Glencoe Physical Science
Features and Benefits

Feature	Description	Page
Dynamic Instructional Strategies	**. . . present clear and comprehensive coverage of physical science.**	
	■ Each engaging chapter opener includes a *Launch Lab* and *Foldables*™.	
	■ *National Geographic Visualizing* features illustrate important concepts in physical science.	[illegible]
A Strong Reading Strand	**. . . encourages active reading and learning for students of all reading levels. In the *Student Edition:***	
	■ *Reading Guides* give students a preview of learning objectives and vocabulary for each section;	125
	■ *Reading Checks* help students check their reading comprehension, and *caption questions* ask students to interpret visuals.	194, 235
	■ *Reading Essentials, An Interactive Student Textbook* is designed to help struggling readers comprehend core content. It is written at a reading level of about two to three grades below the *Student Edition.*	
Math Applications	**. . . provide students with real-world applications of physical science math concepts.**	
	■ *Applying Math* features throughout the chapter allow students to practice important physical science math concepts.	299, 301, 317
	■ *EXTRA Math Problems* are additional opportunities for students to improve their physical science math skills.	834–845
Meeting the Needs of All Students	**. . . facilitates understanding of science concepts for students of all learning levels. In the *Teacher Wraparound Edition:***	
	■ *Differentiated Instruction* strategies help meet the needs of students with learning disabilities and physical challenges, or help create opportunities to enrich and extend students' learning;	323
	■ *Daily Intervention* provides intervention strategies for struggling students; and	326
	■ *Identifying Misconceptions* helps uncover and address common science misconceptions.	355
	■ The *English/Spanish Glossary*, also in the *Student Edition,* helps English-language learners comprehend science terms.	846–870
Extensive Standardized Test Practice	**. . . gives students the opportunity to practice for state and national exams.**	
	■ Each chapter ends with a variety of standardized test practice questions, including *Multiple Choice, Short Response/Grid In,* and *Open Ended.*	412–413
A Variety of Labs	**. . . gets students excited about being involved in physical science. The *Student Edition* provides:**	
	■ *MiniLABs,* traditional labs, and *Design Your Own, Model and Invent,* and *Use the Internet* labs; and	419, 423, 438
	■ *Extra Try at Home Labs* provide opportunities for students to practice their science skills at home with adult supervision using materials from the kitchen, junk drawer, or backyard.	800–812
	■ *Virtual Labs* CD-ROM contains an interactive virtual lab for each chapter. These labs may be too expensive or time-consuming to complete in a classroom laboratory.	242
	■ *Video Labs* reinforce lab techniques and safety skills, offer troubleshooting tips, and give expected outcomes.	518–519
	■ The *Physical Science Lab Manual, Probeware Lab Manual,* and *Science Inquiry Lab Manual* provide additional opportunities to practice laboratory techniques.	
Multi-Level Review	**. . . presents multiple opportunities for all students to review and master content.**	
	■ Section reviews contain a *Summary* of major concepts and a *Self Check* with questions to assess student learning.	511
	■ The *Study Guide* at the end of each chapter allows students to preview, review, and summarize the chapter's main ideas.	561
	■ *Study Guide and Reinforcement* includes study strategies and reinforcement activities to help students grasp core content.	
Teacher Resources	**. . . provide innovative strategies to help new and experienced teachers.**	
	■ *Chapter Resources Fast File* ™ contains important reproducible masters.	568B
	■ Section Focus, Assessment, and Teaching transparencies accompany each chapter.	622C
	■ *Performance Assessment in the Science Classroom* contains assessment guidelines, strategies, sample rubrics, and more.	
Technology	**. . . provides timesaving products to help teachers creatively engage their students.**	
	■ *MindJogger Videoquizzes* (DVD) provide a game-show style interactive quiz for each chapter.	
	■ Easy-to-edit *Interactive Chalkboard* Microsoft® PowerPoint® includes step-by-step lessons, an image bank, review questions, standardized test practice, and transparencies.	
	■ *ExamView® Assessment Suite* CD-ROM in English or Spanish allows you to customize assessment.	
	■ *TeacherWorks* ™ *Plus* DVD-ROM is your all-in-one resource center to help you plan and organize lessons.	
	■ *StudentWorks* ™ *Plus* DVD-ROM solves the heavy backpack problem.	
Online Resources	**. . . enrich the learning experience with the click of a mouse.**	
	■ For prescreened Web links, standardized test practice, self-check quizzes, chapter tests, *Vocabulary PuzzleMaker,* extra math practice, science career information, current science news, and *WebQuest* interactive projects, visit **gpscience.com**.	

SAFETY SYMBOLS

SAFETY SYMBOLS	HAZARD	EXAMPLES	PRECAUTION	REMEDY
DISPOSAL	Special disposal procedures need to be followed.	certain chemicals, living organisms	Do not dispose of these materials in the sink or trash can.	Dispose of wastes as directed by your teacher.
BIOLOGICAL	Organisms or other biological materials that might be harmful to humans	bacteria, fungi, blood, unpreserved tissues, plant materials	Avoid skin contact with these materials. Wear mask or gloves.	Notify your teacher if you suspect contact with material. Wash hands thoroughly.
EXTREME TEMPERATURE	Objects that can burn skin by being too cold or too hot	boiling liquids, hot plates, dry ice, liquid nitrogen	Use proper protection when handling.	Go to your teacher for first aid.
SHARP OBJECT	Use of tools or glassware that can easily puncture or slice skin	razor blades, pins, scalpels, pointed tools, dissecting probes, broken glass	Practice common-sense behavior and follow guidelines for use of the tool.	Go to your teacher for first aid.
FUME	Possible danger to respiratory tract from fumes	ammonia, acetone, nail polish remover, heated sulfur, moth balls	Make sure there is good ventilation. Never smell fumes directly. Wear a mask.	Leave foul area and notify your teacher immediately.
ELECTRICAL	Possible danger from electrical shock or burn	improper grounding, liquid spills, short circuits, exposed wires	Double-check setup with teacher. Check condition of wires and apparatus.	Do not attempt to fix electrical problems. Notify your teacher immediately.
IRRITANT	Substances that can irritate the skin or mucous membranes of the respiratory tract	pollen, moth balls, steel wool, fiberglass, potassium permanganate	Wear dust mask and gloves. Practice extra care when handling these materials.	Go to your teacher for first aid.
CHEMICAL	Chemicals can react with and destroy tissue and other materials	bleaches such as hydrogen peroxide; acids such as sulfuric acid, hydrochloric acid; bases such as ammonia, sodium hydroxide	Wear goggles, gloves, and an apron.	Immediately flush the affected area with water and notify your teacher.
TOXIC	Substance may be poisonous if touched, inhaled, or swallowed.	mercury, many metal compounds, iodine, poinsettia plant parts	Follow your teacher's instructions.	Always wash hands thoroughly after use. Go to your teacher for first aid.
FLAMMABLE	Flammable chemicals may be ignited by open flame, spark, or exposed heat.	alcohol, kerosene, potassium permanganate	Avoid open flames and heat when using flammable chemicals.	Notify your teacher immediately. Use fire safety equipment if applicable.
OPEN FLAME	Open flame in use, may cause fire.	hair, clothing, paper, synthetic materials	Tie back hair and loose clothing. Follow teacher's instruction on lighting and extinguishing flames.	Notify your teacher immediately. Use fire safety equipment if applicable.

Eye Safety
Proper eye protection should be worn at all times by anyone performing or observing science activities.

Clothing Protection
This symbol appears when substances could stain or burn clothing.

Animal Safety
This symbol appears when safety of animals and students must be ensured.

Handwashing
After the lab, wash hands with soap and water before removing goggles.

Glencoe Science

Teacher Wraparound Edition

Physical Science

NATIONAL GEOGRAPHIC

New York, New York Columbus, Ohio Chicago, Illinois Woodland Hills, California

Glencoe Science

Physical Science

The VLA (Very Large Array) is a Y-shaped arrangement of 27 radio antennas on the Plains of San Agustin in New Mexico. Each 25-m antenna can move on tracks. The electronic data collected from the dishes can give a resolution of a 36-km antenna and sensitivity of a 130-m dish, depending on the distance between antennas.

The McGraw·Hill Companies

Send all inquiries to:
Glencoe/McGraw-Hill
8787 Orion Place
Columbus, OH 43240-4027

Student Edition
ISBN: 978-0-07-877962-6
MHID: 0-07-877962-6

Teacher Wraparound Edition
ISBN: 978-0-07-877963-3
MHID: 0-07-877963-4

Printed in the United States of America.

2 3 4 5 6 7 8 9 10 079/055 09 08

Authors

Education Division
Washington, D.C.

Marilyn Thompson, PhD
Assistant Professor, College of Education
Arizona State University
Tempe, AZ

Charles William McLaughlin, PhD
Senior Lecturer
University of Nebraska
Lincoln, NE

Dinah Zike
Educational Consultant
Dinah-Might Activities, Inc.
San Antonio, TX

Contributing Authors

Nancy Ross-Flanigan
Science Writer
Detroit, MI

Margaret K. Zorn
Science Writer
Yorktown, VA

Science Consultants

Jack Cooper
Ennis High School
Ennis, TX

David G. Haase, PhD
North Carolina State University
Raleigh, NC

Michael A. Hoggarth, PhD
Department of Life and
Earth Sciences
Otterbein College
Westerville, OH

Madelaine Meek
Physics Consultant Editor
Lebanon, OH

Cheryl Wistrom
St. Joseph's College
Rensselaer, IN

Carl Zorn, PhD
Staff Scientist
Jefferson Laboratory
Newport News, VA

Series Consultants

MATH

Michael Hopper, DEng.
Manager of Aircraft Certification
L-3 Communications
Greenville, TX

Teri Willard, EdD
Mathematics Curriculum Writer
Belgrade, MT

READING

Elizabeth Babich
Special Education Teacher
Mashpee Public Schools
Mashpee, MA

Barry Barto
Special Education Teacher
John F. Kennedy Elementary
Manistee, MI

Carol A. Senf, PhD
School of Literature, Communication, and Culture
Georgia Institute of Technology
Atlanta, GA

Rachel Swaters-Kissinger
Science Teacher
John Boise Middle School
Warsaw, MO

SAFETY

Aileen Duc, PhD
Science 8 Teacher
Hendrick Middle School, Plano ISD
Plano, TX

Sandra West, PhD
Department of Biology
Texas State University-San Marcos
San Marcos, TX

ACTIVITY TESTERS

Nerma Coats Henderson
Pickerington Lakeview Jr. High School
Pickerington, OH

Mary Helen Mariscal-Cholka
William D. Slider Middle School
El Paso, TX

Science Kit and Boreal Laboratories
Tonawanda, NY

Reviewers

Sharla Adams
IPC Teacher
Allen High School
Allen, TX

Desiree Bishop
Environmental Studies Center
Mobile County Public Schools
Mobile, AL

Tom Bright
Concord High School
Charlotte, NC

Nora M. Prestinari Burchett
Saint Luke School
McLean, VA

Mary Helen Mariscal-Cholka
William D. Slider Middle School
El Paso, TX

Obioma Chukwu
J.H. Rose High School
Greenville, NC

Inga Dainton
Merrilvills High School
Merrilville, IN

Robin Dillon
Hanover Central High School
Cedar Lake, IN

Anthony J. DiSipio, Jr.
8th Grade Science
Octorana Middle School
Atglen, PA

Dwight Dutton
East Chapel Hill High School
Chapel Hill, NC

Carolyn Elliott
South Iredell High School
Statesville, NC

Sueanne Esposito
Tipton High School
Tipton, IN

George Gabb
Great Bridge Middle School
Chesapeake Public Schools
Chesapeake, VA

Nerma Coats Henderson
Pickerington Lakeview Jr.
High School
Pickerington, OH

Maria E. Kelly
Principal
Nativity School
Catholic Diocese of Arlington
Burke, VA

Annette Parrott
Lakeside High School
Atlanta, GA

Darcy Vetro-Ravndal
Hillsborough High School
Tampa, FL

Clabe Webb
Permian High School
Ector County ISD
Odessa, TX

Alison Welch
William D. Slider Middle School
El Paso, TX

Kim Wimpey
North Gwinnett High School
Suwanee, GA

Teacher Advisor Board

The Teacher Advisory Board gave the authors, editorial staff, and the design team feedback on the content and design of the Student Edition. They were instrumental in providing valuable input toward the development of ***Glencoe Physical Science.*** We thank these teachers for their hard work and creative suggestions.

Karen Brown
Theodore High School
Theodore, AL

Bernie Leverett
Sublette High School
Sublette, KS

Armando Miccoli
Adairsville High School
Adairsville, GA

Thom Green
Worthington Kilbourne High School
Worthington, OH

Felecia James
Ellison High School
Killeen, TX

Arla Jo Anderton
Mackenzie Jr. High School
Lubbock, TX

Joe Kowalski
Nikki Rowe High School
McAllen, TX

The Teacher Advisory Board gathers for a photo at the Glencoe/McGraw-Hill headquarters in Columbus, Ohio.

Field Test Schools

Glencoe/McGraw-Hill wishes to thank the following schools that field-tested prepublication manuscript. They were instrumental in providing feedback and verifying the effectiveness of this program.

Bellefontaine High School
Bellefontaine, OH

Mackenzie Junior High School
Lubbock, TX

Sublette High School
Sublette, KS

Adairsville High School
Adairsville, GA

James Rowe High School
McAllen, TX

Teacher Handbook

Table of Contents

Dynamic Instruction

The consistent instructional strategies in each chapter strengthen students' learning—from the beginning of each chapter where students see "Chapter Preview," to the end where they have a chance to test the knowledge they have acquired and prepare for the next lesson.

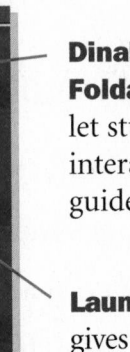

The Big Idea summarizes the chapter content in an overarching statement.

Main Ideas describe the focus of each section and support the Big Idea of the chapter.

Chapter Preview introduces the main concepts.

Science Journal promotes writing and critical-thinking skills.

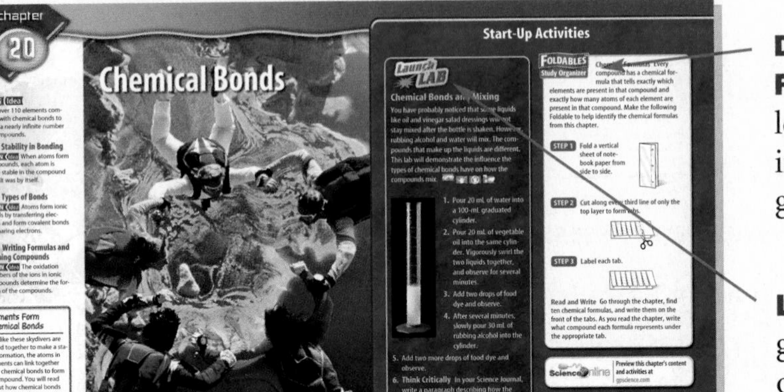

Dinah Zike's Foldables™ let students create interactive study guides.

Launch Lab gives students an opportunity to explore new ideas at the beginning of the chapter.

What You'll Learn at the beginning of each section introduces the main concepts.

Why It's Important provides an answer to "Why do we have to learn this?"

Reading Guide

What You'll Learn	*Why* It's Important	New Vocabulary
■ **Explain** how force and motion are related. ■ **Describe** what inertia is and how it is related to Newton's first law of motion. ■ **Identify** the forces and motion that are present during a car crash.	Force and motion are directly linked—without force, you cannot have motion. **Review Vocabulary** **scientific law:** statement about something that happens in nature that seems to be true all the time	• force • net force • balanced force • inertia

Review Vocabulary reviews a term that helps students better understand section content.

New Vocabulary highlights new terms students will learn in the section.

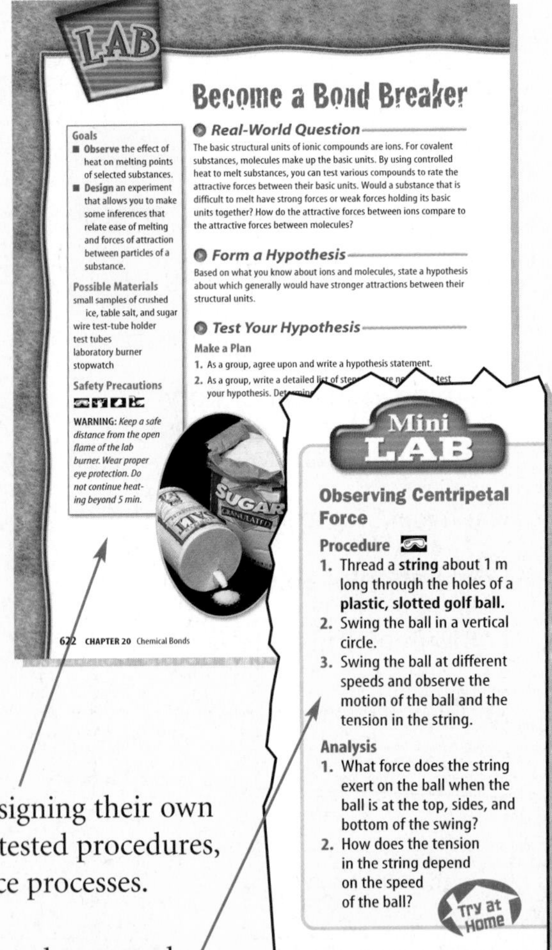

LAB
Become a Bond Breaker
Goals
■ Observe the effect of heat on melting points of selected substances.
■ Design an experiment that allows you to make some inferences that relate ease of melting and forces of attraction between particles of a substance.
Possible Materials
small samples of crushed ice, table salt, and sugar
wire test-tube holder
test tubes
laboratory burner
stopwatch
Safety Precautions
WARNING: Keep a safe distance from the open flame of the lab burner. Wear proper eye protection. Do not continue heating beyond 5 min.
Real-World Question
The basic structural units of ionic compounds are ions. For covalent substances, molecules make up the basic units. By using controlled heat to melt substances, you can test various compounds to rate the attractive forces between their basic units. Would a substance that is difficult to melt have strong forces or weak forces holding its basic units together? How do the attractive forces between ions compare to the attractive forces between molecules?
Form a Hypothesis
Based on what you know about ions and molecules, state a hypothesis about which generally would have stronger attractions between their structural units.
Test Your Hypothesis
Make a Plan
1. As a group, agree upon and write a hypothesis statement.
SUGAR
622 CHAPTER 20 Chemical Bonds
Mini LAB
Observing Centripetal Force
Procedure
1. Thread a string about 1 m long through the holes of a plastic, slotted golf ball.
2. Swing the ball in a vertical circle.
3. Swing the ball at different speeds and observe the motion of the ball and the tension in the string.
Analysis
1. What force does the string exert on the ball when the ball is at the top, sides, and bottom of the swing?
2. How does the tension in the string depend on the speed of the ball?
Try at Home

Labs Whether students are designing their own experiments or following well-tested procedures, they'll learn and practice science processes.

MiniLABs offer students quick and easy-to-do ways to clarify concepts and reinforce skills.

Multi-Level Review and Assessment

Each chapter provides five pages of review and testing to help you evaluate students' knowledge and ability to apply science concepts.

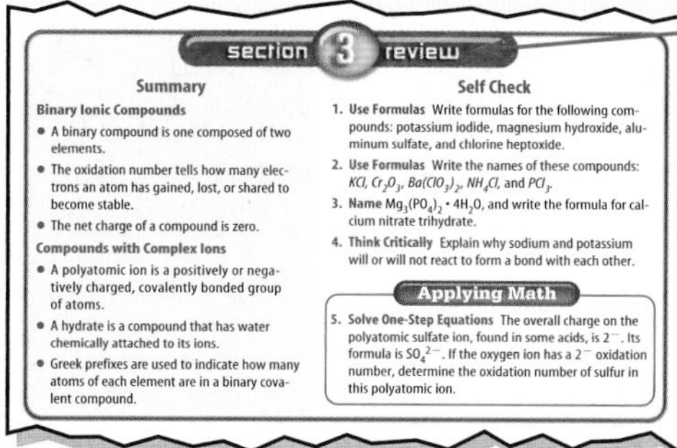

section 3 review

Summary

Binary Ionic Compounds

- A binary compound is one composed of two elements.
- The oxidation number tells how many electrons an atom has gained, lost, or shared to become stable.
- The net charge of a compound is zero.

Compounds with Complex Ions

- A polyatomic ion is a positively or negatively charged, covalently bonded group of atoms.
- A hydrate is a compound that has water chemically attached to its ions.
- Greek prefixes are used to indicate how many atoms of each element are in a binary covalent compound.

Self Check

1. **Use Formulas** Write formulas for the following compounds: potassium iodide, magnesium hydroxide, aluminum sulfate, and chlorine heptoxide.
2. **Use Formulas** Write the names of these compounds: KCl, Cr_2O_3, $Ba(ClO_3)_2$, NH_4Cl, and PCl_3.
3. **Name** $Mg_3(PO_4)_2 \cdot 4H_2O$, and write the formula for calcium nitrate trihydrate.
4. **Think Critically** Explain why sodium and potassium will or will not react to form a bond with each other.

Applying Math

5. **Solve One-Step Equations** The overall charge on the polyatomic sulfate ion, found in some acids, is 2−. Its formula is SO_4^{2-}. If the oxygen ion has a 2− oxidation number, determine the oxidation number of sulfur in this polyatomic ion.

Section Review

- Summary pinpoints important concepts in the section.
- Skill-based questions promote critical thinking skills.

Study Guide

- Main idea summary of each section
- Concept mapping activity to help students visualize the main ideas

Chapter Review

- Using Vocabulary
- Checking Concepts
- Thinking Critically
- Performance Activities
- Applying Math

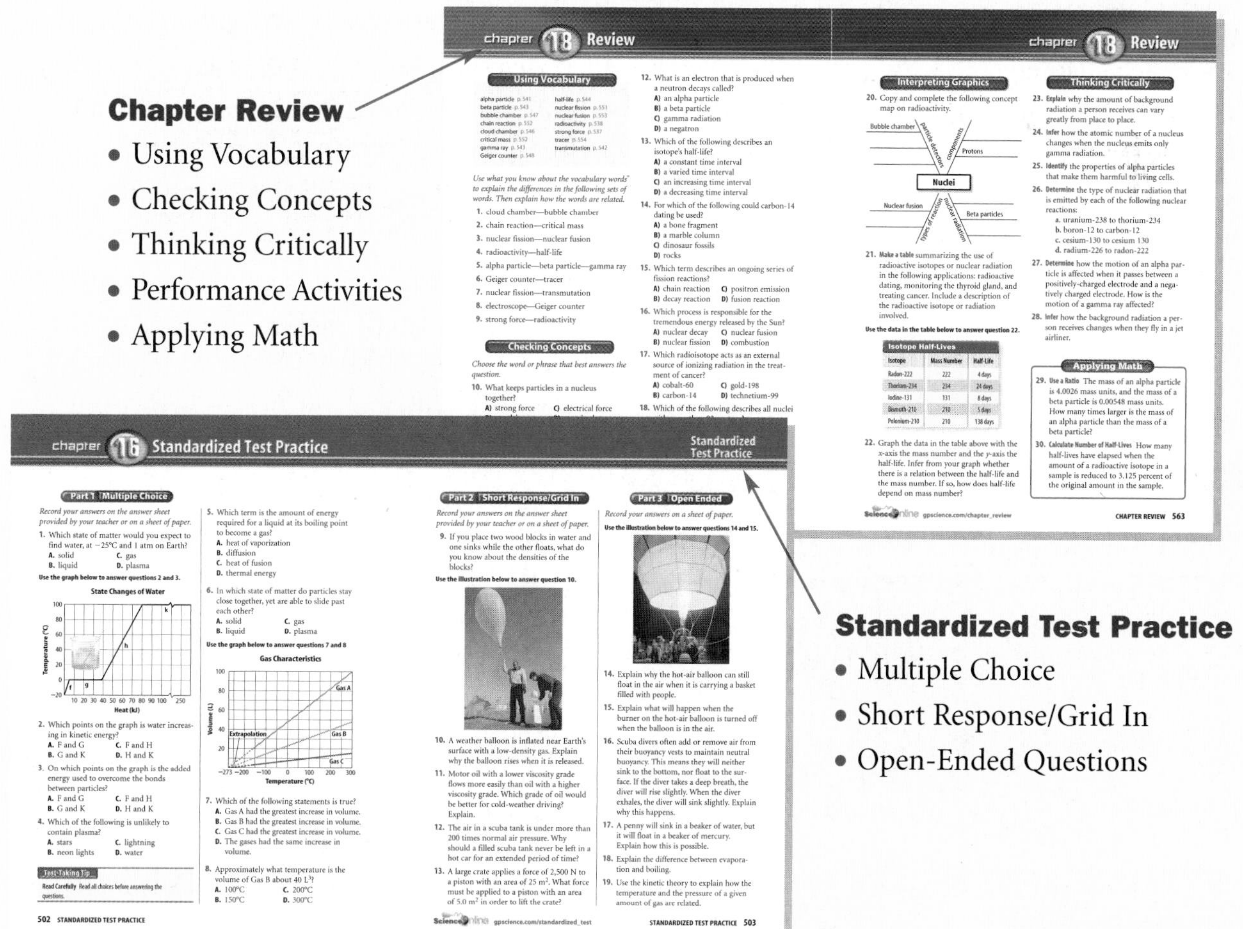

Standardized Test Practice

- Multiple Choice
- Short Response/Grid In
- Open-Ended Questions

Time-Saving Teacher Resources

Glencoe Science provides an extensive array of support materials and resources designed to help you create and customize your science course quickly and easily.

Time-Saving Teacher Resources

FAST FILE Chapter Resources

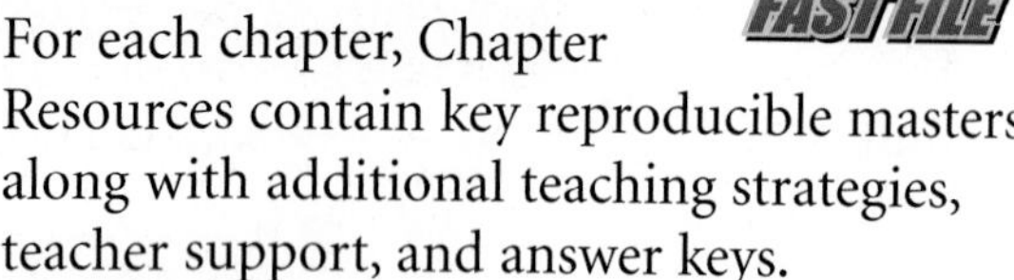

For each chapter, Chapter Resources contain key reproducible masters along with additional teaching strategies, teacher support, and answer keys.

Reproducible Student Resources include:

- Worksheets for all MiniLABs and Labs
- *Directed Reading for Content Mastery* (in English and Spanish), *Reinforcement* and *Enrichment* worksheets for each chapter
- *Section Focus, Teaching,* and *Assessment Transparencies* masters
- Chapter Review and Chapter Test masters

Teacher Support and Planning includes:

- Additional student preparation materials for each chapter
- Spanish Resources provide translations of all objectives, vocabulary, and main ideas
- Answer keys and teaching strategies

Teacher Wraparound Edition

The *Teacher Wraparound Edition* is your key to the teaching resources available. In addition to teaching strategies and suggestions, the *Teacher Wraparound Edition* provides a guide for all print and software materials available for each lesson.

Transparencies

- Section Focus Transparency
- Assessment Transparency
- Teaching Transparency
- Transparency masters and worksheets

Exam*View*® Assessment Suite CD-ROM

- Create, edit, and customize tests
- Create multiple versions of tests
- Translate tests from English to Spanish and vice versa
- Build tests aligned with state standards

Video Labs

- Step-by-step lab procedures for selected *Student Edition* labs
- Lab safety skills
- Teacher support
- Troubleshooting advice
- Located on the Super DVD

Technology Support

TeacherWorks Plus™

This DVD-ROM is your all-in-one resource center. Personalize a lesson plan, access resources from the *Teacher Wraparound Edition,* connect to the Internet, or make a to-do list. These are only a few of the many features that can assist you in the planning and organizing of your lessons.

Includes:

- A calendar feature
- Access to all program blackline masters
- Standards correlations and more

This CD-ROM brings Microsoft® PowerPoint® presentations right to your door. With the large number of graphics provided, students can use a visual approach to learning chapter content.

Includes:

- A pre-made presentation for every chapter
- Image bank and interactive graphics
- Animations and audio clips
- All new section and chapter questions
- Standardized test practice
- Transparencies
- Pre-lab questions for all labs
- Foldables™ directions
- Links to gpscience.com

StudentWorks Plus™

This DVD-ROM combines the Student Edition with a full audio reading of the text so students can both read and listen to the book at the same time.

Includes:

- Complete *Student Edition* on DVD-ROM
- Links to online activities and resources
- Access to all student worksheets

Virtual Labs CD-ROM Program

The Virtual Labs CD-ROM contains a collection of labs that allow students to complete labs that are too expensive, take too long to complete, or might be too dangerous in a classroom laboratory.

gpscience.com

For students:

- Prescreened Internet sites (Web links) that correlate to text chapters
- Interactive activities that review chapter concepts
- Internet Labs where students can share data with each other
- Access to *Student Edition* online
- Interactive self-check quizzes for each chapter section as well as the entire chapter

For teachers:

- *WebQuest* activities
- Teacher Forum for teachers to share activities and ideas

Technology Support

Help Your Students with Reading and Writing

Glencoe Science increases science literacy, improves reading comprehension, and deepens students' understanding of ideas and concepts. The reading strategies are active, constructive, and engaging.

In the *Student Edition*

Reading Checks stimulate quick recall and keep students focused on the main idea.

Caption Questions offer a visual approach to learning. Students are asked to recall what they have read by interpreting the visual.

> **Figure 18** Three allotropes of carbon are depicted here.
> **Identify** *the geometric shapes that make up each allotrope.*

Science Journals provide opportunities to write responses to questions that require critical thinking, to conduct research and write about it, or to practice creative writing skills.

Skill Words such as *compare and contrast, describe, explain,* and *state* are included in the Self Check at the end of each section, in the goals of each Lab, and in the chapter reviews.

Technology Support

Vocabulary PuzzleMaker allows you to create crossword puzzles, jumble puzzles, or word searches in minutes to review chapter vocabulary. The puzzles can be printed or played on the computer screen.

Guided Reading Audio Program (available on MP3-formatted CD-ROMs) provides a comprehensive overview in Spanish and English for auditory learners, students with reading difficulties, and English-language learners (ELL).

In the *Teacher Edition*

Project CRISS™ (Creating Independence through Student-Owned Strategies) strategies are highlighted in the Unit Openers where an activity is supplied that relates to unit content. For more information about Project CRISS™, visit www.projectcriss.com.

Use Science Words features encourage students to look up biology terms. Use these as a pre-reading activity, or have students keep a vocabulary journal.

> **Use Science Words**
> **Word Usage** The distinction between distance and displacement can be confusing. Have students use each of these words correctly in a sentence. Possible response: When I go to school and then back home, my displacement is zero, even though the distance from home to school is 2 km.

Additional Science Journal writing activities promote writing and critical thinking skills and extend the *Student Edition* journaling activity.

Active Reading Strategies utilize a variety of learning styles, and encourage cooperative learning and intrapersonal reflection on chapter content.

Additional Teacher Resources

Reading Essentials provides summaries of each section of the textbook, focusing on the most important scientific concepts.

Reading and Writing in the Science Classroom provides teachers with effective strategies for building students' skills in reading and writing about science.

Reading and Writing

Help Your Students with Reading and Writing

Making Concept Maps and Charts

Bubble Map Students brainstorm and organize words in clusters to describe concepts.

Flow Chart Students logically analyze and draw a sequence of events.

Cause-and-Effect Chart Students visually represent the causes and effects of an event or process.

Supporting-Idea Chart Students make a concept map to analyze relationships between a whole and its parts.

Network-Tree Concept Map Students show a hierarchy and use branching procedures.

Events-Chain Concept Map Students order steps or stages in a linear procedure.

Cycle Concept Map Students show how a series of events interact.

Spider Concept Map Students use for brainstorming and grouping nonrelated terms to a central idea.

Using the Science Journal

Double-Reference Journal Students read and record ideas.

Metacognition Students analyze what and how they have learned.

Learning Journal Students create notes and reflect on the content.

Problem-Solution Journal Students analyze problems and suggest workable solutions.

Speculation About Effects/Prediction Journal Students examine events and speculate about their possible long-term effects.

Synthesis Journal Students reflect on a project, a paper, or a performance task and plan how to apply what they have learned to their own lives.

Reflective Journal Students identify what they learned in an activity and record responses.

Quickwrites Students use spontaneous writing to discover what they already know.

Collaborative Learning Strategies

Pair of Pairs Partners respond to a question and compare their response to other pairs and to the class.

Write-Draw-Discuss Students write about and draw a picture of a concept, then share it with the class.

Active Reading

Learning Reading Have students divide a sheet of paper in half. Have them record research notes, lecture notes, and vocabulary terms related to the laws of motion in the left column. Tell them to use the right column to respond, interpret, question, and analyze left-column entries. L2 **Intrapersonal**

Four-Corner Discussion The class works in four groups to debate a complex issue.

Jigsaw Students work in groups to become experts on a portion of text and share what they've learned with the class.

Buddy Interviews Students interview one another to find out what strategies they use to learn the text.

Reciprocal Teaching Students take turns reading a section of text, retelling it in their own words, then asking questions about it.

News Summary Students are given several minutes to summarize, retell, or analyze an activity for a "TV" audience.

ReQuest The teacher reads aloud an article or story. Student pairs then construct discussion questions and review the content.

Foldables™

Foldables™ are easy-to-make, three-dimensional, interactive graphic organizers that students create out of simple sheets of paper. These unique hands-on tools for studying and reviewing were created exclusively for Glencoe by education specialist Dinah Zike.

Research Behind Foldables™

According to research (Bransford, 1979; Corno, 1994), study strategies help students understand, organize, remember and apply new information presented in science textbooks. Some study strategies include concept mapping, highlighting, outlining, note taking, summarizing, and underlining (Peverly, Brobst, Graham & Shaw, 2003). Glencoe Science offers Dinah Zike's Foldables™ Study Organizers as an organizational tool and study guide for students.

Build Prereading Skills

- Encourages students to prepare for what they will be learning
- Gives students an opportunity to recall what they already know about a subject

Encourage Active Reading and Writing

- Practices basic reading and writing skills
- Develops skills in finding and reporting main ideas
- Organizes information
- Reviews key vocabulary terms

Summarize Content for Review

- Creates a comprehensive, interactive snapshot of the chapter
- Provides preparation support for chapter, unit, and end-of-course exams, as well as standardized tests

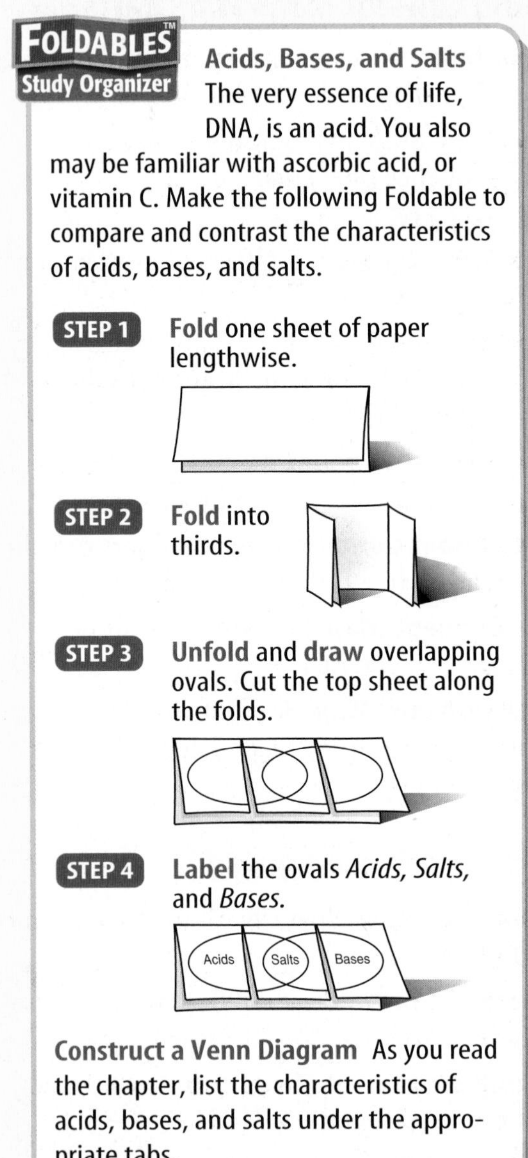

FOLDABLES™
Study Organizer
Acids, Bases, and Salts The very essence of life, DNA, is an acid. You also may be familiar with ascorbic acid, or vitamin C. Make the following Foldable to compare and contrast the characteristics of acids, bases, and salts.
STEP 1 Fold one sheet of paper lengthwise.
STEP 2 Fold into thirds.
STEP 3 Unfold and draw overlapping ovals. Cut the top sheet along the folds.
STEP 4 Label the ovals Acids, Salts, and Bases.
Acids
Salts
Bases
Construct a Venn Diagram As you read the chapter, list the characteristics of acids, bases, and salts under the appropriate tabs.

Dinah Zike's *Teaching with Foldables™ Science*

- Sample presentations of Foldables™ instructions
- More ideas on how to incorporate Foldables™ into your lessons
- Easy-to-read folding instruction pages

Course Planning Guide

Glencoe Science programs provide a complete selection of core concepts that can be presented in a way that meets the needs of all your students. As the teacher, you are in the best position to design a science course that sets the pace at which the content is covered and determines what material should be given the most emphasis. To assist you in planning the course, the following Course Planning Guide is provided.

The chart shown below offers general suggestions for pacing your students through the book. Pacing for both standard class periods and block schedule class periods is given.

Glencoe Physical Science									
Single Period					Block Period				
Chapter	Instruction	Labs	Review & Assessment	Total	Chapter	Instruction	Labs	Review & Assessment	Total
1	4	3	2	9	1	2	1.5	1	4.5
2	3	3	2	8	2	1.5	1.5	1	4
3	3.5	2.5	2	8	3	1.75	1.25	1	4
4	2.5	2.5	2	7	4	1.25	1.25	1	3.5
5	4.5	2.5	2	9	5	2.25	1.25	1	4.5
6	4	4	2	10	6	2	2	1	5
7	4	3	2	9	7	2	1.5	1	4.5
8	4	4	2	10	8	2	2	1	5
9	3	6	2	11	9	1.5	3	1	5.5
10	3.5	2.5	2	8	10	1.75	1.25	1	4
11	4	2.5	2.5	9	11	2	1.25	1.25	4.5
12	3.5	3.5	2	9	12	1.75	1.75	1	4.5
13	4	3	2	9	13	2	1.5	1	4.5
14	4	3	2	9	14	2	1.5	1	4.5
15	2.5	3	1.5	7	15	1.25	1.5	.75	3.5
16	4	3	2	9	16	2	1.5	1	4.5
17	3	4	2	9	17	1.5	2	1	4.5
18	4	3	2	9	18	2	1.5	1	4.5
19	3.5	2.5	2	8	19	1.75	1.25	1	4
20	4	3	2	9	20	2	1.5	1	4.5
21	3	4	2	9	21	1.5	2	1	4.5
22	3.5	2.5	2	8	22	1.75	1.25	1	4
23	3.5	3	1.5	8	23	1.75	1.5	.75	4
24	3.5	2.5	2	8	24	1.75	1.25	1	4
25	3	4	2	9	25	1.5	2	1	4.5

Assessment

Glencoe Science offers the Glencoe Assessment Advantage, a system designed to give you all the tools you need to prepare your students for success in any testing situation.

In the *Student Edition*

Section Review and **Applying Math** questions appear in every chapter.

Chapter Review questions help you evaluate students' knowledge and ability to apply science concepts.

Standardized Test Practice questions at the end of each chapter provide students with additional opportunities to practice their test-taking skills.

In the *Teacher Wraparound Edition*

Assessments located throughout the *Teacher Wraparound Edition* provide methods for assessing students' comprehension with Performance, Process, and Content exercises.

Teacher Classroom Resources

Performance Assessment in the Science Classroom

- Guidelines for assessing the performance of a task
- Reproducible activities for evaluating students
- Sample rubrics and checklists

***Fast File* Chapter Resources** provides six pages of assessement for every chapter including *Testing Concepts, Applying Concepts,* and *Writing Skills.*

Technology Support

MindJogger Videoquizzes are interactive video quizzes set in game show format. Each is designed for the full range of student learning styles.

Exam*View*® Assessment Suite CD-ROM for Windows® and Macintosh® provides an easy way to create, edit, and customize your tests. Select your own test items by objective from two different levels of difficulty, or write and edit your own. Translate tests from English to Spanish and vice versa.

Rubrics

The following rubrics are sample scoring devices for short response and open-ended questions.

Short Response

Points	Description
2	The student demonstrates a thorough understanding of the science of the task. The response may contain minor flaws that do not detract from the demonstration of a thorough understanding.
1	The student has provided a response that is only partially correct.
0	The student has provided a completely incorrect solution or no response at all.

Open Ended

Points	Description
4	The student demonstrates a thorough understanding of the science of the task. The response may contain minor flaws that do not detract from the demonstration of a thorough understanding.
3	The student demonstrates an understanding of the science of the task. The response is essentially correct and demonstrates an essential but less than thorough understanding of the science.
2	The student demonstrates only a partial understanding of the science of the task. Although the student may have used the correct approach to a solution or may have provided a correct solution, the work lacks an essential understanding of the underlying science concepts.
1	The student demonstrates a very limited understanding of the science of the task. The response is incomplete and exhibits many flaws.
0	The student provides a completely incorrect solution or no response at all.

Educational Partnerships

NATIONAL GEOGRAPHIC

Some topics in the chapter either require or benefit from a larger, more detailed visual explanation. The National Geographic Society has created *Visualizing* features that call out an important concept from the chapter and illustrate it in a way that will inform, excite, and motivate your students.

NATIONAL GEOGRAPHIC VISUALIZING SEED DISPERSAL

Figure 18

Plants have many adaptations for dispersing seeds, often enlisting the aid of wind, water, or animals.

▲ Equipped with tiny hooks, burrs cling tightly to fur and feathers.

▲ Pressure builds within the seedpods of this jewelweed plant until the pod bursts, flinging seeds far and wide.

▼ Some seeds buried by animals, such as this squirrel, go uneaten and sprout the next spring.

▼ Dandelion seeds are easily dislodged and sail away on a puff of wind.

▲ Encased in a thick, buoyant husk, a coconut may be carried hundreds of kilometers by ocean currents.

▶ Blackberry seeds eaten by this white-footed mouse will pass through its digestive tract and be deposited in a new location.

SECTION 3 Seed Reproduction 289

TIME SCIENCE AND HISTORY

SCIENCE CAN CHANGE THE COURSE OF HISTORY!

Overcoming the Odds

Guts and determination helped one pioneering doctor to save the lives of thousands

Overcoming the odds is a challenge that many people face. Dr. Samuel Lee Kountz, Jr. had the odds stacked against him. Thanks to his determination he beat them.

Dr. Kountz was interested in kidney transplants, a process that was still brand new in the 1950s. For many patients, a kidney transplant added months or a year to one's life. But then a patient's body would reject the kidney, and the patient would die. Dr. Kountz was determined to see that kidney transplants saved lives and kept patients healthy for years.

A donated organ is on its way to save a life.

Fixing the Problem

Kountz discovered the root of the problem—why and how a patient's body rejected the transplanted kidney. He discovered that the patient's cells attacked and destroyed the small blood vessels of the transplanted kidney. So the new kidney would die from lack of blood-supplied oxygen. From this, doctors knew when to give patients the right kinds of drugs, so that their bodies could overcome the rejection process.

In 1959, Kountz performed the first successful kidney transplant. He went on to develop a procedure to keep body organs healthy for up to 60 hours after being taken from a donor. He also set up a system of organ donor cards through the National Kidney Foundation. And in his career, Dr. Kountz transplanted more than 1,000 kidneys himself—and paved the way for thousands more.

Research What kinds of medical breakthroughs has the last century brought? Locate an article that explains either a recent advance in medicine or the work that doctors and medical researchers are doing. Share your findings with your class.

Science online

TIME

TIME magazine brings science topics and history together to further explain the chapter's main ideas and show how science relates to real life.

Differentiated Instruction

Teaching Strategies

Following each suggested assessment and activity, ability levels are supplied to accommodate all students.

- LS Multiple Learning Styles logos are used throughout the text to indicate strategies that address different learning styles.
- L1 Level 1 activities should be appropriate for students with learning difficulties.
- L2 Level 2 activities should be within the ability range of all students.
- L3 Level 3 activities are designed for above-average students.
- ELL English-Language Learners activities should be within the ability range of English-Language Learners or students who speak English as a second language (ESL).
- COOP LEARN Cooperative Learning activities are designed for small group work.
- PBL Problem-Based Learning activities apply real-world situations to learning.
- P Portfolio strategies represent student products that can be placed into a best-work portfolio.

Identifying Misconceptions

These short, diagnostic, and perscriptive lessons target common science misconceptions.

Necessary Metals Students may think it strange that metals are needed by the body. Explain that the metals calcium, potassium, and sodium, for example, help transmit electrical signals within the nervous system.

Multiple Learning Styles

Look for these italicized designations under various activities to help you target your lessons to each student's preferred learning style.

- ***Kinesthetic*** learners learn through touch, movement, and manipulating objects.
- ***Visual-Spatial*** learners think in terms of images, illustrations, and models.
- ***Interpersonal*** learners understand and work well with other people.
- ***Intrapersonal*** learners can analyze their own strengths and weaknesses and may prefer to work on their own.
- ***Linguistic*** learners write clearly and easily understand the written word.
- ***Logical-Mathematical*** learners understand numbers easily and have highly-developed reasoning skills.

Daily Interventions

Found at the end of each chapter section, this feature is designed to intercept students who are struggling and prescribe a system to help them get back on track. *Reteach* provides reinforcement of the section's concepts through visual activities.

DAILY INTERVENTION

Check for Understanding

Kinesthetic Have a student light a match and allow it to burn. Also, place an ice cube in a glass container and allow it to melt. Have students explain what type of changes took place with each item and describe the final properties of each.

Differentiated Instruction

These activities present various teaching strategies designed to help you meet the special needs of students with learning disabilities, physical challenges, visual impairment, and hearing impairment. Challenge activities provide opportunities for students who excel to engage in activities and research projects that extend the chapter's concepts. English-language learners in the classroom will also find exercises that bridge the gap between language barriers and the chapter content.

> **Differentiated Instruction**
>
> **English-Language Learners** Have students make flashcards with the name of a gland on one side and the hormone it produces on the other. Student pairs can quiz each other using the flashcards.

Cultural Diversity

These readings provide insights into the unique ways in which people of different ethnicities and cultural heritage have approached science. The intent of these features is to build awareness and appreciation for the global community in which we live.

> **Cultural Diversity**
>
> **Tsunami!** Tsunamis occur in many areas around the world and have been reported since ancient times. One of the earliest record tsunamis struck Syria around 2,000 B.C. Thera, one of the Cyclades Islands in the Mediterranean, may be the remnant of a volcano that erupted—causing tsunamis that ended the Minoan civilization on Crete. Tsunami is a Japanese word for "harbor wave." Many have struck the Japanese shore. Because Japan is an island nation, the threat of tsunamis is a national safety concer. Today, by using expected tsunami characteristics, the Japan Meteorological Agency can forecast tsunami heights for the Japanese coastline. This provides residents with the knowledge necessary to move a safe distance away from the shore.

Inquiry-Based Science

The call for more inquiry-based science by the *National Science Education Standards* has been met by Glencoe Science.

Glencoe Science recognizes the importance of conducting inquiry-based science activities in the classroom. The process of doing inquiry models actual science practice, encouraging problem-solving strategies and developing critical thinking skills. Inquiry gets students actively involved in the learning process by allowing them to determine materials, procedures, or the topics and questions they want to investigate.

Inquiry can range from a very structured activity for those students who need more guidance to a more open-ended approach where students lead the investigations. Glencoe Science recognizes that the inquiry activities suggested will not look the same in every classroom. We encourage teachers to modify the suggested activities in a manner that best supports your students.

Glencoe also provides teachers with Alternative Inquiry Labs, teaching strategies or suggestions for making existing labs more inquiry-based.

> **Alternative Inquiry Lab**
>
> **Extend the Experience** To make this Lab an Inquiry Lab, have students examine the magnetic field around the motor, using a compass or iron fillings. Test the armature and rotor before final assembly, as it will be difficult to fit the compass inside the motor. Encourage students to make various adaptations to the motor. Ask them to figure out how to make the motor spin the other way, spin faster, and spin slower. How could the motor be turned into a generator? How could they make the motor consume less power? Finally, students might research how these issues are handled by industry or other questions they find interesting.

Research-Based Learning Strategies

Glencoe Science incorporates the most current and applicable educational research on science learning and follows recommendations from the American Association for the Advancement of Science and the National Science Teachers Association. The following research-based strategies can be found throughout the text.

Learning Strategies

The following research-based strategies can be found throughout the text:

- **Using Prior Knowledge** Glencoe Science encourages students to use their prior knowledge to learn information because this adds relevance to the material. Students are referred back to other parts of the text or to their own real-life experiences.
- **Practicing Important Tasks** By offering students an opportunity to practice important tasks using a variety of labs and activities in the *Student Edition, Teacher Wraparound Edition,* ancillaries and technology, Glencoe Science makes learning fun and relevant for students.
- **Using Visuals to Communicate, Organize, and Reinforce Learning** High-quality art and photos throughout the text communicate concepts more efficiently and reinforce learning, while allowing students to organize information.
- **Motivating Students to Achieve** Active strategies and real-world experiences motivate students to achieve. Throughout Glencoe's programs, students are encouraged to apply their knowledge in ways that will motivate them to learn.
- **Developing Decoding and Reading Comprehension Strategies** Throughout the text, students are supplied with caption questions, reading checks, and other strategies to aid in comprehension.
- **Using Study Strategies** Through the use of highlighting, outlining, note-taking, summarizing, and other such strategies, students can monitor their own progress and organize information more effectively, thereby increasing their scientific literacy. These strategies are found throughout the text and ancillaries.

The use of these strategies within Glencoe Science will help teachers to achieve the goals set forth by the *National Science Education Standards.*

Academic Research

The Glencoe Science White Papers outline the educational strategies on which this program was based. These papers provide the research behind specific examples found in the *Student Edition, Teacher Wraparound Edition,* ancillary program, and technology resources. They highlight the use of educationally sound strategies that help students learn science.

For more information about research, visit glencoe.com.

Field Research and Testing

Feedback from students, teachers, curriculum supervisors, department chairpersons, parents, learning specialists, and science content experts was invaluable in the development of this program. The following pre-publication and post-publication research was conducted.

Prior to Publication

- Detailed classroom teacher and curriculum supervisor **surveys** were conducted by independently contracted researchers.
- A **nationwide panel** of science teachers, curriculum supervisors, and department chairpersons provided countless hours of feedback and assistance throughout program development.
- A wide range of **educator and content reviewers** provided in-depth reviews of and suggestions for manuscripts and pre-publication versions of the program.
- **Face-to-face interviews** with science teachers provided insight into teachers' day-to-day challenges.

Field-Test Results

- Field-test research indicates that test scores increased among students using Glencoe Science programs.
- Nine out of ten students earned higher scores after using Glencoe programs.
- Scores improved among both male and female students.
- Scores improved among both minority and non-minority students.
- Overall, the gap between the average pre-test score and a perfect score closed by 33 percent. Stated differently, on average, **scores increased 77 percent after students used the Glencoe program.**

After Publication

- Field tests were conducted in which students and teachers used a pre-publication manuscript in the classroom.
- Follow-up interviews, observations, and surveys of Glencoe Science users provide ongoing opportunities for program development and verification of program success.

National Education Standards

Correlation of *Glencoe Physical Science* to the National Science Education Standards.

Content Standard	Chapter
(UCP) Unifying Concepts and Processes (Grades 5–8, 9–12)	
1. Systems, order, and organization	1, 2, 3, 5, 6, 8, 9, 10, 11, 12, 13, 14, 15, 16, 17, 18, 19, 20, 21, 22, 23, 24, 25
2. Evidence, models, and explanation	1, 2, 3, 4, 5, 6, 7, 8, 9, 10, 11, 12, 13, 14, 15, 16, 17, 18, 19, 20, 21, 22, 23, 24, 25
3. Change, constancy, and measurement	1, 2, 3, 4, 5, 6, 7, 8, 9, 10, 11, 12, 13, 14, 15, 16, 17, 18, 19, 20, 21, 22, 23, 24, 25
4. Evolution and equilibrium	7, 16, 21
5. Form and function	1, 3, 5, 6, 7, 8, 9, 10, 11, 12, 13, 14, 15, 16, 17, 18, 19, 20, 21, 22, 23, 24, 25
(A) Science as Inquiry (Grades 5–8, 9–12)	
1. Abilities necessary to do scientific inquiry	1, 2, 3, 4, 5, 6, 7, 8, 9, 10, 11, 12, 13, 14, 15, 16, 17, 18, 19, 20, 21, 22, 23, 24, 25
2. Understandings about scientific theory	1, 2, 3, 4, 5, 6, 7, 8, 9, 10, 11, 12, 13, 14, 16, 18, 19, 20, 21, 22, 23, 24, 25
(B) Physical Science (Grades 5–8)	
1. Properties and changes of properties in matter	4, 6, 7, 8, 9, 10, 12, 13, 14, 15, 16, 17, 19, 20, 21, 22, 23, 24, 25
2. Motions and forces	2, 3, 4, 6, 7, 8, 10, 12, 16, 17, 18, 19, 20
3. Transfer of energy	5, 6, 7, 9, 10, 12, 13, 16, 17, 18, 20, 21, 22
(B) Physical Science (Grades 9–12)	
1. Structure of atoms	9, 18, 19, 22, 25
2. Structure and properties of matter	4, 6, 7, 8, 9, 10, 12, 13, 14, 15, 16, 17, 19, 20, 21, 22, 23, 24, 25
3. Chemical Reactions	15, 21, 22, 23
4. Motion and forces	2, 3, 4, 5, 6, 7, 8, 10, 12, 16, 18, 19, 20, 23
5. Conservation of energy and increase in disorder	4, 6, 10, 16, 17
6. Interactions of energy and matter	5, 6, 7, 9, 10, 12, 13, 15, 16, 17, 20, 21, 22
(C) Life Science (Grades 5–8)	
1. Structure and function in living systems	13, 24
4. Populations and ecosystems	17
5. Diversity and adaptations of organisms	6
(C) Life Science (Grades 9–12)	
5. Matter, energy, and organization in living systems	11, 12, 13, 14, 24
6. Behavior of organisms	13
(D) Earth and Space Science (Grades 5–8)	
1. Structure of the Earth system	8, 9, 12
2. Earth's history	8, 9
(D) Earth and Space Science (Grades 9–12)	
1. Energy in the Earth system	8, 9, 12
2. Geochemical cycles	9
3. Origin and evolution of the Earth system	8, 9
(E) Science and Technology (Grades 5–8, 9–12)	
1. Abilities of technological design	1, 5, 6, 9, 14, 16
2. Understandings about science and technology	1, 4, 5, 6, 8, 9, 12, 13, 14, 16, 18, 19, 21, 22, 23, 24, 25

Content Standard	Chapter
(F) Science in Personal and Social Perspectives (Grades 5–8)	
1. Personal health	11, 14, 18, 19, 20, 22, 23
2. Populations, resources, and environments	9, 23
4. Risks and benefits	9
5. Science and technology in society	1, 7
(F) Science in Personal and Social Perspectives (Grades 9–12)	
1. Personal and community health	2, 5, 11, 12, 14, 18, 19, 20, 22, 23, 24
2. Population growth	9
3. Natural resources	9, 12, 13, 21, 24
4. Environmental quality	9, 21, 24
5. Natural and human-induced hazards	1, 2, 9, 11, 12, 18, 21, 23, 24
6. Science and technology in local, national, and global challenges	4, 5, 6, 7, 8, 9, 10, 11, 12, 13, 14, 19, 21, 23, 24, 25
(G) History and Nature of Science (Grades 5–8, 9–12)	
1. Science as a human endeavor	21, 22
2. Nature of science	1, 21
3. History of science	2, 4, 8, 10, 12, 14, 16, 17, 18, 19, 20, 21, 24, 25

How Glencoe Science Aligns with the National Science Education Standards

The correlations at the left and above show the close alignment between Glencoe Science and the grade-appropriate standards. Glencoe Science allows students to discover concepts within each of the content standards and gives students opportunities to make connections among the science disciplines. Hands-on activities and inquiry-based lessons reinforce the science processes emphasized in the standards.

How Glencoe Science Aligns with the NCTM Standards for Grades 9–12

Throughout Glencoe Science, each Applying Math activity provides students with the opportunity to practice and apply some of the mathematical concepts and applications described in the NCTM Standards. These activities serve to reinforce mathematical skills in real-life situations, thus preparing students to meet their needs in an ever-changing world.

Correlation of *Glencoe Physical Science* to NCTM Standards

Math Standard	Page
1. Number and Operations	24, 33, 40, 63, 69, 95, 102, 104, 121, 128, 130, 153, 162, 185, 211, 219, 251, 283, 299, 317, 342, 349, 357, 379, 411, 443, 463, 487, 493, 531, 548, 563, 587, 597, 644, 657, 691, 721, 753, 783
2. Algebra	24, 33, 40, 63, 69, 95, 102, 104, 121, 128, 130, 153, 162, 185, 211, 219, 251, 299, 317, 342, 349, 379, 411, 463, 471, 487, 493, 501, 587, 597, 617, 627, 644, 657, 691, 721, 753
3. Geometry	162, 411
4. Measurement	33, 443, 669
5. Data Analysis and Probability	24, 63, 185, 283, 349, 531, 597, 691, 721, 753, 783
6. Problem Solving	63, 471, 501, 548, 563, 617, 627, 669, 783
7. Reasoning and Proof	501
8. Communication	90, 106, 179
9. Connections	24, 33, 40, 63, 69, 95, 102, 104, 121, 128, 130, 153, 185, 211, 219, 251, 283, 299, 317, 342, 349, 379, 443, 463, 471, 531, 548, 563, 587, 597, 617, 627, 644, 657, 669, 691, 721, 753, 783
10. Representation	644, 657

Learning in the Laboratory

In the *Student Edition*

Working in the lab is perhaps the most exciting part of science. Labs and MiniLABs give your students the hands-on opportunity to create, investigate, and explore science. Students will learn new material, while having fun.

Traditional Labs provide guided inquiry as students hypothesize, plan investigations, and collect and analyze data.

Design Your Own Labs challenge students to design their own experiments that will provide answers to lab problems.

Model and Invent Labs allow students to create a model or invent a product that can demonstrate scientific concepts.

Use the Internet Labs help students share and retrieve data from others around the country and world, by posting data they have collected on gpscience.com. These activities show students the possible range of data, importance of collecting large amounts of data, and data analysis.

MiniLABs and **Applying Science** activities are a quick way for students to practice specific process skills as they learn science concepts. Many of them can be classroom demonstrations or homework assignments.

In the *Teacher Wraparound Edition*

Quick Demos allow students to visualize biology concepts.

Inquiry Labs in each chapter can be used to support inquiry-based science or as alternatives to traditional labs.

Technology Support

Virtual Labs CD-ROM includes a collection of interactive activities involving major chapter themes that allow students to understand science concepts in a virtual setting. These labs provide a way to conduct experiments without classroom time, cost, and safety constraints.

Video Labs show students step-by-step lab procedures while emphasizing important lab safety skills. The lab videos also include teacher support, troubleshooting advice, and expected outcomes.

Additional Resources

Laboratory Activities offer a variety of traditional laboratory experiences that reinforce the biology principles in the text. The *Teacher Wraparound Edition* provides full support.

Probeware Labs present activities for students to explore scientific concepts using a probeware data collection system. These hand-held systems provide a fast and simple way to collect, view, and analyze data in the classroom or during a field investigation. Integrating technology in the classroom is made simple with step-by-step instructions for setting up and using probeware.

Science Inquiry Lab Manual gives students the opportunity to become increasingly independent in stating hypotheses, designing and performing experiments, and collecting and analyzing data.

Safety in the Laboratory

All activities are designed to minimize dangers in the laboratory. Careful laboratory planning and management by both the instructor and the student are essential to a safe laboratory experience. **Local, state, and federal laboratory safety laws and regulations must be strictly followed.** The information provided here is one of the many resources to which you can refer for information about laboratory safety.

Classroom and Laboratory Preparation

1. Label and store chemicals properly and securely. See p. 20T.
2. Store equipment properly and securely and other thing.
   a. Clean and dry all equipment before storing.
   b. Protect electronic equipment and microscopes from dust, humidity, and extreme temperatures.
   c. Number, catalog, and organize equipment.
3. Ensure adequate work space for each student.
4. Ensure adequate classroom and storeroom ventilation.
5. Explain and post safety and evacuation guidelines along with expectations of conduct.
6. Ensure that all safety equipment is functioning properly and is clearly visible.
7. Provide hot plates as a heat source whenever possible. If gas burners are used, know where the central gas supply shutoff valve is located.
8. Ensure that each workstation has a GFCI-protected electrical source.
9. Provide safety goggles consistent with ANSI Standard Z87.1 for each student, including students who wear corrective lenses.

First Day of Class (with students)

1. Distribute and discuss safety rules, safety symbols, and first aid guidelines. Have students to review safety symbols and guidelines.
2. Review safe use of equipment and chemicals.
3. Review use and location of safety equipment.
4. Discuss safe disposal of materials and laboratory cleanup policy.
5. Discuss proper laboratory attitude and conduct.
6. Document students' understanding of the preceding points. Have students sign a safety contract and return it.

Before Each MiniLAB or Lab

1. Perform each investigation yourself before assigning it.
2. Arrange the lab in such a way that equipment and supplies are clearly labeled and easily accessible.
3. Have available only equipment and supplies needed to complete the assigned investigation.
4. Review the procedure with students, emphasizing any caution statements or safety symbols that appear.
5. Be sure all students know the proper procedures to follow if an accident should occur.
6. Provide containers for disposing of chemicals, waste products, and biological specimens. Disposal methods should meet local guidelines.

During the MiniLAB or Lab

1. Make sure the lab is clean and free of clutter.
2. Insist that students wear goggles and aprons.
3. Never allow a student to work alone in the lab.
4. Never allow students to use a cutting device with more than one edge.
5. Students should not point the open end of a heated test tube toward anyone.
6. Remove broken glassware or frayed cords from use. Also clean up any spills immediately. Dilute solutions with water before removing.
7. Be sure all glassware that is to be heated is of a heat-treated type that will not shatter.
8. Remind students that hot glassware looks cool.
9. Prohibit eating and drinking in the lab.

After the MiniLAB or Lab

1. Be sure that the lab is clean.
2. Be certain that students have returned all equipment and disposed of broken glassware and chemicals properly.
3. Be sure that all hot plates and electrical connections are off.
4. Insist that each student wash his or her hands when lab work is completed.

Chemical Storage and Disposal

General Guidelines

Be sure to store all chemicals properly. The following are guidelines commonly used. Your school, city, county, or state may have additional requirements for handling chemicals. It is the responsibility of each teacher to become informed of the rules or guidelines in effect in his or her area.

1. Separate chemicals by reaction type. Strong acids should be stored together. Likewise, strong bases should be stored together and should be separated from acids. Oxidants should be stored away from easily oxidized materials, and so on.
2. Be sure all chemicals are stored in labeled containers indicating contents, concentration, source, date purchased (or prepared), any precautions for handling and storage, and expiration date.
3. Dispose of any outdated or waste chemicals properly according to accepted disposal procedures.
4. Do not store chemicals above eye level.
5. Wood shelving is preferable to metal. All shelving should be firmly attached to the wall and should have anti-roll edges.
6. Store only those chemicals that you plan to use.
7. Hazardous chemicals require special storage containers and conditions. Be sure to know which chemicals those are and the accepted practices for your area. Some substances must be stored outside the building.
8. When working with chemicals or preparing solutions, observe the same general safety precautions that you would expect from students. These include wearing an apron and goggles. Wear gloves and use the fume hood when necessary. Students will want to do as you do whether they admit it or not.
9. If you are a new teacher in a particular laboratory, it is your responsibility to survey the chemicals stored there to be sure they are stored properly. If not, they should be disposed of. Consult the rules and laws in your area concerning which chemicals can be kept in your classroom. For disposal, consult up-to-date disposal information from state and federal governments.

Disposal of Chemicals

Local, state, and federal laws regulate the proper disposal of chemicals. These laws should be consulted before chemical disposal is attempted. Although many substances encountered in the science classroom can be flushed down the drain with plenty of water, it is not safe to assume that this is always true. Teachers who use chemicals should consult the following book from the National Research Council:

Prudent Practices in the Laboratory. Washington, DC: National Academy Press, 1995. This book is useful and was revised in 1995. Current laws in your area would, of course, supersede the information in this book.

DISCLAIMER

Glencoe Publishing Company makes no claims to the completeness of this discussion of laboratory safety and chemical storage. The material presented is not all-inclusive, nor does it address all of the hazards associated with handling, storing, and disposing of chemicals, or with laboratory management.

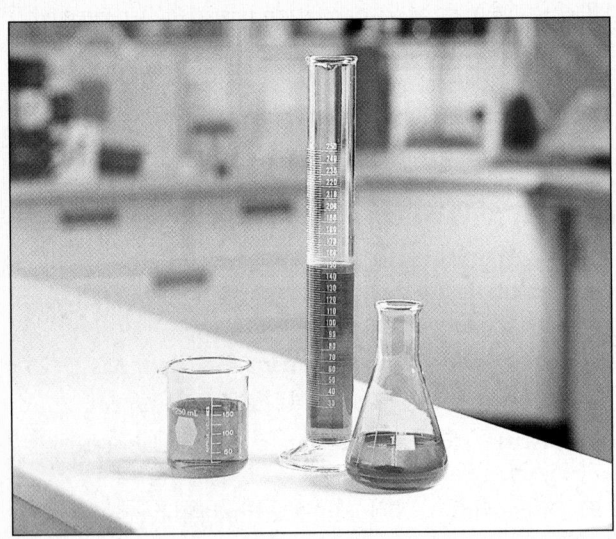

Preparation of Solutions

It is important to use safe laboratory techniques when handling all chemicals. Always check the MSDS (Material Safety Data Sheet) for each chemical before using it in the classroom. Many substances might appear harmless, but might be toxic, corrosive, or very reactive. Chemicals should never be ingested. Use proper techniques to smell any chemical, wear safety goggles and an apron in the laboratory, and observe the following precautions.

1. **Dilution of Acids and Bases** When diluting acids with water, always add the acids to the water. Never add water to acids. When sulfuric acid and sodium hydroxide are added to water, a large amount of thermal energy is released. Use extra care when handling these substances.

2. **Poisonous and Corrosive Liquids or Vapors** Use a fume hood if possible. Examples include hydrochloric acid, acetic acid, nitric acid, and ammonium hydroxide.

3. **Poisonous and Corrosive to Eyes, Lungs, and Skin** Examples include acids, bases, silver nitrate, iodine, and potassium permanganate.

Bromthymol blue: Add 0.5 g bromthymol blue powder to 500 mL distilled water to make a BTB stock solution. Dilute 40 mL BTB stock solution to 2 L with distilled water. Solution should be bright blue. If not, add one drop of NaOH at a time, swirling to mix. Check color.

Hydrochloric acid (HCL) solution: To make a 5% solution, add 13.6 mL concentrated HCl to 73 mL water while stirring. To make a 0.1*M* solution, add 1 mL concentrated hydrochloric acid to 100 mL water while stirring.

Iodine solution/Iodine stain: Dilute 1 part Lugol's solution with 15 parts water.

Lugol's solution: Dissolve 10 g potassium iodide in 100 mL distilled water. Then add and dissolve 5 g iodine. Store in dark bottle. Keeps indefinitely.

Phenolphthalein indicator: From a drug store, buy a package of any laxative that contains phenolphthalein. To make 1% solution, mash 4 tablets and pour the powder into 10 mL of rubbing alcohol. Let mixture soak for 15 minutes. Pour liquid into and store in a dropper bottle.

Potassium permanganate: For a 0.01*M* solution of potassium permanganate, dissolve 0.15 g $KMnO_4$ in 100 mL water.

Red cabbage concentrate: Put 5 leaves of red cabbage in a pot. Add 1 L of water, bring to a boil, and simmer until water turns a deep purple. Pour liquid through a strainer or piece of cheesecloth into a storage bottle. Keep refrigerated.

Salt solution: For a 3.5% salt (NaCl) solution that simulates the concentration of ocean water, dissolve 35 g of salt (NaCl) in 965 mL of water. For a 1% solution (weak), dissolve 1 g of salt (NaCl) in 99 mL of water. For a 6% solution, dissolve 6 g of salt (NaCl) in 94 mL of water.

Silver nitrate solution: To make a 10% solution, put 5 g of silver nitrate in 50 mL of distilled water.

Sugar solution: Add 1 tablespoon of sugar to 1 cup of warm water in a deep jar or flask. Stir to dissolve.

Sodium hydroxide (dilute): To make a 1% solution, dissolve 1 g NaOH in 99 mL of water.

Equipment and Materials List

These easy-to-use tables of equipment and consumable materials can help you prepare for your science classes for the year. Refer to the Chapter Organizer in front of each chapter for a list of equipment and materials used for each laboratory activity in the chapter.

Consumables

Material	Launch Lab (Chapter)	MiniLab (Chapter-Section)	Lab (Chapter-Section)
agar gel	21		
alcohol–rubbing, amyl, ethanol	20	22-4	24-2, 24-4
alum			23-2
aluminum foil		3-1, 8-1, 16-2, 25-1	7-3, 12-2, 15-1
antacid tablet		23-1	
bag, plastic		19-1	15-1
baking soda		23-3	15-2
balloon	16	16-3, 20-2	
battery–6-V dry cell, D cell	4, 7	7-3	7-2, 7-3, 8-3
bead, plastic		6-2	
beans, dried	17		1-3, 18-4
boxes, cardboard			4-1, 9-3
bread	24		
bulb(s)–flashlight, fluorescent, incandescent	7	7-2, 13-3	7-3
butter or wax		6-2	
cabbage			23-2
can of food		5-2	
candies–colored, green, red, yellow		18-2	18-4
candle		9-1	6-2
cardboard			5-3, 19-3
cardboard tube			8-3, 14-3
cereal		19-1	
chalk	23		15-1
chlorine standard solution		19-2	
clay		15-1, 18-4	13-4, 14-3
coffee can lids	9		
coffee filter			23-2
construction paper, red	12		
copper(II) bromide		21-4	
copper(II) sulfate	19		
corn meal			1-3
corn syrup		16-2	16-3
craft stick			25-3
cream of tartar			23-2
cups, foam		1-3, 8-1, 13-3	6-3
detergent, dish	13		16-3
envelope	17		
eraser		3-1	
filter, paper	23		
food coloring	6, 15, 20	16-2	
fruit preservative			23-2
glue		25-2	18-4, 25-3
gravel or pebbles		15-1, 25-2	
grease pencil			23-2
gumdrops		24-1	19-3
hydrochloric acid, 1*M*		23-1	
hydrogen peroxide, 3%			21-4
index cards		21-1	20-1
indicator, universal	21	23-1	
juice–orange, purple grape		17-3, 23-3	
manganese dioxide			21-4
milk		17-3	
molasses			16-3

Equipment and Materials List

Material	Launch Lab (Chapter)	MiniLab (Chapter-Section)	Lab (Chapter-Section)
oil, salad			1-3
oil, vegetable	20	16-2	16-3
paint–black, white	9		
pancake syrup			16-3
paper–black, blue, colored, orange, red		17-1, 24-3	4-2, 9-3, 25-3
paper, graph			4-2, 25-3
paper clip(s)	4, 8, 19	4-2, 17-3, 24-3, 25-1	2-3, 7-3, 14-1
paper clips, steel			8-3
paper towel(s)		22-4	19-2
pebbles		15-1	
pepper, black			6-2
peppercorns, whole		16-2	
phenolphthalein indicator solution, 1%			23-3
plaster of paris		20-3	
plastic food wrap	14	13-3	
polystyrene sheets, thin			19-3
poster board		14-1	18-4
potassium permanganate		15-2	
potassium permanganate solution, 0.01*M*			24-2
potato flakes			1-3
raisins		24-1	
rice–brown, white			1-3, 18-4
rope–heavy, light	5		10-1
rubber bands		2-3, 4-1	
salicylic acid			24-4
salt			15-1, 20-3, 22-3
sand		15-1, 25-2	21-4
seeds, dried			18-4
shampoo			16-3
silver nitrate solution		19-2	
soap, borax laundry			25-3
soda		17-3	
sodium chloride	19		
sodium hydrogen sulfite		15-2	
sodium hydroxide solution–dilute (0.1*M*), 6*M*			23-3, 24-2
soft drinks, colorless			23-3
soil		15-1	
spaghetti, thin			19-3
string		3-2, 11-1	1-3, 2-3, 4-2, 5-3, 10-1
strontium chloride	19		
sugar–granular, cubes	18	22-1	20-3, 22-4
sulfuric acid, concentrated			24-4
tape–cellophane, duct, masking	4	2-1, 8-1	1-3, 2-3, 3-3, 4-1, 7-3, 8-3, 9-3, 14-1, 14-3
thread		8-1	
toothpicks		24-1	
vinegar–salad, white		23-3	1-3, 16-3
water–bottled, carbonated, distilled	23	19-2, 22-1	22-3, 22-4
wax paper			23-2
wire–copper, insulated, steel, 22-gauge insulated	7, 25	7-2	7-2, 8-3, 15-1
wool or fur		20-2	
Nonconsumables			
aluminum chimney		9-1	
aluminum sample			19-2
baby food jars		12-2	
balance			1-3, 3-3, 4-1, 5-3
baseball		17-3	3-3
beaker	6, 15, 16, 23, 25	6-2, 9-1, 12-2, 15-2, 16-2, 16-3, 18-4, 23-1	6-2, 6-3, 16-1, 16-3, 21-4, 22-3, 24-4, 25-3, 25-4
board		2-3	5-3
book(s)		8-1, 12-1	2-3, 12-2
bowl		19-1, 20-3	12-2
broom handle	5		
bulb holder			7-2

Equipment and Materials List

Material	Launch Lab (Chapter)	MiniLab (Chapter-Section)	Lab (Chapter-Section)
calcium sample			19-2
can opener, manual		5-2	
cart		2-3	
chair		11-1	
cloth		8-1, 9-2, 11-2, 17-3	
compact disk	13		
compass, magnetic			8-3
conductivity tester		25-1	19-2
container, clear		15-1	13-4
cup, short, opaque		13-1	
dime		17-3	5-3
dishes			19-2
dominoes			18-4
double pulleys			5-3
drinking glass–small, medium-sized		12-1, 22-1, 23-1	
dropper(s)		22-4	23-3
evaporating dish	15		15-2
feather		17-3	
filters, polarizing			13-4
flashlight	13		12-2
funnel, glass	23		
gloves	19		
gloves, heat-resistant	15		
golf ball		17-3	
golf ball, plastic, slotted		3-2	
graduated cylinder, 10-mL	20	1-2	1-3, 15-2, 21-4, 22-4, 23-3, 24-2, 24-4, 25-3
granite			15-1
hair dryer		20-3	
hammer, small			19-2
hot plate	15, 16, 22		6-2, 6-3, 15-2, 16-1, 21-4, 22-4, 22-3, 24-4
knife–butter, paring		8-1	6-3
lab burner	19, 20, 24, 25		20-3
lamp or flashlight			13-4
lens–eyepiece, objective			14-3
light		14-1	
lights, small with sockets			7-3
long exercise rubber band			10-1
magnesium sample			19-2
magnet	8	8-1, 19-1	8-3
magnifying lens			15-2
mallet	10	10-3, 17-3, 18-4	
marbles, glass or steel balls			16-3
marking pen			1-3
measuring cup			1-3
measuring tablespoon			1-3
measuring teaspoon			1-3, 23-2
metal object		11-1	
meterstick	2, 18	2-1	3-3, 4-1, 4-2, 10-3, 11-4, 25-3
microwave		12-2	
mirror, plane			14-1
mitts, thermal	22		6-3
nail(s)–clean aluminum, iron or steel, 16-penny iron	21		8-3
nickel		4-1, 17-3	5-3
nut, steel		16-2	
nylon panty hose			10-1
pan, metal		12-1	
penny		13-1, 17-3, 22-4	
periodic table			20-1
pie plate		10-2	
plastic lid		1-3	
plate		8-1	
power supply, 0-6 V DC			8-3

Material	Launch Lab (Chapter)	MiniLab (Chapter-Section)	Lab (Chapter-Section)
prism, glass	13		
protractor			14-1
quarter			5-3
racquetball			3-3
radio		11-2	11-4
ramps or boards			2-3
ring clamp			16-1
ring stand		4-1, 8-1	2-3, 4-4, 16-4, 22-3, 22-4, 24-4
rock		3-1	
rod–aluminum or nail			8-3
rod–wood, steel, and fiberglass composite			25-3
rod supports			25-3
rubber ball			4-1
rubber hammer		20-3	
rubber stopper, 2-hole, medium			4-2
ruler	11, 18	3-1	5-3, 16-3, 17-3
scale, spring			2-3, 5-3, 25-3
scissors	9		1-3, 3-3, 7-3, 8-3, 14-3, 19-3
sewing needle		8-8	
softball	3		3-3
sound meter			11-4
spatula			19-2
splint, wooden			21-4
spoon–metal, plastic, wooden		6-2, 14-1	
spring scale			2-3, 5-3
spring toy			10-1, 10-3
springs			2-3
stand or support for pulleys			5-3
steel wool	4		
stirrer, copper wire			22-4
stop block		2-3	
stopper		14-3	24-2
stopwatch	2, 3	2-1	3-3, 9-3, 10-1, 10-3, 16-3, 18-4, 20-3
strontium sample			19-2
support for wooden board			5-3
support rod, 30-cm			4-2
support-rod clamp			4-2
table		13-1	
tape measure	16		
teaspoon, small plastic			21-4, 23-2
television		12-1	
television remote control		12-1	
tennis ball	3		3-3, 4-1
test tubes	24	19-2, 21-4	11-3, 20-3, 22-4, 23-3, 24-2, 24-4
test-tube clamp			4-2
test-tube holder, wire	24		20-3, 22-4, 24-4
test-tube rack			11-3, 21-4, 22-4
textbooks		2-3	
thermometer, Celsius		1-3, 13-3	6-3, 9-3, 16-1, 22-3, 22-4, 24-4
tin sample			19-2
tongs	4, 19, 25		
towel			10-1
toy car		2-1	2-3
tray, metal or plastic		1-3	
triple-beam balance			2-3
tuning fork		10-3	
vial			15-1
weight, 9.8 N			5-3
wire mesh			16-1
wood block		3-1	

Suppliers

Equipment Suppliers

American Science & Surplus
P.O. Box 1030
Skokie, IL 60076
(847) 647-0011
www.sciplus.com

Bio-Rad Laboratories
2000 Alfred Nobel Dr.
Life Science Group
Hercules, CA 94547
(800) 424-6723
www.bio-rad.com

Carolina Biological Supply Co.
2700 York Road
Burlington, NC 27215
(800) 334-5551
www.carolina.com

Edmund Scientific Company
60 Pearce Ave.
Tonawanda, NY 14150
(800) 728-6999
www.scientificsonline.com

Fisher Science Education
Educational Materials Division
4500 Turnberry Dr.
Hanover Park, IL 60133
(800) 955-1177
www.fisheredu.com

Flinn Scientific
P.O. Box 219
770 N. Raddant Rd.
Batavia, IL 60510
(800) 452-1261
www.flinnsci.com

Frey Scientific, Div. of Beckley Cardy
100 Paragon Parkway
Mansfield, OH 44903
(800) 225-FREY
www.freyscientific.com

Nasco Science
901 Janesville Avenue
P.O. Box 901
Fort Atkinson, WI 53538-0901
(800) 558-9595
www.enasco.com

Nebraska Scientific
3823 Leavenworth St.
Omaha, NE 68105-1180
(800) 228-7117
nebraskascientific.com

PASCO Scientific
P.O. Box 619011
10101 Foothills Blvd.
Roseville, CA 95747
(800) 772-8700
www.pasco.com

Sargent-Welch/VWR Scientific Products
P.O. Box 4130
Buffalo, NY 14217
(800) SAR-GENT 727-4368
www.SargentWelch.com

Science Kit and Boreal Laboratories
777 East Park Dr.
Tonawanda, NY 14150
(800) 828-7777
www.sciencekit.com

Ward's Natural Science Est.
5100 W. Henrietta Road
P.O. Box 92912
Rochester, NY 14692-9012
(800) 962-2660
www.wardsci.com

Audiovisual Distributors

Bullfrog Films
P.O. Box 149
Oley, PA 19547
(800) 543-FROG(3764)
www.bullfrogfilms.com

Discovery Channel School
Silver Springs, MD 20910
(240) 662-2000
www.discoveryschool.com

Films for the Humanities and Sciences
P.O. Box 2053
Princeton, NJ 08543
(800) 257-5126
www.filmsmediagroup.com

Flinn Scientific
P.O. Box 219
770 N. Raddant Rd.
Batavia, IL 60510
(800) 452-1261
www.flinnsci.com

Frey Scientific, Div. of Beckley Cardy
100 Paragon Parkway
Mansfield, OH 44903
(800) 225-FREY
www.freyscientific.com

National Geographic Society Educational Services
1145 17th Street, N.W.
Washington, DC 20036
(800) 368-2728
www.nationalgeographic.com

Phoenix Learning Group Coronet/MTI Film & Video
2349 Chaffee Dr.
St. Louis, MO 63146
(800) 221-1274
www.phoenixlearninggroup.com

Scholastic, Inc.
555 Broadway
New York, NY 10012-3999
(800) 724-6527
www.scholastic.com

Videodiscovery Inc.
920 N. 34th St.
Suite 300
Seattle, WA 98103
(800) 548-3472

Software Distributors

Boreal Laboratories, Ltd.
399 Vansickle Rd.
St. Catharines, Ontario,
L2S 3T4
Canada
(800) 387-9393
boreal.com

Educational Activities, Inc.
1937 Grand Ave.
Baldwin, NY 11510
(800) 797-3223
www.edact.com

IBM Education
www.solutions.ibm.com/k12

J. Weston Walch, Publisher
321 Valley St.
P.O. Box 658
Portland, ME 04104-0658
(800) 341-6094
www.walch.com

Scholastic, Inc.
555 Broadway
New York, NY 10012-3999
(800) 724-6527
www.scholastic.com

Sunburst Technology
1550 Executive Drive
Elgin, IL 60123
(800) 321-7511
www.SUNBURST.com

Contents In Brief

Contents

unit 1 Energy and Motion—2

chapter 1 The Nature of Science—4

chapter 2 Motion—36

chapter 3 Forces—66

chapter 4 Energy—98

In each chapter, look for these opportunities for review and assessment:
- Reading Checks
- Caption Questions
- Section Review
- Chapter Study Guide
- Chapter Review
- Standardized Test Practice
- Online practice at gpscience.com

chapter 5 Work and Machines—124

chapter 6 Thermal Energy—156

unit 2 Electricity and Energy Resources—188

chapter 7 Electricity—190

Contents

In each chapter, look for these opportunities for review and assessment:

- Reading Checks
- Caption Questions
- Section Review
- Chapter Study Guide
- Chapter Review
- Standardized Test Practice
- Online practice at gpscience.com

chapter 11 Sound—320

chapter 12 Electromagnetic Waves—352

chapter 13 Light—382

chapter 14 Mirrors and Lenses—414

unit 4 The Nature of Matter—446

In each chapter, look for these opportunities for review and assessment:
- **Reading Checks**
- **Caption Questions**
- **Section Review**
- **Chapter Study Guide**
- **Chapter Review**
- **Standardized Test Practice**
- **Online practice at gpscience.com**

Diversity of Matter—566

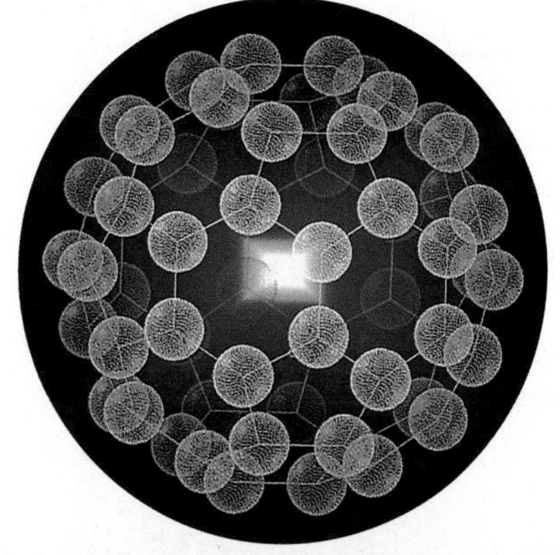

Interactions of Matter—660

Solutions—662

Acids, Bases, and Salts—694

Organic Compounds—724

New Materials Through Chemistry—756

Student Resources—786

In each chapter, look for these opportunities for review and assessment:

- **Reading Checks**
- **Caption Questions**
- **Section Review**
- **Chapter Study Guide**
- **Chapter Review**
- **Standardized Test Practice**
- **Online practice at gpscience.com**

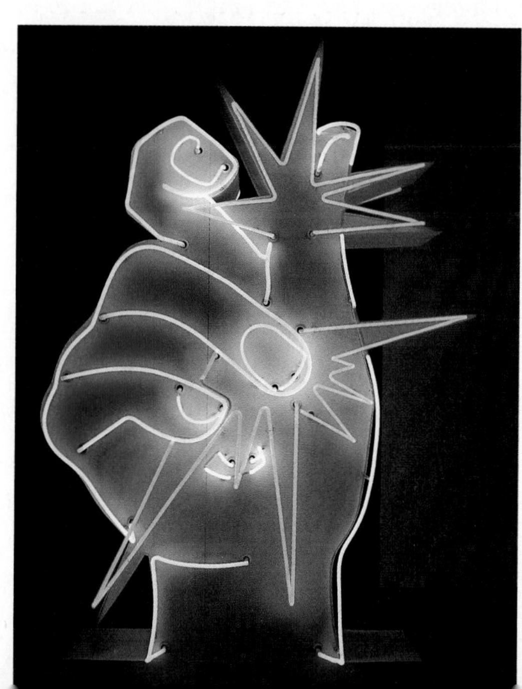

Cross-Curricular Readings

Content Details

NATIONAL GEOGRAPHIC Unit Openers

NATIONAL GEOGRAPHIC VISUALIZING

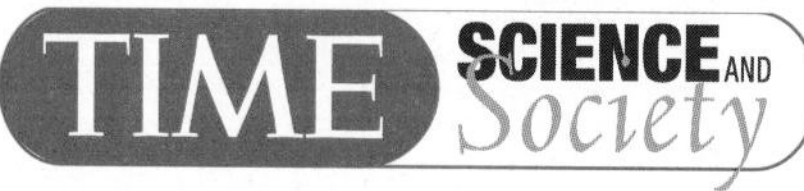

TIME SCIENCE AND HISTORY

Oops! Accidents in SCIENCE

Science and Language Arts

SCIENCE Stats

(DVD) available as a video lab on DVD

Mini LAB

Mini LAB Try at Home

DVD available as a video lab on DVD

Content Details

One-Page Labs

Two-Page Labs

Design Your Own Labs

Model and Invent Labs

Use the Internet Labs

Activities

Applying Math

Applying Science

INTEGRATE

Science Online

Standardized Test Practice

unit 1

Unit Contents

WebQuest ***Roller Coaster Physics*** is an investigation of coaster design, laws of motion, gravity, velocity, and acceleration. Students will use virtual programming to engineer, test, and evaluate roller coaster simulations. As a culminating activity, students will create their own roller coaster model and report on their results.

unit 1 Energy and Motion

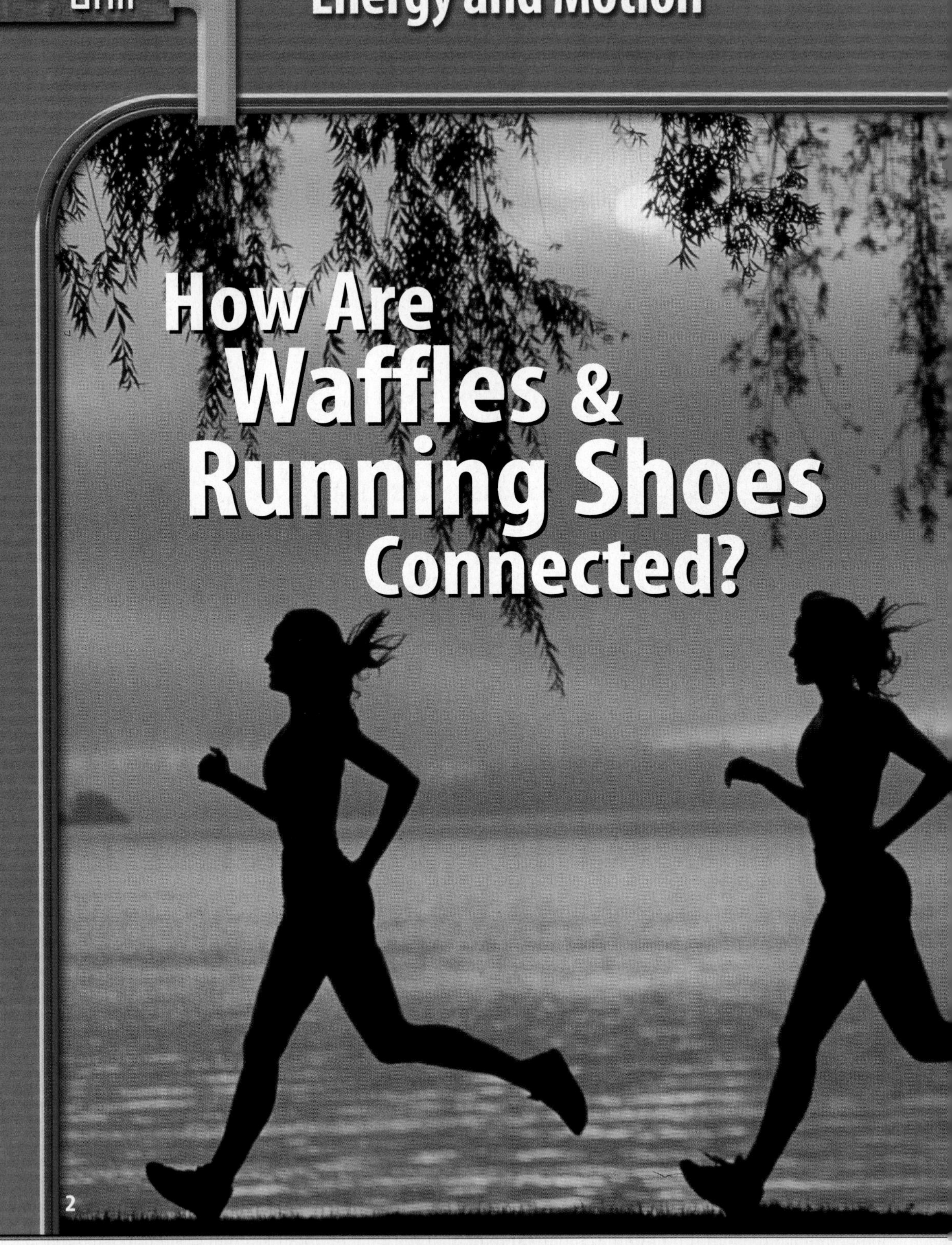
How Are Waffles & Running Shoes Connected?
2

PROJECT CRISS[SM]

Study Skills

Use of Graphics Changing words into pictures enables students to synthesize ideas. After finishing the unit, students in cooperative teams can use large sheets of paper and colored markers to map a selected topic through pictures, words, and diagrams. The various topics could include motion, speed, energy, friction, velocity, force, Newton's laws, inertia, work, and machines. Teams share their free-form maps with the class.

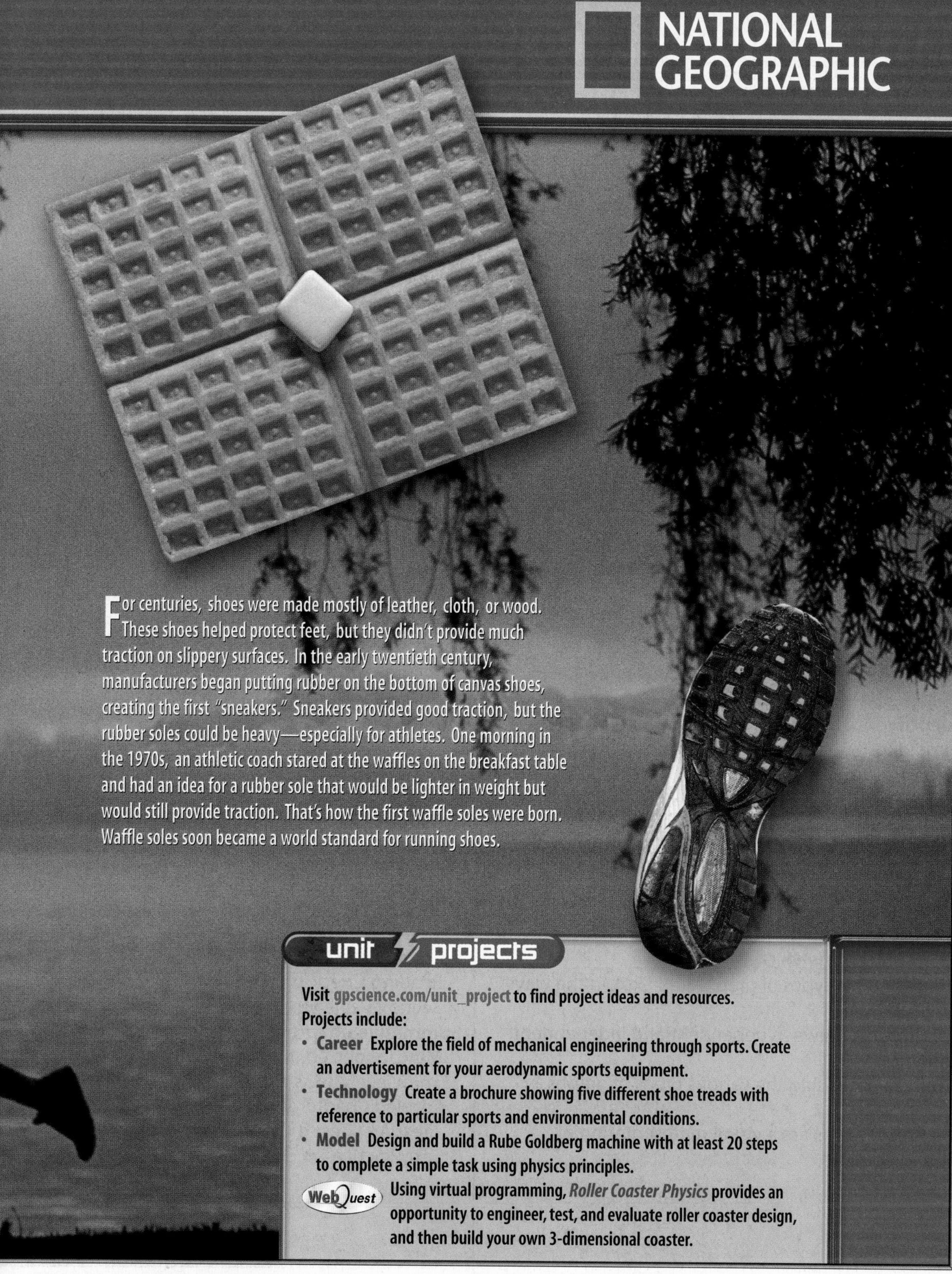

For centuries, shoes were made mostly of leather, cloth, or wood. These shoes helped protect feet, but they didn't provide much traction on slippery surfaces. In the early twentieth century, manufacturers began putting rubber on the bottom of canvas shoes, creating the first "sneakers." Sneakers provided good traction, but the rubber soles could be heavy—especially for athletes. One morning in the 1970s, an athletic coach stared at the waffles on the breakfast table and had an idea for a rubber sole that would be lighter in weight but would still provide traction. That's how the first waffle soles were born. Waffle soles soon became a world standard for running shoes.

unit projects

Visit gpscience.com/unit_project to find project ideas and resources.
Projects include:

- **Career** Explore the field of mechanical engineering through sports. Create an advertisement for your aerodynamic sports equipment.
- **Technology** Create a brochure showing five different shoe treads with reference to particular sports and environmental conditions.
- **Model** Design and build a Rube Goldberg machine with at least 20 steps to complete a simple task using physics principles.

WebQuest Using virtual programming, *Roller Coaster Physics* provides an opportunity to engineer, test, and evaluate roller coaster design, and then build your own 3-dimensional coaster.

NATIONAL GEOGRAPHIC **How Are Waffles & Running Shoes Connected?**

- Ask students how many of them have slipped when wearing an old pair of running shoes because the tread was worn.
- Have students compare the tread pattern in several pairs of their shoes and hypothesize how each affects friction. Ask them how the intended surface affects what type of tread is on the shoe.

unit projects

Career Have students explore the careers available to mechanical engineers in sports—equipment designer or participant. Have students write an advertisement for their particular sport and its equipment, stating why their friction and aerodynamic design is the best for that sport and its conditions. Some choices include car racing, rollerblading or ice skating, bike racing, skiing, bobsledding, or boat, car, or monster-truck competition.

Technology Ask students to examine, sketch, or do rubbings of a variety of soles of shoes. Have students research and then draw conclusions about how the different treads affect the friction between the shoe and the ground. Have students create a brochure showing five different shoe treads with an explanation about how each type of sole might suit a shoe to a particular activity or environmental condition. Students should analyze how today's technology has made advancements in shoe design, sports, and safety possible.

Model Ask students to design and build a Rube Goldberg machine. Have students use and connect everyday machines to achieve a simple task in at least 20 steps. Limits on size and run time inspire creative students to apply physics principles to complete a simple task in a fun and ingenious way. More information on state and national competitions is available at the link below.

Additional Resources For more information, resources, and assessment rubrics, visit gpscience.com/unit_project

The Nature of Science

BIG Idea Science is a method of learning and communicating information about the natural world.

	Content Standards	Learning Objectives	Resources to Assess Mastery
Section 1	**5–8:** UCP.1–3, 5; A.1, 2; F.5; G.2 **9–12:** UCP.1–3, 5; A.1, 2; F.5; G.2	**The Methods of Science** **1. Identify** the steps scientists often use to solve problems. **2. Describe** why scientists use variables. **3. Compare and contrast** science and technology. ***Main Idea*** Scientific investigations don't always proceed with identical steps but do contain similar methods.	**Formative Assessment** Reading Check, pp. 7, 9, 10, 12 Section Review, p. 13 **Summative Assessment** *ExamView® Assessment Suite*
Section 2	5–8: UCP.1–3, 5; A.1, 2; F.5; G.2 **9–12:** UCP.1–3, 5; A.1, 2; F.5; G.2	**Standards of Measurement** **4. Name** the prefixes used in SI and indicate what multiples of ten each one represents. **5. Identify** SI units and symbols for length, volume, mass, density, time, and temperature. **6. Convert** related SI units. ***Main Idea*** Standard measurement units, such as centimeters and seconds, are exact quantities used to compare measurements.	**Formative Assessment** Reading Check, pp. 15, 21 Section Review, p. 21 **Summative Assessment** *ExamView® Assessment Suite*
Section 3	**5–8:** UCP.1–3, 5; A.1, 2; F.5; G.2 **9–12:** UCP.1–3, 5; A.1, 2; F.5; G.2 See pp. 16T–17T for a Key to Standards.	**Communicating with Graphs** **7. Identify** three types of graphs and explain the ways they are used. **8. Distinguish** between dependent and independent variables. **9. Analyze** data using the various types of graphs. ***Main Idea*** Graphs are a visual representation of numerical data.	**Formative Assessment** Reading Check, pp. 22, 25 Section Review, p. 26 **Summative Chapter Assessment** MindJogger, Ch. 1 *ExamView® Assessment Suite* Leveled Chapter Test Test A L1 Test B L2 Test C L3 Test Practice, pp. 34–35

Suggested Pacing				
Period	**Instruction**	**Labs**	**Review & Assessment**	**Total**
Single	4 days	3 days	2 days	9 days
Block	2 blocks	1.5 blocks	1 block	4.5 blocks

Core Instruction	Leveled Resources	Leveled Labs	Pacing: Period		Pacing: Block
Student Text, pp. 4–13 Section Focus Transparency, Ch. 1 Section 1 Interactive Chalkboard, Ch. 1, Section 1 Differentiated Instruction, pp. 7, 10	**Chapter *Fast File* Resources** Directed Reading for Content Mastery L1 Note-taking Worksheet, pp. 33, 34 Reinforcement L2 Enrichment L3 **Reading Essentials,** p. 2 L1 ELL **Science Notebook,** p. 1 ELL	**Launch Lab,** p. 5: nonstandard measuring devices *10 min* L2	**1**	Section 1, pp. 5–10 (includes Launch Lab)	**1**
			2	Section 1, pp. 11–13 (includes Section Review)	
Student Text, pp. 14–21 Section Focus Transparency, Ch. 1, Section 2 Interactive Chalkboard, Ch. 1, Section 2 Identifying Misconceptions, p. 15 Applying Math, p. 16 Differentiated Instruction, pp. 15, 19, 20 Visualizing SI Dimensions, p. 20	**Chapter *Fast File* Resources** Directed Reading for Content Mastery , p. 20 L1 Note-taking Worksheet , pp. 33, 34 Reinforcement, p. 27 L2 Enrichment, p. 30 L3 **Reading Essentials,** p. 9 L1 ELL **Science Notebook,** p. 5 ELL ***Active*Folders**: *Measurement* L1 ELL	**MiniLAB,** p. 19: water, 100-mL graduated cylinder, unsharpened pencil, balance *15 min* L2 (Video Lab)	**3**	Section 2, pp. 12–18	**2**
			4	Section 2, pp. 19–21 (includes MiniLAB and Section Review)	
Student Text, pp. 22–29 Section Focus Transparency, Ch. 1, Section 3 Teaching Transparency, Ch. 1, Section 3 Interactive Chalkboard, Ch. 1, Section 2 Differentiated Instruction, pp. 23, 24 Applying Math, p. 24 Chapter Study Guide, p. 31	**Chapter *Fast File* Resources** Directed Reading for Content Mastery, p. 20 L1 Note-taking Worksheet , pp. 33, 34 Reinforcement, p. 28 L2 Enrichment, p. 31 L3 **Reading Essentials,** p. 16 L1 ELL **Science Notebook,** p. 8 ELL	**MiniLAB,** p. 25: plastic foam cup with lid and straw hole, thermometer, graph paper, timer with second hand, hot water *15 min* L2 **Lab,** p. 27: balance, 100-mL graduated cylinder, measuring cup, measuring spoons, cornmeal, dried beans, dried rice, potato flakes, water, vinegar, salad oil *30 min* L1 L2 L3 **Lab,** pp. 28–29: string, scissors, marking pen, masking tape, miscellaneous objects *75 min* L1 L2 L3 *Lab version A L1 version B L2 L3	**5**	Section 3, pp. 22–26 (includes MiniLab and Section Review)	**3**
			6	Lab:Converting Kitchen Measurements, p. 27	
			7	Lab:Setting High Standards for Measurements, pp. 28–29	**4**
			8	Lab:Setting High Standards for Measurements, pp. 28–29	
			9	Study Guide, Chapter Review, and Test Practice, pp. 31–35	**4.5**

(Video Lab icon) Video Lab

chapter 1 The Nature of Science

Transparencies

Section Focus

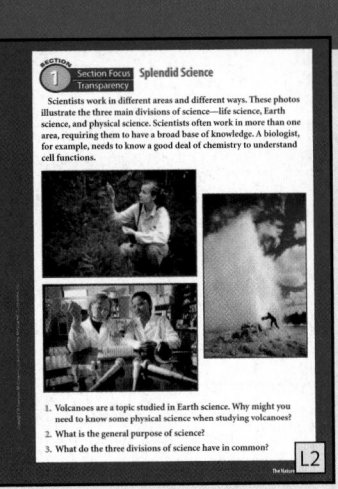

Section 1 Section Focus Transparency **Splendid Science**

Scientists work in different areas and different ways. These photos illustrate the three main divisions of science—life science, Earth science, and physical science. Scientists often work in more than one area, requiring them to have a broad base of knowledge. A biologist, for example, needs to know a good deal of chemistry to understand cell functions.

1. Volcanoes are a topic studied in Earth science. Why might you need to know some physical science when studying volcanoes?
2. What is the general purpose of science?
3. What do the three divisions of science have in common?

L2

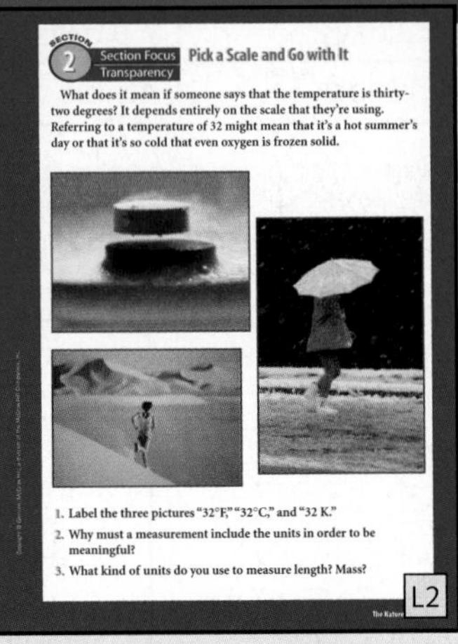

Section 2 Section Focus Transparency **Pick a Scale and Go with It**

What does it mean if someone says that the temperature is thirty-two degrees? It depends entirely on the scale that they're using. Referring to a temperature of 32 might mean that it's a hot summer's day or that it's so cold that even oxygen is frozen solid.

1. Label the three pictures "32°F," "32°C," and "32 K."
2. Why must a measurement include the units in order to be meaningful?
3. What kind of units do you use to measure length? Mass?

L2

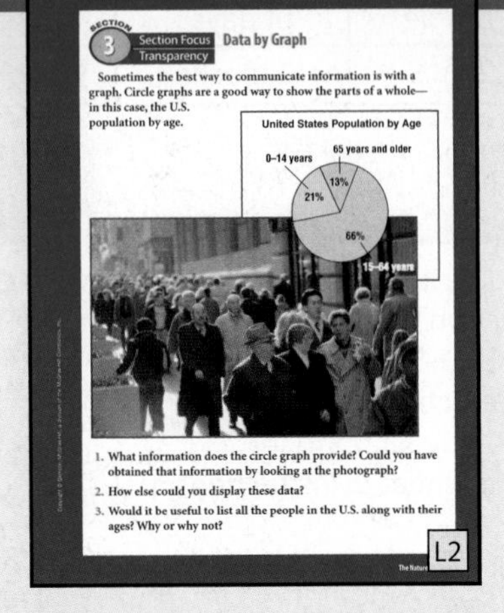

Section 3 Section Focus Transparency **Data by Graph**

Sometimes the best way to communicate information is with a graph. Circle graphs are a good way to show the parts of a whole—in this case, the U.S. population by age.

1. What information does the circle graph provide? Could you have obtained that information by looking at the photograph?
2. How else could you display these data?
3. Would it be useful to list all the people in the U.S. along with their ages? Why or why not?

L2

This is a representation of key blackline masters available in the Teacher Classroom Resources. See Resource Manager boxes within the chapter for additional information.

Assessment

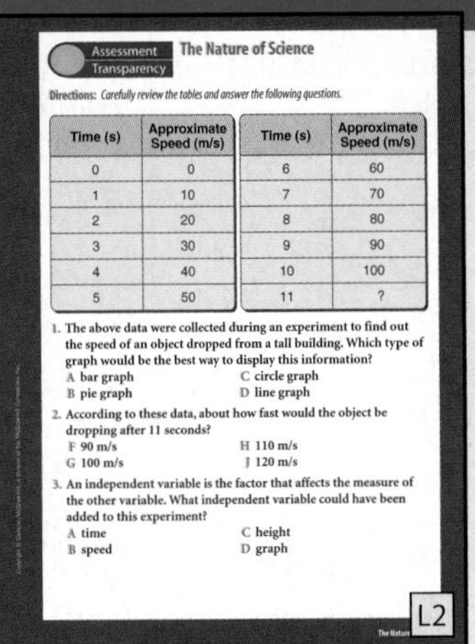

Assessment Transparency **The Nature of Science**

Directions: *Carefully review the tables and answer the following questions.*

Time (s)	Approximate Speed (m/s)	Time (s)	Approximate Speed (m/s)
0	0	6	60
1	10	7	70
2	20	8	80
3	30	9	90
4	40	10	100
5	50	11	?

1. The above data were collected during an experiment to find out the speed of an object dropped from a tall building. Which type of graph would be the best way to display this information?
   A bar graph C circle graph
   B pie graph D line graph
2. According to these data, about how fast would the object be dropping after 11 seconds?
   F 90 m/s H 110 m/s
   G 100 m/s J 120 m/s
3. An independent variable is the factor that affects the measure of the other variable. What independent variable could have been added to this experiment?
   A time C height
   B speed D graph

L2

Teaching

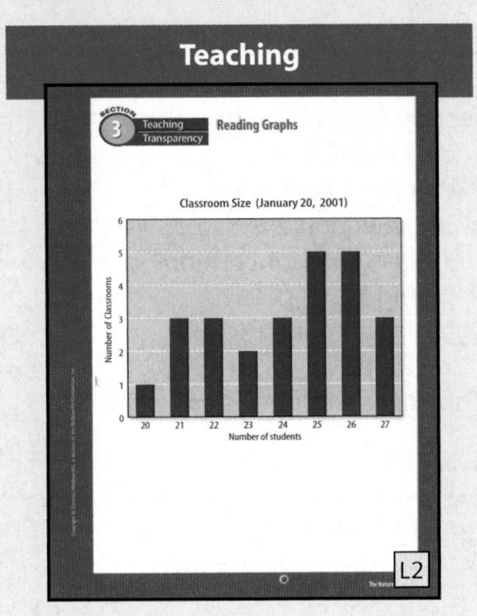

Section 3 Teaching Transparency **Reading Graphs**

L2

Key to Teaching Strategies

The following designations will help you decide which activities are appropriate for your students.

- L1 Level 1 activities should be appropriate for students with learning difficulties.
- L2 Level 2 activities should be within the ability range of all students.
- L3 Level 3 activities are designed for above-average students.
- ELL ELL activities should be within the ability range of English Language Learners.
- COOP LEARN Cooperative Learning activities are designed for small group work.
- LS Multiple Learning Styles logos, as described on page 12T, are used throughout to indicate strategies that address different learning styles.
- P These strategies represent student products that can be placed into a best-work portfolio.
- PBL Problem-Based Learning activities apply real-world situations to learning.

Hands-on Activities

Student Text Lab Worksheet

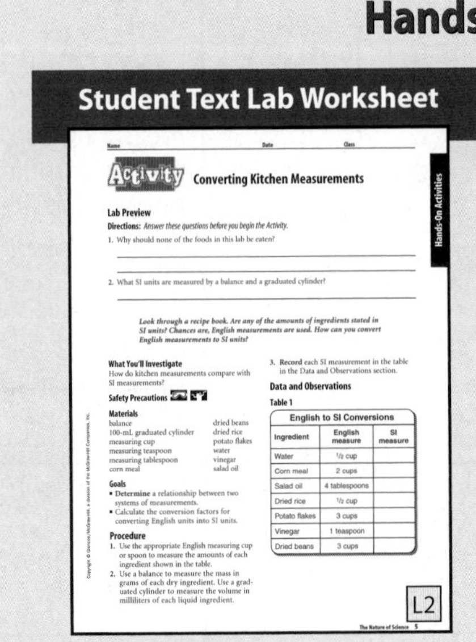

Name Date Class

Activity **Converting Kitchen Measurements**

Hands-On Activities

Lab Preview

Directions: *Answer these questions before you begin the Activity.*

1. Why should none of the foods in this lab be eaten?
2. What SI units are measured by a balance and a graduated cylinder?

Look through a recipe book. Are any of the amounts of ingredients stated in SI units? Chances are, English measurements are used. How can you convert English measurements to SI units?

What You'll Investigate

How do kitchen measurements compare with SI measurements?

Safety Precautions

Materials

balance, 100-mL graduated cylinder, measuring cup, measuring teaspoon, measuring tablespoon, corn meal, dried beans, dried rice, potato flakes, water, vinegar, salad oil

Goals

- **Determine** a relationship between two systems of measurements.
- Calculate the conversion factors for converting English units into SI units.

Procedure

1. Use the appropriate English measuring cup or spoon to measure the amounts of each ingredient shown in the table.
2. Use a balance to measure the mass in grams of each dry ingredient. Use a graduated cylinder to measure the volume in milliliters of each liquid ingredient.
3. **Record** each SI measurement in the table in the Data and Observations section.

Data and Observations

Table 1

English to SI Conversions

Ingredient	English measure	SI measure
Water	½ cup	
Corn meal	2 cups	
Salad oil	4 tablespoons	
Dried rice	½ cup	
Potato flakes	3 cups	
Vinegar	1 teaspoon	
Dried beans	3 cups	

L2

The Nature of Science 5

Laboratory Activities

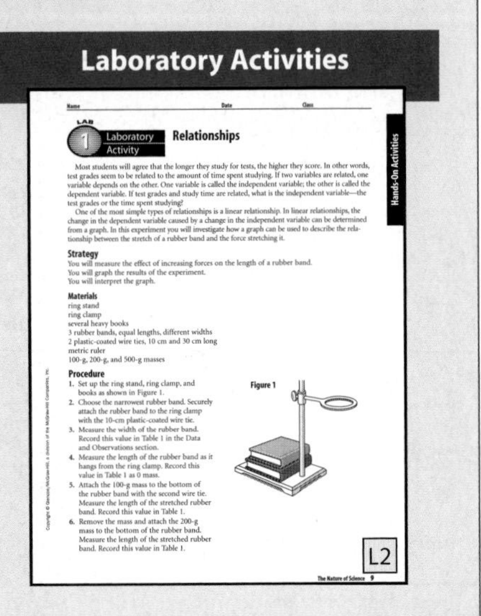

Name Date Class

Lab 1 Laboratory Activity **Relationships**

Hands-On Activities

Most students will agree that the longer they study for tests, the higher they score. In other words, test grades seem to be related to the amount of time spent studying. If two variables are related, one variable depends on the other. One variable is called the independent variable; the other is called the dependent variable. If test grades and study time are related, what is the independent variable—the test grades or the time spent studying?

One of the most simple types of relationships is a linear relationship. In linear relationships, the change in the dependent variable caused by a change in the independent variable can be determined from a graph. In this experiment you will investigate how a graph can be used to describe the relationship between the stretch of a rubber band and the force stretching it.

Strategy

You will measure the effect of increasing forces on the length of a rubber band.
You will graph the results of the experiment.
You will interpret the graph.

Materials

ring stand
ring clamp
several heavy books
3 rubber bands, equal lengths, different widths
2 plastic-coated wire ties, 10 cm and 30 cm long
metric ruler
100-g, 200-g, and 500-g masses

Procedure

1. Set up the ring stand, ring clamp, and books as shown in Figure 1.
2. Choose the narrowest rubber band. Securely attach the rubber band to the ring clamp with the 10-cm plastic-coated wire tie.
3. Measure the width of the rubber band. Record this value in Table 1 in the Data and Observations section.
4. Measure the length of the rubber band as it hangs from the ring clamp. Record this value in Table 1 as 0 mass.
5. Attach the 100-g mass to the bottom of the rubber band with the second wire tie. Measure the length of the stretched rubber band. Record this value in Table 1.
6. Remove the mass and attach the 200-g mass to the bottom of the rubber band. Measure the length of the stretched rubber band. Record this value in Table 1.

Figure 1

L2

The Nature of Science 9

Meeting Different Ability Levels

Content Outline

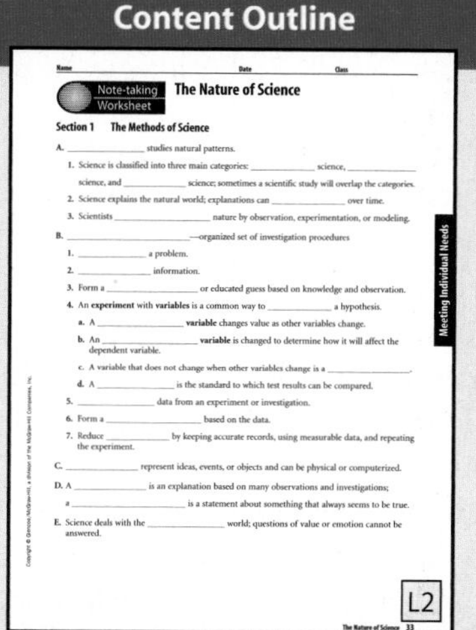

Note-taking Worksheet **The Nature of Science**

Section 1 The Methods of Science

L2

Reinforcement

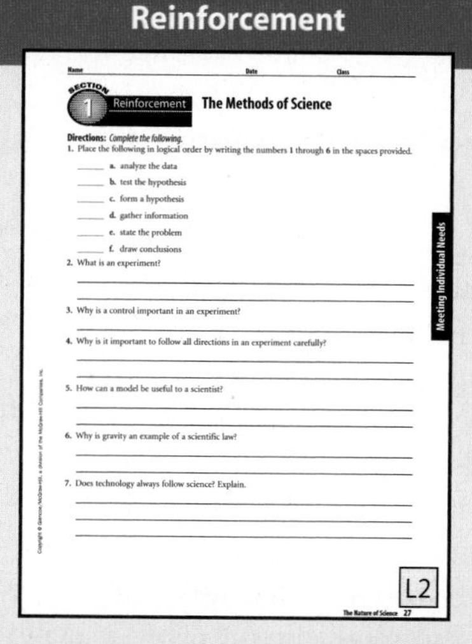

Section 1 Reinforcement **The Methods of Science**

L2

Enrichment

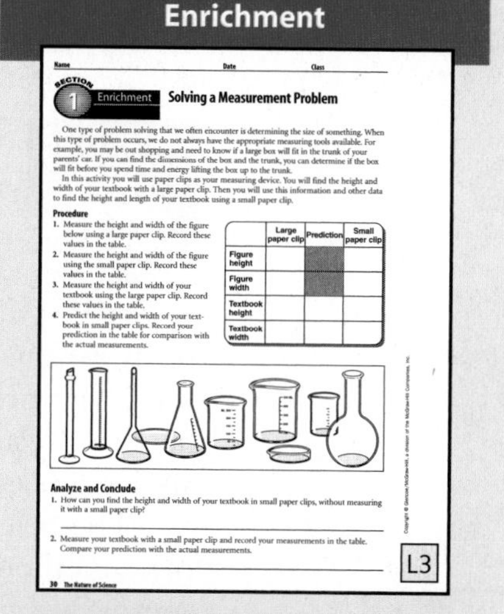

Section 1 Enrichment **Solving a Measurement Problem**

L3

Directed Reading (English/Spanish)

Directed Reading for Content Mastery *Overview* **The Nature of Science**

L1

Study Guide

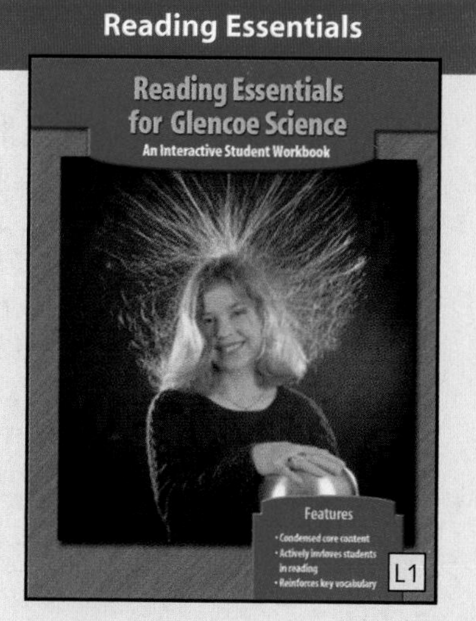

Study Guide
Features
• Contains a study guide page for each section of the chapter
• Reviews key concepts
• Includes answer pages

L2

Reading Essentials

Reading Essentials for Glencoe Science

An Interactive Student Workbook

Features

• Condensed core content

• Actively involves students in reading

• Reinforces key vocabulary

L1

Assessment

Test Practice Workbook

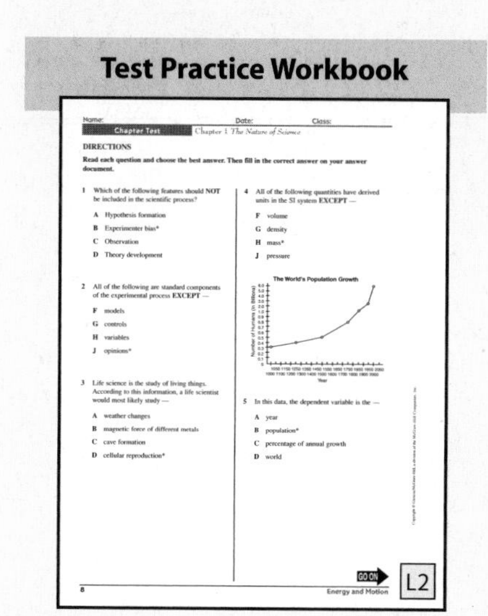

Chapter Test Chapter 1 The Nature of Science

L2

Chapter Review

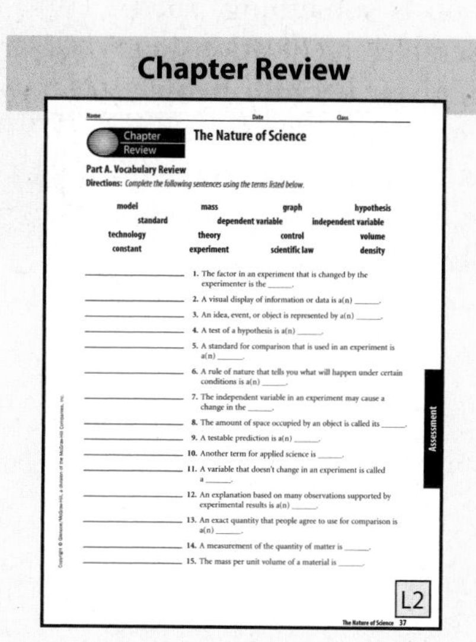

Chapter Review **The Nature of Science**

Part A. Vocabulary Review

L2

Chapter Tests

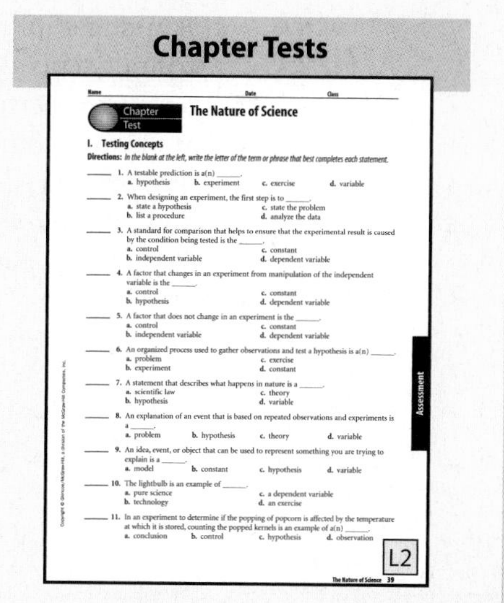

Chapter Test **The Nature of Science**

I. Testing Concepts

L2

Science Content Background

section 1 The Methods of Science

Scientific Methods

Many science educators are no longer using the term "The Scientific Method." This is because there is really no one method; an astronomer works in ways that are very different from those of a medical researcher. Also, science does not always proceed in the linear manner described by "The Scientific Method." The term "scientific methods" indicates that a variety of approaches are employed in scientific inquiry.

Investigations will sometimes use a null hypothesis. This null hypothesis is usually the opposite of the scientist's hypothesis for what will happen in the investigation. Thus if a medical researcher thinks Drug PR will help cure disease PQ, a null hypothesis could be that there will be no difference in symptoms between people who received PR and those who didn't receive it. If the data show that the null hypothesis is false, then this is evidence that the original hypothesis may be correct.

The term *experiment* should be reserved for occasions when scientists or students manipulate a variable to see the result. The independent variable is the thing or variable that is changed. This is done to see the effect on the dependent variable.

In human drug experiments, a drug is given to a treatment group and a placebo is given to a control group. A placebo is something, such as a sugar pill, that resembles medication but contains no drug. It is given because people often get better just because they believe they are taking something that will help even though they are not. The people in the drug experiment don't know whether they are taking the new drug or the placebo.

Using Science—Technology

Pure science is often contrasted with applied science. Pure science seeks knowledge just for the sake of knowledge. Applied science seeks to develop technologies that improve people's lives.

While science certainly leads to the development of technologies, technologies also lead to the development of science. The invention of the light microscope advanced the field of cell biology. Other technologies that have influenced science include gel electrophoresis, telescopes, and particle accelerators.

Barry L. Runk/Grant Heilman Photography, Inc.

Standards of Measurement

Measurement Systems

The SI system of measurement allows easy conversions among SI units. The SI system stops being easy when measurements are converted into English units. A gram is approximately the mass of one regular-size paper clip. A kilometer is 2.5 times around an Olympic track. A liter is just a bit more than a quart of milk.

Measuring Distance

A common metric unit for area is the hectare. One hectare is equal to 10,000 square meters.

Measuring Time and Temperature

Three systems of units are commonly used for temperature. Almost all the people in the world use the Celsius system. People in the United States use the Fahrenheit system. While United States scientists typically use the Celsius or Kelvin system, many United States meteorologists use Fahrenheit. The Kelvin is the official SI unit for temperature.

Measuring Matter

Water has a density of 1 g/cm^3, so if you didn't have a scale you could measure 5 g of water by using a graduated cylinder to measure 5 mL, which is 5 cm^3, of water. Objects that have a density greater than 1 g/cm^3 sink in water and those with a lower density float.

section 3 Communicating with Graphs

Choosing the Right Graph

Line graphs are appropriate for continuous data. Continuous data are numerical data that have an uninterrupted range of values such as time of travel, growth in height of a plant, or current flow in a wire. Bar graphs are appropriate for categorical or nominal data. These are data that fall into defined categories or that have specific names such as boys and girls, types of primates, or types of fruits.

Teacher to Teacher
Erin Peters, Lead Science Teacher
Williamsburg Middle School
Arlington, VA

"When discussing the nature of science it is important to distinguish between observation and inference. Place raisins in carbonated water with yellow food coloring and lead the students to believe that they are 'sewer slugs,' (fictitious) animals that purify sewage. When the students realize the 'animals' are fictitious, begin to analyze which of their statements were observations and which statements were inferences. In addition, discuss what statements are appropriate for a scientific discussion, as opposed to everyday conversations."

Erin Peters

chapter content resources

Internet Resources
For additional content background, visit gpscience.com to:

- access your book online
- find references to related articles in popular science magazines
- access Web links with related content background
- access current events with science journal topics

Print Resources

Science and Technology, by Oxford University, 1993

Classroom Critters and the Scientific Method, by Sally Kneidel, Fulcrum Publishers, 1999

The Wild Side—Weird Science, by Henry Billings, Jamestown Publishers, 2001

ABOUT THE PHOTO

Space Shuttle Experiments The photo shows the launch of the space shuttle *Discovery* on September 29, 1988. This mission carried several experiments on board, including experiments involving protein crystal growth and the aggregation of red blood cells under conditions of apparent weightlessness.

Science Journal Possible answers might include to learn the properties of planets, stars, and galaxies and how they were formed; the history of the universe; and how life on Earth is affected by what happens in space.

BIG Idea

Testing Hypotheses A hypothesis can be thought of as an answer to a scientific question. For a hypothesis to be considered correct, it must make a prediction or predictions that can be tested by experimentation and observation of the natural world. However, even though the hypothesis might be initially verified, at a later time it might be inconsistent with new data and observations. Then a new hypothesis must be proposed, or the existing hypothesis modified, to be consistent with the new information. The new or modified hypothesis again must make predictions that can be verified by experiment or observation before it can be accepted.

Introduce the Chapter Have students list some problems they recently have tried to solve. Ask them to discuss the strategies they used to try to solve their problem. Ask them why they think their strategies worked or didn't work. Was there anything the successful problem-solving strategies had in common?

chapter 1

The Nature of Science

BIG Idea

Science is a method of learning and communicating information about the natural world.

1.1 The Methods of Science

MAIN Idea Scientific investigations don't always proceed with identical steps but do contain similar methods.

1.2 Standards of Measurement

MAIN Idea Standard measurement units, such as centimeters and seconds, are exact quantities used to compare measurements.

1.3 Communicating with Graphs

MAIN Idea Graphs are a visual representation of numerical data.

Out of This World

The space program was developed in response to many unanswered questions. Scientists have worked together to develop ways in which to answer those questions. In this chapter, you will learn how scientists learn about the natural world.

Science Journal

Look at the picture above. Write in your Science Journal why scientists study space.

4

Interactive Chalkboard

This CD-ROM is an editable Microsoft® PowerPoint® presentation that includes:

- an editable presentation for every chapter
- additional chapter questions
- animated graphics
- image bank
- links to gpscience.com

Start-Up Activities

Understanding Measurements

During a track meet, one athlete ran 1 mile in 5 min and another athlete ran 5,000 m in 280 s. The two runners used different units to describe their races, so how can you compare them? Do the following lab to explore how using different units can make it difficult to compare measurements.

1. Measure the distance across your classroom using your foot as a measuring device.
2. Record your measurement and name your measuring unit.
3. Now, have your partner measure the same distance using his or her foot as the measuring device. Record this measurement and make up a different name for the unit.
4. **Think Critically** Explain why you think it might be important to have standard, well-defined units to make measurements.

Preview this chapter's content and activities at gpscience.com

Scientific Processes Make the following Foldable to help identify what you already know, what you want to know, and what you learned about science.

STEP 1 **Fold** a vertical sheet of paper from side to side. Make the front edge about 1.25 cm shorter than the back edge.

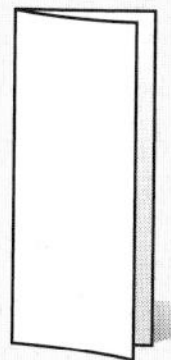

STEP 2 **Turn** lengthwise and **fold** into thirds.

STEP 3 **Unfold and cut** only the top layer along both folds to make three tabs. **Label** each tab.

Identify Questions Before you read the chapter, write what you already know about science under the left tab of your Foldable, and write questions about what you'd like to know under the center tab. After you read the chapter, list what you learned under the right tab.

Purpose Use the Launch Lab activity to introduce students to nonstandard measuring units. L1 ELL COOP LEARN

LS **Interpersonal**

Materials Do not make standard measuring devices, such as metersticks, available.

Teaching Strategy Have students repeat the lab, measuring a different distance.

Think Critically

Only measurements made using the same standard can be easily compared. Standard units of measurement make it possible to compare measurements by different people in different locations.

Assessment

Oral Have students draw cartoons that explain the limitations of the measurements they made. It is difficult to measure fractions of units accurately and to compare data from groups that use different units. Use **Performance Assessment in the Science Classroom,** p. 133.

Dinah Zike Study Fold

Student preparation materials for this Foldable are available in the **Chapter *Fast File* Resources.**

Additional Chapter Media

- Virtual Lab: *How is a controlled experiment performed?*
- Video Lab: *Determining the Density of a Pencil*

section 1 The Methods of Science

1 Motivate

Bellringer

Section Focus Transparencies also are available on the Interactive Chalkboard CD-ROM.

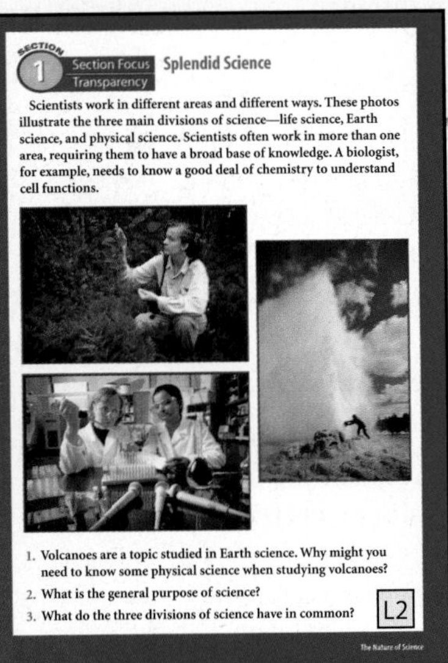

Section 1 Section Focus Transparency **Splendid Science**

Scientists work in different areas and different ways. These photos illustrate the three main divisions of science—life science, Earth science, and physical science. Scientists often work in more than one area, requiring them to have a broad base of knowledge. A biologist, for example, needs to know a good deal of chemistry to understand cell functions.

1. Volcanoes are a topic studied in Earth science. Why might you need to know some physical science when studying volcanoes?
2. What is the general purpose of science?
3. What do the three divisions of science have in common?

L2

The Nature of Science

Tie to Prior Knowledge

What is science? Discuss with students what they believe science to be. Have them compare their ideas with the definition of science given in the text.

Reading Guide

What You'll Learn

- **Identify** the steps scientists often use to solve problems.
- **Describe** why scientists use variables.
- **Compare and contrast** science and technology.

Why It's Important

Using scientific methods will help you solve problems.

Review Vocabulary

investigation: to observe or study by close examination

New Vocabulary

- scientific method
- hypothesis
- experiment
- variable
- dependent variable
- independent variable
- constant
- control
- bias
- model
- theory
- scientific law
- technology

What is science?

Science is not just a subject in school. It is a method for studying the natural world. After all, science comes from the Latin word *scientia,* which means "knowledge." Science is a process that uses observation and investigation to gain knowledge about events in nature.

Nature follows a set of rules. Many rules, such as those concerning how the human body works, are complex. Other rules, such as the fact that Earth rotates about once every 24 h, are much simpler. Scientists ask questions to learn about the natural world.

Major Categories of Science Science covers many different topics that can be classified according to three main categories. (1) Life science deals with living things. (2) Earth science investigates Earth and space. (3) Physical science deals with matter and energy. In this textbook, you will study mainly physical science. Sometimes, though, a scientific study will overlap the categories. One scientist, for example, might study the motions of the human body to understand how to build better artificial limbs. Is this scientist studying energy and matter or how muscles operate? She is studying both life science and physical science. It is not always clear what kind of science you are using, as shown in **Figure 1.**

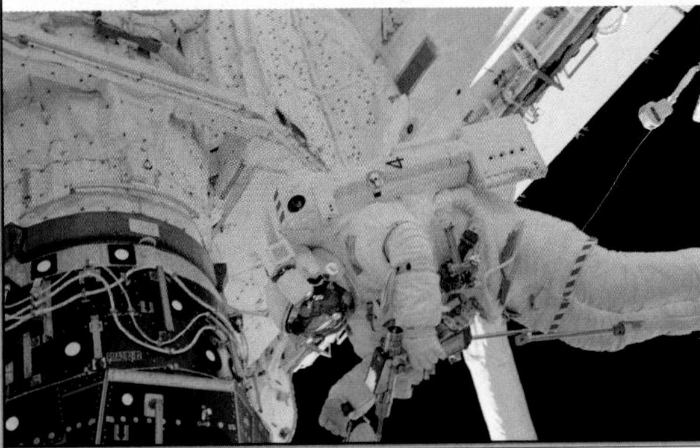

Figure 1 Astronaut Michael Lopez-Alegria uses a pistol grip tool on the *International Space Station.*
Observe *What evidence do you see of the three main branches of science in the photograph?*

Section 1 Resource Manager

Chapter *FAST FILE* Resources
- Transparency Activity, p. 44
- Note-taking Worksheets, pp. 33–34
- Enrichment, p. 30
- Directed Reading for Content Mastery, pp. 19, 20
- Reinforcement, p. 27

Reading and Writing Skill Activities, p. 37

Cultural Diversity, p. 29

Science Inquiry Labs, pp. 13–14

Science Explains Nature Scientific explanations help you understand the natural world. Sometimes these explanations must be modified. As more is learned about the natural world, some of the earlier explanations might be found to be incomplete or new technology might provide more accurate answers.

For example, look at **Figure 2.** In the late eighteenth century, most scientists thought that heat was an invisible fluid with no mass. Scientists observed that heat seemed to flow like a fluid. It also moves away from a warm body in all directions, just as a fluid moves outward when you spill it on the floor.

However, the heat fluid idea did not explain everything. If heat were an actual fluid, an iron bar that had a temperature of 1,000°C should have more mass than it did at 100°C because it would have more of the heat fluid in it. The eighteenth-century scientists thought they just were not able to measure the small mass of the heat fluid on the balances they had. When additional investigations showed no difference in mass, scientists had to change the explanation.

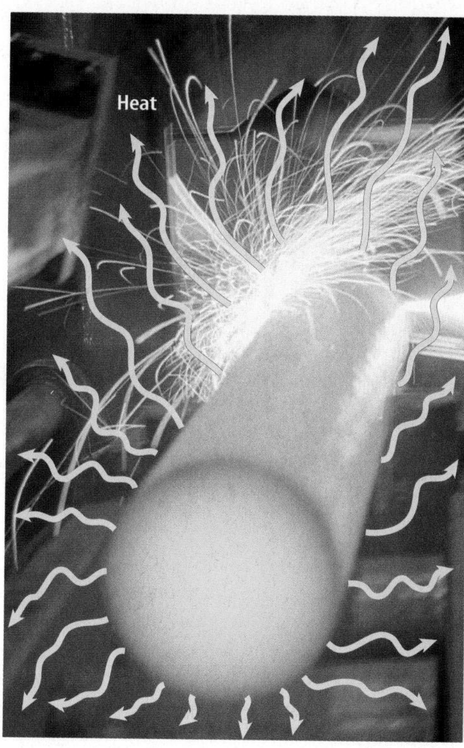

Figure 2 Many years ago, scientists thought that heat, such as in this metal rod, was a fluid.
Infer *how heat acts like a fluid.*

Investigations Scientists learn new information about the natural world by performing investigations, which can be done many different ways. Some investigations involve simply observing something that occurs and recording the observations, perhaps in a journal. Other investigations involve setting up experiments that test the effect of one thing on another. Some investigations involve building a model that resembles something in the natural world and then testing the model to see how it acts. Often, a scientist will use something from all three types of investigation when attempting to learn about the natural world.

Reading Check *Why do scientific explanations change?*

Scientific Methods

Although scientists do not always follow a rigid set of steps, investigations often follow a general pattern. An organized set of investigation procedures is called a **scientific method.** Six common steps found in scientific methods are shown in **Figure 3.** A scientist might add new steps, repeat some steps many times, or skip steps altogether when doing an investigation.

Topic: Prediction
Visit gpscience.com for Web links to information about why leaves change color in the autumn.

Activity Fill a glass with cold water and add a few drops of blue or red food coloring. Cut a piece of celery and place it in the glass. Over the next few days observe what happens to the celery. Make a prediction about why this occurs. Support your answer with evidence.

2 Teach

Activity

Venn Diagram Have students work as a class or in large groups. Have each group make a Venn diagram representing the three main branches of science. Place three overlapping circles on a large sheet of paper or a bulletin board and label each circle with one major category of science. Have them use pictures from newspapers and magazines to fill in the areas on the diagram. Be sure the overlap areas of the circles are large enough to accommodate examples that apply to more than one branch of science. Be sure students can justify each placement. L1 ELL COOP LEARN

LS **Visual-Spatial**

Caption Answers

Figure 1 physical science—pistol grip tool and other instruments; Earth science—event taking place in space; life science—space suit that allows a human body to survive in space

Figure 2 It flows from one location to another.

Reading Check

Answer Scientists are constantly learning new information by performing investigations.

Visual Learning

Figure 2 Discuss with students ways scientists study heat. Point out that scientists study the structure of the materials through which heat travels, why heat travels through them, and what heat really is. L1

LS **Logical-Mathematical**

Differentiated Instruction

Learning Disabled While science can answer many questions about how things work, what they are made of, and where things come from, it cannot answer questions that are opinion-based. Science cannot answer questions about art, politics, or literature. Science cannot tell you what is right, wrong, good, or bad. Have students brainstorm both questions that science can answer and those that science cannot answer. Ask students to explain why science can answer some questions, but not others. L1

Use an Analogy

Finding Class Ask students to describe how they found their different classrooms on the first day of school in this building. Explain that their methods are analogous to the way the scientific methods discussed in this section are used.

Use Science Words

Word Origin The word *experiment* is from the Latin word *experimentum*, which means "proof or test." Have students write entries in their Science Journals explaining how the meaning of the word reflects the meaning of its root. L2 LS **Linguistic**

Fun Fact

Experiments can be done to confirm a hypothesis about how an independent variable affects a dependent variable. They can also be done to confirm a null hypothesis. A null hypothesis states that the independent variable does not affect the dependent variable.

Discussion

Hypothesis Confirmed Why are results that do not confirm a hypothesis important? These experimental results can help scientists adjust and restate hypotheses. L2 LS **Logical-Mathematical**

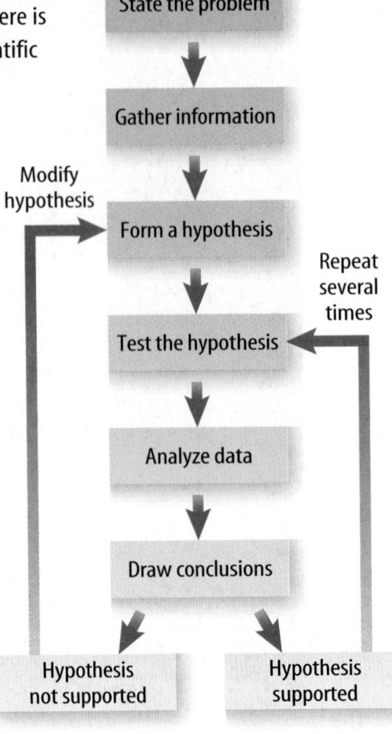

Figure 3 The series of procedures shown here is one way to use scientific methods to solve a problem.

Stating a Problem Many scientific investigations begin when someone observes an event in nature and wonders why or how it occurs. Then the question of "why" or "how" is the problem. Sometimes a statement of a problem arises from an activity that is not working. Some early work on guided missiles showed that the instruments in the nose of the missiles did not always work. The problem statement involved finding a material to protect the instruments from the harsh conditions of flight.

Later, National Aeronautics and Space Administration (NASA) scientists made a similar problem statement. They wanted to build a new vehicle—the space shuttle—that could carry people to outer space and back again. Guided missiles did not have this capability. NASA needed to find a material for the outer skin of the space shuttle that could withstand the heat and forces of reentry into Earth's atmosphere.

Researching and Gathering Information Before testing a hypothesis, it is useful to learn as much as possible about the background of the problem. Have others found information that will help determine what tests to do and what tests will not be helpful? The NASA scientists gathered information about melting points and other properties of the various materials that might be used. In many cases, tests had to be performed to learn the properties of new, recently created materials.

Forming a Hypothesis A **hypothesis** is a possible explanation for a problem using what you know and what you observe. NASA scientists knew that a ceramic coating had been found to solve the guided missile problem. They hypothesized that a ceramic material also might work on the space shuttle.

Testing a Hypothesis Some hypotheses can be tested by making observations. Others can be tested by building a model and relating it to real-life situations. One common way to test a hypothesis is to perform an experiment. An **experiment** tests the effect of one thing on another using controlled conditions.

Cultural Diversity

Herbal Medicine Principles of science have been used to solve problems throughout the world and throughout history. In the rain forests of Central and South America, plants are used to promote healing. For thousands of years the local people have observed and tested plants and learned which ones can be used for medicines. Today scientists from industries that specialize in manufacturing prescription drugs are working with these herbal healers to identify the materials in the plants that have medicinal value.

Variables An experiment usually contains at least two variables. A **variable** is a quantity that can have more than a single value. You might set up an experiment to determine which of three fertilizers helps plants to grow the biggest. Before you begin your tests, you would need to think of all the factors that might cause the plants to grow bigger. Possible factors include plant type, amount of sunlight, amount of water, room temperature, type of soil, and type of fertilizer.

In this experiment, the amount of growth is the **dependent variable** because its value changes according to the changes in the other variables. The variable you change to see how it will affect the dependent variable is called the **independent variable.**

Constants and Controls To be sure you are testing to see how fertilizer affects growth, you must keep the other possible factors the same. A factor that does not change when other variables change is called a **constant.** You might set up one trial, using the same soil and type of plant. Each plant is given the same amount of sunlight and water and is kept at the same temperature. These are constants. Three of the plants receive a different amount of fertilizer, which is the independent variable.

The fourth plant is not fertilized. This plant is a control. A **control** is the standard by which the test results can be compared. Suppose that after several days, the three fertilized plants grow between 2 and 3 cm. If the unfertilized plant grows 1.5 cm, you might infer that the growth of the fertilized plants was due to the fertilizers.

How might the NASA scientists set up an experiment to solve the problem of the damaged tiles shown in **Figure 4?** What are possible variables, constants, and controls?

Reading Check *Why is a control used in an experiment?*

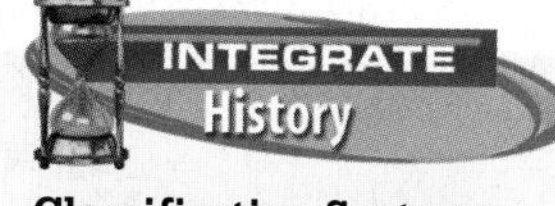

Classification Systems
Through observations of living organisms, Aristotle designed a classification system. Systems used today group organisms according to variables such as habits and physical and chemical features. Research to learn recent reclassifications of organisms. Share your findings with your class.

Figure 4 NASA has had an ongoing mission to improve the space shuttle. A technician is replacing tiles damaged upon reentry into Earth's atmosphere.

Activity

Create a Hypothesis Organize the class into teams and give each team a large index card on which to write a problem for an experiment. Have teams exchange their cards. Each team should generate a hypothesis for the question they hold and write it on the card. Have students exchange cards with a different group. Ask each team to devise an experiment based on the question and hypothesis on the card the team now has. Students should be sure to identify the constants, independent variable, dependent variable, and control in the experiment. L2 COOP LEARN LS **Logical-Mathematical**

Text Question Answer

They might make tiles of many different materials and subject them all to the heat and other stresses encountered by the shuttle. The variables would be the materials used, the constants would be the conditions to which the tiles were subjected, and scientists could use additional tiles that are made from the same materials as the tested tiles for the controls.

The science that deals with the naming and classifying of organisms is called taxonomy. Taxonomists continually collect and analyze data, sometimes changing the way organisms are classified as a result of their findings. Fungi, for example, were classified as plants until data convinced scientists to put fungi in their own kingdom.

Reading Check

Answer A control is a standard to which test results can be compared.

Active Reading

ReQuest To improve listening skills, have students listen carefully as you read the discussion of scientific methods in this section. After the reading, have students construct questions to be discussed in class. You can have students reread the section and participate in the questioning with other students.

Use Science Words

Word Meaning Some of the terms used when analyzing data are *mean, mode, median,* and *average.* These terms have slightly different meanings and can be confusing. Have students define each one. *mean:* a value that is computed by dividing the sum of a set of values by the number of values; *mode:* the most frequent value of a set of data; *median:* a value in an ordered set of values below and above which there is an equal number of values, or, if there is no one middle number, a value which is the arithmetic mean of the two middle values; *average:* same as mean. L2 LS **Linguistic**

Quick Demo

The Scientific Method

Material thermometer, two beakers of hot water, one stirrer, stopwatch, ice cubes

Estimated Time 15 minutes

Procedure Do ice cubes melt faster in hot water when stirred or when left to sit untouched? Perform the steps of the scientific method out of order in front of the class. Ask students to rank the steps in the order they should have occurred. Have them explain why it makes a difference if the scientific method is performed out of order. Repeat the steps in the order the students ranked them. Ask students which way makes more sense.

Fun Fact

It is impossible for any experiment to be completely objective and free from bias. The questions asked include an inherent bias. Scientists work to minimize bias and to be as aware as possible of the bias they introduce.

Reading Check

Answer A bias occurs when what the scientist expects changes how the results are viewed.

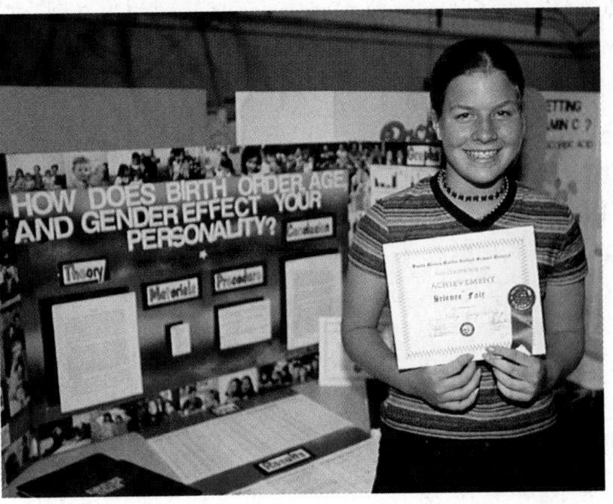

Figure 5 An exciting and important part of investigating something is sharing your ideas with others, as this student is doing at a science fair.

Analyzing the Data An important part of every experiment includes recording observations and organizing the test data into easy-to-read tables and graphs. Later in this chapter you will study ways to display data. When you are making and recording observations, you should include all results, even unexpected ones. Many important discoveries have been made from unexpected occurrences.

Interpreting the data and analyzing the observations is an important step. If the data are not organized in a logical manner, wrong conclusions can be drawn. No matter how well a scientist communicates and shares that data, someone else might not agree with the data. Scientists share their data through reports and conferences. In **Figure 5** a student is displaying her data.

Drawing Conclusions Based on the analysis of your data, you decide whether or not your hypothesis is supported. When lives are at stake, such as with the space shuttle, you must be very sure of your results. For the hypothesis to be considered valid and widely accepted, the experiment must result in the exact same data every time it is repeated. If your experiment does not support your hypothesis, you must reconsider the hypothesis. Perhaps it needs to be revised or your experiment needs to be conducted differently.

Being Objective Scientists also should be careful to reduce bias in their experiments. A **bias** occurs when what the scientist expects changes how the results are viewed. This expectation might cause a scientist to select a result from one trial over those from other trials. Bias also might be found if the advantages of a product being tested are used in a promotion and the drawbacks are not presented.

Scientists can lessen bias by running as many trials as possible and by keeping accurate notes of each observation made. Valid experiments also must have data that are measurable. For example, a scientist performing a global warming study must base his or her data on accurate measures of global temperature. This allows others to compare the results to data they obtain from a similar experiment. Most importantly, the experiment must be repeatable. Findings are supportable when other scientists perform the same experiment and get the same results.

Reading Check *What is bias in science?*

Curriculum Connection

Language Arts Emphasize to students that being objective is important in reporting information in all areas. Have them search through magazines and newspapers and find articles in which the writer's bias has influenced the article. L2 LS **Linguistic**

Differentiated Instruction

Challenge When analyzing the results of many different trials, scientists use the methods of statistics. One of the most useful tools of statistics is normal distribution. Have students find out what this tool is. A normal distribution is a distribution of values that produces a symmetrical bell-shaped curve. It shows the distribution of values that results from many random variables. L3 LS **Logical-Mathematical**

Visualizing with Models

Sometimes, scientists cannot see everything that they are testing. They might be observing something that is too large, too small, or takes too much time to see completely. In these cases, scientists use models. A **model** represents an idea, event, or object to help people better understand it.

Models in History Models have been used throughout history. One scientist, Lord Kelvin, who lived in England in the 1800s, was famous for making models. To model his idea of how light moves through space, he put balls into a bowl of jelly and encouraged people to move the balls around with their hands. Kelvin's work to explain the nature of temperature and heat still is used today.

High-Tech Models Scientific models don't always have to be something you can touch. Today, many scientists use computers to build models. NASA experiments involving space flight would not be practical without computers. The complex equations would take far too long to calculate by hand, and errors could be introduced much too easily.

Another type of model is a simulator, like the one shown in **Figure 6.** An airplane simulator enables pilots to practice problem solving with various situations and conditions they might encounter when in the air. This model will react the way a plane does when it flies. It gives pilots a safe way to test different reactions and to practice certain procedures before they fly a real plane.

Computer Models
Meteorology has changed greatly due to computer modeling. Using special computer programs, meteorologists now are able to more accurately predict disastrous weather. In your Science Journal, describe how computer models might help save lives.

Figure 6 Pilots and astronauts use flight simulators for training. **Explain** *how these models differ from actual airplanes and spacecraft.*

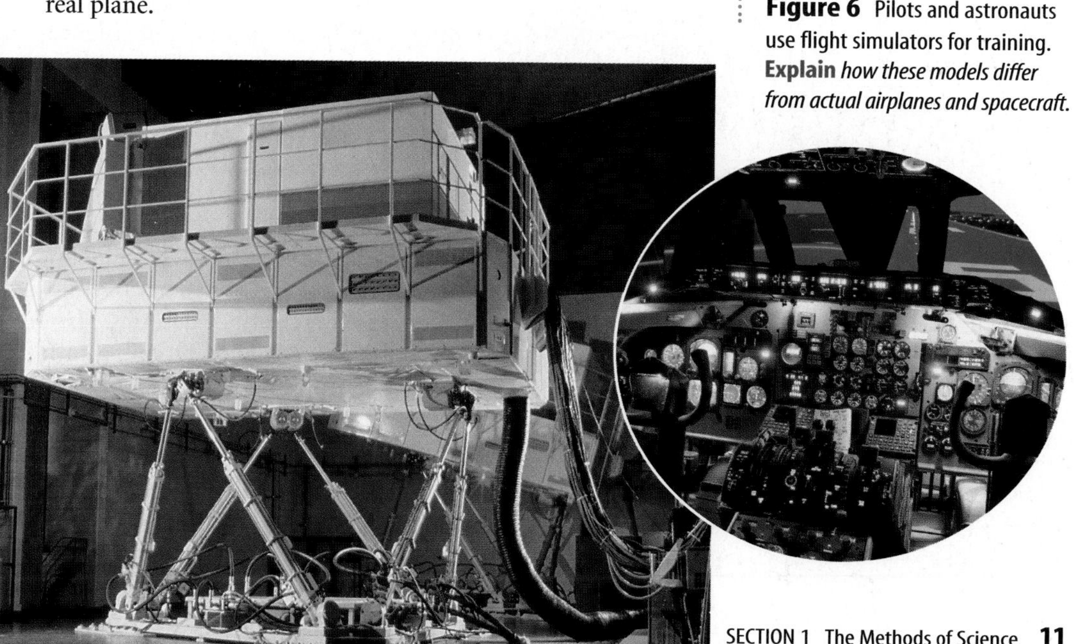

Computer Models Journal entries should include that predictions of severe weather, such as tornadoes, hurricanes, and flooding rains, can warn residents of an area to take precautions or evacuate the area. P

Activity

Studying Models Have students make posters showing situations in which models are used to study something too large to study directly, too small to be studied directly, and too dangerous to be studied directly. Possible answers: the solar system, which is too large to be studied directly; the tiny particles that make up matter, which are too small to be studied directly; and a plane crash, which is too dangerous to be studied directly L2 LS **Visual-Spatial**

Caption Answer

Figure 6 They don't always mimic the real situation exactly. They also don't cause any damage to people or materials when the pilot makes a mistake and crashes.

Reading Check

Answer A theory can change if its supporting data changes. A law is assumed to be true and doesn't change. Also, a law tells what happens but does not explain why. Theories try to explain why things happen.

Caption Answer

Figure 7 No; it cannot be tested

Discussion

Modeling with Computers Why are computers useful for modeling situations? Computers can slow down or speed up action and can show how a process changes over time. They also can be programmed to make predictions based on data put into them. L2 LS **Logical-Mathematical**

Science Journal

Universal Theories Have students investigate theories about the origin of the universe and explain why these theories are not scientific laws. The current main theory is the Big Bang Theory. This theory is not a law because it tries to explain how or why something happens. A law simply describes a pattern. L2 LS **Logical-Mathematical**

Visual Learning

Figure 6 Ask students whether they have used a driving simulator in a video game. Ask them to explain what it taught them about driving and why it does not really equip them to drive. The simulation might give them practice in steering, accelerating, and stopping, but it does not involve roadway experience with other cars. L2 LS **Visual-Spatial**

Inquiry Lab

The Path of Theory Development

Purpose To have students get a better grasp of the evolution of scientific knowledge and the application of scientific method.

Possible Materials index cards

Safety Precautions

- As this lab may involve social commentary, caution students to remain objective.
- Have students use topics from news items only, not from observations about events within the school or about their peers. Make a rule against 'picking on' individuals.

Estimated Time one class period

Teaching Strategies

- Have students record at least three observations about a psychological, social, or scientific phenomenon in their experience.
- Mix the cards up and have students suggest an experiment that could be done to test a hypothesis for each observation. Encourage objective discussion of the viability of each experiment suggested.
- The game can demonstrate that a hypothesis can't be proven, only disproved.
- For each hypothesis that students disprove with observations, have them create a further hypothesis. Explain that this is how real science develops.

For additional inquiry activities, see *Science Inquiry Labs*.

Virtual Labs

Data Collection *How is a controlled experiment performed?*

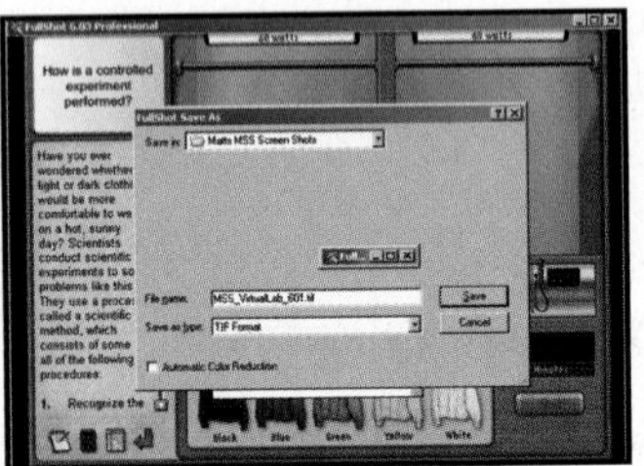

Topic: Archimedes' Principle

Visit gpscience.com for Web links to information about Archimedes' principle.

Activity Place a full soft-drink bottle, water bottle, or container of milk in a tub of water. What happens to the pop bottle or milk container? Would you classify Archimedes' principle as a scientific theory or scientific law?

Scientific Theories and Laws

A scientific **theory** is an explanation of things or events based on knowledge gained from many observations and investigations. It is not a guess. If scientists repeat an investigation and the results always support the hypothesis, the hypothesis can be called a theory. Just because a scientific theory has data supporting it does not mean it will never change. Recall that the theory about heat being a fluid was discarded after further experiments. As new information becomes available, theories can be modified. A theory accepted today might at some time in the future also be discarded.

A **scientific law** is a statement about what happens in nature and that seems to be true all the time. Laws tell you what will happen under certain conditions, but they don't explain why or how something happens. Gravity is an example of a scientific law. The law of gravity says that any one mass will attract another mass. To date, no experiments have been performed that disprove the law of gravity.

A theory can be used to explain a law. For example, many theories have been proposed to explain how the law of gravity works. Even so, there are few theories in science and even fewer laws.

What is the difference between a scientific theory and a scientific law?

Figure 7 Science can't answer all questions.
Analyze *Can anyone prove that you like artwork? Explain.*

The Limitations of Science

Science can help you explain many things about the world, but science cannot explain or solve everything. Although it's the scientist's job to make guesses, the scientist also has to make sure his or her guesses can be tested and verified. But how do you prove that people will like a play or a piece of music? You cannot and science cannot.

Most questions about emotions and values are not scientific questions. They cannot be tested. You might take a survey to get people's opinions about such questions, but that would not prove that the opinions are true for everyone. A survey might predict that you will like the art in **Figure 7,** but science cannot prove that you or others will.

Teacher FYI

Spin-offs Many materials or processes commonly used are spin-offs of scientific research. That is, they result from scientific research done to solve another problem. For example, John Wesley Hyatt was looking for an inexpensive substitute for ivory to make billiard balls. He discovered celluloid, the first practical synthetic plastic. Celluloid was used not only for billiard balls but many other products such as eyeglasses frames, combs, and buttons.

Using Science—Technology

Many people use the terms *science* and *technology* interchangeably, but they are not the same. **Technology** is the application of science to help people. For example, when a chemist develops a new, lightweight material that can withstand great amounts of heat, science is used. When that material is used on the space shuttle, technology is applied. **Figure 8** shows other examples of technology.

Technology doesn't always follow science, however. Sometimes the process of discovery can be reversed. One important historic example of science following technology is the development of the steam engine. The inventors of the steam engine had little idea of how it worked. They just knew that steam from boiling water could move the engine. Because the steam engine became so important to industry, scientists began analyzing how it worked. Lord Kelvin, James Prescott Joule and Sadi Carnot, who lived in the 1800s, learned so much from the steam engine that they developed revolutionary ideas about the nature of heat.

Science and technology do not always produce positive results. The benefits of some technological advances, such as nuclear technology and genetic engineering, are subjects of debate. Being more knowledgeable about science can help society address these issues as they arise.

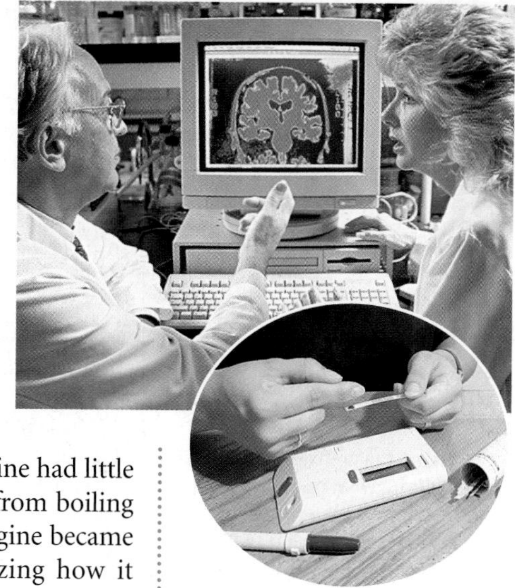

Figure 8 Technology is the application of science.
State *the type of science (life, Earth, or physical) that is applied in these examples of technology.*

section 1 review

Summary

What is science?

- Scientists ask questions and perform investigations to learn more about the natural world.

Scientific Methods

- Scientists perform the six-step scientific method to test their hypotheses.

Visualizing with Models

- Models help scientists visualize concepts.

Scientific Theories and Laws

- A theory is a possible explanation for observations while a scientific law describes a pattern but does not explain why things happen.

Using Science—Technology

- Technology is the application of science into our everyday lives.

Self-Check

1. **Define** the first step a scientist usually takes to solve a problem.
2. **Explain** why a control is needed in a valid experiment.
3. **Think Critically** What is the dependent variable in an experiment that shows how the volume of gas changes with changes in temperature?

Applying Math

4. **Find the Average** You perform an experiment to determine how many breaths a fish takes per minute. Your experiment yields the following data: minute 1: 65 breaths; minute 2: 73 breaths; minute 3: 67 breaths; minute 4: 71 breaths; minute 5: 62 breaths. Calculate the average number of breaths that a fish takes per minute.

gpscience.com/self_check_quiz

Caption Answer

Figure 8 The top picture shows applications of physical science (computer) and life science (medical image). The lower picture shows the application of physical science (instruments) and life science (measuring levels of sugar in blood).

3 Assess

DAILY INTERVENTION

Check for Understanding

Visual-Spatial Review with students the scientific method. On separate sheets of paper, write the parts of the scientific method. Have students place these sheets on a chart in the correct order.

Reteach

Freezing Water Ask students to design an experiment that will determine whether hot water freezes faster than cold water does. Make sure that constants include the amount of water, the size and kind of container, the amount of time in the freezer, and the freezer used. L2 LS **Logical-Mathematical**

Assessment

Performance Have students design and perform an experiment to determine whether microwave popcorn pops better when it has been frozen. Have them identify constants, variables, and a control for the experiment. Use **Performance Assessment in the Science Classroom,** p. 95.

section 1 review

1. Identify the problem.
2. to provide a standard against which test results can be compared
3. volume of gas
4. The fish takes an average of 68 breaths per minute.

section 2

Standards of Measurement

Reading Guide

What You'll Learn

- **Name** the prefixes used in SI and indicate what multiple of ten each one represents.
- **Identify** SI units and symbols for length, volume, mass, density, time, and temperature.
- **Convert** related SI units.

Why It's Important

By using uniform standards, nations can exchange goods and compare information easily.

Review Vocabulary

measurement: the dimensions, capacity, or amount of something

New Vocabulary

- standard
- SI
- volume
- mass
- density

Units and Standards

A **standard** is an exact quantity that people agree to use to compare measurements. Look at **Figure 9.** Suppose you and a friend want to make some measurements to find out whether a desk will fit through a doorway. You have no ruler, so you decide to use your hands as measuring tools. Using the width of his hands, your friend measures the doorway and says it is 8 hands wide. Using the width of your hands, you measure the desk and find it is $7\frac{3}{4}$ hands wide. Will the desk fit through the doorway? You can't be sure. What went wrong? Even though you both used hands to measure, you didn't check to see whether your hands were the same width as your friend's. In other words, you didn't use a measurement standard, so you can't compare the measurements.

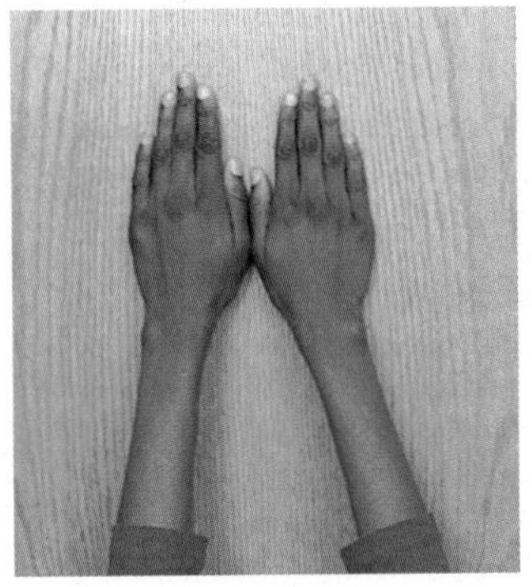

Figure 9 Hands are a convenient measuring tool, but using them can lead to misunderstanding.

Measurement Systems

Suppose the label on a ball of string indicates that the length of the string is 150. Is the length 150 feet, 150 m, or 150 cm? For a measurement to make sense, it must include a number and a unit.

Your family might buy lumber by the foot, milk by the gallon, and potatoes by the pound. These measurement units are part of the English system of measurement, which is commonly used in the United States. Most other nations use the metric system—a system of measurement based on multiples of ten.

1 Motivate

Bellringer

Section Focus Transparencies also are available on the Interactive Chalkboard CD-ROM.

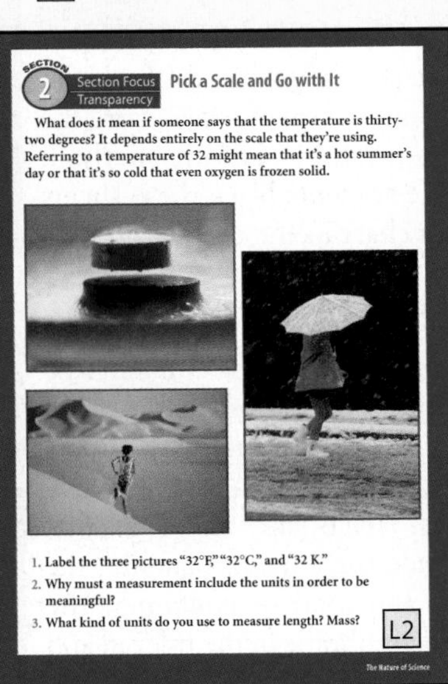

Section 2 Section Focus Transparency **Pick a Scale and Go with It**

What does it mean if someone says that the temperature is thirty-two degrees? It depends entirely on the scale that they're using. Referring to a temperature of 32 might mean that it's a hot summer's day or that it's so cold that even oxygen is frozen solid.

1. Label the three pictures "32°F," "32°C," and "32 K."
2. Why must a measurement include the units in order to be meaningful?
3. What kind of units do you use to measure length? Mass?

L2

The Nature of Science

Tie to Prior Knowledge

Measuring Students are familiar with measurements. Ask them to name the units they commonly use to measure length, mass, volume, and temperature.

Section 2 Resource Manager

Chapter *FAST FILE* Resources

- Transparency Activity, p. 45
- Enrichment, p. 31
- Directed Reading for Content Mastery, p. 20
- MiniLAB, p. 3
- Lab Activity, pp. 9–12
- Reinforcement, p. 28

Physical Science Critical Thinking/Problem Solving, p. 2

Mathematics Skill Activities, p. 61

Reading and Writing Skills Activities, pp. 13, 41

14 CHAPTER 1 The Nature of Science

International System of Units In 1960, an improved version of the metric system was devised. Known as the International System of Units, this system is often abbreviated SI, from the French *Le Systeme Internationale d'Unites.* All **SI** standards are universally accepted and understood by scientists throughout the world. The standard kilogram, which is kept in Sèvres, France, is shown in **Figure 10.** All kilograms used throughout the world must be exactly the same as the kilogram kept in France.

Each type of SI measurement has a base unit. The meter is the base unit of length. Every type of quantity measured in SI has a symbol for that unit. These names and symbols for the seven base units are shown in **Table 1.** All other SI units are obtained from these seven units.

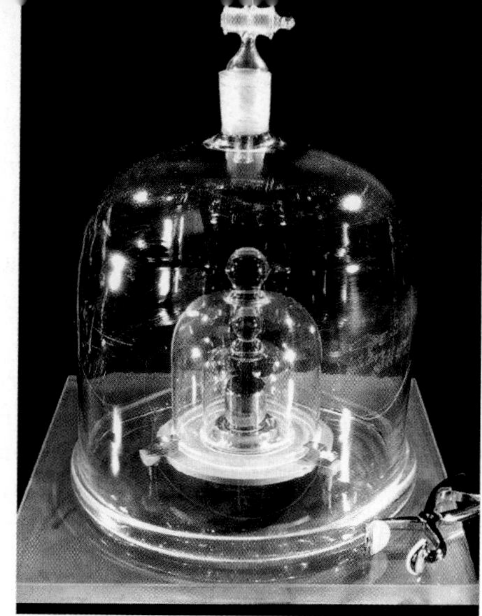

Figure 10 The standard for mass, the kilogram, and other standards are kept at the International Bureau of Weights and Measures in Sèvres, France. **Explain** *the purpose of a standard.*

SI Prefixes The SI system is easy to use because it is based on multiples of ten. Prefixes are used with the names of the units to indicate what multiple of ten should be used with the units. For example, the prefix *kilo-* means "1,000." That means that one kilometer equals 1,000 meters. Likewise, one kilogram equals 1,000 grams. Because *deci-* means "one-tenth," one decimeter equals one tenth of a meter. A decigram equals one tenth of a gram. The most frequently used prefixes are shown in **Table 2.**

Reading Check *How many meters is 1 km? How many grams is 1 dg?*

Table 1 SI Base Units

Quantity Measured	Unit	Symbol
Length	meter	m
Mass	kilogram	kg
Time	second	s
Electric current	ampere	A
Temperature	kelvin	K
Amount of substance	mole	mol
Intensity of light	candela	cd

Table 2 Common SI Prefixes

Prefix	Symbol	Multiplying Factor
Kilo-	k	1,000
Deci-	d	0.1
Centi-	c	0.01
Milli-	m	0.001
Micro-	μ	0.000 001
Nano-	n	0.000 000 001

2 Teach

IDENTIFYING Misconceptions

SI Precision Students may think that SI is more precise than the English system because scientists use it. Point out that both systems can yield equally precise measurements. For instance, a micrometer used by machinists can measure the diameters of bolts to the nearest 0.0001 inch. Scientists use SI because it is easier to use and easier to convert units. Have students measure the length of their textbook using a metric ruler and a ruler calibrated in inches. Have them compare results and note that both measurements can be precise.

Caption Answer

Figure 10 It provides an accepted and understood value for a base unit.

Reading Check

Answer 1,000; one tenth

Science Journal

Standards Have students record in their Science Journals the physical standards for mass, length, and time. The standard mass is the 1 kg of platinum-iridium alloy shown in **Figure 10**. The standard length, 1 meter, is defined as the distance light travels in a vacuum in 1/299,792,458 of a second. The standard time, 1 second, is defined as 9,192,631,770 periods of the radiation of cesium-133 atoms. L3

Differentiated Instruction

Challenge Have students research the standardization of currency. When did it occur? Why? They can compare the need for standard units of measurement with the need for standard currency. It is believed that the first standard coins were produced in Lydia, part of present-day Turkey, in the 600s B.C. The coins were standardized so people knew the exact value of the metal pieces. L3 P LS **Linguistic**

Caption Answer

Figure 11 31 mm

Make a Model

Measurment System Model a new metric measurement system. Organize the class into groups and have each group choose an object to be the basis for its new metric standard of length. Have students make or draw models showing a unit, a deciunit, a centiunit, and a kilounit. L2

LS **Visual-Spatial**

National Math Standards

Correlation to Mathematics Objectives

4

Answers to Practice Problems

1. ? mm = 11 cm × 10 mm/cm

   11 cm × 10 mm/cm = 110 mm

2. 1 mi = 1.6 km

   20,000 mi × 1.6 km = 32000 km

Discussion

Measuring Day Time Point out to students that while in SI the units for time less than 1 s are divided into multiples of ten (the millisecond, nanosecond, etc.), the units for time greater than 1 s are not. Have each student devise a metric system for measuring the amount of time in a day. Accept all responses in which time is divided into units that are multiples of 10. L3 LS **Logical-Mathematical**

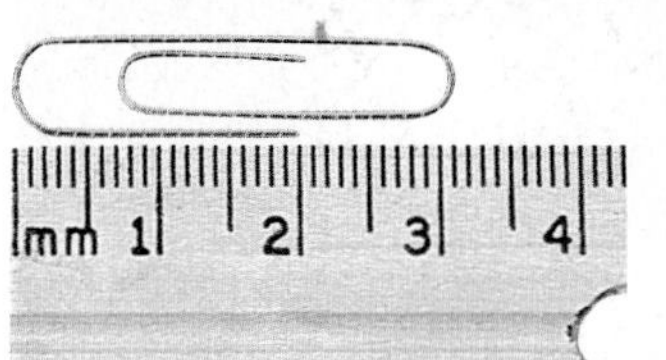

Figure 11 One centimeter contains 10 mm.
Determine *the length of the paper clip in centimeters and millimeters.*

Converting Between SI Units Sometimes quantities are measured using different units as shown in **Figure 11.** A conversion factor is a ratio that is equal to one and is used to change one unit to another. For example, there are 1,000 mL in 1 L, so 1,000 mL = 1 L. If both sides in this equation are divided by 1 L, the equation becomes:

$$\frac{1{,}000\text{ mL}}{1\text{ L}} = 1$$

To convert units, you multiply by the appropriate conversion factor. For example, to convert 1.255 L to mL, multiply 1.255 L by a conversion factor. Use the conversion factor with new units (mL) in the numerator and the old units (L) in the denominator.

$$1.255\text{ L} \times \frac{1{,}000\text{ mL}}{1\text{ L}} = 1{,}255\text{ mL}$$

CONVERSION EQUATIONS

Convert Units How long, in centimeters, is a 3,075–mm rope?

1. **This is what you know:** rope length in mm = 3,075 mm; 1 m = 100 cm = 1,000 mm
2. **This is what you need to find:** rope length in cm
3. **Use this formula:** $\text{length in cm} = \text{length in mm} \times \frac{100\text{ cm}}{1{,}000\text{ mm}}$
4. **Substitute:** $\text{length in cm} = 3{,}075\text{ mm} \times \frac{100\text{ cm}}{1{,}000\text{ mm}} = 307.5\text{ cm}$
5. **Determine the units:** cm = mm × cm/mm

Answer: The rope is 307.5 cm long

Science Online
For more practice problems, go to page 834, and visit gpscience.com/extra_problems.

Practice Problems

1. Your pencil is 11 cm long. How long is it in millimeters?
2. **Challenge** The Bering Land Bridge National Preserve is a summer home to birdlife. Some birds migrate 20,000 miles. If 1 mile equals 1.6 kilometers, calculate the distance birds fly in kilometers.

Teacher FYI

Early Measurement Early measurements were based on body parts. One of the earliest measurements ever recorded was length. The Egyptian cubit was derived from the length of the arm from the elbow to the outstretched fingertips. France's unit of length was the meter, which was defined as being one ten-millionth part of a quarter of Earth's circumference. The production of this standard required a very careful survey to be done which took several years. As more accurate instruments became available, the standard was called into question.

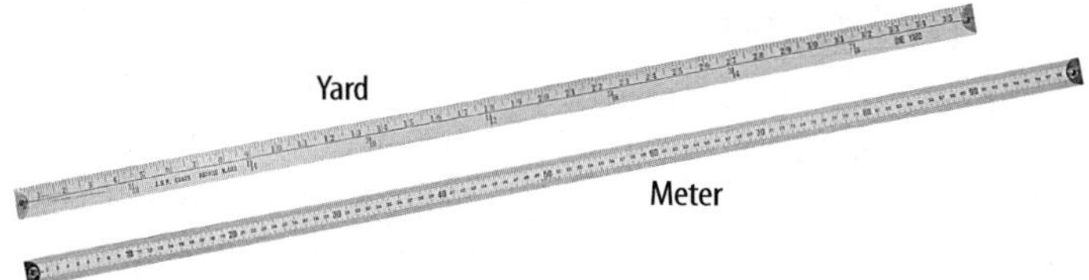

Figure 12 One meter is slightly longer than 1 yard and 100 m is slightly longer than a football field. **Predict** *whether your time for a 100-m dash would be slightly more or less than your time for a 100-yard dash.*

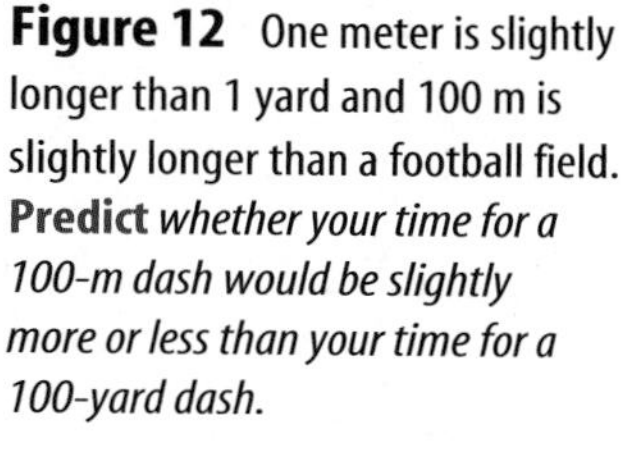

Measuring Distance

The word *length* is used in many different ways. For example, the length of a novel is the number of pages or words it contains. In scientific measurement, however, length is the distance between two points. That distance might be the diameter of a hair or the distance from Earth to the Moon. The SI base unit of length is the meter, m. A baseball bat is about 1 m long. Metric rulers and metersticks are used to measure length. **Figure 12** compares a meter and a yard.

Choosing a Unit of Length As shown in **Figure 13,** the size of the unit you measure with will depend on the size of the object being measured. For example, the diameter of a shirt button is about 1 cm. You probably also would use the centimeter to measure the length of your pencil and the meter to measure the length of your classroom. What unit would you use to measure the distance from your home to school? You probably would want to use a unit larger than a meter. The kilometer, km, which is 1,000 m, is used to measure these kinds of distances.

By choosing an appropriate unit, you avoid large-digit numbers and numbers with many decimal places. Twenty-one kilometers is easier to deal with than 21,000 m. And 13 mm is easier to use than 0.013 m.

Astronomical Units The standard measurement for the distance from Earth to the Sun is called the astronomical unit, AU. The distance is about 150 billion (1.5×10^{11}) m. In your Science Journal, calculate what 1 AU would equal in km.

Figure 13 The size of the object being measured determines which unit you will measure in. A tape measure measures in meters. The micrometer, shown at the right, measures in small lengths. **State** *what unit you think it measures in.*

Caption Answer

Figure 12 slightly more

Figure 13 micrometers

Activity

Rulers Distribute metric rulers and have students identify the millimeter, centimeter, and decimeter markings on the ruler. Have them measure common objects. As they are measuring, have each student choose an object that best represents a centimeter. Allow them to make estimations and use their rulers to check their estimations. L2 IS **Kinesthetic**

Astronomical Units Venus is 0.72 AU from the Sun and Pluto is 39.6 AU from the Sun. 1 AU is about 1.5×10^8 km = 150,000,000 km.

Career Astronomers study objects where they cannot use all of their senses. They cannot touch or smell stars, comets, or planets other than Earth. Astronomers do need good observations skills. The majority of the astronomers do not look through telescopes. They teach and do research in colleges and universities.

Cultural Diversity

Length Through Time Accurate length measurement was important for ancient engineering projects, such as the Nazca lines, the pyramids in Central America and Africa, and the great public buildings found in many cultures. Have students identify some of the units of length used in the ancient world. Lengths used include the cubit and the Roman mile. L2 IS **Linguistic**

Visual Learning

Figure 12 Discuss with students the difference between a meter and a yard. Measure the distance across the classroom or blackboard in both meters and yards and make sure students understand the measurements. Review with students how to convert meters into yards.

Activity

Relative Volume Provide a number of irregularly-shaped containers and a graduated cylinder. Have each student make a hypothesis about the relative volumes of the containers and write down the hypothesis. Then have students test their hypotheses by measuring the volume of each container. Tell them to fill each container completely with water, pour the water into the graduated cylinder, and measure the amount the container held. L2 LS **Kinesthetic**

Caption Answer

Figure 14 1,000 cm^3 are in 1 dm^3.

Topic: International System of Units

Visit gpscience.com for Web links to information about the International System of Units.

Activity Measure four different things in your classroom using a different unit—distance, volume, time, or temperature—for each. Use each unit only once. Write the measurements down and using the common prefixes in **Table 2**, convert them to different units.

Measuring Volume

The amount of space occupied by an object is called its **volume.** If you want to know the volume of a solid rectangle, such as a brick, you measure its length, width, and height and multiply the three numbers and their units together ($V = l \times w \times h$). For a brick, your measurements probably would be in centimeters. The volume would then be expressed in cubic centimeters, cm^3. To find out how much a moving van can carry, your measurements probably would be in meters, and the volume would be expressed in cubic meters, m^3, because when you multiply you add exponents.

Measuring Liquid Volume How do you measure the volume of a liquid? A liquid has no sides to measure. In measuring a liquid's volume, you are indicating the capacity of the container that holds that amount of liquid. The most common units for expressing liquid volumes are liters and milliliters. These are measurements used in canned and bottled foods. A liter occupies the same volume as a cubic decimeter, dm^3. A cubic decimeter is a cube that is 1 dm, or 10 cm, on each side, as in **Figure 14.**

Look at **Figure 14.** One liter is equal to 1,000 mL. A cubic decimeter, dm^3, is equal to 1,000 cm^3. Because 1 L = 1 dm^3, it follows that:

$$1 \text{ mL} = 1 \text{ cm}^3$$

Sometimes, liquid volumes such as doses of medicine are expressed in cubic centimeters.

Suppose you wanted to convert a measurement in liters to cubic centimeters. You use conversion factors to convert L to mL and then mL to cm^3.

$$1.5 \cancel{\text{L}} \times \frac{1{,}000 \cancel{\text{mL}}}{1 \cancel{\text{L}}} \times \frac{1 \text{ cm}^3}{1 \cancel{\text{mL}}} = 1{,}500 \text{ cm}^3$$

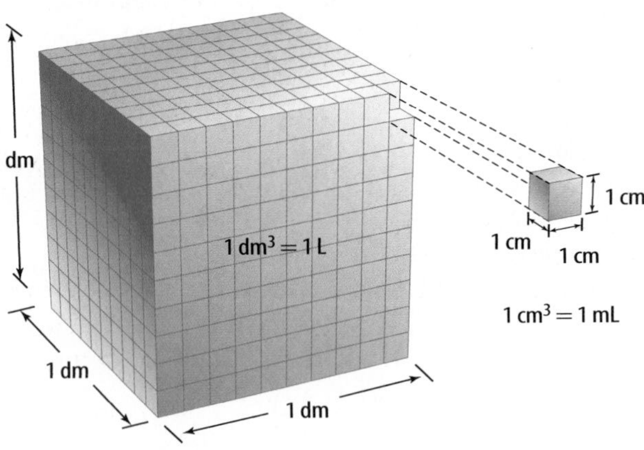

Figure 14 The large cube has a volume of 1 dm^3, which is equivalent to 1 L. **Calculate** *the cubic centimeters (cm^3) in the large cube.*

Curriculum Connection

Math Have students find and record the equations for determining the volumes of shapes such as a cylinder, sphere, square pyramid, and cone. The equation for calculating the volume of a cylinder is $\pi r^2 h$. The equation for the volume of a sphere is $\frac{4}{3}\pi r^3$. The equation for the volume of a square pyramid is $\frac{1}{3}bh$. The equation for the volume of a cone is $\frac{1}{3}\pi r^2 h$. L3 LS **Logical-Mathematical**

Table 3 Densities of Some Materials at 20°C			
Material	Density (g/cm^3)	Material	Density (g/cm^3)
hydrogen	0.000 09	aluminum	2.7
oxygen	0.001 4	iron	7.9
water	1.0	gold	19.3

Measuring Matter

A table-tennis ball and a golf ball have about the same volume. But if you pick them up, you notice a difference. The golf ball has more mass. **Mass** is a measurement of the quantity of matter in an object. The mass of the golf ball, which is about 45 g, is almost 18 times the mass of the table-tennis ball, which is about 2.5 g. A bowling ball has a mass of about 5,000 g. This makes its mass roughly 100 times greater than the mass of the golf ball and 2,000 times greater than the table-tennis ball's mass. To visualize SI units, see **Figure 15** on the following page.

Density A cube of polished aluminum and a cube of silver that are the same size not only look similar but also have the same volume. The mass and volume of an object can be used to find the density of the material the object is made of. **Density** is the mass per unit volume of a material. You find density by dividing an object's mass by the object's volume. For example, the density of an object having a mass of 10 g and a volume of 2 cm^3 is 5 g/cm^3. **Table 3** lists the densities of some familiar materials.

Derived Units The measurement unit for density, g/cm^3, is a combination of SI units. A unit obtained by combining different SI units is called a derived unit. An SI unit multiplied by itself also is a derived unit. Thus the liter, which is based on the cubic decimeter, is a derived unit. A meter cubed, expressed with an exponent—m^3—is a derived unit.

Measuring Time and Temperature

It is often necessary to keep track of how long it takes for something to happen, or whether something heats up or cools down. These measurements involve time and temperature.

Time is the interval between two events. The SI unit for time is the second. In the laboratory, you will use a stopwatch or a clock with a second hand to measure time.

Determining the Density of a Pencil

Procedure

1. Find a **pencil** that will fit in a 100-mL graduated cylinder below the 90-mL mark.
2. Measure the mass of the pencil in grams.
3. Put 90 mL of **water** (initial volume) into a 100-mL **graduated cylinder.** Lower the pencil, eraser first, into the cylinder. Push the pencil down until it is just submerged. Hold it there and record the final volume to the nearest tenth of a milliliter.

Analysis

1. Determine the water displaced by the pencil by subtracting the initial volume from the final volume.
2. Calculate the pencil's density by dividing its mass by the volume of water displaced.
3. Is the density of the pencil greater than or less than the density of water? How do you know?

Mini LAB

Purpose Students measure the mass and volume of a pencil and use these data to find its density. L1 ELL IN Logical-Mathematical

Materials water, 100-mL graduated cylinder, unsharpened pencil, balance

Teaching Strategy The mass measurement should be made using a dry pencil.

Analysis

1. Students should use the equation $d = m/v$. Remind them that 1 mL = 1 cm^3.
2. Check students' paper.
3. Because the pencil floats, its density is less than that of water. Also, its calculated density is less than that of water—1.0.

Assessment

Performance Have students use the same procedure to test the density of another object such as a cork or a rubber stopper. If possible, they could compare their results with the density given in **Table 3** on this page or another density table. Use **Performance Assessment in the Science Classroom,** p. 97.

Curriculum Connection

Math The SI prefix *pico-* is used for tiny measurements. The diameter of a hydrogen nucleus is about 78 picometers. Have students find out what *pico-* means and find the diameter of a hydrogen atom in meters. The prefix means one-trillionth. A hydrogen atom has a diameter of 78 trillionths (78×10^{-12}) of a meter. L2 IN **Logical-Mathematical**

Differentiated Instruction

Behaviorally Disordered Have these students read through the lab a day or two before the class does it. Show them how it works and ask whether they have any questions. Make sure they understand the purpose of the water. When they do the lab, pair them with students who work well in the lab.

SECTION 2 Standards of Measurement 19

NATIONAL GEOGRAPHIC

Visualizing SI Dimensions

Have students examine the pictures and read the captions. Then ask the following questions.

In what units would you measure your height? meters The distance a runner covered in a marathon? kilometers The mass of a pencil? grams

Why wouldn't you measure the distance from Dallas, Texas to Miami, Florida in millimeters? The number of millimeters would be an extremely large number, too big to be able to visualize. What unit should you use? kilometers

Activity

Different Measurements Set up three stations and allow groups to rotate through them. One station should have a balance and several objects that students can mass. Another station should have several containers of liquids and a graduated cylinder so they can measure volumes. The third station should have a metric ruler and meterstick and several objects whose lengths students can determine. Have students measure the objects and compare their measurements when all have finished. L1 LS **Kinesthetic**

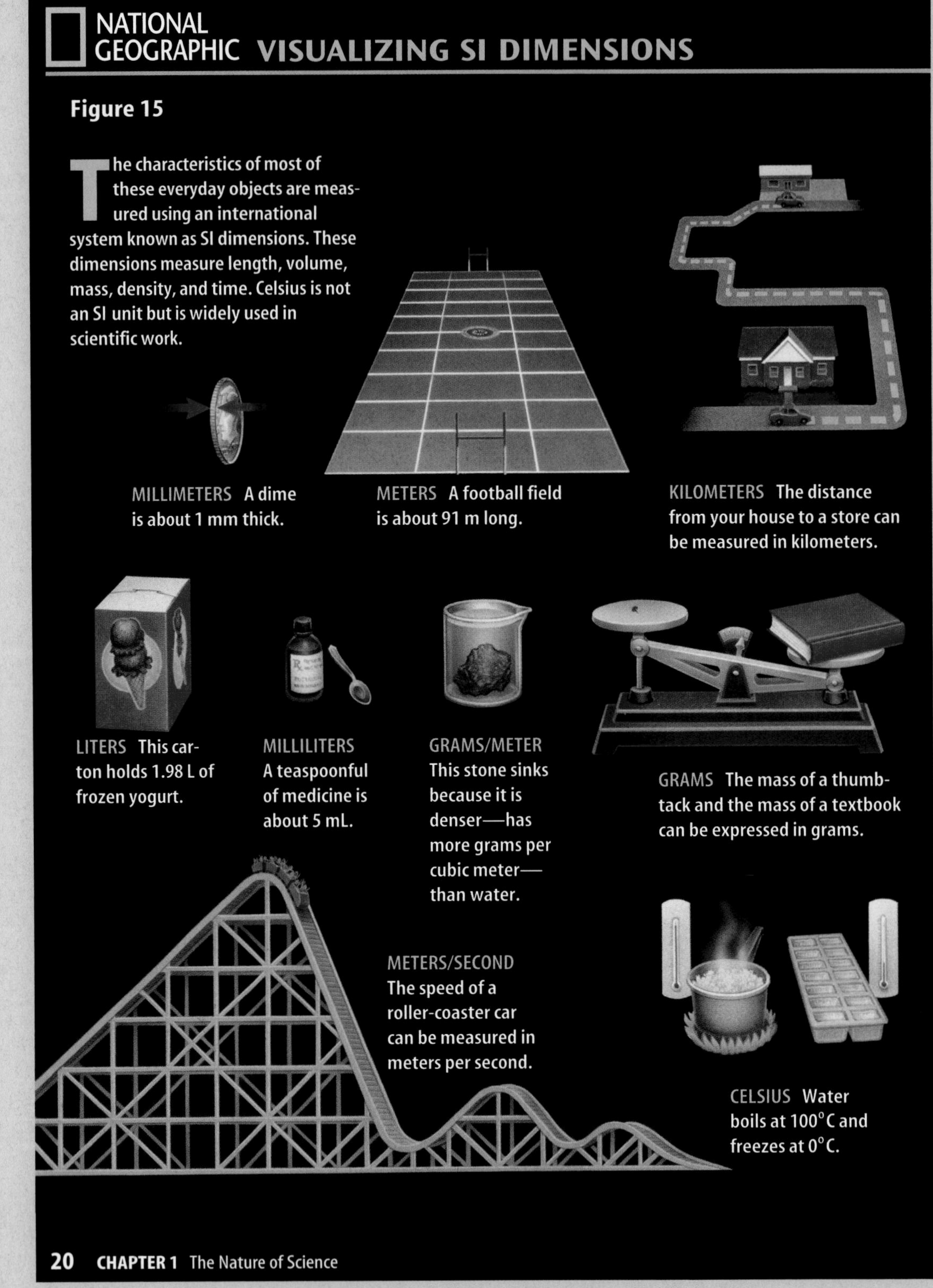

NATIONAL GEOGRAPHIC VISUALIZING SI DIMENSIONS
Figure 15
The characteristics of most of these everyday objects are measured using an international system known as SI dimensions. These dimensions measure length, volume, mass, density, and time. Celsius is not an SI unit but is widely used in scientific work.
MILLIMETERS A dime is about 1 mm thick.
METERS A football field is about 91 m long.
KILOMETERS The distance from your house to a store can be measured in kilometers.
LITERS This carton holds 1.98 L of frozen yogurt.
MILLILITERS A teaspoonful of medicine is about 5 mL.
GRAMS/METER This stone sinks because it is denser—has more grams per cubic meter—than water.
GRAMS The mass of a thumbtack and the mass of a textbook can be expressed in grams.
METERS/SECOND The speed of a roller-coaster car can be measured in meters per second.
CELSIUS Water boils at 100°C and freezes at 0°C.
20 CHAPTER 1 The Nature of Science

Differentiated Instruction

Challenge Have students find the high temperature for the day in Fahrenheit, Celsius, and Kelvin. They can obtain the temperature, probably in Fahrenheit, from a weather report. Have them use the following equations: $C = 5(F - 32)/9$; $C + 273 = K$. L3 LS **Logical-Mathematical**

What's Hot and What's Not You will learn the scientific meaning of the word *temperature* in a later chapter. For now, think of temperature as a measure of how hot or how cold something is.

Look at **Figure 16.** For most scientific work, temperature is measured on the Celsius (C) scale. On this scale, the freezing point of water is 0°C, and the boiling point of water is 100°C. Between these points, the scale is divided into 100 equal divisions. Each one represents 1°C. On the Celsius scale, average human body temperature is 37°C, and a typical room temperature is between 20°C and 25°C.

Kelvin and Fahrenheit The SI unit of temperature is the kelvin (K). Zero on the Kelvin scale (0 K) is the coldest possible temperature, also known as absolute zero. Absolute zero is equal to −273°C, which is 273° below the freezing point of water.

Most laboratory thermometers are marked only with the Celsius scale. Because the divisions on the two scales are the same size, the Kelvin temperature can be found by adding 273 to the Celsius reading. So, on the Kelvin scale, water freezes at 273 K and boils at 373 K. Notice that degree symbols are not used with the Kelvin scale.

The temperature measurement you are probably most familiar with is the Fahrenheit scale, which was based roughly on the temperature of the human body, 98.6°.

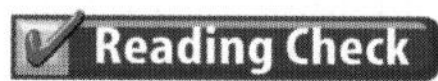

What is the relationship between the Celsius scale and the Kelvin scale?

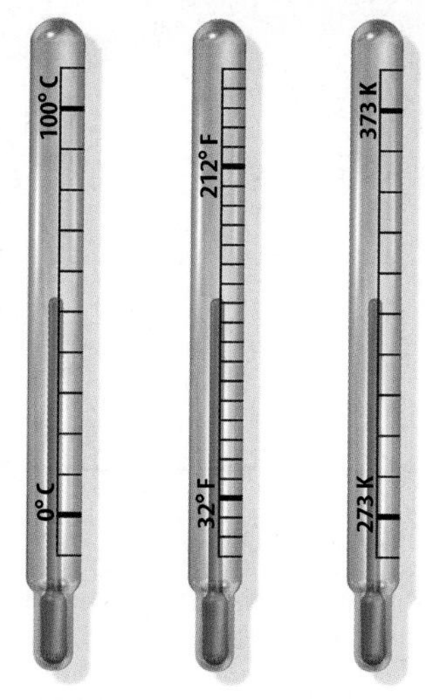

Figure 16 These three thermometers illustrate the scales of temperature between the freezing and boiling points of water.
Compare *the boiling points of the three scales.*

section 2 review

Summary

Units and Standards

- When making measurements, it is important to be accurate.

Measurement Systems

- The International System of Units, or SI, was established to provide a standard of measurement and reduce confusion.
- Conversion factors are used to change one unit to another and involve using a ratio equal to 1.

Measuring

- The size of an object being measured determines which unit you will measure in.

Self Check

1. **Explain** why it is important to have exact standards of measurement.
2. **Explain** why density is a derived unit.
3. **Think Critically** Using a metric ruler, measure a shoe box and a pad of paper. Find the volume of each in cubic centimeters. Then convert the units to mL.

Applying Math

4. **Convert Units** Make the following conversions: 27°C to Kelvin, 20 dg to milligrams, and 3 m to decimeters.
5. **Calculate Density** What is the density of an unknown metal that has a mass of 158 g and a volume of 20 mL? Use **Table 3** to identify this metal.

Caption Answer

Figure 16 The boiling point of water is 373 K, 100°C, and 212°F.

Reading Check

Answer The units are the same size, but zero on the Kelvin scale is 273 units lower than zero on the Celsius scale.

3 Assess

DAILY INTERVENTION

Check for Understanding

Kinesthetic Being able to convert between SI units is important in understanding how scientists operate on a daily basis. Have students measure various objects in centimenters. Then have students convert from centimeters to meter, from meter to kilometer, and centimeter to kilometer.

Reteach

Have each student calculate his or her mass in kilograms. Tell students that at Earth's surface, an object weighing 1 pound has a mass of 0.45 kg. Sample: A student weighing 120 pounds has a mass of 54 kg L2 IS **Logical-Mathematical**

Assessment

Performance Have students develop their own standards and units for measuring time. Have them evaluate their units in terms of how easy it is to replicate results using their standards. Use **Performance Assessment in the Science Classroom,** p. 117.

section 2 review

1. They provide a consistent, known, and accepted value for a base unit.
2. It is obtained by combining two SI units.
3. Check students' work.
4. 300 K; 2000 mg; 30 dm
5. 158.0 g/20.0 mL = 7.90 g/mL; iron

section 3

Communicating with Graphs

Reading Guide

What You'll Learn

- **Identify** three types of graphs and explain the ways they are used.
- **Distinguish** between dependent and independent variables.
- **Analyze** data using the various types of graphs.

Why It's Important

Graphs are a quick way to communicate a lot of information in a small amount of space.

Review Vocabulary

data: information gathered during an investigation or observation

New Vocabulary

- graph

A Visual Display

Scientists often graph the results of their experiments because they can detect patterns in the data easier in a graph than in a table. A **graph** is a visual display of information or data. **Figure 17** is a graph that shows a girl walking her dog. The horizontal axis, or the *x*-axis, measures time. Time is the independent variable because as it changes, it affects the measure of another variable. The distance from home that the girl and the dog walk is the other variable. It is the dependent variable and is measured on the vertical axis, or *y*-axis.

Figure 17 This graph tells the story of the motion that takes place when a girl takes her dog for an 8-min walk.

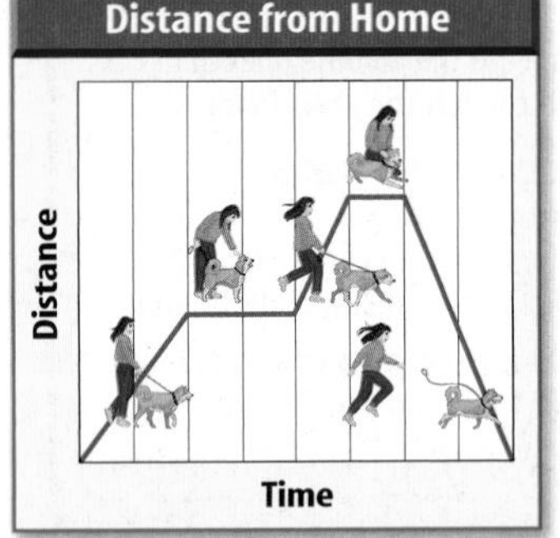

Graphs are useful for displaying numerical information in business, science, sports, advertising, and many everyday situations. Different kinds of graphs—line, bar, and circle—are appropriate for displaying different types of information.

Reading Check *What are three common types of graphs?*

Business people, as well as scientists, need an organized method to display data. Graphs make it easier to understand patterns by displaying data in a visual manner. Scientists often graph their data to detect patterns that would not have been evident in a table. Business people may graph sales dollars to determine trends. Different graphs use different methods for displaying information. The conclusions drawn from graphs must be based on accurate information.

1 Motivate

Bellringer

Section Focus Transparencies also are available on the Interactive Chalkboard CD-ROM.

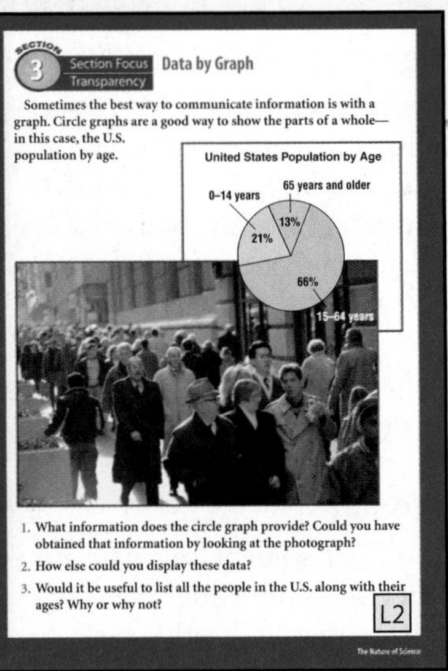

Section 3 Section Focus Transparency **Data by Graph**

Sometimes the best way to communicate information is with a graph. Circle graphs are a good way to show the parts of a whole—in this case, the U.S. population by age.

1. What information does the circle graph provide? Could you have obtained that information by looking at the photograph?
2. How else could you display these data?
3. Would it be useful to list all the people in the U.S. along with their ages? Why or why not?

L2

The Nature of Science

Tie to Prior Knowledge

Finding Graphs Assign students to find graphs in newspapers and magazines and bring them to class. Have student groups develop a classification system for the graphs. L1 IN **Interpersonal**

Section 3 Resource Manager

Chapter *Fast File* Resources

- Transparency Activity, pp. 46, 47–48
- Directed Reading for Content Mastery, pp. 21, 22
- MiniLAB, p. 4
- Enrichment, p. 32
- Reinforcement, p. 29
- Lab Activity, pp. 13–16
- Lab Worksheet, pp. 5–6, 7–8

Lab Management and Safety, p. 71

Reading and Writing Skill Activities, p. 47

Line Graphs

A line graph can show any relationship where the dependent variable changes due to a change in the independent variable. Line graphs often show how a relationship between variables changes over time. You can use a line graph to track many things, such as how certain stocks perform or how the population changes over any period of time—a month, a week, or a year.

You can show more than one event on the same graph as long as the relationship between the variables is identical. Suppose a builder had three choices of thermostats for a new school. He wanted to test them to know which was the best brand to install throughout the building. He installed a different thermostat in classrooms A, B, and C. He set each thermostat at 20°C. He turned the furnace on and checked the temperatures in the three rooms every 5 min for 25 min. He recorded his data in **Table 4.**

Table 4 Room Temperature

Time*	Classroom Temperature (C°) A	B	C
0	16	16	16
5	17	17	16.5
10	19	19	17
15	20	21	17.5
20	20	23	18
25	20	25	18.5

*minutes after turning on heat

The builder then plotted the data on a graph. He could see from the table that the data did not vary much for the three classrooms. So he chose small intervals for the *y*-axis and left part of the scale out (the part between 0° and 15°). See **Figure 18.** This allowed him to spread out the area on the graph where the data points lie. You can see easily the contrast in the colors of the three lines and their relationship to the black horizontal line. The black line represents the thermostat setting and is the control. The control is what the resulting room temperature of the classrooms should be if the thermostats are working efficiently.

Figure 18 The room temperatures of classrooms A, B, and C are shown in contrast to the thermostat setting of 20°C.
Identify *the thermostat that achieved its temperature setting the quickest.*

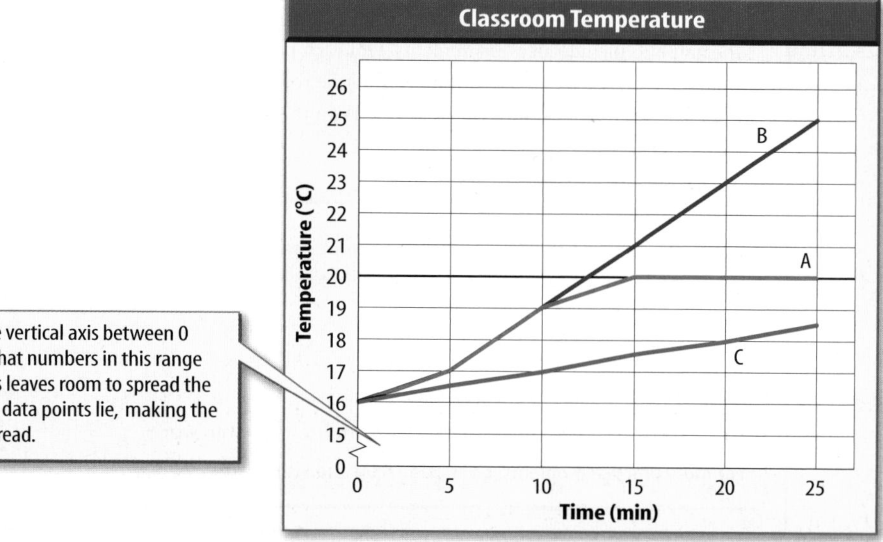

2 Teach

Reading Check

Answer line, bar, and circle graphs

Caption Answer

Figure 18 thermostat A

Discussion

Interpolation v. Extrapolation Explain to students that interpolation is reading graph values between data points, and extrapolation is reading graph values beyond data points. Ask students which process is likely to produce more error. Extrapolation; it goes beyond what has actually been measured in an experiment. L3 IS **Logical-Mathematical**

Activity

Graphing Have student look in the newspaper for information that can be presented as graphs. Have each student explain why they chose that particular graph. Examples can be weather data, motor vehicle ads, or sports statistics.

Visual Learning

Figure 18 Have students practice interpolation (finding data between reference points) and extrapolation (finding data past the range of the reference points) by examining the data provided. Ask them what they would expect the temperature to be in the classroom using thermostat A after 8 min and after 30 min. 18°C and 20°C L3 ELL IS **Visual-Spatial**

Differentiated Instruction

Challenge Graphs are not always a completely objective presentation of data. Graphs are frequently used in advertising to conceal or distort data. Ask students to think of ways that information could be emphasized or underplayed on a graph. A stretched-out vertical scale would emphasize highs and lows. A compressed vertical scale would conceal them. L2 ELL IS **Logical-Mathematical**

Applying Math

National Math Standards

Correlation to Mathematics Objectives

1, 2, 5, 9

Answer to Practice Problem

1. Students could use either bar graphs or line graphs to represent this data. In either case, running time should be on the *y*-axis and year should be on the *x*-axis.
2. Check students' work.
3. The difference in time is 1.2h. % Improvement = 1.2 h/5.2 h × 100 = 23.1%

Quick Demo

Data Tables

Materials none

Estimated Time ten minutes

Purpose Use students' clothing or shoes to demonstrate how to make a data table. For example, you could collect data such as shoe type, shoe color, sleeve length, or clothing type. After completing the data table, complete a bar graph of the information. Reinforce the idea that a bar graph rather than a line graph would be used because a line graph must contain two sets of numbers, while a bar graph can use categories. L2 ELL LS **Visual-Spatial**

Teacher FYI

Charts and Graphs The earliest surviving chart, an illustration of the orbits of the planets over time, dates back to the tenth century. The art of charting and graphing didn't appear again until the 18th century with the introduction of the modern economics graph by William Playfair.

Figure 19 Graphing calculators are valuable tools for making graphs.

Constructing Line Graphs Besides choosing a scale that makes a graph readable, as illustrated in **Figure 18,** other factors are involved in constructing useful graphs. The most important factor in making a line graph is always using the *x*-axis for the independent variable. The *y*-axis always is used for the dependent variable. Because the points in a line graph are related, you connect the points.

Another factor in constructing a graph involves units of measurement. For example, you might use a Celsius thermometer for one part of your experiment and a Fahrenheit thermometer for another. But you must first convert your temperature readings to the same unit of measurement before you make your graph.

In the past, graphs had to be made by hand, with each point plotted individually. Today, scientists use a variety of tools, such as computers and graphing calculators like the one shown in **Figure 19,** to help them draw graphs.

Applying Science

GRAPHING TEMPERATURE In an experiment, you checked the air temperature at certain hours of the day. At 8 A.M., the temperature is 27°C; at noon, the temperature is 32°C; and at 4 P.M., the temperature is 30°C. Graph the results of your experiment.

IDENTIFY known values

time = independent variable which is the *x*-axis

temperature = dependent variable which is the *y*-axis

GRAPH the problem

Graph time on the *x*-axis and temperature on the *y*-axis. Mark the equal increments on the graph to include all measurements. Plot each point on the graph by finding the time on the *x*-axis and moving up until you find the recorded temperature on the *y*-axis. Place a point there. Continue placing points on the graph. Then connect the points from left to right.

Practice Problems

As you train for a marathon, you compare your previous times. In year one, you ran it in 5.2 h; in year two, you ran it in 5 h; in year three, you ran it in 4.8 h; in year four, you ran it in 4.3 h; and in year five, you ran it in 4 h.

1. Make a table of your data.
2. Graph the results of your marathon races.
3. Calculate your percentage of improvement from year 1 to year 5.

For more practice problems, go to page 834, and visit gpscience.com/extra_problems.

Science Journal

Birth Months Take a class survey of the month in which each student's birthday occurs and tally these data on the board. Have students record this information in their Science Journals. Ask each student to make both a bar graph and a circle graph to show the information. L2 LS **Logical-Mathematical** P

Differentiated Instruction

Learning Disabled Have students conduct a survey in class to determine how many of their peers walk to class, how many ride their bike, get a ride, and take the bus. After students gather their data, have them determine which graph will best display the data. Why did they choose that particular graph? What made the other graphs a bad choice?

Bar Graphs

A bar graph is useful for comparing information collected by counting. For example, suppose you counted the number of students in every classroom in your school on a particular day and organized your data as in **Table 5.** You could show these data in a bar graph like the one shown in **Figure 20.** Uses for bar graphs include comparisons of oil, or crop productions, costs, or as data in promotional materials. Each bar represents a quantity counted at a particular time, which should be stated on the graph. As on a line graph, the independent variable is plotted on the *x*-axis and the dependent variable is plotted on the *y*-axis.

Recall that you might need to place a break in the scale of the graph to better illustrate your results. For example, if your data were 1,002, 1,010, 1,030, and 1,040 and the intervals on the scale were every 100 units, you might not be able to see the difference from one bar to another. If you had a break in the scale and started your data range at 1,000 with intervals of ten units, you could make a more accurate comparison.

Reading Check *Describe possible data where using a bar graph would be better than using a line graph.*

Table 5 Classroom Size

Number of Students	Number of Classrooms
20	1
21	3
22	3
23	2
24	3
25	5
26	5
27	3

Figure 20 The height of each bar corresponds to the number of classrooms having a particular number of students.

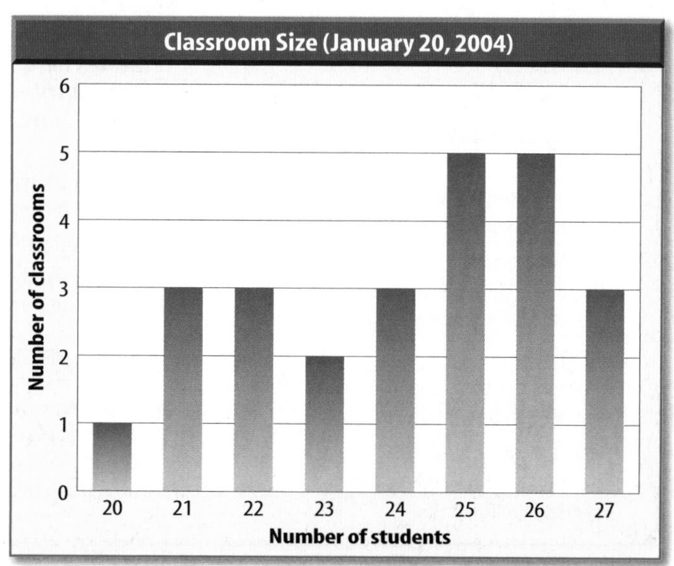

Mini LAB

Observing Change Through Graphing

Procedure

1. Place a **thermometer** in a **plastic foam cup** of hot, but not boiling, **water.**
2. Measure and record the temperature every 30 s for 5 min.
3. Repeat the experiment with freshly heated water. This time, cover the cup with a **plastic lid** in between measurements.

Analysis

1. Make a line graph of the changing temperature from step 2, showing time on the *x*-axis and temperature on the *y*-axis. Using a different color pen, plot the changing temperature from step 3 on the same graph.
2. Use the graph to describe the cooling process in each of the trials.

Try at Home

Purpose Students measure the change in temperature over time and graph the data. L1 ELL LS **Visual-Spatial**

Materials plastic foam cup, matching lid with straw hole, thermometer, graph paper, timer with second hand, hot water

Teaching Strategy Show students how to estimate a reading between marks on the thermometer.

Analysis

1. The slopes of both graphs will be negative and steeper at the beginning. The first graph will be steeper than the second.
2. The temperature decreases most rapidly when it is highest. Adding a lid significantly reduces the rate at which temperature decreases.

Assessment

Process Have students sketch a graph of what they probably would observe if they reversed the process and heated the water in an open glass container. The slope would be positive.

Reading Check

Answer Answers will vary but might include the number of points scored by the local football team for each game of the season.

LAB DEMONSTRATION

Purpose to show students how to draw circle graphs

Preparation Write the following data on the board: Of the people who attended a play, 42 were under 10 years old; 27 were from 11 to 20, and 11 were over 21.

Procedure Determine what percentage of the whole each part represents (percentage = part ÷ whole × 100%). For those under 10, this is ÷ 42/80 × 100% = 52%. A circle contains 360°. To find the number of degrees needed to show each percentage, change the percentage to a decimal number and multiply it by 360°. For those under 10, 360° × 0.52 = 187°.

Assessment

What percentage of the audience were from 11 to 20? $\frac{27}{80}$ × 100% = 34% from 11 to 20 Over 21? $\frac{11}{80}$ × 100% = 14% How many degrees of the circle graph are required for each of these groups? 360° × 0.34 = 122° from 11 to 20; 360° × 0.14 = 50° over 21

3 Assess

DAILY INTERVENTION

Check for Understanding

Logical-Mathematical Tell students that four students scored a D on a test, ten scored a C, seven scored a B, and four scored an A. Ask students what kinds of graphs could be used to display this data. circle graph or bar graph Have each student make a bar graph and a circle graph of the data, choose the graph he or she prefers, and explain the choice. L2

Reteach

Candle Wicks Stick ten birthday cake candles in holders in a long piece of plastic foam. Light the second candle and let it burn for only 5 s. Light the remaining candles in turn, letting the third candle burn for 10 s, the fourth for 15 s, etc. Remove the candles from the holders, clip their wicks, and place them side-by-side, bases aligned, on an overhead projector. Discuss with students what the silhouette displays. L2 LS **Visual-Spatial**

Assessment

Performance If students find line graphs for question six in the Section Review, have them identify the dependent and independent variables. For circle graphs, have them check that the percentages total 100 percent. Use **Performance Assessment in the Science Classroom**, p. 101.

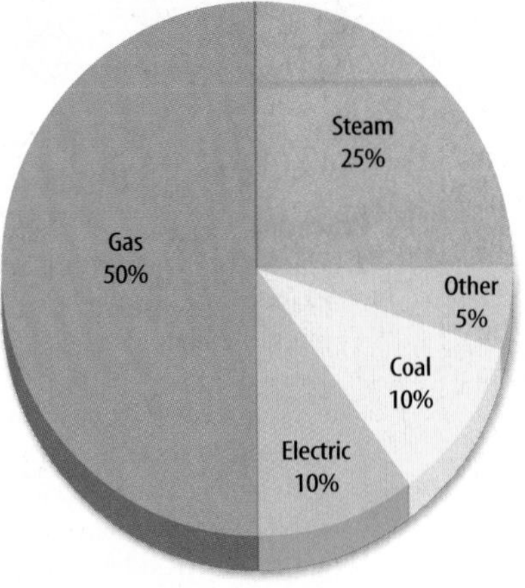

Figure 21 A circle graph shows the different parts of a whole quantity.

Circle Graphs

A circle graph, or pie graph, is used to show how some fixed quantity is broken down into parts. The circular pie represents the total. The slices represent the parts and usually are represented as percentages of the total.

Figure 21 illustrates how a circle graph could be used to show the percentage of buildings in a neighborhood using each of a variety of heating fuels. You easily can see that more buildings use gas heat than any other kind of system. What else does the graph tell you?

To create a circle graph, you start with the total of what you are analyzing. **Figure 21** starts with 72 buildings in the neighborhood. For each type of heating fuel, you divide the number of buildings using each type of fuel by the total (72). You then multiply that decimal by 360° to determine the angle that the decimal makes in the circle. Eighteen buildings use steam. Therefore, $18 \div 72 \times 360° = 90°$ on the circle graph. You then would measure 90° on the circle with your protractor to show 25 percent.

When you use graphs, think carefully about the conclusions you can draw from them. You want to make sure your conclusions are based on accurate information and that you use scales that help make your graph easy to read.

section 3 review

Summary

A Visual Display

- Graphs are a visual representation of data.
- Scientists often graph their data to detect patterns.
- The type of graph used is based on the conclusions you want to identify.

Line Graphs

- A line graph shows how a relationship between two variables changes over time.

Bar Graphs

- Bar graphs are best used to compare information collected by counting.

Circle Graphs

- A circle graph shows how a fixed quantity is broken down into parts.

Self Check

1. **Identify** the kind of graph that would best show the results of a survey of 144 people where 75 ride a bus, 45 drive cars, 15 carpool, and 9 walk to work.
2. **State** which type of variable is plotted on the x-axis and which type is plotted on the y-axis.
3. **Explain** why the points in a line graph are connected.
4. **Think Critically** How are line, bar, and circle graphs similar? How are they different?

Applying Math

5. **Percentage** In a survey, it was reported that 56 out of 245 people would rather drink orange juice in the morning than coffee. Calculate what percentage of a circle graph this data would occupy.

gpscience.com/self_check_quiz

section 3 review

1. bar graph
2. The independent variable is shown on the x-axis and the dependent variable is shown on the y-axis.
3. Points are connected because they are related.
4. All three graphs are used to display data. A line graph shows relationships between two variables. A bar graph can be used to compare information. A circle graph can be used to show percentages.
5. 22.9%

Converting Kitchen Measurements

Look through a recipe book. Are any of the ingredient amounts stated in SI? How can you convert English measurements to SI measurements?

Real-World Question

How do kitchen measurements compare with SI measurements?

Goals

- Determine a relationship between two systems of measurements.
- Calculate the conversion factors for converting English units to SI units.

Materials

balance
100-mL graduated cylinder
measuring cup
measuring teaspoon
measuring tablespoon
cornmeal
dried beans
dried rice
potato flakes
water
vinegar
salad oil

Safety Precautions

Procedure

1. Copy the data table into your Science Journal and record each SI measurement.
2. Use the appropriate English measuring cup or spoon to measure the amounts of each ingredient shown in the table.
3. Use a balance to measure each dry ingredient. Use a graduated cylinder to measure each liquid ingredient.

English to SI Conversions

Ingredient	English Measure	SI Measure
Water	1/2 cup	118 mL
Cornmeal	2 cups	295 g
Salad oil	4 tablespoons	60 mL
Dried rice	1/2 cup	90 g
Potato flakes	3 cups	168 g
Vinegar	1 teaspoon	5 mL
Dried beans	3 cups	510 g

Conclude and Apply

1. **Calculate** the number of grams in one cup of each dry ingredient. Calculate the number of milliliters in one cup, one teaspoon, and one tablespoon of each liquid ingredient.
2. **Write** conversion factors that will convert each English unit to an SI unit for each ingredient.
3. **Calculate** how many milliliters you would measure if a recipe called for three tablespoons of salad oil.
4. **Compare and contrast** your conversion factors for the dry ingredients and your conversion factors for the liquid ingredients.

Write a recipe used in your home converting all the English units to SI units.

Real-World Question

Purpose Students will compare English and metric measurements used in kitchen utensils.

Process Skills compare, contrast, predict, infer

Time Required 30 min

Safety Precautions Instruct students to wear safety goggles. Caution students to never eat or drink anything in science class.

Procedure

Teaching Strategy Have dishwashing liquid available for students to use for clean up.

Troubleshooting Review metric and English units before starting the lab.

Conclude and Apply

1. cornmeal, 148 g; rice, 180 g; potato flakes, 56 g; beans, 170 g; all liquids: 1 c = about 236 mL; 1 Tbsp. = about 15 mL; 1 tsp. = about 5 mL
2. Cornmeal, $\frac{148\text{ g}}{1\text{ c}}$; beans, $\frac{170\text{ g}}{1\text{ c}}$; all liquids, $\frac{236\text{ mL}}{1\text{ c}}$.
3. 45 mL
4. Each conversion factor has *1 c* in the denominator. The solid conversion factors convert a volume unit to a mass unit. The liquid factors convert between two volume units. The solid conversion factors are all different and the liquid factors are all the same.

Assessment

Oral Ask students to write metric/ English unit conversion questions and quiz each other aloud. Use **Performance Assessment in the Science Classroom,** p. 91.

Communicating Your Data

Have students trade recipes and take them home and make the dishes to test whether or not the conversions were done correctly.

Real-World Question

Purpose Students will design and carry out an experiment to show the necessary components of an acceptable measurement system. L1 COOP LEARN

LS **Interpersonal**

Process Skills measure, collect and organize data, make and use tables, separate and control variables, communicate, form operational definitions, make models, use numbers, classify, observe and infer

Time Required one class period to brainstorm; one-half to one class period to complete the activity and summarize results

Materials Have various colors of string available.

Form a Hypothesis

Possible Hypothesis Students may hypothesize that using a defined measurement standard will make it possible for other students to measure objects consistently.

Test Your Hypothesis

Possible Procedures Choose an object such as a piece of chalk, a paper clip, or a book as the standard. Mark the units on the string with a marker or tape. Try several different-sized scale divisions of the base unit to measure halves, quarters, and tenths of units.

Design Your Own

Setting High Standards for Measurements

Real-World Question

To develop the International System of Units, people had to agree on set standards and basic definitions of scale. If you had to develop a new measurement system, people would have to agree with your new standards and definitions. In this activity, your team will use string to devise and test its own SI (String International) system for measuring length. What are the requirements for designing a new measurement system using string?

Goals

- **Design** an experiment that involves devising and testing your own measurement system for length.
- **Measure** various objects with the string measurement system.

Possible Materials

string
scissors
marking pen
masking tape
miscellaneous objects for standards

Safety Precautions

Form a Hypothesis

Based on your knowledge of measurement standards and systems, form a hypothesis that explains how exact units help keep measuring consistent.

Test Your Hypothesis

Make a Plan

1. As a group, agree upon and write out the hypothesis statement.
2. As a group, list the steps that you need to take to test your hypothesis. Be specific, describing exactly what you will do at each step.
3. Make a list of the materials that you will need.

Alternative Inquiry Lab

Real-World Connection Have students research and discuss why other standards in science are necessary. Examples include graphing rules, writing in pen in permanently bound laboratory notebooks (the debacle of the Cold Fusion experiments is a good illustration), and standards in experimental procedures and reporting format.

Researching the history of standards of measurement in antiquity also can be fascinating. Possible topics include the precision of the construction of the Egyptian pyramids, geometry, astronomy, and monolithic construction, the ancient Chinese, the Mayans, the ancient Muslim scientists, and units for trade and barter.

4. **Design** a data table in your Science Journal so it is ready to use as your group collects data.
5. As you read over your plan, be sure you have chosen an object in your classroom to serve as a standard. It should be in the same size range as what you will measure.
6. Consider how you will mark scale divisions on your string. Plan to use different pieces of string to try different-sized scale divisions.
7. What is your new unit of measurement called? Come up with an abbreviation for your unit. Will you name the smaller scale divisions?
8. What objects will you measure with your new unit? Be sure to include objects longer and shorter than your string. Will you measure each object more than once to test consistency? Will you measure the same object as another group and compare your findings?

Follow Your Plan

1. Make sure your teacher approves your plan before you start.
2. Carry out the experiment as it has been planned.
3. **Record** observations that you make and complete the data table in your Science Journal.

Analyze Your Data

1. Which of your string scale systems will provide the most accurate measurement of small objects? Explain.
2. How did you record measurements that were between two whole numbers of your units?

Conclude and Apply

1. When sharing your results with other groups, why is it important for them to know what you used as a standard?
2. **Infer** how it is possible for different numbers to represent the same length of an object.

Compare your conclusions with other students' conclusions. Are there differences? Explain how these may have occurred.

Teaching Strategy Use heavy string to make handling easy. Be sure metersticks and other standard measuring devices are not available to students. Encourage students to use common classroom objects as standards.

Expected Outcome Students will devise and test a measuring system that other groups can use to make consistent measurements. They may encounter errors due to stretching of the string and estimating between units.

Discussion Discuss with students that measurements between two marked units will include one estimated digit. Different people using the same measuring device will be more likely to get the same measurement if the scale divisions are small. The ability to measure and get the same answer is called precision.

Analyze Your Data

1. the system with the smallest divisions, because it is the most precise
2. The final digit was estimated.

Error Analysis Have students analyze how errors could result from the method used to mark their string into smaller units.

Conclude and Apply

1. so they can reproduce your results
2. When the size of the unit of measurement varies, the number of units used to measure an object also must vary.

Assessment

Portfolio Have students tape a sample of their measuring string to an explanation of their standard and measuring system. Then have them write about any problems they solved in the process of developing this system. Students should include this paper in their portfolio. Use **Performance Assessment in the Science Classroom,** p. 159. P

To test their measurement systems, have students exchange strings and use them to measure the same item.

Understanding Literature

Identifying the Main Head Possible answer: The main idea of this selection is that thinking in pictures—has allowed Temple Grandin to solve design problems as an equipment designer.

Answers to Questions

1. They think in pictures.
2. photographs at the cow's eye level
3. Kites and model airplanes
4. **Linking Science and Writing** Remind students that maps and pictures can be models as well as three-dimensional objects.

INTEGRATE Physics **Modeling** The design and use of models can help people predict the characteristics of any system. Because a model can be built, tested, and modified at a reasonably low cost, scientists, architects, and other designers use models to predict the performance of a prototype. If the results obtained from a model are to be applicable to the prototype, a strict set of conditions must be met by the model or the deviations from these conditions must be considered when predicting the behavior of the prototype.

Science and Language Arts

Thinking in Pictures: and other reports from my life with autism[1]

By Temple Grandin

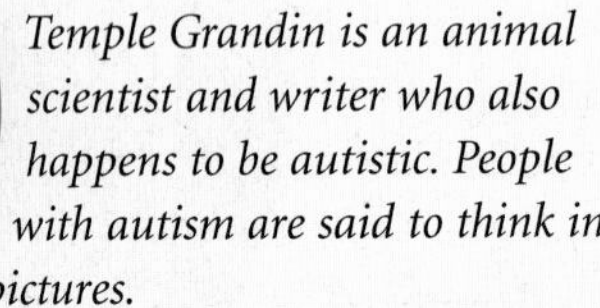

Temple Grandin is an animal scientist and writer who also happens to be autistic. People with autism are said to think in pictures.

I think in pictures. Words are like a second language to me. I translate both spoken and written words into full-color movies, complete with sound, which run like a VCR tape in my head. When somebody speaks to me, his words are instantly translated into pictures. Language-based thinkers often find this phenomenon difficult to understand, but in my job as equipment designer for the livestock industry, visual thinking is a tremendous advantage.

. . . I credit my visualization abilities with helping me understand the animals I work with. Early in my career I used a camera to help give me the animals' perspective as they walked through a chute for their veterinary treatment. I would kneel down and take pictures through the chute from the cow's eye level. Using the photos, I was able to figure out which things scared the cattle.

Every design problem I've ever solved started with my ability to visualize and see the world in pictures. I started designing things as a child, when I was always experimenting with new kinds of kites and model airplanes.

1 Autism is a complex developmental disability that usually appears during the first three years of life. Children and adults with autism typically have difficulties in communicating with others and relating to the outside world.

Understanding Literature

Identifying the Main Idea The most important idea expressed in a paragraph or essay is the main idea. The main idea in a reading might be clearly stated, but sometimes the reader has to summarize the contents of a reading in order to determine its main idea. What do you think is the main idea of the passage?

Respond to the Reading

1. How do people with autism think differently than other people?
2. What did the author use to see from a cow's point of view?
3. What did the author use for models to design things when she was a child?
4. **Linking Science and Writing** Research the use of a scientific model. Write a paragraph stating the main ideas and listing supporting details.

INTEGRATE Physics Models enable scientists to see things that are too big, too small, or are too complex. Scientists might build models of DNA, airplanes, or other equipment. Temple Grandin's visual thinking and ability to make models enables her to predict how things will work when they are put together.

Resources for Teachers and Students

Dr. Temple Grandin Video-Visual Thinking of a Person with Autism, by Temple Grandin, Future Horizons, 1999

Unraveling the Mystery of Autism and Pervasive Development Disorder: A Mother's Story of Research and Recovery, by Karyn Seroussi and Bernard Rimland Ph.D., Simon & Shuster, 2000

Reviewing Main Ideas

Section 1 The Methods of Science

1. Science is a way of learning about the natural world, such as the hurricane shown below, through investigation.

2. Scientific investigations can involve making observations, testing models, or conducting experiments.
3. Scientific experiments investigate the effect of one variable on another. All other variables are kept constant.
4. Scientific laws are repeated patterns in nature. Theories attempt to explain how and why these patterns develop.

Section 2 Standards of Measurement

1. A standard of measurement is an exact quantity that people agree to use as a basis of comparison. The International System of Units, or SI, was established to provide a standard and reduce confusion.
2. When a standard of measurement is established, all measurements are compared to the same exact quantity—the standard. Therefore, all measurements can be compared with one another.
3. The most commonly used SI units include: length—meter, volume—liter, mass—kilogram, and time—second.
4. In SI, prefixes are used to make the base units larger or smaller by multiples of ten.
5. Any SI unit can be converted to any other related SI unit by multiplying by the appropriate conversion factor. These towers are 45,190 cm in height, which is equal to 451.9 m.

Section 3 Communicating With Graphs

1. Graphs are a visual representation of data that make it easier for scientists to detect patterns.
2. Line graphs show continuous changes among related variables. Bar graphs are used to show data collected by counting. Circle graphs show how a fixed quantity can be broken into parts.
3. To create a circle graph, you have to determine the angles for your data.
4. In a line graph, the independent variable is always plotted on the horizontal x-axis. The dependent variable is always plotted on the vertical y-axis.

FOLDABLES Use the Foldable that you made at the beginning of this chapter to help you review scientific processes.

Science Online gpscience.com/interactive_tutor

chapter 1 Study Guide

Reviewing Main Ideas

Summary statements can be used by students to review the major concepts of the chapter.

Science Online

Visit gpscience.com
/self_check_quiz
/interactive_tutor
/vocabulary_puzzlemaker
/chapter_review
/standardized_test

Assessment Transparency

For additional assessment questions, use the *Assessment Transparency* located in the transparency book.

Assessment

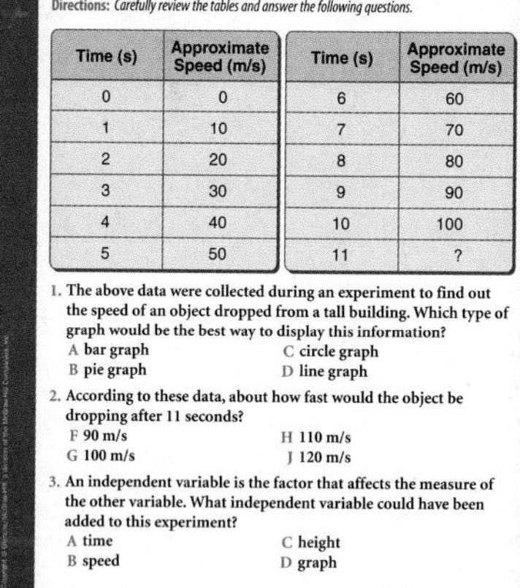
Assessment Transparency The Nature of Science

Directions: *Carefully review the tables and answer the following questions.*

Time (s)	Approximate Speed (m/s)
0	0
1	10
2	20
3	30
4	40
5	50

Time (s)	Approximate Speed (m/s)
6	60
7	70
8	80
9	90
10	100
11	?

1. The above data were collected during an experiment to find out the speed of an object dropped from a tall building. Which type of graph would be the best way to display this information?
   A bar graph C circle graph
   B pie graph D line graph
2. According to these data, about how fast would the object be dropping after 11 seconds?
   F 90 m/s H 110 m/s
   G 100 m/s J 120 m/s
3. An independent variable is the factor that affects the measure of the other variable. What independent variable could have been added to this experiment?
   A time C height
   B speed D graph

L2

The Nature of Science

FOLDABLES Have students use the Foldables that they made at the beginning of the chapter to help them review scientific processes.

Using Vocabulary

1. SI
2. volume
3. standard
4. mass
5. dependent variable
6. graph
7. experiment
8. constant
9. density
10. hypothesis

Checking Concepts

11. B
12. B
13. D
14. D
15. A
16. B
17. D

Interpreting Graphics

18. Independent variable: pot; constant: vegetables; ingredients; dependent variable: heat required, iron content, taste, cooking time
19. Check student page

Thinking Critically

20. Possible answer: The next king's arm would be a different length.
21. Possible advantages: SI is based on powers of 10 conversion is easy because the same prefixes are used for all types of measurements most countries use it. Possible disadvantages: Conversion to SI would be expensive; people are reluctant to change from a familiar system.
22. Bias occurs when a scientist's expectations about the experiment change how he views the results. Running multiple trials, keeping accurate records of measurable data, and designing experiments that can be repeated reduces bias and helps validate data.

Using Vocabulary

bias p. 10	model p. 11
constant p. 9	scientific law p. 12
control p. 9	scientific method p. 7
density p. 19	SI p. 15
dependent variable p. 9	standard p. 14
experiment p. 8	technology p. 13
graph p. 22	theory p. 12
hypothesis p. 8	variable p. 9
independent variable p. 9	volume p. 18
mass p. 19	

Match each phrase with the correct term from the list of vocabulary words.

1. the modern version of the metric system
2. the amount of space occupied by an object
3. an agreed-upon quantity used for comparison
4. the amount of matter in an object
5. a variable that changes as another variable changes
6. a visual display of data
7. a test set up under controlled conditions
8. a variable that does NOT change as another variable changes
9. mass per unit volume
10. an educated guess using what you know and observe

Checking Concepts

Choose the word or phrase that best answers the question.

11. Which of the following questions CANNOT be answered by science?
    A) How do birds fly?
    B) Is this a good song?
    C) What is an atom?
    D) How does a clock work?

12. Which of the following is an example of an SI unit?
    A) foot **C)** pound
    B) second **D)** gallon

13. One one-thousandth is expressed by which prefix?
    A) kilo- **C)** centi-
    B) nano- **D)** milli-

14. Which of the following is SI based on?
    A) inches **C)** English units
    B) powers of five **D)** powers of ten

15. What is the symbol for deciliter?
    A) dL **C)** dkL
    B) dcL **D)** Ld

16. Which of the following is NOT a derived unit?
    A) dm^3 **C)** cm^3
    B) m **D)** g/ml

17. Which of the following is NOT equal to 1,000 mL?
    A) 1 L **C)** 1 dm^3
    B) 100 cL **D)** 1 cm^3

Interpreting Graphics

Use the photo below to answer question 18.

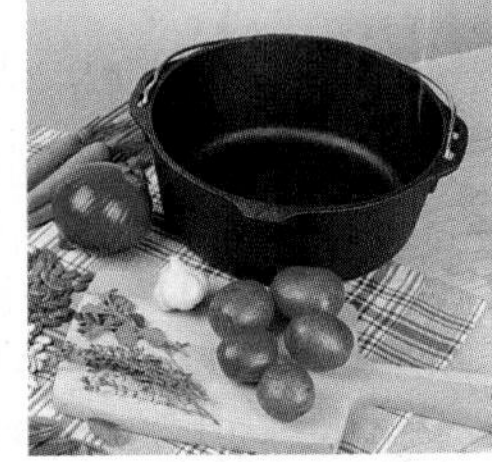

18. The illustrations above show the items needed for an investigation. Which item is the independent variable? Which items are the constants? What might a dependent variable be?

Science Online gpscience.com/vocabulary_puzzlemaker

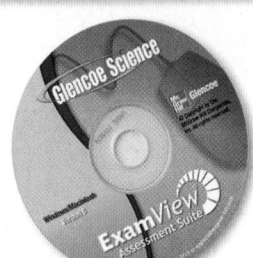

19. Copy and complete this concept map on scientific methods.

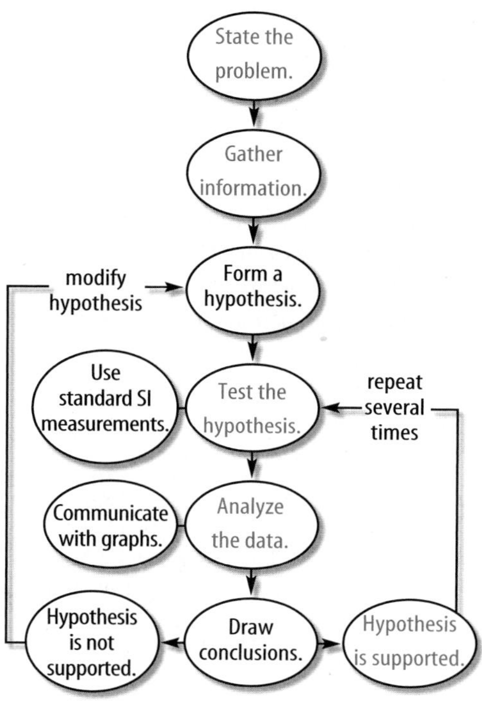

Thinking Critically

20. **Communicate** Standards of measurement used during the Middle Ages often were based on such things as the length of the king's arm. How would you go about convincing people to use a different system of standard units?

21. **Analyze** What are some advantages and disadvantages of adopting SI in the United States?

22. **Identify** when bias occurs in scientific experimentation. Describe steps scientists can take to reduce bias and validate experimental data.

23. **Demonstrate** Not all objects have a volume that is measured easily. If you were to determine the mass, volume, and density of your textbook, a container of milk, and an air-filled balloon, how would you do it?

24. **Apply** Suppose you set a glass of water in direct sunlight for 2 h and measure its temperature every 10 min. What type of graph would you use to display your data? What would the dependent variable be? What would the independent variable be?

25. **Form a Hypothesis** A metal sphere is found to have a density of 5.2 g/cm^3 at 25°C and a density of 5.1 g/cm^3 at 50°C. Form a hypothesis to explain this observation. How could you test your hypothesis?

26. **List** the SI units of length you would use to express the following.
 a. diameter of a hair
 b. width of your classroom
 c. width of a pencil lead
 d. length of a sheet of paper

27. **Compare and contrast** the ease with which conversions can be made among SI units versus conversions among units in the English system.

Applying Math

28. **Convert Units** Make the following conversions.
 A) 1,500 mL to L
 B) 2 km to cm
 C) 5.8 dg to mg
 D) 22°C to K

29. **Calculate the density** of an object having a mass of 17 g and a volume of 3 cm^3.

30. **Solve** A block of wood is 0.4 m by 0.2 m by 0.7 m. Find its dimensions in centimeters. Then find its volume in cubic centimeters.

 gpscience.com/chapter_review

Assessment Resources

 **Reproducible Masters**

Chapter *Fast File* Resources
Chapter Review, pp. 39–40
Chapter Tests, pp. 41–44
Assessment Transparency Activity, p. 51

Glencoe Science Web site
Chapter Review Test
Standardized Test Practice

Glencoe Technology
Assessment Transparency
ExamView® Assessment Suite
MindJogger Videoquiz
Interactive Chalkboard

Thinking Critically

23. Textbook volume could be determined by multiplying its length, width, and height. The volume of the balloon could be determined by measuring the volume of water it displaces. The volume of any irregular object, such as the milk carton, must be determined indirectly. If the object is not harmed by water, volume can be measured by water displacement.

24. A line graph; time would be the independent variable and temperature would be the dependent variable.

25. The metal expands when heated. The hypothesis can be tested by measuring the volume of the ball at the two temperatures.

26. a. nanometer, nm
 b. meter, m
 c. millimeter, mm
 d. centimeter, cm

27. SI measurements are based on powers of ten. There are many different divisions in the English system. Thus, it is easier to convert in SI than in the English system.

Applying Math

National Math Standards

1, 2, 4, 9

28. a. 1.5 L
 b. 200,000 cm
 c. 580 mg
 d. 295 K

29. $D = \frac{m}{V}$

$m = 17\text{ g} \qquad V = 3\text{ cm}^3$

$D = \frac{17\text{ g}}{3\text{ cm}^3} = 5.67\text{ g/cm}^3$

30. 1 meter = 100 cm;
0.4 m = 40 cm;
0.2 m = 20 cm;
0.7 m = 70 cm
$V = \text{length} \times \text{width} \times \text{height}$
$V = 40\text{ cm} \times 70\text{ cm} \times 20\text{ cm}$
$= 56{,}000\text{ cm}^3$

chapter 1 Standardized Test Practice

FAST FILE

Answer Sheet A practice answer sheet can be found at gpscience.com/answer_sheet.

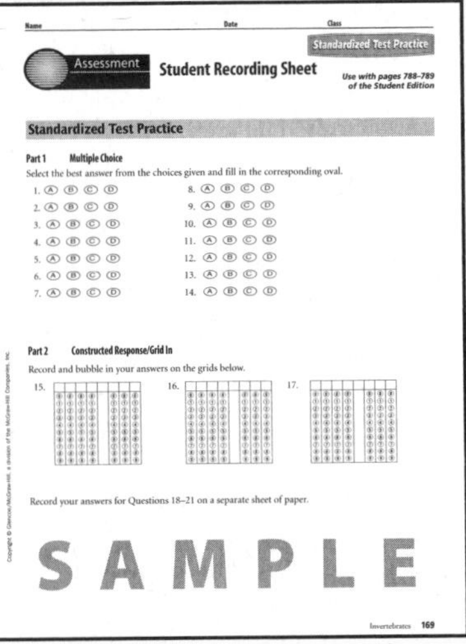
Name Date Class

Standardized Test Practice

Assessment Student Recording Sheet

Use with pages 788–789 of the Student Edition

Standardized Test Practice

Part 1 Multiple Choice

Select the best answer from the choices given and fill in the corresponding oval.

Part 2 Constructed Response/Grid In

Record and bubble in your answers on the grids below.

Record your answers for Questions 18–21 on a separate sheet of paper.

SAMPLE

Part 1 Multiple Choice

1. A
2. C
3. B
4. B
5. C
6. B
7. A
8. D

Part 2 Short Response

9. A scientist may make and record observations about something that is taking place. She might set up an experiment or build a model, run tests, and gather data about her observations.
10. Technology is the application of science to help people. Examples of technology are nearly limitless, but may be grouped into categories including medical tools, equipment designed for entertainment, modes of transportation, or home appliances.
11. Life science deals with living things, Earth science with Earth and space, and physical science with matter and energy. An environmental engineer would be concerned with all three branches. For example, he might study how heat and waste materials emitted by an industrial plant (physical science) affect the air, water, and soil (Earth science) and living organisms (life science) in the vicinity of the plant.
12. a. $615 \text{ mg} \times \frac{1 \text{ g}}{1000 \text{ mg}} = 0.615 \text{ g}$

    b. $75 \text{ dL} \times \frac{1\text{L}}{10 \text{ dL}} \times \frac{1000 \text{ mL}}{1\text{L}} = 7{,}500 \text{ mL}$

    c. $0.95 \text{ km} \times \frac{1000\text{m}}{1 \text{ km}} \times \frac{100 \text{ cm}}{1 \text{ m}} = 95{,}000 \text{ cm}$
13. Volume is the amount of space occupied by an object. The volume of the cube is 4cm × 4 cm × 4 cm, or 64 cm^3. 64 cm^3 = 64 mL.
14. Density is the mass per unit volume of material. The density of this material is 96 grams divided by 64 cm^3, or 1.5g/cm^3.

chapter 1 Standardized Test Practice

Part 1 Multiple Choice

Record your answers on the answer sheet provided by your teacher or on a sheet of paper.

Use the graph below to answer questions 1 and 2.

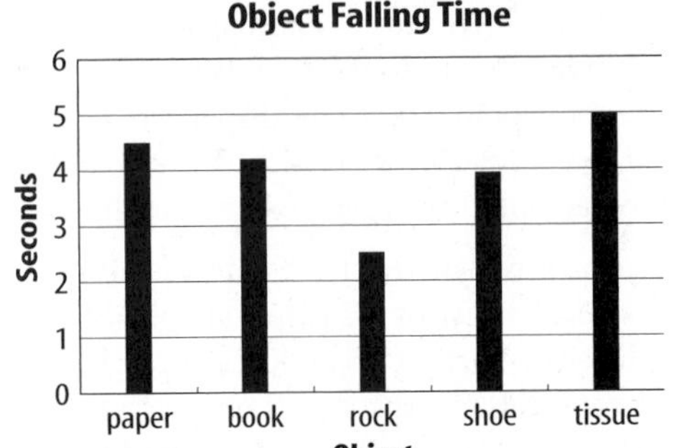

1. Students drop objects from a height and measure the time it takes each to reach the ground. What is the dependent variable in this experiment?
   A. falling time
   B. shoe
   C. drop height
   D. paper
2. What is a constant in this experiment?
   A. throwing some objects and dropping others
   B. measuring different falling times for each object
   C. dropping each object from the same height
   D. dropping a variety of objects
3. Which of the following is a statement about something that happens in nature which seems to be true all the time?
   A. theory
   B. scientific law
   C. hypothesis
   D. conclusion

Test-Taking Tip

Recheck Your Answers Double check your answers before turning in the test.

4. What does the symbol *ns* represent?
   A. millisecond
   B. nanosecond
   C. microsecond
   D. kelvin
5. Which of these best defines mass?
   A. the amount of space occupied by an object
   B. the distance between two points
   C. the quantity of matter in an object
   D. the interval between two events

Use the graph below to answer questions 6 and 7.

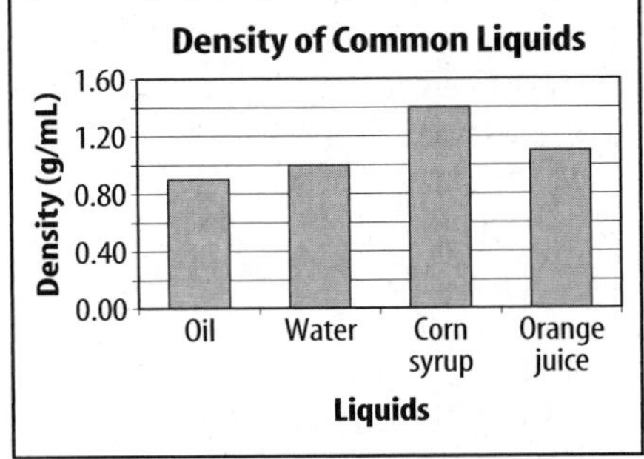

6. Which two liquids have the highest and the lowest densities?
   A. oil and water
   B. oil and corn syrup
   C. orange juice and water
   D. corn syrup and orange juice
7. What is the density of oil in units of mg/cm^3?
   A. 850 mg/cm^3
   B. 85 mg/cm^3
   C. 0.085 mg/cm^3
   D. 8500 mg/cm^3
8. Which type of graph is most useful for showing how the relationship between independent and dependent variables changes over time?
   A. circle graph
   B. bar graph
   C. pictograph
   D. line graph

Part 2 Short Response/Grid In

Part 2 Short Response/Grid In

Record your answers on the answer sheet provided by your teacher or on a sheet of paper.

9. Describe several ways scientists use investigations to learn about the natural world.

10. Define the term *technology.* Identify three ways that technology makes your life easier, safer, or more enjoyable.

11. Describe the three major categories into which science is classified. Which branches of science would be most important to an environmental engineer? Why?

12. Make the following conversions:
   a. 615 mg to g
   b. 75 dL to mL
   c. 0.95 km to cm

Use the illustration below to answer questions 13 and 14.

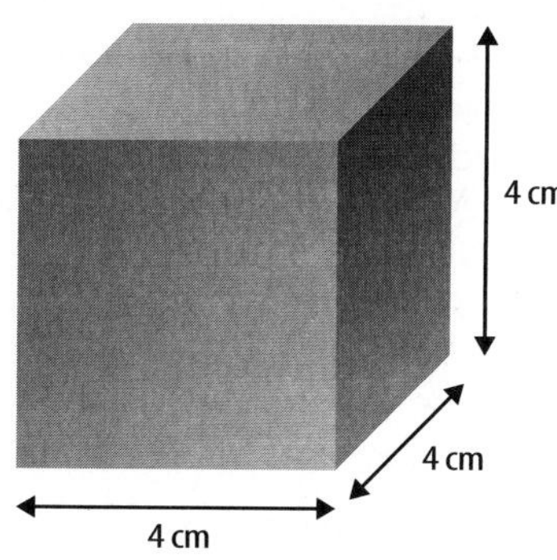

13. Define the term *volume.* Calculate the volume of the cube shown above. Give your answer in cm^3 and mL.

14. Define the term *density.* If the mass of the cube is 96 g, what is the density of the cube material?

15. Why do scientists use graphs when analyzing data?

Part 3 Open Ended

Record your answers on a sheet of paper.

16. A friend frequently misses the morning school bus. Use the scientific method to address this problem.

Use the illustration below to answer questions 17 and 18.

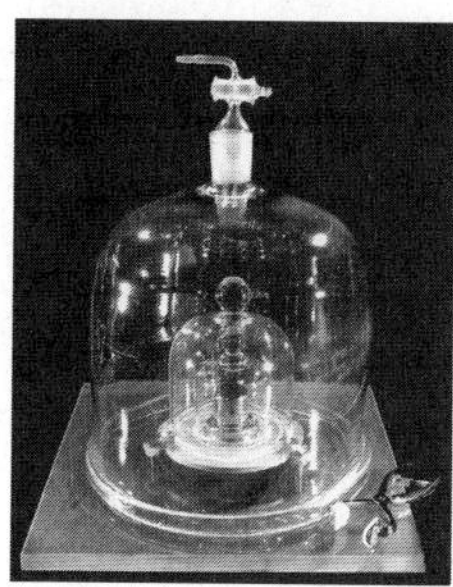

17. What is the standard unit shown in this picture? Why is it kept under cover, in a vacuum-sealed container?

18. Why is this standard important to anyone who makes measurements? Explain why valid experimental results must be based on standards.

19. You must decide what items to pack for a hiking and camping trip. Space is limited, and you must carry all items during hikes. What measurements are important in your preparation?

Use the table below to answer question 20.

Animal Life Span			
	Cow	Dog	Horse
Resting Heart Rate	52 beats per min	95 beats	48 beats per min
Average Life Span	18 years	16 years	27 years

20. Create a graph to display the data shown above.

15. It is easier to detect patterns when examining data in graph form than chart form.

Part 3 Open Ended

16. *The Problem:* Your friend misses the morning school bus. *Gather information:* Learn about the time and location of the bus' arrival and the morning routines in the home. *Possible hypotheses:* You friend should wake earlier, lay her clothes out the night before, or leave the house earlier in order to make the bus. *Test hypotheses, analyze data, and conclude.* Test each hypothesis several times over different mornings. If your friend consistently catches the bus, you can conclude that the hypothesis tested was supported.

17. This is the kilogram, the standard for mass. It is covered in a vacuum-sealed container to prevent any erosion or corrosion which might occur through contact with air, and to keep airborne materials from settling on it, changing its mass.

Part 3 Open Ended

18. All kilograms used throughout the world in various measuring equipment must have the same mass as this standard kilogram. Scientists throughout the world compare experimental data. Because all measurements are made using the same standards, they can be compared to each other in a meaningful, valid way.

19. The length, width, and height of the car packing areas helps determine which items will fit in which spaces. The volume, or total amount of space in the duffel bag and car also determine the items which will fit into each. Mass is important, as massive objects which must be carried on hikes will be difficult to manage.

20. The graph should resemble the one shown below.

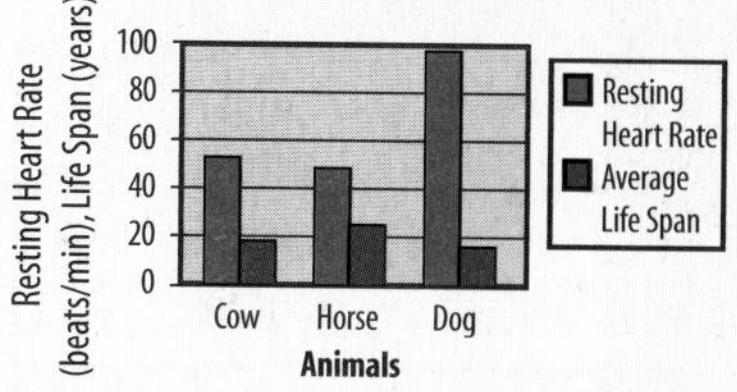

Rubrics

For more help evaluating open-ended assessment questions, see the rubric on p. 10T.

chapter 2 Instructional Planner

Motion

BIG Idea **Motion occurs when an object changes its position.**

	Content Standards	Learning Objectives	Resources to Assess Mastery
Section 1	**5–8:** UCP.1–3; A.1, 2; B.2 **9–12:** UCP.1–3; A.1, 2; B.4	**Describing Motion** 1. **Distinguish** between distance and displacement. 2. **Explain** the difference between speed and velocity. 3. **Interpret** motion graphs. ***Main Idea*** An object's speed depends on how far an object travels in a unit of time.	**Formative Assessment** Reading Check, pp. 39, 42, 43, 44 Section Review, p. 46 **Summative Assessment** *ExamView® Assessment Suite*
Section 2	**5–8:** UCP.1–3; A.1, 2; B.2 **9–12:** UCP.1–3; A.1, 2; B.4	**Acceleration** 4. **Identify** how acceleration, time, and velocity are related. 5. **Explain** how positive and negative acceleration affect motion. 6. **Describe** how to calculate the acceleration of an object. ***Main Idea*** Acceleration describes how the velocity of an object is changing.	**Formative Assessment** Reading Check, p. 51 Section Review, p. 51 **Summative Assessment** *ExamView® Assessment Suite*
Section 3	**5–8:** UCP.1–3; A.1, 2; B.2; G.3 **9–12:** UCP.1–3; A.1, 2; B.4; G.3 See pp. 16T–17T for a Key to Standards.	**Motion and Forces** 7. **Explain** how force and motion are related. 8. **Describe** what inertia is and how it is related to Newton's first law of motion. 9. **Identify** the forces and motion that are present during a car crash. ***Main Idea*** An object's motion changes only if the forces acting on the object are unbalanced.	**Formative Assessment** Reading Check, pp. 53, 55 Section Review, p. 56 **Summative Chapter Assessment** MindJogger, Ch. 2 *ExamView® Assessment Suite* Leveled Chapter Test Test A L1 Test B L2 Test C L3 Test Practice, pp. 64–65

Suggested Pacing				
Period	**Instruction**	**Labs**	**Review & Assessment**	**Total**
Single	3 days	3 days	2 days	8 days
Block	1.5 blocks	1.5 blocks	1 block	4 blocks

<table>
<thead>
<tr><th rowspan="2">Core Instruction</th><th rowspan="2">Leveled Resources</th><th rowspan="2">Leveled Labs</th><th colspan="3">Pacing</th></tr>
<tr><th>Period</th><th></th><th>Block</th></tr>
</thead>
<tbody>
<tr>
<td rowspan="2">Student Text, pp. 36–46
Section Focus Transparency, Ch. 2, Section 1
Teaching Transparency, Ch. 2, Section 1
Interactive Chalkboard, Ch. 2, Section 1
Identifying Misconceptions, pp. 39, 43, 45
Differentiated Instruction, pp. 42, 43
Applying Math, p. 40</td>
<td rowspan="2">Chapter Fast File Resources
Directed Reading for Content Mastery, p. 20 [L1]
Note-taking Worksheet, pp. 33–35
Reinforcement, p. 27 [L2]
Enrichment, p. 30 [L3]
Reading Essentials, p. 20 [L1] ELL
Science Notebook, p. 13 ELL</td>
<td rowspan="2">Launch Lab, p. 37: meterstick , stopwatch, calculator 10 min [L2]

MiniLAB, p. 42: tape, toy car, stopwatch, pencil, meterstick 10 min [L2]</td>
<td>1</td><td>Section 1, pp. 37–42 (includes Launch Lab and MiniLAB)</td><td rowspan="2">1</td>
</tr>
<tr><td>2</td><td>Section 1, pp. 42–46 (includes Section Review)</td></tr>
<tr>
<td>Student Text, pp. 47–51
Section Focus Transparency, Ch. 2, Section 2
Interactive Chalkboard, Ch. 2, Section 2
Differentiated Instruction, p. 49
Visualizing Acceleration, p. 49</td>
<td>Chapter Fast File Resources
Directed Reading for Content Mastery, p. 21 [L1]
Note-taking Worksheet, pp. 33–35
Reinforcement, p. 28 [L2]
Enrichment, p. 31 [L3]
Reading Essentials, p. 28 [L1] ELL
Science Notebook, p. 17 ELL</td>
<td></td>
<td>3</td><td>Section 2, pp. 47–51 (includes Section Review)</td><td rowspan="2">2</td>
</tr>
<tr>
<td rowspan="5">Student Text, pp. 52–59
Section Focus Transparency, Ch. 2, Section 3
Interactive Chalkboard, Ch. 2, Section 3
Identifying Misconceptions, p. 53
Differentiated Instruction, pp. 54, 55
Chapter Study Guide, p. 61</td>
<td rowspan="5">Chapter Fast File Resources
Directed Reading for Content Mastery, pp. 21, 22 [L1]
Note-taking Worksheet, pp. 33–35
Reinforcement, p. 29 [L2]
Enrichment, p. 32 [L3]
Reading Essentials, p. 32 [L1] ELL
Science Notebook, p. 20 ELL
ActiveFolders: Newton's 1st Law of Motion and Forces [L1] ELL</td>
<td rowspan="5">MiniLAB, p. 54: board, textbook, small object, car, rubber bands 10 min [L2]

*Lab, p. 57: tape, paper clip, 10-N spring scale, large book, science book, triple-beam balance 40 min [L1] [L2] [L3] (Video Lab)

*Lab, pp. 58–59 small toy car, ramps or boards, springs or rubber bands, string, stopwatch, meterstick or tape measure, graph paper 75 min [L1] [L2] [L3]

*Lab version A [L1] version B [L2] [L3]</td>
<td>4</td><td>Section 3, pp. 52–56 (includes MiniLAB and Section Review)</td>
</tr>
<tr><td>5</td><td>Lab:Force and Acceleration, p. 57</td><td rowspan="2">3</td></tr>
<tr><td>6</td><td>Lab:Comparing Motion from Different Forces, pp. 58–59</td></tr>
<tr><td>7</td><td>Lab:Comparing Motion from Different Forces, pp. 58–59</td><td rowspan="2">4</td></tr>
<tr><td>8</td><td>Study Guide, Chapter Review, and Test Practice, pp. 119–123</td></tr>
</tbody>
</table>

Video Lab

Transparencies

Section Focus

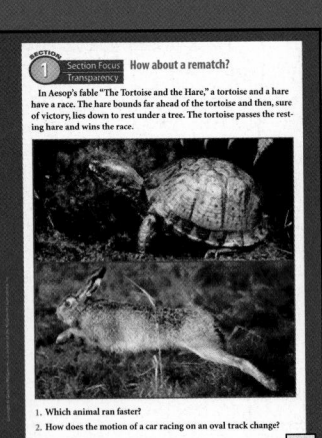

SECTION 1 Section Focus Transparency **How about a rematch?**

In Aesop's fable "The Tortoise and the Hare," a tortoise and a hare have a race. The hare bounds far ahead of the tortoise and then, sure of victory, lies down to rest under a tree. The tortoise passes the resting hare and wins the race.

1. Which animal ran faster?
2. How does the motion of a car racing on an oval track change?

L2

SECTION 2 Section Focus Transparency **On the Edge**

Many people enjoy cross-country and downhill skiing for recreation and for exercise. For others, skiing is a competitive sport. In ski races, fractions of a second can make the difference between winning and finishing second.

1. Describe how the skier's velocity changes during the race.
2. Why does the skier's velocity increase as he races downhill?
3. How does being in a tuck position affect a skier's motion?

L2

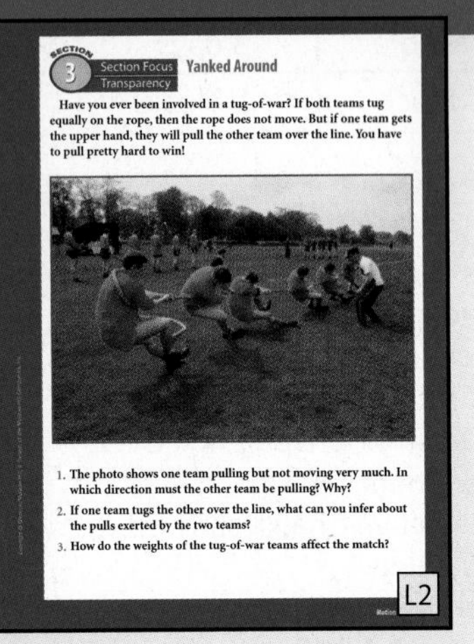

SECTION 3 Section Focus Transparency **Yanked Around**

Have you ever been involved in a tug-of-war? If both teams tug equally on the rope, then the rope does not move. But if one team gets the upper hand, they will pull the other team over the line. You have to pull pretty hard to win!

1. The photo shows one team pulling but not moving very much. In which direction must the other team be pulling? Why?
2. If one team tugs the other over the line, what can you infer about the pulls exerted by the two teams?
3. How do the weights of the tug-of-war teams affect the match?

L2

This is a representation of key blackline masters available in the Teacher Classroom Resources. See Resource Manager boxes within the chapter for additional information.

Assessment

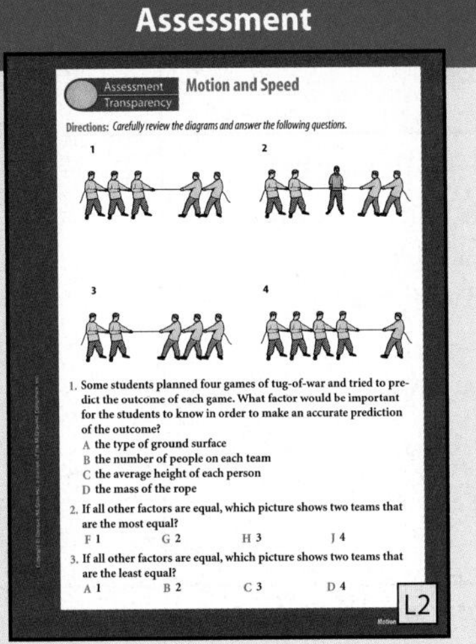

Assessment Transparency **Motion and Speed**

Directions: Carefully review the diagrams and answer the following questions.

1 2 3 4

1. Some students planned four games of tug-of-war and tried to predict the outcome of each game. What factor would be important for the students to know in order to make an accurate prediction of the outcome?
   A the type of ground surface
   B the number of people on each team
   C the average height of each person
   D the mass of the rope
2. If all other factors are equal, which picture shows two teams that are the most equal?
   F 1 G 2 H 3 J 4
3. If all other factors are equal, which picture shows two teams that are the least equal?
   A 1 B 2 C 3 D 4

L2

Teaching

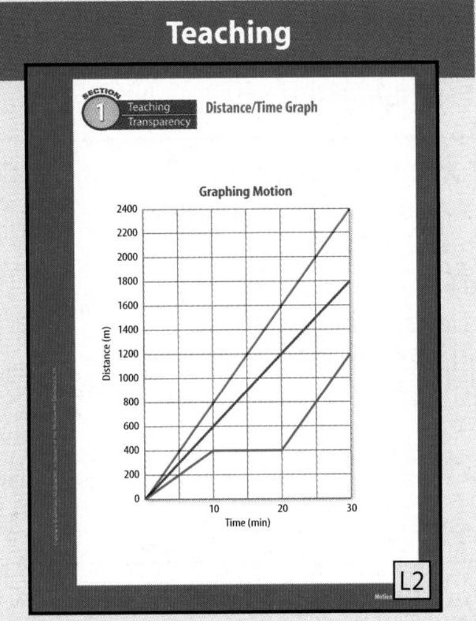

SECTION 1 Teaching Transparency **Distance/Time Graph**

L2

Key to Teaching Strategies

The following designations will help you decide which activities are appropriate for your students.

- **L1** Level 1 activities should be appropriate for students with learning difficulties.
- **L2** Level 2 activities should be within the ability range of all students.
- **L3** Level 3 activities are designed for above-average students.
- **ELL** ELL activities should be within the ability range of English Language Learners.
- **COOP LEARN** Cooperative Learning activities are designed for small group work.
- **LS** Multiple Learning Styles logos, as described on page 12T, are used throughout to indicate strategies that address different learning styles.
- **P** These strategies represent student products that can be placed into a best-work portfolio.
- **PBL** Problem-Based Learning activities apply real-world situations to learning.

Hands-on Activities

Student Text Lab Worksheet

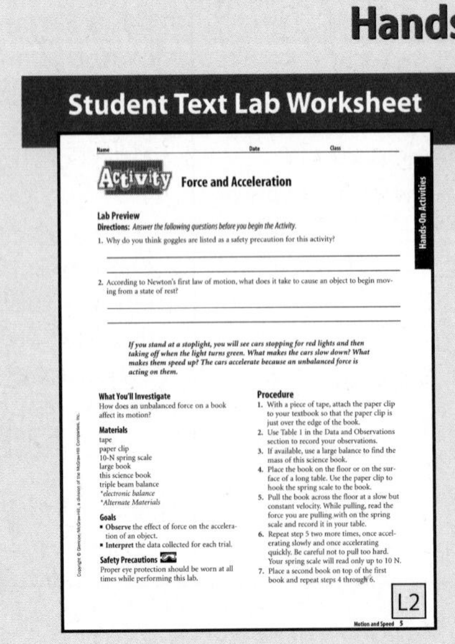

Name Date Class

Activity **Force and Acceleration**

Hands-On Activities

Lab Preview

Directions: *Answer the following questions before you begin the Activity.*

1. Why do you think goggles are listed as a safety precaution for this activity?
2. According to Newton's first law of motion, what does it take to cause an object to begin moving from a state of rest?

If you stand at a stoplight, you will see cars stopping for red lights and then taking off when the light turns green. What makes the cars slow down? What makes them speed up? The cars accelerate because an unbalanced force is acting on them.

What You'll Investigate

How does an unbalanced force on a book affect its motion?

Materials

tape
paper clip
10-N spring scale
large book
this science book
triple beam balance
*electronic balance
*Alternate Materials

Goals

- **Observe** the effect of force on the acceleration of an object.
- **Interpret** the data collected for each trial.

Safety Precautions

Proper eye protection should be worn at all times while performing this lab.

Procedure

1. With a piece of tape, attach the paper clip to your textbook so that the paper clip is just over the edge of the book.
2. Use Table 1 in the Data and Observations section to record your observations.
3. If available, use a large balance to find the mass of this science book.
4. Place the book on the floor or on the surface of a long table. Use the paper clip to hook the spring scale to the book.
5. Pull the book across the floor at a slow but constant velocity. While pulling, read the force you are pulling with on the spring scale and record it in your table.
6. Repeat step 5 two more times, once accelerating slowly and once accelerating quickly. Be careful not to pull too hard. Your spring scale will read only up to 10 N.
7. Place a second book on top of the first book and repeat steps 4 through 6.

L2

Motion and Speed 5

Laboratory Activities

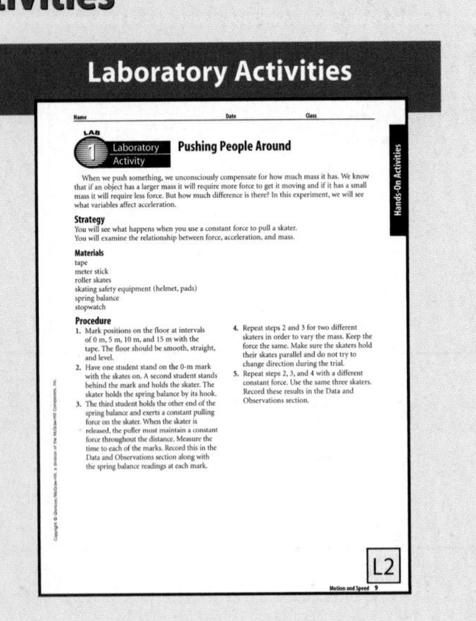

Name Date Class

LAB 1 Laboratory Activity **Pushing People Around**

Hands-On Activities

When we push something, we unconsciously compensate for how much mass it has. We know that if an object has a larger mass it will require more force to get it moving and if it has a small mass it will require less force. But how much difference is there? In this experiment, we will see what variables affect acceleration.

Strategy

You will see what happens when you use a constant force to pull a skater.
You will examine the relationship between force, acceleration, and mass.

Materials

tape
meter stick
roller skates
skating safety equipment (helmet, pads)
spring balance
stopwatch

Procedure

1. Mark positions on the floor at intervals of 0 m, 5 m, 10 m, and 15 m with the tape. The floor should be smooth, straight, and level.
2. Have one student stand on the 0-m mark with the skates on. A second student stands behind the mark and holds the skater. The skater holds the spring balance by its hook.
3. The third student holds the other end of the spring balance and exerts a constant pulling force on the skater. When the skater is released, the puller must maintain a constant force throughout the distance. Measure the time to each of the marks. Record this in the Data and Observations section along with the spring balance readings at each mark.
4. Repeat steps 2 and 3 for two different skaters in order to vary the mass. Keep the force the same. Make sure the skaters hold their skates parallel and do not try to change direction during the trial.
5. Repeat steps 2, 3, and 4 with a different constant force. Use the same three skaters. Record these results in the Data and Observations section.

L2

Motion and Speed 9

Meeting Different Ability Levels

Content Outline

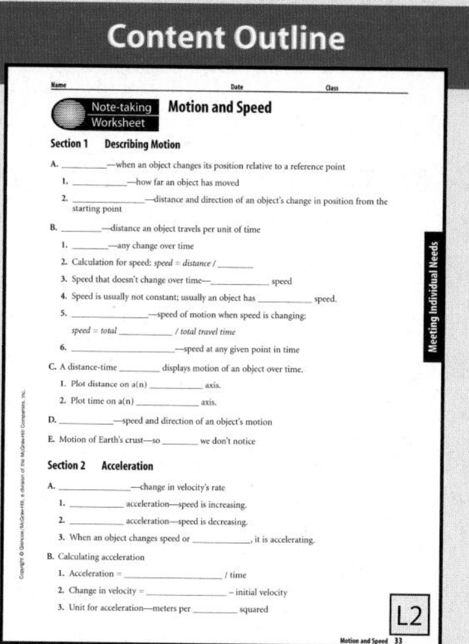

Name Date Class

Note-taking Worksheet **Motion and Speed**

Section 1 Describing Motion

A. ________—when an object changes its position relative to a reference point
1. ________—how far an object has moved
2. ________—distance and direction of an object's change in position from the starting point

B. ________—distance an object travels per unit of time
1. ________—any change over time
2. Calculation for speed: speed = distance / ________
3. Speed that doesn't change over time—________ speed
4. Speed is usually not constant; usually an object has ________ speed.
5. ________—speed of motion when speed is changing: speed = total ________ / total travel time
6. ________—speed at any given point in time

C. A distance-time ________ displays motion of an object over time.
1. Plot distance on a(n) ________ axis.
2. Plot time on a(n) ________ axis.

D. ________—speed and direction of an object's motion

E. Motion of Earth's crust—so ________ we don't notice

Section 2 Acceleration

A. ________—change in velocity's rate
1. ________ acceleration—speed is increasing.
2. ________ acceleration—speed is decreasing.
3. When an object changes speed or ________, it is accelerating.

B. Calculating acceleration
1. Acceleration = ________ / time
2. Change in velocity = ________ − initial velocity
3. Unit for acceleration—meters per ________ squared

Meeting Individual Needs

L2

Motion and Speed 33

Reinforcement

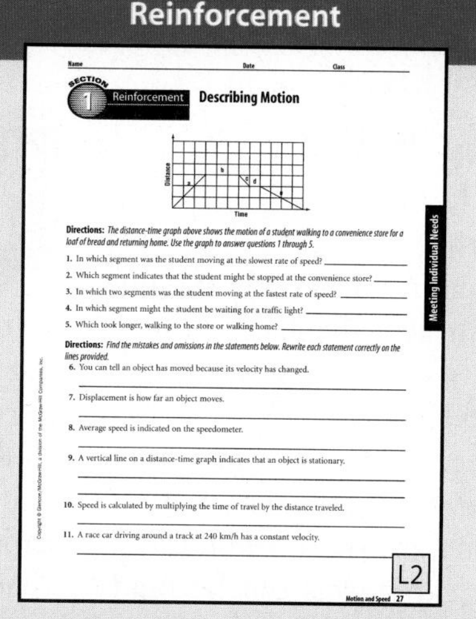

Name Date Class

Section 1 Reinforcement **Describing Motion**

Directions: *The distance-time graph above shows the motion of a student walking to a convenience store for a loaf of bread and returning home. Use the graph to answer questions 1 through 5.*

1. In which segment was the student moving at the slowest rate of speed? ________
2. Which segment indicates that the student might be stopped at the convenience store? ________
3. In which two segments was the student moving at the fastest rate of speed? ________
4. In which segment might the student be waiting for a traffic light? ________
5. Which took longer, walking to the store or walking home? ________

Directions: *Find the mistakes and omissions in the statements below. Rewrite each statement correctly on the lines provided.*

6. You can tell an object has moved because its velocity has changed.
7. Displacement is how far an object moves.
8. Average speed is indicated on the speedometer.
9. A vertical line on a distance-time graph indicates that an object is stationary.
10. Speed is calculated by multiplying the time of travel by the distance traveled.
11. A race car driving around a track at 240 km/h has a constant velocity.

Meeting Individual Needs

L2

Motion and Speed 27

Enrichment

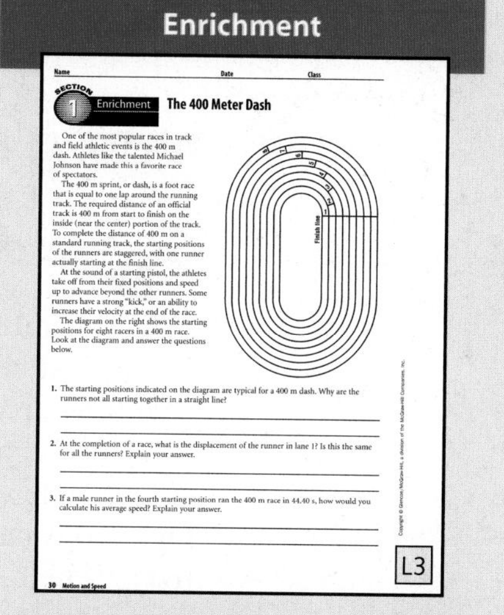

Name Date Class

Section 1 Enrichment **The 400 Meter Dash**

One of the most popular races in track and field athletic events is the 400 m dash. Athletes like the talented Michael Johnson have made this a favorite race of spectators.

The 400 m sprint, or dash, is a foot race that is equal to one lap around the running track. The required distance of an official track is 400 m from start to finish on the inside (near the center) portion of the track. To complete the distance of 400 m on a standard running track, the starting positions of the runners are staggered, with one runner actually starting at the finish line.

At the sound of a starting pistol, the athletes take off from their fixed positions and speed up to advance beyond the other runners. Some runners have a strong "kick," or an ability to increase their velocity at the end of the race.

The diagram on the right shows the starting positions for eight racers in a 400 m race. Look at the diagram and answer the questions below.

1. The starting positions indicated on the diagram are typical for a 400 m dash. Why are the runners not all starting together in a straight line?
2. At the completion of a race, what is the displacement of the runner in lane 1? Is this the same for all the runners? Explain your answer.
3. If a male runner in the fourth starting position ran the 400 m race in 44.40 s, how would you calculate his average speed? Explain your answer.

L3

30 Motion and Speed

Directed Reading (English/Spanish)

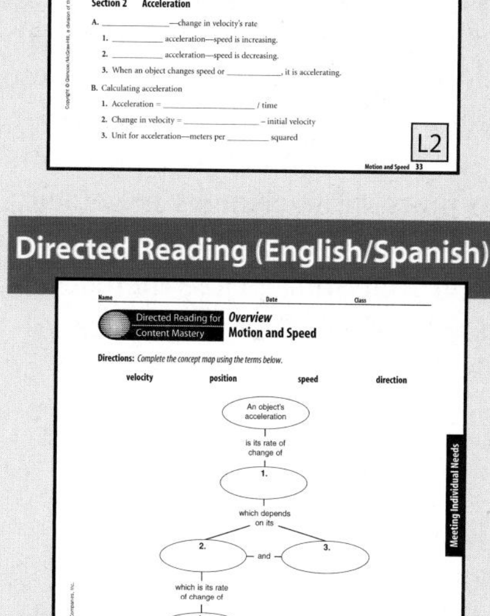

Name Date Class

Directed Reading for Content Mastery *Overview* **Motion and Speed**

Directions: *Complete the concept map using the terms below.*

velocity position speed direction

Directions: *Circle the term in parentheses that correctly completes the sentence.*

5. Newton's first law of motion states that an object's velocity will not change unless it is acted upon by (balanced/unbalanced) forces.
6. The greater a boulder's mass, the (greater/less) inertia it has.
7. Displacement depends on an object's distance and (speed/direction) compared to a starting point.
8. An automobile that slows down when approaching a stop sign has (negative, positive) acceleration.

Meeting Individual Needs

L1

Motion and Speed 19

Study Guide

Reading Essentials

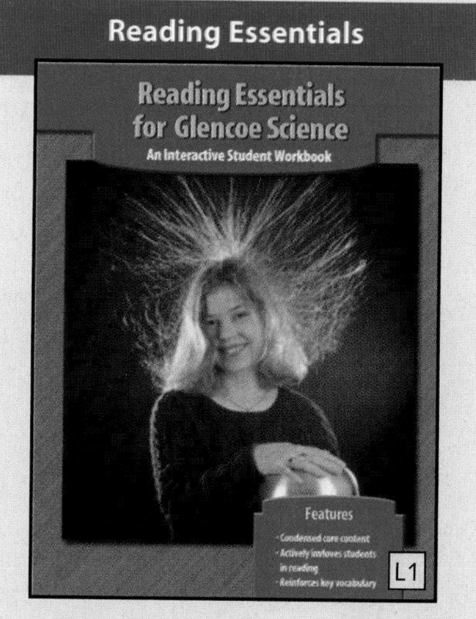

Assessment

Test Practice Workbook

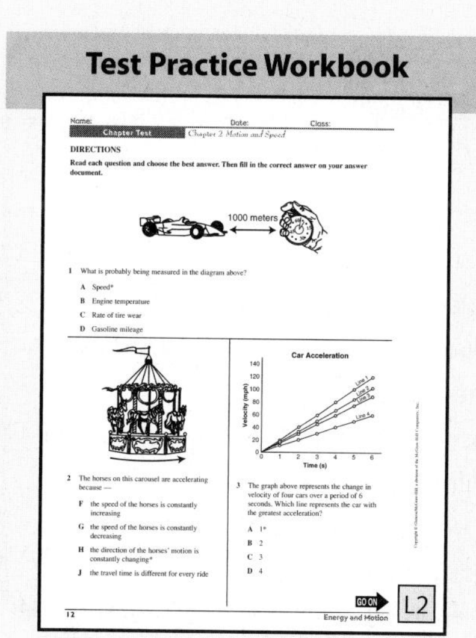

Name: Date: Class:

Chapter Test *Chapter 2 Motion and Speed*

DIRECTIONS

Read each question and choose the best answer. Then fill in the correct answer on your answer document.

1 What is probably being measured in the diagram above?
- A Speed*
- B Engine temperature
- C Rate of tire wear
- D Gasoline mileage

2 The horses on this carousel are accelerating because —
- F the speed of the horses is constantly increasing
- G the speed of the horses is constantly decreasing
- H the direction of the horses' motion is constantly changing*
- J the travel time is different for every ride

3 The graph above represents the change in velocity of four cars over a period of 6 seconds. Which line represents the car with the greatest acceleration?
- A 1*
- B 2
- C 3
- D 4

GO ON

L2

12 Energy and Motion

Chapter Review

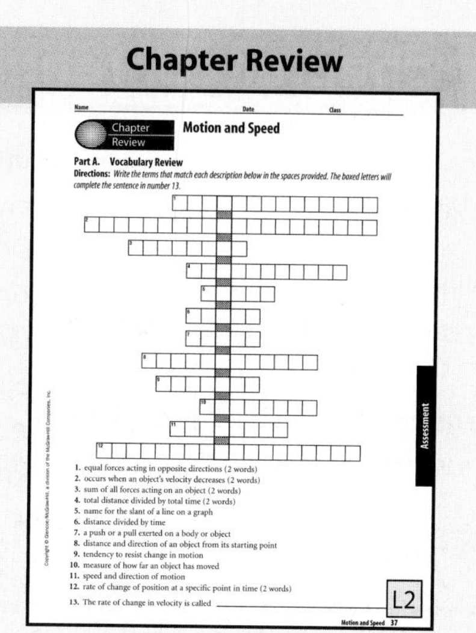

Name Date Class

Chapter Review **Motion and Speed**

Part A. Vocabulary Review

Directions: *Write the terms that match each description below in the spaces provided. The boxed letters will complete the sentence in number 13.*

1. equal forces acting in opposite directions (2 words)
2. occurs when an object's velocity decreases (2 words)
3. sum of all forces acting on an object (2 words)
4. total distance divided by total time (2 words)
5. name for the slant of a line on a graph
6. distance divided by time
7. a push or a pull exerted on a body or object
8. distance and direction of an object from its starting point
9. tendency to resist change in motion
10. measure of how far an object has moved
11. speed and direction of motion
12. rate of change of position at a specific point in time (2 words)
13. The rate of change in velocity is called ________

Assessment

L2

Motion and Speed 37

Chapter Tests

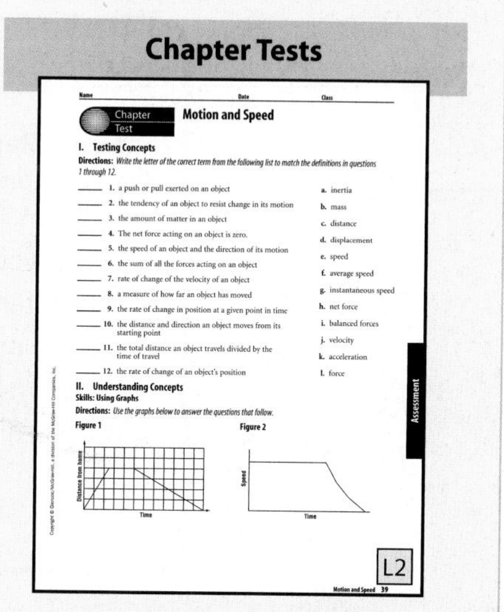

Name Date Class

Chapter Test **Motion and Speed**

I. Testing Concepts

Directions: *Write the letter of the correct term from the following list to match the definitions in questions 1 through 12.*

____	1. a push or pull exerted on an object	a. inertia
____	2. the tendency of an object to resist change in its motion	b. mass
____	3. the amount of matter in an object	c. distance
____	4. The net force acting on an object is zero.	d. displacement
____	5. the speed of an object and the direction of its motion	e. speed
____	6. the sum of all the forces acting on an object	f. average speed
____	7. rate of change of the velocity of an object	g. instantaneous speed
____	8. a measure of how far an object has moved	h. net force
____	9. the rate of change in position at a given point in time	i. balanced forces
____	10. the distance and direction an object moves from its starting point	j. velocity
____	11. the total distance an object travels divided by the time of travel	k. acceleration
____	12. the rate of change of an object's position	l. force

II. Understanding Concepts

Skills: Using Graphs

Directions: *Use the graphs below to answer the questions that follow.*

Figure 1 **Figure 2**

Assessment

L2

Motion and Speed 39

Science Content Background

section 1 Describing Motion

Distance Versus Displacement

A vector quantity has both magnitude and direction, such as a displacement of 15 km east and a velocity of 7 m/s west. Scalar quantities have magnitude only, such as a distance of 5 km and a speed of 6 m/s. The terms *distance* and *displacement* have different meanings. Consider a car going around a round racetrack. The distance the car travels can be read from its odometer, but the car's displacement is its straight-line distance and direction from its starting point. For each lap the odometer increases. But for each lap its displacement at first increases, and then decreases and becomes zero as it returns to the starting point. Speed and velocity also can be contrasted easily. The car traveling around the track may have a constant speed, but its velocity is constantly changing because its direction is constantly changing.

section 2 Acceleration

Acceleration, Speed, and Velocity

An object will move with constant velocity unless a force acts on it. A planet orbiting a star experiences the force of gravity between the star and the planet. This force causes the object to accelerate toward the star and not fly off in straight-line motion. So even though the planet moves with constant speed, it is accelerating.

Acceleration units show changes in velocity divided by time. If velocity is expressed as meters/second and time in seconds, then acceleration is expressed with units of meters per second per second. This is equivalent to m/s/s or (m/s $\times$ 1/s) or m/s^2.

section 3 Motion and Forces

Inertia and Mass

Astronauts in weightless conditions would still have a harder time moving a massive object like a bowling ball than moving a tennis ball. This is because the greater the mass of an object, the greater is its inertia. In the weightless condition, if the bowling ball were not moving, it would be just as hard to push it down as to pick it up.

chapter content resources

Internet Resources

For additional content background, visit gpscience.com to:

- access your book online
- find references to related articles in popular science magazines
- access Web links with related content background
- access current events with science journal topics

Print Resources

Eyewitness: Force and Motion, by Peter Lafferty, Dorling Kindersley Publishing, 2000

Sports Science Projects: The Physics of Balls in Motion (Science Fair Success), by Madeline Goodstein, Enslow Publishers, Inc., 1999

The Science of Soccer, by John Wesson, Institute of Physics Publishing, 2002

The Physics of Hockey, by Alain Hache, John Hopkins University Press, 2002

Misconceptions

Find Out What Students Think

Students may think that . . .

Distance and displacement are the same thing.

Speed and velocity are the same thing.

Students are familiar with scalar quantities and vector quantities, but terms such as *displacement* and *velocity* may cause confusion. Also, the term velocity is frequently used as though it were the same thing as *speed*. Finally, the terms *displacement* and *distance* sound similar, and this may cause confusion between them.

Discussion

Tell students that a turtle and a hare start a race at the same time. The turtle goes straight to the finish line. The hare starts off and deviates along the way. They both finish the race at the same time. Discuss which had the greatest average speed during the race.

Promote Understanding

Activity

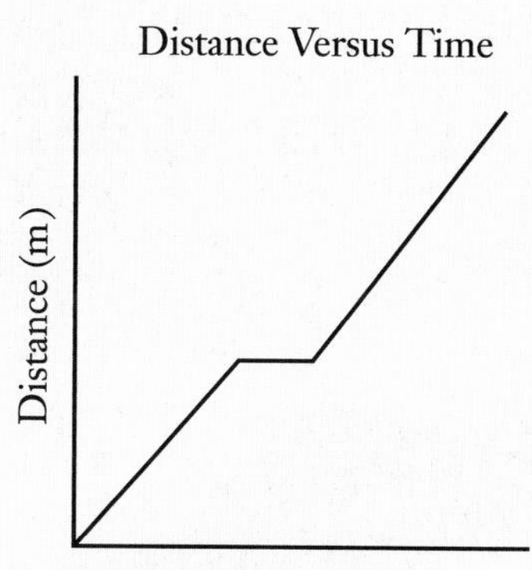

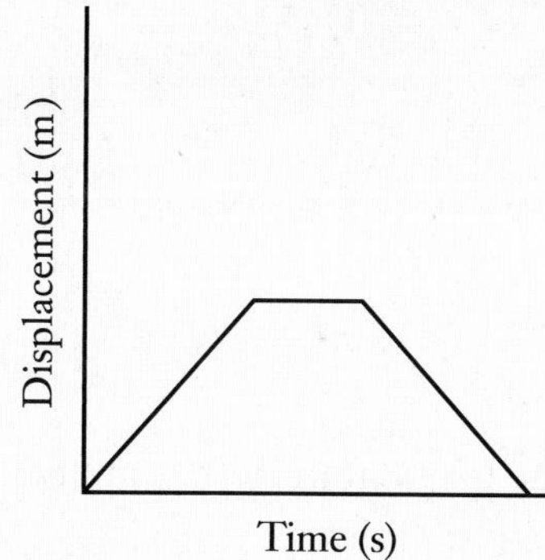

- Draw the graphs on the right on the board. Explain that the distance-time graph and the displacement-time graph each show Samantha's walking motion after she left her house.
- Ask students to supply a possible story to describe her motion. Ask them what she might be doing when the lines of both graphs are horizontal.
- Students should see that the distance-time graph and the displacement-time graph for the same motion look very different. In this case the distance traveled is how far Samantha actually walked. Her displacement shows how far she is from her house.
- A plausible story for both graphs is Samantha walks with constant speed directly away from her house, then rests a bit, and then walks with constant speed directly back to her house. L2

Assess

After completing the chapter, see *Identifying Misconceptions* in the Study Guide at the end of the chapter.

chapter 2

About the Photo

Amusement Park Physics The photo shows a double-loop roller coaster. Engineers use the laws of motion to design rides to be thrilling.

Science Journal Roller coaster and bumper car rides have quick velocity and acceleration changes. A Ferris wheel ride has constant speed but changing velocity due to the change in direction of motion.

BIG Idea

Scalars and Vectors The physical variables that describe motion are of two types—scalars and vectors. Scalars are variables that can be specified with only one number. The distance traveled by an object is a scalar—only one number, the length of the path traveled, needs to be specified. Speed is also a scalar. Vectors are specified with more than one number. In describing motion, vectors include position, displacement, velocity, and acceleration. These variables are usually specified by two numbers—a size and a direction.

Introduce the Chapter Place a battery-powered or wind-up toy vehicle on a long piece of heavy paper and mark its starting position on the paper and on the table or floor. Measure how far the toy travels in 10 s. Place the toy at its starting position. Start the toy again and drag the paper forward for several seconds while the toy is moving. After 10 s, measure the distance the paper has traveled relative to both starting points. Point out that the distance traveled depends on which starting point is used. Explain that either starting point could be chosen.

chapter 2

Motion

BIG Idea

Motion occurs when an object changes its position.

2.1 Describing Motion

MAIN Idea An object's speed depends on how far an object travels in a unit of time.

2.2 Acceleration

MAIN Idea Acceleration describes how the velocity of an object is changing.

2.3 Motion and Forces

MAIN Idea An object's motion changes only if the forces acting on the object are unbalanced.

Taking the Plunge

How would you describe a ride on a roller coaster? You might talk about the thrills you experienced on the high-speed turns or on the breath-taking downhill plunges. The high speeds and sudden changes in speed and direction can all help make the ride a memorable experience.

Science Journal

Write a paragraph describing how three different rides in an amusement park cause you to move.

36

Interactive Chalkboard

This CD-ROM is an editable Microsoft® PowerPoint® presentation that includes:

- an editable presentation for every chapter
- additional chapter questions
- animated graphics
- image bank
- links to gpscience.com

Start-Up Activities

Compare Speeds

A cheetah can run at a speed of almost 120 km/h and is the fastest runner in the world. A horse can reach a speed of 64 km/h; an elephant's top speed is about 40 km/h; and the fastest snake slithers at a speed of about 3 km/h. The speed of an object is calculated by dividing the distance the object travels by the time it takes it to move that distance. How does your speed compare to the speeds of these animals?

1. Use a meterstick to mark off 10 m.
2. Have your partner use a stopwatch to determine how fast you run 10 m.
3. Divide 10 m by your time in seconds to calculate your speed in m/s.
4. Multiply your answer by 3.6 to determine your speed in km/h.
5. **Think Critically** Write a paragraph in your Science Journal comparing your speed with the maximum speed of a cheetah, horse, elephant, and snake. Could you win a race with any of them?

Preview this chapter's content and activities at gpscience.com

Motion Many things are in motion in your everyday life. Make the following Foldable to help you better understand motion as you read the chapter.

STEP 1 **Fold** a sheet of paper in half lengthwise. Make the back edge about 1.25 cm longer than the front edge.

STEP 2 **Fold** in half, then fold in half again to make three folds.

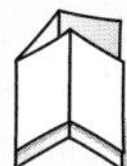

STEP 3 **Unfold and cut** only the top layer along the three folds to make four tabs.

STEP 4 **Label** the tabs.

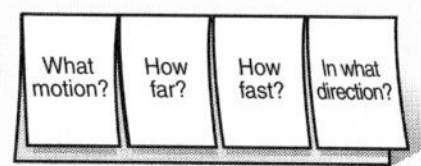

Identify Questions Before you read the chapter, select a motion you can observe and write it under the left tab. As you read the chapter, write answers to the other questions under the appropriate tabs.

37

Purpose Use the Launch Lab to introduce students to the relationship between motion and speed. L2 LS **Kinesthetic**

Preparation Find a location outside where groups of students will have room to mark off their 10-m distances. Assign each group a specific location.

Materials meterstick, stopwatch, calculator

Teaching Strategy Stage a contest between the five students with the greatest speeds to determine the fastest student in the class. Post the top speeds on a classroom bulletin board.

Think Critically

Students would lose races with a cheetah, horse, or elephant. They would win races with a snake.

Assessment

Oral Have students infer a formula for determining the speed of moving objects. Use **Performance Assessment in the Science Classroom**, p. 89.

Dinah Zike Study Fold

Student preparation materials for this Foldable are available in the **Chapter *Fast File* Resources.**

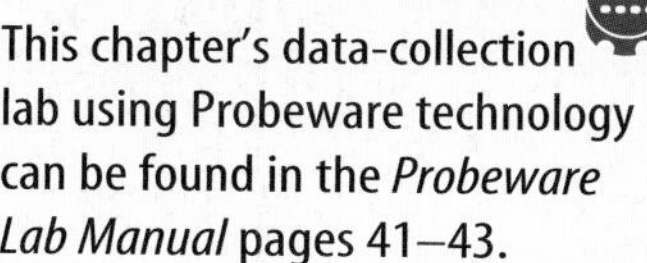

Probeware Labs

This chapter's data-collection lab using Probeware technology can be found in the *Probeware Lab Manual* pages 41–43.

Additional Chapter Media

- Brain POP *Acceleration*
- Virtual Lab: *What is the relationship between distance, average speed, and time?*
- Video Lab: *Force and Acceleration*

1 Motivate

Bellringer

Section Focus Transparencies also are available on the Interactive Chalkboard CD-ROM. L2 

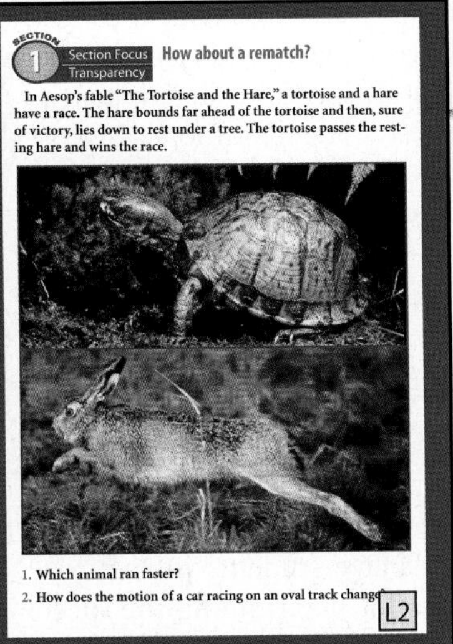
Section 1 Section Focus Transparency — How about a rematch?

In Aesop's fable "The Tortoise and the Hare," a tortoise and a hare have a race. The hare bounds far ahead of the tortoise and then, sure of victory, lies down to rest under a tree. The tortoise passes the resting hare and wins the race.

1. Which animal ran faster?
2. How does the motion of a car racing on an oval track change?

L2

Tie to Prior Knowledge

Speed Limits Ask students to name the speed limits near their school, on the road in front of their homes, or on an interstate highway. Discuss with students the units, such as miles per hour and kilometers per hour, used in speed limits. Tell students they will learn about measuring speed in this section. L1

Caption Answer

Figure 1 Its position relative to the mailbox changed.

section 1

Describing Motion

Reading Guide

What You'll Learn

- **Distinguish** between distance and displacement.
- **Explain** the difference between speed and velocity.
- **Interpret** motion graphs.

Why It's Important

Understanding the nature of motion and how to describe it helps you understand why motion occurs.

Review Vocabulary

instantaneous: occurring at a particular instant of time

New Vocabulary

- distance
- displacement
- speed
- average speed
- instantaneous speed
- velocity

Figure 1 This mail truck is in motion.
Infer *How do you know the mail truck has moved?*

Motion

Are distance and time important in describing running events at the track-and-field meets in the Olympics? Would the winners of the 5-km race and the 10-km race complete the run in the same length of time?

Distance and time are important. In order to win a race, you must cover the distance in the shortest amount of time. The time required to run the 10-km race should be longer than the time needed to complete the 5-km race because the first distance is longer. How would you describe the motion of the runners in the two races?

Motion and Position You don't always need to see something move to know that motion has taken place. For example, suppose you look out a window and see a mail truck stopped next to a mailbox. One minute later, you look out again and see the same truck stopped farther down the street. Although you didn't see the truck move, you know it moved because its position relative to the mailbox changed.

A reference point is needed to determine the position of an object. In **Figure 1,** the reference point might be a tree or a mailbox. Motion occurs when an object changes its position relative to a reference point. The motion of an object depends on the reference point that is chosen. For example, the motion of the mail truck in **Figure 1** would be different if the reference point were a car moving along the street, instead of a mailbox.

Section 1 Resource Manager

Chapter *Fast File* Resources

Transparency Activity, pp. 44, 47–48
Directed Reading for Content Mastery, pp. 19, 20
Note-taking Worksheets, pp. 33–35
MiniLab, p. 3

Mathematics Skill Activities, p. 11
Physical Science Critical Thinking/Problem Solving, p. 2
Life Science Critical Thinking/Problem Solving, p. 14

Frame of Reference After a reference point is chosen, a frame of reference can be created. A frame of reference is a coordinate system in which the position of the objects is measured. The *x-axis* and *y-axis* of the reference frame are drawn so that they intersect the reference point.

Distance In track-and-field events, have you ever run a 50-m dash? A distance of 50 m was marked on the track or athletic field to show you how far to run. An important part of describing the motion of an object is to describe how far it has moved, which is **distance.** The SI unit of length or distance is the meter (m). Longer distances are measured in kilometers (km). One kilometer is equal to 1,000 m. Shorter distances are measured in centimeters (cm). One meter is equal to 100 centimeters.

Displacement Suppose a runner jogs to the 50-m mark and then turns around and runs back to the 20-m mark, as shown in **Figure 2.** The runner travels 50 m in the original direction (north) plus 30 m in the opposite direction (south), so the total distance she ran is 80 m. How far is she from the starting line? The answer is 20 m. Sometimes you may want to know not only your distance but also your direction from a reference point, such as from the starting point. **Displacement** is the distance and direction of an object's change in position from the starting point. The runner's displacement in **Figure 2** is 20 m north.

The length of the runner's displacement and the distance traveled would be the same if the runner's motion was in a single direction. If the runner ran from the starting point to the finish line in a straight line, then the distance traveled would be 50 m and the displacement would be 50 m north.

How do distance and displacement differ?

Speed

Think back to the example of the mail truck's motion in **Figure 1.** You could describe the movement by the distance traveled and by the displacement from the starting point. You also might want to describe how fast it is moving. To do this, you need to know how far it travels in a given amount of time. **Speed** is the distance an object travels per unit of time.

Moving Through Space
Using the Sun as your reference point, you are moving about 30 km through space every second. What is this speed in meters per second?

Figure 2 Distance and displacement are not the same. The runner's displacement is 20 m north of the starting line. However, the total distance traveled is 80 m.

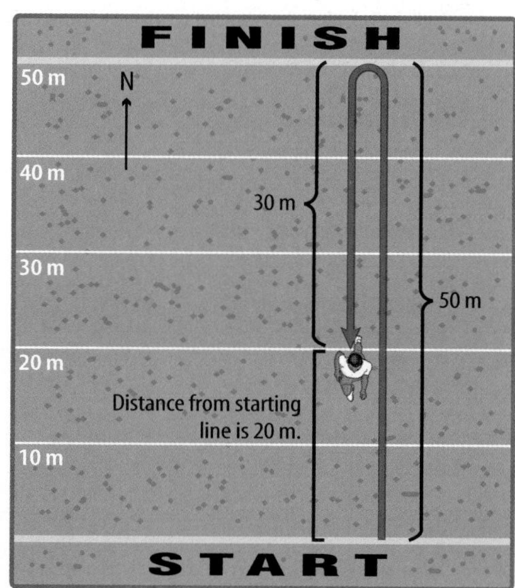

Displacement = 20 m north of starting line
Distance traveled = 50 m + 30 m = 80 m

Visual Learning

Figure 2 Help students understand the information presented in **Figure 2.** As you read the description from the text, have these students follow the path of the runner with their fingers. Then ask students how far the runner ran and how far she is from the starting line. 80 m; 20 m L2

2 Teach

Use Science Words

Word Usage Students may have difficulty with the term *relative* when it is used to describe an object's motion or position. Have them discuss what the word means. Possible answers are "dependent upon" or "with reference to." L1
LS **Linguistic**

IDENTIFYING Misconceptions

Word Differences Students may think that distance and displacement are the same. They may also think speed and velocity are the same. Refer to page F at the beginning of this chapter for teaching strategies that address this misconception.

Reading Check

Answer Distance describes how far an object has moved; displacement includes distance and direction of an object's change in position from its starting point.

Moving Through Space 30,000; 30,000 m/s. The distance Earth travels around the Sun in one year is about 942 billion meters. One year has approximately 31,558,000 seconds. Have students use these numbers to calculate Earth's speed. 942 billion m ÷ 31,558,000 s = 29,850 m/s L3
LS **Logical-Mathematical**

Activity

Different Rates Review the concept of rate by having students measure their breathing rates. Discuss other rates, such as heart rate (pulse) and interest rates. Discuss the units that describe these rates and point out similarities in the units. They are all a number of something per time. L2

LS **Logical-Mathmatical**

SPEED EQUATION

National Math Standards

Correlation to Mathematics Objectives

1, 2, 9,

Answers to Practice Problems

1. 6.0 m/s
2. 0.25 h or 15 min
3. 66 km
4. 3,000 m or 3 km

Activity

Speed Limits Have each student make a table showing all of the speed limits between his or her home and school. The table should begin with the speed limit of the road outside the home and should also give the distance that speed limit is in effect. The table should then give the next speed limit and the distance it is in effect, and so on. Students can then use the formula $t = d/v$ to determine the time it would take them to get to school if they traveled the exact speed limit all the way to school. L2

Use an Analogy

Lined Paper Explain to students that using a reference point to describe motion is analogous to using lines on paper to write. The lines on the paper provide a reference point to keep your writing on a straight line. L2

Calculating Speed Any change over time is called a rate. If you think of distance as the change in position, then speed is the rate at which distance is traveled or the rate of change in position. Speed can be calculated from this equation:

Speed Equation

$$\text{speed (in meters/second)} = \frac{\text{distance (in meters)}}{\text{time (in seconds)}}$$

$$s = \frac{d}{t}$$

In SI units, distance is measured in meters and time is measured in seconds, so the SI unit for speed is meters per second (m/s). Sometimes it is more convenient to express speed in other units, such as kilometers per hour (km/h). **Table 1** shows some convenient units for certain types of motion.

SPEED EQUATION

Solve for Speed A car traveling at a constant speed covers a distance of 750 m in 25 s. What is the car's speed?

1. **This is what you know:** distance: $d = 750\text{m}$; time: $t = 25$ s
2. **This is what you need to find:** speed: s
3. **Use this formula:** $s = \frac{d}{t}$
4. **Substitute:** the values of d and t into the formula and divide. $s = \frac{750}{25} = 30$
5. **Determine the units:** units of $s = \frac{(\text{units of } d)}{(\text{units of } t)} = \frac{\text{m}}{\text{s}} = \text{m/s}$

Answer: The car's speed is 30 m/s.

Science Online

For more practice problems, go to page 834, and visit gpscience.com/extra_problems.

Practice Problems

1. A passenger elevator travels from the first floor to the 60th floor, a distance of 210 m, in 35 s. What is the elevator's speed?
2. A motorcycle is moving at a constant speed of 40 km/h. How long does it take the motorcycle to travel a distance of 10 km?
3. How far does a car travel in 0.75 h if it is moving at a constant speed of 88 km/h?
4. **Challenge** A long-distance runner is running at a constant speed of 5 m/s. How far does the runner travel in 10 minutes?

Cultural Diversity

The Olympics Runners from all over the world participate in track and field events in the Olympics every four years. Have students research the winners and their times and speeds for a track event of their choice for the past five summer Olympics. They should combine their research into a bulletin board and creatively relate it to information in this chapter. L2

Unit of Speed	Examples of Uses	Approximate Speed
km/s	rocket escaping Earth's atmosphere	11.2 km/s
km/h	car traveling at highway speed	100 km/h
cm/yr	geological plate movements	2cm/yr–17 cm/yr

Table 1 Examples of Units of Speed

Motion with Constant Speed Suppose you are in a car traveling on a nearly empty freeway. You look at the speedometer and see that the car's speed hardly changes. If the car neither slows down nor speeds up, the car is traveling at a constant speed. If you are traveling at a constant speed, you can measure your speed over any distance interval.

Changing Speed Usually speed is not constant. Think about riding a bicycle for a distance of 5 km, as in **Figure 3.** As you start out, your speed increases from 0 km/h to 20 km/h. You slow down to 10 km/h as you pedal up a steep hill and speed up to 30 km/h going down the other side of the hill. You stop for a red light, speed up again, and move at a constant speed for a while. Finally, you slow down and then stop. Checking your watch, you find that the trip took 15 min. How would you express your speed on such a trip? Would you use your fastest speed, your slowest speed, or some speed between the two?

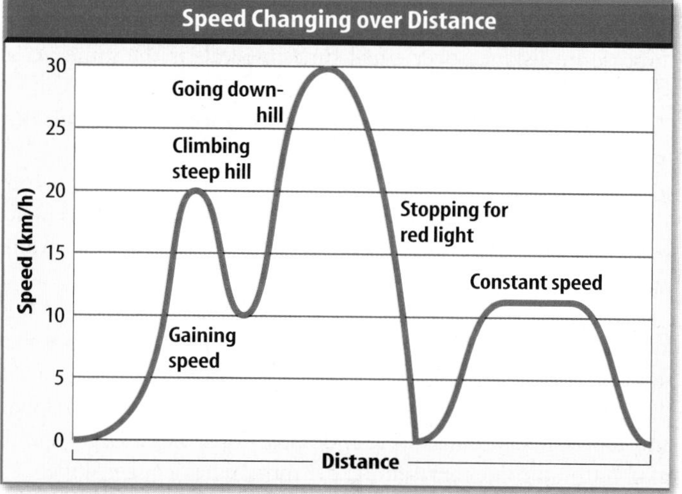

Figure 3 The graph shows how the speed of a cyclist changes during a trip.
Explain *how you describe the speed of an object when the speed is changing.*

Science Online

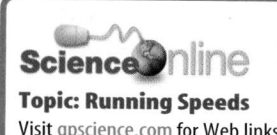

Topic: Running Speeds
Visit gpscience.com for Web links to information about the running speeds of various animals.

Activity In your Science Journal, describe how running fast benefits the survival of animals in the wild.

Quick Demo

Car Ramps

Materials three ramps of various lengths at least 2 m long, toy car, stopwatch, meterstick

Estimated Time 15 minutes

Procedure Make three ramps of various lengths, each at least 2 m long. Have a volunteer start a toy car rolling down one of the ramps while another volunteer times the car's motion with a stopwatch. Ask a third volunteer to measure the distance covered by the car. Write the distance traveled and time elapsed on the board. Repeat the activity with each of the three ramps. Have students determine the average speed for the three runs by dividing the total distance traveled by the total time. L2

Caption Answer

Figure 3 average speed over the entire motion or instantaneous speed at a given time

Discussion

Speed Units Remind students that when the equation for speed is rearranged, we have $t = d/v$. How do time units emerge from this equation?

$m \div (\frac{m}{s}) = m \times \frac{s}{m} = s$

L3

Science Journal

How far do they move? Have students calculate how far each object in **Table 1** moves in one hour and put their calculations and their answers in their Science Journals. rocket: 40,320 km; car: 100 km; geological plate: 0.0002 cm – 0.002 cm L2 LS **Logical-Mathmatical**

Curriculum Connection

Geography Geographers use lines of latitude and longitude to help them describe displacement on Earth. Have students find out how early seafarers determined their latitude and longitude. To find their latitude they used the positions of the stars and the Sun. They had no way to determine longitude until an accurate chronometer was developed in the mid-1700s. L3 LS **Linguistic**

Purpose Students will calculate the average speed and velocity of a car's motion. L2

Materials tape, toy car, stopwatch, pencil, meterstick

Teaching Strategy Try to use cars that will travel in a straight line when pushed gently.

Analysis

average speed = distance/time; The speed would be the same if the car traveled in the opposite direction.

Assessment

Process Have students use their observations to hypothesize why the car eventually comes to a rest. Use **Performance Assessment in the Science Classroom,** p. 93.

Answer possible responses: driving a car in town, riding a bicycle

Discussion

Lightning Strikes Have students use the information in the Applying Math activity to calculate how far a lightning strike is from them if they see the lightning strike 5 seconds before they hear the thunder. Write the solution on the board after the students have had a chance to solve the problem. $v = d \div t$, therefore, $d = vt$; $d = 330$ m/s $\times$ 5 s = 1,650 m = 1.65 km L2

Figure 4 The speed shown on the speedometer gives the instantaneous speed—the speed at one instant in time.

Describing the Motion of a Car

Procedure

1. Mark your starting point on the floor with **tape.**
2. At the starting line, give your **toy car** a gentle push forward. At the same time, start your **stopwatch.**
3. Stop timing when the car comes to a complete stop. Mark the spot on the floor at the front of the car with a **pencil.** Record the time for the entire trip.
4. Use a **meterstick** to measure the distance to the nearest tenth of a centimeter and convert it to meters.

Analysis

Calculate the speed. How would the speed differ if you repeated your experiment in exactly the same way but the car traveled in the opposite direction?

Average Speed Average speed describes speed of motion when speed is changing. **Average speed** is the total distance traveled divided by the total time of travel. It can be calculated using the relationships among speed, distance, and time. For the bicycle trip just described, the total distance traveled was 5 km and the total time was 1/4 h, or 0.25 h. The average speed was:

$$s = \frac{d}{t} = \frac{5 \text{ km}}{0.25 \text{ h}} = 20 \text{ km/h}$$

Instantaneous Speed Suppose you watch a car's speedometer, like the one in **Figure 4,** go from 0 km/h to 60 km/h. A speedometer shows how fast a car is going at one point in time or at one instant. The speed shown on a speedometer is the instantaneous speed. **Instantaneous speed** is the speed at a given point in time.

Changing Instantaneous Speed When something is speeding up or slowing down, its instantaneous speed is changing. The speed is different at every point in time. If an object is moving with constant speed, the instantaneous speed doesn't change. The speed is the same at every point in time.

Reading Check *What are two examples of motion in which the instantaneous speed changes?*

Graphing Motion

The motion of an object over a period of time can be shown on a distance-time graph. Time is plotted along the horizontal axis of the graph and the distance traveled is plotted along the vertical axis of the graph. If the object moves with constant speed, the increase in distance over equal time intervals is the same. As a result, the line representing the object's motion is a straight line.

For example, the graph shown in **Figure 5** represents the motion of three swimmers during a 30-min workout. The straight red line represents the motion of Mary, who swam with a constant speed of 80 m/min over the 30-min workout. The straight blue line represents the motion of Kathy, who swam with a constant speed of 60 m/min during the workout.

The graph shows that the line representing the motion of the faster swimmer is steeper. The steepness of a line on a graph is the slope of the line. The slope of a line on a distance-time graph equals the speed. A horizontal line on a distance-time graph has zero slope, and represents an object at rest. Because Mary has a larger speed than Kathy, the line representing her motion has a larger slope.

Differentiated Instruction

Learning Disabled Perform the calculations for determining average speed on the board to help students understand the process before doing it themselves. After you have done the procedure several times, ask students to do the calculations on their own. L2

Changing Speed The green line represents the motion of Julie, who did not swim at a constant speed. She covered 400 m at a constant speed during the first 10 min, rested for the next 10 min, and then covered 800 m during the final 10 min. During the first 10 min, her speed was less than Mary's or Kathy's, so her line has a smaller slope. During the middle period her speed is zero, so her line over this interval is horizontal and has zero slope. During the last time interval she swam as fast as Mary, so that part of her line has the same slope.

Plotting a Distance-Time Graph On a distance-time graph, the distance is plotted on the vertical axis and the time on the horizontal axis. Each axis must have a scale that covers the range of numbers to be plotted. In **Figure 5** the distance scale must range from 0 to 2,400 m and the time scale must range from 0 to 30 min. Then, each axis can be divided into equal time intervals to represent the data. Once the scales for each axis are in place, the data points can be plotted. After plotting the data points, draw a line connecting the points.

Topic: Olympic Swimming Speeds
Visit gpscience.com for Web links to information about the speeds of Olympic swimmers over the past 60 years.

Activity Make a speed-year graph showing the swimming speeds over time. Are there any trends in the speed data?

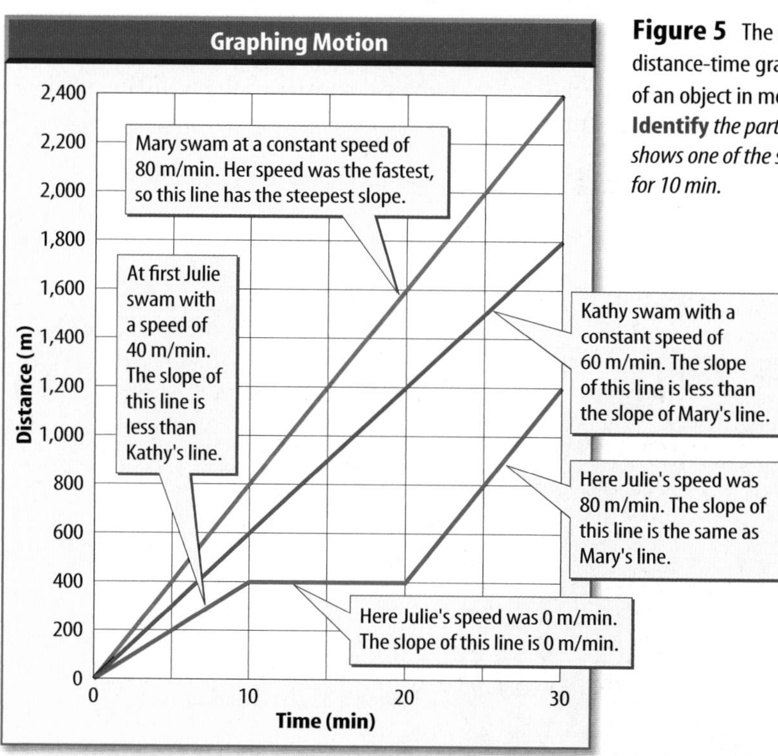

Graphing Motion
Mary swam at a constant speed of 80 m/min. Her speed was the fastest, so this line has the steepest slope.
At first Julie swam with a speed of 40 m/min. The slope of this line is less than Kathy's line.
Kathy swam with a constant speed of 60 m/min. The slope of this line is less than the slope of Mary's line.
Here Julie's speed was 80 m/min. The slope of this line is the same as Mary's line.
Here Julie's speed was 0 m/min. The slope of this line is 0 m/min.
Distance (m)
Time (min)
2,400
2,200
2,000
1,800
1,600
1,400
1,200
1,000
800
600
400
200
0
0
10
20
30

Figure 5 The slope of a line on a distance-time graph gives the speed of an object in motion.
Identify *the part of the graph that shows one of the swimmers resting for 10 min.*

IDENTIFYING Misconceptions

Average Speed Students sometimes interpret the height of a distance-time graph as its slope. The steepness of the straight line of a distance-time graph is the slope. This shows the average speed. The height of the line is the farthest distance the object has traveled in the positive direction.

Visual Learning

Figure 5 In addition to finding the average speed over the entire 30-minute period, students can find the average speed over any time period by dividing the change in distance during the period by the amount of time. What is Julie's average speed during the period 15 min to 25 min? 40 m/min Students should also notice that the instantaneous speed at any point in time is the slope of the line at that point. What is the instantaneous speed of Mary at $t = 5$ min? 80 m/min L2

LS **Visual-Spatial**

Caption Answer

Figure 5 On Julie's graph there is a slope of zero between 10 min and 20 min which represents a speed of 0m/min.

Virtual Labs

d = st *What is the relationship between distance, average speed, and time?*

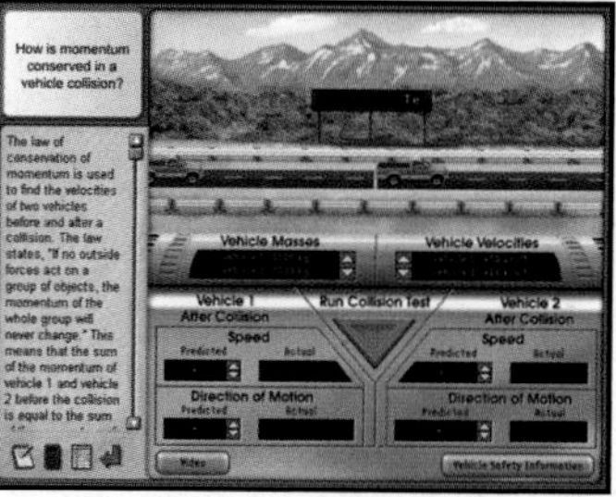

Differentiated Instruction

English-Language Learners Have students cut photos out of magazines showing some type of motion. Have students create a decorative collage of their photos L1 P

Teacher FYI

Vertical Speed It is impossible to have a true vertical line on a distance-time graph. The vertical line would mean the object moved a distance in zero time. To do this, the object would have to go infinitely fast.

Discussion

Velocity Describe the velocity of an object that travels north 6.9 m in 3 s, then turns and travels south 2.8 m in 4 s. velocity = 2.3 m/s north then 0.7 m/s south L2 LS **Logical-Mathematical**

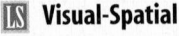

Reading Check

Answer Velocity includes direction; speed does not.

Activity

Changing Velocity Swing a ball on a string around your head at a constant speed. Ask students whether the velocity of the ball is constant or changing. changing, because the direction varies L1 ELL LS **Visual-Spatial**

Controlling Motion

Purpose To design a device that will control the motion of a marble and keep the marble in constant motion for exactly 3 minutes.

Possible Materials Students will choose their own materials. Suggestions: cardboard sheets, cardboard tubes, pizza delivery boxes, or plastic tubing

Estimated Time 2 class periods, outside class time may be required

Teaching Strategy Divide the class into small groups. Students can use a variety of schemes to keep their marble in motion. The goal is to keep the marble in motion exactly 3 min, so the students will have to fine-tune their devices. Encourage students to use gravity, springs, catapults, mouse traps, etc. to make their device fun.

For additional inquiry activities, see Science Inquiry Labs.

Figure 6 The speed of a storm is not enough information to plot the path. The direction the storm is moving must be known, too.

Velocity

You turn on the radio and hear the tail end of a news story about a hurricane, like the one in **Figure 6,** that is approaching land. The storm, traveling at a speed of 20 km/h, is located 100 km east of your location. Should you be worried?

Unfortunately, you don't have enough information to answer that question. Knowing only the speed of the storm isn't much help. Speed describes only how fast something is moving. To decide whether you need to move to a safer area, you also need to know the direction that the storm is moving. In other words, you need to know the velocity of the storm. **Velocity** includes the speed of an object and the direction of its motion.

Escalators like the one shown in **Figure 7** are found in shopping malls and airports. The two sets of passengers pictured are moving at constant speed, but in opposite directions. The speeds of the passengers are the same, but their velocities are different because the passengers are moving in different directions.

Because velocity depends on direction as well as speed, the velocity of an object can change even if the speed of the object remains constant. For example, look at **Figure 7.** The race car has a constant speed and is going around an oval track. Even though the speed remains constant, the velocity changes because the direction of the car's motion is changing constantly.

Reading Check ***How are velocity and speed different?***

Figure 7 For an object to have constant velocity, speed and direction must not be changing.

The people on these two escalators have the same speed. However, their velocities are different because they are traveling in opposite directions.

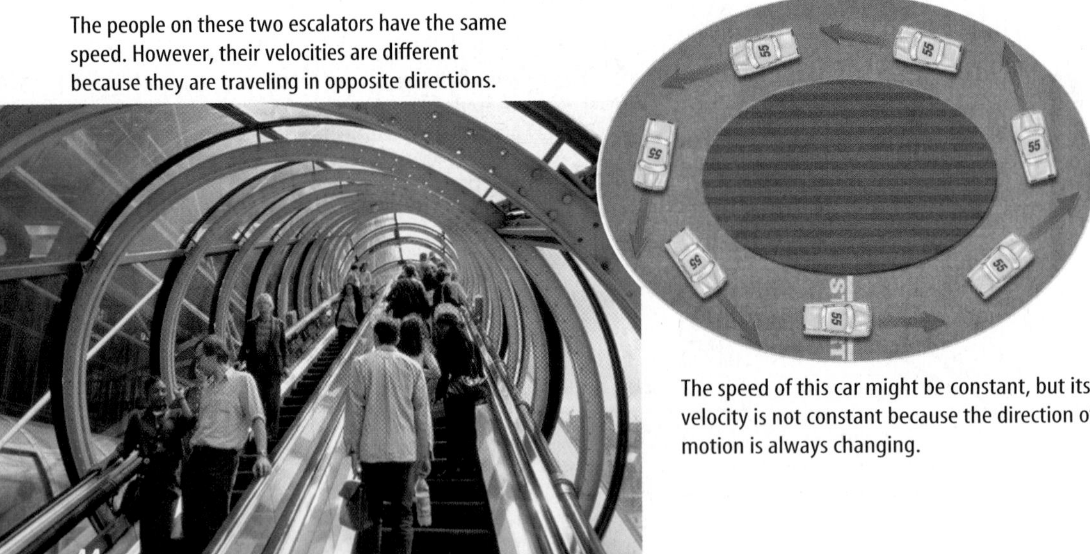

The speed of this car might be constant, but its velocity is not constant because the direction of motion is always changing.

Science Journal

Changing Velocity Have students write brief paragraphs in their Science Journals describing several situations in which speed is constant but velocity is changing. a person walking up and down the aisles of a grocery store at a constant speed, a glider moving up and down in the air at constant speed L2 LS **Linguistic**

Active Reading

ReQuest Have students listen carefully as you read an interesting story or newsworthy item aloud. After the reading, students, alone or in groups, can formulate questions to discuss. Have students participate in a ReQuest related to motion and/or acceleration and the forces that are acting on the object. L2

Motion of Earth's Crust

INTEGRATE Earth Science

Can you think of something that is moving so slowly you cannot detect its motion, yet you can see evidence of its motion over long periods of time? As you look around the surface of Earth from year to year, the basic structure of the planet seems the same. Mountains, plains, lakes, and oceans seem to remain unchanged over hundreds of years. Yet if you examined geological evidence of what Earth's surface looked like over the past 250 million years, you would see that large changes have occurred. **Figure 8** shows how, according to the theory of plate tectonics, the positions of landmasses have changed during this time. Changes in the landscape occur constantly as continents drift slowly over Earth's surface. However, these changes are so gradual that you do not notice them.

About 250 million years ago, the continents formed a supercontinent called Pangaea.

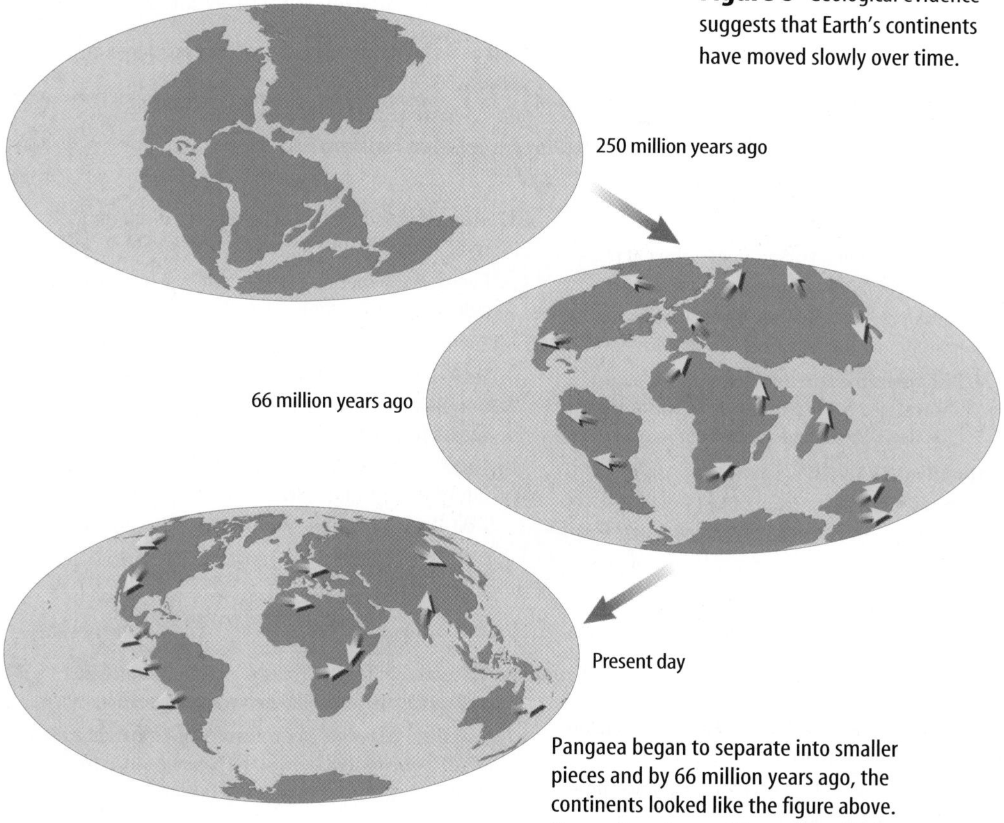

250 million years ago

66 million years ago

Present day

Pangaea began to separate into smaller pieces and by 66 million years ago, the continents looked like the figure above. The continents are still moving today.

Figure 8 Geological evidence suggests that Earth's continents have moved slowly over time.

Activity

Moving Plates When two of Earth's plates move past each other, scientists describe their speeds relative to each other. Use tape to mark two side-by-side tracks on the floor, each 3 m long. Have a student stand at each end of the tracks, and have other students with timers ready to record how long it takes balls to roll from one end of the track to the other end. When you say "go," the students at the ends of the tracks should roll the balls toward each other. The class can then determine the velocity (relative to the floor) of a ball going in one direction and the velocity of the ball going in the other direction. Explain that adding these numbers will give the speed of the balls relative to each other, similar to the speed of two of Earth's plates moving past each other. L2 ELL LS **Kinesthetic**

Activity

Pangaea In the early 1900s, Alfred Wegener, a German meteorologist, developed the theory that all Earth's continents were once part of a single landmass called *Pangaea*. Have students research and discuss evidence that supports this theory. Possible answers: similarities in fossils, glacial sediments, rock layers, structure of the ocean floor between continents L3 LS **Linguistic**

Teacher FYI

Displacement Distance is how far something moves, but displacement includes distance and direction. Velocity measures displacement, so average velocity is the total displacement divided by the time.

Differentiated Instruction

Challenge Have students explore relative velocity. For example, suppose you ride on a train that is going 80 km/h. If you walk toward the front of the train at a speed of 1.2 km/h, your velocity relative to the ground is 81.2 km/h in the direction that the train is moving. If, instead, you walk toward the back of the train at a speed of 1.2 km/h, your velocity relative to the ground is 78.8 km/h in the direction that the train is moving. Have students research other situations that demonstrate the concept of relative velocity. Have students make a poster that explains their example to other students. L3 LS **Logical-Mathematical**

3 Assess

DAILY INTERVENTION

Check for Understanding

Linguistic Have students write a short narrative that could be used to explain the difference between distance and displacement to a younger sibling or to someone in the class that doesn't understand the difference. L2

Reteach

Calculating Average Speed Have students calculate the average speed of a windup or battery-operated toy car using metersticks and a wall clock. L2

Assessment

Performance Provide students with the following problem: Suppose a bus is traveling along the highway. It travels 100 km in the first 2 hours and 120 km in the second 2 hours. It stops for one hour, then it finishes the trip by going 100 km in two hours. Draw a distance-time graph of the bus's motion. Use **Performance Assessment in the Science Classroom**, p. 111. L2

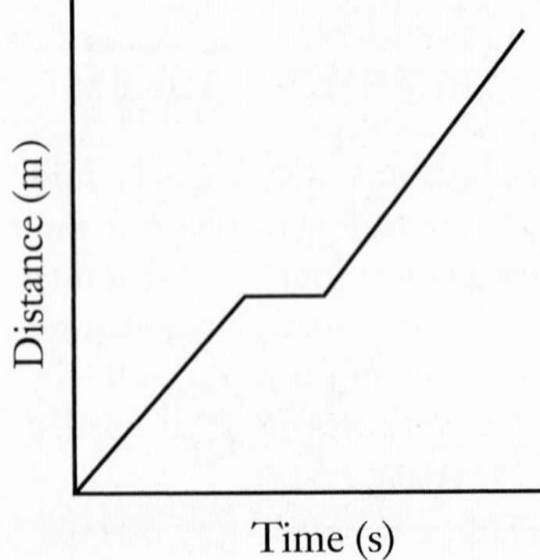

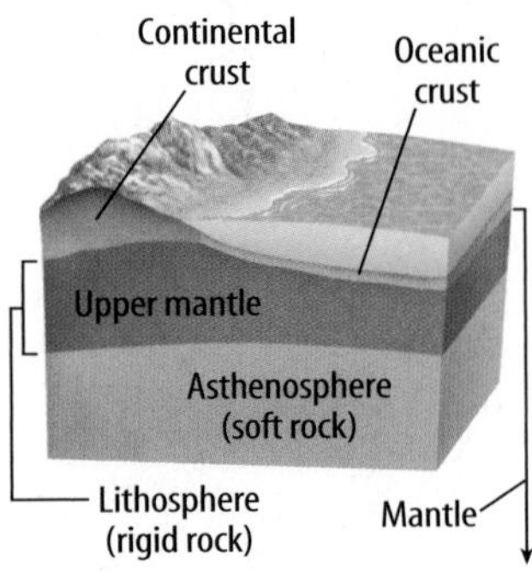

Figure 9 Earth's crust floats over a puttylike interior.

Moving Continents How can continents move around on the surface of Earth? Earth is made of layers, as shown in **Figure 9.** The outer layer is the crust, and the layer just below the crust is called the upper mantle. Together the crust and the top part of the upper mantle are called the lithosphere. The lithosphere is broken into huge sections called plates that slide slowly on the puttylike layers just below. If you compare Earth to an egg, these plates are about as thick as the eggshell. These moving plates cause geological changes such as the formation of mountain ranges, earthquakes, and volcanic eruptions.

The movement of the plates also is changing the size of the oceans and the shapes of the continents. The Pacific Ocean is getting smaller while the Atlantic Ocean is getting larger. The movement of the plates also changes the shape of the continents as they collide and spread apart.

Plates move so slowly that their speeds are given in units of centimeters per year. In California, two plates slide past each other along the San Andreas Fault with an average relative speed of about 1 cm per year. The Australian Plate's movement is one of the fastest, pushing Australia north at an average speed of about 17 cm per year.

section 1 review

Summary

Position and Motion

- The position of an object is determined relative to a reference point.
- Motion occurs when an object changes its position relative to a reference point.
- Distance is the length of the path an object has traveled. Displacement is the distance and direction of a change in position.

Speed and Velocity

- Speed is the distance an object travels per unit time and is given by this equation:

$$s = \frac{d}{t}$$

- The velocity of an object includes the object's speed and its direction of motion relative to a reference point.

Graphing Motion

- On a distance-time graph, time is the horizontal axis and distance is the vertical axis.
- The slope of a line plotted on a distance-time graph is the speed.

Self Check

1. **Infer** whether the size of an object's displacement could be greater than the distance the object travels.
2. **Describe** the motion represented by a horizontal line on a distance-time graph.
3. **Explain** whether, during a trip, a car's instantaneous speed can ever be greater than its average speed.
4. **Describe** the difference between average speed and constant speed.
5. **Think Critically** You are walking toward the back of a bus that is moving forward with a constant velocity. Describe your motion relative to the bus and relative to a point on the ground.

Applying Math

6. **Calculate Speed** Michiko walked a distance of 1.60 km in 30 min. Find her average speed in m/s.
7. **Calculate Distance** A car travels at a constant speed of 30.0 m/s for 0.8 h. Find the total distance traveled in km.

Science Online gpscience.com/self_check_quiz

section 1 review

1. No. The displacement equals the distance only if the object moves in a straight line in a single direction. Otherwise, the displacement is less than the distance.
2. The slope is zero, corresponding to a speed of zero.
3. Yes. The instantaneous speed at various times can be greater or less than the average speed.
4. Average speed is total distance traveled divided by total time; the instantaneous speed can be changing. Constant speed means that the instantaneous speed doesn't change.
5. Relative to the bus, you move backward at your walking speed. Relative to the ground, you move in the same direction as the bus with a speed equal to the bus speed minus your walking speed.
6. 0.89 m/s
7. 86.4 km

section 2

Acceleration

Reading Guide

What You'll Learn
- **Identify** how acceleration, time, and velocity are related.
- **Explain** how positive and negative acceleration affect motion.
- **Describe** how to calculate the acceleration of an object.

Why It's Important
Acceleration occurs all around you as objects speed up, slow down, or change direction.

Review Vocabulary
speed: rate of change of position; can be calculated by dividing the distance traveled by the time taken to travel the distance

New Vocabulary
- acceleration

Acceleration, Speed, and Velocity

You're sitting in a car at a stoplight when the light turns green. The driver steps on the gas pedal and the car starts moving faster and faster. Just as speed is the rate of change of position, **acceleration** is the rate of change of velocity. When the velocity of an object changes, the object is accelerating.

Remember that velocity includes the speed and direction of an object. Therefore, a change in velocity can be either a change in how fast something is moving or a change in the direction it is moving. Acceleration occurs when an object changes its speed, its direction, or both.

Speeding Up and Slowing Down When you think of acceleration, you probably think of something speeding up. However, an object that is slowing down also is accelerating.

Imagine a car traveling through a city. If the speed is increasing, the car has positive acceleration. When the car slows down its speed is decreasing and the car has negative acceleration. In both cases the car is accelerating because its speed is changing.

Acceleration also has direction, just as velocity does. If the acceleration is in the same direction as the velocity, as in **Figure 10,** the speed increases and the acceleration is positive. If the speed decreases, the acceleration is in the opposite direction from the velocity, and the acceleration is negative for the car shown in **Figure 10.**

Figure 10 These cars are both accelerating because their speed is changing.

Acceleration

Velocity

The speed of this car is increasing. The car has positive acceleration.

Acceleration

Velocity

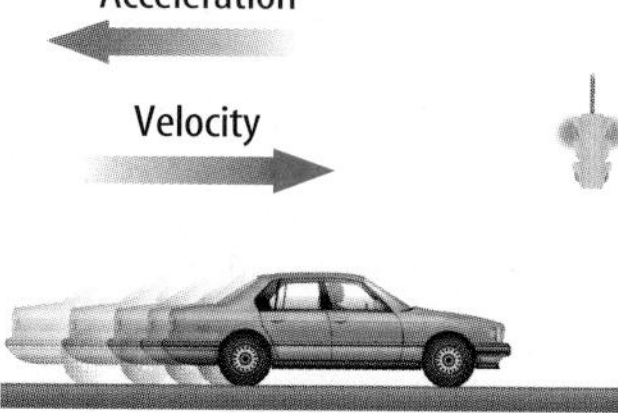

The speed of this car is decreasing. The car has negative acceleration.

Section 2 Resource Manager

Chapter *FAST FILE* Resources
Enrichment, p. 31
Lab Activity, pp. 13–15
Directed Reading for Content Mastery, p. 21
Reinforcement, p. 28

Performance Assessment in the Science Classroom, p. 37

Science Inquiry Labs, pp. 23–24

1 Motivate

Bellringer

Section Focus Transparencies also are available on the Interactive Chalkboard CD-ROM. L2 ELL

Section 2 Section Focus Transparency On the Edge

Many people enjoy cross-country and downhill skiing for recreation and for exercise. For others, skiing is a competitive sport. In ski races, fractions of a second can make the difference between winning and finishing second.

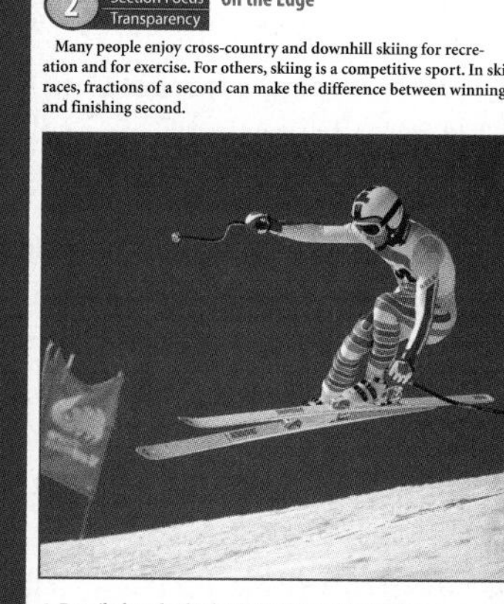

1. Describe how the skier's velocity changes during the race.
2. Why does the skier's velocity increase as he races downhill?
3. How does being in a tuck position affect a skier's motion? L2

Tie to Prior Knowledge

"Stepping on the Gas" Have a student explain the phrase "stepping on the gas." Relate the function of the accelerator to the motion of a car. L2

2 Teach

INTEGRATE History

Aircraft Carriers The U.S. navy was not alone in the development of aircraft carriers. During World War I the British navy converted a merchant-ship hull into the first aircraft carrier with an unobstructed flight deck, the HMS *Argus.* The first U.S. carrier, the USS *Langley*, joined the fleet in March 1922. The Japanese built the first carrier from the keel up, the *Hosyo.* It entered service in December 1922.

Research Have students research modern aircraft carriers including nuclear-powered carriers. Students can prepare a presentation to present to the class using the information they find. L3

Discussion

Acceleration Tell students that, as in the case of speed and velocity, acceleration can be constant or changing, and one can measure instantaneous acceleration as well as average acceleration. Ask students to give examples of constant acceleration, instantaneous acceleration, and average acceleration. constant acceleration: free fall; instantaneous acceleration: the acceleration of a falling rock after it has been falling for 3 s; average acceleration: final velocity of the falling rock when it hits the ground divided by the total time it was falling L3

LS **Logical-Mathematical**

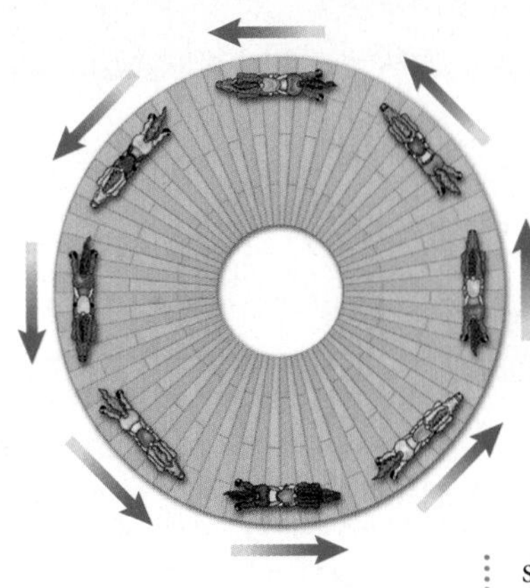

Figure 11 The speed of the horses in this carousel is constant, but the horses are accelerating because their direction is changing constantly.

INTEGRATE History

Aircraft Carriers An aircraft carrier provides a landing strip for airplanes to land and take off at sea. The carrier must be equipped to provide enough negative acceleration to stop a moving plane. The carrier also must be equipped to quickly accelerate planes to allow them to take off on a short runway. In 1911, American pilot Eugene Ely landed on a specially equipped deck on the battleship *Pennsylvania.* The experiment was successful, and today aircraft carriers are an important part of navies worldwide.

Changing Direction A change in velocity can be either a change in how fast something is moving or a change in the direction of movement. Any time a moving object changes direction, its velocity changes and it is accelerating. Think about a horse on a carousel. Although the horse's speed remains constant, the horse is accelerating because it is changing direction constantly as it travels in a circular path, as shown in **Figure 11.** In the same way, Earth is accelerating constantly as it orbits the Sun in a nearly circular path.

Graphs of speed versus time can provide information about accelerated motion. The shape of the plotted curve shows when an object is speeding up or slowing down. **Figure 12** shows how motion graphs are constructed.

Calculating Acceleration

Acceleration is the rate of change in velocity. To calculate the acceleration of an object, the change in velocity is divided by the length of the time interval over which the change occurred.

To calculate the change in velocity, subtract the initial velocity—the velocity at the beginning of the time interval—from the final velocity—the velocity at the end of the time interval. Let v_i stand for the initial velocity and v_f stand for the final velocity. Then the change in velocity is:

$$\text{change in velocity} = \text{final velocity} - \text{initial velocity}$$
$$= v_f - v_i$$

Using this expression for the change in velocity, the acceleration can be calculated from the following equation:

Acceleration Equation

$$\textbf{acceleration} \text{ (in meters/second}^2) = \frac{\text{change in velocity (in meters/second)}}{\text{time (in seconds)}}$$

$$a = \frac{v_f - v_i}{t}$$

Recall that velocity includes both speed and direction. However, if the direction of motion doesn't change and the object moves in a straight line, the change in velocity can be calculated from the change in speed. The change in velocity then is the final speed minus the initial speed.

The unit for acceleration is a unit for velocity divided by a unit for time. In SI units, velocity has units of m/s, and time has units of s, so acceleration has units of m/s^2.

Curriculum Connection

Physical Education Most sports rely on the ability of people to make quick changes in acceleration. Have students find out some of the equipment used in different sports to make acceleration easier. starting blocks for runners and swimmers; cleats on shoes for runners, soccer players, football players, and baseball players; rubber-soled shoes for basketball players; special clothing for reducing wind resistance for all racers L2

Teacher FYI

Feeling Acceleration In the aerospace industry, the accelerations experienced by astronauts and pilots are often expressed as multiples of *g*. The acceleration, caused by gravity (*g*), acting on an object falling freely near Earth's surface is about 9.8 m/s^2. Vertical accelerations as low as 3 *g* can cause pilots to black out.

NATIONAL GEOGRAPHIC VISUALIZING ACCELERATION

Figure 12

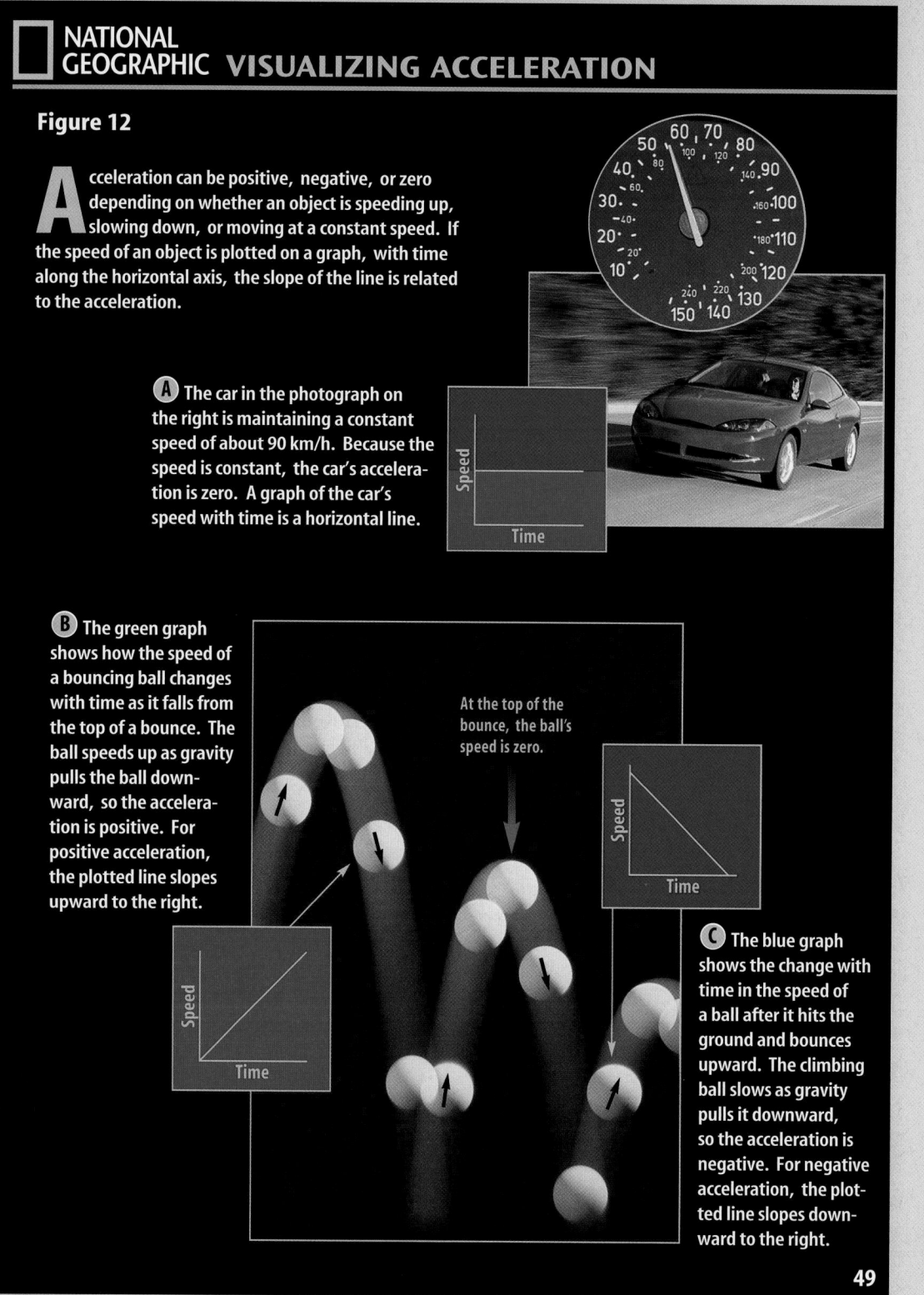

Acceleration can be positive, negative, or zero depending on whether an object is speeding up, slowing down, or moving at a constant speed. If the speed of an object is plotted on a graph, with time along the horizontal axis, the slope of the line is related to the acceleration.

Ⓐ The car in the photograph on the right is maintaining a constant speed of about 90 km/h. Because the speed is constant, the car's acceleration is zero. A graph of the car's speed with time is a horizontal line.

Ⓑ The green graph shows how the speed of a bouncing ball changes with time as it falls from the top of a bounce. The ball speeds up as gravity pulls the ball downward, so the acceleration is positive. For positive acceleration, the plotted line slopes upward to the right.

Ⓒ The blue graph shows the change with time in the speed of a ball after it hits the ground and bounces upward. The climbing ball slows as gravity pulls it downward, so the acceleration is negative. For negative acceleration, the plotted line slopes downward to the right.

49

Visualizing Acceleration

Have students examine the pictures and read the captions. Then ask the following questions.

In the graphs for A, B, and C, how are the slopes of the lines and the accelerations of the objects related? The slope of the line is positive if acceleration is positive, negative if acceleration is negative, and zero if there is no acceleration.

In the graph for B, what is the numerical value of the acceleration of the ball? The numerical value is the same as the acceleration due to gravity, 9.8 m/s^2.

What is the relation between the graphs for B and C? The acceleration of both balls is due to the pull of gravity. Graph B has a positive acceleration due to gravity or $+9.8$ m/s^2 and graph C has a negative acceleration due to gravity or -9.8 m/s^2.

Activity

Rap Songs Have students work in pairs to make up rap songs containing descriptions of the relationship between different types of acceleration and their corresponding graphs. L2

LS **Auditory-Musical**

Differentiated Instruction

Challenge Have students find out what type of information can be obtained by finding the area under a speed-time graph. Explain why this could be a useful tool for scientists. Construct a speed-time graph and find the distance traveled by the object. The numerical value of the area under a speed-time graph is the distance traveled by the object. L3 P

LS **Logical-Mathematical**

Visually Impaired Have a student helper read the text for each graph. Have the helper move his or her finger along the graph while the other student gently lays his or her hand on top of the helper's hand. This can help the visually-impaired student "see" the graph.

Visual Learning

Figure 13 Review with students the graphs in **Figure 13**. Then ask a volunteer to draw on the board the speed-time graph for a car that starts at 0 km/h, accelerates to 30 km/h over a period of 2 minutes, runs at 30 km/h for 10 minutes, then takes 30 seconds to stop. L2

Quick Demo

Sphere Acceleration

Materials about 2 m of clear plastic tubing, small sphere that can freely roll through tubing

Estimated Time 10 minutes

Procedure Have two students hold the tubing in a U-shape. Put the sphere in one end of the tubing. Point out to the students that the sphere has positive acceleration as it rolls downhill in the tubing. The sphere has negative acceleration as it starts to go uphill in the tubing.

Answer They are accelerated.

Calculating Positive Acceleration How is the acceleration for an object that is speeding up different from that of an object that is slowing down? Suppose the jet airliner in **Figure 13** starts at rest at the end of a runway and reaches a speed of 80 m/s in 20 s. The airliner is traveling in a single direction down the runway, so its change in velocity can be calculated from its change in speed. Because it started from rest, its initial speed was zero. Its acceleration can be calculated as follows:

$$a = \frac{(v_f - v_i)}{t} = \frac{(80 \text{ m/s} - 0 \text{ m/s})}{20 \text{ s}} = 4 \text{ m/s}^2$$

The airliner is speeding up, so the final speed is greater than the initial speed and the acceleration is positive.

Calculating Negative Acceleration Now imagine that the skateboarder in **Figure 13** is moving in a straight line at a constant speed of 3 m/s and comes to a stop in 2 s. The final speed is zero and the initial speed was 3 m/s. The skateboarder's acceleration is calculated as follows:

$$a = \frac{(v_f - v_i)}{t} = \frac{(0 \text{ m/s} - 3 \text{ m/s})}{2 \text{ s}} = -1.5 \text{ m/s}^2$$

The skateboarder is slowing down, so the final speed is less than the initial speed and the acceleration is negative. The acceleration always will be positive if an object is speeding up and negative if the object is slowing down.

If the line slopes upward to the right, acceleration is positive.

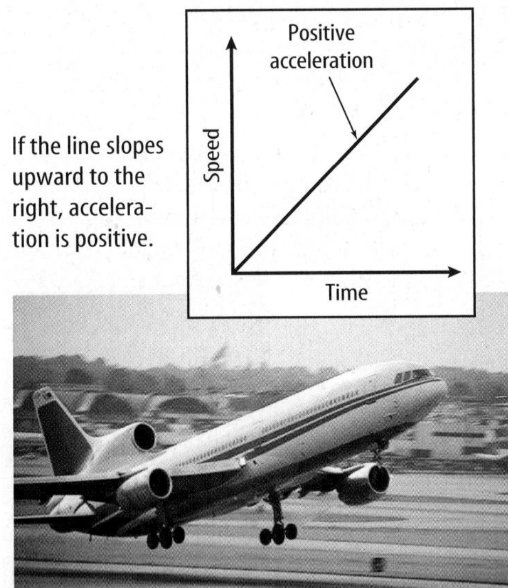

If the line slopes downward to the right, acceleration is negative.

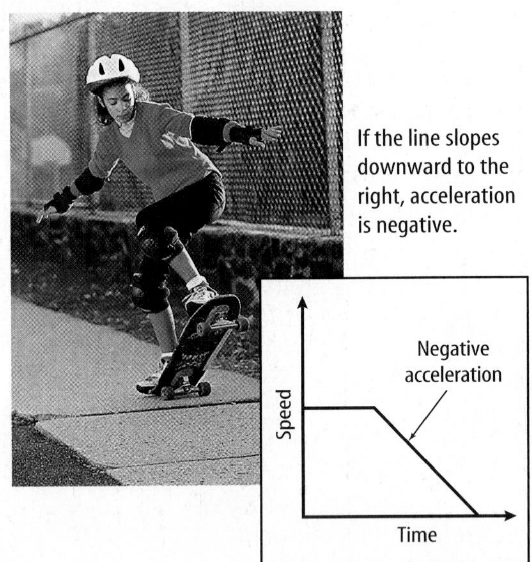

Figure 13 A speed-time graph tells you if acceleration is positive or negative.

LAB DEMONSTRATION

Purpose to demonstrate making a table and graph from distance-time measurements

Materials 8 socks, clock with second hand, meterstick

Preparation Mark a starting place where you have room to walk.

Procedure Start walking at the starting line. Have a student call out every 3 s. Begin walking slowly then steadily increase your speed. Drop a sock every 3 s. Measure the distance from the starting line to each sock. On the board, make a table and a distance-time graph of the data.

Expected Outcome The distance between socks will increase for each 3-second interval.

Assessment

What is the slope of the line after 6 s? The slope will vary with the data. What does this show? the speed L2

Amusement Park Acceleration

Riding roller coasters in amusement parks can give you the feeling of danger, but these rides are designed to be safe. Engineers use the laws of physics to design amusement park rides that are thrilling, but harmless. Roller coasters are constructed of steel or wood. Because wood is not as rigid as steel, wooden roller coasters do not have hills that are as high and steep as some steel roller coasters have. As a result, the highest speeds and accelerations usually are produced on steel roller coasters.

Steel roller coasters can offer multiple steep drops and inversion loops, which give the rider large accelerations. As the rider moves down a steep hill or an inversion loop, he or she will accelerate toward the ground due to gravity. When riders go around a sharp turn, they also are accelerated. This acceleration makes them feel as if a force is pushing them toward the side of the car. **Figure 14** shows one of the fastest roller coasters in the United States.

What happens when riders on a roller coaster go around a sharp turn?

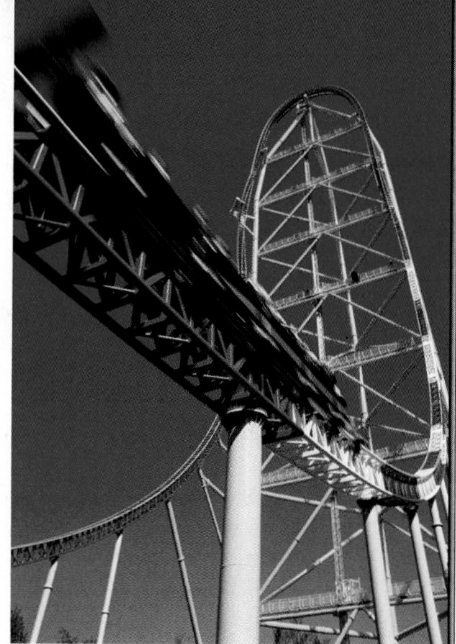

Figure 14 This roller coaster can reach a speed of about 200 km/h in 4 s.

section 2 review

Summary

Acceleration, Speed, and Velocity

- Acceleration is the rate of change of velocity.
- A change in velocity occurs when the speed of an object changes, or its direction of motion changes, or both occur.
- The speed of an object increases if the acceleration is in the same direction as the velocity.
- The speed of an object decreases if the acceleration and the velocity of the object are in opposite directions.

Calculating Acceleration

- Acceleration can be calculated by dividing the change in velocity by the time according to the following equation:

$$a = \frac{v_f - v_i}{t}$$

- The SI unit for acceleration is m/s^2.
- If an object is moving in a straight line, the change in velocity equals the final speed minus the initial speed.

Self Check

1. **Describe** three ways to change the velocity of a moving car.
2. **Determine** the change in velocity of a car that starts at rest and has a final velocity of 20 m/s north.
3. **Explain** why streets and highways have speed limits rather than velocity limits.
4. **Describe** the motion of an object that has an acceleration of 0 m/s^2.
5. **Think Critically** Suppose a car is accelerating so that its speed is increasing. Describe the plotted line on a distance-time graph of the motion of the car.

Applying Math

6. **Calculate Time** A ball is dropped from a cliff and has an acceleration of 9.8 m/s^2. How long will it take the ball to reach a speed of 24.5 m/s?
7. **Calculate Speed** A sprinter leaves the starting blocks with an acceleration of 4.5 m/s^2. What is the sprinter's speed 2 s later?

 gpscience.com/self_check_quiz

3 Assess

DAILY INTERVENTION

Check for Understanding

Kinesthetic Have students work in groups to discuss acceleration experienced by a tennis ball as it is dropped and bounces. Because the velocity of the ball changes direction as it bounces, students must include the direction of the ball's motion when they calculate acceleration. If down is the positive direction, the ball's acceleration is positive when it falls. When the ball rises, its velocity becomes less negative as it moves upward, so its acceleration is again positive. When the ball is in contact with the floor, its acceleration is negative as it slows down in the positive (down) direction, and then speeds up in the negative (up) direction. Have students make a labeled poster illustrating the tennis ball's positive then negative acceleration cycle; a pattern that repeats itself with each bounce. L3

COOP LEARN P IS **Interpersonal**

Reteach

Acceleration Have students demonstrate three ways to accelerate while walking. speeding up, slowing down, changing direction L1

IS **Kinesthetic**

Assessment

Process Think about how motion is affected by gravitational acceleration. Water on Earth falls from a waterfall with an acceleration of 9.8 m/s^2. The gravity of Mars is four-tenths that of Earth. If water were on the surface of Mars, would water fall from a waterfall faster, more slowly, or at the same speed? more slowly Use **Performance Assessment in the Science Classroom,** p. 89. L2

section 2 review

1. speed up, slow down, turn
2. 20 m/s north
3. Velocity includes direction, so to have a velocity limit there would have to be some limit as to the direction in which a car was moving, as well as speed.
4. It's moving in a straight line with constant speed.
5. The plot would be a curved line sloping upward whose slope is increasing.
6. 2.5 s
7. 9.0 m/s

1 Motivate

Bellringer

Section Focus Transparencies also are available on the Interactive Chalkboard CD-ROM. 

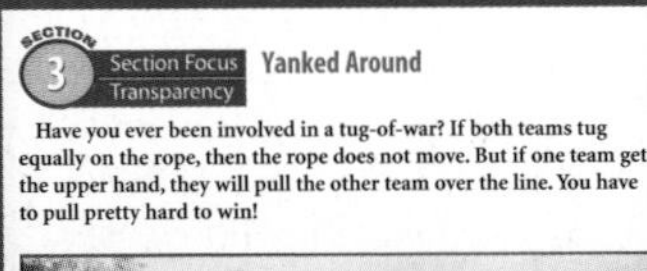

Have you ever been involved in a tug-of-war? If both teams tug equally on the rope, then the rope does not move. But if one team gets the upper hand, they will pull the other team over the line. You have to pull pretty hard to win!

1. The photo shows one team pulling but not moving very much. In which direction must the other team be pulling? Why?
2. If one team tugs the other over the line, what can you infer about the pulls exerted by the two teams?
3. How do the weights of the tug-of-war teams affect the match?

L2

Motion and Speed

Tie to Prior Knowledge

Changing Velocity Ask students to describe things they could do to change the velocity of a soccer ball. Point out that in each case, they are using a push or a pull to change the ball's motion. Tell students that pushes and pulls are forces, and this section discusses how forces change an object's motion. L2

Reading Check

Answer Student answers will vary. possible answer: force of gravity on a falling object

section 3 Motion and Forces

Reading Guide

What You'll Learn

- **Explain** how force and motion are related.
- **Describe** what inertia is and how it is related to Newton's first law of motion.
- **Identify** the forces and motion that are present during a car crash.

Why It's Important

Force and motion are directly linked—without force, you cannot have motion.

Review Vocabulary

scientific law: statement about something that happens in nature that seems to be true all the time

New Vocabulary

- force
- net force
- balanced force
- inertia

What is force?

Passing a basketball to a team member or kicking a soccer ball into the goal are examples of applying force to an object. A **force** is a push or pull. In both examples, the applied force changes the movement of the ball. Sometimes it is obvious that a force has been applied. But other forces aren't as noticeable. For instance, are you conscious of the force the floor exerts on your feet? Can you feel the force of the atmosphere pushing against your body or gravity pulling on your body? Think about all the forces you exert in a day. Every push, pull, stretch, or bend results in a force being applied to an object.

Figure 15 This ball is hit with a force. The racket strikes the ball with a force in the opposite direction of its motion. As a result, the ball changes the direction it is moving.

Changing Motion What happens to the motion of an object when you exert a force on it? A force can cause the motion of an object to change. Think of hitting a ball with a racket, as in **Figure 15.** The racket strikes the ball with a force that causes the ball to stop and then move in the opposite direction. If you have played billiards, you know that you can force a ball at rest to roll into a pocket by striking it with another ball. The force of the moving ball causes the ball at rest to move in the direction of the force. In these cases, the velocities of the ball and the billiard ball were changed by a force.

Section 3 Resource Manager

Chapter *FAST FILE* Resources
- Directed Reading for Content Mastery, pp. 21, 22
- Enrichment, p. 32
- MiniLAB, p. 4
- Reinforcement, p. 29
- Lab Worksheet, pp. 5–6, 7–8

Home and Community Involvement, p. 41

Earth Science Critical Thinking/Problem Solving, p. 9

Cultural Diversity, p. 63

Figure 16 Forces can be balanced and unbalanced.

→ + ← = 0

Net Force = 0

A These students are pushing on the box with an equal force but in opposite directions. Because the forces are balanced, the box does not move.

→ + ← = →

Net Force = →

B These students are pushing on the box with unequal forces in opposite directions. The box will be moved in the direction of the larger force.

→ + → = →

Net Force = →

C These students are pushing on the box in the same direction. The combined forces will cause the box to move.

Balanced Forces Force does not always change velocity. In **Figure 16A,** two students are pushing on opposite sides of a box. Both students are pushing with an equal force but in opposite directions. When two or more forces act on an object at the same time, the forces combine to form the **net force.** The net force on the box in **Figure 16A** is zero because the two forces cancel each other. Forces on an object that are equal in size and opposite in direction are called **balanced forces.**

Unbalanced Forces Another example of how forces combine is shown in **Figure 16B.** When two students are pushing with unequal forces in opposite directions, a net force occurs in the direction of the larger force. In other words, the student who pushes with a greater force will cause the box to move in the direction of the force. The net force that moves the box will be the difference between the two forces because they are in opposite directions. They are considered to be unbalanced forces.

In **Figure 16C,** the students are pushing on the box in the same direction. These forces are combined, or added together, because they are exerted on the box in the same direction. The net force that acts on this box is found by adding the two forces together.

Reading Check *Give another example of an unbalanced force.*

Science Online

Topic: Forces and Fault Lines

Visit gpscience.com for Web links to information about the unbalanced forces that occur along Earth's fault lines.

Activity Use inexpensive materials such as bars of soap to model the forces and movements along the fault lines. Share your models and demonstrations with your class.

2 Teach

Quick Demo

Upward and Downward Force

Materials spring scale and objects with various masses

Estimated Time 10 minutes

Procedure Hold up a spring scale and hang objects of different masses from it. Have a student read the force required to hold up each object. Explain that the upward force exerted by the spring of the spring scale balances the downward gravitational force of the object.

Identifying Misconceptions

Balanced Forces Students often assume no motion means no force, but an object's lack of motion is because the forces acting on it are balanced. Students also may assume that an object in motion has an external force acting on it. Explain that motion may be caused by unbalanced forces, or it may be the result of inertia.

Teacher FYI

Plate Tectonics Scientists do not fully understand the driving force behind the movement of the plates. There appears to be three factors contributing to the movement of the plates: the pull of gravity, convection currents in the mantle, and thermal plumes or vertical columns of molten material in the mantle.

Visual Learning

Figure 16 Tell students that the net force acting on an object is called the resultant force. In **Figure 16A,** the forces are equal and in opposite directions, so the resultant force is zero. In **Figure 16B,** you can calculate the resultant force by subtracting the smaller force from the larger one. How would you calculate the resultant force in **Figure 16C**? Add the two forces together. L2

IS **Visual-Spatial**

Purpose Students will observe the effect of inertia. L2

IS **Kinesthetic**

Materials board, textbooks, block, small object, cart, rubber bands

Analysis

1. Without rubber bands the forces are gravity and the force exerted by the cart on the object. When the cart hits the wall, the object continues moving until the stop block exerts a force on it. The rubber bands exert an additional force on the object. Because the rubber bands can stretch, the object slows down over a longer period of time, reducing the stopping force.
2. In a crash, seat belts reduce the stopping force and decrease damage to passengers.

Assessment

Process Ask students to make diagrams of each run of the cart. Have them use labeled arrows to indicate the forces. Use **Performance Assessment in the Science Classroom,** p. 127.

Make a Model

Unbalanced Forces Use children's blocks to represent boxes similar to those on the previous page. Have student volunteers use a pencil to apply balanced and unbalanced forces to the blocks to force them to move. Have students explain the type of forces that are being applied. L2

Observing Inertia

Procedure

1. Create an inclined plane between 25° and 50° using a **board** and **textbooks.** Place a **stop block** (brick or other heavy object) at the end of the plane.
2. Place a **small object** in a **cart** and allow both to roll down the plane. Record the results in your Science Journal.
3. Secure the object in the cart with **rubber bands** (safety belts). Allow both to roll down the plane again. Record the results.

Analysis

1. Identify the forces acting on the object in both runs.
2. Explain why it is important to wear safety belts in a car.

Try at Home

Inertia and Mass

The dirt bike in **Figure 17** is sliding on the track. This sliding bike demonstrates the property of inertia. **Inertia** (ih NUR shuh) is the tendency of an object to resist any change in its motion. If an object is moving, it will have uniform motion. It will keep moving at the same speed and in the same direction unless an unbalanced force acts on it. The velocity of the object remains constant unless a force changes it. If an object is at rest, it tends to remain at rest. Its velocity is zero unless a force makes it move.

Does a bowling ball have the same inertia as a table-tennis ball? Why is there a difference? You couldn't change the motion of a bowling ball much by swatting it with a table-tennis paddle. However, you easily could change the motion of the table-tennis ball. A greater force would be needed to change the motion of the bowling ball because it has greater inertia. Why is this? Recall that mass is the amount of matter in an object, and a bowling ball has more mass than a table-tennis ball does. The inertia of an object is related to its mass. The greater the mass of an object is, the greater its inertia.

Newton's Laws of Motion Forces change the motion of an object in specific ways. The British scientist Sir Isaac Newton (1642–1727) was able to state rules that describe the effects of forces on the motion of objects. These rules are known as Newton's laws of motion. They apply to the motion of all objects you encounter every day such as cars and bicycles, as well as the motion of planets around the Sun.

Figure 17 This racer is skidding because of inertia. The bike tends to move in a straight line with constant speed despite the efforts of the rider to steer the bike around the curve.

Differentiated Instruction

Challenge Have students prepare a diagram showing the four forces acting on an ice-skater skating forward. Explain why the skater is able to move forward for a relatively long period of time. Possible answer: The four forces are gravity pulling down on the skater, the ice pushing up, the ice pushing forward in response to the skater's push on the ice, and friction pulling the skater back. Since the ice provides relatively little friction, the skater's inertia keeps him or her moving forward for a relatively long time. L3 IS **Logical-Mathematical**

Figure 18 The inertia of the billiard balls causes them to remain at rest until a force is exerted on them by the cue ball.

Newton's First Law of Motion Newton's first law of motion states that an object moving at a constant velocity keeps moving at that velocity unless an unbalanced net force acts on it. If an object is at rest, it stays at rest unless an unbalanced net force acts on it. Does this sound familiar? It is the same as the earlier discussion of inertia. This law is sometimes called the law of inertia. You probably have seen and felt this law at work without even knowing it. **Figure 18** shows a billiard ball striking the other balls in the opening shot. What are the forces involved when the cue ball strikes the other balls? Are the forces balanced or unbalanced? How does this demonstrate the law of inertia?

Reading Check *What is Newton's first law of motion?*

What happens in a crash?

The law of inertia can explain what happens in a car crash. When a car traveling about 50 km/h collides head-on with something solid, the car crumples, slows down, and stops within approximately 0.1 s. Any passenger not wearing a safety belt continues to move forward at the same speed the car was traveling. Within about 0.02 s (1/50 of a second) after the car stops, unbelted passengers slam into the dashboard, steering wheel, windshield, or the backs of the front seats, as in **Figure 19.** They are traveling at the car's original speed of 50 km/h—about the same speed they would reach falling from a three-story building.

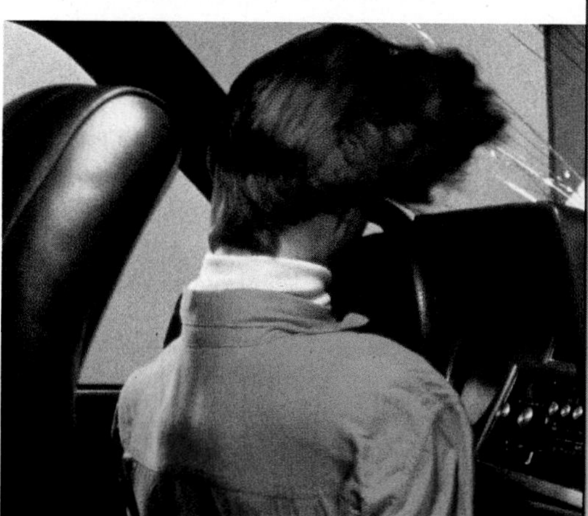

Figure 19 The crash dummy is not restrained in this low-speed crash. Inertia causes the dummy to slam into the steering wheel. **Explain** *how safety belts can help keep passengers from being seriously injured.*

Differentiated Instruction

Learning Disabled Some students may have a hard time visualizing what is occurring when the billiard balls are hit with the cue stick. Get several small balls and demonstrate this on the floor of the classroom. Have students explain what is happening using the terms *force* and *inertia*.

Fun Fact

Although the law of inertia is called Newton's first law, Galileo formulated it before Newton was born. In his writings, Newton credited Galileo for the idea.

Text Question Answer

Force of stick hitting cue ball, force of cue ball hitting other balls, force of balls hitting each other; forces are unbalanced; balls are at rest, then move when a force acts on them.

Reading Check

Answer An object moving at a constant velocity keeps moving at that velocity unless an unbalanced force acts on it.

Activity

Safety Belts Contact your local state patrol office to have an officer speak to the class about the advantages of wearing safety belts. Tell the officer ahead of time that you are studying the forces experienced by a person during a crash so that topic can be addressed. Afterward, have students write in their Science Journals about what they learned from the officer. L2 P

LS **Auditory-Musical**

Discussion

Air Bags How do air bags help prevent injuries during a car crash? Air bags increase the time over which a force acts to slow the motion of a body. The increased time decreases the force required to stop the body, thus reducing the chance for serious injury. L3 LS **Logical-Mathematical**

Caption Answer

Figure 19 The safety belt increases the time it takes for the person to slow down and reduces the force exerted on the person. This results in the passenger receiving less severe injuries.

3 Assess

DAILY INTERVENTION

Check for Understanding

Auditory-Musical Divide students into small groups. Have students create a song that explains balanced and unbalanced forces. Students may perform their song for the class as a review. L2

Reteach

Forces Tie a string around a book and suspend it. Cut the string. Ask students to describe the forces acting on the book before and after you cut the string. Before the string was cut, the force of gravity was pulling down on the book. The string exerted an equal upward force on the book. Since these forces were equal and opposite in direction, the book was at rest. After the string was cut, there was no upward force on the book. The force of gravity was not opposed, so the book fell to the floor. L1 ELL IS **Visual-Spatial**

Assessment

Oral Have students discuss the forces that enable a kite to stay in the air. Gravity pulls down on the kite. The upward force of the wind and the large surface area available for the wind to act upon result in an upward net force on the kite. This upward net force allows the kite to overcome gravity and fly. The tension (force) in the string prevents the kite from flying away. Use **Performance Assessment in the Science Classroom,** p. 89. L2

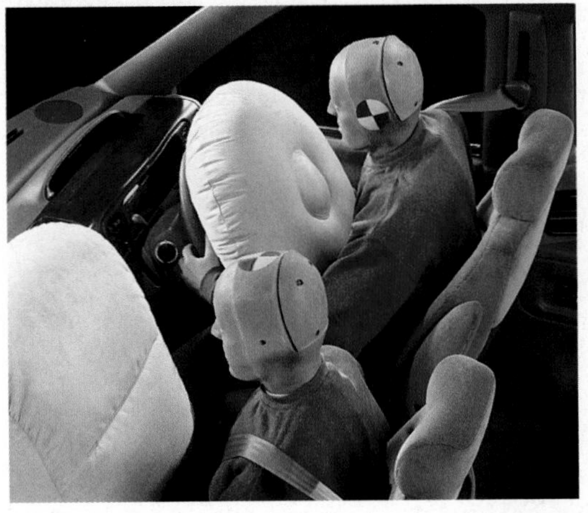

Figure 20 These crash dummies were restrained safely with safety belts in this low-speed crash. Usually humans would have fewer injuries if they were restrained safely during an accident.

Safety Belts The crash dummy wearing a safety belt in **Figure 20** is attached to the car and slows down as the car slows down. The force needed to slow a person from 50 km/h to zero in 0.1 s is equal to 14 times the force that gravity exerts on the person. The belt loosens a little as it restrains the person, increasing the time it takes to slow the person down. This reduces the force exerted on the person. The safety belt also prevents the person from being thrown out of the car. Car-safety experts say that about half the people who die in car crashes would survive if they wore safety belts. Thousands of others would suffer fewer serious injuries.

Air bags also reduce injuries in car crashes by providing a cushion that reduces the force on the car's occupants. When impact occurs, a chemical reaction occurs in the air bag that produces nitrogen gas. The air bag expands rapidly and then deflates just as quickly as the nitrogen gas escapes out of tiny holes in the bag. The entire process is completed in about 0.04 s.

section 3 review

Summary

What is Force?

- A force is a push or a pull on an object.
- The net force on an object is the combination of all the forces acting on the object.
- When the forces on an object are balanced, the net force on the object is zero.
- Unbalanced forces cause the motion of objects to change.

Inertia and Newton's First Law of Motion

- The inertia of an object is the tendency of an object to resist a change in motion.
- The larger the mass of an object, the greater its inertia.
- Newton's first law of motion states that the motion of an object at rest or moving with constant velocity will not change unless an unbalanced net force acts on the object.
- In a car crash, inertia causes an unrestrained passenger to continue moving at the speed of the car before the crash.

Self Check

1. **Infer** whether the inertia of an object changes as the object's velocity changes.
2. **Explain** whether or not there must be an unbalanced net force acting on any moving object.
3. **Explain** Can there be forces acting on an object if the object is at rest?
4. **Infer** the net force on a refrigerator if you push on the refrigerator and it doesn't move.
5. **Think Critically** Describe three situations in which a force changes the velocity of an object.

Applying Math

6. **Calculate Net Force** Two students push on a box in the same direction, and one pushes in the opposite direction. What is the net force on the box if each pushes with a force of 50 N?
7. **Calculate Acceleration** The downward force of gravity and the upward force of air resistance on a ball are both 5 N. What is the ball's acceleration?

Science Online gpscience.com/self_check_quiz

section 3 review

1. No. The inertia is related to the amount of mass and doesn't change.
2. If an object is moving with a constant velocity, then no unbalanced force is acting on it.
3. An object can be at rest if the forces acting on it are balanced.
4. The net force is zero.
5. Possible answers: force exerted by baseball bat changes velocity of pitched ball, gravity causes ball thrown upward to fall, force exerted by person lifts book from desk
6. 50 N in the direction the students are pushing
7. 0 m/s^2

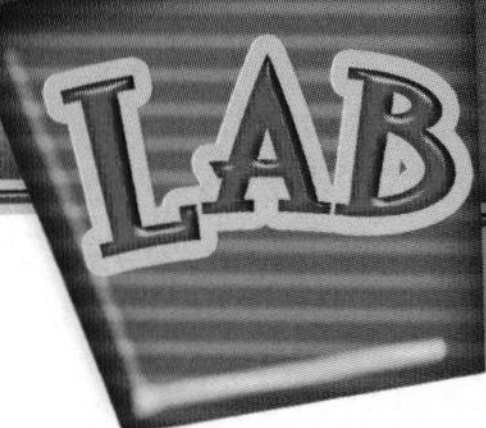

Force AND ACCELERATION

If you stand at a stoplight, you will see cars stopping for red lights and then taking off when the light turns green. What makes the cars slow down? What makes them speed up? Can a study of unbalanced forces lead to a better understanding of these everyday activities?

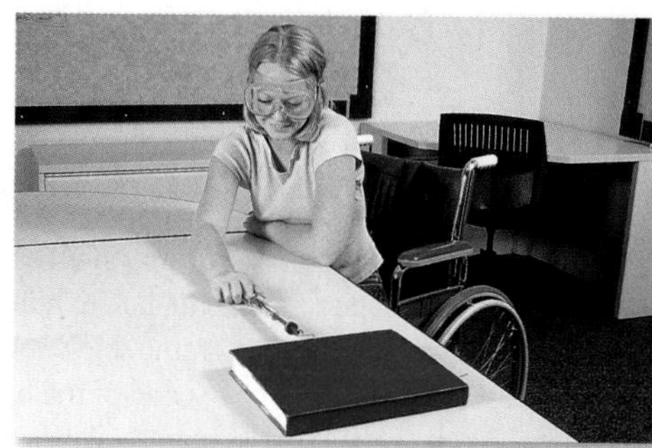

Real-World Question

How does an unbalanced force on a book affect its motion?

Goals

- **Observe** the effect of force on the acceleration of an object.
- **Interpret** the data collected for each trial.

Materials

tape	this science book
paper clip	triple-beam balance
10-N spring scale	**electronic balance*
large book	**Alternate materials*

Safety Precautions

Proper eye protection should be worn at all times while performing this lab.

Procedure

1. With a piece of tape, attach the paper clip to your textbook so that the paper clip is just over the edge of the book.
2. Prepare a data table with the following headings: *Force, Mass.*
3. If available, use a large balance to find the mass of this science book.
4. Place the book on the floor or on the surface of a long table. Use the paper clip to hook the spring scale to the book.
5. Pull the book across the floor or table at a slow but constant velocity. While pulling, read the force you are pulling with on the spring scale and record it in your table.
6. Repeat step 5 two more times, once accelerating slowly and once accelerating quickly. Be careful not to pull too hard. Your spring scale will read only up to 10 N.
7. Place a second book on top of the first book and repeat steps 3 through 6.

Conclude and Apply

1. **Organize** the pulling forces from greatest to least for each set of trials. Do you see a relationship between force and acceleration? Explain your answer.
2. **Explain** how adding the second book changed the results.

Communicating Your Data

Compare your conclusions with those of other students in your class. **For more help, refer to the** Science Skill Handbook.

Real-World Question

Purpose Students will observe the relationship between mass, force, and acceleration. L2

Process Skills observe, compare, infer

Time Required 40 minutes

Procedure

Safety Precautions Students should wear safety goggles while this activity is in progress.

Teaching Strategy Remind students that the spring scale only reads up to 10 N, so they must not pull too hard.

Conclude and Apply

1. As force increased, so did the acceleration.
2. When the second book was added, the force should have increased. If the second book has approximately the same mass as the first book, the force should have doubled.

Assessment

Process Ask students to infer how the pulling force would be different if a book with less mass were pulled. Less force would be required. How would it be different if three of the science books were pulled? More force would be required. Use **Performance Assessment in the Science Classroom,** p. 89. L2

Communicating Your Data

Have students discuss with one another any differences in their results and possible reasons for the differences.

Real-World Question

Purpose Demonstrate how the motion of a toy car is affected by different forces. L2

LS **Kinesthetic**

Process Skills form a hypothesis, design an experiment, separate and control variables, interpret data, measure, use numbers, observe, infer, compare and contrast, recognize cause and effect, communicate, make and use tables, make and use graphs

Time Required 30 minutes to plan the experiment and 45 minutes to make measurements and graph data

Possible Materials Try small springs from molecular model sets to propel the cars by flipping one end of the spring against the car while holding the other end securely.

Use thin springs with loose windings so that they can be easily retracted and released to push the car forward. The string can be used to sharply tug the car. Rubber bands can be used, but they will provide less momentum.

Data Table:

Force Used	Distance	Time	Speed
1			
2			
3			
4			

Form a Hypothesis

Possible Hypothesis Students might hypothesize that the force of the spring will cause the car to go fastest.

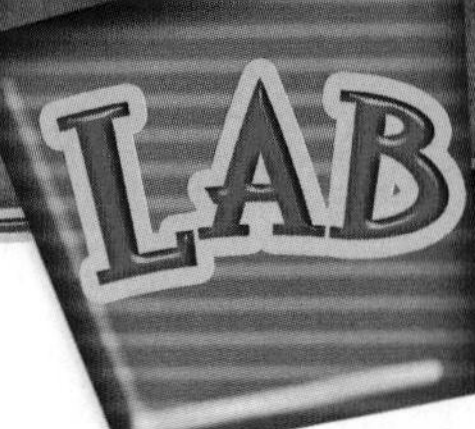

Design Your Own

Comparing Motion from Different Forces

Goals

- **Identify** several forces that you can use to propel a small toy car across the floor.
- **Demonstrate** the motion of the toy car using each of the forces.
- **Graph** the position versus time for each force.
- **Compare** the motion of the toy car resulting from each force.

Possible Materials

small toy car
ramps or boards of different lengths
springs or rubber bands
string
stopwatch
meterstick or tape measure
graph paper

Safety Precautions

Real-World Question

Think about a small ball. How many ways could you exert a force on the ball to make it move? You could throw it, kick it, roll it down a ramp, blow it with a large fan, etc. Do you think the distance and speed of the ball's motion will be the same for all of these forces? Do you think the acceleration of the ball would be the same for all of these types of forces?

Form a Hypothesis

Based on your reading and observations, state a hypothesis about how a force can be applied that will cause the toy car to go fastest.

Test Your Hypothesis

Make a Plan

1. As a group, agree upon the hypothesis and decide how you will test it. Identify which results will confirm the hypothesis that you have written.
2. **List** the steps you will need to test your hypothesis. Be sure to include a control run. Be specific. Describe exactly what you will do in each step. List your materials.
3. **Prepare** a data table in your Science Journal to record your observations.

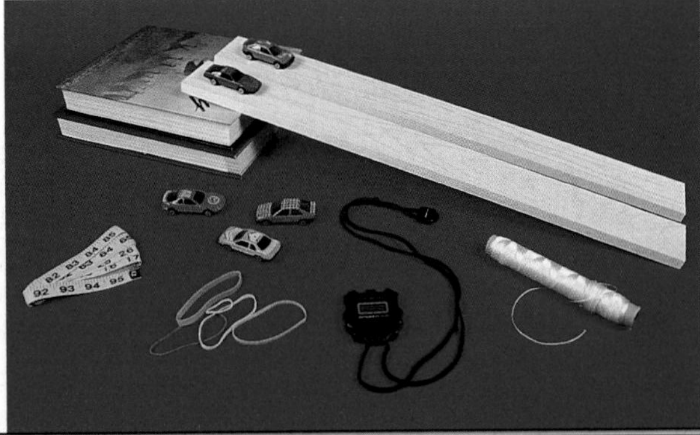

58 CHAPTER 2 Motion

Alternative Inquiry Lab

Real-World Connection To make this Lab an Inquiry Lab, give the students more personal investment into the problem by connecting it to the real world. Tell the students that they are designing a race track for a new type of car racing. They are to design a new race track that will allow stock cars to break speed records in racing. Students should consider safe but innovative ways to increase the speeds of the race cars. L2

Using Scientific Methods

4. **Read** the entire experiment to make sure all steps are in logical order and will lead to a useful conclusion.
5. **Identify** all constants, variables, and controls of the experiment. Keep in mind that you will need to have measurements at multiple points. These points are needed to graph your results. You should make sure to have several data points taken after you stop applying the force and before the car starts to slow down. It might be useful to have several students taking measurements, making each responsible for one or two points.

Follow Your Plan

1. Make sure your teacher approves your plan before you start.
2. Carry out the experiment as planned.
3. While doing the experiment, record your observations and complete the data tables in your Science Journal.

Analyze Your Data

1. **Graph** the position of the car versus time for each of the forces you applied. How can you use the graphs to compare the speeds of the toy car?
2. **Calculate** the speed of the toy car over the same time interval for each of the forces that you applied. How do the speeds compare?

Conclude and Apply

1. **Evaluate** Did the speed of the toy car vary depending upon the force applied to it?
2. **Determine** For any particular force, did the speed of the toy car change over time? If so, how did the speed change? Describe how you can use your graphs to answer these questions.
3. **Draw Conclusions** Did your results support your hypothesis? Why or why not?

Communicating Your Data

Compare your data with those of other students. **Discuss** how the forces you applied might be different from those others applied and how that affected your results.

Test Your Hypothesis

Possible Procedures Position students with stopwatches at points along a track to determine when the car reaches there. One student will provide the initial force to the car by releasing a spring against it, tugging it with a string, etc.

Teaching Strategy Encourage students to provide a sufficient force to enable the car to travel the entire length of the track they have made.

Expected Outcome Although results will vary greatly, students should be able to determine the average speed of the car for each force.

Analyze Your Data

Answers to Questions

1. Some graphs will show a slight increase in speed. Others will show a decrease in speed.
2. Students should calculate the average speed using $v = d/t$.

Error Analysis Ask students to compare their results with other groups and discuss ways the differences could be minimized.

Conclude and Apply

1. yes
2. Answers will vary.
3. Answers will depend on student hypotheses.

Assessment

Process Ask students to draw diagrams showing how friction, gravity, and inertia influenced the motion of the car. Use **Performance Assessment in the Science Classroom,** p. 127. L2

Communicating Your Data

Have students use graphics software to prepare a poster explaining their experiment and the results. Posters should contain sketches showing forces on the car. They might also include graphs of the data. L2

Understanding Literature

Descriptive Writing Angelou is telling us that the power that people have to make changes for better lives is more significant than the universe and the special places people have built on Earth.

Respond to the Reading

1. small, lonely, minuscule, kithless, wayward, floating
2. people
3. **Linking Science and Writing** Remind students that the Moon revolves around Earth. Therefore, their poems should describe how the Moon might see the Sun come and go as it moves around Earth.

Motion In the Middle Ages, most people thought Earth stood still and that the sky moved around Earth. It is now known that the daily movement of the stars is due to Earth's rotation on its axis. This can be proven by focusing a camera on the North Star and leaving the shutter open for several hours. At the same time that Earth rotates, it revolves about the Sun. Earth follows the Sun in its wanderings through the heavens. The Sun revolves around the center of the Milky Way. Earth, a satellite of the Sun, takes part in this journey.

Science and Language Arts

A Brave and Startling Truth

by Maya Angelou

We, this people, on a small and lonely planet
Traveling through casual space
Past aloof stars, across the way of indifferent suns
To a destination where all signs tell us
It is possible and imperative that we learn
A brave and startling truth …

When we come to it
Then we will confess that not the Pyramids
With their stones set in mysterious perfection …
Not the Grand Canyon
Kindled into delicious color
By Western sunsets
These are not the only wonders of the world …

When we come to it
We, this people, on this minuscule and kithless[1]
globe …
We this people on this mote[2] of matter

When we come to it
We, this people, on this wayward[3], floating body
Created on this earth, of this earth
Have the power to fashion for this earth
A climate where every man and every woman
Can live freely without sanctimonious piety[4]
Without crippling fear

When we come to it
We must confess that we
are the possible
We are the miraculous, the
true wonder of the world
That is when, and only
when
We come to it.

Understanding Literature

Descriptive Writing The poet names some special places on Earth. These places, although marvelous, fall short of being really wonderful. How does Angelou contrast Earth's position within the universe to emphasize the importance of people?

Respond to the Reading

1. What adjectives does the poet use to describe Earth?
2. What does the poet believe are the true wonders of the world?
3. **Linking Science and Writing** Write a six-line poem that describes Earth's movement from the point of view of the Moon.

Sometimes a person doesn't need to see movement to know that something has moved. Even though we don't necessarily see Earth's movement, we know Earth moves relative to a reference point such as the Sun. If the Sun is the reference point, Earth moves because the Sun appears to change its position in the sky. The poem describes Earth's movement from a reference point outside of Earth, somewhere in space.

1 to be without friends or neighbors
2 small particle
3 wanting one's own way in spite of the advice or wishes of another
4 a self-important show of being religious

60 CHAPTER 2 Motion

Resources for Teachers and Students

"On the Pulse of Morning" from *The Complete Collected Poems of Maya Angelou*, Maya Angelou, Random House, Inc., 1994

Space Travel, edited by Ben Bova with Anthony R. Lewis, Writer's Digest Books, 1997

Roller Coaster, by David Bennett, Chartwell Books, 1998

Reviewing Main Ideas

Section 1 Describing Motion

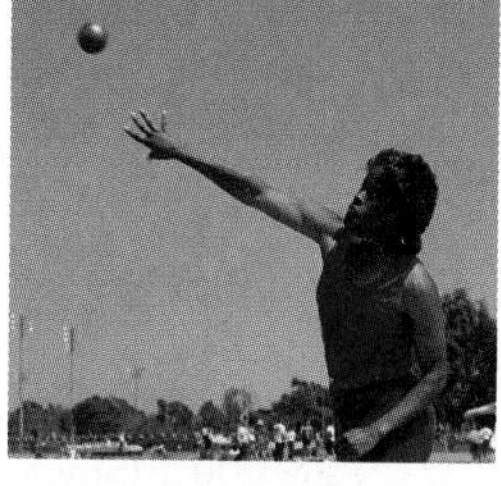

1. Motion is a change of position of a body. Distance is the measure of how far an object moved. Displacement is the distance and direction of an object's change in position from the starting point.
2. A reference point must be specified in order to determine an object's position.
3. The speed of an object can be calculated from this equation:

$$s = \frac{d}{t}$$

4. The slope of a line on a distance-time graph is equal to the speed.
5. Velocity describes the speed and direction of a moving object.

Section 2 Acceleration

1. Acceleration occurs when an object changes speed or changes direction.
2. An object speeds up if its acceleration is in the direction of its motion.
3. An object slows down if its acceleration is opposite to the direction of its motion.
4. Acceleration is the rate of change of velocity, and is calculated from this equation:

$$a = \frac{v_f - v_i}{t}$$

Section 3 Motion and Forces

1. A force is a push or a pull.
2. The net force acting on an object is the combination of all the forces acting on the object.
3. The forces on an object are balanced if the net force is zero.
4. Inertia is the resistance of an object to a change in motion.
5. According to Newton's first law of motion, the motion of an object does not change unless an unbalanced net force acts on the object.

FOLDABLES™ Use the Foldable that you made at the beginning of this chapter to help you review motion.

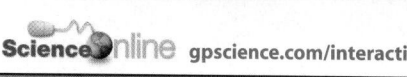

gpscience.com/interactive_tutor

Identifying Misconceptions

Assess

After students have done the activity on page F at the beginning of the chapter and completed the chapter, have them perform this activity.

Materials protractor, paper, ruler, string

Procedure Have each student use the protractor to draw a large circle and label four points 90 degrees apart A, B, C, and D. Have them place an object at point A, and tell them the object will travel around the circle. Their mission is to find the object's distance traveled and displacement at points B, C, and D.

Expected Outcome Use the string to measure the circle or use the formula for a perimeter of a circle. L2

chapter 2 Study Guide

Reviewing Main Ideas

Summary statements can be used by students to review the major concepts of the chapter.

Science Online

Visit gpscience.com
- /self_check_quiz
- /interactive_tutor
- /vocabulary_puzzlemaker
- /chapter_review
- /standardized_test

Assessment Transparency

For additional assessment questions, use the *Assessment Transparency* located in the transparency book.

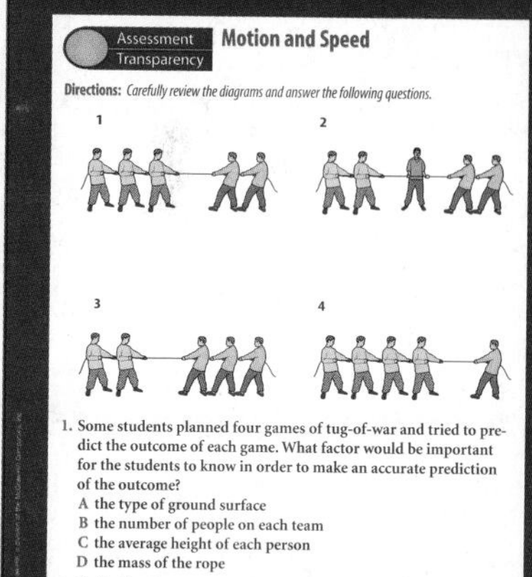

Assessment

Assessment Transparency **Motion and Speed**

Directions: *Carefully review the diagrams and answer the following questions.*

1 2

3 4

1. Some students planned four games of tug-of-war and tried to predict the outcome of each game. What factor would be important for the students to know in order to make an accurate prediction of the outcome?
   A the type of ground surface
   B the number of people on each team
   C the average height of each person
   D the mass of the rope
2. If all other factors are equal, which picture shows two teams that are the most equal?
   F 1 G 2 H 3 J 4
3. If all other factors are equal, which picture shows two teams that are the least equal?
   A 1 B 2 C 3 D 4

L2

Motion and Speed

FOLDABLES™ Have students use their Foldables to review the content of the chapter. On the back, have them write 5 facts that they have learned about motion.

chapter 2 Review

Using Vocabulary

1. Both tell how distance changes with time. Velocity includes the direction.
2. Displacement is distance and direction from a starting point. Distance is how far an object has moved.
3. Both describe rate of change in position. Average speed refers to total distance moved divided by total time elapsed. Instantaneous speed refers to speed at a given point in time.
4. Balanced forces are forces on an object that cancel each other out. Net force is the sum of all forces acting on an object.
5. Force is a push or a pull that one body exerts on another. Inertia is the tendency of an object to resist change in motion.
6. Velocity is the speed and direction of an object. Acceleration is how the velocity changes with time.
7. Velocity is the speed and direction of an object. Instantaneous speed is how fast an object moves at a given point in time.
8. Force is a push or a pull. Net force is the sum of all forces acting on an object.
9. Force is a push or a pull. Acceleration is the change in velocity of an object.

Checking Concepts

10. A
11. B
12. C
13. B
14. A
15. D
16. C

chapter 2 Review

Using Vocabulary

acceleration p. 47
average speed p. 42
balanced force p. 53
displacement p. 39
distance p. 39
force p. 52
inertia p. 54
instantaneous speed p. 42
net force p. 53
speed p. 39
velocity p. 44

Compare and contrast the following pairs of vocabulary words.

1. speed—velocity
2. distance—displacement
3. average speed—instantaneous speed
4. balanced force—net force
5. force—inertia
6. acceleration—velocity
7. velocity—instantaneous speed
8. force—net force
9. force—acceleration

Checking Concepts

Choose the word or phrase that best answers the question.

10. Which of the following do you calculate when you divide the total distance traveled by the total travel time?
    A) average speed
    B) constant speed
    C) variable speed
    D) instantaneous speed
11. Which term below best describes the forces on an object with a net force of zero?
    A) inertia
    B) balanced forces
    C) acceleration
    D) unbalanced forces
12. Which of the following is a proper unit of acceleration?
    A) s/km^2
    B) km/h
    C) m/s^2
    D) cm/s
13. Which of the following is not used in calculating acceleration?
    A) initial velocity
    B) average speed
    C) time interval
    D) final velocity
14. In which of the following conditions does the car NOT accelerate?
    A) A car moves at 80 km/h on a flat, straight highway.
    B) The car slows from 80 km/h to 35 km/h.
    C) The car turns a corner.
    D) The car speeds up from 35 km/h to 80 km/h.
15. What is the tendency for an object to resist any change in its motion called?
    A) net force
    B) acceleration
    C) balanced force
    D) inertia
16. How can speed be defined?
    A) acceleration/time
    B) change in velocity/time
    C) distance/time
    D) displacement/time

Interpreting Graphics

Use the table below to answer question 17.

Distance-Time for Runners

Time (s)	1	2	3	4
Sally's Distance (m)	2	4	6	8
Alonzo's Distance (m)	1	2	2	4

17. Make a distance-time graph that shows the motion of both runners. What is the average speed of each runner? Which runner stops briefly? Over what time interval do they both have the same speed?

gpscience.com/vocabulary_puzzlemaker

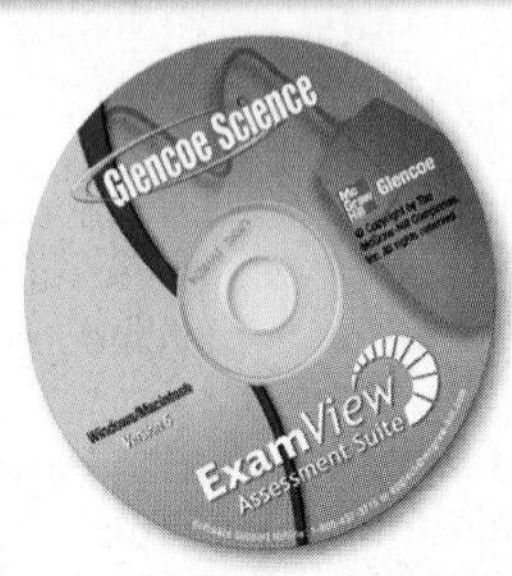

Use the *ExamView® Assessment Suite* CD-ROM to:

- create multiple versions of tests
- create modified tests with one mouse click for inclusion students
- edit existing questions and add your own questions
- build tests aligned with state standards using built-in State Curriculum Tags
- change English tests to Spanish with one mouse click and vice versa

18. Copy and complete this concept map on motion.

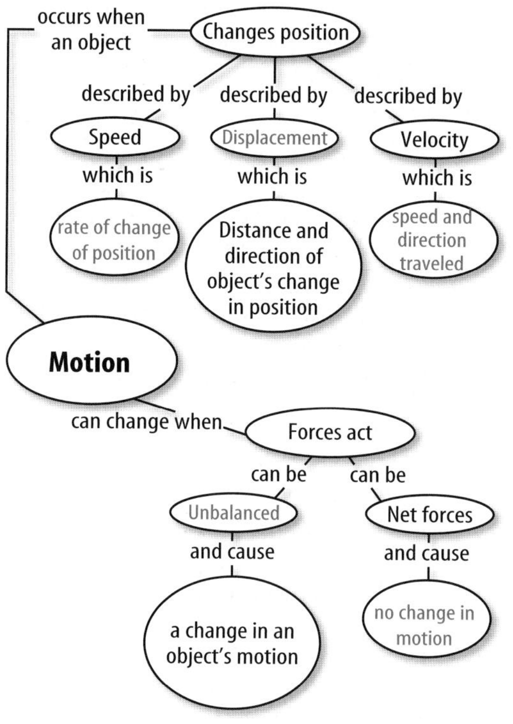

Thinking Critically

19. **Evaluate** Which of the following represents the greatest speed: 20 m/s, 200 cm/s, or 0.2 km/s?

20. **Recognize Cause and Effect** Acceleration can occur when a car is moving at constant speed. What must cause this acceleration?

21. **Explain** why a passenger who is not wearing a safety belt will likely hit the windshield in a head-on collision.

22. **Determine** If you walked 20 m, took a book from a library table, turned around and walked back to your seat, what are the distance traveled and displacement?

23. **Explain** When you are describing the rate that a race car goes around a track, should you use the term *speed* or *velocity* to describe the motion?

Applying Math

24. **Calculate Speed** A cyclist must travel 800 km. How many days will the trip take if the cyclist travels 8 h/day at an average speed of 16 km/h?

25. **Calculate Acceleration** A satellite's speed is 10,000 m/s. After 1 min, it is 5,000 m/s. What is the satellite's acceleration?

26. **Calculate Displacement** A cyclist leaves home and rides due east for a distance of 45 km. She returns home on the same bike path. If the entire trip takes 4 h, what is her average speed? What is her displacement?

27. **Calculate Velocity** The return trip of the cyclist in question 13 took 30 min longer than her trip east, although her total time was still 4 h. What was her velocity in each direction?

Use the graph below to answer question 28.

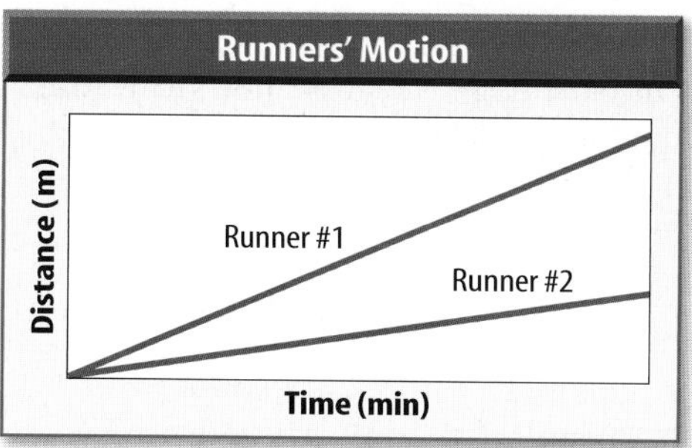

28. **Interpret a Graph** Use the graph to determine which runner had the greatest speed.

 gpscience.com/chapter_review

Assessment Resources

Reproducible Masters

Chapter *Fast File* Resources
Chapter Review, pp. 37–38
Chapter Tests, pp. 39–42
Assessment Transparency Activity, p. 49

Glencoe Science Web site
Chapter Review Test
Standardized Test Practice

Glencoe Technology
Assessment Transparency
ExamView® Assessment Suite
MindJogger Videoquiz
Interactive Chalkboard

chapter 2 Review

Interpreting Graphics

17. Sally's average speed is 2 m/s and Alonzo's is 1 m/s. Alonzo stops briefly; they run at the same speed from 3 s to 4 s.

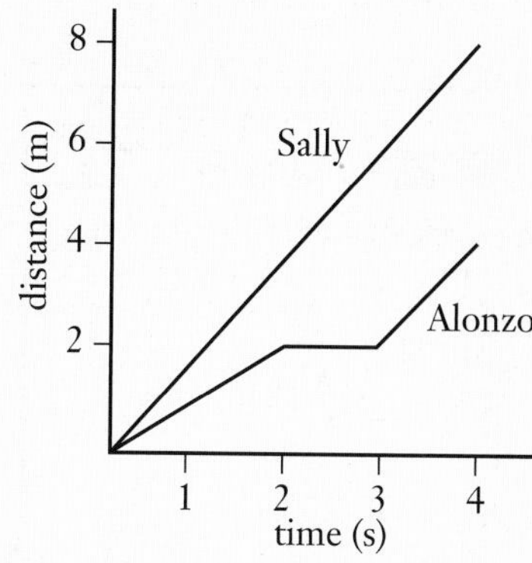

18. See student page.

Thinking Critically

19. 0.2 km/s
20. change in direction
21. The inertia of the unbelted passenger will cause the person to move forward.
22. distance traveled, 40 m; displacement, 0 m
23. speed, because the velocity is constantly changing due to the constant change of direction

Applying Math

National Math Standards

1, 2, 5, 6, 9

24. time = 800 km/16 km/h = 50 h; at 8 h/day, total time is 6 days 2 hours
25. about -83.3 m/s^2
26. 22.5 km/h; displacement is 0
27. Time there is 1.75 hours; time back is 2.25 hours; velocity there is 25.7 km/h; velocity back is -20 km/h.
28. Runner 1 because of the greater slope on the graph

FAST FILE

Answer Sheet A practice answer sheet can be found at gpscience.com/answer_sheet.

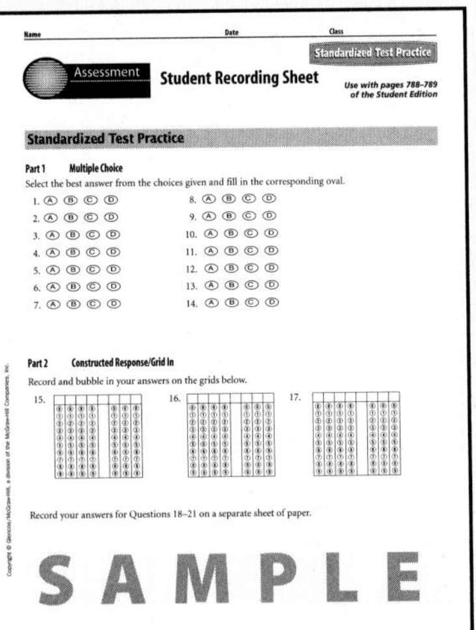
Name Date Class

Standardized Test Practice

Assessment Student Recording Sheet

Use with pages 788–789 of the Student Edition

Standardized Test Practice

Part 1 Multiple Choice

Select the best answer from the choices given and fill in the corresponding oval.

1. Ⓐ Ⓑ Ⓒ Ⓓ 8. Ⓐ Ⓑ Ⓒ Ⓓ
2. Ⓐ Ⓑ Ⓒ Ⓓ 9. Ⓐ Ⓑ Ⓒ Ⓓ
3. Ⓐ Ⓑ Ⓒ Ⓓ 10. Ⓐ Ⓑ Ⓒ Ⓓ
4. Ⓐ Ⓑ Ⓒ Ⓓ 11. Ⓐ Ⓑ Ⓒ Ⓓ
5. Ⓐ Ⓑ Ⓒ Ⓓ 12. Ⓐ Ⓑ Ⓒ Ⓓ
6. Ⓐ Ⓑ Ⓒ Ⓓ 13. Ⓐ Ⓑ Ⓒ Ⓓ
7. Ⓐ Ⓑ Ⓒ Ⓓ 14. Ⓐ Ⓑ Ⓒ Ⓓ

Part 2 Constructed Response/Grid In

Record and bubble in your answers on the grids below.

15. 16. 17.

Record your answers for Questions 18–21 on a separate sheet of paper.

SAMPLE

169

Part 1 Multiple Choice

1. B
2. C
3. C
4. B
5. B
6. C
7. A
8. A
9. C
10. A

Part 2 Short Response

11. Swimmer C is the fastest because the line representing her motion has the larger slope.
12. Swimmers B and C swam at constant speed because their motion is shown by straight lines. Swimmer A did not swim at a constant speed because between 10 and 20 minutes, her speed is zero.
13. You must also know the direction the storm is moving in order to plot its course. This allows you to predict where it will hit land and which people should evacuate.
14. The car could be accelerating if it is changing direction.
15. $-2.2\ m/s^2$

chapter 2 Standardized Test Practice

Part 1 Multiple Choice

Record your answers on the answer sheet provided by your teacher or on a sheet of paper.

1. Sound travels at a speed of 330 m/s. How long does it take for the sound of thunder to travel 1485 m?
   A. 45 s **C.** 4,900 s
   B. 4.5 s **D.** 0.22 s

Use the graph below to answer questions 2–4.

Speed Changing Over Distance

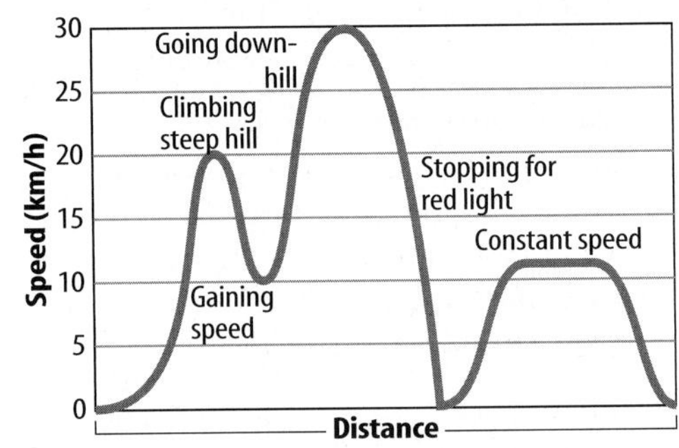

2. The graph shows how a cyclist's speed changed over distance of 5 km. What is the cyclist's average speed if the trip took 0.25 h?
   A. 2 km/h **C.** 20 km/h
   B. 30 km/h **D.** 8 km/h
3. Once the trip was started, how many times did the cyclist stop?
   A. 0 **C.** 2
   B. 4 **D.** 5
4. What was the fastest speed the cyclist traveled?
   A. 20 km/h **C.** 12 km/h
   B. 30 km/h **D.** 10 km/h

Test-Taking Tip

Read Carefully Read each question carefully for full understanding.

5. A skier is going down a hill at a speed of 9 km/s. The hill gets steeper and her speed increases to 18 m/s in 3 s. What is her acceleration?
   A. $9\ m/s^2$ **C.** $27\ m/s^2$
   B. $3\ m/s^2$ **D.** $6\ m/s^2$
6. Which of the following best describes an object with constant velocity?
   A. It is changing direction.
   B. Its acceleration is increasing.
   C. Its acceleration is zero.
   D. Its acceleration is negative.
7. Which of the following is a force?
   A. friction **C.** inertia
   B. acceleration **D.** velocity

Use the table below to answer questions 8 and 9.

Runner	Distance covered (km)	Time (min)
Daisy	12.5	42
Jane	7.8	38
Bill	10.5	32
Joe	8.9	30

8. What is Daisy's average speed?
   A. 0.29 km/min **C.** 2.9 km/min
   B. 530 km/min **D.** 3.4 km/min
9. Which runner has the fastest average speed?
   A. Daisy **C.** Bill
   B. Jane **D.** Joe
10. The movement of the Australian plate pushes Australia north at an average speed of about 17 cm per year. What will Australia's displacement be in meters in 1,000 years?
    A. 170 m north **C.** 1,700 m north
    B. 170 m south **D.** 1,700 m south

Part 3 Open Ended

16. You could speed up, slow down, or change direction.
17. If the object slows down and comes to a stop, its velocity is changing. According to the first law of motion, an unbalanced force must be acting on the object.
18. Possible answer: A box is at rest. You push on the box in one direction and someone else pushes with an equal force in the opposite direction.
19. plane speeds up: force exerted by engine is greater than air resistance, net force is in the forward direction; plane slows down: air resistance is greater than force exerted by engine, net force is in the backward direction

Part 2 Short Response/Grid In

Record your answers on the answer sheet provided by your teacher or on a sheet of paper.

Use the graph below to answer questions 11 and 12.

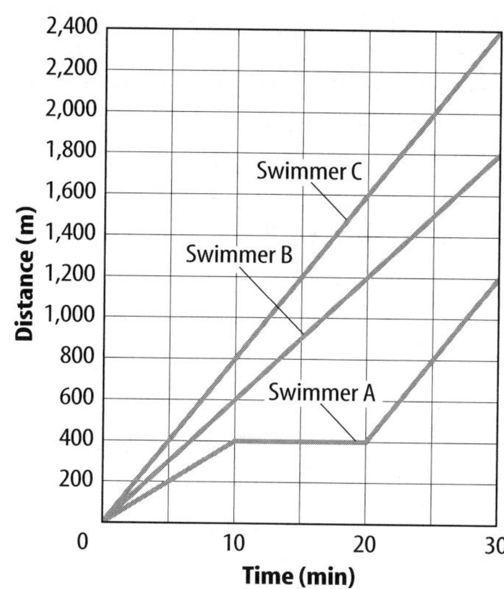

11. The graph shows the motion of three swimmers during a 30-min workout. Which swimmer had the highest average speed over the 30-min time interval?

12. Did all the swimmers swim at a constant speed? Explain how you know.

13. Why is knowing just the speed at which a hurricane is traveling toward land not enough information to be able to warn people to evacuate?

14. If the speedometer on a car indicates a constant speed, can you be sure the car is not accelerating? Explain.

15. If a car is traveling at a speed of 40 km/h and then comes to a stop in 5 s, what is its acceleration in m/s^2?

Part 3 Open Ended

Record your answers on a sheet of paper.

16. Describe three ways that your acceleration could change as you jog along a path through a park.

17. An object in motion slows down and comes to a stop. Use Newton's first law of motion to explain why this happens.

18. Give an example of a force applied to an object that does not change the object's velocity.

19. In an airplane flying at a constant speed, the force exerted by the engine pushing the airplane forward is equal to the opposite force of air resistance. Describe how these forces compare when the plane speeds up and slows down. In which direction is the net force on the airplane in each case?

20. Where would you place the location of a reference point in order to describe the motion of a space probe traveling from Earth to Jupiter? Explain your choice.

Use the table below to answer question 21.

Car	Mass (kg)	Stopping distance(m)
A	1000	80
B	1250	100
C	1500	120
D	2000	160

21. What is the relationship between a car's mass and its stopping distance? How can you explain this relationship?

22. Two cars approach each other. How does the speed of one car relative to the other compare with speed of the car relative to the ground?

20. Possible answer: at the Sun, because Earth and Jupiter move with respect to the Sun

21. The greater the mass of the car, the greater the stopping distance. The greater the mass of the car, the more inertia it has, and the harder it is to change its motion.

22. The speed of one car relative to the other is greater than the speed of that car relative to the ground.

Rubrics

The following rubrics are sample scoring devices for short response and open-ended questions.

Short Response

Points	Description
2	The student demonstrates a thorough understanding of the science of the task. The response may contain minor flaws that do not detract from the demonstration of a thorough understanding.
1	The student has provided a response that is only partially correct.
0	The student has provided a completely incorrect solution or no response at all.

Open Ended

Points	Description
4	The student demonstrates a thorough understanding of the science of the task. The response may contain minor flaws that do not detract from the demonstration of a thorough understanding.
3	The student demonstrates an understanding of the science of the task. The response is essentially correct and demonstrates an essential but less than thorough understanding of the science.
2	The student demonstrates only a partial understanding of the science of the task. Although the student may have used the correct approach to a solution or may have provided a correct solution, the work lacks an essential understanding of the underlying science concepts.
1	The student demonstrates a very limited understanding of the science of the task. The response is incomplete and exhibits many flaws.
0	The student provides a completely incorrect solution or no response at all.

chapter 3 Instructional Planner

Forces

BIG Idea Newton's laws of motion connect the change in an object's motion with the forces acting on it.

	Content Standards	Learning Objectives	Resources to Assess Mastery
Section 1	**5–8:** UCP.1–3, 5; A.1, 2; B.2 **9–12:** UCP.1–3, 5; A.1, 2; B.2, 4	**Newton's Second Law** 1. **Define** Newton's second law of motion. 2. **Apply** Newton's second law of motion. 3. **Describe** the three different types of friction. 4. **Observe** the effects of air resistance on falling objects. ***Main Idea*** The acceleration of an object equals the net force divided by the mass.	Formative Assessment Reading Check, pp. 70, 72 Section Review, p. 74 Summative Assessment *ExamView® Assessment Suite*
Section 2	**5–8:** UCP.1–3, 5; A.1, 2; B.2 **9–12:** UCP.1–3, 5; A.1, 2; B.4	**Gravity** 5. **Describe** the gravitational force. 6. **Distinguish** between mass and weight. 7. **Explain** why objects that are thrown will follow a curved path. 8. **Compare** circular motion with motion in a straight line. ***Main Idea*** Gravity is an attractive force that any two objects with mass exert on each other.	Formative Assessment Reading Check, p. 78 Section Review, p. 79 Summative Assessment *ExamView® Assessment Suite*
Section 3	**5–8:** UCP.1–3, 5; A.1, 2; B.2 **9–12:** UCP.1–3, 5; A.1, 2; B.4 See pp. 16T–17T for a Key to Standards.	**The Third Law of Motion** 9. **State** Newton's third law of motion. 10. **Identify** action and reaction forces. 11. **Calculate** momentum. 12. **Recognize** when momentum is conserved. ***Main Idea*** Forces between two objects are always exerted in pairs.	Formative Assessment Reading Check, p. 84 Section Review, p. 88 Summative Chapter Assessment MindJogger, Ch. 3 *ExamView® Assessment Suite* Leveled Chapter Test Test A L1 Test B L2 Test C L3 Test Practice, pp.96–97

Suggested Pacing				
Period	Instruction	Labs	Review & Assessment	Total
Single	3.5 days	2.5 days	2 days	8 days
Block	1.75 blocks	1.25 blocks	1 block	4 blocks

Core Instruction	Leveled Resources	Leveled Labs	Pacing Period		Block
Student Text, pp. 66–74 Section Focus Transparency, Ch. 3, Section 1 Interactive Chalkboard, Ch. 3, Section 1 Identifying Misconceptions, p. 70 Differentiated Instruction, pp. 71, 72 Applying Math, p. 69	**Chapter *Fast File* Resources** Directed Reading for Content Mastery, p. 20 L1 Note-taking Worksheet, pp. 33, 34 Reinforcement, p. 27 L2 Enrichment, p. 30 L3 **Reading Essentials,** p. 36 L1 ELL **Science Notebook,** p. 25 ELL ***Active*Folders**: *Newton's 2nd Law of Motion* L1 ELL	**Launch Lab,** p. 67: softball, meterstick, tennis ball, stopwatch, paper *10 min* L2 **MiniLAB,** p. 71: ice cube, rock, eraser, wood block, aluminum foil, metal or plastic tray, metric ruler *10 min* L2	1	Section 1, pp. 67–70 (includes Launch Lab)	1
			2	Section 2, pp. 70-74 (includes MiniLAB and Section Review)	
Student Text, pp. 75–82 Section Focus Transparency, Ch. 3, Section 2 Teaching Transparency, Ch. 3, Section 2 Interactive Chalkboard, Ch. 3, Section 2 Identifying Misconceptions, p. 77 Differentiated Instruction, pp. 76, 77, 80, 81	**Chapter *Fast File* Resources** Directed Reading for Content Mastery, p. 20 L1 Note-taking Worksheet, pp. 33, 34 Reinforcement, p. 28 L2 Enrichment, p. 31 L3 **Reading Essentials,** p. 42 L1 ELL **Science Notebook,** p. 29 ELL	**MiniLAB,** p. 81: string, plastic; slotted golf ball *15 min* L2	3	Section 2, pp. 75-80	2
			4	Section 2, pp. 81-82 (includes MiniLAB and Section Review)	
Student Text, pp. 83–91 Section Focus Transparency, Ch. 3, Section 3 Interactive Chalkboard, Ch. 3, Section 3 Visualizing Rocket Motion, p. 85 Differentiated Instruction, pp. 85, 86 Applying Math, p. 86 Chapter Study Guide, p. 93	**Chapter *Fast File* Resources** Directed Reading for Content Mastery, pp. 21, 22 L1 Note-taking Worksheet, pp. 33, 34 Reinforcement, p. 29 L2 Enrichment, p. 32 L3 **Reading Essentials,** p. 48 L1 ELL **Science Notebook,** p. 32 ELL ***Active*Folders**: *Newton's 3rd Law of Motion* L1 ELL	***Lab,** p. 89: paper (4 sheets), scissors, meterstick, stopwatch, masking tape *30 min* L1 L2 L3 ***Lab,** pp. 90–91: meterstick, softball, racquetball, tennis ball, baseball, stopwatch, masking tape, balance *45 min* L1 L2 L3 (Video Lab) *Lab version A L1 version B L2 L3	5	Section 3, pp. 83–88	3
			6	Lab: Measuring the Effects of Air Resistance, p. 89	
			7	Lab: The Momentum of Colliding Objects, pp. 90–91	4
			8	Study Guide, Chapter Review, and Test Practice, pp. 93–97	

(Video Lab icon) Video Lab

Transparencies

Section Focus

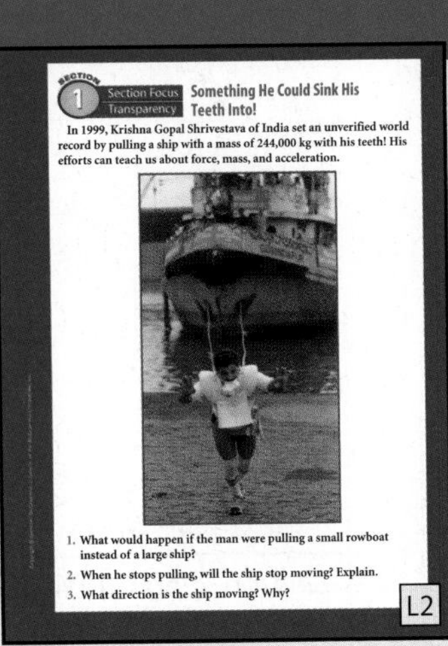
SECTION 1 Section Focus Transparency

Something He Could Sink His Teeth Into!

In 1999, Krishna Gopal Shrivestava of India set an unverified world record by pulling a ship with a mass of 244,000 kg with his teeth! His efforts can teach us about force, mass, and acceleration.

1. What would happen if the man were pulling a small rowboat instead of a large ship?
2. When he stops pulling, will the ship stop moving? Explain.
3. What direction is the ship moving? Why?

L2

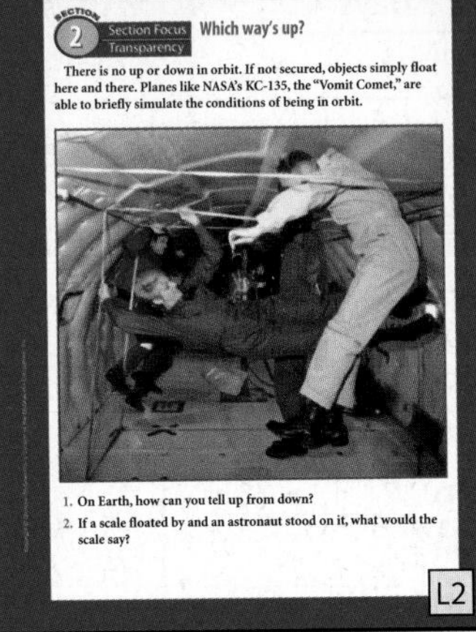
SECTION 2 Section Focus Transparency

Which way's up?

There is no up or down in orbit. If not secured, objects simply float here and there. Planes like NASA's KC-135, the "Vomit Comet," are able to briefly simulate the conditions of being in orbit.

1. On Earth, how can you tell up from down?
2. If a scale floated by and an astronaut stood on it, what would the scale say?

L2

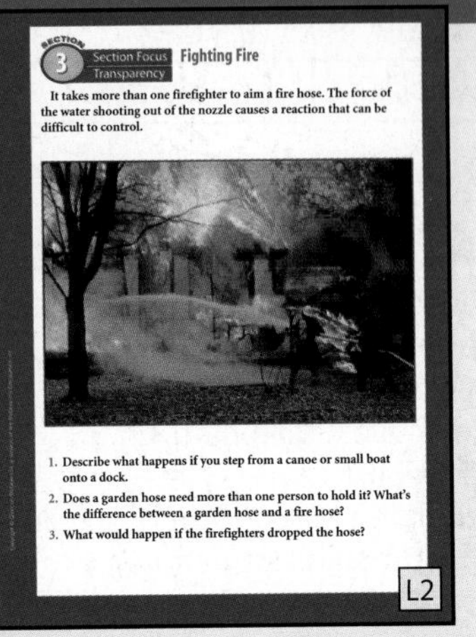
SECTION 3 Section Focus Transparency

Fighting Fire

It takes more than one firefighter to aim a fire hose. The force of the water shooting out of the nozzle causes a reaction that can be difficult to control.

1. Describe what happens if you step from a canoe or small boat onto a dock.
2. Does a garden hose need more than one person to hold it? What's the difference between a garden hose and a fire hose?
3. What would happen if the firefighters dropped the hose?

L2

This is a representation of key blackline masters available in the Teacher Classroom Resources. See Resource Manager boxes within the chapter for additional information.

Assessment

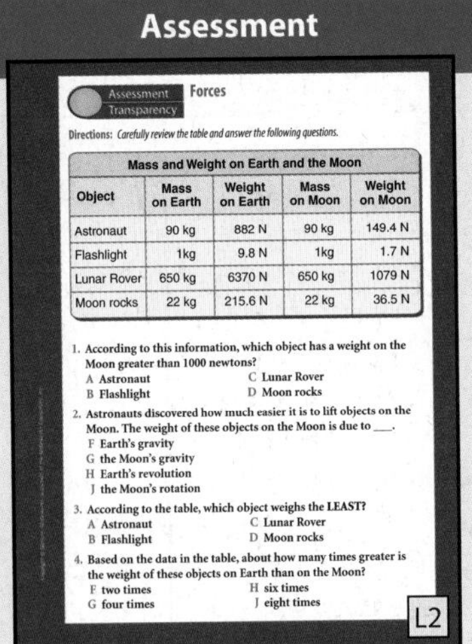
Assessment Transparency

Forces

Directions: Carefully review the table and answer the following questions.

Mass and Weight on Earth and the Moon				
Object	Mass on Earth	Weight on Earth	Mass on Moon	Weight on Moon
Astronaut	90 kg	882 N	90 kg	149.4 N
Flashlight	1kg	9.8 N	1kg	1.7 N
Lunar Rover	650 kg	6370 N	650 kg	1079 N
Moon rocks	22 kg	215.6 N	22 kg	36.5 N

1. According to this information, which object has a weight on the Moon greater than 1000 newtons?
   A Astronaut C Lunar Rover
   B Flashlight D Moon rocks
2. Astronauts discovered how much easier it is to lift objects on the Moon. The weight of these objects on the Moon is due to ___.
   F Earth's gravity
   G the Moon's gravity
   H Earth's revolution
   J the Moon's rotation
3. According to the table, which object weighs the LEAST?
   A Astronaut C Lunar Rover
   B Flashlight D Moon rocks
4. Based on the data in the table, about how many times greater is the weight of these objects on Earth than on the Moon?
   F two times H six times
   G four times J eight times

L2

Teaching

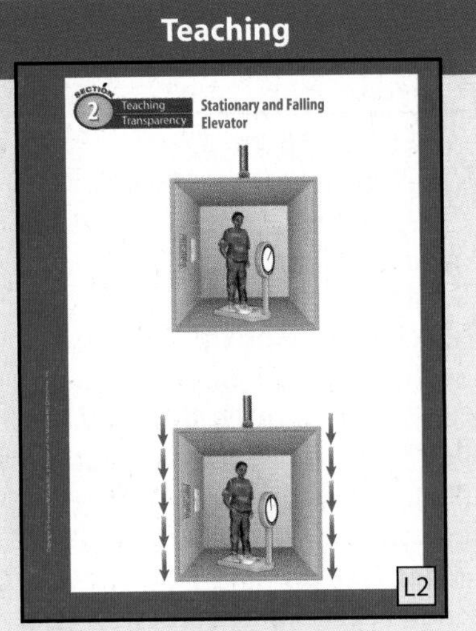
SECTION 2 Teaching Transparency

Stationary and Falling Elevator

L2

Key to Teaching Strategies

The following designations will help you decide which activities are appropriate for your students.

- L1 Level 1 activities should be appropriate for students with learning difficulties.
- L2 Level 2 activities should be within the ability range of all students.
- L3 Level 3 activities are designed for above-average students.
- ELL ELL activities should be within the ability range of English Language Learners.
- COOP LEARN Cooperative Learning activities are designed for small group work.
- LS Multiple Learning Styles logos, as described on page 12T, are used throughout to indicate strategies that address different learning styles.
- P These strategies represent student products that can be placed into a best-work portfolio.
- PBL Problem-Based Learning activities apply real-world situations to learning.

Hands-on Activities

Student Text Lab Worksheet

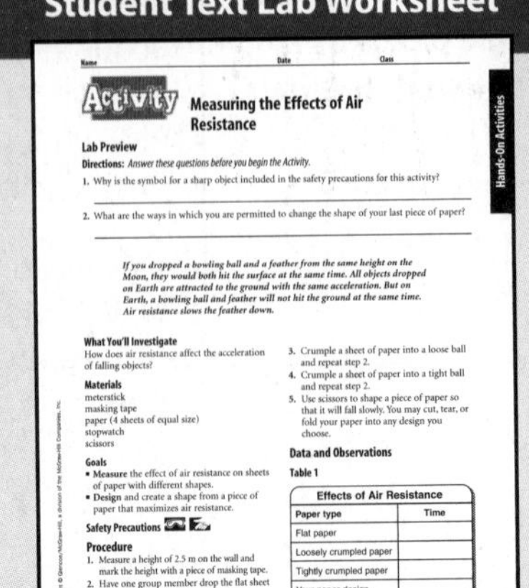
Name Date Class

Activity **Measuring the Effects of Air Resistance**

Hands-On Activities

Lab Preview

Directions: *Answer these questions before you begin the Activity.*

1. Why is the symbol for a sharp object included in the safety precautions for this activity?
2. What are the ways in which you are permitted to change the shape of your last piece of paper?

If you dropped a bowling ball and a feather from the same height on the Moon, they would both hit the surface at the same time. All objects dropped on Earth are attracted to the ground with the same acceleration. But on Earth, a bowling ball and feather will not hit the ground at the same time. Air resistance slows the feather down.

What You'll Investigate

How does air resistance affect the acceleration of falling objects?

Materials

meterstick
masking tape
paper (4 sheets of equal size)
stopwatch
scissors

Goals

- **Measure** the effect of air resistance on sheets of paper with different shapes.
- **Design** and create a shape from a piece of paper that maximizes air resistance.

Safety Precautions

Procedure

1. Measure a height of 2.5 m on the wall and mark the height with a piece of masking tape.
2. Have one group member drop the flat sheet of paper from the 2.5-m mark. Use the stopwatch to time how long it takes for the paper to reach the ground. Record your time in Table 1.
3. Crumple a sheet of paper into a loose ball and repeat step 2.
4. Crumple a sheet of paper into a tight ball and repeat step 2.
5. Use scissors to shape a piece of paper so that it will fall slowly. You may cut, tear, or fold your paper into any design you choose.

Data and Observations

Table 1

Effects of Air Resistance	
Paper type	Time
Flat paper	
Loosely crumpled paper	
Tightly crumpled paper	
Your paper design	

L2

Forces 5

Laboratory Activities

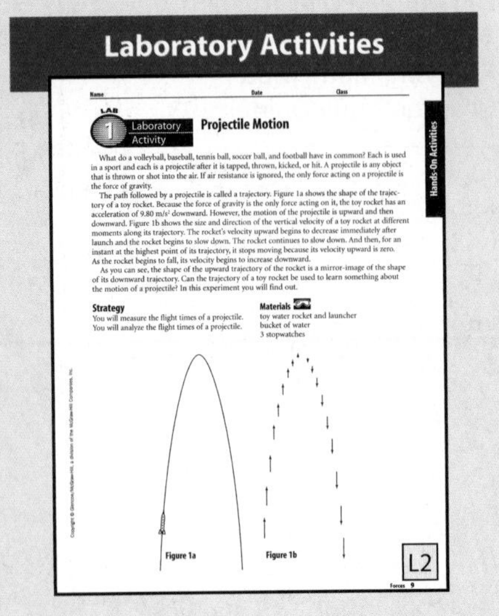
Name Date Class

LAB 1 Laboratory Activity **Projectile Motion**

Hands-On Activities

What do a volleyball, baseball, tennis ball, soccer ball, and football have in common? Each is used in a sport and each is a projectile after it is tapped, thrown, kicked, or hit. A projectile is any object that is thrown or shot into the air. If air resistance is ignored, the only force acting on a projectile is the force of gravity.

The path followed by a projectile is called a trajectory. Figure 1a shows the shape of the trajectory of a toy rocket. Because the force of gravity is the only force acting on it, the toy rocket has an acceleration of 9.80 m/s^2 downward. However, the motion of the projectile is upward and then downward. Figure 1b shows the size and direction of the vertical velocity of a toy rocket at different moments along its trajectory. The rocket's velocity upward begins to decrease immediately after launch and the rocket begins to slow down. The rocket continues to slow down. And then, for an instant at the highest point of its trajectory, it stops moving because its velocity upward is zero. As the rocket begins to fall, its velocity begins to increase downward.

As you can see, the shape of the upward trajectory of the rocket is a mirror-image of the shape of its downward trajectory. Can the trajectory of a toy rocket be used to learn something about the motion of a projectile? In this experiment you will find out.

Strategy

You will measure the flight times of a projectile.
You will analyze the flight times of a projectile.

Materials

toy water rocket and launcher
bucket of water
3 stopwatches

Figure 1a Figure 1b

L2

Forces 9

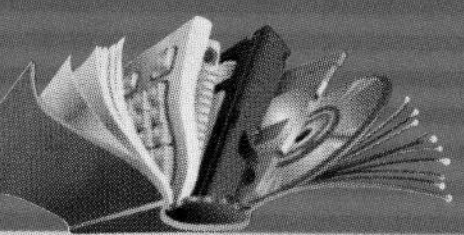

Meeting Different Ability Levels

Content Outline

Name Date Class

Note-taking Worksheet **Forces**

Section 1 Newton's Second Law

A. Force and motion are ________________.

1. An object will have greater ________________ if a greater force is applied to it.
2. The ________________ of an object and the force applied to it affect acceleration.

B. Newton's second law of motion connects force, mass, and acceleration in the equation *acceleration equals net force* ________________ *by mass*.

C. ________________—force that opposes motion between two surfaces that are touching each other

1. ________________, areas where surface bumpers stick together, are the source of friction.
2. Friction between two surfaces that are not moving past each other is called ________________ friction.
3. ________________ friction—force that opposes the motion of two surfaces sliding past each other
4. Friction between a rolling object and the surface it rolls on is called ________________ friction.

D. ________________ that opposes the force of gravity

1. The ________________ of air resistance depends on an object's shape, size, and speed.
2. ________________—forces on a falling object are balanced and the object falls with constant speed

Section 2 Gravity

A. Law of ________________—any two masses exert an attractive force on each other

1. ________________ is one of the four basic forces that also include the electromagnetic force, the strong nuclear force, and the weak nuclear force.
2. Gravity is a ________________ force that gives the universe its structure.

B. Due to ________________, all objects fall with the same acceleration regardless of mass.

Meeting Individual Needs

L2

Forces 33

Reinforcement

Name Date Class

SECTION 1 Reinforcement **Newton's Second Law**

Directions: *Use the equation F = m × a to solve the following problems. Show your calculations in the spaces provided.*

1. How much force is needed to accelerate a 1000-kg car at a rate of 3 m/s²?
2. If a 70-kg swimmer pushes off a pool wall with a force of 250 N, at what rate will the swimmer accelerate from the wall?
3. A weightlifter raises a 200-kg barbell with an acceleration of 3 m/s². How much force does the weightlifter use to raise the barbell?
4. A dancer lifts his partner above his head with an acceleration of 2.5 m/s². The dancer exerts a force of 200 N. What is the mass of the partner?

Directions: *Answer the following questions on the lines provided.*

5. What does Newton's second law of motion state?
6. What two factors affect the rate of acceleration of an object?
7. What are the three types of friction and when does each apply?

Meeting Individual Needs

L2

Forces 27

Enrichment

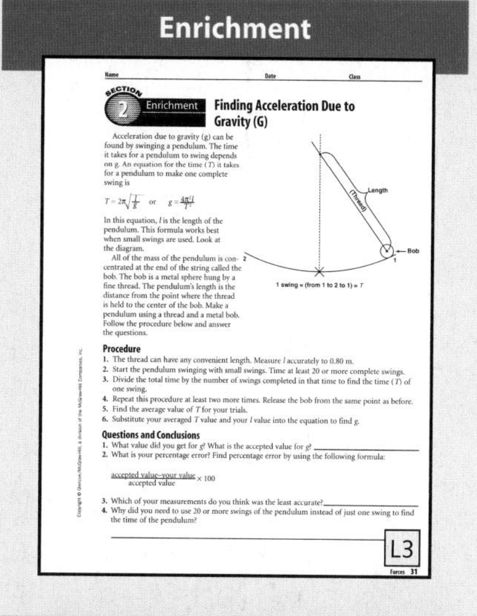

Name Date Class

SECTION 2 Enrichment **Finding Acceleration Due to Gravity (G)**

Acceleration due to gravity (g) can be found by swinging a pendulum. The time it takes for a pendulum to swing depends on g. An equation for the time (T) it takes for a pendulum to make one complete swing is

$T = 2\pi\sqrt{\frac{l}{g}}$ or $g = \frac{4\pi^2 l}{T^2}$

In this equation, l is the length of the pendulum. This formula works best when small swings are used. Look at the diagram.

All of the mass of the pendulum is concentrated at the end of the string called the bob. The bob is a metal sphere hung by a fine thread. The pendulum's length is the distance from the point where the thread is held to the center of the bob. Make a pendulum using a thread and a metal bob. Follow the procedure below and answer the questions.

Length
Thread
Bob
1 swing = (from 1 to 2 to 1) = T

Procedure

1. The thread can have any convenient length. Measure l accurately to 0.80 m.
2. Start the pendulum swinging with small swings. Time at least 20 or more complete swings.
3. Divide the total time by the number of swings completed in that time to find the time (T) of one swing.
4. Repeat this procedure at least two more times. Release the bob from the same point as before.
5. Find the average value of T for your trials.
6. Substitute your averaged T value and your l value into the equation to find g.

Questions and Conclusions

1. What value did you get for g? What is the accepted value for g?
2. What is your percentage error? Find percentage error by using the following formula:

$\frac{\text{accepted value} - \text{your value}}{\text{accepted value}} \times 100$

3. Which of your measurements do you think was the least accurate?
4. Why did you need to use 20 or more swings of the pendulum instead of just one swing to find the time of the pendulum?

L3

Forces 31

Directed Reading (English/Spanish)

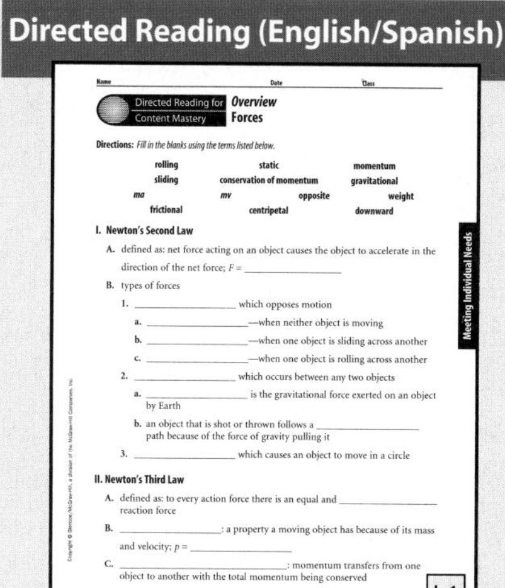

Name Date Class

Directed Reading for Content Mastery *Overview* **Forces**

Directions: *Fill in the blanks using the terms listed below.*

rolling	static	momentum
sliding	conservation of momentum	gravitational
ma	*mv*	opposite
weight	frictional	centripetal
downward		

I. Newton's Second Law

A. defined as: net force acting on an object causes the object to accelerate in the direction of the net force; F = ________________

B. types of forces

1. ________________ which opposes motion
   a. ________________—when neither object is moving
   b. ________________—when one object is sliding across another
   c. ________________—when one object is rolling across another
2. ________________ which occurs between any two objects
   a. ________________ is the gravitational force exerted on an object by Earth
   b. an object that is shot or thrown follows a ________________ path because of the force of gravity pulling it
3. ________________ which causes an object to move in a circle

II. Newton's Third Law

A. defined as: to every action force there is an equal and ________________ reaction force

B. ________________: a property a moving object has because of its mass and velocity; p = ________________

C. ________________: momentum transfers from one object to another with the total momentum being conserved

Meeting Individual Needs

L1

Forces 19

Study Guide

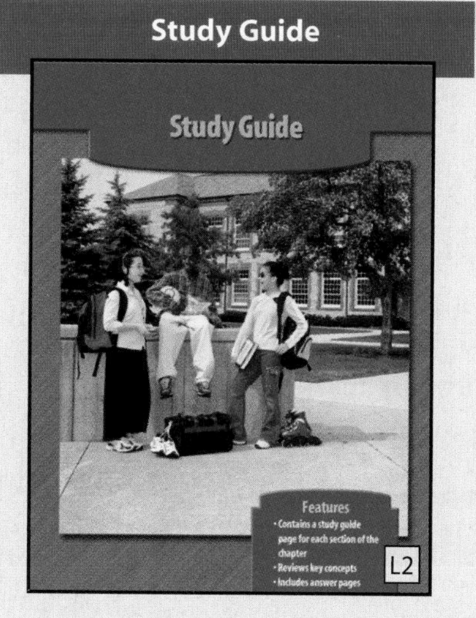

Study Guide
Features
• Contains a study guide page for each section of the chapter
• Reviews key concepts
• Includes answer pages
L2

Reading Essentials

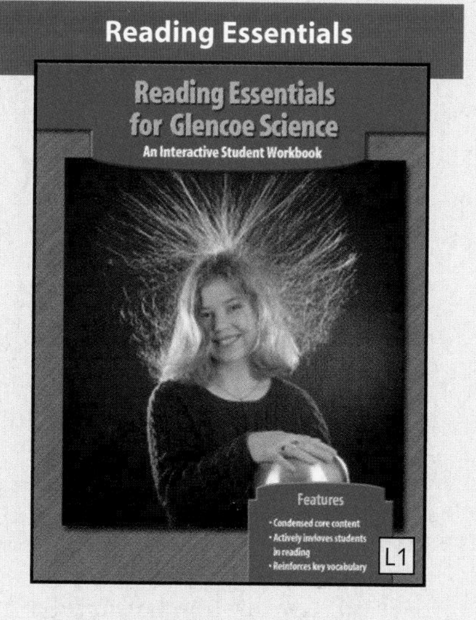

Reading Essentials for Glencoe Science
An Interactive Student Workbook
Features
• Condensed core content
• Actively involves students in reading
• Reinforces key vocabulary
L1

Assessment

Test Practice Workbook

Name: Date: Class:

Chapter Test *Chapter 3 Forces*

DIRECTIONS

Read each question and choose the best answer. Then fill in the correct answer on your answer document.

1 The firefighter feels the hose pushing backwards. What is the most likely cause of this?

A The hose material is very elastic.
B Since the hose is at rest, it tends to stay at rest.
C The force exerted on the water equals the mass of the water times its acceleration.
D The escaping water exerts an equal and opposite force on the hose.*

2 If the same force is applied to each of these balls, which one will have the LEAST acceleration?

F m = 1.0 kg
G m = 7.3 kg
H m = 0.75 kg
J m = 0.5 kg

Different Kinds of Friction

Weight of Object	No Friction: Ideal Force Needed to Push Up Ramp	Static Friction: Force Needed to Start Moving	Sliding Friction: Force Needed to Keep Moving	Rolling Friction: Force Needed to Keep Rolling
400 N	160 N	192 N	176 N	166 N
800 N	300 N	360 N	332 N	310 N
750 N	250 N	300 N	278 N	258 N

3 A ramp is 3 meters long and 1 meter high. Under ideal conditions, this ramp would reduce the force needed to raise an object by a factor of three. However, friction is a force that opposes motion between two surfaces that are touching. According to the chart, which kind of friction opposes motion with the greatest force?

A No friction
B Static friction*
C Sliding friction
D Rolling friction

GO ON

L2

16 Energy and Motion

Chapter Review

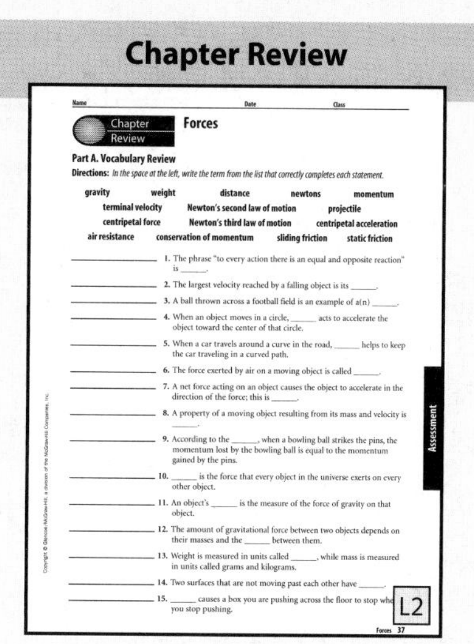

Name Date Class

Chapter Review **Forces**

Part A. Vocabulary Review

Directions: *In the space at the left, write the term from the list that correctly completes each statement.*

gravity, weight, distance, newtons, momentum, terminal velocity, Newton's second law of motion, projectile, centripetal force, Newton's third law of motion, centripetal acceleration, air resistance, conservation of momentum, sliding friction, static friction

1. The phrase "to every action there is an equal and opposite reaction" is ______.
2. The largest velocity reached by a falling object is its ______.
3. A ball thrown across a football field is an example of a(n) ______.
4. When an object moves in a circle, ______ acts to accelerate the object toward the center of that circle.
5. When a car travels around a curve in the road, ______ helps to keep the car traveling in a curved path.
6. The force exerted by air on a moving object is called ______.
7. A net force acting on an object causes the object to accelerate in the direction of the force; this is ______.
8. A property of a moving object resulting from its mass and velocity is ______.
9. According to the ______, when a bowling ball strikes the pins, the momentum lost by the bowling ball is equal to the momentum gained by the pins.
10. ______ is the force that every object in the universe exerts on every other object.
11. An object's ______ is the measure of the force of gravity on that object.
12. The amount of gravitational force between two objects depends on their masses and the ______ between them.
13. Weight is measured in units called ______, while mass is measured in units called grams and kilograms.
14. Two surfaces that are not moving past each other have ______.
15. ______ causes a box you are pushing across the floor to stop when you stop pushing.

Assessment

L2

Forces 37

Chapter Tests

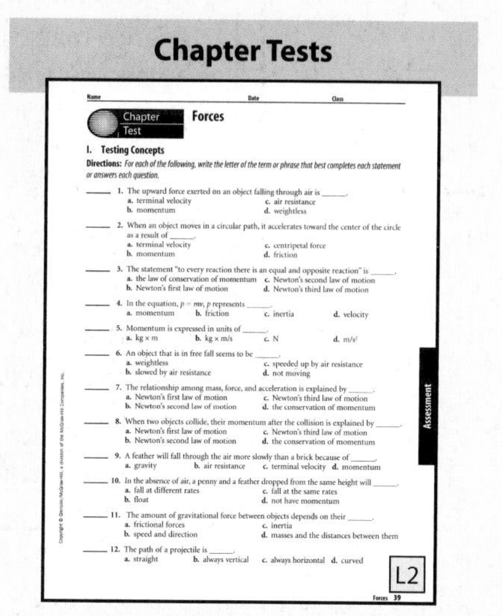

Name Date Class

Chapter Test **Forces**

I. Testing Concepts

Directions: *For each of the following, write the letter of the term or phrase that best completes each statement or answers each question.*

1. The upward force exerted on an object falling through air is ______.
   a. terminal velocity c. air resistance
   b. momentum d. weightless
2. When an object moves in a circular path, it accelerates toward the center of the circle as a result of ______.
   a. terminal velocity c. centripetal force
   b. momentum d. friction
3. The statement "to every reaction there is an equal and opposite reaction" is ______.
   a. the law of conservation of momentum c. Newton's second law of motion
   b. Newton's first law of motion d. Newton's third law of motion
4. In the equation, p = mv, p represents ______.
   a. momentum b. friction c. inertia d. velocity
5. Momentum is expressed in units of ______.
   a. kg × m b. kg × m/s c. N d. m/s²
6. An object that is in free fall seems to be ______.
   a. weightless c. speeded up by air resistance
   b. slowed by air resistance d. not moving
7. The relationship among mass, force, and acceleration is explained by ______.
   a. Newton's first law of motion c. Newton's third law of motion
   b. Newton's second law of motion d. the conservation of momentum
8. When two objects collide, their momentum after the collision is explained by ______.
   a. Newton's first law of motion c. Newton's third law of motion
   b. Newton's second law of motion d. the conservation of momentum
9. A feather will fall through the air more slowly than a brick because of ______.
   a. gravity b. air resistance c. terminal velocity d. momentum
10. In the absence of air, a penny and a feather dropped from the same height will ______.
    a. fall at different rates c. fall at the same rates
    b. float d. not have momentum
11. The amount of gravitational force between objects depends on their ______.
    a. frictional forces c. inertia
    b. speed and direction d. masses and the distances between them
12. The path of a projectile is ______.
    a. straight b. always vertical c. always horizontal d. curved

Assessment

L2

Forces 39

Science Content Background

section 1 Newton's Second Law

Force, Mass, and Acceleration

Dynamics is the study of motion produced by forces. It comes from the Greek word *dynamis*, which means "strength or power." Words such as *dynamite* and *dynamo* share these origins.

Newton's Second Law

It follows from this law that if an object is accelerating, there must be force acting on it. Engines produce forces to make cars positively accelerate. The brakes produce forces to cause negative acceleration. A planet moving with constant speed around a star is constantly changing direction and therefore is accelerating toward the star. This acceleration is due to the force of gravity between the star and the planet.

A force of one Newton is equal to one kilogram meter per second squared ($1N = 1$ kg m/s^2). Thus, when dividing force by mass the kg units cancel leaving the acceleration units of m/s^2.

chapter content resources

Internet Resources

For additional content background, visit gpscience.com to:

- access your book online
- find references to related articles in popular science magazines
- access Web links with related content background
- access current events with science journal topics

Print Resources

Forces and Motion by Peter Lafferty, Raintree Steck-Vaughn Publishers, 2001

Science Projects About the Physics of Sports by Robert Gardner, Enslow Publishers, Inc., 2000

Gravity The Universal Force by Don Nardo, Lucent Books, 1990

Awesome Experiments in Force & Motion by Michael DiSpezio, Sterling Publishing Co., 1998

Air Resistance

When people jump out of high-altitude airplanes they don't keep accelerating. The faster they fall the greater the air resistance acting on them, so their acceleration decreases as they fall. Eventually a sky diver stops accelerating and achieves a constant velocity called the terminal velocity. For humans, terminal velocity is about 53 m/s or 190 km/h. It's a good thing their velocity slows to only 5 to 10 m/s after the parachute opens!

section 2 Gravity

The Law of Gravitation

Newton described the gravitational force between two objects and the distance between them with the following equation: force of gravity = $G \times (\text{mass}_1) \times (\text{mass}_2)/(\text{distance between them})^2$. G is the universal gravitational constant. If the mass of one of the objects quadruples, the force of gravity quadruples. If the distance between the objects quadruples, the force of gravity is reduced by one-sixteenth.

Gravitational Acceleration

The average acceleration due to gravity on Earth is 9.8 m/s^2. This value varies slightly with location. In general the greater the distance from Earth's center, the lower the value, which means gravitational acceleration is smaller on a mountain than in a valley. The acceleration at the equator tends to be less than at the poles. This is because Earth is not a perfect sphere; its poles are somewhat pushed together. The acceleration due to gravity on Mercury is 3.8 m/s^2, while on Jupiter it is 22.9 m/s^2.

Newton's second law can be used to explain why all objects, regardless of mass, fall with the same acceleration due to gravity. Objects with a large mass do have a greater gravitational force acting on them. However, although the force is greater, so is the mass. These offset each other, causing all objects to fall with the same acceleration.

Centripetal Force

An object in circular motion is sometimes said to be experiencing centrifugal force, which really doesn't exist. If you swing a bucket of water on a string, the water seems to be pushed outward, but this is due to the water's inertia. It tends to move in straight-line motion while the bucket is pulled in by the centripetal force of the string. This causes the water to remain at the bottom of the bucket.

The Third Law of Motion

Newton's Third Law

The recoil of a rifle is an interesting application of Newton's laws. When fired, the rifle "kicks back" into the shoulder of the shooter. If the rifle hurts the shoulder, should the shooter use a more massive or a less massive gun? If the guns are firing the same bullets with the same acceleration, the more massive gun will give less kickback. The recoil force will be the same, but the more massive gun will not accelerate as much $(a = F/m)$.

David Young-Wolff/PhotoEdit

Teacher to Teacher

Sarah Vandermeer
St. Charles High School
Columbus, Ohio

"I have one of the smaller and one of the larger students in the class each take a 100-N spring scale. We hook the two scales together, and each student pulls as hard as possible. A third student reads each of the scales and, sure enough, they have the same reading. This is true even if the stronger student causes the smaller one to slide along the floor. You can also get two bathroom scales and place them bottom to bottom between the two students. When they push on the scales against each other, the two scales show the same force."

Sarah Vandermeer

Finding Planets with Newton's Laws

Newton's third law is now being used to find planets in other solar systems. The planets are not directly seen, but their presence is inferred from the behavior of the star in that solar system. More than fifty planets in other solar systems have been found in this way.

Momentum

To hit a home run, a softball player must impart the maximum momentum from his or her body and the bat to the ball. To do this each player must find the bat that gives him or her the best combination of mass and speed. A heavier bat has more mass but the player may not be able to swing it as fast as a lighter bat.

A force applied over time, also called an impulse, can change momentum. The formula describing this relationship is $F \times t = m\ \Delta v$. In softball, following through on a swing can increase the amount of time the bat stays in contact with the ball, and this causes a greater velocity gain by the ball.

About the Photo

Deceleration A person who is properly restrained by an over-the-shoulder seat belt can undergo an acceleration as large as 30 g's (30 times the acceleration of gravity) and still survive in a car accident. The front end of a car going 34 km/h (about 55 mph) would need to collapse over a distance of 1 m for the person to survive.

Science Journal A car with a front that crumples in a crash is safer. It provides a longer distance and a longer time over which a car can decelerate.

BIG Idea

Forces and Changes in Motion According to Newton's first law of motion, the motion of an object changes only when unbalanced forces act on the object. The second law of motion, $a = F_{net}/m$, can be considered an elaboration of the first law. The forces on an object are unbalanced when the net force is not zero. Then, according to the second law, the object has a non-zero acceleration. When an object is accelerating, its velocity is changing. So the second law implies that the motion of an object changes when the forces acting on it are unbalanced.

Introduce the Chapter Give students a small block of wood. Have students give the block a small push and then describe the block's motion. Ask students why the block slows down and stops. Explain to students that friction is a force acting on the block as it slides. Ask students how they could make the block slide farther with the same applied force. Discuss with students how the block would move if there were no friction.

chapter 3

Forces

BIG Idea Newton's laws of motion connect the change in an object's motion with the forces acting on it.

3.1 Newton's Second Law

MAIN Idea The acceleration of an object equals the net force divided by the mass.

3.2 Gravity

MAIN Idea Gravity is an attractive force that any two objects with mass exert on each other.

3.3 The Third Law of Motion

MAIN Idea Forces between two objects are always exerted in pairs.

Who's a dummy?

Crunch! This test dummy would have some explaining to do if this were a traffic accident. But in a test crash, the dummy plays an important role. The forces acting on it during a crash are measured and analyzed in order to learn how to make cars safer.

Science Journal

Predict which would be safer in a head-on crash—a car with a front that crumples, or one with a front that doesn't crumple.

66

Interactive Chalkboard

This CD-ROM is an editable Microsoft® PowerPoint® presentation that includes:

- an editable presentation for every chapter
- additional chapter questions
- animated graphics
- image bank
- links to gpscience.com

Start-Up Activities

The Force of Gravity

The force of Earth's gravity pulls all objects downward. However, objects such as rocks seem to fall faster than feathers or leaves. Do objects with more mass fall faster?

1. Measure the mass of a softball, a tennis ball, and a flat sheet of paper. Copy the data table below and record the masses.
2. Drop the softball from a height of 2.5 m and use a stopwatch to measure the time it takes for the softball to hit the floor. Record the time in your data table.
3. Repeat step 2 using the tennis ball and the flat sheet of paper. Record the times in your data table.
4. Crumple the flat sheet of paper into a ball, and measure the time for the crumpled paper to fall 2.5 m. Record the time in your data table.
5. **Think Critically** Write a paragraph comparing the times it took each item to fall 2.5 m. From your data, infer if the speed of a falling object depends on the object's mass.

Falling Object Data		
Object	Mass	Time
Softball		
Tennis ball		
Flat paper		
Crumpled paper		

The Force of Friction One of the forces you encounter every day is friction. Make the following Foldable to help you compare the three types of friction—static friction, sliding friction, and rolling friction.

STEP 1 **Fold** the top of a vertical piece of paper down and the bottom up to divide the paper into thirds.

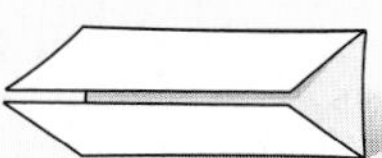

STEP 2 **Unfold and label** the rows *Static Friction, Sliding Friction,* and *Rolling Friction.*

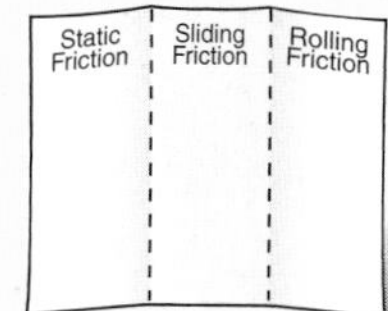

Read and Write As you read, write the definition and give examples of each type of friction.

Preview this chapter's content and activities at gpscience.com

Additional Chapter Media

- What's Science Got to Do With It?: *See Through Science*
- BrainPOP *Newton's Laws of Motion*
- Virtual Lab: *How is momentum conserved in a vehicle collision?*
- Video Lab: *The Momentum of Colliding Objects*

Purpose Use the Launch Lab to introduce students to the seemingly paradoxical phenomenon that, neglecting air resistance, objects with different masses fall with the same velocities. L2 **Visual-Spatial**

Preparation Find a suitable location, such as a stairwell, from which students can drop the balls. Measure a distance of 3 m above the floor, and mark the height with a piece of tape.

Materials softball, meterstick, tennis ball, paper, stopwatch

Teaching Strategy Have students do this lab in pairs so one student can drop the balls while the other observes and determines which object hit the ground first.

Think Critically

Although they differ in mass, the softball, tennis ball, and crumpled paper ball will fall at nearly the same velocity. Air resistance prevents the flat paper from falling with the same velocity as the crumpled paper ball.

Assessment

Process Have students make bar graphs of the data they obtained in this activity. Use **Performance Assessment in the Science Classroom,** p. 111.

Dinah Zike Study Fold

Student preparation materials for this Foldable are available in the Chapter *Fast File* Resources.

Section 1 Newton's Second Law

1 Motivate

Bellringer

Section Focus Transparencies also are available on the Interactive Chalkboard CD-ROM.

L2 ELL

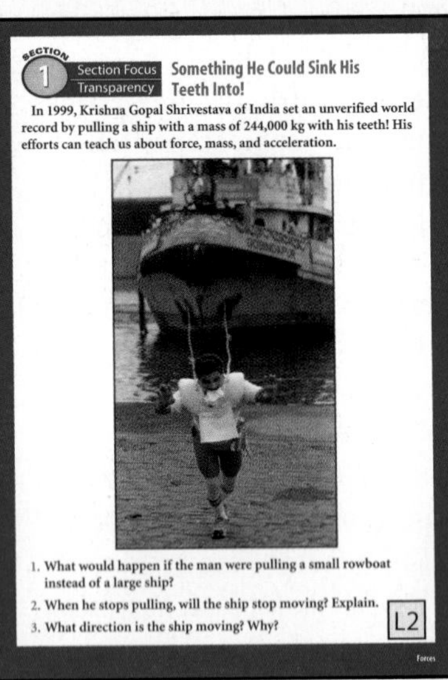

SECTION 1 Section Focus Transparency **Something He Could Sink His Teeth Into!**

In 1999, Krishna Gopal Shrivestava of India set an unverified world record by pulling a ship with a mass of 244,000 kg with his teeth! His efforts can teach us about force, mass, and acceleration.

1. What would happen if the man were pulling a small rowboat instead of a large ship?
2. When he stops pulling, will the ship stop moving? Explain.
3. What direction is the ship moving? Why?

L2

Forces

Text Question Answer

The ball thrown harder has a faster initial speed.

Tie to Prior Knowledge

Movement Ask students what they do when they have heavy objects they need to move. In this section they will learn how the mass of an object affects how fast they can move it, and why some objects keep moving while others stop.

Reading Guide

What You'll Learn

- **Define** Newton's second law of motion.
- **Apply** Newton's second law of motion.
- **Describe** the three different types of friction.
- **Observe** the effects of air resistance on falling objects.

Why It's Important

Newton's second law explains how forces cause the motion of objects to change.

Review Vocabulary

net force: the combination of all forces acting on an object

New Vocabulary

- Newton's second law of motion
- friction
- static friction
- sliding friction
- air resistance

Force, Mass, and Acceleration

The previous chapter discussed Newton's first law of motion which states that the motion of an object changes only if an unbalanced force acts on the object. Newton's second law of motion describes how the forces exerted on an object, like the volleyball in **Figure 1,** its mass, and its acceleration are related.

Force and Acceleration What's different about throwing a ball horizontally as hard as you can and tossing it gently? When you throw hard, you exert a much greater force on the ball. The ball has a greater velocity when it leaves your hand than it does when you throw gently. Thus, the hard-thrown ball has a greater change in velocity, and the change occurs over a shorter period of time. Recall that acceleration is the change in velocity divided by the time it takes for the change to occur. So, a hard-thrown ball has a greater acceleration than a gently thrown ball.

Mass and Acceleration If you throw a softball and a baseball as hard as you can, why don't they have the same speed? The difference is due to their masses. A softball has a mass of about 0.20 kg, but a baseball's mass is about 0.14 kg. The softball has less velocity after it leaves your hand than the baseball does, even though you exerted the same force. If it takes the same amount of time to throw both balls, the softball would have less acceleration. The acceleration of an object depends on its mass as well as the force exerted on it. Force, mass, and acceleration are related.

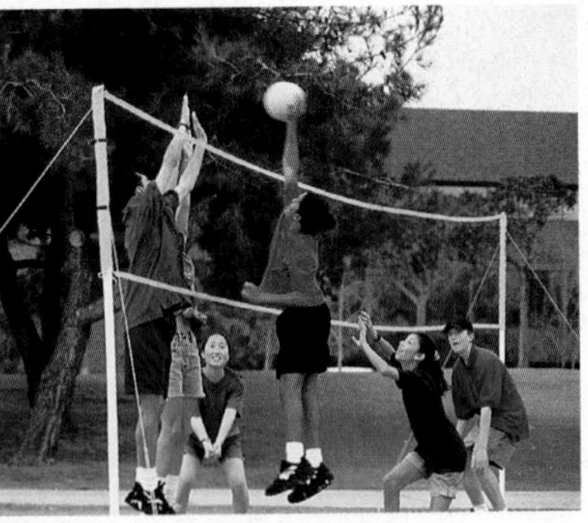

Figure 1 A volleyball's motion changes when an unbalanced force acts on it.

Section 1 Resource Manager

Chapter *FAST FILE* Resources

Transparency Activity, p. 44

Note-taking Worksheets, pp. 33–34

MiniLAB, p. 3

Enrichment, p. 30

Reinforcement, p. 27

Directed Reading for Content Mastery, pp. 19, 20

Lab Activity, pp. 9–12

Reading and Writing Skill Activities, p. 35

Newton's Second Law

According to **Newton's second law of motion,** the acceleration of an object is in the same direction as the net force on the object, and the acceleration can be calculated from the following equation:

The Second Law of Motion Equation

$$\text{acceleration (in meters/second}^2) = \frac{\text{net force (in newtons)}}{\text{mass (in kilograms)}}$$

$$a = \frac{F_{net}}{m}$$

In the above equation, acceleration has units of meters per second squared (m/s^2) and mass has units of kilograms (kg). Just like velocity and acceleration, force has a size and a direction. In SI units, the size of a force is measured in newtons (N). It takes a force of about 3 N to lift a full can of soft drink.

Topic: Motion in Sports
Visit gpscience.com for Web links to information about methods used to analyze the motions of athletes.

Activity Choose a sport and write a report on how analyzing the motions involved in the sport can improve performance and reduce injuries.

SECOND LAW OF MOTION EQUATION

Solve for Acceleration You push a wagon that has a mass of 8kg. If the net force on the wagon is 4 N, what is the wagon's acceleration?

1. **This is what you know:** mass: $m = 8$ kg; net force: $F_{net} = 4$ N
2. **This is what you need to find:** acceleration: a
3. **Use this formula:** $a = \frac{F_{net}}{m}$
4. **Substitute:** the values of m and F_{net} into the formula and divide. $a = \frac{4\text{N}}{8\text{ kg}} = 0.5$
5. **Determine the units:** units of $a = \frac{\text{units of } F_{net}}{\text{units of } m} = \frac{\text{N}}{\text{kg}} = \text{m/s}^2$

Answer: The wagon's acceleration is 0.5 m/s^2.

Practice Problems

1. If the mass of a helicopter is 4,500 kg, and the net force on it is 18,000 N, what is the helicopter's acceleration?
2. What is the net force on a dragster with a mass of 900 kg if its acceleration is 32.0 m/s^2?
3. A car pulled by a tow truck has an acceleration of 2.0 m/s^2. What is the mass of the car if the net force on the car is 3,000 N?
4. **Challenge** What is the net force on skydiver falling with a constant velocity of 10 m/s downward?

Science Online
For more practice problems, go to page 834, and visit gpscience.com/extra_problems.

Teacher FYI

Exceptions to Newton's Second Law Newton's second law fails for particles moving close to the speed of light. At these speeds, a particle's mass increases significantly as velocity increases. This effect is important in particle accelerators. Newton's second law also does not apply in areas of extremely high gravity.

2 Teach

Discussion

Mass and Acceleration Ask students whether they have ever used a "medicine ball." This heavier-than-normal ball is often used during training to build muscle strength and coordination. In order to give the medicine ball the same acceleration as a basketball, how must the force you use when throwing the ball be different? You must use a greater force because the mass of the medicine ball is greater. L2 LS **Logical-Mathematical**

Quick Demo

Newton's Second Law

Materials flexible plastic ruler, table tennis ball, golf ball, flat surface

Estimated Time five minutes

Procedure Place a flexed ruler next to a golf ball and release the ruler. Observe the motion of the ball, and measure the distance it travels. Repeat using a table tennis ball. Be sure to keep the launch force constant by bending the ruler back the same amount each time.

L2  LS **Visual-Spatial**

SECOND LAW EQUATION

National Math Standards

Correlation to Mathematics Objectives

1, 2, 9

Answers to Practice Problems

1. 4.0 m/s^2
2. 28,800 N
3. 1,500 kg
4. If the velocity is constant, the acceleration is zero. Then by the second law, the net force must be zero.

IDENTIFYING Misconceptions

Effect of Surface Area on Friction Friction is nearly independent of the surface area in contact. Friction depends on the microscopic contact areas on the microscopic welds that form when the surfaces are pushed together. If the macroscopic contact area increases, more welds are formed. However, because pressure equals force divided by area, the pressure pushing the surfaces together decreases. This causes the contact area on each weld to become smaller such that the total microscopic contact area remains nearly unchanged.

Text Question Answer

The skateboard moves in a straight line and slows down until it stops.

Reading Check

Answer kinds of surfaces and force pressing them together

Make a Model

Rough Surfaces Students can use modeling clay to show how two surfaces that appear to be smooth and in complete contact are, in fact, microscopically rough. The models should show the bumps and dips on the surfaces and how the surfaces touch only at the bumps. L2 LS **Kinesthetic**

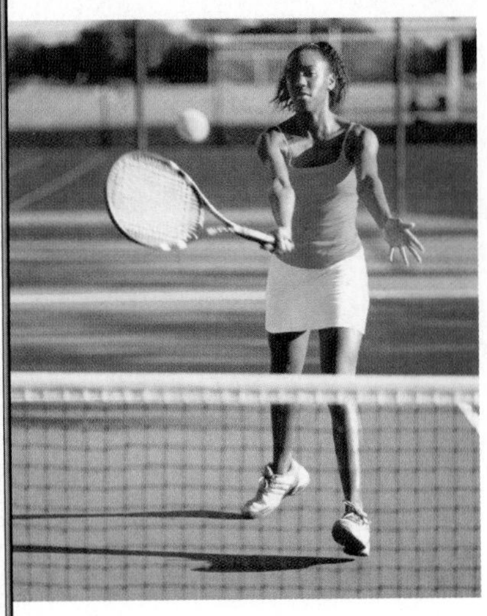

Figure 2 The tennis racket exerts a force on the ball that causes it to accelerate.

Calculating Net Force with the Second Law Newton's second law also can be used to calculate the net force if mass and acceleration are known. To do this, the equation for Newton's second law must be solved for the net force, F_{net}. To solve for the net force, multiply both sides of the above equation by the mass:

$$\cancel{m} \times \frac{F_{net}}{\cancel{m}} = ma$$

The mass, m, on the left side cancels, giving the equation:

$$F_{net} = ma$$

For example, when the tennis player in **Figure 2** hits a ball, the ball might be in contact with the racket for only a few thousandths of a second. Because the ball's velocity changes over such a short period of time, the ball's acceleration could be as high as 5,000 m/s^2. The ball's mass is 0.06 kg, so the net force exerted on the ball would be:

$$F_{net} = ma = (0.06 \text{ kg})\ (5{,}000 \text{ m/s}^2) = 300 \text{ kg m/s}^2 = 300 \text{ N}$$

Friction

Suppose you give a skateboard a push with your hand. According to Newton's first law of motion, if the net force acting on a moving object is zero, it will continue to move in a straight line with constant speed. Does the skateboard keep moving with constant speed after it leaves your hand?

You know the answer. The skate board slows down and finally stops. Recall that when an object slows down it is accelerating. By Newton's second law, if the skateboard is accelerating, there must be a net force acting on it.

The force that slows the skateboard and brings it to a stop is friction. **Friction** is the force that opposes the sliding motion of two surfaces that are touching each other. The amount of friction between two surfaces depends on two factors—the kinds of surfaces and the force pressing the surfaces together.

Reading Check *What does the force of friction between two objects in contact depend on?*

Figure 3 While surfaces might look and even feel smooth, they can be rough at the microscopic level.

What causes friction? Would you believe the surface of a highly polished piece of metal is rough? **Figure 3** shows a microscopic view of the dips and bumps on the surface of a polished silver teapot. If two surfaces are in contact, welding or sticking occurs where the bumps touch each other. These microwelds are the source of friction.

LAB DEMONSTRATION

Purpose to observe properties of friction

Materials 2 heavy wood blocks (about 10 cm × 15 cm × 5 cm thick) 2 nails or eyelet screws, string, strip of sandpaper as wide as the blocks, smooth surface

Procedure Pound nails or insert eyelet screws in the center of one 5-cm side and one 15-cm side of one wood block. Attach the spring scale and pull the block across a smooth surface. Record the force. Repeat on a rough surface, and with the second block on top. Repeat with the block on its end.

Expected Outcome There is more friction on a rough surface. Friction doubles if the mass doubles. The area of contact doesn't affect friction.

Assessment

What would happen if a third block were put on top of the second block? The frictional force would be triple.

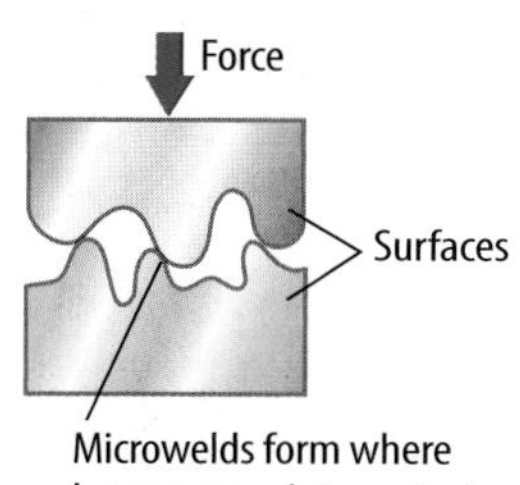

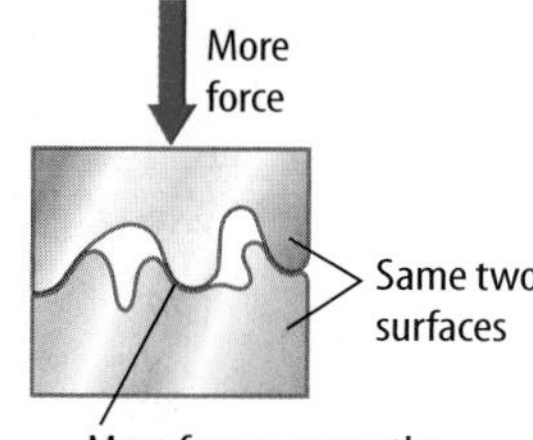

Figure 4 Friction is due to microwelds formed between two surfaces. The larger the force pushing the two surfaces together is, the stronger the microwelds will be.
Explain *how the area of contact between the surfaces changes when they are pushed together.*

Sticking Together The larger the force pushing the two surfaces together is, the stronger these microwelds will be, because more of the surface bumps will come into contact, as shown in **Figure 4.** To move one surface over the other, a force must be applied to break the microwelds.

Static Friction Suppose you have filled a cardboard box, like the one in **Figure 5,** with books and want to move it. It's too heavy to lift, so you start pushing on it, but it doesn't budge. Is that because the mass of the box is too large? If the box doesn't move, then it has zero acceleration. According to Newton's second law, if the acceleration is zero, then the net force on the box is zero. Another force that cancels your push must be acting on the box. That force is friction due to the microwelds that have formed between the bottom of the box and the floor. This type of friction is called static friction. **Static friction** is the frictional force that prevents two surfaces from sliding past each other. In this case, your push is not large enough to break the microwelds, and the box does not move.

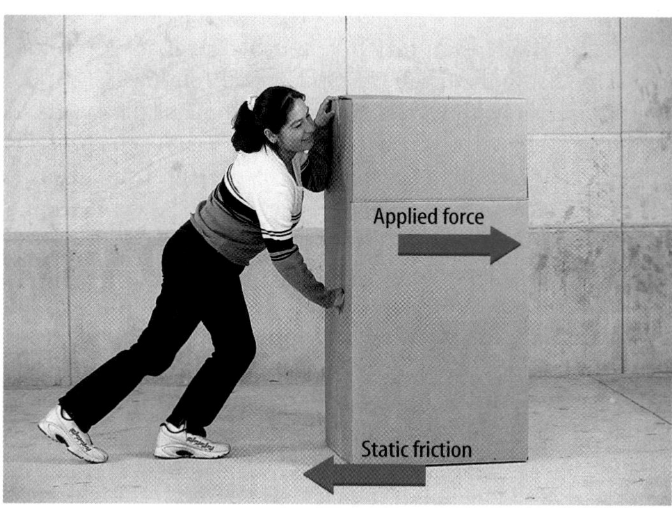

Figure 5 The box doesn't move because static friction is equal to the applied force.
Infer *the net force on the box.*

Mini LAB

Comparing Friction

Procedure

1. Place an **ice cube,** a **rock,** an **eraser,** a **wood block,** and a square of **aluminum foil** at one end of a **metal** or **plastic tray.**
2. Slowly lift the end of the tray with the items.
3. Have a partner use a **metric ruler** to measure the height of the raised end of the tray at which each object slides to the other end. Record the heights in your **Science Journal.**

Analysis

1. List the height at which each object slid off the tray.
2. Why did the objects slide off at different heights?
3. What type of friction acted on each object?

Caption Answer

Figure 4 The area of contact increases.

Purpose Students observe the effect of friction on several materials L2 IN **Kinesthetic**

Materials ice cube, rock, eraser, wood block, square of aluminum foil, metal or plastic tray, metric ruler

Teaching Strategy Have an empty jar or beaker available for the ice cubes.

Analysis

1. The ice cube should slide first, followed by the aluminum foil, rock, wood block, and eraser
2. The static friction varied between the tray and the objects. The greater the static friction, the steeper the tray needed to be before that object moved.
3. Static friction before sliding, sliding friction once sliding began.

Assessment

Oral Ask students to list several ways to increase the friction between tires and ice. Put chains on tires, make tires with steel grips, add sand or some other abrasive to ice, add weight to the car. Use **PASC,** p. 93.

Caption Answer

Figure 5 The net force is zero.

Differentiated Instruction

Challenge In general, the smoother two surfaces are the less friction there is between them. However, if surfaces are extremely smooth, they actually have more friction between them. Have students rub two new glass slides together and compare this to the resistance felt when rubbing older, scratched slides together. Ask them to explain this effect. Extremely smooth surfaces have a greater true contact area (more bumps are in contact). L3 IN **Kinesthetic**

Visual Learning

Figure 4 The number of bumps where the two surfaces touch is actually quite small. If pressure on the surface is increased, the area over which the surfaces touch increases, so friction increases. Have students demonstrate the effect of increasing pressure on friction with various objects.

Use Science Words

Word Origin Have students find the origin of the word *friction.* The word *friction* comes from the Latin word *fricare*, which means "to rub." L2 LS **Linguistic**

Reading Check

Answer Sliding friction is caused by microwelds breaking and reforming as one surface slides on another.

Figure 6 Sliding friction acts in the direction opposite the motion of the sliding box.

Sliding Friction You ask a friend to help you move the box, as in **Figure 6.** Pushing together, the box moves. Together you and your friend have exerted enough force to break the microwelds between the floor and the bottom of the box. But if you stop pushing, the box quickly comes to a stop. This is because as the box slides across the floor, another force—sliding friction—opposes the motion of the box. **Sliding friction** is the force that opposes the motion of two surfaces sliding past each other. Sliding friction is caused by microwelds constantly breaking and then forming again as the box slides along the floor. To keep the box moving, you must continually apply a force to overcome sliding friction.

Reading Check *What causes sliding friction?*

Figure 7 Rolling friction between the train's wheels and the track is reduced by making both from steel. This reduces the deformation that occurs as the wheel rolls on the track.

Rolling Friction You may have watched a car stuck in snow, ice, or mud spin its wheels. The driver steps on the gas, but the wheels just spin without the car moving. To make the car move, sand or gravel may be spread under the wheels. When a wheel is spinning there is sliding friction between the wheels and surface. Spreading sand or gravel on the surface increases the sliding friction until the wheel stops slipping and begins rolling.

As a wheel rolls over a surface, the wheel digs into the surface, causing both the wheel and the surface to be deformed. Static friction acts over the deformed area where the wheel and surface are in contact, producing a frictional force called rolling friction. Rolling friction is the frictional force between a rolling object and the surface it rolls on. Rolling friction would cause the train in **Figure 7** to slow down and come to a stop, just as sliding friction causes a sliding object to slow down and come to a stop.

Differentiated Instruction

Learning Disabled Provide students with an assortment of toy cars. Have them examine the cars and roll them around and then identify all the sources of friction in the cars that hinder the cars' movement. Ask them to suggest ways to decrease the friction so the cars will roll more easily. Suggestions might include adding lubrication, making the contacting surfaces smoother, using different materials for the contacting surfaces, and adding ball bearings. L1 LS **Kinesthetic**

Visual Learning

Figure 6 Tell students that the coefficient of static friction is equal to the force needed to start a body moving across a surface divided by the weight of the body being moved. If the students in the picture had to push with a force of 400 N to start the 900 N box moving, what is the coefficient of static friction between the box and the floor? $\frac{400\text{ N}}{900\text{ N}} = 0.44$ L3 LS **Logical-Mathematical**

Air Resistance

When an object falls toward Earth, it is pulled downward by the force of gravity. However, a friction-like force called **air resistance** opposes the motion of objects that move through the air. Air resistance causes objects to fall with different accelerations and different speeds. If there were no air resistance, then all objects, like the apple and the feather shown in **Figure 8,** would fall with the same acceleration.

Air resistance acts in the opposite direction to the motion of an object through air. If the object is falling downward, air resistance acts upward on the object. The size of the air resistance force also depends on the size and shape of an object. Imaging dropping two identical plastic bags. One is crumpled into a ball and the other is spread out. When the bags are dropped, the crumbled bag falls faster than the spread out-bag. The downward force of gravity on both bags is the same, but the upward force of air resistance on the crumpled bag is less. As a result, the net downward force on the crumpled bag is greater, as shown in **Figure 9.**

The amount of air resistance on an object depends on the speed, size, and shape of the object. Air resistance, not the object's mass, is why feathers, leaves, and pieces of paper fall more slowly than pennies, acorns, and apples.

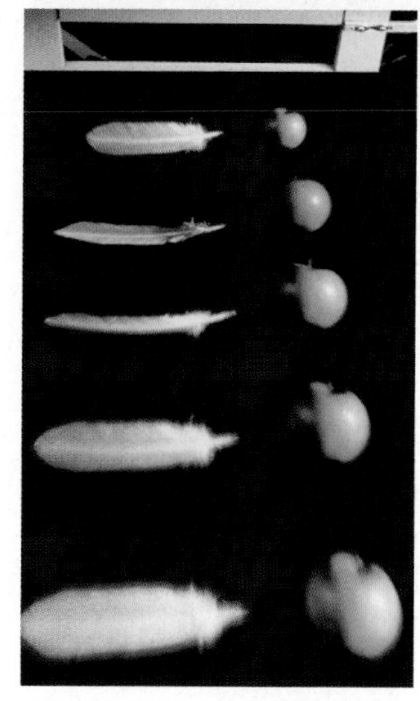

Figure 8 This photograph shows an apple and feather falling in a vacuum. The photograph was taken using a strobe light that flashes on and off at a steady rate. Because there is no air resistance in a vacuum, the feather and the apple fall with the same acceleration.

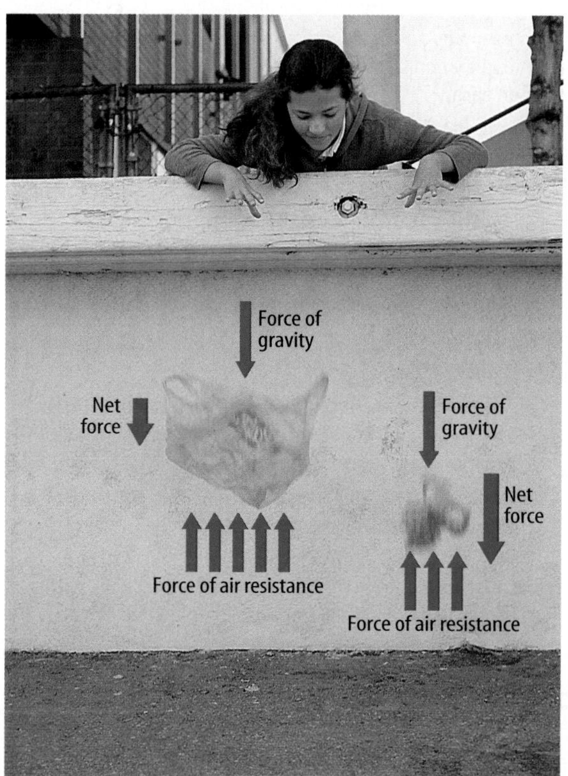

Figure 9 Because of its greater surface area, the bag on the left has more air resistance acting on it as it falls.

Discussion

Parachutes Why does using a parachute make it possible for sky divers to jump safely out of an airplane? The parachute has a large surface area. This causes a great deal of air resistance, which makes the sky diver fall slowly enough to land safely. L2 IS **Logical-Mathematical**

Activity

Air Resistance Have students show how air resistance affects the way an object falls by making a parachute out of string and cloth and attaching it to a small object. Suggest that students compare the rates at which the object falls when it is attached to the parachute and when it is not. L1 ELL IS **Kinesthetic**

Visual Learning

Figure 9 On August 2, 1971, during the *Apollo 15* mission, astronaut David Scott dropped a hammer and a feather onto the Moon's surface. This demonstration proved Galileo's conjecture that two objects would fall at the same rate in a vacuum, regardless of their mass.

Fun Fact

Friction works for us more often than it works against us. Static friction is necessary to get and keep a wheel rolling, and without sliding friction we would have to run into stationary objects (like brick walls) in order come to a stop.

Science Journal

Falling Objects Have students describe in their Science Journals how the velocity and acceleration of an object change as it falls from a tall building. Initially, velocity increases causing the air resistance force to increase until it equals the force of gravity at the object's terminal velocity. The velocity is then constant and acceleration is zero until the object hits the ground. L2 P IS **Logical-Mathematical**

Discussion

Terminal Velocity What happens to an object's velocity and acceleration when the object reaches terminal velocity? After reaching terminal velocity, the object's velocity remains constant, so its acceleration is zero.

3 Assess

DAILY INTERVENTION

Check for Understanding

Kinesthetic Have (or draw on the board) three boxes that are the same size but have different masses. Ask how the students could tell which is heaviest without actually picking it up. You could push it along the floor. The most difficult to push is the heaviest if the boxes are made from the same material so that the frictional forces are the same.

Reteach

Friction Have students demonstrate how rolling friction is less than sliding friction by pulling a rubber band attached to a toy car. If the car is pulled on its wheels, the rubber band barely extends. If the car is pulled on its top, the rubber band extends much more. L2 ELL IS **Kinesthetic**

Assessment

Oral Have students work in small groups to discuss various sports they enjoy. They should explain how static, sliding, and rolling friction are important for the sport. Use **Performance Assessment in the Science Classroom,** p. 169.

Figure 10 The force of air resistance on an open parachute balances the force of gravity on the sky diver when the parachute is falling slowly.

Terminal Velocity As an object falls, the downward force of gravity causes the object to accelerate. For example, after falling 2,000 m, without the effects of air resistance the sky diver's speed would be almost 200 m/s, or over 700 km/h.

However, as an object falls faster, the upward force of air resistance increases. This causes the net force on a sky diver to decrease as the sky diver falls. Finally, the upward air resistance force becomes large enough to balance the downward force of gravity. This means the net force on the object is zero. Then the acceleration of the object is also zero, and the object falls with a constant speed called the terminal velocity. The terminal velocity is the highest speed a falling object will reach.

The terminal velocity depends on the size, shape, and mass of a falling object. The air resistance force on an open parachute, like the one in **Figure 10,** is much larger than the air resistance on the sky diver with a closed parachute. With the parachute open, the terminal velocity of the sky diver becomes small enough that the sky diver can land safely.

section 1 review

Summary

Force, Mass, and Acceleration

- The greater the force on an object, the greater the object's acceleration.
- The acceleration of an object depends on its mass as well as the force exerted on it.

Newton's Second Law

- Newton's second law of motion states that the acceleration of an object is in the direction of the net force on the object, and can be calculated from this equation:

$$a = \frac{F_{net}}{m}$$

Friction

- Friction is the force that opposes motion between two surfaces that are touching each other.
- Friction depends on the types of surfaces and the force pressing the surfaces together.
- Friction results from the microwelds formed between surfaces that are in contact.

Air Resistance

- Air resistance is a force that acts on objects that move through the air.

Self Check

1. **State** Newton's second law of motion.
2. **Infer** why an object with a smaller mass has a larger acceleration than a larger mass if the same force acts on each.
3. **Explain** why the frictional force between two surfaces increases if the force pushing the surfaces together increases.
4. **Compare** the force of air resistance and the force of gravity on an object falling at its terminal velocity.
5. **Think Critically** Why does coating surfaces with oil reduce friction between the surfaces?

Applying Math

6. **Convert Units** show that the units N/kg can be written using only units of meters (m) and seconds (s). Is this a unit of mass, acceleration or force?
7. **Calculate Mass** You push yourself on a skateboard with a force of 30 N and accelerate at 0.5 m/s^2. Find the mass of the skateboard if your mass is 58 kg.
8. **Calculate Sliding Friction** You push a 2-kg book with a force of 5 N. Find the force of sliding friction on the book if it has an acceleration of 1.0 m/s^2.

Science Online gpscience.com/self_check_quiz

section  review

1. Acceleration of an object is in the direction of the net force and equals the net force divided by the mass.
2. $F = ma$; so if mass decreases and the force stays constant, the acceleration must increase.
3. The contact area between the surfaces increases and more microwelds are formed.
4. The two forces are equal and in opposite directions.
5. The oil reduces the contact area between the surfaces so fewer microwelds are formed.
6. $\text{N/kg} = \frac{(\text{kg} \times \text{m/s}^2)}{\text{kg}} = \text{m/s}^2$
   This is a unit of acceleration.
7. $\frac{m = F/a = (25\text{ N})}{(0.5\text{ m/s}^2)} = 50\text{ kg}$
   $50\text{ kg} - 48\text{ kg} = 2\text{kg}$
8. $F = ma = 2.0\text{ kg} \times 1.0\text{ m/s}^2 = 2\text{ N}$
   $5\text{ N} - 2\text{ N} = 3\text{ N}$

section 2

Gravity

Reading Guide

What You'll Learn

- **Describe** the gravitational force.
- **Distinguish** between mass and weight.
- **Explain** why objects that are thrown will follow a curved path.
- **Compare** circular motion with motion in a straight line.

Why It's Important

There is a gravitational force between you and every other object in the universe.

Review Vocabulary

acceleration: the rate of change of velocity which occurs when an object changes speed or direction

New Vocabulary

- gravity
- weight
- centripetal acceleration
- centripetal force

What is gravity?

There's a lot about you that's attractive. At this moment, you are exerting an attractive force on everything around you—your desk, your classmates, even the planet Jupiter millions of kilometers away. It's the attractive force of gravity.

Anything that has mass is attracted by the force of gravity. **Gravity** is an attractive force between any two objects that depends on the masses of the objects and the distance between them. This force increases as the mass of either object increases, or as the objects move closer, as shown in **Figure 11.**

You can't feel any gravitational attraction between you and this book because the force is weak. Only Earth is both close enough and has a large enough mass that you can feel its gravitational attraction. While the Sun has much more mass than Earth, the Sun is too far away to exert a noticeable gravitational attraction on you. And while this book is close, it doesn't have enough mass to exert an attraction you can feel.

Gravity—A Basic Force Gravity is one of the four basic forces. The other basic forces are the electromagnetic force, the strong nuclear force, and the weak nuclear force. The two nuclear forces only act on particles in the nuclei of atoms. Electricity and magnetism are caused by the electromagnetic force. Chemical interactions between atoms and molecules also are due to the electromagnetic force.

Figure 11 The gravitational force between two objects depends on their masses and the distance between them.

If the mass of either of the objects increases, the gravitational force between them increases.

If the objects are closer together, the gravitational force between them increases.

Section 2 Resource Manager

Chapter *Fast File* Resources

Transparency Activity, pp. 45, 47–48

Directed Reading for Content Mastery, p. 20

Enrichment, p. 25

MiniLAB, p. 4

Reinforcement, p. 28

Performance Assessment in the Science Classroom, p. 37

Earth Science Critical Thinking/Problem Solving, p. 5

Life Science Critical Thinking/Problem Solving, p. 14

Cultural Diversity, p. 25

1 Motivate

Bellringer

Section Focus Transparencies also are available on the Interactive Chalkboard CD-ROM. L2 ELL

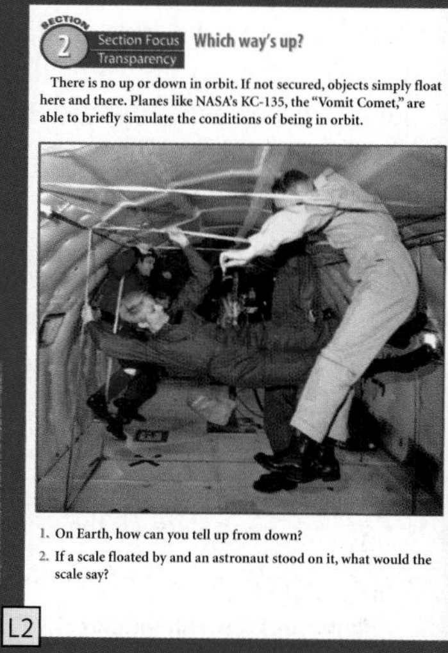

Tie to Prior Knowledge

Gravity's Effect on a Football Ask students to describe how a football must be thrown for a long pass. Explain that in this section they will learn how the force of gravity affects the motion of projectiles such as a football.

2 Teach

Quick Demo

Gravitational Acceleration

Materials water, bucket, plastic cup

Estimated Time five minutes

Procedure Punch a hole in the bottom of the cup. Place your finger over the hole in the bottom of the cup and fill it with water. Hold the cup as high over your head as you can, and let it drop into the bucket. Have students observe that the water and the cup fall at the same rate, so no water drains out of the cup as it falls. L2 ELL
LS **Visual-Spatial**

Fun Fact

Newton's law of gravitation states that the gravitational attraction between two objects is

$F = \frac{G(m_1m_2)}{d_2}$, where d is the distance between the two objects and G is the universal gravitational constant. In 1798, Henry Cavendish performed experiments that verified Newton's law. Based on his work and the work of others, the value of G is now known to be approximately $6.67 \times 10^{-11} m^3/kg \cdot s^2$.

Topic: Gravity on Other Planets

Visit gpscience.com Web links to information about the gravitational acceleration near the surface of different planets in the solar system.

Activity Make a graph with the gravitational acceleration on the *y*-axis, and the planet's mass on the *x*-axis. Infer from your graph how the gravitational acceleration depends on a planet's mass.

The Law of Universal Gravitation

For thousands of years people everywhere have observed the stars and the planets in the night sky. Gradually, data were collected on the motions of the planets by a number of observers. Isaac Newton used some of these data to formulate the law of universal gravitation, which he published in 1687. This law can be written as the following equation.

The Law of Universal Gravitation

$$\text{gravitational force} = (\text{constant}) \times \frac{(\text{mass 1}) \times (\text{mass 2})}{(\text{distance})^2}$$

$$F = G\frac{m_1m_2}{d^2}$$

In this equation G is a constant called the universal gravitational constant, and d is the distance between the two masses, m_1 and m_2. The law of universal gravitation enables the force of gravity to be calculated between any two objects if their masses and the distance between them are known.

The Range of Gravity According to the law of universal gravitation, the gravitational force between two masses decreases rapidly as the distance between the masses increases. For example, if the distance between two objects increases from 1 m to 2 m, the gravitational force between them becomes one fourth as large. If the distance increases from 1 m to 10 m, the gravitational force between the objects is one hundredth as large.

However, no matter how far apart two objects are, the gravitational force between them never completely goes to zero. Because the gravitational force between two objects never disappears, gravity is called a long-range force.

Finding Other Planets Earth's motion around the Sun is affected by the gravitational pulls of the other planets in the solar system. In the same way, the motion of every planet in the solar system is affected by the gravitational pulls of all the other planets.

In the 1840s the most distant planet known was Uranus. The motion of Uranus calculated from the law of universal gravitation disagreed slightly with its observed motion. Some astronomers suggested that there must be an undiscovered planet affecting the motion of Uranus. Using the law of universal gravitation and Newton's laws of motion, two astronomers independently calculated the orbit of this planet. As a result of these calculations, the planet Neptune, shown in **Figure 12,** was found in 1846.

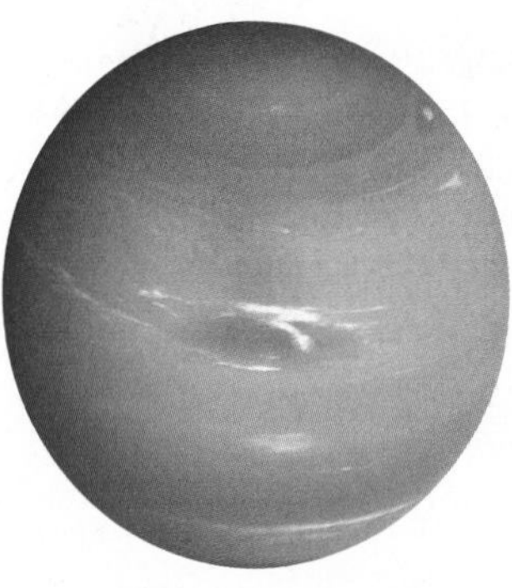

Figure 12 The location of the planet Neptune in the night sky was correctly predicted using Newton's laws of motion and the law of universal gravitation.

Science Journal

Lower Gravity Ask students to imagine that, during the next few days, the gravitational force of Earth gradually becomes half of what it is now. Have students write in their Science Journals about the sort of changes that would take place. Students might describe slow-moving waterfalls, soaring tennis balls, or a thinner atmosphere. L2 LS **Linguistic**

Differentiated Instruction

Challenge Have students show how Newton's first law can be derived from Newton's second law. Newton's 2nd Law says $F = ma$. If $F = 0$ then $a = 0$. If $a = 0$ the object will continue either sitting still or moving in a straight line at constant velocity L3 LS **Logical-Mathematical**

Earth's Gravitational Acceleration

If you dropped a bowling ball and a marble at the same time, which would hit the ground first? Suppose the effects of air resistance are small enough to be ignored. When all forces except gravity acting on an a falling object can be ignored, the object is said to be in free fall. Then all objects near Earth's surface would fall with the same acceleration, just like the two balls in **Figure 13.**

Close to Earth's surface, the acceleration of a falling object in free fall is about 9.8 m/s^2. This acceleration is given the symbol g and is sometimes called the acceleration of gravity. By Newton's second law of motion, the force of Earth's gravity on a falling object is the object's mass times the acceleration of gravity. This can be expressed by the equation:

Force of Earth's Gravity

force of gravity (N) = mass (kg) × acceleration of gravity (m/s^2)

$$F = mg$$

For example, the gravitational force on a sky diver with a mass of 60 kg would be

$$F = mg = (60 \text{ kg})\ (9.8 \text{ m/s}^2) = 588 \text{ N}$$

Weight Even if you are not falling, the force of Earth's gravity still is pulling you downward. If you are standing on a floor, the net force on you is zero. The force of Earth's gravity pulls you downward, but the floor exerts an upward force on you that balances gravity's downward pull.

Whether you are standing, jumping, or falling, Earth exerts a gravitational force on you. The gravitational force exerted on an object is called the object's **weight.** Because the weight of an object on Earth is equal to the force of Earth's gravity on the object, weight can be calculated from this equation:

Weight Equation

weight (N) = mass (kg) × acceleration of gravity (m/s^2)

$$W = mg$$

On Earth where g equals 9.8 m/s^2, a cassette tape weighs about 0.5 N, a backpack full of books could weigh 100 N, and a jumbo jet weighs about 3.4 million N. A sky diver with a mass of 60 kg has a weight of 588 N. Under what circumstances would the net force on the sky diver equal the sky diver's weight?

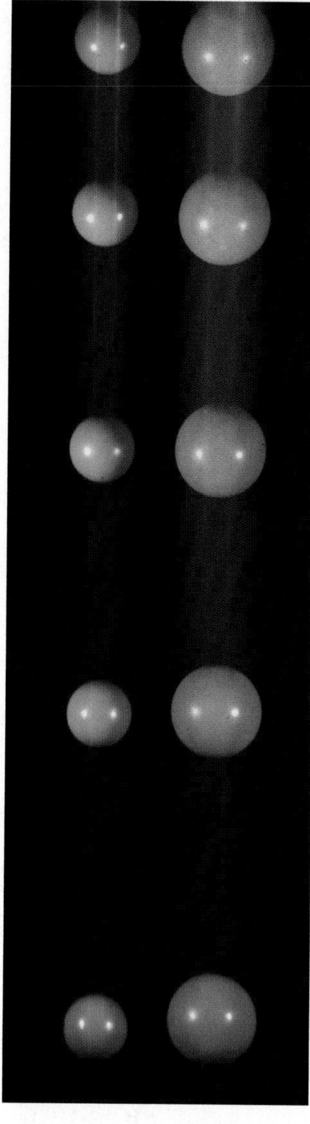

Figure 13 Time-lapse photography shows that two balls of different masses fall at the same rate.

Quick Demo

Mass and Falling Speed

Materials golf ball, table tennis ball

Estimated Time 15 minutes

Procedure Bring a golf ball and a table tennis ball to class. Have volunteers determine the mass of each ball and write it on the board. Then drop both balls from the same height for the class to observe. Have the class decide whether one ball hit the floor before the other. L2 IS **Visual-Spatial**

Text Question Answer

The bowling ball and the marble would hit the ground at the same time. They have the same acceleration, so their velocities are the same as they fall.

Misconceptions

Mass Versus Weight People in Europe and other places that use SI units usually express their weight in kilograms. This is technically incorrect, as the kilogram is a unit of mass, not weight.

Differentiated Instruction

Challenge Ask students to identify the force that opposes gravity and enables objects to float in water. The buoyant force of the water acts on an object with a force equal to the weight of the water displaced by the object. If the buoyant force is equal to the force of gravity pulling on the object, the object will float. This occurs when the object is less dense than water. L3 IS **Logical-Mathematical**

Discussion

Weight and Mass Why is it that an object has mass in and of itself but must interact with another object in order to have weight? Mass is a measure of the amount of matter an object contains. Weight is a measure of gravitational force, which only occurs between objects. L2 LS **Logical-Mathematical**

Activity

Collecting Data To help students become familiar with the relationship between an object's mass and its weight on Earth, have groups of students work together to make a table listing the weights and masses of various objects. Students first should use a balance to determine the object's mass in kilograms, and then calculate its weight by multiplying the mass by 9.8 m/s^2. L2 ELL LS **Kinesthetic**

Reading Check

Answer Weight equals mass times acceleration due to gravity.

Quick Demo

Simulating Gravity

Materials marble, shallow pan

Estimated Time 15 minutes

Procedure One way to overcome weightlessness in space is to build a space station in the shape of a large, doughnut-shaped ring called a torus. If the torus is set spinning in outer space, the centripetal force would cause people inside to feel as if they are being pushed toward the outer wall, simulating gravity. Demonstrate this to students by swirling a marble in a shallow pan. L3 LS **Visual-Spatial**

Figure 14 On the Moon, the gravitational force on the astronaut is less than it is on Earth. As a result, the astronaut can take longer steps and jump higher than on Earth.

Weight and Mass Weight and mass are not the same. Weight is a force and mass is a measure of the amount of matter an object contains. However, according to the weight equation on the previous page, weight and mass are related. Weight increases as mass increases.

The weight of an object usually is the gravitational force between the object and Earth. But the weight of an object can change, depending on the gravitational force on the object. For example, the acceleration of gravity on the Moon is 1.6 m/s^2, about one sixth as large as Earth's gravitational acceleration. As a result, a person, like the astronaut in **Figure 14,** would weigh only about one sixth as much on the Moon as on Earth. **Table 1** shows how various weights on Earth would be different on the Moon and some of the planets.

Reading Check *How are weight and mass related?*

Weightlessness and Free Fall

You've probably seen pictures of astronauts and equipment floating inside the space shuttle. Any item that is not fastened down seems to float throughout the cabin. They are said to be experiencing the sensation of weightlessness.

However, for a typical mission, the shuttle orbits Earth at an altitude of about 400 km. According the law of universal gravitation, at 400-km altitude the force of Earth's gravity is about 90 percent as strong as it is at Earth's surface. So an astronaut with a mass of 80 kg still would weigh about 700 N in orbit, compared with a weight of about 780 N at Earth's surface.

Table 1 Weight Comparison Table

Weight on Earth (N)	Weight on Other Bodies in the Solar System (N)				
	Moon	Venus	Mars	Jupiter	Saturn
75	12	68	28	190	87
100	17	90	38	254	116
150	25	135	57	381	174
500	84	450	190	1,270	580
700	119	630	266	1,778	812
2,000	333	1,800	760	5,080	2,320

Teacher FYI

Acceleration Due to Gravity Near Earth's surface, acceleration due to gravity (g) is approximately 9.8 m/s^2. This value varies by only a fraction of a percent even on top of Mount Everest. The value of g decreases as you travel away from Earth's surface. At a height of 1,000 km, it is about 3/4 the value at Earth's surface.

Active Reading

Reflective Journal In this strategy, students record their responses to the various activities, and what they learned from each. Have them divide sheets of paper into 5 columns titled *What I did, What I learned, Questions I have, What surprised me* and *Overall Response.* Have students write a Reflective Journal entry for the activities about gravity in this section.

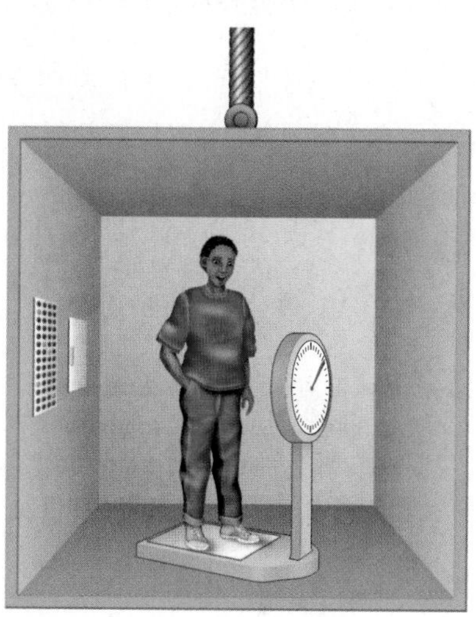

A When the elevator is stationary, the scale shows the boy's weight.

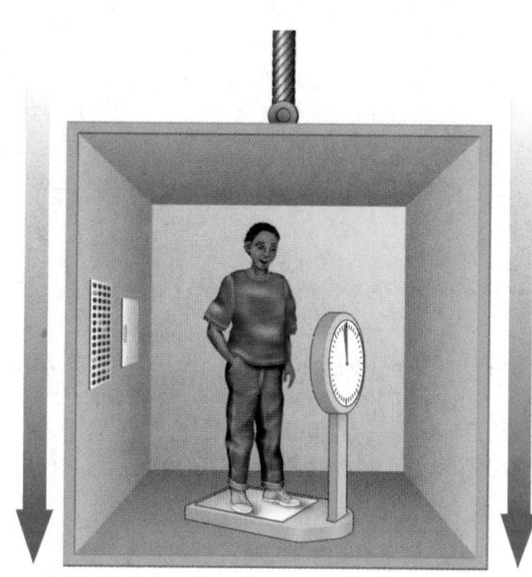

B If the elevator were in free fall, the scale would show a zero weight.

Floating in Space So what does it mean to say that something is weightless in orbit? Think about how you measure your weight. When you stand on a scale, as in **Figure 15A,** you are at rest and the net force on you is zero. The scale supports you and balances your weight by exerting an upward force. The dial on a scale shows the upward force exerted by the scale, which is your weight. Now suppose you stand on a scale in an elevator that is falling, as in **Figure 15B.** If you and the scale were in free fall, then you no longer would push down on the scale at all. The scale dial would say you have zero weight, even though the force of gravity on you hasn't changed.

A space shuttle in orbit is in free fall, but it is falling around Earth, rather than straight downward. Everything in the orbiting space shuttle is falling around Earth at the same rate, in the same way you and the scale were falling in the elevator. Objects in the shuttle seem to be floating because they are all falling with the same acceleration.

Figure 15 The boy pushes down on the scale with less force when he and the scale are falling at the same rate.

Gravity and Earth's Atmosphere Apart from simply keeping your feet on the ground, gravity is important for life on Earth for other reasons, too. Because Earth has a sufficient gravitational pull, it can hold around it the oxygen/nitrogen atmosphere necessary for sustaining life. Research other ways in which gravity has played a role in the formation of Earth.

Projectile Motion

If you've tossed a ball to someone, you've probably noticed that thrown objects don't always travel in straight lines. They curve downward. That's why quarterbacks, dart players, and archers aim above their targets. Anything that's thrown or shot through the air is called a projectile. Earth's gravity causes projectiles to follow a curved path.

Activity

Using a Spring Scale Have students hang an object from a spring scale to determine its weight. Next, have them compare this with the force recorded on the scale when the object is moved rapidly up and rapidly down. Have students explain the results. The downward force exerted by the object on the scale is the force recorded on the scale, and equals the upward force exerted by the scale on the object. When the object isn't accelerating, the scale exerts an upward force on the object equal to its weight. When the object is accelerating upward, the upward force on the object exerted by the scale is greater than its weight. When the object is accelerating downward, the upward force on the object exerted by the scale is less than its weight. L3 LS **Logical-Mathematical**

Gravity and Earth's Atmosphere The force of gravity also has caused the shape of Earth and other bodies in the solar system to be spherical. During Earth's formation, gravity caused denser materials such as iron and nickel to sink toward the center of Earth, where they now form Earth's core. Less dense materials such as silicates and water were left at Earth's surface, where they now form Earth's crust and oceans.

Use Science Words

Word Origins Ask students to find the origin of the word *projectile.* The word *projectile* comes from the Latin prefix *pro-,* which means "forward," and the Latin verb *iacere,* which means "to throw." L2 LS **Linguistic**

Curriculum Connection

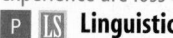

Health Pictures of objects floating around in a spaceship make weightlessness look like fun, but weightlessness can have an adverse effect on the health of astronauts. Have students research this problem and use a word processor to prepare a report about some effects. Some problems astronauts experience are loss of bone density and muscle atrophy. L2 P LS **Linguistic**

Inquiry Lab

Distance and Launch Angle

Purpose Students design an experiment to show how the horizontal distance traveled by a projectile is affected by its initial launch angle.

Possible Materials meterstick, protractor, rubber bands, boards about 5 cm × 12 cm, nails, small rubber stopper, or a toy rubber-tipped dart gun

Estimated Time one class period

Possible Procedure

1. Have the students build a slingshot using the board, nails and rubber band, to launch the rubber stopper (or use the dart gun).
2. Launch the rubber stopper at different angles from the same elevation. Keep the launch forces the same.
3. Measure the horizontal distance traveled by the projectile at each angle.
4. Plot the results on a graph of angle versus distance.
5. Infer which angles give the greatest horizontal distance

Teaching Strategy

Wear protective eye gear, and caution students not to aim at anything breakable or each other. They should find that complementary angles give the same horizontal distance. L3

LS **Logical-Mathematical**

For additional inquiry activities, see *Science Inquiry Labs.*

Visual Learning

Figure 16 Point out that the spacing of the balls with respect to horizontal is identical. This shows that the balls have the same vertical acceleration. Ask students what the result would be if one of the balls had greater mass. The result would be the same. L2 LS **Visual-Spatial**

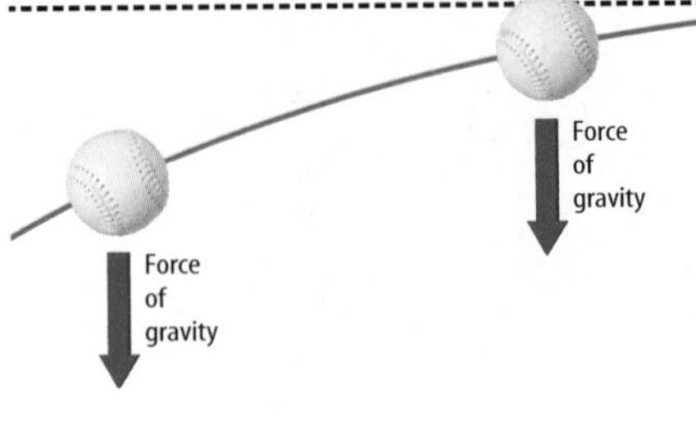

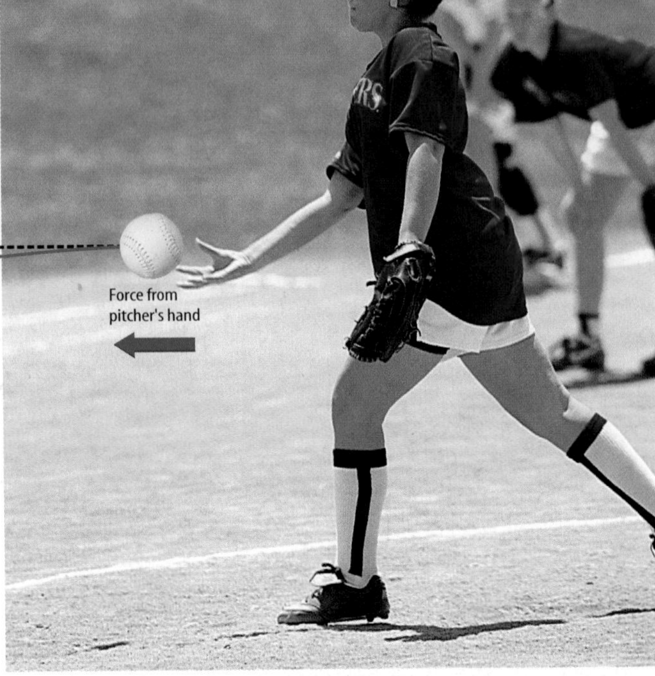

Figure 16 The pitcher gives the ball a horizontal motion. Gravity, however, is pulling the ball down. The combination of these two motions causes the ball to move in a curved path.

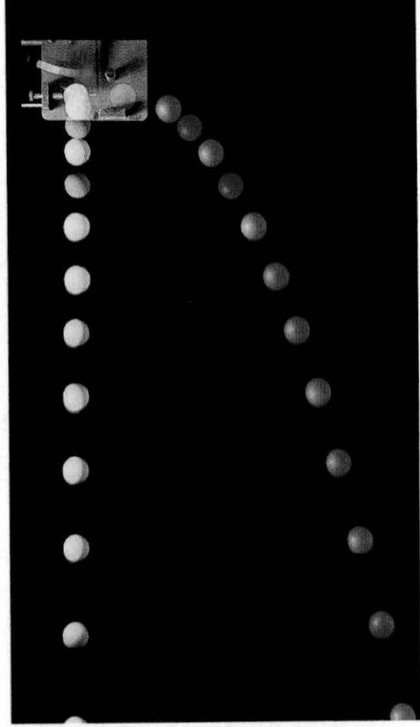

Figure 17 Multiflash photography shows that each ball has the same acceleration downward, whether it's thrown or dropped.

Horizontal and Vertical Motions When you throw a ball, like the pitcher in **Figure 16,** the force exerted by your hand pushes the ball forward. This force gives the ball horizontal motion. After you let go of the ball, no force accelerates it forward, so its horizontal velocity is constant, if you ignore air resistance.

However, when you let go of the ball, gravity can pull it downward, giving it vertical motion. Now the ball has constant horizontal velocity but increasing vertical velocity. Gravity exerts an unbalanced force on the ball, changing the direction of its path from only forward to forward and downward. The result of these two motions is that the ball appears to travel in a curve, even though its horizontal and vertical motions are completely independent of each other.

Horizontal and Vertical Distance If you were to throw a ball as hard as you could from shoulder height in a perfectly horizontal direction, would it take longer to reach the ground than if you dropped a ball from the same height? Surprisingly, it won't. A thrown ball and one dropped will hit the ground at the same time. Both balls in **Figure 17** travel the same vertical distance in the same amount of time. However, the ball thrown horizontally travels a greater horizontal distance than the ball that is dropped.

Differentiated Instruction

Challenge Have students explain the following problem, using both diagrams and written expression: If one bullet is dropped from the same altitude and at the same time that an identical bullet is fired from a gun, they both hit the ground at the same time (but not the same place). Which bullet will hit first if one is fired at an upward angle at the same time the second is dropped? When the gun is fired horizontally, both bullets have the same initial vertical speed (0) and the same vertical acceleration (9.8 m/s^2). They land at the same time. But when one bullet is fired at an upward angle, they do not have the same initial vertical speed. L3 LS **Logical-Mathematical**

Centripetal Force

Look at the path the ball follows as it travels through the curved tube in **Figure 18.** The ball may accelerate in the straight sections of the pipe maze if it speeds up or slows down. However, when the ball enters a curve, even if its speed does not change, it is accelerating because its direction is changing. When the ball goes around a curve, the change in the direction of the velocity is toward the center of the curve. Acceleration toward the center of a curved or circular path is called **centripetal acceleration.**

According to the second law of motion, when the ball has centripetal acceleration, the direction of the net force on the ball also must be toward the center of the curved path. The net force exerted toward the center of a curved path is called a **centripetal force.** For the ball moving through the tube, the centripetal force is the force exerted by the walls of the tube on the ball.

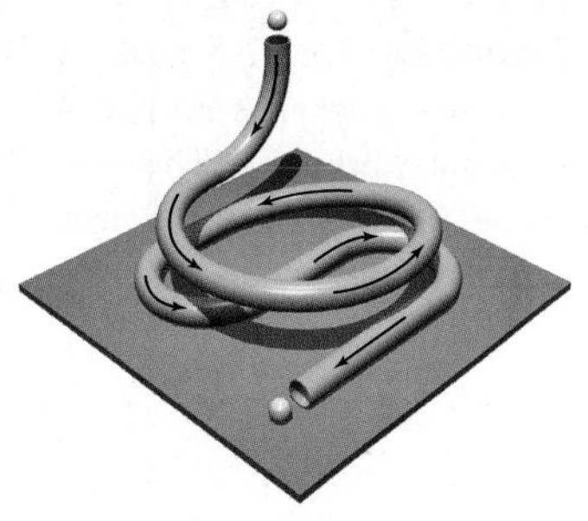

Figure 18 When the ball moves through the curved portions of the tube, it is accelerating because its velocity is changing. **Identify** *the forces acting on the ball as it falls through the tube.*

Centripetal Force and Traction When a car rounds a curve on a highway, a centripetal force must be acting on the car to keep it moving in a curved path. This centripetal force is the frictional force, or the traction, between the tires and the road surface. If the road is slippery and the frictional force is small, the centripetal force might not be large enough to keep the car moving around the curve. Then the car will slide in a straight line. Anything that moves in a circle, such as the people on the amusement park ride in **Figure 19,** is doing so because a centripetal force is accelerating it toward the center.

Mini LAB

Observing Centripetal Force

Procedure

1. Thread a **string** about 1 m long through the holes of a **plastic, slotted golf ball.**
2. Swing the ball in a vertical circle.
3. Swing the ball at different speeds and observe the motion of the ball and the tension in the string.

Analysis

1. What force does the string exert on the ball when the ball is at the top, sides, and bottom of the swing?
2. How does the tension in the string depend on the speed of the ball?

Try at Home

Figure 19 Centripetal force keeps these riders moving in a circle.

Use Science Words

Word Usage Have students explain how the definition of the word *centripetal* describes the force exerted on a ball on a string that you swing around your head. *Centripetal* means "moving toward the center." The tension in the string pulls the ball toward the center. L2

LS **Linguistic**

Caption Answer

Figure 18 gravity, force exerted by wall of tube on ball

Mini LAB

Purpose to observe the effect of centripetal force

Materials string; plastic, slotted golf ball

Analysis

1. centripetal force
2. The faster the ball swings, the more tension there is on the string.

Assessment

Process Show students a picture of a satellite in orbit. Ask them to explain how centripetal force acts on the satellite. The centripetal force of Earth's gravity pulls the satellite toward Earth. Use **Performance Assessment in the Science Classroom,** p. 89.

Differentiated Instruction

Learning Disabled Make sure students realize that as an object moves in a circle, its change in direction is toward the center of the circle. Students can show this by moving a brick along the edge of a large circle. Every time they move the brick, they must twist it a bit so it fits on the circle. This twist shows the change in direction.

3 Assess

DAILY INTERVENTION

Check For Understanding

Visual-Kinesthetic Toss a tennis ball gently across the room to a student who will catch it. Ask the students to describe the vertical motion of the ball. Did it ever speed up, slow down or stop vertically? It slowed down on the way up, stopped and then sped up on the way down. Ask them to describe the horizontal motion in similar terms. What causes the change in vertical motion of the ball? gravity Is there any horizontal accelerating force once the ball is released? no

Reteach

Measure the Fall Have students measure the distance that either of the two balls shown in **Figure 13** fell between each flash. They can use a bar graph to show distance fallen versus flash number. Ask them to explain how this graph supports the idea that the balls are accelerating downward. The balls fall farther between successive flashes.

L2 ELL P LS **Visual-Spatial**

Oral Ask students to explain why the astronauts and everything else in the space shuttle behave as if they were weightless. Everything in the shuttle is in free fall as the shuttle orbits the Earth. Use **Performance Assessment in the Science Classroom,** p. 89.

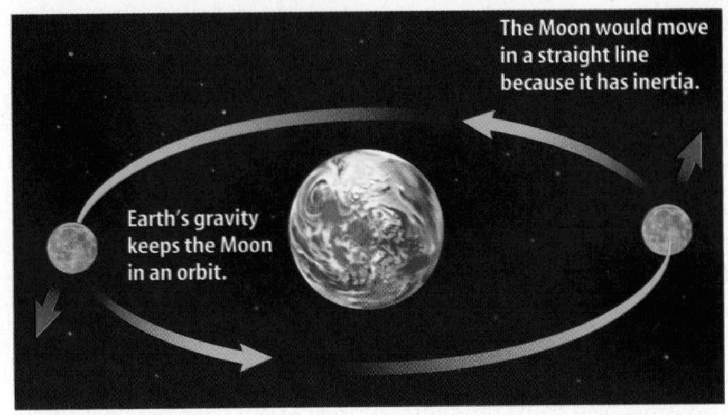

The Moon would move in a straight line because it has inertia.
Earth's gravity keeps the Moon in an orbit.

Figure 20 The Moon would move in a straight line except that Earth's gravity keeps pulling it toward Earth. This gives the Moon a nearly circular orbit.

Gravity Can Be a Centripetal Force Imagine whirling an object tied to a string above your head. The string exerts a centripetal force on the object that keeps it moving in a circular path. In the same way, Earth's gravity exerts a centripetal force on the Moon that keeps it moving in a nearly circular orbit, as shown in **Figure 20.**

section 2 review

Summary

Gravity

- According to the law of universal gravitation, the gravitational force between two objects depends on the masses of the objects and the distance between them.
- The acceleration due to gravity near Earth's surface has the value 9.8 m/s^2.
- Near Earth's surface, the gravitational force on an object with mass, m, is given by:

$$F = mg$$

Weight

- The weight of an object is related to its mass according to the equation:

$$W = mg$$

- An object in orbit seems to be weightless because it is falling around Earth.

Projectile Motion and Centripetal Force

- Projectiles follow a curved path because their horizontal motion is constant, but gravity causes the vertical motion to be changing.
- The net force on an object moving in a circular path is called the centripetal force.

Self Check

1. **Describe** how the gravitational force between two objects depends on the mass of the objects and the distance between them.
2. **Distinguish** between the mass of an object and the object's weight.
3. **Explain** what causes the path of a projectile to be curved.
4. **Describe** the force that causes the planets to stay in orbit around the Sun.
5. **Think Critically** Suppose Earth's mass increased, but Earth's diameter didn't change. How would the acceleration of gravity near Earth's surface change?

Applying Math

6. **Calculate Weight** On Earth, what is the weight of a large-screen TV that has a mass of 75 kg?
7. **Calculate Gravity on Mars** Find the acceleration of gravity on Mars if a person with a mass of 60.0 kg weighs 222 N on Mars.
8. **Calculate Force** Find the force exerted by a rope on a 10-kg mass that is hanging from the rope.

gpscience.com/self_check_quiz

section 2 review

1. It increases as the mass of one or both objects increases, and it decreases as the distance between the objects increases.
2. Mass is a measure of the amount of matter an object contains. Weight is a measure of the force of gravity on an object. Weight changes if the gravitational force changes.
3. vertical motion and horizontal motion
4. The Sun's gravitational force keeps them in orbit.
5. Standing on Earth's surface, you would be attracted by a larger mass, so the force of Earth's gravity and the acceleration of gravity would be greater.
6. Weight $= mg$ $= 75 \text{ kg} \times 9.8 \text{ m/s}^2 = 735 \text{ N}$
7. $a = F/m = \frac{(222 \text{ N})}{(60 \text{ kg})} = 3.7 \text{ m/s}^2$
8. $F = ma = 10.0 \text{ kg} \times 9.8 \text{ m/s}^2$ $= 98 \text{ N}$ (Because of Newton's third Law, the rope exerts the same force up on the mass as the mass exerts down on the rope.)

section 3

The Third Law of Motion

Reading Guide

What You'll Learn
- **State** Newton's third law of motion.
- **Identify** action and reaction forces.
- **Calculate** momentum.
- **Recognize** when momentum is conserved.

Why It's Important

The third law of motion explains how you affect Earth when you walk, and how Earth affects you.

Review Vocabulary

velocity: describes the speed and direction of a moving object

New Vocabulary
- Newton's third law of motion
- momentum

Newton's Third Law

Push against a wall and what happens? If the wall is sturdy enough, usually nothing happens. If you pushed against a wall while wearing roller skates, you would go rolling backwards. Your action on the wall produced a reaction—movement backwards. This is a demonstration of Newton's third law of motion.

Newton's third law of motion describes action-reaction pairs this way: When one object exerts a force on a second object, the second one exerts a force on the first that is equal in strength and opposite in direction. Another way to say this is "to every action force there is an equal and opposite reaction force."

Action and Reaction When a force is applied in nature, a reaction force occurs at the same time. When you jump on a trampoline, for example, you exert a downward force on the trampoline. Simultaneously, the trampoline exerts an equal force upward, sending you high into the air.

Action and reaction forces are acting on the two skaters in **Figure 21.** The male skater is pulling upward on the female skater, while the female skater is pulling downward on the male skater. The two forces are equal, but in opposite directions.

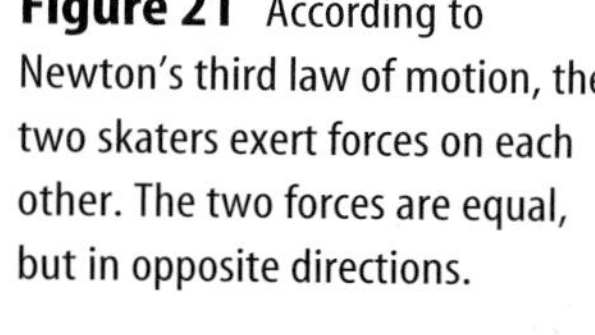

Figure 21 According to Newton's third law of motion, the two skaters exert forces on each other. The two forces are equal, but in opposite directions.

Section 3 Resource Manager

Chapter *FAST FILE* Resources

Transparency Activity, p. 46

Directed Reading for Content Mastery, pp. 21–22

Lab Activity, pp. 13–16

Enrichment, p. 32

Lab Worksheet, pp. 5–6, 7–8

Reinforcement, p. 29

Home and Community Involvement, p. 49

Performance Assessment in the Science Classroom, p. 36

1 Motivate

Bellringer

Section Focus Transparencies also are available on the Interactive Chalkboard CD-ROM.

L2 ELL

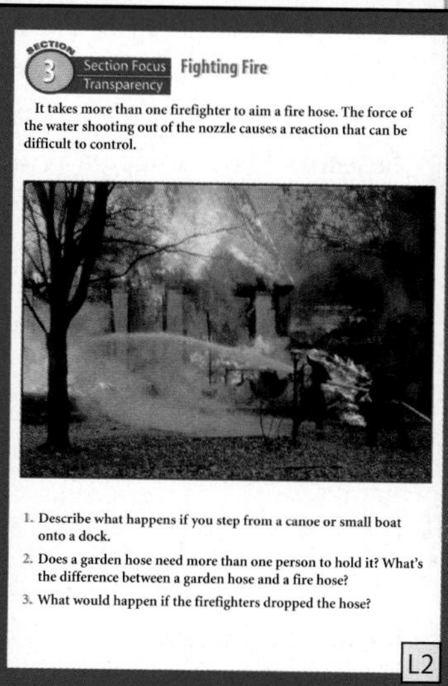

Section 3 Section Focus Transparency **Fighting Fire**

It takes more than one firefighter to aim a fire hose. The force of the water shooting out of the nozzle causes a reaction that can be difficult to control.

1. Describe what happens if you step from a canoe or small boat onto a dock.
2. Does a garden hose need more than one person to hold it? What's the difference between a garden hose and a fire hose?
3. What would happen if the firefighters dropped the hose?

L2

Tie to Prior Knowledge

Motion of Different Objects Have students recall the motion of an untied, inflated balloon and the motion of a rocket. Tell them that the motions of the balloon and the rocket are governed by Newton's third law of motion. In this section they will learn more about Newton's third law.

2 Teach

Text Question Answer

She pushes the water backward.

Space Some scientists think that living in outer space may arrest the spread of arthritis and be beneficial because stress on bones is much smaller than on Earth. Medical research is being carried out in outer space that could lead to a better understanding of diseases such as sickle-cell anemia.

Research Have students research the different kinds of medical projects done on space-shuttle missions.

Reading Check

Answer They are acting on different objects.

Quick Demo

Newton's Third Law

Materials party balloon, tape, 15-m piece of string, plastic straw, two vertical supports 10 m apart

Estimated Time two minutes

Procedure Put the string through the straw and stretch it between two vertical supports about 10 m apart. Blow up the balloon and tape it to the straw. Let go and have the students observe that air molecules pushing against the front of the balloon propels it backward.

Visual Learning

Figure 22 Review the forces that move the car shown here. Draw the car on the board, and indicate gas particles inside the rocket engine. Emphasize that the action force is the rocket engine pushing the gas particles, and the reaction force is the gas particles against the rocket engine. L2 LS **Visual-Spatial**

Space Astronauts who stay in outer space for extended periods of time may develop health problems. Their muscles, for example, may begin to weaken because they don't have to exert as much force to get the same reaction as they do on Earth. A branch of medicine called space medicine deals with the possible health problems that astronauts may experience. Research some other health risks that are involved in going into outer space. Do trips into outer space have any positive health benefits?

Action and Reaction Forces Don't Cancel If action and reaction forces are equal, you might wonder how some things ever happen. For example, how does a swimmer move through the water in a pool if each time she pushes on the water, the water pushes back on her? According to the third law of motion, action and reaction forces act on different objects. Thus, even though the forces are equal, they are not balanced because they act on different objects. In the case of the swimmer, as she "acts" on the water, the "reaction" of the water pushes her forward. Thus, a net force, or unbalanced force, acts on her so a change in her motion occurs. As the swimmer moves forward in the water, how does she make the water move?

Reading Check *Why don't action and reaction forces cancel?*

Rocket Propulsion Suppose you are standing on skates holding a softball. You exert a force on the softball when you throw the softball. According to Newton's third law, the softball exerts a force on you. This force pushes you in the direction opposite the softball's motion. Rockets use the same principle to move even in the vacuum of outer space. In the rocket engine, burning fuel produces hot gases. The rocket engine exerts a force on these gases and causes them to escape out the back of the rocket. By Newton's third law, the gases exert a force on the rocket and push it forward. The car in **Figure 22** uses a rocket engine to propel it forward. **Figure 23** shows how rockets were used to travel to the Moon.

Figure 22 If more gas is ejected from the rocket engine, or expelled at a greater velocity, the rocket engine will exert a larger force on the car.

Science Journal

Newton's Third Law Have students use Newton's third law to describe the similarities between a person walking on a sidewalk and a fish swimming in the ocean. A person exerts a force on the sidewalk, and the sidewalk pushes back on the person, moving the person forward. A fish pushes on water, and the reaction force of the water on the fish propels the fish forward. L1 LS **Linguistic**

Cultural Diversity

And the Rockets' Red Glare Centuries ago, the Chinese invented gunpowder. Although it was first used during celebrations, gunpowder was quickly adapted for war purposes. By the fourteenth century, Chinese armies were using it in rockets. When the gunpowder ignited, it expelled hot gases, which propelled the rockets forward.

NATIONAL GEOGRAPHIC **VISUALIZING ROCKET MOTION**

Figure 23

On the afternoon of July 16, 1969, *Apollo 11* lifted off from Cape Kennedy, Florida, bound for the Moon. Eight days later, the spacecraft returned to Earth, splashing down safely in the Pacific Ocean. The motion of the spacecraft to the Moon and back is governed by Newton's laws of motion.

◀ *Apollo 11* roars toward the Moon. At launch, a rocket's engines must produce enough force and acceleration to overcome the pull of Earth's gravity. A rocket's liftoff is an illustration of Newton's third law: For every action there is an equal and opposite reaction.

▲ As *Apollo* rises, it burns fuel and ejects its rocket booster engines. This decreases its mass, and helps *Apollo* move faster. This is Newton's second law in action: As mass decreases, acceleration can increase.

▶ The lunar module uses other engines to slow down and ease into a soft touchdown on the Moon. A day later, the same engines lift the lunar module again into outer space.

▲ After the lunar module returns to *Apollo,* the rocket fires its engines to set it into motion toward Earth. The rocket then shuts off its engines, moving according to Newton's first law. As it nears Earth, the rocket accelerates at an increasing rate because of Earth's gravity.

Visualizing Rocket Motion

Have students examine the pictures and read the captions. Then ask the following questions.

When *Apollo 11* was launched, what were the equal and opposite forces? The thrust from the rocket engines pushed on the rocket and the rocket pushed back.

As *Apollo* ejected its spent rocket booster, what equation described the relationship between mass and acceleration? $F = ma$

As the rocket returns to Earth, why is the rocket able to shut off its engines? The rocket will continue to move toward Earth after the engines are turned off because of inertia.

Activity

Apollo 11 Have the students write a poem about the *Apollo 11* mission and Newton's laws of motion. L2 LS **Linguistics**

Fun Fact

Squids and octopuses use Newton's third law as a means of propulsion. They take in water and forcibly expel it through a siphon in a sudden spurt that pushes them through the water. Squids are very streamlined and can achieve speeds of 37 km/h.

Differentiated Instruction

English-Language Learners Have students write a sentence that describes or includes each of the following words, and then organize the sentences into a paragraph about space travel: rocket, force, spacecraft, booster rocket, gravity, planet, the Moon.

Challenge Have students research the *Apollo 13* mission. Students should find out how the astronauts used Newton's law to safely return to Earth after a potentially life-threatening disaster occurred on-board. Have the students make multimedia presentations to the class about what they learned. L3 P

Discussion

Momentum in Football Momentum is important to football players, who use it to stop players on the other team. What can a football player do to increase his or her momentum? run faster or increase his or her mass

Momentum Equation

National Math Standards

Correlation to Mathematics Objectives

1, 2, 9

Answers to Practice Problems

1. 36,400 kg • m/s
2. 40 m/s
3. 65 kg
4. The momentum of the basketball is three times greater.

Virtual Labs

Crash! *How is momentum conserved in a vehicle collision?*

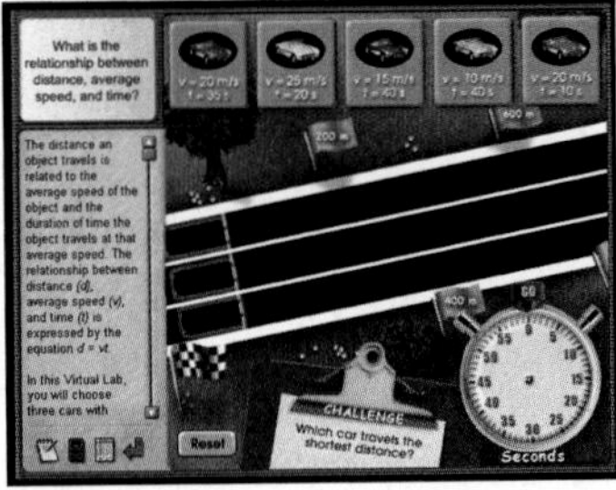

Momentum

A moving object has a property called momentum that is related to how much force is needed to change its motion. The **momentum** of an object is the product of its mass and velocity. Momentum is usually given the symbol p and can be calculated with the following equation:

Momentum Equation

momentum (kg m/s) = **mass** (kg) × velocity (m/s)

$$p = mv$$

The unit for momentum is kg•m/s. Just like velocity, momentum has a size and a direction. Suppose you know the speed of an object. Then the size of the momentum can be calculated by substituting the speed for the velocity in the above equation.

Momentum Equation

Solve for Momentum At the end of a race, a sprinter with a mass of 80.0 kg has a speed of 10.0 m/s. What is the sprinter's momentum?

1. **This is what you know:** mass: m = **80.0 kg**; velocity: v = **10.0 m/s**
2. **This is what you need to find:** momentum: p
3. **Use this formula:** $p = mv$
4. **Substitute:** the values of m and v into the formula and multiply. $p = (\mathbf{80.0})(10.0) = \mathbf{800.0}$
5. **Determine the units:** units of p = (units of m) × (units of v) = **kg** × m/s = **kg•m/s**

Answer: The sprinter's momentum is 800.0 kg m/s.

Science Online For more practice problems, go to page 834, and visit gpscience.com/extra_problems.

Practice Problems

1. What is the momentum of a car with a mass of 1,300 kg traveling at a speed of 28 m/s?
2. A baseball has a momentum of 6.0 kg•m/s. If the mass of the baseball is 0.15 kg, what is the baseball's speed?
3. What is the mass of a person walking at a speed of 0.8 m/s if the person's momentum is 52.0 kg•m/s?
4. **Challenge** The mass of a basketball is three times greater than the mass of a softball. Compare the momentum of a softball and a basketball if they both are moving at the same speed.

Differentiated Instruction

Challenge Newton actually worded his second law to state that force equals the change in momentum divided by the change in time. Explain how this is equivalent to, $F = ma$.

$F = ma$; $\Delta p = m\Delta v$; $F = \frac{\Delta p}{t}$

$F = \frac{(m\Delta v)}{t}$; $a = \frac{\Delta v}{t}$ so $F = ma$

L3 LS **Logical-Mathematical**

Teacher FYI

Momentum, Force, and Time The momentum change depends on the size of the net force acting on an object and the time over which the net force acts. A large force acting for a short time and a small force acting for a longer time can cause equal changes in momentum.

Force and Changing Momentum

If you catch a baseball, your hand might sting, even if you use a baseball glove. Your hand stings because the baseball exerted a force on your hand when it came to a stop, and its momentum changed.

Recall that acceleration is the difference between the initial and final velocity, divided by the time. Also, from Newton's second law, the net force on an object equals its mass times its acceleration. By combining these two relationships, Newton's second law can be written in this way:

$$F = (mv_f - mv_i)/t$$

In this equation mv_f is the final momentum and mv_i is the initial momentum. The equation says that the net force exerted on an object can be calculated by dividing its change in momentum by the time over which the change occurs. When you catch a ball, your hand exerts a force on the ball that stops it. The force you exert on the ball equals the force the ball exerts on your hand. This force depends on the mass and initial velocity of the ball, and how long it takes the ball to stop.

Law of Conservation of Momentum

The momentum of an object doesn't change unless its mass, velocity, or both change. Momentum, however, can be transferred from one object to another. Consider the game of pool shown in **Figure 24.**

When the cue ball hits the group of balls that are motionless, the cue ball slows down and the rest of the balls begin to move. The momentum the group of balls gained is equal to the momentum that the cue ball lost. The total momentum of all the balls just before and after the collision would be the same. If no other forces act on the balls, their total momentum is conserved—it isn't lost or created. This is the law of conservation of momentum—if a group of objects exerts forces only on each other, their total momentum doesn't change.

Figure 24 Momentum is transferred in collisions. **A** Before the collision, only the cue ball has momentum. **B** When the cue ball strikes the other balls, it transfers some of its momentum to them.

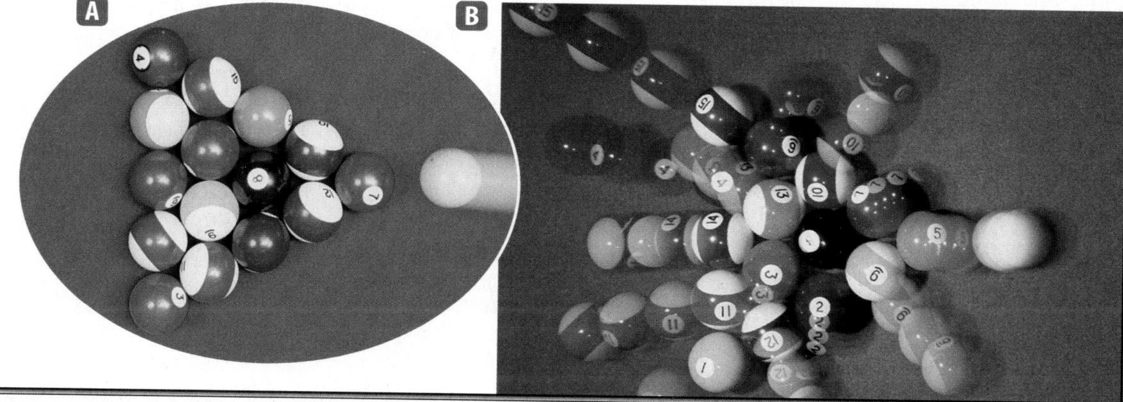

Use an Analogy

Money as Momentum Conservation of momentum can be compared with the use of money to buy and sell things. People may exchange money back and forth with each other, but unless more is minted by the government, the amount of money remains constant.

Discussion

Recoil Speed In a circus, a 50-kg clown is shot out of a cannon at 20 m/s. What is the recoil speed of the cannon if it has a mass of 250 kg? Because momentum is conserved, the momentum of the cannon will be equal to the momentum of the clown. The momentum of the clown is 50 kg × 20 m/s = 1,000 kg · m/s. For the cannon, therefore, mv = 1,000 kg · m/s = (250 kg)v. Solving for v, you find that v = (1,000 kg · m/s) ÷ 4 250 kg = 4 m/s.

L2 IS **Logical-Mathematical**

Quick Demo

Conservation of Momentum

Materials two marbles, ring stand, glue

Estimated Time 15 minutes

Procedure Demonstrate conservation of momentum using two identical marbles. Use superglue to attach a string to one marble. Fasten the string to a ring stand so the marble hangs just above the tabletop. Place the second marble on the table next to the first marble. Pull back the first marble, making sure the string is taut, and release it toward the other marble. The momentum of the first marble is transferred to the second. L2 IS **Visual-Spatial**

Visual Learning

Figure 24 Point out that the balls scatter left and right as they are deflected by the cue ball. Tell students that momentum is conserved separately in each direction. The sum of the forward velocities of the balls equals the cue ball's initial velocity. The sum of the left velocities is equal to the sum of the right velocities. Why do the balls eventually slow and stop? friction

Caption Answer

Figure 25 They will move away from each other with the same speed.

Visual Learning

Figure 25 Tell students that to apply conservation of momentum you must define the system you are referring to. Have them define the system shown in **Figure 25.** the table and the pucks L2 LS **Visual-Spatial**

3 Assess

DAILY INTERVENTION

Check for Understanding

Visual-Kinesthetic Have two students of different sizes stand facing one another and push on each others hands, palm to palm without either one pushing the other over. Ask who is exerting the larger force. They both exert the same force. Have one student stand in stockinged feet so that he or she slides when pushed. Now which one exerts the greater force? They are still the same. Ask, if the forces are the same, why does one move and not the other? One has a higher frictional force keeping him or her stationary.

Reteach

Action/reaction Ask students to draw and explain action/reaction force arrows for a box sitting on the ground and for a person running. L2 LS **Visual-Spatial**

Assessment

Process Provide students with photographs of various types of activities or collisions. Have them describe how momentum is conserved in each situation. Use **Performance Assessment in the Science Classroom,** p. 89.

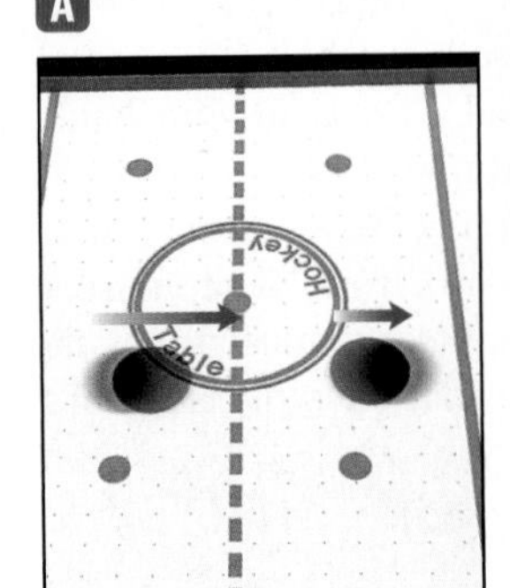

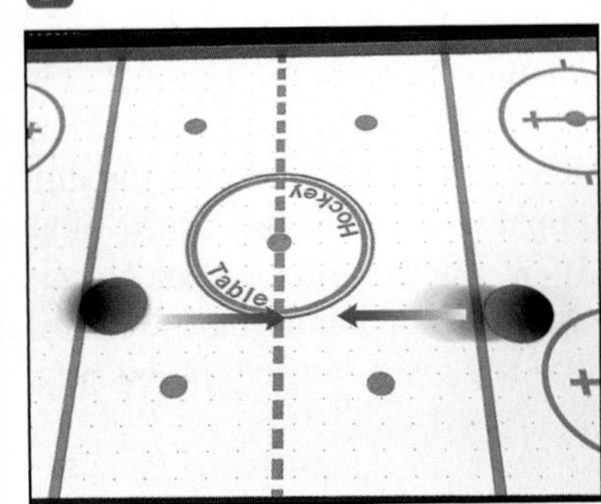

Figure 25 The results of a collision depend on the momentum of each object. **A** When the first puck hits the second puck from behind, it gives the second puck momentum in the same direction. **B** If the pucks are speeding toward each other with the same speed, the total momentum is zero.
Predict *how the pucks will move after they collide.*

When Objects Collide Collisions of two air hockey pucks are shown in **Figure 25.** Suppose one of the pucks was moving in one direction and another struck it from behind. The first puck would continue to move in the same direction but more quickly. The second puck has given it more momentum in the same direction. What if two pucks of equal mass were moving toward each other with the same speed? They would have the same momentum, but in opposite directions. So the total momentum would be zero. After the pucks collide, each would reverse direction, and move with the same speed. The total momentum would be zero again.

section 3 review

Summary

Newton's Third Law

- According to Newton's third law of motion, for every action force, there is an equal and opposite reaction force.
- Action and reaction forces act on different objects.

Momentum

- The momentum of an object is the product of its mass and velocity:

$$p = mv$$

- The net force on an object can be calculated by dividing its change in momentum by the time over which the change occurs.

The Law of Conservation of Momentum

- According to the law of conservation of momentum, if objects exert forces only on each other, their total momentum is conserved.
- In a collision, momentum is transferred from one object to another.

Self Check

1. **Determine** You push against a wall with a force of 50 N. If the wall doesn't move, what is the net force on you?
2. **Explain** how a rocket can move through outer space where there is no matter for it to push on.
3. **Compare** the momentum of a 6,300-kg elephant walking 0.11 m/s and a 50-kg dolphin swimming 10.4 m/s.
4. **Describe** what happens to the momentum of two billiard balls that collide.
5. **Think Critically** A ballet director assigns slow, graceful steps to larger dancers, and quick movements to smaller dancers. Why is this plan successful?

Applying Math

6. **Calculate Momentum** What is the momentum of a 100-kg football player running at a speed of 4 m/s?
7. **Calculate Force** What is the force exerted by a catcher's glove on a 0.15-kg baseball moving at 35 m/s that is stopped in 0.02 s?

gpscience.com/self_check_quiz

section 3 review

1. You are not moving, so $F = 0$. The wall pushes back on you with a force = to the force you push on it. The static friction between your feet and the floor keeps you from moving.
2. The rocket exerts a force on gas molecules, pushing them backward. The gas molecules exert a force on the rocket, pushing it forward.
3. The dolphin's momentum is $p = (50\ \text{kg})(10.4\ \text{m/s}) =$ 520 kg·m/s. The elephant's momentum is $p = (6{,}300\ \text{kg})(0.11\ \text{m/s}) =$ 693 kg·m/s.
4. The two balls exchange momentum.
5. It takes less force for a person with less mass to move quickly than for a person with more mass to do so.
6. $p = mv = 100\ \text{kg} \times 4\ \text{m/s} = 400\ \text{kg m/s}$
7. $F = \frac{(mv_f - mv_i)}{t} = 0 - \frac{(0.15\ \text{kg} \times 35\ \text{m/s})}{(0.02\ \text{s})} = 262\ \text{N}$

MEASURING THE EFFECTS OF AIR RESISTANCE

If you dropped a bowling ball and a feather from the same height on the Moon, they would both hit the surface at the same time. All objects dropped on Earth are attracted to the ground with the same acceleration. But on Earth, a bowling ball and a feather will not hit the ground at the same time. Air resistance slows the feather down.

Real-World Question

How does air resistance affect the acceleration of falling objects?

Goals

- **Measure** the effect of air resistance on sheets of paper with different shapes.
- **Design** and create a shape from a piece of paper that maximizes air resistance.

Materials

paper (4 sheets of equal size)
scissors
meterstick
stopwatch
masking tape

Safety Precautions

Procedure

1. Copy the data table above in your Science Journal, or create it on a computer.
2. Measure a height of 2.5 m on the wall and mark the height with a piece of masking tape.
3. Have one group member drop the flat sheet of paper from the 2.5-m mark. Use the stopwatch to time how long it takes for the paper to reach the ground. Record your time in your data table.

Effects of Air Resistance

Paper Type	Time
Flat paper	
Loosely crumpled paper	Answers will vary.
Tightly crumpled paper	
Your paper design	

4. Crumple a sheet of paper into a loose ball and repeat step 3.
5. Crumple a sheet of paper into a tight ball and repeat step 3.
6. Use scissors to shape a piece of paper so that it will fall slowly. You may cut, tear, or fold your paper into any design you choose.

Conclude and Apply

1. **Compare** the falling times of the different sheets of paper.
2. **Explain** why the different-shaped papers fell at different speeds.
3. **Explain** how your design caused the force of air resistance on the paper to be greater than the air resistance on the other paper shapes.

Communicating Your Data

Compare your paper design with the designs created by your classmates. As a class, compile a list of characteristics that increase air resistance.

Real-World Question

Purpose Students will observe the effect of air resistance on the gravitational acceleration of different shaped sheets of paper. L2 Kinesthetic

Process Skills measure, recognize cause and effect, formulate models, compare, infer

Time Required 30 minutes

Procedure

Alternate Materials Make sure the sheets of paper are identical.

Safety Precautions Caution students to be careful when standing on stools or ladders.

Teaching Strategies

- Stage a contest to determine which design maximizes the effect of air resistance.
- Have students practice timing the falling paper before entering data in their tables.

Troubleshooting Have students do at least three trials for each paper drop and record the average time in their data table.

Conclude and Apply

1. Shapes with greater exposed surface areas will create more air resistance and fall more slowly.
2. Answers will vary.
3. A spread eagle position increases the surface area of the diver allowing more air resistance to slow her fall.

Assessment

Process Show students several photographs of falling sky divers and ask them to analyze the sky divers' body positions and infer the order of their velocities. Use **Performance Assessment in the Science Classroom,** p. 89.

Communicating Your Data

Encourage students to electronically represent their design using the appropriate software.

Real-World Question

Purpose Students will observe the effects of mass and velocity on the momentum of rolling objects. L2 LS **Kinesthetic**

Process Skills observe, measure, compare, use numbers, use space/time relationship, sequence, recognize cause and effect, infer

Time Required one class period

Procedure

Alternate Materials A foam rubber ball, golf ball, or hockey ball could replace the tennis ball and racquetball.

Safety Precautions Caution students never to throw the balls during the activity and to roll the baseball only when other students are clear of the ball's path.

Teaching Strategy Have students practice rolling the balls at different speeds and rolling the balls into the softball. Clear away floor space in your room or take students outside to provide enough space for each group.

LAB

The Momentum of Colliding Objects

Goals

- **Observe** and calculate the momentum of different balls.
- **Compare** the results of collisions involving different amounts of momentum.

Materials

meterstick
softball
racquetball
tennis ball
baseball
stopwatch
masking tape
balance

Safety Precautions

Real-World Question

Many scientists hypothesize that dinosaurs became extinct 65 million years ago when an asteroid collided with Earth. The asteroid's diameter was probably no more than 10 km. Earth's diameter is more than 12,700 km. How could an object that size change Earth's climate enough to cause the extinction of animals that had dominated life on Earth for 140 million years? The asteroid could have caused such damage because it may have been traveling at a velocity of 50 m/s, and had a huge amount of momentum. The combination of an object's velocity and mass will determine how much force it can exert. How do the mass and velocity of a moving object affect its momentum?

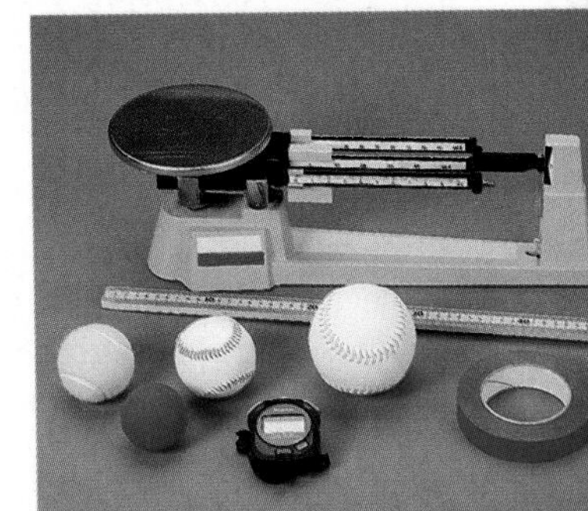

Momentum of Colliding Balls

Action	Time	Velocity	Mass	Momentum	Distance softball moved
Racquetball rolled slowly			0.04		
Racquetball rolled quickly			0.04		
Tennis ball rolled slowly	Answers will vary.	Answers will vary.	0.06	Answers will vary.	Answers will vary.
Tennis ball rolled quickly			0.06		
Baseball rolled slowly			0.14		
Baseball rolled quickly			0.14		

Active Reading

Synthesis Journal In this strategy, students reflect on a project, a paper, or a performance task and plan for personal application. Have each student divide a sheet of paper in three sections and record *What I did, What I learned,* and *How I can use it.* Have students write a Synthesis Journal related to this lab.

Alternative Inquiry Lab

Momentum Supply students with the materials listed for this lab, and ask them to find a way to give each ball the same momentum. Have them design a data table, and a method to test when the momentum of each ball is equal to the others.

90 CHAPTER 3 Forces

Using Scientific Methods

Procedure

1. Copy the data table on the previous page in your Science Journal.
2. Use the balance to measure the mass of the racquetball, tennis ball, and baseball. Record these masses in your data table.
3. Measure a 2-m distance on the floor and mark it with two pieces of masking tape.
4. Place the softball on one piece of tape. Starting from the other piece of tape, slowly roll the racquetball toward the center of the softball.
5. Use a stopwatch to time how long it takes the racquetball to roll the 2-m distance and hit the softball. Record this time in your data table.
6. Measure and record the distance the racquetball moved the softball.
7. Repeat steps 4–6, rolling the racquetball quickly.
8. Repeat steps 4–6, rolling the tennis ball slowly, then quickly.
9. Repeat steps 4–6, rolling the baseball slowly, then quickly.

Distance Softball Moved and Momentum of Colliding Ball

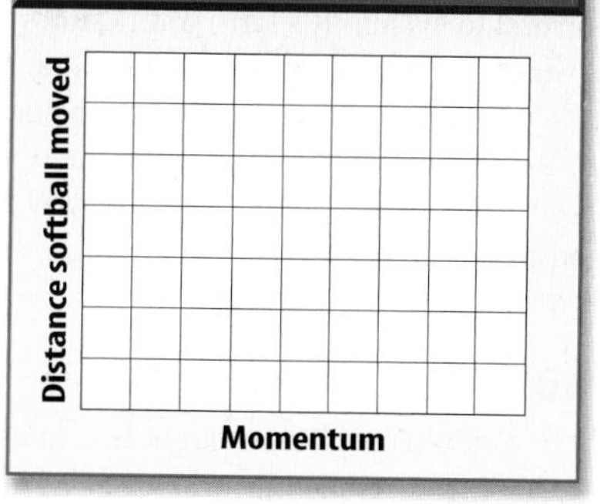

(Graph grid — vertical axis: Distance softball moved; horizontal axis: Momentum)

Analyze Your Data

1. **Calculate** the momentum for each type of ball and action using the formula $p = mv$. Record your calculations in the data table.
2. **Graph** the relationship between the momentum of each ball and the distance the softball was moved using a graph like the one shown.

Conclude and Apply

1. **Infer** from your graph how the distance the softball moves after each collision depends on the momentum of the ball that hits it.
2. **Explain** how the motion of the balls after they collide can be determined by Newton's laws of motion.

Communicating Your Data

Compare your graph with the graphs made by other students in your class. **Discuss** why the graphs might look different.

Tie to Prior Knowledge Students will be aware that more massive moving objects and objects traveling with greater speeds will produce more force.

Analyze Your Data

Expected Outcome The high velocity baseball will have the greatest momentum, and the slow velocity racquetball will have the least momentum.

Answers to Questions

1. Calculations for momentum should show that momentum increases as mass/velocity increases.
2. The graph should have a positive (diagonally upward) slope.

Error Analysis Have students compare their graphs with other lab groups. Ask which of their predictions matched their results, and have them explain those that did not. Have students identify possible sources of measurement, timing or procedural errors.

Conclude and Apply

1. The graph should show that as the momentum of the colliding ball increases, so does the distance the softball moves.
2. By the third law of motion, when the balls collide, they exert the same force on each other. The softball has the larger mass, so according to the second law its acceleration will be less than the smaller ball. The softball will move more slowly after the collision and the other ball will move more quickly.

Assessment

Oral Ask students if it is possible for an object to have a negative value for momentum. Yes; velocity has both direction and magnitude. Once a positive direction is chosen, velocity in the other direction is negative and momentum is negative. Use **Performance Assessment in the Science Classroom,** p. 89.

Communicating Your Data

Divide the class into small groups for the discussion so that all students have the opportunity to describe their experiences with the sports.

TIME

Content Background

Newton's three laws of motion and the law of universal gravitation have proven to be able to describe the motion of objects ranging from galaxies to raindrops. Newton believed that the forces involved in the behavior of ordinary objects, such as the forces that caused an apple to fall from a tree, were the same forces that controlled the motions of planets and moons. The law of universal gravitation and the three laws of motion applied to all objects. Newton also believed that matter was made of indivisible particles and that the forces of gravity, electricity, and magnetism determined the behavior of these particles.

Newton was correct in that gravity, electricity, and magnetism also act at the atomic level. However, the gravitational force is so much weaker than the electromagnetic force that it can be ignored at the atomic level. In addition, there are two other forces, the strong and weak nuclear forces, that are involved in nuclear reactions and were unknown to Newton.

Historical significance

What Newton contributed to science during his first 25 years cannot be underestimated. More than 300 years later, scientists and engineers still use his laws to understand natural phenomena and to design and develop new technologies.

TIME **SCIENCE** AND HISTORY

SCIENCE CAN CHANGE THE COURSE OF HISTORY!

Newton and the Plague

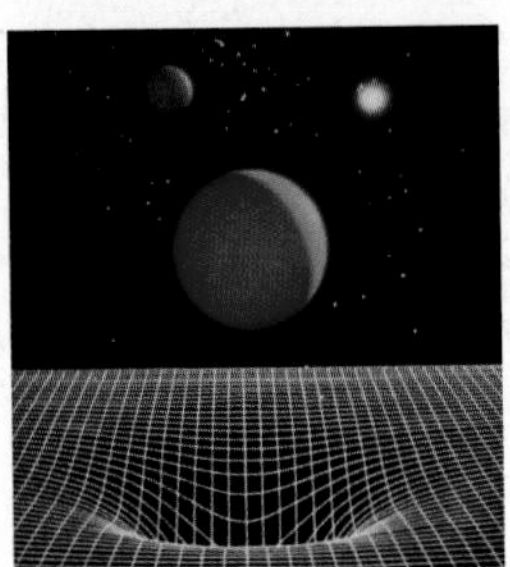

In Einstein's theory of general relativity, gravity is due to a distortion in space-time.

In 1665, the bubonic plague swept through England and other parts of Europe. Isaac Newton, then a 23-year-old university student, returned to his family's farm until Cambridge university reopened. To occupy his time, Newton made a list of 22 questions. During the next 18 months, Newton buried himself in the search for answers. And in that brief time, Newton developed calculus, the three laws of motion, and the universal law of gravitation!

The Laws of Motion

Earlier philosophers thought that force was necessary to keep an object moving. By analyzing the data collected by Galileo and others, Newton realized that forces did not cause motion. Instead, forces cause a change in motion. Newton came to understand that force and acceleration were related and that objects exert equal and opposite forces on each other. Newton's three laws of motion were able to explain how all things moved, from an apple falling from a tree to the motions of the moon and the planets, in terms of force, mass, and acceleration.

Isaac Newton was a university student when he developed the laws of motion.

What is gravity?

Using the calculus and data on the motion of the planets, Newton deduced the law of universal gravitation. This law enabled the force of gravity between any two objects to be calculated, if their masses and the distance between them were known.

Newton was able to show mathematically that the law of universal gravitation predicted that the planets' orbits should be ellipses, just as Johannes Kepler had discovered two generations earlier. The application of Newton's laws of motion and the law of universal gravitation also were able to explain phenomena such as tides, the motion of the moon and the planets, and the bulge at the Earth's equator.

A Different View of Gravity

In 1916, Albert Einstein proposed a different model for gravity called the general theory of relativity. In Einstein's model, objects create distortions in space-time, like a bowling ball dropped on a sheet. What we see as the force of gravity is the motion of an object on distorted space-time. Today, Einstein's theory is used to help explain the nature of the big bang and the structure of the universe.

Investigate Research how both Newton's law of gravitation and Einstein's general theory of relativity have been used to develop the current model of the universe.

For more information, visit gpscience.com/time

Investigate The existence of dark matter has been hypothesized to explain the rotations and motions of galaxies which seem to violate Newton's laws of motion. For Newton's laws to be satisfied, these galaxies must contain additional matter that has not been detected directly. Einstein's general theory of relativity explains how the structure of space-time changed as the universe expanded after the big bang.

Resources for Teachers and Students

Isaac Newton: The Greatest Scientist of All Time Margaret Jean Anderson, Enslow Publishers, Incorporated., 1996

Albert Einstein: Physicist and Genius. Joyce Goldenstern, Enslow Publishers, Incorporated., 1994

Reviewing Main Ideas

Section 1 Newton's Second Law

1. Newton's second law of motion states that a net force causes an object to accelerate in the direction of the net force and that the acceleration is given by

$$a = \frac{F_{net}}{m}$$

2. Friction is a force opposing the sliding motion of two surfaces in contact. Friction is caused by microwelds that form where the surfaces are in contact.

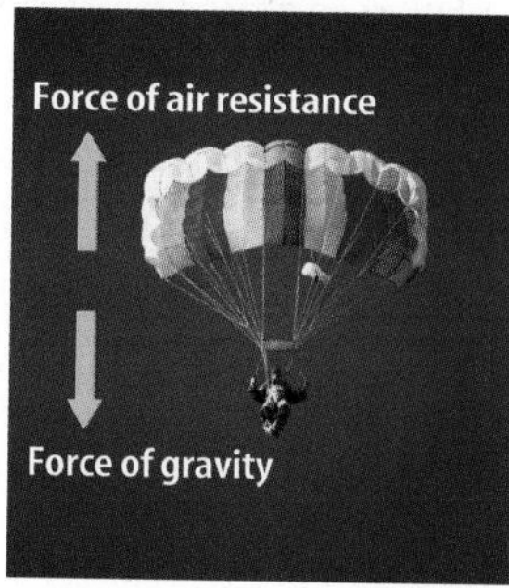

3. Air resistance opposes the motion of objects moving through the air.

Section 2 Gravity

1. Gravity is an attractive force between any two objects with mass. The gravitational force depends on the masses of the objects and the distance between them.
2. The gravitational acceleration, g, near Earth's surface equals 9.8 m/s^2. The force of gravity on an object with mass, m, is:

$$F = mg$$

3. The weight of an object near Earth's surface is:

$$W = mg$$

4. Projectiles travel in a curved path because of their horizontal motion and vertical acceleration due to gravity.
5. The centripetal force is the net force on an object in circular motion and is directed toward the center of the circular path.

Section 3 The Third Law of Motion

1. Newton's third law of motion states that for every action there is an equal and opposite reaction.
2. The momentum of an object can be calculated by the equation $p = mv$.

3. When two objects collide, momentum can be conserved. Some of the momentum from one object is transferred to the other.

FOLDABLES Use the Foldable that you made at the beginning of this chapter to help you review the different types of friction.

Science Online gpscience.com/interactive_tutor

chapter 3 Study Guide

Reviewing Main Ideas

Summary statements can be used by students to review the major concepts of the chapter.

Visit gpscience.com
/self_check_quiz
/interactive_tutor
/vocabulary_puzzlemaker
/chapter_review
/standardized_test

Assessment Transparency

For additional assessment questions, use the *Assessment Transparency* located in the transparency book.

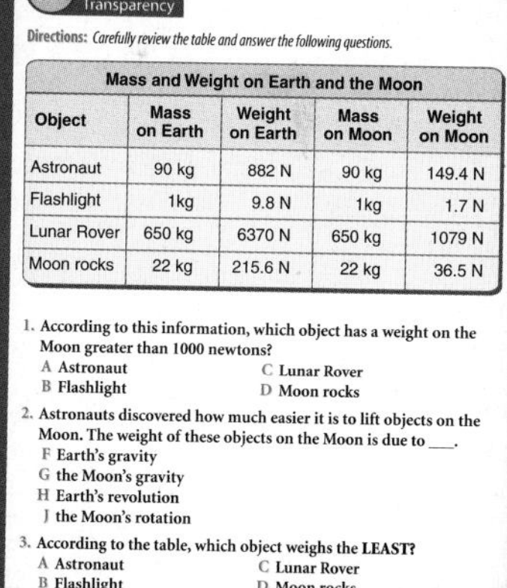

Assessment Transparency **Forces**

Directions: *Carefully review the table and answer the following questions.*

Mass and Weight on Earth and the Moon				
Object	Mass on Earth	Weight on Earth	Mass on Moon	Weight on Moon
Astronaut	90 kg	882 N	90 kg	149.4 N
Flashlight	1kg	9.8 N	1kg	1.7 N
Lunar Rover	650 kg	6370 N	650 kg	1079 N
Moon rocks	22 kg	215.6 N	22 kg	36.5 N

1. According to this information, which object has a weight on the Moon greater than 1000 newtons?
   A Astronaut
   B Flashlight
   C Lunar Rover
   D Moon rocks
2. Astronauts discovered how much easier it is to lift objects on the Moon. The weight of these objects on the Moon is due to ___.
   F Earth's gravity
   G the Moon's gravity
   H Earth's revolution
   J the Moon's rotation
3. According to the table, which object weighs the LEAST?
   A Astronaut
   B Flashlight
   C Lunar Rover
   D Moon rocks
4. Based on the data in the table, about how many times greater is the weight of these objects on Earth than on the Moon?
   F two times
   G four times
   H six times
   J eight times

L2

Forces

FOLDABLES Have students use their Foldables to review the content of this chapter. Identify the action of sliding, rolling, and static friction on a moving bicycle. Sliding fraction exists around the axles and between the brake pads and the tire. Rolling friction between the tires and the road pushes the bicycle forward.

Using Vocabulary

1. Newton's third law of motion
2. static friction
3. weight
4. centripetal force
5. gravity
6. Newton's second law of motion

Checking Concepts

7. D
8. A
9. B
10. B
11. B
12. C
13. A
14. C

Interpreting Graphics

15. See students' page
16. C
17. The force of air resistance is different on the different objects.
18. A

Using Vocabulary

air resistance p. 73
centripetal acceleration p. 81
centripetal force p. 81
friction p. 70
gravity p. 75
momentum p. 86
Newton's 2nd law of motion p. 69
Newton's 3rd law of motion p. 83
sliding friction p. 72
static friction p. 71
weight p. 77

Complete each statement using a word(s) from the vocabulary list above.

1. The way in which objects exert forces on each other is described by ________.
2. ________ prevents surfaces in contact from sliding past each other.
3. The ________ of an object is different on other planets in the solar system.
4. When an object moves in a circular path, the net force is called a(n) ________.
5. The attractive force between two objects that depends on their masses and the distance between them is ________.
6. ________ relates the net force exerted on an object to its mass and acceleration.

Checking Concepts

Choose the best answer for each question.

7. What is the gravitational force exerted on an object called?
   A) centripetal force
   B) friction
   C) momentum
   D) weight
8. Which of the following best describes why projectiles move in a curved path?
   A) They have horizontal velocity and vertical acceleration.
   B) They have momentum.
   C) They have mass.
   D) They have weight.
9. Which of the following explains why astronauts seem weightless in orbit?
   A) Earth's gravity is much less in orbit.
   B) The space shuttle is in free fall.
   C) The gravity of Earth and the Sun cancel.
   D) The centripetal force on the shuttle balances Earth's gravity.
10. Which of the following exerts the strongest gravitational force on you?
   A) the Moon
   B) Earth
   C) the Sun
   D) this book

Use the graph below to answer question 11.

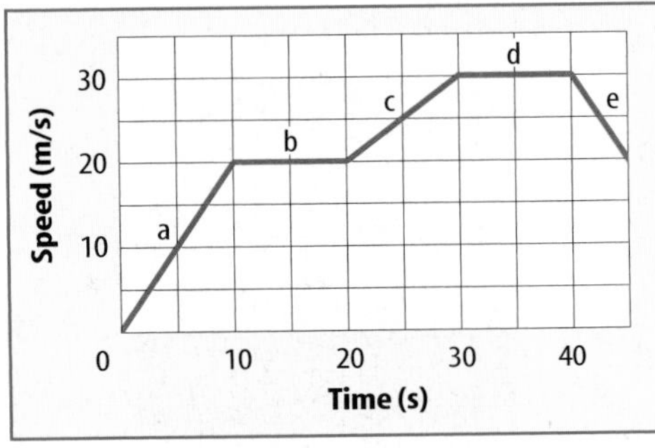

11. The graph shows the speed of a car moving in a straight line. Over which segments are the forces on the car balanced?
   A) A and C
   B) B and D
   C) C and E
   D) D only
12. Which of the following is true about an object in free fall?
   A) Its acceleration depends on its mass.
   B) It has no inertia.
   C) It pulls on Earth, and Earth pulls on it.
   D) Its momentum is constant.
13. The acceleration of an object is in the same direction as which of the following?
   A) net force
   B) air resistance
   C) static friction
   D) gravity
14. Which of the following is NOT a force?
   A) weight
   B) friction
   C) momentum
   D) air resistance

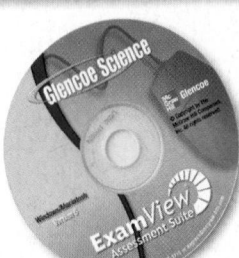

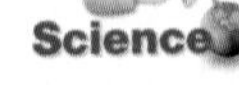
Science Online gpscience.com/vocabulary_puzzlemaker

Interpreting Graphics

15. Copy and complete the following concept map on forces.

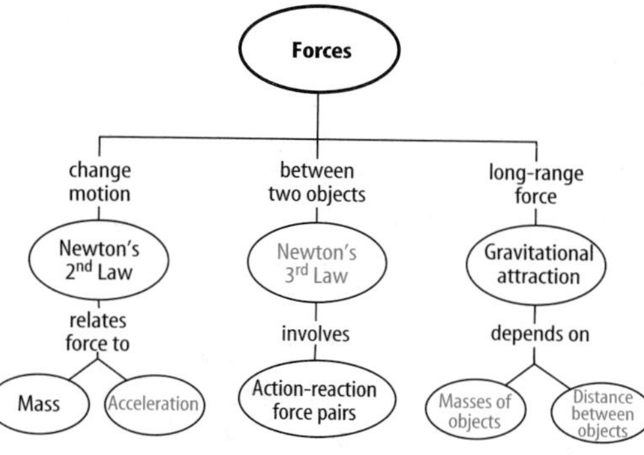

Use the table below to answer questions 16–18.

Time of Fall for Dropped Objects

Object	Mass (g)	Time of Fall (s)
A	5.0	2.0
B	5.0	1.0
C	30.0	0.5
D	35.0	1.5

16. If the objects in the data table above all fell the same distance, which object fell with the greatest average speed?

17. Explain why all four objects don't fall with the same speed.

18. On which object was the force of air resistance the greatest?

Thinking Critically

19. **Determine** the direction of the net force on a book sliding on a table if the book is slowing down.

20. **Explain** whether there can be any forces acting on a car moving in a straight line with constant speed.

21. **Explain** You pull a door open. If the force the door exerts on you is equal to the force you exert on the door, why don't you move?

22. **Predict** Suppose you are standing on a bathroom scale next to a sink. How does the reading on the scale change if you push down on the sink?

23. **Describe** the action and reaction force pairs involved when an object falls toward Earth. Ignore the effects of air resistance.

Applying Math

24. **Calculate Mass** Find your mass if a scale on Earth reads 650 N when you stand on it.

25. **Calculate Acceleration of Gravity** You weigh yourself at the top of a high mountain and the scale reads 720 N. If your mass is 75 kg, what is the acceleration of gravity at your location?

Use the figure below to answer question 26.

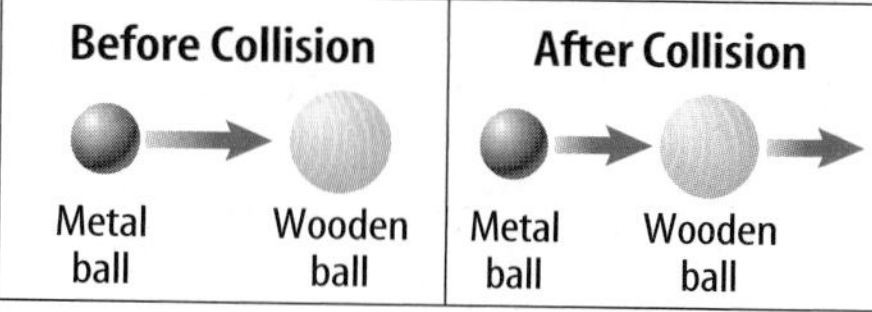

26. **Calculate Speed** The 2-kg metal ball moving at a speed of 3 m/s strikes a 1-kg wooden ball that is at rest. After the collision, the speed of the metal ball is 1 m/s. Assuming momentum is conserved, what is the speed of the wooden ball?

27. **Calculate Mass** Find the mass of a car that has a speed of 30 m/s and a momentum of 45,000 kg,m/s.

28. **Calculate Sliding Friction** A box being pushed with a force of 85 N slides along the floor with a constant speed. What is the force of sliding friction on the box?

Science Online gpscience.com/chapter_review

Thinking Critically

19. The book is slowing down, so the acceleration is in the direction opposite the motion. The net force is in the same direction as the acceleration.

20. Yes, there can be forces acting on the car, but the forces are balanced so that the net force is zero.

21. The force of static friction between your feet and the floor balances the force the door exerts on you.

22. The reading on the scale decreases because the sink pushes up on you. The upward force exerted by the scale and the sink now balance your weight, so the force exerted by the scale decreases.

23. Earth pulls on the object and the object pulls on Earth.

Applying Math

National Math Standards

1, 2, 9

24. $m = \frac{F}{g} = \frac{(650\text{ N})}{(9.8\text{ m/s}^2)} = 66.3\text{ kg}$

25. $g = \frac{F}{m} = \frac{(720\text{ N})}{(75\text{ kg})} = 9.6\text{ m/s}^2$

26. $m_1v_1 = m_1v_1' + m_2v_2$

$2\text{ kg} \times 3\text{ m/s} = 6\text{ kg m/s}$

$2\text{ kg} \times 1\text{ m/s} = 2\text{ kg m/s}$

$6\text{ kg m/s} - 2\text{ kg m/s} = 4\text{ kg m/s}$

$\frac{(4\text{ kg m/s})}{1\text{ kg}} = 4\text{ m/s}$

27. $m = \frac{p}{v} = \frac{(45{,}000\text{ kg m/s})}{(30\text{ m/s})} = 1500\text{ kg}$

28. $F = 85\text{ N}$

Assessment Resources

Reproducible Masters

Chapter *Fast File* Resources
- Chapter Review, pp. 39–40
- Chapter Tests, pp. 41–44
- Assessment Transparency Activity, p. 51

Glencoe Science Web site
- Chapter Review Test
- Standardized Test Practice

Glencoe Technology
- Assessment Transparency
- *ExamView® Assessment Suite*
- MindJogger Videoquiz
- Interactive Chalkboard

Answer Sheet A practice answer sheet can be found at gpscience.com/answer_sheet.

Name Date Class

Standardized Test Practice

Assessment Student Recording Sheet *Use with pages 788–789 of the Student Edition*

Standardized Test Practice

Part 1 Multiple Choice

Select the best answer from the choices given and fill in the corresponding oval.

1.–14. Ⓐ Ⓑ Ⓒ Ⓓ

Part 2 Constructed Response/Grid In

Record and bubble in your answers on the grids below.

15. 16. 17.

Record your answers for Questions 18–21 on a separate sheet of paper.

SAMPLE

169

Part 1 Multiple Choice

1. C **4.** C **7.** B

2. C **5.** A

3. A **6.** B

chapter 3 Standardized Test Practice

Part 1 Multiple Choice

Record your answers on the answer sheet provided by your teacher or on a sheet of paper.

1. The net force on an object moving with constant speed in circular motion is in which direction?

A. downward

B. opposite to the object's motion

C. toward the center of the circle

D. in the direction of the object's velocity

Use the table below to answer questions 2–4.

Object in Free Fall with Air Resistance	
Time (s)	**Speed (m/s)**
0	0
1	9.1
2	15.1
3	18.1
4	19.3
5	19.9

2. According to the trend in these data, which of the following values is most likely the speed of the object after falling for 6 s?

A. 26.7 m/s **C.** 20.1 m/s

B. 15.1 m/s **D.** 0 m/s

3. Over which of the following time intervals is the acceleration of the object the greatest?

A. 0 s to 1 s

B. 1 s to 2 s

C. 4 s to 5 s

D. The acceleration is constant.

4. Over which of the following time intervals is the force on the object the smallest?

A. 0 s to 1 s **C.** 4 s to 5 s

B. 1 s to 2 s **D.** The force is constant.

5. Which of the following would cause the gravitational force between object A and object B to increase?

A. Decrease the distance between them.

B. Increase the distance between them.

C. Decrease the mass of object A.

D. Decrease the mass of both objects.

Use the graphs below to answer questions 6–7.

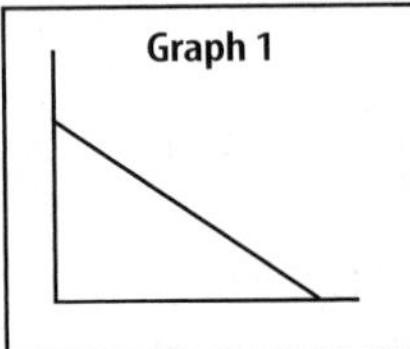

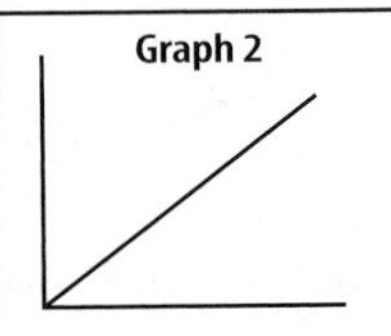

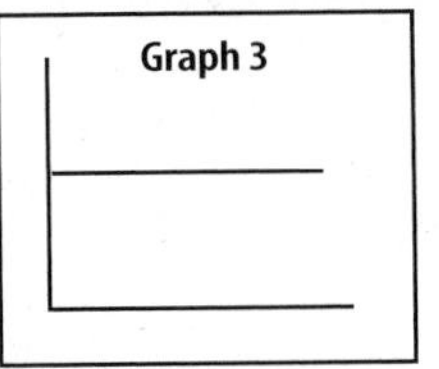

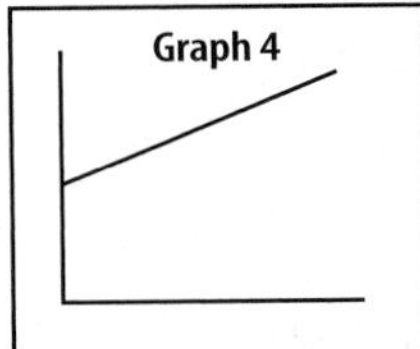

6. Which of the graphs above shows how the force on an object changes if the mass increases and the acceleration stays constant?

A. Graph 1 **C.** Graph 3

B. Graph 2 **D.** Graph 4

7. Which of the graphs above shows how the force on an object changes if the acceleration increases and the mass stays constant?

A. Graph 1 **C.** Graph 3

B. Graph 2 **D.** Graph 4

Test-Taking Tip

Keep Track of Time If you are taking a timed test, keep track of time during the test. If you find you are spending too much time on a multiple-choice question, mark your best guess and move on.

Part 2 Short Response/Grid In

8. 90 N

9. Force of gravity on skydiver $= (60\ \text{kg})(9.8\ \text{m/s}^2) = 588\ \text{N}$, net force on sky diver $= 588\ \text{N} - 300\ \text{N} = 288\ \text{N}$,

$$a = \frac{F_{net}}{m} = \frac{(288\ \text{N})}{(60\ \text{kg})} = 4.8\ \text{m/s}^2$$

10. The mass of the truck decreases while the net force remains the same, so the truck's acceleration increases.

11. Both balls have fallen the same distance after one second. Their vertical motion is independent of their horizontal motion.

12. It is less, because an object at this height is farther from Earth than an object at Earth's surface. According to the law of universal gravitation, the force of gravity decreases as the distance between objects increases. Because the force of gravity decreases, the acceleration of gravity decreases.

Part 2 Short Response/Grid In

Record your answers on the answer sheet provided by your teacher or on a sheet of paper.

8. You are pushing a 30-kg wooden crate across the floor. The force of sliding friction on the crate is 90 N. How much force must you exert on the crate to keep it moving with a constant velocity?

9. A sky diver with a mass of 60 kg jumps from an airplane. Five seconds after jumping the force of air resistance on the sky diver is 300 N. What is the sky diver's acceleration five seconds after jumping?

10. A pickup truck is carrying a load of gravel. The driver hits a bump and gravel falls out, so that the mass of the truck is one half as large after hitting the bump. If the net force on the truck doesn't change, how does the truck's acceleration change?

Use the figure below to answer question 11.

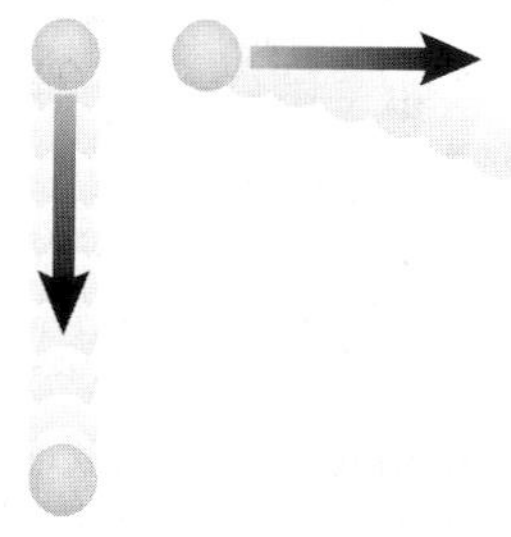

11. Two balls are at the same height. One ball is dropped and the other initially moves horizontally, as shown in the figure above. After one second, which ball has fallen the greatest vertical distance?

12. How does the acceleration of gravity 5,000 km above Earth's surface compare with the acceleration of gravity at Earth's surface?

Part 3 Open Ended

Record your answers on a sheet of paper.

13. You push on a rolling ball so that the direction of your push is different from the direction of the ball's motion. After you push, will the ball be moving in the same direction that you pushed? Explain.

14. Two balls are dropped from an airplane. Both balls are the same size, but one has a mass ten-times greater than the other. The force of air resistance on each ball depends on the ball's speed. Explain whether both balls will reach the same terminal velocity.

Use the graph below to answer question 15.

Speed of Sliding Book

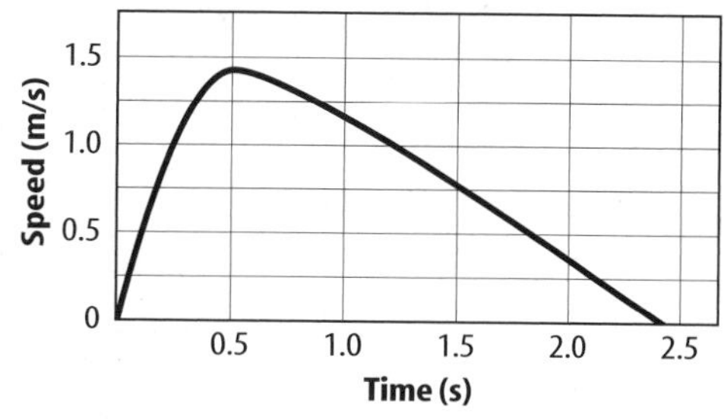

15. The graph above shows the how the speed of a book changes as it slides across a table. Over what time interval is the net force on the book in the opposite direction of the book's motion?

16. When the space shuttle is launched from Earth, the rocket engines burn fuel and apply a constant force on the shuttle until they burn out. Explain why the shuttles acceleration increases while the rocket engines are burning fuel.

17. Catching a hard-thrown baseball with your bare hand can cause your hand to sting. Explain why using a baseball glove reduces the sting when you catch a ball.

Part 3 Open Ended

13. No. The ball will accelerate in the direction of your push. The change in its velocity will be in the direction of your push, so the ball will change direction.

14. To reach terminal velocity, the force of air resistance on the more massive ball must be greater to balance its larger weight. Air resistance becomes larger as the ball's speed increases, so the more massive ball will be moving faster when air resistance is large enough to balance its greater weight.

15. After 0.5 s the book is slowing down, so the acceleration is opposite to the book's direction of motion, and the net force is opposite to the book's direction of motion.

16. The mass of the rockets is decreasing as the fuel burns, but the force exerted by the rocket engines remains the same. By the second law of motion, the acceleration then must increase.

17. The baseball glove increases the amount of time needed for the ball to come to a stop. The change in momentum is the same as when you catch the ball with your bare hand, but because the time needed for the change to occur is greater, the force exerted by the ball on your hand is less.

Rubrics

For more help evaluating open-ended assessment questions, see the rubric on p. 10T.

Energy

BIG Idea Every change that occurs requires energy.

	Content Standards	Learning Objectives	Resources to Assess Mastery
Section 1	**5–8:** UCP.2, 3, 5; A.1, 2; B.1, 3 **9–12:** UCP.2, 3, 5; A.1, 2; B.2, 4	**The Nature of Energy** **1. Distinguish** between kinetic and potential energy. **2. Calculate** kinetic energy. **3. Describe** different forms of potential energy. ***Main Idea*** There are different forms of energy, including potential energy and kinetic energy.	**Formative Assessment** Reading Check, pp. 101, 103 Section Review, p. 105 **Summative Assessment** *ExamView® Assessment Suite*
Section 2	**5–8:** UCP.2, 3, 5; A.1; B.1, 3, G.3 **9–12:** UCP.2, 3, 5; A.1, 2; B.2, 4, 5; G.3 See pp. 16T–17T for a Key to Standards.	**Conservation of Energy** **4. Describe** how energy can be transformed from one form to another. **5. Explain** how the mechanical energy of a system is the sum of the kinetic and potential energy. **6. Discuss** the law of conservation of energy. ***Main Idea*** Energy cannot be created or destroyed, but only can change from one form to another.	**Formative Assessment** Reading Check, pp. 109, 111 Section Review, p. 115 **Summative Chapter Assessment** MindJogger, Ch. 4 *ExamView® Assessment Suite* Leveled Chapter Test Test A L1 Test B L2 Test C L3 Test Practice, pp. 122–123

Suggested Pacing				
Period	**Instruction**	**Labs**	**Review & Assessment**	**Total**
Single	2.5 days	2.5 days	2 days	7 days
Block	1.25 blocks	1.25 blocks	1 block	3.5 blocks

<table>
<tr><th rowspan="2">Core Instruction</th><th rowspan="2">Leveled Resources</th><th rowspan="2">Leveled Labs</th><th colspan="3">Pacing</th></tr>
<tr><th>Period</th><th></th><th>Block</th></tr>
<tr><td rowspan="3">Student Text, pp. 98–106
Section Focus Transparency, Ch. 4, Section 1
Teaching Transparency, Ch. 4, Section 1
Interactive Chalkboard, Ch. 4, Section 1
Differentiated Instruction, p. 101
Applying Math, pp. 102, 104</td><td rowspan="3">Chapter Fast File Resources
Directed Reading for Content Mastery, p. 20 [L1]
Note-taking Worksheet, pp. 31, 32
Reinforcement, p. 27 [L2]
Enrichment, p. 29 [L3]
Reading Essentials, p. 52 [L1] ELL
Science Notebook, p. 37 ELL
ActiveFolders: Energy [L1] ELL</td><td>Launch Lab, p. 99: D-cell batteries (2), non-coated paper clips (2), tape, metal tongs, steel wool 15 min [L2]</td><td>1</td><td>Section 1, pp. 99–102 (includes Launch Lab)</td><td rowspan="2">1</td></tr>
<tr><td>MiniLAB, p. 103: nickel, rubber band, meterstick 15 min [L2]</td><td>2</td><td>Section 1, pp. 103–105 (includes MiniLAB and Section Review)</td></tr>
<tr><td>*Lab, p. 106: tennis ball, rubber ball, balance, meterstick, masking tape, cardboard box 30 min [L1] [L2] [L3] (Video Lab)</td><td>3</td><td>Lab: Bouncing Balls, p. 106</td><td rowspan="2">2</td></tr>
<tr><td rowspan="4">Student Text, pp. 107–117
Section Focus Transparency, Ch. 4, Section 2
Interactive Chalkboard, Ch. 4, Section 2
Identifying Misconceptions, pp. 109, 114
Differentiated Instruction, pp. 108, 112
Visualizing Energy Transformation, p. 110
Chapter Study Guide, p. 119</td><td rowspan="4">Chapter Fast File Resources
Directed Reading for Content Mastery, pp. 21, 22 [L1]
Note-taking Worksheet, pp. 31, 32
Reinforcement, p. 28 [L2]
Enrichment, p. 30 [L3]
Reading Essentials, p. 58 [L1] ELL
Science Notebook, p. 41 ELL
ActiveFolders: Law of Conservation of Energy [L1] ELL</td><td>MiniLAB, p. 112: paper clip 5 min [L2]</td><td>4</td><td>Section 2, pp. 107–111</td></tr>
<tr><td rowspan="2">*Lab, pp. 116–117: ring stand, test-tube clamp, support–rod clamp, support rod, medium stopper (2-hole), string, meterstick, graph paper 45 min [L1] [L2] [L3]</td><td>5</td><td>Section 2, pp. 111–115 (includes MiniLAB and Section Review)</td><td rowspan="2">3</td></tr>
<tr><td>6</td><td>Lab: Swinging Energy, pp. 116–117</td></tr>
<tr><td>*Lab version A [L1]
version B [L2] [L3]</td><td>7</td><td>Study Guide, Chapter Review, and Test Practice, pp. 119–123</td><td>3.5</td></tr>
</table>

(Video Lab icon) Video Lab

Transparencies

Section Focus

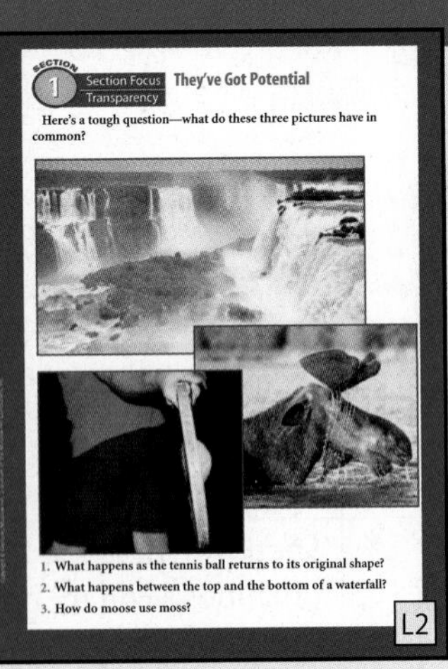
Section 1 Section Focus Transparency **They've Got Potential**

Here's a tough question—what do these three pictures have in common?

1. What happens as the tennis ball returns to its original shape?
2. What happens between the top and the bottom of a waterfall?
3. How do moose use moss?

L2

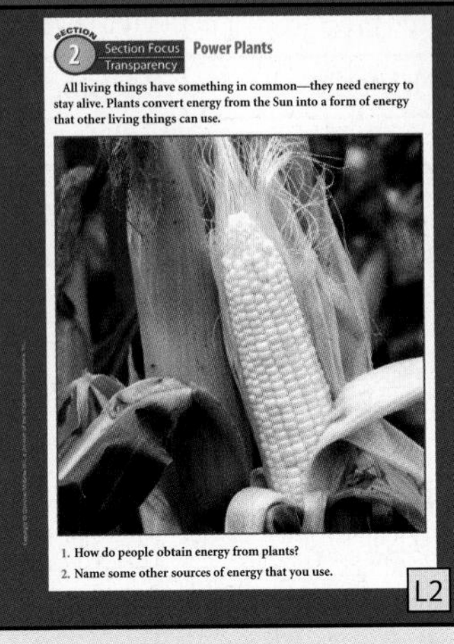
Section 2 Section Focus Transparency **Power Plants**

All living things have something in common—they need energy to stay alive. Plants convert energy from the Sun into a form of energy that other living things can use.

1. How do people obtain energy from plants?
2. Name some other sources of energy that you use.

L2

This is a representation of key blackline masters available in the Teacher Classroom Resources. See Resource Manager boxes within the chapter for additional information.

Assessment

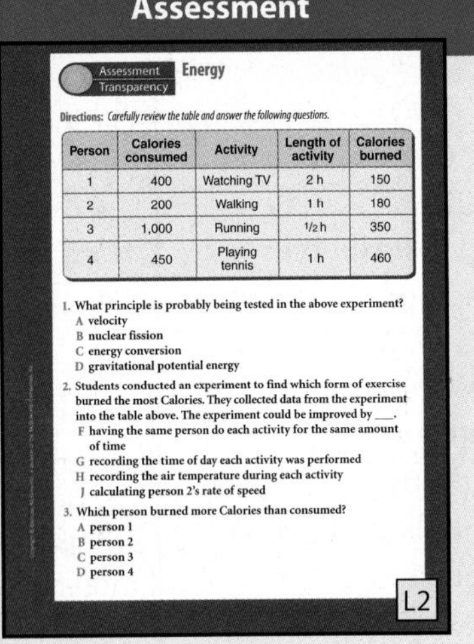
Assessment Transparency **Energy**

Directions: *Carefully review the table and answer the following questions.*

Person	Calories consumed	Activity	Length of activity	Calories burned
1	400	Watching TV	2 h	150
2	200	Walking	1 h	180
3	1,000	Running	1/2 h	350
4	450	Playing tennis	1 h	460

1. What principle is probably being tested in the above experiment?
   A velocity
   B nuclear fission
   C energy conversion
   D gravitational potential energy
2. Students conducted an experiment to find which form of exercise burned the most Calories. They collected data from the experiment into the table above. The experiment could be improved by ___.
   F having the same person do each activity for the same amount of time
   G recording the time of day each activity was performed
   H recording the air temperature during each activity
   J calculating person 2's rate of speed
3. Which person burned more Calories than consumed?
   A person 1
   B person 2
   C person 3
   D person 4

L2

Teaching

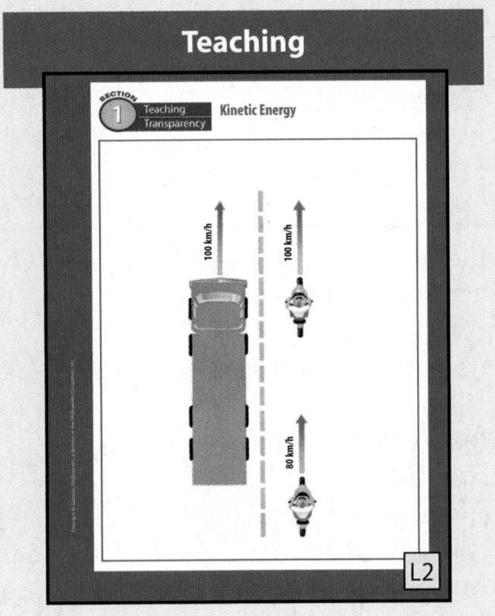
Section 1 Teaching Transparency **Kinetic Energy**

L2

Key to Teaching Strategies

The following designations will help you decide which activities are appropriate for your students.

- L1 Level 1 activities should be appropriate for students with learning difficulties.
- L2 Level 2 activities should be within the ability range of all students.
- L3 Level 3 activities are designed for above-average students.
- ELL ELL activities should be within the ability range of English Language Learners.
- COOP LEARN Cooperative Learning activities are designed for small group work.
- LS Multiple Learning Styles logos, as described on page 12T, are used throughout to indicate strategies that address different learning styles.
- P These strategies represent student products that can be placed into a best-work portfolio.
- PBL Problem-Based Learning activities apply real-world situations to learning.

Hands-on Activities

Student Text Lab Worksheet

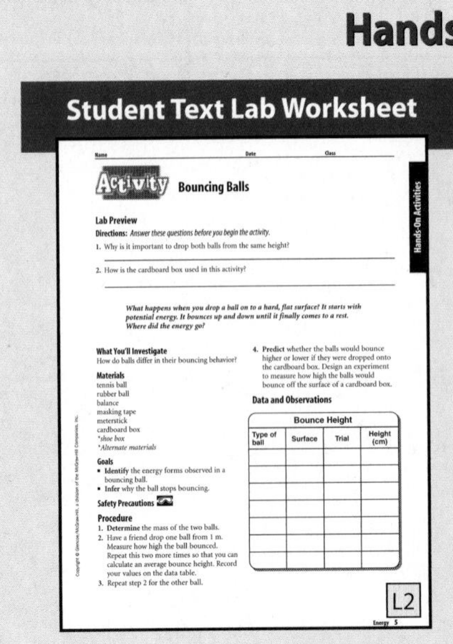
Name Date Class

Activity **Bouncing Balls**

Lab Preview

Directions: *Answer these questions before you begin the activity.*

1. Why is it important to drop both balls from the same height?
2. How is the cardboard box used in this activity?

What happens when you drop a ball on to a hard, flat surface? It starts with potential energy. It bounces up and down until it finally comes to a rest. Where did the energy go?

What You'll Investigate
How do balls differ in their bouncing behavior?

Materials
tennis ball
rubber ball
balance
masking tape
meterstick
cardboard box
*shoe box
*Alternate materials

Goals
- **Identify** the energy forms observed in a bouncing ball.
- **Infer** why the ball stops bouncing.

Safety Precautions

Procedure
1. **Determine** the mass of the two balls.
2. Have a friend drop one ball from 1 m. Measure how high the ball bounced. Repeat this two more times so that you can calculate an average bounce height. Record your values on the data table.
3. Repeat step 2 for the other ball.
4. **Predict** whether the balls would bounce higher or lower if they were dropped onto the cardboard box. Design an experiment to measure how high the balls would bounce off the surface of a cardboard box.

Data and Observations

Bounce Height			
Type of ball	Surface	Trial	Height (cm)

Hands-On Activities

Copyright © Glencoe/McGraw-Hill, a division of the McGraw-Hill Companies, Inc.

L2

Energy 5

Laboratory Activities

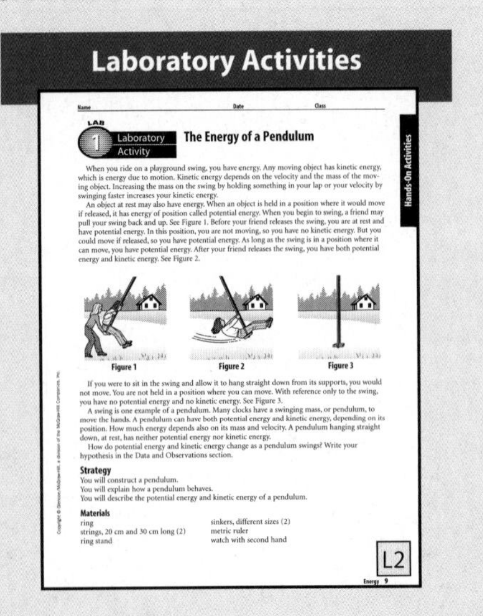
Name Date Class

LAB 1 Laboratory Activity **The Energy of a Pendulum**

When you ride on a playground swing, you have energy. Any moving object has kinetic energy, which is energy due to motion. Kinetic energy depends on the velocity and the mass of the moving object. Increasing the mass on the swing by holding something in your lap or your velocity by swinging faster increases your kinetic energy.

An object at rest may also have energy. When an object is held in a position where it would move if released, it has energy of position called potential energy. When you begin to swing, a friend may pull your swing back and up. See Figure 1. Before your friend releases the swing, you are at rest and have potential energy. In this position, you are not moving, so you have no kinetic energy. But you could move if released, so you have potential energy. As long as the swing is in a position where it can move, you have potential energy. After your friend releases the swing, you have both potential energy and kinetic energy. See Figure 2.

Figure 1 Figure 2 Figure 3

If you were to sit in the swing and allow it to hang straight down from its supports, you would not move. You are not held in a position where you can move. With reference only to the swing, you have no potential energy and no kinetic energy. See Figure 3.

A swing is one example of a pendulum. Many clocks have a swinging mass, or pendulum, to move the hands. A pendulum can have both potential energy and kinetic energy, depending on its position. How much energy depends also on its mass and velocity. A pendulum hanging straight down, at rest, has neither potential energy nor kinetic energy.

How do potential energy and kinetic energy change as a pendulum swings? Write your hypothesis in the Data and Observations section.

Strategy
You will construct a pendulum.
You will explain how a pendulum behaves.
You will describe the potential energy and kinetic energy of a pendulum.

Materials
ring
strings, 20 cm and 30 cm long (2)
ring stand
sinkers, different sizes (2)
metric ruler
watch with second hand

Hands-On Activities

Copyright © Glencoe/McGraw-Hill, a division of the McGraw-Hill Companies, Inc.

L2

Energy 9

Resource Manager

Meeting Different Ability Levels

Content Outline

Name Date Class

Note-taking Worksheet **Energy**

Section 1 The Nature of Energy

A. Energy is the ability to cause ________.
1. **Kinetic energy**—Energy in the form of ________
   a. The amount of kinetic energy an object has depends on its ________ and its ________.
   b. Kinetic energy = ½ ________ × velocity²
   c. ________—The SI unit used to measure energy
2. **Potential energy**—Energy stored in a ________ object, giving it the potential to cause change
3. **Elastic potential energy**—Energy stored by things that ________
4. **Chemical potential energy**—Energy stored in ________ between atoms
5. **Gravitational potential energy**—Energy stored by things that are ________
   a. The amount of GPE an object has depends on its ________, the acceleration due to ________, and its ________.
   b. GPE = mass in kilograms × 9.8 m/s² × height in ________

Section 2 Conservation of Energy

A. Energy conversions—energy changing from one ________ to another
1. Fuels store energy in the form of ________ energy.
2. ________ energy—the total amount of potential and kinetic energy in a system

B. Law of Conservation of Energy—Energy may change from one form to another, but the ________ of energy never changes.
1. Example—As a swing moves back and forth, its energy continually converts from ________ to ________ and back.
2. If the energy of the swing decreases, then the energy of some other object must ________ by an equal amount.
3. Friction converts some of the mechanical energy into ________ energy.

L2

Energy 31

Reinforcement

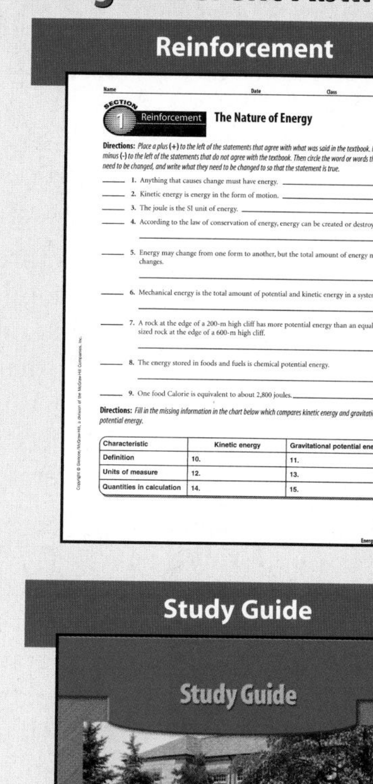

Name Date Class

Section 1 Reinforcement **The Nature of Energy**

Directions: *Place a plus (+) to the left of the statements that agree with what was said in the textbook. Place a minus (-) to the left of the statements that do not agree with the textbook. Then circle the word or words that need to be changed, and write what they need to be changed to so that the statement is true.*

____ 1. Anything that causes change must have energy.
____ 2. Kinetic energy is energy in the form of motion.
____ 3. The joule is the SI unit of energy.
____ 4. According to the law of conservation of energy, energy can be created or destroyed.
____ 5. Energy may change from one form to another, but the total amount of energy never changes.
____ 6. Mechanical energy is the total amount of potential and kinetic energy in a system.
____ 7. A rock at the edge of a 200-m high cliff has more potential energy than an equal-sized rock at the edge of a 600-m high cliff.
____ 8. The energy stored in foods and fuels is chemical potential energy.
____ 9. One food Calorie is equivalent to about 2,800 joules.

Directions: *Fill in the missing information in the chart below which compares kinetic energy and gravitational potential energy.*

Characteristic	Kinetic energy	Gravitational potential energy
Definition	10.	11.
Units of measure	12.	13.
Quantities in calculation	14.	15.

L2

Energy 27

Enrichment

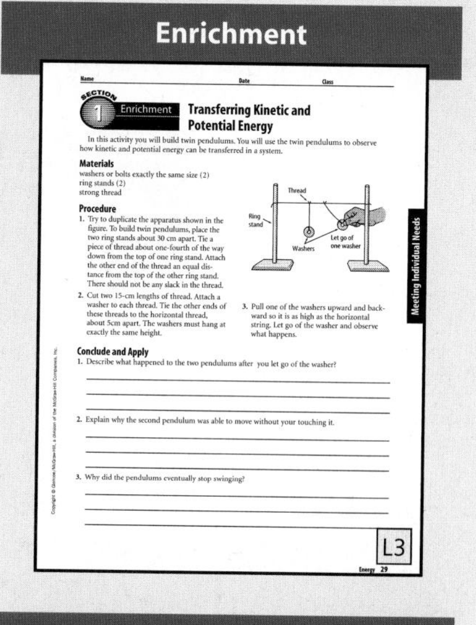

Name Date Class

Section 1 Enrichment **Transferring Kinetic and Potential Energy**

In this activity you will build twin pendulums. You will use the twin pendulums to observe how kinetic and potential energy can be transferred in a system.

Materials
washers or bolts exactly the same size (2)
ring stands (2)
strong thread

Procedure
1. Try to duplicate the apparatus shown in the figure. To build twin pendulums, place the two ring stands about 30 cm apart. Tie a piece of thread about one-fourth of the way down from the top of one ring stand. Attach the other end of the thread an equal distance from the top of the other ring stand. There should not be any slack in the thread.
2. Cut two 15-cm lengths of thread. Attach a washer to each thread. Tie the other ends of these threads to the horizontal thread, about 5cm apart. The washers must hang at exactly the same height.
3. Pull one of the washers upward and backward so it is as high as the horizontal string. Let go of the washer and observe what happens.

Conclude and Apply
1. Describe what happened to the two pendulums after you let go of the washer?
2. Explain why the second pendulum was able to move without your touching it.
3. Why did the pendulums eventually stop swinging?

L3

Energy 29

Directed Reading (English/Spanish)

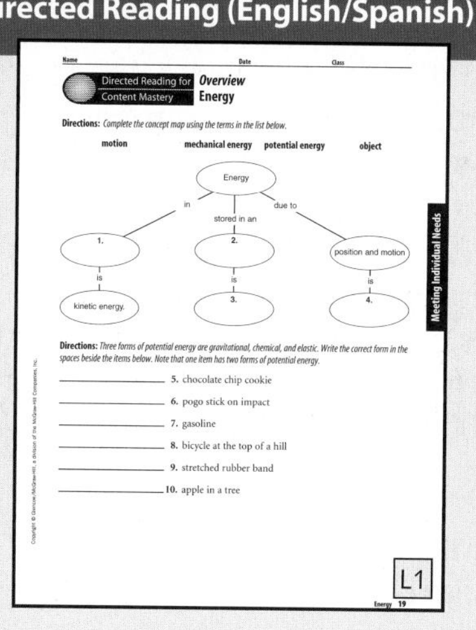

Name Date Class

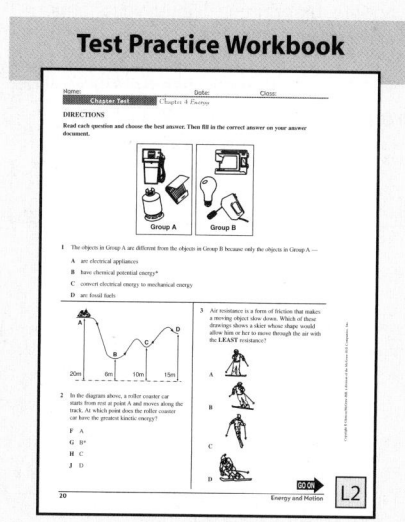

Directed Reading for Content Mastery ***Overview* Energy**

Directions: *Complete the concept map using the terms in the list below.*

motion mechanical energy potential energy object

Directions: *Three forms of potential energy are gravitational, chemical, and elastic. Write the correct form in the spaces beside the items below. Note that one item has two forms of potential energy.*

________ 5. chocolate chip cookie
________ 6. pogo stick on impact
________ 7. gasoline
________ 8. bicycle at the top of a hill
________ 9. stretched rubber band
________ 10. apple in a tree

L1

Energy 19

Study Guide

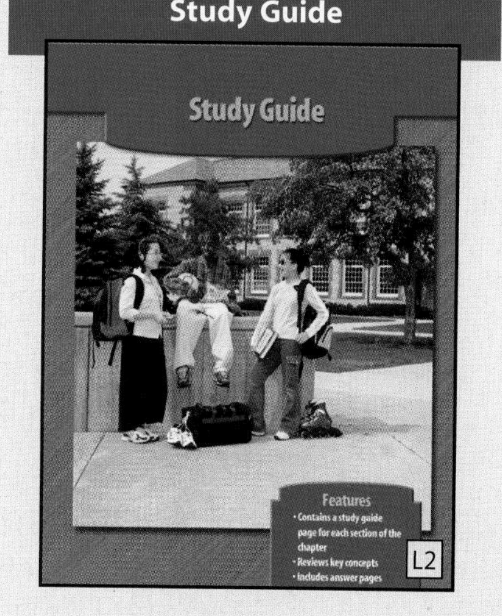

Reading Essentials

Assessment

Test Practice Workbook

Name: Date: Class:

Chapter Test *Chapter 4 Energy*

DIRECTIONS

Read each question and choose the best answer. Then fill in the correct answer on your answer document.

Group A Group B

1 The objects in Group A are different from the objects in Group B because only the objects in Group A —
A are electrical appliances
B have chemical potential energy*
C convert electrical energy to mechanical energy
D are fossil fuels

2 In the diagram above, a roller coaster car starts from rest at point A and moves along the track. At which point does the roller coaster car have the greatest kinetic energy?
F A
G B*
H C
J D

3 Air resistance is a form of friction that makes a moving object slow down. Which of these drawings shows a skier whose shape would allow him or her to move through the air with the LEAST resistance?

A B C D

GO ON

L2

20 Energy and Motion

Chapter Review

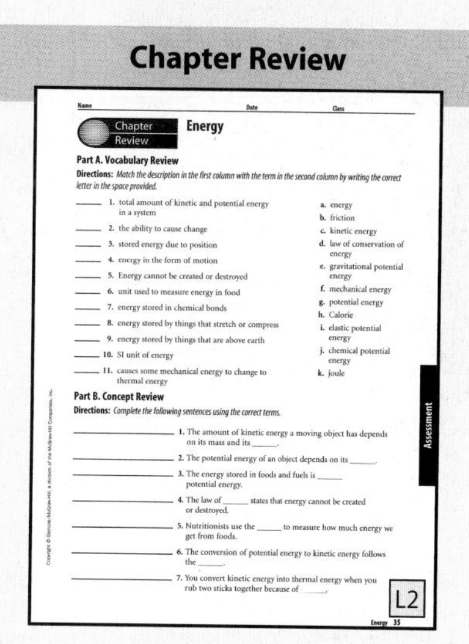

Name Date Class

Chapter Review **Energy**

Part A. Vocabulary Review

Directions: *Match the description in the first column with the term in the second column by writing the correct letter in the space provided.*

____ 1. total amount of kinetic and potential energy in a system
____ 2. the ability to cause change
____ 3. stored energy due to position
____ 4. energy in the form of motion
____ 5. Energy cannot be created or destroyed
____ 6. unit used to measure energy in food
____ 7. energy stored in chemical bonds
____ 8. energy stored by things that stretch or compress
____ 9. energy stored by things that are above earth
____ 10. SI unit of energy
____ 11. causes some mechanical energy to change to thermal energy

a. energy
b. friction
c. kinetic energy
d. law of conservation of energy
e. gravitational potential energy
f. mechanical energy
g. potential energy
h. Calorie
i. elastic potential energy
j. chemical potential energy
k. joule

Part B. Concept Review

Directions: *Complete the following sentences using the correct terms.*

1. The amount of kinetic energy a moving object has depends on its mass and its ____.
2. The potential energy of an object depends on its ____.
3. The energy stored in foods and fuels is ____ potential energy.
4. The law of ____ states that energy cannot be created or destroyed.
5. Nutritionists use the ____ to measure how much energy we get from foods.
6. The conversion of potential energy to kinetic energy follows the ____.
7. You convert kinetic energy into thermal energy when you rub two sticks together because of ____.

L2

Energy 35

Chapter Tests

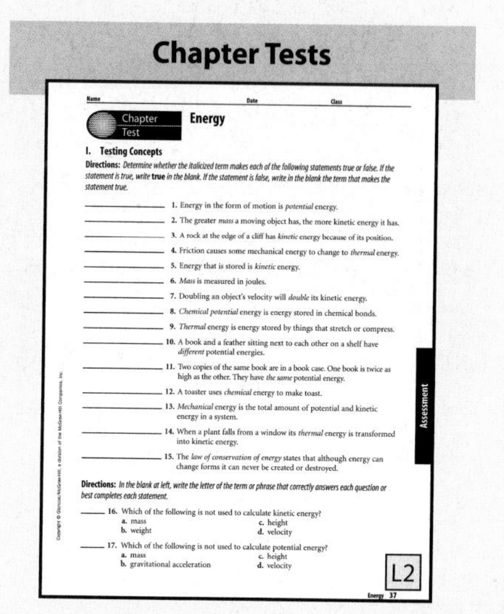

Name Date Class

Chapter Test **Energy**

I. Testing Concepts

Directions: *Determine whether the italicized term makes each of the following statements true or false. If the statement is true, write* **true** *in the blank. If the statement is false, write in the blank the term that makes the statement true.*

____ 1. Energy in the form of motion is *potential energy.*
____ 2. The greater *mass* a moving object has, the more kinetic energy it has.
____ 3. A rock at the edge of a cliff has *kinetic energy* because of its position.
____ 4. Friction causes some mechanical energy to change to *thermal energy.*
____ 5. Energy that is stored is *kinetic energy.*
____ 6. *Mass* is measured in joules.
____ 7. Doubling an object's velocity will *double* its kinetic energy.
____ 8. *Chemical potential energy* is energy stored in chemical bonds.
____ 9. *Thermal energy* is energy stored by things that stretch or compress.
____ 10. A book and a feather sitting next to each other on a shelf have *different* potential energies.
____ 11. Two copies of the same book are in a book case. One book is twice as high as the other. They have *the same* potential energy.
____ 12. A toaster uses *chemical* energy to make toast.
____ 13. *Mechanical* energy is the total amount of potential and kinetic energy in a system.
____ 14. When a plant falls from a window its *thermal* energy is transformed into kinetic energy.
____ 15. The *law of conservation of energy* states that although energy can change forms it can never be created or destroyed.

Directions: *In the blank at left, write the letter of the term or phrase that correctly answers each question or best completes each statement.*

____ 16. Which of the following is not used to calculate kinetic energy?
a. mass
b. weight
c. height
d. velocity

____ 17. Which of the following is not used to calculate potential energy?
a. mass
b. gravitational acceleration
c. height
d. velocity

L2

Energy 37

Science Content Background

section 1 The Nature of Energy

What is energy?

Energy is not matter. Electromagnetic energy can exist independent of matter. Other forms of energy, such as chemical energy, can only exist with matter.

Kinetic Energy

The equation for kinetic energy states that $KE = \frac{1}{2}mv^2$. This means that as an object's velocity doubles its kinetic energy quadruples.

Kinetic comes from a Greek word for movement. The word *cinema*—used to describe moving pictures or movies—shares the same root word.

Potential Energy

Potential energy is energy due to an object's position or condition. A rock on a cliff has potential energy due to its position, while the energy stored in a starch molecule is due to the condition of the bonds between the atoms in that molecule.

Hooke's law describes the relationship between stress and strain in a spring. The amount of force is directly proportional to the compression or extension of the spring. The amount of potential energy depends on the amount of compression or extension and the elasticity of the spring.

Without friction, the work done to lift an object is equal to the object's gain in potential energy. Consider the two equations: *work = force × distance and potential energy = mass × gravitational acceleration × height.* The force needed to lift an object is equivalent to the object's mass multiplied by the acceleration due to gravity. The distance traveled is the height. So in this case, these two equations are equivalent.

If you took a one-kilogram mass to a distance from Earth that corresponds to the distance to the Moon, the mass would have a potential energy relative to Earth of 62,000,000 joules or 62 mega-joules. This is small compared to its potential energy relative to the Sun, which would be 190,000 mega-joules.

Albert Copley/Visuals Unlimited

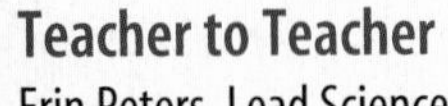

Teacher to Teacher

Erin Peters, Lead Science Teacher
Williamsburg Middle School
Arlington, Virginia

"This game will show that you trace every type of energy back to the sun. Pick any activity, for example, "doing your homework," then follow it backwards. Pushing your pencil is mechanical energy which comes from the chemical energy of eating lunch, which comes from food, which gets its energy from the sun."

Erin Peters

section 2 Conservation of Energy

Changing Forms of Energy

In our common experiences on Earth, energy is neither created nor destroyed, but is often transformed from one form into another. People use these energy transformations to do work. In most energy transformations, heat is produced.

Energy is not recycled in ecosystems like matter is recycled. Much of the energy that flows through ecosystems is transformed to heat. As energy flows from organism to organism, more and more is transformed as heat. This flow of energy can be visually represented as food chains. The Sun supplies energy to plants, which start almost all food chains.

Conversions Between Kinetic and Potential Energy

As an object falls, its gravitational potential energy is converted into kinetic energy. Therefore, if you know the falling object's initial potential energy, you can calculate the velocity it attains just before it hits the ground using the equation $GPE = mgh$. A 0.06 kg tennis ball dropped from a height of 2.9 m starts with 1.7 J of energy. Solving the kinetic energy equation for v gives 7.54 m/s.

The joule is the SI unit of energy and work. It has the units $kg{\cdot}m^2/s^2$. In work calculations a joule is sometimes called a newton-meter. Since a newton is composed of the units $kg \cdot m/s^2$, multiplying newtons by meters results in $kg \cdot m^2/s^2$, or joules.

The Law of Conservation of Energy

The law of conservation of energy works for most of our calculations, but Einstein suggested that mass could be converted to energy and energy into mass. Einstein's famous equation, $E = mc^2$ shows the relationship between mass and energy and explains the incredible power unleashed by atomic bombs. So the law of conservation of energy should more accurately be called the law of conservation of energy and mass.

chapter content resources

Internet Resources

For additional content background, visit **gpscience.com** to:

- access your book online
- find references to related articles in popular science magazines
- access Web links with related content background
- access current events with science journal topics

Print Resources

Forces, Motion and Energy Book Two, by Robert Friedhoffer, Franklin Watts Publishers, 1992

Physics for Every Kid, by Janice VanCleave, John Wiley & Sons Publishers, 1991

Great Ideas in Physics, by Alan Lightman, McGraw-Hill, 2000

The Handbook to the Universe, by Richard Paul, Chicago Review Press, 1993

Frank Rossotto/The Stock Market

About the Photo

Energy To reach a maximum height, a pole-vaulter must convert as much kinetic energy as possible into potential energy. The bending of the pole transforms kinetic energy into elastic potential energy, then into gravitational potential energy.

Science Journal Walking upstairs and taking the escalator take the same amount of energy as long as the change in elevation is the same. In the first case the energy is provided by the person and in the second it is provided by the escalator.

BIG Idea

Energy, Work, and Change Energy is often defined as the ability to do work. Strictly speaking, this definition refers to mechanical energy, that is, the sum of the kinetic and potential energy of an object. When work is done on an object, the mechanical energy of the object increases. When an object does work, mechanical energy is transferred from the object, and its mechanical energy decreases. However, not all processes in which energy is transferred involve work being done. For example, no work is done when an atom absorbs or emits photons as electrons change energy levels. But any process in which energy is transferred results in a change occurring.

Introduce the Chapter On the chalkboard compile a list of changes that students have observed in the world around them. Ask students to describe what changed and how it changed. Discuss with students whether something was transferred to or away from the object that changed.

chapter 4

Energy

BIG Idea
Every change that occurs requires energy.

4.1 The Nature of Energy
MAIN Idea There are different forms of energy, including potential energy and kinetic energy.

4.2 Conservation of Energy
MAIN Idea Energy cannot be created or destroyed, but only can change from one form to another.

A Big Lift

How does this pole vaulter go from standing at the end of a runway to climbing through the air? The answer is energy. During her vault, energy originally stored in her muscles is converted into other forms of energy that enable her to soar.

Science Journal
Which takes more energy: walking up stairs or taking an escalator? Explain your reasoning.

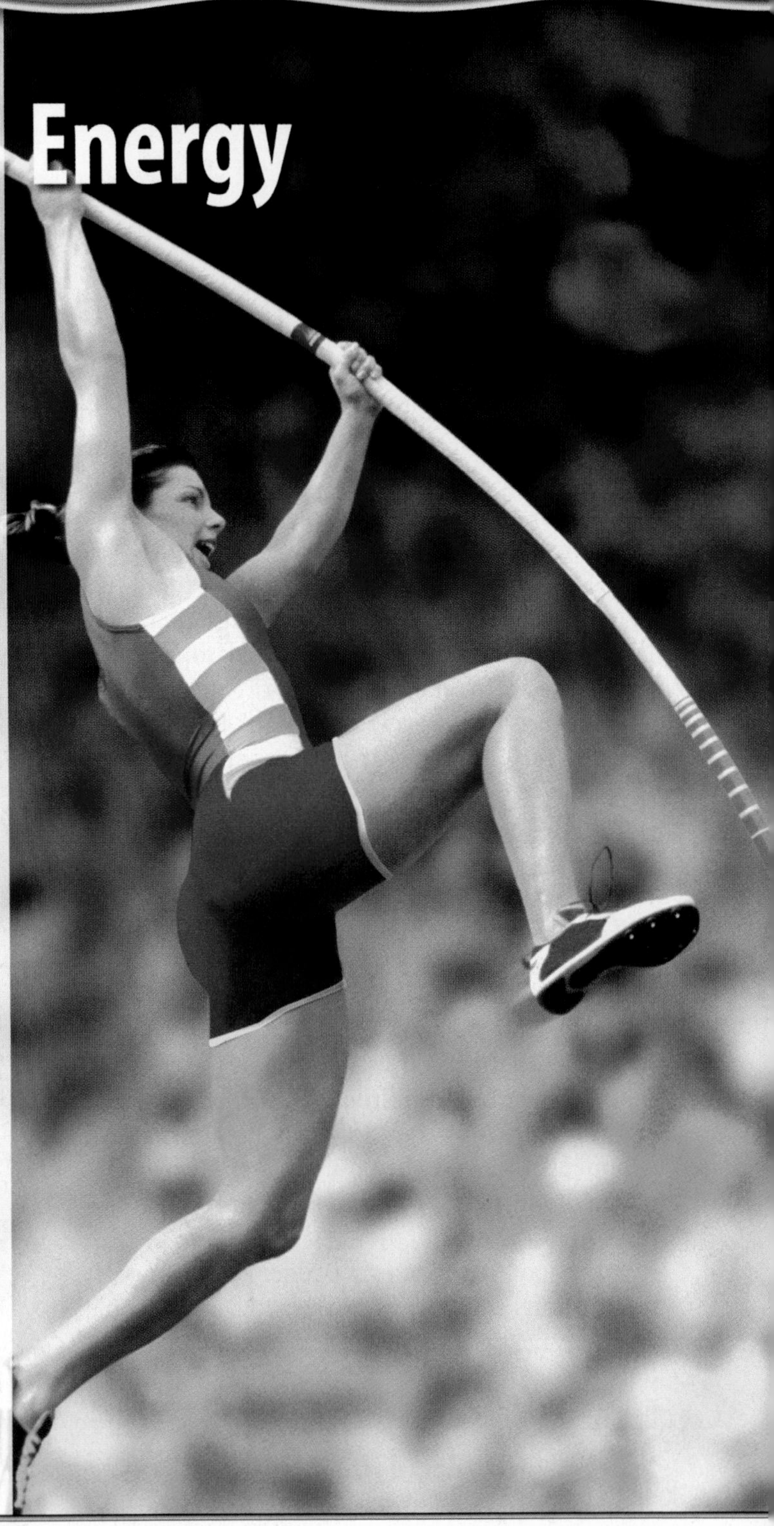

98

Interactive Chalkboard

This CD-ROM is an editable Microsoft® PowerPoint® presentation that includes:
- an editable presentation for every chapter
- additional chapter questions
- animated graphics
- image bank
- links to gpscience.com

Start-Up Activities

Energy Conversions

One of the most useful inventions of the nineteenth century was the electric lightbulb. Being able to light up the dark has enabled people to work and play longer. A lightbulb converts electrical energy to heat energy and light, another form of energy. The following lab shows how electrical energy is converted into other forms of energy.

WARNING: *Steel wool can become hot—connect to battery only for a brief time.*

1. Obtain two D-cell batteries, two non-coated paper clips, tape, metal tongs and some steel wool. Separate the steel wool into thin strands and straighten the paper clips.
2. Tape the batteries together and then tape one end of each paper clip to the battery terminals.
3. While holding the steel wool with the tongs, briefly complete the circuit by placing the steel wool in contact with both the paper clip ends.
4. **Think Critically** In your Science Journal, describe what happened to the steel wool. What changes did you observe?

Preview this chapter's content and activities at gpscience.com

FOLDABLES Study Organizer

Energy Make the following Foldable to help you identify what you already know, what you want to know, and what you learned about energy.

STEP 1 **Fold** a vertical sheet of paper from side to side. Make the front edge about 1 cm shorter than the back edge.

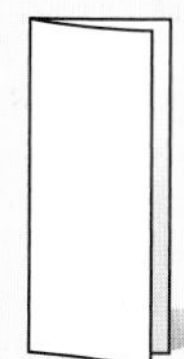

STEP 2 **Turn** lengthwise and **fold** into thirds.

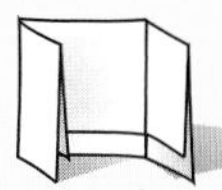

STEP 3 **Unfold and cut** only the top layer along both folds to make three tabs.

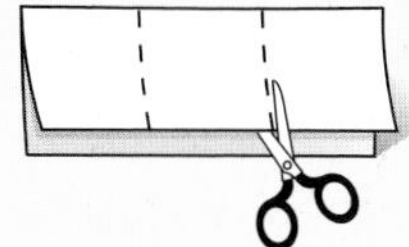

STEP 4 **Label** each tab as shown.

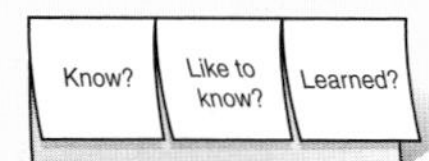

Question Before you read this chapter, write what you already know about energy under the left tab of your Foldable, and write questions about what you'd like to know under the center tab. After you read the chapter, list what you learned under the right tab.

99

Purpose Use the Launch Lab to introduce students to the conversion of electricity to light and heat. L1 COOP LEARN

LS **Kinesthetic**

Materials 2 D-cell batteries, 2 non-coated paper clips, tape, metal tongs, steel wool

Teaching Strategy Inform students that the steel wool can become quite hot.

Think Critically

When connected to the batteries, the steel wool gives off light and heat.

Assessment

Content Have students investigate how a light bulb works and write a paragraph comparing it with the model they made in this activity. Use **Performance Assessment in the Science Classroom,** p. 159.

Dinah Zike Study Fold

Student preparation materials for this Foldable are available in the **Chapter *Fast File* Resources.**

Additional Chapter Media

- What's Science Got to Do With It?: *Sports Drinks*
- BrainPOP *Kinetic Energy*
- Virtual Lab: *How is energy converted from one form to another?*
- Video Lab: *Bouncing Balls*

section 1

The Nature of Energy

1 Motivate

Bellringer

Section Focus Transparencies also are available on the Interactive Chalkboard CD-ROM. L2 

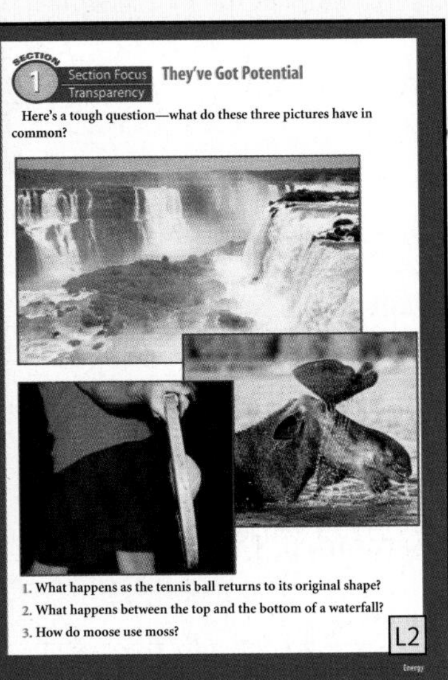

Tie to Prior Knowledge

Common Energy Ask students to describe how the word *energy* is commonly used. They might mention fuel energy or energy from the Sun. Explain that in this section they will learn the scientific definition of energy.

Reading Guide

What **You'll Learn**

- **Distinguish** between kinetic and potential energy.
- **Calculate** kinetic energy.
- **Describe** different forms of potential energy.
- **Calculate** gravitational potential energy.

Why **It's Important**

All of the changes that occur around you every day involve the conversion of energy from one form to another.

Review Vocabulary

gravity: the attractive force between any two objects that have mass

New Vocabulary

- kinetic energy
- joule
- potential energy
- elastic potential energy
- chemical potential energy
- gravitational potential energy

What is energy?

Wherever you are sitting as you read this, changes are taking place—lightbulbs are heating the air around them, the wind might be rustling leaves, or sunlight might be glaring off a nearby window. Even you are changing as you breathe, blink, or shift position in your seat.

Every change that occurs—large or small—involves energy. Imagine a baseball flying through the air. It hits a window, causing the glass to break as shown in **Figure 1.** The window changed from a solid sheet of glass to a number of broken pieces. The moving baseball caused this change—a moving baseball has energy. Even when you comb your hair or walk from one class to another, energy is involved.

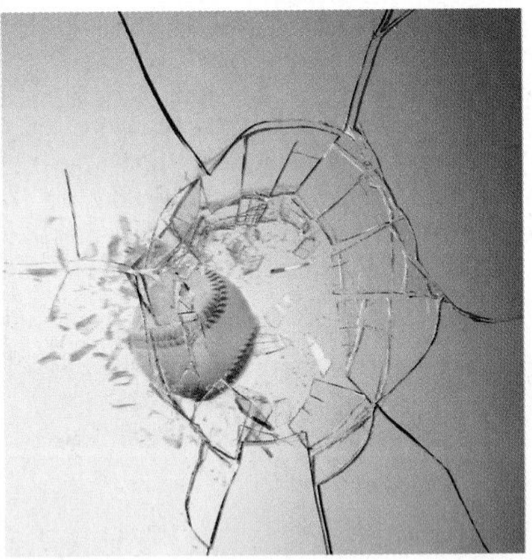

Figure 1 The baseball caused changes to occur when it hit the window.
Describe *the changes that are occurring.*

Change Requires Energy When something is able to change its environment or itself, it has energy. Energy is the ability to cause change. The moving baseball had energy. It certainly caused the window to change. Anything that causes change must have energy. You use energy to arrange your hair to look the way you want it to. You also use energy when you walk down the halls of your school between classes or eat your lunch. You even need energy to yawn, open a book, and write with a pen.

Section 1 Resource Manager

Chapter *FAST FILE* Resources

Transparency Activity, p. 42, 45–46
Note-taking Worksheets, pp. 31–32
MiniLAB, p.3
Directed Reading for Content Mastery, pp. 19, 20
Lab Activity, pp. 9–12
Enrichment, p. 29
Reinforcement, p. 7
Lab Worksheet, pp. 5–6

Reading and Writing Skill Activities, p. 35

Different Forms of Energy

Turn on an electric light, and a dark room becomes bright. Turn on your CD player, and sound comes through your headphones. In both situations, energy moves from one place to another. These changes are different from each other, and differ from the baseball shattering the window in **Figure 1.** This is because energy has several different forms—electrical, chemical, radiant, and thermal.

Figure 2 shows some examples of everyday situations in which you might notice energy. Is the chemical energy stored in food the same as the energy that comes from the Sun or the energy stored in gasoline? Radiant energy from the Sun travels a vast distance through space to Earth, warming the planet and providing energy that enables green plants to grow. When you make toast in the morning, you are using electrical energy. In short, energy plays a role in every activity that you do.

Figure 2 Energy can be stored and it can move from place to place.
Infer *which materials are storing chemical energy.*

Reading Check *What are some different forms of energy?*

An Energy Analogy Money can be used in an analogy to help you understand energy. If you have $100, you could store it in a variety of forms—cash in your wallet, a bank account, travelers' checks, or gold or silver coins. You could transfer that money to different forms. You could deposit your cash into a bank account or trade the cash for gold. Regardless of its form, money is money. The same is true for energy. Energy from the Sun that warms you and energy from the food that you eat are only different forms of the same thing.

2 Teach

Caption Answer

Figure 1 The window breaks.

Figure 2 Energy is stored in the gasoline and in the food.

Discussion

Storage and Motion Name some objects that store energy and some examples of energy in motion. Possible answers: stored—springs, muscles in our bodies; motion—bouncing ball, spinning top, baseball flying through the air L1 LS **Linguistic**

Reading Check

Answer thermal energy, chemical energy, radiant energy, and electrical energy

Text Question Answer

Energy stored in food and gasoline is chemical potential energy. Energy from the sun is in the form of heat and electromagnetic radiation.

Fun Fact

Mitochondria are organelles that convert chemical energy into forms cells can use. This is why they are also known as the powerhouses of living cells. Mitochondria have their own DNA separate from nuclear DNA but cannot re-produce themselves without help from the cell's nucleus.

Differentiated Instruction

English-Language-Learners Have students list ways they can warm up. Possible answers: sit by the fire, sit in the sun, wrap up in blankets, run in place, rub their hands together. Then have them classify whether they warmed up from kinetic (moving) energy, or emitted (stored) heat energy. ELL

Science Journal

Different Forms of Energy Have students make a list in their Science Journals of the different types of energy mentioned in the text. Have them list several examples of how they use each form of energy every day. L2 LS **Linguistic**

Use Science Words

Word Origin Have students look up the words *kinetic* and *potential* in the dictionary. *Kinetic* comes from the Greek root *kinein* (to move) and *potential* from the Latin root *potens* (power). Ask a volunteer to state how the words *kinetic* and *potential* reflect the meanings of their roots. Possible answer: Kinetic energy is energy of movement. Potential energy is stored energy due to position, waiting to be unleashed. L1 IS **Linguistic**

Quick Demo

Kinetic Energy

Materials one heavy ball, one light ball, two identical balls and a table top.

Estimated Time five minutes

Procedure

1. Show students two balls; one heavy and one light. Roll them across the table at about the same speed. Ask: Which ball has the greater kinetic energy? If the velocity of both balls is the same, the ball with the greater mass has the greater kinetic energy.
2. Show the students two identical balls. Roll the balls across the table but roll one ball faster than the other. Ask: Which ball has the greater kinetic energy? The ball with the greater speed. L1

IS **Logical-Mathematical**

Kinetic Energy Equation

National Math Standards

1, 2, 9

Answers to Practice Problems

1. 120 J
2. 1,500 kg
3. 10 m/s
4. Kinetic energy depends on the speed squared. So if the speed doubles, the kinetic energy increases by four times.

Topic: Glacier Flow

Visit gpscience.com for Web links to information about the speeds at which glaciers flow.

Activity For the five fastest glaciers, calculate the kinetic energy a 1 kg block of ice in each glacier would have.

Kinetic Energy

When you think of energy, you might think of action—or objects in motion, like the baseball that shatters a window. An object in motion does have energy. **Kinetic energy** is the energy a moving object has because of its motion. The kinetic energy of a moving object depends on the object's mass and its speed.

Kinetic Energy Equation

$$\text{kinetic energy (in joules)} = \frac{1}{2}\,\text{mass (in kg)} \times [\text{speed (in m/s)}]^2$$

$$KE = \frac{1}{2}mv^2$$

In this equation, the symbol v represents speed. The SI unit of energy is the joule, abbreviated J. If you drop a softball from a height of about 0.5 m, it has a kinetic energy of about 1J just before it hits the floor. According to the above equation, the unit J is equal to the combination of units kg m^2/s^2.

Kinetic Energy Equation

Solve for Kinetic Energy A jogger with a mass of 60.0 kg is moving at a speed of 3.0 m/s. What is the jogger's kinetic energy?

1. **This is what you know:** mass: $m = 60.0$ kg; speed: $v = 3.0$ m/s
2. **This is what you need to find:** kinetic energy: KE
3. **Use this formula:** $KE = \frac{1}{2}mv^2$
4. **Substitute:** the values of m and v into the formula and multiply. $KE = \frac{1}{2}(60.0)(3.0)^2 = \frac{1}{2}(60.0)(9.0) = 270$
5. **Determine the units:** units of KE = (units of m) × (units of v)^2 = kg × $(m/s)^2$ = kg·m^2/s^2 = J

Answer: The jogger's kinetic energy is 270 J.

Practice Problems

1. A baseball with a mass of 0.15 kg is moving at a speed of 40 m/s. What is the baseball's kinetic energy?
2. A sprinter has a mass of 80.0 kg and a kinetic energy of 4,000 J. What is the sprinter's speed?
3. **Challenge** A car with a mass of 1,500 kg doubles its speed from 50 km/h to 100 km/h. By how many times does the kinetic energy of the car increase?

Science Online For more practice problems, go to page 834, and visit gpscience.com/extra_problems.

Curriculum Connection

Geography On May 18, 1980, Mount St. Helens in the state of Washington erupted in a devastating volcanic explosion. The tremendous energy of the eruption hurled hot ash and rock more than 16 kilometers. Have students do research to discover other geologic events in history that have involved large amounts of energy. Have each student make a table listing the examples they find and where each event occurred. Possible events: earthquakes in 1964 in Alaska, in 1991 in southern California, in 1995 in Kobe, Japan, and in 2001 in India; and eruptions of the volcanoes Krakatau in 1883 and Mount Vesuvius in 79 A.D. L2 IS **Visual-Spatial** P

Figure 3 As natural gas burns, it combines with oxygen to form carbon dioxide and water. In this chemical reaction, chemical potential energy is released.

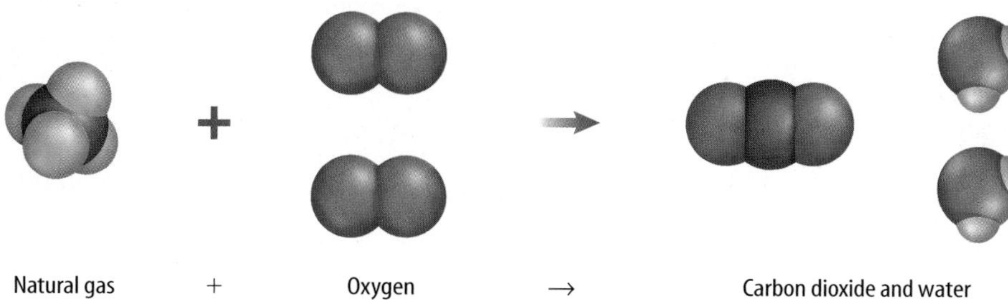

Potential Energy

Energy doesn't have to involve motion. Even motionless objects can have energy. This energy is stored in the object. Therefore, the object has potential to cause change. A hanging apple in a tree has stored energy. When the apple falls to the ground, a change occurs. Because the apple has the ability to cause change, it has energy. The hanging apple has energy because of its position above Earth's surface. Stored energy due to position is called **potential energy.** If the apple stays in the tree, it will keep the stored energy due to its height above the ground. If it falls, that stored energy of position is converted to energy of motion.

Elastic Potential Energy Energy can be stored in other ways, too. If you stretch a rubber band and let it go, it sails across the room. As it flies through the air, it has kinetic energy due to its motion. Where did this kinetic energy come from? Just as the apple hanging in the tree had potential energy, the stretched rubber band had energy stored as elastic potential energy. **Elastic potential energy** is energy stored by something that can stretch or compress, such as a rubber band or spring.

Chemical Potential Energy The cereal you eat for breakfast and the sandwich you eat at lunch also contain stored energy. Gasoline stores energy in the same way as food stores energy—in the chemical bonds between atoms. Energy stored in chemical bonds is **chemical potential energy. Figure 3** shows a molecule of natural gas. Energy is stored in the bonds that hold the carbon and hydrogen atoms together and is released when the gas is burned.

How is elastic potential energy different from chemical potential energy?

Interpreting Data from a Slingshot

Procedure

1. Using two fingers, carefully stretch a **rubber band** on a table until it has no slack.
2. Place a **nickel** on the table, slightly touching the midpoint of the rubber band.
3. Push the nickel back 0.5 cm into the rubber band and release. Measure the distance the nickel travels.
4. Repeat step 3, each time pushing the nickel back an additional 0.5 cm.

Analysis

1. How did the takeoff speed of the nickel depend on the distance that you stretched the rubber band?
2. How did the kinetic energy of the nickel depend on the distance the rubber band was stretched?

Use an Analogy

Saving Money Suggest to students that potential energy is analogous to money in a savings account. The money is not in use now, but it's ready for you to use when needed.

Purpose Students observe the relationship between the elastic potential energy and kinetic energy of an object. L1 COOP LEARN IS **Kinesthetic**

Materials nickel, rubber band, meterstick

Teaching Strategy Have students work in pairs and take turns making the measurements.

Troubleshooting Be sure students don't pull the rubber band back too far. The nickel can quickly travel a long distance.

Analysis

1. The farther you stretch the band, the faster the nickel moves.
2. The greater the speed of the nickel, the greater its kinetic energy.

Assessment

Process Have students predict how their results would differ on a rough surface. Have them test their hypotheses by repeating the activity on sandpaper. Use **Performance Assessment in the Science Classroom,** p. 93.

Reading Check

Answer Elastic potential energy is energy stored by things that stretch or compress. Chemical potential energy is energy stored in chemical bonds.

Visual Learning

Figure 3 What forms of energy are given off when natural gas burns? light and heat (thermal energy)

The Myth of Sisyphus Sisyphus had to continually provide the rock with gravitational potential energy only to have it turn into kinetic energy again.

Quick Demo

Gravitational Potential Energy

Materials three tennis balls, bookshelf or something with three different heights to put them on.

Estimated Time 5 minutes

Procedure

1. Demonstrate the idea of gravitational potential energy by placing the three tennis balls on level surfaces at different heights. Ask: How do the gravitational potential energies of the three balls compare? *GPE increases with height. The ball that is highest has the greatest GPE and the ball that is nearest the ground has the lowest GPE.* L1

LS **Logical-Mathematical**

Potential Energy Equation

National Math Standards

Correlation to Mathematics Objectives

1, 2, 9

Answers to Practice Problems

1. 2.9 J
2. 50 m
3. 60 kg
4. The gravitational potential energy would increase by four times.

The Myth of Sisyphus In Greek mythology, a king named Sisyphus angered the gods by attempting to delay death. As punishment, he was doomed for eternity to endlessly roll a huge stone up a hill, only to have it roll back to the bottom again. Explain what caused the potential energy of the stone to change as it moved up and down the hill.

Gravitational Potential Energy Anything that can fall has stored energy called gravitational potential energy. **Gravitational potential energy** (GPE) is energy stored by objects due to their position above Earth's surface. The GPE of an object depends on the object's mass and height above the ground. Gravitational potential energy can be calculated from the following equation.

Gravitational Potential Energy Equation

gravitational potential energy (J) = mass (kg) × acceleration of gravity (m/s^2) × height (m)

$$GPE = mgh$$

In this equation, the acceleration of gravity has the symbol g. On Earth, the acceleration of gravity has the value 9.8 m/s^2. Like all forms of energy, gravitational potential energy is measured in joules.

Potential Energy Equation

Solve for Gravitational Potential Energy What is the gravitational potential energy of a ceiling fan that has a mass of 7.0 kg and is 4.0 m above the ground?

1. **This is what you know:** mass: m = **7.0 kg**; height: h = **4.0 m**; acceleration of gravity: g = 9.8 m/s^2
2. **This is what you need to find:** gravitational potential energy: *GPE*
3. **Use this formula:** $GPE = mgh$
4. **Substitute:** the values of m, g, and h into the formula and multiply. $GPE = (7.0)(9.8)(4.0) = 274$
5. **Determine the units:** units of *GPE* = (units of m) × (units of g) × (units of h) = kg × m/s^2 × m = kg·m^2/s^2 = J

Answer: The gravitational potential energy of the ceiling fan is 274 J.

Science Online For more practice problems, go to page 834, and visit gpscience.com/extra_problems.

Practice Problems

1. Find the GPE of a coffee mug with a mass of 0.3 that is on a counter top 1-m high above the ground.
2. How high above the ground is a baseball with a mass of 0.15 kg that has a GPE of 73.5 J?
3. A rock climber is 200 m above the ground and has a GPE of 117,600 J. What is the rock climber's mass?
4. **Challenge** Suppose the mass of an object and it's height above the ground both were to double. How would the object's gravitational potential energy change?

Cultural Diversity

Working with Energy During World War II, O.S. (Ozzie) Williams became the first African American aeronautical engineer hired by Republic Aviation, Inc. Later, his work included the application of solar and wind energy to the needs of Africa. Have students find other scientists who have spent much of their careers working with energy. Ask students to present their findings in oral reports to the class. L2

LS **Interpersonal**

Changing GPE Look at the objects in the bookcase in **Figure 4.** Which of these objects has the most gravitational potential energy? According to the equation for gravitational potential energy, the GPE of an object can be increased by increasing its height above the ground. If two objects are at the same height, then the object with the larger mass has more gravitational potential energy.

In **Figure 4,** suppose the green vase on the lower shelf and the blue vase on the upper shelf have the same mass. Then the blue vase on the upper shelf has more gravitational potential energy because it is higher above the ground.

Imagine what would happen if the two vases were to fall. As they fall and begin moving, they have kinetic energy as well as gravitational potential energy. As the vases get closer to the ground, their gravitational potential energy decreases. At the same time, they are moving faster, so their kinetic energy increases. The vase that was higher above the floor has fallen a greater distance. As a result, the vase that initially had more gravitational potential energy will be moving faster and have more kinetic energy when it hits the floor.

Figure 4 An object's gravitational potential energy increases as its height increases.

section 1 review

Summary

Energy

- Energy is the ability to cause change.
- Forms of energy include electrical, chemical, thermal, and radiant energy.

Kinetic Energy

- Kinetic energy is the energy a moving object has because of its motion.
- The kinetic energy of a moving object can be calculated from this equation:

$$KE = \frac{1}{2}mv^2$$

Potential Energy

- Potential energy is stored energy due to the position of an object.
- Different forms of potential energy include elastic potential energy, chemical potential energy, and gravitational potential energy.
- Gravitational potential energy can be calculated from this equation:

$$GPE = mgh$$

Self Check

1. **Explain** whether an object can have kinetic energy and potential energy at the same time.
2. **Describe** three situations in which the gravitational potential energy of an object changes.
3. **Explain** how the kinetic energy of a truck could be increased without increasing the truck's speed.
4. **Think Critically** The different molecules that make up the air in a room have on average the same kinetic energy. How does the speed of the different air molecules depend on their masses?

Applying Math

5. **Calculate Kinetic Energy** Find the kinetic energy of a ball with a mass of 0.06 kg moving at 50 m/s.
6. **Use Ratios** A boulder on top of a cliff has potential energy of 8,800 J, and has twice the mass of a boulder next to it. What is the GPE of the smaller boulder?
7. **Calculate GPE** An 80-kg diver jumps from a 10-m high platform. What is the gravitational potential energy of the diver halfway down?

 gpscience.com/self_check_quiz

3 Assess

DAILY INTERVENTION

Check for Understanding

Kinetic Energy Roll a fist-sized piece of soft modeling clay into a ball and drop it on the floor. Ask: Where is the kinetic energy of the clay ball the greatest? What happened to the kinetic energy when the clay ball hit the floor? What other kinds of energy were formed from the kinetic energy of the ball? The kinetic energy is greatest just before the ball hits the floor. It then turned into sound energy and heat.

Reteach

Energy Transformation Perform several tasks, such as clapping your hands, walking across the room, tossing a ball across the room, or turning on a light. Ask students to identify the energy transformations that occur during each task. L1 ELL

 **Visual-Spatial**

Assessment

Process Tell students that a 5 kg bowling ball is on a rack 1.5 m above the ground. Have them calculate the GPE of the ball. $5 \text{ kg} \times 9.8 \text{ m/s}^2 \times 1.5 \text{ m} = 73.5 \text{ J}$ Use **Performance Assessment in the Science Classroom,** p. 101.

section 1 review

1. Yes, an object that is moving above Earth's surface will have kinetic energy and potential energy.
2. An object is raised higher, an object falls to a lower height, and the mass of an object above Earth's surface changes.
3. The kinetic energy could be increased by increasing the truck's mass.
4. Molecules with smaller masses will be moving faster.
5. $KE = \frac{1}{2}mv^2$

   $KE = \frac{1}{2}(0.06 \text{ kg})(50 \text{ m/s})^2$

   $KE = 75 \text{ J}$
6. $\frac{GPE_1}{m_1} = \frac{GPE_2}{m_2}$

   $\frac{8800 \text{ J}}{2x} = \frac{GPE_2}{x}$

   $4400 \text{ J} = GPE$
7. $PE = mgh = 80 \text{ kg} \times 9.8 \text{ m/s}^2 \times 10 \text{ m} = 7800 \text{ J}$

   $PE = mgh = 80 \text{ kg} \times 9.8 \text{ m/s}^2 \times 5 \text{ m} = 3900 \text{ J}$

Real-World Question

Purpose Students observe how the GPE of a falling ball is converted to kinetic energy and elastic potential energy, enabling the ball to bounce. L2 COOP LEARN **Kinesthetic**

Process Skills observing and inferring, predicting, comparing, recognizing cause and effect

Time Required 30 minutes

Procedure

Alternate Materials table tennis ball, book

Safety Precautions Caution students to let the balls drop and not throw them down.

Teaching Strategy Explain that it is only possible to measure the approximate height of the ball's bounce.

Troubleshooting Have students hold a meter stick vertically next to the drop zone and watch closely to estimate bounce heights.

Conclude and Apply

1. Use the formula: $GPE = m\text{ (kg)} \times 9.8\text{ m/s}^2 \times h\text{ (m)}$.
2. Average height = sum of heights ÷ number of trials. Answers will vary.
3. The balls don't bounce as high on the box. Some of the kinetic energy the ball has when it hits the box is transferred to the box, causing the box to vibrate. This energy is then unavailable to help propel the ball up.
4. Some balls store more elastic potential energy than others.

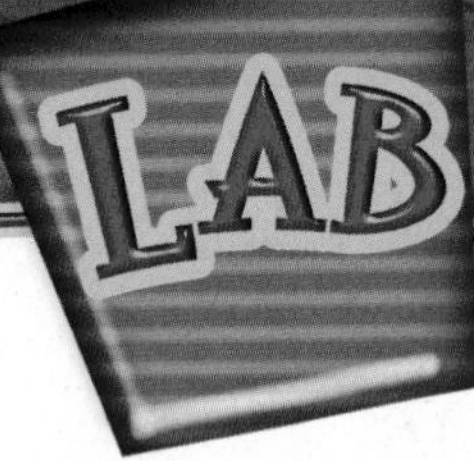

Bouncing Balls

What happens when you drop a ball onto a hard, flat surface? It starts with potential energy. It bounces up and down until it finally comes to a rest. Where did the energy go?

Real-World Question

Why do bouncing balls stop bouncing?

Goals

- **Identify** the forms of energy observed in a bouncing ball.
- **Infer** why the ball stops bouncing.

Materials

tennis ball
rubber ball
balance
meterstick
masking tape
cardboard box
*shoe box

*Alternate materials

Safety Precautions

Procedure

1. **Measure** the mass of the two balls.
2. Have a partner drop one ball from 1 m. Measure how high the ball bounced. Repeat this two more times so you can calculate an average bounce height. Record your values on the data table.
3. Repeat step 2 for the other ball.
4. **Predict** whether the balls would bounce higher or lower if they were dropped onto the cardboard box. Design an experiment to measure how high the balls would bounce off the surface of a cardboard box.

Bounce Height

Type of Ball	Surface	Trial	Height (cm)
Tennis	Floor	1	36
Tennis	Floor	2	34
Tennis	Floor	3	37
Rubber	Floor	1	54
Rubber	Floor	2	56
Rubber	Floor	3	56
Tennis	Box	1	29

Conclude and Apply

1. **Calculate** the gravitational potential energy of each ball before dropping it.
2. **Calculate** the average bounce height for the three trials under each condition. Describe your observations.
3. **Compare** the bounce heights of the balls dropped on a cardboard box with the bounce heights of the ballls dropped on the floor. Hint: *Did you observe any movement of the box when the balls bounced?*
4. **Explain** why the balls bounced to different heights, using the concept of elastic potential energy.

Meet with three other lab teams and compare average bounce heights for the tennis ball on the floor. Discuss why your results might differ. **For more help, refer to the** Science Skill Handbook.

Assessment

Process Demonstrate how the bounce height of a ball becomes lower and lower each time it bounces. Have students infer why this happens. Each time the ball bounces, part of its energy is converted to other forms of energy, such as thermal energy and sound. Use **Performance Assessment in the Science Classroom,** p. 89.

Students can use a computer graphics program to prepare a display of their activity results. They should be allowed freedom to make their own design, but the picture should clearly show how the balls bounced higher off the floor than off the box.

Section 2 Conservation of Energy

Reading Guide

What You'll Learn
- **Describe** how energy can be transformed from one form to another.
- **Explain** how the mechanical energy of a system is the sum of the kinetic and potential energy.
- **Discuss** the law of conservation of energy.

Why It's Important
All the energy transformations that occur inside you and around you obey the law of conservation of energy.

Review Vocabulary
friction: a force that opposes the sliding motion of two surfaces that are touching each other

New Vocabulary
- mechanical energy
- law of conservation of energy

Changing Forms of Energy

Unless you were talking about potential energy, you probably wouldn't think of the book on top of a bookshelf as having much to do with energy—until it fell. You'd be more likely to think of energy as race cars roar past or as your body uses energy from food to help it move, or as the Sun warms your skin on a summer day. These situations involve energy changing from one form to another form.

Transforming Electrical Energy You use many devices every day that convert one form of energy to other forms. For example, you might be reading this page in a room lit by lightbulbs. The lightbulbs transform electrical energy into light so you can see. The warmth you feel around the bulb is evidence that some of that electrical energy is transformed into thermal energy, as illustrated in **Figure 5.** What other devices have you used today that make use of electrical energy? You might have been awakened by an alarm clock, styled your hair, made toast, listened to music, or played a video game. What form or forms of energy is electrical energy converted to in these examples?

Figure 5 A lightbulb is a device that transforms electrical energy into light energy and thermal energy.
Identify *other devices that convert electrical energy to thermal energy.*

1 Motivate

Bellringer

Section Focus Transparencies also are available on the Interactive Chalkboard CD-ROM.

L2 ELL

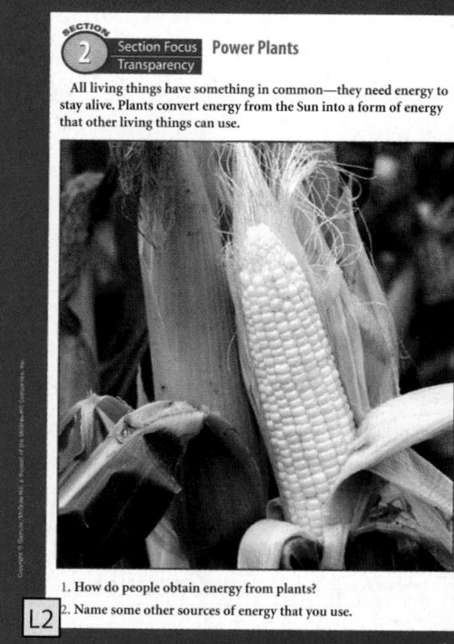

L2

Tie to Prior Knowledge

Skateboarding Discuss the various forms of energy involved in skateboarding.

Text Question Answer

alarm clock—sound; hair styler—heat or kinetic; toaster—heat; music—sound; video game—light

Caption Answer

Figure 5 Possible answers: heater, electric stove, iron, hair dryer

Section 2 Resource Manager

Chapter *FAST FILE* Resources
- Transparency Activity, p. 53
- Directed Reading for Content Mastery, pp. 21–22
- Lab Activity, pp. 13–15
- Enrichment, p. 30
- MiniLAB, p.4
- Lab Worksheet, pp. 7–8
- Reinforcement, p. 28

Cultural Diversity, p. 53
Home and Community Involvement, p. 36
Physical Science Critical Thinking/Problem Solving, p. 17

2 Teach

Visual Learning

Figure 6 Review the energy conversions at work in an internal combustion engine. Then discuss how a diesel engine works. In a diesel engine, the air in the cylinder is compressed to a high pressure and becomes very hot. When the fuel is sprayed into the cylinder, it ignites in the hot air without the need of a spark plug. What energy conversions take place in a diesel engine? Chemical potential energy is converted to thermal energy and then to kinetic energy. L2 LS **Logical-Mathematical**

Make a Model

Converting Energy Have students work in groups to make models that show the conversion from potential energy to kinetic energy. They might choose to use a spring, windup car, or ball to demonstrate the idea. L1 COOP LEARN LS **Kinesthetic**

Quick Demo

Energy Conversion

Materials rubber "superball"

Estimated Time five minutes

Procedure Demonstrate conversion of gravitational potential energy to kinetic energy and back again by dropping a rubber "superball" from different heights. Point out that the higher the drop, the greater its final velocity and the higher it rebounds. Also, notice the ball never quite bounces to its original height. Ask: Why does the ball not return to its original height each time the ball bounces? Some of the energy is converted to heat each time the ball hits the floor.

Text Question Answer

Mechanical energy is the sum of all potential and kinetic energies. As one transforms into another, the mechanical energy remains constant.

In a car, a spark plug fires, initiating the conversion of chemical potential energy into thermal energy.

As the hot gases expand, thermal energy is converted into kinetic energy.

Figure 6 In the engine of a car, several energy conversions occur.

Transforming Chemical Energy Fuel stores energy in the form of chemical potential energy. For example, the car or bus that might have brought you to school this morning probably runs on gasoline. The engine transforms the chemical potential energy stored in gasoline molecules into the kinetic energy of a moving car or bus. Several energy conversions occur in this process, as shown in **Figure 6.** An electric spark ignites a small amount of fuel. The burning fuel produces thermal energy. So chemical energy is changed to thermal energy. The thermal energy causes gases to expand and move parts of the car, producing kinetic energy.

Some energy transformations are less obvious because they do not result in visible motion, sound, heat, or light. Every green plant you see converts light energy from the Sun into energy stored in chemical bonds in the plant. If you eat an ear of corn, the chemical potential energy in the corn is transformed into other forms of energy by your body.

Conversions Between Kinetic and Potential Energy

You have experienced many situations that involve conversions between potential and kinetic energy. Systems such as bicycles, roller coasters, and swings can be described in terms of potential and kinetic energy. Even launching a rubber band or using a bow and arrow involves energy conversions. To understand the energy conversions that occur, it is helpful to identify the mechanical energy of a system. **Mechanical energy** is the total amount of potential and kinetic energy in a system and can be expressed by this equation.

$$\text{mechanical energy} = \text{potential energy} + \text{kinetic energy}$$

In other words, mechanical energy is energy due to the position and the motion of an object or the objects in a system. What happens to the mechanical energy of an object as potential and kinetic energy are converted into each other?

Differentiated Instruction

Challenge Remind students that work is the transfer of energy, is measured in the same units as energy, and can be calculated using the formula W 5 F 3 d. Provide students the following scenario: The kinetic energy of a hockey puck is 20 J as it moves from ice onto the cement surrounding the rink. By how much is its energy decreased if it stops on the cement? 20 J If the cement causes a frictional force of 10 N on the puck, how far does it slide? $-10\text{ N} \cdot d = -20\text{ J}$, therefore $d = 2.0\text{ m}$ What happens to this energy? It is converted into heat. L3 LS **Mathematical**

Falling Objects Standing under an apple tree can be hazardous. An apple on a tree, like the one in **Figure 7,** has gravitational potential energy due to Earth pulling down on it. The apple does not have kinetic energy while it hangs from the tree. However, the instant the apple comes loose from the tree, it accelerates due to gravity. As it falls, it loses height so its gravitational potential energy decreases. This potential energy is transformed into kinetic energy as the velocity of the apple increases.

Look back at the equation for mechanical energy. If the potential energy is being converted into kinetic energy, then the mechanical energy of the apple doesn't change as it falls. The potential energy that the apple loses is gained back as kinetic energy. The form of energy changes, but the total amount of energy remains the same.

Reading Check *What happens to the mechanical energy of the apple as it falls from the tree?*

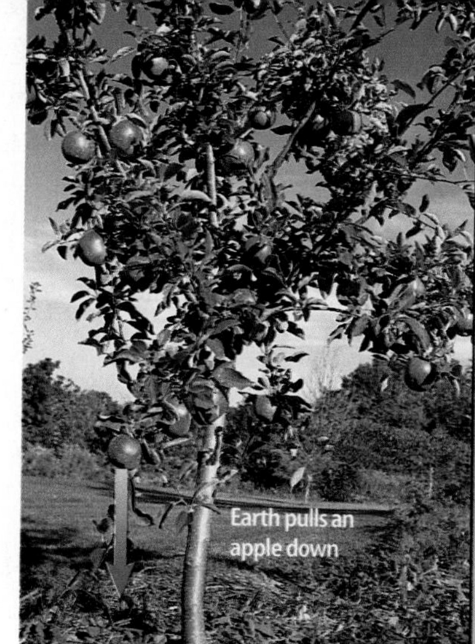

Figure 7 Objects that can fall have gravitational potential energy.
Apply *What objects around you have gravitational potential energy?*

Energy Transformations in Projectile Motion Energy transformations also occur during projectile motion when an object moves in a curved path. Look at **Figure 8.** When the ball leaves the bat, it has mostly kinetic energy. As the ball rises, its velocity decreases, so its kinetic energy must decrease, too. However, the ball's gravitational potential energy increases as it goes higher. At its highest point, the baseball has the maximum amount of gravitational potential energy. The only kinetic energy it has at this point is due to its forward motion. Then, as the baseball falls, gravitational potential energy decreases while kinetic energy increases as the ball moves faster. However, the mechanical energy of the ball remains constant as it rises and falls.

Figure 8 Kinetic energy and gravitational potential energy are converted into each other as the ball rises and falls.

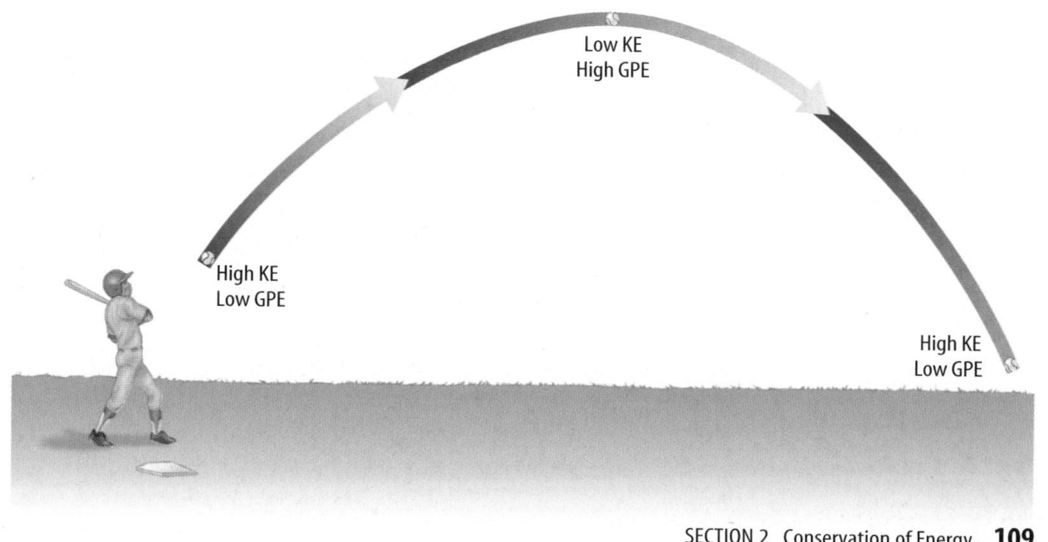

Reading Check

Answer Potential energy decreases; kinetic energy increases; total mechanical energy remains constant.

Caption Answer

Figure 7 Any objects that are elevated have GPE.

Discussion

Riding an Elevator You are riding in an elevator. How do your kinetic and potential energies relative to the elevator change as you go up? Neither changes. L1

Teacher FYI

Free Fall Rate If there is no air resistance, then two objects that start falling at the same time from the same height will hit the ground at the same time. The rate of free fall does not depend on mass. But an object with larger mass has more GPE before it falls and has more kinetic energy as it falls. In other words, it will hurt more when it hits your head.

Identifying Misconceptions

Pendulum Swing Some students may not realize that when the bob of a pendulum reaches its maximum height, it momentarily stops, and when it is at its lowest part of its swing, its velocity is highest. Sketch a pendulum on the board and use arrows to show movement. Explain that the bob must briefly stop to change directions. Because it has no velocity, it has no kinetic energy at this point.

Curriculum Connection

History Students have probably heard the tale of Isaac Newton discovering gravity when an apple fell from a tree onto his head. Have students investigate this story to determine if it is a myth or a true occurrence. Have students share their findings with the class. Newton is purported to have said himself that the fall of the apple "occasioned" his "notion of gravitation." L3 IN **Interpersonal**

NATIONAL GEOGRAPHIC

Visualizing Energy Transformations

Have students examine the pictures and read the captions. Then ask the following questions.

As the student goes from point A to B, why is her kinetic energy increasing? because her velocity is increasing

What force accelerates the student as she goes from point A to the lowest point and slows down the student as she goes from the lowest point to point D? gravity

Activity

Model Swings The movement of the swing is similar to the movement of a pendulum. Provide students with a 1-meter piece of string with a large washer tied to the end of it. Ask students to simulate the movement of the swing or a pendulum using the string and washer. Have students experiment to see if the length of the string has any relationship to the time it takes the washer to make one complete period, going from point A on the diagram to point D and back to point A again. Caution students not to swing string and washer strongly or near other students.

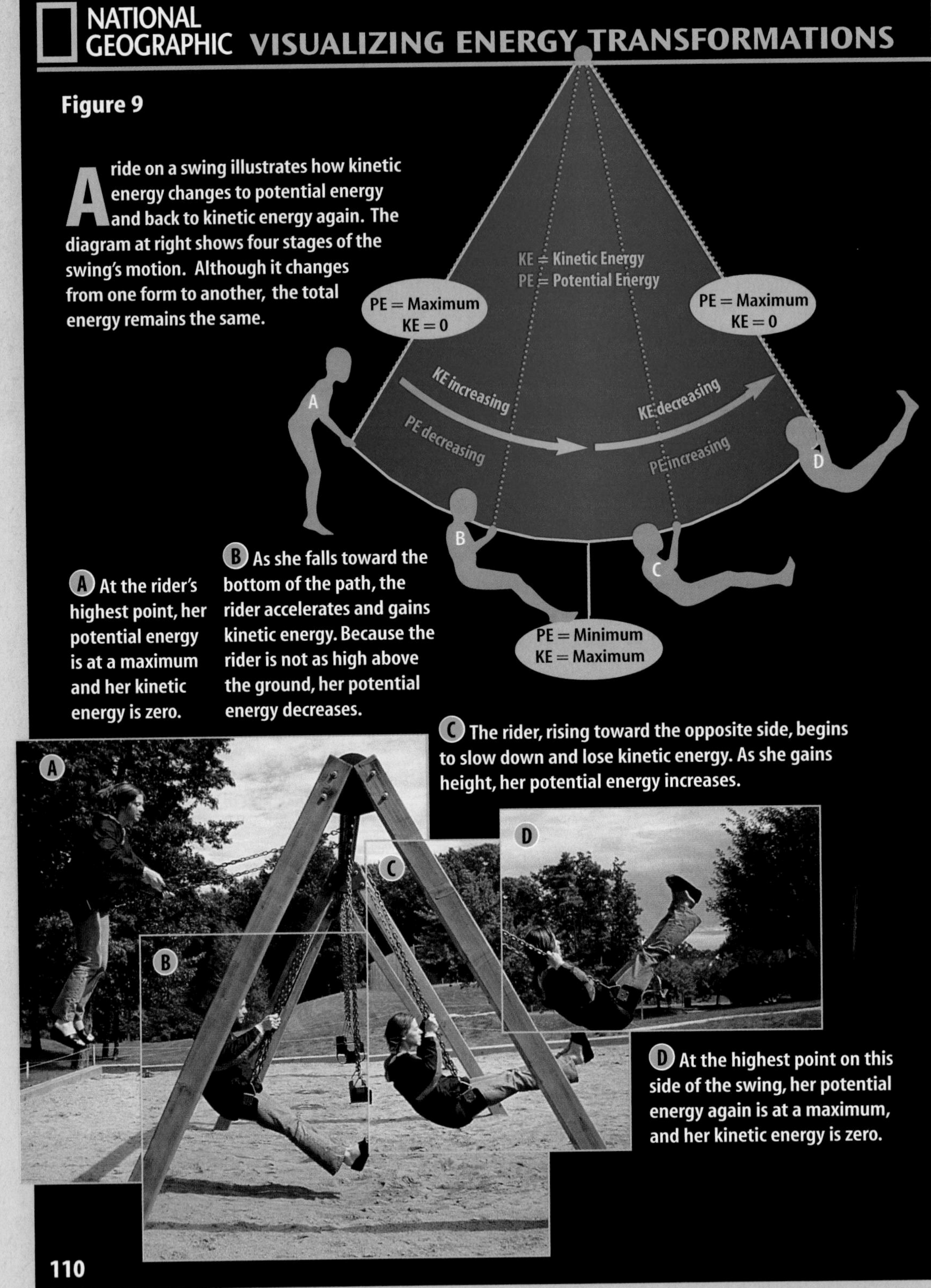

NATIONAL GEOGRAPHIC VISUALIZING ENERGY TRANSFORMATIONS
Figure 9
A ride on a swing illustrates how kinetic energy changes to potential energy and back to kinetic energy again. The diagram at right shows four stages of the swing's motion. Although it changes from one form to another, the total energy remains the same.
KE = Kinetic Energy
PE = Potential Energy
PE = Maximum KE = 0
PE = Maximum KE = 0
KE increasing
PE decreasing
KE decreasing
PE increasing
PE = Minimum KE = Maximum
A At the rider's highest point, her potential energy is at a maximum and her kinetic energy is zero.
B As she falls toward the bottom of the path, the rider accelerates and gains kinetic energy. Because the rider is not as high above the ground, her potential energy decreases.
C The rider, rising toward the opposite side, begins to slow down and lose kinetic energy. As she gains height, her potential energy increases.
D At the highest point on this side of the swing, her potential energy again is at a maximum, and her kinetic energy is zero.
110

LAB DEMONSTRATION

Purpose to demonstrate the conservation of mechanical energy

Materials 2 m plastic tubing, 2 ring stands with clamps, marble

Preparation Form a U-shaped tunnel by clamping each end of the tubing to a ring stand. The ends should be at identical heights.

Procedure Hold a marble slightly above one end of the tubing. Have students predict the height the marble will reach on the opposite side. Release and discuss the result. Rearrange the tubing to form various shaped tunnels and repeat the activity.

Expected Outcome There should be a slight loss in mechanical energy.

Assessment

How was the mechanical energy affected as the marble traveled along the tubing? Air resistance on a marble inside a plastic tube is negligible. What are possible causes of this? friction from the tubing

Energy Transformations in a Swing When you ride on a swing, like the one shown in **Figure 9,** part of the fun is the feeling of almost falling as you drop from the highest point to the lowest point of the swing's path. Think about energy conservation to analyze such a ride.

The ride starts with a push that gets you moving, giving you kinetic energy. As the swing rises, you lose speed but gain height. In energy terms, kinetic energy changes to gravitational potential energy. At the top of your path, potential energy is at its greatest. Then, as the swing accelerates downward, potential energy changes to kinetic energy. At the bottom of each swing, the kinetic energy is at its greatest and the potential energy is at its minimum. As you swing back and forth, energy continually converts from kinetic to potential and back to kinetic. What happens to your mechanical energy as you swing?

The Law of Conservation of Energy

When a ball is thrown into the air or a swing moves back and forth, kinetic and potential energy are constantly changing as the object speeds up and slows down. However, mechanical energy stays constant. Kinetic and potential energy simply change forms and no energy is destroyed.

This is always true. Energy can change from one form to another, but the total amount of energy never changes. Even when energy changes form from electrical to thermal and other energy forms as in the hair dryer shown in **Figure 10,** energy is never destroyed. Another way to say this is that energy is conserved. This principle is recognized as a law of nature. The **law of conservation of energy** states that energy cannot be created or destroyed. On a large scale, this law means that the total amount of energy in the universe does not change.

Reading Check *What law states that the total amount of energy never changes?*

Conserving Resources You might have heard about energy conservation or been asked to conserve energy. These ideas are related to reducing the demand for electricity and gasoline, which lowers the consumption of energy resources such as coal and fuel oil. The law of conservation of energy, on the other hand, is a universal principle that describes what happens to energy as it is transferred from one object to another or as it is transformed.

Energy and the Food Chain One way energy enters ecosystems is when green plants transform radiant energy from the Sun into chemical potential energy in the form of food. Energy moves through the food chain as animals that eat plants are eaten by other animals. Some energy leaves the food chain, such as when living organisms release thermal energy to the environment. Diagram a simple biological food chain showing energy conservation.

Figure 10 The law of conservation of energy requires that the total amount of energy going into a hair dryer must equal the total amount of energy coming out of the hair dryer.

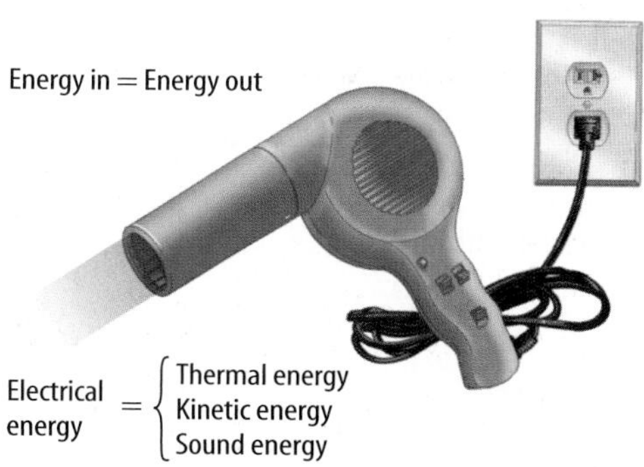

Energy and the Food Chain In a food chain, arrows show the direction in which energy moves from one organism to the next. Possible food chain: grass → rabbit → fox

Career Find out how environmental scientists in your area use data on numbers and kinds of plants and animals to evaluate the health of an ecosystem.

Use Science Words

Word Meaning The word *conservation* means to keep from being lost or wasted. Discuss why this is an appropriate word to use for the principle of conservation of energy. Possible answer: It is appropriate because energy is never lost. L2

LS **Linguistic**

Text Question Answer:

Mechanical energy remains constant

Answer the law of conservation of energy

Virtual Labs

Energy Conversion *How is energy converted from one form to another?*

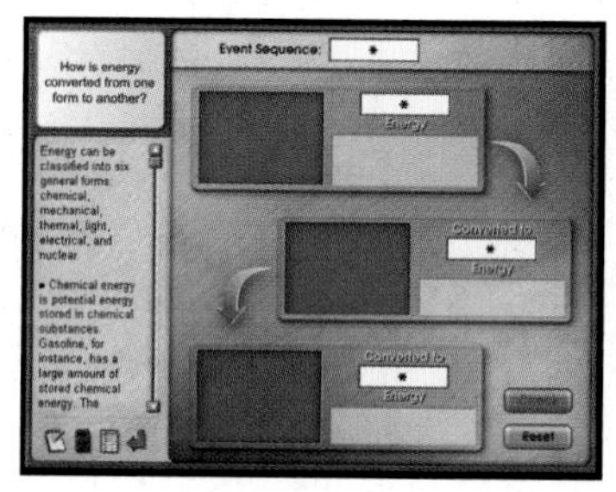

Science Journal

Have students create a flow diagram that traces the conversion of solar energy into different forms of energy on earth. Possible answers: Plants convert solar energy into food for animals who move around. Plants also feed people who use machines and electricity to do work. Heat energy from the sun causes warm air to rise which causes wind energy, and it fuels the water cycle. P

Purpose Students observe how kinetic energy can change into thermal energy. L1

LS **Intrapersonal**

Materials paper clip

Teaching Strategy Have students use uncoated clips that are not too thick or brittle to easily bend.

Safety Precaution Students should be careful of the sharp ends of the paper clip when bending it.

Analysis

1. It went up. Some mechanical energy from the paper clip was converted to thermal energy.
2. Chemical energy from the body is converted to kinetic energy that is transferred to the paper clip. Mechanical energy is converted to thermal energy by collisions of the molecules in the paper clip.

Assessment

Oral Have students discuss other examples of the process modeled by this activity. Possible answer: bicycle or car tires heat up as they roll along the road. Use **Performance Assessment in the Science Classroom,** p. 89.

Caption Answer

Figure 11 Both the kinetic and potential energy decrease as friction and air resistance transform the swing's mechanical energy into thermal energy.

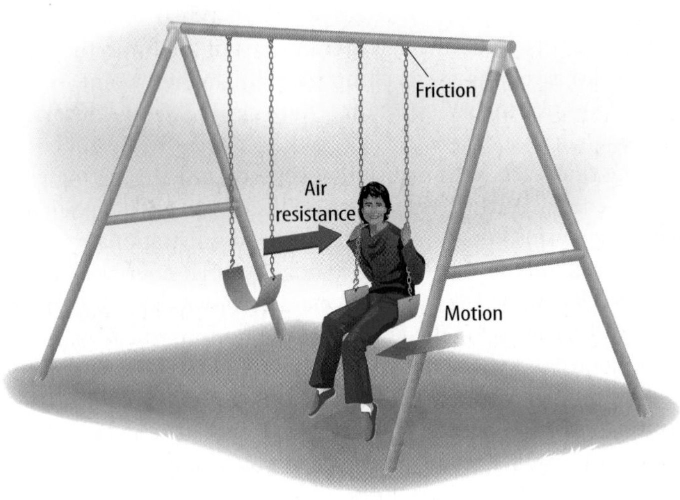

Figure 11 In a swing, mechanical energy is transformed into thermal energy because of friction and air resistance.
Infer *how the kinetic and potential energy of the swing change with time.*

Energy Transformations in a Paper Clip

Procedure

1. Straighten a **paper clip.** While holding the ends, touch the paper clip to the skin just below your lower lip. Note whether the paper clip feels warm, cool, or about room temperature.
2. Quickly bend the paper clip back and forth five times. Touch it below your lower lip again. Note whether the paper clip feels warmer or cooler than before.

Analysis

1. What happened to the temperature of the paper clip? Why?
2. Explain the energy conversions that take place as you bend the paper clip.

Try at Home

Is energy always conserved? You might be able to think of situations where it seems as though energy is not conserved. For example, while coasting along a flat road on a bicycle, you know that you will eventually stop if you don't pedal. If energy is conserved, why wouldn't your kinetic energy stay constant so that you would coast forever? In many situations, it might seem that energy is destroyed or created. Sometimes it is hard to see the law of conservation of energy at work.

The Effect of Friction You know from experience that if you don't continue to pump a swing or be pushed by somebody else, your arcs will become lower and you eventually will stop swinging. In other words, the mechanical (kinetic and potential) energy of the swing seems to decrease, as if the energy were being destroyed. Is this a violation of the law of conservation of energy?

It can't be—it's the law! If the energy of the swing decreases, then the energy of some other object must increase by an equal amount to keep the total amount of energy the same. What could this other object be that experiences an energy increase? To answer this, you need to think about friction. With every movement, the swing's ropes or chains rub on their hooks and air pushes on the rider, as illustrated in **Figure 11.** Friction and air resistance cause some of the mechanical energy of the swing to change to thermal energy. With every pass of the swing, the temperature of the hooks and the air increases a little, so the mechanical energy of the swing is not destroyed. Rather, it is transformed into thermal energy. The total amount of energy always stays the same.

Fun Fact

Many people have tried to develop a perpetual motion machine, a device which, once set in motion, would forever make more energy than it uses. Conservation of energy means that such a machine is impossible.

Differentiated Instruction

Learning Disabled To help students see how friction affects the velocity and therefore the kinetic energy of objects, have them roll marbles across a smooth table and then across a piece of carpet. Explain that the marbles move more slowly on the carpet and have less kinetic energy because the frictional force opposes their motion.

 **Kinesthetic**

Converting Mass into Energy You might have wondered how the Sun unleashes enough energy to light and warm Earth from so far away. A special kind of energy conversion—nuclear fusion—takes place in the Sun and other stars. During this process a small amount of mass is transformed into a tremendous amount of energy. An example of a nuclear fusion reaction is shown in **Figure 12.** In the reaction shown here, the nuclei of the hydrogen isotopes deuterium and tritium undergo fusion.

Nuclear Fission Another process involving the nuclei of atoms, called nuclear fission, converts a small amount of mass into enormous quantities of energy. In this process, nuclei do not fuse—they are broken apart, as shown in **Figure 12.** In either process, fusion or fission, mass is converted to energy. In processes involving nuclear fission and fusion, the total amount of energy is still conserved if the energy content of the masses involved are included. Then the total energy before the reaction is equal to the total energy after the reaction, as required by the law of conservation of energy. The process of nuclear fission is used by nuclear power plants to generate electrical energy.

Topic: Nuclear Fusion
Visit gpscience.com for Web links to information about using nuclear fusion as a source of energy in electric power plants.

Activity Make a table listing the advantages and disadvantages of using nuclear fusion as an energy source.

Figure 12 Mass is converted to energy in the processes of fusion and fission.

Nuclear fusion

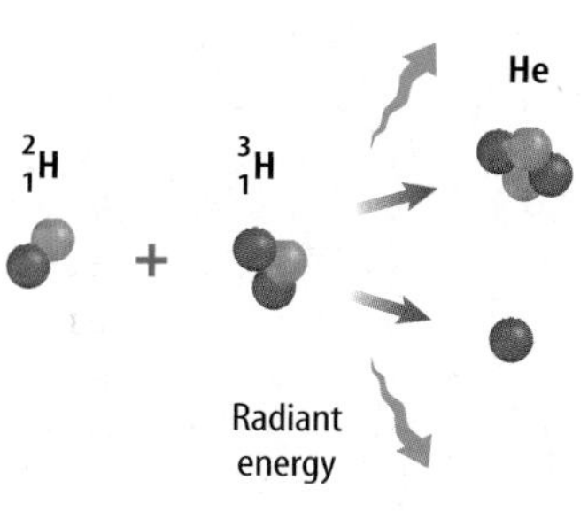

Mass $^2_1$H + Mass $^3_1$H > Mass **He** +Mass **neutron**

In this fusion reaction, the combined mass of the two hydrogen nuclei is greater than the mass of the helium nucleus, He, and the neutron.

Nuclear fission

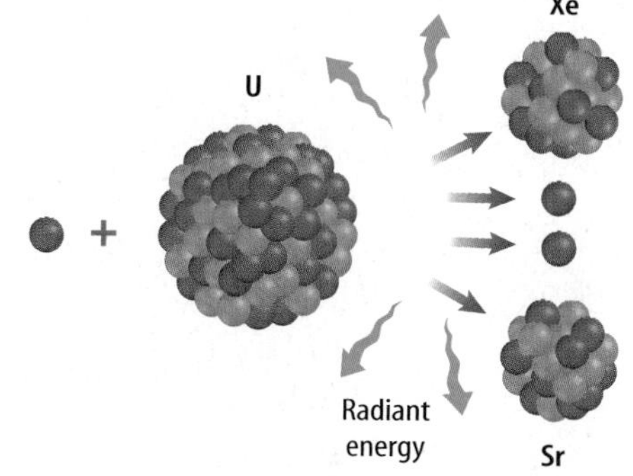

Mass **U** + Mass **neutron** > Mass **Xe** + Mass **Sr** + Mass **neutrons**

In nuclear fission, the mass of the large nucleus on the left is greater than the combined mass of the other two nuclei and the neutrons.

Use Science Words

Word Meaning Have students use a dictionary to look up the words *fusion* and *fission.* Ask them to explain why these are appropriate terms for the nuclear processes discussed in this section. Fusion is combining of things—in nuclear fusion, nuclei combine. Fission is splitting apart of things—in nuclear fission, nuclei split apart. L1 IN **Linguistic**

Inquiry Lab

Calculate Energy

Purpose to calculate elastic potential energy and kinetic energy in a rubber band

Possible Materials rubber band, Newton scale, meterstick, pan balance, stopwatch.

Estimated Time 30 minutes

Procedure Have students devise a method to calculate and a method to check the elastic potential energy of a rubber band using the mater-ials listed. Remind them that velocity can be calculated using the horizontal distance traveled and the time to fall. Have them graph force to pull vs distance pulled, and force to pull vs. velocity.

Safety Precautions Caution students not to shoot rubber bands at each other.

Teaching Strategy

The elastic potential energy can be calculated by multiplying the force to pull times the distance pulled. It should nearly equal the kinetic energy which can be calculated from the mass and velocity. The force vs. distance graph should be a straight diagonal line because they are directly proportional. Force vs. velocity will be a curve.

For additional inquiry activities, see *Science Inquiry Labs.*

Teacher FYI

Chain Reaction In the process of fission, neutrons are released. They initiate further fission, beginning a chain reaction. For the chain reaction to continue, sufficient fissionable material must be present. The amount of material needed to sustain a chain reaction is known as the critical mass.

SECTION 2 Conservation of Energy 113

The Human Body—Balancing the Energy Equation

What forms of energy discussed in this chapter can you find in the human body? With your right hand, reach up and feel your left shoulder. With that simple action, stored potential energy within your body was converted to the kinetic energy of your moving arm. Did your shoulder feel warm to your hand? Some of the chemical potential energy stored in your body is used to maintain a nearly constant internal temperature. A portion of this energy also is converted to the excess heat that your body gives off to its surroundings. Even the people shown standing in **Figure 13** require energy conversions to stand still.

Energy Conversions in Your Body The complex chemical and physical processes going on in your body also obey the law of conservation of energy. Your body stores energy in the form of fat and other chemical compounds. This chemical potential energy is used to fuel the processes that keep you alive, such as making your heart beat and digesting the food you eat. Your body also converts this energy to heat that is transferred to your surroundings, and you use this energy to make your body move. **Table 1** shows the amount of energy used in doing various activities. To maintain a healthy weight, you must have a proper balance between energy contained in the food you eat and the energy your body uses.

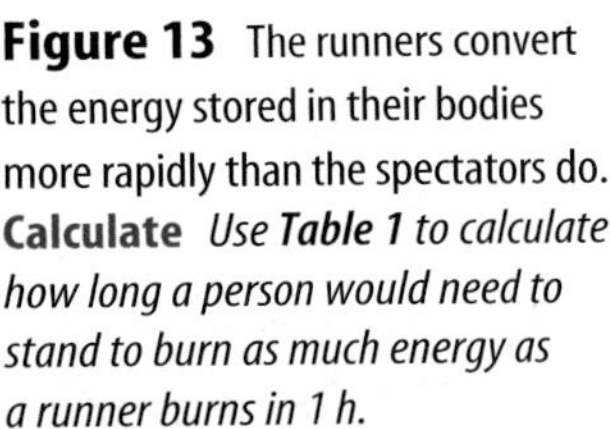

Figure 13 The runners convert the energy stored in their bodies more rapidly than the spectators do. **Calculate** *Use **Table 1** to calculate how long a person would need to stand to burn as much energy as a runner burns in 1 h.*

IDENTIFYING Misconceptions

Human Conversions Students may confuse energy transformations with changes in matter. Some may state that food is converted into energy in the body. During digestion, chemical compounds in food are converted into compounds that muscle cells use to enable muscles to move.

Use Science Words

Word Origin The word *calorie* originates from the eighteenth-century word *caloric*, which was a hypothetical weightless fluid that scientists thought flowed from hot objects to cold objects. Ask students to find out how caloric theory contributed to the idea of conservation of energy. Benjamin Thompson (1753–1814), working in a German munitions factory noticed that canons became very hot during the boring process even though the canon and the borer were initially cold. He concluded that heat was a form of energy produced by friction. Similar experiments by other scientists confirmed that heat was a form of energy and not a fluid, and that it was energy that was being conserved and not caloric. L2 LS **Linguistic**

Caption Answer

Figure 13 7 to 8 hours depending on body type

Visual Learning

Table 1 Have students think back over the past 24 hours and make a list of the things they did. Have them use the table to find out about how many Calories of energy they used.

Cultural Diversity

Energy in Martial Arts Karate, which means "empty hand," originated on Okinawa in the 17th century. A trained karateka can break a thin concrete block with his or her hand. Have students research the meanings of the names of other forms of martial arts and where they originated. Possible martial arts include judo, aikido, and tae kwon do. L2 LS **Intrapersonal**

Active Reading

Learning Journal Have students draw a vertical line down each page of a Learning Journal and record research notes, lecture notes, or vocabulary terms in the left column. In the right column, they respond to, interpret, question, or analyze the left column entries. Students can write a Learning Journal while reading about conservation of energy.

Food Energy Your body has been busy breaking down your breakfast into molecules that can be used as fuel. The chemical potential energy in these molecules supplies the cells in your body with the energy they need to function. Your body also can use the chemical potential energy stored in fat for its energy needs. The food Calorie (C) is a unit used by nutritionists to measure how much energy you get from various foods—1 C is equivalent to about 4,184 J. Every gram of fat a person consumes can supply 9 C of energy. Carbohydrates and proteins each supply about 4 C of energy per gram.

Look at the labels on food packages. They provide information about the Calories contained in a serving, as well as the amounts of protein, fat, and carbohydrates.

Table 1 Calories Used in 1 h

Type of Activity	Body Frames		
	Small	Medium	Large
Sleeping	48	56	64
Sitting	72	84	96
Eating	84	98	112
Standing	96	112	123
Walking	180	210	240
Playing tennis	380	420	460
Bicycling (fast)	500	600	700
Running	700	850	1,000

section 2 review

Summary

Energy Transformations

- Energy can be transformed from one form to another.
- Devices such as lightbulbs, hair dryers, and automobile engines convert one form of energy into other forms.
- The mechanical energy of a system is the sum of the kinetic and potential energy in the system:

  mechanical energy = KE + PE
- In falling, projectile motion, and swings, kinetic and potential energy are transformed into each other and the mechanical energy doesn't change.

The Law of Conservation of Energy

- According to the law of conservation of energy, energy cannot be created or destroyed.
- Friction converts mechanical energy into thermal energy.
- Fission and fusion are nuclear reactions that convert a small amount of mass in a nucleus into an enormous amount of energy.

Self Check

1. **Explain** how friction affects the mechanical energy of a system.
2. **Describe** the energy transformations that occur as you coast down a long hill on a bicycle and apply the brakes, causing the brake pads and bicycle rims to feel warm.
3. **Explain** how energy is conserved when nuclear fission or fusion occurs.
4. **Think Critically** A roller coaster is at the top of a hill and rolls to the top of a lower hill. If mechanical energy is conserved, on the top of which hill is the kinetic energy of the roller coaster larger?

Applying Math

5. **Calculate Kinetic Energy** The potential energy of a swing is 200 J at its highest point and 50 J at its lowest point. If mechanical energy is conserved, what is the kinetic energy of the swing at its lowest point?
6. **Calculate Thermal Energy** The mechanical energy of a bicycle at the top of a hill is 6,000 J. The bicycle stops at the bottom of the hill by applying the brakes. If the potential energy of the bicycle is 2,000 J at the bottom of the hill, how much thermal energy was produced?

Science Online gpscience.com/self_check_quiz

3 Assess

DAILY INTERVENTION

Check for Understanding

Fission v. Fusion Have students use models to demonstrate nuclear fission and nuclear fusion. Students could use marbles for neutrons and protons, with clay to hold them together.
L2 LS **Visual-Spatial**

Reteach

Energy and Calories Show students pictures of people performing various activities, such as those listed in Table 1. Ask students to order the pictures according to how quickly they burn calories. Students should also identify types of energy conversion in each activity.
L1 LS **Visual-Spatial**

Assessment

Process Have students draw diagrams illustrating some of the changing forms of energy involved in bouncing a basketball. Chemical energy from the body changes to kinetic energy to lift the ball. This energy is transferred to the ball as potential energy. As the ball falls, this changes to kinetic energy. As the ball hits the floor, part of the energy changes to sound, part is transferred to the floor, and most is returned to the ball as elastic potential energy, enabling the ball to bounce. Use **Performance Assessment in the Science Classroom,** p. 127.

section 2 review

1. Friction converts mechanical energy into thermal energy.
2. As you coast down the hill, some of your potential energy is being transformed into potential energy. When you apply the brakes, friction between the brake pads and the bicycle rims convert kinetic energy into thermal energy.
3. A small amount of mass is converted into energy.
4. The top of the lower hill. The roller coaster has less potential energy at the top of the lower hill. The difference between the roller coaster's potential energy at the top of the higher hill and lower hill has been converted into kinetic energy.
5. 150 J; The mechanical energy is constant, so the decrease in potential energy = 150 J = increase in kinetic energy. Because the kinetic energy is zero at the top of the swing, the kinetic energy at the bottom is 150 J.
6. 4.000 J; The decrease in mechanical energy equals the thermal energy produced.

Real-World Question

Purpose Construct a pendulum to compare the exchange of potential and kinetic energy. L2 COOP LEARN IS **Kinesthetic**

Process Skills measuring, collecting and organizing data, observing and inferring, communicating, making and using tables, comparing and contrasting, recognizing cause and effect, forming a hypothesis, designing an experiment, using numbers, separating and controlling variables

Time Required one class period

Possible Materials Have additional materials available (string, extra ring stands, banner paper, masking tape).

Safety Precautions Students should wear safety goggles when swinging the stoppers.

Form a Hypothesis

Possible Hypothesis Students may suggest that the crossarm's interference halfway up the length of the string will cause the maximum height to decrease by one half. In fact, the shape of the pendulum's path will change, but the height on the opposite end should still be close to the original height.

Design Your Own

Swinging Energy

Goals

- **Construct** a pendulum to compare the exchange of potential and kinetic energy when a swing is interrupted.
- **Measure** the starting and ending heights of the pendulum.

Possible Materials

ring stand
test-tube clamp
support-rod clamp, right angle
30-cm support rod
2-hole, medium rubber stopper
string (1 m)
metersticks
graph paper

Safety Precautions

WARNING: *Be sure the base is heavy enough or well anchored so that the apparatus will not tip over.*

Real-World Question

Imagine yourself swinging on a swing. What would happen if a friend grabbed the swing's chains as you passed the lowest point? Would you come to a complete stop or continue rising to your previous maximum height? How does the motion and maximum height reached by a swing change if the swing is interrupted?

Form a Hypothesis

Examine the diagram on this page. How is it similar to the situation in the introductory paragraph? An object that is suspended so that it can swing back and forth is called a pendulum. Hypothesize what will happen to the pendulum's motion and final height if its swing is interrupted.

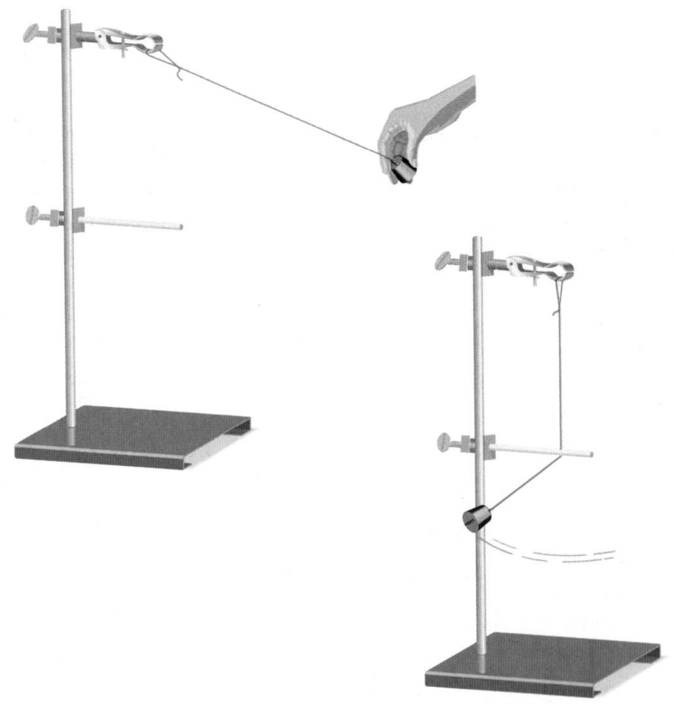

Alternative Inquiry Lab

Energy Loss Have students determine the loss of energy from friction after the pendulum has swung 10 times. Have them measure the mass of the stopper, calculate its initial potential energy, using its initial height, and calculate its ending potential energy using the height after 10 swings. The difference is the amount of energy lost. Have them do this exercise both with and without cross-arm interference. L3 IS **Kinesthetic**

Test Your Hypothesis

Make a Plan

1. As a group, write your hypothesis and list the steps that you will take to test it. Be specific. Also list the materials you will need.
2. **Design** a data table and place it in your Science Journal.
3. Set up an apparatus similar to the one shown in the diagram.
4. **Devise** a way to measure the starting and ending heights of the stopper. Record your starting and ending heights in a data table. This will be your control.
5. **Decide** how to release the stopper from the same height each time.
6. Be sure you test your swing, starting it above and below the height of the cross arm. How many times should you repeat each starting point?

Follow Your Plan

1. Make sure your teacher approves your plan before you start.
2. Carry out the approved experiment as planned.
3. While the experiment is going on, write any observations that you make and complete the data table in your Science Journal.

Analyze Your Data

1. When the stopper is released from the same height as the cross arm, is the ending height of the stopper exactly the same as its starting height? Use your data to support your answer.
2. **Analyze** the energy transfers. At what point along a single swing does the stopper have the greatest kinetic energy? The greatest potential energy?

Conclude and Apply

1. **Explain** Do the results support your hypothesis?
2. **Compare** the starting heights to the ending heights of the stopper. Is there a pattern? Can you account for the observed behavior?
3. **Discuss** Do your results support the law of conservation of energy? Why or why not?
4. **Infer** What happens if the mass of the stopper is increased? Test it.

Communicating Your Data

Compare your conclusions with those of the other lab teams in your class. **For more help, refer to the** Science Skill Handbook.

Test Your Hypothesis

Possible Procedures Set up the pendulum and start it moving. Measure the height at which the stopper was released to start the pendulum. When the pendulum is on the far side of its swing, insert the crossarm. Measure the height to which the pendulum swings after it hits the crossarm.

Teaching Strategy Tape white paper to a wall behind the pendulum for marking stopper height.

Troubleshooting The swing of the pendulum will be irregular if the crossarm inhibits movement of only one side of the pendulum's swing. Suggest students find a way to have the cross arm limit swing in both directions.

Expected Outcome Students will observe that even with the crossarm, the approximate original height is reached.

Analyze Your Data

1. no
2. Kinetic is greatest at the bottom; potential is greatest at the top.

Conclude and Apply

1. Answers will vary with results.
2. Ending heights are lower. Friction slows the stopper and removes some energy from the system.
3. Yes; the apparent loss of energy is due to friction.
4. Kinetic and potential energy increase; the person must pull harder to stop the swing.

Assessment

Process When started from the same height, a pendulum without interference from a crossarm will remain in motion longer than a pendulum with an arm. Ask students to discuss and explain this. Some energy transfers to the crossarm. Use **Performance Assessment in the Science Classroom**, p. 89. L2 **Interpersonal**

Have students use a word processing program to write a short description of their experiment. They may wish to use a computer graphics program to make sketches that help explain the results.

TIME

Content Background

The construction of a perpetual motion machine has been the dream of inventors for centuries. However, the first and second laws of thermodynamics make this impossible. In any real machine, friction causes some of the machine's mechanical energy to be converted to heat that cannot be recovered. As a result, the first law of thermodynamics requires that energy be continually supplied to any machine to keep it moving.

Discussion

Thermodynamics What are the two laws of energy that make perpetual motion machines impossible? 1st Law: Energy cannot be created or destroyed; it only changes form. 2nd Law: Heat flows only from hot to cold.

Historical Significance

Perpetual motion machines have been around at least since Villand de Honnecourt made drawings of one in the 13th century. Between 1635 and 1903, 600 patents were granted for purported free-energy machines. One inventor fooled scientists with a machine that appeared to run on water. He raised five million dollars from investors who later learned that it was actually based on hidden air tubes. In spite of the massive fraud that was found, there are still believers in his "technology" today.

TIME **SCIENCE AND HISTORY** SCIENCE CAN CHANGE THE COURSE OF HISTORY!

The Impossible Dream

A machine that keeps on going? It has been tried for hundreds of years.

Many people have tried throughout history—and failed—to build perpetual-motion machines. In theory, a perpetual-motion machine would run forever and do work without a continual source of energy. You can think of it as a car that you could fill up once with gas, and the car would run forever. Sound impossible? It is!

Science Puts Its Foot Down

For hundreds of years, people have tried to create perpetual-motion machines. But these machines won't work because they violate two of nature's laws. The first law is the law of conservation of energy, which states that energy cannot be created or destroyed. It can change form—say, from mechanical energy to electrical energy—but you always end up with the same amount of energy that you started with.

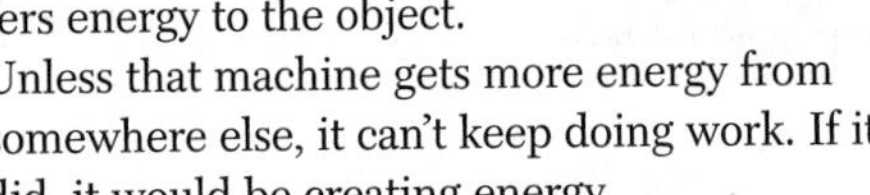

How does that apply to perpetual-motion machines? When a machine does work on an object, the machine transfers energy to the object. Unless that machine gets more energy from somewhere else, it can't keep doing work. If it did, it would be creating energy.

The second law states that heat by itself always flows from a warm object to a cold object. Heat will only flow from a cold object to a warm object if work is done. In the process, some heat always escapes.

To make up for these energy losses, energy constantly needs to be transferred to the machine. Otherwise, it stops. No perpetual motion. No free electricity. No devices that generate more energy than they use. No engine motors that run forever without refueling. Some laws just can't be broken.

Visitors look at the Keely Motor, the most famous perpetual-motion machine fraud of the late 1800s.

Analyze **Using your school or public-library resources, locate a picture or diagram of a perpetual-motion machine. Figure out why it won't run forever. Explain to the class what the problem is.**

Science Online For more information, visit gpscience.com/time

Analyze Ask students to think about how perpetual motion machines might be helpful to science and technology if the laws of thermodynamics did not exist. Start a dialogue addressing the thousands of scam artists who have tried in vain to sell their perpetual motion machines.

Resources for Teachers and Students

"Exploiting Zero-Point Energy", by Philip Yam, *Scientific American*, December 1997

Perpetual Motion: The History of An Obsession, by Arthur W.J.G. OrdHume, Barnes and Noble Books, 1998

Reviewing Main Ideas

Section 1 The Nature of Energy

1. Energy is the ability to cause change.
2. Energy can have different forms, including kinetic, potential, and thermal energy.

3. Moving objects have kinetic energy that depends on the object's mass and velocity, and can be calculated from this equation:

$$KE = \frac{1}{2}mv^2$$

4. Potential energy is stored energy. An object can have gravitational potential energy that depends on its mass and its height, and is given by this equation:

$$GPE = mgh$$

Section 2 Conservation of Energy

1. Energy can change from one form to another. Devices you use every day transform one form of energy into other forms that are more useful.
2. Falling, swinging, and projectile motion all involve transformations between kinetic energy and gravitational potential energy.
3. The total amount of kinetic energy and gravitational potential energy in a system is the mechanical energy of the system:

$$\text{mechanical energy} = KE + GPE$$

4. The law of conservation of energy states that energy never can be created or destroyed. The total amount of energy in the universe is constant.

5. Friction converts mechanical energy into thermal energy, causing the mechanical energy of a system to decrease.
6. Mass is converted into energy in nuclear fission and fusion reactions. Fusion and fission occur in the nuclei of certain atoms, and release tremendous amounts of energy.

FOLDABLES™ Use the Foldable you made at the beginning of this chapter to review what you learned about energy.

Science Online gpscience.com/interactive_tutor

chapter 4 Study Guide

Reviewing Main Ideas

Summary statements can be used by students to review the major concepts of the chapter.

Science Online

Visit gpscience.com
/self_check_quiz
/interactive_tutor
/vocabulary_puzzlemaker
/chapter_review
/standardized_test
/field_guide

Assessment Transparency

For additional assessment questions, use the *Assessment Transparency* located in the transparency book.

Assessment

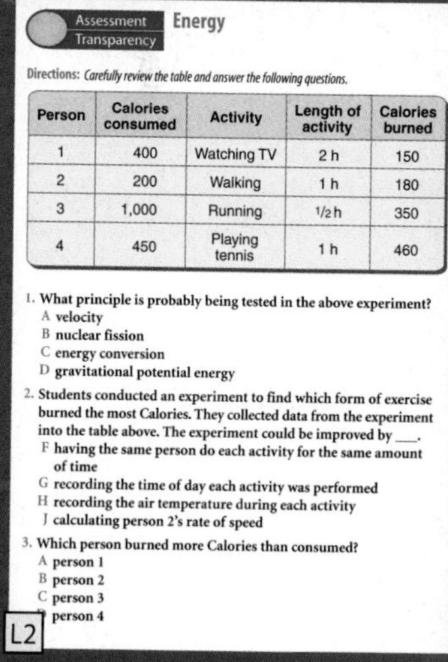

Assessment Transparency **Energy**

Directions: *Carefully review the table and answer the following questions.*

Person	Calories consumed	Activity	Length of activity	Calories burned
1	400	Watching TV	2 h	150
2	200	Walking	1 h	180
3	1,000	Running	1/2 h	350
4	450	Playing tennis	1 h	460

1. **What principle is probably being tested in the above experiment?**
   A velocity
   B nuclear fission
   C energy conversion
   D gravitational potential energy
2. **Students conducted an experiment to find which form of exercise burned the most Calories. They collected data from the experiment into the table above. The experiment could be improved by ___.**
   F having the same person do each activity for the same amount of time
   G recording the time of day each activity was performed
   H recording the air temperature during each activity
   J calculating person 2's rate of speed
3. **Which person burned more Calories than consumed?**
   A person 1
   B person 2
   C person 3
   D person 4

L2

Energy

FOLDABLES™ Have students use their Foldables to review the content of the chapter. On the back of the paper, have students write a paragraph about what they learned about energy.

Using Vocabulary

1. mechanical energy
2. elastic potential energy
3. joule
4. potential energy
5. kinetic energy
6. law of conservation of energy

Checking Concepts

7. D
8. B
9. B
10. A
11. D
12. C

Interpreting Graphics

13. See student page.
14. height = 0.50 m, GPE = 0.24 J, KE = 0.24 J; height = 0.75 m, GPE = 0.37 J, KE = 0.37 J; height = 1.0 m, GPE = 0.49 J, KE = 0.49; The GPE and KE are equal.
15. four times, from 400 J to 1,600 J
16. 2,400 J. It will be four times greater than the KE at 25 m/s, which is 600 J.
17. 100 J. It is one fourth the KE at 20 m/s.

chapter 4 Review

Using Vocabulary

chemical potential energy p. 103	joule p. 102
elastic potential energy p. 103	kinetic energy p. 102
gravitational potential energy p. 104	law of conservation of energy p. 111
	mechanical energy p. 108
	potential energy p. 103

Complete each statement using a word(s) from the vocabulary list above.

1. If friction can be ignored, the ________ of a system doesn't change.
2. The energy stored in a compressed spring is ________.
3. The ________ is the SI unit for energy.
4. When a book is moved from a higher shelf to a lower shelf, its ________ changes.
5. The muscles of a runner transform chemical potential energy into ________.
6. According to the ________ the amount of energy in the universe doesn't change.

Checking Concepts

Choose the word or phrase that best answers the question.

7. What occurs when energy is transferred from one object to another?
   A) an explosion
   B) a chemical reaction
   C) nuclear fusion
   D) a change
8. For which of the following is kinetic energy converted into potential energy?
   A) a boulder rolls down a hill
   B) a ball is thrown upward
   C) a swing comes to a stop
   D) a bowling ball rolls horizontally
9. The gravitational potential energy of an object changes when which of the following changes?
   A) the object's speed
   B) the object's mass
   C) the object's temperature
   D) the object's length
10. Friction causes mechanical energy to be transformed into which of these forms?
    A) thermal energy **C)** kinetic
    B) nuclear energy **D)** potential
11. The kinetic energy of an object changes when which of the following changes?
    A) the object's chemical potential energy
    B) the object's volume
    C) the object's direction of motion
    D) the object's speed
12. When an energy transformation occurs, which of the following is true?
    A) Mechanical energy doesn't change.
    B) Mechanical energy is lost.
    C) The total energy doesn't change.
    D) Mass is converted into energy.

Interpreting Graphics

13. Copy and complete the following concept map on energy.

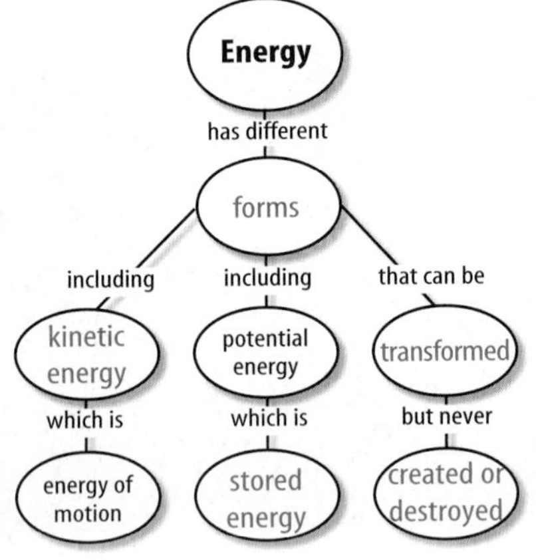

Science Online gpscience.com/vocabulary_puzzlemaker

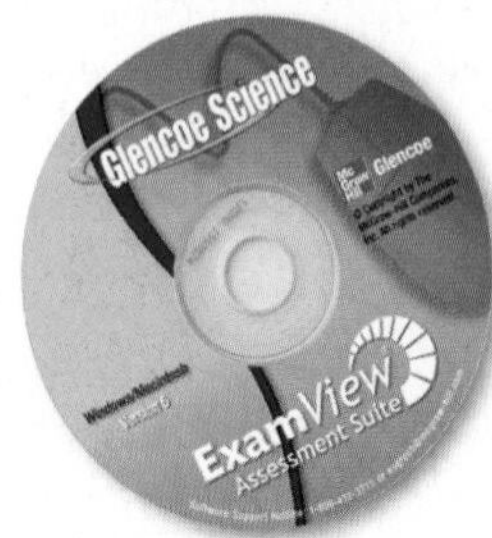

Use the *ExamView® Assessment Suite* CD-ROM to:

- create multiple versions of tests
- create modified tests with one mouse click for inclusion students
- edit existing questions and add your own questions
- build tests aligned with state standards using built-in State Curriculum Tags
- change English tests to Spanish with one mouse click and vice versa

Use the table below to answer question 14.

Toy Cars Rolling Down Ramps

Ramp Height (m)	Speed at Bottom (m/s)	GPE (J)	KE (J)
0.50	3.13		
0.75	3.83		
1.00	4.43		

14. **Make and Use Tables** Three toy cars, each with a mass of 0.05 kg, roll down ramps with different heights. The height of each ramp and the speed of each car at the bottom of each ramp is given in the table. Copy and complete the table by calculating the GPE of each car at the top of the ramp and the KE for each car at the bottom of the ramp to two decimal places. How do the values of GPE and KE you calculate compare?

Use the graph below to answer questions 15–17.

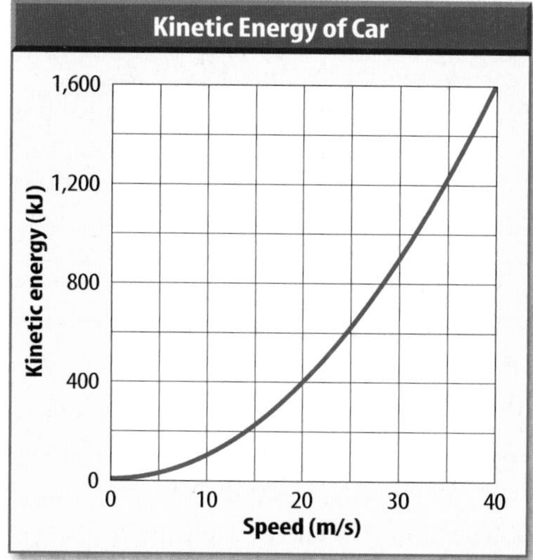

15. When the car's speed doubles from 20 m/s to 40 m/s, by how many times does the car's kinetic energy increase?

16. Using the graph, estimate the car's kinetic energy at a speed of 50 m/s.

17. If the car's kinetic energy at a speed of 20 m/s is 400 kJ, what is the car's kinetic energy at a speed of 10 m/s?

Thinking Critically

18. **Describe** the energy changes that occur in a swing. Explain how energy is conserved as the swing slows down and stops.

19. **Explain** why the law of conservation of energy must also include changes in mass.

20. **Infer** why the tires of a car get hot when the car is driven.

21. **Diagram** On a cold day you rub your hands together to make them warm. Diagram the energy transformations that occur, starting with the chemical potential energy stored in your muscles.

Applying Math

22. **Calculate Kinetic Energy** What is the kinetic energy of a 0.06-kg tennis ball traveling at a speed of 150 m/s?

23. **Calculate Potential Energy** A boulder with a mass of 2,500 kg rests on a ledge 200 m above the ground. What is the boulder's potential energy?

24. **Calculate Mechanical Energy** What is the mechanical energy of a 500-kg roller-coaster car moving with a speed of 3 m/s at the top of hill that is 30 m high?

25. **Calculate Speed** A boulder with a mass of 2,500 kg on a ledge 200 m above the ground falls. If the boulder's mechanical energy is conserved, what is the speed of the boulder just before it hits the ground?

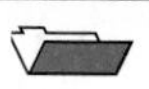

chapter Review 4

Thinking Critically

18. At the highest point of the swing, the potential energy is a maximum and the kinetic energy is zero. As the swing falls, potential energy is converted into kinetic energy. At the bottom of the swing, the kinetic energy is maximum and the potential energy is a minimum. As the swing moves, friction and air resistance convert the swing's mechanical energy to thermal energy, causing it to slow down and stop.

19. In nuclear fission and nuclear fusion, a small amount of mass is converted into energy.

20. The flexing of the tires as the car is moving coverts elastic potential energy in the tire to thermal energy.

21. Diagram should be: chemical potential energy $\longrightarrow$ kinetic energy of hands $\longrightarrow$ thermal energy.

Applying Math

National Math Standards

1, 2, 9

22. 1,350 J

23. 4,900,000 J

24. $KE = 2{,}250$ J, $GPE = 147{,}000$ J, mechanical energy $= 149{,}250$ J

25. $KE = 4{,}900{,}000$ J, $v = 62.6$ m/s

Assessment Resources

Reproducible Masters

Chapter *Fast File* Resources
Chapter Review, pp. 39–40
Chapter Tests, pp. 41–44
Assessment Transparency Activity, p. 51

Glencoe Science Web site
Chapter Review Test
Standardized Test Practice

Glencoe Technology
Assessment Transparency
ExamView® Assessment Suite
MindJogger Videoquiz
Interactive Chalkboard

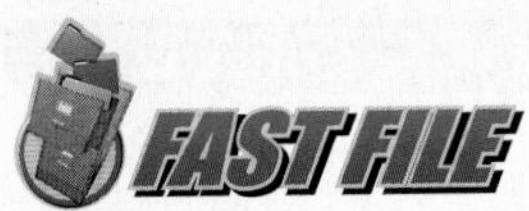

Answer Sheet A practice answer sheet can be found at gpscience.com/answer_sheet.

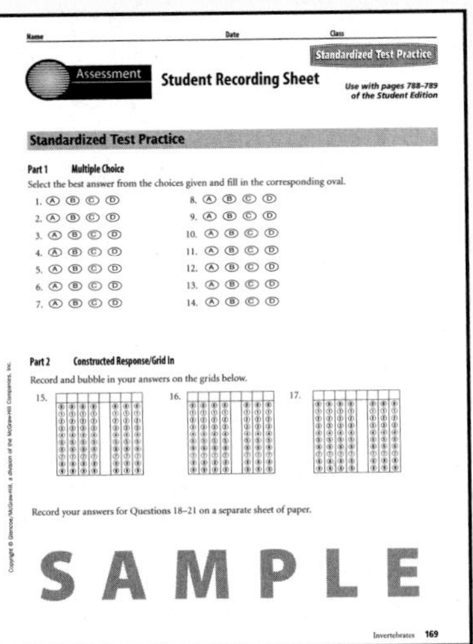
Name Date Class

Standardized Test Practice

Assessment Student Recording Sheet

Use with pages 788–789 of the Student Edition

Standardized Test Practice

Part 1 Multiple Choice

Select the best answer from the choices given and fill in the corresponding oval.

1. Ⓐ Ⓑ Ⓒ Ⓓ	8. Ⓐ Ⓑ Ⓒ Ⓓ
2. Ⓐ Ⓑ Ⓒ Ⓓ	9. Ⓐ Ⓑ Ⓒ Ⓓ
3. Ⓐ Ⓑ Ⓒ Ⓓ	10. Ⓐ Ⓑ Ⓒ Ⓓ
4. Ⓐ Ⓑ Ⓒ Ⓓ	11. Ⓐ Ⓑ Ⓒ Ⓓ
5. Ⓐ Ⓑ Ⓒ Ⓓ	12. Ⓐ Ⓑ Ⓒ Ⓓ
6. Ⓐ Ⓑ Ⓒ Ⓓ	13. Ⓐ Ⓑ Ⓒ Ⓓ
7. Ⓐ Ⓑ Ⓒ Ⓓ	14. Ⓐ Ⓑ Ⓒ Ⓓ

Part 2 Constructed Response/Grid In

Record and bubble in your answers on the grids below.

15. 16. 17.

Record your answers for Questions 18–21 on a separate sheet of paper.

SAMPLE

Invertebrates 169

Part 1 Multiple Choice

1. C
2. B
3. B
4. C
5. A
6. D
7. C
8. D
9. B
10. C

Part 2 Short Response

11. Mass changes to energy in nuclear reactions.
12. 38 J
13. thermal energy
14. sound energy, kinetic energy (moving air), thermal energy
15. the highest point of its trajectory
16. The ball's mechanical energy remains constant. Its value depends on the energy given to it by the batter.
17. An object at rest can have potential energy.
18. 3 m/s

Part 3 Open Ended

19. An atom of uranium combines with a neutron. The uranium breaks apart into a xenon atom, a strontium atom, and two neutrons. Radiant energy is released during the process. The original mass of the neutron and the uranium atom is greater than the mass of the xenon atom, the mass of the strontium atom, and the masses of the two neutrons. The remaining mass is converted to energy.
20. It is less. Some of the mass of the particles before the reaction is converted into energy during the reaction.

---

chapter 4 Standardized Test Practice

Part 1 Multiple Choice

Record your answers on the answer sheet provided by your teacher or on a sheet of paper.

1. What is the potential energy of a 5.0-kg object located 2.0 m above the ground?
   A. 2.5 J **C.** 98 J
   B. 10 J **D.** 196 J

Use the figure below to answer questions 2–4.

Kinetic Energy of Falling Rock

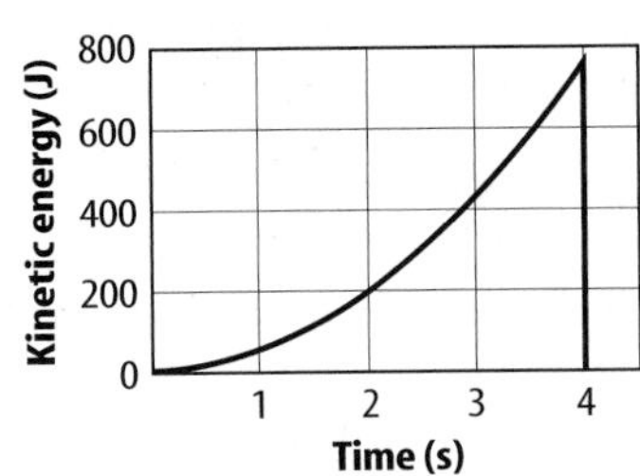

2. According to the graph, which of the following is the best estimate for the kinetic energy of the rock after it has fallen for 1 s?
   A. 100 J **C.** 200 J
   B. 50 J **D.** 0 J
3. According to the graph, which of the following is the best estimate for the potential energy of the rock before it fell?
   A. 400 J **C.** 200 J
   B. 750 J **D.** 0 J
4. If the rock has a mass of 1 kg, which of the following is the speed of the rock after it has fallen for 2 s?
   A. 10 m/s **C.** 20 m/s
   B. 100 m/s **D.** 200 m/s
5. Which of the following describes the energy conversions in a car's engine?
   A. chemical to thermal to mechanical
   B. chemical to electrical to mechanical
   C. thermal to mechanical to chemical
   D. kinetic to potential to mechanical
6. What is the difference in the gravitational potential energy of a 7.75 kg book that is 1.50 m above the ground and a 9.53 kg book that is 1.75 m above the ground?
   A. 0.28 J **C.** 11.7 J
   B. 5.1 J **D.** 49.5 J
7. A box with a mass of 14.8 kg sits on the floor. How high would you have to lift the box to for it to have a gravitational potential energy of 355 J?
   A. 1.62 m **C.** 2.45 m
   B. 2.40 m **D.** 4.90 m

Use the figure below to answer questions 8 and 9.

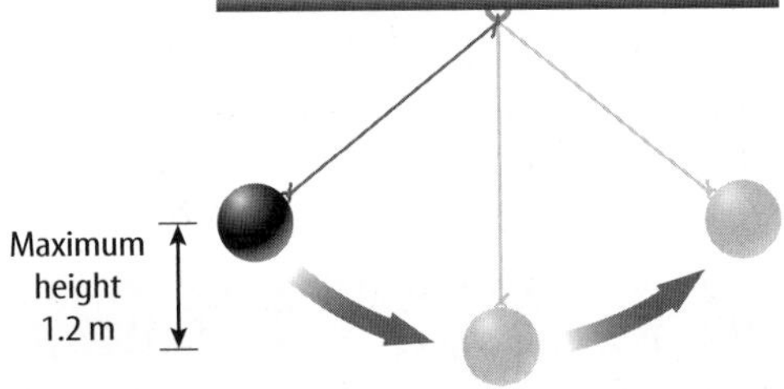

8. At its highest point, the pendulum is 1.2 m above the ground and has a gravitational potential energy of 62 J. If the gravitational potential energy is 10 J at its lowest point, what is the pendulum's kinetic energy at this point?
   A. 0 J **C.** 62 J
   B. 31 J **D.** 52 J
9. What is the mass of the pendulum bob?
   A. 2.7 kg **C.** 6.3 kg
   B. 5.3 kg **D.** 52 kg
10. The SI unit of energy is the joule (J). Which of the following is an equivalent way of expressing this unit?
    A. kg•m **C.** $kg{\cdot}m^2/s^2$
    B. kg•m/s **D.** $kg{\cdot}m/s^2$

Part 2 Short Response/Grid In

Record your answers on the answer sheet provided by your teacher or on a sheet of paper.

11. Explain why the law of conservation of energy also includes mass when applied to nuclear reactions.

12. A student walks to school at a speed of 1.2 m/s. If the student's mass is 53 kg, what is the student's kinetic energy?

13. A book sliding across a horizontal table slows down and comes to a stop. The book's kinetic energy was converted into what form of energy?

14. Electrical energy was converted into which forms of energy by a hair dryer?

Use the figure below to answer questions 15 and 16.

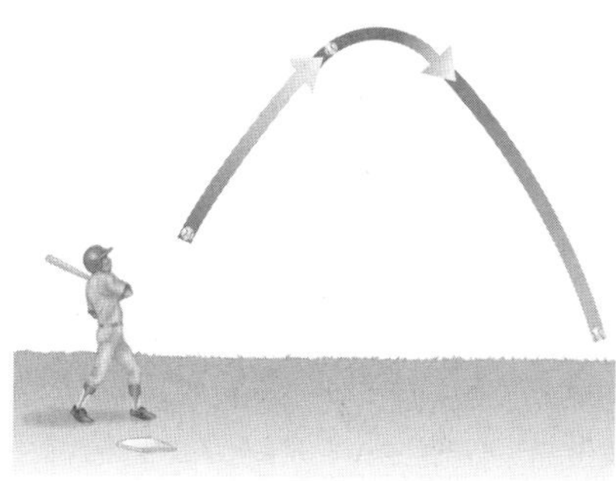

15. At what point on the ball's path is the ball's kinetic energy lowest but its gravitational potential energy highest?

16. How does the mechanical energy of the ball change from the moment just after the batter hits it to the moment just before it touches the ground?

17. Explain whether it is possible for an object at rest to have energy.

18. Find the speed of a 5.6-kg bowling ball that has a kinetic energy of 25.2 J.

Part 3 Open Ended

Record your answers on a sheet of paper.

Use the figure below to answer questions 19 and 20.

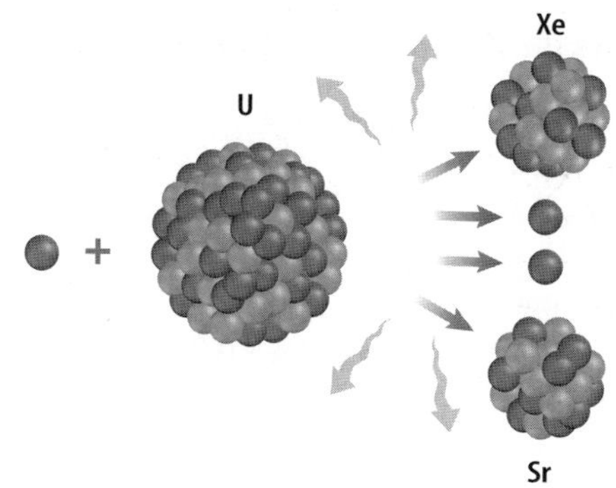

19. Describe the process shown in the figure above, and explain how it obeys the law of conservation of energy.

20. Describe how the total mass of the particles before the reaction occurs compares to the total mass of the particles produced by the reaction.

21. Is the mechanical energy of a liter of water at the top of a waterfall greater than, the same as, or less than the mechanical energy of a liter of water just before it reaches the bottom of the waterfall? Explain.

22. Name and describe some examples of how different forms of energy can be stored.

23. Describe a process in which energy travels through the environment and changes from one form to another.

Test-Taking Tip

Show All your Work For constructed response questions, show all your work and any calculations on your answer sheet.

Question 19 On your answer sheet, list the energy changes that occur during each for each step of the process that you can think of.

21. Just for a ball falling from a table, the mechanical energy of the falling water remains constant as it falls.

22. Possible answer: Chemical potential energy is stored in the molecular bonds of food and fuels. Gravitational potential energy is stored in objects above the ground. Elastic potential energy is stored in a spring that is compressed or in a rubber band that is stretched.

23. Possible answer: Radiant energy from the Sun travels to Earth and is absorbed by plants. The plants store this as chemical potential energy. An animal eats the plant and gains the energy from it. The animal uses part of the energy for everyday activity and stores part of the energy as chemical potential energy in its body.

Rubrics

The following rubrics are sample scoring devices for short response and open-ended questions.

Short Response

Points	Description
2	The student demonstrates a thorough understanding of the science of the task. The response may contain minor flaws that do not detract from the demonstration of a thorough understanding.
1	The student has provided a response that is only partially correct.
0	The student has provided a completely incorrect solution or no response at all.

Open Ended

Points	Description
4	The student demonstrates a thorough understanding of the science of the task. The response may contain minor flaws that do not detract from the demonstration of a thorough understanding.
3	The student demonstrates an understanding of the science of the task. The response is essentially correct and demonstrates an essential but less than thorough understanding of the science.
2	The student demonstrates only a partial understanding of the science of the task. Although the student may have used the correct approach to a solution or may have provided a correct solution, the work lacks an essential understanding of the underlying science concepts.
1	The student demonstrates a very limited understanding of the science of the task. The response is incomplete and exhibits many flaws.
0	The student provides a completely incorrect solution or no response at all.

Work and Machines

BIG Idea Machines make doing work easier by changing the force needed to do the work.

	Content Standards	Learning Objectives	Resources to Assess Mastery
Section 1	**5–8:** UCP.1–3; A.1, 2; B.2, 3 **9–12:** UCP.1–3, 5; A.1, 2; B.1; B.4, 6	**Work** 1. **Explain** the meaning of work. 2. **Describe** how work and energy are related. 3. **Calculate** work. 4. **Calculate** power. ***Main Idea*** Work is done when a force causes something to move.	**Formative Assessment** Reading Check, pp. 127, 129 Section Review, p. 131 **Summative Assessment** *ExamView® Assessment Suite*
Section 2	**5–8:** UCP.1–3, 5; A.1, 2; B.2, 3 **9–12:** UCP.1–3, 5; A.1, 2; B.1; B.4, 6	**Using Machines** 5. **Explain** how machines make doing work easier. 6. **Calculate** the mechanical advantage of a machine. 7. **Calculate** the efficiency of a machine. ***Main Idea*** A machine can change the force needed to do a job, but it can't reduce the amount of work needed.	**Formative Assessment** Reading Check, pp. 133, 136 Section Review, p. 137 **Summative Assessment** *ExamView® Assessment Suite*
Section 3	**5–8:** UCP.1–3, 5; A.1, 2; B.2, 3 **9–12:** UCP.1–3, 5; A.1, 2; B.1; B.4, 6 See pp. 16T–17T for a Key to Standards.	**Simple Machines** 8. **Describe** the six types of simple machines. 9. **Explain** how the different types of simple machines make doing work easier. 10. **Calculate** the ideal mechanical advantage of the different types of simple machines. ***Main Idea*** Compound machines are made from six types of simple machines.	**Formative Assessment** Reading Check, p. 142 Section Review, p. 146 **Summative Chapter Assessment** MindJogger, Ch. 5 *ExamView® Assessment Suite* Leveled Chapter Test Test A L1 Test B L2 Test C L3 Test Practice, pp. 154–155

Suggested Pacing				
Period	Instruction	Labs	Review & Assessment	Total
Single	4.5 days	2.5 days	2 days	9 days
Block	2.25 blocks	1.25 blocks	1 block	4.5 blocks

Core Instruction	Leveled Resources	Leveled Labs	Pacing: Period		Pacing: Block
Student Text, pp. 124–131 Section Focus Transparency, Ch. 5, Section 1 Interactive Chalkboard, Ch. 5, Section 1 Differentiated Instruction, pp. 127, 129 Applying Math, pp. 128, 130	**Chapter *Fast File* Resources** Directed Reading for Content Mastery, p. 22 L1 Note-taking Worksheet, pp. 35–37 Reinforcement, p. 29 L2 Enrichment, p. 32 L3 **Reading Essentials,** p. 66 L1 ELL **Science Notebook,** p. 45 ELL ***Active*Folders**: *Work & Simple Machines* L1 ELL	**Launch Lab**, p. 125: broom handles (2), rope *10 min* L2	1	Section 1, pp. 125–129 (includes Launch Lab)	1
		MiniLAB, p. 129: stairs, stopwatch or clock, meterstick *15 min* L2 (Video Lab)	2	Section 1, pp. 129–131 (includes MiniLAB and Section Review)	
Student Text, pp. 132–137 Section Focus Transparency, Ch. 5, Section 2 Interactive Chalkboard, Ch. 5, Section 2 Identifying Misconceptions, p. 135 Differentiated Instruction, p. 133	**Chapter *Fast File* Resources** Directed Reading for Content Mastery, p. 22 L1 Note-taking Worksheet, pp. 35–37 Reinforcement, p. 30 L2 Enrichment, p. 33 L3 **Reading Essentials,** p. 71 L1 ELL **Science Notebook,** p. 49 ELL ***Active*Folders**: *Work & Simple Machines* L1 ELL	**MiniLAB**, p. 134: can of food, manual can opener, metric ruler *10 min* L2	3	Section 2, pp. 132–134 (includes MiniLAB)	2
			4	Section 2, pp. 135–137 (includes Section Review)	
Student Text, pp. 138–149 Section Focus Transparency, Ch. 5, Section 3 Teaching Transparency, Ch. 5, Section 3 Interactive Chalkboard, Ch. 5, Section 3 Visualizing Levers In The Human Body, p. 140 Identifying Misconceptions, p. 143 Differentiated Instruction, pp. 139, 141, 143 Chapter Study Guide, p. 151	**Chapter *Fast File* Resources** Directed Reading for Content Mastery, pp. 23, 24 L1 Note-taking Worksheet, pp. 35–37 Reinforcement, p. 31 L2 Enrichment, p. 34 L3 **Reading Essentials,** p. 77 L1 ELL **Science Notebook,** p. 52 ELL ***Active*Folders**: *Work & Simple Machines* L1 ELL	***Lab**, p. 147: stiff cardboard (30 cm x 30 cm), coins (quarter, dime, nickel), balance, metric ruler *40 min* L1 L2 L3	5	Section 3, pp. 138–142	3
			6	Section 3, pp. 143–146 (includes Section Review)	
		***Lab**, pp. 148–149: spring scale, weight (1 kg mass), double pulleys (2), string, stand or support, wooden board (40 cm), support for board (10 cm high *45 min* L1 L2 L3	7	Lab:Levers, p. 147	4
			8	Lab:Using Simple Machines, pp. 148–149	
		*Lab version A L1 version B L2 L3	9	Study Guide, Chapter Review, and Test Practice, pp. 151–155	4.5

Video Lab

Work and Machines

Transparencies

Section Focus

Section 1 Section Focus Transparency **Onward and Upward**

Backpacking is a lot of fun, but it also can be a lot of work. Whether hoisting the pack onto your back to start the hike or trudging up a long hill, you'll need to exert a good deal of effort to get to the next camp.

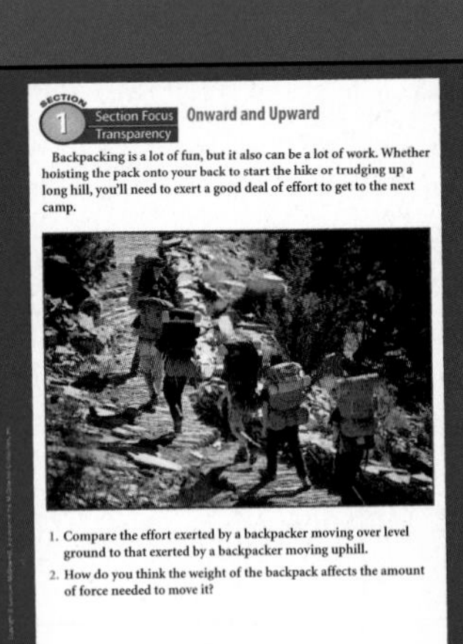

1. Compare the effort exerted by a backpacker moving over level ground to that exerted by a backpacker moving uphill.
2. How do you think the weight of the backpack affects the amount of force needed to move it?

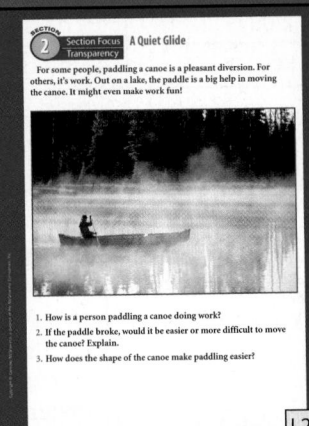

L2

Section 2 Section Focus Transparency **A Quiet Glide**

For some people, paddling a canoe is a pleasant diversion. For others, it's work. Out on a lake, the paddle is a big help in moving the canoe. It might even make work fun!

1. How is a person paddling a canoe doing work?
2. If the paddle broke, would it be easier or more difficult to move the canoe? Explain.
3. How does the shape of the canoe make paddling easier?

L2

Section 3 Section Focus Transparency **Moving Day**

Moving can be a chore. Packing boxes, moving them, then unpacking everything can be hard work. But machines can help. Some machines are simple, while others can be very complicated. This mover uses a selection of machines to help make moving day much easier.

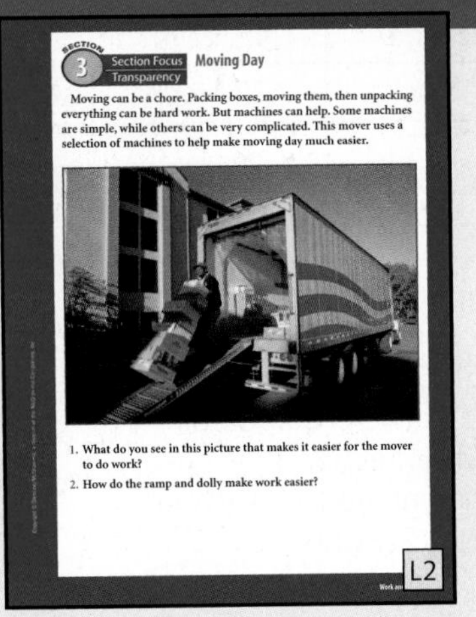

1. What do you see in this picture that makes it easier for the mover to do work?
2. How do the ramp and dolly make work easier?

L2

This is a representation of key blackline masters available in the Teacher Classroom Resources. See Resource Manager boxes within the chapter for additional information.

Assessment

Assessment Transparency **Work and Machines**

Directions: Carefully review the table and the diagram and answer the following questions.

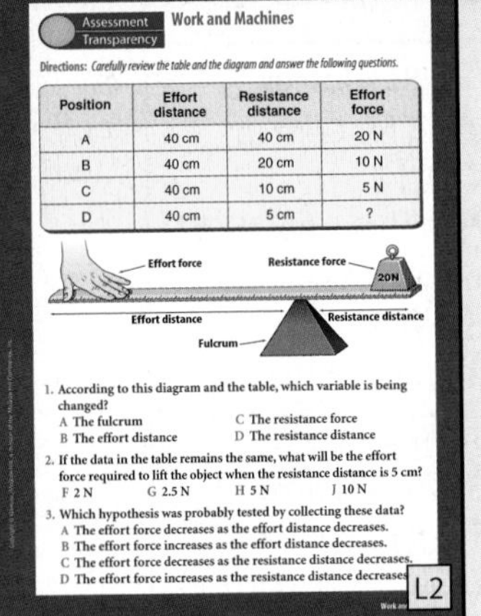

Position	Effort distance	Resistance distance	Effort force
A	40 cm	40 cm	20 N
B	40 cm	20 cm	10 N
C	40 cm	10 cm	5 N
D	40 cm	5 cm	?

1. According to this diagram and the table, which variable is being changed?
   A The fulcrum
   B The effort distance
   C The resistance force
   D The resistance distance
2. If the data in the table remains the same, what will be the effort force required to lift the object when the resistance distance is 5 cm?
   F 2 N G 2.5 N H 5 N J 10 N
3. Which hypothesis was probably tested by collecting these data?
   A The effort force decreases as the effort distance decreases.
   B The effort force increases as the effort distance decreases.
   C The effort force decreases as the resistance distance decreases.
   D The effort force increases as the resistance distance decreases.

L2

Teaching

Section 3 Teaching Transparency **Simple Machines**

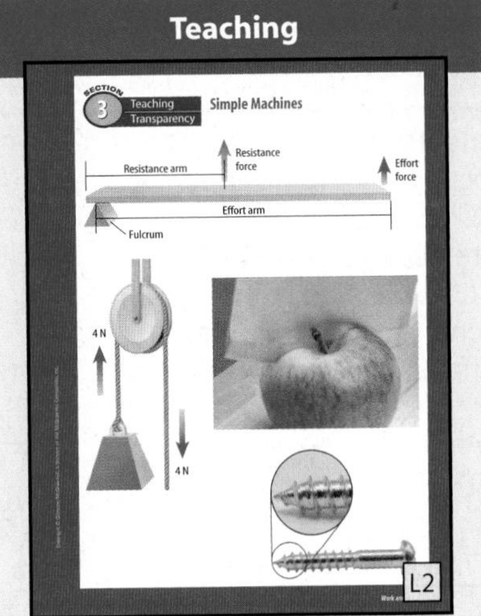

L2

Key to Teaching Strategies

The following designations will help you decide which activities are appropriate for your students.

L1 Level 1 activities should be appropriate for students with learning difficulties.

L2 Level 2 activities should be within the ability range of all students.

L3 Level 3 activities are designed for above-average students.

ELL ELL activities should be within the ability range of English Language Learners.

COOP LEARN Cooperative Learning activities are designed for small group work.

LS Multiple Learning Styles logos, as described on page 12T, are used throughout to indicate strategies that address different learning styles.

P These strategies represent student products that can be placed into a best-work portfolio.

PBL Problem-Based Learning activities apply real-world situations to learning.

Hands-on Activities

Student Text Lab Worksheet

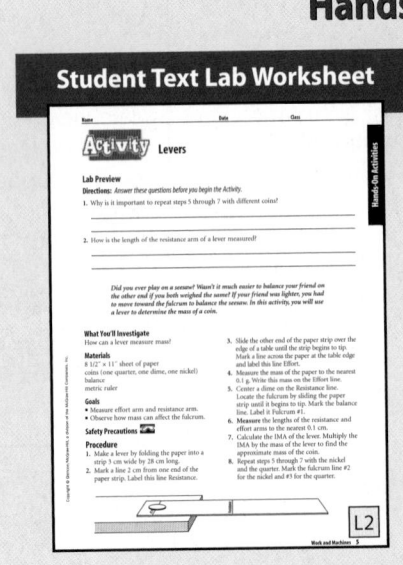

Activity **Levers**

Lab Preview

Directions: Answer these questions before you begin the Activity.

1. Why is it important to repeat steps 5 through 7 with different coins?
2. How is the length of the resistance arm of a lever measured?

L2

Laboratory Activities

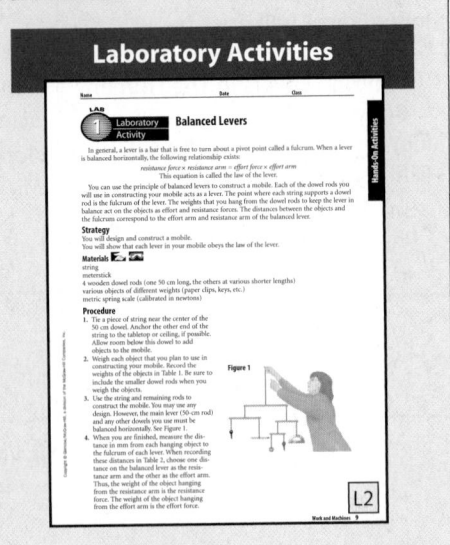

Laboratory Activity 1 **Balanced Levers**

L2

Meeting Different Ability Levels

Content Outline

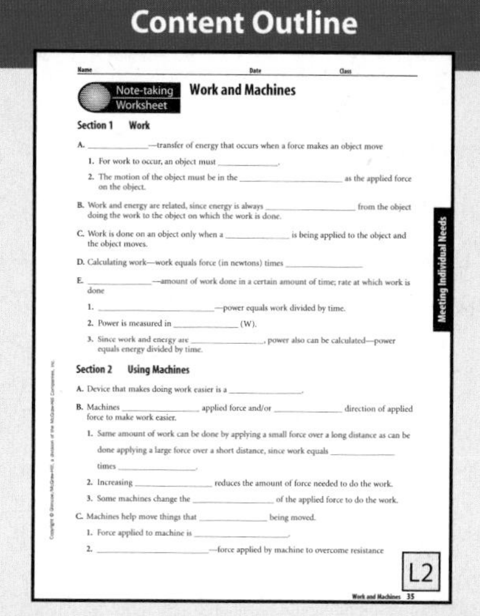

Reinforcement

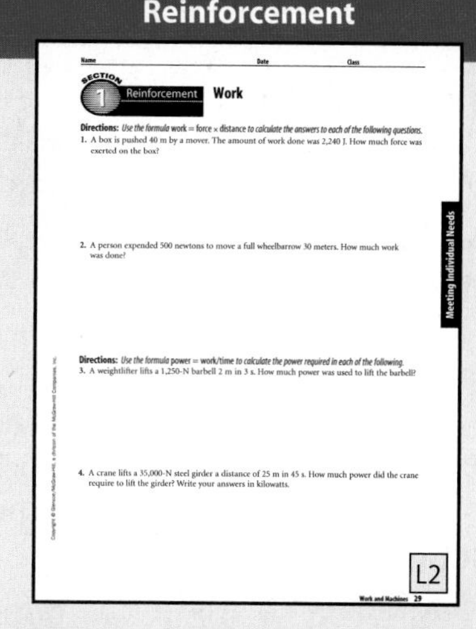

Enrichment

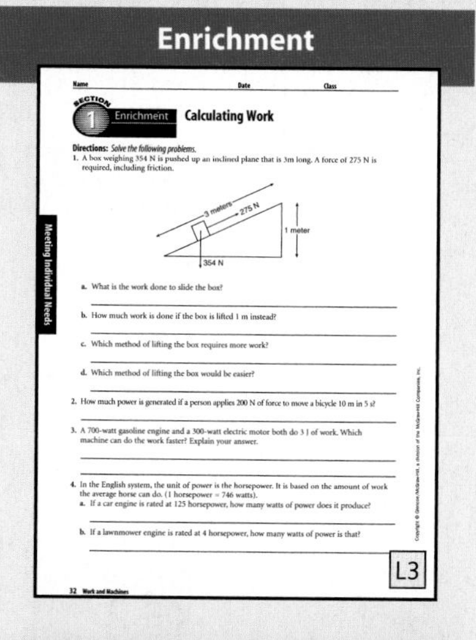

Directed Reading (English/Spanish)

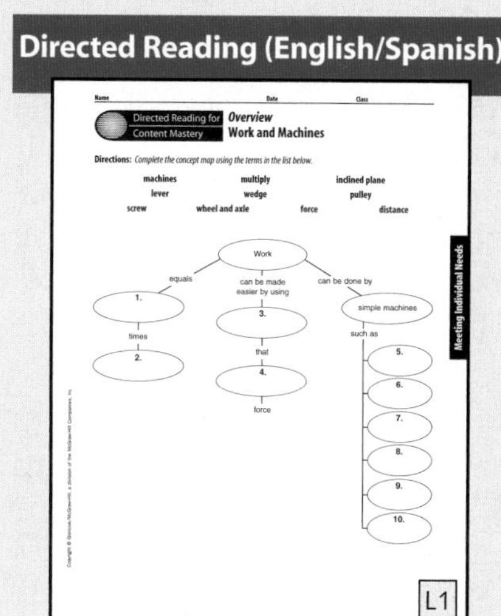

Study Guide

Reading Essentials

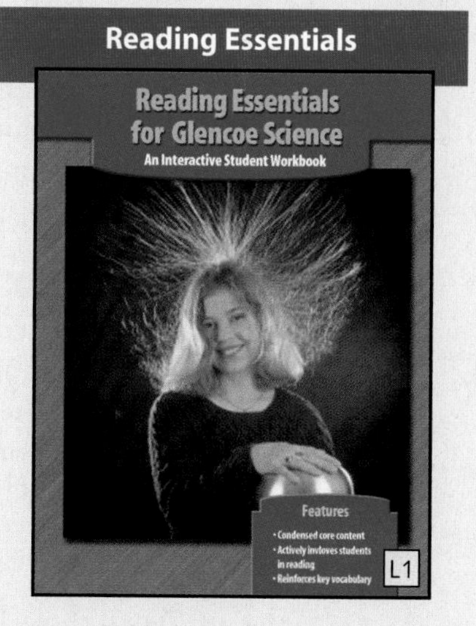

Assessment

Test Practice Workbook

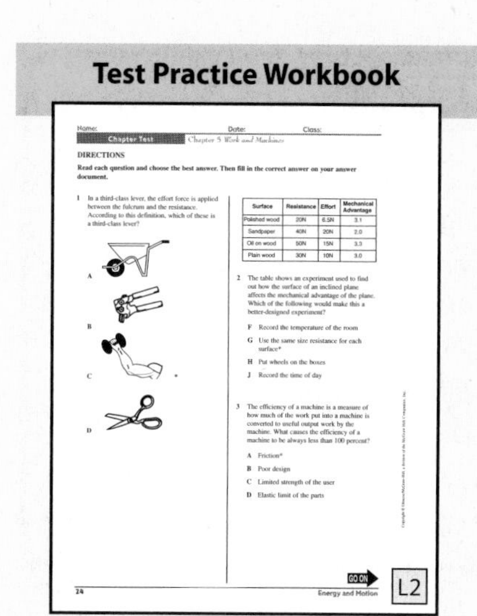

Chapter Review

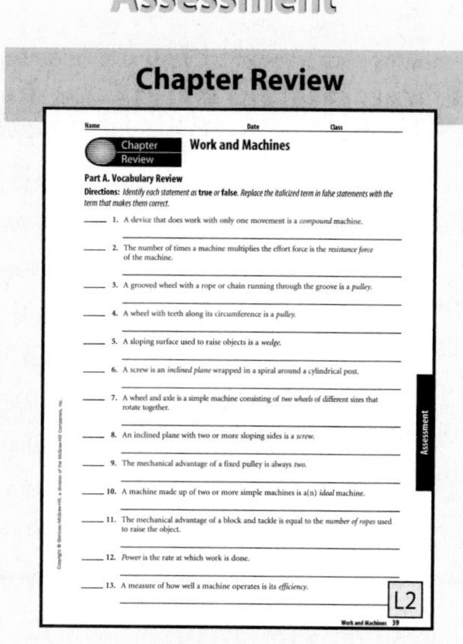

Chapter Tests

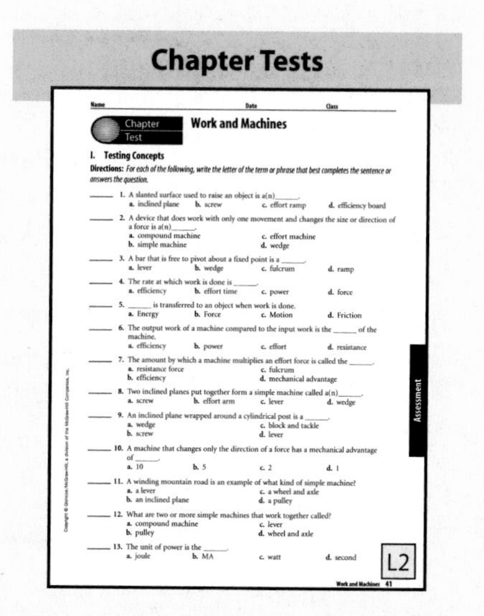

Science Content Background

Work

Power

The horsepower is a common, although nonmetric, unit of power. It was originally created by James Watt to compare his steam engines to the power of a horse. It is equivalent to 746 watts.

Using Machines

Making Work Easier

Many machines allow a person to use less effort to do a job such as lifting an engine or opening a soda bottle. These machines do not reduce the amount of work that must be done. A smaller force must be applied over a greater distance to do the work.

Mechanical Advantage and Efficiency

A machine converts an input force to an output force. The ratio of the output force to the input force is the mechanical advantage of the machine. For a real machine, the output work done by the machine is always less than the input work. Friction always transforms some of the input work into heat. The efficiency of a machine is the output work divided by the input work.

Simple Machines

Pulleys

When counting the number of ropes supporting a load to determine the mechanical advantage, the rope that is actually pulled is not counted. An easier means of determining the mechanical advantage of a block and tackle system is to count the number of pulleys.

Wheel and Axles

The diameter of the wheel is greater than the diameter of the axle. So a force applied on the wheel moves through a greater distance in one revolution than the force applied by the axle. If the amount of work done on the wheel is nearly equal to the amount of work done by the axle, then the force exerted on the wheel must be less than the force applied by the axle.

Wedges

A wedge is useful for two reasons. A downward force applied to a wedge is converted to a horizontal force exerted perpendicular to the sides of the wedge. Also, the wedge is narrower at one end. As a result, the narrow tip of the wedge exerts a higher pressure than the wider edge. This helps the wedge to penetrate materials.

chapter content resources

Internet Resources

For additional content background, visit **gpscience.com** to:

- access your book online
- find references to related articles in popular science magazines
- access Web links with related content background
- access current events with science journal topics

Print Resources

The New Way Things Work, David MacCaulay, Houghton Mifflin Company, 1998

Physics Matters! Vol. 2, John O. E. Clark, Grolier Educational, 2001

Simple Machines Series by David Glover, Rigby Press, 1997

How Things Work, Neil Ardley, Reader's Digest Book, 1995

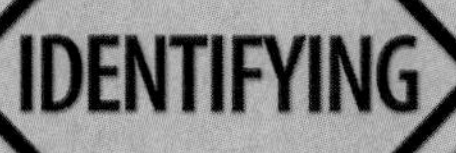

IDENTIFYING Misconceptions

Find Out What Students Think

Students may think that . . .

A simple machine allows us to do less work.

The term *machine* often makes people think of things such as cars and power tools. By using fuel or electrical energy to do work, these machines do allow people to do less work. This conception of machines may create the misconception that simple machines also allow people to do less work. Additionally, the force used on a simple machine provides an immediate sensation to the worker. Using a simple machine to do a task often requires less effort and so it feels easier than doing the task without the machine, and this may contribute to the idea that less work is being done.

Activity

Ask students to write explanations of why people use simple machines such as the lever, pulley, and inclined plane. Have a few students read their explanations to the class. Then have the class try to decide which is the best explanation. L2

Promote Understanding

Activity

Show students a picture of movers pushing a large object up a ramp into the truck. Why do they use this ramp? Lead the discussion so students debate whether the movers do it to do less work or to use less effort. Have students do the following activity to find the answer. Organize the class into groups and give each group a spring scale, ruler, wooden plank, wood block with hook, and string. Tell them to follow these steps:

- Use the spring scale to lift the block from the floor to a chair, and note the reading from the scale as it rises.
- Measure the height of the chair, and multiply force times distance to obtain the work done lifting the block.
- Rest the plank on the chair so it rises at about a 45° angle from the ground. Pull the block up the plane to the chair, and measure the effort used by reading the scale while the block is moving.
- Measure the distance the block traveled and calculate the amount of work done.
- Compare the amounts of effort used and the amounts of work done in the two situations.

The results show that the simple machine made it easier to lift the load, but the amount of work students did with the ramp was the same or greater than the work done just lifting the block. L2

Assess

After completing the chapter, see *Identifying Misconceptions* in the Study Guide at the end of the chapter.

About the Photo

Compound Machines Riding a mountain bike takes a lot of work, especially over rough terrain. But the gears and levers, wheels and axles help the rider accomplish that work with less effort, and with more power. Compound machines like bicycles are excellent examples of how combinations of simple machines make both work and play easier.

Science Journal Accept all reasonable answers.

BIG Idea

Machines and Work A machine is a device that does work on something (the output work) when work is done on the machine (the input work). The law of conservation of energy prevents the output work from being greater than the input work—a machine cannot create energy. However, the advantage of using a machine is that, compared to the output work, the input work can be done in a different way that is easier for the user of the machine. For example, in lifting an object using a first-class lever, the user can apply a smaller force on the lever (the input force) than the lever applies on the object (the output force). However, because the input work and output work are equal, the input force must be applied over a greater distance than the output force.

Introduce the Chapter Ask students to give examples of machines they have used and list their examples on the chalkboard. Have students describe what the machine does and what must be done to the machine to make it work. Discuss whether something always must move when a machine is used.

chapter 5

Work and Machines

BIG Idea
Machines make doing work easier by changing the force needed to do the work.

5.1 Work
MAIN Idea Work is done when a force causes something to move.

5.2 Using Machines
MAIN Idea A machine can change the force needed to do a job, but it can't reduce the amount of work needed.

5.3 Simple Machines
MAIN Idea Compound machines are made from six types of simple machines.

Work with Me

Have you ever thought of a mountain bike as a machine? A mountain bike is actually a combination of simple machines. Like all machines, a bicycle makes doing a job easier. A mountain bike, for example, helps you travel faster than you could by running or walking.

Science Journal
Diagram a bicycle and identify the parts you think are simple machines.

124

Interactive Chalkboard

This CD-ROM is an editable Microsoft® PowerPoint® presentation that includes:

- an editable presentation for every chapter
- additional chapter questions
- animated graphics
- image bank
- links to gpscience.com

Start-Up Activities

Doing Work with a Simple Machine

Did you know you can lift several times your own weight with the help of a pulley? Before the hydraulic lift was invented, a car mechanic used pulleys to raise a car off the ground. In this lab you'll see how a pulley can increase a force.

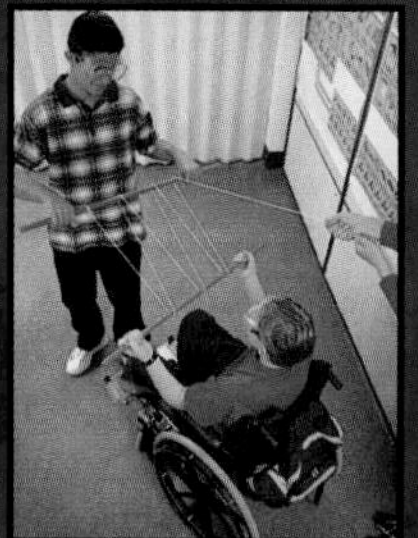

1. Tie a rope several meters in length to the center of a broom handle. Have one student hold both ends of the handle.
2. Have another student hold the ends of a second broom handle and face the first student as shown in the photo.
3. Have a third student loop the free end of the rope around the second handle, making six or seven loops.
4. The third student should stand to the side of one of the handles and pull on the free end of the rope. The two students holding the broom handles should prevent the handles from coming together.
5. **Think Critically** Describe how the applied force was changed. What would happen if the number of rope loops were increased?

Work and Machines Make the following Foldable to help you understand how machines make doing work easier.

STEP 1 **Fold** a vertical sheet of paper in half from top to bottom .

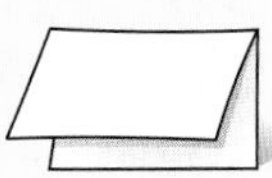

STEP 2 **Fold** in half from side to side with the fold at the top.

STEP 3 **Unfold** the paper once. **Cut** only the fold of the top flap to make two tabs.

STEP 4 **Turn** the paper vertically and **label** the front tabs as shown.

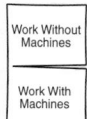

Work Without Machines

Work With Machines

List Before you read the chapter, list five examples of work you do without machines, and five examples of work you do with machines. Next to each example, rate the effort needed to do the work on a scale of 1 (little effort) to 3 (much effort).

Preview this chapter's content and activities at gpscience.com

125

Purpose Use the Launch Lab to introduce students to the force multiplying power of simple machines. L2 IN **Kinesthetic**

Preparation Cut 8-m lengths of rope and collect two broom handles for each group.

Materials broom handles (2), 8-m length of rope

Teaching Strategy Tell the students holding the broom handles that they must keep the handles parallel to each other and they cannot place their hands or fingers on the rope.

Think Critically

The applied force was increased. The third group member easily could pull the broom handles together. Increasing the number of rope loops would increase the applied force even more.

Assessment

Performance Ask each group to predict how the results of the lab would have differed if the rope had been wrapped only twice around the poles. Ask students to test their predictions. The pulley will have far less mechanical advantage, and the student pulling on the rope will not be able to pull the two handles together as easily. Use **Performance Assessment in the Science Classroom**, p. 93.

Dinah Zike Study Fold

Student preparation materials for this Foldable are available in the **Chapter *Fast File* Resources.**

Additional Chapter Media

- BrainPOP *Pulleys*
- Virtual Lab: *How is a controlled experiment performed?*
- Video Lab: *Calculating Your Work and Power*

1 Motivate

Bellringer

Section Focus Transparencies also are available on the Interactive Chalkboard CD-ROM.

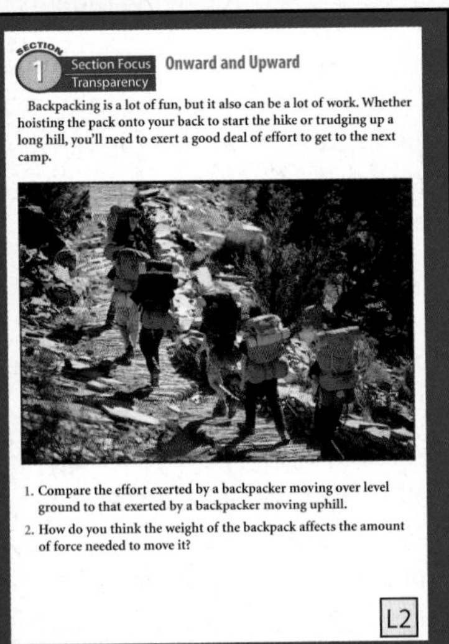
SECTION 1 Section Focus Transparency **Onward and Upward**

Backpacking is a lot of fun, but it also can be a lot of work. Whether hoisting the pack onto your back to start the hike or trudging up a long hill, you'll need to exert a good deal of effort to get to the next camp.

1. Compare the effort exerted by a backpacker moving over level ground to that exerted by a backpacker moving uphill.
2. How do you think the weight of the backpack affects the amount of force needed to move it?

L2

Work and Machines

Tie to Prior Knowledge

Student Work Ask students what types of work they do. They might mention cutting grass, taking out garbage, or caring for a younger sibling. In this section they will learn that the scientific definition of work is different from the everyday definition.

section 1

Work

Reading Guide

What You'll Learn

- **Explain** the meaning of work.
- **Describe** how work and energy are related.
- **Calculate** work.
- **Calculate** power.

Why It's Important

Doing work is another way of transferring energy from one place to another.

Review Vocabulary

energy: the ability to cause change

New Vocabulary

- work
- power

What is work?

Have you done any work today? To many people, the word *work* means something they do to earn money. In that sense, work can be anything from filling fast-food orders or loading trucks to teaching or doing word processing on a computer. The word *work* also means exerting a force with your muscles. Someone might say they have done work when they push as hard as they can against a wall that doesn't move. However, in science the word *work* is used in a different way.

Work Makes Something Move Press your hand against the surface of your desk as hard as you can. Have you done any work? The answer is no, no matter how tired your effort makes you feel. Remember that a force is a push or a pull. In order for work to be done, a force must make something move. **Work** is the transfer of energy that occurs when a force makes an object move. If you push against the desk and nothing moves, then you haven't done any work.

Doing Work There are two conditions that have to be satisfied for work to be done on an object. One is that the applied force must make the object move, and the other is that the movement must be in the same direction as the applied force.

For example, if you pick up a pile of books from the floor as in **Figure 1,** you do work on the books. The books move upward, in the direction of the force you are applying. If you hold the books in your arms without moving the books, you are not doing work on the books. You're still applying an upward force to keep the books from falling, but no movement is taking place.

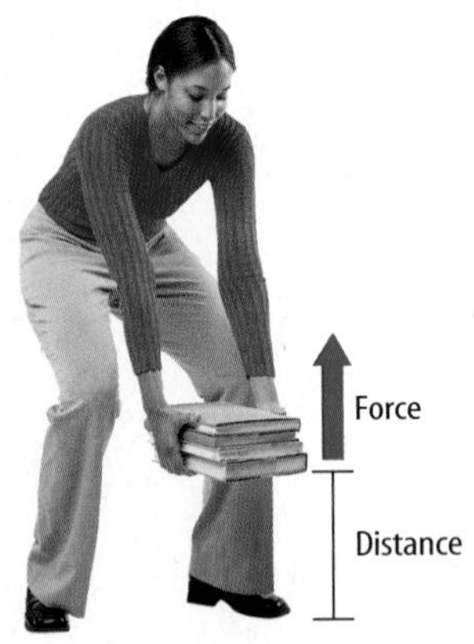

Figure 1 When you lift a stack of books, your arms apply a force upward and the books move upward. Because the force and distance are in the same direction, your arms have done work on the books.

Section 1 Resource Manager

Chapter *FAST FILE* Resources

- Transparency Activity, p. 46
- Directed Reading for Content Mastery, pp. 21, 22
- Note-taking Worksheets, pp. 35–37
- MiniLAB, p. 3
- Enrichment, p. 32
- Reinforcement, p. 29

Mathematics Skill Activities, p. 11

Cultural Diversity, p. 63

126 CHAPTER 5 Work and Machines

Force and Direction of Motion When you carry books while walking, like the student in **Figure 2,** you might think that your arms are doing work. After all, you are exerting a force on the books with your arms, and the books are moving. Your arms might even feel tired. However, in this case the force exerted by your arms does no work on the books. The force exerted by your arms on the books is upward, but the books are moving horizontally. The force you exert is at right angles to the direction the books are moving. As a result, your arms exert no force in the direction the books are moving.

Reading Check *How are an applied force and an object's motion related when work is done?*

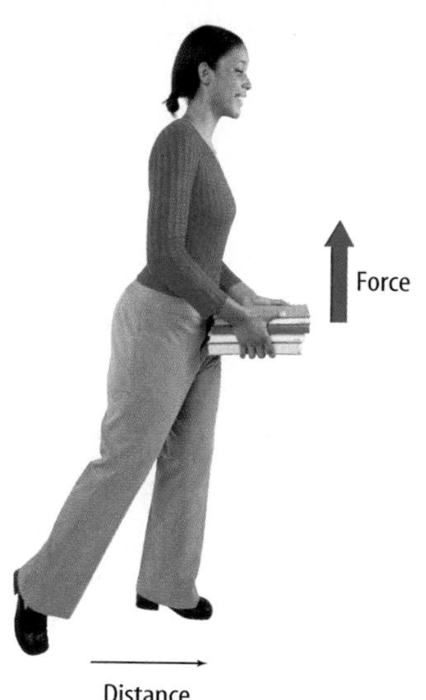

Figure 2 If you hold a stack of books and walk forward, your arms are exerting a force upward. However, the distance the books move is horizontal. Therefore your arms are not doing work on the books.

Work and Energy

How are work and energy related? When work is done, a transfer of energy always occurs. This is easy to understand when you think about how you feel after carrying a heavy box up a flight of stairs. Remember that when the height of an object above Earth's surface increases, the potential energy of the object increases. You transferred energy from your moving muscles to the box and increased its potential energy by increasing its height.

You may recall that energy is the ability to cause change. Another way to think of energy is that energy is the ability to do work. If something has energy, it can transfer energy to another object by doing work on that object. When you do work on an object, you increase its energy. The student carrying the box in **Figure 3** transfers chemical energy in his muscles to the box. Energy is always transferred from the object that is doing the work to the object on which the work is done.

Figure 3 By carrying a box up the stairs, you are doing work. You transfer energy to the box. **Explain** *how the energy of the box changes as the student climbs the stairs.*

2 Teach

Activity

Analyzing Forces Have a volunteer press against the wall. Ask students whether or not the person is doing work on the wall. No, because the wall is not moving in the direction of the applied force. Repeat this demonstration for various other activities, such as raising an object vertically or carrying an object horizontally. If there is more than one force involved, help students analyze which forces are doing work and which are not. L2 LS **Kinesthetic**

Reading Check

Answer The applied force and the object's motion must be in the same direction for work to be done.

Caption Answer

Figure 3 The potential energy of the box increases as the box is moved up the stairs because the height of the box increases.

Virtual Labs

Work, Force, Distance
What is the relationship between work, force, and distance?

Science Journal

Relating Work and Energy Have students write descriptions in their Science Journals of situations they have seen or been a part of in which work has been done or energy has been transferred. Ask them to include at least one example of a situation in which energy was transferred but no work was done. L2 LS **Linguistic**

Differentiated Instruction

Challenge Have students use the definition of work to define power in terms of velocity. Ask students to relate this to the power of a car.

$$P = \frac{W}{t} = \frac{(F \times d)}{t} = F \times \left(\frac{d}{t}\right) = F \times v,$$

where v is the rate at which the car is moving L3 LS **Logical-Mathematical**

Quick Demo

Calculating Work

Materials spring scale, 1-kg mass

Estimated Time 5 minutes

Procedure Hook a spring scale to a 1-kg mass. Using the spring scale, raise the mass 1 m over a period of 1 s. Let students read the spring scale, which should read approximately 1 N. Tell them you have just done 1 J of work. Give students the opportunity to repeat your demonstration. L2

IS **Visual-Spatial**

Activity

Joule The unit of work is the joule. Ask students to express a joule in basic SI units. $W = F \times d = m \times a \times d$; therefore, $1\ J = 1\ kg \cdot \frac{m^2}{s^2}$ L2

IS **Logical-Mathematical**

Work Equation

National Math Standards

Correlation to Mathematics Objectives

1, 2, 9

Answers to Practice Problems

1. 375 J
2. 150 m
3. 4,800 N
4. The gravitational force $= mg = (5.0)(9.8) = 49$ N. $W = Fd = (49\ N)(2.0\ m) = 98$ J

Discussion

Bow and Arrow Force Suppose you used a force of 50 N to shoot an arrow, and the arrow flew 25 m. As you shot the arrow, the bow string moved the arrow 1 m. Did you do 1,250 J of work or 50 J of work? Explain. You did 50 J of work because after the arrow left the bow, it was flying loose in the air and was not experiencing any force from you.

L2 IS **Logical-Mathematical**

Calculating Work The amount of work done depends on the amount of force exerted and the distance over which the force is applied. When a force is exerted and an object moves in the direction of the force, the amount of work done can be calculated as follows.

Work Equation

work (in joules) = applied force (in newtons) × distance (in meters)

$$W = Fd$$

In this equation, force is measured in newtons (N) and distance is measured in meters (m). Recall that doing work on an object increases its energy. This means that work, like energy, is measured in units of joules (J). The amount of work needed to lift a basketball from your waist to your head would be about 4 J.

Work Equation

Solve for Work You push a refrigerator with a force of 100 N. If you move the refrigerator a distance of 5 m while you are pushing, how much work do you do?

1. **This is what you know:** applied force: $F = 100$ N; distance: $d = 5$ m
2. **This is what you need to find:** work: W
3. **Use this formula:** $W = Fd$
4. **Substitute:** the values of F and d into the formula and multiply. $W = (100)(5) = 500$
5. **Determine the units:** units of W = (units of F) × (units of d) = N × m = J

Answer: The work done is 500 J.

Science Online
For more practice problems, go to page 834, and visit gpscience.com/extra_problems.

Practice Problems

1. A couch is pushed with a force of 75 N and moves a distance of 5 m across the floor. How much work is done in moving the couch?
2. A lawn mower is pushed with a force of 80 N. If 12,000 J of work are done in mowing a lawn, what is the total distance the lawn mower was pushed?
3. The brakes on a car do 240,000 J of work in stopping the car. If the car travels a distance of 50 m while the brakes are being applied, what is the force the brakes exert on the car?
4. **Challenge** The force needed to lift an object is equal in size to the gravitational force on the object. How much work is done in lifting an object with a mass of 5.0 kg a vertical distance of 2.0 m?

Curriculum Connection

History James Prescott Joule was a British scientist who lived from 1818 to 1889. Ask students to find out why the unit of work was named for him. Joule established the relationship between heat and mechanical energy, called the mechanical equivalent of heat. L2

IS **Linguistic**

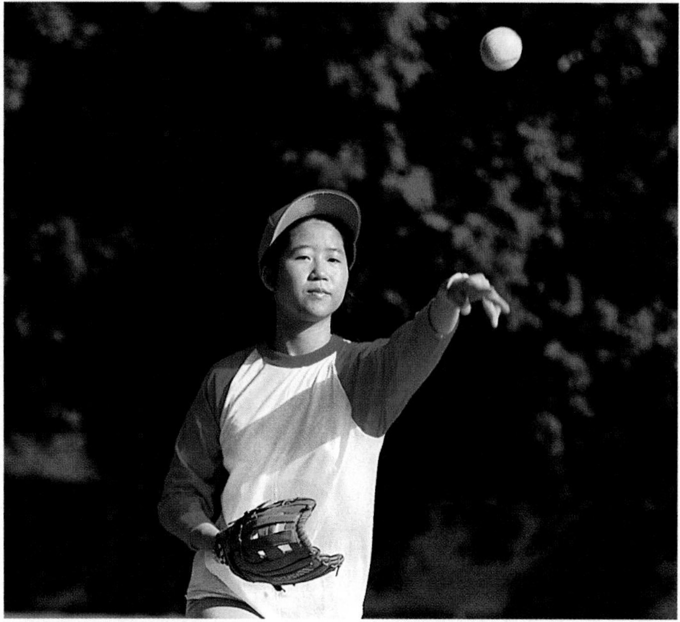

Figure 4 A pitcher exerts a force on the ball to throw it to the catcher. After the ball leaves her hand, she no longer is exerting any force on the ball. She does work on the ball only while it is in her hand.

When is work done? Suppose you give a book a push and it slides along a table for a distance of 1 m before it comes to a stop. The distance you use to calculate the work you did is how far the object moves while the force is being applied. Even though the book moved 1 m, you do work on the book only while your hand is in contact with it. The distance in the formula for work is the distance the book moved while your hand was pushing on the book. As **Figure 4** shows, work is done on an object only when a force is being applied to the object.

Power

Suppose you and another student are pushing boxes of books up a ramp to load them into a truck. To make the job more fun, you make a game of it, racing to see who can push a box up the ramp faster. The boxes weigh the same, but your friend is able to push a box a little faster than you can. She moves a box up the ramp in 30 s. It takes you 45 s. You both do the same amount of work on the books because the boxes weigh the same and are moved the same distance. The only difference is the time it takes to do the work.

In this game, your friend has more power than you do. **Power** is the amount of work done in one second. It is a rate—the rate at which work is done.

Reading Check *How is power related to work?*

Calculating Your Work and Power

Procedure

1. Find a set of **stairs** that you can safely walk and run up. Measure the vertical height of the stairs in meters.
2. Record how many seconds it takes you to walk and run up the stairs.
3. Calculate the work you did in walking and running up the stairs using $W = Fd$. For force, use your weight in newtons (your weight in pounds times 4.5).
4. Use the formula $P = W/t$ to calculate the power you needed to walk and run up the stairs.

Analysis

1. Is the work you did walking and running the steps the same?
2. Which required more power—walking or running up the steps? Why?

Mini LAB

Purpose Students measure work and power. L2 IS **Kinesthetic**

Materials stairs, stopwatch or clock, meterstick

Teaching Strategy Suggest students work in pairs so one can time while the other climbs the stairs.

Safety Precautions Caution students to choose a set of stairs that they can run without slipping.

Analysis

1. Yes; the work is independent of speed.
2. More power is used running than walking, because you do the same amount of work in less time.

Assessment

Content Have students work in small groups to write short rhymes to help them remember the relationships among force, distance, work, and power. Use **Performance Assessment in the Science Classroom,** p. 151.

Reading Check

Answer Power is the amount of work done per second.

Teacher FYI

Power The metric unit of power is the watt, or joule/s. The power of heating and cooling units is often given in British thermal units (Btu) per second. One Btu per second is about 1,055 watts. The power of motors and engines is usually given in horsepower. One horsepower is equal to about 746 watts.

Differentiated Instruction

Physically Challenged Students in wheelchairs can do the MiniLab by using a ramp instead of stairs. Students can time themselves going up the ramp at a slow rate, and then time themselves going up the ramp quickly. Point out that in order to calculate the force, students will need to know the weight of the wheelchair in newtons. L2

Visual Learning

Figure 4 Point out that work is done by the pitcher only while she still has the ball in her hand. The distance over which she moves her arm to throw the ball and the force with which she throws it determine how much work she does. After she lets go of the ball, work is done by gravity to make it fall. L2

Discussion

Work v. Power Suppose two students are asked to unpack identical cartons of books. One student completes the job in ten minutes, while the other takes twenty minutes. Which student did more work? Both students did the same amount of work. Which student used more power? the one who finished in the least amount of time L2 LS **Logical-Mathematical**

Use Science Words

Word Usage The word *power* is often used in the context of politics. Ask students to explain how this usage of the word *power* is analogous to the scientific use of the term. The more power a politician has, the shorter the period of time he or she needs to cause changes. L2 LS **Linguistic**

Fun Fact

One horsepower was the average amount of work a horse could do in one day. Watt underestimated the amount of work his engines could do by about 67 percent so that he would not be accused of exaggeration.

Power Equation

National Math Standards

Correlation to Mathematics Objectives

1, 2, 9

Answers to Practice Problems

1. 25 W
2. $W = Pt = (130\ \text{W})(600\ \text{s}) = 78{,}000\ \text{J}$
3. $t = W/P = (10{,}000\ \text{J})/(500\ \text{W}) = 20\ \text{s}$
4. $150\ \text{hp} = (150\ \text{hp})(745\ \text{W/hp}) = 111{,}750\ \text{W}$. $W = Pt = (111{,}750\ \text{W})(10\ \text{s}) = 1{,}117{,}500\ \text{J}$

Calculating Power Power is the rate at which work is done. To calculate power, divide the work done by the time that is required to do the work.

Power Equation

$$\text{Power (in watts)} = \frac{\text{work (in joules)}}{\text{time (in seconds)}}$$

$$P = \frac{W}{t}$$

The SI unit for power is the watt (W). One watt equals one joule of work done in one second. It takes about 20 W of power to lift a 2-L bottle of soft drink a distance of 1 m in 1 s. Because the watt is a small unit, power often is expressed in kilowatts. One kilowatt (kW) equals 1,000 W.

Power Equation

Solve for Power You do 900 J of work in pushing a sofa. If it took 5 s to move the sofa, how much power did you use?

1. **This is what you know:** work done: $W = 900\ \text{J}$; time: $t = 5\ \text{s}$
2. **This is what you need to find:** power: P
3. **Use this formula:** $P = \frac{W}{t}$
4. **Substitute:** the values of W and t into the formula and divide. $P = \frac{900}{5} = 180$
5. **Determine the units:** units of $P = \frac{\text{units of } W}{\text{units of } t} = \text{J/s} = \text{W}$

Answer: The power used is 180 W.

The symbol for work, *W*, is usually italicized. However, the abbreviation for watt, W, is not italicized.

Science Online
For more practice problems, go to page 834, and visit gpscience.com/extra_problems.

Practice Problems

1. In lifting a baby from a crib, 50 J of work are done. How much power is needed if the baby is lifted in 2.0 s?
2. If a runner's power is 130 W as she runs, how much work is done by the runner in 10 minutes?
3. The power produced by an electric motor is 500 W. How long will it take the motor to do 10,000 J of work?
4. **Challenge** One horsepower is a unit of power equal to 745 W. How much work can be done by a 150 horsepower engine in 10 s?

Curriculum Connection

Health Nutritionists recommend a daily diet of about 9,000,000 J (2,100 Cal) to maintain health. Have students calculate the average power that this diet would generate in a 24-hour period. There are 60 × 60 × 24 = 86,400 seconds in 24 hours. Therefore, the amount of power is 9,000,000 J ÷ 86,400 s = 104 watts. L2 LS **Logical-Mathematical**

Power and Energy Doing work is a way of transferring energy from object to another. Just as power is the rate at which work is done, power is also the rate at which energy is transferred. When energy is transferred, the power involved can be calculated by dividing the energy transferred by the time needed for the transfer to occur.

Power Equation for Energy Transfer

$$\text{power (in watts)} = \frac{\text{energy transferred (in joules)}}{\text{time (in seconds)}}$$

$$P = \frac{E}{t}$$

For example, when the lightbulb in **Figure 5** is connected to an electric circuit, energy is transferred from the circuit to the lightbulb filament. The filament converts the electrical energy supplied to the lightbulb into heat and light. The power used by the lightbulb is the amount of electrical energy transferred to the lightbulb each second.

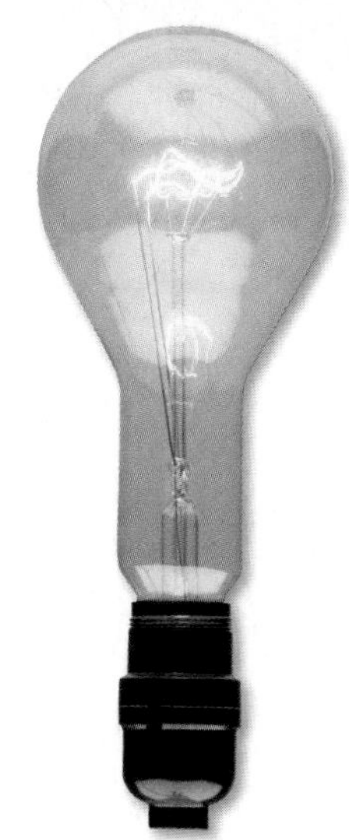

Figure 5 This 100 W lightbulb converts electrical energy into light and heat at a rate of 100 J/s.

section 1 review

Summary

Work and Energy

- Work is done on an object when a force is exerted on the object and it moves in the direction of the force.
- If a force, F, is exerted on object while the object moves a distance, d, in the direction of the force, the work done is

$$W = Fd$$

- When work is done on an object, energy is transferred to the object.

Power

- Power is the rate at which work is done or energy is transferred.
- When work is done, power can be calculated from the equation

$$P = \frac{W}{t}$$

- When energy is transferred, power can be calculated from the equation

$$P = \frac{E}{t}$$

Self Check

1. **Explain** how the scientific definition of work is different from the everyday meaning.
2. **Describe** a situation in which a force is applied, but no work is done.
3. **Explain** how work and energy are related.
4. **Think Critically** In which of the following situations is work being done?
   a. A person shovels snow off a sidewalk.
   b. A worker lifts bricks, one at a time, from the ground to the back of a truck.
   c. A roofer's assistant carries a bundle of shingles across a construction site.

Applying Math

5. **Calculate Force** Find the force a person exerts in pulling a wagon 20 m if 1,500 J of work are done.
6. **Calculate Work** A car's engine produces 100 kW of power. How much work does the engine do in 5 s?
7. **Calculate Energy** A color TV uses 120 W of power. How much energy does the TV use in 1 hour?

Science Online gpscience.com/self_check_quiz

3 Assess

DAILY INTERVENTION

Check for Understanding

Logical-Mathematical Have students make a chart that compares the work done and the power it took for each of five students to climb the stairs in the MiniLAB in this section. Which value is the same for all five students? work done Which values are different? power What one variable determines the difference in values? time L2

Reteach

Work and Power Ask students to name various activities they enjoy. Have the class discuss the work done and the amount of power used while performing each activity. L2 IS **Interpersonal**

Assessment

Portfolio Have students make posters that define the SI units for force, work, and power and illustrate the relationships among them. Use **Performance Assessment in the Science Classroom,** p. 145. L2 P

section 1 review

1. The scientific definition requires that a force act on an object and that the object move in the direction of that force. The everyday meaning requires that an effort be exerted.
2. Accept any answer in which a force is applied but the object does not move in the direction of the force.
3. Work is a way of transferring energy from one object to another.
4. **a.** Work is being done when the snow is lifted up by the shovel. Work also is done if the person tosses the snow out of the shovel. **b.** Work is done when the worker lifts the brick off the ground and pushes the brick along the bed of the truck. **c.** The assistant does no work while carrying the shingles.
5. $F = \frac{W}{d} = \frac{1{,}500\text{ J}}{20\text{ m}} = 75\text{ N}$

6. $W = Pt = (100{,}000\text{ J\s})(5\text{ s}) = 500{,}000\text{ J}$
7. $E = Pt = (120\text{ J\s})(1\text{ h})\left(\frac{60\text{ min}}{1\text{ h}}\right)\left(\frac{60\text{ s}}{1\text{ min}}\right) = 20\text{ s}$

1 Motivate

Bellringer

Section Focus Transparencies also are available on the Interactive Chalkboard CD-ROM.

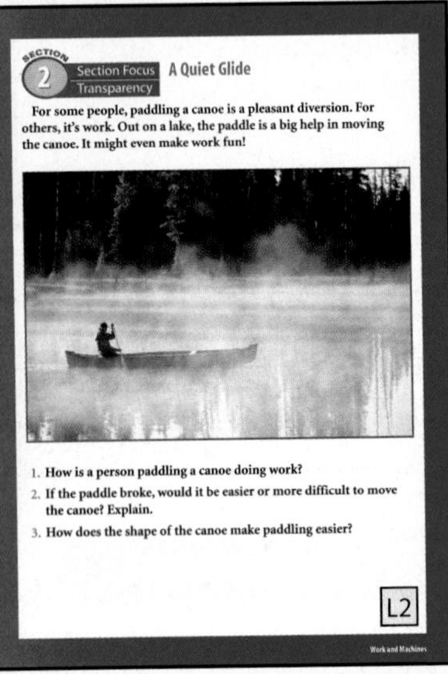

Section 2 Section Focus Transparency A Quiet Glide

For some people, paddling a canoe is a pleasant diversion. For others, it's work. Out on a lake, the paddle is a big help in moving the canoe. It might even make work fun!

1. How is a person paddling a canoe doing work?
2. If the paddle broke, would it be easier or more difficult to move the canoe? Explain.
3. How does the shape of the canoe make paddling easier?

L2

Work and Machines

Tie to Prior Knowledge

Easier Work Ask students to name ways that machines make work easier. They might mention that a shovel makes lifting dirt easier, and a hammer makes pushing a nail into wood easier. In this section, students will use the scientific definition of work to learn how machines make work easier.

section 2

Using Machines

Reading Guide

***What* You'll Learn**

- **Explain** how machines make doing work easier.
- **Calculate** the mechanical advantage of a machine.
- **Calculate** the efficiency of a machine.

***Why* It's Important**

Cars, stairs, and teeth are all examples of machines that make your life easier.

Review Vocabulary

force: a push or a pull

New Vocabulary

- machine
- input force
- output force
- mechanical advantage
- efficiency

What is a machine?

A **machine** is a device that makes doing work easier. When you think of a machine you may picture a device with an engine and many moving parts. However, machines can be simple. Some, like knives, scissors, and doorknobs, are used every day to make doing work easier.

Making Work Easier

Machines can make work easier by increasing the force that can be applied to an object. A screwdriver increases the force you apply to turn a screw. A second way that machines can make work easier is by increasing the distance over which a force can be applied. A leaf rake is an example of this type of machine. Machines also can make work easier by changing the direction of an applied force. A simple pulley changes a downward force to an upward force.

Figure 6 A car jack is an example of a machine that increases an applied force.

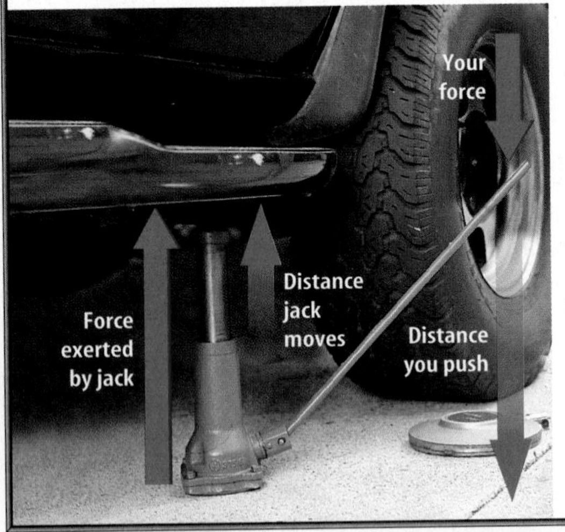

Increasing Force A car jack, like the one in **Figure 6,** is an example of a machine that increases an applied force. The upward force exerted by the jack is greater than the downward force you exert on the handle. However, the distance you push the handle downward is greater than the distance the car is pushed upward. Because work is the product of force and distance, the work done by the jack is not greater than the work you do on the jack. The jack increases the applied force, but it doesn't increase the work done.

Section 2 Resource Manager

Chapter *FAST FILE* Resources
Transparency Activity, p. 47
Directed Reading for Content Mastery, p. 22
MiniLAB, p. 4
Enrichment, p. 33
Reinforcement, p. 30
Physical Science Critical Thinking/Problem Solving, p. 3

Figure 7 Whether the mover slides the chair up the ramp or lifts it directly into the truck, she will do the same amount of work. Doing the work over a longer distance allows her to use less force.

Force and Distance Why does the mover in **Figure 7** push the heavy furniture up the ramp instead of lifting it directly into the truck? It is easier for her because less force is needed to move the furniture.

The work done in lifting an object depends on the change in height of the object. The same amount of work is done whether the mover pushes the furniture up the long ramp or lifts it straight up. If she uses a ramp to lift the furniture, she moves the furniture a longer distance than if she just raised it straight up. If work stays the same and the distance is increased, then less force will be needed to do the work.

How does a ramp make lifting an object easier?

Changing Direction Some machines change the direction of the force you apply. When you use the car jack, you are exerting a force downward on the jack handle. The force exerted by the jack on the car is upward. The direction of the force you applied is changed from downward to upward. Some machines change the direction of the force that is applied to them in another way. The wedge-shaped blade of an ax is one example. When you use an ax to split wood, you exert a downward force as you swing the ax toward the wood. As **Figure 8** shows, the blade changes the downward force into a horizontal force that splits the wood apart.

Figure 8 An ax blade changes the direction of the force from vertical to horizontal.

2 Teach

Discussion

Everyday Machines Ask students to name devices that make work easier but aren't normally called machines in everyday conversations. Some examples are a bicycle, a can opener, and a rake. Discuss how each device makes work easier. L1 LS **Linguistic**

Activity

Changing Force Direction Have students experiment with lifting a load using a simple fixed pulley and using a screwdriver to pry the lid off a can. For each activity, have students try to do the job without changing the direction of force. L2 LS **Kinesthetic**

Reading Check

Answer Less force is needed to lift an object when using a ramp.

Differentiated Instruction

Learning Disabled Have students push a heavy box up a gentle ramp. Keep the ramp the same height, but make it shorter and therefore steeper. Then ask students to push the box again. Do this several times with increasingly shorter and steeper ramps to help students understand the relationship between the distance the box moves and the force required to move it. L1

Challenge Tell students that some machines have a mechanical advantage that is less than 1. Have them find out why these machines are still useful. In these machines the input force is greater than the output force. These machines can be useful if they increase the distance an object moves or its speed. L3 LS **Logical-Mathematical.**

Purpose Students observe how machines multiply a person's force of effort. L2

Kinesthetic

Materials can of food, manual can opener, metric ruler

Teaching Strategy Explain to students that the length of the can opener handle is the diameter of the circle or "wheel" that they must turn the handle around to be able to move the small circle or "axle" of the cutting blade. The can opener functions as a wheel and axle. To gain force from the cutting blade, they must move the handle a greater distance.

WARNING: *Do not touch can opener's cutting blades or cut edges of the can's lid.*

Analysis

1. The can opener easily opens the can, but the can would be impossible to open using just the cutting blade.
2. Answers will vary, but cutting blades generally measure 2 cm while the diameter of the circle formed by turning the handle ranges from 8 to 10 cm.
3. The added distance the student must turn the handle multiplies the amount of force applied by the cutting blade to the can.

Assessment

Process Show students a door handle and ask them to infer how the handle multiplies the force of the person opening the door. Like the can opener, the door handle works as a wheel and axle. The handle is the large "wheel" that easily turns the metal rod or "axle" inserted into the door lock. Use **Performance Assessment in the Science Classroom,** p. 89.

Figure 9 A crowbar increases the force you apply and changes its direction.

Mini LAB

Machines Multiplying Force

Procedure

1. Open a **can of food** using a **manual can opener.** *WARNING: Do not touch can opener's cutting blades or cut edges of the can's lid.*
2. Use a **metric ruler** to measure the diameter of the cutting blade of the can opener.
3. Measure the length of the handle you turn.

Analysis

1. Compare how difficult it is to open the can using the can opener with how difficult it would have been to open the can by turning the cutting blade with a smaller handle.
2. Compare the diameter of the cutting blade with the diameter of the circle formed by turning the can opener's handle.
3. Infer why a can opener makes it easier to open a metal can.

Try at Home

The Work Done by Machines

To pry the lid off a wooden crate with a crowbar, you'd slip the end of the crowbar under the edge of the crate lid and push down on the handle. By moving the handle downward, you do work on the crowbar. As the crowbar moves, it does work on the lid, lifting it up. **Figure 9** shows how the crowbar increases the amount of force being applied and changes the direction of the force.

When you use a machine such as a crowbar, you are trying to move something that resists being moved. For example, if you use a crowbar to pry the lid off a crate, you are working against the friction between the nails in the lid and the crate. You also could use a crowbar to move a large rock. In this case, you would be working against gravity—the weight of the rock.

Input and Output Forces Two forces are involved when a machine is used to do work. You exert a force on the machine, such as a bottle opener, and the machine then exerts a force on the object you are trying to move, such as the bottle cap. The force that is applied to the machine is called the **input force.** F_{in} stands for the input force. The force applied by the machine is called the **output force,** symbolized by F_{out}. When you try to pull a nail out with a hammer as in **Figure 10,** you apply the input force on the handle. The output force is the force the claw applies to the nail.

Two kinds of work need to be considered when you use a machine—the work done by you on the machine and the work done by the machine. When you use a crowbar, you do work when you apply force to the crowbar handle and make it move. The work done by you on a machine is called the input work and is symbolized by W_{in}. The work done by the machine is called the output work and is abbreviated W_{out}.

Science Journal

Work In and Work Out Have students choose two simple machines that they have used. For each simple machine, write a short paragraph describing the work in and the work out. Describe how the machine simplifies a task. Machines used might include shovel, bicycle, broom, screwdriver, and scissors. L2

Linguistic

Curriculum Connection

Art Leonardo da Vinci is famous for such well-known paintings as *Mona Lisa* and *The Last Supper*. However, he was also the inventor of an extraordinary collection of machines. Have students research Leonardo da Vinci and prepare a computer presentation showing how his work with mechanical devices inspired much of the technology we use today. L2 **Visual-Spatial** P

134 CHAPTER 5 Work and Machines

Conserving Energy Remember that energy is always conserved. When you do work on the machine, you transfer energy to the machine. When the machine does work on an object, energy is transferred from the machine to the object. Because energy cannot be created or destroyed, the amount of energy the machine transfers to the object cannot be greater than the amount of energy you transfer to the machine. A machine cannot create energy, so W_{out} is never greater than W_{in}.

However, the machine does not transfer all of the energy it receives to the object. In fact, when a machine is used, some of the energy transferred changes to heat due to friction. The energy that changes to heat cannot be used to do work, so W_{out} is always smaller than W_{in}.

Figure 10 When prying a nail out of a piece of wood with a claw hammer, you exert the input force on the handle of the hammer, and the claw exerts the output force. **Describe** *how the hammer changes the input force.*

Ideal Machines Remember that work is calculated by multiplying force by distance. The input work is the product of the input force and the distance over which the input force is exerted. The output work is the product of the output force and the distance over which that force is exerted.

Suppose a perfect machine could be built in which there was no friction. None of the input work or output work would be converted to heat. For such an ideal machine, the input work equals the output work. So for an ideal machine,

$$W_{in} = W_{out}$$

Suppose the ideal machine increases the force applied to it. This means that the output force, F_{out}, is greater than the input force, F_{in}. Recall that work is equal to force times distance. If F_{out} is greater than F_{in}, then W_{in} and W_{out} can be equal only if the input force is applied over a greater distance than the output force is exerted over.

For example, suppose the hammer claw in **Figure 10** moves a distance of 1 cm to remove a nail. If an output force of 1,500 N is exerted by the claw of the hammer, and you move the handle of the hammer 5 cm, you can find the input force as follows.

$$W_{in} = W_{out}$$
$$F_{in}\, d_{in} = F_{out}\, d_{out}$$
$$F_{in}\,(0.05 \text{ m}) = (1{,}500 \text{ N})\,(0.01 \text{ m})$$
$$F_{in}\,(0.05 \text{ m}) = 15 \text{ N·m}$$
$$F_{in} = 300 \text{ N}$$

Because the distance you move the hammer is longer than the distance the hammer moves the nail, the input force is less than the output force.

Quick Demo

Changing Energy

Materials wood, claw hammer

Estimated Time five minutes

Procedure Bring to class a piece of wood with a nail pounded almost all the way into it. In front of the class, use a claw hammer to pull the nail out of the wood. Invite students to touch the warm nail to show how some of the work was converted to thermal energy. L2 IS **Visual-Kinesthetic**

Caption Answer

Figure 10 The hammer produces an output force that is greater than the input force, but the output force is applied over a shorter distance than the input force.

Always Work Students may think that simple machines allow us to do less work. See page F at the beginning of this chapter for teaching strategies that address this misconception.

Visual Learning

Figure 10 Point out the fact that although this hammer is not an ideal machine, most of the input work is converted to work done on the nail. This means that $W_{in} \approx W_{out}$. Since work = force × distance, if the hammer handle is moved a large distance with a small force, then the claw, which moves a short distance, will exert a large force. Have students draw a diagram to show this relationship. L2 IS **Visual-Spatial**

Activity

Crowbar *MA* Ask students to calculate the mechanical advantage of a crowbar to which you apply 100 N of force to lift a 250-N rock.

$MA = \frac{F_{out}}{F_{in}} = 250\text{ N} \div 100\text{N} = 2.5$

 **Logical-Mathematical**

Mechanical advantage also can be determined by dividing the input distance by the output distance.

INTEGRATE Chemistry

Efficiency Graphite is composed of carbon atoms formed into linked hexagons, arranged in weakly bonded layers. Graphite is useful as a lubricant because the layers can slide easily over one another. When graphite is applied to the moving parts of machines, the sliding of the layers reduces the effects of friction.

Research Have students research other types of lubricants such as Teflon, lithium grease, Freon and tungsten oxide that are used in industry to help cut down on wear and tear and heat loss due to friction between moving parts in machines. L2

Reading Check

Answer because some of the input work is converted into thermal energy by friction

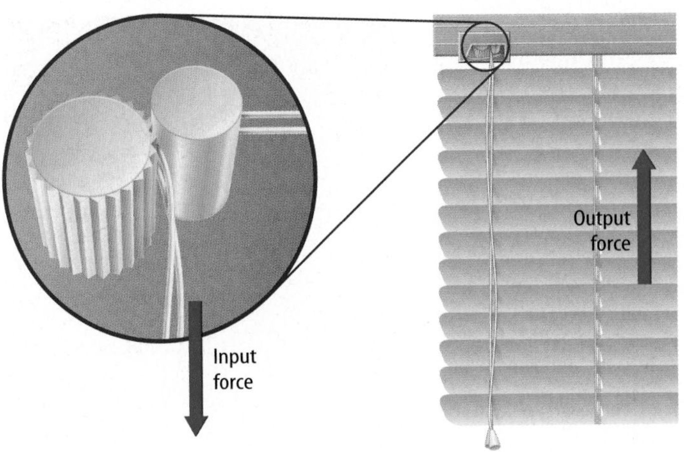

Figure 11 Window blinds use a machine that changes the direction of an input force. A downward pull on the cord is changed to an upward force on the blinds. The input and output forces are equal, so the MA is 1.

Graphite Lubricant
Graphite is a solid that sometimes is used as a lubricant to increase the efficiency of machines. Find out what element graphite is made of and why graphite is a good lubricant.

Mechanical Advantage

Machines like the car jack, the ramp, the crow bar, and the claw hammer make work easier by making the output force greater than the input force. The ratio of the output force to the input force is the **mechanical advantage** of a machine. The mechanical advantage of a machine can be calculated from the following equation.

Mechanical Advantage Equation

$$\text{mechanical advantage} = \frac{\text{output force (in newtons)}}{\text{input force (in newtons)}}$$

$$MA = \frac{F_{out}}{F_{in}}$$

Figure 11 shows that the mechanical advantage equals one when only the direction of the input force changes.

Ideal Mechanical Advantage The mechanical advantage of an a machine without friction is called the ideal mechanical advantage, or IMA. The IMA can be calculated by dividing the input distance by the output distance. For a real machine, the IMA would be the mechanical advantage of the machine if there were no friction.

Efficiency

For real machines, some of the energy put into a machine is always converted into heat by frictional forces. For that reason, the output work of a machine is always less than the work put into the machine.

Efficiency is a measure of how much of the work put into a machine is changed into useful output work by the machine. A machine with high efficiency produces less heat from friction so more of the input work is changed to useful output work.

 ***Why is the output work always less than the input work for a real machine?***

Teacher FYI

***MA* Information** Mechanical advantage (*MA*) is output force divided input force. If *MA* is less than 1, the input force is greater than the output force. If *MA* equals 1, the machine only changes the direction of the input force. If *MA* is greater than 1, the machine increases the output force.

Calculating Efficiency To calculate the efficiency of a machine, the output work is divided by the input work. Efficiency is usually expressed as a percentage by this equation:

Efficiency Equation

$$\text{efficiency (\%)} = \frac{\text{output work (in joules)}}{\text{input work (in joules)}} \times 100\%$$

$$\textit{efficiency} = \frac{W_{out}}{W_{in}} \times 100\%$$

In an ideal machine there is no friction and the output work equals the input work. So the efficiency of an ideal machine is 100 percent. In a real machine, friction causes the output work to always be less than the input work. So the efficiency of a real machine is always less than 100 percent.

Increasing Efficiency Machines can be made more efficient by reducing friction. This usually is done by adding a lubricant, such as oil or grease, to surfaces that rub together, as shown in **Figure 12.** A lubricant fills in the gaps between the surfaces, enabling the surfaces to slide past each other more easily.

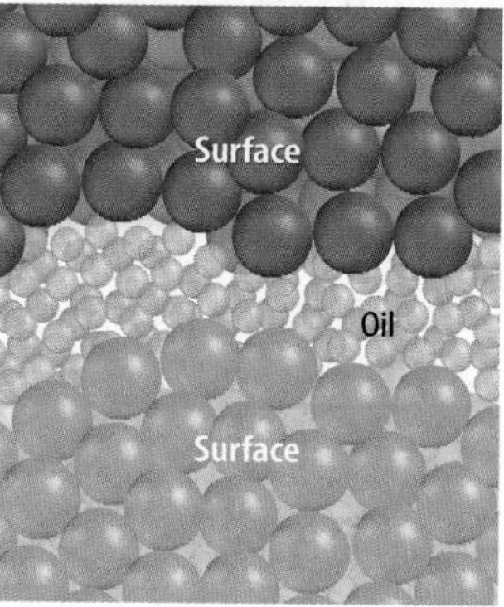

Figure 12 Oil reduces the friction between two surfaces. Oil fills the space between the surfaces so high spots don't rub against each other.

section 2 review

Summary

Work and Machines

- Machines make doing work easier by changing the applied force, changing the distance over which the force is applied, or changing the direction of the applied force.
- Because energy cannot be created or destroyed, the output work cannot be greater than the input work.
- In a real machine, some of the input work is converted into heat by friction.

Mechanical Advantage and Efficiency

- The mechanical advantage of a machine is the output force divided by the input force:
$$MA = \frac{F_{out}}{F_{in}}$$
- The efficiency of a machine is the output work divided by the input work times 100%:
$$\textit{efficiency} = \frac{W_{out}}{W_{in}} \times 100\%$$

Self Check

1. **Describe** the circumstances for which the output work would equal the input work in a machine.
2. **Infer** how lubricating a machine affects the output force exerted by the machine.
3. **Explain** why in a real machine the output work is always less than the input work.
4. **Think Critically** The mechanical advantage of a machine is less than one. Compare the distances over which the input and output forces are applied.

Applying Math

5. **Calculate** the mechanical advantage of a hammer if the input force is 125 N and the output force is 2,000 N.
6. **Calculate Efficiency** Find the efficiency of a machine that does 800 J of work if the input work is 2,400 J.
7. **Calculate Force** Find the force needed to lift a 2,000-N weight using a machine with a mechanical advantage of 15.

Science Online gpscience.com/self_check_quiz

3 Assess

DAILY INTERVENTION

Check for Understanding

Kinesthetic Set up a wood ramp so that the ramp is 3× longer than the height. Use a spring balance to pull a smooth wood block up the ramp. Measure the force and calculate the work done. Tape a strip of sandpaper as wide as the wood along the length of the ramp and repeat the procedure. Ask the students which machine was more efficient and why. Ask how they could improve the efficiency of the second ramp without removing the sandpaper. They could put something smooth over the sandpaper. L2

Reteach

Machines Bring in various simple machines for students to examine. For each one, have students decide whether the machine works by increasing force, increasing distance, changing the direction of the force. L2 LS **Visual-Spatial**

Assessment

Process Have each student choose a machine and prepare a presentation showing different ways to reduce friction in the machine and increase its efficiency. Possible ways of reducing friction include using bearings, wheels, or a lubricant. Use **Performance Assessment in the Science Classroom,** p. 143 L2 P

section 2 review

1. The machine would have to be an ideal machine in which there was no friction.
2. Friction is a force that opposes the motion of two surface sliding past each other. Lubricating a machine increases the output force because it decreases friction.
3. In a real machine, some of the input work is converted into thermal energy by friction.
4. The distance over which the output force is applied is greater than the distance that the input force is applied.
5. $MA = \frac{F_{out}}{F_{in}} = 16$
6. $eff = \frac{W_{out}}{W_{in}} \times 100\% = 33\%$
7. $F_{in} = \frac{F_{out}}{MA} = 133$ N

1 Motivate

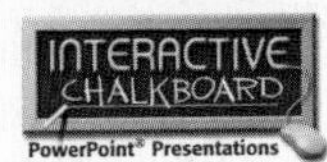

Bellringer

Section Focus Transparencies also are available on the Interactive Chalkboard CD-ROM. L2 ELL

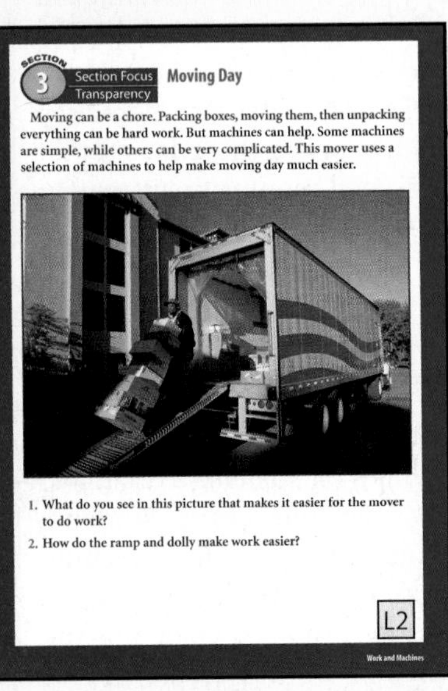
Section 3 Section Focus Transparency — Moving Day

Moving can be a chore. Packing boxes, moving them, then unpacking everything can be hard work. But machines can help. Some machines are simple, while others can be very complicated. This mover uses a selection of machines to help make moving day much easier.

1. What do you see in this picture that makes it easier for the mover to do work?
2. How do the ramp and dolly make work easier?

L2

Work and Machines

Tie to Prior Knowledge

Define *MA* Ask students to define mechanical advantage. the number of times a machine multiplies the effort force applied to it Tell them that in this section they will learn how the design of a simple machine affects its mechanical advantage. L2

Simple Machines

Reading Guide

***What* You'll Learn**

- **Describe** the six types of simple machines.
- **Explain** how the different types of simple machines make doing work easier.
- **Calculate** the ideal mechanical advantage of the different types of simple machines.

***Why* It's Important**

All complex machines, such as cars, are made of simple machines. Even your body contains simple machines.

Review Vocabulary

compound: composed of separate elements or parts

New Vocabulary

- simple machine
- lever
- pulley
- wheel and axle
- inclined plane
- screw
- wedge
- compound machine

Figure 13 There are three classes of levers.

First-class Lever
The fulcrum is between the input force and the output force.

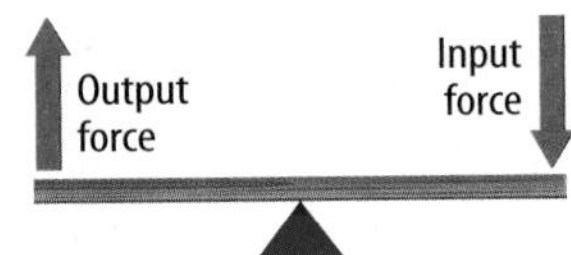

Second-class Lever
The output force is between the fulcrum and the input force.

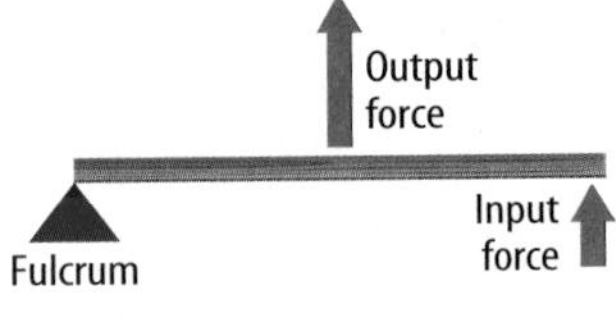

Third-class Lever
The input force is between the fulcrum and the output force.

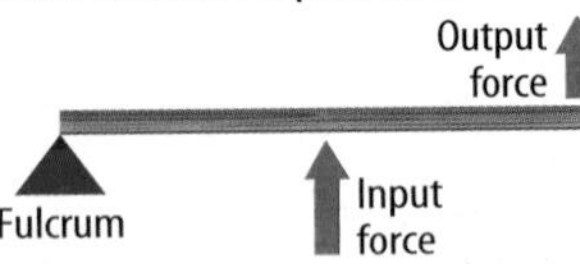

Types of Simple Machines

If you cut your food with a knife, or use a screwdriver, or even chew your food, you are using a simple machine. A **simple machine** is a machine that does work with only one movement of the machine. There are six types of simple machines: lever, pulley, wheel and axle, inclined plane, screw, and wedge. The pulley and the wheel and axle are modified levers, and the screw and the wedge are modified inclined planes.

Levers

You've used a lever if you've used a wheelbarrow, or a lawn rake, or swung a baseball bat. A **lever** is a bar that is free to pivot or turn around a fixed point. The fixed point the lever pivots on is called the fulcrum. The input arm of the lever is the distance from the fulcrum to the point where the input force is applied. The output arm is the distance from the fulcrum to the point where the output force is exerted by the lever.

The output force produced by a lever depends on the lengths of the input arm and the output arm. If the output arm is longer than the input arm, the law of conservation of energy requires that the output force be less than the input force. If the output arm is shorter than the input arm, then the output force is greater than the input force.

There are three classes of levers, as shown in **Figure 13.** The differences among the three classes of levers depend on the locations of the fulcrum, the input force, and the output force.

Section 3 Resource Manager

Chapter *Fast File* Resources
- Transparency Activity, p. 48, 49–50
- Directed Reading for Content Mastery, pp. 23, 24
- Lab Activity, pp. 9–11, 13–18
- Enrichment, p. 34
- Lab Worksheet, pp. 5–6, 7–8
- Reinforcement, p. 31

Home and Community Involvement, p. 35

Physical Science Critical Thinking/Problem Solving, pp. 6, 7

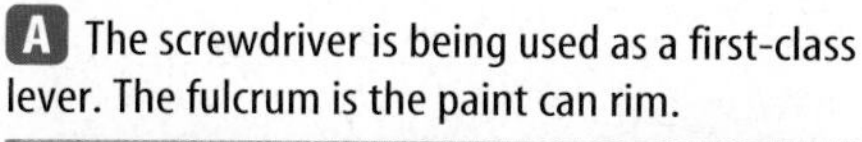

Figure 14 Levers are classified by the location of the input force, output force, and the fulcrum.

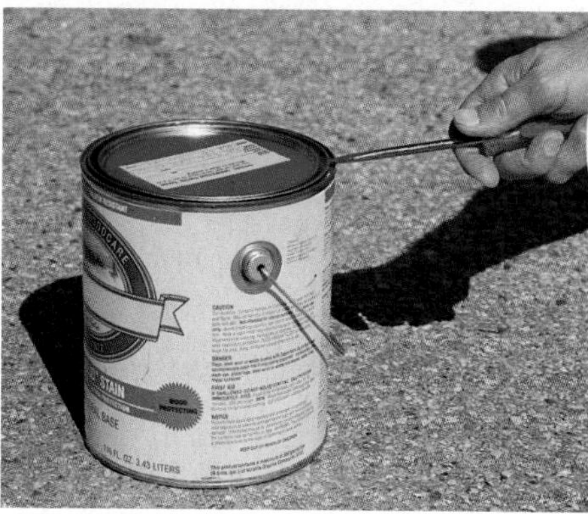

A The screwdriver is being used as a first-class lever. The fulcrum is the paint can rim.

B A wheelbarrow is a second-class lever. The fulcrum is the wheel.

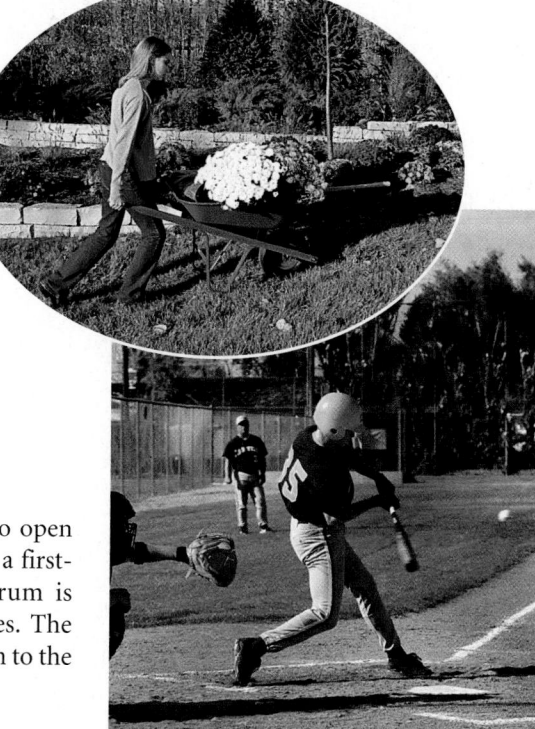

C A baseball bat is a third-class lever. The fulcrum here is this batter's left hand.

First-Class Lever The screwdriver used to open the paint can in **Figure 14A** is an example of a first-class lever. For a first-class lever, the fulcrum is located between the input and output forces. The output force is always in the opposite direction to the input force in a first-class lever.

Second-Class Lever For a second-class lever, the output force is located between the input force and the fulcrum. Look at the wheelbarrow in **Figure 14B.** You apply an upward input force on the handles, and the wheel is the fulcrum. The output force is exerted between the input force and fulcrum. For a second-class lever, the output force is always greater than the input force.

Third-Class Lever Many pieces of sports equipment, such as a baseball bat, are third-class levers. For a third-class lever, the input force is applied between the output force and the fulcrum. The right-handed batter in **Figure 14C,** applies the input force with the right hand and the left hand is the fulcrum. The output force is exerted by the bat above the right hand. The output force is always less than the input force in a third-class lever. Instead, the distance over which the output force is applied is increased.

Every lever can be placed into one of these classes. Each class can be found in your body, as shown in **Figure 15** on the next page.

2 Teach

Quick Demo

Classifying Levers

Materials several different kinds of levers, such as crow bars, screwdrivers, nut crackers, bottle openers, tweezers, fishing poles

Estimated Time 10 minutes

Procedure Display several examples of each of the three classes of levers for students to examine and handle. First-class levers would be pliers, screwdrivers, and crowbars. Second-class levers are nutcrackers, wheelbarrows, and bottle openers. Third-class levers are tweezers, baseball bats, and fishing poles. L2 IS **Kinesthetic**

Use Science Words

Word Origin Have students look up the word *fulcrum* in a dictionary to determine its origin. Ask a volunteer to explain how the meaning of the word reflects its root. The word *fulcrum* comes from the Latin root fulcire, meaning "to support." A fulcrum acts as a support around which a lever moves. L1 IS **Linguistic**

Differentiated Instruction

Challenge Have students create a computer presentation describing the three classes of levers. The description should include the locations of the fulcrum, input force, and output force. If possible, have students create an animated presentation to present to the class. L3

Cultural Diversity

Chinese Wheelbarrow The wheelbarrow, a second-class lever, was invented in China sometime in or before the first century B.C. The Chinese called their wheeled devices such things as wooden goat, wooden sheep, wooden ox, and gliding horse. How does a wheelbarrow give a worker more power? It allows the worker to do more work in a shorter amount of time. L1 IS **Logical-Mathematical**

SECTION 3 Simple Machines 139

NATIONAL GEOGRAPHIC

Visualizing Levers in the Human Body

Have students examine the pictures and read the captions. Then ask the following questions.

Newborn babies are not able to support their heads and they must be carefully supported. Why is this? The unborn baby floats in fluid and does not have to support its own head. After birth, these muscles must be strengthened.

Explain why your forearm becomes more muscular when you do curls with a dumbbell. When you increase the output force (the dumbbell), your input force (muscle in your forearm) must also increase. Repeating curls increases the muscle mass in your forearm over time.

Activity

Other Body Levers Find other levers in your body. Make a poster showing the various kinds that you find. For each example, mark the fulcrum, input force, and output force. L2 LS **Visual-Spatial**

Figure 15

▲ Fulcrum
▼ Input force
▲ Output force

All three types of levers—first-class, second-class, and third-class—are found in the human body. The forces exerted by muscles in your body can be increased by first-class and second-class levers, while third-class levers increase the range of movement of a body part. Examples of how the body uses levers to help it move are shown here.

▲ FIRST-CLASS LEVER The fulcrum lies between the input force and the output force. Your head acts like a first-class lever. Your neck muscles provide the input force to support the weight of your head.

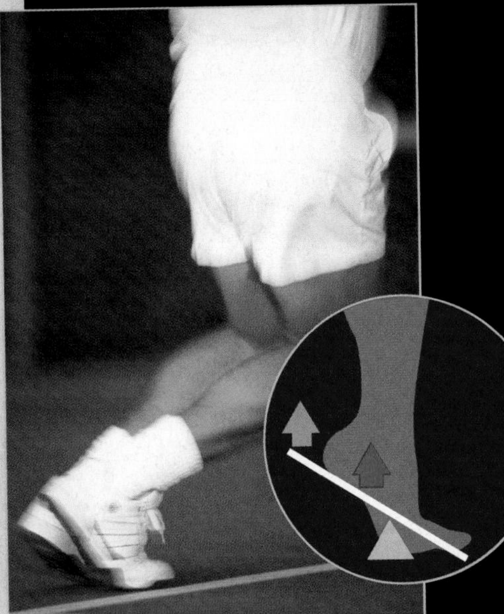

◀ SECOND-CLASS LEVER The output force is between the fulcrum and the input force. Your foot becomes a second-class lever when you stand on your toes.

▶ THIRD-CLASS LEVER The input force is between the fulcrum and the output force. A third-class lever increases the range of motion of the output force. When you do a curl with a dumbbell, your forearm is a third-class lever.

Figure 16 A fixed pulley is another form of the lever.
Infer *the lengths of the input arm and output arm in a pulley.*

Ideal Mechanical Advantage of a Lever The ideal mechanical advantage, or IMA, can be calculated for any machine by dividing the input distance by the output distance. For a lever, the input distance is the length of the input arm and the output distance is the length of the output arm. The IMA of a lever can be calculated from this equation:

Ideal Mechanical Advantage of a Lever

$$\text{ideal mechanical advantage} = \frac{\text{length of input arm (m)}}{\text{length of output arm (m)}}$$

$$\text{IMA} = \frac{L_{in}}{L_{out}}$$

Pulleys

A **pulley** is a grooved wheel with a rope, chain, or cable running along the groove. A fixed pulley is a modified first-class lever, as shown in **Figure 16.** The axle of the pulley acts as the fulcrum. The two sides of the pulley are the input arm and output arm. A pulley can change the direction of the input force or increase input force, depending on whether the pulley is fixed or movable. A system of pulleys can change the direction of the input force and make it larger.

Fixed Pulleys The cable attached to an elevator passes over a fixed pulley at the top of the elevator shaft. A fixed pulley, such as the one in **Figure 17,** is attached to something that doesn't move, such as a ceiling or wall. Because a fixed pulley changes only the direction of force, the IMA is 1.

Figure 17 A fixed pulley changes only the direction of your force. You need to apply an input force of 4 N to lift the 4-N weight.

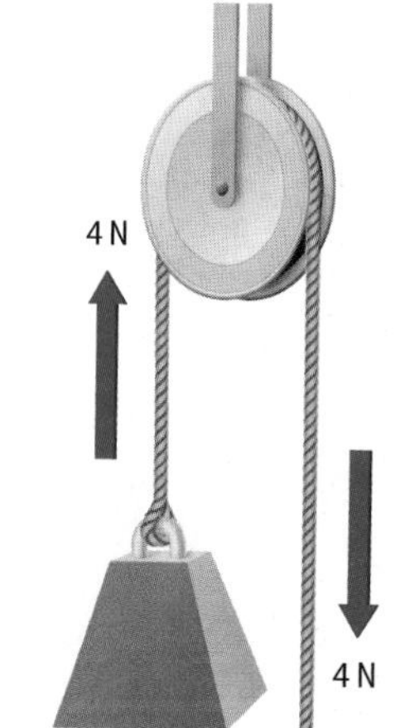

Activity

Calculate *IMA* Ask students to calculate the *IMA* of a lever whose output arm is 1 m long and whose input arm is 80 cm long. What class of lever is this? *IMA* = 0.8 m ÷ 1.0 m = 0.8; this must be a third-class lever. L2 LS **Logical-Mathematical**

Caption Answer

Figure 16 the radius of the pulley

Make a Model

Belt Pulleys Some pulleys, such as drive pulleys in automobiles, consist of two or more grooved wheels connected by a circular belt. Have students work in pairs to make models of a belt pulley. One student can hold two spools with pencils through the holes. Have students connect the spools with a large rubber band. The other student can turn the spools to show how turning one rotates the other in the same direction. If possible, use one small spool and one large spool. The students can see that the speed of the pulleys is inversely related to their diameter. L3 LS **Kinesthetic**

Discussion

Fixed Pulleys The *IMA* of a single fixed pulley is 1. What is the benefit of using a fixed pulley? A fixed pulley allows a person to raise objects to high places while the person stays at ground level. L2 LS **Logical-Mathematical**

Visual Learning

Figure 16 Point out that a fixed pulley, like that shown in **Figure 16,** is a type of first-class lever because the fulcrum is between the input force and the output force. A movable pulley, like that shown on the next page, is a type of second-class lever. The point where the rope is attached to the ceiling is the fulcrum, and the output force is between the fulcrum and the input force. L3 LS **Visual-Spatial**

Differentiated Instruction

Challenge Have students design and build a mousetrap using ramps, pulleys, and levers. If supplies are not available, they can draw their design on a poster and present it to the class. L3

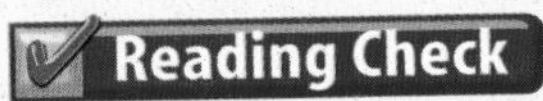

Answer by increasing the distance you must pull

Inquiry Lab

Finding Balance

Purpose Students infer how to include the mass of a lever into the input force.

Possible Materials meterstick, string, hanging weights (5 g, 10 g, 50 g, 100 g), vertical support, horizontal bar (to hang meter stick on)

Estimated Time 50 minutes

Procedure

1. Hang a meterstick about 10 cm off center and hang various combinations of weights on the two ends so that the meterstick balances.
2. Derive an equation to determine the exact location for any given combination of weights to make the stick remain balanced.

Teaching Strategy

Students should find that the heavier of the two weights will always be on the short side of the meterstick. They may even find the location for just one weight to balance the meterstick.

The equation is:

$F_{in}d_{in} + W_s d_s = F_{out}d_{out}$

Where W_s = weight of the meterstick and d_s = distance from the center of the meterstick to the fulcrum. L2

For additional inquiry activities, see *Science Inquiry Labs*.

Figure 18 A movable pulley and a pulley system called a block and tackle reduce the force needed to lift a weight.

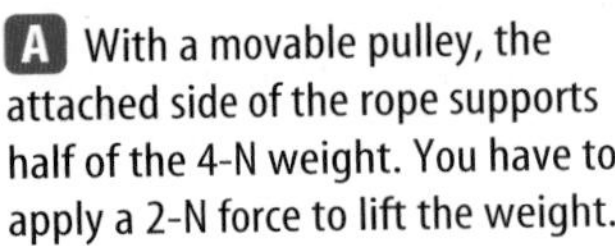

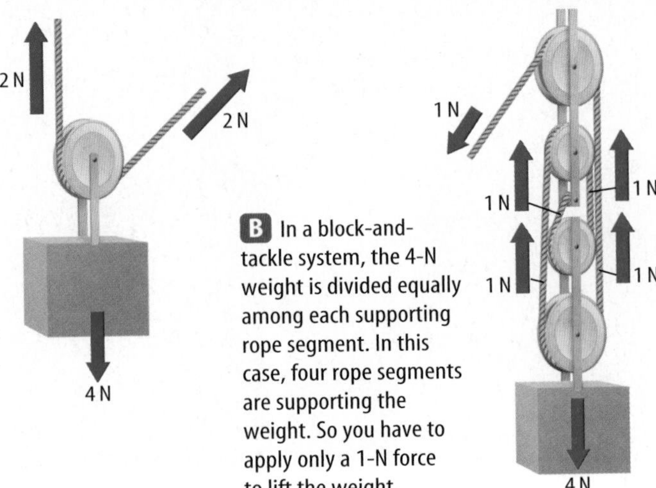

A With a movable pulley, the attached side of the rope supports half of the 4-N weight. You have to apply a 2-N force to lift the weight.

B In a block-and-tackle system, the 4-N weight is divided equally among each supporting rope segment. In this case, four rope segments are supporting the weight. So you have to apply only a 1-N force to lift the weight.

Movable Pulleys A pulley in which one end of the rope is fixed and the wheel is free to move is called a movable pulley. Unlike a fixed pulley, a movable pulley does multiply force. Suppose a 4-N weight is hung from the movable pulley in **Figure 18A.** The ceiling acts like someone helping you to lift the weight. The rope attached to the ceiling will support half of the weight—2 N. You need to exert only the other half of the weight—2 N—in order to support and lift the weight. The output force exerted on the weight is 4 N, and the applied input force is 2 N. Therefore the IMA of the movable pulley is 2.

For a fixed pulley, the distance you pull the rope downward equals the distance the weight moves upward. For a movable pulley, the distance you pull the rope upward is twice the distance the weight moves upward.

Reading Check *How does a movable pulley reduce the input force needed to lift a weight?*

The Block and Tackle A system of pulleys consisting of fixed and movable pulleys is called a block and tackle. **Figure 18B** shows a block and tackle made up of two fixed pulleys and two movable pulleys. If a 4-N weight is suspended from the movable pulley, each rope segment supports one fourth of the weight, reducing the input force to 1 N. The IMA of a pulley system is equal to the number of rope segments that support the weight. The block and tackle shown in **Figure 18B** has a IMA of 4. The IMA of a block and tackle can be increased by increasing the number of pulleys in the pulley system.

LAB DEMONSTRATION

Purpose to measure the mechanical advantage of various pulley systems

Materials one small, single-sheave pulley; two small, 2-ring tandem pulleys; cord; 1-kg mass; 10-N spring scale

Procedure Use a spring scale to measure the forces required to lift a 1-kg mass using a single fixed pulley, then a single movable pulley, and finally, a block and tackle.

Expected Outcome The *IMA*s are, respectively, 1, 2, and 4.

Assessment

Which system(s) increased force? movable pulley and block and tackle Which system(s) changed direction of the force? single fixed pulley and block and tackle Which system(s) increased force and changed direction? block and tackle L2

Figure 19 The handle on a pencil sharpener is part of a wheel and axle. You apply a force to the handle. This force is made larger by the wheel and axle, making it easy to turn the sharpening mechanism.

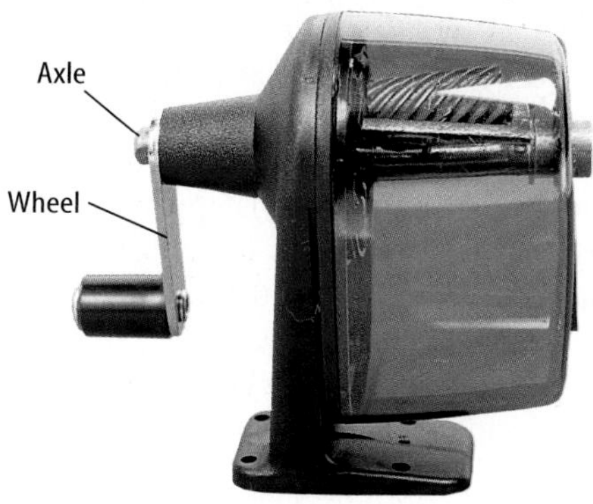

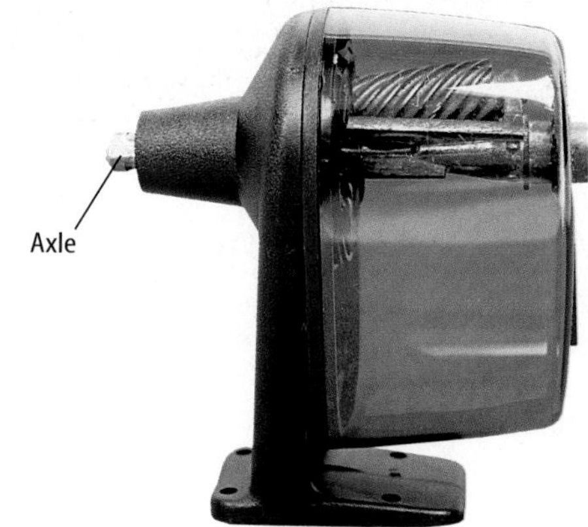

Wheel and Axle

Could you use the pencil sharpener in **Figure 19** if the handle weren't attached? The handle on the pencil sharpener is part of a wheel and axle. A **wheel and axle** is a simple machine consisting of a shaft or axle attached to the center of a larger wheel, so that the wheel and axle rotate together. Doorknobs, screwdrivers, and faucet handles are examples of wheel and axles. Usually the input force is applied to the wheel, and the output force is exerted by the axle.

Mechanical Advantage of the Wheel and Axle A wheel and axle is another modified lever. The center of the axle is the fulcrum. The input force is applied at the rim of the wheel. So the length of the input arm is the radius of the wheel. The output force is exerted at the rim of the axle. So the length of the output arm is the radius of the axle. The ideal mechanical advantage of a lever is the length of the input arm divided by the length of the output arm. So the IMA of a wheel and axle is given by this equation:

Ideal Mechanical Advantage of Wheel and Axle

$$\text{ideal mechanical advantage} = \frac{\text{radius of wheel (m)}}{\text{radius of axle (m)}}$$

$$IMA = \frac{r_w}{r_a}$$

According to this equation, the IMA of a wheel and axle can be increased by increasing the radius of the wheel.

Text Question Answer

No, it would be difficult to turn the axle with your fingers.

Discussion

Lifting a Car A person uses a block and tackle to lift an automobile engine that weighs 1,800 N. The person must exert a force of 300 N to lift the engine. How many ropes support the engine? Explain how you know. Six; the *IMA* is 1,800 N ÷ 300 N = 6, and in a pulley system, the *IMA* equals the number of supporting ropes. L2

IDENTIFYING Misconceptions

Skating The wheel and axle on a skateboard or a pair of in-line skates is not the simple machine known as the wheel and axle. In the simple machine, the wheel and axle rotate together. Usually a small force is applied to the wheel and is translated to a larger force moving over the smaller distance of the axle. The wheels and axles on skateboards and in-line skates are rollers that help the vehicles move with less friction. The axle is fixed and the wheel rotates around the axle.

Curriculum Connection

Math Supply students with several common wheels and axles, such as doorknobs or beaters from an electric mixer. Have them measure the radius of the wheel and the radius of the axle for each item and calculate its *IMA*. L2 LS **Logical-Mathematical**

Differentiated Instruction

English-Language Learners Use visual aids to show students what simple machines look like. Then have students write descriptions of simple machines in their homes. Examples could be a lever, an inclined plane, and a pulley. L2

Activity

Inclined Plane Create an inclined plane by resting a board against a stack of books. Have students measure the input and output distances and calculate the *IMA*. Then ask students to use a spring scale to measure the force required to lift a toy car vertically and the force required to drag it up the ramp. Have them use the numbers they measured for distance and force and calculate the amount of work done pulling the toy car along the ramp and lifting it vertically. Are the two amounts of work the same? Why or why not? The two amounts of work should be close. Any difference is due to inaccurate measurements and loss of energy to friction. L2 ELL IS **Kinesthetic**

Figure 20 If an input force is applied to the larger gear, and it rotates clockwise, the smaller gear rotates counterclockwise. The output force exerted by the smaller gear is less than the input force applied to the larger gear.

Gears A gear is a wheel and axle with the wheel having teeth around its rim. When the teeth of two gears interlock, turning one gear causes the other gear to turn.

When two gears of different sizes are interlocked, they rotate at different rates. Each rotation of the larger gear causes the smaller gear to make more than one rotation. If the input force is applied to the larger gear, the output force exerted by smaller gear is less than the input force.

Gears also may change the direction of the force as shown in **Figure 20.** When the larger gear in is rotated clockwise, the smaller gear rotates counterclockwise.

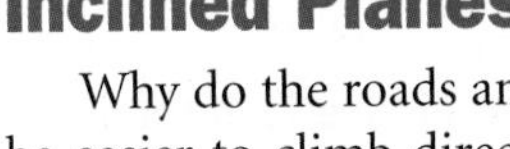

Inclined Planes

Why do the roads and paths on mountains zigzag? Would it be easier to climb directly up a steep incline or walk a longer path gently sloped around the mountain? A sloping surface, such as a ramp that reduces the amount of force required to do work, is an **inclined plane.**

Mechanical Advantage of an Inclined Plane You do the same work by lifting a box straight up or pushing it up an inclined plane. But by pushing the box up an inclined plane, the input force is exerted over a longer distance compared to lifting the box straight up. As a result the input force is less than the force needed to lift the box straight upward. The IMA of an inclined plane can be calculated from this equation.

Ideal Mechanical Advantage of Inclined Plane

$$\text{ideal mechanical advantage} = \frac{\text{length of slope (m)}}{\text{height of slope (m)}}$$

$$\text{IMA} = \frac{l}{h}$$

The IMA of an inclined plane for a given height is increased by making the plane longer.

When you think of an inclined plane, you normally think of moving an object up a ramp—you move and the inclined plane remains stationary. The screw and the wedge, however, are variations of the inclined plane in which the inclined plane moves and the object remains stationary.

Science Online

Topic: Nanorobots

Visit gpscience.com for Web links to information about how tiny robots called nanorobots might be used as microsurgical instruments.

Activity Use the information you find to make a diagram of a nanorobot that might be used to perform surgery.

Visual Learning

Figure 20 Point out that the teeth on the gears must be the same size in order to rotate smoothly. Tell students that the ratio of the number of teeth on the gears determines the speed that the gears turn and the *IMA*. If the small gear has 24 teeth and the large gear has 72 teeth, how much faster will the small gear turn? What is the *IMA*? The large gear will make one-third of a turn for each full turn of the small gear, so the small gear will turn three times faster. The *IMA* is 3. L2 IS **Logical-Mathematical**

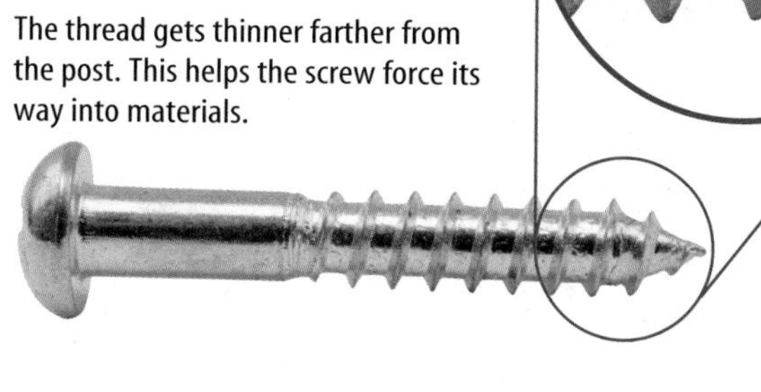

Figure 21 A screw has an inclined plane that wraps around the post of the screw.

The thread gets thinner farther from the post. This helps the screw force its way into materials.

Many lids, such as those on peanut butter jars, also contain threads.

The Screw

A **screw** is an inclined plane wrapped in a spiral around a cylindrical post. If you look closely at the screw in **Figure 21,** you'll see that the threads form a tiny ramp that runs upward from its tip. You apply the input force by turning the screw. The output force is exerted along the threads of the screw. The IMA of a screw is related to the spacing of the threads. The IMA is larger if the threads are closer together. However, if the IMA is larger, more turns of the screw are needed to drive it into some material.

How do you remove the lid off a jar of peanut butter, like in **Figure 21?** If you look closely, you see threads similar to the ones on the screw in **Figure 21.** Where else can you find examples of a screw?

The Wedge

Like the screw, the wedge is also a simple machine where the inclined plane moves through an object or material. A **wedge** is an inclined plane with one or two sloping sides. It changes the direction of the input force.

Look closely at the knife in **Figure 22.** One edge is sharp, and it slopes outward at both sides, forming an inclined plane. As it moves through the apple, the downward input force is changed to a horizontal force, forcing the apple apart.

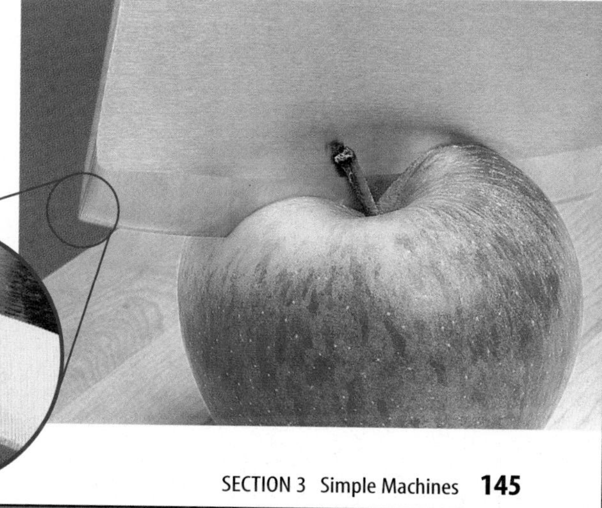

Figure 22 A knife blade is a wedge. As you cut through the apple, it pushes the halves of the apple apart.

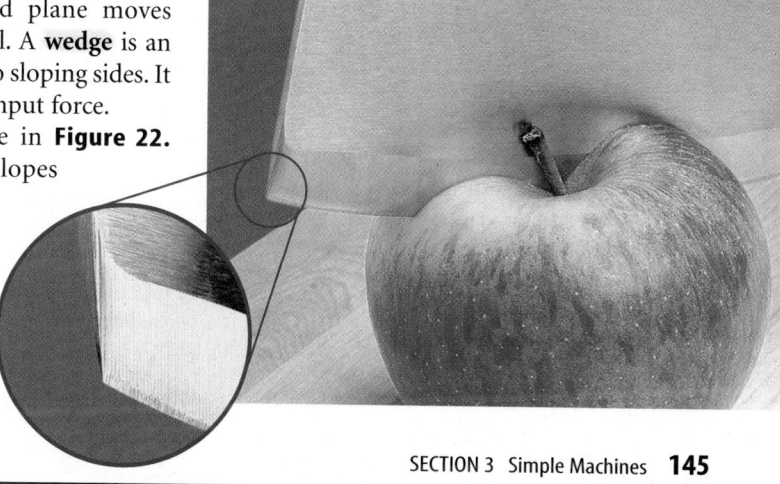

Make a Model

Archimedes Screw An Archimedes' screw is a type of revolving screw used to lift water. This simple device was invented in the third century B.C. by the Greek scientist Archimedes. Have interested students make a model of an Archimedes' screw, using plastic sheeting attached to a dowel. L3 LS **Kinesthetic**

Teacher FYI

Screw Parts The threads of a screw are the windings. The pitch is the distance from a point on one thread to a point directly above it on the next thread. The pitch determines the force you must exert to turn a screw.

Text Question Answer

Other examples of a screw include an auger, a cork screw for opening wine bottles, and a spiral stair case.

Activity

Wedge *IMA* The ideal mechanical advantage of a wedge is calculated by dividing the length of one side of the wedge by the width of the wedge at the thick end. Ask students to calculate the mechanical advantage of a wedge that is 12 cm long and 5 cm wide. $MA = 12\text{ cm} \div 5\text{ cm} = 2.4$ L3 LS **Logical-Mathematical**

Active Reading

Write–Draw–Discuss This strategy encourages students to actively participate in reading and lectures, assimilating content creatively. Have students write about the different simple machines, clarify their ideas, and then make illustrations or drawings of the machines and how they work. Ask students to share responses with the class and display several examples. L2

Fun Fact

In a compound machine, the output force of one of its simple machines becomes the input force of another. For a compound machine made of two simple machines, $MA = MA_2 \times MA_1$.

3 Assess

DAILY INTERVENTION

Check for Understanding

Logical-Mathematical Have students brainstorm how to organize information about the six kinds of simple machines into a table. Include the type of machine, an example of each type, and a brief description of how it works. You may want to include other information such as mechanical advantage and efficiency. L2

Reteach

Arrows From construction paper, cut three arrows, about 10, 20, and 30 cm long. Make a similar set in another color. Label the first set of arrows F_{in} and the second set F_{out}. Collect examples of simple machines. Ask volunteers to choose a machine and use the arrows to show the direction and relative sizes of F_{in} and F_{out}. L2

ELL IS **Visual-Spatial**

Assessment

Process Ask students to compare and contrast pulleys and gears. Both use wheels. Gears have teeth, but pulleys don't. Pulleys use a cord to move the wheels. Gears are pulled by interlocking teeth or a chain. L2

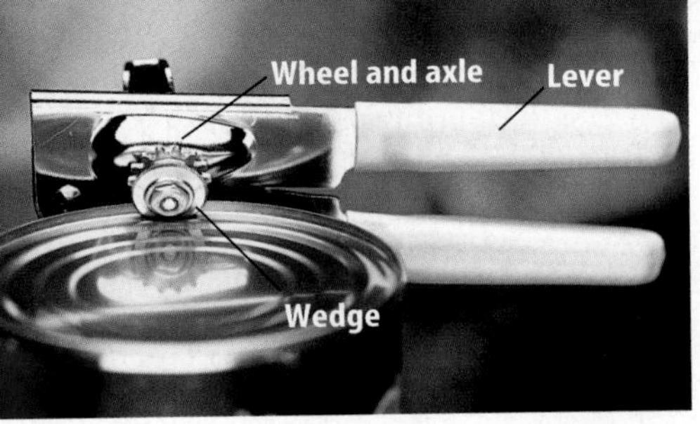

Figure 23 A compound machine, such as a can opener, is made up of simple machines.

Compound Machines

Some of the machines you use every day are made up of several simple machines. Two or more simple machines that operate together form a **compound machine.**

Look at the can opener in **Figure 23.** To open the can you first squeeze the handles together. The handles act as a lever and increase the force applied on a wedge, which then pierces the can. You then turn the handle, a wheel and axle, to open the can.

A car is also a compound machine. Burning fuel in the cylinders of the engine causes the pistons to move up and down. This up-and-down motion makes the crankshaft rotate. The force exerted by the rotating crankshaft is transmitted to the wheels through other parts of the car, such as the transmission and the differential. Both of these parts contain gears, that can change the rate at which the wheels rotate, the force exerted by the wheels, and even reverse the direction of rotation.

section 3 review

Summary

The Lever Family

- A lever is a bar that is free to pivot about a fixed point called the fulcrum.
- There are three classes of levers based on the relative locations of the input force, output force, and the fulcrum.
- A pulley is a grooved wheel with a rope, chain, or cable placed in the groove and is a modified form of a lever.
- The IMA of a lever is the input arm divided by the output arm.
- A wheel and axle consists of a shaft or axle attached to the center of a larger wheel.

The Inclined Plane Family

- An inclined plane is a ramp or sloping surface that reduces the force needed to do work.
- The IMA of an inclined plane is the length of the plane divided by the height of the plane.
- A screw consists of an inclined plane wrapped around a shaft.
- A wedge is an inclined plane that moves and can have one or two sloping surfaces.

Self Check

1. **Classify** a screwdriver as one of the six types of simple machine. Explain how the IMA of screw driver could be increased.
2. **Determine** for which class of lever the output force is always greater than the input force. For which class is the output force always less than the input force?
3. **Make a diagram** of a bicycle and label the parts of a bicycle that are simple machines.
4. **Think Critically** Use the law of conservation of energy to explain why in a second-class lever the distance over which the input force is applied is always greater than the distance over which the output force is applied.

Applying Math

5. **Calculate IMA** What is the IMA of a car's steering wheel if the wheel has a diameter of 40 cm and the shaft it's attached to has a diameter of 4 cm?
6. **Calculate Output Arm Length** A lever has an IMA of 4. If the length of the input arm is 1.0 m, what is the length of the output arm?
7. **Calculate IMA** A 6.0 m ramp runs from a sidewalk to a porch that is 2.0 m above the sidewalk. What is the ideal mechanical advantage of this ramp?

section 3 review

1. wheel and axle; by increasing the radius of the handle of the screw-driver
2. second-class lever; third-class lever
3. Check students' diagrams.
4. The input work cannot be greater than the output work. The input force is always less than the output force, so the input distance must be greater than the output distance.
5. $IMA = \frac{r_w}{r_a} = \frac{(40 \text{ cm})}{(4 \text{ cm})} = 10$
6. $L_{out} = \frac{(1.0 \text{ m})}{4} = 0.25 \text{ m}$
7. $IMA = \frac{l}{h} = \frac{(6.0 \text{ m})}{(2.0 \text{ m})} = 3$

Levers

Have you ever tried to balance a friend on a seesaw? If your friend was lighter, you had to move toward the fulcrum. In this lab, you will usethe same method to measure the mass of a coin.

Real-World Question

How can a lever be used to measure mass?

Goals

- **Measure** the lengths of the input arm and output arm of a lever.
- **Calculate** the ideal mechanical advantage of a lever.
- **Determine** the mass of a coin.

Materials

stiff cardboard, 3 cm by 30 cm
coins (one quarter, one dime, one nickel)
balance
metric ruler

Safety Precautions

Procedure

1. **Measure** the mass of each coin.
2. Mark a line 2 cm from one end of the cardboard strip. Label this line *Output*.
3. Slide the other end of the cardboard strip over the edge of a table until the strip begins to tip. Mark a line across the strip at the table edge and label this line *Input*.
4. **Measure** the mass of the strip to the nearest 0.1 g. Write this mass on the input line.
5. Center a dime on the output line. Slide the cardboard strip until it begins to tip. Mark the balance line. Label it *Fulcrum 1*.

6. **Measure** the lengths of the output and input arms to the nearest 0.1 cm.
7. Calculate the IMA of the lever. Multiply the IMA by the mass of the lever to find the approximate mass of the coin.
8. Repeat steps 5 through 7 with the nickel and the quarter. Mark the fulcrum line *Fulcrum 2* for the nickel and *Fulcrum 3* for the quarter.

Conclude and Apply

1. **Explain** why there might be a difference between the mass of each coin measured by the balance and the mass measured using the lever.
2. **Explain** what provides the input and output force for the lever.
3. **Explain** why the IMA of the lever changes as the mass of the coin changes.

Communicating Your Data

Compare your results with those of other students in your class. **For more help, refer to the Science Skill Handbook.**

BENCH TESTED

Real-World Question

Purpose Students calculate the mechanical advantage of levers. L1 LS **Logical-Mathematical**

Process Skills measure, use numbers, interpret data, classify, observe and infer, compare and contrast, recognize cause and effect, form operational definitions, interpret scientific illustrations

Time Required 40 minutes

Procedure

Teaching Strategies

- Be sure students understand how to use a balance to accurately get a mass of their coin.
- Some students may need help labeling their strips of cardboard.

Conclude and Apply

1. There will be some experimental error in this process.
2. The input force is the weight of the coin. The output force is the weight of the cardboard extended over the edge of the table.
3. because the input force changes with the changes in the weights of the coins

Communicating Your Data

Have students use graphics software to draw diagrams that explain the lab and illustrate their results.

Assessment

Oral Evaluate student understanding of the lever design by having them explain to the class how they performed the calculations. Use **Performance Assessment in the Science Classroom,** p. 101.

Real-World Question

Purpose Students will make models of different simple machines to lift a weight and compare the forces used. L2 COOP LEARN IN **Kinesthetic**

Process Skills observe, use numbers, communicate, measure, infer, compare and contrast, recognize cause and effect, interpret data, formulate models, make and use tables

Time Required one class period

Materials The block and tackle can be difficult to set up unless the pulleys and string sizes are matched. The pulleys should be made for block and tackle use. The small pulleys typically available from hardware stores will work, but can be difficult to handle as they don't usually have the needed fastening points on both top and bottom. Be sure to arrange the double pulley and single pulley as illustrated.

Safety Precautions Be sure students wear eye protection for this lab.

Model and Invent

Using Simple Machines

Goals

- **Model** lifting devices based on a block and tackle and on an inclined plane.
- **Calculate** the output work that will be accomplished.
- **Measure** the force needed by each machine to lift a weight.
- **Calculate** the input work and efficiency for each model machine.
- **Select** the best machine for your job based on the force required.

Possible Materials

spring scale, 0–10 N range
9.8-N weight (1 kg mass)
two double pulleys
string for pulleys
stand or support for the pulleys
wooden board, 40 cm long
support for board, 10 cm high

Safety Precautions

Real-World Question

You are the contractor on a one-story building with a large air-conditioner. How can you get the air conditioner to the roof? How can you minimize the force needed to lift an object? What machines could you use? Consider a fixed pulley with ideal mechanical advantage (*IMA*) = 1, a movable pulley with *IMA* = 2, a block and tackle with one fixed double pulley and one movable double pulley with *IMA* = 4, and an inclined plane with *IMA* = slope / height = 4. How can you find the efficiency of machines?

Make the Model

1. Work in teams of at least two. **Collect** all the needed equipment.
2. Sketch a model for each lifting machine. **Model** the inclined plane with a board 40-cm long and raised 10 cm at one end. Include a control in which the weight is lifted while being suspended directly from the spring scale.
3. Make a table for data.
4. Is the pulley support high enough that the block and tackle can lift a weight 10 cm?
5. Obtain your teacher's approval of your sketches and data table before proceeding.

Problem Data

	Control	Inclined Plane	Block and Tackle
Ideal Mechanical Advantage, *IMA*	1	4	4
Input force, F_{in}, N	Will vary	Will vary	Will vary
Input distance, d_{in}, m	0.10	0.40	0.10
Output force, F_{out}, N	9.8	9.8	9.8
Output distance, d_{out}, m	0.10	0.10	0.10
$Work_{in} = F_{in}\ d_{in}$, Joules	Will vary	Will vary	Will vary
$Work_{out} = F_{out}\ d_{out}$, Joules	0.98	0.98	0.98
$Efficiency = (Work_{out}/Work_{in}) \times 100\%$	Will vary	Will vary	Will vary

Using Scientific Methods

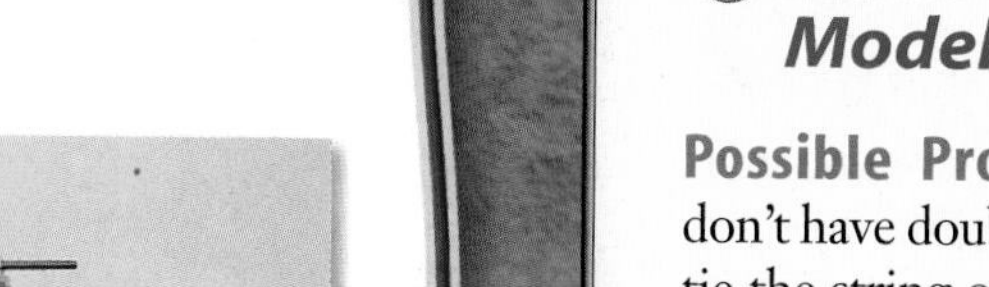

Test the Model

1. Tie the weight to the spring scale and measure the force required to lift it. Record the input force in your data table under *Control,* along with the 10-cm input distance.
2. Assemble the inclined plane so that the weight can be pulled up the ramp at a constant rate. The 40-cm board should be supported so that one end is 10 cm higher.
3. Tie the string to the spring scale and measure the force required to move the weight up the ramp at a constant speed. Record this input force under *Inclined Plane* in your data table. Record 40 cm as the input distance for the inclined plane.
4. Assemble the block and tackle using one fixed double pulley and one movable single pulley.
5. Tie the weight to the single pulley and tie the spring scale to the string at the top of the upper double pulley.
6. **Measure** the force required to lift the weight with the block and tackle. Record this input force.
7. **Measure** the length of string that must be pulled to raise the weight 10 cm. Record this input distance.

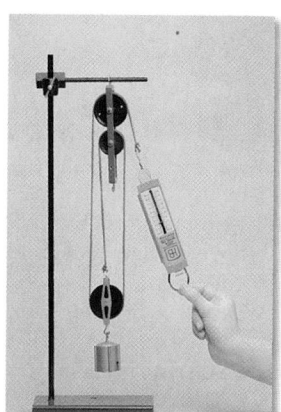

Analyze Your Data

1. **Calculate** the output work for all three methods of lifting the 9.8-N weight a distance of 10 cm.
2. **Calculate** the input work and the efficiency for the control, the inclined plane, and the block and tackle.
3. **Compare** the efficiencies of each of the three methods of lifting.

Conclude and Apply

1. **Explain** how you might improve the efficiency of the machine in each case.
2. **Infer** what types of situations would require use of a ramp over a pulley to help lift something.
3. **Infer** which machines would be most likely to be affected by friction.

Communicating Your Data

Make a poster showing how the best machine would be used to lift the air conditioner to the roof of your building.

Make a Model

Possible Procedures If you don't have double pulleys, you can tie the string on the single pulley, as shown, and loop the string over a horizontal bar, then around the moveable pulley and then around the bar again instead.

Teaching Strategy Teams of two will be required to simplify assembly of apparatus and measurements.

Troubleshooting When students pull on the weight using the spring scale, make sure they pull slowly, smoothly, and at constant speed. Jerky pulling will lead to the use of unnecessarily large forces.

Test Your Model

Expected Outcome Students will build models of three simple machines and use them to model lifting an air conditioner to a roof. L2

Analyze Your Data

1. Output work is the same for all three, 0.98 J.
2. Answers will vary.
3. The block and tackle require the lowest force. The reason for the efficiency difference is probably the difference in the friction between the ramp and the block and tackle.

Conclude and Apply

1. You could improve both by lubricating the ramp and the pulleys.
2. Answers will vary.
3. Answers will vary. A slick ramp will be less affected by friction than a rusty pulley. A well-oiled pulley will work better than a rough-surfaced ramp.

Assessment

Process Have students make bar graphs of the different amounts of force used and work done using each machine. Use **Performance Assessment in the Science Classroom,** p. 111. L2

Communicating Your Data

Have students compare their posters. Did they all agree on the best machine? Display student posters in the classroom. L2

Content Background

The current vision of nanotechnology and its possible uses was discussed in a book by Dr. K. Eric Drexler in 1986. He envisioned the precise construction of advanced materials from chemically pure ingredients, eliminating the toxic byproducts of conventional manufacturing. The long-term goals for molecular manufacturing range from ultra-small computers and space construction to the alleviation of disease, hunger and pollution. As developments increase at a rapid pace, many questions arise concerning the possible use and misuse of the new technology.

Discussion

Nanobots What would be the advantage of having nanobots perform medical tasks now done by drugs or surgery? Possible answer: By acting on a cell-by-cell basis nanobots can avoid damaging healthy cells and reduce recovery time. L2 LS **Logical-Mathematical**

Activity

Precision drawing Divide the class into groups of three or four. Assign a word to each group. Each group will use four different ways to spell out the word using sand on black paper, each time making the word as small as possible. The first time students put on gloves, the second time they will use their bare fingers to move the sand. For the third time, have them use an implement such as a craft stick to move the sand to make the word, and finally, provide students with tweezers and a magnifying glass. Ask students to compare their smallest word with 500 nanometers. L2 LS **Kinesthetic**

TIME SCIENCE AND Society

SCIENCE ISSUES THAT AFFECT YOU!

The Science of very, very small

This is the smallest guitar in the world. It is about as big as a human white blood cell. Each of its six silicon strings is 100 atoms wide. You can see the guitar only with an electron microscope.

Imagine an army of tiny robots, each no bigger than a bacterium swimming through your bloodstream.

Welcome to the world of nanotechnology—the science of creating molecular-sized machines. These machines are called nanobots.

The smallest of these machines are only billionths of a meter in size. They are so tiny that they can do work on the molecular scale.

ANATOMY OF A NANOPROBE

Acoustic relay attached to an onboard computer sends and receives ultrasound to communicate with medical team
Pumps remove toxins from the body and dispense drugs
Outer shell made of strong chemically inert diamonds
Sensors and manipulators detect illnesses and perform cell-by-cell surgery
WIDTH OF A HUMAN HAIR
TYPICAL PROBE SIZE

Up to 10 trillion nanorobots, each as small as 1/200th the width of a human hair, might be injected at once

Small, Smaller, Smallest

Nanotechnologists are predicting that within a few decades they will be creating nanobots that can do just about anything, as long as it's small. Already, nanotechnologists have built gears 10,000 times thinner than a human hair. They've also built tiny molecular "motors" only 50 atoms long. At Cornell University, nanotechnologists created the world's smallest guitar. It is appoximately the size of a white blood cell and it even has six strings.

In the future, they might transmit your internal vital signs to a nanocomputer, which might be implanted under your skin. There the data could be analyzed for signs of disease. Other nanomachines then could be sent to scrub your arteries clean of dangerous blockages, or mop up cancer cells, or even vaporize blood clots with tiny lasers. These are just some of the possibilities in the imaginations of those studying the new science of nanotechnology.

Design Think up a very small simple or complex machine that could go inside the body and do something. What would the machine do? Where would it go? Share your diagram or design with your classmates.

Science Online
For more information, visit gpscience.com/time

Design Provide time for students to give short presentations of their designs to the class. Ask each student to describe why the tiny machine would do the job better than current technology.

Resources for Teachers and Students

Engines of Creation by K. Eric Drexler, Garden City, N.Y.: Anchor Press/Doubleday, 1986

Nanotechnology: A Gentle Introduction to the Next Big Idea by Mark Ratner, Prentice Hall PTR, 2003

Reviewing Main Ideas

Section 1 Work

1. Work is the transfer of energy when a force makes an object move.
2. Work is done only when force produces motion in the direction of the force.
3. Power is the amount of work, or the amount of energy transferred, in a certain amount of time.

Section 2 Using Machines

1. A machine makes work easier by changing the size of the force applied, by increasing the distance an object is moved, or by changing the direction of the applied force.

2. The number of times a machine multiplies the force applied to it is the mechanical advantage of the machine. The actual mechanical advantage is always less than the ideal mechanical advantage.
3. The efficiency of a machine equals the output work divided by the input work.
4. Friction always causes the output work to be less than the input work, so no real machine can be 100 percent efficient.

Section 3 Simple Machines

1. A simple machine is a machine that can do work with a single movement.
2. A simple machine can increase an applied force, change its direction, or both.
3. A lever is a bar that is free to pivot about a fixed point called a fulcrum. A pulley is a grooved wheel with a rope running along the groove. A wheel and axle consists of two different-sized wheels that rotate together. An inclined plane is a sloping surface used to raise objects. The screw and wedge are special types of inclined planes.
4. A combination of two or more simple machines is called a compound machine.

FOLDABLES™ Use the Foldable that you made at the beginning of this chapter to help you review how machines make doing work easier.

Science Online gpscience.com/interactive_tutor

Identifying Misconceptions

Assess

After students have done the activity on page F and completed the chapter, have them answer the following question.

Julio lifted a box onto a desk. Joshua pushed an identical box up an inclined plane onto the desk. Friction on the inclined plane opposes Joshua's push. Which boy probably used more force in lifting the boxes? Julio Which boy did more work? They did about the same amount of work.

Expected Outcome Students will see that simple machines may reduce the amount of force exerted; but not the work done. L2

chapter 5 Study Guide

Reviewing Main Ideas

Summary statements can be used by students to review the major concepts of the chapter.

Visit gpscience.com
/self_check_quiz
/interactive_tutor
/vocabulary_puzzlemaker
/chapter_review
/standardized_test

Assessment Transparency

For additional assessment questions, use the *Assessment Transparency* located in the transparency book.

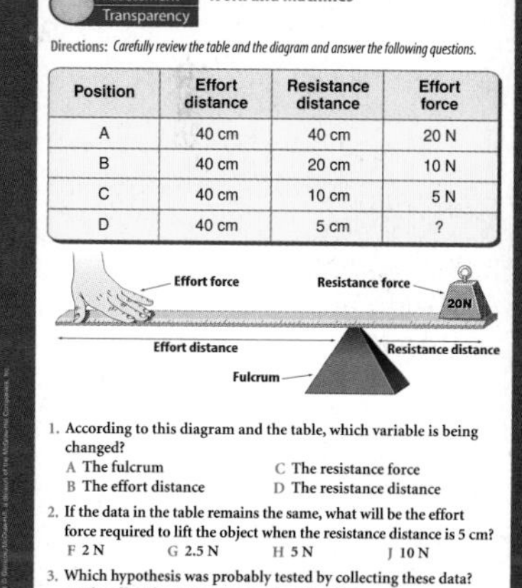
Assessment

Assessment Transparency — Work and Machines

Directions: *Carefully review the table and the diagram and answer the following questions.*

Position	Effort distance	Resistance distance	Effort force
A	40 cm	40 cm	20 N
B	40 cm	20 cm	10 N
C	40 cm	10 cm	5 N
D	40 cm	5 cm	?

1. According to this diagram and the table, which variable is being changed?
   A The fulcrum
   B The effort distance
   C The resistance force
   D The resistance distance
2. If the data in the table remains the same, what will be the effort force required to lift the object when the resistance distance is 5 cm?
   F 2 N
   G 2.5 N
   H 5 N
   J 10 N
3. Which hypothesis was probably tested by collecting these data?
   A The effort force decreases as the effort distance decreases.
   B The effort force increases as the effort distance decreases.
   The effort force decreases as the resistance distance decreases.
   The effort force increases as the resistance distance decreases.

L2

Work and Machines

FOLDABLES™ Have students use their Foldables to review the content of the chapter. Ask them to think of ways to improve the efficiency of the work they do without machines.

Using Vocabulary

1. compound machine
2. inclined plane
3. mechanical advantage
4. pulley
5. output force
6. work
7. Power

Checking Concepts

8. C	13. A
9. B	14. A
10. A	15. B
11. B	16. D
12. C	17. B

Interpreting Graphics

18. See student page.
19. B
20. $F_{out} = 1.3 \times 50\ N = 65\ N$

chapter 5 Review

Using Vocabulary

compound machine p. 146	output force p. 134
efficiency p. 136	power p. 129
inclined plane p. 144	pulley p. 141
input force p. 134	screw p. 145
lever p. 138	simple machine p. 138
machine p. 132	wedge p. 145
mechanical advantage p. 136	wheel and axle p. 143
	work p. 126

Complete each statement using a word(s) from the vocabulary list above.

1. A combination of two or more simple machines is a(n) ________.
2. A wedge is another form of a(n) ________.
3. The ratio of the output force to the input force is the ________ of a machine.
4. A(n) ________ is a grooved wheel with a rope, chain, or cable in the groove.
5. The force exerted by a machine is the ________.
6. Energy is transferred when ________ is done.
7. ________ is the rate at which work is done or energy is transferred.

Checking Concepts

Choose the word or phrase that best answers the question.

8. Using the scientific definition, which of the following is true of work?
   A) It is difficult.
   B) It involves levers.
   C) It involves a transfer of energy.
   D) It is done with a machine.
9. How many types of simple machines exist?
   A) three **C)** eight
   B) six **D)** ten
10. In an ideal machine, which of the following is true?
   A) Work input is equal to work output.
   B) Work input is greater than work output.
   C) Work input is less than work output.
   D) The IMA is always equal to one.
11. Which of these is not done by a machine?
   A) multiply force
   B) multiply energy
   C) change direction of a force
   D) work
12. What term indicates the number of times a machine multiplies the input force?
   A) efficiency
   B) power
   C) mechanical advantage
   D) resistance
13. How could you increase the IMA of an inclined plane?
   A) increase its length
   B) increase its height
   C) decrease its length
   D) make its surface smoother
14. In a wheel and axle, which of the following usually exerts the output force?
   A) the axle **C)** the fulcrum
   B) the wheel **D)** the input arm
15. What is the IMA of screwdriver with a shaft radius of 3 mm and a handle radius of 10 mm?
   A) 0.3 **C)** 30
   B) 3.3 **D)** 13
16. What is the IMA of an inclined plane that is 2.1 m long and 0.7 m high?
   A) 0.3 **C)** 1.5
   B) 2.8 **D)** 3.0
17. Which of the following increases as the efficiency of a machine increases?
   A) work input **C)** friction
   B) work output **D)** IMA

Science Online gpscience.com/vocabulary_puzzlemaker

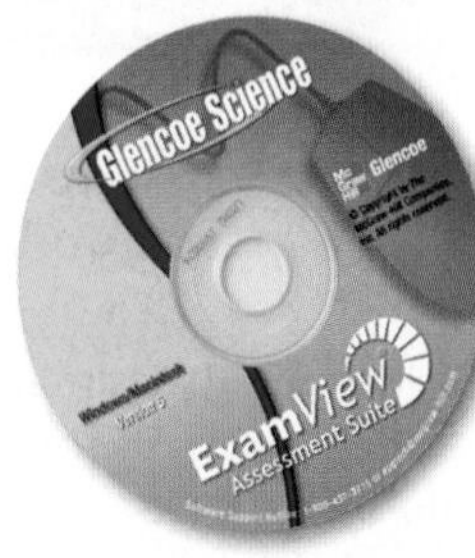

Use the *ExamView® Assessment Suite* CD-ROM to:
- create multiple versions of tests
- create modified tests with one mouse click for inclusion students
- edit existing questions and add your own questions
- build tests aligned with state standards using built-in State Curriculum Tags
- change English tests to Spanish with one mouse click and vice versa

Interpreting Graphics

18. Copy and complete the concept map of simple machines using the following terms: *compound machines, mechanical advantage, output force, work.*

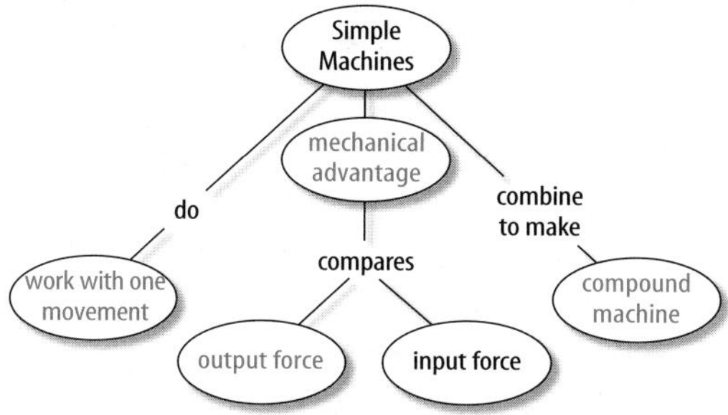

Use the table below to answer questions 19 and 20.

Lever Input and Output Arms

Lever	Input arm (cm)	Output arm (cm)
A	25	75
B	53	42
C	36	36
D	32	99
E	10	30

19. Determine which of the levers listed in the table above has the largest IMA.

20. An input force of 50 N is applied to lever B. If the lever is 100 percent efficient, what is the output force?

Thinking Critically

21. **Describe** how the effort force, resistance force and fulcrum should be arranged so that a child can lift an adult using his own body weight on a see saw.

22. **Determine** what arrangement of movable and fixed pulleys would give a mechanical advantage of 3.

23. **Explain** which would give the best mechanical advantage for driving a screw down into a board: a screwdriver with a long, thin handle, or a screwdriver with a short, fat handle.

Applying Math

24. **Calculate Work** Find the work needed to lift a book weighing 20.0 N 2.0 m.

25. **Calculate Axle Radius** A doorknob has an IMA equal to 8.5. If the diameter of the doorknob is 8.0 cm, what is the radius of the shaft the doorknob is connected to?

26. **Calculate Input Work** A machine has an efficiency of 61 percent. Find the input work if the output work is 140 J.

27. **Calculate Efficiency** Using a ramp 6 m long, workers apply an input force of 1,250 N to move a 2,000-N crate onto a platform 2 m high. What is the efficiency of the ramp?

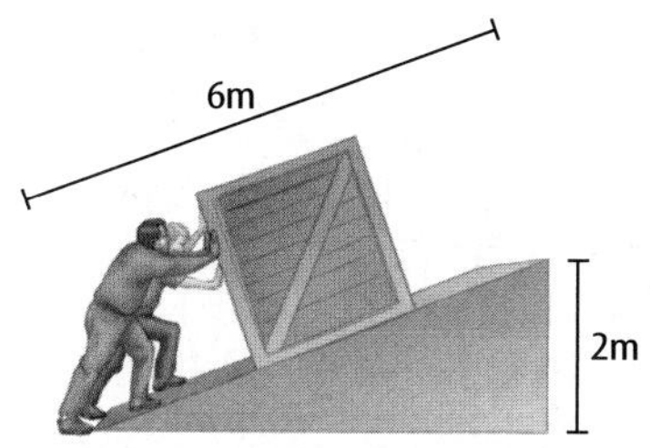

28. **Calculate Power** A person weighing 500 N climbs 3 m. How much power is needed to make the climb in 5 s?

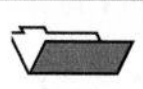
Science Online gpscience.com/chapter_review

Thinking Critically

21. The fulcrum should be moved toward the adult to increase the length of the input arm of the child's lever. This will multiply the input force exerted by the child.

22. A fixed double pulley with a moveable single will give $MA = 3$. Tie the string to the moveable pulley and loop it first through the lower pulley on the fixed double pulley, then through the single, moveable, and finally over the top double pulley. This gives three supporting strings.

23. The one with the fat handle; the screwdriver is being used as a wheel and axle, with the handle acting as the wheel. The screwdriver with the fat handle will therefore have a greater *MA*. The length does not matter.

Applying Math

National Math Standards

1, 2, 9

24. 40 J
25. 0.47 cm
26. 230 J
27. 53%
28. 300 W

Assessment Resources

Reproducible Masters

Chapter *Fast File* Resources
- Chapter Review, pp. 39–40
- Chapter Tests, pp. 41–44
- Assessment Transparency Activity, p. 51

Glencoe Science Web site
- Chapter Review Test
- Standardized Test Practice

Glencoe Technology
- Assessment Transparency
- *ExamView® Assessment Suite*
- MindJogger Videoquiz
- Interactive Chalkboard

FAST FILE

Answer Sheet A practice answer sheet can be found at gpscience.com/answer_sheet.

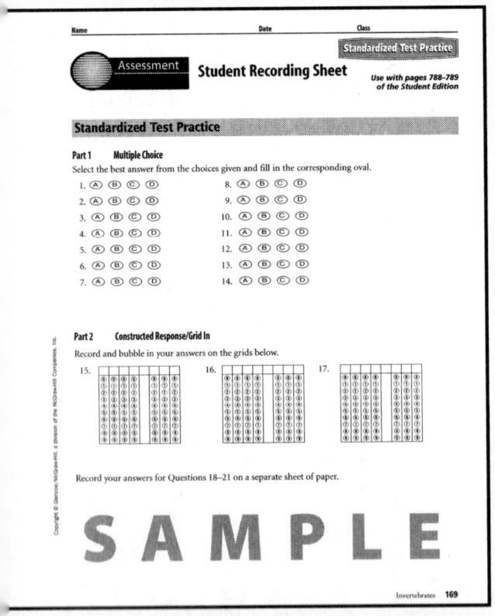

Student Recording Sheet

SAMPLE

Part 1 Multiple Choice

1. B
2. B
3. C
4. D
5. B
6. D
7. C
8. B
9. B

chapter 5 Standardized Test Practice

Part 1 Multiple Choice

Record your answers on the answer sheet provided by your teacher or on a sheet of paper.

Use the figure below to answer questions 1 and 2

1. The figure above shows a doorknob with a radius of 4.8 cm and a mechanical advantage of 4.0. What is the radius of the inner rod that connects the knob to the door?

A. 0.6 cm **C.** 1.8 cm
B. 1.2 cm **D.** 2.4 cm

2. What would happen to the mechanical advantage if the radius of the doorknob were doubled?

A. It would be multiplied by 4.
B. It would be multiplied by 2.
C. It would be divided by 4.
D. It would be divided by 2.

3. A ramp is 2.8 m long and 1.2 m high. How much power is needed to push a box up the ramp in 4.6 s with a force of 96 N?

A. 21 W **C.** 58 W
B. 25 W **D.** 270 W

4. How much work is done in lifting a 9.10-kg box onto a shelf 1.80 m high?

A. 5.06 J **C.** 49.5 J
B. 16.4 J **D.** 161 J

5. What type of simple machine is your foot when you stand on your toes?

A. first-class lever
B. second-class lever
C. third-class lever
D. inclined plane

6. An input force of 80 N is used to lift an object weighing 240 N with a system of pulleys. How far down must the rope around the pulleys be pulled in order to lift the object a distance of 1.4 m?

A. 0.47 m **C.** 2.8 m
B. 1.4 m **D.** 4.2 m

Use the figure below to answer questions 7 and 8.

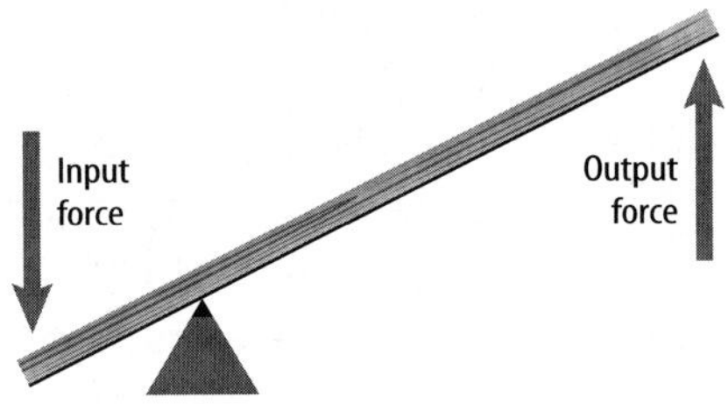

7. If the distance between the lever's input force and the fulcrum is 8 cm, and the distance between the fulcrum and the output force is 24 cm, what is the ideal mechanical advantage of the lever?

A. 4 **C.** 0.33
B. 3 **D.** 0.25

8. Which device uses the same class of lever as that shown in the figure?

A. baseball bat **C.** shovel
B. scissors **D.** wheelbarrow

9. How much more work is done to push a box 2.5 m with a force of 30 N than to push a box 2.0 m with a force of 26 N?

A. 28 J **C.** 4 J
B. 23 J **D.** 56 J

Test-Taking Tip

Don't Panic Stay calm during the test. If you feel yourself getting nervous, close your eyes and take five slow, deep, breaths.

Part 2 Short Response/Grid In

10. 1.89 J
11. 4
12. 5 N
13. 4 N
14. 24 W
15. $eff = \frac{F_{out} \times d_{out}}{F_{in} \times d_{in}} \times 100\%$
16. No, because force is not in the direction of motion.

Part 2 Short Response/Grid In

Record your answers on the answer sheet provided by your teacher or on a sheet of paper.

10. As you throw a ball, you exert a force on ball of 4.2 N. You exert this force on the ball while the ball moves a distance of 0.45 m. The ball leaves your hand and travels a horizontal distance of 8.5 m to your friend. How much work have you done on the ball?

Use the illustration below to answer questions 11–13.

11. What is the ideal mechanical advantage of the pulley system shown in the figure to the right?

12. If the block supported by the pulley system shown above has a weight of 20 N, what is the input force on the rope?

13. If an additional pulley were included in the system shown in the illustration, what would the input force be?

14. A machine does 760 J of work in 32 s. What is the machine's power?

15. Write an equation for the efficiency of a lever if you know the lever's input force and distance as well as the output force and distance.

16. A centripetal force is exerted in a direction perpendicular to the motion of an object in circular motion. Is work done by a centripetal force? Why or why not?

Part 3 Open Ended

Record your answers on a sheet of paper.

17. Is the following statement true? If so, give an example that supports it. If not, explain why.

When work is done, a transfer of energy always occurs, but a transfer of energy does not always mean that work has been done.

18. What are three ways that simple machines can make work easier? For each one, give an example of a machine that makes work easier in that way.

19. Explain what causes friction in a machine and how a lubricant reduces a machine's friction. Describe the change a lubricant would make in the efficiency of a machine.

20. Use the law of conservation of energy to explain why it is impossible for the output work of a machine to be greater than the machine's input work.

Use the illustration below to answer questions 21 and 22.

21. The boy in the photograph to the right is carrying a box to the top of the stairs. Describe how the work that the boy does on the box is related to the energy transfer that occurs. How does the energy of the box change form as the boy carries the box up the stairs?

22. Explain how the work, power, and energy would change if the boy walked faster. How would the work, power, and energy change if the steps were the same height but steeper?

20. When work is done on the machine, energy is transferred to the machine. When the machine does work, energy is transferred from the machine. If energy cannot be created, then the output work cannot be greater than the input work.

21. The chemical energy from the boy's muscles is converted to potential energy to the box. The potential energy of the box increases as the boy increases the height of the box.

22. Work would be the same. Power would increase because the time required to do the work decreased. The energy change of the box would be the same.

Rubrics

For more help evaluating open-ended assessment questions, see the rubric on p. 10T.

Part 3 Open Ended

17. It is true. Doing work is a way of transferring energy from one object to another. Lifting a book transfers energy to the book and increases its potential energy. When thermal energy is transferred from one object to another, the objects can remain at rest. No work is done on the objects, but energy is transferred.

18. changing the direction of force—using a pulley to raise a flag on a flagpole; increasing the distance over which the force is applied—such as pushing a box up a ramp; by increasing the force you apply—using a screw driver

19. Friction in a machine is caused by the moving parts rubbing against each other. A lubricant makes the parts slippery so that the parts do not rub on each other as much. Adding a lubricant decreases friction and increases efficiency.

chapter 6 Instructional Planner

Thermal Energy

BIG Idea **Thermal energy flows from a higher temperature to a lower temperature.**

	Content Standards	Learning Objectives	Resources to Assess Mastery
Section 1	**5–8:** UCP.1–3, 5; A.1, 2; B.1–3 **9–12:** UCP.1–3, 5; A.1–2; B.1; G.2–3	**Temperature and Heat** **1. Define** temperature. **2. Explain** how thermal energy depends on temperature. **3. Explain** how thermal energy and heat are related. **4. Calculate** the change in thermal energy. ***Main Idea*** The atoms and molecules that make up matter are in continual random motion.	**Formative Assessment** Reading Check, pp. 160, 161 Section Review, p. 163 **Summative Assessment** *ExamView® Assessment Suite*
Section 2	**5–8:** UCP.1–3, 5; A.1, 2; B.1–3; C.5 **9–12:** UCP.1–3, 5; A.1–2; B.2, 4, 6	**Transferring Thermal Energy** **5. Compare and contrast** the transfer of thermal energy by conduction, convection, and radiation. **6. Compare and contrast** thermal conductors and insulators. **7. Explain** how insulators are used to control the transfer of thermal energy. ***Main Idea*** There are three ways thermal energy is transferred—conduction, convection, and radiation.	**Formative Assessment** Reading Check, pp. 165, 168, 169 Section Review, p. 170 **Summative Assessment** *ExamView® Assessment Suite*
Section 3	**5–8:** UCP.1–3, 5; A.1, 2; B.1, 3 **9–12:** UCP.1–3, 5; A.1–2; B.2, 4, 5 See pp. 16T–17T for a Key to Standards.	**Using Heat** **8. Describe** common types of heating systems. **9. Describe** the first and second laws of thermodynamics. **10. Explain** how an internal combustion engine works. **11. Explain** how a refrigerator transfers thermal energy from a cool to a warm temperature. ***Main Idea*** Thermal energy can be made useful by controlling its production and movement.	**Formative Assessment** Reading Check, pp. 175, 176, 178 Section Review, p. 179 **Summative Chapter Assessment** MindJogger, Ch. 6 *ExamView® Assessment Suite* Leveled Chapter Test Test A L1 Test B L2 Test C L3 Test Practice, pp. 186–187

Suggested Pacing				
Period	Instruction	Labs	Review & Assessment	Total
Single	4 days	4 days	2 days	10 days
Block	2 blocks	2 blocks	1 block	5 blocks

Core Instruction	Leveled Resources	Leveled Labs	Pacing: Period		Pacing: Block
Student Text, pp. 156–163 Section Focus Transparency, Ch. 6, Section 1 Interactive Chalkboard, Ch. 6, Section 1 Identifying Misconceptions, p. 160 Differentiated Instruction, pp. 161, 162 Applying Math, p. 162	**Chapter *Fast File* Resources** Directed Reading for Content Mastery, p. 20 [L1] Note-taking Worksheet, pp. 33–35 Reinforcement, p. 27 [L2] Enrichment, p. 30 [L3] **Reading Essentials,** p. 84 [L1] ELL **Science Notebook,** p. 57 ELL ***Active*Folders**: *Temperature and Thermal Energy* [L1] ELL	**Launch Lab,** p. 157: beakers (2), water, ice, food coloring, stopwatch *10 min* [L2]	**1**	Section 1, pp. 157–160 (includes Launch Lab)	**1**
			2	Section 1, pp. 161–163 (includes Section Review)	
Student Text, pp. 164–171 Section Focus Transparency, Ch. 6, Section 2 Interactive Chalkboard, Ch. 6, Section 2 Identifying Misconceptions, p. 167 Differentiated Instruction, pp. 166, 168 Visualizing Convection Currents, p. 166	**Chapter *Fast File* Resources** Directed Reading for Content Mastery, p. 20 [L1] Note-taking Worksheet, pp. 33–35 Reinforcement, p. 28 [L2] Enrichment, p. 31 [L3] **Reading Essentials,** p. 90 [L1] ELL **Science Notebook,** p. 61 ELL ***Active*Folders**: *Temperature and Thermal Energy* [L1] ELL	**MiniLAB,** p. 168: window in sunlight *10 min* [L2]	**3**	Section 2, pp. 164–168 (includes MiniLAB)	**2**
		MiniLAB, p. 169: small plastic beads (3), dabs of butter (3), beaker, boiling water, spoons (metal, plastic, wooden) *15 min* [L2]	**4**	Section 2, pp. 169–170 (includes MiniLAB and Section Review)	
		***Lab,** p. 171: burner or hot plate, water, candle, 500-mL beaker, black pepper *45 min* [L1] [L2] [L3]	**5**	Lab:Convection in Gases and Liquids, p. 171	**3**
Student Text, pp. 172–181 Section Focus Transparency, Ch. 6, Section 3 Teaching Transparency, Ch. 6, Section 3 Interactive Chalkboard, Ch. 6, Section 2 Differentiated Instruction, pp. 177, 178 Chapter Study Guide, p. 183	**Chapter *Fast File* Resources** Directed Reading for Content Mastery, pp. 221, 22 [L1] Note-taking Worksheet, pp. 33–35 Reinforcement, p. 29 [L2] Enrichment, p. 32 [L3] **Reading Essentials,** p. 96 [L1] ELL **Science Notebook,** p. 64 ELL	***Lab,** pp. 108–181: thermometers (3), foam cups (2), 400-mL beakers (2), burner or hot plate, thermal mitts (2) *80 min* [L1] [L2] [L3] (Video Lab)	**6**	Section 3, pp. 172–175	
			7	Section 3, pp. 176–179 (includes Section Review)	**4**
			8	Lab:Conduction in Gases, pp. 180–181	
			9	Lab:Conduction in Gases, pp. 180–181	**5**
		*Lab version A [L1] version B [L2] [L3]	**10**	Study Guide, Chapter Review, and Test Practice, pp. 183–187	

(Video Lab icon) Video Lab

Transparencies

Section Focus

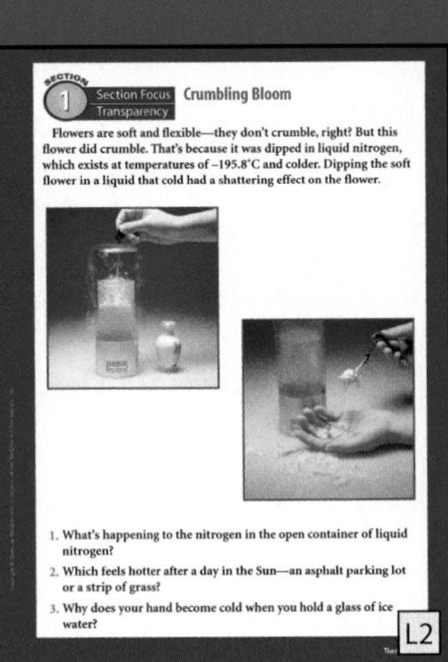
Section 1 Section Focus Transparency Crumbling Bloom

Flowers are soft and flexible—they don't crumble, right? But this flower did crumble. That's because it was dipped in liquid nitrogen, which exists at temperatures of –195.8°C and colder. Dipping the soft flower in a liquid that cold had a shattering effect on the flower.

1. What's happening to the nitrogen in the open container of liquid nitrogen?
2. Which feels hotter after a day in the Sun—an asphalt parking lot or a strip of grass?
3. Why does your hand become cold when you hold a glass of ice water?

L2

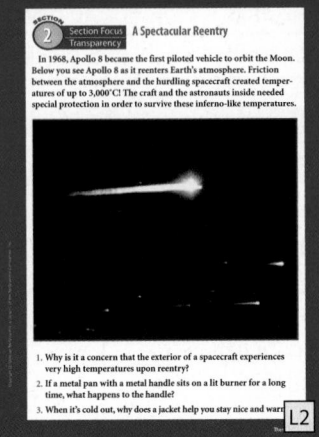

Section 2 Section Focus Transparency A Spectacular Reentry

In 1968, Apollo 8 became the first piloted vehicle to orbit the Moon. Below you see Apollo 8 as it reenters Earth's atmosphere. Friction between the atmosphere and the hurdling spacecraft created temperatures of up to 3,000°C! The craft and the astronauts inside needed special protection in order to survive these inferno-like temperatures.

1. Why is it a concern that the exterior of a spacecraft experiences very high temperatures upon reentry?
2. If a metal pan with a metal handle sits on a lit burner for a long time, what happens to the handle?
3. When it's cold out, why does a jacket help you stay nice and warm?

L2

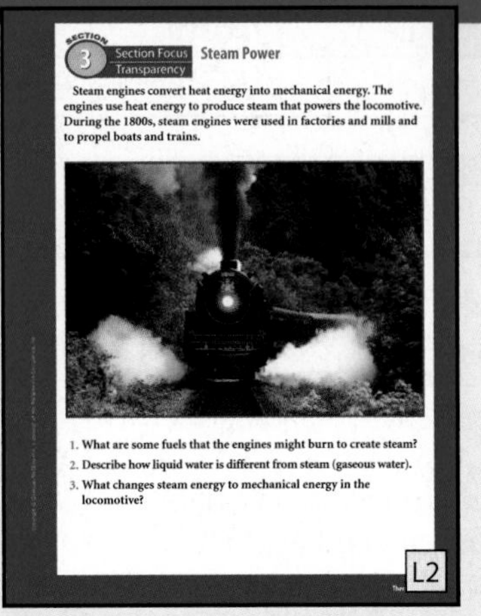
Section 3 Section Focus Transparency Steam Power

Steam engines convert heat energy into mechanical energy. The engines use heat energy to produce steam that powers the locomotive. During the 1800s, steam engines were used in factories and mills and to propel boats and trains.

1. What are some fuels that the engines might burn to create steam?
2. Describe how liquid water is different from steam (gaseous water).
3. What changes steam energy to mechanical energy in the locomotive?

L2

This is a representation of key blackline masters available in the Teacher Classroom Resources. See Resource Manager boxes within the chapter for additional information.

Assessment

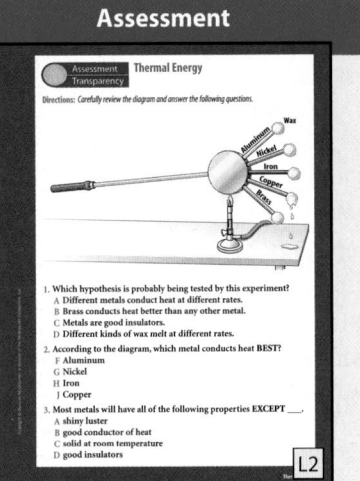

Assessment Transparency Thermal Energy

Directions: Carefully review the diagram and answer the following questions.

1. Which hypothesis is probably being tested by this experiment?
   A Different metals conduct heat at different rates.
   B Brass conducts heat better than any other metal.
   C Metals are good insulators.
   D Different kinds of wax melt at different rates.
2. According to the diagram, which metal conducts heat BEST?
   F Aluminum
   G Nickel
   H Iron
   J Copper
3. Most metals will have all of the following properties EXCEPT ___.
   A shiny luster
   B good conductor of heat
   C solid at room temperature
   D good insulators

L2

Teaching

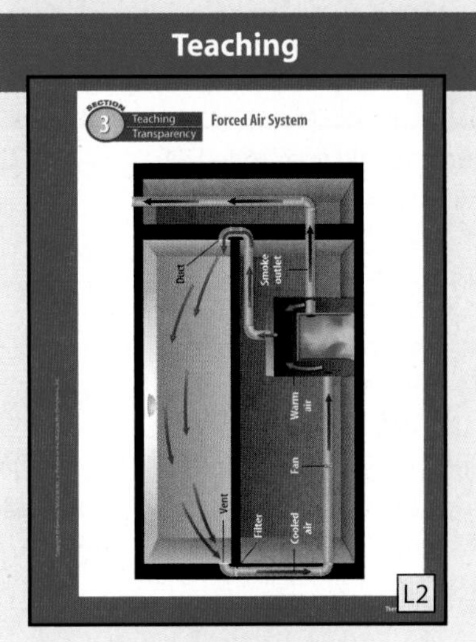
Section 3 Teaching Transparency Forced Air System

L2

Key to Teaching Strategies

The following designations will help you decide which activities are appropriate for your students.

- L1 Level 1 activities should be appropriate for students with learning difficulties.
- L2 Level 2 activities should be within the ability range of all students.
- L3 Level 3 activities are designed for above-average students.
- ELL ELL activities should be within the ability range of English Language Learners.
- COOP LEARN Cooperative Learning activities are designed for small group work.
- LS Multiple Learning Styles logos, as described on page 12T, are used throughout to indicate strategies that address different learning styles.
- P These strategies represent student products that can be placed into a best-work portfolio.
- PBL Problem-Based Learning activities apply real-world situations to learning.

Hands-on Activities

Student Text Lab Worksheet

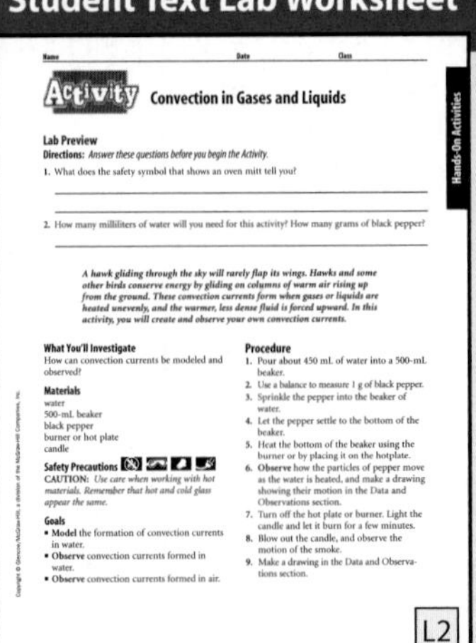
Activity Convection in Gases and Liquids

Hands-On Activities

Lab Preview

L2

Laboratory Activities

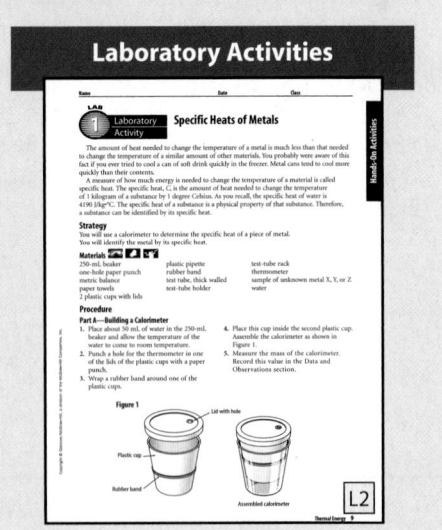

Lab 1 Laboratory Activity Specific Heats of Metals

Hands-On Activities

L2

Resource Manager

Meeting Different Ability Levels

Content Outline

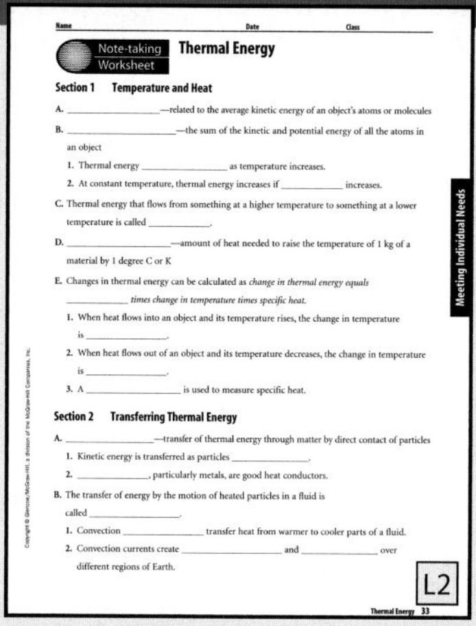

Name Date Class

Note-taking Worksheet **Thermal Energy**

Section 1 Temperature and Heat

A. ____________—related to the average kinetic energy of an object's atoms or molecules

B. ____________—the sum of the kinetic and potential energy of all the atoms in an object

1. Thermal energy ____________ as temperature increases.
2. At constant temperature, thermal energy increases if ____________ increases.

C. Thermal energy that flows from something at a higher temperature to something at a lower temperature is called ____________.

D. ____________—amount of heat needed to raise the temperature of 1 kg of a material by 1 degree C or K

E. Changes in thermal energy can be calculated as *change in thermal energy equals ____________ times change in temperature times specific heat.*

1. When heat flows into an object and its temperature rises, the change in temperature is ____________.
2. When heat flows out of an object and its temperature decreases, the change in temperature is ____________.
3. A ____________ is used to measure specific heat.

Section 2 Transferring Thermal Energy

A. ____________—transfer of thermal energy through matter by direct contact of particles

1. Kinetic energy is transferred as particles ____________.
2. ____________, particularly metals, are good heat conductors.

B. The transfer of energy by the motion of heated particles in a fluid is called ____________.

1. Convection ____________ transfer heat from warmer to cooler parts of a fluid.
2. Convection currents create ____________ and ____________ over different regions of Earth.

Meeting Individual Needs

L2

Thermal Energy 33

Reinforcement

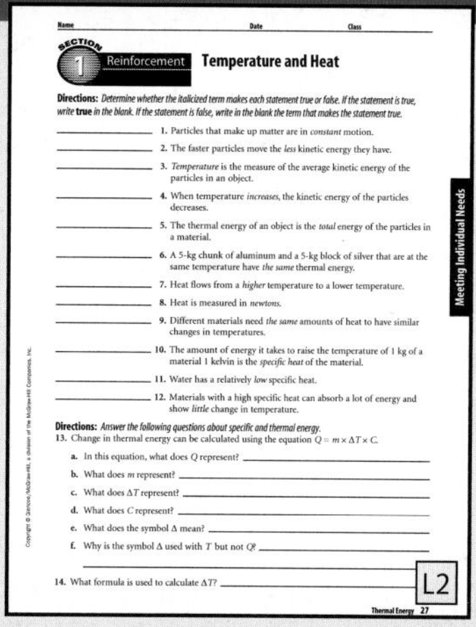

Name Date Class

Section 1 Reinforcement **Temperature and Heat**

Directions: *Determine whether the italicized term makes each statement true or false. If the statement is true, write* **true** *in the blank. If the statement is false, write in the blank the term that makes the statement true.*

____________ 1. Particles that make up matter are in *constant* motion.

____________ 2. The faster particles move the *less* kinetic energy they have.

____________ 3. *Temperature* is the measure of the average kinetic energy of the particles in an object.

____________ 4. When temperature *increases*, the kinetic energy of the particles decreases.

____________ 5. The thermal energy of an object is the *total* energy of the particles in a material.

____________ 6. A 5-kg chunk of aluminum and a 5-kg block of silver that are at the same temperature have *the same* thermal energy.

____________ 7. Heat flows from a *higher* temperature to a lower temperature.

____________ 8. Heat is measured in *newtons*.

____________ 9. Different materials need *the same* amounts of heat to have similar changes in temperature.

____________ 10. The amount of energy it takes to raise the temperature of 1 kg of a material 1 kelvin is the *specific heat* of the material.

____________ 11. Water has a relatively *low* specific heat.

____________ 12. Materials with a high specific heat can absorb a lot of energy and show *little* change in temperature.

Directions: *Answer the following questions about specific and thermal energy.*

13. Change in thermal energy can be calculated using the equation $Q = m \times \Delta T \times C$.

a. In this equation, what does Q represent? ____________

b. What does m represent? ____________

c. What does ΔT represent? ____________

d. What does C represent? ____________

e. What does the symbol Δ mean? ____________

f. Why is the symbol Δ used with T but not Q? ____________

14. What formula is used to calculate ΔT? ____________

Meeting Individual Needs

L2

Thermal Energy 27

Enrichment

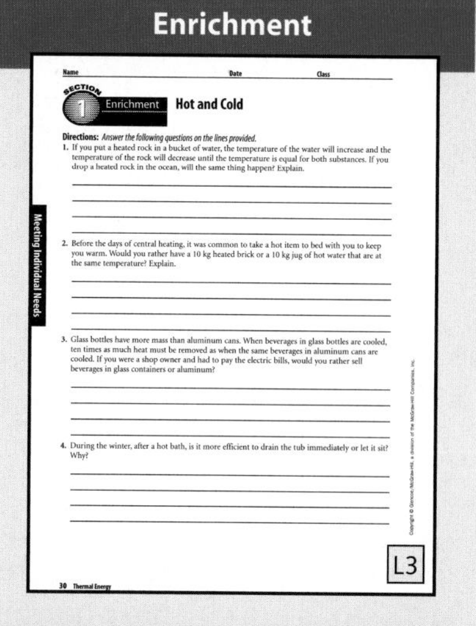

Name Date Class

Section 1 Enrichment **Hot and Cold**

Directions: *Answer the following questions on the lines provided.*

1. If you put a heated rock in a bucket of water, the temperature of the water will increase and the temperature of the rock will decrease until the temperature is equal for both substances. If you drop a heated rock in the ocean, will the same thing happen? Explain.

2. Before the days of central heating, it was common to take a hot item to bed with you to keep you warm. Would you rather have a 10 kg heated brick or a 10 kg jug of hot water that are at the same temperature? Explain.

3. Glass bottles have more mass than aluminum cans. When beverages in glass bottles are cooled, ten times as much heat must be removed as when the same beverages in aluminum cans are cooled. If you were a shop owner and had to pay the electric bills, would you rather sell beverages in glass containers or aluminum?

4. During the winter, after a hot bath, is it more efficient to drain the tub immediately or let it sit? Why?

Meeting Individual Needs

L3

30 Thermal Energy

Directed Reading (English/Spanish)

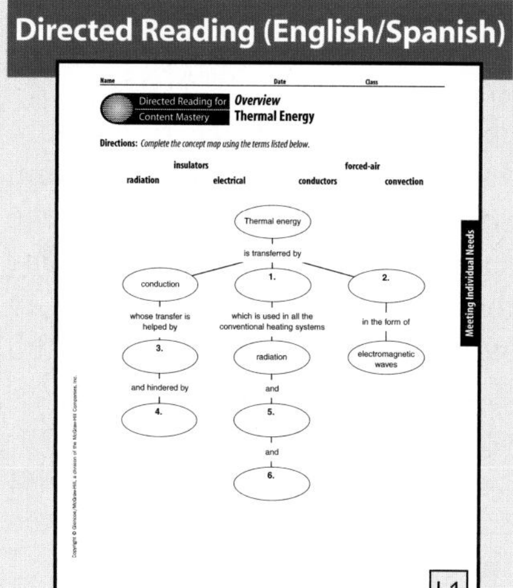

Name Date Class

Directed Reading for Content Mastery **Overview Thermal Energy**

Directions: *Complete the concept map using the terms listed below.*

insulators, forced-air, radiation, electrical, conductors, convection

Meeting Individual Needs

L1

Thermal Energy 19

Study Guide

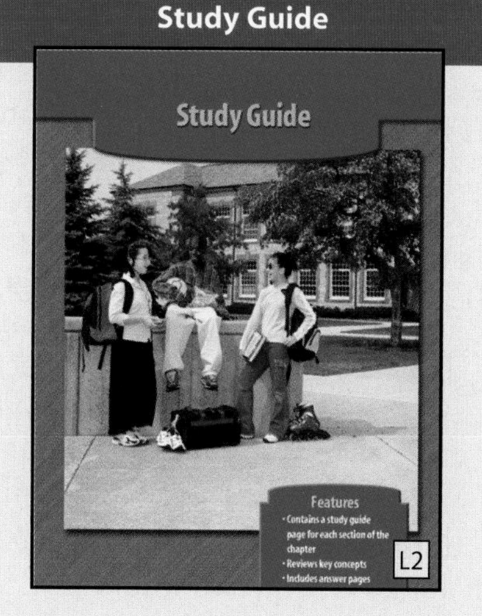

Reading Essentials

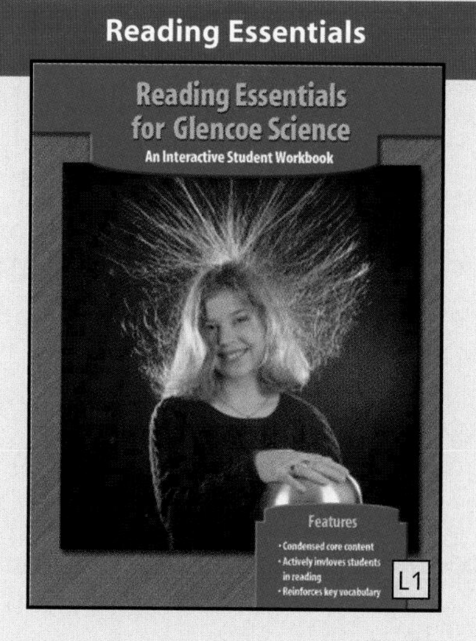

Assessment

Test Practice Workbook

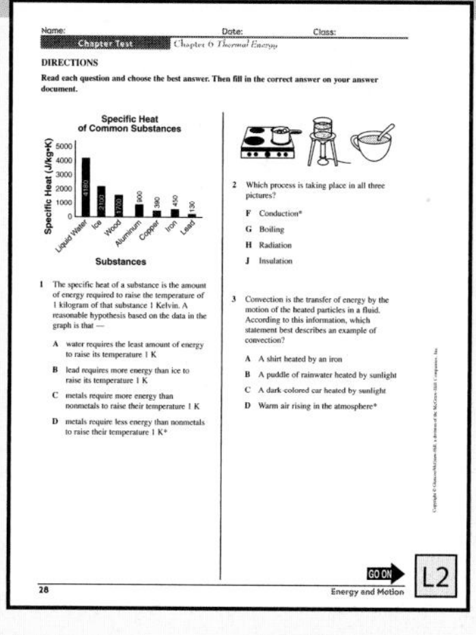

Name: Date: Class:

Chapter Test Chapter 6 Thermal Energy

DIRECTIONS

Read each question and choose the best answer. Then fill in the correct answer on your answer document.

Specific Heat of Common Substances

Specific Heat (J/kg•K)

Liquid Water, Ice, Wood, Aluminum, Copper, Iron, Lead

Substances

1 The specific heat of a substance is the amount of energy required to raise the temperature of 1 kilogram of that substance 1 Kelvin. A reasonable hypothesis based on the data in the graph is that —

A water requires the least amount of energy to raise its temperature 1 K

B lead requires more energy than ice to raise its temperature 1 K

C metals require more energy than nonmetals to raise their temperature 1 K

D metals require less energy than nonmetals to raise their temperature 1 K*

2 Which process is taking place in all three pictures?

F Conduction*

G Boiling

H Radiation

J Insulation

3 Convection is the transfer of energy by the motion of the heated particles in a fluid. According to this information, which statement best describes an example of convection?

A A shirt heated by an iron

B A puddle of rainwater heated by sunlight

C A dark-colored car heated by sunlight

D Warm air rising in the atmosphere*

GO ON

L2

28 Energy and Motion

Chapter Review

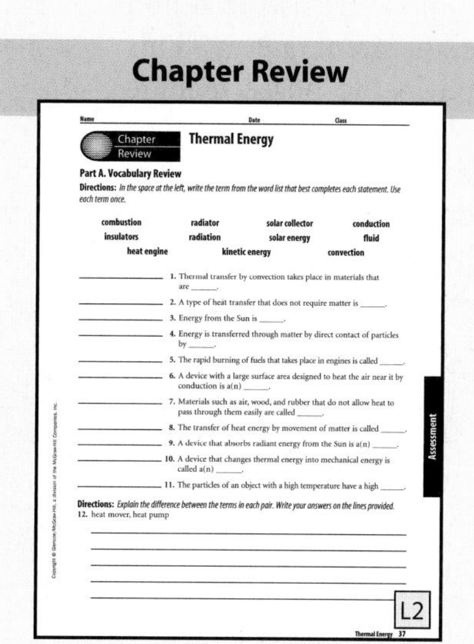

Name Date Class

Chapter Review **Thermal Energy**

Part A. Vocabulary Review

Directions: *In the space at the left, write the term from the word list that best completes each statement. Use each term once.*

combustion, radiator, solar collector, conduction, insulators, radiation, solar energy, fluid, heat engine, kinetic energy, convection

____________ 1. Thermal transfer by convection takes place in materials that are ______.

____________ 2. A type of heat transfer that does not require matter is ______.

____________ 3. Energy from the Sun is ______.

____________ 4. Energy is transferred through matter by direct contact of particles by ______.

____________ 5. The rapid burning of fuels that takes place in engines is called ______.

____________ 6. A device with a large surface area designed to heat the air near it by conduction is a(n) ______.

____________ 7. Materials such as air, wood, and rubber that do not allow heat to pass through them easily are called ______.

____________ 8. The transfer of heat energy by movement of matter is called ______.

____________ 9. A device that absorbs radiant energy from the Sun is a(n) ______.

____________ 10. A device that changes thermal energy into mechanical energy is called a(n) ______.

____________ 11. The particles of an object with a high temperature have a high ______.

Directions: *Explain the difference between the terms in each pair. Write your answers on the lines provided.*

12. heat mover, heat pump

Assessment

L2

Thermal Energy 37

Chapter Tests

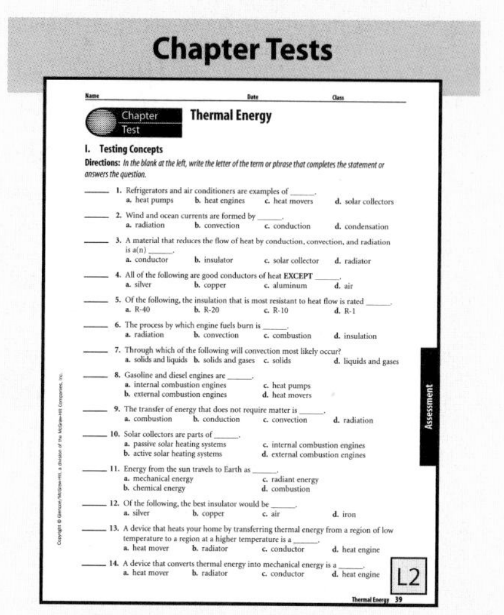

Name Date Class

Chapter Test **Thermal Energy**

I. Testing Concepts

Directions: *In the blank at the left, write the letter of the term or phrase that completes the statement or answers the question.*

____ 1. Refrigerators and air conditioners are examples of ______.
a. heat pumps b. heat engines c. heat movers d. solar collectors

____ 2. Wind and ocean currents are formed by ______.
a. radiation b. convection c. conduction d. condensation

____ 3. A material that reduces the flow of heat by conduction, convection, and radiation is a(n) ______.
a. conductor b. insulator c. solar collector d. radiator

____ 4. All of the following are good conductors of heat EXCEPT ______.
a. silver b. copper c. aluminum d. air

____ 5. Of the following, the insulation that is most resistant to heat flow is rated ______.
a. R-40 b. R-20 c. R-10 d. R-1

____ 6. The process by which engine fuels burn is ______.
a. radiation b. convection c. combustion d. insulation

____ 7. Through which of the following will convection most likely occur?
a. solids and liquids b. solids and gases c. solids d. liquids and gases

____ 8. Gasoline and diesel engines are ______.
a. internal combustion engines b. external combustion engines c. heat pumps d. heat movers

____ 9. The transfer of energy that does not require matter is ______.
a. combustion b. conduction c. convection d. radiation

____ 10. Solar collectors are parts of ______.
a. passive solar heating systems b. active solar heating systems c. internal combustion engines d. external combustion engines

____ 11. Energy from the sun travels to Earth as ______.
a. mechanical energy b. chemical energy c. radiant energy d. combustion

____ 12. Of the following, the best insulator would be ______.
a. silver b. copper c. air d. iron

____ 13. A device that heats your home by transferring thermal energy from a region of low temperature to a region at a higher temperature is a ______.
a. heat mover b. radiator c. conductor d. heat engine

____ 14. A device that converts thermal energy into mechanical energy is a ______.
a. heat mover b. radiator c. conductor d. heat engine

Assessment

L2

Thermal Energy 39

Science Content Background

section 1 Temperature and Heat

Temperature

It is important to differentiate between temperature and thermal energy. A small nail at a temperature of 100°C has less thermal energy than a large hammer at a temperature of 90°C.

The common thermometer is a glass tube filled with colored alcohol or mercury, which expands with increasing heat to give a reading of temperature. Digital thermometers, such as those put into children's ears, rely on the increase in electrical resistance with higher temperature to ascertain temperatures.

Three temperature scales are commonly used around the world. The Celsius scale is used by almost all the people in the world and in most scientific work. The Fahrenheit scale, the oldest scale, is used by people in the United States. The kelvin is the official SI unit for temperature. This scale, used by scientists, is based on absolute zero—the lowest possible temperature. Zero K is a theoretical value not yet observed.

Thermal Energy

Which contains more thermal energy, liquid water at 100°C or steam at 100°C? Anyone who has been burned by steam knows the correct answer—steam! Thermal energy is the sum of both kinetic and potential energy. The steam, although at the same temperature as the liquid water, has more potential, or latent energy. This is the energy it absorbed in the phase change from a liquid to a gas.

Properties of materials can change as they gain or lose thermal energy. For example: most substances expand when they are heated, resistance in wire increases with rises in temperature, the color of some materials is influenced by temperature, and materials can change phase as they gain or lose thermal energy.

Heat

The SI unit of thermal energy is the joule. Calorie is another unit frequently used. One calorie, equal to 4.184 joules, is the amount of heat needed to raise the temperature of one gram of water one degree Celsius. This amount is so small that with food energy, units of kilocalories are used. Kilocalories are also called *Calories*, but with a capital C. So if the package says that chocolate contains 150 Calories, it really has 150,000 calories, or 627,600 joules, of energy.

Specific Heat

Water has a very high specific heat. If you have one gram of water and one gram of aluminum and you add one calorie of heat to each, the water will increase in temperature by about one degree and the aluminum will increase in temperature by about five degrees. The high specific heat of water has important influences on climate. Large bodies of water tend to maintain their temperatures longer than smaller bodies of water. So areas near the ocean often have milder winters and milder summers.

David Young-Wolff/PhotoEdit

Teacher to Teacher

Erin Peters, Lead Science Teacher
Williamsburg Middle School
Arlington, VA

"To demonstrate how mechanical energy can be transformed to thermal energy, drill a hole in the cap of an empty water bottle so that a thermometer can be inserted to fit snuggly in the bottle when the cap is on. Fill it 2/3 full with sand and note the starting temperature. Shake for three minutes and note the final temperature. The shaking causes the particles to rub together, resulting in heat. As an alternative, have students rub their hands together for one minute."

Erin Peters

section 2 Transferring Thermal Energy

Conduction

The term *thermodynamics* comes from Greek words that mean "heat force." The first law of thermodynamics is the law of conservation of energy applied to thermal energy. Thermal energy doesn't just magically disappear or appear, it is transferred to or from other objects or it is created by work.

Things don't transfer coldness, but they do transfer heat. So the ice isn't giving cold to your drink, but the ice is absorbing heat from the beverage. If you touch a piece of wood and a piece of metal that are both at the same temperature, the metal feels colder. The metal conducts the heat away from your finger faster than the wood, giving your finger a cold sensation.

section 3 Using Heat

Solar Heating

Passive solar heating usually features large windows facing south to let the sunlight in during the winter. Materials with high specific heats, such as concrete walls, water barrels, and tile floors, are frequently placed so that they are exposed to the sunlight. The Sun warms these materials, and then during the night, they slowly release the heat to the room.

Using Heat to do Work

No heat engine can be completely efficient. When heat is converted into work by a heat engine, some heat always is released to the surroundings.

chapter content resources

Internet Resources

For additional content background, visit gpscience.com to:

- access your book online
- find references to related articles in popular science magazines
- access Web links with related content background
- access current events with science journal topics

Print Resources

Thermal Physics: Entropy and Free Energies, by Joon Chang Lee, World Scientific Publishing Company, Inc., 2002

Fundamentals of Heat and Mass Transfer, by Frank P. Incropera and David P. DeWitt, John Wiley & Sons, 2001

Fundamentals of Thermodynamics, by Richard E. Sonntag, Claus Borgnakke, and Gordon J. Van Wylen, John Wiley & Sons, 2002

Principles of Refrigeration, by Roy J. Dossat and Thomas J. Horan, Prentice Hall, 2002

Bob Daemmrich/The Image Works

About the Photo

Molten Steel Steel is an alloy of iron and carbon. The carbon content of steel ranges up to 2 percent carbon. Alloys with higher carbon content are classified as cast iron. Steel is widely used to manufacture a wide range of products from skyscrapers to rail cars. It is used extensively because it is relatively inexpensive to process; the raw materials are available in abundance, and because of its desirable properties.

Science Journal Student answers may vary. Accept all reasonable responses.

BIG Idea

Thermal Energy In all objects, the atoms or molecules that make up the object are in continual random motion. This means that at any time any one of these particles can be moving in any direction with various speeds. The reference point for these random motions is the center of mass of the object. The thermal energy of the material is the sum of the kinetic and potential energies of the particles due to their random motion. However, if the object moves, the thermal energy of the object doesn't change, even though the object acquires kinetic energy. When the object moves, its center of mass moves, but the random motion of the particles relative to the center of mass isn't affected.

Introduce the Chapter Remind students that the transfer of energy causes changes. Have students list several situations in which an object became warmer or cooler. Then for each situation have students hypothesize from what object and to what object energy was transferred.

chapter 6

Thermal Energy

BIG Idea Thermal energy flows from a higher temperature to a lower temperature.

6.1 Temperature and Heat

MAIN Idea The atoms and molecules that make up matter are in continual random motion.

6.2 Transferring Thermal Energy

MAIN Idea There are three ways thermal energy is transferred-conduction, convection, and radiation.

6.3 Using Heat

MAIN Idea Thermal energy can be made useful by controlling its production and movement.

Hot Stuff

This hot, glowing liquid will become solid steel when it cools. The difference between liquid and solid steel is energy—thermal energy. Increasing the thermal energy of solid steel can cause it to melt and change into a fiery liquid.

Science Journal Describe things you do to make yourself feel warmer and cooler.

156

Interactive Chalkboard

This CD-ROM is an editable Microsoft® PowerPoint® presentation that includes:

- an editable presentation for every chapter
- additional chapter questions
- animated graphics
- image bank
- links to gpscience.com

Start-Up Activities

Temperature and Kinetic Energy

Hot water can burn your skin, but warm water doesn't. How is hot water different from warm water? You know that the temperature of hot water is higher. The temperature depends on the energy of the water molecules. In hot water, molecules of water are moving faster than they are in warm water. As a result, the kinetic energy of water molecules in hot water is larger. The difference in kinetic energy also has other effects, as you'll see in this lab. 

1. Pour 200 mL of room-temperature water into a beaker.
2. Pour 200 mL of water into a beaker and add some ice.
3. Put one drop of food coloring into each beaker.
4. Compare how quickly the food coloring causes the color of the water to change in each beaker.
5. **Think Critically** Write a paragraph describing the results of your experiment. Infer why the food coloring spread throughout the water in the two beakers at different rates.

Thermal Energy and Heat Make the following Foldable to help you understand thermal energy and heat.

STEP 1 **Fold** a vertical sheet of paper in half from top to bottom.

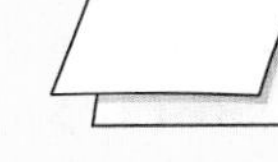

STEP 2 **Fold** in half from side to side with the fold at the top.

STEP 3 **Unfold** the paper once. **Cut** only the fold of the top flap to make two tabs.

STEP 4 **Turn** the paper vertically and **label** the front tabs as shown.

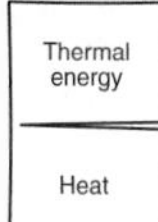

Find Main Ideas As you read the chapter, write the main ideas you find about thermal energy and heat under the appropriate tab.

Science Online | Preview this chapter's content and activities at gpscience.com

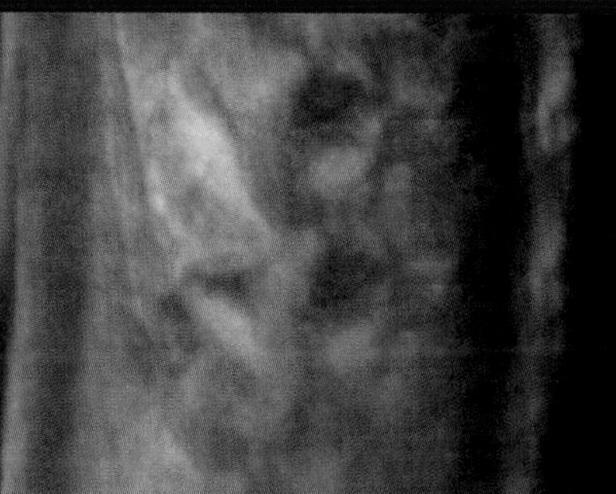

157

Purpose Use the Launch Lab to introduce students to the kinetic theory of matter. L2 ELL

LS **Kinesthetic**

Preparation Obtain enough ice for the class and keep it in a freezer until just prior to the time when students do this lab.

Materials 2 beakers, water, ice, food coloring, stopwatch

Teaching Strategies Suggest students repeat the experiment several times, waiting different amounts of time between adding the ice to the beaker and adding the food coloring.

Think Critically

The food coloring spread faster in the room temperature water than it did in the water with ice. In the warmer water the water molecules move faster and collide more often with the food coloring molecules making them move faster.

Assessment

Portfolio Have students draw colored sketches showing the water in each beaker every minute until all the water in each beaker has changed color. Make sure they label each sketch with the time. Use **Performance Assessment in the Science Classroom,** p. 127. L2 ELL

LS **Visual-Spatial**

Dinah Zike Study Fold

Student preparation materials for this Foldable are available in the Chapter *Fast File* Resources.

Additional Chapter Media

- What's Science Got to Do With It?: *Tractor Pulls*
- Virtual Lab: *How do the insulation properties of various materials compare?*
- Video Lab: *Conduction in Gases*

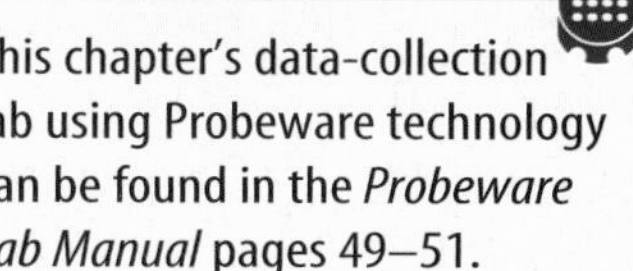

Probeware Labs

This chapter's data-collection lab using Probeware technology can be found in the *Probeware Lab Manual* pages 49–51.

1 Motivate

INTERACTIVE
CHALKBOARD
PowerPoint® Presentations

Bellringer

Section Focus Transparencies also are available on the Interactive Chalkboard CD-ROM.

L2 ELL

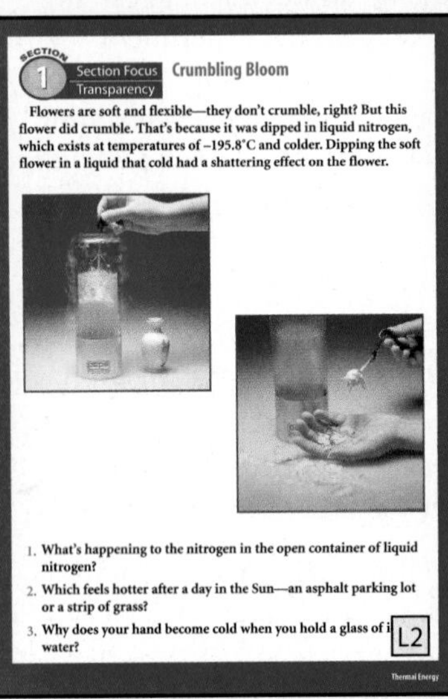

SECTION 1 Section Focus Transparency **Crumbling Bloom**

Flowers are soft and flexible—they don't crumble, right? But this flower did crumble. That's because it was dipped in liquid nitrogen, which exists at temperatures of −195.8°C and colder. Dipping the soft flower in a liquid that cold had a shattering effect on the flower.

1. What's happening to the nitrogen in the open container of liquid nitrogen?
2. Which feels hotter after a day in the Sun—an asphalt parking lot or a strip of grass?
3. Why does your hand become cold when you hold a glass of ice water?

L2

Thermal Energy

Tie to Prior Knowledge

Specific Heat Ask students whether they have ever noticed that some materials heat up faster than others. Tell students that the amount of heat it takes to make a substance warm up is called its specific heat, one of the things they will learn about in this section.

section 1

Temperature and Heat

Reading Guide

What You'll Learn

- **Define** temperature.
- **Explain** how thermal energy depends on temperature.
- **Explain** how thermal energy and heat are related.
- **Calculate** the change in thermal energy.

Why It's Important

Cars, buses, trucks, and airplanes could not operate without thermal energy.

Review Vocabulary

kinetic energy: the energy an object has due to its motion

New Vocabulary

- temperature
- thermal energy
- heat
- specific heat

Temperature

You use the words hot and cold to describe temperature. Something is hot when its temperature is high. When you heat water on a stove, its temperature increases. How are temperature and heat related?

Matter in Motion The matter around you is made of tiny particles—atoms and molecules. In all materials these particles are in constant, random motion; moving in all directions at different speeds. Because these particles are moving, they have kinetic energy. The faster they move, the more kinetic energy they have. **Figure 1** shows that particles move faster in hot objects than in cooler objects.

Figure 1 The particles in an object are in constant random motion.

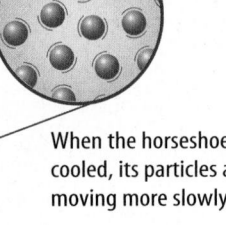

When the horseshoe is hot, the particles in it move faster.
When the horseshoe has cooled, its particles are moving more slowly.

Section 1 Resource Manager

Chapter *FAST FILE* Resources
- Transparency Activity, p. 44
- Note-taking Worksheets, pp. 33–35
- Enrichment, p. 30
- Directed Reading for Content Mastery, pp. 19, 20
- Reinforcement, p. 27
- Lab Activity, pp. 9–12

Mathematics Skill Activities, p. 11

Reading and Writing Skill Activities, p. 33

Earth Science Critical Thinking/Problem Solving, p. 10

Temperature The temperature of an object and the kinetic energy of its atoms and molecules are related. The **temperature** of an object is a measure of the average kinetic energy of the particles in the object. As the temperature of an object increases, the average speed of the particles in random motion increases. The temperature of hot tea is higher than the temperature of iced tea because the particles in the hot tea are moving faster on average. In SI units, temperature is measured in kelvins (K). A more commonly used temperature scale is the Celsius scale. One kelvin degree is the same size as one Celsius degree.

Thermal Energy

If you let cold butter sit at room temperature for a while, it warms and becomes softer. Because the air in the room is at a higher temperature than the butter, particles in air have more kinetic energy than butter particles. Collisions between particles in butter and particles in air transfer energy from the faster-moving particles in air to the slower-moving butter particles. The butter particles then move faster and the temperature of the butter increases.

Particles in the butter can exert attractive forces on each other. Recall that Earth exerts an attractive gravitational force on a ball. When the ball is above the ground, the ball and Earth are separated, and the ball has potential energy. In the same way, atoms and particles that exert attractive forces on each other have potential energy when they are separated. The sum of the kinetic and potential energy of all the particles in an object is the **thermal energy** of the object. Because the kinetic energy of the butter particles increased as it warmed, the thermal energy of the butter increased.

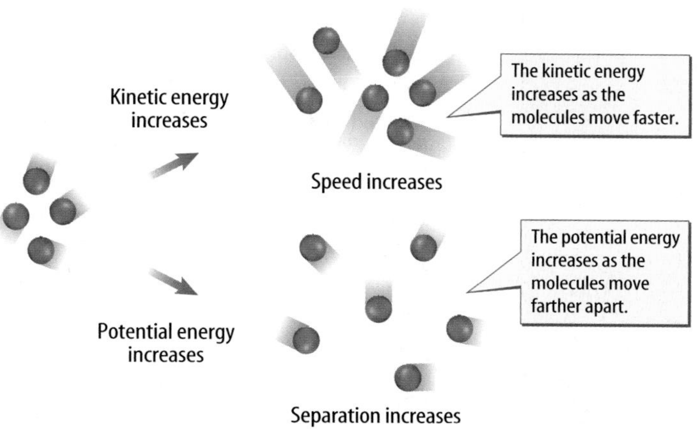
Kinetic energy increases
Speed increases
The kinetic energy increases as the molecules move faster.
Potential energy increases
Separation increases
The potential energy increases as the molecules move farther apart.

Figure 2 The thermal energy of a substance is the sum of the kinetic and potential energy of its molecules.
Infer *why increasing the temperature of an object increases its thermal energy.*

2 Teach

Visual Learning

Figure 1 Point out to students that the horseshoe in **Figure 1** bends easily when it is very hot. When the horseshoe cools, it is rigid. Why is the horseshoe in **Figure 1** more malleable when it is hot than when it is cool? When the horseshoe is hot, its quickly moving particles easily realign into new positions. When it has cooled down its particles are moving more slowly and resist realigning into new positions. L2 LS **Logical-Mathematical**

Teacher FYI

Shivering One way the human body maintains its internal temperature is through rapid vibration known as shivering.

Fun Fact

Water is a unique substance. Unlike most materials that expand when heated, water at temperatures of 1°, 2°, or 3°C contracts when heated. Water is most dense at 4°C. This property allows ice to float in your glass of water, and keeps ponds from freezing from the bottom up.

Caption Answer

Figure 2 Increasing the temperature increases the kinetic energy of the particles.

Active Reading

Quickwrites This strategy, sometimes called freewrite, lets students use spontaneous writing to discover what they already know. Have students write a list of ideas about heat and then share these ideas with the class. Next, have students write about these ideas freely without worrying about punctuation, spelling, and grammar. Have students use a Quickwrite to share ideas about thermal energy and heat. L2 LS **Linguistic**

IDENTIFYING Misconceptions

Maintaining Heat During cold weather, people often close doors and windows to keep the cold out. Since cold is the absence of heat, they are actually attempting to keep the heat inside, not keep the cold out.

Visual Learning

Figure 3 Why is it necessary to stir the ice cream while it is freezing? Stirring allows the ice cream mix to cool evenly and more quickly. L2 P LS **Logical-Mathematical**

Reading Check

Answer Heat is thermal energy that flows from something with a higher temperature to something with a lower temperature.

Reading Check

Answer the amount of heat that is needed to raise the temperature of 1kg of water by 1°C

Topic: Weather Satellites
Visit gpscience.com for Web links to information about how weather satellites use thermal energy to acquire weather data.

Activity Draw a diagram showing how a satellite uses thermal energy to produce images.

Thermal Energy and Temperature Thermal energy and temperature are related. When the temperature of an object increases, the average kinetic energy of the particles in the object increases. Because thermal energy is the total kinetic and potential energy of all the particles in an object, the thermal energy of the object increases when the average kinetic energy of its particles increases. Therefore, the thermal energy of an object increases as its temperature increases.

Thermal Energy and Mass Suppose you have a glass and a beaker of water that are at the same temperature. The beaker contains twice as much water as the glass. The water in both containers is at the same temperature, so the average kinetic energy of the water molecules is the same in both containers. But there are twice as many water molecules in the beaker as there are in the glass. So the total kinetic energy of all the molecules is twice as large for the water in the beaker. As a result, even though they are at the same temperature, the water in the beaker has twice as much thermal energy as the water in the glass does. If the temperature doesn't change, the thermal energy in an object increases if the mass of the object increases.

Heat

Can you tell if someone has been sitting in your chair? Perhaps you've noticed that your chair feels warm, and maybe you concluded that someone has been sitting in it recently. The chair feels warmer because thermal energy from the person's body flowed to the chair and increased its temperature.

Heat is thermal energy that flows from something at a higher temperature to something at a lower temperature. Heat is a form of energy, so it is measured in joules—the same units that energy is measured in. Heat always flows from warmer to cooler materials. How did the ice cream in **Figure 3** become cold? Heat flowed from the warmer liquid ingredients to the cooler ice-and-salt mixture. The liquid ingredients released enough thermal energy to become cold enough to form solid ice cream. Meanwhile, the ice-and-salt solution absorbed thermal energy, causing some of the ice to melt.

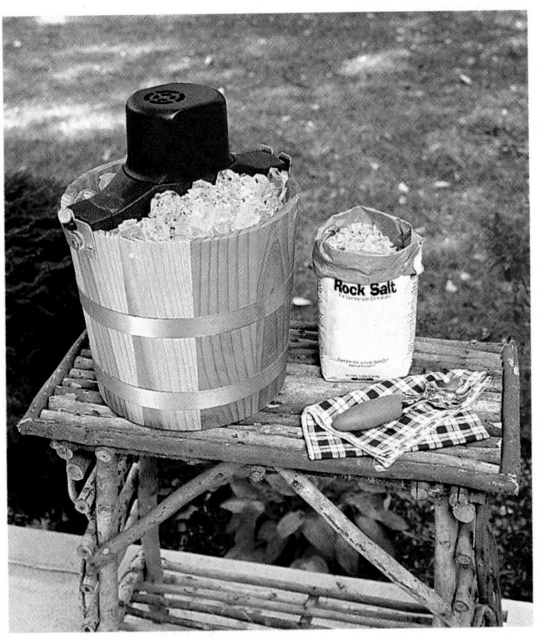

Figure 3 Heat flows from the warmer ingredients inside the container to the ice-and-salt mixture.

Reading Check *How are heat and thermal energy related?*

Curriculum Connection

History Have a group of students report on the experiments of James Joule that quantitatively related thermal energy and work. Joule used falling weights to turn paddles that stirred water and raised its temperature. He calculated the mechanical energy of the falling weights and the heat energy from the increase in temperature of the water. L2 COOP LEARN LS **Linguistic**

Science Journal

Body Heat Have students describe in their Science Journals how thermal energy flows when an oral thermometer is used to take someone's temperature. The thermometer usually has a temperature lower than that of a human body, 37°C (98.6°F). In the mouth, thermal energy moves from the body to the thermometer, raising the temperature of the material in the thermometer. L2 LS **Logical-Mathematical** P

Specific Heat

If you are at the beach in the summertime, you might notice that the ocean seems much cooler than the air or sand. Even though energy from the Sun is falling on the air, sand, and water at the same rate, the temperature of the water has changed less than the temperature of the air or sand has.

As a substance absorbs heat, its temperature change depends on the nature of the substance, as well as the amount of heat that is added. For example, compared to 1 kg of sand, the amount of heat that is needed to raise the temperature of 1 kg of water by 1°C is about six times greater. So the ocean water at the beach would have to absorb six times as much heat as the sand to be at the same temperature. The amount of heat that is needed to raise the temperature of 1 kg of some material by 1°C is called the **specific heat** of the material. Specific heat is measured in joules per kilogram degree Celsius [J/(kg °C)]. **Table 1** shows the specific heats of some familiar materials.

Table 1 Specific Heat of Some Common Materials

Substance	Specific Heat [J/(kg°C)]
Water	4,184
Wood	1,760
Carbon (graphite)	710
Glass	664
Iron	450

Reading Check *What is the specific heat of a material?*

Water as a Coolant Compared with the other common materials in **Table 1,** water has the highest specific heat. **Figure 4** shows why this is. Because water can absorb heat without a large change in temperature, it is useful as a coolant. A coolant is a subtance that is used to absorb heat. For example, water is used as the coolant in the cooling systems of automobile engines. As long as the water temperature is lower than the engine temperature, heat will flow from the engine to the water. Compared to other materials, the temperature of water will increase less.

Figure 4 The specific heat of water is high because water molecules form strong bonds with each other.

When heat is added, some of the added heat has to break some of these bonds before the molecules can start moving faster.

In metals, electrons can move freely. When heat is added, no strong bonds have to be broken before the electrons can start moving faster.

Discussion

Specific Heat Why do metal pans and serving spoons often have plastic handles? Plastic is not a good conductor of heat. Plastic has a higher specific heat than metal. It will remain cool to the touch. L2 IS **Logical-Mathematical**

Activity

SI Practice To give students practice working with SI, have them convert the specific heats given in **Table 1** from units of $\frac{J}{(kg \cdot K)}$ to $\frac{J}{(g \cdot K)}$

water — $\frac{1kg}{1{,}000g} \cdot \frac{4{,}184J}{kg \cdot K} = \frac{4.184\,J}{(g \cdot K)}$

wood — $\frac{1.760\,J}{(g \cdot K)}$;

carbon — $\frac{0.710\,J}{(g \cdot K)}$;

glass — $\frac{0.664\,J}{(g \cdot K)}$;

iron — $\frac{0.450\,J}{(g \cdot K)}$

L2 IS **Logical-Mathematical**

Quick Demo

Comparing Specific Heat

Materials large beaker, crushed ice, water, three test tubes, sand (or table salt), iron filings, starch-based packing peanuts

Estimated Time 15 minutes

Procedure Partially fill a large beaker with crushed ice. Add water to fill voids in the ice. Place a thermometer in each test tube. Partially fill each test tube with one of the following materials: sand, iron filings, and packing peanuts. Break up packing peanuts, if needed. Adjust the thermometer so that it does not touch the bottom of the test tube. It should be completely surrounded by the packing material. Place the test tubes in the beaker of ice water. Record the temperature of each test tube every minute for 5 minutes. To remove the packing peanuts from the test tube, add water to the test tube to dissolve the peanuts.

Differentiated Instruction

Challenge The Dulong-Petit law, discovered in 1819 by two French scientists, relates specific heat to atomic weight. Have students learn more about this law and how it has been used. According to the law, the specific heat of a solid element is inversely related to its atomic weight. L3 IS **Linguistic**

Visual Learning

Figure 4 Explain that the attractive forces between water molecules are very strong, which means they have a lot of energy. These forces must be overcome to allow water molecules to gain kinetic energy and heat up. The atoms of the metal don't have the same strong attractive forces between them, so it takes less energy to make them move and heat up. L2 IS **Visual-Spatial**

Coastal Climates There is a narrow band of land that runs along coastal areas that experiences little temperature differences throughout the year. The proximity to the water moderates the temperatures in these areas.

Use Science Words

Word Origin Have students use their dictionaries to identify the origin of the word *thermal.* The word *thermal* comes from the Greek word *therme,* meaning "heat." Many English words derive from this root, including thermos, which insulates hot and cold beverages. L2 LS **Linguistic**

Thermal Energy Equation

National Math Standards

Correlation to Mathematics Objectives

1, 2, 3

Teaching Strategy

Follow the steps in the example problem.

Answer to Practice Problem

1. 306,000 J
2. 0.15 kg
3. 35.0°C

Coastal Climates The high specific heat of water causes large bodies of water to heat up and cool down more slowly than land masses. As a result, the temperature changes in coastal areas tend to be less extreme than they are farther inland.

Changes in Thermal Energy The thermal energy of an object changes when heat flows into or out of the object. If Q is the change in thermal energy and C is specific heat, the change in thermal energy can be calculated from the following equation:

Thermal Energy Equation

change in thermal energy (J) = mass (kg) × change in temperature (°C) × specific heat $\left(\frac{J}{kg°C}\right)$

$$Q = m(T_f - T_i)C$$

In this equation, T_f is the final temperature of the object and T_i is the initial temperature of the object. The temperature change, $T_f - T_i$, has units of °C.

Thermal Energy Equation

Solve for Thermal Energy A wooden block has a mass of 20.0 kg and specific heat of 1,700 J/(kg°C). Find the change in thermal energy of the block as it warms from 15°C to 25°C.

1. **This is what you know:** mass: m = 20.0 kg; final temperature: T_f = 25°C; initial temperature: T_i = 15°C; specific heat: C = 1,700 J/(kg °C)
2. **This is what you need to find:** change in thermal energy: Q
3. **Use this formula:** $Q = m(T_f - T_i)C$
4. **Substitute:** the values of m, T_f, T_i and C into the formula, do the subtraction, and then multiply.
   $Q = (20.0)(25 - 15)(1{,}700)$
   $= (20.0)(10)(1{,}700) = 340{,}000$
5. **Determine the units:** units of Q = (units of m) (units of $T_f - T_i$) (units of C)
   $= \cancel{kg} \times \cancel{°C} \times \frac{J}{\cancel{kg}\,\cancel{°C}} = J$

Answer: The change in the block's thermal energy is 340,000 J.

Science Online
For more practice problems, go to page 834, and visit gpscience.com/extra_problems.

Practice Problems

1. The air in a living room has a mass of 60.0 kg and a specific heat of 1,020.0 J/(kg °C). What is the change in thermal energy of the air when it warms from 20°C to 25°C.
2. The thermal energy of water in a mug increases by 12,552 J when the water is heated from 20.0°C to 40.0°C. If the specific heat of water is 4,184 J/(kg °C), what is the mass of the water?
3. **Challenge** A block has a mass of 0.20 kg, a specific heat of 710 J/(kg °C), and is at a temperature of 20.0°C. What is the block's final temperature if its thermal energy increases by 2,130 J?

Differentiated Instruction

Learning Disabled To help students calculate changes in thermal energy, make sure they know what each variable in the formula means, and show the places where numerical values are put in. Be sure to show them how to calculate the change in temperature. L2 LS **Logical-Mathematical**

Measuring Specific Heat

The specific heat of a material can be measured using a device called a calorimeter, shown in **Figure 5.** The specific heat of a material can be determined if the mass of the material, its change in temperature, and the amount of heat absorbed or released are known. In a calorimeter, a heated sample transfers heat to a known mass of water. The energy absorbed by the water can be calculated by measuring the water's temperature change. Then the thermal energy released by the sample equals the thermal energy absorbed by the water.

Using a Calorimeter To measure the specific heat of a material, the mass of a sample of the material is measured, as is the initial temperature of the water in the calorimeter. The material is then heated, its temperature measured, and the sample is placed in the water in the inner chamber of the calorimeter. The sample cools as heat is transferred to the water, and the temperature of the water increases. The transfer of heat continues until the sample and the water are at the same temperature. Then the initial and final temperatures of the water are known, and the amount of heat gained by the water can be calculated.

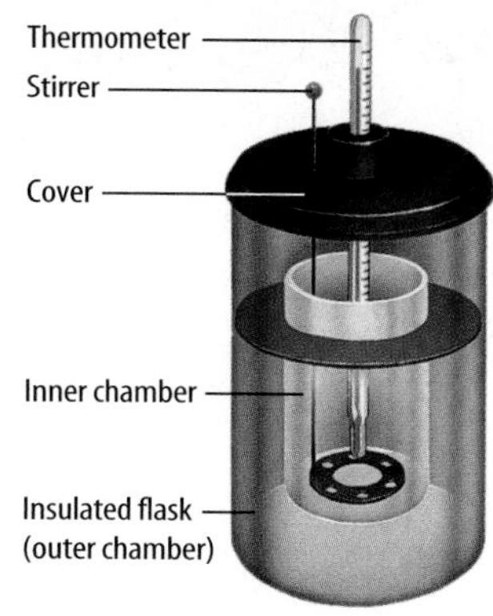

Figure 5 A calorimeter can be used to measure the specific heat of materials. The sample is placed in the inner chamber.

section 1 review

Summary

Temperature

- The temperature of an object is a measure of the average kinetic energy of the particles that make up the object.

Thermal Energy and Heat

- Thermal energy is the sum of the kinetic and potential energy of all the particles in an object.
- If temperature is constant, the thermal energy increases when the mass increases.
- Heat is thermal energy that is transferred from an object at a higher temperature to an object at a lower temperature.

Specific Heat

- The specific heat of a material is the amount of heat needed to raise the temperature of 1 kg of the material 1°C.
- The change in thermal energy of an object can be calculated from this equation

$$Q = m(T_f - T_i)C$$

Self Check

1. **Explain** how energy moves when you touch a block of ice with your hand.
2. **Describe** how the thermal energy of an object changes when the object's temperature changes.
3. **Infer** When heat flows between two objects, does the temperature increase of one object always equals the temperature decrease of the other object? Explain.
4. **Explain** why the specific heat of water is higher than the specific heat of most other substances.
5. **Think Critically** Explain whether or not the following statement is true: for any two objects, the one with the higher temperature always has more thermal energy.

Applying Math

6. **Calculate** the change in thermal energy of the water in a pond with a mass of 1,000 kg and a specific heat of 4,184 J/(kg °C) if the water cools by 1°C.
7. **Calculate** the specific heat of a metal if 0.5 kg of the metal absorb 9,000 J of heat as it warms by 10°C.

Science Online gpscience.com/self_check_quiz

3 Assess

DAILY INTERVENTION

Check for Understanding

Linguistic Have students write three sample test questions about the information in this section. Have students exchange papers with another student. Have students write a complete answer to the sample questions they now have. Have students return the papers to the original owner. Have students check the answers. Answer any questions that students may have. L2 LS

Reteach

Specific Heat Ask students to look at specific heat values from their book and think about cooking food on top of a stove. Ask them why an iron or copper pan is used to heat food. These materials have low specific heats, which means that they heat up quickly, since a small amount of heat is needed for each degree of temperature change. These materials can heat food quickly. L2 LS **Logical-Mathematical**

Assessment

Process Ask students to imagine that equal masses of water and alcohol are put into identical pans and heated for ten minutes. At the end of ten minutes, the alcohol has a higher temperature. What does this tell you about the specific heat of alcohol? The alcohol must have a lower specific heat since its temperature rose more with the same amount of thermal energy added. Use **Performance Assessment in the Science Classroom,** p. 89.

section 1 review

1. Thermal energy transfers from your hand to the block of ice as the particles in your hand strike the particles of ice where your hand touches the ice.
2. Temperature is the average kinetic energy of the particles in the object. Kinetic energy is one of the components of thermal energy—as kinetic energy changes, thermal energy changes.
3. No. The temperature change depends on the specific heat of each material.
4. Molecules of water have strong bonds between them that require energy to break before an increase of kinetic energy of the particles can occur.
5. It is false. Thermal energy depends on the amount of material and the potential energy of the particles in the objects.
6. −4,184,000 J
7. 1,800 J/(kg°C)

Transferring Thermal Energy

Reading Guide

What You'll Learn

- **Compare and contrast** the transfer of thermal energy by conduction, convection, and radiation.
- **Compare and contrast** thermal conductors and insulators.
- **Explain** how insulators are used to control the transfer of thermal energy.

Why It's Important

You must be able to control the flow of thermal energy to keep from being too hot or too cold.

Review Vocabulary

density: the mass per unit volume of a substance

New Vocabulary

- conduction
- convection
- radiation
- insulator

Conduction

Thermal energy is transferred from place to place by conduction, convection, and radiation. **Conduction** is the transfer of thermal energy by collisions between particles in matter. Conduction occurs because particles in matter are in constant motion.

Collisions Transfer Thermal Energy Thermal energy is transferred when one end of a metal spoon is heated by a Bunsen burner, as shown in **Figure 6.** The kinetic energy of the particles near the flame increases. Kinetic energy is transferred when these particles collide with neighboring particles. Thermal energy is transferred by collisions between particles with more kinetic energy and particles with less kinetic energy. As these collisions continue, thermal energy is transferred from one end of the spoon to the other end of the spoon. When heat is transferred by conduction, thermal energy is transferred from place to place without transferring matter. Thermal energy is transferred by the collisions between particles, not by movement of matter.

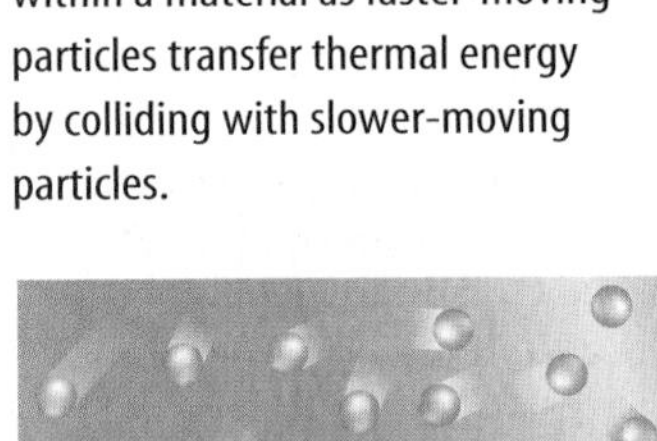

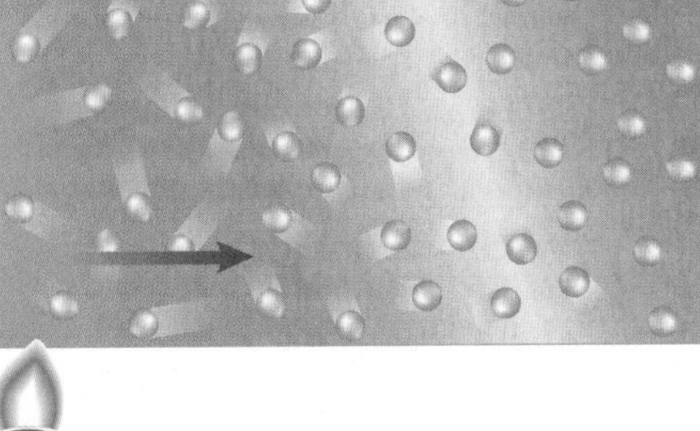

Figure 6 Conduction occurs within a material as faster-moving particles transfer thermal energy by colliding with slower-moving particles.

INTERACTIVE CHALKBOARD PowerPoint® Presentations

Bellringer

Section Focus Transparencies also are available on the Interactive Chalkboard CD-ROM.

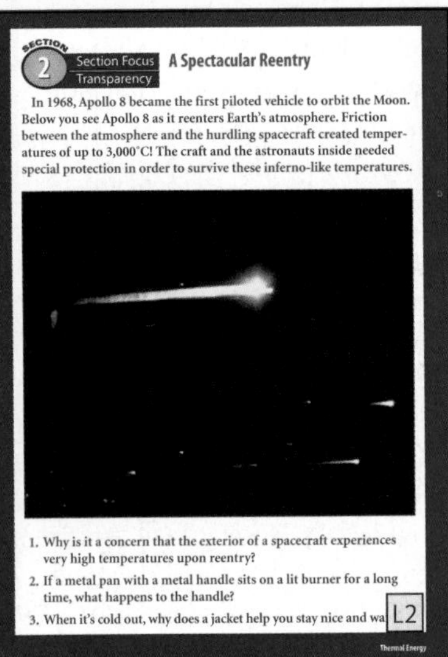

Section 2 Section Focus Transparency **A Spectacular Reentry**

In 1968, Apollo 8 became the first piloted vehicle to orbit the Moon. Below you see Apollo 8 as it reenters Earth's atmosphere. Friction between the atmosphere and the hurdling spacecraft created temperatures of up to 3,000°C! The craft and the astronauts inside needed special protection in order to survive these inferno-like temperatures.

1. Why is it a concern that the exterior of a spacecraft experiences very high temperatures upon reentry?
2. If a metal pan with a metal handle sits on a lit burner for a long time, what happens to the handle?
3. When it's cold out, why does a jacket help you stay nice and wa

L2

Thermal Energy

Tie to Prior Knowledge

Conductors Ask students to recall whether they have ever been burned by touching a hot object. What type of material was the hot object made of? It probably was made of a good conductor that transferred its thermal energy to the student's hand by conduction.

Section 2 Resource Manager

Chapter *FAST FILE* Resources

Transparency Activity, p. 45
Directed Reading for Content Mastery, p. 20
MiniLAB, pp. 3–4
Enrichment, p. 31
Lab Worksheet, pp. 5–6
Lab Activity, pp. 13–15
Reinforcement, p. 28

Life Science Critical Thinking/Problem Solving, pp. 10, 12

Physical Science Critical Thinking/Problem Solving, p. 2

164 CHAPTER 6 Thermal Energy

Heat Conductors Although heat can be transferred by conduction in all materials, the rate at which heat moves depends on the material. Heat moves faster by conduction in solids and liquids than in gases. In gases, particles are farther apart, so collisions with other particles occur less frequently than they do in solids or liquids.

The best conductors of heat are metals. In a piece of metal, there are electrons that are not bound to individual atoms, but can move easily through the metal. Collisions between these electrons and other particles in the metal enable thermal energy to be transferred more quickly than in other materials. Silver, copper and aluminum are among the best conductors of heat.

Convection

Unlike solids, liquids and gases can flow and are classified as fluids. In fluids, thermal energy can be transferred by convection. **Convection** is the transfer of thermal energy in a fluid by the movement of warmer and cooler fluid from place to place. When conduction occurs, more energetic particles collide with less energetic particles and transfer thermal energy. When convection occurs, more energetic particles move from one place to another.

As the particles move faster, they tend to be farther apart. As a result, a fluid expands as its temperature increases. Recall that density is the mass of a material divided by its volume. When a fluid expands, its volume increases, but its mass doesn't change. As a result, its density decreases. The same is true for parts of a fluid that have been heated. The density of the warmer fluid, therefore, is less than that of the surrounding cooler fluid.

Heat Transfer by Currents How does convection occur? Look at the lamp shown in **Figure 7.** Some of these lamps contain oil and alcohol. When the oil is cool, its density is greater than the alcohol, and it sits at the bottom of the lamp. When the two liquids are heated, the oil becomes less dense than the alcohol. Because it is less dense than the alcohol, it rises to the top of the lamp. As it rises, it loses heat by conduction to the cooler fluid around it. When the oil reaches the top of the lamp, it has become cool enough that it is denser than the alcohol, and it sinks. This rising-and-sinking action is a convection current. Convection currents transfer heat from warmer to cooler parts of the fluid. In a convection current, both conduction and convection transfer thermal energy.

Reading Check *How are conduction and convection different?*

Figure 7 The heat from the light at the bottom of the lamp causes one fluid to expand more than the other. This creates convection currents in the lamp.
Explain *why the substances in the lamp rise and sink.*

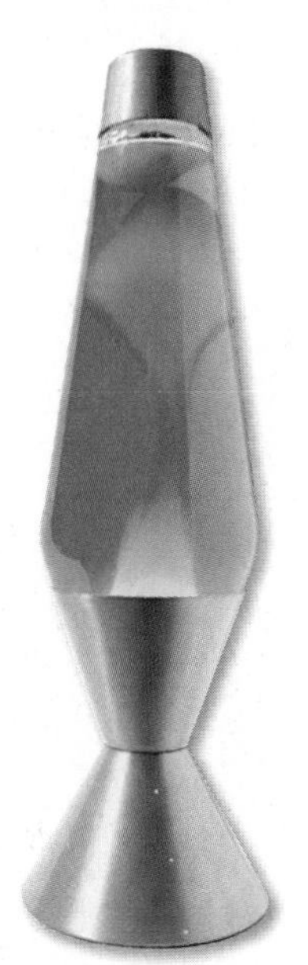

2 Teach

Use an Analogy

Kicking a Soccer Ball Explain that transferring energy to a soccer ball by kicking it is similar to transferring thermal energy through a material by conduction. Both the soccer ball and the molecules in the material are given energy as they collide with something else.

Caption Answer

Figure 7 The substances rise and sink due to density changes as the substance warms and cools.

Answer In conduction, heated particles collide with each other and transfer their energy. In convection, fluid particles move from one location to another, and carry their energy with them.

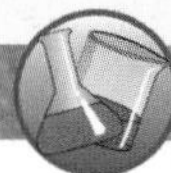

LAB DEMONSTRATION

Purpose to observe the effect of temperature on convection

Materials three 250-mL beakers, one 600-mL beaker, food coloring, dropper, hot plate, ice

Procedure Fill the 600-mL beaker two-thirds full of ice. Put water in the small beakers. Using the dropper, gently place a drop of food coloring in the bottom of each beaker. Place one beaker on a heated hot plate, one on the ice, and one in your hand.

Expected Outcome Greater heat causes more convection.

Assessment

Why did the food coloring disperse only in some beakers? The hot plate and hand warmth caused convection. No convection occurred in the cold water.

Visualizing Convection Currents

Have students examine the pictures and read the captions. Then ask the following questions.

Why does the air lose its moisture as it rises and cools at the equator? The water vapor in the air condenses as the air cools.

Why does the dry air create a zone of deserts at the tropics? The dry air causes moisture to evaporate out of the ground. Since there is a continuous stream of hot, dry air that blows across the land, any water on the ground is vaporized and carried away. In addition to this drying process, there is insufficient rainfall to replenish the moisture.

Activity

World Map Have students obtain or draw a world map. Ask students to locate and mark the equator and both tropics. Have them find the major rain forests and deserts of the world and mark them on their map. L2 ELL

LS **Visual-Spatial**

NATIONAL GEOGRAPHIC **VISUALIZING CONVECTION CURRENTS**

Figure 8

When the Sun beats down on the equator, warm, moist air begins to rise. As it rises, the air cools and loses its moisture as rain that sustains rain forests near the equator. Convection currents carry the now dry air farther north and south. Some of this dry air descends at the tropics, where it creates a zone of deserts.

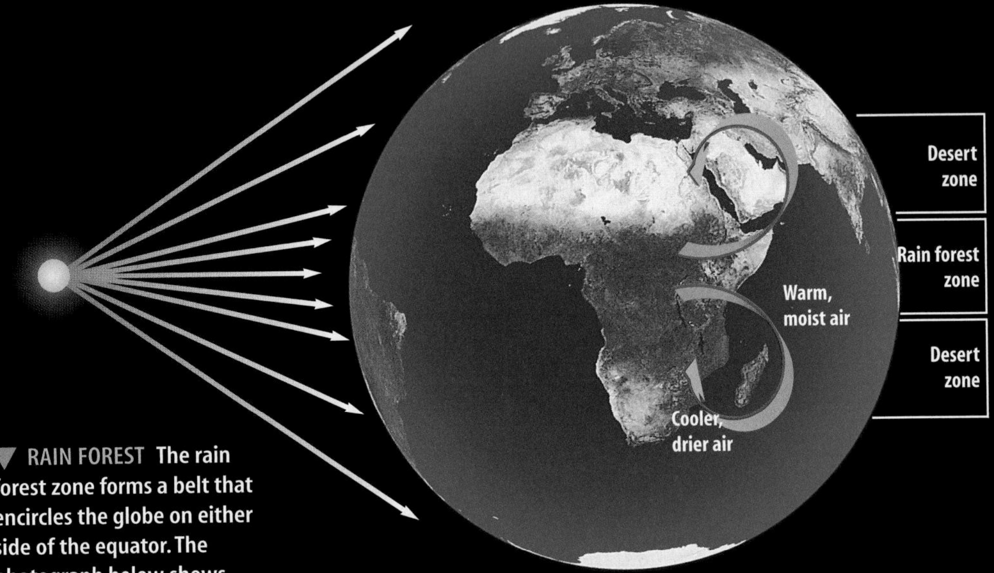

▼ RAIN FOREST The rain forest zone forms a belt that encircles the globe on either side of the equator. The photograph below shows a rain forest near the Congo River in central Africa.

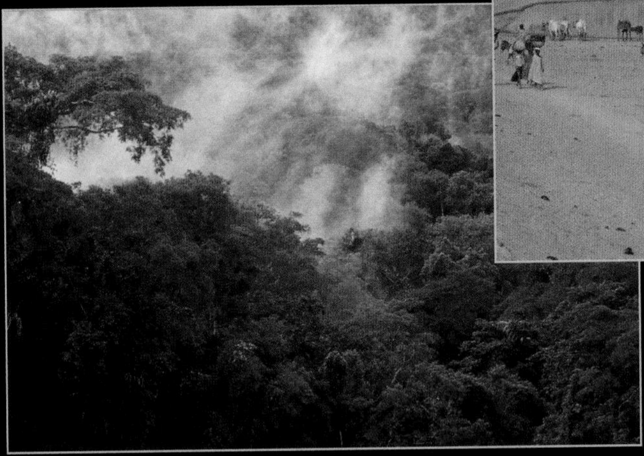

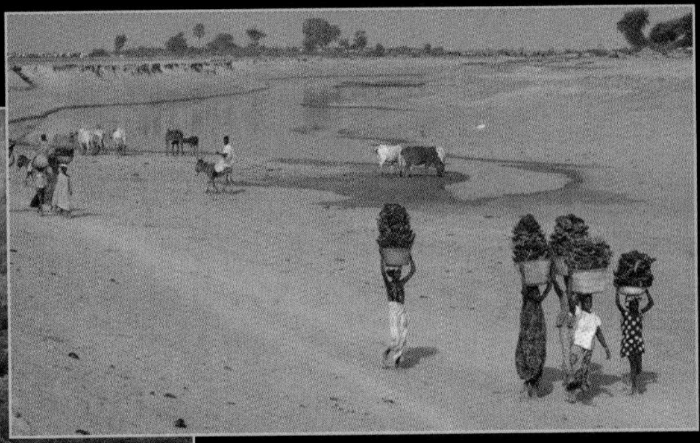

▲ DESERT Like many of the great desert regions of the world, the Sahara, in northern Africa, is largely a result of atmospheric convection currents. Here, a group of nomads gather near a dried-up river in Mali.

Differentiated Instruction

Challenge Have students research the living conditions of the peoples in the desert areas discussed in this feature. Students should find out how they obtain food, shelter, and how they cope with their harsh conditions. Ask students to give an oral report of their findings to their class. L3 LS **Auditory-Musical**

Desert and Rain Forests Earth's atmosphere is made of various gases and is a fluid. The atmosphere is warmer at the equator than it is at the north and south poles. Also, the atmosphere is warmer at Earth's surface than it is at higher altitudes. These temperature differences create convection currents that carry heat to cooler regions. **Figure 8** shows how these convection currents create rain forests and deserts over different regions of Earth's surface.

Radiation

Earth gets heat from the Sun, but how does that heat travel through space? Almost no matter exists in the space between Earth and the Sun, so heat cannot be transferred by conduction or convection. Instead, the Sun's heat reaches Earth by radiation.

Radiation is the transfer of energy by electromagnetic waves. These waves can travel through space even when no matter is present. Energy that is transferred by radiation often is called radiant energy. When you stand near a fire and warm your hands, much of the warmth you feel has been transferred from the fire to your hands by radiation.

Radiant Energy and Matter When radiation strikes a material, some of the energy is absorbed, some is reflected, and some may be transmitted through the material. **Figure 9** shows what happens to radiant energy from the Sun as it reaches Earth. The amount of energy absorbed, reflected, and transmitted depends on the type of material. Materials that are light-colored reflect more radiant energy, while dark-colored materials absorb more radiant energy. When radiant energy is absorbed by a material, the thermal energy of the material increases.

For example, when a car sits outside in the Sun, some of the radiation from the Sun passes through the transparent car windows. Materials inside the car absorb some of this radiation and become hot. Radiation can pass through solids, liquids, and gases.

Radiation in Solids, Liquids, and Gases The transfer of energy by radiation is most important in gases. In a solid, liquid or gas, radiant energy can travel through the space between molecules. Molecules can absorb this radiation and emit some of the energy they absorbed. This energy then travels through the space between molecules, and is absorbed and emitted by other molecules. Because molecules are much farther apart in gases than in solids or liquids, radiation usually passes more easily through gases than through solids or liquids.

Figure 9 Not all of the Sun's radiation reaches Earth. Some of it is reflected by the atmosphere. Some of the radiation that does reach the surface is also reflected.

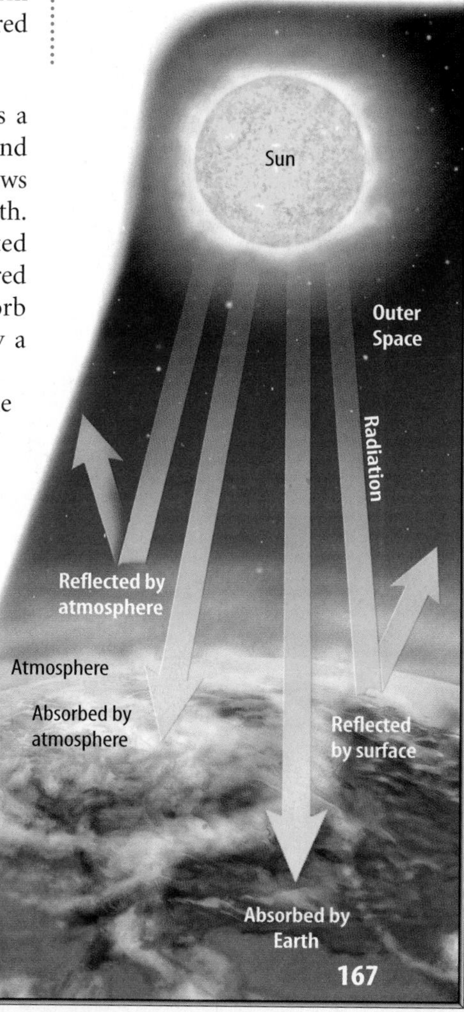

Fun Fact

The Amazon River drains the Amazon Rain Forest. The Amazon River is the largest watershed system in the world in terms of watershed area, number of tributaries, and volume of water discharged. It is estimated that one fifth of all the fresh water that drains into the ocean is discharged by the Amazon River.

Use Science Words

Word Origin Have students look up the origins of the words *conduction*, *convection*, and *radiation* in a dictionary. Students should find that the words come from the Latin roots *conducere* (to lead) and *convehere* (to bring together), and *radius* (ray), respectively. Ask volunteers to connect the meaning of each word with its root. L2 ELL IS **Linguistic**

IDENTIFYING Misconceptions

Radiation Students may confuse radiation as a form of heat transfer with nuclear radiation or radioactivity. Both types of radiation involve the sending out of energy as waves or particles. In nuclear radiation, radioactive nuclei of atoms break down and emit particles and electromagnetic waves. In thermal radiation, matter emits electromagnetic waves of much lower frequency.

Discussion

Radiant Energy Why is it important that the amount of radiant energy that reaches the Earth stays within a narrow range? Too much or too little energy from the Sun would result in the death of many organisms. L1 IS **Logical-Mathematical**

Curriculum Connection

Social Studies Very large cities can be measurably warmer than the surrounding countryside—as much as six or eight degrees warmer on a hot summer day. The main reason for these urban heat islands is thought to be their combination of paved land and tall, crowded buildings. Concrete, tar, and brick have lower specific heat than grass and trees, so they become hotter in the sun. They are good heat conductors, and at night the tall buildings radiate heat back and forth between them, rather than letting it escape quickly. Cities also generate their own heat through vehicles, factories, and even air conditioners. Have students draw diagrams showing heat flow in a large city and heat flow in the countryside. L2 IS **Visual-Spatial** P

Purpose Students observe the effect of glass on heat from the Sun. L2 ELL IS **Kinesthetic**

Materials window in sunlight

Teaching Strategies Make sure students find a window in a place where results won't be affected by heating or air conditioning.

Safety Precautions Advise students not to look directly at the Sun.

Analysis

1. by radiation
2. Answers will vary, depending on outdoor temperature, wind, and indoor climate control.
3. Yes; the student can feel the effect of the Sun's heat inside the window.

Assessment

Process Have each student write up the procedure used and results obtained for this MiniLAB in a lab report. Use **Performance Assessment in the Science Classroom,** p. 119.

Text Question Answer

Possible answer: Animals of a given species are generally larger in colder climates. This gives them a smaller surface area-to-volume ratio, making it easier for them to retain heat.

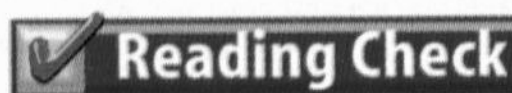

Answer Possible answers: antarctic fur seal's thick fur, emperor penguin's thick layer of blubber, scaly skin of the desert spiny lizard, black feathers on a penguin's back

Observing Heat Transfer by Radiation

Procedure

1. On a sunny day, go outside and place the back of your hand in **direct sunlight** for 2 min.
2. Go inside and find a **window exposed to direct sunlight.**
3. Place the back of your hand in the sunlight that has passed through the window for 2 min.

Analysis

1. Explain how heat was transferred from the Sun to your skin when you were outside.
2. Compare how warm your skin felt inside and outside.
3. Was thermal energy transferred through the glass in the window? Explain.

Try at Home

Controlling Heat Flow

You might not realize it, but you probably do a number of things every day to control the flow of heat. For example, when it's cold outside, you put on a coat or a jacket before you leave your home. When you reach into an oven to pull out a hot dish, you might put a thick, cloth mitten over your hand to keep from being burned. In both cases, you used various materials to help control the flow of heat. Your jacket kept you from getting cold by reducing the flow of heat from your body to the surrounding air. And the oven mitten kept your hand from being burned by reducing the flow of heat from the hot dish.

As shown in **Figure 10,** almost all living things have special features that help them control the flow of heat. For example, the antarctic fur seal's thick coat and the emperor penguin's thick layer of blubber help keep them from losing heat. This helps them survive in a climate in which the temperature is often below freezing. In the desert, however, the scaly skin of the desert spiny lizard has just the opposite effect. It reflects the Sun's rays and keeps the animal from becoming too hot. An animal's color also can play a role in keeping it warm or cool. The black feathers on the penguin's back, for example, allow it to absorb radiant energy. Can you think of any other animals that have special adaptations for cold or hot climates?

Reading Check *What are two animal adaptations that control the flow of heat?*

Figure 10 Animals have different features that help them control heat flow.

The antarctic fur seal grows a coat that can be as much as 10 cm thick.

The emperor penguin has a thick layer of blubber and thick, closely spaced feathers, which help reduce the loss of body heat.

The scaly skin of the desert spiny lizard not only reflects sunlight but it also prevents water loss. This is important in a dry environment.

Differentiated Instruction

Learning Disabled Obtain samples of insulation materials for students to observe. Point out the air pockets in the insulation samples for students to see. Materials may include fiber fill, fleece, and building insulation. If fiberglass is used, put the sample in a plastic bag to protect the students. Do not allow students to remove the material from the bag. L1 ELL IS **Visual-Spatial**

Science Journal

Wet Blanket Have students describe in their journals whether they think a wet blanket would keep them as warm as a dry blanket and why. Responses might include that a dry blanket has air trapped among the fibers, and air is a poor heat conductor. The wet blanket contains water which is a better conductor than air, and would be a poorer insulator than the dry blanket. L2 IS **Logical-Mathematical**

Figure 11 The tiny pockets of air in fleece make it a good insulator. They help reduce the flow of the jogger's body heat to the colder outside air.

Insulators

A material in which heat flows slowly is an **insulator.** Examples of materials that are insulators are wood, some plastics, fiberglass, and air. Materials, such as metals, that are good conductors of heat are poor insulators. In these materials, heat flows more rapidly from one place to another.

Gases, such as air, are usually much better insulators than solids or liquids. Some types of insulators contain many pockets of trapped air. These air pockets conduct heat poorly and also keep convection currents from forming. Fleece jackets, like the one shown in **Figure 11,** work in the same way. When you put the jacket on, the fibers in the fleece trap air and hold this air next to you. This air slows down the flow of your body heat to the colder air outside the jacket. Gradually, the air trapped by the fleece is warmed by your body heat, and underneath the jacket you are wrapped in a blanket of warm air.

Reading Check *Why does trapped air make a material like fleece a good insulator?*

Insulating Buildings Insulation, or materials that are insulators, helps keep warm air from flowing out of buildings in cold weather and from flowing into buildings in warm weather. Building insulation is usually made of some fluffy material, such as fiberglass, that contains pockets of trapped air. The insulation is packed into a building's outer walls and attic, where it reduces the flow of heat between the building and the surrounding air.

Insulation helps furnaces and air conditioners work more effectively, saving energy. In the United States, about 55 percent of the energy used in homes is used for heating and cooling.

Mini LAB

Comparing Thermal Conductors

Procedure

1. Obtain a **plastic spoon,** a **metal spoon,** and a **wooden spoon** with similar lengths.
2. Stick a small **plastic bead** to the handle of each spoon with a dab of **butter or wax.** Each bead should be the same distance from the tip of the spoon.
3. Stand the spoons in a **beaker,** with the beads hanging over the edge of the beaker.
4. Carefully pour **boiling water** to a depth of about 5 cm in the beaker holding the spoons.

Analysis

1. In what order did the beads fall from the spoons?
2. Describe how heat was transferred from the water to the beads.
3. Rank the spoons in their ability to conduct heat.

Reading Check

Answer Air is a good insulator. It reduces the rate at which heat is transferred to the colder, outside air.

Quick Demo

Insulators

Materials insulated travel mug, hot liquid

Estimated Time 10 minutes

Procedure Fill an insulated travel mug with a hot liquid such as water or coffee. Pass the mug around the class to allow students to feel the outside of the mug. Have students explain why the outside of the mug did not become hot. The insulating material reduces the rate at which heat is transferred from the liquid to the outside of the mug.

Purpose Students observe the thermal conductivity of a metallic alloy, plastic, and wood. L2 ELL LS **Kinesthetic**

Materials Each group will need: metallic, plastic, and wooden spoons (similar length), three small plastic beads, and three small dabs of butter, beaker, and boiling water.

Teaching Strategies Have students place their beakers on paper towels to catch butter drips.

Safety Precautions Students should be careful when handling boiling water.

Analysis

1. metal, plastic, then wood
2. by conduction through the spoons and the wax
3. metal, plastic, wood

Assessment

Process Have students draw cartoons explaining why items in the kitchen are made of insulators or conductors. Use **PASC,** p. 133.

Visual Learning

Figure 11 Discuss with students how the light jacket can keep the jogger warm, despite the snow and the wintry temperatures. Is the jacket producing heat? No; because the jogger is warm-blooded, she generates her own heat, which does not escape easily through the fleece jacket. L2 LS **Logical-Mathematical**

Teacher FYI

Insulation Asbestos is an effective insulator. It has been used to insulate hot water pipes, to make safety clothing for firefighters, and to protect brake linings. Scientists have discovered that the disease asbestosis can result from breathing in asbestos fibers, so its use has been significantly decreased.

3 Assess

DAILY INTERVENTION

Check for Understanding

Interpersonal Have students quiz one another on the three means by which thermal energy is transferred. conduction, convection, radiation L2 LS

Reteach

Heat Transfer Have students brainstorm about which method of heat transfer would most concern an astronaut floating in space. Heat radiation between the suit and outer space would be of serious concern. L3 LS **Logical-Mathematical**

Assessment

Oral Have students describe the forms of thermal energy transfer they might experience when they go to a beach or pool on a hot summer day. How might they use insulation to increase their comfort? Answers might include conduction from hot sand or concrete, convection while in the water, and radiation from the Sun. Insulators could include sandals and a towel. Use **Performance Assessment in the Science Classroom,** p. 89.

Virtual Labs

Insulation *How do the insulation properties of various materials compare?*

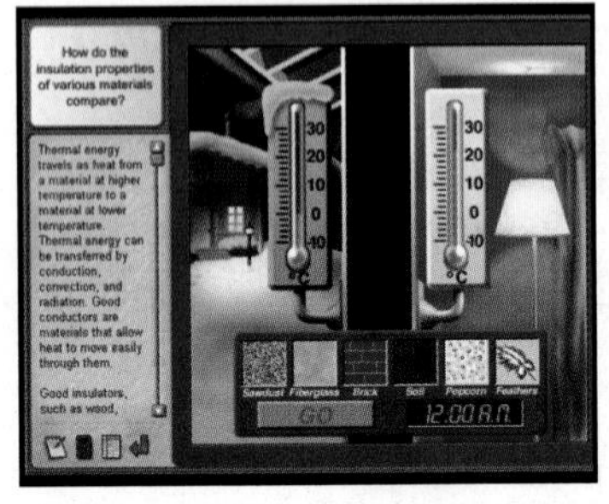

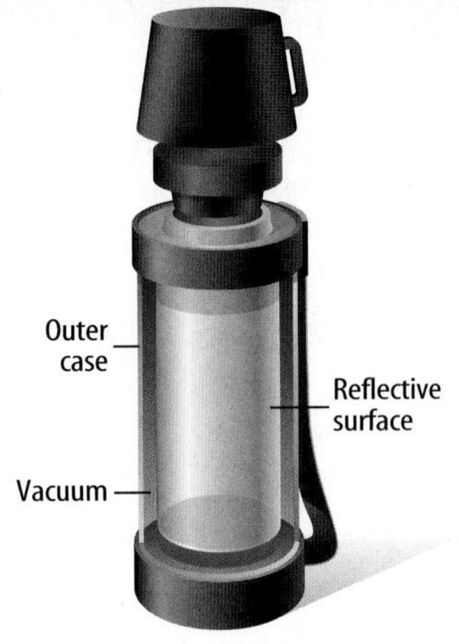

Figure 12 A thermos bottle uses a vacuum and reflective surfaces to reduce the flow of heat into and out of the bottle. The vacuum prevents heat flow by conduction and convection. The reflective surfaces reduce the heat transfer by radiation.

Reducing Heat Flow in a Thermos You might have used a thermos bottle, like the one in **Figure 12,** to carry hot soup or iced tea. A thermos bottle reduces the flow of heat into and out of the liquid in the bottle, so that the temperature of the liquid hardly changes over a number of hours. To do this, a thermos bottle has two glass walls. The air between the two walls is removed so there is a vacuum between the glass layers. Because the vacuum contains almost no matter, it prevents heat transfer by conduction or convection between the liquid and the air outside the thermos.

To further reduce the flow of heat into or out of the liquid, the inside and outside glass surface of a thermos bottle is coated with aluminum to make each surface highly reflective. This causes electromagnetic waves to be reflected at each surface. The inner relective surface prevents radiation from transferring heat out of the liquid. The outer reflective surface prevents radiation from transferring heat into the liquid.

Think about the things you do to stay warm or cool. Sitting in the shade reduces the heat transferred to you by radiation. Opening or closing windows reduces heat transfer by convection. Putting on a jacket reduces the heat transferred from your body by conduction. In what other ways do you control the flow of heat?

section 2 review

Summary

Conduction

- Conduction is the transfer of thermal energy by collisions between more energetic and less energetic particles.
- Conduction occurs in solids, liquids, and gases. Metals are the best conductors of heat.

Convection

- Convection is the tranfer of thermal energy by the movement of warmer and cooler material.
- Convection occurs in fluids. Rising of warmer fluid and sinking of cooler fluid forms a convection current.

Radiation

- Radiation is the transfer of energy by electromagnetic waves.

Controlling Heat Flow

- Insulators are used to reduce the rate of heat transfer from one place to another.

Self Check

1. **Explain** why materials that are good conductors of heat are poor insulators.
2. **Explain** why the air temperature near the ceiling of a room tends to be warmer than near the floor.
3. **Predict** whether plastic foam, which contains pockets of air, would be a good conductor or a good insulator.
4. **Describe** how a convection current occurs.
5. **Think Critically** Several days after a snowfall, the roofs of some homes on a street have almost no snow on them, while the roofs of other houses are still snow-covered. Describe what would cause this difference.

Applying Math

6. **Calculate Solar Radiation** Averaged over a year in the central United States, radiation from the sun transfers about 200 W to each square meter of Earth's surface. If a house is 10 m long by 10 m wide, how much solar energy falls on the house each second?

Science Online gpscience.com/self_check_quiz

section 2 review

1. Heat passes easily through good heat conductors. They increase the rate at which heat is transferred. A good insulator decreases the rate at which heat is transferred.
2. Warm air rises because the faster-moving particles are farther apart making the air less dense than the cool air.
3. It would be a good insulator because the air pockets do not easily transfer heat.
4. Convection occurs when more energetic particles move from one place to another. Convection currents transfer heat from warmer to cooler parts of the fluid.
5. The snow-covered houses are better insulated. Not enough heat escaped to melt the snow.
6. $\frac{200\text{ W}}{1\text{ m}^2} = \frac{x}{100\text{ m}^2}$; $x = 20{,}000$ W

Convection in Gases and Liquids

A hawk gliding through the sky will rarely flap its wings. Hawks and some other birds conserve energy by gliding on columns of warm air rising up from the ground. These convection currents form when gases or liquids are heated unevenly, and the warmer, less dense fluid is forced upward.

Real-World Question

How can convection currents be modeled and observed?

Goals

- **Model** the formation of convection currents in water.
- **Observe** convection currents formed in water.
- **Observe** convection currents formed in air.

Materials

burner or hot plate
water
candle
500-mL beaker
black pepper

Safety Precautions

WARNING: *Use care when working with hot materials. Remember that hot and cold glass appear the same.*

Procedure

1. Pour 450 mL of water into the beaker.
2. Use a balance to measure 1 g of black pepper.
3. Sprinkle the pepper into the beaker of water and let it settle to the bottom of the beaker.
4. Heat the bottom of the beaker using the burner or by placing it on the hotplate.
5. **Observe** how the particles of pepper move as the water is heated, and make a drawing showing their motion in your Science Journal.
6. Turn off the hot plate or burner. Light the candle and let it burn for a few minutes.
7. Blow out the candle, and observe the motion of the smoke.
8. Make a drawing of the movement of the smoke in your Science Journal.

Conclude and Apply

1. **Describe** how the particles of pepper moved as the water became hotter.
2. **Explain** how the motion of the pepper particles is related to the motion of the water.
3. **Explain** how a convection current formed in the beaker.
4. **Explain** why the motion of the pepper changed when the heat was turned off.
5. **Predict** how the pepper would move if the water were heated from the top.
6. **Describe** how the smoke particles moved when the candle was blown out.
7. **Explain** why the smoke moved as it did.

Communicating Your Data

Compare your conclusions with other students in your class. **For more help, refer to the** Science Skill Handbook.

Assessment

Process Ask each student to make an events chain for each of the convection currents observed. Use **Performance Assessment in the Science Classroom**, p. 163. L2 ELL IS **Visual-Spatial**

Communicating Your Data

Have each group observe the convection current patterns created by the experiments of other groups. Ask students to explain any differences in results.

Real-World Question

Purpose Students will model and observe convection currents. L2 ELL IS **Kinesthetic**

Process Skills make models, observe, record data, predict

Time Required one class period

Procedure

Alternate Materials Other fine grained spices that are insoluble in water can replace the black pepper.

Safety Precautions Caution students never to taste foods during science class. Caution them not to touch the hot plate when it is on.

Teaching Strategy Ask students to bring in insoluble particles from home to be used during their experiments.

Conclude and Apply

1. The particles swirled upward.
2. As the water heated, the convection currents in the water carried the black pepper upwards.
3. The water was hotter in the bottom of the beaker because it was nearer the heat source. The hot water rose in the beaker and the cool water sank.
4. There was no longer a temperature gradient in the beaker so convection stopped.
5. The pepper would stay on the top because hot water is less dense than cool water.
6. The smoke rose as long as there was a heat source. The rise of the smoke became slower as the wick cooled.
7. Smoke particles were carried upward by the convection currents in air.

section 3

Using Heat

1 Motivate

Bellringer

Section Focus Transparencies also are available on the Interactive Chalkboard CD-ROM.

SECTION 3 Section Focus Transparency **Steam Power**

Steam engines convert heat energy into mechanical energy. The engines use heat energy to produce steam that powers the locomotive. During the 1800s, steam engines were used in factories and mills and to propel boats and trains.

1. What are some fuels that the engines might burn to create steam?
2. Describe how liquid water is different from steam (gaseous water).
3. What changes steam energy to mechanical energy in the locomotive?

L2

Thermal Energy

Tie to Prior Knowledge

Energy Sources Have students identify the energy sources and the types of energy used in their home heating systems. From a class poll, rank the energy sources from most used to least used. Compare and contrast some of the common ones mentioned.

Reading Guide

What You'll Learn
- **Describe** common types of heating systems.
- **Describe** the first and second laws of thermodynamics.
- **Explain** how an internal combustion engine works.
- **Explain** how a refrigerator transfers thermal energy from a cool to a warm temperature.

Why It's Important

Imagine your life without heating systems, cooling systems, and cars.

Review Vocabulary

work: the product of the force exerted on an object and the distance the object moves in the direction of the force

New Vocabulary
- solar collector
- thermodynamics
- first law of thermodynamics
- second law of thermodynamics
- heat engine
- internal combustion engine

Heating Systems

Almost everywhere in the United States air temperatures at some time become cold enough that a source of heat is needed. As a result, most homes and public buildings contain some type of heating system. The best heating system for any building depends on the local climate and how the building is constructed.

All heating systems require some source of energy. In the simplest and oldest heating system, wood or coal is burned in a stove. The heat that is produced by the burning fuel is transferred from the stove to the surrounding air by conduction, convection, and radiation. One disadvantage of this system is that heat transfer from the room in which the stove is located to other rooms in the building can be slow.

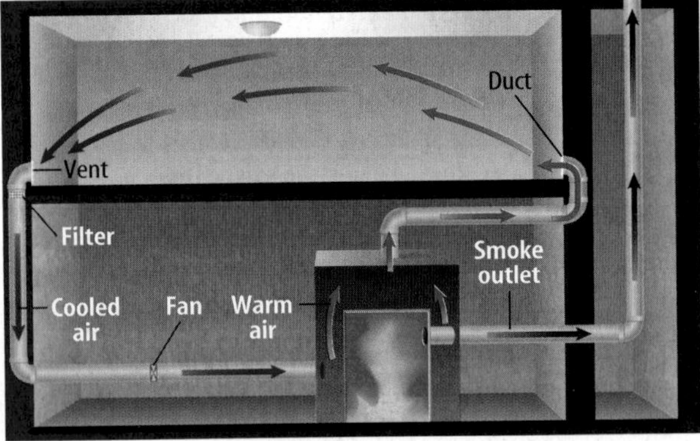

Figure 13 In forced-air systems, air heated by the furnace gets blown through ducts that usually lead to every room.

Forced-Air Systems The most common type of heating system in use today is the forced-air system, shown in **Figure 13.** In this system, fuel is burned in a furnace and heats a volume of air. A fan then blows the warm air through a series of large pipes called ducts. The ducts lead to openings called vents in each room. Cool air returns through additional vents to the furnace, where it is reheated.

Section 3 Resource Manager

Chapter *FAST FILE* Resources
- Transparency Activity, pp. 46, 47–48
- Enrichment, p. 32
- Directed Reading for Content Mastery, pp. 21–22
- Reinforcement, p. 29
- Lab Worksheet, pp. 7–8

Home and Community Involvement, p. 38

Cultural Diversity, p. 41

Physical Science Critical Thinking/Problem Solving, p. 17

Science Inquiry Labs, pp. 21–22

Performance Assessment in the Science Classroom, p. 41

Radiator Systems Before forced-air systems were widely used, many homes and buildings were heated by radiators. A radiator is a closed metal container that contains hot water or steam. The thermal energy contained in the hot water or steam is transferred to the air surrounding the radiator by conduction. This warm air then moves through the room by convection.

In radiator heating systems, fuel burned in a central furnace heats a tank of water. A system of pipes carries the hot water to radiators in the rooms of the building. After the water cools, it flows through the pipes back to the water tank and is reheated. In some radiator systems, the water is heated to produce steam that flows through the pipes to the radiators. As the steam cools, it condenses into water and flows back to the tank.

Electric Heating Systems An electric heating system has no central furnace. Instead, electrically heated coils placed in floors and in walls heat the surrounding air by conduction. Heat is then distributed through the room by convection. Electric heating systems are not as widely used as forced-air systems. However, in warmer climates the walls and floors of some buildings may not be thick enough to contain pipes and ducts. Then an electric heating system might be the only practical way to provide heat.

Solar Heating

The Sun emits an enormous amount of radiant energy that strikes Earth every day. The radiant energy from the Sun can be used to help heat homes and buildings. There are two types of systems that use the Sun's energy for heating—passive solar heating systems and active solar heating systems.

Passive Solar Heating In passive solar heating systems, materials inside a building absorb radiant energy from the Sun during the day and heat up. At night when the building begins to cool, thermal energy absorbed by these materials helps keep the room warm. **Figure 14** shows a room in a house that uses passive solar heating. Walls of windows receive the maximum amount of sunlight during the day. The other walls are heavily insulated and have few or no windows to reduce heat loss at night.

Figure 14 In a passive solar heating system, radiant energy from the Sun is transferred to the room through windows. Windows also prevent air inside from mixing with cooler air outside.
Infer *in which regions of the United States passive solar systems would be practical.*

2 Teach

Discussion

Heating Water Why is water rather than other fluids used in home heating systems? The specific heat of water is high compared with that of other fluids. Thus, it carries more heat per unit of mass and loses it more slowly, keeping the room warm longer. L2 LS **Logical-Mathematical**

Quick Demo

Observe Radiant Heating

Materials electric space heater

Estimated Time five minutes

Procedure Bring a small electric space heater to class. Plug the heater in and have the students observe the electric coils heat the area around the heater. Students can put their hands near the heater to feel the heat. Explain to students that the wires have resistance to the electric current that flows through them. The wires become hot due to this resistance. Heat is transferred to the room by radiation. A small fan is often part of the design of the heater. This fan helps transfer the heat into the room.

Caption Answer

Figure 14 All regions of the U.S. should be able to use passive solar systems to some degree of effectiveness.

Cultural Diversity

Home Heating Have students find out how the Inuit use convection currents to regulate heat inside igloos. The Inuit make the entranceways to their igloos lower than the inside. Because cold air is denser than warm air, the coldest air in the igloo sinks into the entranceway, leaving the warmer air inside the igloo. L3 LS **Logical-Mathematical**

Inquiry Lab

Passive Solar Heating

Purpose To research, explore, and observe passive solar heating, have students design and construct buildings out of small boxes that include design elements for passive solar heating. L2 ELL IS **Kinesthetic**

Possible Materials small boxes such as shoe boxes, cardboard, assorted colors of paper, clear sheeting such as overhead transparencies, insulating materials, resources to research passive solar heating

Estimated Time two weeks outside class time

Teaching Strategies

- Compass orientation of the building can maximize sun exposure.
- Students should have windows exposed to the Sun to collect solar energy.
- Buildings should be insulated to retain heat.
- Windows should have provisions for blocking the Sun during the summer to maintain comfort in the building.
- The color and type of flooring material should be considered for desired heat absorption.
- Students may provide a way to test their design. Have students take temperature measurements to show that a comfortable temperature is maintained.
- Students may find other design elements that should be included during their research.
- Students could present their models to architects involved in future school building plans for their consideration.

For additional inquiry activities, see *Science Inquiry Labs*.

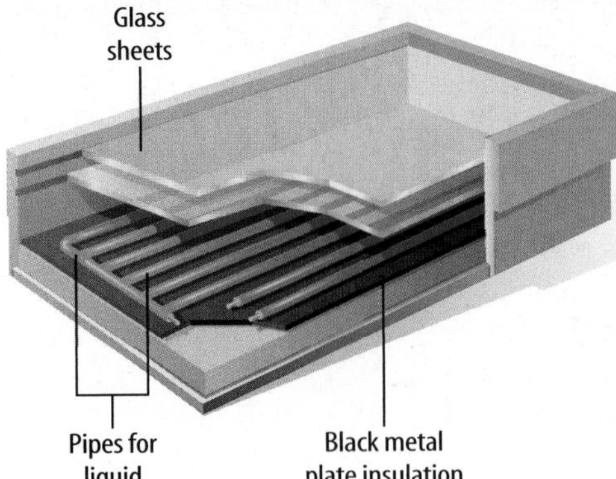

Figure 15 This active solar heating system uses solar collectors mounted on the roof to absorb solar energy. The absorbed energy heats a liquid that is circulated throughout the house.

Active Solar Heating Active solar heating systems use **solar collectors** that absorb radiant energy from the Sun. The collectors usually are installed on the roof or south side of a building. Radiant energy from the Sun heats air or water in the solar collectors. One type of active solar collector is shown in **Figure 15.** The black metal plate absorbs radiant energy from the Sun. The absorbed energy heats water in pipes just above the plate. A pump circulates the hot water to radiators in rooms of the house. The cooled water then is pumped back to the collector to be reheated.

Topic: Solar Heating
Visit gpscience.com for Web links to information about systems that use solar energy to heat buildings.

Activity Draw a diagram showing how an active solar heating system is used to heat a home.

Thermodynamics

There is another way to increase the thermal energy of an object besides adding heat. Have you ever rubbed your hands together to warm them on a cold day? Your hands get warmer and their thermal energy and temperature increase, even though there is no heat flowing to them. You did work on your hands by rubbing them together. The work you did caused the thermal energy of your hands to increase. Thermal energy, heat, and work are related, and the study of the relationship among them is **thermodynamics.**

Heat and Work Increase Thermal Energy You can warm your hands by placing them near a fire, so that heat is added to your hands by radiation. If you rub your hands and hold them near a fire, the increase in thermal energy of your hands is even greater. Both the work you do and the heat transferred from the fire increase the thermal energy of your hands.

In the example above your hands can be considered as a system. A system can be a group of objects such as a galaxy, or a car's engine, or something as simple as a ball. In fact, a system is anything you can draw a boundary around, as shown in **Figure 16.** The heat transferred to a system is the amount of heat flowing into the system that crosses the boundary. The work done on a system is the work done by something outside the system's boundary.

Cultural Diversity

Solar Brick-Making Passive solar heating can be used to make buildings as well as warm them. In the ancient Near East and Egypt, and still among some Native Americans of the desert Southwest, solar heat has been used to harden adobe clay into brick. Adobe is a fine-grained clay found in combination with sand and silt. People mix it with straw, form it into bricks, and bake the bricks in the Sun for one to two weeks. The bricks are sturdy enough to make multistory buildings, and some adobe structures have lasted for several centuries. Have students look up photos of Taos Pueblo (New Mexico) or cliff dwellings. L2 ELL IS **Visual-Spatial**

The First Law of Thermodynamics According to the **first law of thermodynamics,** the increase in thermal energy of a system equals the work done on the system plus the heat transferred to the system. Doing work on a system is a way of adding energy to a system. As a result, the temperature of a system can be increased by adding heat to the system, doing work on the system, or both. The first law of thermodynamics is another way of stating the law of conservation of energy. The increase in energy of a system equals the energy added to the system.

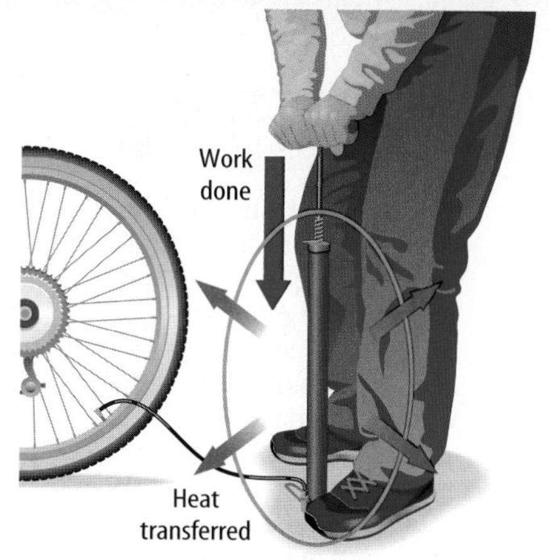

Figure 16 A bicycle air pump can be a system. Work is done on the system by pushing down on the handle. This causes the pump to become warm, and heat is transferred from the system to the outside air.

Closed and Open Systems A system is an open system if heat flows across the boundary or if work is done across the boundary. Then energy is added to the system. If no heat flows across the boundary and there is no outside work done, then the system is a closed system. According to the first law of thermodynamics, the thermal energy of a closed system doesn't change. There may be processes going on in the system that are converting one form of energy into another, but the total energy of the system doesn't change. Because energy cannot be created or destroyed, the total energy stays constant in a closed system.

The Second Law of Thermodynamics When heat flows from a warm object to a cool object the thermal energy of the warm object decreases and the thermal energy of the cool object increases. According to the law of conservation of energy or the first law of thermodynamics, the increase in thermal energy of the cool object equals the decrease in thermal energy of the warm object.

Can heat flow spontaneously from a cold object to warm object? This process never happens, but it wouldn't violate the first law of thermodynamics. The first law would require only that the decrease in thermal energy of the cool object would be equal to the increase in thermal energy of the warm object.

Reading Check ***How does heat flow from a warm to a cool object satisfy the first law of thermodynamics?***

However, the flow of heat spontaneously from a cool object to a warm object never happens because it violates another law—the second law of thermodynamics. One way to state the **second law of thermodynamics** is that it is impossible for heat to flow from a cool object to a warmer object unless work is done. For example, if you hold an ice cube in your hand, no work is done. As a result, heat flows only from your warmer hand to the colder ice.

Use Science Words

Word Usage Have students use the words active and passive in sentences that are not related to solar energy and then show how these general meanings transfer to scientific use. Possible answers: She is active in her chess club; in fact, she's the president. An active solar heating system collects and distributes radiant energy. A seat belt is a passive restraint. It is designed so that once you fasten it, it does the restraining merely by being in place. A passive solar system is designed so that once you set it up, it heats the house merely by being in place. L2 LS **Linguistic**

Discussion

Solar Power How is the solar calculator that a student may have similar to active solar heating? Possible answer: Both use radiant solar energy, one converting it into heat, the other converting it into electricity to run a calculator. L2 LS **Logical-Mathematical**

Reading Check

Answer According to the first law of thermodynamics, the increase in thermal energy of the cool object equals the decrease of thermal energy of the warm object.

Science Journal

Heating Systems Have students investigate the types of heating that are common in your area and why, and find information about initial cost, efficiency, and maintenance requirements of different systems. Have students write their findings in their Science Journals. L2 LS **Linguistic**

Nature's Heat Engines Diagrams should show that warm water from the ocean evaporates, rises, and then condenses in thunderstorm clouds that surround the eye of a hurricane. The heat for the hurricane heat engine comes from the latent heat released as the water in these thunderstorms changes from gas to liquid. In order for a hurricane to get started, water temperature must be at least 25.5°C (78°F).

Career Have students research a career as a hurricane chaser. These brave scientists fly directly into the eye of a hurricane to collect data. Have students find out why these scientists collect this data and who employs these scientists. L2 LS **Linguistic**

Reading Check

Answer Even if there were no friction, the second law of thermodynamics prevents heat from being converted completely into work.

Fun Fact

In engines with several cylinders, the piston in each cylinder goes through a four-stroke cycle. However, at any given time, the pistons in the various cylinders are in different positions.

Discussion

Types of Engines Would you prefer to own a car with a four-cylinder, six-cylinder, or eight-cylinder engine? Why? Answers may include concerns about fuel use, acceleration, and power going uphill. L2 LS **Logical-Mathematical**

Nature's Heat Engines
Hurricanes are storms that form over the ocean in regions of low pressure. Because hurricanes use heat from warm ocean water to produce strong winds, they are sometimes called nature's heat engines. Research hurricanes and draw a diagram showing how they are like a heat engine.

Converting Heat to Work

If you give a book sitting on a table a push, the book will slide and come to a stop. Friction between the book and the table converted the work you did on the book to heat. As a result, the book and the table became slightly warmer.

In the example above, work was converted completely into heat. Is it possible to do the reverse, and convert heat completely into work? Even though this process would not violate the first law of thermodynamics, it also is forbidden by the second law of thermodynamics. The second law of thermodynamics makes it impossible to build a device that converts heat completely into work.

Reading Check *Why can't heat be convered completely into work?*

A device that converts heat into work is a **heat engine.** A car's engine is an example of a heat engine. A car's engine converts the chemical energy in gasoline into heat. The engine then transforms some of the thermal energy into work by rotating the car's wheels, as shown in **Figure 17.** However, only about 25 percent of the heat released by the burning gasoline is converted into work, and the rest is transferred to the engine's surroundings.

Internal Combustion Engines The heat engine in a car is an **internal combustion engine** in which fuel is burned inside the engine in chambers or cylinders. Automobile engines usually have four, six, or eight cylinders. Each cylinder contains a piston that moves up and down. Each up-and-down movement of the piston is called a stroke. Automobile and diesel engines have four different strokes. **Figure 18** shows the four-stroke cycle in an automobile engine.

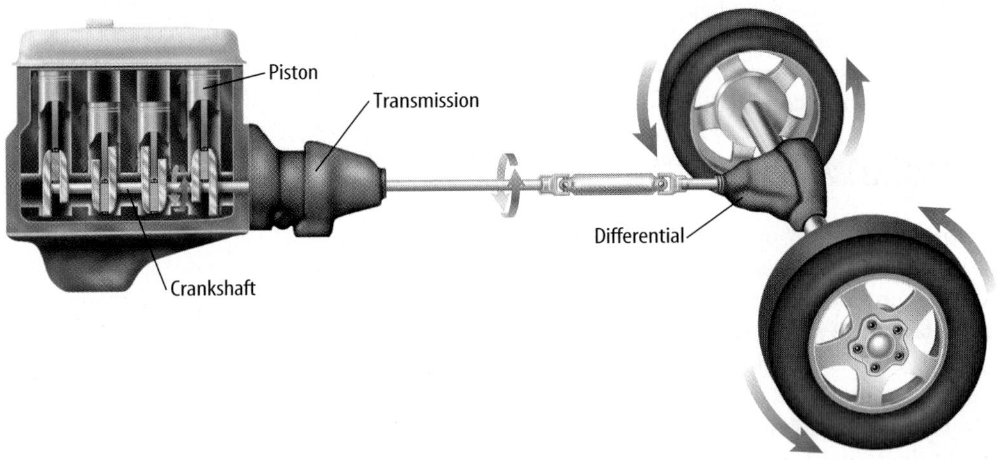

Figure 17 Burning fuel in the engine's cylinders produces thermal energy that is converted into work as the pistons move up and down. The crankshaft, transmission, and differential convert the up and down motion of the pistons into rotation of the wheels.

Science Journal

Invention's Impact Have students write short paragraphs in their Science Journals about the impact of the internal combustion engine on everyday life. They should consider not only cars but tractors, lawn mowers, cement trucks, moving vans, airplanes, and other applications of this technology L2 LS **Linguistic**

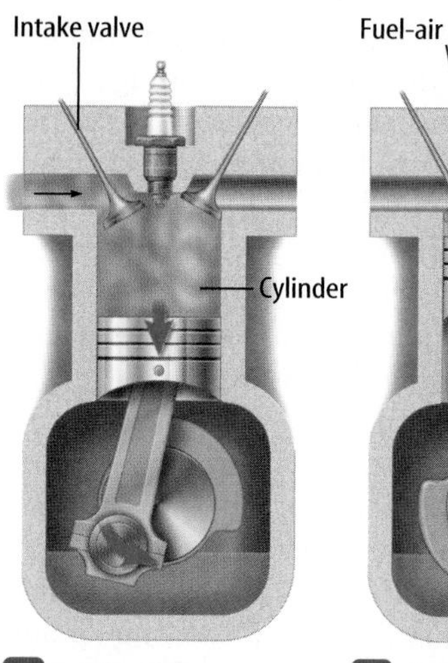

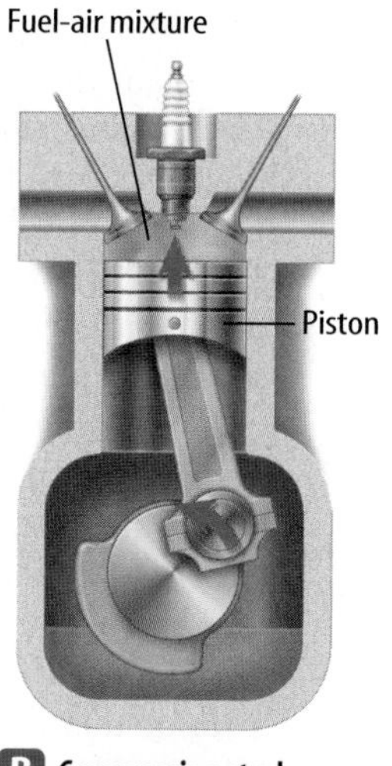

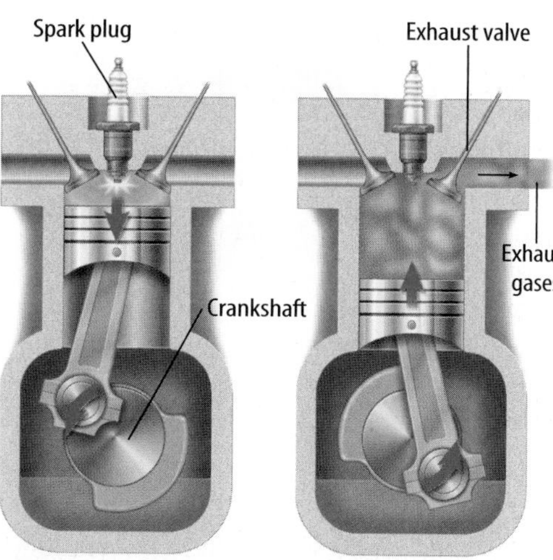

A Intake stroke The intake valve opens as the piston moves downward, drawing a mixture of gasoline and air into the cylinder.

B Compression stroke The intake valve closes as the piston moves upward, compressing the fuel-air mixture.

C Power stroke A spark plug ignites the fuel-air mixture. As the mixture burns, hot gases expand, pushing the piston down.

D Exhaust stroke As the piston moves up, the exhaust valve opens, and the hot gases are pushed out of the cylinder.

Figure 18 The up-and-down movement of a piston in an automobile engine consists of four separate strokes. These four strokes form a cycle that is repeated many times a second by each piston. **Determine** *whether eliminating friction would make the engine 100 percent efficient.*

Friction and the Efficiency of Heat Engines Almost three fourths of the heat produced in an internal combustion engine is not converted into useful work. Friction between moving parts causes some of the work done by the engine to be converted into heat. However, even if friction were totally eliminated, a heat engine still could not convert heat completely into work and be 100 percent efficient. Instead, the efficiency of an internal combustion engine depends on the difference in the temperature of the burning gases in the cylinder and the temperature of the air outside the engine. Increasing the temperature of the burning gases makes the engine more efficient.

Heat Movers

How can the inside of a refrigerator stay cold? The second law of thermodynamics prevents heat from spontaneously flowing from inside the refrigerator to the warmer room. However, the second law of thermodynamics allows heat to move from a cold to a warm object if work is done in the process. A refrigerator does work as it moves heat from inside the refrigerator to the warmer room. The energy to do the work comes from the electrical energy the refrigerator obtains from an electrical outlet. You can think of a refrigerator as a heat mover that does work to move heat from a cooler temperature to a warmer temperature.

Visual Learning

Figure 18 Read aloud the descriptions of each of the cycles in a four-cycle engine. Ask students to trace on the diagram each process as you read it. L2 IS **Auditory-Musical**

Caption Answer

Figure 18 The second law of thermodynamics prevents a heat engine from converting heat completely into work so that it is 100 percent efficient.

Fun Fact

The maximum efficiency possible for any heat engine is called the ideal efficiency and depends only on the highest and lowest temperatures in the engine cycle. The ideal efficiency of a four-cycle gasoline engine such as those used in automobiles is between 40 and 50%. This means that no matter how the engine is designed, it can never be more efficient than this.

Differentiated Instruction

Challenge The statement that heat can be made to flow from the cool refrigerator to the warm room only if work is done is one way to state the second law of thermodynamics. Have students find out who first stated the second law of thermodynamics and how he stated it. Have students write a brief report. The second law of thermodynamics was first stated by Rudolph Clausius and Lord Kelvin and was based on work done by Sadi Carnot. Clausius' version of the second law says it is impossible for any self-acting machine to convey heat continuously from one body to another at a higher temperature. L3 IS **Linguistic**

Teacher FYI

Blood Flow To regulate body temperature, blood flow to the skin is automatically adjusted. When the environment is too cold, blood is drawn away from the skin and sent to more vital organs. When the environment is hot, more blood is sent to the skin so that its heat can be exchanged with the environment.

Teacher FYI

Evaporation Evaporation explains why you shiver when you get out of a lake or pool, even on a hot day, or when you get out of the bathtub even into a warm room. It also explains why it's important to drink liquids when you're exercising or the day is hot. As your body sweats to cool off, you can become dehydrated.

Reading Check

Answer Work is done when the compressor compresses the coolant vapor, causing its temperature to increase.

Make a Model

Heat Pumps Have students work in small groups to look up heat pumps and then draw two diagrams: one showing how a heat pump cools during warm weather, and the second showing how a heat pump warms during cool weather. L2 LS **Visual-Spatial**

COOP LEARN

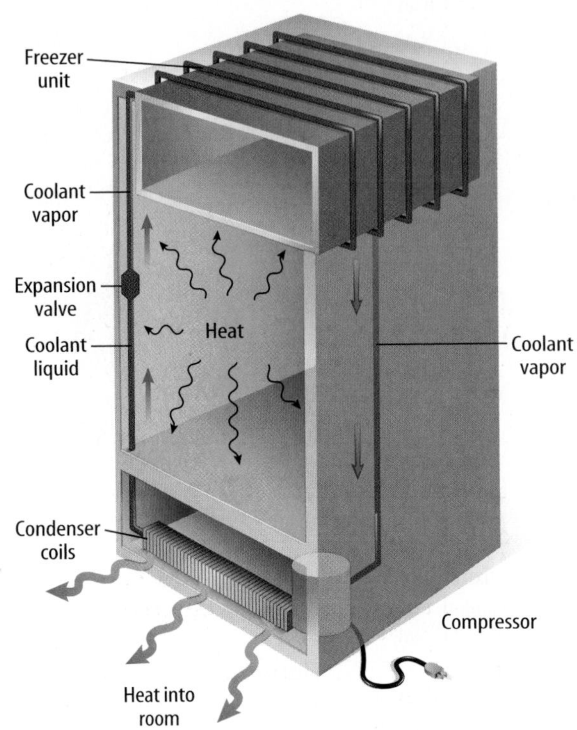

Figure 19 A refrigerator must do work on the coolant in order to transfer heat from inside the refrigerator to the warmer air outside. Work is done when the compressor compresses the coolant vapor, causing its temperature to increase.

Refrigerators A refrigerator contains a coolant that is pumped through pipes on the inside and outside of the refrigerator. The coolant is a special substance that evaporates at a low temperature. **Figure 19** shows how a refrigerator operates. Liquid coolant is pumped through an expansion valve and changes into a gas. When the coolant changes to a gas, it cools. The cold gas is pumped through pipes inside the refrigerator, where it absorbs thermal energy. As a result, the inside of the refrigerator cools.

The gas then is pumped to a compressor that does work by compressing the gas. This makes the gas warmer than the temperature of the room. The warm gas is pumped through the condenser coils. Because the gas is warmer than the room, thermal energy flows from the gas to the room. Some of this heat is the thermal energy that the coolant gas absorbed from the inside of the refrigerator. As the gas gives off heat, it cools and changes to a liquid. The liquid coolant then is changed back to a gas, and the cycle is repeated.

Reading Check *How does a refrigerator do work on the coolant?*

Air Conditioners and Heat Pumps An air conditioner is another type of heat mover. It operates like a refrigerator, except that warm air from the room is forced to pass over tubes containing the coolant. The warm air is cooled and is forced back into the room. The thermal energy that is absorbed by the coolant is transferred to the air outdoors. Refrigerators and air conditioners are heat engines working in reverse—they use mechanical energy supplied by the compressor motor to move thermal energy from cooler to warmer areas.

A heat pump is a two-way heat mover. In warm weather, it operates as an air conditioner. In cold weather, a heat pump operates like an air conditioner in reverse. The coolant gas is cooled and is pumped through pipes outside the house. There, the coolant absorbs heat from the outside air. The coolant is then compressed and pumped back inside the house, where it releases heat.

Curriculum Connection

Health Sweat glands exist in the dermis, the inner layer of skin lying below the epidermis. Although sweat itself has little smell, it contains bacteria that produce ammonia. Have students find out how deodorants work. Some deodorants kill the bacteria, while others cover the smell with perfume. Antiperspirants block the pores to prevent the secretion of sweat. L2 LS **Linguistic**

Differentiated Instruction

English-Language Learners To help students understand the refrigeration cycle, have them construct a simple diagram or schematic of the process. Students should identify where heat transfers occur. L2 ELL LS **Visual-Spatial**

The Human Coolant After exercising on a warm day, you might feel hot and be drenched with sweat. But your temperature would be close to your normal body temperature of 37°C. Your body uses evaporation to keep its internal temperature constant. When a liquid changes to a gas, energy is absorbed from the liquid's surroundings. As you exercise, your body generates sweat from tiny glands within your skin. As the sweat evaporates, it carries away heat, as shown in **Figure 20,** making you cooler.

Energy Transformations Produce Heat Every day many energy transformations occur around you that convert one form of energy into a more useful form. However, usually when these energy transformations occur, some heat is produced. For example, friction converts mechanical energy into thermal energy when the shaft of an electric motor or an electric generator rotates. The thermal energy produced in these energy transformations is no longer in a useful form and is transferred into the surroundings by conduction and convection.

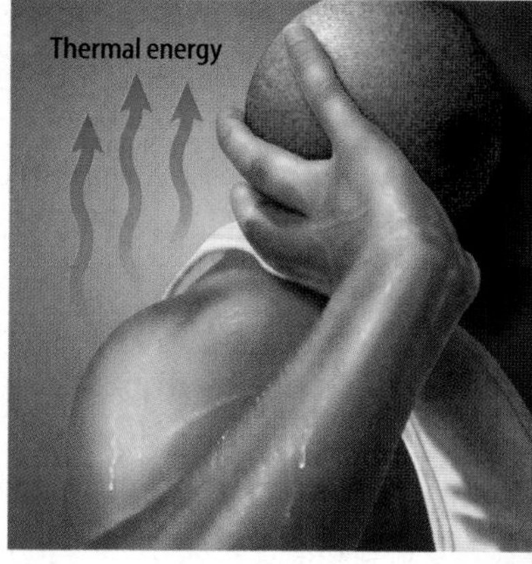

Figure 20 As perspiration evaporates from your skin, it carries heat away, cooling your body.

section 3 review

Summary

Heating Systems

- A forced-air heating system uses a fan to force air heated by a furnace through a system of ducts.
- Radiator and electric heating systems transfer heat to rooms by conduction and convection.
- Solar heating systems convert radiant energy from the Sun to thermal energy.

Thermodynamics

- The first law of thermodynamics states that the increase in thermal energy of a system equals the work done on the system plus the heat added to the system.
- One way to state the second law of thermodynamics is that heat will not flow from a hot to a cold object unless work is done.

Converting Heat to Work

- The second law of thermodynamics states that heat cannot be converted completely into work.
- A heat engine converts heat into work.
- A refrigerator moves heat by doing work on the coolant.

Self Check

1. **Explain** how the thermal energy of a closed system changes with time.
2. **Compare and contrast** an active solar heating system with a radiator system.
3. **Explain** whether or not a heat engine could be made 100 percent efficient by eliminating friction.
4. **Diagram** how the thermal energy of the coolant changes as it flows in a refrigerator.
5. **Think Critically** Suppose you vigorously shake a bottle of fruit juice. Predict how the temperature of the juice will change. Explain your reasoning.

Applying Math

6. **Calculate Change in Thermal Energy** You push down on the handle of a bicycle pump with a force of 20 N. The handle moves 0.3 m, and the pump does not absorb or release any heat. What is the change in thermal energy of the bicycle pump?
7. **Calculate Work** The thermal energy released when a gallon of gasoline is burned in a car's engine is 140 million J. If the engine is 25 percent efficient, how much work does it do when one gallon of gasoline is burned?

gpscience.com/self_check_quiz

3 Assess

DAILY INTERVENTION

Check for Understanding

Logical-Mathematical Have students work in small groups to think of as many ways as they can to keep a house warmer in the winter and then to categorize those ways according to energy source. L2 LS COOP LEARN

Reteach

Four-Stroke Engine Have students make flash cards with the names of the strokes of the four-stroke cycle of an internal combustion engine. On the reverse side of each card, have them write descriptions of the stroke. Partners can then test each other by shuffling the cards and sequencing them by both name and description. L2 LS **Linguistic** COOP LEARN

Assessment

Portfolio Have students make posters or drawings showing heat flow in any of the heating or cooling systems or engines studied. Some may be simpler than others, but all should show areas of high and low temperature and direction of heat flow. Use **Performance Assessment in the Science Classroom,** p. 145. L2 LS **Visual-Spatial** P

section 3 review

1. In an open system, heat flows across the boundary or work is done across the boundary. In a closed system, no heat flows across the boundary and no work is done across the boundary. The thermal energy stays constant.
2. Both systems use hot water and radiators to heat a home. In a conventional radiator system, fuel is used to heat the water. In an active solar heating system, the Sun's radiant energy is used to heat the water.
3. The second law of thermodynamics states that it is impossible to build a device that is 100% efficient. Increasing the temperature of the burning gases can increase the efficiency, but it will never be 100% efficient.
4. Check students' drawings.
5. The temperature of the juice will increase because you do work on the juice as you shake it.
6. $W = Fd = (20\text{ N})(0.3\text{ m}) = 6\text{ N}\cdot\text{m} = 6\text{ J}$
7. $(0.25)(140{,}000{,}000\text{J}) = 35{,}000{,}000\text{ J}$

Real-World Question

Purpose Students will observe how heat is transferred by conduction in liquids and gases. L2
Kinesthetic COOP LEARN

Process Skills collect data, measure, make and use tables, record data, make and use graphs, interpret data

Time Required 80 minutes

Procedure

Alternate Materials The knife used for cutting the foam cup should have a thin blade. A kitchen paring knife works well, but scissors are an acceptable substitute.

Safety Precautions Students should be careful while handling hot liquids. Caution them to use care while cutting with the knife. Number the knives and collect them before the end of class.

Teaching Strategies

- Have students work in small groups for this lab. Two students can call out the temperature readings as another student records them.
- Remind students that heat transfer by conduction occurs by touch. The particless have to touch in order for conduction to occur.

Conduction in Gases

Goals

- **Measure** temperature changes in air near a heat source.
- **Observe** conduction of heat in air.

Materials

thermometers (3)
foam cups (2)
400-mL beakers (2)
burner or hot plate
paring knife
thermal mitts (2)

Safety Precautions

WARNING: *Use care when handling hot water. Pour hot water using both hands.*

Real-World Question

Does smog occur where you live? If so, you may have experienced a temperature inversion. Usually the Sun warms the ground, and the air above it. When the air near the ground is warmer than the air above, convection occurs. This convection also carries smoke and other gases emitted by cars, chimneys, and smokestacks upward into the atmosphere. If the air near the ground is colder than the air above, convection does not occur. Then smoke and other pollutants can be trapped near the ground, sometimes forming smog. How does the insulating properties of air cause a temperature inversion to occur?

Procedure

1. Using the paring knife, carefully cut the bottom from one foam cup.
2. Use a pencil or pen to poke holes about 2 cm from the top and bottom of each foam cup.
3. Turn both cups upside down, and poke the ends of the thermometers through the upper holes and lower holes, so both thermometers are supported horizontally. The bulb end of both thermometers should extend into the middle of the bottomless cup.

Alternative Inquiry Lab

Weather Research To extend this lab into an Inquiry Lab, have students research the effects of convection of energy on weather patterns. Topics to research may include explaining typical local weather patterns, tornados, hurricanes, Chinook winds, trade winds, ocean currents, weather in relation to geographic features (such as mountains or plains), the ocean's effect on weather, hail storms, cloud formations, or any other suitable topic. Have students explain the phenomenon using an experiment, poster, model, or computer-generated presentation and written or oral descriptions.

4. Heat about 350 mL of water to about 80°C in one of the beakers.
5. Place an empty 400-mL beaker on top of the bottomless cup. Record the temperature of the two thermometers in your data table.
6. Add about 100 mL of hot water to the empty beaker. After one minute, record the temperatures of the thermometers in a data table like the one shown here.
7. Continue to record the temperatures every minute for 10 min. Add hot water as needed to keep the temperature of the water at about 80°C.

Air Temperatures in Foam Cup

Time (min)	Upper Thermometer (°C)	Lower Thermometer (°C)
0		
1		
2	Measured temperatures will vary.	
3		
4		
5		

Analyze Your Data

1. **Graph** the temperatures measured by the upper and lower thermometers on the same graph. Make the vertical *y*-axis the temperature and the horizontal *x*-axis the time.
2. **Calculate** the total temperature change for both thermometers by subtracting the initial temperature from the final temperature.
3. **Calculate** the average rate of temperature change for each thermometer by dividing the total temperature change by 10 min.

Conclude and Apply

1. **Explain** whether convection can occur in the foam cup if it's being heated from the top.
2. **Describe** how heat was transferred through the air in the foam cup.
3. **Explain** why the average rate of temperature change was different for each thermometer.

Your Data

Compare your results with other students in your class. **Identify** the factors caused the average rate of temperature change to be different for different groups.

Analyze Your Data

Expected Outcome The heat source is at the top of the container. Heat transfer by convection cannot occur, therefore the heat transfer must occur by conduction.

Answers to Questions

1. Check students' graphs.
2. Answers will vary. Check students' work.
3. Answers will vary. Check students' work.

Error Analysis Have each group compare its results with those of another group. If the data disagree, have students list reasons for the discrepancy.

Conclude and Apply

1. No. If the cup is heated from the top, the air at the top becomes warmer and less dense than the air below. As a result, this air does not sink and transfer heat to the cooler air below.
2. Because convection could not occur, heat was transferred by conduction in the air.
3. The thermometer at the top was closer to the hot water, so it took less time for heat to be transferred to the air around it. Heat had to be transferred by conduction to the lower thermometer. Because heat moves slowly through air, it took more time for heat to reach this thermometer and the temperature change of this thermometer occurred more slowly.

Assessment

Oral Ask students to use the kinetic theory to explain why heat transfers in the following order: from fastest to slowest solids, liquids, and gases. Use **Performance Assessment in the Science Classroom,** p. 89.

Communicating Your Data

Have students compare results with other groups and discuss differences noted. Why might these differences have occurred?

LAB 181

Content Background

The energy in the Sun is generated by the fusion of hydrogen atoms to form helium. Since the Sun is composed primarily of hydrogen atoms, the fuel for this reaction is readily available. The energy radiated from the Sun provides Earth with an environment that can support life, as we know it. The Sun provides energy for photosynthesis to occur, which provides a food source for many organisms. It provides heat, which combined with our atmosphere and water sources, provides a moderate temperature range that supports life. Despite all of these uses of solar energy a large portion of the energy that arrives on Earth's surface is not used. Scientists are attempting to develop technology that will enable people to use more of the Sun's energy.

Activity

Solar Energy Have students research the various ways people use solar energy. Students should make oral presentations to share their information with their class.

L2 IS **Auditory-Musical**

Differentiated Instruction

Challenge Solar energy from the Sun travels at a speed of 299,274 km/s. Express this number in scientific notation using three significant digits. 3.00×10^5 km/s Express this number in m/s using three significant digits and scientific notation. 3.00×10^8 m/s L3

SCIENCE Stats

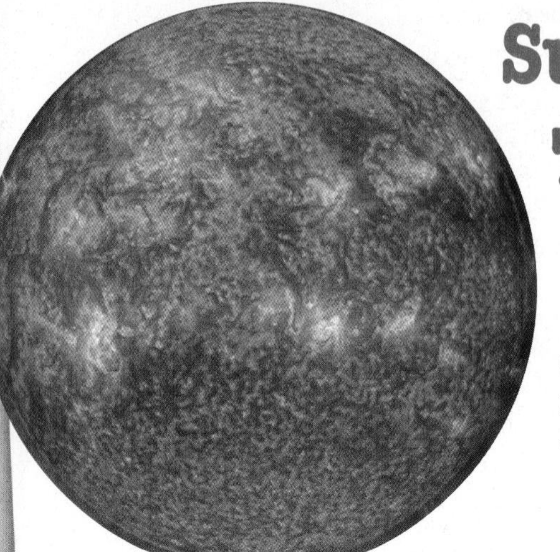

Surprising Thermal Energy

Did you know...

. . . The average amount of solar energy that reaches the United States each year is about 600 times greater than the nation's annual energy demands.

. . . When a space shuttle reenters Earth's atmosphere at more than 28,000 km/h, its outer surface is heated by friction to nearly 1,650°C. This temperature is high enough to melt steel.

. . . A lightning bolt heats the air in its path to temperatures of about 25,000°C. That's about 4 times hotter than the average temperature on the surface of the Sun.

Applying Math

1. The highest recorded temperature on Earth is 58°C and the lowest is −89°C. What is the range between the highest and lowest recorded temperatures?
2. What is the average temperature of the surface of the Sun? Draw a bar graph comparing the temperature of a lightning bolt to the temperature of the surface of the Sun.
3. The Sun is almost 150 million km from Earth. How long does it take solar energy to reach Earth if it travels at 300,000 km/s?

Applying Math

Teaching Strategies

- Review with students how to find range for question 1.
- Discuss which units should be used to mark the *y*-axis on the bar graph for the question 2.
- Provide graph paper to assist the students with question 2.

Answers

1. 147° C
2. 6,250° C. Check students' graphs.
3. 500 s = 8 min and 20 s

Reviewing Main Ideas

Section 1 Temperature and Heat

1. The temperature of a material is a measure of the average kinetic energy of the molecules in the material.
2. Heat is thermal energy that flows from a higher to a lower temperature.

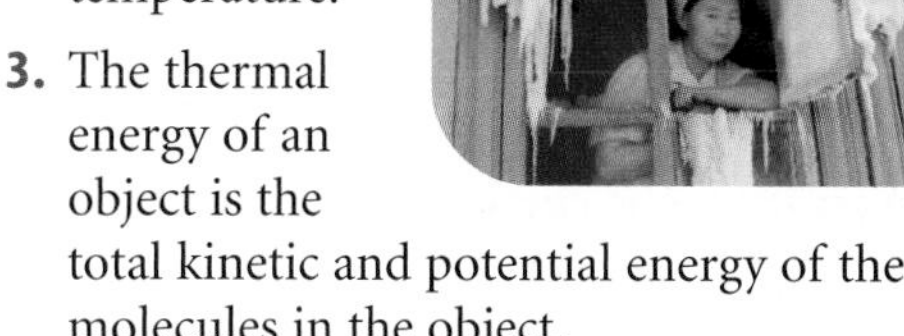

3. The thermal energy of an object is the total kinetic and potential energy of the molecules in the object.
4. The specific heat is the amount of heat needed to raise the temperature of 1 kg of a substance by 1°C.

Section 2 Transferring Thermal Energy

1. Conduction occurs when thermal energy is transferred by collisions between particles. Matter is not transferred when conduction occurs.
2. Convection occurs in a fluid as warmer and cooler fluid move from place to place.
3. Radiation is the transfer of energy by electromagnetic waves. Radiation can transfer energy through empty space.
4. Heat flows more easily in materials that are conductors than in insulators.
5. Some insulating materials contain pockets of trapped air that reduce the flow of heat.

Section 3 Using Heat

1. Conventional heating systems use air, hot water, and steam to transfer thermal energy through a building.
2. A solar heating system converts radiant energy from the Sun to thermal energy. Active solar systems use solar collectors to absorb the thermal radiant energy.
3. According to the first law of thermodynamics, the increase in the thermal energy of a system equals the work done on the system and the amount of heat added to the system.
4. The second law of thermodynamics states that heat cannot flow from a colder to a hotter temperature unless work is done, and that heat cannot be converted completely into work.
5. Heat engines convert heat into work. The efficiency of a heat engine can never be 100 percent. Refrigerators transfer heat from a cooler to a warmer temperature by doing work on the coolant.

FOLDABLES Use the Foldable that you made at the beginning of this chapter to help you review thermal energy.

Science Online gpscience.com/interactive_tutor

chapter 6 Study Guide

Reviewing Main Ideas

Summary statements can be used by students to review the major concepts of the chapter.

Science Online

Visit gpscience.com
/self_check_quiz
/interactive_tutor
/vocabulary_puzzlemaker
/chapter_review
/standardized_test
/field_guide

Assessment Transparency

For additional assessment questions, use the *Assessment Transparency* located in the transparency book.

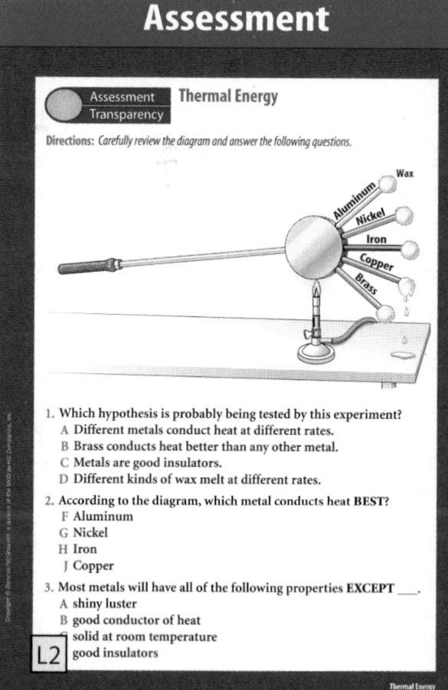

Assessment

Assessment Transparency **Thermal Energy**

Directions: *Carefully review the diagram and answer the following questions.*

1. Which hypothesis is probably being tested by this experiment?
   A Different metals conduct heat at different rates.
   B Brass conducts heat better than any other metal.
   C Metals are good insulators.
   D Different kinds of wax melt at different rates.
2. According to the diagram, which metal conducts heat BEST?
   F Aluminum
   G Nickel
   H Iron
   J Copper
3. Most metals will have all of the following properties EXCEPT ___.
   A shiny luster
   B good conductor of heat
   C solid at room temperature
   D good insulators

L2

Thermal Energy

FOLDABLES Have students use their Foldables to review the content of the chapter. On the back of the paper, have students write a paragraph comparing and contrasting temperature and thermal energy.

CHAPTER STUDY GUIDE 183

Using Vocabulary

1. heat engine
2. heat
3. solar collector
4. specific heat
5. temperature
6. conductor

Checking Concepts

7. B
8. A
9. D
10. A
11. B
12. C
13. A
14. A
15. C

Interpreting Graphics

16. See student page.
17. See student page.

chapter 6 Review

Using Vocabulary

conduction p. 164
convection p. 165
first law of thermodynamics p. 175
heat p. 160
heat engine p. 176
insulator p. 169
internal combustion engine p. 176
radiation p. 167
second law of thermodynamics p. 175
solar collector p. 174
specific heat p. 161
temperature p. 159
thermal energy p. 159
thermodynamics p. 174

Complete each statement using a word(s) from the vocabulary list above.

1. A ________ is a device that converts thermal energy into mechanical energy.
2. ________ is energy that is transferred from warmer to cooler materials.
3. A ________ is a device that absorbs the Sun's radiant energy.
4. The energy required to raise the temperature of 1 kg of a material 1°C. is a material's ________.
5. ________ is a measure of the average kinetic energy of the particles in a material.
6. Heat flows easily in a(n) ________.

Checking Concepts

Choose the word or phrase that best answers the question.

7. Which is NOT a method of heat transfer?
   A) conduction **C)** radiation
   B) specific heat **D)** convection
8. In which of the following devices is fuel burned inside chambers called cylinders?
   A) internal combustion engine
   B) radiator
   C) heat pump
   D) air conditioner
9. During which phase of a four-stroke engine are waste gases removed?
   A) power stroke **C)** compression stroke
   B) intake stroke **D)** exhaust stroke
10. Which of the following materials is a poor insulator of heat?
    A) iron **C)** air
    B) feathers **D)** plastic
11. Which of the following devices is an example of a heat mover?
    A) solar panel
    B) refrigerator
    C) internal combustion engine
    D) diesel engine
12. Which term describes the measure of the average kinetic energy of the particles in an object?
    A) potential energy
    B) thermal energy
    C) temperature
    D) specific heat
13. Which of these is NOT used to calculate change in thermal energy?
    A) volume
    B) temperature change
    C) specific heat
    D) mass
14. Which of the following processes does NOT require the presence of particles of matter?
    A) radiation **C)** convection
    B) conduction **D)** combustion
15. Which of the following is the name for thermal energy that is transferred only from a higher temperature to a lower temperature?
    A) potential energy
    B) kinetic energy
    C) heat
    D) solar energy

Science Online gpscience.com/vocabulary_puzzlemaker

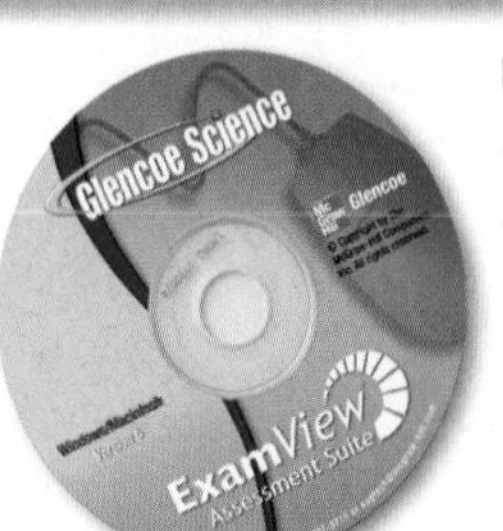

Use the *ExamView® Assessment Suite* CD-ROM to:
- create multiple versions of tests
- create modified tests with one mouse click for inclusion students
- edit existing questions and add your own questions
- build tests aligned with state standards using built-in State Curriculum Tags
- change English tests to Spanish with one mouse click and vice versa

Interpreting Graphics

16. Complete the following events-chain concept map to show how an active solar heating system works.

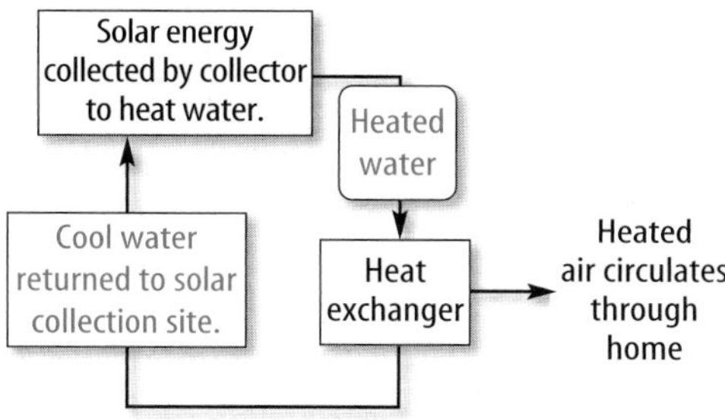

17. Copy and complete this concept map.

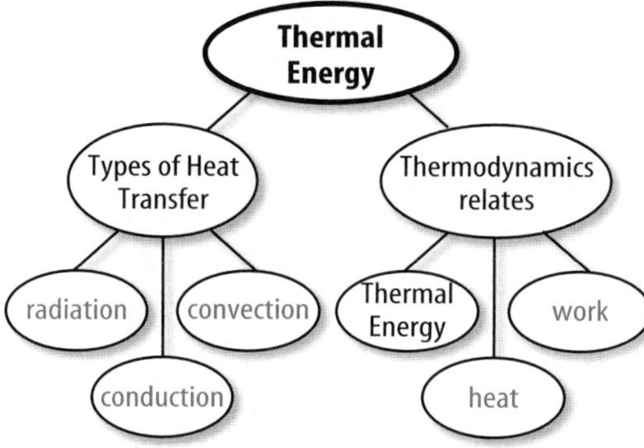

Thinking Critically

18. Explain On a hot day a friend suggests that you can make your kitchen cooler by leaving the refrigerator door open. Explain whether leaving the refrigerator door open would cause the air temperature in the kitchen to decrease.

19. Explain Which has the greater amount of thermal energy, one liter of water at 50°C or two liters of water at 50°C?

20. Explain whether or not the following statement is true: If the thermal energy of an object increases, the temperature of the object must also increase.

21. Predict Suppose a beaker of water is heated from the top. Predict which is more likely to occur in the water—heat transfer by conduction or convection. Explain.

22. Classify Order the events that occur in the removal of heat from an object by a refrigerator. Draw the complete cycle, from the placing of a warm object in the refrigerator to the changes in the coolant.

Applying Math

Use the table below to answer questions 23 to 25.

Specific Heat of Materials

Material	Specific Heat (J/kg°C)
Water	4,184
Copper	385
Silver	235
Graphite	710
Iron	450

23. Calculate Thermal Energy How much thermal energy is needed to raise the temperature of 4.0 kg of water from 25°C to 75°C?

24. Calculate Temperature Change How does the temperature of 33.0 g of graphite change when it absorbs 350 J of thermal energy?

25. Calculate Mass A hot iron ball is dropped into 200.0 g of cooler water. The water temperature increases by 2.0°C and the temperature of the ball decreases by 18.6°C. What is the mass of the iron ball?

Science Online gpscience.com/chapter_review

chapter Review 6

Thinking Critically

18. It would not cool the kitchen. The thermal energy from the kitchen that is transferred to the refrigerator coolant would be transferred back to the kitchen from the condenser coils.

19. Thermal energy is the sum of the kinetic and potential energy of the water molecules. Doubling the amount of water will double the thermal energy.

20. It is not true. The increase in thermal energy may increase the potential energy so that the temperature remains unchanged.

21. If the water is heated from the top, conduction will occur instead of convection. The warm water on the top is less dense than the cooler water below and will not sink.

22. Heat transferred from the warm object to the coolant in refrigerator, coolant is compressed and the temperature rises, heat transferred from the warm coolant to the outside air, the coolant expands as it passes through expansion valve and cools.

Applying Math

National Math Standards

1, 2, 5, 9

23. $Q = m \times (T_{final} - T_{initial}) \times C$
$= (4.0\ \text{kg})(50\ ^\circ\text{C})(4{,}184\ \text{J/kg} \cdot ^\circ\text{C})$
$= 836{,}800\ \text{J}$

24. increases by 14.9 °C

25. Heat lost by ball = heat gained by water = (0.2 kg)(2.0 °C)(4,184 J/kg · °C) = 1,673 J. mass of ball = 200 g

Assessment Resources

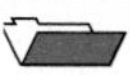
Reproducible Masters

Chapter *Fast File* Resources
Chapter Review, pp. 37–38
Chapter Tests, pp. 39–42
Assessment Transparency Activity, p. 49

Glencoe Science Web site
Chapter Review Test
Standardized Test Practice

Glencoe Technology
Assessment Transparency
ExamView® Assessment Suite
MindJogger Videoquiz
Interactive Chalkboard

Answer Sheet A practice answer sheet can be found at gpscience.com/answer_sheet.

Name Date Class

Standardized Test Practice

Assessment Student Recording Sheet

Use with pages 788–789 of the Student Edition

Standardized Test Practice

Part 1 Multiple Choice

Select the best answer from the choices given and fill in the corresponding oval.

1. Ⓐ Ⓑ Ⓒ Ⓓ 8. Ⓐ Ⓑ Ⓒ Ⓓ
2. Ⓐ Ⓑ Ⓒ Ⓓ 9. Ⓐ Ⓑ Ⓒ Ⓓ
3. Ⓐ Ⓑ Ⓒ Ⓓ 10. Ⓐ Ⓑ Ⓒ Ⓓ
4. Ⓐ Ⓑ Ⓒ Ⓓ 11. Ⓐ Ⓑ Ⓒ Ⓓ
5. Ⓐ Ⓑ Ⓒ Ⓓ 12. Ⓐ Ⓑ Ⓒ Ⓓ
6. Ⓐ Ⓑ Ⓒ Ⓓ 13. Ⓐ Ⓑ Ⓒ Ⓓ
7. Ⓐ Ⓑ Ⓒ Ⓓ 14. Ⓐ Ⓑ Ⓒ Ⓓ

Part 2 Constructed Response/Grid In

Record and bubble in your answers on the grids below.

15. 16. 17.

Record your answers for Questions 18–21 on a separate sheet of paper.

SAMPLE

Part 1 Multiple Choice

1. D
2. A
3. A
4. C
5. C
6. A
7. D

Part 2 Short Response

8. Heat is thermal energy that flows from something at a higher temperature to something at a lower temperature. Heat is measured in units of joules.
9. Possible answer: Energy travels from the Sun to the Earth by electromagnetic waves. This is an example of radiation. During earthquakes, energy travels by seismic waves through the Earth. This is an example of conduction.
10. Materials that are light-colored reflect more radiant energy, while dark-colored materials absorb more radiant energy.
11. It has a high specific heat, meaning it can absorb heat without a large change in temperature.

chapter 6 Standardized Test Practice

Part 1 Multiple Choice

Record your answers on the answer sheet provided by your teacher or on a sheet of paper.

1. The difference between the boiling point and the freezing point of potassium is 695.72 K. What is the difference between the two points on the Celsius temperature scale?

A. 100.00°C **C.** 422.57°C
B. 275.15°C **D.** 695.72°C

Use the table below to answer questions 2 and 3.

Material	Specific Heat [J/(kg °C)]
Copper	385
Gold	449
Lead	129
Tin	228
Zinc	388

2. According to the table above, a 2-kg block of which of the following materials would require 898 joules of heat to increase its temperature by 1°C?

A. gold **C.** tin
B. lead **D.** zinc

3. Which of the following materials would require the most heat to raise a 5-kg sample of the material from 10°C to 50°C?

A. gold **C.** tin
B. lead **D.** zinc

4. Automobile engines usually are four-stroke engines. During which stroke does the spark from a spark plug ignite the fuel-air mixture?

A. the intake stroke
B. the compression stroke
C. the power stroke
D. the exhaust stroke

5. A refrigerator is an example of what type of device that removes thermal energy from one location and transfers it to another location at a differrent temperature?

A. condenser **C.** heat mover
B. conductor **D.** heat pump

6. The temperature of a 24.5-g block of aluminum decreases from 30.0°C to 21.5°C. If aluminum has a specific heat of 897 J/(kg°C), what is the change in thermal energy of the block of aluminum?

A. 187 J **C.** 5,820 J
B. 2,590 J **D.** 187,000 J

Use the figure below to answer question 7.

7. The photograph above shows a pot of boiling water. What type of heat transfer causes the water at the top of the pot to become hot?

A. conduction
B. convection
C. convection and radiation
D. conduction and convection

Test-Taking Tip

Read All the Information On a bar graph, line up each bar with its corresponding value by laying your pencil between the two points.

12. The type of heat transfer is conduction. The heat source increases the kinetic energy of nearby particles. This energy moves through the material by collisions among particles.
13. No. Thermal energy only flows from warmer to cooler objects. The block of ice would absorb heat from the material.
14. In warm weather, a heat pump operates as an air conditioner. In cold weather, a heat pump operates like an air conditioner in reverse.

Part 3 Open Ended

15. The mass of water in the calorimeter and its temperature are measured. A sample of material of known mass is heated and its temperature is measured. The heated sample is then placed in the calorimeter. Heat flows from the sample to the water until they both reach the same temperature. The increase in thermal energy

Part 2 Short Response/Grid In

Record your answers on the answer sheet provided by your teacher or on a sheet of paper.

8. Define the term *heat* and tell what units are used to measure heat.

9. Give an example of how waves transfer energy by radiation. Give an example of how energy is transferred by conduction.

10. How is the color of a material related to its absorption and reflection of radiant energy?

11. What property of water makes it useful as a coolant?

Use the figure below to answer questions 12 and 13.

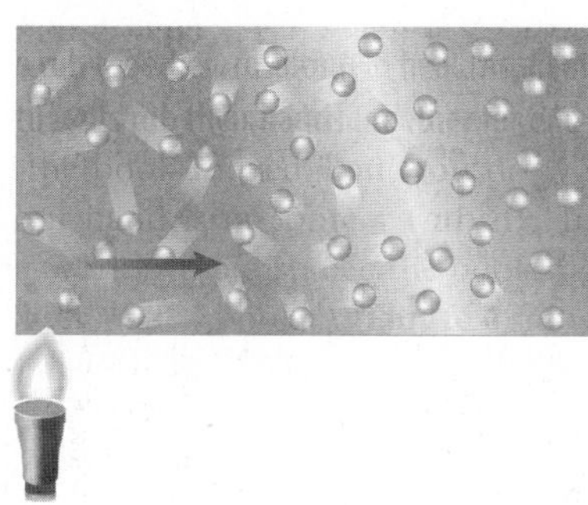

12. The illustration above shows a heat source below one end of a material. Heat is transferred from the warmer part of the material to the cooler part. Name and describe the type of heat transfer illustrated in the figure.

13. If the heat source were replaced by a block of ice, would cold be transferred through the material in the same way? Explain why or why not.

14. How is a heat pump different from an air conditioner?

Part 3 Open Ended

Record your answers on a sheet of paper.

Use the figure below to answer question 15.

15. The calorimeter in the illustration above is composed of inner and outer chambers that surround a thick layer of air. Describe the process by which the calorimeter is used to measure the specific heat of materials.

16. Define the terms *temperature* and *thermal energy.* Explain how the temperature and thermal energy of an object are related.

17. Conduction can occur in solids, liquids, and gases. Explain why solids and liquids are better conductors of heat than gases.

18. Explain why radiation usually passes more easily through gases than through solids or liquids.

19. Suppose you have a glass half-filled with 250 mL of water at a temperature of 30°C. You then add 250 mL of water at the same temperature to the glass. Explain any changes in the water's temperature and thermal energy.

20. Explain how changes in a fluid's density enables convection to occur.

of the water, which is equal to the thermal energy lost by the sample, can be calculated. Because the mass of the sample, its change in temperature, and the change in thermal energy are known, the sample's specific heat can be calculated.

16. Temperature is the average kinetic energy of an object's particles. Thermal energy is the total kinetic and potential energy of all the particles of an object. When the average kinetic energy of the particles increase, the total kinetic and potential energy increases. Thus, when the temperature of an object increases, the thermal energy increases.

17. The particles in solids and liquids are usually much closer together than they are in gases. This means they collide with one another more often, enabling them to conduct heat more effectively.

18. In a solid, liquid, or gas, radiant energy can travel through the space between molecules. Molecules can absorb this radiation and re-emit some of the energy they absorbed. This energy then travels through the space and on to other molecules as it is passed through the material. Because molecules are much farther apart in gases than in solids or liquids, radiation usually passes more easily through gases than through solids or liquids.

19. Temperature is the average kinetic energy of the water's molecules. Because the temperature is the same for the beginning and the added water, the average kinetic energy, and therefore the temperature, remains unchanged. The thermal energy, however, doubles. Thermal energy is the total kinetic and potential energy of the molecules. When you double the number of molecules, the total kinetic and potential energy double, even though the average kinetic energy remains the same.

20. Convection is the transfer of energy in a fluid by the movement of the heated particles. When a fluid is heated, the particles move faster, As the particles move faster, they tend to be farther apart. The fluid expands as its temperature increases. The volume of the fluid increases, but its mass remains unchanged. The result is that the density of the fluid increases. Convection occurs when the warmer, less-dense fluid rises above the cooler, denser fluid.

Rubrics

For more help evaluating open-ended assessment questions, see the rubric on p. 10T.

unit 2

Unit Contents

WebQuest *MagLev Trains: Floating Locomotives* is an investigation of magnets and how they work. Using online resources, students study different types of magnetic levitation, design and build a maglev train, then test and refine their models. Class presentations reflect student designs, procedures, refinements, and results.

PROJECT CRISS[SM]

Study Skills

Discussion Provide students with sticky notes. Have students read through one or more chapters in the unit, either at home or as an in-class assignment. As they read, they should use the sticky notes to mark topics or examples they find especially interesting or difficult. They may use the notes for short descriptions or questions they may have, or to mark uses for electricity, magnetism, or nuclear energy that they find interesting.

In the late 1800s, a mysterious form of radiation called X rays was discovered. One French physicist wondered whether uranium would give off X rays after being exposed to sunlight. He figured that if X rays were emitted, they would make a bright spot on a wrapped photographic plate. But the weather turned cloudy, so the physicist placed the uranium and the photographic plate together in a drawer. Later, on a hunch, he developed the plate and found that the uranium had made a bright spot anyway. The uranium was giving off some kind of radiation even without being exposed to sunlight! Scientists soon determined that the atoms of uranium are radioactive—that is, they give off particles and energy from their nuclei. In today's nuclear power plants, this energy is harnessed and converted into electricity. This electricity provides some of the power used in homes to operate everything from lamps to toasters.

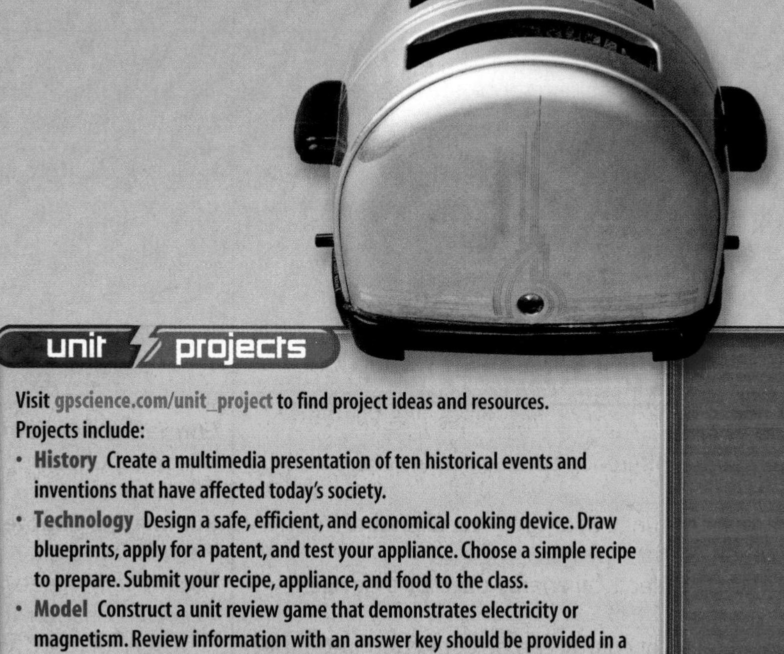

unit projects

Visit gpscience.com/unit_project to find project ideas and resources.
Projects include:

- **History** Create a multimedia presentation of ten historical events and inventions that have affected today's society.
- **Technology** Design a safe, efficient, and economical cooking device. Draw blueprints, apply for a patent, and test your appliance. Choose a simple recipe to prepare. Submit your recipe, appliance, and food to the class.
- **Model** Construct a unit review game that demonstrates electricity or magnetism. Review information with an answer key should be provided in a well-designed, marketable package.

Using the *MagLev Trains* WebQuest, research, design, build, and test your own version of a maglev train, then present your model to the class.

NATIONAL GEOGRAPHIC How Are Clouds & Toasters Connected?

- Ask students to list the connections between clouds and toasters. You might want them to use a concept map to relate one step to another.
- Students might start this activity with negative ideas about nuclear energy. Have them make a two-column table they can use to list the positive and negative aspects of nuclear energy as they learn more about it.
- Ask students to brainstorm what geographic areas might most likely use nuclear power to produce electricity and why. Most nuclear power plants are in regions of the country with the highest populations, where there is the greatest need.

unit projects

History Have students research ten historical events and inventions that have affected communication, energy use, or technology development today. Students prepare a brief summary of these events, how they relate to each other, and how they affect their everyday lives. Students then display the information to their classmates in a creative multimedia presentation.

Technology Ask students to design a safe, efficient, and economical cooking device that uses energy other than fossil fuels. Have students draw blueprints, apply to the teacher for a "patent" on their original device, test their appliance with a recipe, and then submit the recipe, appliance, and cooked food for teacher and peer evaluation.

Model Have students design and construct a unit review game or toy that demonstrates electricity or magnetism as one of its characteristics. The completed model should contain directions for use, an ample amount of unit review information with answer guide, and be contained in a well-designed box, ready for the game-store market. Display each creative, quality product for class review, as well as evaluation by peers and teachers for educational review value, electric and magnetic modeling, construction quality, safety, and enjoyment.

Additional Resources For more information, resources, and assessment rubrics, visit gpscience.com/unit_project

Electricity

BIG Idea **The flow of electric charges in a circuit is a source of electrical energy.**

	Content Standards	Learning Objectives	Resources to Assess Mastery
Section 1	**5–8:** UCP.2, 3, 5; A.1, 2; B.1, 2 **9–12:** UCP.2, 3, 5; A.1, 2; B.2, 4	**Electric Charge** 1. **Describe** how electric charges exert forces on each other. 2. **Compare** the strengths of electric and gravitational forces. 3. **Distinguish** between conductors and insulators. 4. **Explain** how objects become electrically charged. ***Main Idea*** Like electric charges attract each other and unlike charges repel.	**Formative Assessment** Reading Check, pp. 193, 194 Section Review, p. 199 **Summative Assessment** *ExamView® Assessment Suite*
Section 2	**5–8:** UCP.2, 3, 5; A.1, 2; B.1, 2 **9–12:** UCP.2, 3, 5; A.1, 2; B.2, 4	**Electric Current** 5. **Describe** how voltage difference causes current to flow. 6. **Explain** how batteries produce a voltage difference in a circuit. 7. **List** the factors that affect an object's electrical resistance. 8. **Define** Ohm's law. ***Main Idea*** A voltage difference causes electrons to flow in a circuit.	**Formative Assessment** Reading Check, pp. 200, 204 Section Review, p. 205 **Summative Assessment** *ExamView® Assessment Suite*
Section 3	**5–8:** UCP.2–5; A.1, 2; B.1–3; F.5 **9–12:** UCP.2, 3, 5; A.1, 2; B.2, 4, 6; F.6 See pp. 16T–17T for a Key to Standards.	**Electrical Energy** 9. **Describe** the difference between series and parallel circuits. 10. **Recognize** the function of circuit breakers and fuses. 11. **Calculate** electrical power. 12. **Calculate** the electrical energy used by a device. ***Main Idea*** Electrical energy can be converted into other forms of energy in a circuit.	**Formative Assessment** Reading Check, pp. 207, 210 Section Review, p. 213 **Summative Chapter Assessment** MindJogger, Ch. 7 *ExamView® Assessment Suite* Leveled Chapter Test Test A L1 Test B L2 Test C L3 Test Practice, pp. 220–221

Suggested Pacing				
Period	**Instruction**	**Labs**	**Review & Assessment**	**Total**
Single	4 days	3 days	2 days	9 days
Block	2 blocks	1.5 blocks	1 block	4.5 blocks

Core Instruction	Leveled Resources	Leveled Labs	Pacing Period		Block
Student Text, pp. 190–199 Section Focus Transparency, Ch. 7, Section 1 Interactive Chalkboard, Ch. 7, Section 1 Identifying Misconceptions, p. 196 Differentiated Instruction, pp. 195, 197 Visualizing Lightning, p. 197	**Chapter *Fast File* Resources** Directed Reading for Content Mastery, p. 18 L1 Note-taking Worksheet, pp. 31–33 Reinforcement, p. 25 L2 Enrichment, p. 28 L3 **Reading Essentials,** p. 102 L1 ELL **Science Notebook,** p. 69 ELL ***Active*Folders**: *Electricity* L1 ELL	**Launch Lab**, p. 191: battery, flashlight bulb, insulated wire, electrical tape or battery holder *15 min* L2 **MiniLAB**, p. 198: transparent tape *10 min* L2	**1**	Section 1, pp. 191–194 (includes Launch Lab)	**1**
			2	Section 1, pp. 195–199 (includes MiniLAB and Section Review)	
Student Text, pp. 200–206 Section Focus Transparency, Ch. 7, Section 2 Interactive Chalkboard, Ch. 7, Section 2 Identifying Misconceptions, pp. 201, 203, 204	**Chapter *Fast File* Resources** Directed Reading for Content Mastery, p. 19 L1 Note-taking Worksheet, pp. 31–33 Reinforcement, p. 26 L2 Enrichment, p. 29 L3 **Reading Essentials,** p. 108 L1 ELL **Science Notebook,** p. 73 ELL	**MiniLAB**, p. 202: D-cell batteries (2), 3-volt bulbs and sockets (3), insulated wire *15 min* L2 ***Lab**, p. 206: battery, flashlight bulb, bulb holder, insulated wire *40 min* L1 L2 L3	**3**	Section 2, pp. 200–203 (includes MiniLAB)	**2**
			4	Section 2, pp. 203–205 (includes Section Review)	
			5	Lab:Indentifying Conductors and Insulators, p. 206	**3**
Student Text, pp. 207–215 Section Focus Transparency, Ch. 7, Section 3 Teaching Transparency, Ch. 7, Section 3 Interactive Chalkboard, Ch. 7, Section 2 Applying Math, pp. 211, 212 Differentiated Instruction, p. 212 Chapter Study Guide, p. 217	**Chapter *Fast File* Resources** Directed Reading for Content Mastery, pp. 19, 20 L1 Note-taking Worksheet, pp. 31–33 Reinforcement, p. 27 L2 Enrichment, p. 30 L3 **Reading Essentials,** p. 114 L1 ELL **Science Notebook,** p. 76 ELL	***Lab**, pp. 214–215: 6-V dry-cell battery, small lights with sockets (3), aluminum foil, paper clips, tape, scissors, paper *45 min* L1 L2 L3 *Lab version A L1 version B L2 L3	**6**	Section 3, pp. 207–210	
			7	Section 3, pp. 210–213 (includes Section Review)	**4**
			8	Lab:Comparing Series and Parallel Circuits, pp. 214–215	
			9	Study Guide, Chapter Review, and Test Practice, pp. 214–215	**4.5**

Video Lab

Transparencies

Section Focus

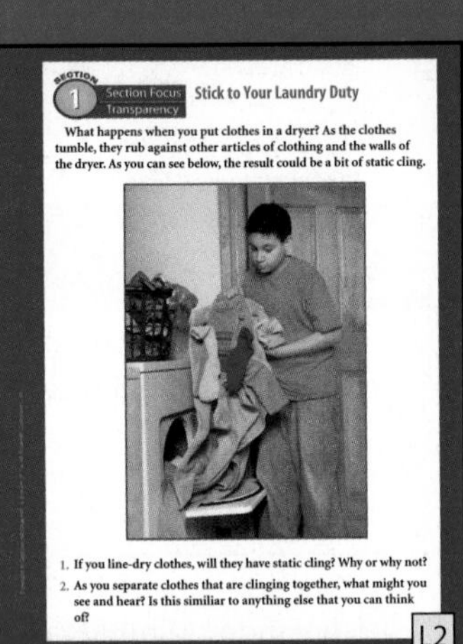
Section 1 Section Focus Transparency
Stick to Your Laundry Duty

What happens when you put clothes in a dryer? As the clothes tumble, they rub against other articles of clothing and the walls of the dryer. As you can see below, the result could be a bit of static cling.

1. If you line-dry clothes, will they have static cling? Why or why not?
2. As you separate clothes that are clinging together, what might you see and hear? Is this similiar to anything else that you can think of?

L2

Section 2 Section Focus Transparency
Go with the Flow

Do you see how the water flows down the cliff? Water takes the path of least resistance—it flows where it's easiest for water to go. Electric currents flow and experience resistance, too.

1. Which do you think has more energy, the waterfall in the picture or Niagara Falls which are higher and have move water flowing over? Explain your answer.
2. How do people use the energy in water currents?

L2

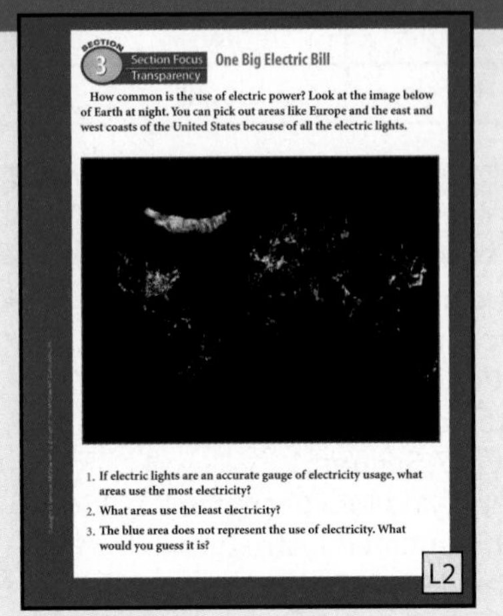
Section 3 Section Focus Transparency
One Big Electric Bill

How common is the use of electric power? Look at the image below of Earth at night. You can pick out areas like Europe and the east and west coasts of the United States because of all the electric lights.

1. If electric lights are an accurate gauge of electricity usage, what areas use the most electricity?
2. What areas use the least electricity?
3. The blue area does not represent the use of electricity. What would you guess it is?

L2

This is a representation of key blackline masters available in the Teacher Classroom Resources. See Resource Manager boxes within the chapter for additional information.

Assessment

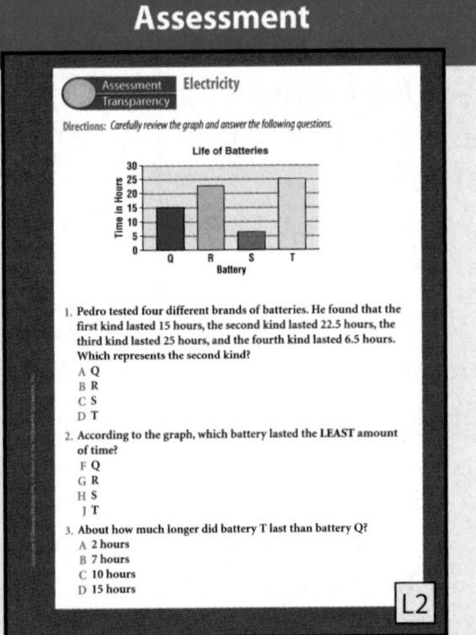
Assessment Transparency
Electricity

Directions: *Carefully review the graph and answer the following questions.*

1. Pedro tested four different brands of batteries. He found that the first kind lasted 15 hours, the second kind lasted 22.5 hours, the third kind lasted 25 hours, and the fourth kind lasted 6.5 hours. Which represents the second kind?
   A Q
   B R
   C S
   D T
2. According to the graph, which battery lasted the **LEAST** amount of time?
   F Q
   G R
   H S
   J T
3. About how much longer did battery T last than battery Q?
   A 2 hours
   B 7 hours
   C 10 hours
   D 15 hours

L2

Teaching

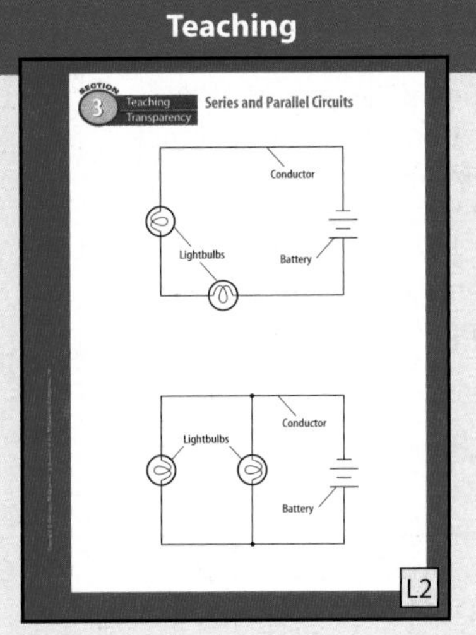
Section 3 Teaching Transparency
Series and Parallel Circuits

L2

Key to Teaching Strategies

The following designations will help you decide which activities are appropriate for your students.

- L1 Level 1 activities should be appropriate for students with learning difficulties.
- L2 Level 2 activities should be within the ability range of all students.
- L3 Level 3 activities are designed for above-average students.
- ELL ELL activities should be within the ability range of English Language Learners.
- COOP LEARN Cooperative Learning activities are designed for small group work.
- LS Multiple Learning Styles logos, as described on page 12T, are used throughout to indicate strategies that address different learning styles.
- P These strategies represent student products that can be placed into a best-work portfolio.
- PBL Problem-Based Learning activities apply real-world situations to learning.

Hands-on Activities

Student Text Lab Worksheet

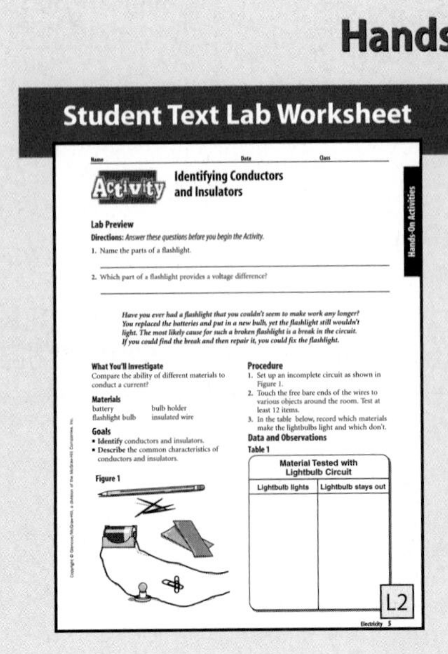
Name Date Class

Activity: Identifying Conductors and Insulators

Hands-On Activities

Lab Preview

Directions: *Answer these questions before you begin the Activity.*

1. Name the parts of a flashlight.
2. Which part of a flashlight provides a voltage difference?

Have you ever had a flashlight that you couldn't seem to make work any longer? You replaced the batteries and put in a new bulb, yet the flashlight still wouldn't light. The most likely cause for such a broken flashlight is a break in the circuit. If you could find the break and then repair it, you could fix the flashlight.

What You'll Investigate
Compare the ability of different materials to conduct a current?

Materials
battery, bulb holder, flashlight bulb, insulated wire

Goals
- **Identify** conductors and insulators.
- **Describe** the common characteristics of conductors and insulators.

Figure 1

Procedure
1. Set up an incomplete circuit as shown in Figure 1.
2. Touch the free bare ends of the wires to various objects around the room. Test at least 12 items.
3. In the table below, record which materials make the lightbulbs light and which don't.

Data and Observations

Table 1

Material Tested with Lightbulb Circuit	
Lightbulb lights	Lightbulb stays out

L2

Electricity 5

Laboratory Activities

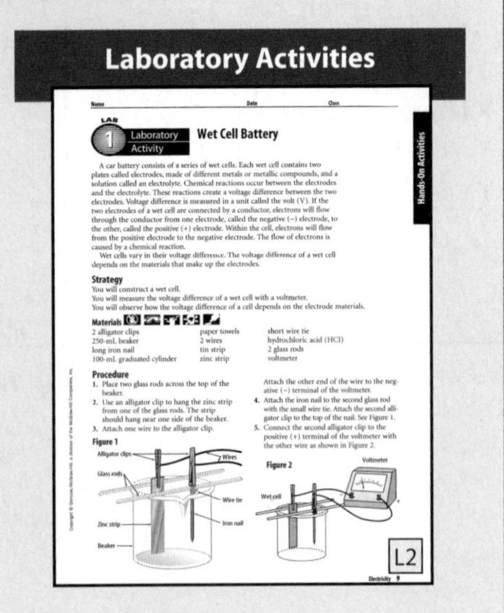
Name Date Class

Lab 1 Laboratory Activity
Wet Cell Battery

Hands-On Activities

A car battery consists of a series of wet cells. Each wet cell contains two plates called electrodes, made of different metals or metallic compounds, and a solution called an electrolyte. Chemical reactions occur between the electrodes and the electrolyte. These reactions create a voltage difference between the two electrodes. Voltage difference is measured in a unit called the volt (V). If the two electrodes of a wet cell are connected by a conductor, electrons will flow through the conductor from one electrode, called the negative (−) electrode, to the other, called the positive (+) electrode. Within the cell, electrons will flow from the positive electrode to the negative electrode. The flow of electrons is caused by a chemical reaction.

Wet cells vary in their voltage difference. The voltage difference of a wet cell depends on the materials that make up the electrodes.

Strategy
You will construct a wet cell.
You will measure the voltage difference of a wet cell with a voltmeter.
You will observe how the voltage difference of a cell depends on the electrode materials.

Materials
2 alligator clips, 250-mL beaker, long iron nail, 100-mL graduated cylinder, paper towels, 2 wires, tin strip, zinc strip, short wire tie, hydrochloric acid (HCl), 2 glass rods, voltmeter

Procedure
1. Place two glass rods across the top of the beaker.
2. Use an alligator clip to hang the zinc strip from one of the glass rods. The strip should hang near one side of the beaker.
3. Attach one wire to the alligator clip. Attach the other end of the wire to the negative (−) terminal of the voltmeter.
4. Attach the iron nail to the second glass rod with the small wire tie. Attach the second alligator clip to the top of the nail. See Figure 1.
5. Connect the second alligator clip to the positive (+) terminal of the voltmeter with the other wire as shown in Figure 2.

Figure 1

Figure 2

L2

Electricity 9

Meeting Different Ability Levels

Content Outline

Note-taking Worksheet — Electricity

Section 1 Electric Charge

Meeting Individual Needs

L2

Reinforcement

Section 1 Reinforcement — Electric Charge

Meeting Individual Needs

L2

Enrichment

Section 1 Enrichment — Electricity in Everyday Life

Activity	Prediction	Result and explanation
1. Run a plastic comb through your hair several times. Hold the comb next to a stream of running water.		
2. Tie two inflated balloons together with a string. Hold the balloons next to each other and rub both with a piece of wool.		
3. Hold a piece of newspaper flat against the wall. Stroke across the surface of the newspaper with your hand.		
4. Stretch a piece of clear plastic food wrap over a glass jar and fold down the sides.		
5. Add an antistatic dryer sheet to some clothes in a dryer. Turn the dryer on for 15 minutes.		

L3

Directed Reading (English/Spanish)

Directed Reading for Content Mastery — Overview — Electricity

Meeting Individual Needs

L1

Study Guide

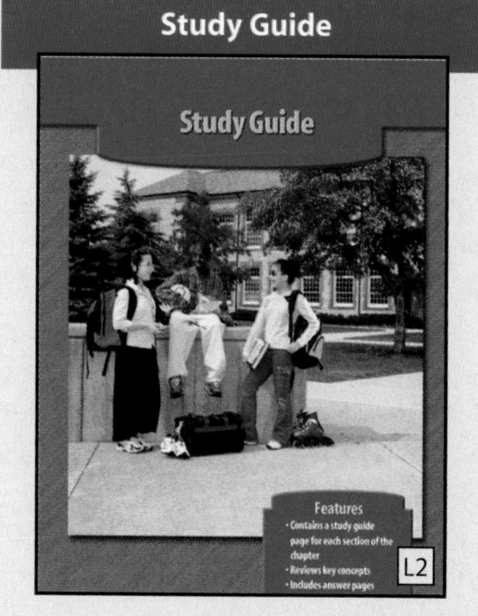

Study Guide
Features
• Contains a study guide page for each section of the chapter
• Reviews key concepts
• Includes answer pages
L2

Reading Essentials

Reading Essentials for Glencoe Science
An Interactive Student Workbook
Features
• Condensed core content
• Actively involves students in reading
• Reinforces key vocabulary
L1

Assessment

Test Practice Workbook

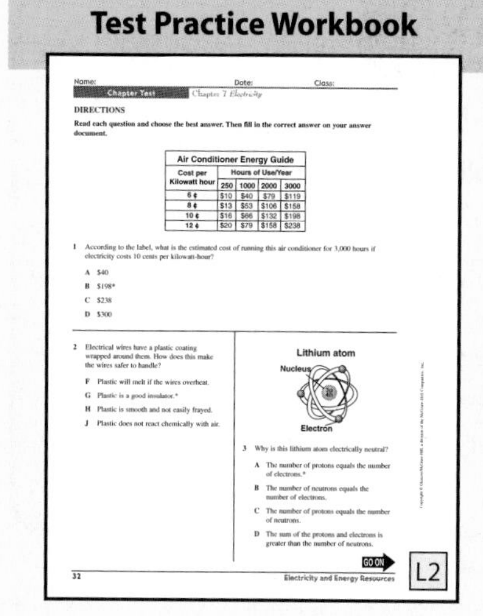

Chapter Test — Chapter 7 Electricity

Air Conditioner Energy Guide

Cost per Kilowatt hour	250	1000	2000	3000
6 ¢	$10	$40	$79	$119
8 ¢	$13	$53	$106	$158
10 ¢	$16	$66	$132	$198
12 ¢	$20	$79	$158	$238

L2

Chapter Review

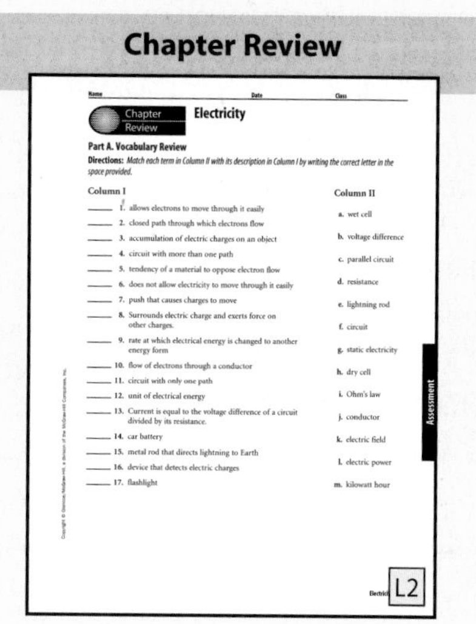

Chapter Review — Electricity

Part A. Vocabulary Review

Assessment

L2

Chapter Tests

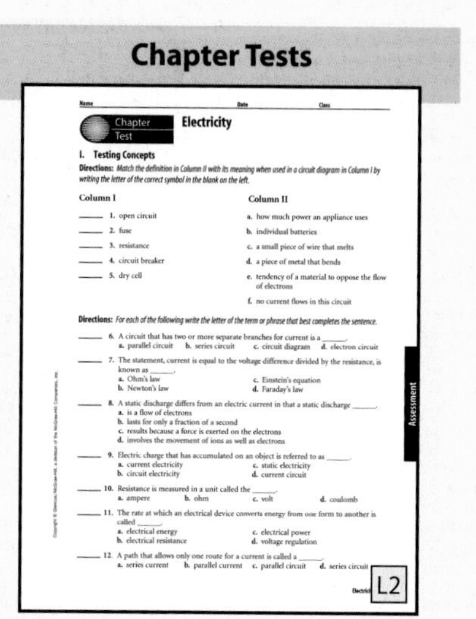

Chapter Test — Electricity

I. Testing Concepts

Assessment

L2

Science Content Background

section 1 Electric Charge

Positive and Negative Charge

Waterfalls produce airborne negative charges. Some people believe these charges make us feel happy and healthy. Ion machines were created to produce negative charges in houses and offices.

Transferring Charge

Benjamin Franklin invented the lightning rod to protect homes by transferring charge. It was a metal rod that was grounded through a wire. The top of the rod was sharpened to a point. Recently scientists discovered that the rods actually work better if they are not sharpened at the top.

section 2 Electric Current

Current and Voltage Difference

Electric current flows from a region of high electric potential energy to low electric potential energy. Electric charge loses electric potential energy as it flows through a circuit just as a ball loses gravitational potential energy when it falls. The electric potential energy lost by a coulomb of charge from one point to another is the voltage difference between the two points. This energy can be used to do useful tasks, such as run electric motors. A battery increases the electrical potential energy of charges, just as lifting a ball increases the ball's gravitational potential energy. All circuits contain electric resistance that converts some electric potential energy to heat as charges move through the circuit.

Electric current has the unit of the ampere, which is defined as one coulomb per second. One coulomb is equivalent to the charge of 6.25×10^{18} electrons.

section 3 Electrical Energy

Series and Parellel Circuits

We pay the electric company for our use of electrical energy. The electrons that transfer electrical energy are not used up in the process; they keep flowing.

In a series circuit with three different resistors, the current at all points in the circuit is the same but the voltage difference across each resistor is different. In a parallel circuit with three different resistors, the voltage difference across the resistors is the same but the current is different.

Electric Power

Electric power is found by multiplying current (coulombs/second) times voltage (joules/coulomb), giving units of joules/second, which is equivalent to a watt.

chapter content resources

Internet Resources

For additional content background, visit gpscience.com to:

- access your book online
- find references to related articles in popular science magazines
- access Web links with related content background
- access current events with science journal topics

Print Resources

Electricity, by Wendy Baker, Alexandra Parsons, Andrew Haslam, Two-Can Publishing, 2000

Electricity, by John Farndon, Benchmark Books, 2000

Electricity (Discovery Channel School Science), by Richie Chevat, Jacqueline A. Ball, Joellyn M. Ausanka, Steve Grey, Gareth Stevens Publishing, May 2003

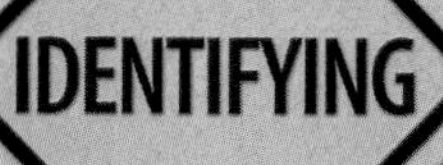

Misconceptions

Find Out What Students Think

Students may think that . . .

Voltage is the same at different places in a circuit and it exists only when current flows. Because electrons and the flow of charge that make up electricity cannot be seen directly, electricity can be difficult to understand and terms such as voltage, current, power, and energy can be confusing. Of all these terms, voltage is the most abstract and can be the most difficult to grasp. Because of the omnipresence of batteries, students are probably familiar with the volt as a unit of measure. This may conceal their misconceptions about voltage. They may confuse the relationship between voltage and current and may come to the wrong conclusion that voltage is a consequence of current and not the cause of it. They also may have inaccurate conceptions of how voltages in a circuit vary.

Activity

Draw the circuit shown in the figure below on the board, and ask students to predict and write what the voltages will be between the points A–B, B–C, C–D, B–D, and A–E.

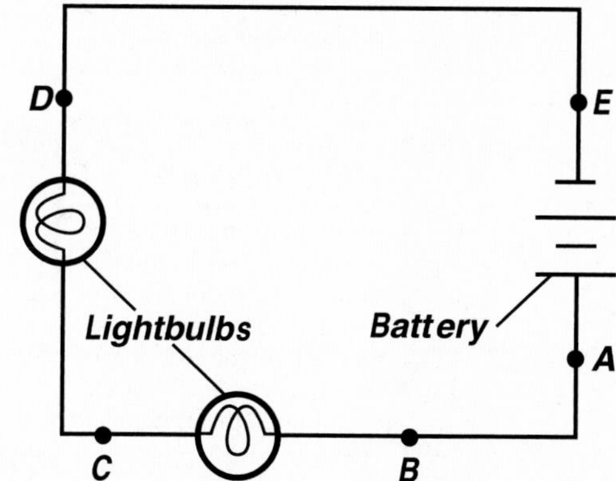

Promote Understanding

Activity

Give each group of students four wires, two flashlight bulbs in sockets, a D battery in a battery holder, and a voltmeter. Ask students to make a series circuit using the battery, bulbs, and four wires. Caution students not to touch a hot bulb.

- Instruct them in the use of the voltmeter. Then have them refer to the figure above and record the voltages between points A–B, A–E, B–C, B–D, and C–D.
- The experimental results should show a voltage of approximately 1.5 volts across points A–E, and B–D, an approximate voltage of 0.75 volts across B–C and C–D, and zero across A–B.
- Have them compare their experimental results with the predictions they made in the previous activity.
- Remove the lightbulb at points B–C from the circuit to leave a gap in the circuit.
- Ask students what they think the voltage across points B–C will now be. Have them share their thoughts and then test their ideas.
- The voltage across the gap should be approximately 1.5 volts.

Assess

After completing the chapter, see *Identifying Misconceptions* in the Study Guide at the end of the chapter.

About the Photo

Keeping the Lights On The photo shows the Bay Bridge, which connects Oakland and San Francisco, California. Cities are connected to large power distribution grids, or networks. Energy is transmitted from generating plants, which are often hundreds of miles away. Regional control centers regulate the flow of energy within and between power grids.

Science Journal Possible answers: lamp–light energy and thermal energy; hair dryer–thermal energy and kinetic energy; toaster–thermal energy, TV–light energy and sound; CD player–sound.

BIG Idea

Electric Current In a metal wire, outer electrons around metal atoms are loosely bound and can move easily. In an open circuit, these electrons are in random motion, constantly colliding with other electrons and the atoms in the wire. When the circuit is closed, an electric field is produced in the wire. Electrons continue to move in random motion, but the electric field makes them accelerate toward the positive terminal between collisions. This acceleration causes electrons to slowly drift toward the positive terminal.

Introduce the Chapter Have students make a table with three columns in which they list 5–10 electrical appliances found in their home. In the next column, have them list how many hours a day each appliance is used. In the third column, they should list how many hours a month each appliance is used. Finally, have students rank appliances according to how much they think it costs to operate each appliance.

chapter 7

Electricity

BIG Idea The flow of electric charges in a circuit is a source of electrical energy.

7.1 Electric Charge
MAIN Idea Like electric charges attract each other and unlike charges repel.

7.2 Electric Current
MAIN Idea A voltage difference causes electrons to flow in a circuit.

7.3 Electrical Energy
MAIN Idea Electrical energy can be converted into other forms of energy in a circuit.

Shine on Brightly

Electricity lights up this city so that people can continue to work or have fun when it gets dark. Electric lights and other electric devices operate by converting electrical energy into other forms of energy.

Science Journal

For five electric devices, list the form of energy electrical energy is converted into by each device.

190

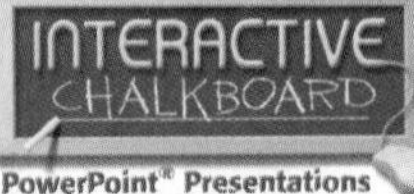

Interactive Chalkboard

This CD-ROM is an editable Microsoft® PowerPoint® presentation that includes:

- an editable presentation for every chapter
- additional chapter questions
- animated graphics
- image bank
- links to gpscience.com

Start-Up Activities

Electric Circuits

No lights! No CD players! No computers, video games or TVs! Without electricity, many of the things that make your life enjoyable wouldn't exist. For these devices to operate, electric current must flow in the electric circuits that are part of the device. Under what conditions does electric current flow in an electric circuit?

1. Obtain a battery, a flashlight bulb, and some wire.
2. Connect the materials so that the lightbulb lights.
3. Draw diagrams of all the ways that you were able to light the bulb.
4. Record a few of the ways that didn't work.
5. Can you light the bulb using only one wire and one battery?
6. **Think Critically** Write a paragraph describing the requirements to light the bulb. Write out a procedure for lighting the bulb and have a classmate follow your procedure.

Electricity Make the following Foldable to help you organize information about electricity.

STEP 1 **Fold** a vertical sheet of paper from top to bottom. Make the top edge about 2 cm shorter than the bottom edge.

STEP 2 **Turn** lengthwise and fold into thirds.

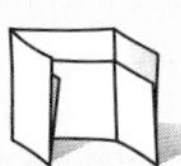

STEP 3 **Unfold and cut** only the top layer along both folds to make three tabs.

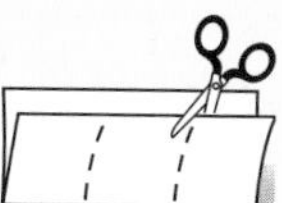

STEP 4 **Label** the Foldable as shown.

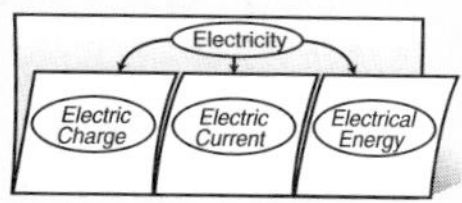

Organize Information As you read Chapter 7, organize the information you find about electric charge, electric current, and electrical energy under the appropriate tab.

Preview this chapter's content and activities at gpscience.com

Additional Chapter Media

- What's Science Got to Do With It?: *Shock Treatment*
- BrainPOP: *Static Electricity*
- Virtual Lab: *How are voltage, current, and resistance related?*
- Video Lab: *Identifying Conductors and Insulators*

Purpose Students explore how electric light circuits work.

L2 ELL IN Kinesthetic

Preparation Strip insulation off the ends of the wires.

Materials battery, flashlight bulb, insulated wire, electrical tape or battery holder

Teaching Strategy If battery holders are used, demonstrate how to attach the wires to the clips. If not, show students how to tape the stripped ends of the wires to the battery.

Think Critically

In order to light the bulb, a continuous path must be made from the battery, through a wire, to the bottom of the bulb. The path must then lead from the side of the bulb, through another wire, and back to the battery.

Assessment

Process Have students make a list of configurations that did NOT light the bulb. Have them infer what was wrong in each. Use **Performance Assessment in the Science Classroom**, p. 89. L2 IN **Logical-Mathematical**

Dinah Zike Study Fold

Student preparation materials for this Foldable are available in the Chapter *Fast File* Resources.

Probeware Labs

This chapter's data-collection lab using Probeware technology is included on the *Video Labs CD-ROM*. See the *Probeware Lab Manual* pages 53–55 for student worksheets.

section 1

Electric Charge

Reading Guide

What You'll Learn

- **Describe** how electric charges exert forces on each other.
- **Compare** the strengths of electric and gravitational forces.
- **Distinguish** between conductors and insulators
- **Explain** how objects become electrically charged.

Why It's Important

The electrical energy that all electrical devices use comes from the forces electric charges exert on each other.

Review Vocabulary

atom: the smallest particle of an element

New Vocabulary

- static electricity
- law of conservation of charge
- conductor
- insulator
- charging by contact
- charging by induction

Positive and Negative Charge

Why does walking across a carpeted floor and then touching something sometimes result in a shock? The answer has to do with electric charge. Atoms contain particles called protons, neutrons, and electrons, as shown in **Figure 1.** Protons and electrons have electric charge, and neutrons have no electric charge.

There are two types of electric charge. Protons have positive electric charge and electrons have negative electric charge. The amount of positive charge on a proton equals the amount of negative charge on an electron. An atom contains equal numbers of protons and electrons, so the positive and negative charges cancel out and an atom has no net electric charge. Objects with no net charge are said to be electrically neutral.

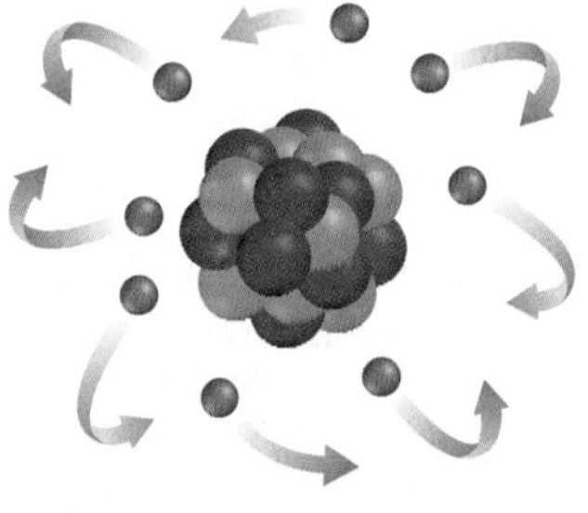

Figure 1 The center of an atom contains protons (orange) and neutrons (blue). Electrons (red) swarm around the atom's center.

Transferring Charge Electrons are bound more tightly to some atoms and molecules. For example, compared to the electrons in carpet atoms, electrons are bound more tightly to the atoms in the soles of your shoes. **Figure 2** shows that when you walk on the carpet, electrons are transferred from the carpet to the soles of your shoes. The soles of your shoes have an excess of electrons and become negatively charged. The carpet has lost electrons and has an excess of positive charge. The carpet has become positively charged. The accumulation of excess electric charge on an object is called **static electricity.**

Motivate

Bellringer

Section Focus Transparencies also are available on the Interactive Chalkboard CD-ROM. L2 ELL

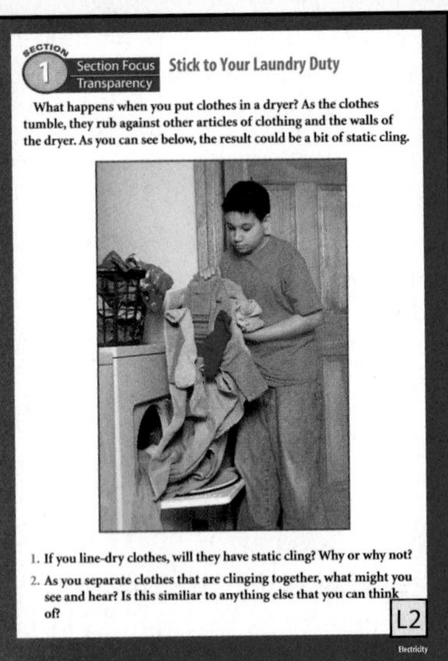

Section 1 Section Focus Transparency — Stick to Your Laundry Duty

What happens when you put clothes in a dryer? As the clothes tumble, they rub against other articles of clothing and the walls of the dryer. As you can see below, the result could be a bit of static cling.

1. If you line-dry clothes, will they have static cling? Why or why not?
2. As you separate clothes that are clinging together, what might you see and hear? Is this similiar to anything else that you can think of?

L2

Electricity

Tie to Prior Knowledge

Static Cling Ask students whether they have ever noticed clothes sticking together when they are taken out of the dryer. Explain that this is caused by static electricity, the topic of this section. L2 LS **Visual-Spatial**

Section 1 Resource Manager

Chapter FAST FILE Resources

- Transparency Activity, p.42
- Note-taking Worksheets, pp. 31–33
- Directed Reading for Content Mastery, pp. 17,18
- Enrichment, p. 28
- MiniLAB, p. 3
- Reinforcement, p. 25

Before the shoe scuffs against the carpet, both the sole of the shoe and the carpet are electrically neutral.

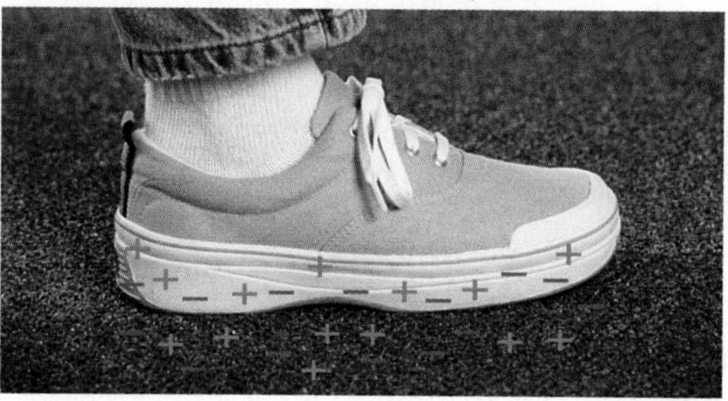

As the shoes scuff against the carpet, electrons are transferred from the carpet to the soles of the shoes.

Figure 2 Atoms in the shoe's sole hold their electrons more tightly than atoms in the carpet hold their electrons.

Conservation of Charge When an object becomes charged, charge is neither created nor destroyed. Usually it is electrons that have moved from one object to another. According to the **law of conservation of charge,** charge can be transferred from object to object, but it cannot be created or destroyed. Whenever an object becomes charged, electric charges have moved from one place to another.

Reading Check *How does an object become charged?*

Charges Exert Forces Have you noticed how clothes sometimes cling together when removed from the dryer? These clothes cling together because of the forces electric charges exert on each other. **Figure 3** shows that unlike charges attract other, and like charges repel each other. The force between electric charges also depends on the distance between charges. The force decreases as the charges get farther apart.

Just as for two electric charges, the force between any two objects that are electrically charged decreases as the objects get farther apart. This force also depends on the amount of charge on each object. As the amount of charge on either object increases, the electrical force also increases.

As clothes tumble in a dryer, the atoms in some clothes gain electrons and become negatively charged. Meanwhile the atoms in other clothes lose electrons and become positively charged. Clothes that are oppositely charged attract each other and stick together.

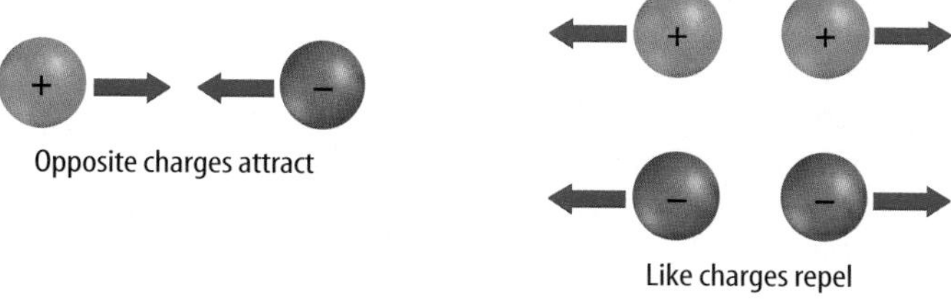
Opposite charges attract
Like charges repel

Figure 3 Positive and negative charges exert forces on each other.

2 Teach

Activity

Changes Have students use balloons, glass rods, polystyrene, puffed cereal, and pieces of silk and wool cloth to explore the ideas of positive and negative charge and the law of conservation of charge. L2 ELL
LS **Kinesthetic**

Use an Analogy

Swarming Bees Reinforce the idea that electrons, not atoms, move to cause static electricity by describing an atom as being like a swarm of bees (the electrons) around honey (the tightly held protons and neutrons). L1
LS **Visual-Spatial**

Reading Check

Answer Electrons move from one object to another. The object that gains electrons becomes negatively charged. The one that loses electrons becomes positively charged.

Science Journal

Flyaway Hair Have students write a paragraph in their journals in which they use conservation of charge to explain why hair combed on a dry day may become "flyaway hair." Before combing, both the comb and hair have equal numbers of positive and negative charges. Combing causes hair to lose electrons to the comb. The hairs then have like charges on them and repel one another. This makes them "fly away." L2 LS **Linguistic, Logical-Mathematical, Intrapersonal**

Discussion

Conductivity Explain that, when substances are categorized as conductors, semiconductors, and insulators, they are being ranked according to the ease with which electrons move around in them (their conductivity). Then have students explain, in terms of electrons, the two extreme limits of conductivity; that is, what would zero conductivity mean and what would the maximum possible conductivity mean? Zero conductivity means that no electrons can move. Maximum conductivity means that electrons move freely; there is no resistance to electron movement. L2 LS **Logical-Mathematical**

Use Science Words

Word Meaning Students may have heard the word *semiconductor.* A semiconductor is a material, such as silicon or germanium, that is neither a good insulator nor a good conductor on its own, but becomes a good conductor when a tiny impurity is added to it. Have students find what semiconductors are used for. Semiconductors are used in computer chips and to make electronic components such as transistors and diodes. L3 LS **Linguistic**

Reading Check

Answer The electric force between protons and electrons is greater than the gravitational force between the particles.

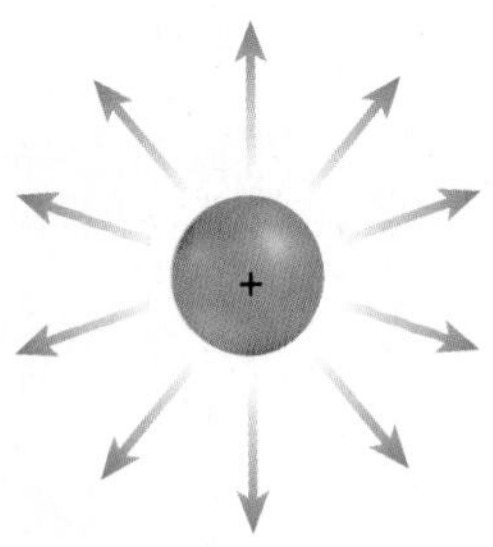

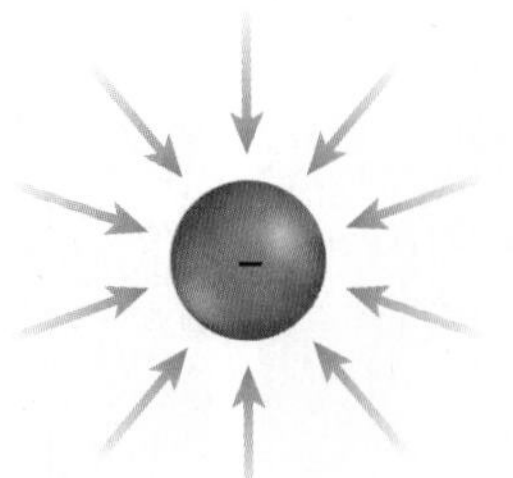

Figure 4 Surrounding every electric charge is an electric field that exerts forces on other electric charges. The arrows point in the direction a positive charge would move.

Electric Fields You might have seen bits of paper fly up and stick to a charged balloon. The bits of paper do not need to touch the charged balloon for an electric force to act on them. If the balloon and the paper are not touching, what causes the paper to move?

An electric field surrounds every electric charge, as shown in **Figure 4,** and exerts the force that causes other electric charges to be attracted or repelled. Any charge that is placed in an electric field will be pushed or pulled by the field. Electric fields are represented by arrows that show how the electric field would make a positive charge move.

Comparing Electric and Gravitational Forces The force of gravity between you and Earth seems to be strong. Yet, compared with electric forces, the force of gravity is much weaker. For example, the attractive electric force between a proton and an electron in a hydrogen atom is about a thousand trillion trillion trillion times larger, or 10^{39} times larger, than the attractive gravitational force between the two particles.

In fact, all atoms are held together by electric forces between protons and electrons that are tremendously larger than the gravitational forces between the same particles. The chemical bonds that form between atoms in molecules also are due to the electric forces between the atoms. These electric forces are much larger than the gravitational forces between the atoms.

Reading Check *Compare the strength of electric and gravitational forces between protons and electrons.*

Figure 5 As you walk across a carpeted floor, excess electrons can accumulate on your body. When you reach for a metal doorknob, electrons flow from your hand to the doorknob and you see a spark.

However, the electric forces between the objects around you are much less than the gravitational forces between them. Most objects that you see are nearly electrically neutral and have almost no net electric charge. As a result, there is usually no noticeable electric force between these objects. But even if a small amount of charge is transferred from one object to another, the electric force between the objects can be noticeable.

For example, you probably have noticed your hair being attracted to a rubber comb after you comb your hair. Transferring about one trillionth of the electrons in a single hair to the comb results in an electric force strong enough to overcome the force of gravity on the strand of hair.

194 CHAPTER 7 Electricity

Curriculum Connection

Ancient Greeks and Electricity Have students research what ancient Greeks knew about electricity. Ancient people knew that if amber was rubbed, it would become charged. *Elektron* is Greek for "amber." L2 LS **Linguistic, Intrapersonal**

Visual Learning

Figure 5 On a dry day, bring in pieces of wool carpeting to have students reproduce the effects shown. Have them explain the transfer of charges that occur. L1 ELL LS **Visual-Spatial, Logical-Mathematical**

Conductors and Insulators

If you reach for a metal doorknob after walking across a carpet, you might see a spark. The spark is caused by electrons moving from your hand to the doorknob, as shown in **Figure 5.** Recall that electrons were transferred from the carpet to your shoes. How did these electrons move from your shoes to your hand?

Conductors A material in which electrons are able to move easily is a **conductor.** Electrons on your shoes repel each other and some are pushed onto your skin. Because your skin is a better conductor than your shoes, the electrons spread over your skin, including your hand.

The best electrical conductors are metals. The atoms in metals have electrons that are able to move easily through the material. Electric wires usually are made of copper because copper metal is one of the best conductors.

Insulators A material in which electrons are not able to move easily is an **insulator.** Electrons are held tightly to atoms in insulators. Most plastics are insulators. The plastic coating around electric wires, shown in **Figure 6,** prevents a dangerous electric shock when you touch the wire. Other good insulators are wood, rubber, and glass.

Charging Objects

You might have noticed socks clinging to each other after they have been tumbling in a clothes dryer. Rubbing two materials together can result in a transfer of electrons. Then one material is left with a positive charge and the other with an equal amount of negative charge. The process of transferring charge by touching or rubbing is called **charging by contact.**

Figure 6 The plastic coating around wires is an insulator. A damaged electrical cord is hazardous when the conducting wire is exposed.

Fun Fact

The process of charging by contact is known as *triboelectricity.* The triboelectric properties of materials are of significant interest to scientists working on missions to Mars. The dry, windy conditions on Mars provide an ideal environment for triboelectric charging.

Teacher FYI

Charging by Friction The process of charge transfer by rubbing is often called *charging by friction.* This term can be misleading because the process requires only light contact, not heating. The rubbing increases the area of contact, thereby enhancing the charge transfer.

Active Reading

Cause-and-Effect Chart Have students design a Cause-and-Effect Chart for static electricity. In the center, students write the topic, in this case, static electricity. To the left, they write the apparent causes of static electricity. On the right, they write the apparent effects of static electricity. L2 LS **Linguistic, Logical-Mathematical, Visual-Spatial**

Differentiated Instruction

Challenge Have students investigate various conductors and insulators. Suggest that they design and make a circuit to test these objects. They also should make a chart to show which items are conductors and which are insulators. L3 LS P **Kinesthetic**

Caption Answer

Figure 7 from the ballon to the sweater

Discussion

Winter Shocks Why are you more likely to get shocked when you touch a door handle in the winter than in the summer? In winter, the air in homes and buildings is often dry. Dry air is an insulator and doesn't easily discharge the excess charge on your body. The charge is therefore more likely to remain until your hand nears a door handle. L2 LS **Logical-Mathematical**

Use Science Words

Word Meaning Ask students to look up the word *static* and tell one reason why this word is appropriate for the term *static electricity* and one reason why the word is misleading. The word static means "not moving." It is true that static electricity is not in continual motion like current electricity. However, a static discharge is far from motionless; it is a very rapid, though noncontinuous, transfer of charge. L2 LS **Linguistic**

Franklin's Kite Students may have heard the tale of Benjamin Franklin's kite being struck by lightning. Fortunately, the kite was *not* struck by lightning, but a negative charge from the air collected on a wire attached to the kite and traveled down the wet string. The sparks Franklin observed enabled him to show (as French scientists had done a month before) the relation between lightning and electricity.

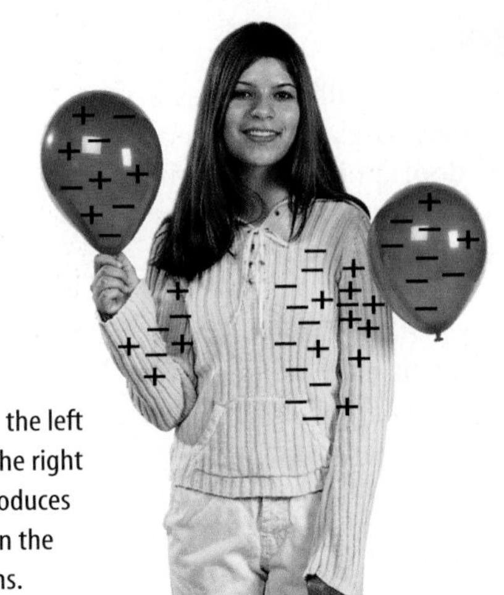

Figure 7 The balloon on the left is neutral. The balloon on the right is negatively charged. It produces a positively charged area on the sleeve by repelling electrons.
Determine *the direction of the force acting on the balloon.*

Charging at a Distance

Because electrical forces act at a distance, charged objects brought near a neutral object will cause electrons to rearrange their positions on the neutral object. Suppose you charge a balloon by rubbing it with a cloth. If you bring the negatively charged balloon near your sleeve, the extra electrons on the balloon repel the electrons in the sleeve. The electrons near the sleeve's surface move away from the balloon, leaving a positively charged area on the surface of the sleeve, as shown in **Figure 7.** As a result, the negatively charged balloon attracts the positively charged area of the sleeve. The rearrangement of electrons on a neutral object caused by a nearby charged object is called **charging by induction.** The sweater was charged by induction. The balloon will now cling to the sweater, being held there by an electrical force.

Lightning Have you ever seen lightning strike Earth? Lightning is a large static discharge. A static discharge is a transfer of charge between two objects because of a buildup of static electricity. A thundercloud is a mighty generator of static electricity. As air masses move and swirl in the cloud, areas of positive and negative charge build up. Eventually, enough charge builds up to cause a static discharge between the cloud and the ground. As the electric charges move through air, they collide with atoms and molecules. These collisions cause the atoms and molecules in air to emit light. You see this light as a spark, as shown in **Figure 8.**

Topic: Lightning
Visit gpscience.com for Web links to information about lightning strikes.

Activity Make a table listing tips on how people can protect themselves from lightning.

Thunder Not only does lightning produce a brilliant flash of light, it also generates powerful sound waves. The electrical energy in a lightning bolt rips electrons off atoms in the atmosphere and produces great amounts of heat. The surrounding air temperature can rise to about 30,000°C—several times hotter than the Sun's surface. The heat causes air in the bolt's path to expand rapidly, producing sound waves that you hear as thunder.

The sudden discharge of so much energy can be dangerous. It is estimated that Earth is struck by lightning about 100 times every second. Lightning strikes can cause power outages, injury, loss of life, and fires.

Science Journal

Thunderstorm Safety You often hear the warning, "Don't stand near a tree during a thunderstorm." Ask students to explain the reasoning behind this warning based on what they have learned in this section. Trees are more susceptible to lightning strikes because they are often the tallest objects around. L2 LS **Logical-Mathematical**

NATIONAL GEOGRAPHIC VISUALIZING LIGHTNING

Figure 8

Storm clouds can form when humid, sun-warmed air rises to meet a colder air layer. As these air masses churn together, the stage is set for the explosive electrical display we call lightning. Lightning strikes when negative charges at the bottom of a storm cloud are attracted to positive charges on the ground.

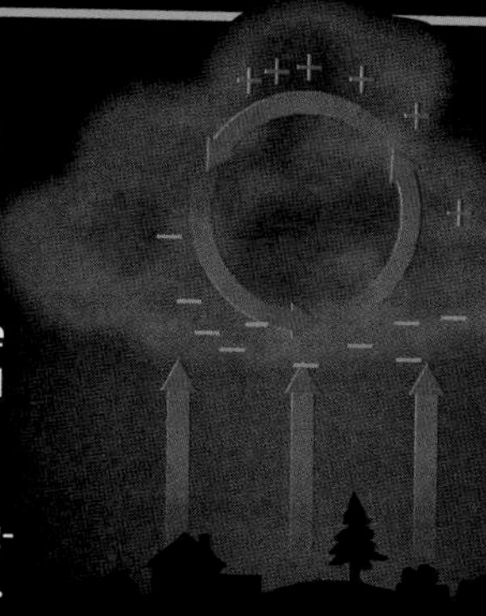

A Convection currents in the storm cloud cause charge separation. The top of the cloud becomes positively charged, the bottom negatively charged.

B Negative charges on the bottom of the cloud induce a positive charge on the ground below the cloud by repelling negative charges in the ground.

C When the bottom of the cloud has accumulated enough negative charges, the attraction of the positive charges below causes electrons in the bottom of the cloud to move toward the ground.

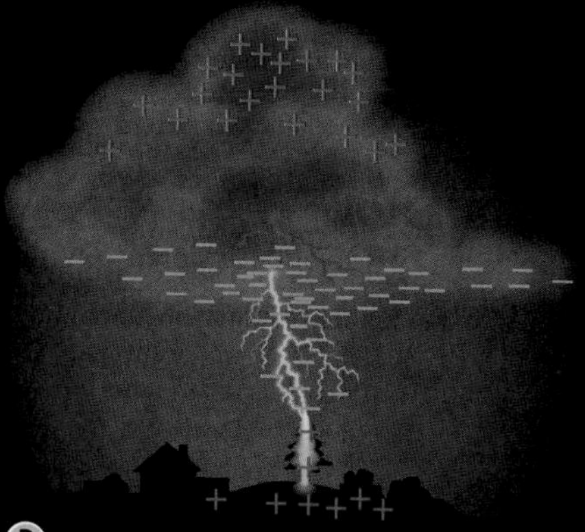

D When the electrons get close to the ground, they attract positive charges that surge upward, completing the connection between cloud and ground. This is the spark you see as a lightning flash.

INTRA-CLOUD LIGHTNING never strikes Earth and can occur ten times more often in a storm than cloud-to-ground lightning.

SECTION 1 Electric Charge 197

Visualizing Lightning

Have students examine the pictures and read the captions. Then ask the following questions.

When the warm humid air rises to meet the cold air, what causes the air masses to churn together? convection currents

What electric property causes the negative charges in the cloud to be attracted to the positive charges in the ground? like charges repel and unlike charges attract

Why does the ground below a cloud have a concentration of positive charges? because the negative charges in the bottom of the cloud repel the negative charges in the ground and attract the positive charges L2 LS **Visual-Spatial, Logical Mathematical**

Activity

Lightning Posters Have students research the different types of lightning and have them make posters illustrating them. If possible, students also could include statistical data involving the number of strikes that occur per year in their area. L2 LS **Visual-Spatial, Linguistic, Logical-Mathematical**

Differentiated Instruction

Challenge Have students find out more about storm chasers. These professionals intentionally go to areas where tornadoes, hurricanes, typhoons, etc. are occurring to study them. Students should report to the class what they learn. L3 LS **Visual-Spatial**

Text Question Answer

Possible answers: faucet (if plumbing is metal), electrical outlet ground

Purpose Students analyze how charged objects interact with each other. L1 ELL IS **Logical-Mathematical** IS **Kinesthetic**

Materials transparent tape

Teaching Strategy Cellophane tape often works, but transparent tape is better.

Analysis

1. The tapes attracted each other because they had opposite charges. When pulled apart, one became positively charged and one became negatively charged.
2. The pieces of tape repelled each other because they had like charges. Pulling both strips off the surface charged each the same way.

Assessment

Process Have students write up the procedures and results for this MiniLAB as lab reports. Use **Performance Assessment in the Science Classroom,** p. 119. L2 IS **Linguistic**

Figure 9 A lightning rod directs the charge from a lightning bolt safely to the ground.

Investigate Charged Objects

Procedure

1. Fold over about 1 cm on the end of a **roll of transparent tape** to make a handle. Tear off a strip of tape about 10 cm long.
2. Stick the strip to a clean, dry, smooth surface, such as a countertop. Make another identical strip and stick it directly on top of the first.
3. Pull both pieces off the counter together and pull them apart. Then bring the nonsticky sides of both tapes together. What happens?
4. Now stick the two strips of tape side by side on the smooth surface. Pull them off and bring the nonsticky sides near each other again.

Analysis

1. What happened when you first brought the pieces close together? Were they charged alike or opposite? What might have caused this?
2. What did you observe when you brought the pieces together the second time? How were they charged? What did you do differently that might have changed the behavior?

Try at Home

Grounding The sensitive electronics in a computer can be harmed by large static discharges. A discharge can occur any time that charge builds up in one area. Providing a path for charge to reach Earth prevents any charge from building up. Earth is a large, neutral object that is also a conductor of charge. Any object connected to Earth by a good conductor will transfer any excess electric charge to Earth. Connecting an object to Earth with a conductor is called grounding. For example, buildings often have a metal lightning rod that provides a conducting path from the highest point on the building to the ground to prevent damage by lightning, as shown in **Figure 9.**

Plumbing fixtures, such as metal faucets, sinks, and pipes, often provide a convenient ground connection. Look around. Do you see anything that might act as a path to the ground?

Detecting Electric Charge

The presence of electric charges can be detected by an electroscope. One kind of electroscope is made of two thin, metal leaves attached to a metal rod with a knob at the top. The leaves are allowed to hang freely from the metal rod. When the device is not charged, the leaves hang straight down, as shown in **Figure 10A.**

Suppose a negatively charged balloon touches the knob. Because the metal is a good conductor, electrons travel down the rod into the leaves. Both leaves become negatively charged as they gain electrons, as shown in **Figure 10B.** Because the leaves have similar charges, they repel each other.

If a glass rod is rubbed with silk, electrons move away from the atoms in the glass rod and build up on the silk. The glass rod becomes positively charged.

Visual Learning

Figure 9 The lightning rod's long, narrow shape causes charges induced into it to bunch together and produce a strong electric field. This electric field causes nearby air molecules to be ionized, enabling charges to travel from the storm cloud to the lightning rod. This reduces the likelihood of a lightning strike elsewhere. Look for lightning rods on buildings in your area. L2 IS **Visual-Spatial**

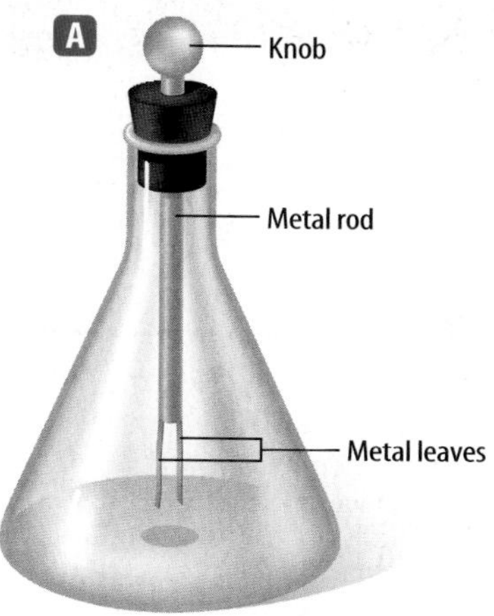

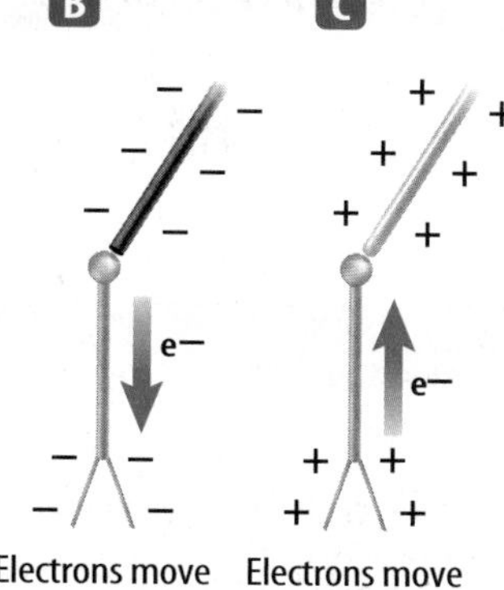

Figure 10 Notice the position of the leaves on the electroscope when they are **A** uncharged, **B** negatively charged, and **C** positively charged.
Infer *How can you tell whether an electroscope is positively or negatively charged?*

When the positively charged glass rod is brought into contact with the metal knob of an uncharged electroscope, electrons flow out of the metal leaves and onto the rod. The leaves repel each other because each leaf becomes positively charged as it loses electrons, as shown in **Figure 10C.**

section 1 review

Summary

Positive and Negative Charge

- There are two types of electric charge—positive charge and negative charge.
- Electric charges can be transferred between objects, but cannot be created or destroyed.
- Like charges repel and unlike charges attract.
- An electric charge is surrounded by an electric field that exerts forces on other charges.

Electrical Conductors and Insulators

- A conductor contains electrons that can move easily. The best conductors are metals.
- The electrons in an electrical insulator do not move easily. Rubber, glass, and most plastics are examples of insulators.

Charging Objects

- Electric charge can be transferred between objects by bringing them into contact.
- Charging by induction occurs when the electric field around a charged object rearranges electrons in a nearby neutral object.

Checking Concepts

1. **Define** static electricity.
2. **Describe** how lightning is produced.
3. **Explain** why if charge cannot be created or destroyed, electrically neutral objects can become electrically charged.
4. **Predict** what would happen if you touched the knob of a positively charged electroscope with another positively charged object.
5. **Think Critically** Humid air is a better electrical conductor than dry air. Explain why you're more likely to receive a shock after walking across a carpet when the air is dry than when the air is humid.

Applying Math

6. **Determine Lightning Strikes** Suppose Earth is struck by 100 lighting strikes each second. How many times is Earth struck by lightning in one day?
7. **Calculate Electric Force** A balloon with a mass of 0.020 kg is charged by rubbing and then is stuck to the ceiling. If the acceleration of gravity is 9.8 m/s^2, what is the electrical force on the balloon?

Science Online gpscience.com/self_check_quiz

Caption Answer

Figure 10 A rod with an opposite charge will cause the leaves to fall.

3 Assess

DAILY INTERVENTION

Check for Understanding

Kinesthetic/ Interpersonal Pair up students and have one pair (one of which has long fine hair) come to the front of the class. Give the pair an inflated balloon. Have one student rub the balloon on his clothing then bring it near the other's long fine hair. Observe the attraction of the hair to the balloon. Have pairs of students confer and write down the answers to these questions: What causes the hair to be attracted to the balloon? What kind of transfer of electric charge occurs? How does the charge on the balloon compare to that on the hair? Discuss the students' answers. L2 IS **Linguistic, Logical-Mathematical**

Reteach

Detecting Electric Charge Use an electroscope to touch various objects, some of which are charged. Have students discuss the results based on what they have learned. L1 ELL IS **Visual-Spatial, Kinesthetic, Logical-Mathematical**

Assessment

Content Have students create posters showing the different methods of transferring electric charge. Use **PASC,** p. 145. L2 IS **Visual Spatial**

section 1 review

1. Static electricity is the accumulation of excess electric charge on an object.
2. Lightning occurs when excess negative charge in clouds discharges to regions of positive charge on the ground or in other clouds.
3. Electrically neutral objects can become charged when they gain or lose electric charges.
4. The leaves of the electroscope would remain apart.
5. Excess electric charge remains on an object in dry air, which is an insulator. Humid air is a better conductor and allows any excess electric charge to drain away into the air.
6. 8,640,000 times/day.
7. 0.20 N

1 Motivate

Bellringer

Section Focus Transparencies also are available on the Interactive Chalkboard CD-ROM. L2 ELL

SECTION 2 Section Focus Transparency **Go with the Flow**

Do you see how the water flows down the cliff? Water takes the path of least resistance—it flows where it's easiest for water to go. Electric currents flow and experience resistance, too.

1. Which do you think has more energy, the waterfall in the picture or Niagara Falls which are higher and have more water flowing over? Explain your answer.
2. How do people use the energy in water currents?

L2

Electricity

Tie to Prior Knowledge

Battery Trouble Ask students if they have ever tried to play a CD in a portable CD player, only to find that the batteries were dead. Ask students what they know about what happens when a battery dies. Explain that when it dies, the battery stops producing enough electric current to operate the CD player. Tell students that in this section, they will learn what an electric current is and how it is produced. L2 LS **Logical-Mathematical**

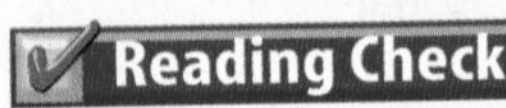

Answer the net movement of electric charge in a single direction

section 2

Electric Current

Reading Guide

***What* You'll Learn**

- **Describe** how voltage difference causes current to flow.
- **Explain** how batteries produce a voltage difference in a circuit.
- **List** the factors that affect an object's electrical resistance.
- **Define** Ohm's law.

***Why* It's Important**

You control electric current every time you change the volume on a TV, stereo, or CD player.

Review Vocabulary

pressure: amount of force exerted per unit area

New Vocabulary

- electric current
- voltage difference
- circuit
- resistance
- Ohm's law

Figure 11 Electric forces in a material cause electric current to flow, just as forces in the water cause water to flow.

The force that causes water to flow is related to a pressure difference.

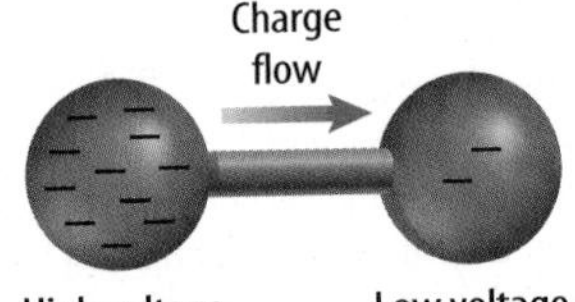

The force that causes a current to flow is related to a voltage difference.

Current and Voltage Difference

When a spark jumps between your hand and a metal doorknob, electric charges move quickly from one place to another. The net movement of electric charges in a single direction is an **electric current.** In a metal wire, or any material, electrons are in constant motion in all directions. As a result, there is no net movement of electrons in one direction. However, when an electric current flows in the wire, electrons continue their random movement, but they also drift in the direction that the current flows.

Electric current is measured in amperes. One ampere is equal to 6,250 million billion electrons flowing past a point every second.

Reading Check *What is electric current?*

Voltage Difference The movement of an electron in an electric current is similar to a ball bouncing down a flight of stairs. Even though the ball changes direction when it strikes a stair, the net motion of the ball is downward. The downward motion of the ball is caused by the force of gravity. When a current flows, the net movement of electric charges is caused by an electric force acting on the charges.

In some ways, the electric force that causes charges to flow is similar to the force acting on the water in a pipe. Water flows from higher pressure to lower pressure, as shown in **Figure 11.** In a similar way, electric charge flows from higher voltage to lower voltage. A **voltage difference** is related to the force that causes electric charges to flow. Voltage difference is measured in volts.

Section 2 Resource Manager

Chapter *Fast File* Resources

- Transparency Activity, p.43
- Directed Reading for Content Mastery, pp. 19
- MiniLAB, p. 4
- Enrichment, p. 29
- Lab Activity, pp. 9–12
- Reinforcement, p. 26
- Lab Worksheet, pp. 5–6

Home and Community Involvement, p. 25

Mathematics Skill Activities, p. 3

Figure 12 Water or electric current will flow continually only through a closed loop. If any part of the loop is broken or disconnected, the flow stops.

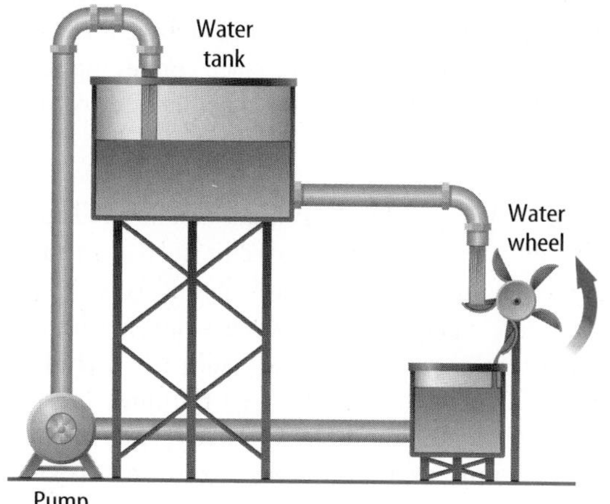

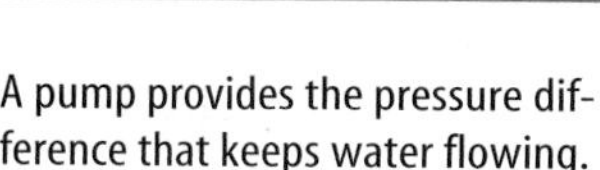
A pump provides the pressure difference that keeps water flowing.

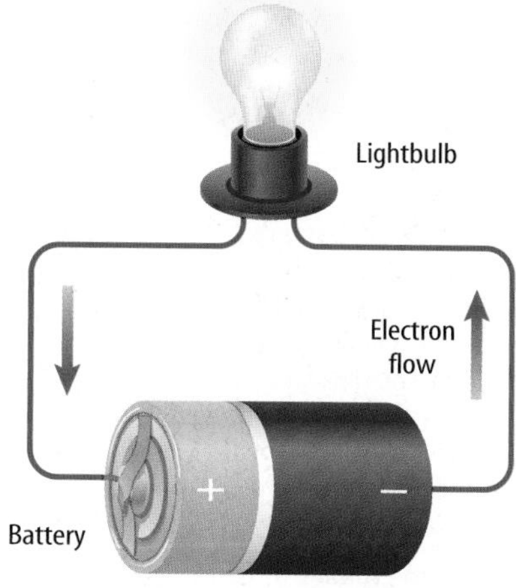

A battery provides the voltage difference that keeps electric current flowing.

Electric Circuits A way to have flowing water perform work is shown in **Figure 12.** Water flows out of the tank and falls on a paddle wheel, causing it to rotate. A pump then provides a pressure difference that lifts the water back up into the tank. The constant flow of water would stop if the pump stopped working. The flow of water also would stop if one of the pipes broke. Then water no longer could flow in a closed loop, and the paddle wheel would stop rotating.

Figure 12 also shows an electric current doing work by lighting a lightbulb. Just as the water current stops flowing if there is no longer a closed loop to flow through, the electric current stops if there is no longer a closed path to follow. A closed path that electric current follows is a **circuit.** If the circuit in Figure 12 is broken by removing the battery, or the light bulb, or one of the wires, current will not flow.

Batteries

In order to keep water flowing continually in the water circuit in **Figure 12,** a pump is used to provide a pressure difference. In a similar way, to keep an electric current continually flowing in the electric circuit in **Figure 12,** a voltage difference needs to be maintained in the circuit. A battery can provide the voltage difference that is needed to keep current flowing in a circuit. Current flows as long as there is a closed path that connects one battery terminal to the other battery terminal.

Teacher FYI

Battery Makeup A 9-volt battery is actually composed of six small 1.5-volt batteries connected in series. A 12-volt car battery is a series of six 2-volt batteries.

2 Teach

IDENTIFYING Misconceptions

Current Students might believe that positive charges flow through wires. Early researchers labeled the direction of current flow from the positive terminal to the negative terminal of a battery. This established the convention. After the discovery of the electron, researchers realized that the electrons actually move from the negative terminal to the positive terminal. Today, we talk about conventional current, which is the direction of the hypothetical flow of positive charges. However, it is negatively-charged electrons that flow in a wire. It is important for students to learn these distinctions and to realize that positive charges do not flow through the wire.

Quick Demo

Simple Cell

Materials small glass or plastic container about three-fourths full of acid solution (lemon juice, tomato juice, or vinegar), strip of copper, strip of zinc or silver, two wires with alligator clips, sensitive voltmeter (0-1 VDC)

Estimated Time five minutes

Procedure Clip one end of a wire to one metal strip and the other end to the voltmeter. Repeat for the second metal strip and wire. Place the metal strips in the acid solution, taking care that the strips do not touch each other. Have a student read the voltage difference that the cell produces between the two electrodes.

Purpose Students discover the effect of adding an additional battery to a circuit. COOP LEARN

L2 **Kinesthetic, Visual-Spatial,** IS **Logical-Mathematical**

Materials D-cell batteries (2), 3-volt bulbs and sockets (3), insulated wire

Safety Precautions Caution students to leave the bulbs burning only long enough to make observations, and to not touch a hot bulb.

Troubleshooting Connecting more than two batteries per lamp in series will shorten the bulb's life or cause it to burn out.

Analysis

1. 1.5 volts, 3.0 volts
2. As the voltage difference increases across the lamp, the charge flowing through it increases.

Assessment

Performance Have students design and label several possible arrangements showing how to light a bulb at different levels of brightness. Have them demonstrate each method. Use **Performance Assessment in the Science Classroom,** p. 127. L2 IS **Kinesthetic, Visual-Spatial**

Caption Answer

Figure 13 The chemical reactions occur when the battery is connected in a circuit.

Mini LAB

Investigating Battery Addition

Procedure

1. Make a circuit by using wire to link two **bulbs** and one **D-cell battery** in a loop. Observe the brightness of the bulbs.
2. Assemble a new circuit by linking two bulbs and two D-cell batteries in a loop. Observe the brightness of the bulbs.

Analysis

1. What is the voltage difference of each D cell? Add them together to find the total voltage difference for the circuit you tested in step 2.
2. Assuming that a brighter bulb indicates a greater current, what can you conclude about the relationship between the voltage difference and current?

Dry-Cell Batteries You probably are most familiar with dry-cell batteries. A cell consists of two electrodes surrounded by a material called an electrolyte. The electrolyte enables charges to move from one electrode to the other. Look at the dry cell shown in **Figure 13.** One electrode is the carbon rod, and the other is the zinc container. The electrolyte is a moist paste containing several chemicals. The cell is called a dry cell because the electrolyte is a moist paste, and not a liquid solution.

INTEGRATE Chemistry When the two terminals of a dry-cell battery are connected in a circuit, such as in a flashlight, a reaction involving zinc and several chemicals in the paste occurs. Electrons are transferred between some of the compounds in this chemical reaction. As a result, the carbon rod becomes positive, forming the positive (+) terminal. Electrons accumulate on the zinc, making it the negative (−) terminal.

The voltage difference between these two terminals causes current to flow through a closed circuit. You make a battery when you connect two or more cells together to produce a higher voltage difference.

Wet-Cell Batteries Another commonly used type of battery is the wet-cell battery. A wet cell, like the one shown in **Figure 13,** contains two connected plates made of different metals or metallic compounds in a conducting solution. A wet-cell battery contains several wet cells connected together.

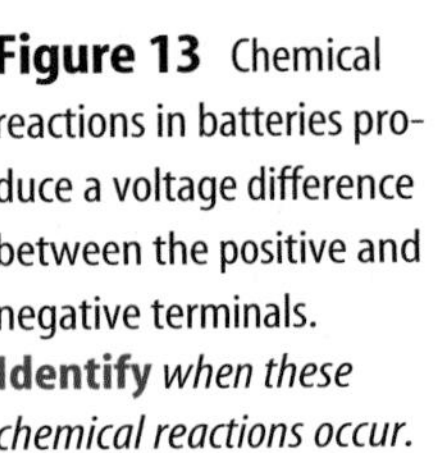

Figure 13 Chemical reactions in batteries produce a voltage difference between the positive and negative terminals. **Identify** *when these chemical reactions occur.*

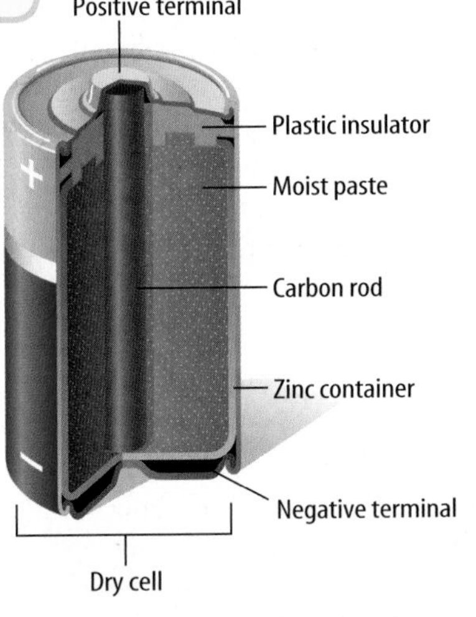

In this dry cell, chemical reactions in the moist paste transfer electrons to the zinc container.

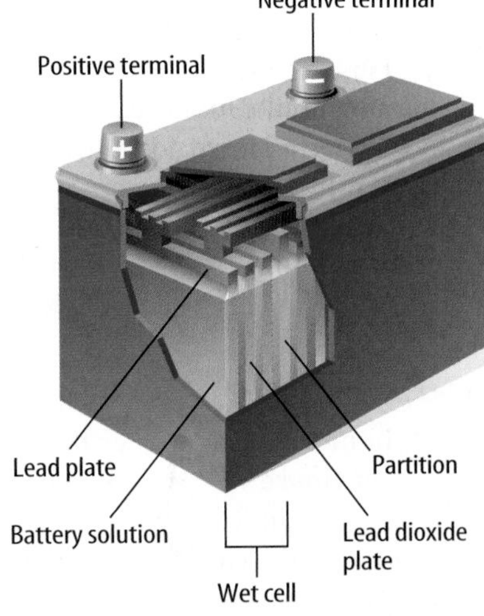

In this wet cell, chemical reactions transfer electrons from the lead plates to the lead dioxide plates.

Visual Learning

Figure 13 Each cell of a battery has an *electrolyte* (a chemical that conducts charge) and two *electrodes* (terminals). One electrode provides electrons to the electrolyte. The other electrode takes electrons from the electrolyte. In dry cells the electrolyte is a paste, and in wet cells it is a liquid. What are the electrodes in this figure? In the dry cell, they are the carbon rod and the zinc container. In the wet cell, they are the lead dioxide and lead plates. L2 IS **Visual-Spatial**

Lead-Acid Batteries Most car batteries are lead-acid batteries, like the wet-cell battery shown in **Figure 13.** A lead-acid battery contains a series of six wet cells made up of lead and lead dioxide plates in a sulfuric acid solution. The chemical reaction in each cell provides a voltage difference of about 2 V, giving a total voltage difference of 12 V. As a car is driven, the alternator recharges the battery by sending current through the battery in the opposite direction to reverse the chemical reaction.

A voltage difference is provided at electrical outlets, such as a wall socket. This voltage difference usually is higher than the voltage difference provided by batteries. Most types of household devices are designed to use the voltage difference supplied by a wall socket. In the United States, the voltage difference across the two holes in a wall socket is usually 120 V. Some wall sockets supply 240 V, which is required by appliances such as electric ranges and electric clothes dryers.

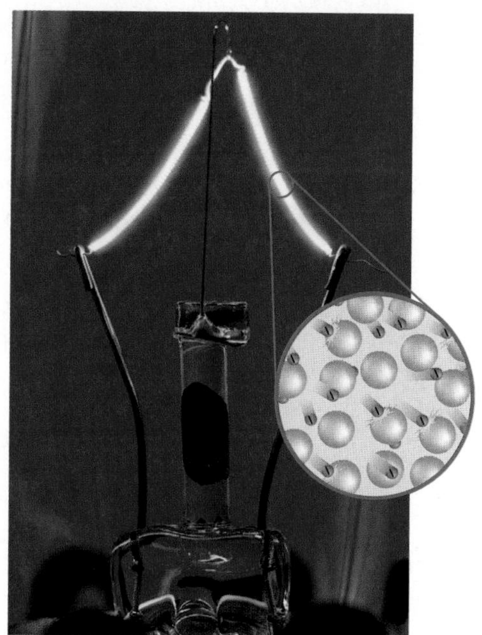

Figure 14 As electrons move through the filament in a lightbulb, they bump into metal atoms. Due to the collisions, the metal heats up and starts to glow.
Describe *the energy conversions that occur in a lightbulb filament.*

Resistance

Flashlights use dry-cell batteries to provide the electric current that lights a lightbulb. What makes a lightbulb glow? Look at the lightbulb in **Figure 14.** Part of the circuit through the bulb is a thin wire called a filament. As the electrons flow through the filament, they bump into the metal atoms that make up the filament. In these collisions, some of the electrical energy of the electrons is converted into thermal energy. Eventually, the metal filament becomes hot enough to glow, producing radiant energy that can light up a dark room.

Resisting the Flow of Current Electric current loses energy as it moves through the filament because the filament resists the flow of electrons. **Resistance** is the tendency for a material to oppose the flow of electrons, changing electrical energy into thermal energy and light. With the exception of some substances that become superconductors at low temperatures, all materials have some electrical resistance. Electrical conductors have much less resistance than insulators. Resistance is measured in ohms (Ω).

Copper is an excellent conductor and has low resistance to the flow of electrons. Copper is used in household wiring because only a small amount of electrical energy is converted to thermal energy as current flows in copper wires.

IDENTIFYING Misconceptions

Voltage Students sometimes think that voltage is the same at different places in a circuit and it exists only when current flows. See page 192F for teaching strategies that address this misconception.

Use an Analogy

Water Flow You can describe resistance by building on the analogy of charge flow being similar to water flow. Suppose a jug of water has a large hole in one side and a small hole in the other side. More water will flow out of the large hole. Similarly, a wire with a large diameter has less resistance and therefore carries greater current than a smaller-diameter wire.

Discussion

Making Heat Should the heating elements on a stove top be made of high-resistance or low-resistance material? high-resistance L2
LS **Logical-Mathematical**

Caption Answer

Figure 14 Electrical energy is converted into thermal energy and radiant energy.

Curriculum Connection

Math In a car battery, the following chemical reaction occurs: $Pb + PbO_2 + H_2SO_4 \rightarrow PbSO_4 + H_2O$. Use coefficients to balance this equation. $Pb + PbO_2 + 2H_2SO_4 \rightarrow 2PbSO_4 + 2H_2O$

Reading Check

Answer The resistance increases as the length of the wire increases and as its thickness decreases.

IDENTIFYING Misconceptions

Static Danger When it comes to electricity and our bodies, it often is true that high voltages are dangerous and low voltages are safer. Students frequently are not aware of a common situation where this is not true. In many static electricity situations, such as walking across a carpet, sparks of 1,500 volts or higher are generated. No damage occurs to our bodies because there is little actual current flow.

Virtual Labs

Electric Charges *How are voltage, current, and resistance related?*

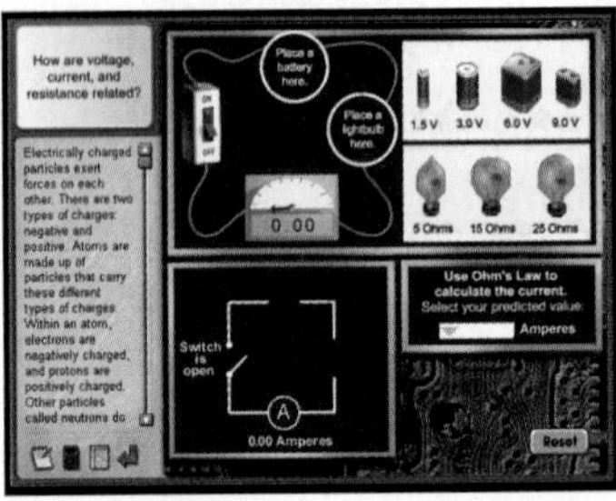

Temperature, Length, and Thickness The electric resistance of most materials usually increases as the temperature of the material increases. The resistance of an object such as a wire also depends on the length and diameter of the wire. The resistance of a wire, or any conductor, increases as the wire becomes longer. The resistance also increases as the wire becomes thinner.

In a 60 watt lightbulb, the filament is a piece of tungsten wire made into a short coil a few cm long. The uncoiled wire is about 2 m long and only about 0.25 mm thick. Even though tungsten metal is a good conductor, by making the wire thin and long, the resistance of the filament is made large enough to cause the bulb to glow.

Reading Check *How does changing the length and thickness of a wire affect its resistance?*

The Current in a Simple Circuit

A simple electric circuit contains a source of voltage difference, such as a battery, a device, such as lightbulb, that has resistance, and conductors that connect the device to the battery terminals. When the wires are connected to the battery terminals, current flows in the closed path. An example of a simple circuit is shown in **Figure 15.**

The voltage difference, current, and resistance in a circuit are related. If the voltage difference doesn't change, decreasing the resistance increases the current in the circuit, as shown in **Figure 15.** Also, if the resistance doesn't change, increasing the voltage difference increases the current.

Figure 15 The amount of current flowing through a circuit is related to the amount of resistance in the circuit.

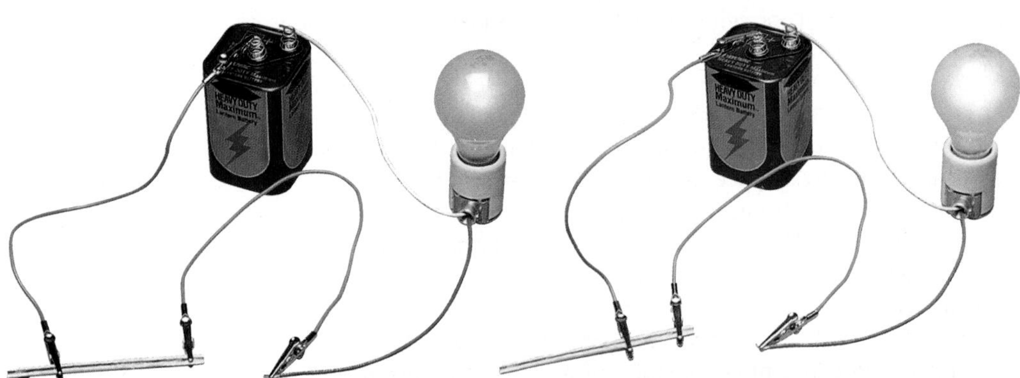

When the clips on the graphite rod are farther apart, the resistance of the rod in the circuit is larger. As a result, less current flows in the circuit and the lightbulb is dim.

When the clips on the graphite rod are closer together, the resistance of the rod in the circuit is less. As a result, more current flows in the circuit and the lightbulb is brighter.

Teacher FYI

High-Temperature Conductivity Conductivity depends on temperature. A higher temperature causes more movement of atoms and generally results in lower conductivity. However, the increased movement of atoms in some substances, such as carbon and semiconductors, frees electrons so that higher temperatures for these substances means higher conductivity.

204 CHAPTER 7 Electricity

Ohm's Law The relationship between voltage difference, current and resistance in a circuit is known as Ohm's law. According to **Ohm's law,** the current in a circuit equals the voltage difference divided by the resistance. If I stands for electric current, Ohm's law can be written as the following equation.

Ohm's Law

$$\text{current (in amperes)} = \frac{\text{voltage difference (in volts)}}{\text{resistance (in ohms)}}$$

$$I = \frac{V}{R}$$

Ohm's law provides a way to measure the resistance of objects and materials. First the equation above is written as:

$$R = \frac{V}{I}$$

An object is connected to a source of voltage difference and the current flowing in the circuit is measured. The object's resistance then equals the voltage difference divided by the measured current.

Current and the Human Body When an electric shock occurs, an electric current moves through some part of the body. The damage caused by an electric shock depends on how large the current is. Research the effects of current on the human body. Make a table showing the effects on the body at different amounts of current.

section 2 review

Summary

Current and Voltage Difference

- Electric current is the net movement of electric charge in a single direction.
- A voltage difference is related to the force that causes charges to flow.
- A circuit is a closed, conducting path.

Batteries

- Chemical reactions in a battery produce a voltage difference between the positive and negative battery terminals.
- Two commonly used types of batteries are dry-cell batteries and wet-cell batteries.

Resistance and Ohm's Law

- Resistance is the tendency of a material to oppose the flow of electrons.
- Ohm's law relates the current, I, resistance, R, and voltage difference, V, in a circuit:

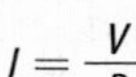

$$I = \frac{V}{R}$$

Self Check

1. **Compare and contrast** a current traveling through a circuit with a static discharge.
2. **Explain** how a carbon-zinc dry cell produces a voltage difference between the positive and negative terminals.
3. **Identify** two ways to increase the current in a simple circuit.
4. **Compare and contrast** the flow of water in a pipe and the flow of electrons in a wire.
5. **Think Critically** Explain how the resistance of a lightbulb filament changes after the light has been turned on.

Applying Math

6. **Calculate** the voltage difference in a circuit with a resistance of 25 Ω if the current in the circuit is 0.5 A.
7. **Calculate Resistance** A current of 0.5 A flows in a 60-W lightbulb when the voltage difference between the ends of the filament is 120 V. What is the resistance of the filament?

Science Online gpscience.com/self_check_quiz

Current and the Human Body Currents of about 0.5 mA can cause a slight shock to a person. Higher currents cause increasing degrees of pain and loss of muscle control. Currents higher than about 150 mA will likely result in death.

3 Assess

DAILY INTERVENTION

Check for Understanding

Visual-Logical Without students seeing, reverse one battery in a flashlight. Show students that the flashlight does not work. Ask them to suggest possible reasons why an electric circuit may not work. L2 LS **Logical-Mathematical, Visual-Spatial**

Reteach

Ohm's Law Use the diagram below to help students remember how to rearrange Ohm's law. When the desired variable is covered, the other two variables are in proper mathematical order. L2 LS **Visual-Spatial**

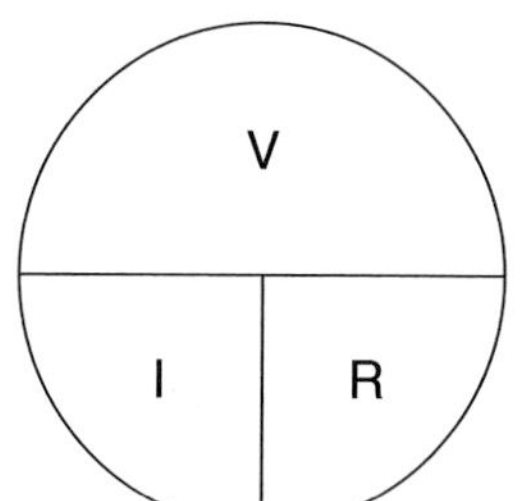

section 2 review

1. Both are a movement of electrons from the negative to the positive charge. A circuit has a continuous current provided by a voltage source. A static discharge is a very rapid, noncontinuous transfer of charge.
2. A chemical reaction causes a negative charge on the zinc container and a positive charge on the carbon rod.
3. Increasing the voltage difference or decreasing the resistance will increase the current.
4. Water flow is the movement of molecules, not just electrons. The larger the diameter of pipe or wire, the greater the flow of water or electrons.
5. A lightbulb filament heats up as an electic current flows through it, causing an increase in the wire's resistance. According to Ohm's Law, the highter resistance results in a lower current.
6. 12.5 volts
7. 240 ohms

Assessment

Process Show the students a flashlight and ask them to draw its electric circuit. Have them calculate the current that flows if the resistance of the bulb is 20 ohms. Circuit should show battery, wires, bulb, and possibly a switch. The current will depend on voltage of batteries. L2 P LS **Visual-Spatial, Logical-Mathematical**

Real-World Question

Purpose Students will compare the conductivity of various materials. L2 IN **Kinesthetic, Visual-Spatial**

Process collect data, make and use tables, record observations, draw conclusions

Time Required 40 minutes

Procedure

Teaching Strategy Have a collection of items ready for students to test, but let students offer additional items to be tested.

Troubleshooting Make sure all connections in the circuit have good contact.

Conclude and Apply

1. Answers will vary. Students should realize that metallic items will conduct electricity.
2. They are metallic.
3. They are nonmetallic.
4. Materials that allow the lightbulb to glow have metallic bonding. Materials that do not allow the lightbulb to glow are nonmetallic.
5. Metallic materials will conduct electricity; bad connections will prevent the lightbulb from lighting.
6. Answers will vary.

Identifying Conductors and Insulators

The resistance of an insulator is so large that only a small current flows when it is connected in a circuit. As a result, a lightbulb connected in a circuit with an insulator usually will not glow. In this lab, you will use the brightness of a lightbulb to identify conductors and insulators.

Real-World Question

What materials are conductors and what materials are insulators?

Goals

- **Identify** conductors and insulators.
- **Describe** the common characteristics of conductors and insulators.

Materials

battery
flashlight bulb
bulb holder
insulated wire

Safety Precautions 

Procedure

1. Set up an incomplete circuit as pictured in the photograph.
2. Touch the free bare ends of the wires to various objects around the room. Test at least 12 items.
3. Copy the table below. In your table, record which materials make the lightbulb glow and which don't.

Material Tested with Lightbulb Circuit	
Lightbulb Glows	Lightbulb Doesn't Glow
Results will vary	Results will vary

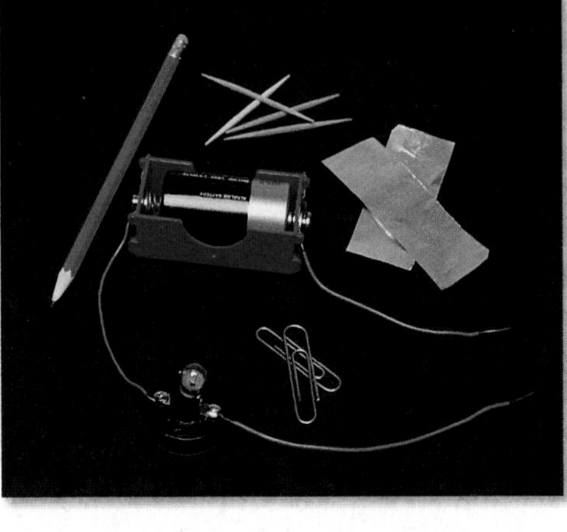

Conclude and Apply

1. Is there a pattern to your data?
2. Do all or most of the materials that light the lightbulb have something in common?
3. Do all or most of the materials that don't light the lightbulb have something in common?
4. **Explain** why one material may allow the lightbulb to light and another prevent the lightbulb from lighting.
5. **Predict** what other materials will allow the lightbulb to light and what will prevent the lightbulb from lighting.
6. **Classify** all the materials you have tested as conductors or insulators.

Communicating Your Data

Compare your conclusions with those of other students in your class. **For more help, refer to the** Science Skill Handbook.

Assessment

Process Silicon is an element that is nonconductive. Have students make posters illustrating how scientists treat silicon to alter its conductivity and how the altered silicon is used. Use **Performance Assessment in the Science Classroom,** p. 145 L2 IN **Visual-Spatial, Logical-Mathematical**

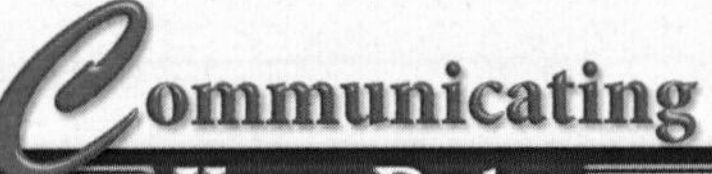

Students should discuss why their conclusions did or did not agree. They can cite references to support their arguments. L3 IN **Linguistic, Logical-Mathematical**

section

Electrical Energy

Reading Guide

What You'll Learn

- **Describe** the difference between series and parallel circuits.
- **Recognize** the function of circuit breakers and fuses.
- **Calculate** electrical power.
- **Calculate** the electrical energy used by a device.

Why It's Important

When you use an electric appliance, such as a hair dryer or a toaster oven, you pay for the electrical energy you use.

Review Vocabulary

energy: the ability to cause change

New Vocabulary

- series circuit
- parallel circuit
- electrical power

Series and Parallel Circuits

Look around. How many electrical devices such as lights, clocks, stereos, and televisions do you see that are plugged into electrical outlets? Circuits usually include three components. One is a source of voltage difference that can be provided by a battery or an electrical outlet. Another is one or more devices that use electrical energy. Circuits also include conductors such as wires that connect the devices to the source of voltage difference to form a closed path.

Think about using a hair dryer. The dryer must be plugged into an electrical outlet to operate. A generator at a power plant produces a voltage difference across the outlet, causing charges to move when the circuit is complete. The dryer and the circuit in the house contain conducting wires to carry current. The hair dryer turns the electrical energy into thermal energy and mechanical energy. When you unplug the hair dryer or turn off its switch, you open the circuit and break the path of the current. To use electrical energy, a complete circuit must be made. There are two kinds of circuits.

Series Circuits One kind of circuit is called a series circuit. In a **series circuit,** the current has only one loop to flow through, as shown in **Figure 16.** Series circuits are used in flashlights and some holiday lights.

Reading Check *How many loops are in a series circuit?*

Figure 16 A series circuit provides only one path for the current to follow.
Infer *What happens to the brightness of each bulb as more bulbs are added?*

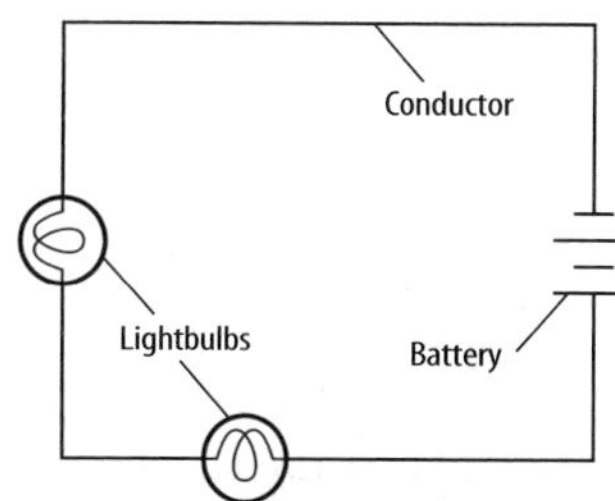

1 Motivate

Bellringer

Section Focus Transparencies also are available on the Interactive Chalkboard CD-ROM.

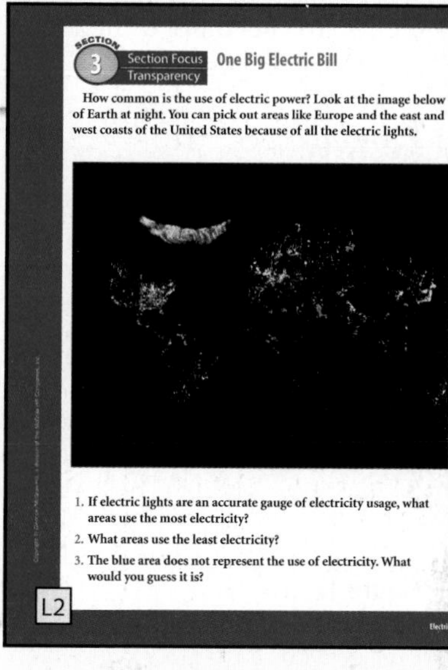

Tie to Prior Knowledge

Real Circuits Discuss with students what they learned in the last section about how resistance, voltage, and current are related. Tell them that this section will apply those terms to circuits in real devices. L2 IS **Auditory**

Reading Check

Answer one

Caption Answer

Figure 16 The brightness decreases.

Section 3 Resource Manager

Chapter *FAST FILE* Resources

Transparency Activity, pp. 44, 45–46
Enrichment, p. 30
Directed Reading for Content Mastery, pp. 19, 20
Lab Activity, pp. 13–14
Lab Worksheet, pp. 7–8
Reinforcement, p. 27
Mathematics Skill Activities, p. 9

2 Teach

Electrician Electricians must have good reading and comprehension skills to interpret and apply building code requirements and to use wiring diagrams. Electricians also must have basic math skills to calculate the materials required for a job and to calculate costs.

Career Research the requirements to become a licensed electrician in your state.

Activity

Examine Circuits Have several small devices with electric circuits, partially taken apart, in the room for students to examine. Possible displays include a small radio, a flashlight, a telephone, and a light fixture with two or more bulbs. L3 ELL IS **Kinesthetic**

Caption Answer

Figure 17 It is the same.

Electrician The installation of electrical wiring in any building usually requires an electrician. Electricians must have a thorough understanding of electricity. They also must constantly be aware of the safety issues involved in working with electricity. Research other skills that electricians must have.

Open Circuit If you have ever decorated a window or a tree with a string of lights, you might have had the frustrating experience of trying to find one burned-out bulb. How can one faulty bulb cause the whole string to go out? Because the parts of a series circuit are wired one after another, the amount of current is the same through every part. When any part of a series circuit is disconnected, no current flows through the circuit. This is called an open circuit. The burned-out bulb causes an open circuit in the string of lights.

Parallel Circuits What would happen if your home were wired in a series circuit and you turned off one light? This would cause an open circuit, and all the other lights and appliances in your home would go out, too. This is why houses are wired with parallel circuits. **Parallel circuits** contain two or more branches for current to move through. Look at the parallel circuit in **Figure 17.** The current can flow through both or either of the branches. Because all branches connect the same two points of the circuit, the voltage difference is the same in each branch. Then, according to Ohm's law, more current flows through the branches that have lower resistance.

Parallel circuits have several advantages. When one branch of the circuit is opened, such as when you turn a light off, the current continues to flow through the other branches. Houses, automobiles, and most electrical systems use parallel wiring so individual parts can be turned off without affecting the entire circuit.

Figure 17 In parallel circuits, the current follows more than one path.
Describe *how the voltage difference will compare in each branch.*

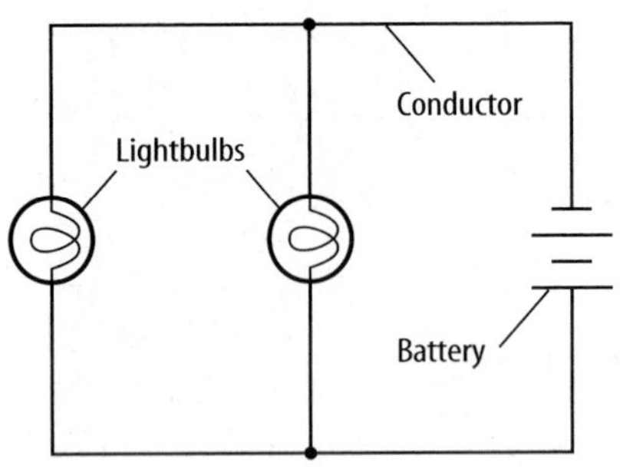

LAB DEMONSTRATION

Purpose to demonstrate series and parallel circuits

Materials battery, small lightbulbs (2), ammeters (2), wire

Procedure Set up a series circuit with the two lightbulbs. Include ammeters in two places in the circuit. Disconnect one lamp so the circuit is broken. Do the same for a parallel circuit.

Expected Outcome In the series circuit, the entire circuit is broken when the lamp is disconnected. For the parallel circuit, the circuit is only broken in the branch with the disconnected lamp.

Assessment

Why do results differ for the two circuits? Series-current has only one path so it is the same everywhere; parallel-current has two paths, so it is split between the paths. L2 IS **Logical-Mathematical, Visual-Spatial**

Figure 18 The wiring in a house must allow for the individual use of various appliances and fixtures. **Identify** *the type of circuit that is most common in household wiring.*

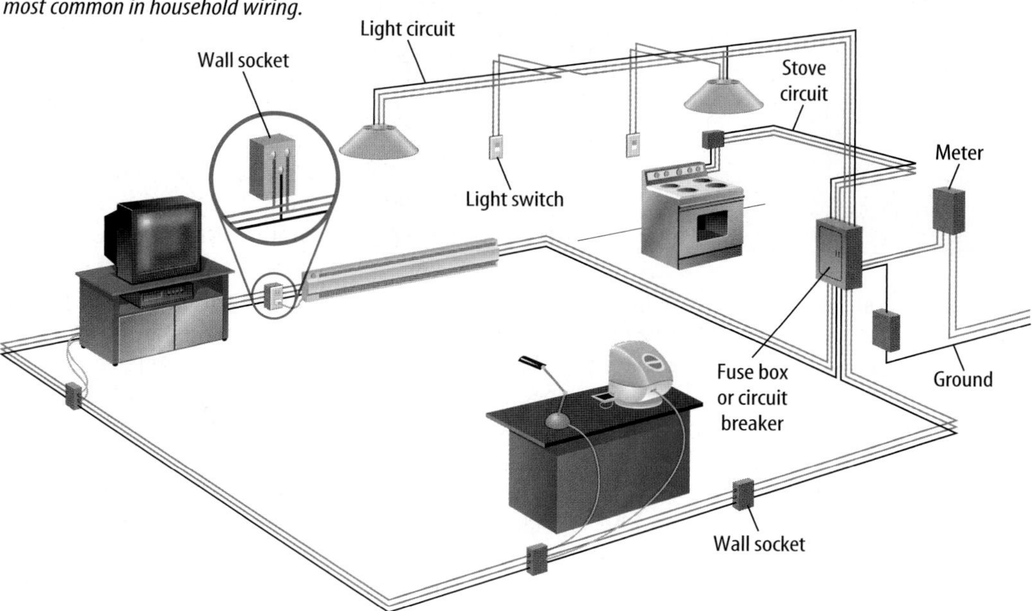

Household Circuits

Count how many different things in your home require electrical energy. You don't see the wires because most of them are hidden behind the walls, ceilings, and floors. This wiring is mostly a combination of parallel circuits connected in an organized and logical network. **Figure 18** shows how electrical energy enters a home and is distributed. In the United States, the voltage difference in most of the branches is 120 V. In some branches that are used for electric stoves or electric clothes dryers, the voltage difference is 240 V. The main switch and circuit breaker or fuse box serve as an electrical headquarters for your home. Parallel circuits branch out from the breaker or fuse box to wall sockets, major appliances, and lights.

In a house, many appliances draw current from the same circuit. If more appliances are connected, more current will flow through the wires. As the amount of current increases, so does the amount of heat produced in the wires. If the wires get too hot, the insulation can melt and the bare wires can cause a fire. To protect against overheating of the wires, all household circuits contain either a fuse or a circuit breaker.

Activity

Circuit Diagrams Draw several circuit diagrams on the board and have students identify them either as series circuits or as parallel circuits. At this point, avoid combination series/parallel circuits. L2 LS **Visual-Spatial**

Caption Answer

Figure 18 parallel circuit

Quick Demo

Series or parallel circuit?

Materials string of minature lights (should be three-wire type)

Estimated Time 10 minutes

Procedure Hang the string of lights across the front of the classroom and plug them in. Have students predict whether the circuit is series or parallel. Remove one bulb from the first half of the string. One section of the lights should go out. Discuss why one section went out but not the other. Have a student draw a possible circuit diagram on the board. L2

LS **Visual-Spatial, Logical-Mathematical, Kinesthetic**

Teacher FYI

Resistance In a series circuit, total resistance is equal to the sum of the individual resistances: $R_{total} = R_1 + R_2 + \ldots$ In a parallel circuit, the total resistance is calculated as follows: $1/R_{total} = 1/R_1 + 1/R_2 + \ldots$ The total resistance is less than any single resistance in a parallel circuit.

Visual Learning

Figure 18 Students should notice that all wiring in the house first runs through the fuse box or circuit breaker for protection. Why are three lines shown in the wiring? One line is ground; the other two are for the closed-current path. L2 LS **Visual-Spatial, Logical-Mathematical**

Caption Answer

Figure 19 a circuit breaker because it can be easily reset, whereas a fuse must be replaced

Make a Model

Fuses Students can learn about the behavior of fuses by constructing a simple circuit containing a battery and a lightbulb. To model a fuse, include as part of the circuit's wiring a strip of aluminum foil about 3 cm long. The strip should have a thin middle section that is about 1 mm wide. When the circuit is completed, the thin part of the foil will quickly melt, opening the circuit, and the light will go out, as occurs when a real fuse blows. L2 LS **Kinesthetic, Visual-Spatial**

Reading Check

Answer to protect against overheating and possible fire if the current in a wire becomes too high

A

B

Figure 19 Two useful devices to prevent electric circuits from overheating are A fuses and B circuit breakers.
Evaluate *which device, a fuse or a circuit breaker, would be more convenient to have in the home.*

Fuses When you hear that somebody has "blown a fuse," it means that the person has lost his or her temper. This expression comes from the function of an electrical fuse, shown in **Figure 19A,** which contains a small piece of metal that melts if the current becomes too high. When it melts, it causes a break in the circuit, stopping the flow of current through the overloaded circuit. To enable current to flow again in the circuit, you must replace the blown fuse with a new one. However, before you replace the blown fuse, you should turn off or unplug some of the appliances. Too many appliances in use at the same time is the most likely cause for the overheating of the circuit.

Circuit Breaker A circuit breaker, shown in **Figure 19B,** is another device that prevents a circuit from overheating and causing a fire. A circuit breaker contains a piece of metal that bends when the current in it is so large that it gets hot. The bending causes a switch to flip and open the circuit, stopping the flow of current. Circuit breakers usually can be reset by pushing the switch to its "on" position. Again, before you reset a circuit breaker, you should turn off or unplug some of the appliances from the overloaded circuit. Otherwise, the circuit breaker will switch off again.

Reading Check *What is the purpose of fuses and circuit breakers in household circuits?*

Electric Power

The reason that electricity is so useful is that electrical energy is converted easily to other types of energy. For example, electrical energy is converted to mechanical energy as the blades of a fan rotate to cool you. Electrical energy is converted to light energy in lightbulbs. A hair dryer changes electrical energy into thermal energy. The rate at which electrical energy is converted to another form of energy is the **electric power.**

The electric power used by appliances varies. Appliances often are labeled with a power rating that describes how much power the appliance uses, as shown in **Figure 20.** Appliances that have electric heating elements, such as ovens and hair dryers, usually use more electric power than other appliances.

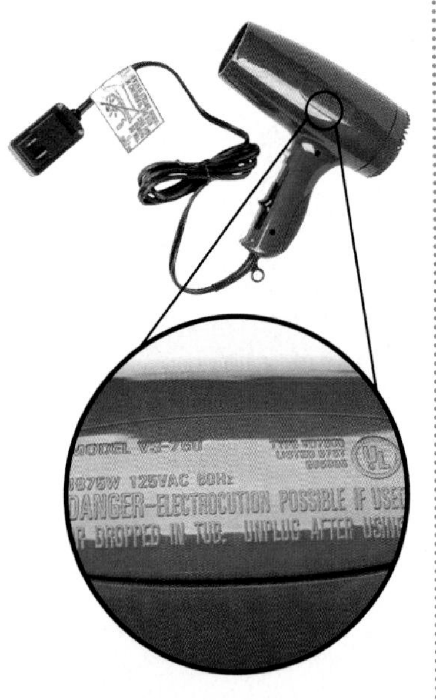

Figure 20 All appliances come with a power rating.

Cultural Diversity

Electric Lighting Lewis H. Latimer, the son of a former slave, taught himself to be a draftsman when he was a teenager. In 1880, Latimer was hired by the United States Electric Lighting Company, where he invented the first carbon-filament electric lamp and an inexpensive way to produce the filaments. In 1883, he joined Thomas Edison, and in 1890, he published the first textbook on electric lighting—*Incandescent Electric Lighting*. In 1918, the Edison Pioneers organization was formed to honor some of the people who worked with Thomas Edison as the "creators of the electric industry." One member was Lewis H. Latimer.

Calculating Electric Power The electric power used depends on the voltage difference and the current. Electric power can be calculated from the following equation.

Electric Power Equation

electric power (in watts) = **current** (in amperes) × **voltage difference** (in volts)

$$P = IV$$

The unit for power is the watt (W). Because the watt is a small unit of power, electric power is often expressed in kilowatts (kW). One kilowatt equals 1,000 watts.

ELECTRIC POWER EQUATION

Solve for Power The current in a clothes dryer is 15 A when it is plugged into a 240-volt outlet. How much electric power does the clothes dryer use?

1. **This is what you know:** current: $I = 15\ A$; voltage difference: $V = 240\ V$
2. **This is what you need to find:** power: P
3. **Use this formula:** $P = IV$
4. **Substitute:** the values of I and V into the formula and multiply. $P = (15)(240) = 3{,}600$
5. **Determine the units:** units of P = (units of I) × (units of V) = **amperes** × **volts** = watts

Answer: The power used by the dryer is 3,600 watts, which also equal to 3.6 kilowatts.

Science Online
For more practice problems, go to page 834, and visit gpscience.com/extra_problems.

Practice Problems

1. A toaster oven is plugged into an outlet where the voltage difference is 120 V. How much power does the toaster oven use if the current in the oven is 10 A?
2. A VCR that is not playing still uses 10.0 W of power. What is the current in the VCR if it is plugged into a 120-V outlet?
3. A flashlight bulb uses 2.4 W of power when the current in the bulb is 0.8 A. What is the voltage difference supplied by the batteries?
4. **Challenge** A hair dryer uses 1.2 kW of power when it is plugged into a 120-V outlet and turned on. What is the current in the hair dryer?

Use Science Words

Word Origin Many units of measurement in science are named for people who did related research. Have students investigate the origins of the words *ampere*, *watt*, and *volt*. The ampere is named after André Marie Ampère, who proposed the relationship between electricity and magnetism. The watt is named after James Watt, who created the first efficient steam engine and first used the word horsepower. The volt is named after Alessandro Volta, who observed that a conducting liquid produced a continuous transfer of electrons, a phenomenon later called electric current. L2 LS **Linguistic**

ELECTRIC POWER EQUATION

National Math Standards

Correlation to Mathematics Objectives

1, 2, 9

Answers to Practice Problems

1. 1,200 W or 1.2 kW
2. 0.083 A
3. 3 V
4. 10 A

Science Journal

Power, Voltage, Current, and Resistance Remind students that they have been given Ohm's law, and the formula for electric power. Have them write both formulas in their Science Journals and combine them to relate power to resistance. $I = V/R$; $P = IV$; therefore $P = V/R \times V = V^2/R$; also, $V = IR$, so $P = I \times IR = I^2 R$. L2 LS **Linguistic, Logical-Mathematical**

Fun Fact

Benjamin Franklin was first to use the terms *positive* and *negative* to describe charged objects. He also invented the lightning rod.

Electrical Energy Equation

National Math Standards

Correlation to Mathematics Objectives

1, 2, 9

Answers to Practice Problems

1. 7 kWh
2. 4 h
3. 4 kW
4. 0.015 kWh

Topic: Energy

Visit gpscience.com for Web links to information about the cost of electrical energy around the country.

Activity Using a blank map of the United States, create a key showing the relative energy costs in different states in different colors. With a partner, color in the states to create a visual map of energy costs. Give your map a title.

Electrical Energy Using electric power costs money. However, electric companies charge by the amount of electrical energy used, rather than by the electric power used. Electrical energy usually is measured in units of kilowatt hours (kWh) and can be calculated from this equation:

Electric Energy Equation

electrical energy (in kWh) = electric power (in kW) × time (in hours)

$$E = Pt$$

In the above equation, electric power is in units of kW and the time is the number of hours that the electric power is used.

Electrical Energy Equation

Solve for Electrical Energy A microwave oven with a power rating of 1,200 W is used for 0.25 h. How much electrical energy is used by the microwave?

1. **This is what you know:** electric power used: P = 1,200 W = 1.2 kW; time: t = 0.25 h
2. **This is what you need to find:** electrical energy used: E
3. **Use this formula:** $E = Pt$
4. **Substitute:** the values of P and t into the formula and multiply. $E = (1.2)(0.25) = 0.30$
5. **Determine the units:** units of E = (units of P) × (units of t) = kW × h = kWh

Answer: The electrical energy used is 0.30 kWh.

Science Online

For more practice problems, go to page 834, and visit gpscience.com/extra_problems.

Practice Problems

1. A refrigerator operates on average for 10.0 h a day. If the power rating of the refrigerator is 700 W, how much electrical energy does the refrigerator use in one day?
2. A TV with a power rating of 200 W uses 0.8 kWh of electrical energy in one day. For how many hours was the TV on during this day?
3. An electric dryer is operated for 0.75 h and uses 3.0 kWh of electrical energy. What is the power rating of the clothes dryer?
4. **Challenge** An electric light is plugged into a 120-V outlet. If the current in the bulb is 0.5 A, how much electrical energy is used by the bulb in 15 minutes?

Differentiated Instruction

Challenge Have students work in pairs to research and build a Leyden jar, a device used to store electric energy. **WARNING:** *Warn students not to use any flammable materials in their construction.* L3 LS **Visual-Spatial, Kinesthetic** COOP LEARN

The Cost of Using Electrical Energy

The cost of using the appliance can be computed by multiplying the electrical energy used by the amount the power company charges for each kWh. For example, if a 100-W lightbulb is left on for 5 h, the amount of electrical energy used is

$$E = Pt = (0.1 \text{ kW})\ (5 \text{ h}) = 0.5 \text{ kWh}$$

If the power company charges $0.10 per kWh, the cost of using the bulb for 5 h is

$$\begin{aligned} \text{cost} &= (\text{kWh used})\ (\text{cost per kWh}) \\ &= (0.5 \text{ kWh})\ (\$0.10/\text{kWh}) = \$0.05 \end{aligned}$$

The cost of using some household appliances is given in **Table 1,** where the cost per kWh is assumed to be $0.09/kWh.

Table 1 Cost of Using Home Appliances

Appliance	Hair Dryer	Stereo	Color Television
Power rating	1,000	100	200
Hours used daily	0.25	2.0	4.0
kWh used monthly	7.5	6.0	24.0
Cost per kWh	$0.09	$0.09	$0.09
Monthly cost	$0.68	$0.54	$2.16

section 3 review

Summary

Series and Parallel Circuits

- A series circuit has only one path that current can flow in.
- A parallel circuit has two or more branches that current can flow in.
- Household wiring usually consists of a number of connected parallel circuits.
- Fuses and circuit breakers are used to prevent wires from overheating when the current flowing in the wires becomes too large.

Electric Power

- Electric power is the rate at which electrical energy is converted into other forms of energy.
- Electric power can be calculated by multiplying the current by the voltage difference:

$$P = IV$$

Electrical Energy

- The electrical energy used can be calculated by multiplying the power by the time:

$$E = Pt$$

- Electric power companies charge customers for the amount of electrical energy they use.

Checking Concepts

1. **Explain** how electric power and electrical energy are related.
2. **Discuss** why fuses and circuit breakers are used in household circuits.
3. **Explain** what determines the current in each branch of a parallel circuit.
4. **Explain** whether or not a fuse or circuit breaker should be connected in parallel to the circuit it is protecting.
5. **Think Critically** A parallel circuit consisting of four branches is connected to a battery. Explain how the amount of current that flows out of the battery is related to amount of current in the branches of the circuit.

Applying Math

6. **Calculate** the current flowing into a desktop computer plugged into a 120-V outlet if the power used is 180 W.
7. **Calculate Electric Power** A circuit breaker is tripped when the current in the circuit is greater than 15 A. If the voltage difference is 120 V, what is the power being used when the circuit breaker is tripped?
8. **Calculate** the monthly cost of using a 700-W refrigerator that runs for 10 h a day if the cost per kWh is $0.09.

gpscience.com/self_check_quiz

section 3 review

1. Power is the rate at which electrical energy is converted to another form of energy. The amount of electrical energy used is the power times the time the power is used.
2. Fuse and circuit breakers stop the flow of current in a circuit when the circuit becomes overloaded. This prevents the wires from becoming so hot they melt or start a fire.
3. The current is determined by the resistance of each branch. The voltage differences across each branch are the same.
4. A fuse or circuit breaker must be connected in series, not parallel, to the circuit it is protecting in order to and stop the flow of current.
5. The current flowing out of the battery is equal to the sum of the currents in the four branches.
6. 1.5 A
7. The power is greater than 1.8 kW.
8. $18.90 (30 days)

Teacher FYI

Horsepower In the United States, the power of car engines is rated using the British unit horsepower (hp). One horsepower is equal to 746 watts.

3 Assess

DAILY INTERVENTION

Check for Understanding

Visual-Spatial Have students work in pairs to draw a model of the lights, switches, and wall outlets that are in the classroom. The drawing should be similar to that shown in Figure 18 and show that switches are wired in series while outlets and some lights are wired in parallel. L2 LS **Interpersonal, Visual-Spatial**

Reteach

Process Bring in an energy rating label from a new appliance. Have students use the voltage and current specifications of the appliance to determine its power, the energy it will use, and the cost of operation. L2 LS **Visual-Spatial, Logical-Mathematical**

Assessment

Process Ask students to write paragraphs that compare and contrast series and parallel circuits. Charge flows through both types of circuits. A series circuit has only one loop through which charge can flow; a parallel circuit has more than one. Use **PASC,** p. 157. L2 LS **Linguistic,** P **Logical-Mathematical**

Real-World Question

Purpose Students will design and test parallel and series circuits. L1 COOP LEARN

LS **Logical-Mathematical**

Process Skills observe, communicate, classify, compare and contrast, recognize cause and effect, interpret data, use numbers, experiment, hypothesize

Time Required one class period

Materials The lightbulb voltage requirements should closely match the battery voltage so bulbs don't burn out quickly.

Alternate Materials Obtain economical low-voltage lightbulbs by cutting apart a string of Christmas minilights. Insulated wire may be used instead of foil.

Safety Precautions To avoid overheating the wire, students should hook up the battery only long enough to make observations.

Form a Hypothesis

Possible Hypothesis If a bulb is removed from a series circuit, all lights will go out. In a parallel circuit, the remaining bulbs will stay lit. Lights shine brightest in the parallel circuit.

Test Your Hypothesis

Possible Procedures Series circuits should have a single path with lights in a chain. Parallel circuits should have the lights on three separate paths.

Design Your Own

Comparing Series and Parallel Circuits

Goals
- **Design** and construct series and parallel circuits.
- **Compare** and contrast the behaviors of series and parallel circuits.

Possible Materials
6-V dry-cell battery
small lights with sockets (3)
aluminum foil
paper clips
tape
scissors
paper

Safety Precautions
Some parts of circuits can become hot. Do not leave the battery connected or the circuit closed for more than a few seconds at a time. Never connect the positive and negative terminals of the dry-cell battery directly without including at least one bulb in the circuit.

Real-World Question

Imagine what a bedroom might be like if it were wired in series. For an alarm clock to keep time and wake you in the morning, your lights and anything else that uses electricity would have to be on. Fortunately, most outlets in homes are wired in parallel circuits on separate branches of the main circuit. How do the behaviors of series and parallel circuits compare?

Form a Hypothesis

Predict what will happen to the other bulbs when one bulb is unscrewed from a series circuit and from a parallel circuit. Explain your prediction. Also, form a hypothesis to explain in which circuit the lights shine the brightest.

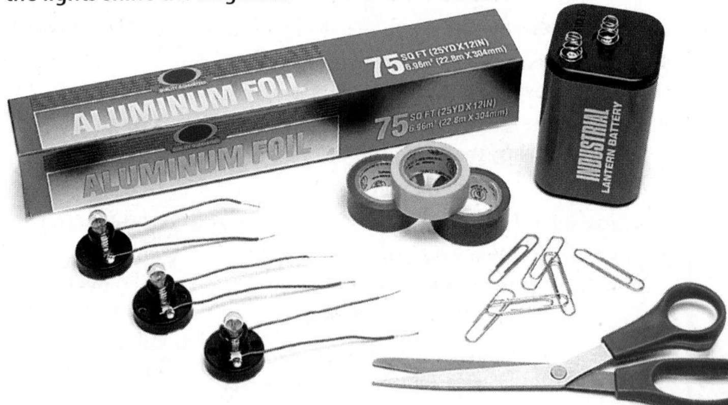

Differentiated Instruction

Visually Impaired Instead of using lamps, this activity can be performed using buzzers in the circuits. A visually impaired student could be paired with a sighted student to aid in circuit construction. L2 LS COOP LEARN **Kinesthetic, Visual-Spatial**

Alternative Inquiry Lab

Test a Hypothesis To extend this Lab into an Inquiry Lab, have students hypothesize how $V = IR$ applies to parallel circuits, and experiment to test those hypotheses. For this experiment, supply light bulbs with different power ratings. Have students use Ohm's law to calculate the current through each lightbulb. Then have them compare the results of their calculations with their observations.

Test Your Hypothesis

Make a Plan

1. As a group, agree upon and write the hypothesis statement.
2. Work together determining and writing the steps you will take to test your hypothesis. Include a list of the materials you will need.
3. How will your circuits be arranged? On a piece of paper, draw a large parallel circuit of three lights and the dry-cell battery as shown. On the other side, draw another circuit with the three bulbs arranged in series.
4. Make conducting wires by taping a 30-cm piece of transparent tape to a sheet of aluminum foil and folding the foil over twice to cover the tape. Cut these to any length that works in your design.

Follow Your Plan

1. Make sure your teacher approves your plan before you start.
2. Carry out the experiment. **WARNING:** *Leave the circuit on for only a few seconds at a time to avoid overheating.*
3. As you do the experiment, record your predictions and your observations in your Science Journal.

Analyze Your Data

1. **Predict** what will happen in the series circuit when a bulb is unscrewed at one end. What will happen in the parallel circuit?
2. **Compare** the brightness of the lights in the different circuits. Explain.
3. **Predict** what happens to the brightness of the bulbs in the series circuit if you complete it with two bulbs instead of three bulbs. Test it. How does this demonstrate Ohm's law?

Conclude and Apply

1. Did the results support your hypothesis? Explain by using your observations.
2. Where in the parallel circuit would you place a switch to control all three lights? Where would you place a switch to control only one light? Test it.

Communicating Your Data

Prepare a poster to highlight the differences between a parallel and a series circuit. Include possible practical applications of both types of circuits. **For more help, refer to the** Science Skill Handbook.

Troubleshooting Students may design a circuit having two lightbulbs in parallel that are wired in series with the third light. Although interesting, this will not help students completely explore the behavior of each of the circuits independently. L2 IS **Visual-Spatial, Kinesthetic**

Expected Outcome When a light in series is removed, all the lights go out. In a parallel circuit, when a light is removed, others remain lit.

Analyze Your Data

Answers to Questions

1. In series, the current will stop and all bulbs will go out. In parallel, the charge will flow through other branches and the other bulbs will remain lit.
2. The lights are brighter in parallel because more current flows through each loop than the loop with three bulbs in a series circuit.
3. It will be brighter because of less resistance in the circuit.

Error Analysis Have students analyze their circuits for possible sources of errors. dead batteries, burned-out bulbs, poor connections with the aluminum foil

Conclude and Apply

1. Answers depend on student hypotheses.
2. between the battery and a wire leading to one side of the lights; along the wire that goes to only one of the lights

Assessment

Oral Ask students to discuss why houses and buildings are wired in parallel and not in series. In a series circuit, all lights and appliances would have to be on at the same time; if one is off or burned out, no charge flows anywhere in the circuit. L2 IS **Logical-Mathematical**

Communicating Your Data

Have students use a computer graphics program to draw sketches of circuits for their posters. They can also use the computer to write any explanations they wish to include on their posters. L3 IS **Visual-Spatial, Logical-Mathematical**

Understanding Literature

Pre-Reading Activity Ask students to do a clustering of terms that define who they are or as Ralph Ellison says "confirms my reality." Each student should put his or her name in the center of a cluster that includes elements that define his or her identity such as ethnic heritage, extracurricular activities, and family members. L2 IN **Linguistic**

Respond to the Reading

Connect Ask students if they can remember a time they were unfairly judged or misunderstood simply because their outward appearance was different from others around them.

Respond Tell students to be aware of their responses as they read about the invisible man. His description of himself might make them think that anyone who is judged by others is an outsider. Ask students if the invisible man has a positive view of himself and how the text conveys that it is important for a person to have a positive view of himself or herself. L2 IN **Linguistic, Logical-Mathematical**

Answers to Questions

1. Ectoplasm is the outer layer of a part of the cell. Epidermis is the outer layer of skin.
2. The narrator says he is "a man of substance, of flesh and bone, fiber and liquids."
3. because he has wired his ceiling with 1,369 lights

Science and Language Arts

Invisible Man

by Ralph Ellison

I am an invisible man. No, I am not a spook like those who haunted Edgar Allen Poe; nor am I one of your Hollywood-movie ectoplasms.[1] A am a man of substance, of flesh and bone, fiber and liquids—and I might even be said to possess a mind. I am invisible, understand, simply because people refuse to see me.... Nor is my invisibility exactly a matter of biochemical accident to my epidermis.[2] That invisibility to which I refer occurs because of a peculiar disposition ... of those with whom I come in contact....

.... Now don't jump to the conclusion that because I call my home a "hole" it is damp and cold like a grave.... Mine is a warm hole.

My hole is warm and full of light. Yes, *full* of light. I doubt if there is a brighter spot in all New York than this hole of mine.... Perhaps you'll think it strange that an invisible man should need light, desire light, love light. Because maybe it is exactly because I *am invisible.* Light confirms my reality, gives birth to my form.... I myself, after existing some twenty years, did not become alive until I discovered my invisibility.

... In my hole in the basement there are exactly 1,369 lights. I've wired the entire ceiling, every inch of it.... Though invisible, I am in the great American tradition of tinkers. That makes me kin to Ford, Edison and Franklin.

1 The outer layer of a part of the cell.

2 The outer layer of skin.

Ralph Ellison

Understanding Literature

Prologue A prologue is an introduction to a novel, play, or other work of literature. Often a prologue contains useful information about events to come in the story. Foreshadowing is the use of clues by the author to prepare readers for future events or recurring themes.

Respond to the Reading

1. What clues does the narrator give that he is not really invisible?
2. Why does the narrator believe he is in the "great American tradition of tinkers"?
3. **Linking Science and Writing** Write a prologue to a make-believe book describing Edison's invention of the lightbulb. Recall that a prologue is not a summary of the book. Rather, it can state general themes that the work of literature will address or set the stage or describe the setting of the story.

If all 1,369 lightbulbs were all wired together in a series circuit, the electrical resistance in the circuit would be high. By Ohm's law, the current in the circuit would be low and the bulbs wouldn't glow. If all the bulbs were wired in a parallel circuit, so much current would flow in the circuit that the connecting wires would melt. For the bulbs to light, the narrator must have wired them in many independent circuits.

Resources for Teachers and Students

Juneteenth, by Ralph Ellison, Random House, 1999

The African American Century, by Henry Louis Gates, Jr. and Cornel West, The Free Press, 2000

Reviewing Main Ideas

Section 1 Electric Charge

1. There are two types of electric charge—positive charge and negative charge.
2. Electric charges exert forces on each other. Like charges repel and unlike charges attract.
3. Electric charges can be transferred from one object to another, but cannot be created or destroyed.
4. Electrons can move easily in an electrical conductor. Electrons do not move easily in an insulator.
5. Objects can be charged by contact or by induction. Charging by induction occurs when a charged object is brought near an electrically neutral object.

Section 2 Electric Current

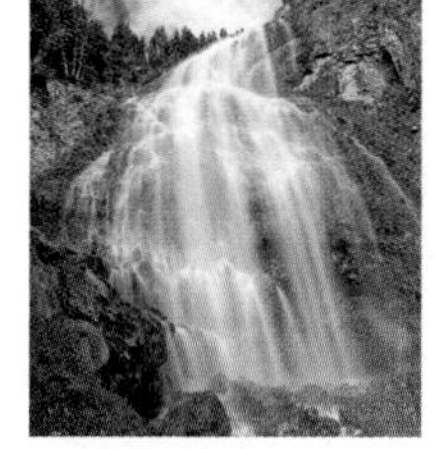

1. Electric current is the net movement of electric charges in a single direction. A voltage difference causes an electric current to flow.
2. A circuit is a closed path along which charges can move. Current will flow continually only along a circuit that is unbroken.
3. Chemical reactions in a battery produce a voltage difference between the positive and negative terminals of the battery.
4. Electrical resistance is the tendency of a material to oppose the flow of electric current.
5. In an electric circuit, the voltage difference, current, and resistance are related by Ohm's law:

$$I = \frac{V}{R}$$

Section 3 Electrical Energy

1. Current has only one path in a series circuit and more than one path in a parallel circuit.
2. Circuit breakers and fuses prevent excessive current from flowing in a circuit.
3. Electrical power is the rate at which electrical energy is used, and can be calculated from $P = IV$.
4. The electrical energy used by a device can be calculated from the equation $E = Pt$.

FOLDABLES Use the Foldable you made at the beginning of the chapter to help you review electric charge, electric current, and electrical energy.

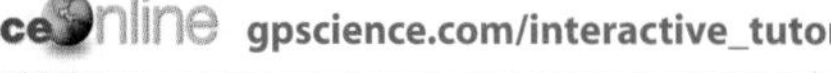
gpscience.com/interactive_tutor

Identifying Misconceptions

Assess

Materials D-battery (1), flashlight (1), bulb in socket (1), switch (1), wires (5), voltmeter (1)

Procedure Have each group set up a circuit. Ask students to predict the voltage between the two sides of the switch when it is open and when it is closed. Students can use voltmeters to test their predictions.

Expected Outcome Voltage varies across different points in a circuit and can exist without current flow. A voltage exists across the two sides of the switch when it is open. The voltage approaches zero when it is closed. L2 COOP LEARN

LS **Logical-Mathematical, Kinesthetic, Visual-Spatial**

Reviewing Main Ideas

Summary statements can be used by students to review the major concepts of the chapter.

Visit gpscience.com
/self_check_quiz
/interactive_tutor
/vocabulary_puzzlemaker
/chapter_review
/standardized_test

Assessment Transparency

For additional assessment questions, use the *Assessment Transparency* located in the transparency book.

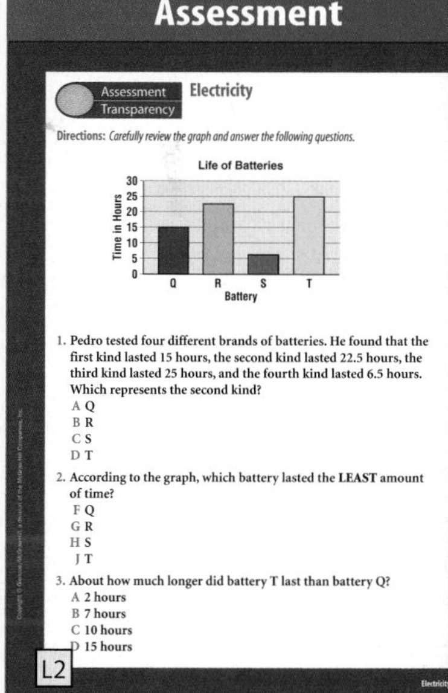
Assessment

Assessment Transparency **Electricity**

Directions: *Carefully review the graph and answer the following questions.*

1. Pedro tested four different brands of batteries. He found that the first kind lasted 15 hours, the second kind lasted 22.5 hours, the third kind lasted 25 hours, and the fourth kind lasted 6.5 hours. Which represents the second kind?
   A Q
   B R
   C S
   D T
2. According to the graph, which battery lasted the **LEAST** amount of time?
   F Q
   G R
   H S
   J T
3. About how much longer did battery T last than battery Q?
   A 2 hours
   B 7 hours
   C 10 hours
   D 15 hours

L2

Electricity

FOLDABLES Have students use their Foldables to review the content of the chapter. On the back of the paper, have students write a paragraph about the nature of the forces between magnets.

chapter 7 Review

Using Vocabulary

1. series circuit
2. static electricity
3. voltage difference
4. the law of conservation of charge
5. Resistance
6. charging by contact

Checking Concepts

7. C
8. C
9. C
10. A
11. B
12. A
13. A

Interpreting Graphics

14. circuit A—2.6 Ω; circuit B—10 Ω; circuit C—30 Ω; circuit D—3.3 Ω The line is curved, descending from left to right. As the resistance becomes larger, the current decreases toward zero. As the resistance approaches zero, the current approaches infinity.
15. See student page.

chapter 7 Review

Using Vocabulary

charging by contact p. 195
charging by induction p. 196
circuit p. 201
conductor p. 195
electric current p. 200
electrical power p. 210
insulator p. 195
law of conservation of charge p. 193
Ohm's law p. 205
parallel circuit p. 208
resistance p. 203
series circuit p. 207
static electricity p. 192
voltage difference p. 200

Complete each statement using a word(s) from the vocabulary list above.

1. A(n) ________ is a circuit with only one path for current to follow.
2. An accumulation of excess electric charge is ________.
3. The electric force that makes current flow in a circuit is related to the ________.
4. According to ________, electric charge cannot be created or destroyed.
5. ________ is the result of electrons colliding with atoms as current flows in a material.
6. Charging a balloon by rubbing it on wool is an example of ________.

Checking Concepts

Choose the word or phrase that best answers the question.

7. Which of the following is a conductor?
   A) glass **C)** tungsten
   B) wood **D)** plastic
8. Resistance in wires causes electrical energy to be converted into which form of energy?
   A) chemical energy
   B) nuclear energy
   C) thermal energy
   D) sound
9. The electric force between two charged objects depends on which of the following?
   A) their masses and their separation
   B) their speeds
   C) their charge and their separation
   D) their masses and their charge
10. An object becomes positively charged when which of the following occurs?
   A) loses electrons **C)** gains electrons
   B) loses protons **D)** gains neutrons
11. Which of the following does NOT provide a voltage difference in a circuit?
   A) wet cell **C)** electrical outlet
   B) wires **D)** dry cell
12. A commonly used unit for electrical energy is which of the following?
   A) kilowatt-hour **C)** ohm
   B) ampere **D)** newton
13. Which of the following is the rate at which appliances use electrical energy?
   A) power **C)** resistance
   B) current **D)** speed

Interpreting Graphics

Use the table below to answer question 14.

Current in Electric Circuits

Circuit	Current (A)
A	2.3
B	0.6
C	0.2
D	1.8

14. The table shows the current in circuits that were each connected to a 6-V dry cell. Calculate the resistance of each circuit. Graph the current versus the resistance of each circuit. Describe the shape of the line on your graph.

Science Online gpscience.com/vocabulary_puzzlemaker

Use the *ExamView® Assessment Suite* CD-ROM to:

- create multiple versions of tests
- create modified tests with one mouse click for inclusion students
- edit existing questions and add your own questions
- build tests aligned with state standards using built-in State Curriculum Tags
- change English tests to Spanish with one mouse click and vice versa

15. Copy and complete the following concept map on electric current.

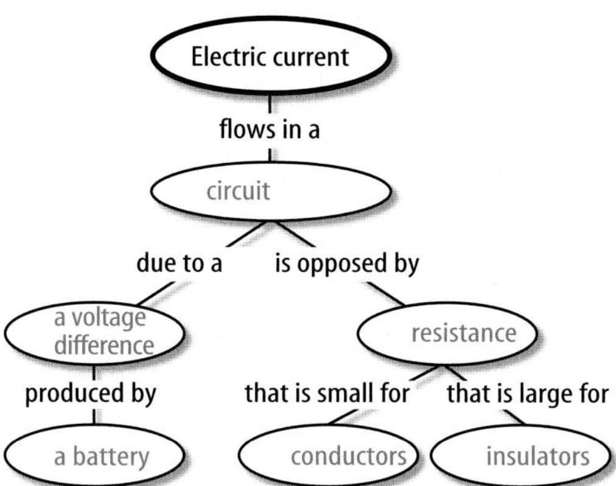

Thinking Critically

16. **Identify and Manipulate Variables** Design an experiment to test the effect on current and voltage differences in a circuit when two identical batteries are connected in series. What is your hypothesis? What are the variables and controls?

17. **Explain** A metal rod is charged by induction when a negatively-charged plastic rod is brought nearby. Explain how the net charge on the metal rod has changed.

18. **Predict** You walk across a carpet on a dry day and touch a glass doorknob. Predict whether or not you would receive an electric shock. Explain your reasoning.

19. **Explain** The electric force between electric charges is much larger than the gravitational force between the charges. Why then is the gravitational force between Earth and the Moon much larger than the electric force between Earth and the Moon?

20. **Diagram** Draw a circuit diagram showing how a stereo, a TV, and a computer can be connected to a single source of voltage difference, such that turning off one appliance does not turn off all the others. Include a circuit breaker in your diagram that will protect all the appliances.

Applying Math

21. **Calculate Current** Using the information in the circuit diagram below, compute the current flowing in the circuit.

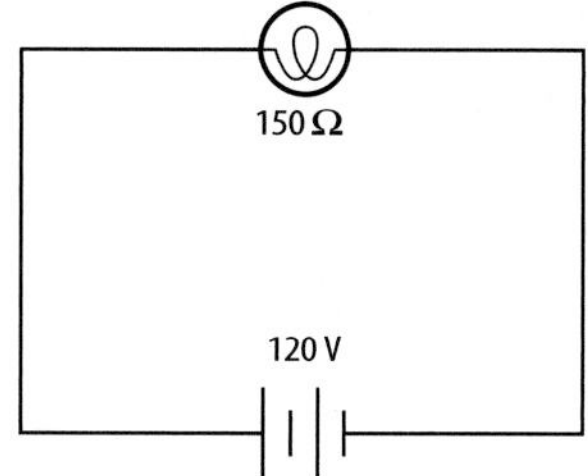

22. **Calculate Current** A toy car with a resistance of 20 Ω is connected to a 3-V battery. How much current flows in the car?

23. **Calculate Electrical Energy** The current flowing in an appliance connected to a 120-V source is 2 A. How many kilowatt-hours of electrical energy does the appliance use in 4 h?

24. **Calculate Electrical Energy Cost** A self-cleaning oven uses 5,400 W when cleaning the oven. If it takes 1.5 h to clean, how many kilowatt-hours of electricity are used? At a cost of $0.09 per kWh, what does it cost to clean the oven?

25. **Calculate Power** A calculator uses a 9-V battery and draws 0.1 A of current. How much power does it use?

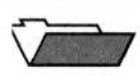
Science Online gpscience.com/chapter_review

Assessment Resources

Reproducible Masters

Chapter *Fast File* Resources
Chapter Review, pp. 39–40
Chapter Tests, pp. 41–44
Assessment Transparency Activity, p. 51

Glencoe Science Web site
Chapter Review Test
Standardized Test Practice

Glencoe Technology
Assessment Transparency
ExamView® Assessment Suite
MindJogger Videoquiz
Interactive Chalkboard

chapter 7 Review

Thinking Critically

16. The hypothesis should include the voltage doubling and the current doubling. Variables should include the voltage of the second battery. Controls should include testing the voltage of the second battery.
17. The net charge does not change since electrons are not lost nor gained, only displaced.
18. No, the glass doorknob is an insulator and resists being charged inductively.
19. The net charge on Earth or the Moon is nearly zero. So the electric force is very small.
20. Drawings will vary but should show the appliances in parallel branches with a circuit breaker in series with the voltage source.

Applying Math

National Math Standards
1, 2, 9

21. 0.8 V
22. 0.15 V
23. 0.96 kWh
24. 8.1 kWh, $.73
25. 0.9 W

Answer Sheet A practice answer sheet can be found at gpscience.com/answer_sheet.

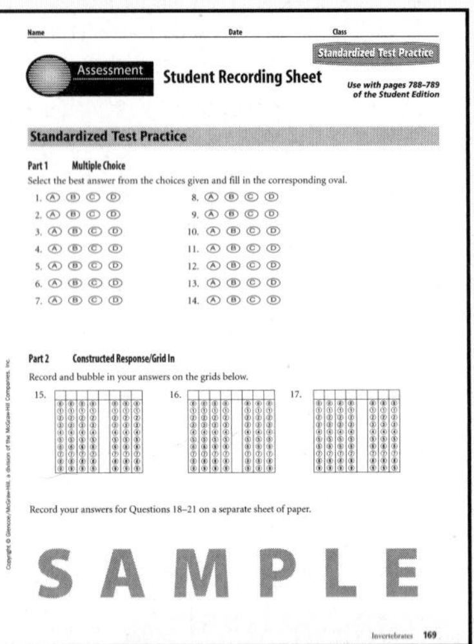
Name Date Class

Standardized Test Practice

Assessment Student Recording Sheet

Use with pages 788–789 of the Student Edition

Standardized Test Practice

Part 1 Multiple Choice

Select the best answer from the choices given and fill in the corresponding oval.

1. Ⓐ Ⓑ Ⓒ Ⓓ
2. Ⓐ Ⓑ Ⓒ Ⓓ
3. Ⓐ Ⓑ Ⓒ Ⓓ
4. Ⓐ Ⓑ Ⓒ Ⓓ
5. Ⓐ Ⓑ Ⓒ Ⓓ
6. Ⓐ Ⓑ Ⓒ Ⓓ
7. Ⓐ Ⓑ Ⓒ Ⓓ
8. Ⓐ Ⓑ Ⓒ Ⓓ
9. Ⓐ Ⓑ Ⓒ Ⓓ
10. Ⓐ Ⓑ Ⓒ Ⓓ
11. Ⓐ Ⓑ Ⓒ Ⓓ
12. Ⓐ Ⓑ Ⓒ Ⓓ
13. Ⓐ Ⓑ Ⓒ Ⓓ
14. Ⓐ Ⓑ Ⓒ Ⓓ

Part 2 Constructed Response/Grid In

Record and bubble in your answers on the grids below.

15. 16. 17.

Record your answers for Questions 18–21 on a separate sheet of paper.

SAMPLE

Invertebrates 169

Part 1 Multiple Choice

1. C
2. B
3. A
4. C
5. B
6. D
7. C
8. B
9. C
10. B

Part 1 Multiple Choice

Record your answers on the answer sheet provided by your teacher or on a sheet of paper.

1. Which of the following is true about two adjacent electric charges?
A. If both are positive, they attract.
B. If both are negative, they attract.
C. If one is positive and one is negative, they attract.
D. If one is positive and one is negative, they repel.

The figure below shows a negatively charged electroscope. Use the figure to answer questions 2 and 3.

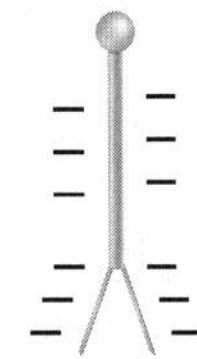

2. If a negatively-charged rod is brought close to, but not touching, the knob, the two leaves will
A. move closer together.
B. move farther apart.
C. not move at all.
D. become positively charged.

3. If a positively charged rod touches the knob, the two leaves will
A. move closer together.
B. move farther apart.
C. not move at all.
D. become positively charged.

4. Which of these is the SI unit of current?
A. volt **C.** ampere
B. ohm **D.** watt

5. A kilowatt-hour is a unit of
A. power. **C.** current.
B. electric energy. **D.** resistance.

6. When two objects become charged by contact, which of the following is true?
A. The net charge on each object doesn't change.
B. Both become negatively charged.
C. Both become positively charged.
D. Electrons are transferred.

7. When an object becomes charged by induction, which of the following best describes the net charge on the object?
A. The net charge increases.
B. The net charge decreases.
C. The object is electrically neutral.
D. The net charge is negative.

Use the figure below to answer questions 8, 9, and 10.

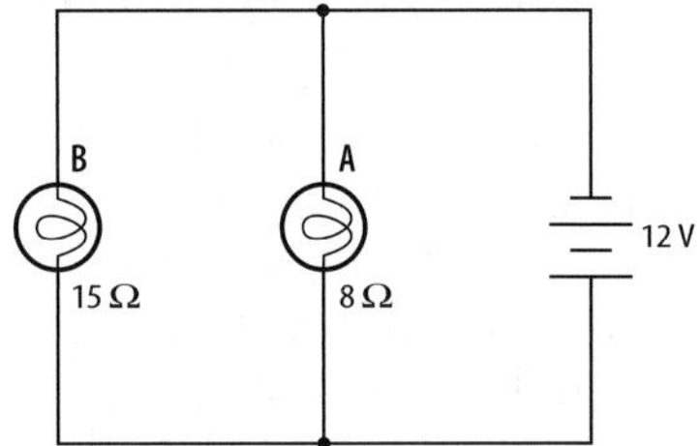

8. Which of the following is the same for each lightbulb?
A. current in the filament
B. voltage difference
C. electric resistance
D. charging by induction

9. Which of the following is the current that flows through lightbulb B?
A. 1.25 A **C.** 0.8 A
B. 0.67 A **D.** 1.5 A

10. Which of the following is the electric power used by lightbulb A?
A. 8 W **C.** 12 W
B. 18 W **D.** 15 W

Part 2 Short Response/Grid In

11. $P = IV = 2.5\ A \times 12\ V = 30\ W$

12. $E = Pt$
$= 100\ W \times \frac{1\ kW}{1000\ W} \times 20\ h$
$= 2\ kW\text{-}h$

13. $12\ \Omega$

14. 30 W h

15. The current will double since the resistance is half.

16. They repel each other because they have the same charge.

17. $E = Pt$
$= 250\ W \times \frac{1\ kW}{1000\ W}$
$\times 4\ h\backslash day \times 30\ days$
$= 30\ kW\text{-}h$, cost $= E \times$ rate
$= 30\ kW\text{-}h \times \frac{\$0.10}{kW\text{-}h} = \$3.00$

Part 2 | Short Response/Grid In

Record your answers on the answer sheet provided by your teacher or on a sheet of paper.

11. The current flowing through a lightbulb is 2.5 A. The lamp is connected to a battery supplying a voltage difference of 12 V. What is the power used by the lightbulb?

12. A person spends four hours a day in a room, but leaves a 100-W lightbulb burning 24 hours a day. How much energy would be saved if the bulb burned for only the four hours the person was in the room?

Use the figure below to answer questions 13, 14, and 15.

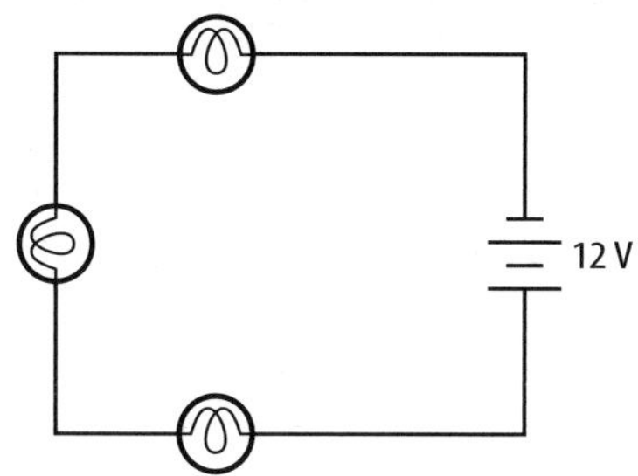

13. If the current in the circuit is 1.0 A, what is the total resistance of the circuit?

14. If the current in the circuit is 1.0 A, how much electrical energy is used by the circuit in 2.5 h?

15. How does the current in the circuit change if one of the lightbulbs is removed and the circuit is reconnected?

16. Two balloons are rubbed with a piece of wool. Describe what happens as the balloons are brought close together.

17. Calculate the cost of the electrical energy used by a TV for 30 days if the TV is on for four hours a day and the TV uses 250 W. Assume that the cost of electrical energy is $0.10 per kWh.

Part 3 | Open Ended

Record your answers on a sheet of paper.

18. Explain how a refrigerator with a power rating of 650 W can use more electrical energy in a day than a hair dryer with a power rating of 1,000 W.

19. Two copper wires have the same length and the same temperature. However, the electric resistance of wire A is twice as large as the resistance of wire B. Explain how wire A and wire B are different.

20. A rubber rod rubbed on hair becomes negatively charged. A glass rod rubbed with a piece of silk becomes positively charged. Suppose the charged rubber rod is suspended so it is free to rotate. Describe how the rubber rod moves as the piece of silk is brought close to it.

Use the table below to answer question 21.

Resistance of Copper Wire	
Length (m)	**Resistance (Ω)**
10	0.8
20	1.6
25	2.0
30	2.4

21. Suppose you were asked to estimate the resistance of a 5-m length of wire based on data in the table. What additional information would be needed to make your estimate more accurate?

22. The filament in a 75-W lightbulb has a smaller electric resistance than the filament in a 40-W lightbulb. Describe two ways the filament in the 75-W bulb could be different from the filament in the 40-W lightbulb.

Science Online gpscience.com/standardized_test

Part 3 | Open Ended

18. A refrigerator operates several hours a day, while a hair dryer operates less than an hour a day.

19. The diameter of wire A is smaller than that of wire B.

20. The negatively charged rubber rod is attracted to the positively charged piece of silk.

21. The temperature, material, and diameter of the 5 m wire must be the same as the wire in the table.

22. The 75-W bulb filament could be shorter or have a larger diameter than the 40-W light bulb.

Rubrics

The following rubrics are sample scoring devices for short response and open-ended questions.

Short Response

Points	Description
2	The student demonstrates a thorough understanding of the science of the task. The response may contain minor flaws that do not detract from the demonstration of a thorough understanding.
1	The student has provided a response that is only partially correct.
0	The student has provided a completely incorrect solution or no response at all.

Open Ended

Points	Description
4	The student demonstrates a thorough understanding of the science of the task. The response may contain minor flaws that do not detract from the demonstration of a thorough understanding.
3	The student demonstrates an understanding of the science of the task. The response is essentially correct and demonstrates an essential but less than thorough understanding of the science.
2	The student demonstrates only a partial understanding of the science of the task. Although the student may have used the correct approach to a solution or may have provided a correct solution, the work lacks an essential understanding of the underlying science concepts.
1	The student demonstrates a very limited understanding of the science of the task. The response is incomplete and exhibits many flaws.
0	The student provides a completely incorrect solution or no response at all.

Magnetism and Its Uses

BIG Idea **A magnet is surrounded by a magnetic field that exerts a force on other magnets.**

	Content Standards	Learning Objectives	Resources to Assess Mastery
Section 1	**5–8:** UCP.1–3, 5; A.1, 2; B.1, 2; D.1, 2 **9–12:** UCP.1–3, 5; A.1, 2; B.2, 4; D.1, 3	**Magnetism** 1. **Explain** how a magnet exerts a force. 2. **Describe** the properties of temporary and permanent magnets. 3. **Explain** why some materials are magnetic and some are not. 4. **Model** magnetic behavior using magnetic domains. ***Main Idea*** Like magnetic poles repel each other and unlike poles attract each other.	**Formative Assessment** Reading Check, pp. 224, 226 Section Review, p. 230 **Summative Assessment** *ExamView® Assessment Suite*
Section 2	**5–8:** UCP.1–3, 5; A.1, 2; B.1, 2; G.3 **9–12:** UCP.1–3, 5; A.1, 2; B.2, 4; G.3	**Electricity and Magnetism** 5. **Describe** the magnetic field produced by an electric current. 6. **Explain** how an electromagnet produces a magnetic field. 7. **Describe** how electromagnets are used. 8. **Explain** how an electric motor operates. ***Main Idea*** An electric current in a wire is surrounded by a magnetic field.	**Formative Assessment** Reading Check, pp. 233, 234 Section Review, p. 237 **Summative Assessment** *ExamView® Assessment Suite*
Section 3	**5–8:** UCP.1–3, 5; A.1, 2; B.1, 2; G.3 **9–12:** UCP.1–3, 5; A.1, 2; B.2, 4; G.3 See pp. 16T–17T for a Key to Standards.	**Producing Electric Current** 9. **Define** electromagnetic induction. 10. **Describe** how a generator produces an electric current. 11. **Distinguish** between alternating current and direct current. 12. **Explain** how a transformer can change the voltage of an alternating current. ***Main Idea*** A changing magnetic field can produce an electric current in a wire loop.	**Formative Assessment** Reading Check, pp. 239, 243 Section Review, p. 244 **Summative Chapter Assessment** MindJogger, Ch. 8 *ExamView® Assessment Suite* Leveled Chapter Test Test A L1 Test B L2 Test C L3 Test Practice, pp. 252–253

Suggested Pacing				
Period	Instruction	Labs	Review & Assessment	Total
Single	4 days	4 days	2 days	10 days
Block	2 blocks	2 blocks	1 block	5 blocks

Core Instruction	Leveled Resources	Leveled Labs	Pacing: Period		Pacing: Block
Student Text, pp. 222–230 Section Focus Transparency, Ch. 8, Section 1 Interactive Chalkboard, Ch. 8, Section 1 Identifying Misconceptions, p. 228 Differentiated Instruction, pp. 225, 229 Applying Science, p. 228	**Chapter *Fast File* Resources** Directed Reading for Content Mastery, p. 20 L1 Note-taking Worksheet, pp. 33–35 Reinforcement, p. 27 L2 Enrichment, p. 30 L3 **Reading Essentials,** p. 120 L1 ELL **Science Notebook,** p. 81 ELL ***Active*Folders**: *Magnetism* L1 ELL	**Launch Lab**, p. 223: bar magnet, small paper clips *10 min* L2 **MiniLAB**, p. 227: bar magnet, ring stand, thread, paper clip, tape, book, paper, aluminum foil, fabric, butter knife *20 min* L2 **MiniLAB**, p. 229: plastic foam cup, magnet, sewing needle, tape, plate, water *15 min* L2	1	Section 1, pp. 223–226 (includes Launch Lab)	1
			2	Section 1, pp. 227–228 (includes MiniLAB)	1
			3	Section 1, pp. 229–230 (includes MiniLAB and Section Review)	2
Student Text, pp. 231–237 Section Focus Transparency, Ch. 8, Section 2 Interactive Chalkboard, Ch. 8, Section 2 Differentiated Instruction, pp. 232, 236	**Chapter *Fast File* Resources** Directed Reading for Content Mastery, p. 21 L1 Note-taking Worksheet, pp. 33–35 Reinforcement, p. 28 L2 Enrichment, p. 31 L3 **Reading Essentials,** p. 125 L1 ELL **Science Notebook,** p. 85 ELL ***Active*Folders**: *Magnetism* L1 ELL		4	Section 2, pp. 231–234	2
			5	Section 2, pp. 235–237 (includes Section Review)	3
Student Text, pp. 238–247 Section Focus Transparency, Ch. 8, Section 3 Teaching Transparency, Ch. 8, Section 3 Interactive Chalkboard, Ch. 8, Section 2 Visualizing Motors and Generators, p. 241 Identifying Misconceptions, p. 239 Differentiated Instruction, p. 241 Chapter Study Guide, p. 249	**Chapter *Fast File* Resources** Directed Reading for Content Mastery, pp. 21, 22 L1 Note-taking Worksheet, pp. 33–35 Reinforcement, p. 29 L2 Enrichment, p. 32 L3 **Reading Essentials,** p. 131 L1 ELL **Science Notebook,** p. 88 ELL	***Lab**, p. 245: cardboard tube, bar magnet, insulated wire, scissors, galvanometer or ammeter *45 min* L1 L2 L3 (Video Lab) ***Lab**, pp. 246–247: 22-guage insulated wire, 16-penny iron nail, aluminum rod or nail, 0-6 V DC power supply, 1.5-V D-cell batteries (3), steel paper clips, magnetic compass, duct tape *60 min* L1 L2 L3 *Lab version A L1 version B L2 L3	6	Section 3, pp. 238–244 (includes Section Review)	3
			7	Lab:Magnets, Coils, and Circuits, p. 245	4
			8	Lab:Controlling Electromagnets, pp. 246–247	4
			9	Lab:Controlling Electromagnets, pp. 246–247	5
			10	Study Guide, Chapter Review, and Test Practice, pp. 249–253	5

Video Lab

chapter  Magnetism and Its Uses

Transparencies

Section Focus

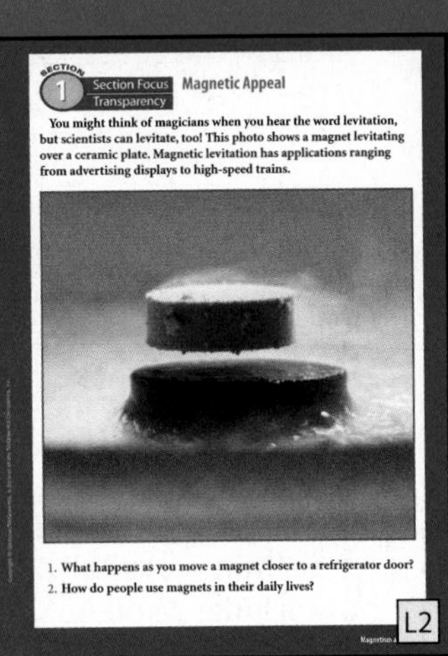
Section 1 Section Focus Transparency Magnetic Appeal

You might think of magicians when you hear the word levitation, but scientists can levitate, too! This photo shows a magnet levitating over a ceramic plate. Magnetic levitation has applications ranging from advertising displays to high-speed trains.

1. What happens as you move a magnet closer to a refrigerator door?
2. How do people use magnets in their daily lives?

L2

Section 2 Section Focus Transparency It Was an Age of Small Appliances

Many common household items contain small motors. Some examples are fans, vacuums, and hairdryers. What other appliances are pictured below?

1. Which items use electricity? Which items have motors?
2. Name some ways you have used electric current today.

L2

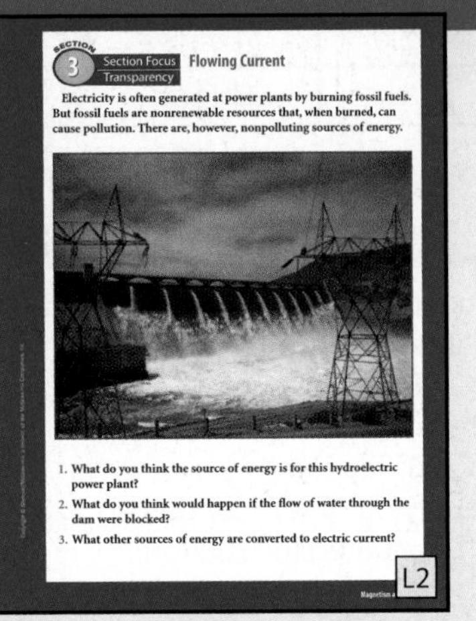
Section 3 Section Focus Transparency Flowing Current

Electricity is often generated at power plants by burning fossil fuels. But fossil fuels are nonrenewable resources that, when burned, can cause pollution. There are, however, nonpolluting sources of energy.

1. What do you think the source of energy is for this hydroelectric power plant?
2. What do you think would happen if the flow of water through the dam were blocked?
3. What other sources of energy are converted to electric current?

L2

This is a representation of key blackline masters available in the Teacher Classroom Resources. See Resource Manager boxes within the chapter for additional information.

Assessment

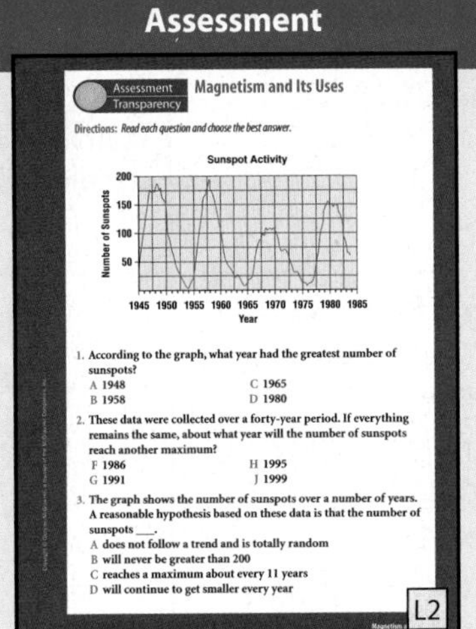
Assessment Transparency Magnetism and Its Uses

Directions: Read each question and choose the best answer.

1. According to the graph, what year had the greatest number of sunspots?
   A 1948 C 1965
   B 1958 D 1980
2. These data were collected over a forty-year period. If everything remains the same, about what year will the number of sunspots reach another maximum?
   F 1986 H 1995
   G 1991 J 1999
3. The graph shows the number of sunspots over a number of years. A reasonable hypothesis based on these data is that the number of sunspots ___.
   A does not follow a trend and is totally random
   B will never be greater than 200
   C reaches a maximum about every 11 years
   D will continue to get smaller every year

L2

Teaching

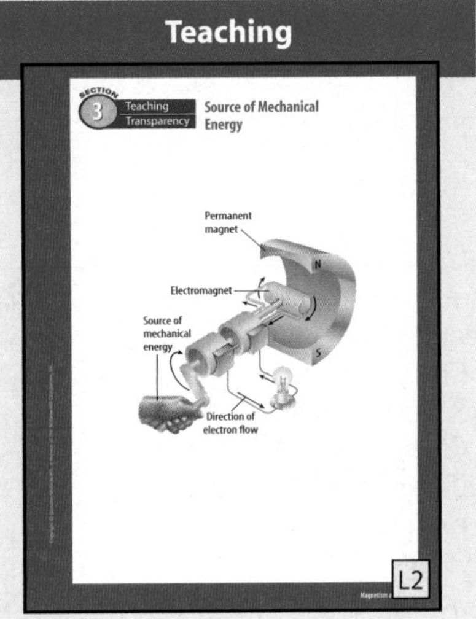
Section 3 Teaching Transparency Source of Mechanical Energy

L2

Key to Teaching Strategies

The following designations will help you decide which activities are appropriate for your students.

L1 Level 1 activities should be appropriate for students with learning difficulties.

L2 Level 2 activities should be within the ability range of all students.

L3 Level 3 activities are designed for above-average students.

ELL ELL activities should be within the ability range of English Language Learners.

COOP LEARN Cooperative Learning activities are designed for small group work.

LS Multiple Learning Styles logos, as described on page 12T, are used throughout to indicate strategies that address different learning styles.

P These strategies represent student products that can be placed into a best-work portfolio.

PBL Problem-Based Learning activities apply real-world situations to learning.

Hands-on Activities

Student Text Lab Worksheet

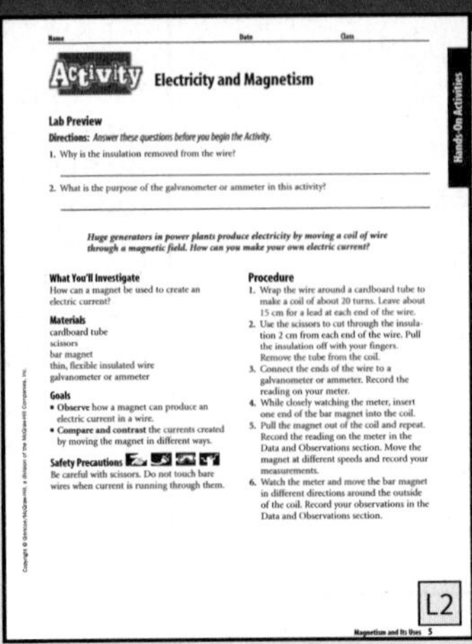
Activity Electricity and Magnetism

L2

Laboratory Activities

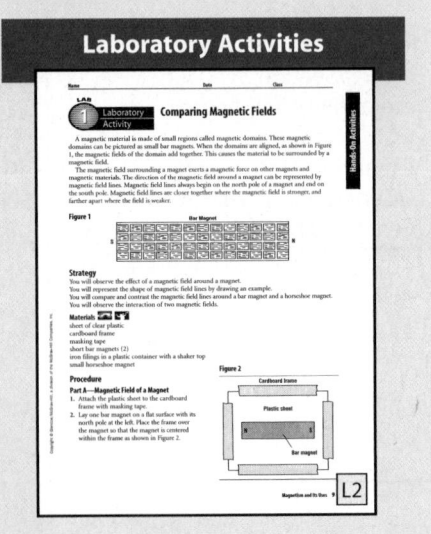

Lab 1 Laboratory Activity Comparing Magnetic Fields

L2

Resource Manager

Meeting Different Ability Levels

Content Outline

Name Date Class

Note-taking Worksheet — Magnetism and Its Uses

Section 1 Magnetism

A. Magnetism—the properties and __________ of magnets

1. Interaction between two magnets, called magnetic __________, increases as magnets move closer together.
2. A magnetic __________, which exerts the magnetic force, surrounds a magnet, and is strongest __________ to the magnet.

B. Magnetic __________—the regions of a magnet where the magnetic force exerted by the magnet is strongest

1. All magnets have a __________ pole and a __________ pole.
2. Like poles __________. Unlike poles __________.
3. Earth has magnetic poles.
   a. A compass needle is a small bar magnet that can freely __________.
   b. A compass needle always points __________.

C. Magnetic materials—__________, cobalt, and nickel

1. The magnetic field created by each __________ exerts a force on nearby atoms.
2. Magnetic domains—groups of atoms with __________ magnetic poles
   a. In a magnet, the like poles of all the domains point in the __________ direction.
   b. __________ magnets are made by placing a magnetic material in a strong magnetic field, forcing a large number of magnetic domains to line up.

Section 2 Electricity and Magnetism

A. Moving charges and magnetic fields

1. Moving charges, like those in an electric current, produce __________ fields.
   a. The magnetic __________ around a current-carrying wire forms a circular pattern about the wire.
   b. The direction of the field depends on the __________ of the current.
   c. The __________ of the magnetic field depends on the amount of current flowing in the wire.

Meeting Individual Needs

L2

Magnetism and Its Uses 33

Reinforcement

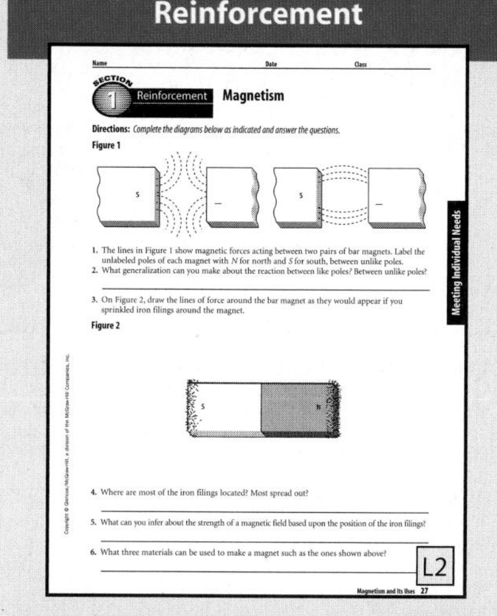
Name Date Class

Section 1 Reinforcement — Magnetism

Directions: Complete the diagrams below as indicated and answer the questions.

Figure 1

1. The lines in Figure 1 show magnetic forces acting between two pairs of bar magnets. Label the unlabeled poles of each magnet with N for north and S for south, between unlike poles.
2. What generalization can you make about the reaction between like poles? Between unlike poles?
3. On Figure 2, draw the lines of force around the bar magnet as they would appear if you sprinkled iron filings around the magnet.

Figure 2

4. Where are most of the iron filings located? Most spread out?
5. What can you infer about the strength of a magnetic field based upon the position of the iron filings?
6. What three materials can be used to make a magnet such as the ones shown above?

Meeting Individual Needs

L2

Magnetism and Its Uses 27

Enrichment

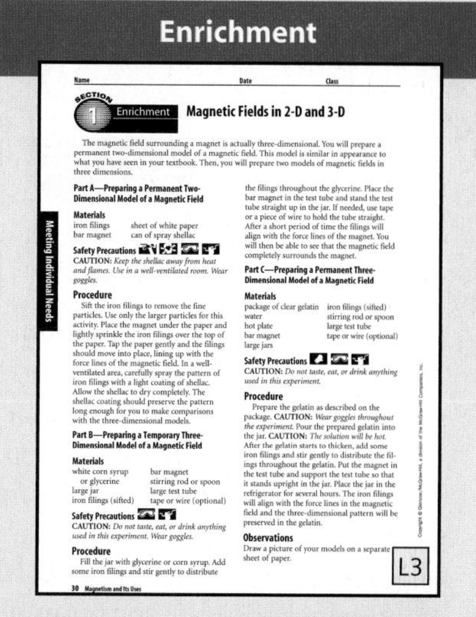
Name Date Class

Section 1 Enrichment — Magnetic Fields in 2-D and 3-D

The magnetic field surrounding a magnet is actually three-dimensional. You will prepare a permanent two-dimensional model of a magnetic field. This model is similar in appearance to what you have seen in your textbook. Then, you will prepare two models of magnetic fields in three dimensions.

Part A—Preparing a Permanent Two-Dimensional Model of a Magnetic Field

Materials: iron filings, sheet of white paper, bar magnet, can of spray shellac

Safety Precautions

CAUTION: Keep the shellac away from heat and flames. Use in a well-ventilated room. Wear goggles.

Procedure

Part B—Preparing a Temporary Three-Dimensional Model of a Magnetic Field

Part C—Preparing a Permanent Three-Dimensional Model of a Magnetic Field

Observations

Meeting Individual Needs

L3

30 Magnetism and Its Uses

Directed Reading (English/Spanish)

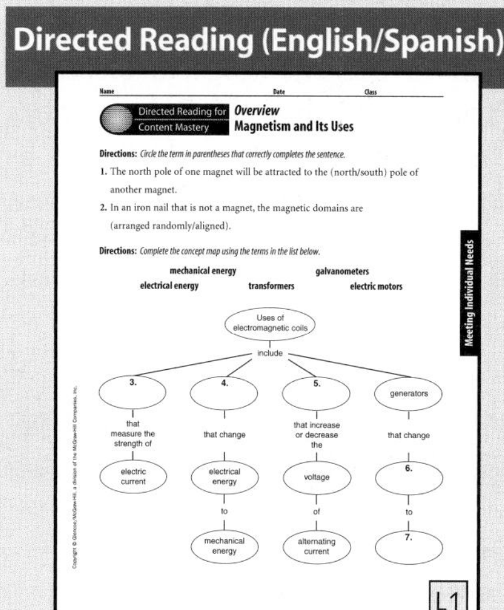
Name Date Class

Directed Reading for Content Mastery — Overview — Magnetism and Its Uses

Directions: Circle the term in parentheses that correctly completes the sentence.

1. The north pole of one magnet will be attracted to the (north/south) pole of another magnet.
2. In an iron nail that is not a magnet, the magnetic domains are (arranged randomly/aligned).

Directions: Complete the concept map using the terms in the list below.

mechanical energy, galvanometers, electrical energy, transformers, electric motors

Meeting Individual Needs

L1

Magnetism and Its Uses 19

Study Guide

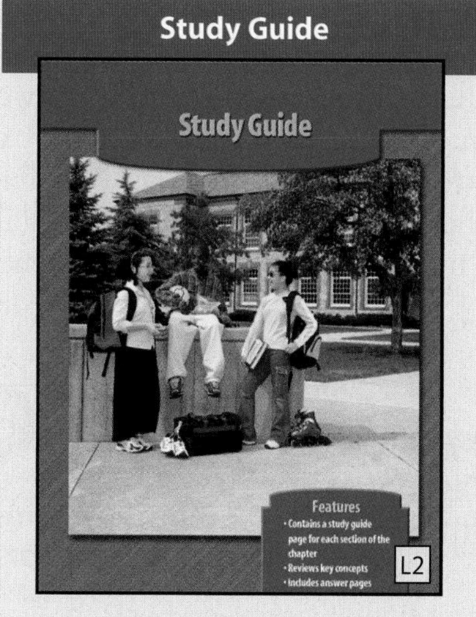

Reading Essentials

Assessment

Test Practice Workbook

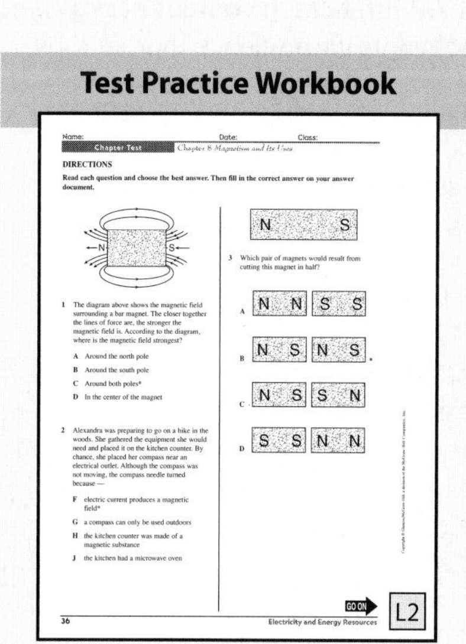
Name: Date: Class:

Chapter Test — Chapter 8 Magnetism and Its Uses

DIRECTIONS

Read each question and choose the best answer. Then fill in the correct answer on your answer document.

1 The diagram above shows the magnetic field surrounding a bar magnet. The closer together the lines of force are, the stronger the magnetic field is. According to the diagram, where is the magnetic field strongest?

A Around the north pole
B Around the south pole
C Around both poles*
D In the center of the magnet

2 Alexandra was preparing to go on a bike in the woods. She gathered the equipment she would need and placed it on the kitchen counter. By chance, she placed her compass near an electrical outlet. Although the compass was not moving, the compass needle turned because —

F electric current produces a magnetic field*
G a compass can only be used outdoors
H the kitchen counter was made of a magnetic substance
J the kitchen had a microwave oven

3 Which pair of magnets would result from cutting this magnet in half?

A N N S S
B N S N S*
C N S S N
D S S N N

L2

36 Electricity and Energy Resources

Chapter Review

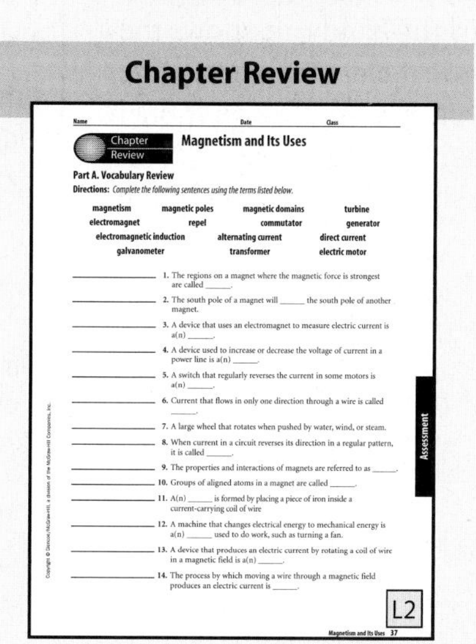
Name Date Class

Chapter Review — Magnetism and Its Uses

Part A. Vocabulary Review

Directions: Complete the following sentences using the terms listed below.

magnetism, magnetic poles, magnetic domains, turbine, electromagnet, repel, commutator, generator, electromagnetic induction, alternating current, direct current, galvanometer, transformer, electric motor

1. The regions on a magnet where the magnetic force is strongest are called __________.
2. The south pole of a magnet will __________ the south pole of another magnet.
3. A device that uses an electromagnet to measure electric current is a(n) __________.
4. A device used to increase or decrease the voltage of current in a power line is a(n) __________.
5. A switch that regularly reverses the current in some motors is a(n) __________.
6. Current that flows in only one direction through a wire is called __________.
7. A large wheel that rotates when pushed by water, wind, or steam.
8. When current in a circuit reverses its direction in a regular pattern, it is called __________.
9. The properties and interactions of magnets are referred to as __________.
10. Groups of aligned atoms in a magnet are called __________.
11. A(n) __________ is formed by placing a piece of iron inside a current-carrying coil of wire.
12. A machine that changes electrical energy to mechanical energy is a(n) __________ used to do work, such as turning a fan.
13. A device that produces an electric current by rotating a coil of wire in a magnetic field is a(n) __________.
14. The process by which moving a wire through a magnetic field produces an electric current is __________.

Assessment

L2

Magnetism and Its Uses 37

Chapter Tests

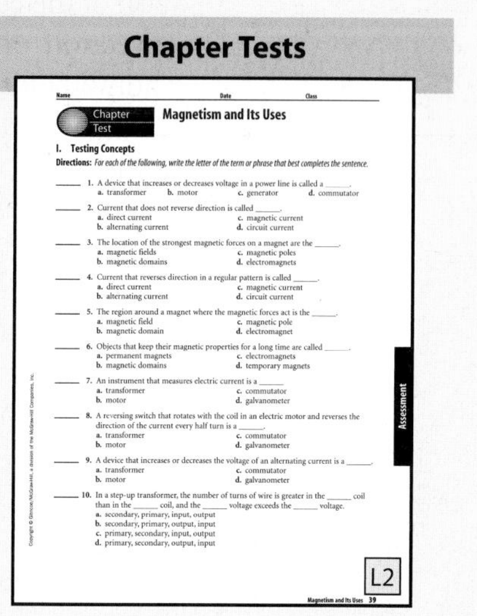
Name Date Class

Chapter Test — Magnetism and Its Uses

I. Testing Concepts

Directions: For each of the following, write the letter of the term or phrase that best completes the sentence.

1. A device that increases or decreases voltage in a power line is called a __________. a. transformer b. motor c. generator d. commutator
2. Current that does not reverse direction is called __________. a. direct current b. alternating current c. magnetic current d. circuit current
3. The location of the strongest magnetic forces on a magnet are the __________. a. magnetic fields b. magnetic domains c. magnetic poles d. electromagnets
4. Current that reverses direction in a regular pattern is called __________. a. direct current b. alternating current c. magnetic current d. circuit current
5. The region around a magnet where the magnetic forces act is the __________. a. magnetic field b. magnetic domain c. magnetic pole d. electromagnet
6. Objects that keep their magnetic properties for a long time are called __________. a. permanent magnets b. magnetic domains c. electromagnets d. temporary magnets
7. An instrument that measures electric current is a __________. a. transformer b. motor c. commutator d. galvanometer
8. A reversing switch that rotates with the coil in an electric motor and reverses the direction of the current every half turn is a __________. a. transformer b. motor c. commutator d. galvanometer
9. A device that increases or decreases the voltage of an alternating current is a __________. a. transformer b. motor c. commutator d. galvanometer
10. In a step-up transformer, the number of turns of wire is greater in the __________ coil than in the __________ coil, and the __________ voltage exceeds the __________ voltage. a. secondary, primary, input, output b. secondary, primary, output, input c. primary, secondary, input, output d. primary, secondary, output, input

Assessment

L2

Magnetism and Its Uses 39

Science Content Background

section 1 Magnetism

Magnets

In 1269 Petrus Peregrinus published an article describing the properties of lodestone. He reported that if it is hung freely, lodestone orients in a north-south plane but does not point exactly to true North. He also noted that like poles repel and unlike poles attract, and that iron can be magnetized by contact with it.

Magnetic Materials

A common definition of magnetism is the ability to attract iron. Steel is composed of iron and carbon molecules that form a strong material used in many common products. Steel is magnetic because it contains iron. This property allows cars to be lifted by electromagnets in junkyards and soup can lids to be held by the magnet on a can opener. Cobalt and nickel are also attracted to magnets. Iron, nickel, and cobalt are called ferromagnetic materials.

section 2 Electricity and Magnetism

Electric Current and Magnetism

Frictional forces usually act in the opposite direction to the motion of an object. For example, air resistance on a car traveling north acts toward the south. The magnetic field produced by an electric current acts at right angles to the direction of the current. The right-hand rule shows the direction of the magnetic field in a wire. The thumb points in the direction of the conventional current, or the way a positive charge would flow in a wire. The fingers then show the direction of the magnetic field.

section 3 Producing Electric Current

From Mechanical to Electrical Energy

Niagara Falls generates significant tourism and electricity. In order to keep the tourism industry vibrant, only about 55 percent of the water that goes over the falls is diverted into turbines in the daytime; at night this amount is increased to 75 percent.

Transformers

The ability of alternating current (AC) to be transformed into higher and lower voltages gives it an advantage over direct current (DC) in electrical power distribution. Increasing the voltage does not create energy because current decreases as voltage increases. This increase does, however, result in more efficient transmission. This efficiency becomes significant as electricity travels through miles of wire.

chapter content resources

Internet Resources

For additional content background, visit gpscience.com to:

- access your book online
- find references to related articles in popular science magazines
- access Web links with related content background
- access current events with science journal topics

Print Resources

Magnetic Materials: Fundamentals and Device Applications, by Nicola A. Spaldin, Cambridge University Press, 2003

Modern Magnetic Materials: Principles and Applications, by Robert C. O'Handley, Wiley InterScience, 1999

Electricity, Magnetism, and Light, by Wayne Saslow, Academic Press, 2002

Waves: Principles of Light, Electricity, and Magnetism (Secrets of the Universe), by Paul Fleisher, Lerner Publications Company, 2001

Misconceptions

Find Out What Students Think

Students may think that . . .

All metals are magnetic.

Students are aware of common properties of metals such as the fact that they are good conductors of electricity and heat. It is natural for students to extend these similarities to magnetism and think that all metals can be attracted by a magnet. Lack of first-hand experience with magnets and metals makes this misconception common, even in adults. In addition, iron alloys are omnipresent, so people's limited experiences with magnets may lead them to believe that all metals are magnetic.

Activity

Ask students to draw two columns on their papers and label one *Attracted to a Magnet* and the other *Not Attracted to a Magnet.* Then ask that they place the following words into the appropriate columns: *iron, lead, plastic, copper, steel, aluminum, nickel, cobalt, oxygen,* and *wood.* Have students form groups and discuss any differences in opinion about which items belong in each column. The iron, steel, nickel, and cobalt are attracted to a magnet, and the lead, plastic, copper, aluminum, oxygen and wood are not. L2

Promote Understanding

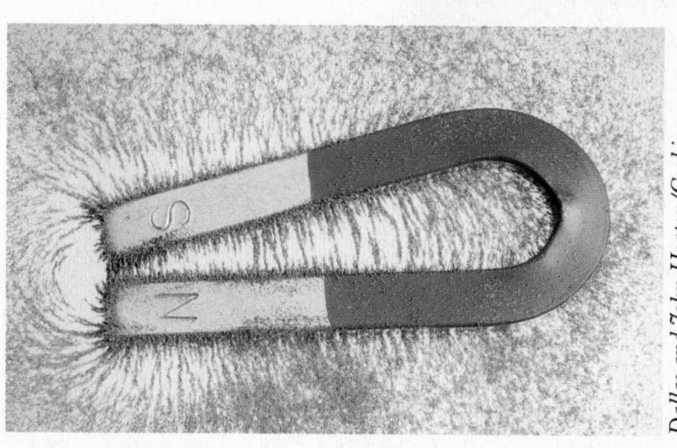

Dallas and John Heaton/Corbis

Activity

Provide students with different metals and nonmetals and with magnets with which to test them. The materials should include easily obtainable ferromagnetic materials such as iron and steel as well as nonferromagnetic metals such as aluminum and copper. Make sure to include nonmetals, even though most students will realize that these are not magnetic.

- Have students use the magnets to test for attraction and sort materials that are and are not magnetic.
- On the board, make a class list of the results.
- Help students realize that iron (Fe) is a magnetic material, so things made from iron, including steel, are attracted to magnets.
- Explain that cobalt (Co) and nickel (Ni) are also magnetic materials.
- Have students locate iron, cobalt, and nickel on a periodic table of the elements. Point out that on the periodic table, these metals are in the same row and are next to each other. L2

Assess

After completing the chapter, see *Identifying Misconceptions* in the Study Guide at the end of the chapter.

About the Photo

Aurora These colorful light displays occur primarily in the upper latitudes of the Northern and Southern Hemispheres. Auroras that occur in the Northern Hemisphere are called aurora borealis or northern lights.

Science Journal Student responses will vary, but may include magnets attract some metals, likes repel, and opposites attract.

BIG Idea

Magnetic Fields Electric fields are produced by electric charges. However, there are two ways that magnetic fields are produced. One way is by an electric charge in motion. Any moving electric charge is surrounded by a magnetic field. Magnetic fields also surround certain particles, such as electrons, that have a quantum-mechanical property called spin. Particles that have spin are not actually spinning around an internal axis, but in some ways behave as if they were. In most materials, the magnetic fields due to both the motion of electrons and their spin cancels out. However, in ferromagnetic materials, such as iron, cobalt, and nickel, the magnetic fields due to electron spin don't completely cancel. As a result, each atom in these materials behaves like a tiny magnet.

Introduce the Chapter Give students two bar magnets with their poles marked. Have students show that like poles repel and unlike poles attract. Then give students magnets of different shapes, such as horseshoe magnets and disk magnets. Have students identify the poles on these magnets.

chapter 8

Magnetism and Its Uses

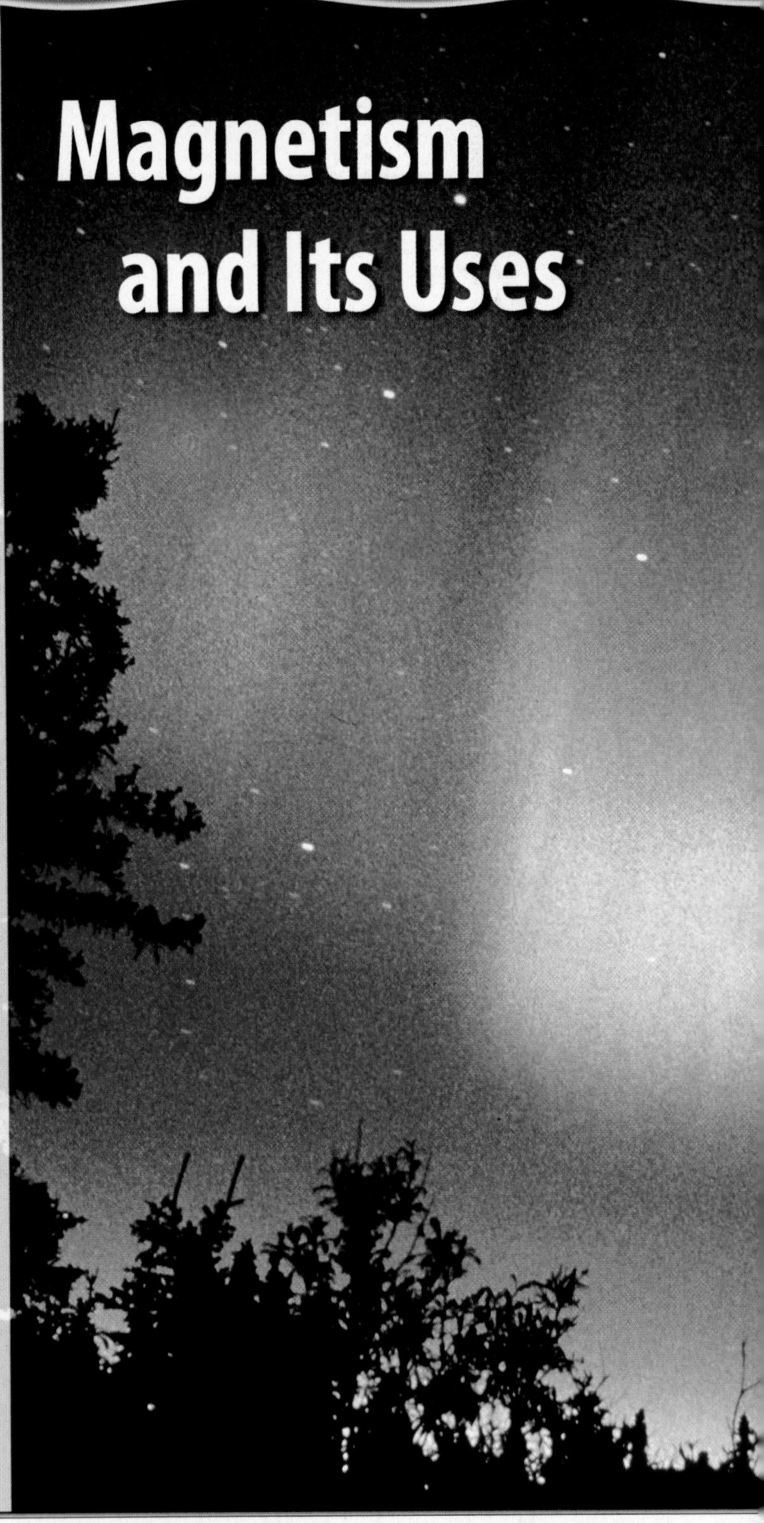

BIG Idea A magnet is surrounded by a magnetic field that exerts a force on other magnets.

8.1 Magnetism

MAIN Idea Like magnetic poles repel each other and unlike poles attract each other.

8.2 Electricity and Magnetism

MAIN Idea An electric current in a wire is surrounded by a magnetic field.

8.3 Producing Electric Current

MAIN Idea A changing magnetic field can produce an electric current in a wire loop.

A Natural Light Show

Have you ever seen an aurora? Auroras result when the Sun emits a blast of charged particles. These blasts cause charged particles trapped by Earth's magnetic field to collide with atoms in the upper atmosphere. The light you see as an aurora is emitted as these collisions occur.

Science Journal List three things you know about magnets.

222

Interactive Chalkboard

This CD-ROM is an editable Microsoft® PowerPoint® presentation that includes:

- an editable presentation for every chapter
- additional chapter questions
- animated graphics
- image bank
- links to gpscience.com

Start-Up Activities

The Strength of Magnets

Did you know that magnets are used in TV sets, computers, stereo speakers, electric motors, and many other devices? Magnets also help create images of the inside of the human body. Even Earth acts like a giant bar magnet. How do magnets work?

1. Hold a bar magnet horizontally and put a paper clip on one end. Touch a second paper clip to the end of the first one. Continue adding paper clips until none will stick to one end of the chain. Copy the data table below and record the number of paper clips the magnet held. Remove the paper clips from the magnet.
2. Repeat step 1 three more times. First, start the chain about 2 cm from the end of the magnet. Second, start the chain near the center of the magnet. Third, start the chain at the other end of the magnet.
3. **Think Critically** Infer which part of the magnet exerts the strongest attraction. Compare the attraction at the center of the magnet with the attraction at the ends.

Magnet/Paper Clip Data

	Paper Clip Chain (number of clips)
Trial 1 (end)	
Trial 2 (2 cm)	
Trial 3 (center)	
Trial 4 (other end)	

Using Magnets Many devices you use contain magnets that help convert one form of energy to another. Make the following Foldable to help you understand how magnets are used to transform electrical and mechanical energy.

STEP 1 **Fold** a sheet of paper in half lengthwise.

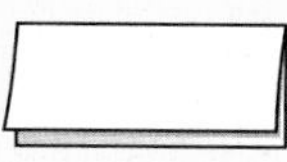

STEP 2 **Fold** the paper down about 2 cm from the top.

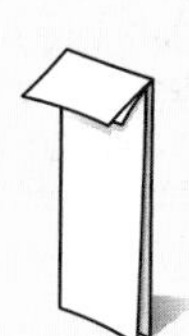

STEP 3 **Open and draw** lines along the top fold. **Label** as shown.

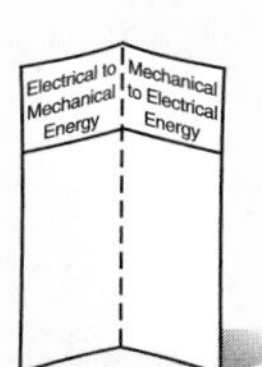

Summarize As you read the chapter, summarize how magnets are used to convert electrical energy to mechanical energy in the left column, and how magnets are used to convert mechanical energy to electrical energy in the right column.

Preview this chapter's content and activities at gpscience.com

223

Purpose Use the Launch Lab to illustrate the fact that the strength of a magnetic field varies over the length of a bar magnet. L2 ELL IN **Kinesthetic**

Preparation Test the bar magnets to see approximately how many paper clips each team will need. Small clips make it easier to observe differences in field strength.

Materials bar magnet, many small paper clips of the same size

Teaching Strategy If you have a variety of bar magnets, have the class compare results after finishing the activity. Ask students why the paper clips need to be the same size. so you can compare the numbers picked up

Think Critically

The two ends of the magnet are equally strong. The middle is weaker. Some magnets will not hold any clips there.

Assessment

Process Have students sketch a graph showing how the strength of the magnetic field changes over the length of the magnet. Use **Performance Assessment in the Science Classroom,** p. 127.

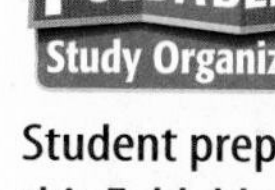

Dinah Zike Study Fold

Student preparation materials for this Foldable are available in the **Chapter *Fast File* Resources.**

Additional Chapter Media

-  *Magnetism*
- Virtual Lab: *How does a generator work?*
- Video Lab: *Electricity and Magnetism*

1 Motivate

Bellringer

Section Focus Transparencies also are available on the Interactive Chalkboard CD-ROM.

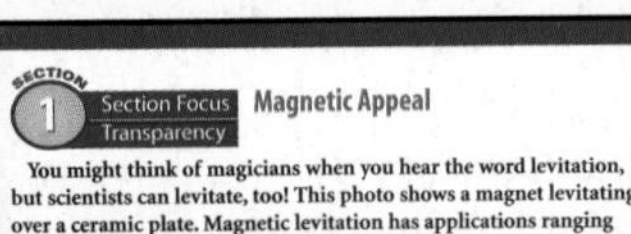

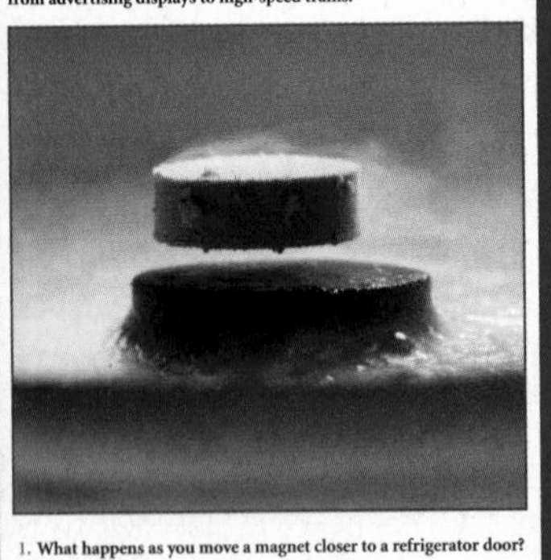

Section 1 Section Focus Transparency — Magnetic Appeal

You might think of magicians when you hear the word levitation, but scientists can levitate, too! This photo shows a magnet levitating over a ceramic plate. Magnetic levitation has applications ranging from advertising displays to high-speed trains.

1. What happens as you move a magnet closer to a refrigerator door?
2. How do people use magnets in their daily lives?

L2

Tie to Prior Knowledge

Magnets Discuss with students places where they have seen or used magnets. Most will have used magnets on refrigerator doors and in science classes. Explain that magnets are also used in such items as stereo speakers, televisions, and floppy disks.

section 1

Magnetism

Reading Guide

What You'll Learn

- **Explain** how a magnet exerts a force.
- **Describe** the properties of temporary and permanent magnets.
- **Explain** why some materials are magnetic and some are not.
- **Model** magnetic behavior using magnetic domains.

Why It's Important

Without the forces exerted by magnets, you could not use televisions, computers, CD players, or even refrigerators.

Review Vocabulary

electric field: surrounds an electric charge and exerts a force on other electric charges

New Vocabulary

- magnetism
- magnetic field
- magnetic pole
- magnetic domain

Magnets

More than 2,000 years ago Greeks discovered deposits of a mineral that was a natural magnet. They noticed that chunks of this mineral could attract pieces of iron. This mineral was found in a region of Turkey that then was known as Magnesia, so the Greeks named the mineral magnetic. The mineral is now called magnetite. In the twelfth century Chinese sailors used magnetite to make compasses that improved navigation. Since then many devices have been developed that rely on magnets to operate. Today, the word **magnetism** refers to the properties and interactions of magnets. **Figure 1** shows a device you might be familiar with that uses magnets and magnetism.

Figure 1 Magnets can be found in many devices you use everyday, such as TVs, video games, telephones. Headphones and CD players also contain magnets.

Magnetic Force You probably have played with magnets and might have noticed that two magnets exert a force on each other. Depending on which ends of the magnets are close together, the magnets either repel or attract each other. You might have noticed that the interaction between two magnets can be felt even before the magnets touch. The strength of the force between two magnets increases as magnets move closer together and decreases as the the magnets move farther apart.

Reading Check *What does the force between two magnets depend on?*

Section 1 Resource Manager

Chapter *Fast File* Resources

- Transparency Activity, p. 44
- Directed Reading for Content Mastery, pp. 19, 20
- Note-taking Worksheets, pp. 33–35
- MiniLAB, pp. 3, 4
- Enrichment, p. 30
- Lab Activity, pp. 9–12
- Reinforcement, p. 27

Mathematics Skill Activities, p. 47

Figure 2 A magnet is surounded by a magnetic field.

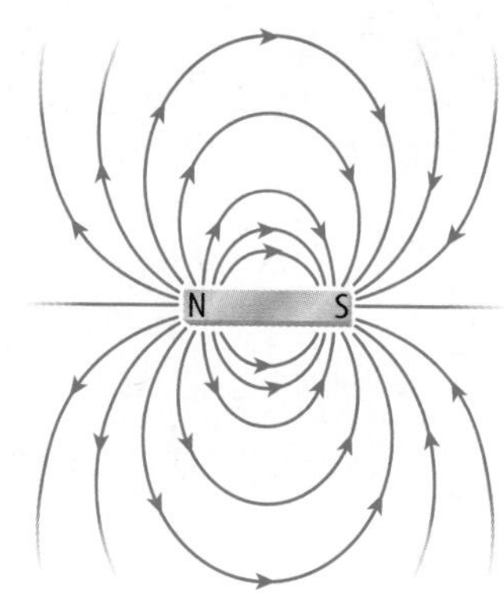

A magnet's magnetic field is represented by magnetic field lines.

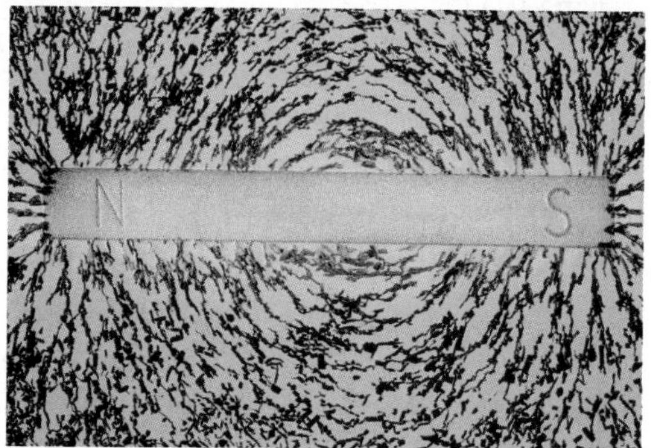

Iron filings sprinkled around a magnet line up along the magnetic field lines.

Magnetic Field A magnet is surrounded by a magnetic field. A **magnetic field** exerts a force on other magnets and objects made of magnetic materials. The magnetic field is strongest close to the magnet and weaker far away. The magnetic field can be represented by lines of force, or magnetic field lines. **Figure 2** shows the magnetic field lines surrounding a bar magnet. A magnetic field also has a direction. The direction of the magnetic field around a bar magnet is shown by the arrows of the left side of **Figure 2.**

Magnetic Poles Look again at **Figure 2.** Do you notice that the magnetic field lines are closest together at the ends of the bar magnet? These regions, called the **magnetic poles,** are where the magnetic force exerted by the magnet is strongest. All magnets have a north pole and a south pole. For a bar magnet, the north and south poles are at the opposite ends.

Figure 3 shows the north and south poles of magnets with more complicated shapes. The two ends of a horseshoe-shaped magnet are the north and south poles. A magnet shaped like a disk has opposite poles on the top and bottom of the disk. Magnetic field lines always connect the north pole and the south pole of a magnet.

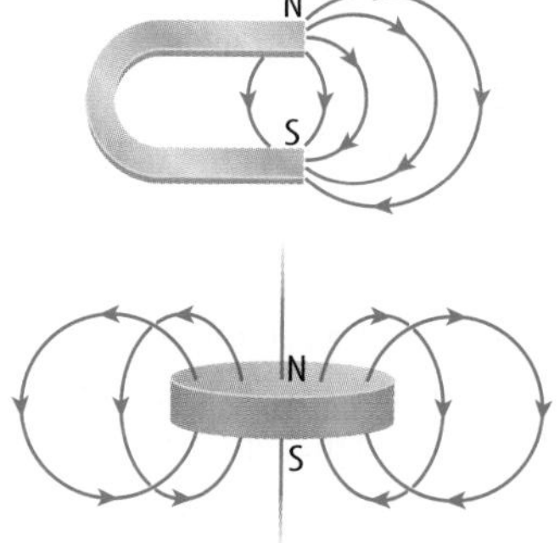

Figure 3 The magnetic field lines around horseshoe and disk magnets begin at each magnet's north pole and end at the south pole.
Identify *where the magnetic field is strongest.*

2 Teach

Answer The distance between the two magnets.

Use an Analogy

Earth's Attraction A magnet's field, like a gravitational field, affects objects without touching them, even at a great distance. The faraway north magnetic pole attracts a compass needle, like the distant Sun holds Earth in orbit.

Use Science Words

Word Meaning Have students find out what *field* means in physics. A field is a region of space with a physical property (such as gravitational force, fluid pressure, etc.) that has a definite value at every point in the region. Compare and contrast this with other meanings of *field.* Other meanings also refer to areas, such as a meadow, a playing field, a background region, or even an area of interest. L3 LS **Linguistic**

Activity

Magnets Divide the class into small groups and provide each group with a set of magnets. Allow students to observe the properties and behaviors of the magnets. L1

Caption Answer

Figure 3 at the magnetic poles

Differentiated Instruction

Visually Impaired For students who cannot see the field lines in the illustrations and demonstrations, provide an opportunity to experiment with strong magnets. Make sure these students can feel the forces of attraction and repulsion between the magnets. L1 LS **Kinesthetic**

SECTION 1 Magnetism 225

Quick Demo

Magnetic Fields

Materials overhead projector, iron filings or an iron nail and file, petri dish or 2 overhead sheets, several different magnets

Estimated Time 15 minutes

Procedure Show magnetic fields on the overhead projector. Make iron filings by rubbing a metal file on an iron nail. Place the iron filings in a covered petri dish or between two overhead sheets. Place different magnets on top of the filings on the projector. Then show the fields between attracting and repelling poles, and how the fields change as you move the magnets slowly toward or away from each other. This demonstrates how field strength diminishes with distance. L2

ELL IS Visual-Spatial

Reading Check

Answer Like poles repel each other; unlike poles attract.

Teacher FYI

Traveling Poles Earth's magnetic poles do not perfectly align with Earth's geographic poles, the endpoints of the axis about which Earth rotates. Also, Earth's magnetic field is not fixed. The north magnetic pole has traveled about 10 km/year over the past century, and, many times in the past, magnetic north and south have switched places.

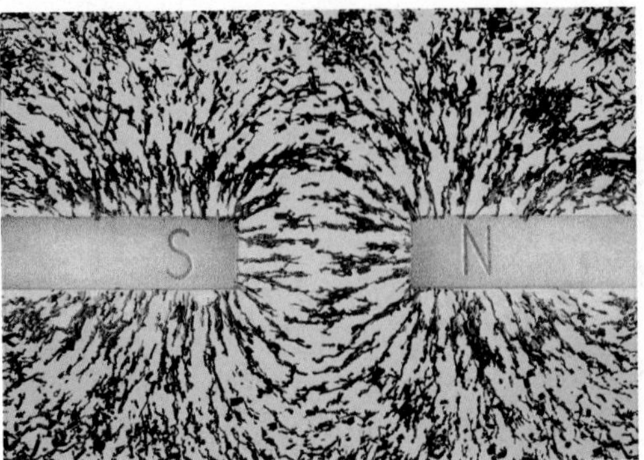

Unlike poles closest together

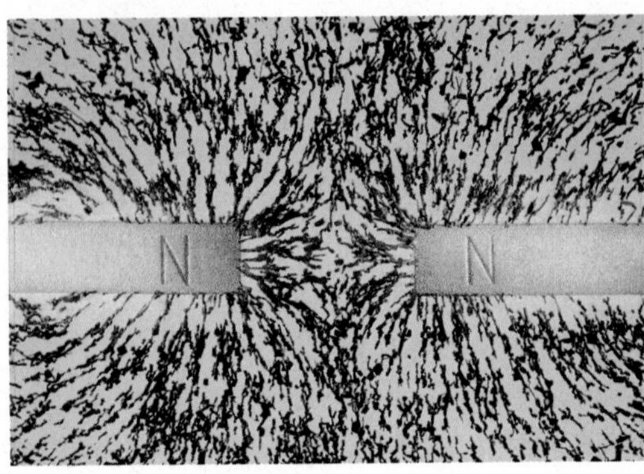

Like poles closest together

Figure 4 Two magnets can attract or repel each other, depending on which poles are closest together.

How Magnets Interact Two magnets can either attract or repel each other. Two north poles or two south poles of two magnets repel each other. However, north poles and south poles always attract each other. Like magnetic poles repel each other and unlike poles attract each other. When two magnets are brought close to each other, their magnetic fields combine to produce a new magnetic field. **Figure 4** shows the magnetic field that results when like poles and unlike poles of bar magnets are brought close to each other.

Reading Check *How do magnetic poles interact with each other?*

Magnetic Field Direction When a compass is brought near a bar magnet, the compass needle rotates. The compass needle is a small bar magnet with a north pole and a south pole. The force exerted on the compass needle by the magnetic field causes the needle to rotate. The compass needle rotates until it lines up with the magnetic field lines, as shown in **Figure 5.** The north pole of a compass points in the direction of the magnetic field. This direction is always away from a north magnetic pole and toward a south magnetic pole.

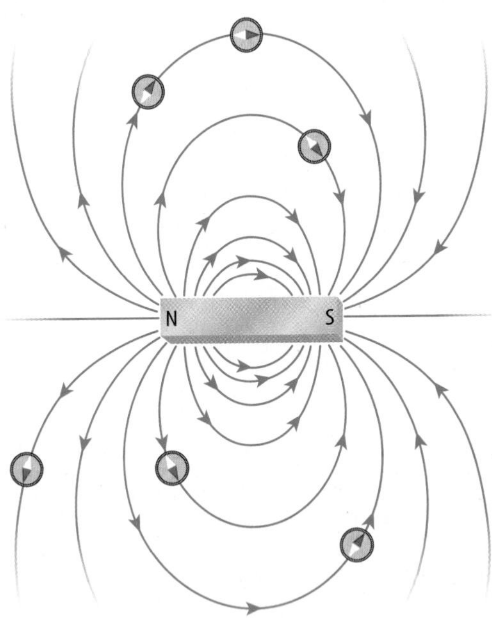

Figure 5 Compass needles placed around a bar magnet line up along magnetic field lines. The north poles of the compass needles are shaded red.

Visual Learning

Figure 4 What do you think happens to the magnetic force in the gaps between the lines? The force is still there even though the lines don't show it. L2

Cultural Diversity

Compasses Compasses were invented in China. By the ninth century A.D., the Chinese had discovered that magnetic north does not exactly coincide with geographic north. The compass was used for navigation at sea starting about 1,000 years ago (850–1050 A.D.). Before that they were used for a type of divination based on geographic features.

INTEGRATE Earth Science

Earth's Magnetic Field A compass can help determine direction because the north pole of the compass needle points north. This is because Earth acts like a giant bar magnet and is surrounded by a magnetic field that extends into space. Just as with a bar magnet, the compass needle aligns with Earth's magnetic field lines, as shown in **Figure 6.**

Earth's Magnetic Poles The north pole of a magnet is defined as the end of the magnet that points toward the geographic north. Sometimes the north pole and south pole of magnets are called the north-seeking pole and the south-seeking pole. Because opposite magnetic poles attract, the north pole of a compass is being attracted by a south magnetic pole. So Earth is like a bar magnet with its south magnetic pole near its geographic north pole.

Currently, Earth's south magnetic pole is located in northern Canada about 1,500 km from the geographic north pole. However, Earth's magnetic poles move slowly with time. Sometimes Earth's magnetic poles switch places so that Earth's south magnetic pole is the southern hemisphere near the geographic south pole. Measurements of magnetism in rocks show that Earth's magnetic poles have changed places over 150 times in the past seventy million years.

No one is sure what produces Earth's magnetic field. Earth's inner core is made of a solid ball of iron and nickel, surrounded by a liquid layer of molten iron and nickel. According to one theory, circulation of the molten iron and nickel in Earth's outer core produces Earth's magnetic field.

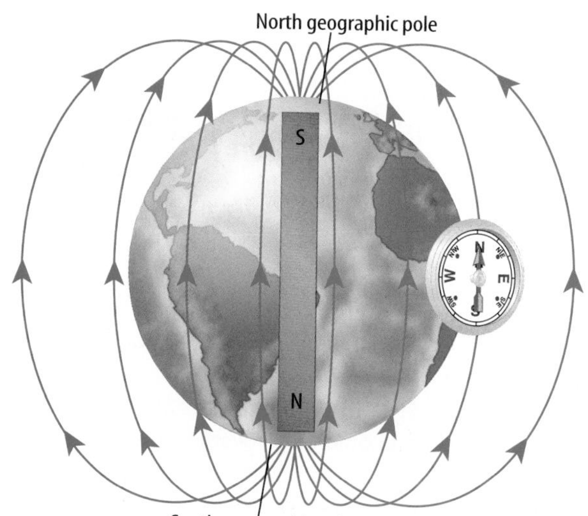

Figure 6 A compass needle aligns with the magnetic field lines of Earth's magnetic field.
Predict *Which way would a compass needle point if Earth's magnetic poles switched places?*

Mini LAB

Observing Magnetic Interference

Procedure

1. Clamp a **bar magnet** to a **ring stand.** Tie a **thread** around one end of a **paper clip** and stick the paper clip to one pole of the magnet.
2. Anchor the other end of the thread under a **book** on the table. Slowly pull the thread until the paper clip is suspended below the magnet but not touching the magnet.
3. Without touching the paper clip, slip a piece of paper between the magnet and the paper clip. Does the paper clip fall?
4. Try other materials, such as **aluminum foil, fabric,** or a **butter knife.**

Analysis

1. Which materials caused the paper clip to fall? Why do you think these materials interfered with the magnetic field?
2. Which materials did not cause the paper clip to fall? Why do you think these materials did not interfere with the magnetic field?

Mini LAB

Purpose Students observe that magnetic fields extend beyond the magnet and through barriers, and that some materials can affect the field. L2 ELL
LS **Kinesthetic**

Materials bar magnet, ring stand, 50 cm of thread, paper clip, tape, book, paper, aluminum foil, fabric, butter knife

Teaching Strategy Have students compare magnetic force to gravitational force. Remind students that gravitational force also acts through barriers.

Analysis

1. Some metals cause the paper clip to fall. These metals can be magnetized, so they affect the magnetic field.
2. Paper, glass, and plastic do not affect the field. The magnetic force is not affected by materials that cannot be magnetized.

Assessment

Process Have students examine the refrigerator door at home. Does it appear to be metal, or another material? Relate this to the lab. The plastic coating on some refrigerator doors does not interfere with the attraction between a magnet and the underlying metal. Use **Performance Assessment in the Science Classroom,** p. 89.

Caption Answer

Figure 6 toward the south magnetic pole in the southern hemisphere

Discussion

North Star What natural body has been used for centuries in the Northern Hemisphere to find the north-south direction? The North Star or the Pole star.

Fun Fact

Earth's magnetic field lines are not parallel to the surface. A delicately balanced magnetized needle can be used to measure the dip of the magnetic field, as well as its direction.

Curriculum Connection

History The compass was an important invention for navigation at sea. Have students research and write reports about some of the sea routes used before and after the invention of the compass. Most European exploration occurred after the adoption of the compass. Polynesian islanders and Vikings managed long sea voyages without the compass, depending on knowledge of the skies and the sea to find their way. L2 P LS **Kinesthetic**

Magnets in Organisms Animals may perceive Earth's magnetic field by mechanical effects, where the magnetite is deflected like a compass needle. They may also sense field variations that cause electrical induction within the animal.

Applying Science

Answers

1. A magnet will attract about 65% of the total mass of the car. Other metals (such as aluminum and copper) are not magnetic and will not be attracted.
2. 525 Kg
3. 9.75×10^9Kg

IDENTIFYING Misconceptions

Magnetic Metals Students may think that all metals are magnetic. See p. 222F for teaching strategies that address this misconception.

Magnets in Organisms Some organisms may use Earth's magnetic field to help find their way around. Some species of birds, insects, and bacteria have been shown to contain small amounts of the mineral magnetite. Research how one species uses Earth's magnetic field, and report your findings to your class.

Magnetic Materials

You might have noticed that a magnet will not attract all metal objects. For example, a magnet will not attract pieces of aluminum foil. Only a few metals, such as iron, cobalt, or nickel, are attracted to magnets or can be made into permanent magnets. What makes these elements magnetic? Remember that every atom contains electrons. Electrons have magnetic properties. In the atoms of most elements, the magnetic properties of the electrons cancel out. But in the atoms of iron, cobalt, and nickel, these magnetic properties don't cancel out. Each atom in these elements behaves like a small magnet and has its own magnetic field.

Even though these atoms have their own magnetic fields, objects made from these metals are not always magnets. For example, if you hold an iron nail close to a refrigerator door and let go, it falls to the floor. However, you can make the nail behave like a magnet temporarily.

Applying Science

How can magnetic parts of a junk car be salvaged?

Every year over 10 million cars containing plastics, glass, rubber, and various metals are scrapped. Magnets are often used to help retrieve some of these materials from scrapped cars. The materials can then be reused, saving both natural resources and energy. Once the junk car has been fed into a shredder, big magnets can easily separate many of its metal parts from its nonmetal parts. How much of the car does a magnet actually help separate? Use your ability to interpret a circle graph to find out.

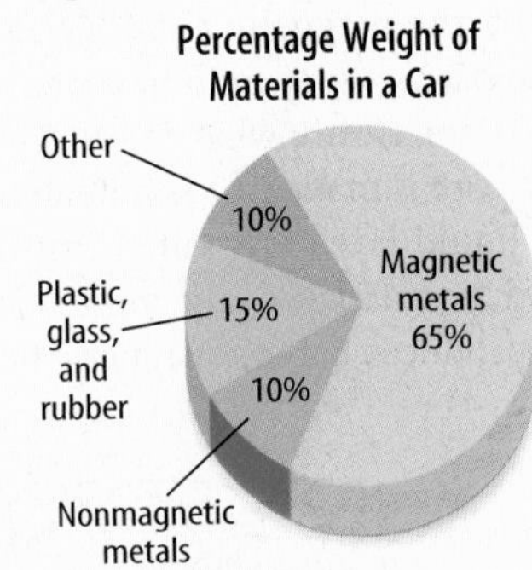

Identifying the Problem

The graph at the right shows the average percent by weight of the different materials in a car. Included in the magnetic metals are steel and iron. The nonmagnetic metals refer to aluminum, copper, lead, zinc, and magnesium. According to the chart, how much of the car can a magnet separate for recycling?

Solving the Problem

1. What percent of the car's weight will a magnet recover?
2. A certain scrapped car has a mass of 1,500 kg. What is the mass of the materials in this car that cannot be recovered using a magnet?
3. If the average mass of a scrapped car is 1,500 kg, and 10 million cars are scrapped each year, what is the total mass of iron and steel that could be recovered from scrapped cars each year?

LAB DEMONSTRATION

Purpose to show how a hard blow can magnetize a steel rod aligned with Earth's magnetic field

Materials compass, steel rod, hammer, paper clips, protractor

Preparation Use the compass to mark a line on the ground running north–south.

Procedure Position the rod along the north-south line as shown. Sharply rap the south end of the rod with a hammer.

Expected Outcome The rod becomes magnetized and will pick up a few clips. Repeat if needed, as this effect depends on hitting the rod just right.

Assessment

What happened to the magnetic domains in the steel rod when it was struck with the hammer? They were jolted and could realign. Enough of the magnetic domains realigned along Earth's field lines to make a magnet. L2

Magnetic Domains—A Model for Magnetism In iron, cobalt, nickel, and some other magnetic materials, the magnetic field created by each atom exerts a force on the other nearby atoms. Because of these forces, large groups of atoms align their magnetic poles so that almost all like poles point in the same direction. The groups of atoms with aligned magnetic poles are called **magnetic domains.** Each domain contains an enormous number of atoms, yet the domains are too small to be seen with the unaided eye. Because the magnetic poles of the individual atoms in a domain are aligned, the domain itself behaves like a magnet with a north pole and a south pole.

Lining Up Domains An iron nail contains an enormous number of these magnetic domains, so why doesn't the nail behave like a magnet? Even though each domain behaves like a magnet, the poles of the domains are arranged randomly and point in different directions, as shown in **Figure 7.** As a result, the magnetic fields from all the domains cancel each other out.

If you place a magnet against the same nail, the atoms in the domains orient themselves in the direction of the nearby magnetic field, as shown on the right in **Figure 7.** The like poles of the domains point in the same direction and no longer cancel each other out. The nail itself now acts as a magnet. But when the external magnetic field is removed, the constant motion and vibration of the atoms bump the magnetic domains out of their alignment. The magnetic domains in the nail return to random arrangement. For this reason, the nail is only a temporary magnet. Paper clips and other objects containing iron also can become temporary magnets.

Mini LAB

Making Your Own Compass

Procedure

WARNING: *Use care when handling sharp objects.*

1. Cut off the bottom of a **plastic foam cup** to make a polystyrene disk.
2. Magnetize a **sewing needle** by continuously stroking the needle in the same direction with a magnet for 1 min.
3. **Tape** the needle to the center of the foam disk.
4. Fill a **plate** with **water** and float the disk, needle-side up, in the water.
5. Bring the magnet close to the foam disk.

Analysis

1. How did the needle and disk move when you placed them in the water? Explain.
2. How did the needle and disk move when the magnet was brought near it? Explain.

Try at Home

Figure 7 Magnetic materials contain magnetic domains.

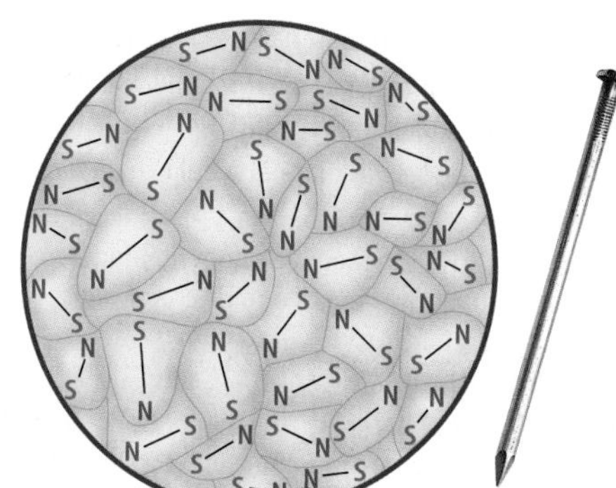

A normal iron nail is made up of microscopic domains that are arranged randomly.

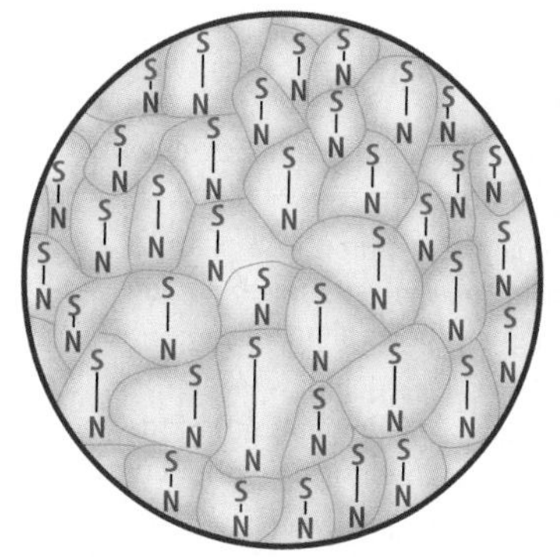

The domains will align themselves along the magnetic field lines of a nearby magnet.

Use an Analogy

Rope Pulling Lining up magnetic domains is like getting a group of people to pull together on one end of a rope. If each person pulls the rope in a different direction, the pulls cancel each other and nothing happens. If they all pull together in one direction, the individual forces add together.

Purpose Students will make a compass. L2 IN **Kinesthetic**

Materials plastic foam cup, magnet, sewing needle, tape, plate, water

Teaching Strategy Remind students that the sewing needle contains, or is made of, iron.

Safety Precautions Caution students to handle the needle with care.

Analysis

1. The needle aligned with Earth's north and south poles.
2. The needle swung around to point toward the magnet. The magnet's field is stronger than Earth's at that distance, so the needle tries to line up with the magnet's north and south poles.

Assessment

Oral What causes the needle to become magnetic when you stroke it with the magnet? The magnet rearranges the domains so that they line up and make the needle magnetic. Use **Performance Assessment in the Science Classroom,** p. 89.

Differentiated Instruction

Challenge Ask students to research if cooling a magnet would reduce its magnetic properties. Have students write a short report to present to the class. As objects cool, there is less atomic motion, and so there would be less opportunity for the magnetic domains to rearrange. L3

Teacher FYI

Rock Minerals Iron minerals in some rocks (such as basalt) align themselves with Earth's magnetic field if the rock forms under the right conditions. This provides a record of Earth's changing magnetic field, which is studied by geologists and those hoping to determine Earth's past climates.

SECTION 1 Magnetism 229

3 Assess

DAILY INTERVENTION

Check for Understanding

Visual-Spatial Have students use **Figure 4** to make illustrations of the magnetic field of two bar magnets with like poles near each other and with unlike poles near each other. Have students clearly label the poles on the illustrations. L2

Reteach

Magnetizing a Nail Hang a nail, by the flat head, from the end of a bar magnet. Next, place the nail and a compass on the overhead to show that the nail has N and S poles. LS **Visual-Spatial** L2

Assessment

Performance Ask students to use a compass to map the magnetic field of a large horseshoe magnet. Use **Performance Assessment in the Science Classroom**, p. 97. L2

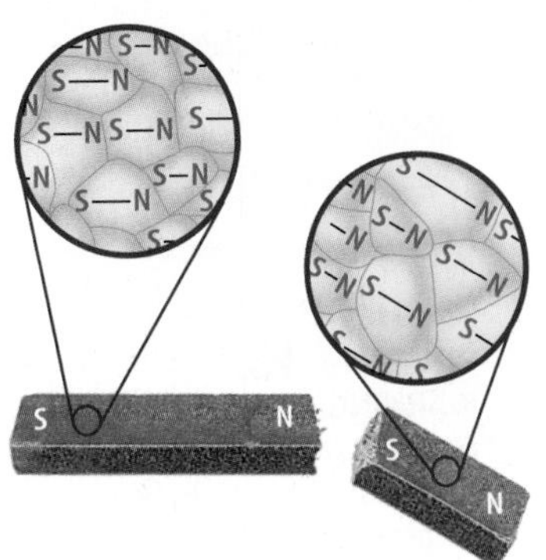

Figure 8 Each piece of a broken magnet still has a north and a south pole.

Permanent Magnets A permanent magnet can be made by placing a magnetic material, such as iron, in a strong magnetic field. The strong magnetic field causes the magnetic domains in the material to line up. The magnetic fields of these aligned domains add together and create a strong magnetic field inside the material. This field prevents the constant motion of the atoms from bumping the domains out of alignment. The material is then a permanent magnet.

But even permanent magnets can lose their magnetic behavior if they are heated. Heating causes atoms in the magnet to move faster. If the permanent magnet is heated enough, its atoms may be moving fast enough to jostle the domains out of alignment. Then the permanent magnet loses its magnetic field and is no longer a magnet.

Can a pole be isolated? What happens when a magnet is broken in two? Can one piece be a north pole and one piece be a south pole? Look at the domain model of the broken magnet in **Figure 8.** Recall that even individual atoms of magnetic materials act as tiny magnets. Because every magnet is made of many aligned smaller magnets, even the smallest pieces have both a north pole and a south pole.

section 1 review

Summary

Magnets

- Magnets are surrounded by a magnetic field that exerts a force on magnetic materials.
- Magnets have a north pole and a south pole.
- Like magnetic poles repel and unlike poles attract.

Magnetic Materials

- Iron, cobalt, and nickel are magnetic elements because their atoms behave like magnets.
- Magnetic domains are regions in a material that contain an enormous number of atoms with their magnetic poles aligned.
- A magnetic field causes domains to align. In a temporary magnet, the domains return to random alignment when the field is removed.
- In a permanent magnet, a stong magnetic field aligns domains and they remain aligned when the field is removed.

Self Check

1. **Describe** what happens when you move two unlike magnetic poles closer together. Draw a diagram to illustrate your answer.
2. **Describe** how a compass needle moves when it is placed in a magnetic field.
3. **Explain** why only certain materials are magnetic.
4. **Predict** how the properties of a bar magnet would change if it were broken in half.
5. **Explain** how heating a bar magnet would change its magnetic field.
6. **Think Critically** Use the magnetic domain model to explain why a magnet sticks to a refrigerator door.

Applying Math

7. **Calculate Number of Domains** The magnetic domains in a magnet have an average volume of 0.0001 mm^3. If the magnet has dimensions 50 mm by 10 mm by 4 mm, how many domains does the magnet contain?

gpscience.com/self_check_quiz

section 1 review

1. The poles attract one another.
2. It aligns itself along the field lines.
3. The atoms of magnetic materials are themselves individual magnets. They form magnetic domains containing large numbers of atoms. Each domain is a magnet. A magnet brought nearby causes domains to align so they are attracted to the nearest pole of the magnet.
4. Each piece still would contain large numbers of domains and have a north pole and a south pole. Because each piece contains few domains, the magnetic field of each piece would be weaker.
5. When the magnet is heated, the atoms in the magnet move faster. If the atoms are moving fast enough, collisions with other atoms may cause atoms in domains to become unaligned. This would reduce the magnetic field.
6. If the metal in the door contains a magnetic material, the magnetic domains align when the magnet is brought close so the opposite poles of the domains attract the closest pole of the magnet.
7. $(50mm)(10mm)(4mm)/0.0001\ mm^3 = 2.0 \times 10^7$

230 CHAPTER 8 Magnetism and Its Uses

section 2

Electricity and Magnetism

Reading Guide

What You'll Learn

- **Describe** the magnetic field produced by an electric current.
- **Explain** how an electromagnet produces a magnetic field.
- **Describe** how electromagnets are used.
- **Explain** how an electric motor operates.

Why It's Important

Electric motors contained in many of the devices you use every day operate because electric currents produce magnetic fields.

Review Vocabulary

electric current: the flow of electric charges in a wire or any conductor

New Vocabulary

- electromagnet
- solenoid
- galvanometer
- electric motor

Electric Current and Magnetism

In 1820, Hans Christian Oersted, a Danish physics teacher, found that electricity and magnetism are related. While doing a demonstration involving electric current, he happened to have a compass near an electric circuit. He noticed that the flow of the electric current affected the direction the compass needle pointed. Oersted hypothesized that the electric current must produce a magnetic field around the wire, and the direction of the field changes with the direction of the current.

Moving Charges and Magnetic Fields Oersted's hypothesis that an electric current creates a magnetic field was correct. It is now known that moving charges, like those in an electric current, produce magnetic fields. Around a current-carrying wire the magnetic field lines form circles, as shown in **Figure 8.** The direction of the magnetic field around the wire reverses when the direction of the current in the wire reverses. As the current in the wire increases the strength of the magnetic field increases. As you move farther from the wire the strength of the magnetic field decreases.

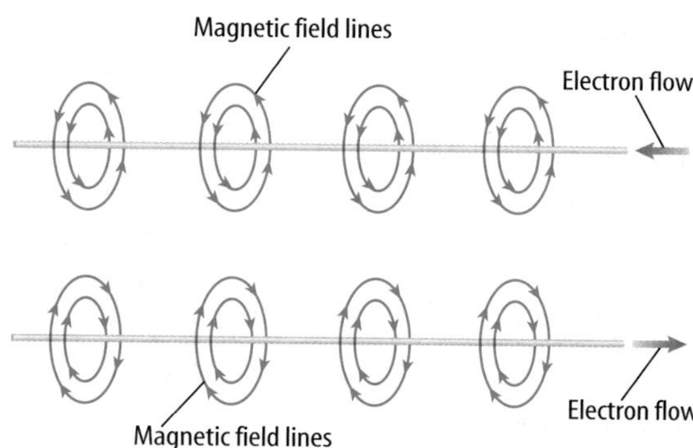

Figure 8 When electric current flows through a wire, a magnetic field forms around the wire. The direction of the magnetic field depends on the direction of the current in the wire.

1 Motivate

Bellringer

Section Focus Transparencies also are available on the Interactive Chalkboard CD-ROM. L2 ELL

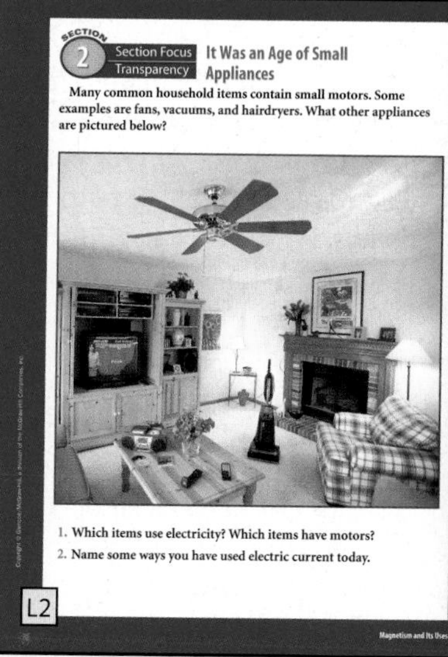

Tie to Prior Knowledge

Electric Motors Ask students to name some items that run by electric motors. Possible answers: fan, CD player, tape player. Explain that this section describes how electricity and magnetism work together in electric motors to make things move.

Section 2 Resource Manager

Chapter *Fast File* Resources

Transparency Activity, p. 45
Directed Reading for Content Mastery, p. 21
Lab Activity, pp. 13–16
Enrichment, p. 31
Reinforcement, p. 28

Physical Science Critical Thinking/Problem Solving, p. 17

2 Teach

Fun Fact

The source of Earth's magnetic field is still not well understood. One hypothesis is that convection currents of molten rock deep in Earth's core generate electric currents, which in turn generate a magnetic field, just like the current in a wire.

Discussion

Crane's Magnet Explain that a crane can have a grabbing end to pick up an object, or it can use an electromagnet. Compare the two cranes. Possible responses: the electromagnet will only work on certain types of metals, while the mechanical crane can lift anything it can wrap around. The strength of the mechanical crane depends on the materials it is made from and how they are attached; the strength of the electromagnet crane depends on these factors plus the number of turns in the coil and the strength of the current running through it. L2 **Logical-Mathematical**

Caption Answer

Figure 9B The direction of the magnetic field would be reversed.

Electromagnets

The magnetic field that surrounds a current-carrying wire can be made much stronger in an electromagnet. An **electromagnet** is a temporary magnet made by wrapping a wire coil carrying a current around an iron core. When a current flows through a wire loop, such as the one shown in **Figure 9A,** the magnetic field inside the loop is stronger than the field around a straight wire. A single wire wrapped into a cylindrical wire coil is called a **solenoid.** The magnetic field inside a solenoid is stronger than the field in a single loop. The magnetic field around each loop in the solenoid combines to form the field shown in **Figure 9B.**

If the solenoid is wrapped around an iron core, an electromagnet is formed, as shown in **Figure 9C.** The solenoid's magnetic field magnetizes the iron core. As a result, the field inside the solenoid with the iron core can be more than 1,000 times greater than the field inside the solenoid without the iron core.

Figure 9 An electromagnet is made from a current-carrying wire.

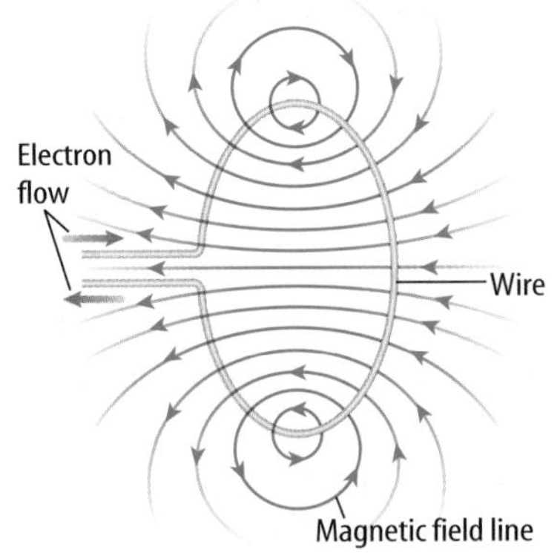

A The magnetic fields around different parts of the wire loop combine to form the field inside the loop.

Properties of Electromagnets Electromagnets are temporary magnets because the magnetic field is present only when current is flowing in the solenoid. The strength of the magnetic field can be increased by adding more turns of wire to the solenoid or by increasing the current passing through the wire.

An electromagnet behaves like any other magnet when current flows through the solenoid. One end of the electromagnet is a north pole and the other end is a south pole. If placed in a magnetic field, an electromagnet will align itself along the magnetic field lines, just as a compass needle will. An electromagnet also will attract magnetic materials and be attracted or repelled by other magnets. What makes electromagnets so useful is that their magnetic properties can be controlled by changing the electric current flowing through the solenoid.

When current flows in the electromagnet and it moves toward or away from another magnet, electric energy is converted into mechanical energy to do work. Electromagnets do work in various devices such as stereo speakers and electric motors.

B When many loops of current-carrying wire are formed into a solenoid, the magnetic field is increased inside the solenoid. The solenoid has a north pole and a south pole.
Predict *how the field would change if the current reversed direction.*

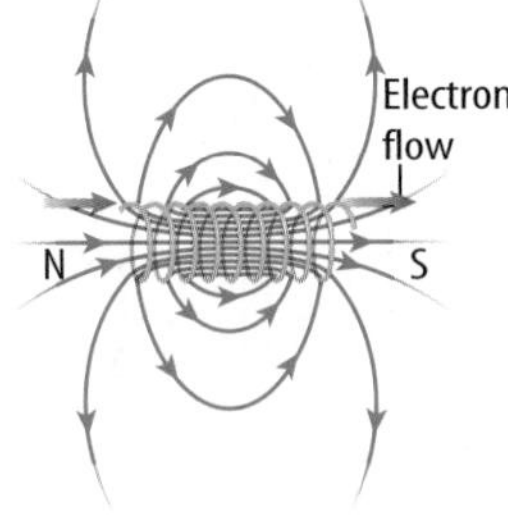

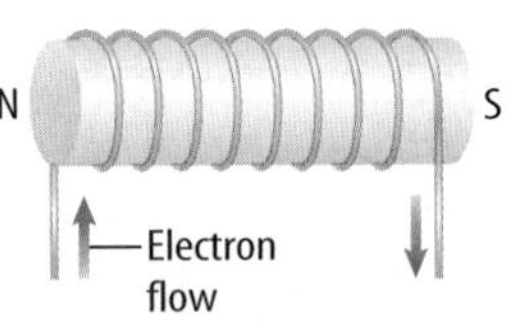

C A solenoid wrapped around an iron core forms an electromagnet.

Differentiated Instruction

English-Language Learners For students who have difficulty following diagrams and complex descriptions, focus on the basic definitions—for example, that a motor converts electricity into motion. Provide a chance for students to observe, handle, and take apart a simple motor or generator. L1 LS **Kinesthetic**

Teacher FYI

Electrons Each electron in an atom acts like a tiny electromagnet—the electron orbiting the nucleus is a loop of electric current, just like electrons moving in a wire. An electron also has "spin,"—a quantum physics characteristic that contributes to the magnetic field generated by the electron.

232 CHAPTER 8 Magnetism and Its Uses

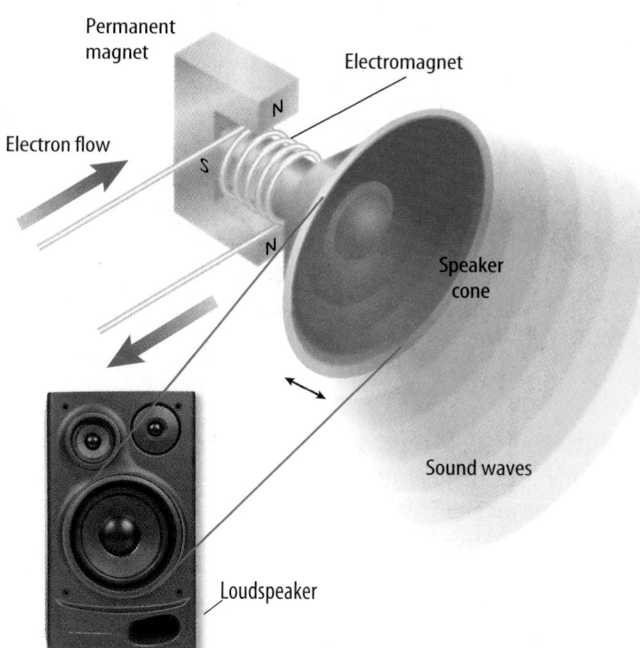

Figure 10 The electromagnet in a speaker converts electrical energy into mechanical energy to produce sound.
Explain *why a speaker needs a permanent magnet to produce sound.*

Using Electromagnets to Make Sound How does musical information stored on a CD become sound you can hear? The sound is produced by a loudspeaker that contains an electromagnet connected to a flexible speaker cone that is usually made from paper, plastic, or metal. The electromagnet changes electrical energy to mechanical energy that vibrates the speaker cone to produce sound, as shown on **Figure 10.**

Reading Check *How does a stereo speaker use an electromagnet to produce sound?*

When you listen to a CD, the CD player produces a voltage that changes according to the musical information on the CD. This varying voltage produces a varying electric current in the electromagnet connected to the speaker cone. Both the amount and the direction of the electric current change, depending on the information on the CD. The varying electric current causes both the strength and the direction of the magnetic field in the electromagnet to change. The electromagnet is surrounded by a permanent, fixed magnet. The changing direction of the magnetic field in the electromagnet causes the electromagnet to be attracted to or repelled by the permanent magnet. This makes the electromagnet move back and forth, causing the speaker cone to vibrate and reproduce the sound that was recorded on the CD.

Quick Demo

Electromagnets

Materials large nail, battery, battery holder, wire

Estimated Time 15 minutes

Procedure Make an electromagnet by connecting a battery to a wire coiled 20 times around a large nail. Demonstrate that the nail picks up no paper clips before the wire is connected and several when it is connected. When the wire again is disconnected, the paper clips should fall. However, the nail will still be slightly magnetized and may pick up one or two paper clips after the current is turned off. **WARNING:** The wire will heat up if it is left connected, so disconnect the battery as soon as you are done. L2 LS **Visual-Spatial**

Visual Learning

Figure 10 Have students analyze the diagram of the speaker. Review step by step the process in which electrical energy is converted to sound energy. Make sure students understand that the changing electrical signal causes a changing magnetic field in the electromagnet, and that the interaction of that magnetic field with the magnetic field of the permanent magnet causes the electromagnet to move.

Reading Check

Answer The electromagnet changes electrical energy to mechanical energy that vibrates parts of the speaker to produce sound.

Caption Answer

Figure 10 The permanent magnet attracts and repels the electromagnet causing the speaker cone to vibrate and produce sound.

Curriculum Connection

History Have students find out how Alexander Graham Bell used an electromagnet in the first telephone and present their findings to the class. L2 LS **Linguistic**

Inquiry Lab

Observing an Electric Motor

Purpose To construct and observe a simple electric motor.

Possible Materials pliable bare copper wire, stiff bare copper wire, D-cell battery, D-cell battery holder, wire cutters or pliers, permanent magnet, tape

Estimated Time one class period

Teaching Strategies

- Students can brainstorm about how they will construct a simple electric motor by creating a coil of wire suspended above a permanent magnet.
- The battery can be used to create a flow of current in the wire coil.
- Students can observe the principles of an electric motor.
- Allow students to explore other questions that arise.

For additional inquiry activities, see *Science Inquiry Labs*.

Reading Check

Answer when current flows in the solenoid, like poles of the electromagnet are repelled by and attracted to the poles of the permanent magnet. This causes the electromagnet to rotate.

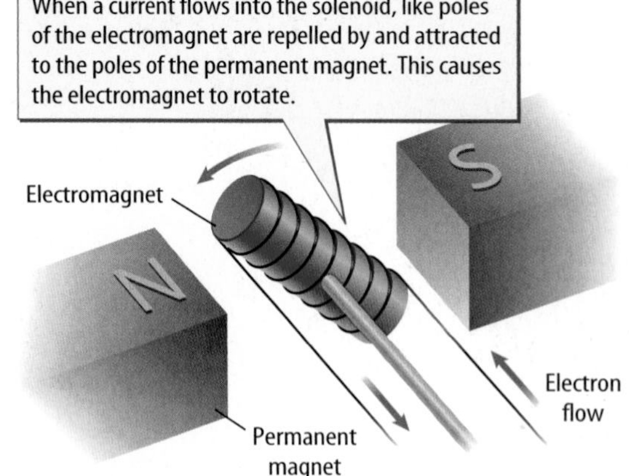
When a current flows into the solenoid, like poles of the electromagnet are repelled by and attracted to the poles of the permanent magnet. This causes the electromagnet to rotate.
Electromagnet
N
S
Electron flow
Permanent magnet

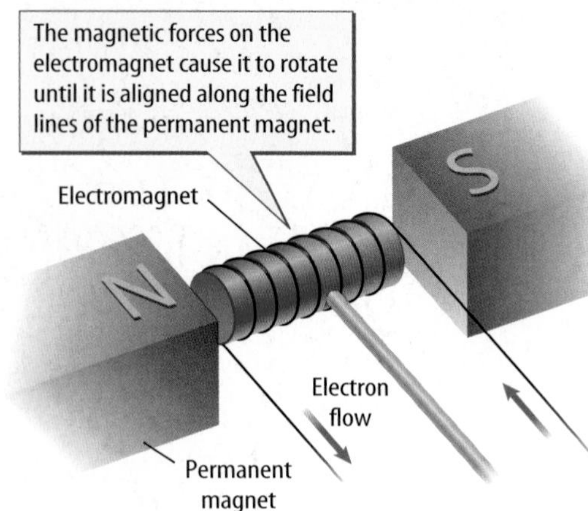
The magnetic forces on the electromagnet cause it to rotate until it is aligned along the field lines of the permanent magnet.
Electromagnet
N
S
Electron flow
Permanent magnet

Figure 11 An electromagnet can be made to rotate in a magnetic field.

Making an Electromagnet Rotate The forces exerted on an electromagnet by another magnet can be used to make the electromagnet rotate. **Figure 11** shows an electromagnet suspended between the poles of a permanent magnet. The poles of the electromagnet are repelled by the like poles and attracted by the unlike poles of the permanent magnet. When the electromagnet is in the position shown on the left side of **Figure 11,** there is a downward force on the left side and an upward force on the right side of the electromagnet forces. These forces cause the electromagnet to rotate as shown.

Reading Check *How can a permanent magnet cause an electromagnet to rotate?*

The electromagnet continues to rotate until its poles are next to the opposite poles of the permanent magnet, as shown on the right side of **Figure 11.** In this position, the forces on the north and south poles of the electromagnet are in opposite directions. Then the net force on the electromagnet is zero, and the electromagnet stops rotating.

One way to change the forces that make the electromagnet rotate is to change the current in the electromagnet. Increasing the current increases the strength of the forces between the two magnets.

Galvanometers You've probably noticed the gauges in the dashboard of a car. One gauge shows the amount of gasoline left in the tank, and another shows the engine temperature. How does a change in the amount of gasoline in a tank or the water temperature in the engine make a needle move in a gauge on the dashboard? These gauges are **galvanometers,** which are devices that use an electromagnet to measure electric current.

Cultural Diversity

China The first dial and pointer devices were made in China, using compass needles. Modern dials and pointers, including galvanometers, descend from these early Chinese devices.

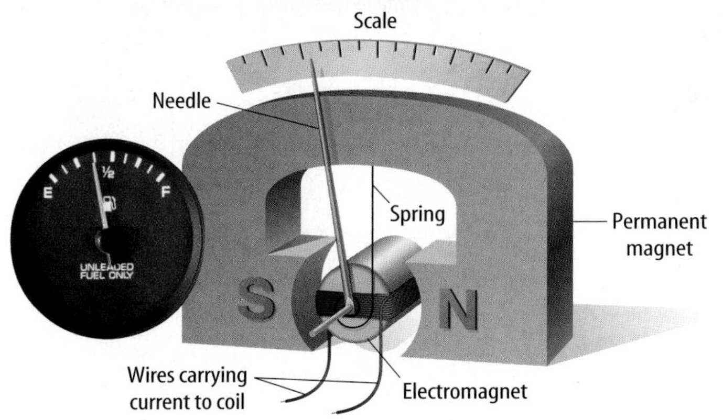

Figure 12 The rotation of the needle in a galvanometer depends on the amount of current flowing in the electromagnet. The current flowing into the galvanometer in a car's fuel gauge changes as the amount of fuel changes.

Using Galvanometers An example of a galvanometer is shown in **Figure 12.** In a galvanometer, the electromagnet is connected to a small spring. Then the electromagnet rotates until the force exerted by the spring is balanced by the magnetic forces on the electromagnet. Changing the current in the electromagnet causes the needle to rotate to different positions on the scale.

For example, a car's fuel gauge uses a galvanometer. A float in the fuel tank is attached to a sensor that sends a current to the fuel gauge galvanometer. As the level of the float in the tank changes, the current sent by the sensor changes. The changing current in the galvanometer causes the needle to rotate by different amounts. The gauge is calibrated so that the current sent when the tank is full causes the needle to rotate to the full mark on the scale.

Electric Motors

On sizzling summer days, do you ever use an electric fan to keep cool? A fan uses an **electric motor,** which is a device that changes electrical energy into mechanical energy. The motor in a fan turns the fan blades, moving air past your skin to make you feel cooler.

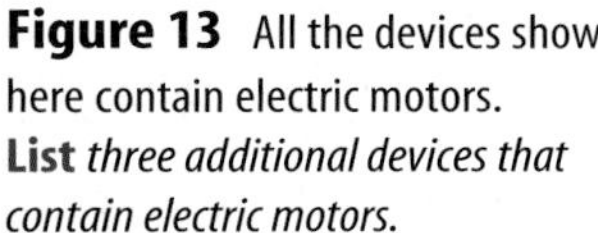

Figure 13 All the devices shown here contain electric motors. **List** *three additional devices that contain electric motors.*

Electric motors are used in all types of industry, agriculture, and transportation, including airplanes and automobiles. If you were to look carefully, you probably could find electric motors in every room of your house. Almost every appliance in which something moves contains an electric motor. Electric motors are used in devices such as in VCRs, CD players, computers, hair dryers, and other appliances shown in **Figure 13.**

Use Science Words

Word Origin Have students use a dictionary to find the origin of the word *motor*. It is derived from the Latin word for move. L2 IS **Linguistic**

Activity

Hobby Motors Bring a set of direct current hobby motors to class. Have students take them apart and identify the different parts. L2

Discussion

Galvanometers Have students describe all the dials with pointers they can find in their homes, school, cars, etc. Which ones are galvanometers? Possible answer: Older voltmeters and ammeters contain galvanometers. Some gauges in a car are galvanometers. A clock is an example of a motorized measuring device that is not a galvanometer. L3 IS **Logical-Mathematical**

Caption Answer

Figure 13 Answers will vary.

Curriculum Connection

History Have students research the history of the development of electric motors. Have them present their findings in the form of a newspaper article. The first commercially useful electric motor was a reversible DC electrical generator built in the early 1870s by Zénobe-Théophile Gramme. The first practical AC motor was built in 1888 by Nikola Tesla. L2 P IS **Linguistic**

Use an Analogy

Waterwheel An electric motor is like a waterwheel. A force (running water, magnetism) applied to a wheel (paddle of wheel, end of magnet) turns an axle. In either case, things can be attached to the axle to use the mechanical energy produced.

Make a Model

Simple Electric Motors Have students use **Figures 14** as a guide to make models of simple electric motors. L3 LS **Kinesthetic**

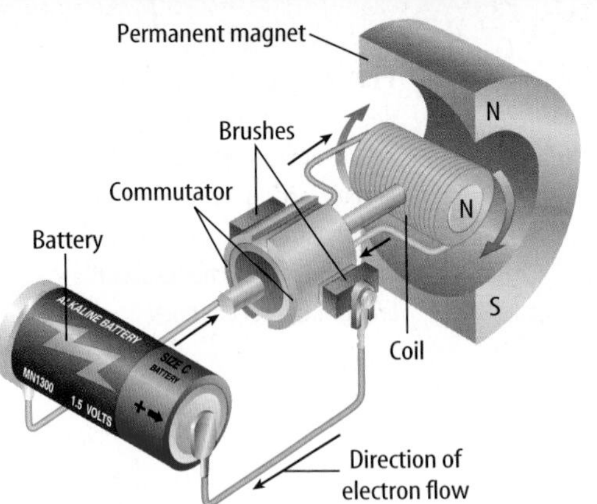

Step 1 When a current flows in the coil, the magnetic forces between the permanent magnet and the coil cause the coil to rotate.

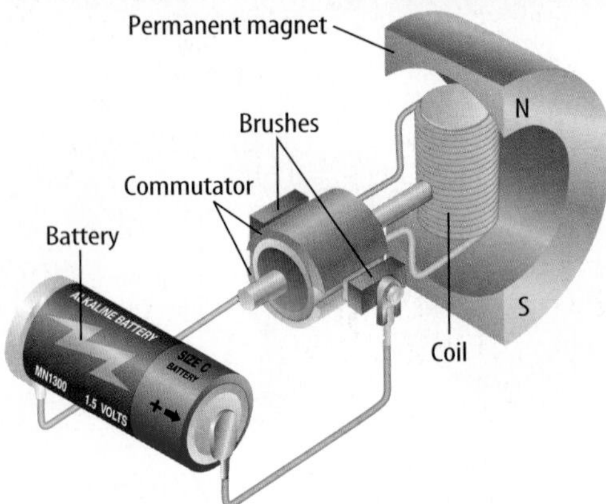

Step 2 In this position, the brushes are not in contact with the commutator and no current flows in the coil. The inertia of the coil keeps it rotating.

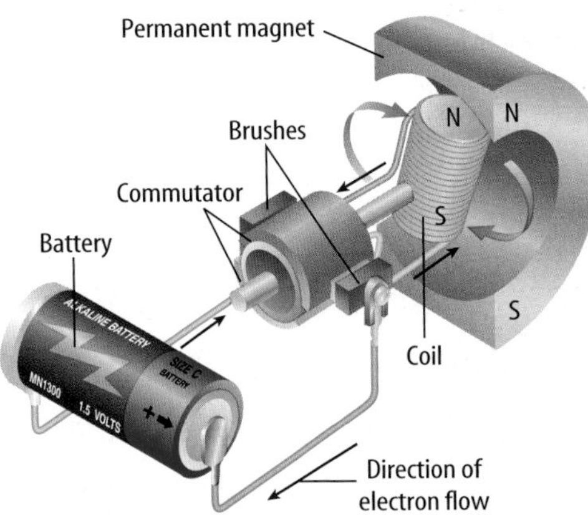

Step 3 The commutator reverses the direction of the current in the coil. This flips the north and south poles of the magnetic field around the coil.

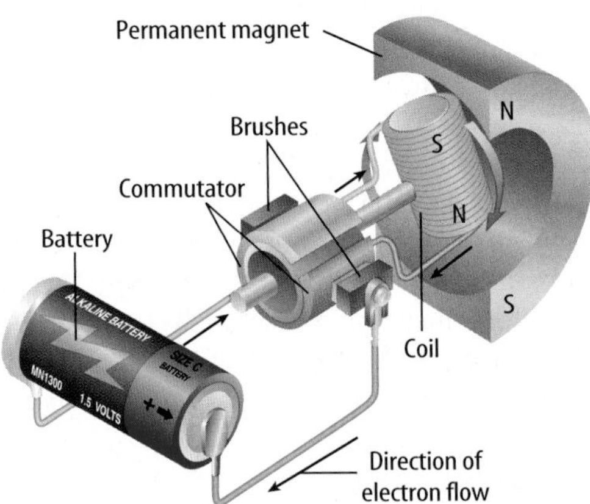

Step 4 The coil rotates until its poles are opposite the poles of the permanent magnet. The commutator reverses the current, and the coil keeps rotating.

Figure 14 In a simple electric motor, a coil rotates between the poles of a permanent magnet. To keep the coil rotating, the current must change direction twice during each rotation.

A Simple Electric Motor A diagram of the simplest type of electric motor is shown in **Figure 14.** The main parts of a simple electric motor include a wire coil, a permanent magnet, and a source of electric current, such as a battery. The battery produces the current that makes the coil an electromagnet. A simple electric motor also includes components called brushes and a commutator. The brushes are conducting pads connected to the battery. The brushes make contact with the commutator, which is a conducting metal ring that is split. Each half of the commutator is connected to one end of the coil so that the commutator rotates with the coil. The brushes and the commutator form a closed electric circuit between the battery and the coil.

Differentiated Instruction

Challenge Have students find out more about how the commutator in an electric motor works. Have students prepare an oral presentation to present to the class. The commutator rotates with the electromagnet and alternately contacts the positive and negative terminals of the power source. The reversing current causes the poles of the rotating electromagnet to switch and rotate toward the opposite pole of the permanent magnet. L3 LS **Logical-Mathematical**

Making the Motor Spin When current flows in the coil, the forces between the coil and the permanent magnet cause the coil to rotate, as shown in step 1 of **Figure 14.** The coil continues to rotate until it reaches the position shown in step 2. Then the brushes no longer make contact with the commutator, and no current flows in the coil. As a result, there are no magnetic forces exerted on the coil. However, the inertia of the coil causes it to continue rotating.

In step 3 the coil has rotated so that the brushes again are in contact with the commutator. However, the halves of the commutator that are in contact with the positive and negative battery terminals have switched. This causes the current in the commutator to reverse direction. Now the top of the electromagnet is a north magnetic pole and the bottom is a south pole. These poles are repelled by the nearby like poles of the permanent magnet, and the magnet continues to rotate.

In step 4, the coil rotates until its poles are next to the opposite poles of the permanent magnet. Then the commutator again reverses the direction of the current, enabling the coil to keep rotating. In this way, the coil is kept rotating as long the battery remains connected to the commutator.

Topic: Electric Motors
Visit gpscience.com for Web links to information about electric motors.

Activity Using the information provided at these links, construct a simple electric motor.

section 2 review

Summary

Electric Current and Magnetic Fields

- A magnetic field surrounds a moving electric charge.
- The strength of the magnetic field surrounding a current-carrying wire depends on the amount of current.

Electromagnets

- An electromagnet is a temporary magnet consisting of a current-carrying wire wrapped around an iron core.
- The magnetic properties of an electromagnet can be controlled by changing the current in the coil.
- A galvanometer uses an electromagnet to measure electric current.

Electric Motors

- In a simple electric motor, an electromagnet rotates between the poles of a permanent magnet.

Self Check

1. **Explain** why, if the same current flows in a wire coil and a single wire loop, the magnetic field inside the coil is stronger than the field inside the loop.
2. **Describe** two ways you could change the strength of the magnetic field produced by an electromagnet.
3. **Predict** how the magnetic field produced by an electromagnet would change if the iron core were replaced by an aluminum core.
4. **Explain** why it is necessary to continually reverse the direction of current flow in the coil of an electric motor.
5. **Think Critically** A bar magnet is repelled when an electromagnet is brought close to it. Describe how the bar magnet would have moved if the current in the electromagnet had been reversed.

Applying Math

6. **Use a Ratio** The magnetic field strength around a wire at a distance of 1 cm is twice as large as at a distance of 2 cm. How does the field strength at 0.5 cm compare to the field strength at 1 cm?

3 Assess

DAILY INTERVENTION

Check for Understanding

Kinesthetic Divide the class into groups. Provide each group with D-cell batteries, a few meters of insulated wire, and iron bolts. Ask the groups to construct electromagnets. **WARNING:** The bolt cores will become hot if the current is left connected. Make sure students disconnect the wire from the battery when they are not using the electromagnet. L2 ELL COOP LEARN

LS **Kinesthetic**

Reteach

Electromagnets Make two electromagnets from iron nails wrapped in wire. Wrap the first one with only a few coils, the second one with many coils. Have students compare the strength of the two electromagnets as you attempt to pick up a number of paper clips. L2

LS **Visual-Spatial**

Assessment

Oral Demonstrate the different speeds on a fan or mixer. Ask students how they think the speed is varied. To make the appliance rotate faster, the amount of current passing through the coil of the electric motor is increased. To slow down the appliance, the amount of current is decreased. Use **Performance Assessment in the Science Classroom,** p. 89. L2

section 2 review

1. The magnetic field around each bit of wire has the same strength, but when the wire is looped, the fields combine, making a stronger field.
2. by varying the electric current passing through it or by changing the number of loops
3. The magnetic field would be weaker because aluminum is not a magnetic material. The only magnetic field would be that created by the looped wire.
4. When an end of the coil moves past a pole of the permanent magnet, reversing the current causes the end of the coil to be attracted to the other pole of the permanent magnet. Repeating this process keeps the coil continually rotating in the same direction.
5. The bar magnet would have been attracted to the electromagnet because the pole would have been opposite to what it was.
6. It would be twice as large as the strength at 1 cm and four times the strength at 2 cm.

section 3

Producing Electric Current

1 Motivate

Bellringer

Section Focus Transparencies also are available on the Interactive Chalkboard CD-ROM. L2 

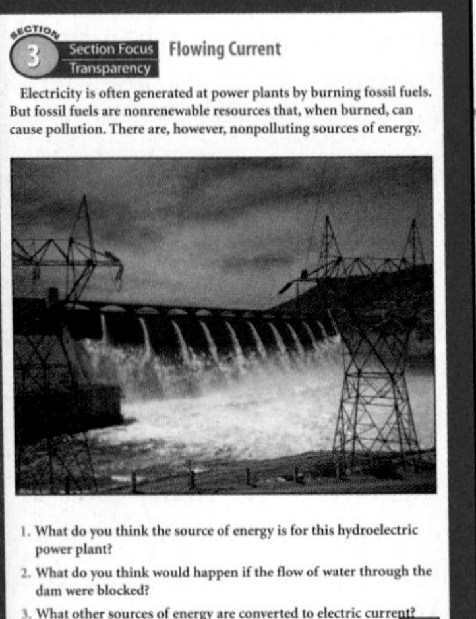

Section Focus Transparency
Flowing Current
Electricity is often generated at power plants by burning fossil fuels. But fossil fuels are nonrenewable resources that, when burned, can cause pollution. There are, however, nonpolluting sources of energy.
1. What do you think the source of energy is for this hydroelectric power plant?
2. What do you think would happen if the flow of water through the dam were blocked?
3. What other sources of energy are converted to electric current?
L2

Tie to Prior Knowledge

Windmills Ask students if they have ever seen a windmill. Refer them to **Figure 18** and have them describe the motion of the blades and what the force of the wind is doing to the generators that they are connected to. L2

Reading Guide

What You'll Learn

- **Define** electromagnetic induction.
- **Describe** how a generator produces an electric current.
- **Distinguish** between alternating current and direct current.
- **Explain** how a transformer can change the voltage of an alternating current.

Why It's Important

Electromagnetic induction enables power plants to generate the electric current an appliance uses when you plug it into an electric outlet.

Review Vocabulary

voltage difference: a measure of the electrical energy provided by charges as they flow in a circuit

New Vocabulary

- electromagnetic induction
- generator
- turbine
- direct current (DC)
- alternating current (AC)
- transformer

From Mechanical to Electrical Energy

Working independently in 1831, Michael Faraday in Britain and Joseph Henry in the United States both found that moving a loop of wire through a magnetic field caused an electric current to flow in the wire. They also found that moving a magnet through a loop of wire produces a current. In both cases, the mechanical energy associated with the motion of the wire loop or the magnet is converted into electrical energy associated with the current in the wire. The magnet and wire loop must be moving relative to each other for an electric current to be produced. This causes the magnetic field inside the loop to change with time. In addition, if the current in a wire changes with time, the changing magnetic field around the wire can also induce a current in a nearby coil. The generation of a current by a changing magnetic field is **electromagnetic induction.**

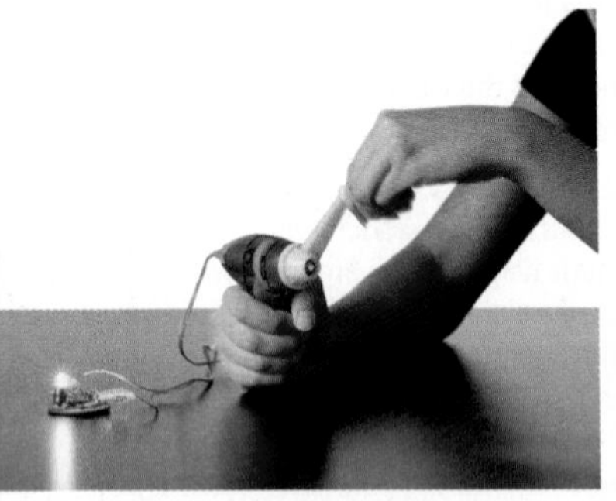

Figure 15 The coil in a generator is rotated by an outside source of mechanical energy. Here the student supplies the mechanical energy that is converted into electrical energy by the generator.

Generators Most of the electrical energy you use every day is provided by generators. A **generator** uses electromagnetic induction to transform mechanical energy into electrical energy. **Figure 15** shows one way a generator converts mechanical energy to electrical energy. The mechanical energy is provided by turning the handle on the generator.

An example of a simple generator is shown in **Figure 16.** In this type of generator, a current is produced in the coil as the coil rotates between the poles of a permanent magnet.

Section 3 Resource Manager

Chapter *Fast File* Resources

Transparency Activity, pp. 46, 47–48

Directed Reading for Content Mastery, pp. 21–22

Enrichment, p. 32

Reinforcement, p. 29

Lab Worksheet, pp. 5–6, 7–8

Home and Community Involvement, p. 37

Cultural Diversity, p. 53

Performance Assessment in the Science Classroom, p. 53

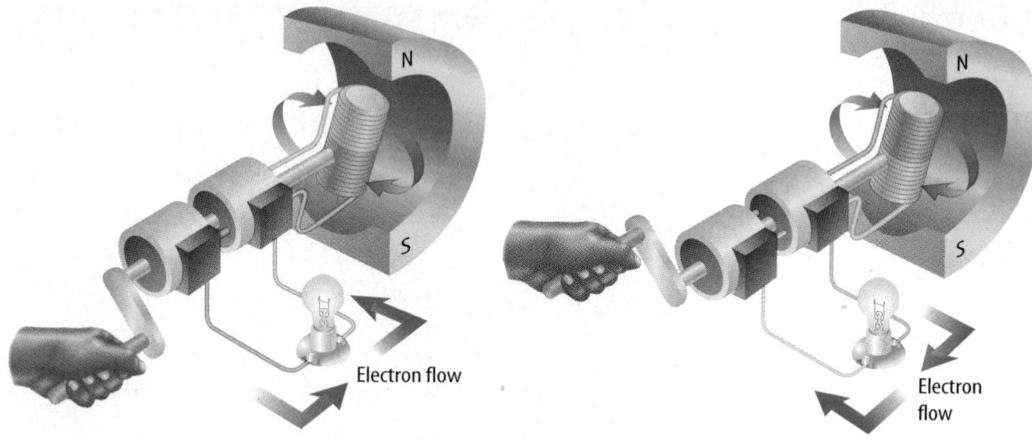

Figure 16 The current in the coil changes direction each time the ends of the coil move past the poles of the permanent magnet. **Explain** *how the frequency of the changing current can be controlled.*

Switching Direction As the generator's wire coil rotates through the magnetic field of the permanent magnet, current flows through the coil. After the wire coil makes one-half of a revolution, the ends of the coil are moving past the opposite poles of the permanent magnet. This causes the current to change direction. In a generator, as the coil keeps rotating, the current that is produced periodically changes direction. The direction of the current in the coil changes twice with each revolution, as **Figure 16** shows. The frequency with which the current changes direction can be controlled by regulating the rotation rate of the generator. In the United States, current is produced by generators that rotate 60 times a second, or 3,600 revolutions per minute.

Reading Check *For each revolution of the coil, how many times does the current change direction?*

Using Electric Generators The type of generator shown in **Figure 16** is used in a car, where it is called an alternator. The alternator provides electrical energy to operate lights and other accessories. Spark plugs in the car's engine also use this electrical energy to ignite the fuel in the cylinders of the engine. Once the engine is running, it provides the mechanical energy that is used to turn the coil in the alternator.

Suppose that instead of using mechanical energy to rotate the coil in a generator, the coil was fixed, and the permanent magnet rotated instead. In fact, the current generated would be the same as when the coil rotates and the magnet doesn't move. The huge generators used in electric power plants are made this way. The current is produced in the stationary coil, and mechanical energy is used to rotate the magnet.

2 Teach

Reading Check

Answer twice

IDENTIFYING Misconceptions

Magnetic Fields Some students may think that a magnetic field alone is enough to produce a current. Emphasize that the magnetic field must be changing to induce a current in the wire coil. A stationary magnet and loop will not generate a current.

Use Science Words

Word Meaning The expression *electromagnetic induction* is related to the word *induce*. Have students find the common meaning of induce and use it in a sentence. Induce means to move to a course of action, to cause; sample sentence: The king induced his knights to follow his lead. L2 LS **Linguistic**

Caption Answer

Figure 16 by regulating the rotation rate of the generator

Science Journal

History of Technology A turbine transforms straight-line motion into rotational motion. One of the oldest means of transforming motion this way is the waterwheel. Have students write paragraphs in their Science Journals comparing the design of a waterwheel with that of a hydroelectric turbine. L2 LS **Linguistic**

Discussion

Number of Power Plants Why is electricity usually generated at a few large plants, rather than many small ones? Possible answer: Generating plants are often located near rivers, dams, or other energy sources. Multiple small plants would require redundant resources and would be more expensive to build. L3 LS **Logical-Mathematical**

Power Plant Operator These operators control and monitor the boilers, turbines, generators, and other equipment at power generating plants. Power plant operators may use computers for many tasks including generating reports of daily operations or unusual incidents.

Research Have students research the future employment outlook for this career.

Quick Demo

Generating Current

Materials hand-operated generator, wire, bulb socket, lightbulb

Estimated Time ten minutes

Procedure Attach wire leads to the hand generator and to the bulb socket containing a lightbulb. Slowly turn the hand generator to light the bulb. Additional lightbulbs can be added in parallel or in series. Vary the speed that you turn the hand generator and show students the effect on the brightness of the lights.

Figure 17 Each of these generators at Hoover Dam can produce over 100,000 kW of electric power. In these generators, a rotating magnet induces an electric current in a stationary wire coil.

Power Plant Operator Many daily activities require electricity. Power plant operators control the machinery that generates electricity. Operators must have a high school diploma. College-level courses may be helpful. Research to find employers in your area that hire power plant operators.

Generating Electricity for Your Home You probably do not have a generator in your home that supplies the electrical energy you need to watch television or wash your clothes. This electrical energy comes from a power plant with huge generators like the one in **Figure 17.** The coils in these generators have many coils of wire wrapped around huge iron cores. The rotating magnets are connected to a **turbine** (TUR bine)—a large wheel that rotates when pushed by water, wind, or steam.

For example, some power plants first produce thermal energy by burning fossil fuels or using the heat produced by nuclear reactions. This thermal energy is used to heat water and produce steam. Thermal energy is then converted to mechanical energy as the steam pushes the turbine blades. The generator then changes the mechanical energy of the rotating turbine into the electrical energy you use. In some areas, fields of windmills, like those in **Figure 18,** can be used to capture the mechanical energy in wind to turn generators. Other power plants use the mechanical energy in falling water to drive the turbine. Both generators and electric motors use magnets to produce energy conversions between electrical and mechanical energy. **Figure 19** summarizes the differences between electric motors and generators.

Figure 18 The propeller on each of these windmills is connected to an electric generator. The rotating propeller rotates a coil or a permanent magnet.

Curriculum Connection

Geography Solar power can be used to generate electricity. A very large array is needed to generate enough electricity for a city, and only very sunny sites will do. Ask students to research and report on areas in the United States that are suitable for such solar generators. Large solar arrays have been proposed for the Southwest's deserts, particularly those in California. L2 P LS **Linguistic**

Visual Learning

Figure 18 In the 1920s and 1930s, before rural areas had access to electricity from power plants, people sometimes used small windmills to run water pumps or household generators. The windmills shown are much larger, of course. Windmills on "wind farms," such as the one shown in the figure, can be as big as 50 meters in diameter and stand several building stories high.

NATIONAL GEOGRAPHIC VISUALIZING MOTORS AND GENERATORS

Figure 19

Electric motors power many everyday machines, from CD players to vacuum cleaners. Generators produce the electricity those motors need to run. Both motors and generators use electromagnets, but in different ways. The table below compares motors and generators.

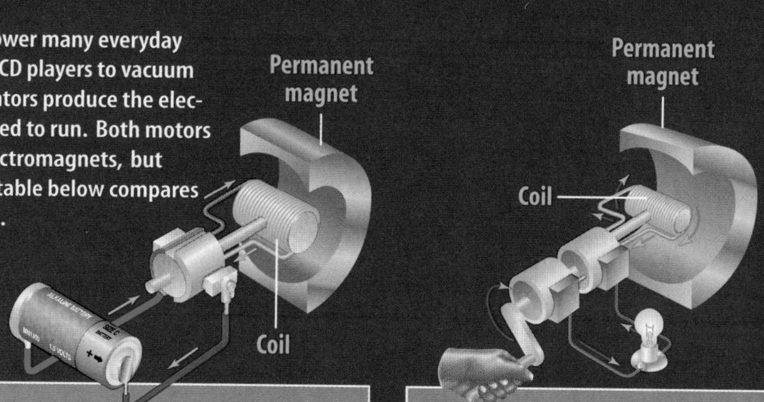

Permanent magnet

Coil

Permanent magnet

Coil

	Electric Motor	Generator
What does it do?	Changes electricity into movement 	Changes movement into electricity 
What makes its electromagnetic coil rotate?	Attractive and repulsive forces between the coil and the permanent magnet 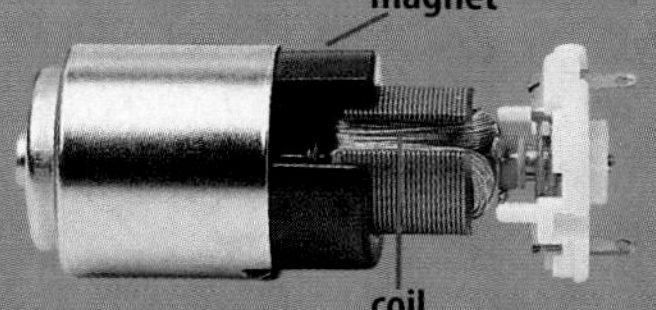 (magnet, coil)	An outside source of mechanical energy 
What is the source of the current that flows in its coil?	An outside power source 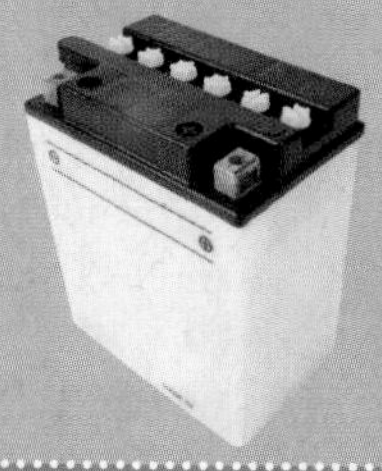	Electromagnetic induction from moving the coil through the field of the permanent magnet 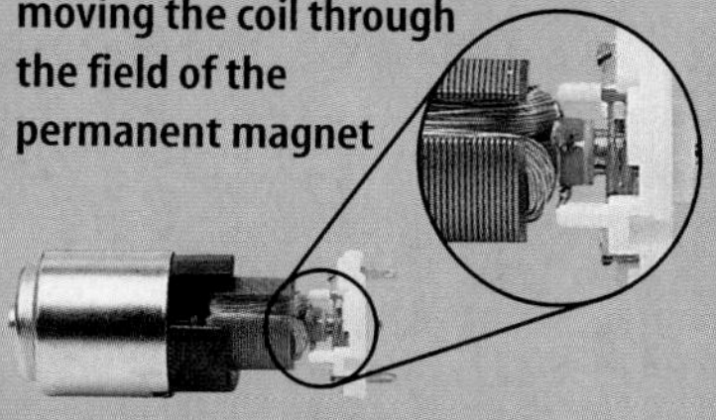
How often does the current in the coil change direction?	Twice during each rotation of the coil	Twice during each rotation of the coil

Have students examine the pictures and read the captions. Then ask the following questions.

In what way is an electric motor the opposite of a generator? In what way is it the same? Opposite: A motor changes electricity into movement, while a generator changes movement into electricity. Same: The current in the coil changes direction twice during each rotation of the coil.

What kind of movement produces the electricity in hydroelectric generators? moving water In windmills? moving air In a bicycle generator? moving bicycle wheel

Activity

Hand-Cranked Power Have small groups of students research power supplies used for camping or emergency situations that produce electricity from a hand-cranked generator. These devices include flashlights, lanterns, and radios. Have students make oral presentations about how these devices work and in what situations they would be most useful. L2 COOP LEARN

LS **Logical-Mathematical**

Differentiated Instruction

Challenge Students could research the differences between AC and DC generators and make labeled posters illustrating the differences between these two ways that electricity is transmitted. L3 LS **Visual-Spatial**

Teacher FYI

Current Disagreement Thomas Edison advocated the use of DC to transmit electric current. One of his workers, Nikola Tesla, argued that an AC current would be better. Edison and Tesla parted ways, and Tesla went to work for Edison's competitor, the Westinghouse Company. Today, electric current in the United States is distributed using AC.

Virtual Labs

Generators *How does a generator work?*

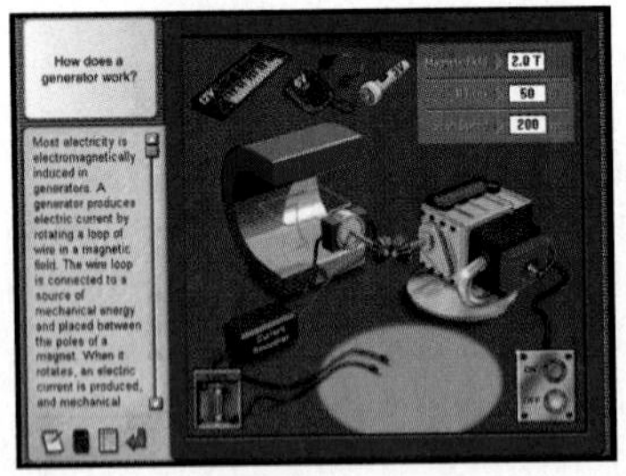

Topic: Transformers
Visit gpscience.com for links to information about how transformers transmit electric current.

Activity In England, voltage from an outlet is greater than required for U.S. appliances. Using information found at these links, diagram a transformer that would allow a U.S. appliance to operate in England.

Direct and Alternating Currents

Modern society relies heavily on electricity. Just how much you rely on electricity becomes obvious during a power outage. Out of habit, you might walk into a room and flip on the light switch. You might try to turn on a radio or television or check the clock to see what time it is. Because power outages sometimes occur, some electrical devices, like the radio in **Figure 20,** use batteries as a backup source of electrical energy. However, the current produced by a battery is different than the current from an electric generator.

A battery produces a direct current. **Direct current** (DC) flows only in one direction through a wire. When you plug your CD player or any other appliance into a wall outlet, you are using alternating current. **Alternating current** (AC) reverses the direction of the current in a regular pattern. In North America, generators produce alternating current at a frequency of 60 cycles per second, or 60 Hz. The electric current produced by a generator changes direction twice during each cycle, or each rotation, of the coil. So a 60-Hz alternating current changes direction 120 times each second.

Electronic devices that use batteries as a backup energy source usually require direct current to operate. When the device is plugged into a wall outlet, electronic components inside the device convert the alternating current to direct current and also reduce the voltage of the alternating current.

Figure 20 Some devices, like this radio, can use either direct or alternating current. Electronic components in these devices change alternating current from an electric outlet to direct current.

Transmitting Electrical Energy

The alternating current produced by an electric power plant carries electrical energy that is transmitted along electric transmission lines. However, when the electric energy is transmitted along power lines, some of the electrical energy is converted into heat due to the electrical resistance of the wires. The heat produced in the power lines warms the wires and the surrounding air and can't be used to power electrical devices. Also, the electrical resistance and heat production increases as the wires get longer. As a result, large amounts of heat can be produced when electrical energy is transmitted over long distances.

One way to reduce the heat produced in a power line is to transmit the electrical energy at high voltages, typically around 150,000 V. However, electrical energy at such high voltage cannot enter your home safely, nor can it be used in home appliances. Instead, a transformer is used to decrease the voltage.

Science Journal

Nikola Tesla Tell students that the inventor Nikola Tesla brought alternating current into wide usage. Have students find out where he was from, when he lived, and how he spread the use of alternating current, and write their findings in their Science Journals. Tesla lived from 1856 to 1943. He was Serbian, born in Croatia. He sold George Westinghouse the idea of alternating current. L2 LS **Linguistic**

Transformers

A **transformer** is a device that increases or decreases the voltage of an alternating current. A transformer is made of a primary coil and a secondary coil. These wire coils are wrapped around the same iron core, as shown in **Figure 21.** As an alternating current passes through the primary coil, the coil's magnetic field magnetizes the iron core. The magnetic field in the primary coil changes direction as the current in the primary coil changes direction. This produces a magnetic field in the iron core that changes direction at the same frequency. The changing magnetic field in the iron core then induces an alternating current with the same frequency in the secondary coil.

The voltage in the primary coil is the input voltage and the voltage in the secondary coil is the output voltage. The output voltage divided by the input voltage equals the number of turns in the secondary coil divided by the number of turns in the primary coil.

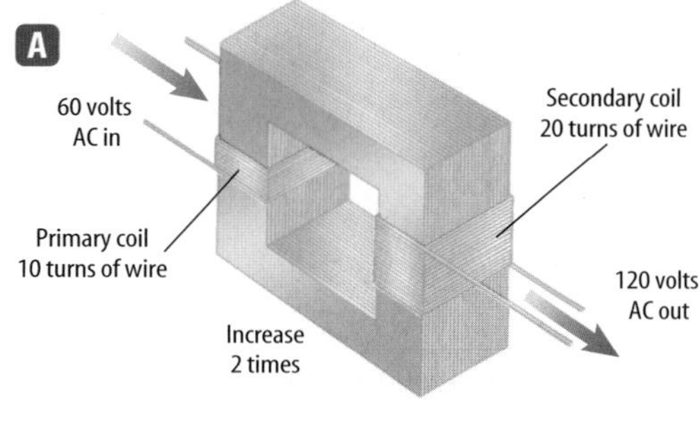

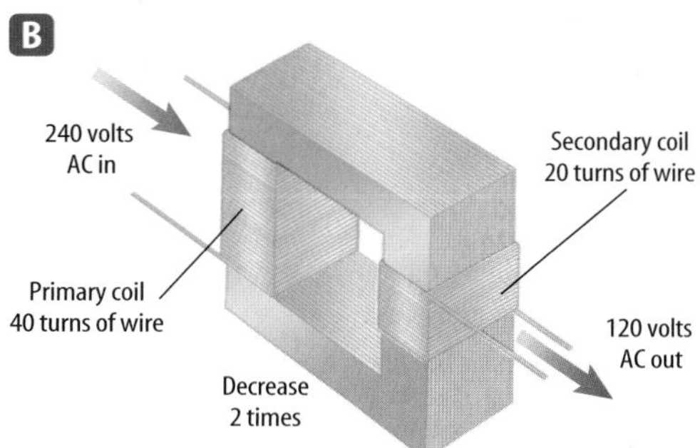

Figure 21 Transformers can increase or decrease voltage. **A** A step-up transformer increases voltage. The secondary coil has more turns than the primary coil does. **B** A step-down transformer decreases voltage. The secondary coil has fewer turns than the primary coil does.
Infer *whether a transformer could change the voltage of a direct current.*

Reading Check *How does a transformer produce an alternating current in the secondary coil?*

Step-Up Transformer A transformer that increases the voltage so that the output voltage is greater than the input voltage is a step-up transformer. In a step-up transformer the number of wire turns on the secondary coil is greater than the number of turns on the primary coil. For example, the secondary coil of the step-up transformer in **Figure 21A** has twice as many turns as the primary coil has. So the ratio of the output voltage to the input voltage is two, and the output voltage is twice as large as the input voltage. For this transformer an input voltage of 60 V in the primary coil would be increased to 120 V in the secondary coil.

Step-Down Transformer A transformer that decreases the voltage so that the output voltage is less than the input voltage is a step-down transformer. In a step-down transformer the number of wire turns on the secondary coil is less than the number of turns on the primary coil. In **Figure 21B** the secondary coil has half as many turns as the primary coil has, so the ratio of the output voltage to the input voltage is one-half. The input voltage of 240 V in the primary coil is reduced to a voltage of 120 V in the secondary coil.

Teacher FYI

Eddy Currents Eddy currents can be generated in transformers by the changing magnetic field around the core. Because the magnetic fields generated by the eddy current oppose the original field, power is lost. The cores of transformers are often made out of many thin, laminated strips of metal instead of one big iron loop. Insulating glue between the strips restricts the eddy currents to individual strips, where they cannot grow very large. This makes the transformer more efficient.

Activity

Finding Transformers Take students outside and find the transformers leading into the school. Ask students to find the transformers near their homes as well, and compare them. Caution students to not touch or get too close to the transformers. L1 ELL
Visual-Spatial

Reading Check

Answer The changing magnetic field in the iron core induces an alternating current with the same frequency in the secondary coil.

Caption Answer

Figure 21 No, a direct current does not produce a changing magnetic field in the primary or secondary coil. So electromagnetic induction does not occur.

Active Reading

Write-Draw-Discuss This strategy encourages students to actively participate in reading and lectures, assimilating content creatively. Have students write about electric motors, generators, and transformers, clarify their ideas, then make illustrations or drawings. Ask students to share responses with the class and display several examples. L2

Caption Answer

Figure 22 The step-up transformer and step-down transformer

3 Assess

DAILY INTERVENTION

Check for Understanding

Visual-Spatial Have students draw a diagram of a generator and label the parts. Have students write a brief description about how the generator works. L2

Reteach

Visual-Spatial Use **Figure 19** to tie the electric generator to the electric motor. Have students explain what each is used for and how each uses the connection between electricity and magnetism. L2 LS

Assessment

Content Ask students to work in teams to design a human-powered device for generating electrical energy. As an example, describe how a stationary bicycle could be modified to rotate the electromagnet in a generator. Use **Performance Assessment in the Science Classroom,** p. 117. L2

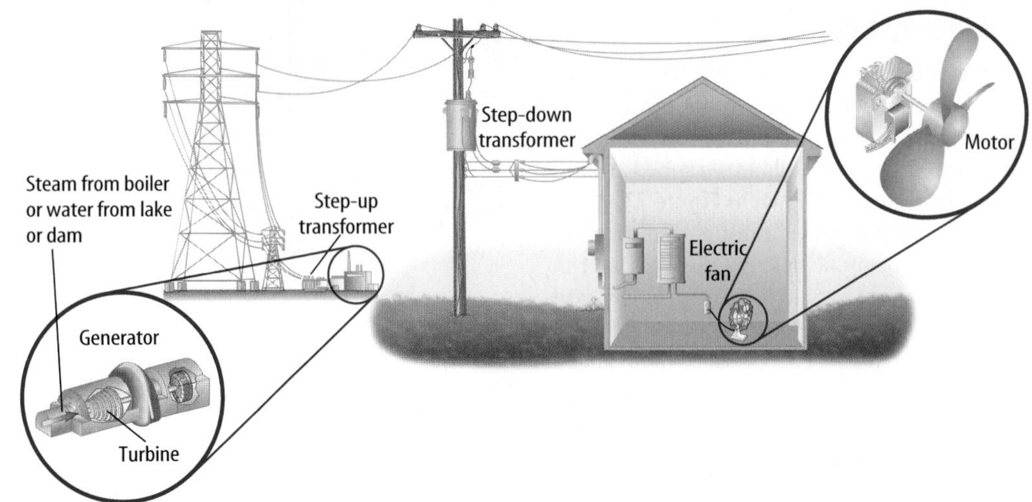

Figure 22 Many steps are involved in the creation, transportation, and use of the electric current in your home.
Identify *the steps that involve electromagnetic induction.*

Transmitting Alternating Current Power plants commonly produce alternating current because the voltage can be increased or decreased with transformers. Although step-up transformers and step-down transformers change the voltage at which electrical energy is transmitted, they do not change the amount of electrical energy transmitted. **Figure 22** shows how step-up and step-down transformers are used in transmitting electrical energy from power plants to your home.

section 3 review

Summary

From Mechanical to Electrical Energy

- An electric current is produced by moving a wire loop through a magnetic field or a magnet through a wire loop.
- A generator can produce an electric current by rotating a wire coil in a magnetic field.

Direct and Alternating Currents

- A direct current flows in one direction. An alternating current changes direction in a regular pattern.

Transformers

- A transformer changes the voltage of an alternating current. The voltage can be increased or decreased.
- The changing magnetic field in the primary coil of a transformer induces an alternating current in the secondary coil.

Self Check

1. **Describe** the energy conversions that occur when water falls on a paddle wheel connected to a generator that is connected to electric lights.
2. **Compare and contrast** a generator with an electric motor.
3. **Explain** why the output voltage from a transformer is zero if a direct current flows through the primary coil.
4. **Explain** why electric current produced by power plants is transmitted as alternating current.
5. **Think Critically** A magnet is pushed into the center of a wire loop, and then stops. What is the current in the wire loop after the magnet stops moving? Explain.

Applying Math

6. **Use a Ratio** A transformer has 1,000 turns of wire in the primary coil and 50 turns in the secondary coil. If the input voltage is 2400 V, what is the output voltage?

gpscience.com/self_check_quiz

section 3 review

1. falling water strikes paddle wheel and wheel begins to turn—kinetic energy to mechanical energy; turning paddle wheel turns shaft of generator—mechanical energy to electrical energy; electrical energy flows to electric lights—electrical energy to heat and light
2. An electric motor converts electrical energy to mechanical energy and a generator coverts mechanical energy to electrical energy.
3. Only an alternating current induces the voltage in the transformer.
4. Alternating current is used because transformers can increase or decrease voltage. This enables power to be transmitted at high voltage to minimize the energy converted into heat. The voltage then is reduced to lower levels for safe use.
5. zero; Either the magnet or the wire loop must be moving to induce current.
6. $\frac{\text{Voltage}_{out}}{\text{Voltage}_{in}} = \frac{\text{turns}_{seondary}}{\text{turns}_{primary}}$

   $\frac{50}{1000} = \frac{\text{Voltage}_{out}}{2400\text{ V}}$

   $\text{Voltage}_{out} = 120\text{ V}$

BENCH TESTED

Magnets, Coils, and Currents

Huge generators in power plants produce electricity by moving magnets past coils of wire. How does that produce an electric current?

Real-World Question

How can a magnet and a wire coil be used to produce an electric current?

Goals

- **Observe** how a magnet and a wire coil can produce an electric current in a wire.
- **Compare** the currents created by moving the magnet and the wire coil in different ways.

Materials

cardboard tube
bar magnet
insulated wire
scissors
galvanometer or ammeter

Safety Precautions

WARNING: *Do not touch bare wires when current is running through them.*

Procedure

1. Wrap the wire around the cardboard tube to make a coil of about 20 turns. Remove the tube from the coil.
2. Use the scissors to cut and remove 2 cm of insulation from each end of the wire.
3. Connect the ends of the wire to a galvanometer or ammeter. Record the reading on your meter.
4. Insert one end of the magnet into the coil and then pull it out. Record the current. Move the magnet at different speeds inside the coil and record the current.

5. Watch the meter and move the bar magnet in different ways around the outside of the coil. Record your observations.
6. Repeat steps 3 through 4, keeping the magnet stationary and moving the wire coil.

Conclude and Apply

1. How was the largest current generated?
2. Does the current generated always flow in the same direction? How do you know?
3. **Predict** what would happen if you used a coil made with fewer turns of wire.
4. **Infer** whether a current would have been generated if the cardboard tube were left in the coil. Why or why not? Try it.

Communicating Your Data

Compare the currents generated by different members of the class. What was the value of the largest current that was generated? How was this current generated?

Real-World Question

Purpose Students observe electromagnetic induction of a current. L1 LS **Kinesthetic**

Process Skills observe and infer, interpret data, draw conclusions, recognize cause and effect, compare and contrast, make models

Time Required 45 minutes

Procedure

Alternate Materials One end of a horseshoe magnet can replace the bar magnet.

Teaching Strategy Be sure the galvanometer is on the most sensitive scale and that students form complete circuits.

Conclude and Apply

1. Faster motion produces more current, as does moving the magnet in the coil rather than outside it.
2. No; the needle was deflected in different directions depending on whether the magnet moved in or out of the coil.
3. A smaller current would be induced.
4. Yes; electric and magnetic fields are not affected by the cardboard.

Assessment

Performance Ask each student to make a poster that shows the design of the experiment they used and explains what each piece of equipment does. To one side, they should list how changes in the setup change the current induced. Use **Performance Assessment in the Science Classroom,** p. 145. L1

Communicating Your Data

Ask students to include suggestions for how they could make a stronger current. Possible answers: increase the number of coils; make the coils closer to the moving magnet; use a stronger magnet

Real-World Question

Purpose Students will assemble an electromagnet and then attempt to control its strength by changing its construction. L2

LS Kinesthetic

Process Skills form a hypothesis, identify and manipulate variables, make and use tables, observe

Time Required 60 minutes

Possible Materials Iron 16-penny nails are available through science supply companies. If nails are purchased locally, make sure they are made of iron.

Alternate Materials Students can use either an electric power supply or batteries for the electric current in their electromagnets. A knife switch can be included for easier current control.

Safety Precautions Closely monitor students who are using an electric power supply to ensure that they do not apply more than 6 volts.

Form a Hypothesis

Possible Hypothesis The more loops that are used in the construction of the electromagnet the stronger the magnetic field it will generate.

Test Your Hypothesis

Possible Procedures Wrap wire around a nail about 15 times. Tape it in place, leaving about 20 cm loose on each end. Connect the wire ends to the terminals of a battery.

Design Your Own

Controlling Electromagnets

Goals
- **Measure** relative strengths of electromagnets.
- **Determine** which factors affect the strength of an electromagnet.

Possible Materials
22-gauge insulated wire
16-penny iron nail
aluminum rod or nail
0-6 V DC power supply
three 1.5-V "D" cells
steel paper clips
magnetic compass
duct tape (to hold "D" cells together)

Safety Precautions

WARNING: *Do not leave the electromagnet connected for long periods of time because the battery will run down. Magnets will get hot with only a few turns of wire. Use caution in handling them when current is flowing through the coil. Do not apply voltages higher than 6 V to your electromagnets.*

Real-World Question

You use electromagnets every day when you use stereo speakers, power door locks, and many other devices. To make these devices work properly, the strength of the magnetic field surrounding an electromagnet must be controlled. How can the magnetic field produced by an electromagnet be made stronger or weaker? Think about the components that form an electromagnet. Make a hypothesis about how changing these components would affect the strength of the electromagnet's magnetic field.

Form a Hypothesis

As a group, write down the components of an electromagnet that might affect the strength of its magnetic field.

Make a Plan

1. Write your hypothesis for the best way to control the magnetic field strength of an electromagnet.
2. **Decide** how you will assemble and test the electromagnets. Which features will you change to determine the effect on the strength of the magnetic fields? How many changes will you need to try? How many electromagnets do you need to build?
3. **Decide** how you are going to test the strength of your electromagnets. Several ways are possible with the materials listed. Which way would be the most sensitive? Be prepared to change test methods if necessary.

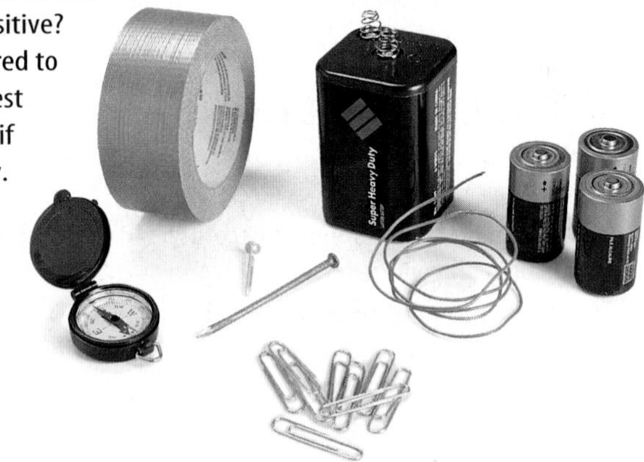

246 CHAPTER 8 Magnetism and Its Uses

Alternative Inquiry Lab

Using Electromagnets Extend this Lab into an Inquiry Lab by building on the experience gained performing this lab. Encourage your students to use what they have learned to brainstorm uses for electromagnets. Have student groups each choose one question to explore. Ask them to list the materials they need to explore their questions. Unsafe or impractical questions should be eliminated. Students should have their plans for their additional experiments approved before continuing. Conduct the experiments after all necessary materials have been gathered. L3

4. Write your plan of investigation. Make sure your plan tests only one variable at a time.

Follow Your Plan

1. Before you begin to build and test the electromagnets, make sure your teacher approves of your plan.
2. Carry out your planned investigation.
3. Record your results.

Analyze Your Data

1. **Make a table** showing how the strength of your electromagnet depends on changes you made in its construction or operation.
2. **Examine** the trends shown by your data. Are there any data points which seem out of line? How can you account for them?

Testing Electromagnets

Trial	Electromagnet Construction Features	Strength of Electromagnet
	Student answers will vary.	

Conclude and Apply

1. **Describe** how the electromagnet's magnetic-field strength depended on its construction or operation.
2. **Identify** the features of the electromagnet's construction that had the greatest effect on its magnetic-field strength. Which do you think would be easiest to control?
3. **Explain** how you could use your electromagnet to make a switch. Would it work with both AC and DC?
4. **Evaluate** whether or not your results support your hypothesis. Why or why not?

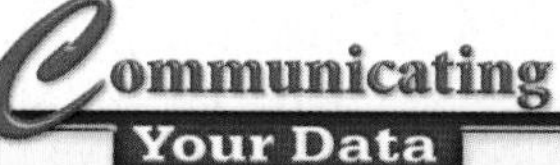

Compare your group's result with those of other groups. Did any other group use a different method to test the strength of the magnet? Did you get the same results?

Determine how many paper clips the magnetized nail will pick up. Vary the number of wire loops and the number of batteries to observe the effect on the strength of the nail's magnetization.

Teaching Strategy Remind students that the polarity of the electromagnet can be reversed by changing the direction of the current flow.

Expected Outcome Increasing the number of loops in the electromagnet or the number of batteries increases the strength of the magnetic field.

Analyze Your Data

1. Check each group's table.
2. Answers will vary.

Error Analysis Have students compare their results and their hypotheses and explain why differences occurred.

Conclude and Apply

1. The strength of the magnetic field increased when the number of loops or number of batteries increased.
2. Adding additional batteries had the greatest effect and would be easiest to control.
3. Accept all reasonable responses. One way to make a switch would be to use the electromagnet to close and open a circuit. When current flows in the electromagnet, it pulls the metal strip to close a circuit. When current doesn't flow in the electromagnet, the spring pulls the metal strip back and opens the circuit.
4. Answers will vary.

Assessment

Process Students should research how a doorbell works and make drawings illustrating what they find. Use **Performance Assessment in the Science Classroom,** p. 127. L2

When comparing various methods used to test the strength of the magnet, students should consider the masses of the objects used and their composition. L2

Content Background

Magnetic resonance imaging (MRI) is a noninvasive diagnostic technique that uses nuclear magnetic resonance (NMR) to image the structure of the body. Unhampered by bone and capable of producing images in a variety of planes, MRI is used in the diagnosis of brain tumors and disorders, spinal disorders, multiple sclerosis, and cardiovascular diseases. The procedure is considered to be without risk to the patient.

Types of magnetic resonance include electron paramagnetic resonance (EPR), also known as electron spin resonance (ESR), involving the magnetic effect of electrons, and nuclear magnetic resonance (NMR), involving the magnetic effects of protons and neutrons in the nuclei of atoms. The NMR resonant frequency provides information about the molecular material in which the nuclei reside.

Discussion

X Rays How are X rays used differently from MRI? Possible Answer: X rays are used for the diagnosis of problems in hard tissue areas of the body while MRI is used to diagnose soft tissue disorders. L2 **Logical-Mathematical**

Historical Significance

Make sure students understand that MRI has only been developed in the last twenty-five years, which is a very short period of time in the span of history. Start a discussion that will get students to think about the medical advances that have been made possible by MRI. For example, because of MRI doctors are now able to diagnose birth defects and operate on babies in the womb.

TIME SCIENCE AND HISTORY

SCIENCE CAN CHANGE THE COURSE OF HISTORY!

Body Art

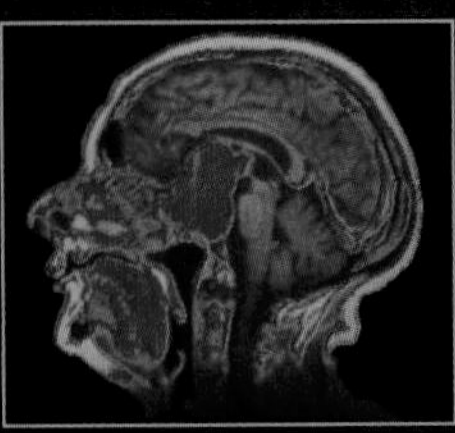

The surgeon turns the computer screen so the patient can see it. Pointing to a colorful image of the patient's brain, she reassures the worried patient. "This MRI shows exactly where your tumor is. We can remove it with little danger to you."

MRI for the Soft Stuff

MRI stands for "magnetic resonance imaging." It's a way to take 3-D pictures of the inside of your body. Before the 1980s, doctors could x-ray solid tissue like bones, but had no way to see soft tissue like the brain. Well, they had one way—surgery, which sometimes caused injury and infection, risking a patient's health.

MRI uses a strong magnet and radio waves. Tissues in your body contain water molecules that are made of oxygen and hydrogen atoms.

The nucleus of a hydrogen atom is a proton, which behaves like a tiny magnet. A strong magnetic field inside the MRI tube makes these proton magnets line up in the direction of the field. Radio waves are then applied to the body. The protons absorb some of the radio-wave energy, and flip their direction.

When the radio waves are turned off, the protons realign themselves with the magnetic field and emit the energy they absorbed. Different tissues in the body absorb and emit different amounts of energy. The emitted energy is detected, and a computer uses this information to form images of the body.

Your brain is getting bigger!

MRI has turned into an important research tool. For example, researchers using MRI have found that the brain grows rapidly through adolescence. Before this research, people thought that the brain stopped growing in childhood. MRI has proved that adolescents are getting bigger brains all the time.

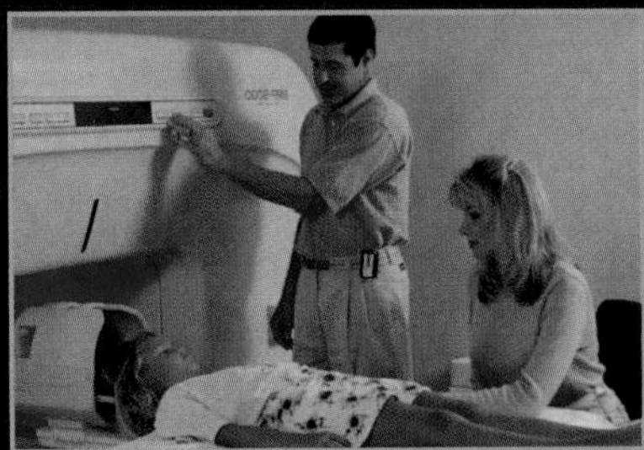

This patient is about to be placed in an MRI machine.

Interview As an oral history project, interview a retired physician or surgeon. Ask him or her to discuss with you how tools such as the MRI changed during his or her career. Make a list of the tools and how they have helped improve medicine.

For more information, visit gpscience.com/time

Interview If any of the students' parents work in the health field, ask them for suggestions of people students can interview. Conduct a brainstorming session to establish questions for the students to ask during their interviews to help them focus on relevant facts. Encourage them to write down their questions before the interview to ease this process. L2

Resources for Teachers and Students

Functional MRI (Medical Radiology) by C.T.W. Moonen (Editor) and P.A. Bandettini (Editor). Springer-Verlag, 2000

Imaging of Soft Tissue Tumors by A.M.A. De Schepper, and others, eds. Springer Verlag 2001

Reviewing Main Ideas

Section 1 Magnetism

1. A magnetic field surrounds a magnet and exerts a magnetic force.
2. All magnets have two poles: a south pole and a north pole.

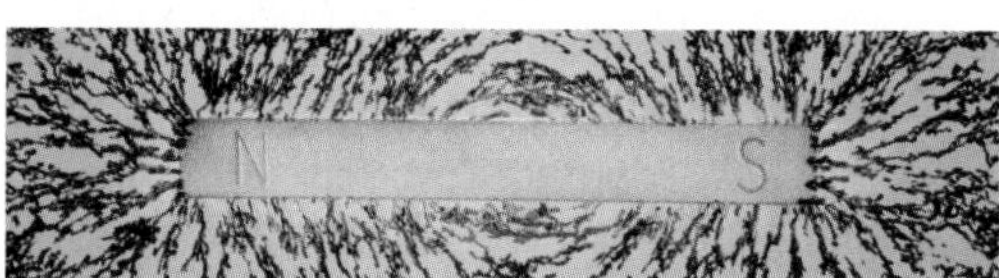

3. Opposite poles of magnets attract; like poles repel.
4. Groups of atoms with aligned magnetic poles are called magnetic domains.

Section 2 Electricity and Magnetism

1. An electric current flowing through a wire produces a magnetic field.
2. An electric current passing through a coil of wire can produce a magnetic field inside the coil. The coil becomes an electromagnet. One end of the coil is the north pole, and the other end is the south pole.

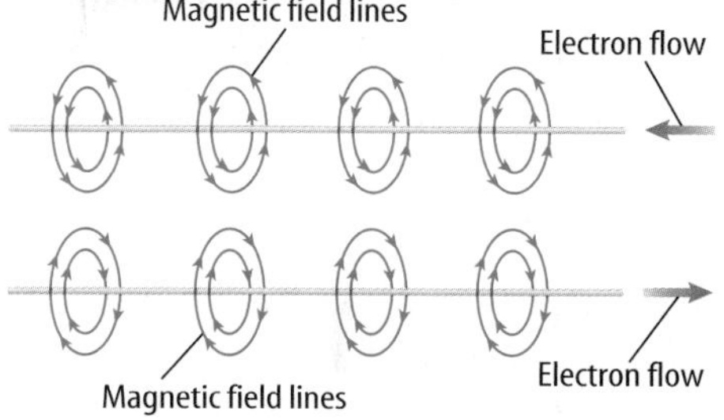

3. The magnetic field around an electromagnet depends on the current and the number of coils.
4. An electric motor contains a rotating electromagnet that converts electrical energy to mechanical energy.

Section 3 Producing Electric Current

1. By moving a magnet near a wire, you can create an electric current in the wire. This is called electromagnetic induction.

2. A generator produces electric current by rotating a coil of wire in a magnetic field. Generators at the base of this dam convert the kinetic energy in falling water into electric energy.
3. Direct current flows in one direction through a wire; alternating current reverses the direction of current flow in a regular pattern.
4. The number of turns of wire in the primary and secondary coils of a transformer determines whether it increases or decreases voltage.

FOLDABLES Use the Foldable that you made at the beginning of this chapter to help you review magnets and magnetism.

Science Online gpscience.com/interactive_tutor

Identifying Misconceptions

Assess

After students have done the lab on page 222F and completed the chapter, have them perform this lab.

Materials PVC pipe, aluminum or copper pipe, circular magnet

Procedure Drop a circular magnet down the length of each pipe and note how long it takes to get to the bottom.

Expected Outcome The magnet travels slower down the metal tube because the falling magnet creates an electric current in the pipe, which creates a magnetic field that slows it down. L2

chapter 8 Study Guide

Reviewing Main Ideas

Summary statements can be used by students to review the major concepts of the chapter.

Science Online

Visit gpscience.com
/self_check_quiz
/interactive_tutor
/vocabulary_puzzlemaker
/chapter_review
/standardized_test

Assessment Transparency

For additional assessment questions, use the *Assessment Transparency* located in the transparency book.

Assessment

Assessment Transparency **Magnetism and Its Uses**

Directions: *Read each question and choose the best answer.*

Sunspot Activity (Number of Sunspots 50–200; Year 1945–1985)

1. According to the graph, what year had the greatest number of sunspots?
   A 1948
   B 1958
   C 1965
   D 1980
2. These data were collected over a forty-year period. If everything remains the same, about what year will the number of sunspots reach another maximum?
   F 1986
   G 1991
   H 1995
   J 1999
3. The graph shows the number of sunspots over a number of years. A reasonable hypothesis based on these data is that the number of sunspots ___.
   A does not follow a trend and is totally random
   B will never be greater than 200
   C reaches a maximum about every 11 years
   D will continue to get smaller every year

L2

Magnetism and Its Uses

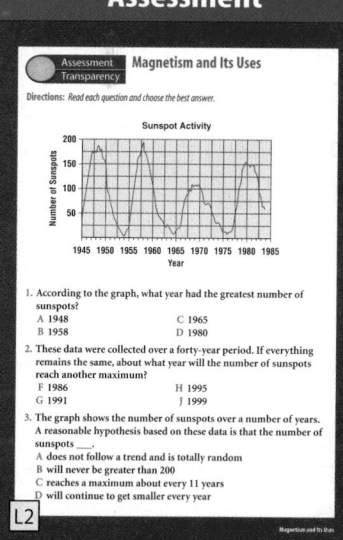

FOLDABLES Have students use their Foldables to review the content of the chapter. On the back of the paper, have students write a paragraph describing how electric motors and electric generators work.

CHAPTER STUDY GUIDE 249

Using Vocabulary

1. transformer
2. magnetic pole
3. Direct current
4. magnetism
5. solenoid
6. magnetic domain
7. galvanometer

Checking Concepts

8. A
9. A
10. C
11. D
12. B
13. B
14. C

Interpreting Graphics

15. Both use a coil, an electromagnet, and a permanent magnet; in both cases the magnets move relative to one another. In an AC generator, a force turns one of the magnets, generating alternating electric current in the electromagnet. In a DC motor, electricity causes a magnet to turn, thereby turning whatever is attached to it.
16. permanent magnet—forces the electromagnet to spin; electromagnet—creates magnetic poles that try to align with the poles of the permanent magnet; the poles switch causing the electromagnet to spin which turns a shaft; current source-provides the electric current that creates the electromagnet
17. See **Figure 15.**
18. about 8 μT
19. The magnetic field strength decreases more rapidly closer to the wire. The magnetic field strength plunges until about 6 cm, then the strength begins to level off to about 2 μT.
20. 2 μT

chapter 8 Review

Using Vocabulary

alternating current (AC) p. 242	generator p. 238
direct current (DC) p. 242	magnetic domains p. 229
electric motor p. 235	magnetic field p. 225
electromagnet p. 232	magnetic pole p. 225
electromagnetic induction p. 238	magnetism p. 224
galvanometer p. 234	solenoid p. 232
	transformer p. 243
	turbine p. 240

Complete each statement with the correct vocabulary word or words.

1. A(n) ________ can be used to change the voltage of an alternating current.
2. A(n) ________ is the region where the magnetic field of a magnet is strongest.
3. ________ does not change direction.
4. The properties and interactions of magnets are called ________.
5. A(n) ________ can rotate in a magnetic field when a current passes through it.
6. The magnetic poles of atoms are aligned in a(n) ________.
7. A device that uses an electromagnet to measure electric current is a(n) ________.

Checking Concepts

Choose the word or phrase that best answers the question.

8. Where is the magnetic force exerted by a magnet strongest?
   A) both poles
   B) south poles
   C) north poles
   D) center
9. Which change occurs in an electric motor?
   A) electrical energy to mechanical energy
   B) thermal energy to wind energy
   C) mechanical energy to electrical energy
   D) wind energy to electrical energy
10. What happens to the magnetic force as the distance between two magnetic poles decreases?
   A) remains constant
   B) decreases
   C) increases
   D) decreases then increases
11. Which of the following best describes what type of magnetic poles the domains at the north pole of a bar magnet have?
   A) north magnetic poles only
   B) south magnetic poles only
   C) no magnetic poles
   D) north and south magnetic poles
12. Which of the following would not change the strength of an electromagnet?
   A) increasing the amount of current
   B) changing the current's direction
   C) inserting an iron core inside the coil
   D) increasing the number of loops
13. Which of the following would NOT be part of a generator?
   A) turbine
   B) battery
   C) electromagnet
   D) permanent magnet
14. Which of the following describes the direction of the electric current in AC?
   A) is constant
   B) is direct
   C) changes regularly
   D) changes irregularly

Interpreting Graphics

15. Copy and complete this Venn diagram. Include the functions, part names, and power sources for these devices.

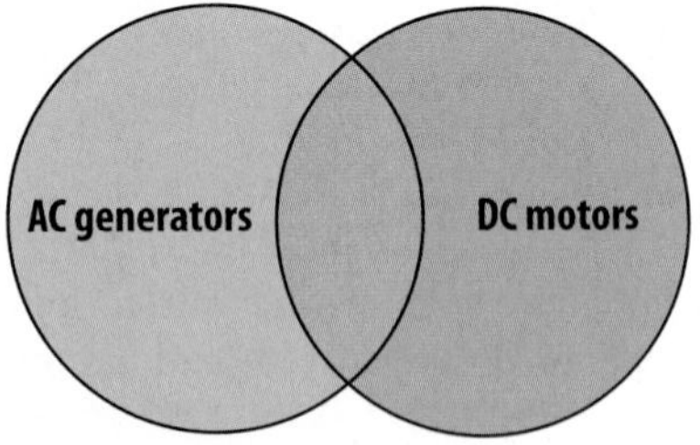

Science Online gpscience.com/vocabulary_puzzlemaker

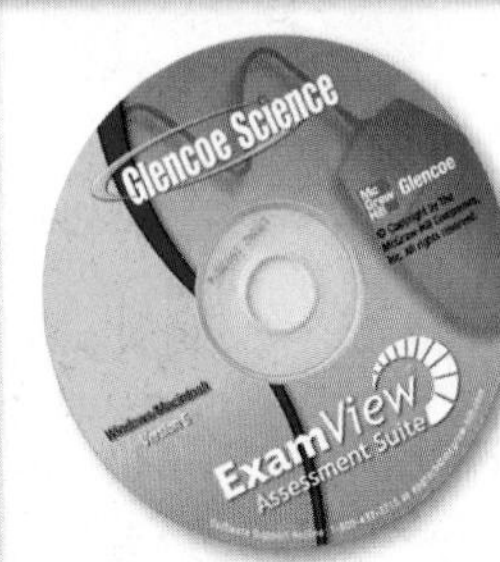

Use the diagram below to answer questions 16 and 17.

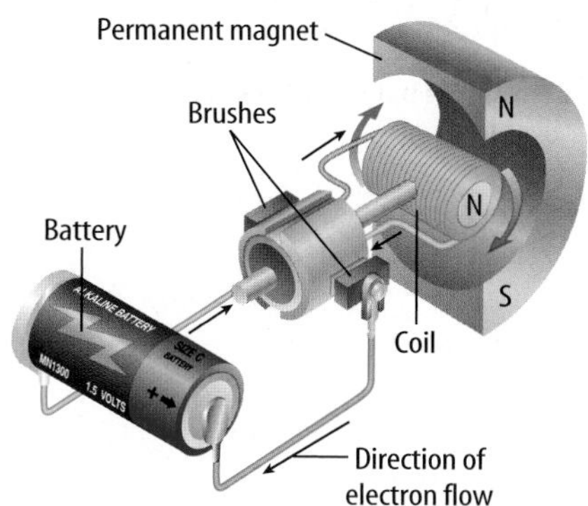

16. Using the diagram, describe the function of the permanent magnet, the electromagnet, and the current source in a simple electric motor.
17. Describe the sequence of steps that occur in an electric motor that forces the coil to spin. Include the role of the commutator in your description.

Use the graph below to answer questions 18–20.

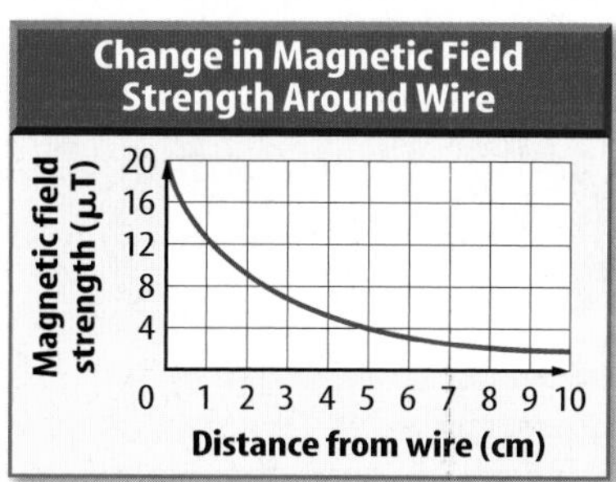

18. How much larger is the magnetic field strength 1 cm from the wire compared to 5 cm from the wire?
19. Does the magnetic field strength decrease more rapidly with distance closer to the wire or farther from the wire? Explain.
20. Using the graph, estimate the magnetic field strength 11 cm from the wire.

Thinking Critically

21. **Infer** how you could you use a horseshoe magnet to find the direction north.
22. **Explain** In Europe, generators produce alternating current at a frequency of 50 Hz. Would the electric appliances you use in North America work if you plugged them into an outlet in Europe? Why or why not?
23. **Predict** Two generators are identical except for the loops of wire that rotate through their magnetic fields. One has twice as many turns of wire as the other one does. Which generator would produce the most electric current? Why?
24. **Explain** why a bar magnet will attract an iron nail to either its north pole or its south pole, but attract another magnet to only one of its poles.
25. **Compare and contrast** electromagnetic induction and the formation of electromagnets.

Applying Math

26. **Calculate** A step-down transformer reduces a 2,400-V current to 120 V. If the primary coil has 500 turns of wire, how many turns of wire are there on the secondary coil?
27. **Use a Ratio** To produce a spark, a spark plug requires a current at about 12,000 V. A car's engine uses a type of transformer called an induction coil to change the input voltage from 12 V to 12,000 V. In the induction coil, what is the ratio of the number of wire turns on the primary coil to the number of turns on the secondary coil?

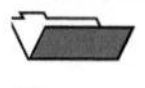
Science Online gpscience.com/chapter_review

Assessment Resources

Reproducible Masters

Chapter *Fast File* Resources
Chapter Review, pp. 37–38
Chapter Tests, pp. 39–42
Assessment Transparency Activity, p. 49

Glencoe Science Web site
Chapter Review Test
Standardized Test Practice

Glencoe Technology
Assessment Transparency
ExamView® Assessment Suite
MindJogger Videoquiz
Interactive Chalkboard

chapter Review 8

Thinking Critically

21. Possible answer: suspend it by the middle so it can rotate; the south end should be attracted to magnetic north
22. No; North American appliances do not work in Europe unless they are made to operate at both frequencies. If the appliance is designed for dual operation, only an adapter is required. Most North American appliances require adapters, a converter, and a transformer to adjust the current and to accommodate the outlet designs in Europe.
23. The generator with twice as many loops will produce the most current because more wire loops pass through the magnetic field.
24. The magnetic domains in the nail become aligned so they are always attracted to the nearest pole of the bar magnet. The domains in a bar magnet are aligned in a fixed direction.
25. Both are related to current flowing in a wire. Electromagnetic induction is the generation of a current by a changing magnetic field. An electromagnet is formed when a wire is wrapped around an iron core and current flows through the wire.

Applying Math

National Math Standards

1, 2, 9

26. $\frac{\text{Voltage}_{out}}{\text{Voltage}_{in}} = \frac{\text{turns}_{seondary}}{\text{turns}_{primary}}$

$\frac{120\text{ V}}{2{,}400\text{ V}} = \frac{\text{turns}_{secondary}}{500\text{ turns}}$

$\text{turns}_{secondary} = 25\text{ turns}$

27. Use the reciprocal of the equation in problem 26.

$\frac{\text{turns}_{primary}}{\text{turns}_{secondary}} = \frac{\text{Voltage}_{in}}{\text{Voltage}_{out}},$

$\frac{\text{turns}_{primary}}{\text{turns}_{secondary}} =$

$\frac{12\text{ V}}{12{,}000\text{ V}} = \frac{1}{1000}$

the ratio is 1:1,000

Answer Sheet A practice answer sheet can be found at gpscience.com/answer_sheet.

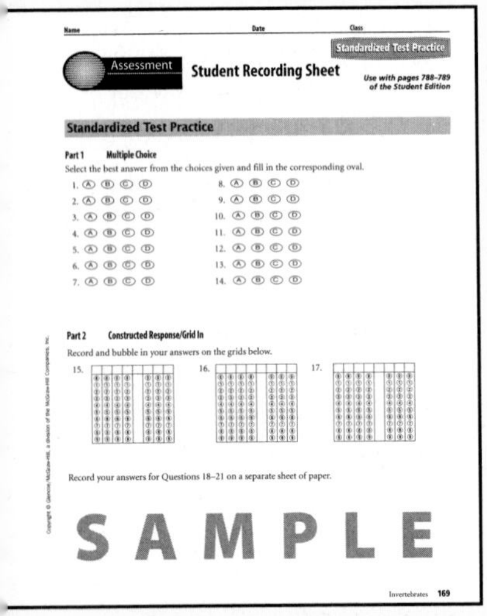

Name Date Class

Standardized Test Practice

Assessment Student Recording Sheet

Use with pages 788–789 of the Student Edition

Standardized Test Practice

Part 1 Multiple Choice

Select the best answer from the choices given and fill in the corresponding oval.

1. Ⓐ Ⓑ Ⓒ Ⓓ 8. Ⓐ Ⓑ Ⓒ Ⓓ
2. Ⓐ Ⓑ Ⓒ Ⓓ 9. Ⓐ Ⓑ Ⓒ Ⓓ
3. Ⓐ Ⓑ Ⓒ Ⓓ 10. Ⓐ Ⓑ Ⓒ Ⓓ
4. Ⓐ Ⓑ Ⓒ Ⓓ 11. Ⓐ Ⓑ Ⓒ Ⓓ
5. Ⓐ Ⓑ Ⓒ Ⓓ 12. Ⓐ Ⓑ Ⓒ Ⓓ
6. Ⓐ Ⓑ Ⓒ Ⓓ 13. Ⓐ Ⓑ Ⓒ Ⓓ
7. Ⓐ Ⓑ Ⓒ Ⓓ 14. Ⓐ Ⓑ Ⓒ Ⓓ

Part 2 Constructed Response/Grid In

Record and bubble in your answers on the grids below.

15. 16. 17.

Record your answers for Questions 18–21 on a separate sheet of paper.

SAMPLE

Invertebrates 169

Part 1 Multiple Choice

1. C
2. D
3. C
4. B
5. D

Part 2 Short Response

6. efficiency $= \frac{\text{power output}}{\text{power input}} \times 100\,\%$,

so: power input

$= \frac{\text{power output}}{\text{efficiency}} \times 100\,\%$

$= \frac{30{,}000\text{ kW}}{85\%} \times 100\,\%$

$= 35{,}300\text{ kW}$

7. The kinetic energy of the coasting bicycle is converted into electrical energy if the generator is turned on. The bicycle will coast farther if the generator is turned off and the generator is not reducing the kinetic energy at a quicker rate.

8. number of rotations

$= \left(\frac{\text{rotations}}{\text{second}}\right) \times (\text{seconds})$

$= \left(\frac{50\text{ rotations}}{\text{second}}\right) \times (3600\text{ seconds})$

$= 180{,}000$ rotations

chapter 8 Standardized Test Practice

Part 1 Multiple Choice

Record your answers on the answer sheet provided by your teacher or on a sheet of paper.

A group of students built a transformer by wrapping 50 turns of wire on one side of an iron ring to form the primary coil. They then wrapped 10 turns of wire around the opposite side to form the secondary coil. Their results are shown in the table below.

Use the table below to answer questions 1–3.

Voltage and Current in a Transformer

Trial	Input Voltage (V)	Primary Coil Current (A)	Output Voltage (V)	Secondary Coil Current (A)
1	5	0.1	1	0.5
2	10	0.2	2	1.0
3	20	0.2	4	1.0
4	50	0.5	10	2.5

1. What is the ratio of the input voltage to the output voltage for this transformer?
   A. 1:2.5 **C.** 5:1
   B. 4:1 **D.** 1:5

2. What is the ratio of the primary coil current to the secondary coil current?
   A. 1:2.5 **C.** 5:1
   B. 4:1 **D.** 1:5

3. The ratio of the secondary coil current to the primary coil current equals which of the following?
   A. the ratio of the secondary coil wire turns to the primary coil wire turns
   B. the ratio of the output voltage to the input voltage
   C. the ratio of the primary coil wire turns to the secondary wire turns
   D. It always equals one.

Use the figure below to answer questions 4 and 5.

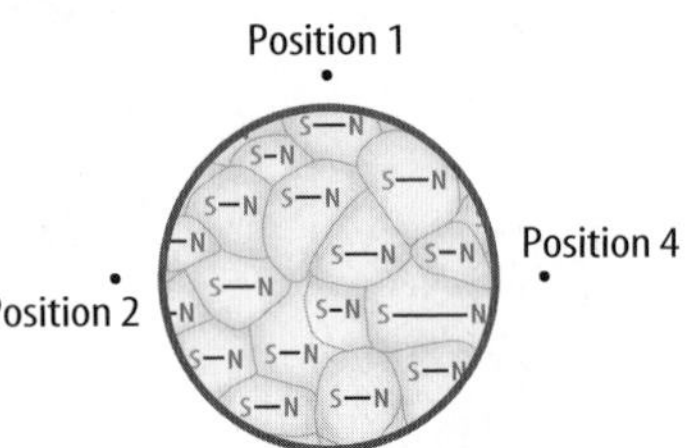

4. A steel paper clip is sitting on a desk. The figure above shows the magnetic domains in a section of the paper clip after the north pole of a magnet has been moved close to it. According to the diagram, the magnet's north pole is most likely at which of the following positions?
   A. position 1 **C.** position 3
   B. position 2 **D.** position 4

5. Which of the following diagrams shows the orientation of the needle of a compass that is placed at position 2?

A.

C.

B.

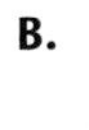

D.

Test-Taking Tip

Read All the Information If a question includes a text passage and a graphic, carefully read the information in the text passage and the graphic before answering the question.

Question 3 Review the information in the text above the table and the information in the table.

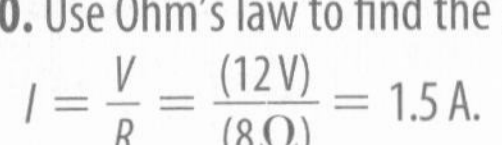

Part 2 Short Response/Grid In

9. First find the output voltage:
$\frac{\text{Voltage}_{\text{out}}}{\text{Voltage}_{\text{in}}} = \frac{\text{turns}_{\text{secondary}}}{\text{turns}_{\text{primary}}}$,
so: $\text{voltage}_{\text{out}} =$
$(\text{voltage}_{\text{in}}) \times \frac{(\text{turns}_{\text{secondary}})}{(\text{turns}_{\text{primary}})}$
$= (120\text{ V}) \times \frac{(2\text{ turns})}{(20\text{ turns})}$
$= 12\text{ V}$

10. Use Ohm's law to find the current:
$I = \frac{V}{R} = \frac{(12\text{ V})}{(8\,\Omega)} = 1.5\text{ A}.$

Part 3 Open Ended

11. No current will flow because the magnet and the coil are not moving relative to each other.

12. Only an alternating current can induce a voltage in the secondary coil of a transformer. A battery supplies a direct current, so the output voltage is zero and no current flows.

Part 2 Short Response/Grid In

Record your answers on the answer sheet provided by your teacher or on a sheet of paper.

6. A hydroelectric power plant uses water to spin a turbine attached to a generator. The generator produces 30,000 kW of electric power. If the turbine and generator are 85 percent efficient, how much power does the falling water supply to the turbine?

7. A bicycle has a small electric generator that is used to light a headlight. The generator is made to spin by rubbing against a wheel. Will the bicycle coast farther on a level surface if the light is turned on or turned off?

8. An electric motor rotates 60 times per second if the current source is 60 Hz alternating current. How many times will an electric motor rotate in one hour if the current source is changed to 50 Hz alternating current?

Use the figure below to answer questions 9 and 10.

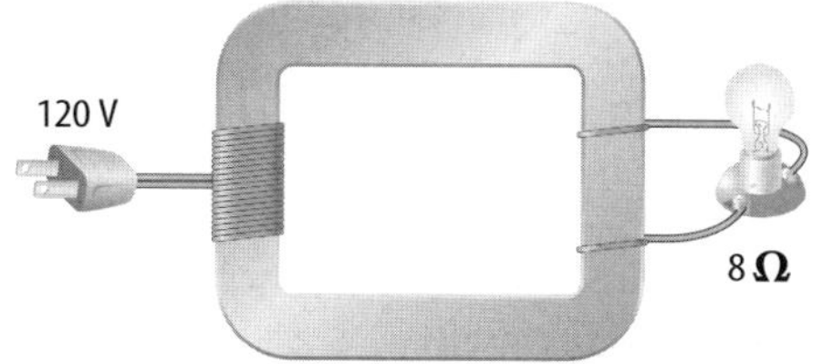

9. A step-down transformer is plugged into a 120-V electric outlet and a light is plugged into the transformer. The transformer has 20 turns on the primary coil and 2 turns on the secondary coil. What is the voltage at the output coil?

10. If the light has a resistance of 8 Ω, what is the current in the light?

Part 3 Open Ended

Record your answers on a sheet of paper.

11. A bar magnet is placed inside a wire coil. The bar magnet and coil are then carried across a room. Explain whether an electric current will flow in the coil as the magnet and coil are moving.

12. A student connects a battery to a step-up transformer in order to boost the voltage. Explain why a small electric motor does not spin when it is connected to the secondary coil of the transformer.

Use the figure below to answer question 13.

Effect of Rotation on Generator Voltage

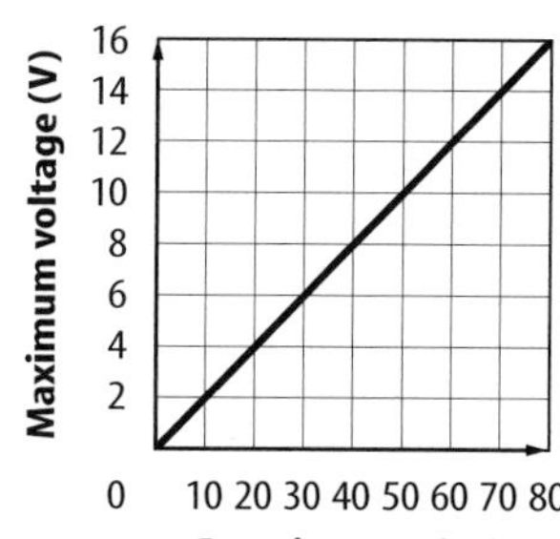

13. The graphic above shows how the voltage produced by a generator depends on the rotation rate of the coil. Explain whether this generator could produce household AC current which is 120 V at 60 Hz.

14. Describe how a permanent magnet is similar to and different from a piece of unmagnetized iron.

15. Compare and contrast the behavior and properties of positive and negative electric charges with north and south magnetic poles.

13. When the generator is rotating at 60 Hz, it produces 12 V. Therefore this generator could not produce household AC current.

14. Both a permanent magnet and the unmagnetized iron contain magnetic domains. In the permanent magnet, most of the domains are aligned so their north poles point in the same direction. In the unmagnetized iron, the poles of the domains point in random directions. The magnet is surrounded by a magnetic field, and the iron isn't.

15. Similarities: Types of electric charge exist, positive and negative. Two types of magnetic poles exist, north and south. Electric charges exert forces on each other. Magnetic poles exert forces on each other. Like charges repel and unlike attract. Like poles repel, unlike attract. Differences: positive and negative charges exist separately, north and south poles don't exist separately.

Rubrics

The following rubrics are sample scoring devices for short response and open-ended questions.

Short Response

Points	Description
2	The student demonstrates a thorough understanding of the science of the task. The response may contain minor flaws that do not detract from the demonstration of a thorough understanding.
1	The student has provided a response that is only partially correct.
0	The student has provided a completely incorrect solution or no response at all.

Open Ended

Points	Description
4	The student demonstrates a thorough understanding of the science of the task. The response may contain minor flaws that do not detract from the demonstration of a thorough understanding.
3	The student demonstrates an understanding of the science of the task. The response is essentially correct and demonstrates an essential but less than thorough understanding of the science.
2	The student demonstrates only a partial understanding of the science of the task. Although the student may have used the correct approach to a solution or may have provided a correct solution, the work lacks an essential understanding of the underlying science concepts.
1	The student demonstrates a very limited understanding of the science of the task. The response is incomplete and exhibits many flaws.
0	The student provides a completely incorrect solution or no response at all.

Energy Sources

BIG Idea The energy in an energy source is transformed into other forms of energy that are used by humans.

	Content Standards	Learning Objectives	Resources to Assess Mastery
Section 1	**5–8:** UCP.1–3, 5; A.1, 2; B.1, 3; D.1, 2; F.2 **9–12:** UCP.1–3, 5; A.1, 2; B.2, 6; D.1–3	**Fossil Fuels** 1. **Discuss** properties and uses of fossil fuels. 2. **Explain** how fossil fuels are formed. 3. **Describe** how the chemical energy in fossil fuels is converted into electrical energy. ***Main Idea*** Burning fossil fuels produces thermal energy that is converted into other useful forms of energy.	**Formative Assessment** Reading Check, p. 259 Section Review, p. 263 **Summative Assessment** *ExamView® Assessment Suite*
Section 2	**5–8:** UCP.1–3, 5; A.1, 2; B.1; F.2, 4 **9–12:** UCP.1–3, 5; A.1, 2; B.1, 2; F.2, 4	**Nuclear Eenrgy** 4. **Explain** how a nuclear reactor converts nuclear energy to thermal energy. 5. **Describe** advantages and disadvantages of using nuclear energy to produce electricity. 6. **Discuss** nuclear fusion as a possible energy source. ***Main Idea*** Nuclear power plants convert thermal energy produced by the fission of uranium atoms into electrical energy.	**Formative Assessment** Reading Check, pp. 266, 269 Section Review, p. 270 **Summative Assessment** *ExamView® Assessment Suite*
Section 3	**5–8:** UCP.1–3, 5; A.1, 2; D.1, 2; F.2, 4 **9–12:** UCP.1–3, 5; A.1, 2; D.1–3; F.2, 4 See pp. 16T–17T for a Key to Standards.	**Renewable Energy Sources** 7. **Analyze** the need for alternate energy sources. 8. **Describe** alternate methods for generating electricity. 9. **Compare** the advantages and disadvantages of various alternate energy sources. ***Main Idea*** Renewable energy sources are not used up because they are replaced as they are used.	**Formative Assessment** Reading Check, pp. 273, 275 Section Review, p. 276 **Summative Chapter Assessment** MindJogger, Ch. 9 *ExamView® Assessment Suite* Leveled Chapter Test Test A L1 Test B L2 Test C L3 Test Practice, pp. 284–285

Suggested Pacing				
Period	**Instruction**	**Labs**	**Review & Assessment**	**Total**
Single	3 days	6 days	2 days	11 days
Block	1.5 blocks	3 blocks	1 block	5.5 blocks

Core Instruction	Leveled Resources	Leveled Labs	Pacing Period		Block
Student Text, pp. 254–263 Section Focus Transparency, Ch. 9, Section 1 Interactive Chalkboard, Ch. 9, Section 1 Differentiated Instruction, pp. 257, 258, 260, 262 Visualizing the Formation of Fossil Fuels, p. 258	**Chapter *Fast File* Resources** Directed Reading for Content Mastery , p. 20 [L1] Note-taking Worksheet, pp. 33–35 Reinforcement , p. 27 [L2] Enrichment , p. 30 [L3] **Reading Essentials,** p. 136 [L1] ELL **Science Notebook,** p. 93 ELL	**Launch Lab,** p. 255: scissors, coffee can with lid (2), paint (white, black), thermometer *25 min* [L2]	**1**	Section 1, pp. 225–258 (includes Launch Lab)	**1**
		MiniLAB, p. 259: candle, beaker, water, aluminum foil *25 min* [L2]	**2**	Section 1, pp. 259–263 (includes MiniLAB and Section Review)	
Student Text, pp. 264–270 Section Focus Transparency, Ch. 9, Section 2 Teaching Transparency, Ch. 9, Section 2 Interactive Chalkboard, Ch. 9, Section 2 Identifying Misconceptions, p. 267 Applying Science, p. 269 Differentiated Instruction, pp. 265, 268	**Chapter *Fast File* Resources** Directed Reading for Content Mastery , p. 20 [L1] Note-taking Worksheet, pp. 33–35 Reinforcement , p. 28 [L2] Enrichment , p. 31 [L3] **Reading Essentials,** p. 143 [L1] ELL **Science Notebook,** p. 97 ELL		**3**	Section 2, pp. 264–266	**2**
			4	Section 2, pp. 267–270 (includes Section Review)	
Student Text, pp. 271–279 Section Focus Transparency, Ch. 9, Section 3 Interactive Chalkboard, Ch. 9, Section 3 Identifying Misconceptions, p. 273 Differentiated Instruction, pp. 272, 274, 275 Chapter Study Guide, p. 281	**Chapter *Fast File* Resources** Directed Reading for Content Mastery , pp. 21, 22 [L1] Note-taking Worksheet, pp. 33–35 Reinforcement , p. 29 [L2] Enrichment , p. 32 [L3] **Reading Essentials,** p. 149 [L1] ELL **Science Notebook,** p. 100 ELL	**MiniLAB,** p. 272: cloth, watch or clock, water, scissors *20 min* [L2]	**5**	Section 3, pp. 271–273 (includes MiniLAB)	**3**
		***Lab,** p. 277: small cardboard boxes,colored paper, paper (black, white), tape or glue, thermometer, watch with second hand *45 min* [L1] [L2] [L3] (Video Lab)	**6**	Section 3, pp. 274–276 (includes Section Review)	
			7	Lab:Solar Heating, p. 277	**4**
		***Lab,** pp. 278–279: Internet access *135 min* [L1] [L2] [L3]	**8**	Lab:How much does energy really cost?, pp. 278–279	
			9	Lab:How much does energy really cost?, pp. 278–279	**5**
			10	Lab:How much does energy really cost?, pp. 278–279	
		*Lab version A [L1] version B [L2] [L3]	**11**	Study Guide, Chapter Review, and Test Practice, pp. 281–285	**5.5**

Video Lab

Transparencies

Section Focus

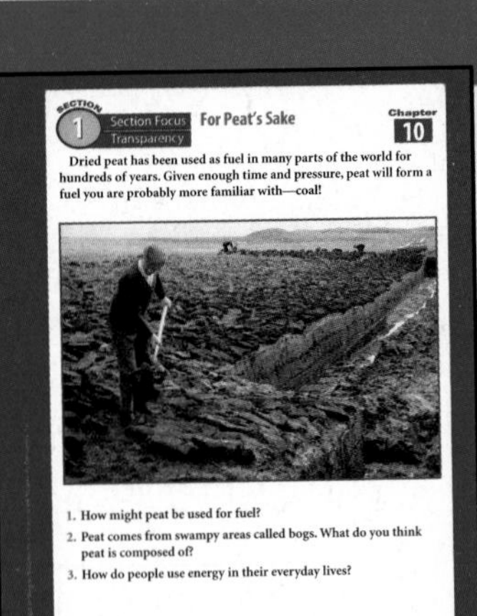
Section 1 Section Focus Transparency — For Peat's Sake — Chapter 10

Dried peat has been used as fuel in many parts of the world for hundreds of years. Given enough time and pressure, peat will form a fuel you are probably more familiar with—coal!

1. How might peat be used for fuel?
2. Peat comes from swampy areas called bogs. What do you think peat is composed of?
3. How do people use energy in their everyday lives?

L2

Section 2 Section Focus Transparency — Atomic Core

The first self-sustaining nuclear reaction was achieved in 1942 by a team of scientists led by Enrico Fermi. Today, nuclear power plants use the energy released by nuclear reactions to create electricity. The photo below shows the core of a nuclear reactor waiting to be lowered into position underwater.

1. How might nuclear energy be transformed into electrical energy?
2. How might nuclear power plants reduce pollution from fossil fuels? Do you think there are any disadvantages to nuclear power?

L2

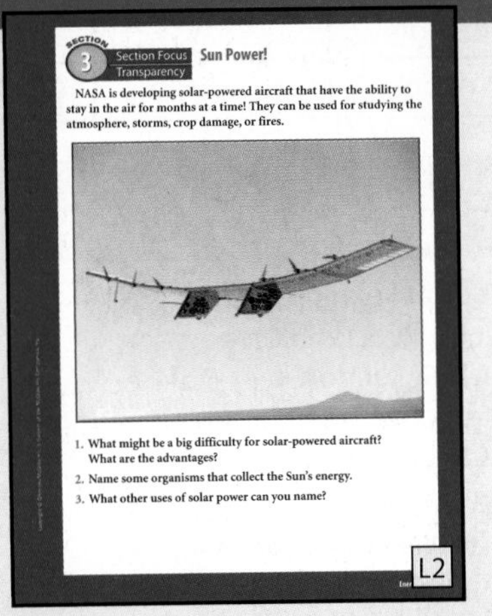
Section 3 Section Focus Transparency — Sun Power!

NASA is developing solar-powered aircraft that have the ability to stay in the air for months at a time! They can be used for studying the atmosphere, storms, crop damage, or fires.

1. What might be a big difficulty for solar-powered aircraft? What are the advantages?
2. Name some organisms that collect the Sun's energy.
3. What other uses of solar power can you name?

L2

This is a representation of key blackline masters available in the Teacher Classroom Resources. See Resource Manager boxes within the chapter for additional information.

Assessment

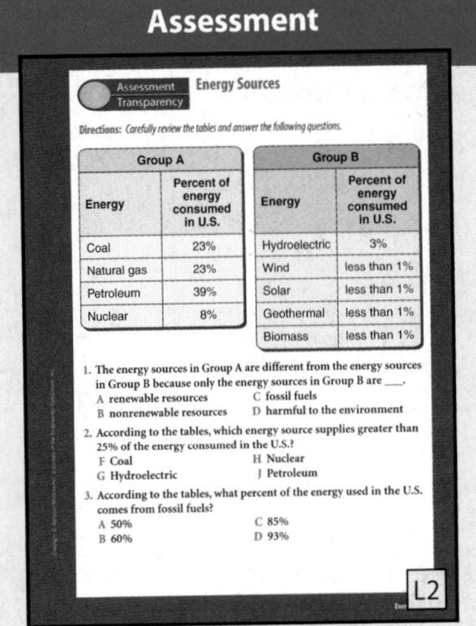
Assessment Transparency — Energy Sources

Directions: *Carefully review the tables and answer the following questions.*

Group A	
Energy	Percent of energy consumed in U.S.
Coal	23%
Natural gas	23%
Petroleum	39%
Nuclear	8%

Group B	
Energy	Percent of energy consumed in U.S.
Hydroelectric	3%
Wind	less than 1%
Solar	less than 1%
Geothermal	less than 1%
Biomass	less than 1%

1. The energy sources in Group A are different from the energy sources in Group B because only the energy sources in Group B are ____.
   A renewable resources C fossil fuels
   B nonrenewable resources D harmful to the environment
2. According to the tables, which energy source supplies greater than 25% of the energy consumed in the U.S.?
   F Coal H Nuclear
   G Hydroelectric J Petroleum
3. According to the tables, what percent of the energy used in the U.S. comes from fossil fuels?
   A 50% C 85%
   B 60% D 93%

L2

Teaching

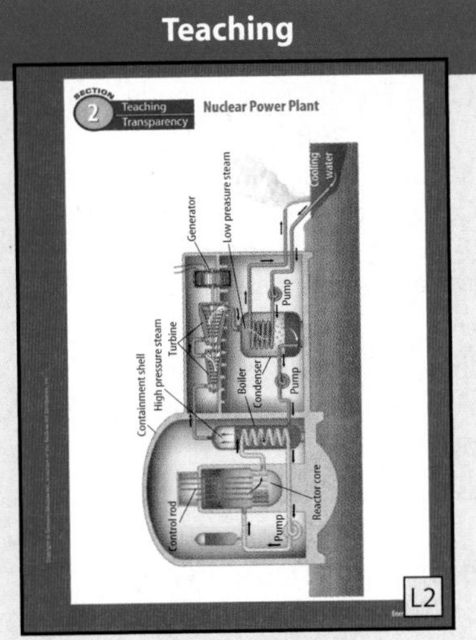
Section 2 Teaching Transparency — Nuclear Power Plant

Key to Teaching Strategies

The following designations will help you decide which activities are appropriate for your students.

- L1 Level 1 activities should be appropriate for students with learning difficulties.
- L2 Level 2 activities should be within the ability range of all students.
- L3 Level 3 activities are designed for above-average students.
- ELL ELL activities should be within the ability range of English Language Learners.
- COOP LEARN Cooperative Learning activities are designed for small group work.
- LS Multiple Learning Styles logos, as described on page 12T, are used throughout to indicate strategies that address different learning styles.
- P These strategies represent student products that can be placed into a best-work portfolio.
- PBL Problem-Based Learning activities apply real-world situations to learning.

Hands-on Activities

Student Text Lab Worksheet

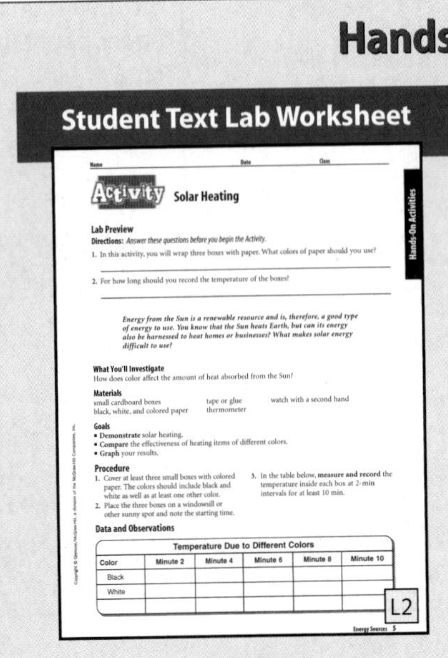
Name Date Class

Activity — Solar Heating

Lab Preview

Directions: *Answer these questions before you begin the Activity.*

1. In this activity, you will wrap three boxes with paper. What colors of paper should you use?
2. For how long should you record the temperature of the boxes?

Energy from the Sun is a renewable resource and is, therefore, a good type of energy to use. You know that the Sun heats Earth, but can its energy also be harnessed to heat homes or businesses? What makes solar energy difficult to use?

What You'll Investigate

How does color affect the amount of heat absorbed from the Sun?

Materials

small cardboard boxes; black, white, and colored paper; tape or glue; thermometer; watch with a second hand

Goals

- **Demonstrate** solar heating.
- **Compare** the effectiveness of heating items of different colors.
- **Graph** your results.

Procedure

1. Cover at least three small boxes with colored paper. The colors should include black and white as well as at least one other color.
2. Place the three boxes on a windowsill or other sunny spot and note the starting time.
3. In the table below, **measure and record** the temperature inside each box at 2-min intervals for at least 10 min.

Data and Observations

Temperature Due to Different Colors					
Color	Minute 2	Minute 4	Minute 6	Minute 8	Minute 10
Black					
White					

Hands-On Activities — Energy Sources 5 — L2

Laboratory Activities

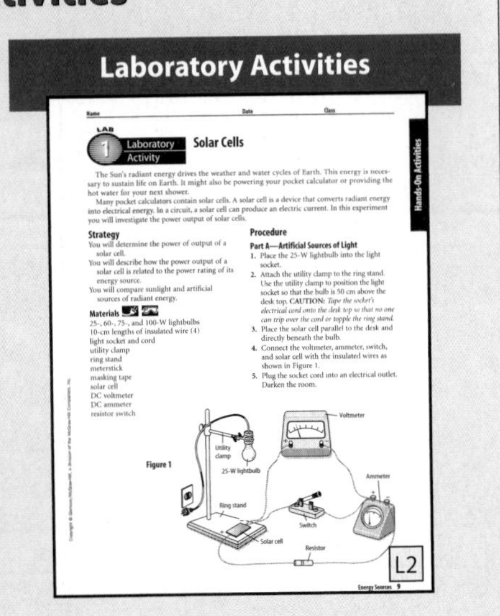
Name Date Class

Lab 1 Laboratory Activity — Solar Cells

The Sun's radiant energy drives the weather and water cycles of Earth. This energy is necessary to sustain life on Earth. It might also be powering your pocket calculator or providing the hot water for your next shower.

Many pocket calculators contain solar cells. A solar cell is a device that converts radiant energy into electrical energy. In a circuit, a solar cell can produce an electric current. In this experiment you will investigate the power output of solar cells.

Strategy

You will determine the power of output of a solar cell.
You will describe how the power output of a solar cell is related to the power rating of its energy source.
You will compare sunlight and artificial sources of radiant energy.

Materials

25-, 60-, 75-, and 100-W lightbulbs; 10-cm lengths of insulated wire (4); light socket and cord; utility clamp; ring stand; meterstick; masking tape; solar cell; DC voltmeter; DC ammeter; resistor switch

Procedure

Part A—Artificial Sources of Light

1. Place the 25-W lightbulb into the light socket.
2. Attach the utility clamp to the ring stand. Use the utility clamp to position the light socket so that the bulb is 50 cm above the desk top. **CAUTION:** *Tape the socket's electrical cord onto the desk top so that no one can trip over the cord or topple the ring stand.*
3. Place the solar cell parallel to the desk and directly beneath the bulb.
4. Connect the voltmeter, ammeter, switch, and solar cell with the insulated wires as shown in Figure 1.
5. Plug the socket cord into an electrical outlet. Darken the room.

Figure 1

Hands-On Activities — Energy Sources 9 — L2

Resource Manager

Meeting Different Ability Levels

Content Outline

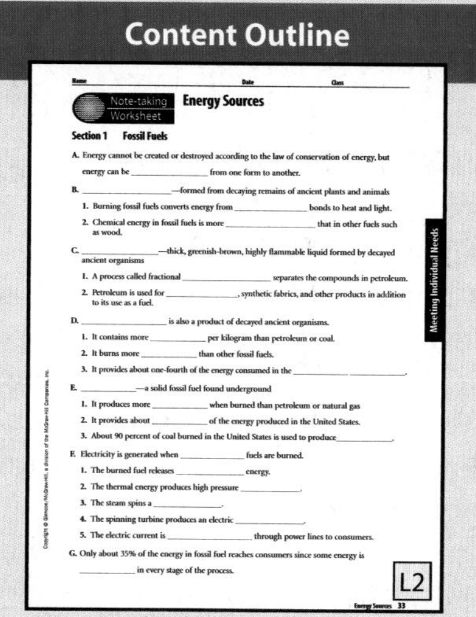

Name Date Class

Note-taking Worksheet **Energy Sources**

Section 1 Fossil Fuels

A. Energy cannot be created or destroyed according to the law of conservation of energy, but energy can be ________ from one form to another.

B. ________—formed from decaying remains of ancient plants and animals

1. Burning fossil fuels converts energy from ________ bonds to heat and light.
2. Chemical energy in fossil fuels is more ________ that in other fuels such as wood.

C. ________—thick, greenish-brown, highly flammable liquid formed by decayed ancient organisms

1. A process called fractional ________ separates the compounds in petroleum.
2. Petroleum is used for ________, synthetic fabrics, and other products in addition to its use as a fuel.

D. ________ is also a product of decayed ancient organisms.

1. It contains more ________ per kilogram than petroleum or coal.
2. It burns more ________ than other fossil fuels.
3. It provides about one-fourth of the energy consumed in the ________.

E. ________—a solid fossil fuel found underground

1. It produces more ________ when burned than petroleum or natural gas
2. It provides about ________ of the energy produced in the United States.
3. About 90 percent of coal burned in the United States is used to produce________.

F. Electricity is generated when ________ fuels are burned.

1. The burned fuel releases ________ energy.
2. The thermal energy produces high pressure ________.
3. The steam spins a ________.
4. The spinning turbine produces an electric ________.
5. The electric current is ________ through power lines to consumers.

G. Only about 35% of the energy in fossil fuel reaches consumers since some energy is ________ in every stage of the process.

L2

Energy Sources 33

Reinforcement

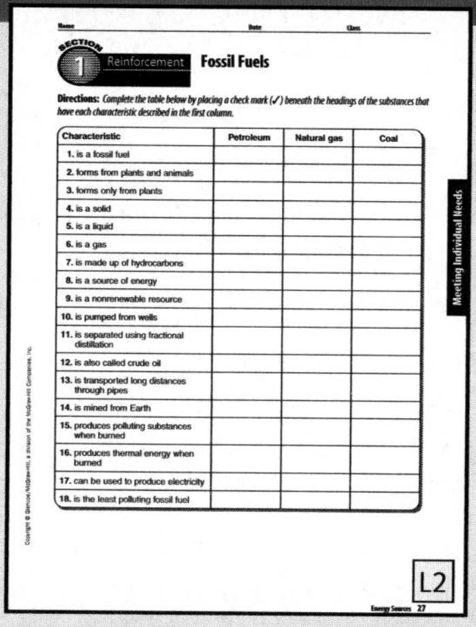

Name Date Class

SECTION 1 Reinforcement **Fossil Fuels**

Directions: Complete the table below by placing a check mark (✓) beneath the headings of the substances that have each characteristic described in the first column.

Characteristic	Petroleum	Natural gas	Coal
1. is a fossil fuel			
2. forms from plants and animals			
3. forms only from plants			
4. is a solid			
5. is a liquid			
6. is a gas			
7. is made up of hydrocarbons			
8. is a source of energy			
9. is a nonrenewable resource			
10. is pumped from wells			
11. is separated using fractional distillation			
12. is also called crude oil			
13. is transported long distances through pipes			
14. is mined from Earth			
15. produces polluting substances when burned			
16. produces thermal energy when burned			
17. can be used to produce electricity			
18. is the least polluting fossil fuel			

L2

Energy Sources 27

Enrichment

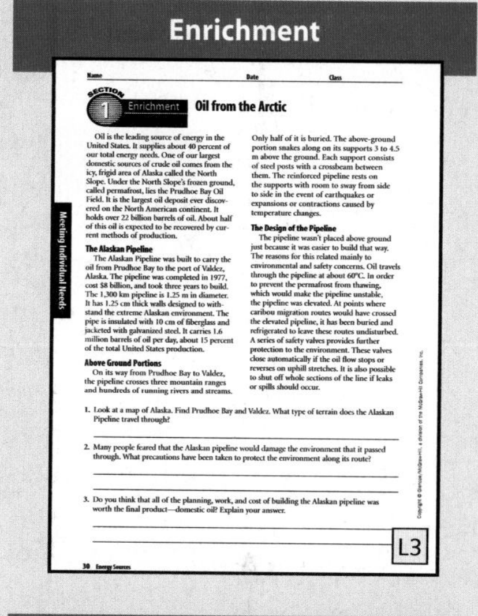

Name Date Class

SECTION 1 Enrichment **Oil from the Arctic**

Oil is the leading source of energy in the United States. It supplies about 40 percent of our total energy needs. One of our largest domestic sources of crude oil comes from the icy, frigid area of Alaska called the North Slope. Under the North Slope's frozen ground, called permafrost, lies the Prudhoe Bay Oil Field. It is the largest oil deposit ever discovered on the North American continent. It holds over 22 billion barrels of oil. About half of this oil is expected to be recovered by current methods of production.

The Alaskan Pipeline

The Alaskan Pipeline was built to carry the oil from Prudhoe Bay to the port of Valdez, Alaska. The pipeline was completed in 1977, cost $8 billion, and took three years to build. The 1,300 km pipeline is 1.25 m in diameter. It has 1.25 cm thick walls designed to withstand the extreme Alaskan environment. The pipe is insulated with 10 cm of fiberglass and jacketed with galvanized steel. It carries 1.6 million barrels of oil per day, about 15 percent of the total United States production.

Above Ground Portions

On its way from Prudhoe Bay to Valdez, the pipeline crosses three mountain ranges and hundreds of running rivers and streams. Only half of it is buried. The above-ground portion snakes along on its supports 3 to 4.5 m above the ground. Each support consists of steel posts with a crossbeam between them. The reinforced pipeline rests on the supports with room to sway from side to side in the event of earthquakes or expansions or contractions caused by temperature changes.

The Design of the Pipeline

The pipeline wasn't placed above ground just because it was easier to build that way. The reasons for this related mainly to environmental and safety concerns. Oil travels through the pipeline at about 60°C. In order to prevent the permafrost from thawing, which would make the pipeline unstable, the pipeline was elevated. At points where caribou migration routes would have crossed the elevated pipeline, it has been buried and refrigerated to leave these routes undisturbed. A series of safety valves provides further protection to the environment. These valves close automatically if the oil flow stops or reverses on uphill stretches. It is also possible to shut off whole sections of the line if leaks or spills should occur.

1. Look at a map of Alaska. Find Prudhoe Bay and Valdez. What type of terrain does the Alaskan Pipeline travel through?
2. Many people feared that the Alaskan pipeline would damage the environment that it passed through. What precautions have been taken to protect the environment along its route?
3. Do you think that all of the planning, work, and cost of building the Alaskan pipeline was worth the final product—domestic oil? Explain your answer.

L3

30 Energy Sources

Directed Reading (English/Spanish)

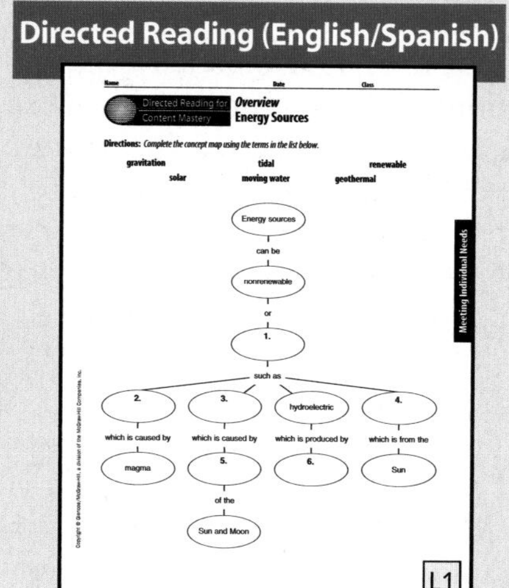

Name Date Class

Directed Reading for Content Mastery ***Overview*** **Energy Sources**

Directions: Complete the concept map using the terms in the list below.

gravitation, tidal, renewable, solar, moving water, geothermal

Energy sources
can be
nonrenewable
or
1.
such as
2.
3.
hydroelectric
4.
which is caused by
which is caused by
which is produced by
which is from the
magma
5.
6.
Sun
of the
Sun and Moon

L1

Energy Sources 19

Study Guide

Study Guide
Features
• Contains a study guide page for each section of the chapter
• Reviews key concepts
• Includes answer pages
L2

Reading Essentials

Reading Essentials for Glencoe Science
An Interactive Student Workbook
Features
• Condensed core content
• Actively involves students in reading
• Reinforces key vocabulary
L1

Assessment

Test Practice Workbook

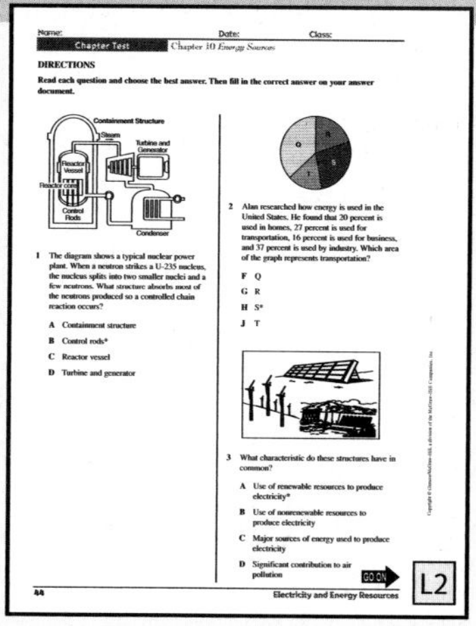

Name: Date: Class:

Chapter Test — Chapter 10 Energy Sources

DIRECTIONS

Read each question and choose the best answer. Then fill in the correct answer on your answer document.

1 The diagram shows a typical nuclear power plant. When a neutron strikes a U-235 nucleus, the nucleus splits into two smaller nuclei and a few neutrons. What structure absorbs most of the neutrons produced so a controlled chain reaction occurs?

A Containment structure
B Control rods*
C Reactor vessel
D Turbine and generator

2 Alan researched how energy is used in the United States. He found that 20 percent is used in homes, 27 percent is used for transportation, 16 percent is used for business, and 37 percent is used by industry. Which area of the graph represents transportation?

F Q
G R
H S*
J T

3 What characteristic do these structures have in common?

A Use of renewable resources to produce electricity*
B Use of nonrenewable resources to produce electricity
C Major sources of energy used to produce electricity
D Significant contribution to air pollution

L2

44 Electricity and Energy Resources

Chapter Review

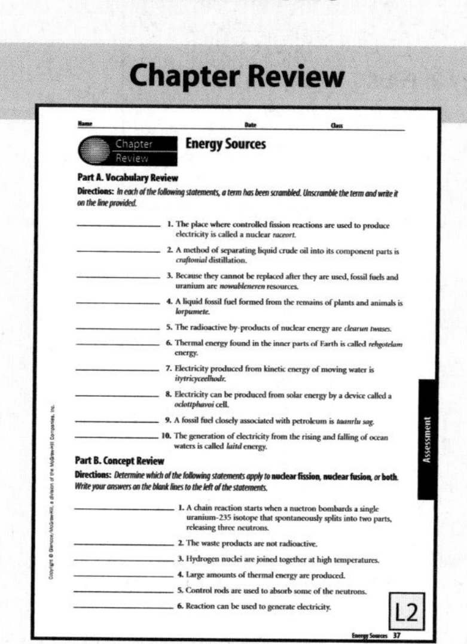

Name Date Class

Chapter Review **Energy Sources**

Part A. Vocabulary Review

Directions: In each of the following statements, a term has been scrambled. Unscramble the term and write it on the line provided.

1. The place where controlled fission reactions are used to produce electricity is called a nuclear *racoent*.
2. A method of separating liquid crude oil into its component parts is *craftionial* distillation.
3. Because they cannot be replaced after they are used, fossil fuels and uranium are *nonwablerenen* resources.
4. A liquid fossil fuel formed from the remains of plants and animals is *lorpumete*.
5. The radioactive by-products of nuclear energy are *clearun twases*.
6. Thermal energy found in the inner parts of Earth is called *rehgotelom* energy.
7. Electricity produced from kinetic energy of moving water is *ityrcicyrdhoelc*.
8. Electricity can be produced from solar energy by a device called a *oclotphavoi* cell.
9. A fossil fuel closely associated with petroleum is *taurelu sag*.
10. The generation of electricity from the rising and falling of ocean waters is called *lidat* energy.

Part B. Concept Review

Directions: Determine which of the following statements apply to nuclear fission, nuclear fusion, or both. Write your answers on the blank lines to the left of the statements.

1. A chain reaction starts when a neutron bombards a single uranium-235 isotope that spontaneously splits into two parts, releasing three neutrons.
2. The waste products are not radioactive.
3. Hydrogen nuclei are joined together at high temperatures.
4. Large amounts of thermal energy are produced.
5. Control rods are used to absorb some of the neutrons.
6. Reaction can be used to generate electricity.

L2

Energy Sources 37

Chapter Tests

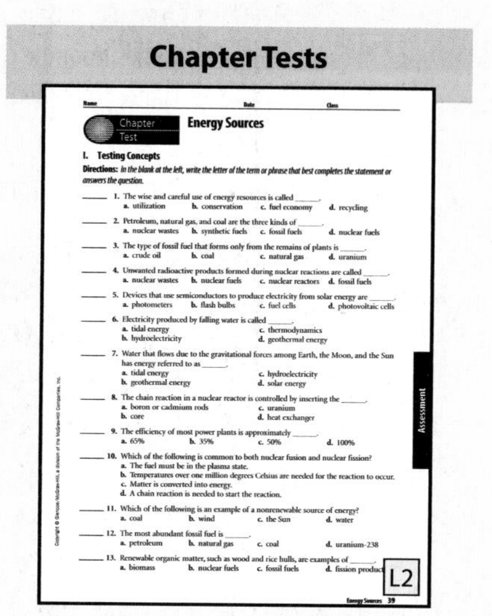

Name Date Class

Chapter Test **Energy Sources**

I. Testing Concepts

Directions: In the blank at the left, write the letter of the term or phrase that best completes the statement or answers the question.

1. The wise and careful use of energy resources is called ____. a. utilization b. conservation c. fuel economy d. recycling
2. Petroleum, natural gas, and coal are the three kinds of ____. a. nuclear wastes b. synthetic fuels c. fossil fuels d. nuclear fuels
3. The type of fossil fuel that forms only from the remains of plants is ____. a. crude oil b. coal c. natural gas d. uranium
4. Unwanted radioactive products formed during nuclear reactions are called ____. a. nuclear wastes b. nuclear fuels c. nuclear reactors d. fossil fuels
5. Devices that use semiconductors to produce electricity from solar energy are ____. a. photometers b. flash bulbs c. fuel cells d. photovoltaic cells
6. Electricity produced by falling water is called ____. a. tidal energy b. hydroelectricity c. thermodynamics d. geothermal energy
7. Water that flows due to the gravitational forces among Earth, the Moon, and the Sun has energy referred to as ____. a. tidal energy b. geothermal energy c. hydroelectricity d. solar energy
8. The chain reaction in a nuclear reactor is controlled by inserting the ____. a. boron or cadmium rods b. core c. uranium d. heat exchanger
9. The efficiency of most power plants is approximately ____. a. 65% b. 35% c. 50% d. 100%
10. Which of the following is common to both nuclear fusion and nuclear fission? a. The fuel must be in the plasma state. b. Temperatures over one million degrees Celsius are needed for the reaction to occur. c. Matter is converted into energy. d. A chain reaction is needed to start the reaction.
11. Which of the following is an example of a nonrenewable source of energy? a. coal b. wind c. the Sun d. water
12. The most abundant fossil fuel is ____. a. petroleum b. natural gas c. coal d. uranium-238
13. Renewable organic matter, such as wood and rice hulls, are examples of ____. a. biomass b. nuclear fuels c. fossil fuels d. fission products

L2

Energy Sources 39

Science Content Background

section 1 Fossil Fuels

Making Fossil Fuels

Fossil fuels were once living organisms that obtained energy directly or indirectly from the Sun and can therefore be considered a type of solar energy. Unlike the direct use of solar energy, burning fossil fuels produces carbon dioxide gas and other pollutants.

Kerosene was once the most important product from petroleum because of its use in kerosene lanterns. Kerosene is now used mainly as a fuel for jet engines.

Generating Electricity

Whether using fossil fuels, geothermal energy, or nuclear power, the generation of electricity involves heating water to produce steam to turn turbines. Hydropower, wind, and tidal energy turn turbines, but water is not heated to produce steam.

Teacher to Teacher
Erin Peters,
Lead Science Teacher
Williamsburg Middle School
Arlington, VA

"I ask the students to think of an activity such as doing your homework. Trace the energy sources back to the Sun. For example, pushing your pencil is mechanical energy, which comes from the chemical energy of eating lunch, which comes from food, which gets its energy from the Sun."

Erin Peters

section 2 Nuclear Energy

Using Nuclear Energy

When nuclear fission and nuclear fusion occur, a small amount of mass is converted into energy. The connection between mass and energy is given by Einstein's famous equation $E=mc^2$. This equation showed that a small amount of mass is converted into an enormous amount of energy.

Gamma ray exposure is sometimes compared to the equivalent exposure in X rays. For example, a nuclear weapons worker may have had a yearly dose that is equivalent to one chest X ray. Compared to X rays or other types of nuclear radiation, gamma rays are the most energetic. As a result, they penetrate the farthest into living tissue and can cause the most biological damage.

France is the world leader in electrical power generation from nuclear fission. Approximately three-quarters of France's electrical energy is generated by this process.

The only approved permanent storage site in the United States for radioactive wastes is Yucca Mountain in Nevada. Some scientists believe this is a good site because it is far from major populations, it has low levels of rainfall, and the water table is very deep.

section 3

Renewable Energy Sources

Energy from the Sun

The materials required to generate electricity from solar energy are expensive. The materials to use the Sun's energy for heating are, however, relatively inexpensive. Piping and a box with a glass roof are the fundamental parts of many solar water heaters. Currently about one million homes in the United States use solar water heating. Some states, such as North Carolina and Arizona, give tax incentives for the installation of solar water heaters. Passive solar heating of spaces in houses is another low-cost way to use the Sun's energy. New houses are increasingly being designed with windows facing the south to absorb the Sun's energy in wintertime. Overhangs on the houses prevent the Sun's entry in the summertime.

Energy from Inside Earth

You don't need to live near a volcano to use geothermal energy. Heat pumps, in use in 400,000 United States homes, take advantage of fairly constant below-ground temperatures. The temperature range in the first ten feet of soil is 10° to 15.5°C (50° to 60°F). This usually means the soil is warmer than the winter air and cooler than the summer air. In a heat pump, air either gains or loses heat to the ground before entering a heating or cooling unit.

Alternative Fuels

When animal manure is decomposed by anaerobic fermentation, methane gas is produced. This can be collected and used as a source of fuel for, among other things, generating electricity. Farms with 700 head of cattle can produce enough methane to power approximately 50 homes. Methane is a greenhouse gas, and this process helps prevent additional methane from entering the atmosphere.

chapter content resources

Internet Resources

For additional content background, visit gpscience.com to:

- access your book online
- find references to related articles in popular science magazines
- access Web links with related content background
- access current events with science journal topics

Print Resources

Achieving Energy Independence—One Step at a Time, by Jeffrey R. Yago, Dunimis Technology, 1999

Power with Nature: Solar and Wind Energy Demystified, by Rex A. Ewing, PixyJack Press, 2003

Alternative Energy: Facts, Statistics, and Issues, by Paula Berinstein, Oryx Press, 2001

Tomorrow's Energy: Hydrogen, Fuel Cells, and the Prospects for a Cleaner Planet, by Peter Hoffmann, MIT Press, 2002

Bill Banaszewski/Visuals Unlimited

About the Photo

Auto Assembly Line Robots do the welding on automobile frames at this automobile assembly plant in Chicago, Illinois. This plant opened in 1924 and currently produces three different vehicles. More than 66 cars per hour can be assembled. A typical automobile body might have hundreds of spot welds. At this plant, over 480 robots do all the welding.

Science Journal Student responses will vary. The majority of the United States uses fossil fuels to generate electrical power, but there are areas of the country that have other energy sources.

BIG Idea

Useful Thermal Energy Energy comes in different forms, but perhaps the most useful form of energy is thermal energy. Thermal energy produced by burning fossil fuels and by the nuclear fission of uranium is used to generate almost 90 percent of the electrical energy used in the United States. Almost all vehicles in the United States are powered by the thermal energy produced by burning fossil fuels. Thermal energy is also used to heat buildings and power other engines and machines. Over 90 percent of the energy used in the United States is either thermal energy or a form of energy that comes from the conversion of thermal energy.

Introduce the Chapter Remind students that energy cannot be created or destroyed. Ask students to identify the forms of energy produced by various appliances they use. Then, ask students to trace back the energy conversions that produce these forms of energy as far as they can.

chapter 9

Energy Sources

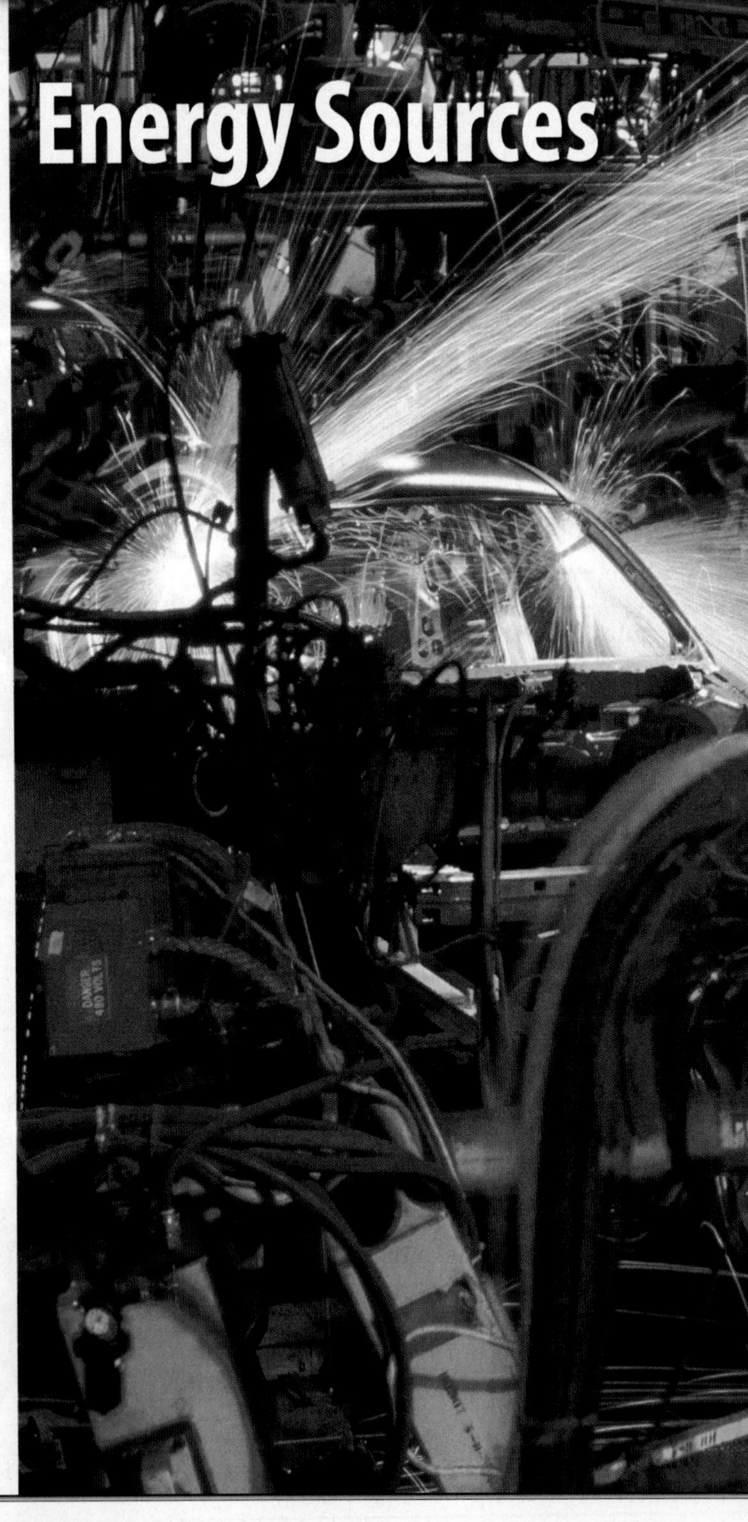

BIG Idea

The energy in an energy source is transformed into other forms of energy that are used by humans.

9.1 Fossil Fuels

MAIN Idea Burning fossil fuels produces thermal energy that is converted into other useful forms of energy

9.2 Nuclear Energy

MAIN Idea Nuclear power plants convert thermal energy produced by the fission of uranium atoms into electrical energy.

9.3 Renewable Energy Sources

MAIN Idea Renewable energy sources are not used up because they are replaced as they are used.

Doing the Robot

A car uses the chemical energy in gasoline to make it run. But energy is also needed to make a car. For example, these welding robots use energy to join pieces of a car together. Even the materials that a car is made from, such as aluminum and plastic, are produced using energy.

Science Journal

Describe how your day would be different if the electric power were off all day.

254

Interactive Chalkboard

This CD-ROM is an editable Microsoft® PowerPoint® presentation that includes:

- an editable presentation for every chapter
- additional chapter questions
- animated graphics
- image bank
- links to gpscience.com

Start-Up Activities

Heating with Solar Energy

The Sun constantly bathes our planet with enormous amounts of energy. This energy can be captured and used to make electricity, heat homes, and provide hot water. How can the Sun's energy be used to heat water?

1. Use scissors to poke a small hole in the center of two coffee can lids.
2. Fill a coffee can that has been painted black with water at room temperature. Snap on the lid and push a thermometer through the hole in the lid. Record the temperature.
3. Repeat step 2 using the coffee can that has been painted white.
4. Place both cans in direct sunlight. After 15 min, record the temperature of the water in both cans again.
5. **Think Critically** Write a paragraph explaining why the temperature change differed between the two cans.

Preview this chapter's content and activities at gpscience.com

FOLDABLES™ Study Organizer

Energy Sources There are many sources of energy. Make the following Foldable to help you organize information about various types of energy sources.

STEP 1 **Fold** a sheet of paper in half lengthwise. Make the back edge about 5 cm longer than the front edge.

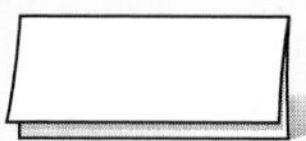

STEP 2 **Turn** the paper so the fold is on the bottom. Then **fold** it into thirds.

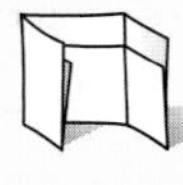

STEP 3 **Unfold and cut** only the top layer along both folds to make three tabs.

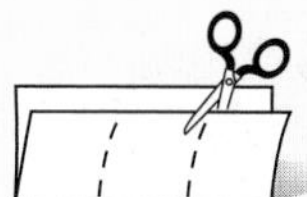

STEP 4 **Label** the Foldable as shown.

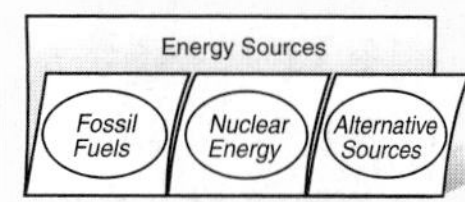

Summarize As you read this chapter, summarize important information about each type of energy source under the appropriate tab.

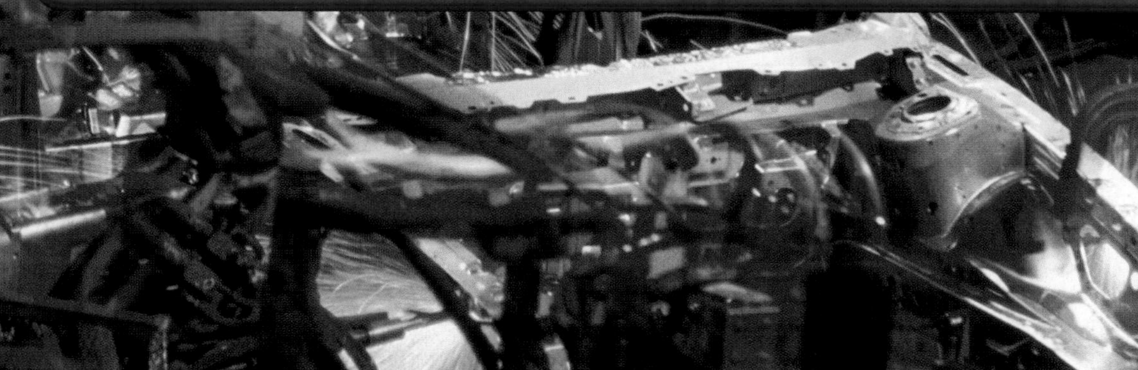

Purpose Use the Launch Lab to show students how one form of energy can be transformed into another form that we can use. L2 ELL LS **Kinesthetic**

Preparation To save time, you may want to paint coffee cans and cut holes in the lids ahead of time.

Materials scissors, coffee cans with lids, white paint, black paint, water, thermometer

Teaching Strategy Identify a place that gets direct sunlight where students can leave the cans for 15 minutes.

Think Critically

The temperature change is greater in the black can because the color black absorbs more energy than the color white.

Assessment

Process Ask students to make data tables and to record in the tables the temperature readings for each can every two minutes. Use **Performance Assessment in the Science Classroom**, p. 109.

Dinah Zike Study Fold

Student preparation materials for this Foldable are available in the Chapter *FAST FILE* Resources.

Additional Chapter Media

- Virtual Lab: *How much electricity is used in a house?*
- Video Lab: *Solar Heating*

section 1

Fossil Fuels

1 Motivate

INTERACTIVE CHALKBOARD
PowerPoint® Presentations

Bellringer

Section Focus Transparencies also are available on the Interactive Chalkboard CD-ROM. L2 ELL

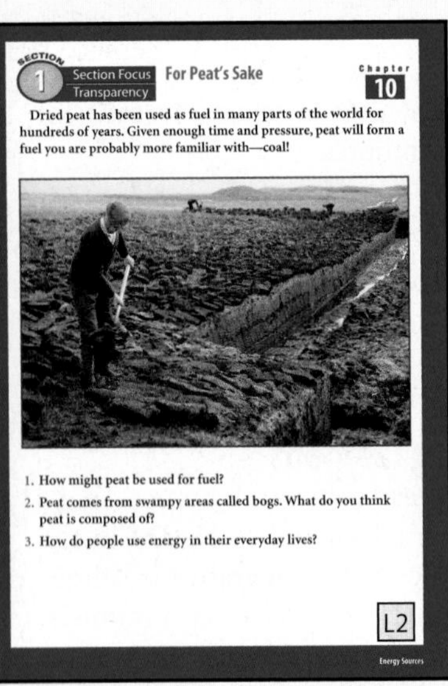
Section 1 Section Focus Transparency — For Peat's Sake — Chapter 10

Dried peat has been used as fuel in many parts of the world for hundreds of years. Given enough time and pressure, peat will form a fuel you are probably more familiar with—coal!

1. How might peat be used for fuel?
2. Peat comes from swampy areas called bogs. What do you think peat is composed of?
3. How do people use energy in their everyday lives?

L2

Energy Sources

Tie to Prior Knowledge

Energy Source Ask students to name the last time they rode in a bus or car. Tell them that the energy that made the vehicle move came from fossil fuels. In this section, they will learn about various types of fossil fuels that are useful sources of energy.

Reading Guide

What You'll Learn

- **Discuss** properties and uses of fossil fuels.
- **Explain** how fossil fuels are formed.
- **Describe** how the chemical energy in fossil fuels is converted into electrical energy.

Why It's Important

Fossil fuels are used to generate most of the energy you use every day.

Review Vocabulary

chemical potential energy: the energy stored in the chemical bonds between atoms in molecules

New Vocabulary

- fossil fuel
- petroleum
- nonrenewable resource

Figure 1 Energy is used in many ways.

Automobiles burn gasoline to provide energy.

Using Energy

How many different ways have you used energy today? You can see energy being used in many ways, throughout the day, such as those shown in **Figure 1.** Furnaces and stoves use thermal energy to heat buildings and cook food. Air conditioners use electrical energy to move thermal energy outdoors. Cars and other vehicles use mechanical energy to carry people and materials from one part of the country to another.

Transforming Energy According to the law of conservation of energy, energy cannot be created or destroyed. Energy can only be transformed, or converted, from one form to another. To use energy means to transform one form of energy to another form of energy that can perform a useful function. For example, energy is used when the chemical energy in fuels is transformed into thermal energy that is used to heat your home.

Sometimes energy is transformed into a form that isn't useful. For example, when an electric current flows through power lines, about 10 percent of the electrical energy is changed to thermal energy. This reduces the amount of useful electrical energy that is delivered to homes, schools, and businesses.

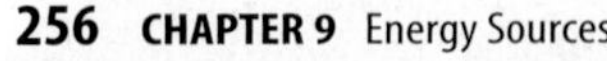

Power lines like these carry the electrical energy you use every day.

Section 1 Resource Manager

Chapter *FAST FILE* Resources
- Transparency Activity, p. 44
- Note-taking Worksheets, pp. 33–35
- Directed Reading for Content Mastery, pp. 19, 20
- MiniLAB, p. 3
- Enrichment, p. 30
- Reinforcement, p. 27

Cultural Diversity, p. 45, 49
Performance Assessment in the Science Classroom, p. 48
Science Inquiry Labs, pp. 31–32
Physical Science Critical Thinking/Problem Solving, p. 14

Energy Use in the United States More energy is used in the United States than in any other country in the world. **Figure 2** shows energy usage in the United States. About 20 percent of the energy is used in homes for heating and cooling, to run appliances, and to provide lighting and hot water. About 27 percent is used for transportation, powering vehicles such as cars, trucks, and aircraft. Another 16 percent is used by businesses to heat, cool, and light stores, shops, and office buildings. Finally, about 37 percent of this energy is used by industry and agriculture to manufacture products and produce food. **Figure 2** also shows the main sources of the energy used in the United States. Almost 85 percent of the energy used in the United States comes from burning petroleum, natural gas, and coal. Nuclear power plants provide about eight percent of the energy used in the United States.

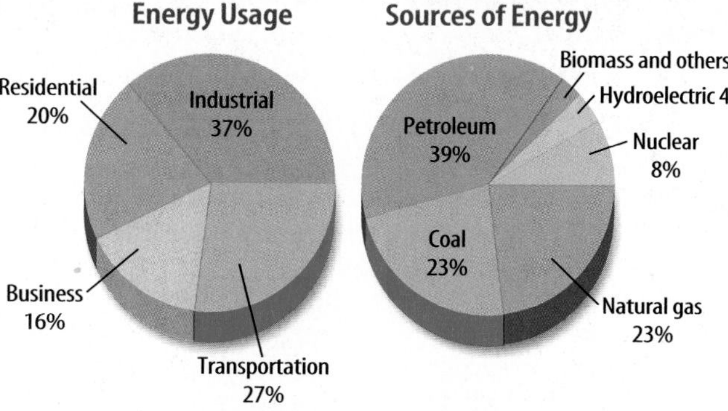

Figure 2 These circle graphs show where energy is used in the United States and sources of this energy.

Making Fossil Fuels

In one hour of freeway driving a car might use several gallons of gasoline. It may be hard to believe that it took millions of years to make the fuels that are used to produce electricity, provide heat, and transport people and materials. **Figure 4** on the next page shows how coal, petroleum, and natural gas are formed by the decay of ancient plants and animals. Fuels such as petroleum, or oil, natural gas, and coal are called **fossil fuels** because they are formed from the decaying remains of ancient plants and animals.

Concentrated Energy Sources When fossil fuels are burned, carbon and hydrogen atoms combine with oxygen molecules in the air to form carbon dioxide and water molecules. This process converts the chemical potential energy that is stored in the chemical bonds between atoms to heat and light. Compared to other fuels such as wood, the chemical energy that is stored in fossil fuels is more concentrated. For example, burning 1 kg of coal releases two to three times as much energy as burning 1 kg of wood. **Figure 3** shows the amount of energy that is produced by burning different fossil fuels.

Figure 3 The bar graph shows the amount of energy released by burning one gram of four different fuels. **Determine** *the ratio of the energy content of natural gas to the energy content of wood.*

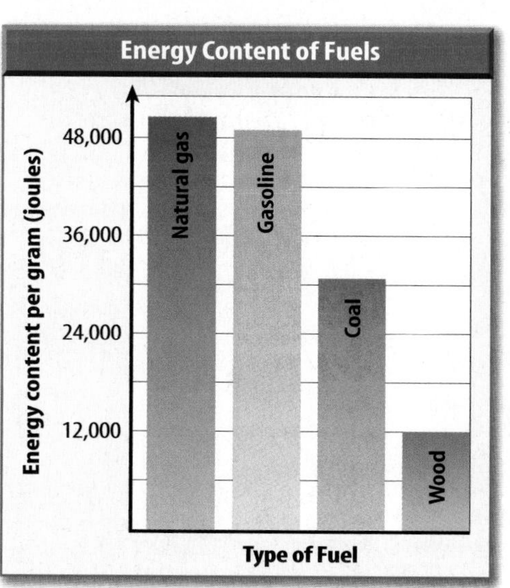

2 Teach

Fun Fact

Fossil fuels currently supply nearly 90 percent of all the energy consumed by the industrially developed nations of the world

Caption Answer

Figure 3 About 4:1

Discussion

Fossil Fuels Are fossil fuels still being made today? The physical and chemical processes that made fossil fuels are still acting on decaying organic matter on Earth's crust. However, the rate at which new fuel is being made is tiny compared with the rate at which it is being used. L3 LS **Logical-Mathematical**

Differentiated Instruction

Challenge Ask students to find out how much energy is used per person in other developed nations, compared with the amount used in the United States. Have students make a graph showing their results. In most other developed nations, about half as much energy is used per person as is used in the United States. L3 LS **Logical-Mathematical**

Curriculum Connection

Language Arts Power outages sometimes occur because of severe snowstorms, flooding, or other natural disasters. Have each student write a story about how he or she would survive an imaginary week-long loss of electricity, natural gas, and gasoline. Students should describe their daily routines and include ideas for alternate sources of energy. L2 LS **Linguistic** P

Visualizing the Formation of Fossil Fuels

Have students examine the pictures and read the captions. Then ask the following question.

Why do oil and gas sometimes bubble to the surface, while coal never does? Oil (a liquid) and natural gas (a gas) are less dense than the surrounding rock. Coal is a solid and its density is not low enough for it to rise to the surface.

Activity

Fossil Fuel Concentrations Divide the class into three groups. Assign each group a different fossil fuel: coal, oil, and natural gas. Have students in each group research the locations of deposits of the fuel and plot the distribution on an outline map of the world. Display the three maps and discuss which parts of the world have the largest concentrations of each fossil fuel. L2 LS **Visual-Spatial**

Differentiated Instruction

Challenge Have students research the discoveries of bog mummies that have been made by peat cutters in northern Europe where peat is still sometimes used as a fuel. Have students write reports on the conditions that caused the peat bogs to form and that also mummified the bodies. L3 LS **Linguistic**

NATIONAL GEOGRAPHIC

VISUALIZING THE FORMATION OF FOSSIL FUELS

Figure 4

Oil and natural gas form when organic matter on the ocean floor, gradually buried under additional layers of sediment, is chemically changed by heat and crushing pressure. The oil and gas may bubble to the surface or become trapped beneath a dense rock layer. Coal forms when peat—partially decomposed vegetation—is compressed by overlying sediments and transformed first into lignite (soft brown coal) and then into harder, bituminous (buh TYEW muh nus) coal. These two processes are shown below.

HOW OIL AND NATURAL GAS ARE FORMED

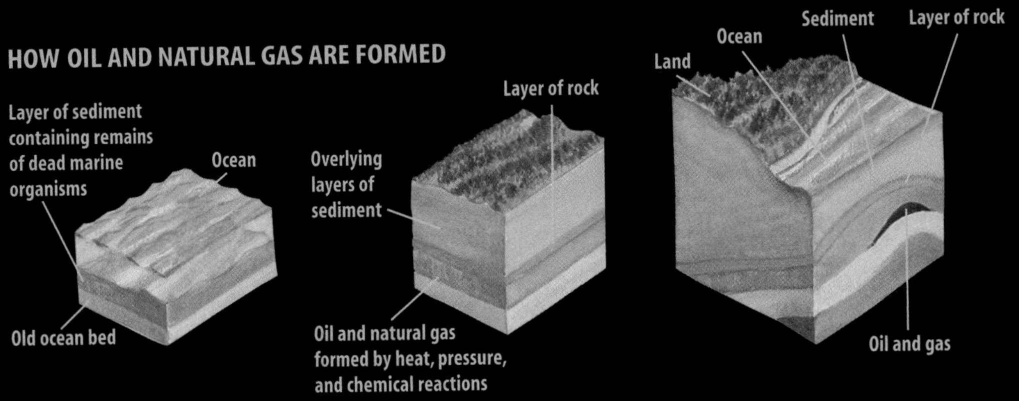

HOW COAL IS FORMED

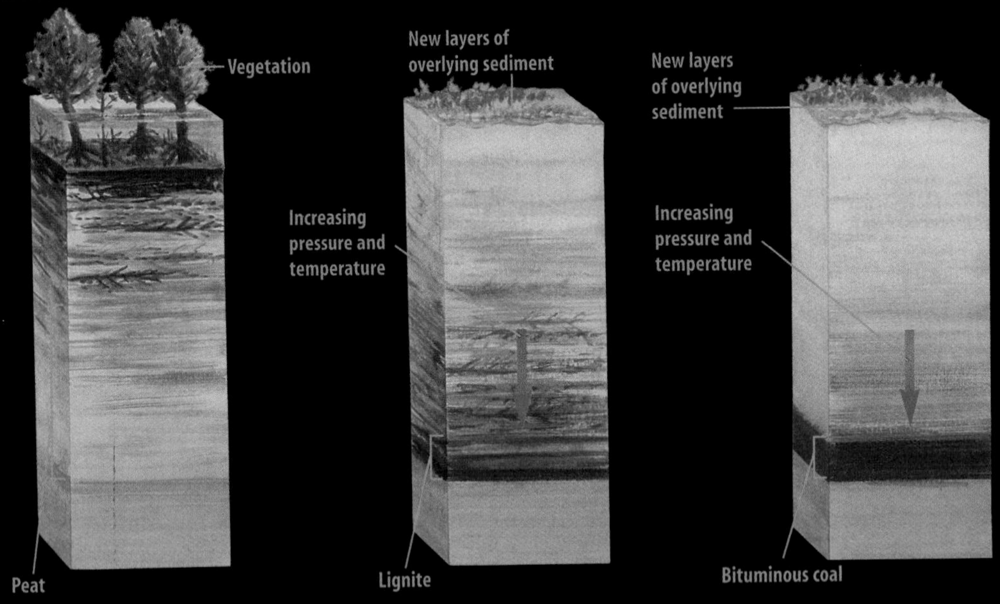

258 CHAPTER 9 Energy Sources

Teacher FYI

OPEC The Organization of Petroleum Exporting Countries (OPEC) is a group of eleven countries that own most of the world's crude oil reserves. They work together to coordinate petroleum policy. Member nations are Algeria, Indonesia, Iran, Iraq, Kuwait, Libya, Nigeria, Qatar, Saudi Arabia, the United Arab Emirates, and Venezuela.

Petroleum

Millions of gallons of petroleum, or crude oil, are pumped every day from wells deep in Earth's crust. **Petroleum** is a highly flammable liquid formed by decayed ancient organisms, such as microscopic plankton and algae. Petroleum is a mixture of thousands of chemical compounds. Most of these compounds are hydrocarbons, which means their molecules contain only carbon atoms and hydrogen atoms.

Separating Hydrocarbons The different hydrocarbon molecules found in petroleum have different numbers and arrangements of carbon and hydrogen atoms. The composition and structure of hydrocarbons determines their properties.

The many different compounds that are found in petroleum are separated in a process called fractional distillation. This separation occurs in the tall towers of oil-refinery plants. First, crude oil is pumped into the bottom of the tower and heated. The chemical compounds in the crude oil boil and vaporize according to their individual boiling points. Materials with the lowest boiling points rise to the top of the tower as vapor and are collected. Hydrocarbons with high boiling points, such as asphalt and some types of waxes, remain liquid and are drained off through the bottom of the tower.

Reading Check *What is fractional distillation used for?*

Other Uses for Petroleum Not all of the products obtained from petroleum are burned to produce energy. About 15 percent of the petroleum-based substances that are used in the United States go toward nonfuel uses. Look around at the materials in your home or classroom. Do you see any plastics? In addition to fuels, plastics and synthetic fabrics are made from the hydrocarbons found in crude petroleum. Also, lubricants such as grease and motor oil, as well as the asphalt used in surfacing roads, are obtained from petroleum. Some synthetic materials produced from petroleum are shown in **Figure 5.**

Designing an Efficient Water Heater

Procedure

1. Measure and record the mass of a **candle.**
2. Measure 50 mL of **water** into a **beaker.** Record the temperature of the water.
3. Use the lighted candle to increase the temperature of the water by 10°C. Put out the candle and measure its mass again.
4. Repeat steps 1 to 3 with an **aluminum chimney** surrounding the candle to help direct the heat upward.

Analysis

1. Compare the mass change in the two trials. Does a smaller or larger mass change in the candle show greater efficiency?
2. Gas burners are used to heat hot-water tanks. What must be considered in the design of these heaters?

Figure 5 The objects shown here are made from chemical compounds found in petroleum.
Identify *four objects in your classroom that are made from petroleum.*

Purpose Students determine how heating efficiency can be improved. L1 ELL IN **Kinesthetic**

Materials candle, water, foil, 100-mL beaker, thermometer, ring stand and ring, balance, wire gauze, graduated cylinder

Teaching Strategies

- Demonstrate how to set up the equipment. Place wire gauze between the ring stand and the beaker for more even heating.
- Encourage students to experiment with chimney size, shape, and location. Soot on the beaker improves the efficiency of heating.

Analysis

1. The mass changes less when the chimney is used. A smaller change in mass shows greater efficiency.
2. directing the flow of heat, controlling heating so that water will not turn to steam and expand

Assessment

Oral How would the results differ if the temperature of the water were increased by 30° C in each case? There would be a greater change in the candle's mass, especially if the chimney were not used.

Reading Check

Answer to separate the many different compounds found in petroleum

Caption Answer

Figure 5 Student answers will vary but may include tennis shoes, plastic chairs, plastic trash bags, and synthetic fabrics such as fleece, polyester, nylon, and rayon.

Cultural Diversity

Oil-Rich Countries More than 65 percent of the world's oil reserves are in the Middle East. Have students research some of the changes that have occurred in these countries since oil was discovered in them. Possible answer: the economies of these countries are now based on income from the sale of oil. They have better health care, roads, schools, and other public facilities than they had before. L3 P IN **Linguistic**

Curriculum Connection

History In 1973, the Arab oil embargo caused an energy crisis in the United States that forced people to carefully examine their dependence on oil. Have groups of students research this topic and create computer presentations about related major events since that time. Topics might include the economic recession caused by the oil crisis or causes of the Persian Gulf War. L3 IN **Interpersonal**

Discussion

Odorless Gas Natural gas has almost no odor. Why might natural gas distributors add an odorant to the gas? so you can tell if there is a gas leak L2 LS **Logical-Mathematical**

Inquiry Lab

Conserving Resources

Purpose to survey fellow student's efforts to conserve energy, to compile results, and to offer energy conservation tips and techniques

Possible Materials copies of student-generated survey to pass out to fellow students

Estimated Time 2 class periods or 2 hours outside of class

Teaching Strategies

- Students should be divided into small groups. Have students write a student survey that will ask questions about energy conservation. Questions such as "Do you turn the lights off when you leave the room?" should be written.
- Students should compile the results of the survey. Students can use their math skills to determine the percentages of the types of responses.
- Have students prepare a brochure to be distributed to students in their school presenting their compilation and tips and techniques for conserving energy.

For additional inquiry activities, see *Science Inquiry Labs*.

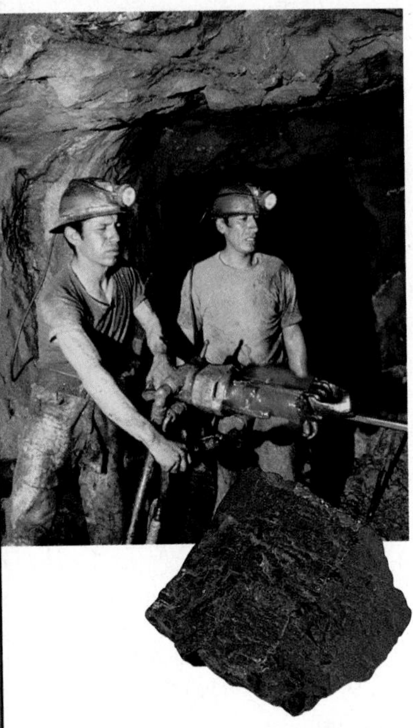

Figure 6 Coal mines usually are located deep underground.

Natural Gas

The chemical processes that produce petroleum as ancient organisms decay also produce gaseous compounds called natural gas. These compounds rise to the top of the petroleum deposit and are trapped there. Natural gas is composed mostly of methane, CH_4, but it also contains other hydrocarbon gases such as propane, C_3H_8, and butane, C_4H_{10}. Natural gas is burned to provide energy for cooking, heating, and manufacturing. About one fourth of the energy consumed in the United States comes from burning natural gas. There's a good chance that your home has a stove, furnace, hot-water heater, or clothes drier that uses natural gas.

Natural gas contains more energy per kilogram than petroleum or coal does. It also burns more cleanly than other fossil fuels, produces fewer pollutants, and leaves no residue such as ash.

Coal

Coal is a solid fossil fuel that is found in mines underground, such as the one shown in **Figure 6.** In the first half of the twentieth century, most houses in the United States were heated by burning coal. In fact, during this time, coal provided more than half of the energy that was used in the United States. Now, almost two-thirds of the energy used comes from petroleum and natural gas, and only about one-fourth comes from coal. About 90 percent of all the coal that is used in the United States is burned by power plants to generate electricity.

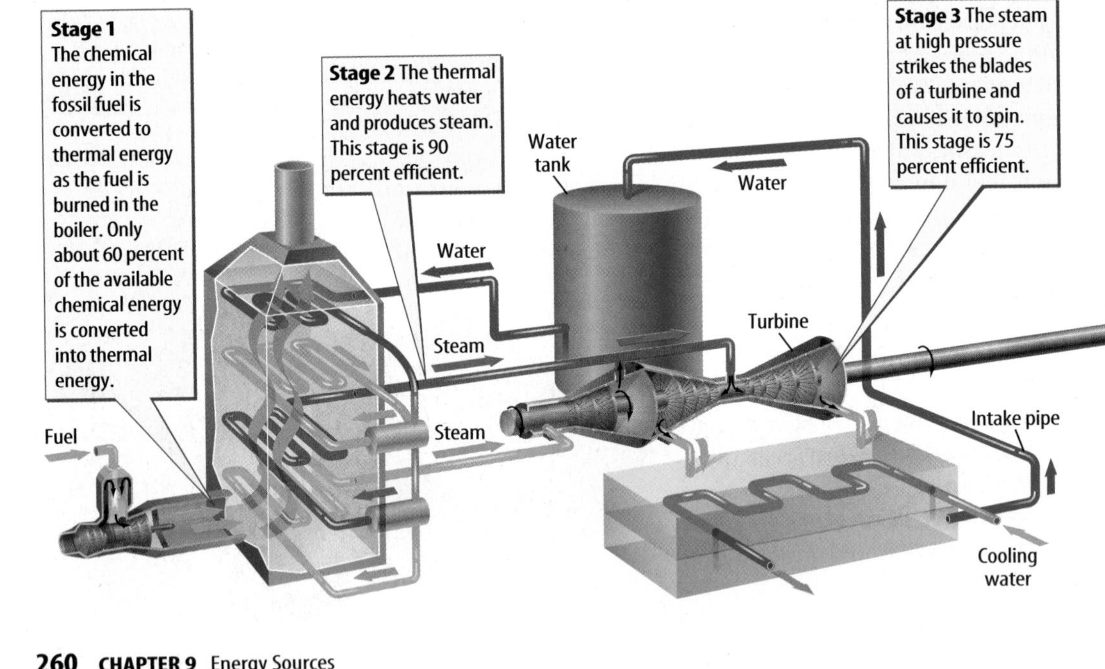

Stage 1 The chemical energy in the fossil fuel is converted to thermal energy as the fuel is burned in the boiler. Only about 60 percent of the available chemical energy is converted into thermal energy.
Stage 2 The thermal energy heats water and produces steam. This stage is 90 percent efficient.
Stage 3 The steam at high pressure strikes the blades of a turbine and causes it to spin. This stage is 75 percent efficient.
Water tank
Water
Water
Steam
Steam
Turbine
Fuel
Intake pipe
Cooling water

Differentiated Instruction

Challenge Fluidized-bed combustion of coal burns coal more efficiently and produces fewer pollutants than conventional coal boilers. Have students find out more about this technology. Have students draw a diagram detailing how this process works. L3 LS **Logical-Mathematical**

Teacher FYI

U.S. Coal Reserves The four largest coal reserves in the United States are the Four Corners Region near northern New Mexico, the Powder River Basin in Montana and Wyoming, the Eastern Interior Region around Illinois, and the Appalachian Region from Pennsylvania to Alabama.

Origin of Coal Coal mines were once the sites of ancient swamps. Coal formed from the organic material that was deposited as the plants that lived in these swamps died. Worldwide, the amount of coal that is potentially available is estimated to be 20 to 40 times greater than the supply of petroleum.

Coal also is a complex mixture of hydrocarbons and other chemical compounds. Compared to petroleum and natural gas, coal contains more impurities, such as sulfur and nitrogen compounds. As a result, more pollutants, such as sulfur dioxide and nitrogen oxides, are produced when coal is burned.

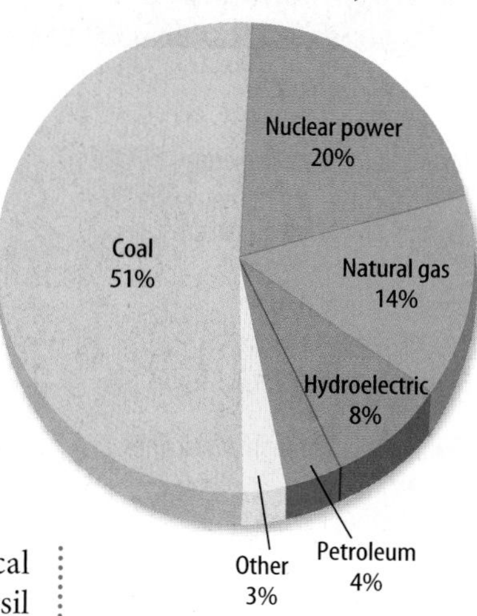

Figure 7 This circle graph shows the percentage of electricity generated in the United States that comes from various energy sources.

Generating Electricity

Figure 7 shows that almost 70 percent of the electrical energy used in the United States is produced by burning fossil fuels. How is the chemical energy contained in fossil fuels converted to electrical energy in an electric power station?

The process is shown in **Figure 8.** In the first stage, fuel is burned in a boiler or combustion chamber, and it releases thermal energy. In the second stage, this thermal energy heats water and produces steam under high pressure. In the third stage, the steam strikes the blades of a turbine, causing it to spin. The shaft of the turbine is connected to an electric generator. In the fourth stage, electric current is produced when the spinning turbine shaft rotates magnets inside the generator. In the final stage, the electric current is transmitted to homes, schools, and businesses through power lines.

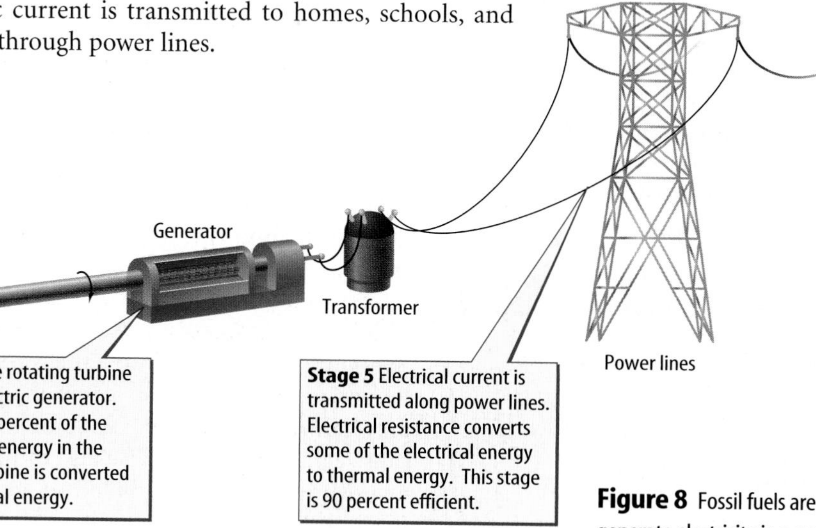

Generator
Transformer
Power lines
Stage 4 The rotating turbine spins an electric generator. Ninety-five percent of the mechanical energy in the rotating turbine is converted into electrical energy.
Stage 5 Electrical current is transmitted along power lines. Electrical resistance converts some of the electrical energy to thermal energy. This stage is 90 percent efficient.

Figure 8 Fossil fuels are burned to generate electricity in a power plant. **Determine** *which stage in this process is the most inefficient.*

Quick Demo

Coal Formation

Materials peat; four different types of coal such as lignite, subbituminous, bituminous, and anthracite

Estimated Time 10 minutes

Procedure Have students examine the peat and the different types of coal. Have students infer how the coal was formed. What are the differences in the conditions that formed the coal? The four types of coal are distinguished by the pressure that produced them. Lignite is produced when rock and soil pressed down on buried peat, causing it to dry out and harden. Further pressure produces subbituminous coal, then bituminous coal, and finally anthracite. L2 LS **Visual-Spatial**

Discussion

Power Sources Electricity became the major source of power in the United States during the twentieth century. What were the sources of power before that? Possible answers include running water and steam.

L2 LS **Logical-Mathematical**

Visual Learning

Figure 7 Review with students the information shown in **Figure 7.** What are the percentages of the three energy sources that are fossil fuels? What do they add up to? Coal 51%, natural gas 14%, and petroleum 4%. These add up to 69%. L2 LS **Visual-Spatial**

Caption Answer

Figure 8 Stage 1

Curriculum Connection

History Electricity has been a major source of power in the United States for less than 100 years. Have students research the early history of the use of electricity in the United States. In 1882, Edison opened an electric power plant that lit light bulbs. The first electric power was direct current. Power plants now produce alternating current. L3 LS **Linguistic**

Discussion

Energy Loss What is the primary way in which energy is lost in power plants? Energy is lost as heat.

Activity

Pollution Diagrams Have students draw diagrams showing how burning fossil fuels causes pollution. Diagrams might illustrate smog formed when fossil fuels are burned, and the effects of ozone near Earth's surface. Students might also draw plants using devices that remove the pollutants before they can reach the air. L3 LS **Visual-Spatial** P

Discussion

Alternatives What might happen when readily available fossil fuels are used up? Possible answers: Alternative energy sources will be developed; companies will exploit more expensive sources of fossil fuels; people's way of life will change because energy will become more expensive to use. L2

LS **Logical-Mathematical**

Virtual Labs

Electricity *How much electricity is used in a house?*

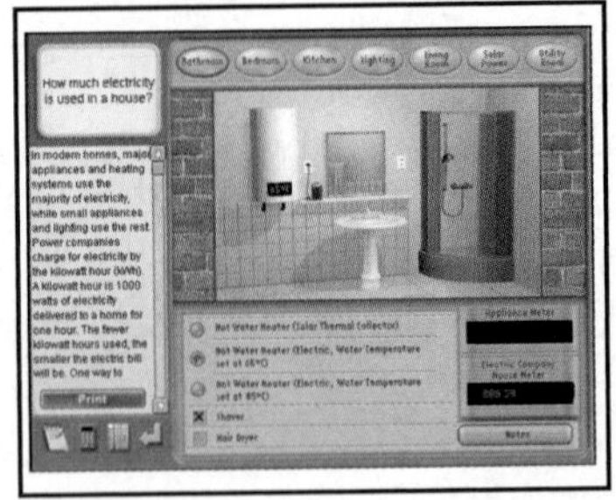

Table 1 Efficiency of Fossil Fuel Conversion

Process	Efficiency (%)
Chemical to thermal energy	60
Conversion of water to steam	90
Steam-turning turbine	75
Turbine spins electric generator	95
Transmission through power lines	90
Overall efficiency	35

Efficiency of Power Plants

When fossil fuels are burned to produce electricity, not all the chemical energy in the fuel is converted to electrical energy. In every stage of the process, some energy is converted into forms of energy that can't be used.

The overall efficiency of the entire process is given by multiplying the efficiencies of each stage of the process shown in **Table 1.** If you were to do this, you'd find that the resulting overall efficiency is only about 35 percent. This means that only about 35 percent of the energy contained in the fossil fuels is delivered to homes, schools, and businesses as electrical energy. The other 65 percent is converted mainly into thermal energy when the chemical energy in fuel is transformed into electrical energy that is delivered to energy users.

The Costs of Using Fossil Fuels

Although fossil fuels are a useful source of energy for generating electricity and providing the power for transportation, their use has some undesirable side effects. When petroleum products and coal are burned, smoke is given off that contains small particles called particulates. These particulates cause breathing problems for some people. Burning fossil fuels also releases carbon dioxide. **Figure 9** shows how the carbon dioxide concentration in the atmosphere has increased from 1960 to 2000. One consequence of increasing the atmospheric carbon dioxide concentration could be to cause Earth's surface temperature to increase.

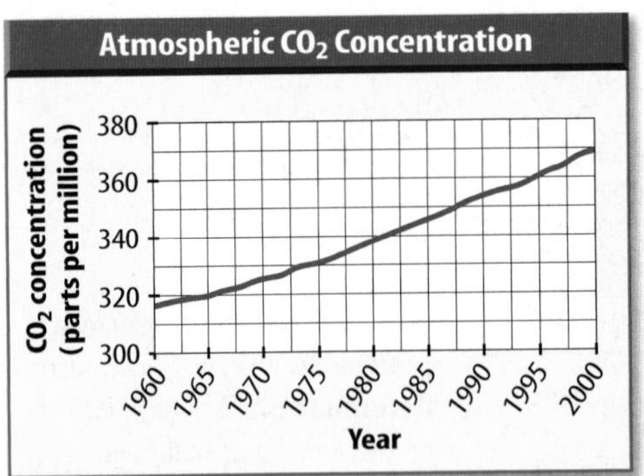

Figure 9 The carbon dioxide concentration in Earth's atmosphere has been measured at Mauna Loa in Hawaii. From 1960 to 2000, the carbon dioxide concentration has increased by about 16 percent.

Using Coal The most abundant fossil fuel is coal, but coal contains even more impurities than oil or natural gas. Many electric power plants that burn coal remove some of these pollutants before they are released into the atmosphere. Removing sulfur dioxide, for example, helps to prevent the formation of compounds that might cause acid rain. Mining coal also can be dangerous. Miners risk being killed or injured, and some suffer from lung diseases caused by breathing coal dust over long periods of time.

Differentiated Instruction

Learning Disabled To help students understand the math involved in finding the total efficiency of a power plant, discuss a two-step process in which the efficiency of the first step is 50 percent and the efficiency of the second step is 50 percent. Fill a beaker with water. Pour off half ($100\% \times 50\% = 50\%$). Then pour off half again ($50\% \times 50\% = 25\%$).

262 CHAPTER 9 Energy Sources

Nonrenewable Resources

All fossil fuels are **nonrenewable resources,** which means they are resources that cannot be replaced by natural processes as quickly as they are used. Therefore, fossil fuel reserves are decreasing at the same time that population and industrial demands are increasing. **Figure 10** shows how the production of oil might decline over the next 50 years as oil reserves are used up. As the production of energy from fossil fuels continues, the remaining reserves of fossil fuels will decrease. Fossil fuels will become more difficult to obtain, causing them to become more costly in the future.

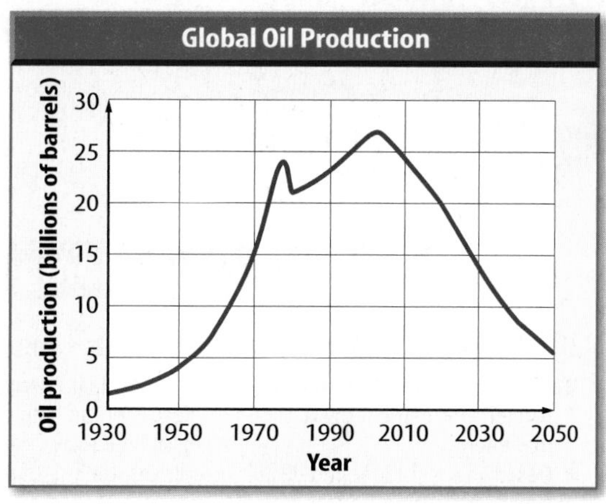

Figure 10 Some predictions show that worldwide oil production will peak by 2005 and then decline rapidly over the following 50 years.

Conserving Fossil Fuels

Even as reserves of fossil fuels decrease and they become more costly, the demand for energy continues to increase as the world's population increases. One way to meet these energy demands would be to reduce the use of fossil fuels and obtain energy from other sources.

section 1 review

Summary

Using Energy

- Energy cannot be created or destroyed, but can only be transformed from one form to another.

Fossil Fuels

- Petroleum, natural gas, and coal are fossil fuels formed by the decay of ancient plants and animals.
- Petroleum is a mixture of thousands of chemical compounds, most of which are hydrocarbons.
- About 90 percent of all coal used in the United States is burned by power plants to produce electricity.

Generating Electricity

- Power plants burn fossil fuels to produce steam that spins turbines attached to electric generators.

Self Check

1. **Describe** the advantages and disadvantages of using fossil fuels to generate electricity.
2. **Explain** how the different chemical compounds in crude oil are separated.
3. **Describe** how fossil fuels are formed.
4. **Name** three materials that are derived from the chemical compounds in petroleum.
5. **Think Critically** If fossil fuels are still forming, why are they considered to be a nonrenewable resource?

Applying Math

6. **Interpret a Graph** According to the graph in **Figure 9,** by how many parts per million did the concentration of atmospheric carbon dioxide increase from 1960 to 2000?
7. **Use a Table** In **Table 1,** if the efficiency of converting chemical to thermal energy was 90 percent, what would be the overall efficiency be?

Science Online gpscience.com/self_check_quiz

3 Assess

DAILY INTERVENTION

Check for Understanding

Interpersonal Divide the class into small groups. Assign each group a topic from the section. Each group should present the main ideas from that section to the rest of the class.

Reteach

Evaluating Fossil Fuels Organize the class into teams of three. Have each team consider the advantages and disadvantages of using petroleum, natural gas, and coal. Have the teams combine their lists and report their conclusions. L2 COOP LEARN

LS **Interpersonal**

Assessment

Process Have students make a bulletin board comparing and contrasting the ways people obtain petroleum and coal. Petroleum is a liquid, so it is pumped from wells drilled deep into Earth's crust. Coal also comes from underground, but it is a solid, so it must be mined. Use **Performance Assessment in the Science Classroom,** p. 131.

section 1 review

1. Advantages: Fossil fuels are an inexpensive source of energy. They are plentiful for the near-term; Disadvantages: Fossil fuels may cause environmental damage when removed from Earth, when transported, and when burned.
2. They are separated by fractional distillation, in which each compound vaporizes at its own boiling point, rises, and is collected.
3. Fossil fuels are formed when organic matter is chemically changed by heat and pressure.
4. Possible answers: plastics, grease, gasoline, asphalt
5. We are using fossil fuels faster than they are being replaced.
6. about 50 parts per million
7. 52%

CLE 3202.2.5: Distinguish between nuclear fission and nuclear fusion.

section 2

Nuclear Energy

1 Motivate

Bellringer

INTERACTIVE CHALKBOARD PowerPoint® Presentations

Section Focus Transparencies also are available on the Interactive Chalkboard CD-ROM. L2 ELL

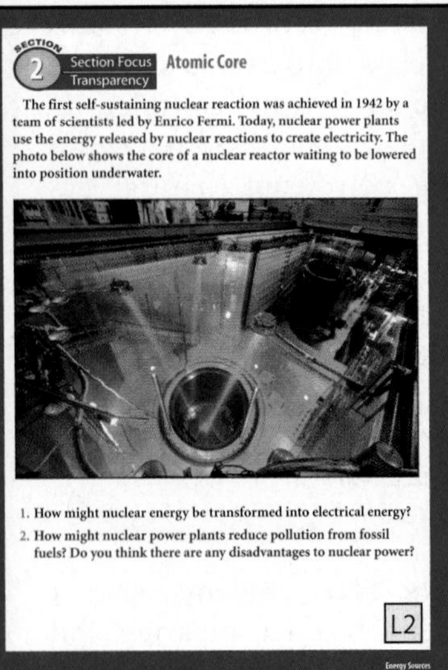

Section 2 Section Focus Transparency Atomic Core

The first self-sustaining nuclear reaction was achieved in 1942 by a team of scientists led by Enrico Fermi. Today, nuclear power plants use the energy released by nuclear reactions to create electricity. The photo below shows the core of a nuclear reactor waiting to be lowered into position underwater.

1. How might nuclear energy be transformed into electrical energy?
2. How might nuclear power plants reduce pollution from fossil fuels? Do you think there are any disadvantages to nuclear power?

L2

Tie to Prior Knowledge

Nuclear Energy Uses Ask students to name ways that nuclear energy is used. Possible answers: diagnose and treat illnesses, nuclear weapons, generate power

Reading Guide

What You'll Learn

- **Explain** how a nuclear reactor converts nuclear energy to thermal energy.
- **Describe** advantages and disadvantages of using nuclear energy to produce electricity.
- **Discuss** nuclear fusion as a possible energy source.

Why It's Important

Using nuclear energy to produce electricity can help reduce the use of fossil fuels. However, like all energy sources, the use of nuclear energy has advantages and disadvantages.

Review Vocabulary

nuclear fission: the process of splitting an atomic nucleus into two or more nuclei with smaller masses

New Vocabulary

- nuclear reactor
- nuclear waste

Using Nuclear Energy

Over the past several decades, electric power plants have been developed that generate electricity without burning fossil fuels. Some of these power plants, such as the one shown in **Figure 11,** convert nuclear energy to electrical energy. Energy is released when the nucleus of an atom breaks apart. In this process, called nuclear fission, an extremely small amount of mass is converted into an enormous amount of energy. Today almost 20 percent of all the electricity produced in the United States comes from nuclear power plants. Overall, nuclear power plants produce about eight percent of all the energy consumed in the United States. In 2003, there were 104 nuclear reactors producing electricity at 65 nuclear power plants in the United States.

Figure 11 A nuclear power plant generates electricity using the energy released in nuclear fission. Each of the domes contain a nuclear reactor. A cooling tower is on the left.

Nuclear Reactors

A **nuclear reactor** uses the energy from controlled nuclear reactions to generate electricity. Although nuclear reactors vary in design, all have some parts in common, as shown in **Figure 12.** They contain a fuel that can be made to undergo nuclear fission; they contain control rods that are used to control the nuclear reactions; and they have a cooling system that keeps the reactor from being damaged by the heat produced. The actual fission of the radioactive fuel occurs in a relatively small part of the reactor known as the core.

Section 2 Resource Manager

Chapter FAST FILE Resources

Transparency Activity, pp. 45, 47–48
Directed Reading for Content Mastery, p. 20
Transparency Activity, pp. 47–48
Enrichment, p. 31
Reinforcement, p. 28

Earth Science Critical Thinking/Problem Solving, p. 2
Cultural Diversity, p. 59
Mathematics Skill Activities, p. 47

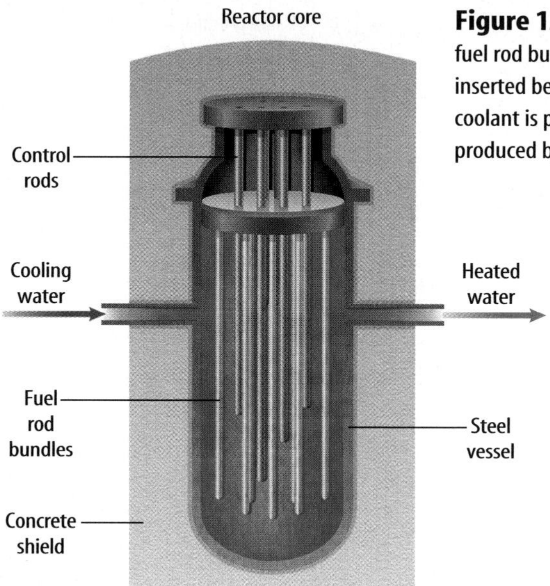

Figure 12 The core of a nuclear reactor contains the fuel rod bundles. Control rods that absorb neutrons are inserted between the fuel rod bundles. Water or another coolant is pumped through the core to remove the heat produced by the fission reaction.

Nuclear Fuel Only certain elements have nuclei that can undergo fission. Naturally occurring uranium contains an isotope, U-235, whose nucleus can split apart. As a result, the fuel that is used in a nuclear reactor is usually uranium dioxide. Naturally occurring uranium contains only about 0.7 percent of the U-235 isotope. In a reactor, the uranium usually is enriched so that it contains three percent to five percent U-235.

The Reactor Core The reactor core contains uranium dioxide fuel in the form of tiny pellets like the ones in **Figure 13.** The pellets are about the size of a pencil eraser and are placed end to end in a tube. The tubes are then bundled and covered with a metal alloy, as shown in **Figure 13.** The core of a typical reactor contains about a hundred thousand kilograms of uranium in hundreds of fuel rods. For every kilogram of uranium that undergoes fission in the core, 1 g of matter is converted into energy. The energy released by this gram of matter is equivalent to the energy released by burning more than 3 million kg of coal.

Figure 13 Nuclear fuel pellets are stacked together to form fuel rods. The fuel rods are bundled together, and the bundle is covered with a metal alloy.

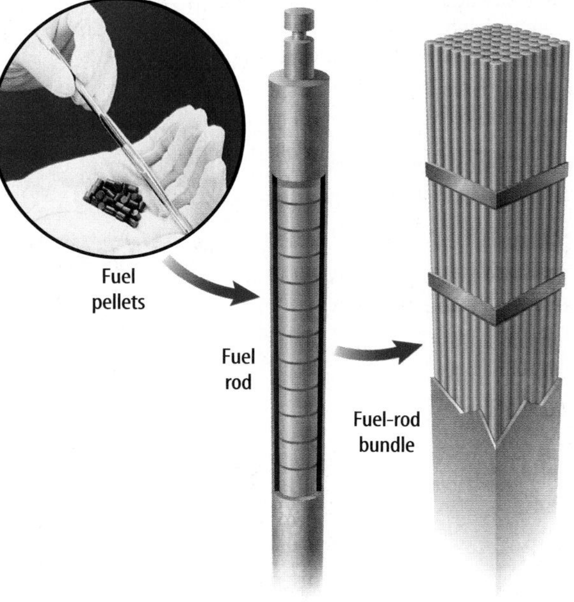

2 Teach

Teacher FYI

Energy Supplies In an average American's lifetime, more than 1 million kg of coal would be needed to supply the person's energy needs. In contrast, if nuclear reactors were used instead of coal, about 1,100 uranium fuel pellets would be needed to supply the same amount of energy.

Visual Learning

Figure 12 The distance the control rods extend into the reactor core controls the reaction. If the control rods are inserted completely, they absorb too many neutrons and the reaction halts. If they are removed completely, the reaction is uncontained. How do you think control rods are programmed to respond in an emergency? They insert completely to stop the reaction. L2 LS **Logical-Mathematical**

Discussion

Rod-Shaped Why do you think the fuel and control used in the reactor are rod-shaped? to allow the water to flow freely around them and provide cooling L2 LS **Visual-Spatial**

Quick Demo

Nuclear Fuel Pellets

Materials mini-marshmallows, test tubes (larger diameter than marshmallows), rubber band

Estimated Time five minutes

Procedure Use mini-marshmallows to represent the uranium dioxide fuel. Use test tubes to represent the reactor rods. Put the mini-marshmallows into the test tubes. Bundle several test tubes together with the rubber band to represent the bundled fuel rods.

Differentiated Instruction

Visually Impaired Use refillable erasers for mechanical pencils to symbolize the fuel pellets, allow students to feel what the fuel pellets are shaped like. A large soda straw can be used to symbolize the fuel rods. Students can put the erasers in the straw to symbolize packing the fuel rod.

Curriculum Connection

Social Studies The use of nuclear reactions in commercial power plants to produce electricity has been the subject of intense controversy. Organize the class into two teams and have them debate the issue. Arguments for nuclear power include its efficiency and nonreliance on fossil fuels. Arguments against nuclear power include safety hazards and disposal of nuclear waste. L3 LS **Logical-Mathematical**

Use an Analogy

Foxes and Rabbits If rabbits live and breed in an environment rich in rabbit food but in which there are no rabbit predators, the rabbit population will boom very quickly. This is analogous to the uncontrolled chain reaction that can occur in a nuclear reactor. The introduction of foxes into the rabbit environment controls the size of the rabbit population just as the introduction of control rods controls the number of neutrons available to participate in the nuclear reaction.

Caption Answer

Figure 14 The neutrons strike other U-235 nuclei breaking them apart into fission products and neutrons or they are absorbed by control rods.

Reading Check

Answer a nuclear reaction in which the products of one reaction start another reaction

Make a Model

Reactor Core Have students work in pairs to make models of the core of a nuclear reactor. Models should include some fuel rods, some control rods, and a coolant. One possible model could use test tubes filled with different substances to represent the fuel rods and the control rods, a test tube rack to represent the core, and water as the coolant. L2 LS **Kinesthetic**

Ukraine The Ukraine borders eastern Europe and is located east of Poland and north of Romania.

Research Have students research the Chernobyl accident. Have them find out what caused the accident and the damages that resulted from it.

Figure 14 When a neutron strikes the nucleus of a U-235 atom, the nucleus splits apart into two smaller nuclei. In the process two or three neutrons also are emitted. The smaller nuclei are called fission products. **Explain** *what happens to the neutrons that are released in this reaction.*

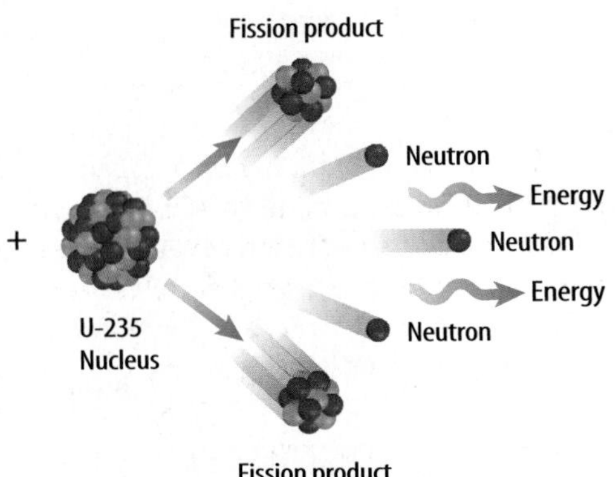

INTEGRATE Earth Science

Uranium-Lead Dating Uranium is used to determine the age of rocks. As uranium decays into lead at a constant rate, the age of a rock can be found by comparing the amount of uranium to the amount of lead produced. Uranium-lead dating is used by scientists to date rocks as old as 4.6 billion years. Research other methods used to determine the age of rocks.

Nuclear Fission How does the nuclear reaction proceed in the reactor core? Neutrons that are produced by the decay of U-235 nuclei are absorbed by other U-235 nuclei. When a U-235 nucleus absorbs a neutron, it splits into two smaller nuclei and two or three additional neutrons, as shown in **Figure 14.** These neutrons strike other U-235 nuclei, causing them to release two or three more neutrons each when they split apart.

Because every uranium atom that splits apart releases neutrons that cause other uranium atoms to split apart, this process is called a nuclear chain reaction. In the chain reaction involving the fission of uranium nuclei, the number of nuclei that are split can more than double at each stage of the process. As a result, an enormous number of nuclei can be split after only a small number of stages. For example, if the number of nuclei involved doubles at each stage, after only 50 stages more than a quadrillion nuclei might be split.

Nuclear chain reactions take place in a matter of milliseconds. If the process isn't controlled, the chain reaction will release energy explosively rather than releasing energy at a constant rate.

Reading Check *What is a nuclear chain reaction?*

Controlling the Chain Reaction To control the chain reaction, some of the neutrons that are released when U-235 splits apart must be prevented from striking other U-235 nuclei. These neutrons are absorbed by rods containing boron or cadmium that are inserted into the reactor core. Moving these control rods deeper into the reactor causes them to absorb more neutrons and slow down the chain reaction. Eventually, only one of the neutrons released in the fission of each of the U-235 nuclei strikes another U-235 nucleus, and energy is released at a constant rate.

Visual Learning

Figure 14 The tremendous energy from the fission process shown here is mostly transferred to the smaller nuclei and the neutrons, but part of the energy is released as gamma radiation. What are two ways a chain reaction can be avoided? by introducing materials that absorb neutrons and by decreasing the amount of U-235 so there aren't enough atoms to continue the process L2 LS **Logical-Mathematical**

Active Reading

Think-Pair-Share This strategy encourages students to think first before discussing their ideas or thoughts about a topic. Students are asked to respond to a question by writing a response. After thinking for a few minutes, partners share responses to the question. Finally, ask students to share responses with the class.

Nuclear Power Plants

Nuclear fission reactors produce electricity in much the same way that conventional power plants do. **Figure 15** shows how a nuclear reactor produces electricity. The thermal energy released in nuclear fission is used to heat water and produce steam. This steam then is used to drive a turbine that rotates an electric generator. To transfer thermal energy from the reactor core to heat water and produce steam, the core is immersed in a fluid coolant. The coolant absorbs heat from the core and is pumped through a heat exchanger. There thermal energy is transferred from the coolant and boils water to produce steam. The overall efficiency of nuclear power plants is about 35 percent, similar to that of fossil fuel power plants.

The Risks of Nuclear Power

Producing energy from nuclear fission has several advantages. Nuclear power plants do not produce the air pollutants that are released by fossil-fuel burning power plants. Also, nuclear power plants don't produce carbon dioxide.

However, there are also disadvantages to using nuclear power. For example, if an accident occurs, a nuclear plant could release radioactive materials that could harm the environment. Nuclear power plants also produce radioactive waste materials that must be safely disposed of.

Ukraine The worst nuclear accident in history occurred at the Chernobyl nuclear power plant in the Ukraine in 1986. Many people in the area suffered from radiation sickness. Use a map or atlas to find the location of the Ukraine. Write a description of the location in your Science Journal.

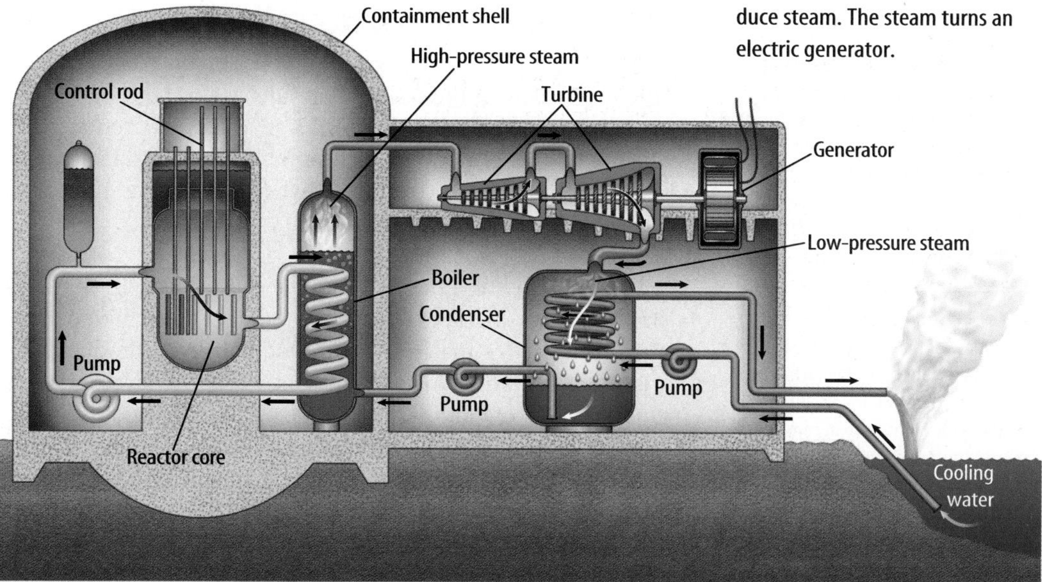

Figure 15 A nuclear power plant uses the heat produced by nuclear fission in its core to produce steam. The steam turns an electric generator.

Uranium-Lead Dating The ratio of amounts of thorium-230 to uranium-234 has been used to date calcium carbonate. Rocks are also dated from the fossils they contain.

IDENTIFYING Misconceptions

Contaminated Water The water that is used as a coolant in reactor cores becomes contaminated with radioactive material. This water is not the same water that is cooled and released into streams and rivers. The water that is released into the environment does not come into direct contact either with the reactor core or with the water that cools the reactor core. It exchanges heat with the contaminated water through a heat exchanger.

Science Journal

Nuclear Power Plants Ask students to identify the nuclear power plant located closest to their community and write their findings in their Science Journals. Have them include the plant's name and location, when it began operation, how much electricity it generates, and its operating history. Answers will depend on the location of their community. L3

LS **Linguistic**

Teacher FYI

Chernobyl After the Chernobyl accident in 1986, people all over the world became concerned about the safety of nuclear reactors. Although all reactors have some risks, reactors in the United States are far safer than the one in Chernobyl. Most importantly, the Chernobyl reactor did not have a containment shell that could prevent the escape of radioactive materials.

Activity

Nuclear Waste Disposal Ask students to generate ideas for nuclear waste disposal. Remind them to consider short-term and long-term effects as well as the various types of waste. Have students share their ideas in small groups and arrive at a class consensus about the best methods of disposal. L2 IS **Interpersonal**

Figure 16 An explosion occurred at the Chernobyl reactor in the Ukraine after graphite control rods caught fire. The explosion shattered the reactor's roof.

The Release of Radioactivity One of the most serious risks of nuclear power is the escape of harmful radiation from power plants. The fuel rods contain radioactive elements with various half-lives. Some of these elements could cause damage to living organisms if they were released from the reactor core. Nuclear reactors have elaborate systems of safeguards, strict safety precautions, and highly trained workers in order to prevent accidents. In spite of this, accidents have occurred.

For example, in 1986 in Chernobyl, Ukraine, an accident occurred when a reactor core overheated during a safety test. Materials in the core caught fire and caused a chemical explosion that blew a hole in the reactor, as shown in **Figure 16.** This resulted in the release of radioactive materials that were carried by winds and deposited over a large area. As a result of the accident, 28 people died of acute radiation sickness. It is possible that 260,000 people might have been exposed to levels of radiation that could affect their health.

In the United States, power plants are designed to prevent accidents such as the one that occurred at Chernobyl. But many people still are concerned that similar accidents are possible.

The Disposal of Nuclear Waste

After about three years, not enough fissionable U-235 is left in the fuel pellets in the reactor core to sustain the chain reaction. The spent fuel contains radioactive fission products in addition to the remaining uranium. **Nuclear waste** is any radioactive by-product that results when radioactive materials are used.

Science Online

Topic: Storing Nuclear Wastes

Visit gpscience.com for Web links to information about storing nuclear wastes.

Activity Obtain a map or sketch an outline of the United States. Mark the locations of the nuclear waste sites that you found. What do these locations have in common? Why do you think these locations were chosen over other sites that were closer to the nuclear waste generating sites?

Low-Level Waste Low-level nuclear wastes usually contain a small amount of radioactive material. They usually do not contain radioactive materials with long half-lives. Products of some medical and industrial processes are low-level wastes, including items of clothing used in handling radioactive materials. Low-level wastes also include used air filters from nuclear power plants and discarded smoke detectors. Low-level wastes usually are sealed in containers and buried in trenches 30 m deep at special locations. When dilute enough, low-level waste sometimes is released into the air or water.

Differentiated Instruction

Challenge On March 28, 1979, an accident occurred at the Three-Mile Island Nuclear Plant near Harrisburg, Pennsylvania. Have students find out more about this incident and report their findings to the class. The accident caused a small amount of hydrogen gas to escape the containment shell. Emergency cooling systems eventually contained the problem, but some radiation was released. This accident focused the nation's attention on the potential dangers of nuclear reactors. L3 IS **Linguistic**

High-Level Waste High-level nuclear waste is generated in nuclear power plants and by nuclear weapons programs. After spent fuel is removed from a reactor, it is stored in a deep pool of water, as shown in **Figure 17.** Many of the radioactive materials in high-level nuclear waste have short half-lives. However, the spent fuel also contains materials that will remain radioactive for tens of thousands of years. For this reason, the waste must be disposed of in extremely durable and stable containers.

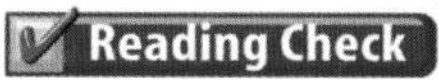
What is the difference between low-level and high-level nuclear wastes?

One method proposed for the disposal of high-level waste is to seal the waste in ceramic glass, which is placed in protective metal-alloy containers. The containers then are buried hundreds of meters below ground in stable rock formations or salt deposits. It is hoped that this will keep the material from contaminating the environment for thousands of years.

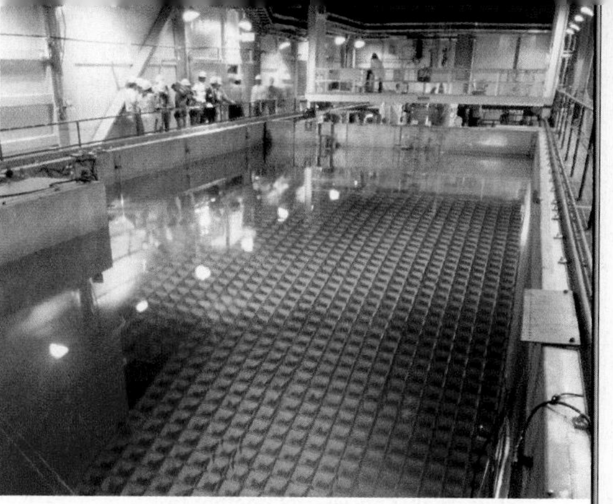

Figure 17 Spent nuclear fuel rods are placed underwater after they are removed from the reactor core. The water absorbs the nuclear radiation and prevents it from escaping into the environment.

Discussion

Nuclear Waste Sites What are some problems that must be addressed when deciding on a site for nuclear waste? Safe transportation from other sites, possible terrorist plans for theft, political changes on policies and funding, proper storage capability to prevent the risk of radioactive materials from entering the environment L2

LS **Logical-Mathematical**

Reading Check

Answer Low-level nuclear wastes usually contain only a small amount of radioactive material with short half-lives. High-level nuclear wastes are usually highly radioactive and contain material with long half-lives.

Applying Science

Can a contaminated radioactive site be reclaimed?

In the early 1900s, with the discovery of radium, extensive mining for the element began in the Denver, Colorado, area. Radium is a radioactive element that was used to make watch dials and instrument panels that glowed in the dark. After World War I, the radium industry collapsed. The area was left contaminated with 97,000 tons of radioactive soil and debris containing heavy metals and radium, which is now known to cause cancer. The soil was used as fill, foundation material, left in place, or mishandled.

Radium
88
Ra
(226)

Identifying the Problem

In the 1980s, one area became known as the Denver Radium Superfund Site and was cleaned up by the Environmental Protection Agency. The land then was reclaimed by a local commercial establishment.

Solving the Problem

1. The contaminated soil was placed in one area and a protective cap was placed over it. This area also was restricted from being used for residential homes. Explain why it is important for the protective cap to be maintained and why homes could not be built in this area.
2. The advantages of cleaning up this site are economical, environmental, and social. Give an example of each.

Applying Science

Answers

1. The cap has to be maintained to prevent contaminated soil from reaching people. Homes can't be built in this area because all of the contaminated soil may not have been removed and some contamination may have reached the groundwater.
2. Advantages: Economic: jobs, revenue for the community, tax for the state, increase in property values. Environmental: elimination of long-term risks for contaminated material, prevention of the migration of metals through the soil, protection of the public from contaminated land and water. Social: improvement of the aesthetic quality of the land, commercial buildings can be built.

LAB DEMONSTRATION

Purpose to demonstrate how shielding decreases radiation levels

Materials alpha, beta, and gamma sources; Geiger counter; 3 lead sheets

Procedure Place the alpha source near the Geiger counter. Note the intensity measured by the counter. Place a lead sheet between the source and the counter, and note the change in intensity. Repeat for the beta source using one lead sheet and for the gamma source using first one, then two, then three lead sheets.

Expected Outcome One lead sheet blocks the alpha and beta radiation. The intensity of the gamma radiation decreases with additional shielding.

Assessment

How were measurements affected by the amount of shielding? Increased shielding meant less radiation was measured.

SECTION 2 Nuclear Energy 269

Fun Fact

Nuclear fusion produces more energy than nuclear fission. The nuclear fusion of hydrogen to form helium releases about eight times the amount of energy as does the nuclear fission of an equal mass of uranium-235.

3 Assess

DAILY INTERVENTION

Check for Understanding

Visual-Spatial Have students draw a diagram of atoms undergoing nuclear fission and nuclear fusion. Students should label the reactants and products of each reaction, as well as the type of atom that is undergoing the process.

Reteach

Nuclear Reactors Have each student make a simple sketch of a nuclear reactor, showing the major parts of the reactor and describing the function of each of them. L2 LS **Visual-Spatial** P

Assessment

Content Nuclear fission is a chain reaction. Have students draw diagrams showing the chain reaction and how it is controlled in nuclear power plants. Use **PASC**, p. 163.

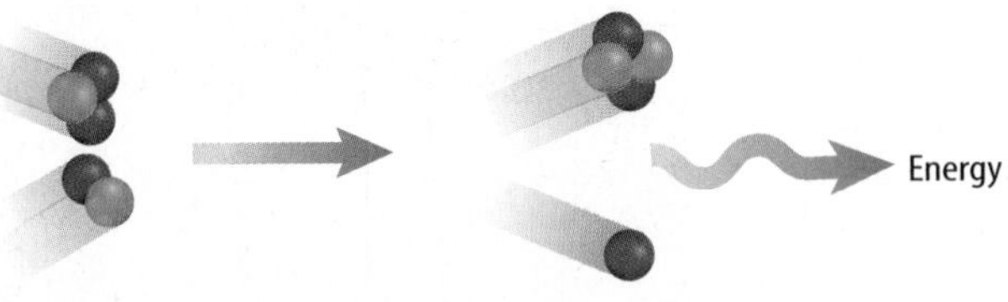
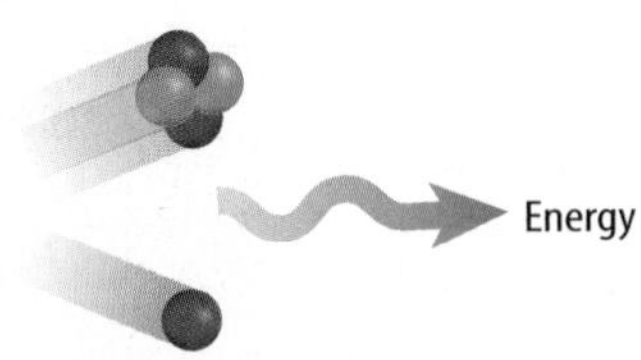

Figure 18 In nuclear fusion, two smaller nuclei join together to form a larger nucleus. Energy is released in the process. In the reaction shown here, two isotopes of hydrogen come together to form a helium nucleus.
Identify *the source of the energy released in a fusion reaction.*

Nuclear Fusion

The Sun gives off a tremendous amount of energy through a process called thermonuclear fusion. Thermonuclear fusion is the joining together of small nuclei at high temperatures, as shown in **Figure 18.** In this process, a small amount of mass is converted into energy. Fusion is the most concentrated energy source known.

An advantage of producing energy using nuclear fusion is that the process uses hydrogen as fuel. Hydrogen is abundant on Earth. Another advantage is that the product of the reaction is helium. Helium is not radioactive and is chemically nonreactive.

One disadvantage of fusion is that it occurs only at temperatures of millions of degrees Celsius. Research reactors often consume more energy to reach and maintain these temperatures than they produce. Another problem is how to contain a reaction that occurs at such extreme conditions. Until solutions to these and other problems are found, the use of nuclear fusion as an energy source is not practical.

section 2 review

Summary

Using Nuclear Energy

- Nuclear power plants produce about eight percent of the energy used each year in the United States.

Nuclear Power Plants

- Nuclear reactors use the energy released in the fission of U-235 to produce electricity.
- The energy released in the fission reaction is used to make steam. The steam drives a turbine that rotates an electric generator.

The Risks of Nuclear Energy

- Nuclear power generation produces high-level nuclear wastes.
- Organisms could be damaged if radiation is released from the reactor.
- Nuclear waste is the radioactive by-product produced by using radioactive materials.

Self Check

1. **Explain** why a chain reaction occurs when uranium-235 undergoes fission.
2. **Describe** how the chain reaction in a nuclear reactor is controlled.
3. **Compare** the advantages and disadvantages of nuclear power plants and those that burn fossil fuels.
4. **Describe** the advantages and disadvantages of using nuclear fusion reactions as a source of energy.
5. **Think Critically** A research project produced 10 g of nuclear waste with a short half-life. How would you classify this waste and how would it be disposed of?

Applying Math

6. **Use Percentages** Naturally occurring uranium contains 0.72 percent of the isotope uranium-235. What is the mass of uranium-235 in 2,000 kg of naturally-occurring uranium?

Science Online gpscience.com/self_check_quiz

section 2 review

1. Neutrons are produced when U-235 undergoes decay. These neutrons are absorbed by other U-235 neutrons which release more neutrons when they decay.
2. Control rods are used to absorb excess neutrons.
3. Advantages: Nuclear power plants do not release air pollutants or carbon dioxide; Disadvantages: The mining of uranium can cause environmental damage. The possible escape of harmful radiation and the disposal of nuclear wastes are additional disadvantages of nuclear power generation.
4. Advantages: A small amount of mass is converted into a large amount of energy. Hydrogen is an abundant fuel source; Disadvantages: The reaction occurs at difficult-to-maintain temperatures. The extreme temperatures involved make the reaction hard to contain.
5. It is a low-level waste that should be sealed in an insulated container and buried in a repository.
6. 14.4 kg

section 3

Renewable Energy Sources

Reading Guide

What You'll Learn

- **Analyze** the need for alternate energy sources.
- **Describe** alternate methods for generating electricity.
- **Compare** the advantages and disadvantages of various alternate energy sources.

Why It's Important

The primary sources of energy in the United States are nonrenewable, so alternative energy sources need to be explored.

Review Vocabulary

radiant energy: the energy carried by an electromagnetic wave

New Vocabulary

- renewable resource
- photovoltaic cell
- hydroelectricity
- geothermal energy
- biomass

Energy Options

The demand for energy increases continually, but supplies of fossil fuels are decreasing. Using more nuclear reactors to produce electricity will produce more high-level nuclear waste that has to be disposed of safely. As a result, other sources of energy that can meet Earth's increasing energy demands are being developed. Some alternative energy sources are renewable resources. A **renewable resource** is an energy source that is replaced nearly as quickly as it is used.

Energy from the Sun

The average amount of solar energy that falls on the United States in one day is more than the total amount of energy used in the United States in one year. Because only about one billionth of the Sun's energy falls on Earth, and because the Sun is expected to continue producing energy for several billion years, solar energy cannot be used up. Solar energy is a renewable resource.

Many devices use solar energy for power including solar-powered calculators similar to the one in **Figure 19.** These devices use a **photovoltaic cell** that converts radiant energy from the Sun directly into electrical energy. Photovoltaic cells also are called solar cells.

Figure 19 This calculator uses a solar cell to produce the electricity it needs to operate.

1 Motivate

Bellringer

Section Focus Transparencies also are available on the Interactive Chalkboard CD-ROM. L2 ELL

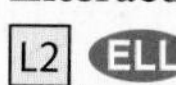

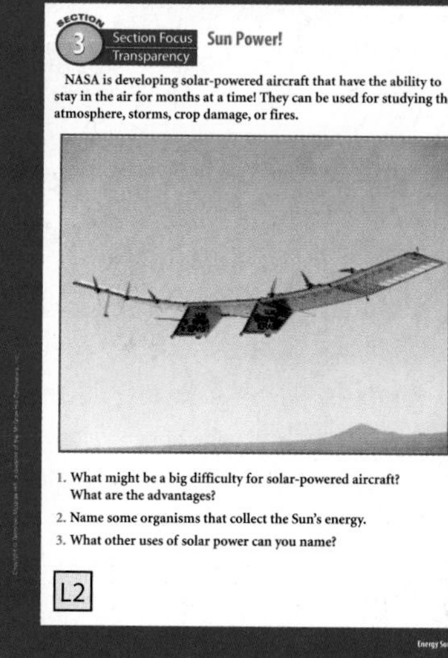

Section 3 Section Focus Transparency Sun Power!

NASA is developing solar-powered aircraft that have the ability to stay in the air for months at a time! They can be used for studying the atmosphere, storms, crop damage, or fires.

1. What might be a big difficulty for solar-powered aircraft? What are the advantages?
2. Name some organisms that collect the Sun's energy.
3. What other uses of solar power can you name?

L2

Tie to Prior Knowledge

Alternative Energy Sources Every day we turn on lights and ride in cars. Ask students what it would be like if suddenly our sources of fossil fuels ran out. Explain that this section describes alternative sources of energy.

Caption Answer

Figure 18 A small amount of mass is converted into energy.

Section 3 Resource Manager

Chapter *Fast File* Resources

- Transparency Activity, p. 46
- MiniLAB, p. 4
- Enrichment, p. 32
- Directed Reading for Content Mastery, pp. 21–22
- Reinforcement, p. 29
- Lab Worksheet, pp. 5–6, 7–8
- Lab Activities, pp. 9–12, 13–16

Home and Community Involvement, p. 42

Mathematics Skill Activities, p. 31

2 Teach

Use Science Words

Word Meaning Why are solar cells also known as photovoltaic cells? *Photo* - means "light," and *voltaic* refers to electricity. L2 IS **Linguistic**

Caption Answer

Figure 20 possible answers are a calculator and a highway sign that displays messages using lights

Purpose to analyze the use of solar energy

L2 ELL IS **Kinesthetic**

Materials piece of cloth, watch or clock, water, scissors

Analysis

1. Answers will vary, but the cloth in direct sunlight should dry faster.
2. Answers will vary depending on the season and weather conditions. Factors such as temperature, wind velocity, cloudiness, and humidity will affect the time needed.
3. Hang clothes in the sun to dry instead of using an electric dryer. Open shades and curtains to warm a room with direct sunlight in cool weather, and close shades and curtains to keep a room cool in warm weather.

Assessment

Oral Ask students to identify the dependent and independent variables and the constants in this experiment. The dependent variable is drying time and the independent variable is location of the cloth. Constants include size, type, and initial dampness of the cloth.

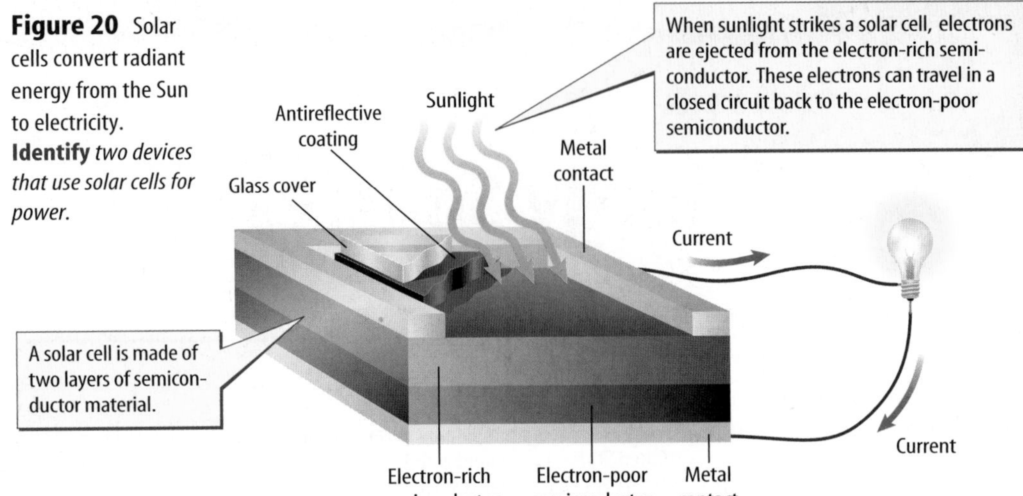
When sunlight strikes a solar cell, electrons are ejected from the electron-rich semiconductor. These electrons can travel in a closed circuit back to the electron-poor semiconductor.
Sunlight
Antireflective coating
Glass cover
Metal contact
Current
A solar cell is made of two layers of semiconductor material.
Current
Electron-rich semiconductor
Electron-poor semiconductor
Metal contact

Figure 20 Solar cells convert radiant energy from the Sun to electricity.
Identify *two devices that use solar cells for power.*

Using Solar Power at Home

Procedure

1. Cut a piece of **cloth** into four equal sized pieces.
2. Wet the pieces and wring them out so they are the same dampness.
3. Spread the pieces out to dry—two pieces inside and two pieces outdoors. One piece of each set should be in direct sunlight and one piece should be in the shade.
4. In your **Science Journal,** record the time it takes for each cloth piece to dry.

Analysis

1. How long did it take for each cloth piece to dry?
2. What conditions determined how quickly the cloth dried?
3. Infer how you can use solar energy in your home to conserve electricity.

Try at Home

How Solar Cells Work Solar cells are made of two layers of semiconductor materials sandwiched between two layers of conducting metal, as shown in **Figure 20.** One layer of semiconductor is rich in electrons, while the other layer is electron poor. When sunlight strikes the surface of the solar cell, electrons flow through an electrical circuit from the electron-rich semiconductor to the electron-poor material. This process of converting radiant energy from the Sun directly to electrical energy is only about 7 percent to 11 percent efficient.

Using Solar Energy Producing large amounts of electrical energy using solar cells is more expensive than producing electrical energy using fossil fuels. However, in remote areas where electric distribution lines are not available, the use of solar cells is a practical way of providing electrical power.

Currently, the most promising solar technologies are those that concentrate the solar power into a receiver. One such system is called the parabolic trough. The trough focuses the sunlight on a tube that contains a heat-absorbing fluid such as synthetic oil or liquid salt. The heated fluid is circulated through a boiler where it generates steam to turn a turbine, generating electricity.

The worlds' largest concentrating solar power plant is located in the Mojave Desert in California. This facility consists of nine units that generate over 350 megawatts of power. These nine units can generate enough electrical power to meet the needs of approximately 500,000 people. These units use natural gas as a backup power source for generating electricity at night and on cloudy days when solar energy is unavailable.

Visual Learning

Figure 20 The semiconductor layers of this solar cell form a diode, a device that allows current to flow in only one direction. Thin metal strips on top of the cell serve as contacts for collecting the current. One advantage of solar cells is that they have no moving parts. Why does this make them attractive for use on satellites in space? Solar cells require no maintenance and no fuel.

Differentiated Instruction

Learning Disabled Have students bring in devices that use solar cells, such as toys and calculators. Show how the devices stop working if the solar cell's light source is blocked. L1 ELL IS **Visual-Spatial**

Energy from Water

Just as the expansion of steam can turn an electric generator, rapidly moving water can as well. The gravitational potential energy of the water can be increased if the water is retained by a high dam. This potential energy is released when the water flows through tunnels near the base of the dam. **Figure 21** shows how the rushing water spins a turbine, which rotates the shaft of an electric generator to produce electricity. Dams built for this purpose are called hydroelectric dams.

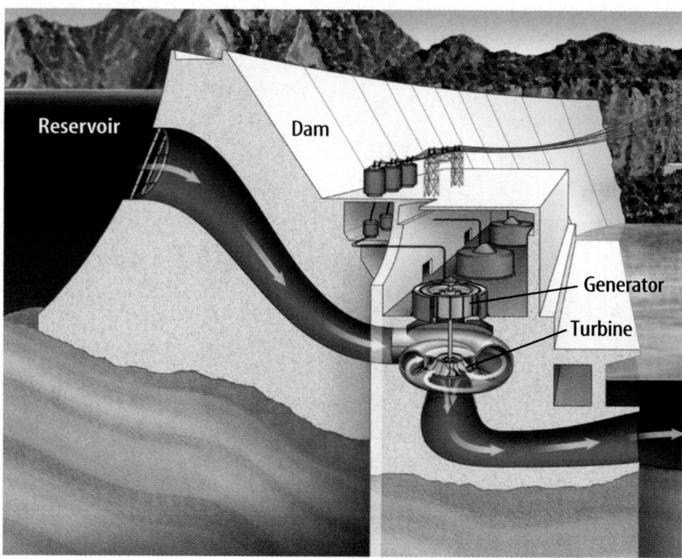

Figure 21 The potential energy in water stored behind the dam is converted to electrical energy in a hydroelectric power plant.
Diagram *the energy conversions that occur as a hydroelectric dam produces electrical energy.*

Using Hydroelectricity Electricity produced from the energy of moving water is called **hydroelectricity.** Currently about 8 percent of the electrical energy used in the United States is produced by hydroelectric power plants. Hydroelectric power plants are an efficient way to produce electricity with almost no pollution. Because no exchange of heat is involved in producing steam to spin a turbine, hydroelectric power plants are almost twice as efficient as fossil fuel or nuclear power plants.

Reading Check *Why are hydroelectric power plants more efficient than fossil fuel power plants?*

Another advantage is that the bodies of water held back by dams can form lakes that can provide water for drinking and crop irrigation. These lakes also can be used for boating and swimming. Also, after the initial cost of building a dam and a power plant, the electricity is relatively cheap.

However, artificial dams can disturb the balance of natural ecosystems. Some species of fish that live in the ocean migrate back to the rivers in which they were hatched to breed. This migration can be blocked by dams, which causes a decline in the fish population. Fish ladders, such as those shown in **Figure 22,** have been designed to enable fish to migrate upstream past some dams. Also, some water sources suitable for a hydroelectric power plant are located far from the regions needing power.

Figure 22 Fish ladders enable fish to migrate upstream past dams.

Discussion

Water Use Water is a free and renewable resource. Why, then, doesn't it supply more of our energy needs? Most sites suitable for developing hydroelectric power are already in use. Hydroelectric plants cannot be built in other locations because they disrupt the natural ecosystems or the geography of the location does not make it practical. L2 LS **Logical-Mathematical**

Caption Answer

Figure 21 The kinetic energy of falling water produces mechanical energy when it strikes and rotates the turbine. The turbine rotates a shaft of an electric generator that transforms mechanical energy to electrical energy.

Identifying Misconceptions

Alternative Energy Sources Students may think that because an alternative energy source isn't economical on a large scale that it isn't useful. Explain that many alternative energy sources, such as hydroelectricity, solar power, and wind power, are ideal for use on a small scale in rural areas or in developing societies.

Reading Check

Answer Hydroelectric power plants do not have a loss of energy converting thermal energy to mechanical energy. The falling water provides the mechanical energy required to turn the turbine to generate electricity.

Teacher FYI

Waterwheels Waterwheels probably first provided energy around the first century B.C. They have been used to turn levers and run machines, such as sawmills and grain grinders. Falling water was harnessed to provide electricity at Niagara Falls in 1896.

Cultural Diversity

The Amish and Electricity The Amish in the United States avoid modern technology and focus on a simple life based on family, church, and community. Have students find out more about how the Amish use technology. Some Amish will use such things as telephones and cars without owning them. Some have their own electrical generators, but do not tap into public power supplies. L3 LS **Linguistic**

Teacher FYI

Tidal Energy The Annapolis Royal tidal energy plant is located on the Bay of Fundy between New Brunswick and Nova Scotia in Canada, which has tides up to 17 meters high. These are the highest tides in the world. L3

LS **Linguistic**

Discussion

Tide Height Why do some coastal areas have higher tides than others? The height of the tide is increased by geographical features, such as the shapes of bays and inlets and the slope of the ocean floor.

Fun Fact

Tidal energy is possible only if the difference between high and low tides is more than 5 m. A higher tide difference means the plant can produce more electricity at a lower cost. A dam is needed to hold back the water at high tide. The dam's high construction cost makes it cheaper to build tidal plants on narrow inlets.

Quick Demo

Windmills

Materials toy pinwheel

Estimated Time five minutes

Procedure Use a toy pinwheel to demonstrate how a windmill works. Blow gently into the pinwheel forcing it to spin.

Figure 23 This tidal energy plant at Annapolis Royal, Nova Scotia, generates 20 megawatts of electric power.

Energy from the Tides

The gravity of the Moon and Sun causes bulges in Earth's oceans. As Earth rotates, the two bulges of ocean water move westward. Each day, the level of the ocean on a coast rises and falls continually. Hydroelectric power can be generated by these ocean tides. As the tide comes in, the moving water spins a turbine that generates electricity. The water is then trapped behind a dam. At low tide the water behind the dam flows back out to the ocean, spinning the turbines and generating electric power.

Tidal energy is nearly pollution free. The efficiency of a tidal power plant is similar to that of a conventional hydroelectric power plant. However, only a few places on Earth have large enough differences between high and low tides for tidal energy to be a useful energy source. The only tidal power station in use in North America is at Annapolis Royal, Nova Scotia, shown in **Figure 23.** Tidal energy probably will be a limited source of energy in the future.

Harnessing the Wind

You might have seen a windmill on a farm or pictures of windmills in a book. These windmills use the energy of the wind to pump water. Windmills also can use the energy of the wind to generate electricity. Wind spins a propeller that is connected to an electric generator. Windmill farms, like the one shown in **Figure 24,** may contain several hundred windmills.

However, only a few places on Earth consistently have enough wind to rely on wind power to meet energy needs. Also, windmills are only about 20 percent efficient on average. Research is underway to improve the design of wind generators and increase their efficiency. Other disadvantages of wind energy are that windmills can be noisy and change the appearance of a landscape. Also, they can disrupt the migration patterns of some birds. However, wind generators do not consume any nonrenewable natural resources, and they do not pollute the atmosphere or water.

Figure 24 Wind energy is converted to electricity as the spinning propeller turns a generator.

Teacher FYI

Tidal Power Plants The world's first and largest tidal power plant began operating in 1967 at the Rance River in France, with a capacity of 240 MW. The Annapolis Royal plant in Canada has a 20 MW capacity, and the tidal plant near Murmansk in Russia has a capacity of 0.4 MW.

Differentiated Instruction

English-Language Learners Have students create a poster showing different types of renewable energy sources. Have students find a real location or an example that uses each type of renewable energy to generate power. Include these examples on the poster. P

Energy from Inside Earth

INTEGRATE Earth Science Earth is not completely solid. Heat is generated within Earth by the decay of radioactive elements. This heat is called geothermal heat. Geothermal heat causes the rock beneath Earth's crust to soften and melt. This hot molten rock is called magma. The thermal energy that is contained in hot magma is called **geothermal energy.**

In some places, Earth's crust has cracks or thin spots that allow magma to rise near the surface. Active volcanoes, for example, permit hot gases and magma from deep within Earth to escape. Perhaps you have seen a geyser, like Old Faithful in Yellowstone National Park, shooting steam and hot water. The water that shoots from the geyser is heated by magma close to Earth's surface. In some areas, this hot water can be pumped into houses to provide heat.

What two natural phenomena are caused by geothermal heat?

Geothermal Power Plants

Geothermal energy also can be used to generate electricity, as shown in **Figure 25.** Where magma is close to the surface, the surrounding rocks are also hot. A well is drilled and water is pumped into the ground, where it makes contact with the hot rock and changes into steam. The steam then returns to the surface, where it is used to rotate turbines that spin electric generators.

The efficiency of geothermal power plants is about 16 percent. Although geothermal power plants can release some gases containing sulfur compounds, pumping the water created by the condensed steam back into Earth can help reduce this pollution. However, the use of geothermal energy is limited to areas where magma is relatively close to the surface.

Topic: Geothermal Energy
Visit gpscience.com for Web links to information about geothermal energy.

Activity Using the information that you find write a paragraph describing why current facilities are located where they are.

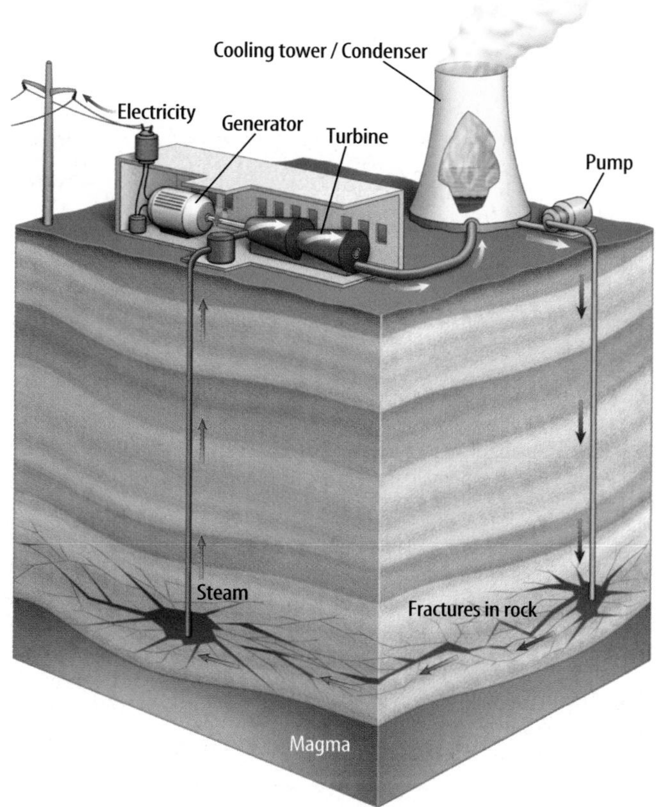

Figure 25 A geothermal power plant converts geothermal energy to electrical energy. Water is changed to steam by the hot rock. The steam is pumped to the surface where it turns a turbine attached to an electric generator.

Discussion

Geothermal Energy Most sources of geothermal energy are in areas with high volcanic activity. Geothermal energy is used on a large scale in Japan, Iceland, Italy, New Zealand, and California. Is geothermal energy renewable? Explain. Heat from a particular reservoir can be used up faster than it can be replaced, so it is not renewable. However, radioactive decay will provide a constant heat source for millions of years. L3 LS **Logical-Mathematical**

Use Science Words

Word Meaning Why is heat from Earth called "geothermal"? *Geo* means "Earth," and *thermal* means "heat." L2 LS **Linguistic**

Reading Check

Answer volcanoes and geysers

Visual Learning

Figure 25 In a geothermal plant such as the one shown here, after the steam has turned the turbine, the steam is condensed and returned to the rock through the injection well. Why is the water returned to the rock formation? to maintain the supply of water needed to produce steam L2 LS **Logical-Mathematical**

Differentiated Instruction

Challenge Have students research and write descriptions of the various forces that affect wind. They might write about the effects of temperature and pressure, surface obstacles, Earth's rotation, sea breezes, and mountain breezes. L3 LS **Logical-Mathematical**

Discussion

Alternative Fuels Using biomass and other alternative fuels reduces dependence on foreign oil. Why is this desirable? Political disagreements could reduce access to foreign oil because of strained relations with some countries. L3 LS **Logical-Mathematical**

3 Assess

DAILY INTERVENTION

Check for Understanding

Interpersonal Have the students work in small groups. Each group should choose one of the energy sources discussed in the chapter. Have the students devise a plan describing how their chosen energy source could be used in their community.

Reteach

Renewable Energy Sources Ask students to list the six energy sources discussed in this section. Once the students have a complete list, ask them to write a sentence about each source, describing how it can be used to provide energy. L2 LS **Linguistic**

Assessment

Performance Have students work in small groups to design and create a system for heating water using solar power. Use **Performance Assessment in the Science Classroom,** p. 117.

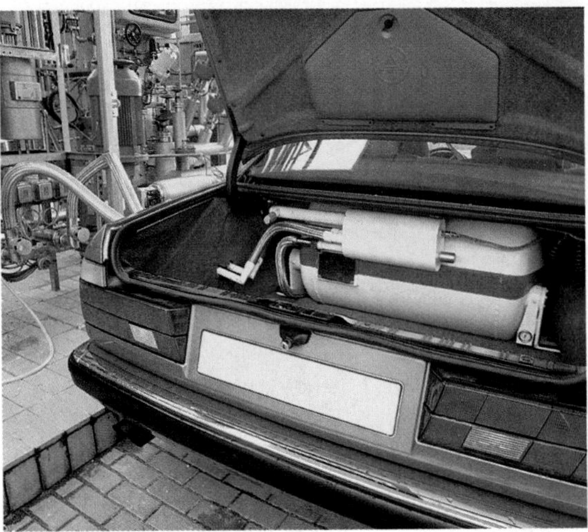

Figure 26 Hydrogen may one day replace gasoline as a fuel for automobiles. Burning hydrogen produces water vapor, instead of carbon dioxide.

Alternative Fuels

The use of fossil fuels would be greatly reduced if cars could run on other fuels or sources of energy. For example, cars have been developed that use electrical energy supplied by batteries as a power source. Hybrid cars use both electric motors and gasoline engines. Hydrogen gas is another possible alternative fuel. It produces only water vapor when it burns and creates no pollution. **Figure 26** shows a car that is equipped to use hydrogen as fuel.

Biomass Fuels Could any other materials be used to heat water and produce electricity like fossil fuels and nuclear fission? Biomass can be burned in the presence of oxygen to convert the stored chemical energy to thermal energy. **Biomass** is renewable organic matter, such as wood, sugarcane fibers, rice hulls, and animal manure. Converting biomass is probably the oldest use of natural resources for meeting human energy needs.

section 3 review

Summary

Energy Options

- The development of alternative energy sources can help reduce the use of fossil fuels.

Solar Energy

- Photovoltaic cells, or solar cells, convert radiant energy from the Sun into electrical energy.
- Producing large amounts of energy from solar cells is more expensive than using fossil fuels.

Other Renewable Energy Sources

- Hydroelectric power plants convert the potential energy in water to electrical energy.
- Tidal energy, wind energy, and geothermal energy can be converted into electrical energy, but are useable only in certain locations.
- Alternative fuels such as hydrogen could be used to power cars, and biomass can be burned to provide heat.

Self Check

1. **Explain** the need to develop and use alternative energy sources.
2. **Describe** three ways that solar energy can be used.
3. **Explain** how the generation of electricity by hydroelectric, tidal, and wind sources are similar to each other.
4. **Explain** why geothermal energy is unlikely to become a major energy source.
5. **Think Critically** What single energy source do most energy alternatives depend on, either directly or indirectly?

Applying Math

6. **Use Percentages** A house uses solar cells that generate 6.0 kW of electrical power to supply some of its energy needs. If the solar panels supply the house with 40 percent of the power it needs, how much power does the house use?

gpscience.com/self_check_quiz

section 3 review

1. The use of alternative energy sources can cause the use of fossil fuels to be reduced. This would make the supply of fossil fuels last longer, and reduce the emission of pollutants and carbon dioxide into the atmosphere.
2. Possible answers: Let the sun warm and light rooms. Use solar panels for heating water or air. Use photovoltaic cells to produce electricity.
3. They are all renewable sources. Each of these spins a turbine to rotate the shaft of an electric generator.
4. It is limited to areas where magma is relatively close to the surface.
5. the Sun
6. 15 kW

Solar Heating

Energy from the Sun is absorbed by Earth and makes its temperature warmer. In a similar way, solar energy also is absorbed by solar collectors to heat water and buildings.

Real-World Question

Does the rate at which an object absorbs solar energy depend on the color of the object?

Goals

- **Demonstrate** solar heating.
- **Compare** the effectiveness of heating items of different colors.
- **Graph** your results.

Materials

small cardboard boxes
black, white, and colored paper
tape or glue
thermometer
watch with a second hand

Procedure

1. Cover at least three small boxes with colored paper. The colors should include black and white as well as at least one other color.
2. Copy the data table into your Science Journal. Replace *Other color* with whatever color you are using.
3. Place the three objects on a windowsill or other sunny spot and note the starting time.
4. **Measure and record** the temperature inside each box at 2-min intervals for at least 10 min.

Temperature Due to Different Colors

Color	2 min	4 min	6 min	8 min	10 min
Black	Students answers will vary.				
White					
Other color					

Conclude and Apply

1. **Graph** your data using a line graph.
2. **Describe** the shapes of the lines on your graph. What color heated up the fastest? Which heated up the slowest?
3. **Explain** why the colored boxes heated at different rates.
4. **Infer** Suppose you wanted to heat a tub of water using solar energy. Based on the results of this activity, what color would you want the tub to be? Explain.
5. **Explain** why you might want to wear a white or light-colored shirt on a hot, sunny, summer day.

Communicating Your Data

Compare your results with those of other students in your class. Discuss any differences found in your graphs, particularly if different colors were used by different groups.

Real-World Question

Purpose Students demonstrate how various colors absorb solar energy differently and graph the results. L2 IS **Kinesthetic**

Process Skills observe, infer, compare and contrast, recognize cause and effect, communicate, make and use tables, make and use graphs, interpret data

Time Required 45 minutes

Procedure

Teaching Strategy Suggest students work in pairs to make measurements. One student can read the thermometer as the other student fills in the data table. Have students work individually to prepare their graphs.

Troubleshooting Students should cover each box in a way that does not allow heat to escape.

Conclude and Apply

1. Suggest students use a different color line for each color of paper.
2. The lines all sloped upward. Black heated the fastest. White heated the slowest.
3. Black absorbs more light energy, which makes it heat faster, and white absorbs less light energy, which makes it heat more slowly.
4. Because black heats up faster, you would want the tub to be black.
5. You would want to wear a white or light-colored shirt because it absorbs less light energy and wouldn't heat up as quickly.

Assessment

Content Have students make cartoons illustrating situations in which the color of something is important to its temperature. For example, dark-colored car seats are hotter in summer than those with a light color. Use **Performance Assessment in the Science Classroom,** p. 133.

Communicating Your Data

Have students use a computer graphing program to prepare their graphs. Encourage them to make their graphs as clear as possible so that others can understand the results easily. Remind students that a clear presentation of data is important to help others benefit from their work.

Real-World Question

Internet Students will use Internet sites that can be accessed by visiting gpscience.com/internet_lab. They will investigate the costs and environmental impacts of different energy sources.

Non-Internet Sources Product information publications often have comparison data for energy sources such as batteries, as well as energy efficiency ratings for appliances.

Time Required about three days

Make a Plan

Preparation

Internet Visit gpscience.com/internet_lab to run through the steps students will follow.

Non-Internet Sources Collect magazines and periodicals that list efficiencies of energy sources and appliances.

Follow Your Plan

Teaching Strategy Remind students that they should consider how different energy sources, such as rechargeable batteries and disposable batteries, affect the environment.

LAB Use the Internet

How much does energy really co$t?

Goals

- **Identify** three energy sources that people use.
- **Determine** the cost of the energy produced by each source.
- **Describe** the environmental impact of each source.

Data Source

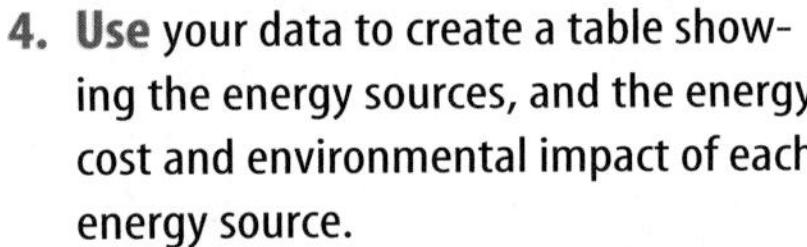

Visit gpscience.com/internet_lab for more information about energy sources and for data collected by other students.

Real-World Question

You know that it costs money to produce energy. Using energy also can have an impact on the environment. For example, coal costs less than some other fuels. However, combustion is a chemical reaction that can produce pollutants, and burning coal produces more pollution than burning other fossil fuels, such as natural gas. Even energy sources, such as hydroelectric power, that don't produce pollution can have an impact on the environment. What are some of the environmental impacts of the evergy sources used in the United States? How can these environmental impacts be compared to the cost of the energy produced?

Make a Plan

1. **Research** the various sources of energy used in different areas of the United States and choose three energy sources to investigate.
2. **Research** the cost of the consumer of 1 kWh of electrical energy generated by energy sources you have choosen.
3. **Determine** the effects each of the three energy sources has on the environment.

4. **Use** your data to create a table showing the energy sources, and the energy cost and environmental impact of each energy source.
5. **Decide** how you will evaluate the environmental impact of each of your energy sources.
6. **Write** a summary describing which of your three energy sources is the most cost-effective for producing energy. Consider the cost of the energy and your evaluation of the environmental impact in making your decision. Use information from your research to support your conclusions.

Alternative Inquiry Lab

Real-World Connection To make this Lab an Inquiry Lab, give the students a more personal investment into the problem by connecting it to the real world. Divide the students into small groups. Each group will start a small imaginary manufacturing facility. The facility must be powered primarily by some type of renewable energy. At least 60 percent of the power for the facility must come from an on-site renewable energy source. Have students investigate the types of energy sources available for their area. Students should develop a site plan for their facility that includes a site for their renewable energy source. This lab will help students develop problem-solving skills, critical-thinking skills, and team-building skills.

Follow Your Plan

1. Make sure your teacher approves your plan before you start.
2. **Record** your data in your Science Journal.

Analyze Your Data

1. Of the energy sources you investigated, which is the most expensive to use? The least expensive?
2. Which energy source do you think has the most impact on the environment? The least impact?

Energy Sources

Energy Source	Cost per kWh	Environmental Impacts
Energy source 1	Student answers will vary.	
Energy source 2		
Energy source 3		

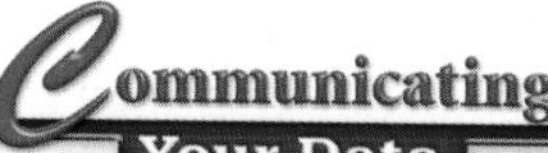

Conclude and Apply

1. **Explain** Of the energy sources you investigated, which is the least expensive energy source? Which is the best choice to use? Why or why not?
2. **Explain** Of the energy sources you investigated, how did the environmental impact of using that energy source influence your choice of the best energy solution?
3. **Evaluate** Which data support your decision?

Communicating Your Data

Find this lab using the link below. Post your data in the table provided. **Compare** your data to those of other students.

Science Online
gpscience.com/internet_lab

Analyze Your Data

1. Answers may vary. Remind students to consider the costs of producing energy sources as they evaluate the cost of using each source.
2. Answers may vary. Students should evaluate different environmental impacts of energy sources, such as water pollution and pollutants released into the ground.

Conclude and Apply

1. To support their answers, ask students to provide specific facts to explain why an energy source is the least expensive or the most expensive and the best choice.
2. Student responses should describe how the chosen energy source affects the environment.
3. Information from scientific and energy industry sources may provide data to support students' hypotheses.

Assessment

Process Have students make displays describing their findings. Displays should include the items that were investigated, students' hypotheses, different energy sources that could be used to operate the items, and the cost and environmental impact of each energy source. Use **Performance Assessment in the Science Classroom,** p. 135.

Communicating Your Data

Have students design a rating system to evaluate the environmental impact of various energy sources. After analyzing each energy source for each criterion, students can make bar graphs representing their results.

TIME

Content Background

Nuclear energy is a complicated subject. Images of the devastation from atomic explosions and sensational accounts of the dangers of radiation have created fear regarding anything labeled *nuclear*. The abstract nature of the subject offers little comfort to the layman.

Radiation occurs when an unstable atom ejects particles or energy from its nucleus in the process of becoming stable. Fission, the splitting of an atom into two smaller atoms, releases neutrons. These neutrons collide with other nuclei, causing them to split and emit neutrons. This process can cause a chain reaction. Nuclear fission reactions can release high-energy electromagnetic radiation called gamma rays, which can only be blocked by lead or thick concrete.

Discussion

Drawbacks Are there any drawbacks to wind, hydroelectric, or tidal power technologies? Possible answers: Wind and tide generation are variable and restricted to a localized area. Hydroelectric power requires building dams, which then have an impact on wildlife habitats. Wind and hydro power use much more land area per kilowatt than the other sources of power.

Investigate the Issue

Have students research the feasibility of power sources not discussed in the article such as fusion and fuel cells. Discuss whether any of these might replace currently available sources.

TIME SCIENCE AND Society

SCIENCE ISSUES THAT AFFECT YOU!

Reacting to Nuclear Energy

Most people agree that thanks to energy sources, we have many things that make our quality of life better. Energy runs our cars, lights our homes, and powers our appliances. What many people don't agree on is where that energy should come from.

Almost all of the world's electric energy is produced by thermal power plants. Most of these plants burn fossil fuels—such as coal, oil, and natural gas—to produce energy. Nuclear energy is produced by fission, which is the splitting of an atom's nucleus. People in favor of nuclear energy argue that, unlike fossil fuels, nuclear energy is nonpolluting.

Opponents counter, though, that the poisonous radioactive waste created in nuclear reactors qualifies as pollution—and will be lingering in the ground and water for hundreds of thousands of years.

Supporters of nuclear energy also cite the spectacular efficiency of nuclear energy—one metric ton of nuclear fuel produces the same amount of energy as up to 3 million tons of coal. Opponents point out that uranium is in very short supply and, like fossil fuels, is likely to run out in the next 100 years.

Opponents worry that as utilities come under less government regulation, safety standards will be ignored in the interest of profit. This could result in more accidents like the one that occurred at Chernobyl in the Ukraine. There, an explosion in the reactor core released radiation over a wide area.

Supporters counter that it will never be in the best interests of those running nuclear plants to relax safety standards since those safety standards are the best safeguard of workers' health. They cite the overall good safety record of nuclear power plants.

This site at Yucca Mountain, Nevada, is the location of a proposed high-level nuclear waste storage facility. Here radioactive materials would be buried for tens of thousands of years.

Debate **Form three teams and have each team defend one of the views presented here. If you need more information, go to the Glencoe Science Web site. "Debrief" after the debate. Did the arguments change your understanding of the issues?**

For more information, visit gpscience.com/time

Debate Have the teams use the knowledge they gained from the activity and investigation above to help them investigate the cost per kilowatt of one of the technologies discussed. Remind students to keep in mind the amount and type of pollution caused by each technology and by processing its fuel. Ask teams for recommendations about future energy production.

Resources for Teachers and Students

American Nuclear Society, 555 North Kensington Avenue, LaGrange Park, Illinois 60526 USA

Quarks and Sparks: The Story of Nuclear Power (Science and Society Series), by J. S. Kidd and Renee A. Kidd, New York: Facts on File (1999)

American Wind Energy Association, 122 C Street, NW, Suite 380, Washington, DC 20001

Reviewing Main Ideas

Section 1 Fossil Fuels

1. Fossil fuels include oil, natural gas,and coal. They formed from the buried remains of plants and animals.
2. Fossil fuels can be burned to supply energy for generating electricity. Petroleum also is used to make plastics and synthetic fabrics.

3. Fossil fuels are nonrenewable energy resources. They can be replaced, but it takes millions of years.

Section 2 Nuclear Energy

1. A nuclear reactor transforms the energy from a controlled nuclear chain reaction to electrical energy.
2. Nuclear wastes must be contained and disposed of carefully so radiation from nuclear decay will not leak into the environment. These low-level nuclear wastes are buried to protect living organisms.

3. Nuclear fusion releases energy when two nuclei combine. Fusion only occurs at high temperatures that are difficult to produce in a laboratory.

Section 3 Renewable Energy Sources

1. Alternative energy resources can be used to supplement or replace nonrenewable energy resources.
2. Other sources of energy for generating electricity include hydroelectricity and solar, wind, tidal, and geothermal energy. Each source has its advantages and disadvantages. Also, some of these sources can damage the environment.
3. Although some alternative energy sources produce less pollution than fossil fuels do and are renewable, their use often is limited to the regions where the energy source is available. For example, tides can be used to generate electricity in coastal regions only.

4. It may be possible to use hydrogen as a fuel for automobiles and other vehicles. Biomass, such as wood and other renewable organic matter, has been used as fuel for thousands of years.

FOLDABLES Use the Foldable that you made at the beginning of the chapter to help you review energy sources.

Science Online gpscience.com/interactive_tutor

chapter 9 Study Guide

Reviewing Main Ideas

Summary statements can be used by students to review the major concepts of the chapter.

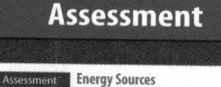

Visit gpscience.com
/self_check_quiz
/interactive_tutor
/vocabulary_puzzlemaker
/chapter_review
/standardized_test
/field_guide

Assessment Transparency

For additional assessment questions, use the *Assessment Transparency* located in the transparency book.

Assessment

Assessment Transparency **Energy Sources**

Directions: *Carefully review the tables and answer the following questions.*

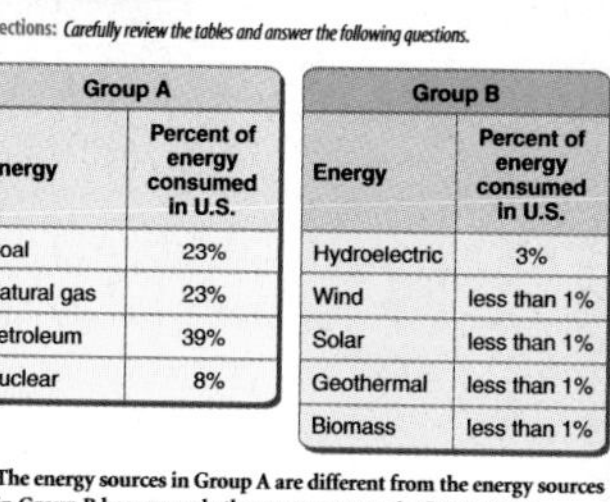

Group A	
Energy	Percent of energy consumed in U.S.
Coal	23%
Natural gas	23%
Petroleum	39%
Nuclear	8%

Group B	
Energy	Percent of energy consumed in U.S.
Hydroelectric	3%
Wind	less than 1%
Solar	less than 1%
Geothermal	less than 1%
Biomass	less than 1%

1. The energy sources in Group A are different from the energy sources in Group B because only the energy sources in Group B are ___.
   A renewable resources C fossil fuels
   B nonrenewable resources D harmful to the environment
2. According to the tables, which energy source supplies greater than 25% of the energy consumed in the U.S.?
   F Coal H Nuclear
   G Hydroelectric J Petroleum
3. According to the tables, what percent of the energy used in the U.S. comes from fossil fuels?
   A 50% C 85%
   B 60% D 93%

L2

Energy Sources

FOLDABLES Have students use their Foldables to review the content of the chapter. On the back of the paper, have the students write the advantages and disadvantages of each type of energy source that is listed on the Foldable.

Using Vocabulary

1. photovoltaic cell
2. Geothermal energy
3. renewable resource
4. Fossil fuel
5. nonrenewable
6. nuclear waste

Checking Concepts

7. C
8. A
9. C
10. B
11. A
12. C
13. D
14. C
15. D
16. B

chapter 9 Review

Using Vocabulary

biomass p. 276
fossil fuel p. 257
geothermal energy p. 275
hydroelectricity p. 273
nonrenewable resource p. 263
nuclear reactor p. 264
nuclear waste p. 268
petroleum p. 259
photovoltaic cell p. 271
renewable resource p. 271

Complete each statement using a term from the vocabulary list above.

1. A(n) ________ uses the Sun to generate electricity.
2. ________ makes use of thermal energy inside the Earth.
3. Energy produced by the rise and fall of ocean levels is a(n) ________.
4. ________ includes the following: oil, natural gas, and coal.
5. Fossil fuels are a(n) ________ because they are being used up faster than they are being made.
6. A special caution should be taken in disposing of ________.

Checking Concepts

Choose the word or phrase that best answers the question.

7. Why are fossil fuels considered to be nonrenewable resources?
   A) They are no longer being produced.
   B) They are in short supply.
   C) They are not being produced as fast as they're being used.
   D) They contain hydrocarbons.
8. To generate electricity, nuclear power plants produce which of the following?
   A) steam **C)** plutonium
   B) carbon dioxide **D)** water
9. What is a major disadvantage of using nuclear fusion reactors?
   A) use of hydrogen as fuel
   B) less radioactivity produced
   C) extremely high temperatures required
   D) use of only small nuclei
10. How are spent nuclear fuel rods usually disposed of?
    A) burying them in a community landfill
    B) storing them in a deep pool of water
    C) burying them at the reactor site
    D) releasing them into the air
11. How much energy in the United States comes from burning petroleum, natural gas, and coal?
    A) 85% **C)** 65%
    B) 35% **D)** 25%
12. Solar cells would be more practical to use if they were which of the following?
    A) pollution free **C)** less expensive
    B) nonrenewable **D)** larger
13. Which energy source uses water that is heated naturally by Earth's internal heat?
    A) hydroelectricity **C)** tidal energy
    B) nuclear fission **D)** geothermal energy
14. What do hydrocarbons react with when fossil fuels are burned?
    A) carbon dioxide **C)** oxygen
    B) carbon monoxide **D)** water
15. Which of the following is NOT a source of nuclear waste?
    A) products of fission reactors
    B) materials with short half-lives
    C) some medical and industrial products
    D) products of coal-burning power plants
16. Which of the following is the source of almost all of Earth's energy resources?
    A) plants **C)** magma
    B) the Sun **D)** fossil fuels

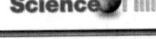

Science Online gpscience.com/vocabulary_puzzlemaker

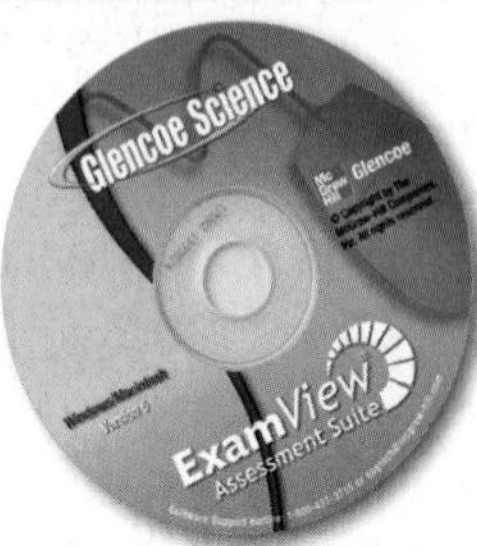

Use the *ExamView® Assessment Suite* CD-ROM to:

- create multiple versions of tests
- create modified tests with one mouse click for inclusion students
- edit existing questions and add your own questions
- build tests aligned with state standards using built-in State Curriculum Tags
- change English tests to Spanish with one mouse click and vice versa

Interpreting Graphics

17. Copy and complete the table below describing possible effects of changes in the normal operation of a nuclear reactor.

Reactor Problems

Cause	Effect
The cooling water is released hot.	Pollution of the environment results.
The control rods are removed.	More heat is produced in the core.
The cooling system fails.	The reactor core overheats and meltdown occurs.

18. Copy and complete this concept map.

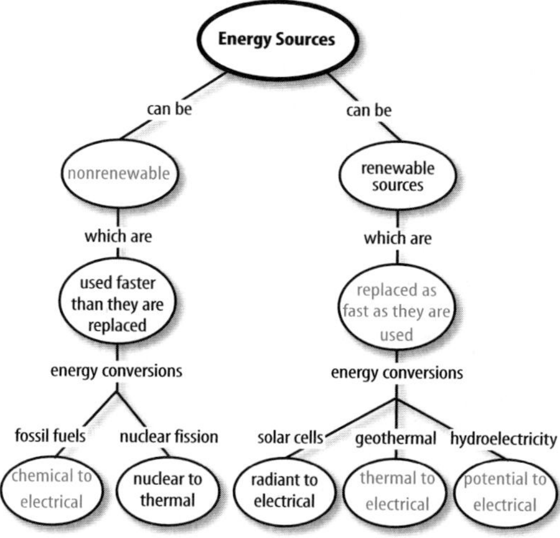

Thinking Critically

19. **Infer** why alternative energy resources aren't more widely used.

20. **Infer** whether fossil fuels should be conserved if renewable energy sources are being developed.

21. **Infer** Suppose new reserves of fossil fuels were found and a way to burn these fuels was developed that did not release pollutants and carbon dioxide into the atmosphere. Should fossil fuels still be conserved? Explain

22. **Explain** why coal is considered a nonrenewable energy source, but biomass, such as wood, is considered a renewable energy source.

23. **Make a table** listing two advantages and two disadvantages for each of the following energy sources: fossil fuels, hydroelectricity, wind turbines, nuclear fission, solar cells, and geothermal energy.

Applying Math

24. **Convert Units** Crude oil is sold on the world market in units called barrels. A barrel of crude oil contains 42 gallons. If 1 gallon is 3.8 liters, how many liters are there in a barrel of crude oil?

Use the table below to answer question 25.

High-Production Coal Mines

Coal Mine	Metric tons/year
North Antelope Rochelle	6.78×10^7
Black Thunder	6.13×10^7

25. **Use Percentages** Nine of the top coal producing mines are located in Wyoming. Production information on two of the mines is in the table above. A total of about 1.02×10^9 metric tons is produced per year in the United States. What percentage do these two coal mines contribute to the total yearly coal production in the U.S.?

Science Online gpscience.com/chapter_review

Assessment Resources

Reproducible Masters

Chapter *Fast File* Resources
- Chapter Review, pp. 37–38
- Chapter Tests, pp. 39–42
- Assessment Transparency Activity, p. 49

Glencoe Science Web site
- Chapter Review Test
- Standardized Test Practice

Glencoe Technology
- Assessment Transparency
- *ExamView® Assessment Suite*
- MindJogger Videoquiz
- Interactive Chalkboard

Interpreting Graphics

17. See student page.
18. See student page.

Thinking Critically

19. Alternative energy resources are not widely used because the necessary technology does not yet exist, is too expensive, or has limited applicability.
20. Fossil fuels should be conserved because they are used to produce useful materials such as plastic.
21. These new sources would still be nonrenewable energy sources. Conserving fossil fuel would make them last longer.
22. Biomass can be replaced in several years by replanting. Coal takes millions of years to form.
23. Fossil fuels: inexpensive and plentiful, but are nonrenewable and produce pollutants. Hydroelectricity: renewable and inexpensive, but can affect local ecosystems and has limited availability. Wind turbines: nonpolluting and use a renewable energy source, but are noisy and have limited availability. Nuclear power: nonpolluting and inexpensive, but problems exist with nuclear waste disposal, and risks of nuclear accidents. Solar cells : use a renewable resource that is available everywhere, but inefficient and expensive. Geothermal energy: uses a renewable resource and does not produce carbon dioxide, but is inefficient and has limited availability.

Applying Math

National Math Standards

1,5,9

24. $\frac{42\ gallons}{1\ barrel} \times \frac{3.8\ liters}{1\ gallon} =$

$159.6 \frac{liters}{barrel} = 160 \frac{liters}{barrel}$

25. $\frac{1.291 \times 10^8 \text{ metric tons/year}}{1.02 \times 10^9 \text{ metric tons/year}} =$

$0.127 = 12.7\%$

FAST FILE

Answer Sheet A practice answer sheet can be found at gpscience.com/answer_sheet.

Student Recording Sheet

SAMPLE

Part 1 Multiple Choice

1. D
2. B
3. A
4. D
5. A
6. B
7. A

Part 2 Short Response

8. no energy lost in producing steam to spin a turbine
9. to produce electricity
10. the conversion of chemical energy in the fuel into heat
11. They usually are sealed in containers and buried in trenches 30 m deep at special locations. If the waste is extremely low-level, the waste sometimes is released into the air or water.
12. A fuel rod contains tiny pellets of uranium dioxide fuel. A fuel rod consists of many of these pellets placed end to end in a tube and covered with a metal alloy.
13. to stop or slow the nuclear chain reaction by absorbing neutrons released during the reaction; Moving these control rods deeper into the reactor allows them to absorb more neutrons and slow down the reaction.
14. Fusion reactions occur only at temperatures of millions of degrees Celsius. Creating and maintaining these high temperatures requires enormous amounts of energy.

Part 3 Open Ended

15. Use **Figure 14** to check students' sketches.
16. At a nuclear power plant, thermal energy released in nuclear fission is used to heat water and produce steam. This steam is used to drive a turbine that rotates an electric generator. The fission process

Part 1 Multiple Choice

Record your answers on the answer sheet provided by your teacher or on a sheet of paper.

Use the graph below to answer questions 1 and 2.

Sources of Electricity

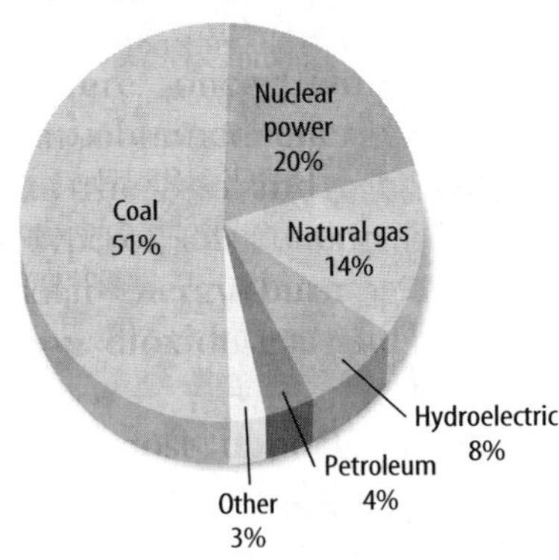

1. The graph above shows the percentage of electricity generated in the United States that comes from various energy sources. According to the graph, about what percentage comes from fossil fuels?

A. 51% **C.** 65%
B. 55% **D.** 69%

2. The graph shows that approximately what percentage of electricity comes from nonrenewable energy sources?

A. 97% **C.** 69%
B. 89% **D.** 55%

3. Which of the following is a typical efficiency for a solar cell?

A. 10% **C.** 75%
B. 50% **D.** 95%

4. Which of the following best describes wind mills used for the production of electricity?

A. They are quiet.
B. They can be used anywhere.
C. They are 90 percent efficient.
D. They are nonpolluting.

5. Which of the following forms only from ancient plant material, not from ancient animal remains?

A. coal **C.** natural gas
B. crude oil **D.** petroleum

Use the table below to answer questions 6 and 7.

Efficiency of Fossil Fuel Conversion

Process	Efficiency (%)
Chemical to thermal energy	60
Conversion of water to steam	90
Steam spins turbine	75
Turbine spins electric generator	95
Transmission through power lines	90

6. The table above shows the efficiency of different steps in the conversion of fossil fuels to electricity at a power plant. According to the table, what is the efficiency for converting chemical energy in the fossil fuels to heat, and then converting water to steam?

A. 30% **C.** 75%
B. 54% **D.** 90%

7. What is the overall efficiency shown in the table for converting chemical energy in fossil fuels to electricity?

A. 35% **C.** 90%
B. 82% **D.** 95%

Test-Taking Tip

Determine the Information Needed Concentrate on what the question is asking about a table, instead of all the information in the table.

Question 7 Read the question carefully to determine which rows in the table contain the information needed to answer the question.

Part 2 Short Response/Grid In

Record your answers on the answer sheet provided by your teacher or on a sheet of paper.

8. Explain why hydroelectric power plants are almost twice as efficient as fossil fuel or nuclear power plants.
9. About 90 percent of the coal that is used in the United States is used for what purpose?
10. What is the most inefficient stage in the production of electrical energy at a fossil-fuel burning power plant?
11. Describe the typical disposal method for low-level nuclear wastes.

Use the illustration below to answer questions 12 and 13.

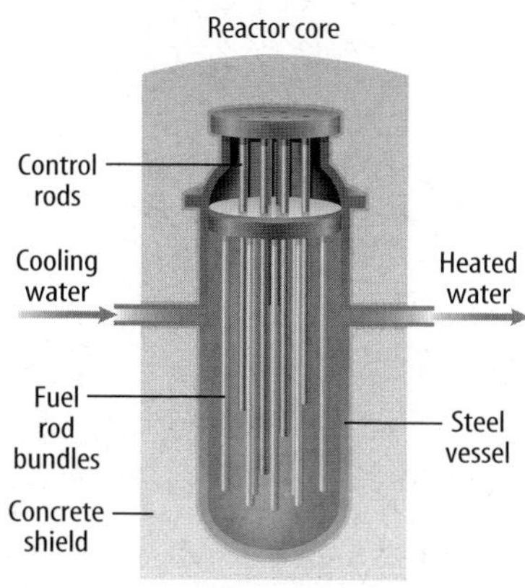

12. The core of a nuclear reactor might contain hundreds of fuel rods. Describe the composition of a fuel rod.
13. Describe the purpose of the control rods and explain how their placement in the reactor affects the nuclear chain reaction.
14. Fusion is the most concentrated energy source known. Why, then, is it not used at nuclear plants to make electricity?

Part 3 Open Ended

Record your answers on a sheet of paper.

Use the photograph below to answer questions 15 and 16.

15. The photograph above shows a nuclear power plant that generates electricity using the energy released in nuclear fission of uranium-235. Draw a sketch showing this fission process. Describe your sketch and explain how the process results in a chain reaction.
16. Explain how a nuclear reactor at a nuclear power plant produces electricity. What is the purpose of the large tower shown in the photograph?
17. Explain how the steam that is used to run turbines is produced at a geothermal power plant.
18. Describe two advantages and three disadvantages of using solar energy to generate electricity.
19. Explain why biomass is considered a renewable energy source.
20. Describe the processes that form oil, natural gas, and coal.
21. What is the difference between low-level and high-level nuclear waste? Describe an example of each type.

20. The formation of oil and natural gas begins when organic matter on the ocean floor is gradually buried under additional layers of sediment. Heat and crushing preasure gradually change the organic matter chemically. The oil and gas may bubble to the surface or become trapped beneath a dense rock layer. Coal forms when partially decomposed vegetation known as peat is compressed by overlying sediments. It is first transformed into lignite (a soft brown coal) and then into bituminous coal (a harder coal)
21. Low-level nuclear waste usually contains a small amount of radioactive material. Some examples are products of some medical and industrial processes, clothing used in handling radioactive materials, air filters from nuclear power plants, and discarded smoke detectors. High-level nuclear waste contains a significant amount of nuclear material. It is generated in nuclear power plants and by nuclear weapons programs. Spent fuel from a nuclear reactor is a high-level nuclear waste.

Rubrics

For more help evaluating open-ended assessment questions, see the rubric on p. 10T.

occurs in the reactor. The cooling occurs in the round tower.

17. A well is drilled and water is pumped down the well, where it makes contact with the hot rock and changes to steam. The steam is then forced to the surface.
18. Advantages: solar energy is widely available and renewable. Disadvantages: cost; electricity can be generated only during the day; large area must be covered with solar cells or solar collectors.
19. Some types of plant material used as fuel can be replanted every year, others can be grown over several years. Because the rate at which biomass fuels are used is low, these fuels can be replenished as rapidly as they are used.

Unit Contents

WebQuest *Created Gemstones: The Real Thing?* is a real-life scenario. Given the task of purchasing a natural gemstone or one manufactured in a laboratory, students research to discover how natural gems form, what their chemical, physical, and optical properties are, as well as how their flaws are corrected and their colors enhanced.

unit 3 **Energy on the Move**

How Are Glassblowing & X Rays Connected?

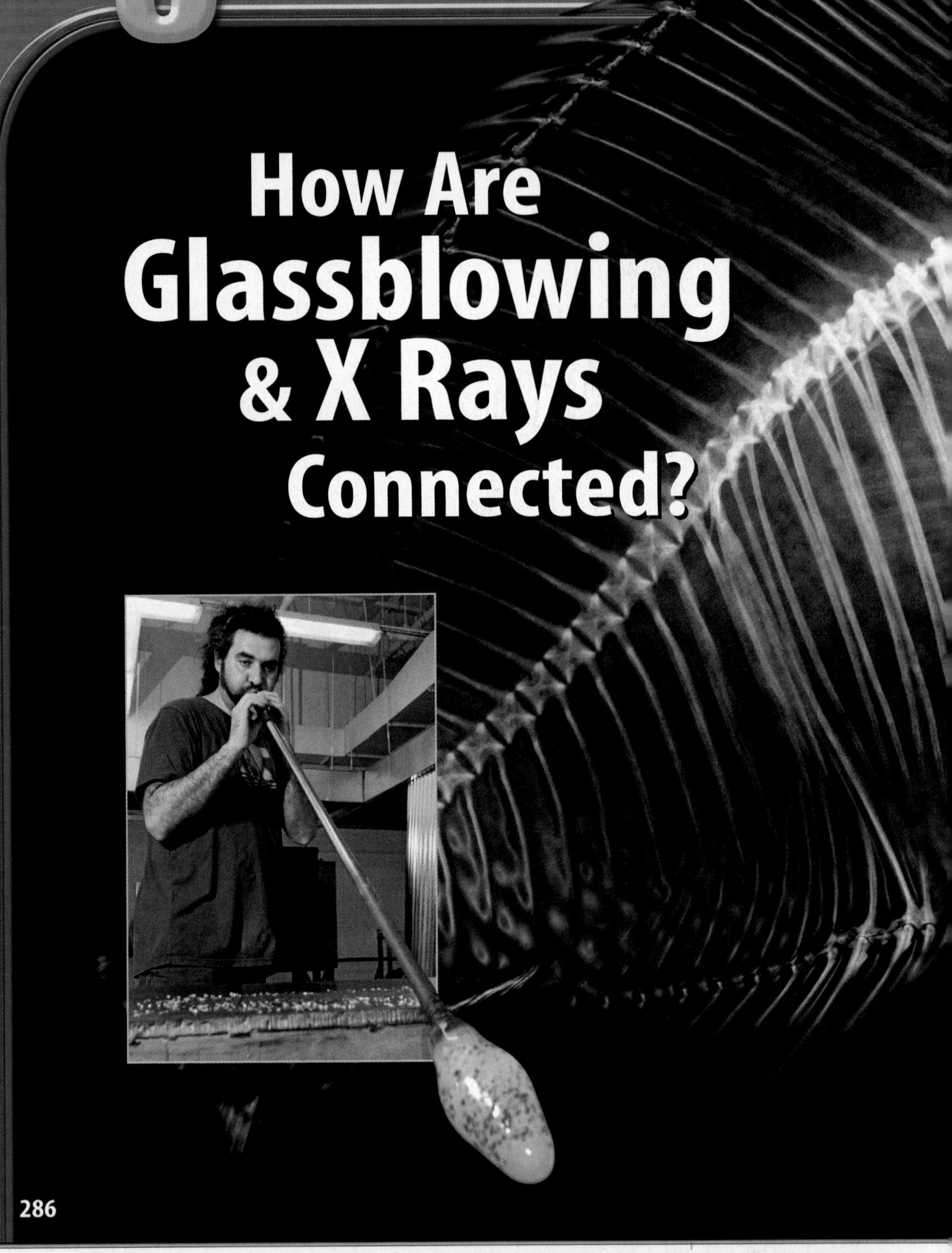

286

PROJECT CRISS[SM]

Study Skills

Vocabulary Students expand their knowledge to extend beyond a strict definition. Students use a definition map in this unit to better understand essential vocabulary. The center box of the map might contain the word "wave." One arm would answer the question, "What is it?" Another arm would answer, "What are the types of waves?" Cooperative teams would continue the map until they have reached a full definition of the word.

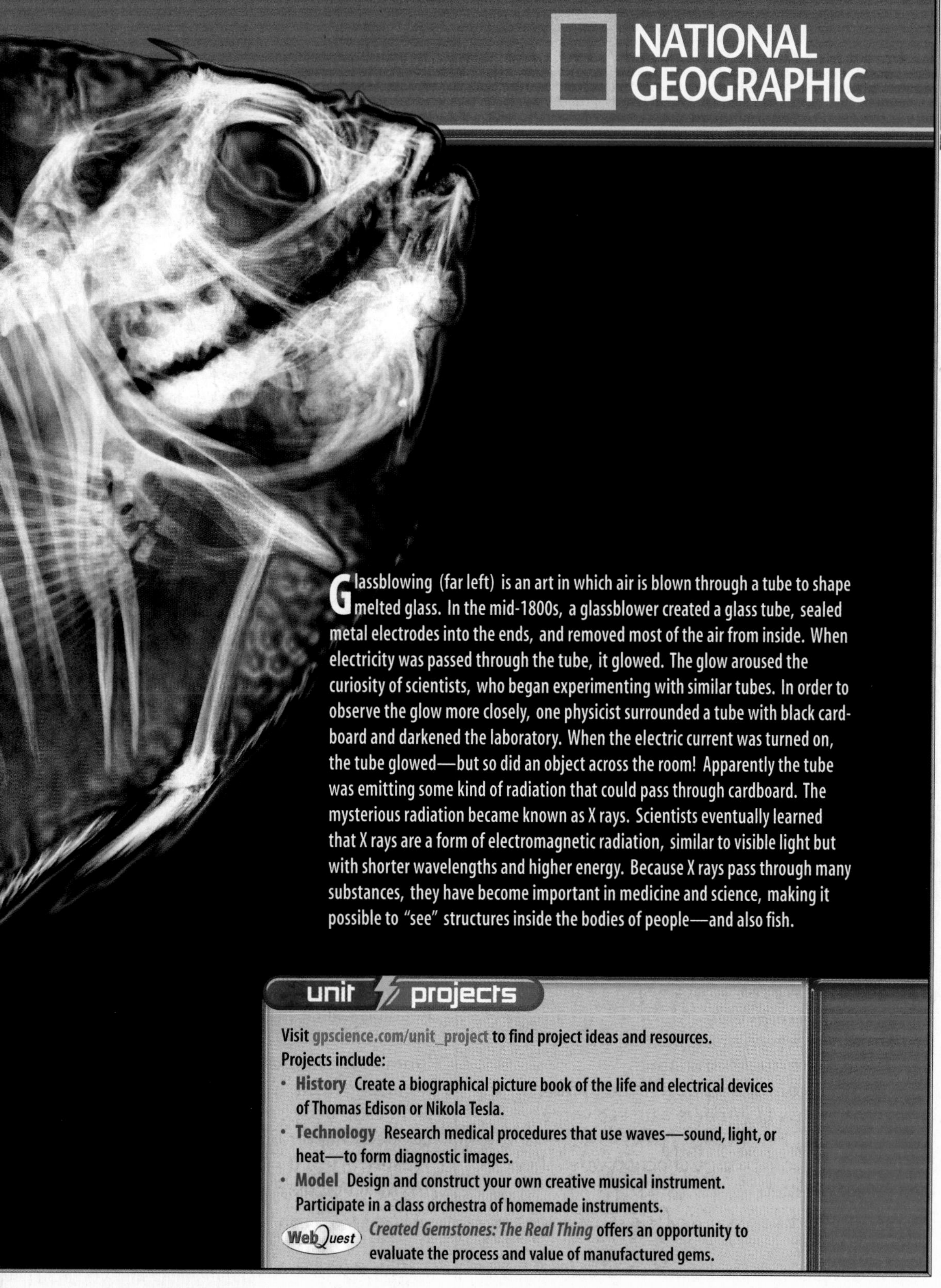

Glassblowing (far left) is an art in which air is blown through a tube to shape melted glass. In the mid-1800s, a glassblower created a glass tube, sealed metal electrodes into the ends, and removed most of the air from inside. When electricity was passed through the tube, it glowed. The glow aroused the curiosity of scientists, who began experimenting with similar tubes. In order to observe the glow more closely, one physicist surrounded a tube with black cardboard and darkened the laboratory. When the electric current was turned on, the tube glowed—but so did an object across the room! Apparently the tube was emitting some kind of radiation that could pass through cardboard. The mysterious radiation became known as X rays. Scientists eventually learned that X rays are a form of electromagnetic radiation, similar to visible light but with shorter wavelengths and higher energy. Because X rays pass through many substances, they have become important in medicine and science, making it possible to "see" structures inside the bodies of people—and also fish.

unit projects

Visit gpscience.com/unit_project to find project ideas and resources.
Projects include:

- **History** Create a biographical picture book of the life and electrical devices of Thomas Edison or Nikola Tesla.
- **Technology** Research medical procedures that use waves—sound, light, or heat—to form diagnostic images.
- **Model** Design and construct your own creative musical instrument. Participate in a class orchestra of homemade instruments.

WebQuest *Created Gemstones: The Real Thing* offers an opportunity to evaluate the process and value of manufactured gems.

unit projects

History Ask students to prepare information on the life and inventions of either Nikola Tesla or Thomas Edison. Have students write and illustrate a biographical picture book highlighting ten or more electrical devices invented by their scientist.

Technology Working in small groups, have students research medical procedures that use waves, sound, or light to form diagnostic images. Procedures may include MRI, CAT scan, X rays, thermal imaging, or ultrasound. Have students create an advertisement or news broadcast about their particular procedure to demonstrate how their image is formed, its benefits and limitations, and any related health risks.

Model Ask students to design their own creative musical instrument. Instruments should demonstrate a full scale and be able to be tuned to the proper pitch. Applying appropriate physics terms, students should be able to explain how their instrument produces a variety of sounds. Using a simple musical score ("Twinkle, Twinkle Little Star," for example) have students participate in an all-class orchestra with their physics musical instruments.

Additional Resources For more information, resources, and assessment rubrics, visit gpscience.com/unit_project

NATIONAL GEOGRAPHIC How Are Glassblowing & X Rays Connected?

- Tell students that X rays can be used on things that are not living. For example, they are helpful in locating cracks and overstressed areas in buildings and other structures.
- Ask students to brainstorm as many examples of energy on the move as they can. In addition to X rays and other types of electromagnetic radiation, such as visible light, lists might include transfer of heat from one place to another or the movement of an object, such as a bouncing ball.

Waves

BIG Idea **Waves transfer energy from place to place without transferring matter.**

	Content Standards	Learning Objectives	Resources to Assess Mastery
Section 1	**5–8:** UCP.1–3, 5; A.1, 2; B.1–3 **9–12:** UCP.1–3, 5; A.1, 2; B.2, 4–6	**The Nature of Waves** 1. **Recognize** that waves carry energy but not matter. 2. **Define** mechanical waves. 3. **Compare and contrast** transverse waves and compressional waves. ***Main Idea*** Waves move through matter as energy is transferred from particle to particle.	**Formative Assessment** Reading Check, pp. 291, 293 Section Review, p. 295 **Summative Assessment** *ExamView® Assessment Suite*
Section 2	**5–8:** UCP.1–3, 5; A.1, 2; B.1–3 **9–12:** UCP.1–3, 5; A.1, 2; B.2, 4, 6	**Wave Properties** 4. **Define** wavelength, frequency, period, and amplitude. 5. **Describe** the relationship between frequency and wavelength. 6. **Explain** how a wave's energy and amplitude are related. 7. **Calculate** wave speed. ***Main Idea*** Wave properties depend on the vibrations of the wave source and the material in which the wave moves.	**Formative Assessment** Reading Check, pp. 297, 298 Section Review, p. 301 **Summative Assessment** *ExamView® Assessment Suite*
Section 3	**5–8:** UCP.1–3, 5; A.1, 2; B.1–3; G.3 **9–12:** UCP.1–3, 5; A.1, 2; B.2, 4–6; G.3 See pp. 16T–17T for a Key to Standards.	**The Behavior of Waves** 8. **State** the law of reflection. 9. **Explain** why waves change direction when they travel from one material to another. 10. **Compare and contrast** refraction and diffraction. 11. **Describe** how waves interfere with each other. ***Main Idea*** Waves can change direction when they interact with matter.	**Formative Assessment** Reading Check, pp. 304, 306 Section Review, p. 311 **Summative Chapter Assessment** MindJogger, Ch. 10 *ExamView® Assessment Suite* Leveled Chapter Test Test A L1 Test B L2 Test C L3 Test Practice, pp. 318–319

Suggested Pacing				
Period	Instruction	Labs	Review & Assessment	Total
Single	3.5 days	2.5 days	2 days	8 days
Block	1.75 blocks	1.25 blocks	1 block	4 blocks

Core Instruction	Leveled Resources	Leveled Labs	Pacing: Period		Pacing: Block
Student Text, pp. 288–295 Section Focus Transparency, Ch. 10, Section 1 Interactive Chalkboard, Ch. 10, Section 1 Identifying Misconceptions, p. 291 Differentiated Instruction, pp. 292, 294 Visualizing Formation of Ocean Waves, p. 294	**Chapter *Fast File* Resources** Directed Reading for Content Mastery, p. 20 L1 Note-taking Worksheet, pp. 33–35 Reinforcement, p. 27 L2 Enrichment, p. 30 L3 **Reading Essentials,** p. 156 L1 ELL **Science Notebook,** p. 105 ELL ***Active*Folders**: *Waves* L1 ELL	**Launch Lab**, p. 289: marbles, textbook, pen or pencil *5 min* L2	1	Section 1, pp. 289–295 (includes Launch Lab and Section Review)	1
Student Text, pp. 296–302 Section Focus Transparency, Ch. 10, Section 2 Teaching Transparency, Ch. 10, Section 2 Interactive Chalkboard, Ch. 10, Section 2 Identifying Misconceptions, p. 299 Applying Math, p. 299 Differentiated Instruction, pp. 297, 300	**Chapter *Fast File* Resources** Directed Reading for Content Mastery, p. 20 L1 Note-taking Worksheet, pp. 33–35 Reinforcement, p. 28 L2 Enrichment, p. 31 L3 **Reading Essentials,** p. 161 L1 ELL **Science Notebook,** p. 109 ELL ***Active*Folders**: *Waves* L1 ELL	**MiniLAB**, p. 297: pie plate or wide pan, water *10 min* L2 ***Lab**, p. 302: coiled spring toys (metal , plastic), rope (heavy, light), string, long rubber band, cloth towel, nylon panty hose, stopwatch *30 min* L1 L2 L3	2	Section 2, pp. 296–298 (includes MiniLAB)	1
			3	Section 2, pp. 298–301 (includes Section Review)	2
			4	Lab:Waves in Different Mediums, p. 302	2
Student Text, pp. 303–313 Section Focus Transparency, Ch. 10, Section 3 Interactive Chalkboard, Ch. 10, Section 3 Differentiated Instruction, p. 305 Chapter Study Guide, p. 315	**Chapter *Fast File* Resources** Directed Reading for Content Mastery, pp. 21, 22 L1 Note-taking Worksheet, pp. 33–35 Reinforcement, p. 29 L2 Enrichment, p. 32 L3 **Reading Essentials,** p. 167 L1 ELL **Science Notebook,** p. 112 ELL	**MiniLAB**, p. 311: tuning forks (3), mallet *10 min* L2 ***Lab**, pp. 312–313: long spring, rope, or hose; meterstick; stopwatch *45 min* L1 L2 L3 (Video Lab) *Lab version A L1 version B L2 L3	5	Section 3, pp. 303–307	3
			6	Section 3, pp. 308–311 (includes MiniLAB and Section Review)	3
			7	Lab:Measuring Wave Properties, pp. 312–313	4
			8	Study Guide, Chapter Review, and Test Practice, pp. 315–319	4

Video Lab

chapter 10 Waves

Transparencies

Section Focus

Section 1 Section Focus Transparency — Wave to the Camera

How many waves can you pick out in this scene? Is light described as a wave? If you were there when this photograph was taken, you might also mention sound waves.

1. Describe the different waves in this picture.
2. If you are swimming underwater, can you still hear the noises around you? What does this tell you about sound waves?
3. What does light travel through as it goes from the Sun to the eyes of an underwater swimmer?

L2

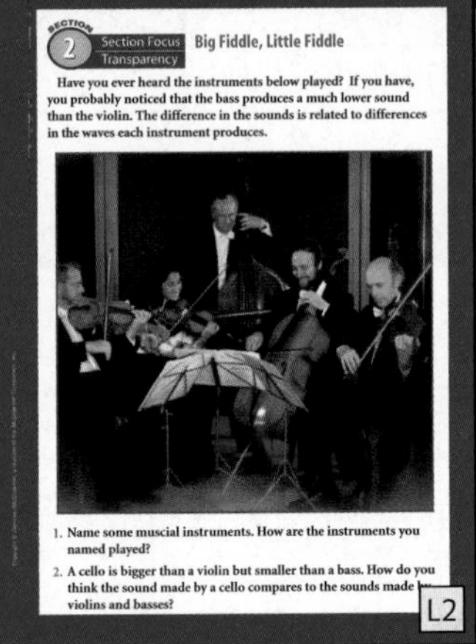

Section 2 Section Focus Transparency — Big Fiddle, Little Fiddle

Have you ever heard the instruments below played? If you have, you probably noticed that the bass produces a much lower sound than the violin. The difference in the sounds is related to differences in the waves each instrument produces.

1. Name some muscial instruments. How are the instruments you named played?
2. A cello is bigger than a violin but smaller than a bass. How do you think the sound made by a cello compares to the sounds made by violins and basses?

L2

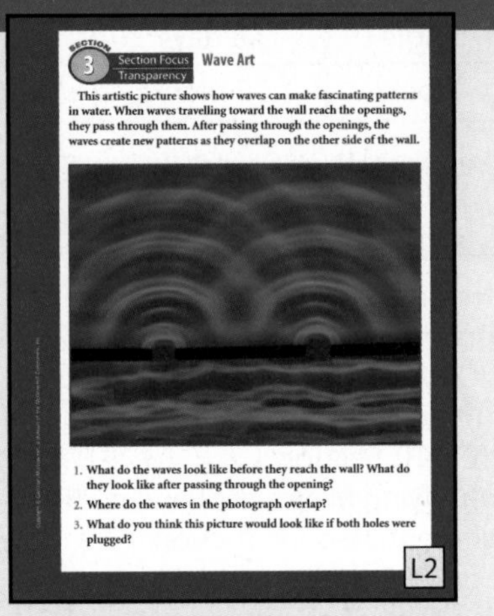

Section 3 Section Focus Transparency — Wave Art

This artistic picture shows how waves can make fascinating patterns in water. When waves travelling toward the wall reach the openings, they pass through them. After passing through the openings, the waves create new patterns as they overlap on the other side of the wall.

1. What do the waves look like before they reach the wall? What do they look like after passing through the opening?
2. Where do the waves in the photograph overlap?
3. What do you think this picture would look like if both holes were plugged?

L2

This is a representation of key blackline masters available in the Teacher Classroom Resources. See Resource Manager boxes within the chapter for additional information.

Assessment

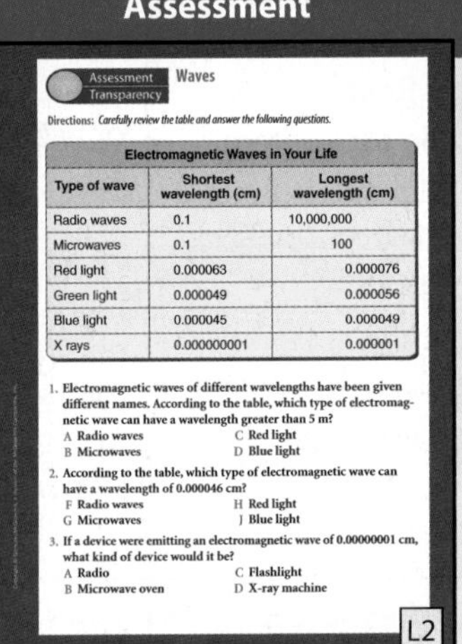

Assessment Transparency — Waves

Directions: Carefully review the table and answer the following questions.

Electromagnetic Waves in Your Life

Type of wave	Shortest wavelength (cm)	Longest wavelength (cm)
Radio waves	0.1	10,000,000
Microwaves	0.1	100
Red light	0.000063	0.000076
Green light	0.000049	0.000056
Blue light	0.000045	0.000049
X rays	0.000000001	0.000001

1. Electromagnetic waves of different wavelengths have been given different names. According to the table, which type of electromagnetic wave can have a wavelength greater than 5 m?
   A Radio waves C Red light
   B Microwaves D Blue light
2. According to the table, which type of electromagnetic wave can have a wavelength of 0.000046 cm?
   F Radio waves H Red light
   G Microwaves J Blue light
3. If a device were emitting an electromagnetic wave of 0.00000001 cm, what kind of device would it be?
   A Radio C Flashlight
   B Microwave oven D X-ray machine

L2

Teaching

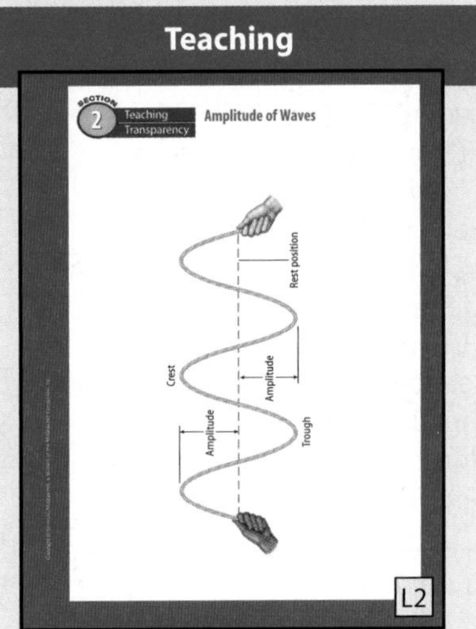

Section 2 Teaching Transparency — Amplitude of Waves

L2

Key to Teaching Strategies

The following designations will help you decide which activities are appropriate for your students.

L1 Level 1 activities should be appropriate for students with learning difficulties.

L2 Level 2 activities should be within the ability range of all students.

L3 Level 3 activities are designed for above-average students.

ELL ELL activities should be within the ability range of English Language Learners.

COOP LEARN Cooperative Learning activities are designed for small group work.

LS Multiple Learning Styles logos, as described on page 12T, are used throughout to indicate strategies that address different learning styles.

P These strategies represent student products that can be placed into a best-work portfolio.

PBL Problem-Based Learning activities apply real-world situations to learning.

Hands-on Activities

Student Text Lab Worksheet

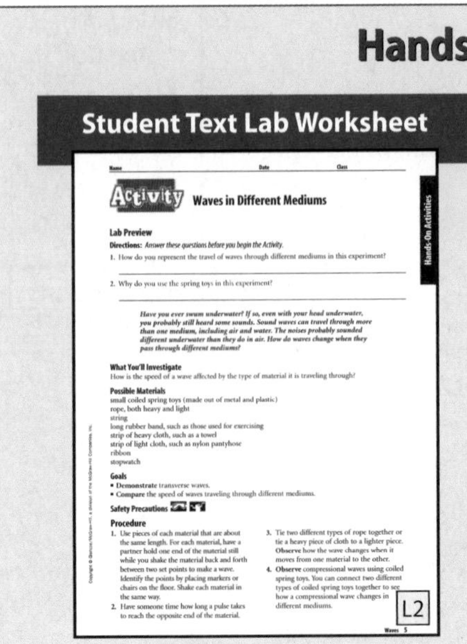

Activity — Waves in Different Mediums

Lab Preview

L2

Laboratory Activities

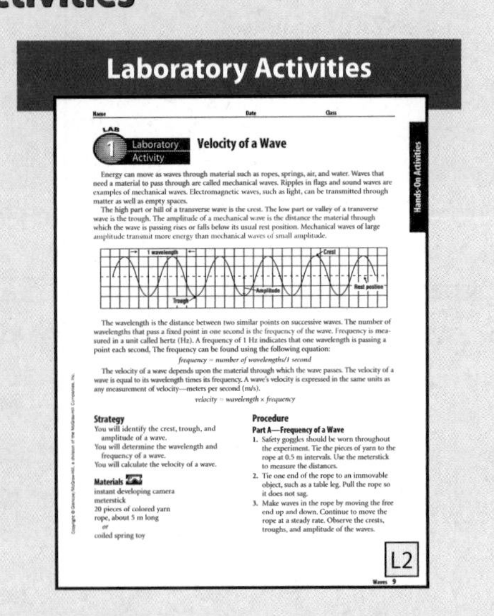

Lab 1 Laboratory Activity — Velocity of a Wave

L2

Meeting Different Ability Levels

Content Outline

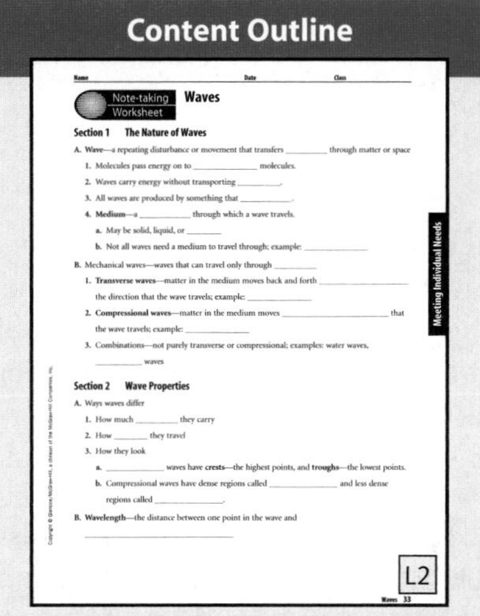
Note-taking Worksheet — Waves

Section 1 The Nature of Waves

Section 2 Wave Properties

L2

Reinforcement

Reinforcement — Section 1 — The Nature of Waves

L2

Enrichment

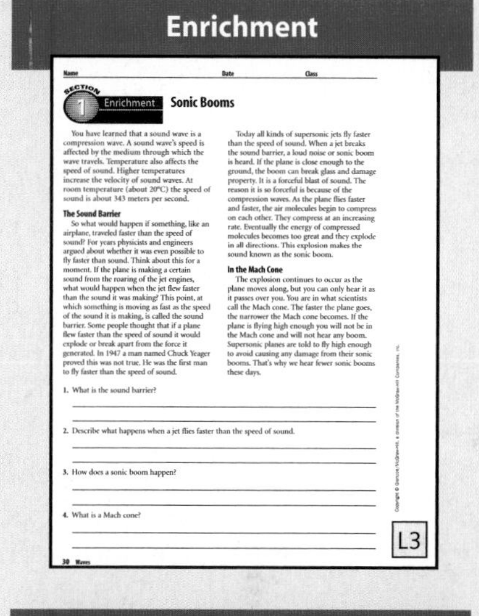
Enrichment — Section 1 — Sonic Booms

L3

Directed Reading (English/Spanish)

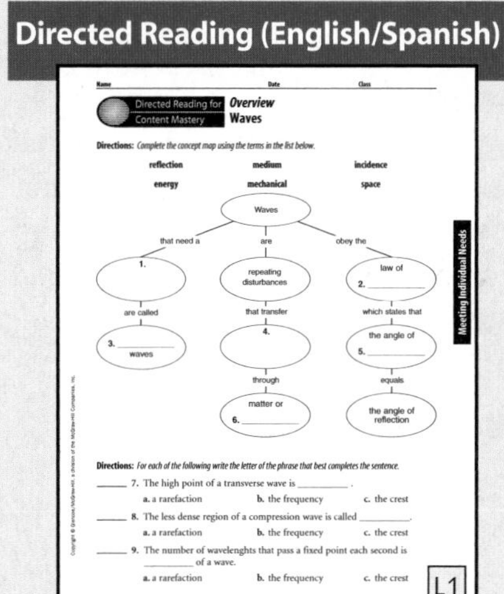
Directed Reading for Content Mastery — Overview — Waves

L1

Study Guide

Reading Essentials

Assessment

Test Practice Workbook

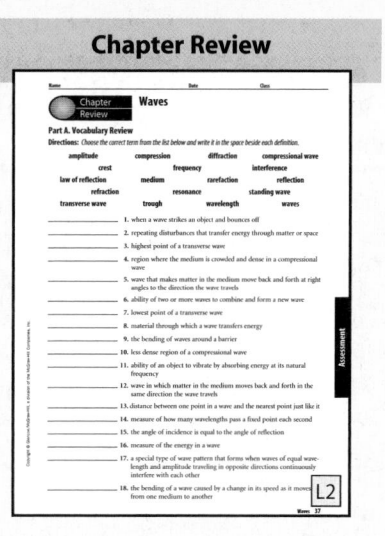

Chapter Test — Chapter 11 Waves

L2

Chapter Review

Chapter Review — Waves

Part A. Vocabulary Review

L2

Chapter Tests

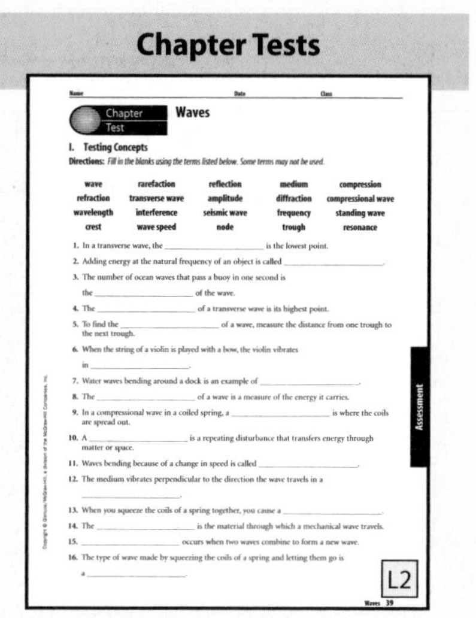
Chapter Test — Waves

I. Testing Concepts

L2

Science Content Background

The Nature of Waves

What's in a wave?

From radio waves to light waves to sound waves, we are immersed in a world of waves.

Waves transfer energy from one place to another. Mechanical waves such as sound and water need a medium to travel through. These waves create disturbances in the medium as they travel. The particles of the medium, however, do not move with the wave as it travels.

Waves can be transverse waves or compressional waves. In a transverse wave, the particles in the medium are displaced perpendicular to the direction of the wave motion. In a compressional wave, the particles move back and forth in the same direction as the wave moves. Transverse waves cannot travel through fluids. Earthquakes produce both transverse waves (S waves) and compressional waves (P waves).

section 2

Wave Properties

Wavelength

A great deal of variation exists in the wavelengths of electromagnetic waves. Electromagnetic waves with wavelengths greater than about 1 mm are radio waves. These waves have the longest wavelengths. Light wavelengths range from about 400 to 700 nanometers. One nanometer is 0.000000001 m or 10^{-9} m.

Frequency

Frequency and period are related. Frequency is how often something happens in a given time. Period is the time for something to happen. Thus for a wave, frequency is equal to the reciprocal of the period. Frequency is expressed as cycles per second, and period is seconds per cycle.

Amplitude and Energy

The amplitude of a wave is the maximum displacement of the particles in the medium from their resting position. Attractive forces between the particles in the medium act like springs that pull the particles back to their original position when the wave passes.

The energy carried by a wave is proportional to the square of the amplitude. Thus, higher ocean waves produce more damage. Doubling the height of the wave makes the energy carried four times greater.

The Behavior of Waves

Refraction and Diffraction

Waves do not always travel in a straight line. Refraction and diffraction cause waves to change direction. Refraction occurs when waves change speed as they pass from one material into another. Diffraction occurs when a wave strikes an obstacle or an opening.

chapter content resources

Internet Resources

For additional content background, visit gpscience.com to:

- access your book online
- find references to related articles in popular science magazines
- access Web links with related content background
- access current events with science journal topics

Print Resources

Basic Physics: A Self-Teaching Guide, by Karl F. Kuhn, John Wiley and Sons, 1996

Waves in the Ocean and Atmosphere: Introduction to Wave Dynamics, by Joseph Pedlosky, Springer Verlag, 2003

Wave Motion, by J. Billingham and A.C. King, Cambridge University Press, 2001

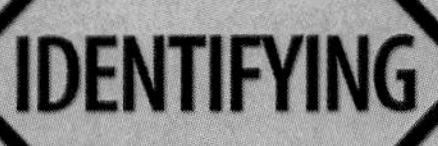

Misconceptions

Find Out What Students Think

Students may think that . . .

When a wave travels through a medium, particles of the medium travel along with the wave. Students have probably seen water waves hit land and flow up the beach. They may even have felt the force of an ocean wave pushing them towards the beach. Because these waves encounter the shore, they move differently from normal waves. But they do form lasting impressions. Thus, it is understandable that students would think that the medium travels with the wave.

Demonstration

Draw the figure below on the board. Tell students to imagine a rock is dropped into the water at Point A. Ask students to predict where each of the floating bobs will end up after ten waves go by the bobs.

Promote Understanding

Activity

Students make two models of waves—one that is incorrrect and one that is correct.

Model 1 (incorrect): Place on the floor alternating strips of green and red tape 2 m apart so they form the outline of a large circle. Have students walk slowly around the circle. Tell them to duck down when they get to a strip of green tape and to walk on their toes when they get to a strip of red tape. Students move up and down as they walk around the room.

Model 2 (correct): This resembles the "wave" done by fans at sporting events. Have students stand in a circle and not leave their positions. Start the wave by having a student reach up high, pause, duck down low, pause, and return to normal standing. After the first person rises, the second person rises and does the same thing. Each person in turn passes the wave around the circle.

Ask students to analyze the two models of waves and write which one they think is the better model and why.

Assess

After completing the chapter, see *Identifying Misconceptions* in the Study Guide at the end of the chapter.

About the Photo

Ocean Waves This area in Hawaii is known for huge ocean waves. Distant storms in the north Pacific supply the energy for gigantic waves that are legendary among surfers.

Science Journal Student responses will vary, but may include that they know waves occur in different materials, that they take different forms, even that they involve energy and motion. Students may want to learn about their causes and effects.

BIG Idea

Wave Speed and Density The speed of a wave in any material depends on the strength of the forces between the particles—atoms or molecules—in the material. The stronger these forces are, the greater the wave speed. In general, waves move faster in solids and liquids than in gases, because particles are much closer in solids and liquids. This results in stronger forces between particles than in gases. As a result, wave speeds in different materials are not primarily due to differences in density. For example, even though the density of silver is almost four times the density of aluminum, the speed of sound in silver is only about one-half the speed in aluminum.

Introduce the Chapter Tie a piece of ribbon in the center of a long piece of thin rope. Make a pulse on the rope by quickly moving one end back and forth. Ask students how the ribbon moved as the pulse passed. Have students compare the position of the ribbon before and after the pulse passed. Ask students if any pieces of the rope were carried along with the pulse.

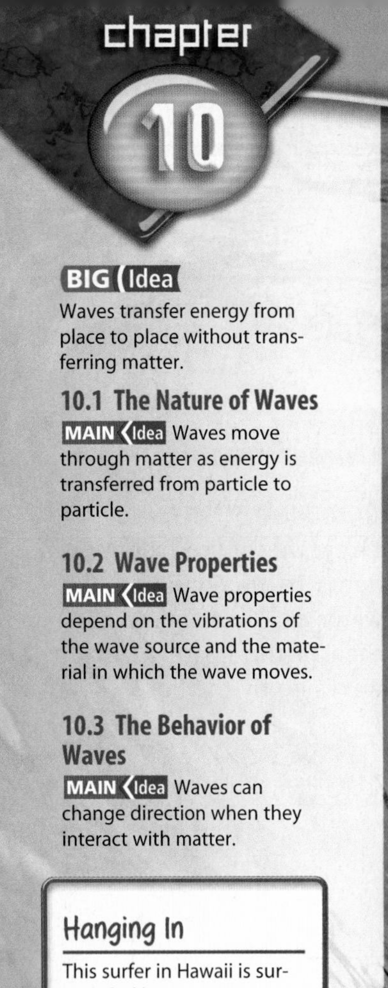

Waves

BIG Idea Waves transfer energy from place to place without transferring matter.

10.1 The Nature of Waves
MAIN Idea Waves move through matter as energy is transferred from particle to particle.

10.2 Wave Properties
MAIN Idea Wave properties depend on the vibrations of the wave source and the material in which the wave moves.

10.3 The Behavior of Waves
MAIN Idea Waves can change direction when they interact with matter.

Hanging In

This surfer in Hawaii is surrounded by an ocean wave that forms a huge tube of water. But even sitting at your desk, you are also surrounded by waves. Everything you see or hear is brought to you by waves. Easy to see-like this ocean wave-or invisible, all waves carry energy.

Science Journal Write down three things you already know about waves and one thing you would like to learn about waves.

288

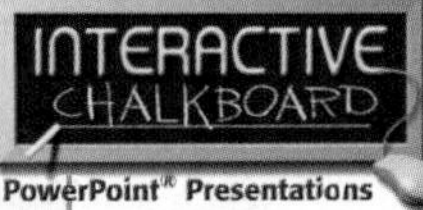

Interactive Chalkboard

This CD-ROM is an editable Microsoft® PowerPoint® presentation that includes:

- an editable presentation for every chapter
- additional chapter questions
- animated graphics
- image bank
- links to gpscience.com

Start-Up Activities

How do waves transfer energy?

Light enters your eyes and sound strikes your ears, enabling you to sense the world around you. Light and sound are waves that carry energy from one place to another. Do waves carry anything else along with their energy? Does a wave transfer matter too? In this activity you'll observe one way that waves can transfer energy.

1. Place your textbook flat on your desk. Line up four marbles on the groove at the edge of the textbook so that the marbles are touching each other.
2. Hold the first three marbles in place using three fingers of one hand.
3. Use your other hand to tap the first marble with a pen or pencil.
4. Observe the behavior of the fourth marble.
5. **Think Critically** Write a paragraph explaining how the fourth marble reacted to the pen tap. Draw a diagram showing how energy was transferred through the marbles.

Preview this chapter's content and activities at gpscience.com

FOLDABLES™ Study Organizer

Types of Waves Make the following Foldable to compare and contrast two types of waves.

STEP 1 **Fold** one sheet of paper lengthwise.

STEP 2 **Fold** into thirds.

STEP 3 **Unfold and draw** overlapping ovals. Cut the top sheet along the folds.

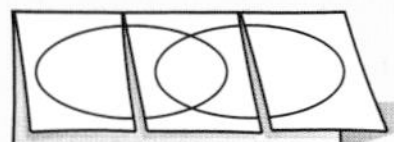

STEP 4 **Label** the ovals as shown.

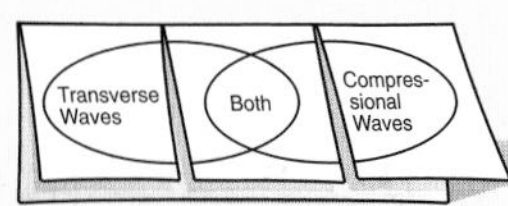

Construct a Venn Diagram As you read this chapter, list properties and characteristics unique to transverse waves under the left tab, those unique to compressional waves under the middle tab, and those common to both under the middle tab.

289

Additional Chapter Media

-  *Waves*
- Virtual Lab: *What are some characteristics of waves?*
- Video Lab: *Measuring Wave Properties*

Purpose Use the Launch Lab to illustrate for students energy moving through matter. L2

LS **Kinesthetic**

Preparation Obtain enough marbles of the same size so that each student can have four.

Materials marbles, textbook

Teaching Strategy Instruct students to make sure books are on a flat surface. Make sure students hold the marbles so they are touching one another.

Think Critically

Students should notice that the fourth marble moved even though the first three marbles stayed in place. This shows that energy transferred through the first three marbles, which caused the fourth marble to move without matter being transferred.

Assessment

Performance Have students write short paragraphs explaining what happens if the marbles are held in place without touching each other and why. After the first marble hits the second marble nothing happens. This is because the energy of the first marble is transferred to the air, which transfers very little energy to the next marble. Use **Performance Assessment in the Science Classroom,** p. 157.

Dinah Zike Study Fold

Student preparation materials for this Foldable are available in the Chapter *Fast File* Resources.

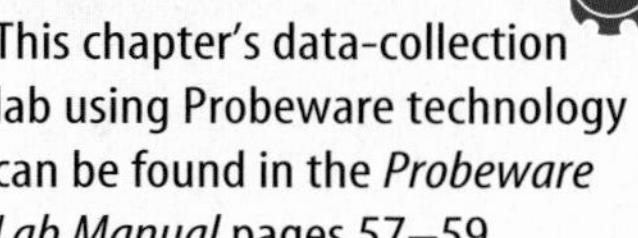

This chapter's data-collection lab using Probeware technology can be found in the *Probeware Lab Manual* pages 57–59.

The Nature of Waves

1 Motivate

Bellringer

Section Focus Transparencies also are available on the Interactive Chalkboard CD-ROM.

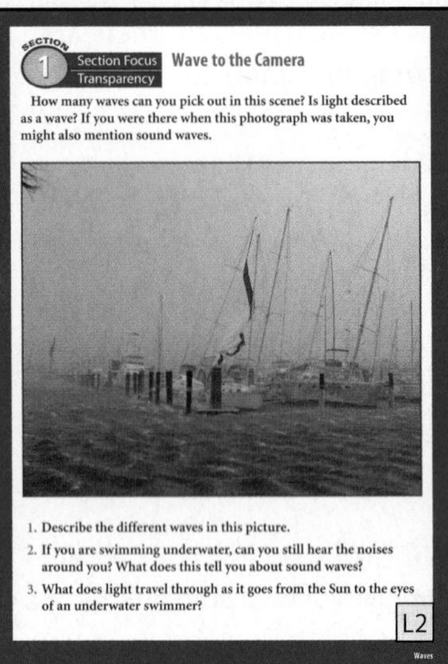

Tie to Prior Knowledge

Energy Review the idea of energy and have students give examples of waves. Emphasize to students that waves transfer energy but not matter.

Reading Guide

What You'll Learn
- **Recognize** that waves carry energy but not matter.
- **Define** mechanical waves.
- **Compare and contrast** transverse waves and compressional waves.

Why It's Important
You can see and hear the world around you because of the energy carried by waves.

Review Vocabulary
energy: the ability to cause change

New Vocabulary
- wave
- medium
- transverse wave
- compressional wave

What's in a wave?

A surfer bobs in the ocean waiting for the perfect wave, microwaves warm up your leftover pizza, and sound waves from your CD player bring music to your ears. Do these and other types of waves have anything in common with one another?

A **wave** is a repeating disturbance or movement that transfers energy through matter or space. For example, ocean waves disturb the water and transfer energy through it. During earthquakes, energy is transferred in powerful waves that travel through Earth. Light is a type of wave that can travel through empty space to transfer energy from one place to another, such as from the Sun to Earth.

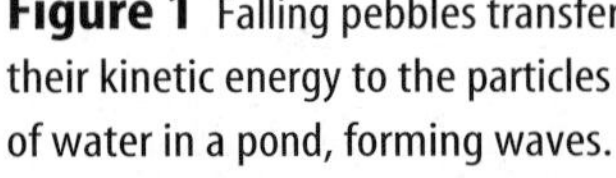

Figure 1 Falling pebbles transfer their kinetic energy to the particles of water in a pond, forming waves.

Waves and Energy

Kerplop! A pebble falls into a pool of water and ripples form. As **Figure 1** shows, the pebble causes a disturbance that moves outward in the form of a wave. Because it is moving, the falling pebble has energy. As it splashes into the pool, the pebble transfers some of its energy to nearby water molecules, causing them to move. Those molecules then pass the energy along to neighboring water molecules, which, in turn, transfer it to their neighbors. The energy moves farther and farther from the source of the disturbance. What you see is energy traveling in the form of a wave on the surface of the water.

Section 1 Resource Manager

Chapter *FAST FILE* Resources
- Transparency Activity, p. 44
- Directed Reading for Content Mastery, pp. 19, 20
- Note-taking Worksheets, pp. 33–35
- Enrichment, p. 30
- Reinforcement, p. 27

Cultural Diversity, p. 43
Science Inquiry Labs, pp. 25–26
Reading and Writing Skill Activities, p. 7
Earth Science Critical Thinking/Problem Solving, p. 9

Waves and Matter Imagine you're in a boat on a lake. Approaching waves bump against your boat, but they don't carry it along with them as they pass. The boat does move up and down and maybe even a short distance back and forth because the waves transfer some of their energy to it. But after the waves have moved on, the boat is still in nearly the same place. The waves don't even carry the water along with them. Only the energy carried by the waves moves forward. All waves have this property—they carry energy without transporting matter from place to place.

Reading Check *What do waves carry?*

Making Waves A wave will travel only as long as it has energy to carry. For example, when you drop a pebble into a puddle, the ripples soon die out and the surface of the water becomes still again.

Suppose you are holding a rope at one end, and you give it a shake. You would create a pulse that would travel along the rope to the other end, and then the rope would be still again, as **Figure 2** shows. Now suppose you shake your end of the rope up and down for a while. You would make a wave that would travel along the rope. When you stop shaking your hand up and down, the rope will be still again. It is the up-and-down motion of your hand that creates the wave.

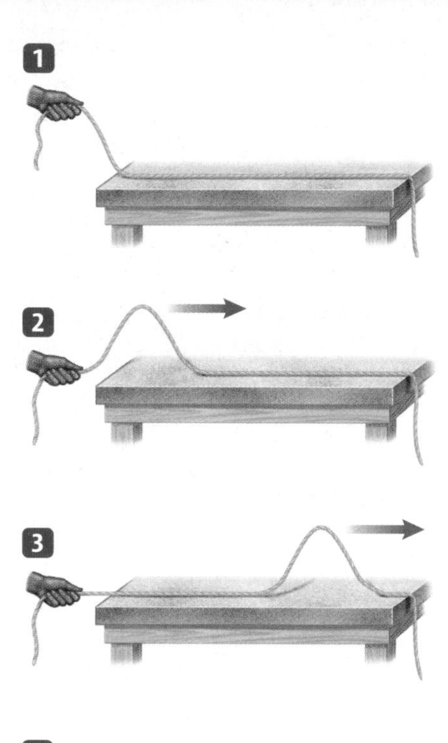

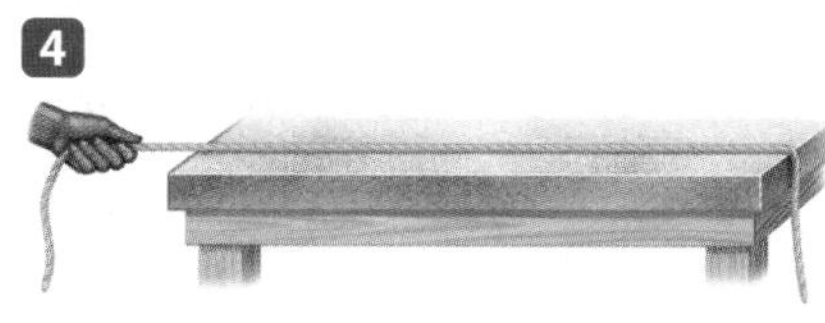

Figure 2 A wave will exist only as long as it has energy to carry. **Explain** *what happened to the energy that was carried by the wave in this rope.*

Anything that moves up and down or back and forth in a rhythmic way is vibrating. The vibrating movement of your hand at the end of the rope created the wave. In fact, all waves are produced by something that vibrates.

Mechanical Waves

Sound waves travel through the air to reach your ears. Ocean waves move through water to reach the shore. In both cases, the matter the waves travel through is called a **medium.** The medium can be a solid, a liquid, a gas, or a combination of these. For sound waves the medium is air, and for ocean waves the medium is water. Not all waves need a medium. Some waves, such as light and radio waves, can travel through space. Waves that can travel only through matter are called mechanical waves. The two types of mechanical waves are transverse waves and compressional waves.

2 Teach

Caption Answer

Figure 2 It was transferred to the end of the rope and then to the surrounding air.

Quick Demo

Wave Motion

Materials table-tennis ball, wide pan of water, small rock

Estimated Time five minutes

Procedure Place the table-tennis ball in the pan about halfway between the center and the edge of the pan. When the water is still, drop the rock into the pan. The ball moves up and down, but not horizontally in the direction in which the wave moves. L2 LS **Visual-Spatial**

Reading Check

Answer energy

IDENTIFYING Misconceptions

Wave Motion Students may think that when a wave travels through a medium, particles of the medium travel along with the wave. See the beginning of this chapter for teaching strategies that address this misconception.

LAB DEMONSTRATION

Purpose to demonstrate the movement of a wave through matter

Materials rope, broom

Preparation Tie the end of a rope to the handle of a broom.

Procedure Rest the broom upright in the corner of the room. Send a wave through the rope.

Expected Outcome Students will see the wave travel through the rope and cause the broom to shake or fall down.

Assessment

Where did the energy that caused the broom to shake or fall come from? from the hand moving the rope How did the energy get to the broom? It traveled along the rope in a wave. L2

Use Science Words

Word Meaning Tell students that the word *transverse* means "acting, lying, or being across; set crosswise." What makes a transverse wave transverse? When a transverse wave travels through a medium, the particles of the medium move crosswise to the direction in which the wave moves. L2 LS **Linguistic**

Activity

Wave Types Have students use a coiled spring toy to make both transverse and compressional waves. Have them compare and contrast how the waves look and the different things they did to make the two different types of waves. L1 ELL LS **Kinesthetic**

Teacher FYI

Wave Names Another name for a compressional wave is longitudinal wave. Sound waves are examples of this type of wave.

Caption Answer

Figure 4 Possible answer: sound wave

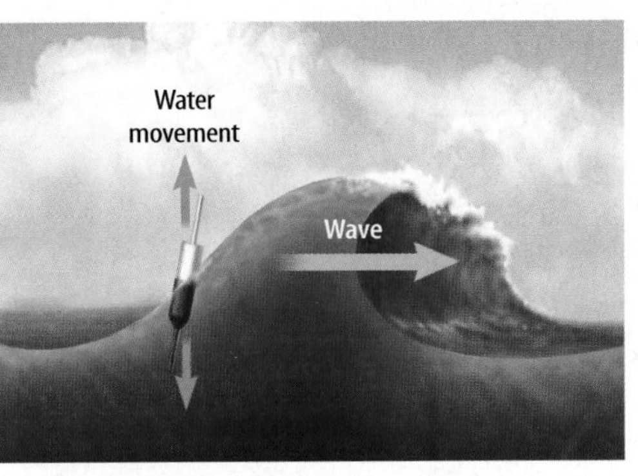

Figure 3 A water wave travels horizontally as the water moves vertically up and down.

Transverse Waves In a **transverse wave,** matter in the medium moves back and forth at right angles to the direction that the wave travels. For example, **Figure 3** shows how a wave in the ocean moves horizontally, but the water that the wave passes through moves up and down. When you shake one end of a rope while your friend holds the other end, you are making transverse waves. The wave and its energy travel from you to your friend as the rope moves up and down.

Compressional Waves In a **compressional wave,** matter in the medium moves back and forth along the same direction that the wave travels. You can model compressional waves with a coiled spring toy, as shown in **Figure 4.** Squeeze several coils together at one end of the spring. Then let go of the coils, still holding onto coils at both ends of the spring. A wave will travel along the spring. As the wave moves, it looks as if the whole spring is moving toward one end. Suppose you watched the coil with yarn tied to it as in **Figure 4.** You would see that the yarn moves back and forth as the wave passes, and then stops moving after the wave has passed. The wave carries energy, but not matter, forward along the spring. Compressional waves also are called longitudinal waves.

Sound Waves Sound waves are compressional waves. When a noise is made, such as when a locker door slams shut and vibrates, nearby air molecules are pushed together by the vibrations. The air molecules are squeezed together like the coils in a coiled spring toy are when you make a compressional wave with it. The compressions travel through the air to make a wave.

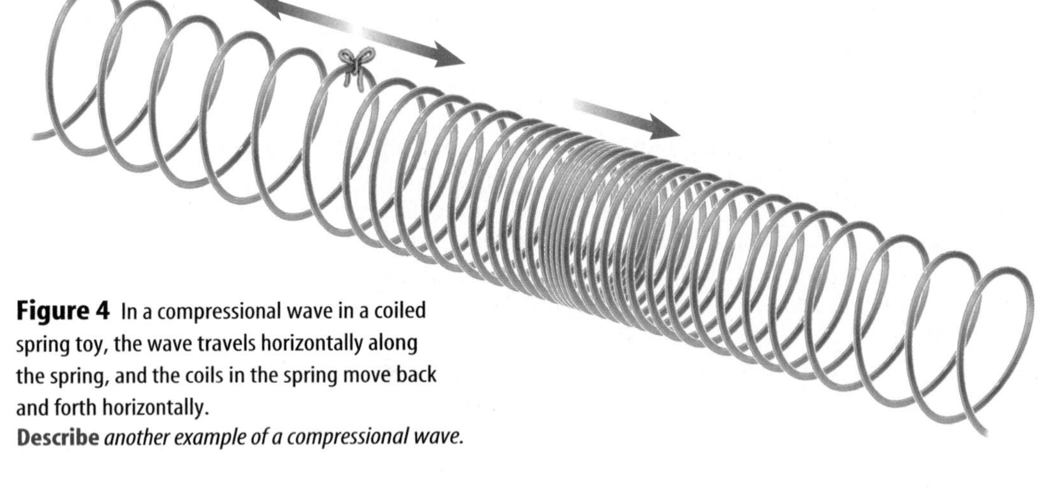

Figure 4 In a compressional wave in a coiled spring toy, the wave travels horizontally along the spring, and the coils in the spring move back and forth horizontally.
Describe *another example of a compressional wave.*

Differentiated Instruction

Visually Impaired Have each visually impaired student place a hand on a section of a rope or spring toy. Make waves in the rope or spring toy. Ask each student to describe how the section he or she is touching moves. Does it move up or down, backwards or forwards? Does it travel from one place to another? L1 ELL COOP LEARN LS **Kinesthetic**

Challenge Have students hypothesize how transverse waves will travel in different kinds of ropes. Then, have students test their hypotheses using different ropes. Ask them to write a single summary sentence that describes the relationship between the wave and type of rope used. Students will find that thick ropes will carry waves, but might require more energy to start wave action than do thin ropes. L3

Sound in Other Materials Sound waves also can travel through other mediums, such as water and wood. Particles in these mediums also are pushed together and move apart as the sound waves travel through them. When a sound wave reaches your ear, it causes your eardrum to vibrate. Your inner ear then sends signals to your brain, and your brain interprets the signals as sound.

Reading Check *How do sound waves travel in solids?*

Water Waves Water waves are not purely transverse waves. The water moves up and down as the waves go by. But the water also moves a short distance back and forth along the direction the wave is moving. This movement happens because the low part of the wave can be formed only by pushing water forward or backward toward the high part of the wave, as in **Figure 5A.** Then as the wave passes, the water that was pushed aside moves back to its initial position, as in **Figure 5B.** In fact, if you looked closely, you would see that the combination of this up-and-down and back-and-forth motion causes water to move in circles. Anything floating on the surface of the water absorbs some of the waves' energy and bobs in a circular motion.

Ocean waves are formed most often by wind blowing across the ocean surface. As the wind blows faster and slower, the changing wind speed is like a vibration. The size of the waves that are formed depends on the wind speed, the distance over which the wind blows, and how long the wind blows. **Figure 6** on the next page shows how ocean waves are formed.

Figure 5 A water wave causes water to move back and forth, as well as up and down. Water is pushed back and forth to form the crests and troughs.

A The low point of a water wave is formed when water is pushed aside and up to the high point of the wave.

B The water that is pushed aside returns to its initial position.

Reading Check

Answer Particles in the solid are pushed together and move apart as sound waves travel through them.

Discussion

Beach Breakers Why do waves break where they meet beaches? As waves of water move into the increasingly shallow area near the shore, the particles of water are forced to move in shallower and shallower ellipses. The wave breaks when it hits the ground as it tries to complete its elliptical path. The energy of the wave dissipates as the water moves up the beach and then falls back into the ocean. [L2]

Science Journal

Wave Diary Have students list in their Science Journals the kinds of waves they see in a typical day, classifying each wave as transverse or compressional. Have them identify the effects each wave's energy produces. [L2] LS **Linguistic**

Visual Learning

Figure 5 When you throw a stone into the water, how does it start the motion of the wave? When the stone hits the water, it pushes down on the water. Why does the wave spread out as it moves? It spreads because the energy moves in all directions from the point of origin. [L2] LS **Visual-Spatial**

Visualizing Formation of Ocean Waves

Have students examine the pictures and read the captions. Then ask the following questions.

What happens to the surface area of water exposed to the wind as waves build up? The surface area increases. How does this affect the waves? The greater surface area means that there is more contact area between the air and water, providing an increased area to which energy may be transferred.

Activity

Observe Waves Use a wave tank or large flat pan such as a cake pan partially filled with water to observe waves. Students can blow across the surface or a fan can be provided to simulate the wind. Students should try to duplicate the four types of seas presented. L2 LS **Kinesthetic**

Teacher FYI

Earthquakes and Waves Earthquakes produce three types of waves, all of which move out in concentric circles from the focus of the earthquake. Primary waves, known as P waves, are compressional waves that travel deep inside Earth. These waves travel the fastest. Secondary waves, called S waves, are transverse waves that can travel only through solids. They also travel deep inside Earth. Most of the damage from earthquakes is caused by surface waves that spread out from the epicenter, the point on Earth's surface above the focus. Surface waves cause both transverse and compressional movement of the ground.

NATIONAL GEOGRAPHIC **VISUALIZING FORMATION OF OCEAN WAVES**

Figure 6

When wind blows across an ocean, friction between the moving air and the water causes the water to move. As a result, energy is transferred from the wind to the surface of the water. The waves that are produced depend on the length of time and the distance over which the wind blows, as well as the wind speed.

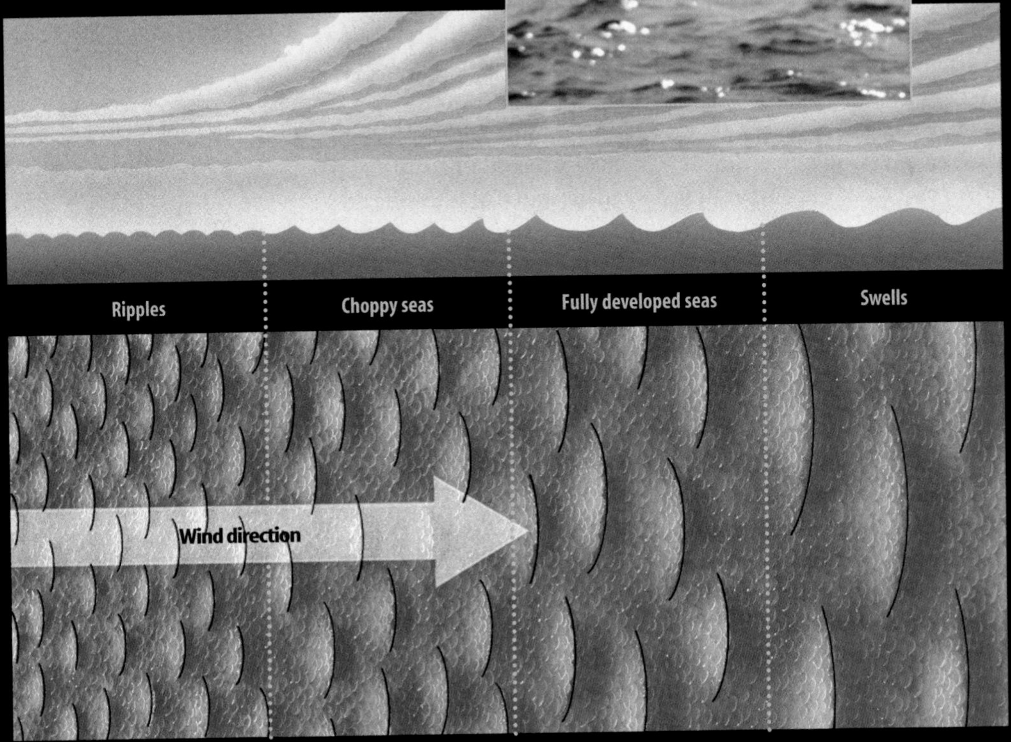

▲ Wind causes ripples to form on the surface of the water. As ripples form, they provide an even larger surface area for the wind to strike, and the ripples increase in size.

▲ Waves that are higher and have longer wavelengths grow faster as the wind continues to blow, but the steepest waves break up, forming whitecaps. The surface is said to be choppy.

▲ The shortest-wavelength waves break up, while the longest-wavelength waves continue to grow. When these waves have reached their maximum height, they form fully developed seas.

▲ After the wind dies down, the waves lose energy and become lower and smoother. These smooth, long-wavelength ocean waves are called swells.

294 CHAPTER 10 Waves

Differentiated Instruction

Challenge Ask students to research the impact to the shoreline when ocean waves repeatedly strike the shore. Have them find what measures are being taken to keep the shoreline unchanged. L3

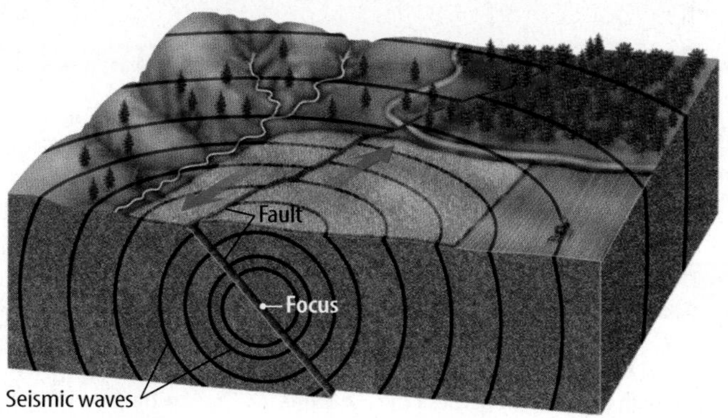

Figure 7 When Earth's crust shifts or breaks, the energy that is released is transmitted outward, causing an earthquake.
Explain *why earthquakes are mechanical waves.*

INTEGRATE Earth Science **Seismic Waves** A guitar string makes a sound when it breaks. The string vibrates for a short time after it breaks and produces sound waves. In a similar way, forces in Earth's crust can cause regions of the crust to shift, bend, or even break. The breaking crust vibrates, creating seismic (SIZE mihk) waves that carry energy outward, as shown in **Figure 7.** Seismic waves are a combination of compressional and transverse waves. They can travel through Earth and along Earth's surface. When objects on Earth's surface absorb some of the energy carried by seismic waves, they move and shake. The more the crust moves during an earthquake, the more energy is released.

Science Online
Topic: Seismic Waves
Visit gpscience.com for Web links to information about seismic waves.

Activity Write a summary of how seismic waves are used to map Earth's interior.

section 1 review

Summary

Waves and Energy
- A wave is a repeating disturbance or movement that transfers energy through matter or space.
- Waves carry energy without transporting matter.
- Waves are produced by something that is vibrating.

Mechanical Waves
- Mechanical waves must travel in matter.
- Mechanical waves can be transverse waves or compressional waves.
- In a transverse wave, matter in the medium moves at right angles to the wave motion.
- In a compressional wave, matter in the medium moves back and forth along the direction of the wave motion.

Self Check

1. **Compare and contrast** a transverse wave and a compressional wave. Give an example of each type.
2. **Describe** the motion of a buoy when a water wave passes. Does it move the buoy forward?
3. **Explain** how you could model a compressional wave using a coiled spring toy.
4. **List** the characteristics of a mechanical wave.
5. **Think Critically** Why do boats need anchors if ocean waves do not carry matter forward?

Applying Math

6. **Calculate Time** The average speed of sound in water is 1,500 m/s. How long would it take a sound wave to travel 9,000 m?

gpscience.com/self_check_quiz

Caption Answer

Figure 7 because they require a medium through which to travel

3 Assess

DAILY INTERVENTION

Check for Understanding

Logical-Mathematical With a partner, have each student draw a diagram of both a transverse wave and a compressional wave. Ask them to label peaks and troughs; compressions and rarefactions, as well as the direction energy moves for each wave. L2

Reteach

Comparing Waves Pair students and give each pair a coiled spring toy. Tie a piece of colored string or yarn around one of the coils. Have students make transverse and then compressional waves in the toy. Ask them to identify what is the same and what is different about the motion of the string with each wave. L2

Assessment

Process Have students do research on earthquakes. Have them find out how the waves form and why they form in the places they do. Have students make events chains of their findings. Use **Performance Assessment in the Science Classroom,** p. 163. P L2

section 1 review

1. Possible answers include that transverse waves move at right angles to the direction the waves travel, while compressional waves move back and forth in the same direction as the waves travel. Water waves are partly transverse waves. Sound waves are compressional waves.
2. A buoy moves up and down when a wave passes. The wave does not move the buoy forward.
3. Pull the ends of the toy apart and anchor them firmly at both ends. Then, squeeze several coils together at one end and release them.
4. Mechanical waves are either transverse or compressional, but always require a medium to travel through.
5. The tide and its related currents will move unanchored boats.
6. 6 seconds

section 2

Wave Properties

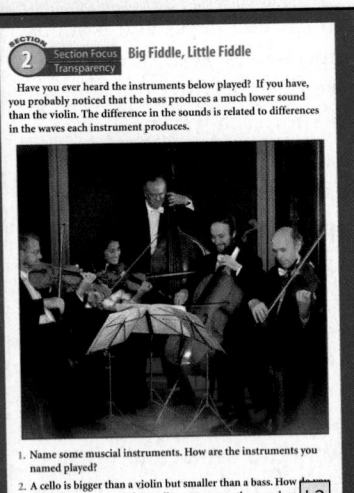

Reading Guide

What You'll Learn

- **Define** wavelength, frequency, period, and amplitude.
- **Describe** the relationship between frequency and wavelength.
- **Explain** how a wave's energy and amplitude are related.
- **Calculate** wave speed.

Why It's Important

Waves with different properties can be used in different ways.

Review Vocabulary

vibration: a back and forth movement

New Vocabulary

- crests
- troughs
- rarefaction
- wavelength
- frequency
- period
- amplitude

The Parts of a Wave

What makes sound waves, water waves, and seismic waves different from each other? Waves can differ in how much energy they carry and in how fast they travel. Waves also have other characteristics that make them different from each other.

Suppose you shake the end of a rope and make a transverse wave. The transverse wave in **Figure 8** has alternating high points, called **crests,** and low points, called **troughs.**

On the other hand, a compressional wave has no crests and troughs. When a compressional wave passes through a medium, it creates regions where the medium becomes crowded together and more dense, as in **Figure 8.** These regions are compressions. When you make compressional waves in a coiled spring, a compression is a region where the coils are close together. **Figure 8** also shows that the coils in the region next to a compression are spread apart, or less dense. This less-dense region of a compressional wave is called a **rarefaction.**

Figure 8 Transverse and compressional waves have different features that travel through a medium and form the wave.

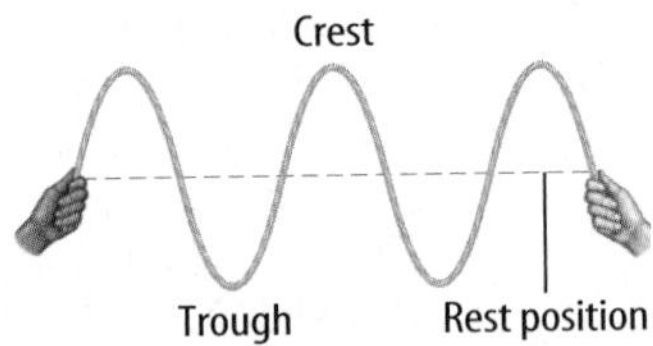

A transverse wave is made of crests and troughs that travel through the medium.

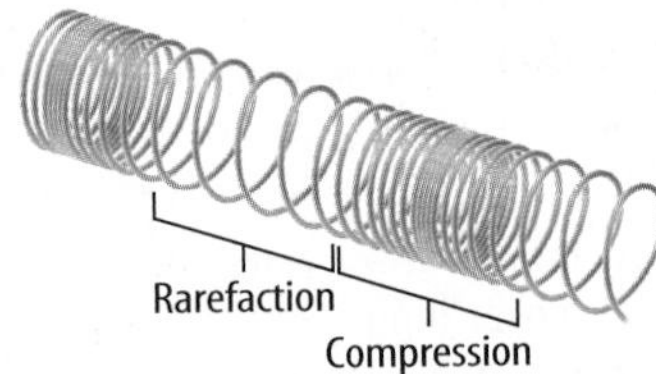

A compressional wave is made of compressions and rarefactions that travel through the medium.

Section 2 Resource Manager

Chapter *FAST FILE* Resources

- Transparency Activity, pp. 45, 47–48
- Directed Reading for Content Mastery, p. 20
- MiniLAB, p. 3
- Enrichment, p. 31
- Lab Activity, pp. 9–11
- Reinforcement, p. 28
- Lab Worksheet, pp. 5–6

Mathematics Skill Activities, p. 9

1 Motivate

Bellringer

Section Focus Transparencies also are available on the Interactive Chalkboard CD-ROM. L2

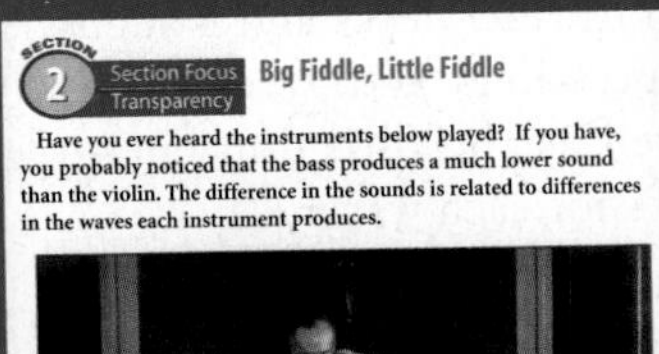

Section 2 Section Focus Transparency **Big Fiddle, Little Fiddle**

Have you ever heard the instruments below played? If you have, you probably noticed that the bass produces a much lower sound than the violin. The difference in the sounds is related to differences in the waves each instrument produces.

1. Name some musical instruments. How are the instruments you named played?
2. A cello is bigger than a violin but smaller than a bass. How do you think the sound made by a cello compares to the sounds made by violins and basses?

L2

Tie to Prior Knowledge

Comparing Waves Have students compare common examples of waves and ask them whether they can identify any similarities among all waves. Tell students that in this section they will learn about the different parts of waves and how these parts determine the amount of energy a wave can carry. L2

Figure 9 One wavelength starts at any point on a wave and ends at the nearest point just like it.

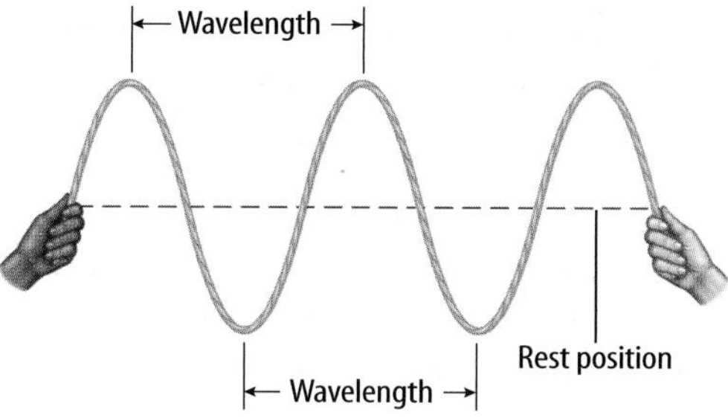

For transverse waves, a wavelength can be measured from crest to crest or trough to trough.

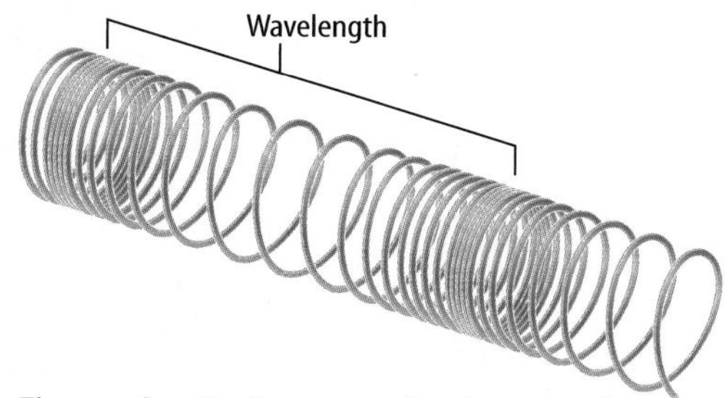

The wavelength of a compressional wave can be measured from compression to compression or from rarefaction to rarefaction.

Wavelength

Waves also have a property called wavelength. A **wavelength** is the distance between one point on a wave and the nearest point just like it. **Figure 9** shows that for transverse waves the wavelength is the distance from crest to crest or trough to trough.

A wavelength in a compressional wave is the distance between two neighboring compressions or two neighboring rarefactions, as shown in **Figure 9.** You can measure from the start of one compression to the start of the next compression or from the start of one rarefaction to the start of the next rarefaction. The wavelengths of sound waves that you can hear range from a few centimeters for the highest-pitched sounds to about 15 m for the deepest sounds.

How is wavelength measured in transverse and compressional waves?

Frequency and Period

When you tune your radio to a station, you are choosing radio waves of a certain frequency. The **frequency** of a wave is the number of wavelengths that pass a fixed point each second. You can find the frequency of a transverse wave by counting the number of crests or troughs that pass by a point each second. The frequency of a compressional wave is the number of compressions or rarefactions that pass a point every second. Frequency is expressed in hertz (Hz). A frequency of 1 Hz means that one wavelength passes by in 1 s. In SI units, 1 Hz is the same as 1/s. The **period** of a wave is the amount of time it takes one wavelength to pass a point. As the frequency of a wave increases, the period decreases. Period has units of seconds.

Observing Wavelength

Procedure

1. Fill a **pie plate or other wide pan** with **water** about 2 cm deep.
2. Lightly tap your finger once per second on the surface of the water and observe the spacing of the water waves.
3. Increase the rate of your tapping, and observe the spacing of the water waves.

Analysis

1. How is the spacing of the water waves related to their wavelength?
2. How does the spacing of the water waves change when the rate of tapping increases?

Try at Home

2 Teach

Reading Check

Answer transverse wave—crest to crest or trough to trough; compressional wave—compression to compression or rarefaction to rarefaction

Purpose to observe the relationship between the wavelength and frequency of a wave L2 ELL IN Kinesthetic

Materials pie plate, water

Teaching Strategy Suggest students use a watch to measure the rate of tapping.

Analysis

1. The closer the waves, the shorter their wavelength.
2. As the rate of tapping increases, the spacing of the waves decreases.

Assessment

Process Have students draw diagrams of the water waves they formed by tapping at two different rates. Ask students to label the wavelength on their diagrams. Use **Performance Assessment in the Science Classroom,** p. 127.

Activity

Compressional Waves Use a metal spring toy to create waves of differing wavelengths, then of differing frequency. Have your students describe how they accomplished each. L2

Teacher FYI

Heinrich Hertz The hertz is named for the German physicist Heinrich Hertz. Hertz showed that radio waves are electromagnetic waves, as is light. He produced electromagnetic waves in his laboratory, and he pioneered broadcasting and receiving radio waves.

Differentiated Instruction

English-Language Learners Have students create an illustrated glossary of new terms. Have students write the term on one side of an index card and the definition and an illustration showing what the term means on the other side of the card.

Quick Demo

Measuring Wavelength

Materials meterstick; overhead transparency, projector and pen

Estimated Time five minutes

Procedure Draw transverse waves on the board or on the overhead transparency. Be sure the wavelengths are of equal size. With a meterstick, measure the wavelength of the waves at several heights. Show students that, no matter which two points are chosen to measure wavelength, if the points correspond, the answer is always the same. L2

LS **Visual-Spatial**

Use Science Words

Word Usage Have students use the word *frequency* to refer to something other than waves. Possible answer: He looked at his watch with great frequency, glancing at it three times in one minute. Have students explain how the everyday use of the word frequency relates to its use in describing waves. When something has a greater frequency, it occurs more often within a given time period. When waves have a greater frequency, more of them pass a particular point within a given time period. L2

LS **Linguistic**

Discussion

Traveling Sound Why does sound travel faster in solids than in gases? The particles in solids are close together, and they bump into each other more often than do the particles in a gas. Why does sound travel faster in warm air than it does in cold air? Gas particles travel faster in warm air than they do in cold air, and they bump into each other more often. L3

LS **Logical-Mathematical**

Reading Check

Answer as frequency increases, wavelength decreases

Wavelength Is Related to Frequency If you make transverse waves with a rope, you increase the frequency by moving the rope up and down faster. Moving the rope faster also makes the wavelength shorter. This relationship is always true—as frequency increases, wavelength decreases. **Figure 10** compares the wavelengths and frequencies of two different waves.

The frequency of a wave is always equal to the rate of vibration of the source that creates it. If you move the rope up, down, and back up in 1 s, the frequency of the wave you generate is 1 Hz. If you move the rope up, down, and back up five times in 1 s, the resulting wave has a frequency of 5 Hz.

Reading Check *How are the wavelength and frequency of a wave related?*

Wave Speed

You're at a large stadium watching a baseball game, but you're high up in the bleachers, far from the action. The batter swings and you see the ball rise. An instant later you hear the crack of the bat hitting the ball. You see the impact before you hear it because light waves travel much faster than sound waves do. Therefore, the light waves reflected from the flying ball reach your eyes before the sound waves created by the crack of the bat reach your ears.

The speed of a wave depends on the medium it is traveling through. Sound waves usually travel faster in liquids and solids than they do in gases. However, light waves travel more slowly in liquids and solids than they do in gases or in empty space. Also, sound waves usually travel faster in a material if the temperature of the material is increased. For example, sound waves travel faster in air at 20°C than in air at 0°C.

Figure 10 The wavelength of a wave decreases as the frequency increases.

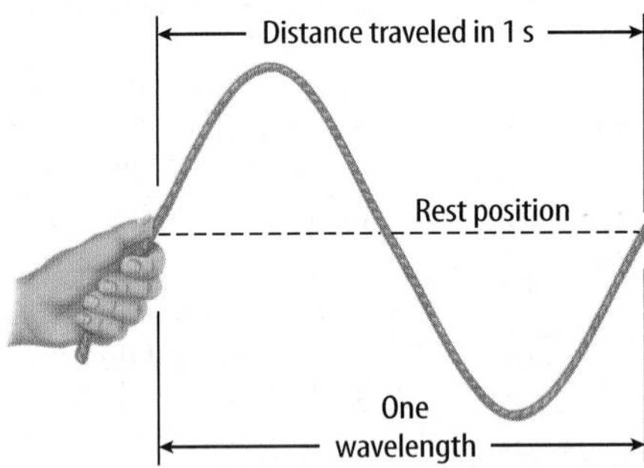

The rope is moved down, up, and down again one time in 1 s. One wavelength is created on the rope.

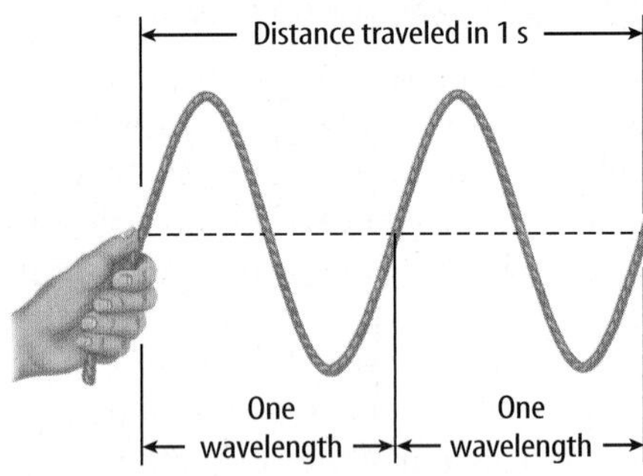

The rope is shaken down, up, and down again twice in 1 s. Two wavelengths are created on the rope.

Visual Learning

Figure 10 Why might it be more difficult to measure the exact wavelength of a compressional wave than that of a transverse wave? It's difficult to determine where compressions begin and where they end. L2 LS **Logical-Mathematical**

Teacher FYI

Speed of Light The first widely accepted value for the speed of light was calculated by Ole Rømer in 1676. He realized that the periods of the orbits of Jupiter's moons appeared shorter when Earth approached Jupiter and longer when Earth receded from Jupiter. His value for the speed of light was about two-thirds of the modern value.

Calculating Wave Speed The speed of a wave depends on the medium in which the wave travels. However, the wave speed, the frequency of the wave, and the wavelength are related. The speed of a wave can be calculated from the following equation:

Wave Speed Equation

speed (in m/s) = frequency (in Hz) × wavelength (in m)

$$v = f\lambda$$

In this equation, v represents the wave speed, f is the frequency, and the Greek letter λ (lambda) represents the wavelength. Why does multiplying the frequency unit Hz by the distance unit m give the unit for speed, m/s? Recall that the SI unit Hz is the same as 1/s. So multiplying m by Hz equals m by 1/s, which equals m/s.

Deadly Ocean Waves Tsunamis can cause serious damage when they hit land. These waves can measure up to 30 m tall and can travel faster than 700 km/h. Research to find which areas of the world are most vulnerable to tsunamis. Describe the effects of a tsunami that has occurred in these areas.

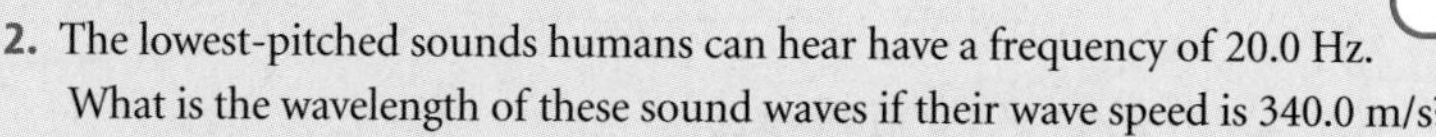

Solve for Wave Speed What is the speed of a sound wave that has a wavelength of 2.00 m and a frequency of 170.5 Hz?

1. **This is what you know:** wavelength: λ = 2.00 m; frequency: f = 170.5 Hz
2. **This is what you need to find:** wave speed: v
3. **Use this formula:** $v = f\lambda$
4. **Substitute:** the values of f and λ into the formula and multiply. $v = (170.5)(2.00) = 341$
5. **Determine the units:** units of v = (units of f) × (units of λ) $= \text{Hz} \times \text{m} = \frac{1}{\text{s}} \times \text{m} = \frac{\text{m}}{\text{s}} = \text{m/s}$

Answer: The speed of the sound wave is 341 m/s

Practice Problems

1. A wave traveling in water has a frequency of 500.0 Hz and a wavelength of 3.00 m. What is the speed of the wave?
2. The lowest-pitched sounds humans can hear have a frequency of 20.0 Hz. What is the wavelength of these sound waves if their wave speed is 340.0 m/s?
3. The highest-pitched sounds humans can hear have a wavelength of 0.017 m in air. What is the frequency of these sound waves if their wave speed is 340.0 m/s?
4. **Challenge** A sound wave with a frequency of 100.0 Hz travels in water with a speed of 1,500.0 m/s and then travels in air with a speed of 340.0 m/s. Compare the wavelength of the sound wave in water to the wavelength of the sound wave in air.

Science Online
For more practice problems, go to page 834, and visit gpscience.com/extra_problems.

INTEGRATE Social Studies

Deadly Ocean Waves all coastal areas of the Pacific Ocean; loss of life, property and land

IDENTIFYING Misconceptions

Tsunamis Tsunamis are sometimes mistakenly called *tidal waves*, which may cause students to think they are related to tides. A tsunami is set off by an underwater geological disturbance; tides are the result of gravitational interactions between Earth, the Moon, and the Sun. Ordinary waves are stirred up by wind. Point out to students that this is a good example of the wide range of disturbances that can transfer energy by waves.

Wave Speed Equation

National Math Standards

Correlation to Mathematics Objectives

1, 2, 9

Answers to Practice Problems

1. 1,500 m/s
2. 17 m
3. 20,000 Hz
4. The wavelength in water is 15 m, and the wavelength in air is 3.4 m; so the wavelength in water is 4.4 times the wavelength in air.

Curriculum Connection

Math Tell students that as frequency decreases, the wavelength increases if the speed of the wave is constant. Ask students what the relationship between wavelength and frequency is called when the wave speed is constant. They are inversely proportional. L3 LS **Linguistic**

Visual Learning

Figure 11 Point out to students the areas of compression and rarefaction in each of the waves in **Figure 11**. Which wave has denser compressions? the top wave Which has the less dense rarefactions? also the top wave L2 LS **Visual-Spatial**

Make a Model

Penny Compressions Have students use pennies and 11 × 17 paper to make models of compression waves. Have students divide the paper into twelve equal sections from left to right. Label the sections R (for rarefaction), T (for transition), and C (for compression). The twelve sections in order should be labeled R, T, C, T, R, T, C, T, R, T, C, T. Tell students to fill the areas with pennies to model a compression wave. The areas of compression should have the most pennies and the areas of rarefaction should have the fewest pennies. Ask students how they would need to move the pennies to increase the amplitude of the wave. Move pennies out of the rarefaction section and put them in the compression section. Have students count the pennies in each section and graph the number of pennies on the y-axis against the distance traveled by the wave on the x-axis. L2 P LS **Visual-Spatial**

Caption Answer

Figure 12 Move the rope only a small distance up and down for smaller amplitude, and a larger distance up and down for greater amplitude.

Amplitude and Energy

Why do some earthquakes cause terrible damage, while others are hardly felt? This is because the amount of energy a wave carries can vary. **Amplitude** is related to the energy carried by a wave. The greater the wave's amplitude is, the more energy the wave carries. Amplitude is measured differently for compressional and transverse waves.

Amplitude of Compressional Waves The amplitude of a compressional wave is related to how tightly the medium is pushed together at the compressions. The denser the medium is at the compressions, the larger its amplitude is and the more energy the wave carries. For example, it takes more energy to push the coils in a coiled spring toy tightly together than to barely move them. The closer the coils are in a compression, the farther apart they are in a rarefaction. So the less dense the medium is at the rarefactions, the more energy the wave carries. **Figure 11** shows compressional waves with different amplitudes.

Figure 11 The amplitude of a compressional wave depends on the density of the medium in the compressions and rarefactions.

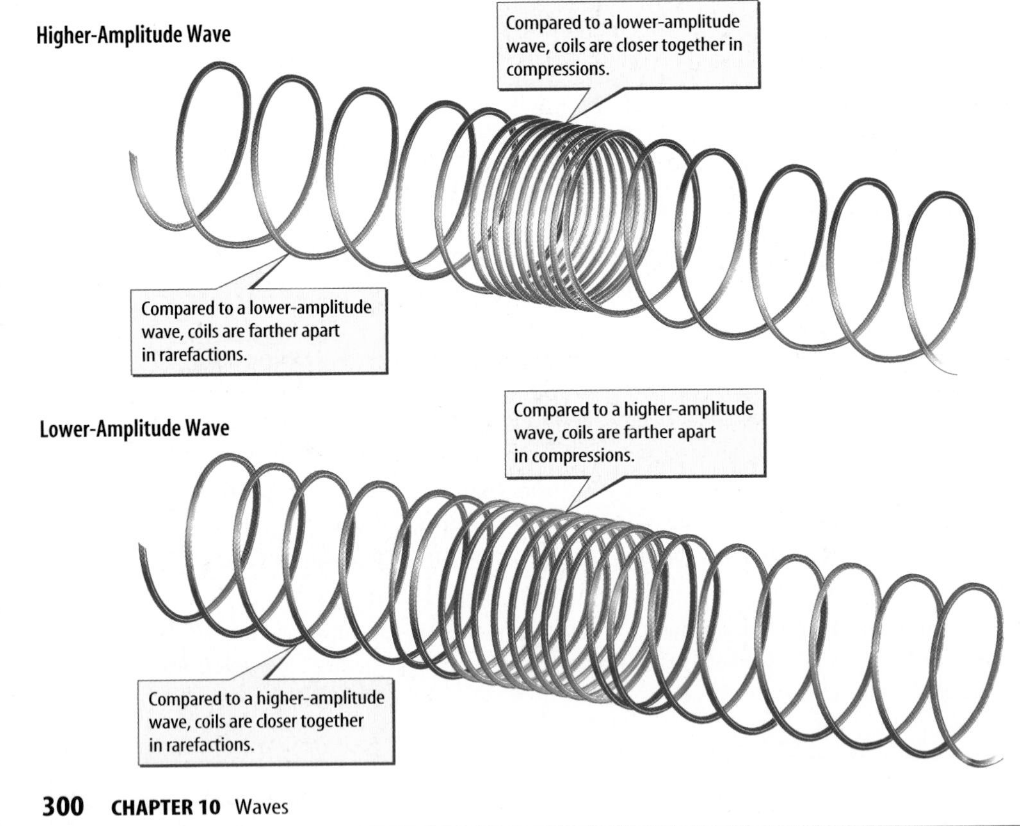
Higher-Amplitude Wave
Compared to a lower-amplitude wave, coils are closer together in compressions.
Compared to a lower-amplitude wave, coils are farther apart in rarefactions.
Lower-Amplitude Wave
Compared to a higher-amplitude wave, coils are farther apart in compressions.
Compared to a higher-amplitude wave, coils are closer together in rarefactions.

Differentiated Instruction

Challenge Tell students that AM stands for "amplitude modulation" and that FM stands for "frequency modulation." Explain that to modulate means to vary the frequency or amplitude. Have students research and report on AM and FM radio technology. In AM signals, the amplitude is varied to convey the message; in FM signals, the frequency is varied. L3 LS **Linguistic**

Curriculum Connection

Music Play a recording of a piece of music for students. Make sure the music includes soft sections and loud sections. Ask students to identify the portions of the music in which the sound waves have a large amplitude and those where the sound waves have a lower amplitude. The loud sections have high amplitude waves and the soft sections have low amplitude waves. L2 LS **Auditory-Musical**

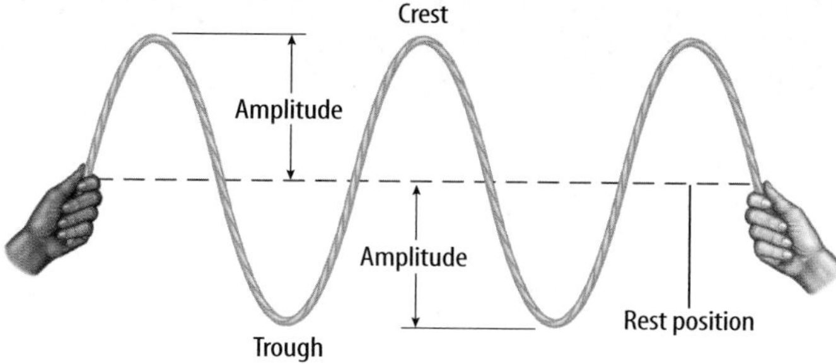

Figure 12 The amplitude of a transverse wave is the distance between a crest or a trough and the position of the medium at rest.
Describe *how you could create waves with different amplitudes in a piece of rope.*

Amplitude of Transverse Waves If you've ever been knocked over by an ocean wave, you know that the higher the wave, the more energy it carries. Remember that the amplitude of a wave increases as the energy carried by the wave increases. So a tall ocean wave has a greater amplitude than a short ocean wave does. The amplitude of any transverse wave is the distance from the crest or trough of the wave to the rest position of the medium, as shown in **Figure 12.**

section 2 review

Summary

The Parts of a Wave

- Transverse waves have repeating high points called crests and low points called troughs.
- Compressional waves have repeating high-density regions called compressions, and low-density regions called rarefactions.

Wavelength, Frequency, and Period

- Wavelength is the distance between a point on a wave and the nearest point just like it.
- Wave frequency is the number of wavelengths passing a fixed point each second.
- Wave period is the amount of time it takes one wavelength to pass a fixed point.

Wave Speed and Amplitude

- The speed of a wave depends on the material it is traveling in, and the temperature.
- The speed of a wave is the product of its frequency and its wavelength:

$$v = f\lambda$$

- As the amplitude of a wave increases, the energy carried by the wave increases.

Self Check

1. **Describe** the difference between a compressional wave with a large amplitude and one with a small amplitude.
2. **Describe** how the wavelength of a wave changes if the wave slows down and its frequency doesn't change.
3. **Explain** how the frequency of a wave changes when the period of the wave increases.
4. **Form a hypothesis** to explain why a sound wave travels faster in a solid than in a gas.
5. **Think Critically** You make a transverse wave by shaking the end of a long rope up and down. Explain how you would shake the end of the rope to make the wavelength shorter. How would you shake the end of the rope to increase the energy carried by the wave?

Applying Math

6. **Calculate** the frequency of a water wave that has a wavelength of 0.5 m and a speed of 4.0 m/s.
7. **Calculate Wavelength** An FM radio station broadcasts radio waves with a frequency of 100,000,000 Hz. What is the wavelength of these radio waves if they travel at a speed of 300,000 km/s?

3 Assess

DAILY INTERVENTION

Check for Understanding

Visual-Spatial Have students draw a diagram of a transverse wave and compressional wave. Have students label the following parts of the waves: trough, crest, rest position, rarefaction, compression, and wavelength.

Reteach

Transverse Waves Give students a piece of string about 60 cm long. Instruct them to work in pairs to shake the string to form a transverse wave. Have students count the number of waves and measure the average wavelength. Suggest that they change the wave so it has a greater amplitude, then change it again so it has shorter wavelengths. What happens to the frequency? It increases with shorter wavelengths, but it should not change with change in amplitude. L2 ELL COOP LEARN

LS **Kinesthetic**

Assessment

Performance Have students shake a coiled spring toy to form a transverse wave, and then determine which variable (amplitude, wavelength, or frequency) cannot be controlled. Wavelength can be controlled only indirectly by changing frequency. Use **PASC**, p. 89. L2

Virtual Labs

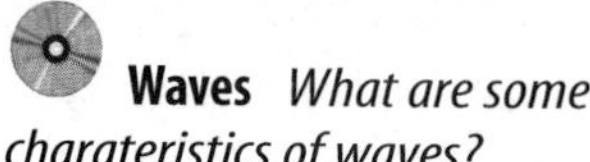

Waves *What are some charateristics of waves?*

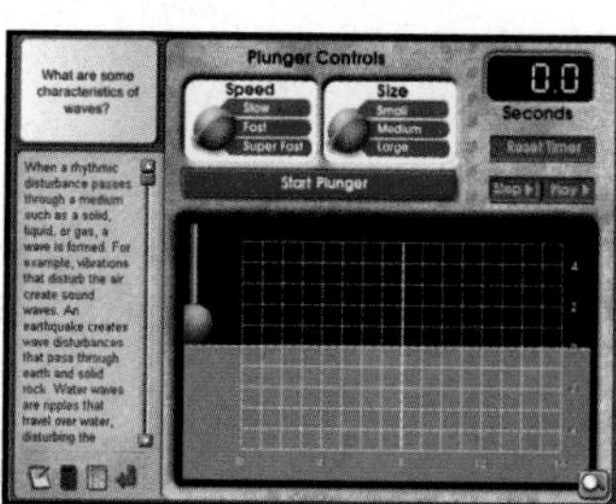

section 2 review

1. A compressional wave with a larger amplitude has particles of the medium closer together in the compressions and farther apart in the rarefactions.
2. The wavelength decreases.
3. as the period increases, the frequency decreases
4. The particles in a solid are more closely spaced, so that collisions between particles occur more frequently than in a gas, where particles are farther apart.
5. To make the wavelength shorter, increase the frequency of the wave by shaking the end of the rope up and down more rapidly. To increase the amplitude, increase the distance that the end of the rope is moved up and down.
6. $f = \frac{v}{\lambda} = \frac{(4.0 \text{ m/s})}{(0.5 \text{ m})} = 8.0 \text{ Hz}$
7. $\lambda = \frac{v}{f} = \frac{(300{,}000{,}000 \text{ m/s})}{(100{,}000{,}000 \text{ Hz})} = 3.0 \text{ m}$

Real-World Question

Purpose Students will generate waves in different types of materials and compare and contrast the behavior of these waves. L2 

Process Skills observe, compare and contrast

Time Required 30 minutes

Procedure

Alternate Materials Telephone cord can be used to demonstrate the behavior of coiled material.

Safety Precautions eye protection, laboratory aprons

Teaching Strategy The strips of cloth and string should be about 1 m long. This will be long enough so that the time for the pulse to move along the strip can be measured. If the strip is too long, the wave energy will die away before the wave reaches the other end.

Troubleshooting If students have difficulty timing the pulses, have them count the wavelengths instead.

Conclude and Apply

1. The amplitude of the wave decreases as it travels from a less dense material to a more dense material.
2. Waves tended to travel faster in the denser material.
3. The speed increased and the amplitude decreased as the waves traveled into denser material.
4. from the movement of the student's hand

Waves in Different Mediums

Have you ever swum underwater? If so, even with your head underwater, you probably still heard some sounds. The noises probably sounded different underwater than they do in air. Waves can change properties when they travel from one medium into another.

Real-World Question

How is the speed of a wave affected by the type of material it is traveling through?

Goals

- **Demonstrate** transverse and compressional waves.
- **Compare** the speed of waves traveling through different mediums.

Possible Materials

coiled spring toys (made out of both metal and plastic)
rope, both heavy and light
string
long rubber band, such as those used for exercising
strip of heavy cloth, such as a towel
strip of light cloth, such as nylon panty hose
stopwatch

Safety Precautions

Procedure

1. Use pieces of each material that are about the same length. For each material, have a partner hold one end of the material still while you shake the material back and forth. Shake each material in the same way.
2. Have someone time how long a pulse takes to reach the opposite end of the material.
3. Tie two different types of rope together or tie a heavy piece of cloth to a lighter piece. Observe how the wave changes when it moves from one material to the other.
4. **Observe** compressional waves using coiled spring toys. You can connect two different types of coiled spring toys together to see how a compressional wave changes in different mediums.

Conclude and Apply

1. **Describe** how the amplitude of the waves changed as they traveled from one material to a different material.
2. **Determine** if the waves travel at the same speed through the different mediums.
3. **Explain** how the waves changed when they moved from one material to another.
4. **Describe** how the waves created in this activity got their energy.

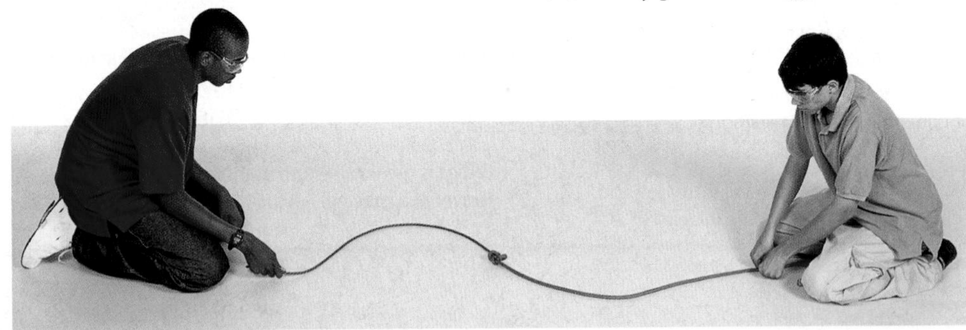

Communicating Your Data

Have students draw diagrams showing the waves they generated in each type of material or combination of materials. Diagrams should include the names of the materials used and should have the amplitude, wavelength, and frequency labeled. L2

Assessment

Process Provide students with a new, different material and ask them to predict the relative amplitude, frequency, and wavelength of the waves they would generate with that material. Give students an opportunity to test their predictions. Use **Performance Assessment in the Science Classroom**, p. 93. L2

section 3

The Behavior of Waves

Reading Guide

What You'll Learn

- **State** the law of reflection.
- **Explain** why waves change direction when they travel from one material to another.
- **Compare and contrast** refraction and diffraction.
- **Describe** how waves interfere with each other.

Why It's Important

You can hear an echo, see shadows, and check your reflection in a mirror because of how waves behave.

Review Vocabulary

perpendicular: a line that forms a 90-degree angle with another line

New Vocabulary

- refraction
- diffraction
- interference
- standing wave
- resonance

Reflection

If you are one of the last people to leave your school building at the end of the day, you'll probably find the hallways quiet and empty. When you close your locker door, the sound echoes down the empty hall. Your footsteps also make a hollow sound. Thinking you're all alone, you may be startled by your own reflection in a classroom window. The echoes and your image looking back at you from the window are caused by wave reflection.

Reflection occurs when a wave strikes an object and bounces off of it. All types of waves—including sound, water, and light waves—can be reflected. How does the reflection of light allow the boy in **Figure 13** to see himself in the mirror? It happens in two steps. First, light strikes his face and bounces off. Then, the light reflected off his face strikes the mirror and is reflected into his eyes.

Figure 13 The light that strikes the boy's face is reflected into the mirror. The light then reflects off the mirror into his eyes.
List *examples of waves that can be reflected.*

Echoes A similar thing happens to sound waves when your footsteps echo. Sound waves form when your foot hits the floor and the waves travel through the air to both your ears and other objects. Sometimes when the sound waves hit another object, they reflect off it and come back to you. Your ears hear the sound again, a few seconds after you first heard your footstep.

Bats and dolphins use echoes to learn about their surroundings. A dolphin makes a clicking sound and listens to the echoes. These echoes enable the dolphin to locate nearby objects.

303

Section 3 Resource Manager

Chapter *Fast File* Resources

- Transparency Activity, p. 46
- Directed Reading for Content Mastery, pp. 21, 22
- Enrichment, p. 32
- Lab Activity, pp. 13–16
- Reinforcement, p. 29
- Lab Worksheet, pp. 7–8
- MiniLAB, p. 4

Reading and Writing Skill Activities, p. 33
Home and Community Involvement, p. 38
Performance Assessment in the Science Classroom, p. 52
Cultural Diversity, p. 61

1 Motivate

INTERACTIVE CHALKBOARD
PowerPoint® Presentations

Bellringer

Section Focus Transparencies also are available on the Interactive Chalkboard CD-ROM.
L2 ELL

Section 3 Section Focus Transparency **Wave Art**

This artistic picture shows how waves can make fascinating patterns in water. When waves travelling toward the wall reach the openings, they pass through them. After passing through the openings, the waves create new patterns as they overlap on the other side of the wall.

1. What do the waves look like before they reach the wall? What do they look like after passing through the opening?
2. Where do the waves in the photograph overlap?
3. What do you think this picture would look like if both holes were plugged?

L2

Waves

Tie to Prior Knowledge

Moving Balls Ask students what happens to a ball when it hits a wall. Ask how a ball might travel differently if moving through water. Tell students that in this section they will learn how a wave behaves when it hits something or when it travels through different media.

Caption Answer

Figure 13 Possible answers: water waves, sound waves, light waves

2 Teach

Activity

Tennis Ball Angles Have students sit on the floor and roll a tennis ball against a wall. Have them first roll the ball directly toward the wall and then at increasing angles to the normal. Ask them what they notice about how the ball bounces off the wall as the angle to the normal is increased. The greater the angle between the normal and the ball's path to the wall, the greater the angle to the normal by the ball's path away from the wall. L1

ELL LS **Kinesthetic**

Use an Analogy

Turning Sleds Ask students whether they've ever ridden on a sled that's moved from snow to ice or mud. If the sled hit the ice or mud at an angle, one of its runners hit the ice or mud before the other. That runner then started moving more quickly or more slowly while the other runner stayed at the original speed, causing the sled to turn. Tell students that this is similar to what happens to a sound, seismic, or light wave when it moves from one medium to another. L2

Reading Check

Answer when a wave changes speed as it moves from one medium to another at an angle

Use Science Words

Word Origins Have students look up the word *refraction* or *refract* in a dictionary and find the Latin word from which it is derived. Ask students why this word is appropriate to use to describe refraction. The word *refract* comes from the Latin word *refringere*, which means "to break up or break open." When you look at the pencil through water, it looks as if it's broken. L2

LS **Linguistic**

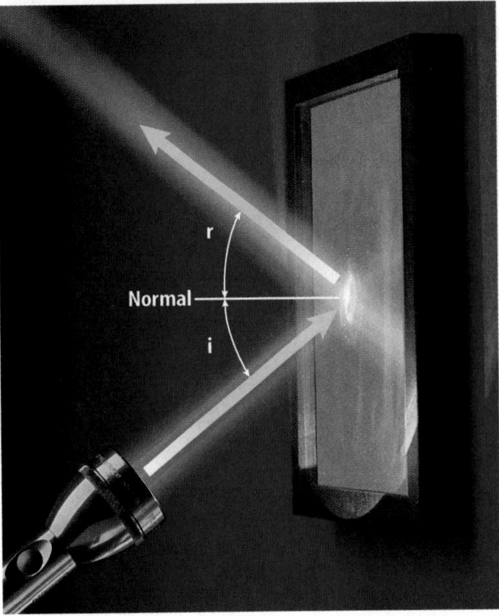

Figure 14 A flashlight beam is made of light waves. When any wave is reflected, the angle of incidence, *i*, equals the angle of reflection, *r*.

The Law of Reflection Look at the two light beams in **Figure 14.** The beam striking the mirror is called the incident beam. The beam that bounces off the mirror is called the reflected beam. The line drawn perpendicular to the surface of the mirror is called the normal. The angle formed by the incident beam and the normal is the angle of incidence, labeled *i*. The angle formed by the reflected beam and the normal is the angle of reflection, labeled *r*. According to the law of reflection, the angle of incidence is equal to the angle of reflection. All reflected waves obey this law. Objects that bounce from a surface sometimes behave like waves that are reflected from a surface. For example, suppose you throw a bounce pass while playing basketball. The angle between the ball's direction and the normal to the floor is the same before and after it bounces.

Refraction

Do you notice anything unusual in **Figure 15?** The pencil looks as if it is broken into two pieces. But if you pulled the pencil out of the water, you would see that it is unbroken. This illusion is caused by refraction. How does it work?

Remember that a wave's speed depends on the medium it is moving through. When a wave passes from one medium to another—such as when a light wave passes from air to water—it changes speed. If the wave is traveling at an angle when it passes from one medium to another, it changes direction, or bends, as it changes speed. **Refraction** is the bending of a wave caused by a change in its speed as it moves from one medium to another. The greater the change in speed is, the more the wave bends.

Reading Check *When does refraction occur?*

Figure 16A on the next page shows what happens when a wave passes into a material in which it slows down. The wave is refracted (bent) toward the normal. **Figure 16B** shows what happens when a wave passes into a medium in which it speeds up. Then the wave is refracted away from the normal.

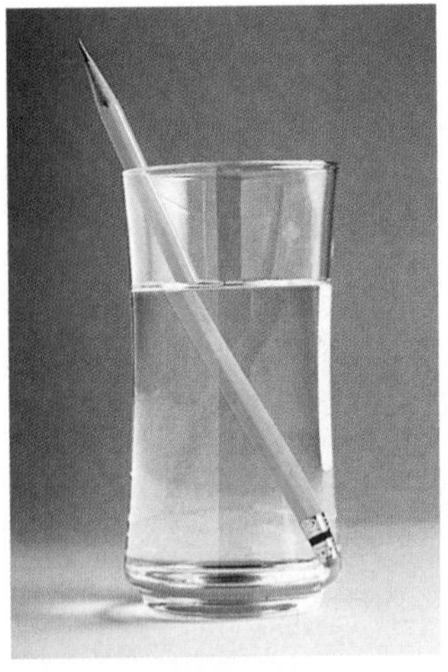

Figure 15 The pencil looks like it is broken at the surface of the water because of refraction.

Science Journal

Ray Diagrams Have students trace into their Science Journals the two photographs on this page. Then ask them to use the tracings to construct ray diagrams of the reflection and refraction shown in each one. Tell them to be sure to add the line normal to the surface in each diagram and to measure and label the angles. L2

LS **Visual-Spatial** P

Figure 16 Light waves travel slower in water than in air. This causes light waves to change direction when they move from water to air or air to water.
Predict *how the beam would bend if the speed were the same in both air and water.*

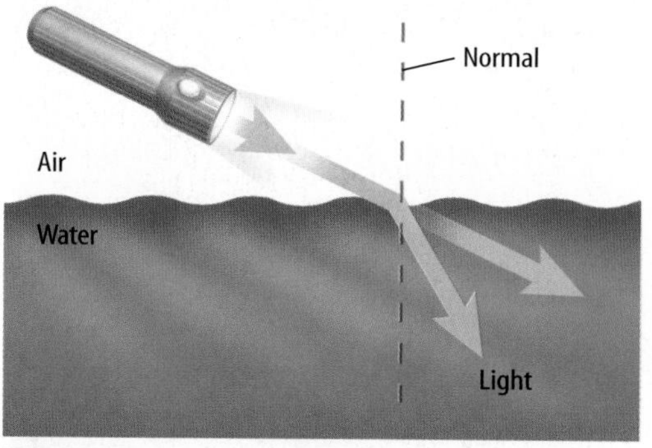

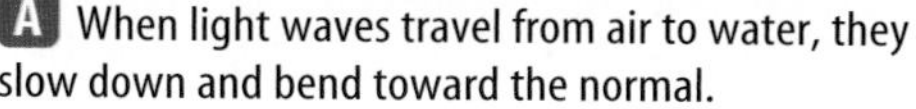

A When light waves travel from air to water, they slow down and bend toward the normal.

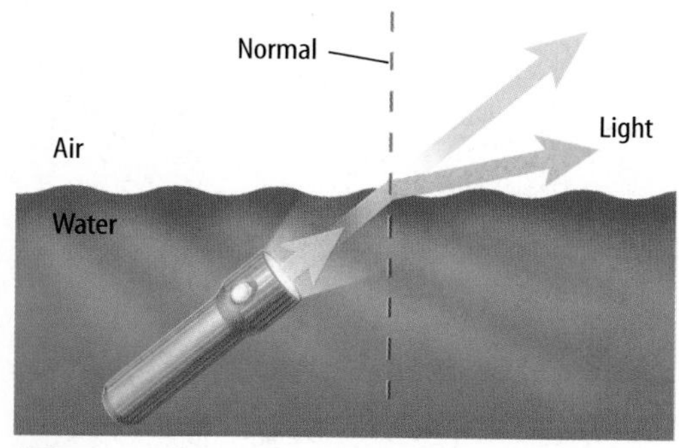

B When light waves travel from water to air, they speed up and bend away from the normal.

Refraction of Light in Water You may have noticed that objects that are underwater seem closer to the surface than they really are. **Figure 17** shows how refraction causes this illusion. In the figure, the light waves reflected from the swimmer's foot are refracted away from the normal and enter your eyes. However, your brain assumes that all light waves have traveled in a straight line. The light waves that enter your eyes seem to have come from a foot that was higher in the water. This is also why the pencil in **Figure 15** seems broken. The light waves coming from the part of the pencil that is underwater are refracted, but your brain interprets them as if they have traveled in a straight line. However, the light waves coming from the part of the pencil above the water are not refracted. So, the part of the pencil that is underwater looks as if it has shifted.

Figure 17 Light waves from the boy's foot bend away from the normal as they pass from water to air. This makes the foot look closer to the surface than it really is.
Infer *whether the boy's knee would seem closer to the surface than it is.*

Caption Answer

Figure 16 The beam wouldn't bend at all. It's the difference in speed that makes the light bend.

Caption Answer

Figure 17 yes, for the same reasons

Inquiry Lab

Addition of Waves

Purpose to model interfering waves

Possible Materials translucent straws, sheet of cardboard or poster paper, marker, tape

Estimated Time one class session

Teaching Strategies

- Make a 2×4 grid on a vertical piece of paper with each cell the same size. Use the top half as one set of x and y axes to draw a sine wave. Draw a sine wave of three times the frequency on the x and y axes formed in the bottom half.
- Cover the top with straws (resting on the halfway line) and tape the straws down. Use the marker to trace the sine wave onto the straws. Number the straws on their bottom ends from left to right. Now remove the tape and cut out the sine wave from the tops of the straws.
- Place the bottoms of the straws along the bottom wave. The tops of the straws now show the wave formed by the addition of these two waves.
- You can also try this on a graphing calculator. Graph $y = \sin(x)$, $y = \sin(3x)$, then $y = \sin(x) + \sin(3x)$.
- Extend this lab to other wave additions. Allow students to explore other questions about waves.

For additional inquiry activities, see *Science Inquiry Labs*.

Differentiated Instruction

Challenge Light travels at a different speed through glass than it does through air. Ask students to find out whether light travels faster or slower in glass than it does in air. slower Have students research to discover how refraction of light waves through glass is made useful in optometry. Ask them to depict their findings on an informational poster. L3 LS **Logical-Mathematical**

Teacher FYI

Medium Refraction How much a wave will be refracted when passing from one medium to another depends on the media involved, the angle of the wave, and sometimes its frequency. Some waves with higher frequencies are refracted more than those with lower frequencies in some media.

Quick Demo

Observing Diffraction

Materials petri dish, water, pen or pencil, overhead projector, scissors, small pieces of cardboard

Estimated Time 10 minutes

Procedure Place the water-filled petri dish on the overhead projector. Use the pen or pencil to make waves in the water. Cut the cardboard pieces into several different shapes, and place them into the dish, one at a time and in different combinations. Have students observe how each piece or combination of pieces causes a different diffraction pattern. L2 ELL IS **Visual-Spatial**

Answer refraction occurs when waves change direction as they change speed; diffraction occurs when waves bend around an object

Make a Model

Slit Diffraction Have students use rectangular glass baking dishes and flat pieces of metal or plastic to make a model of the diffraction of water waves through a slit. Have students tape two flat pieces of metal or plastic so they stand vertically across the width of the baking dish. Be sure they leave an open slit between the two pieces. Then have students fill the baking dish with water, use pencils to generate waves, and observe the diffraction. Suggest that students experiment with slit widths until they find the one that diffracts the water waves the most. L2 IS **Kinesthetic**

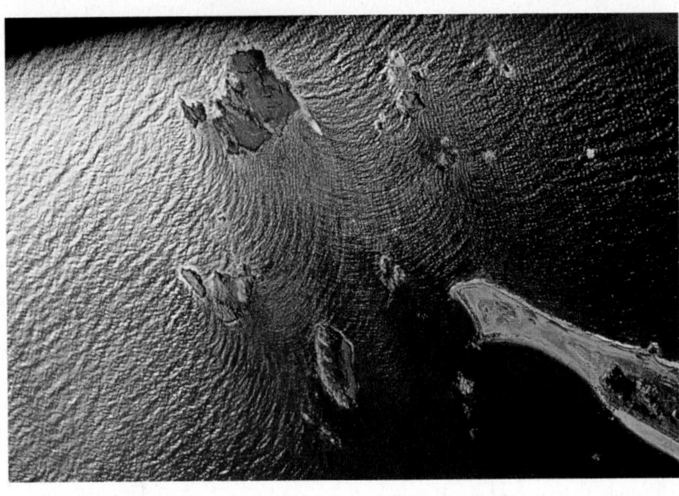

Figure 18 Diffraction causes ocean waves to change direction as they pass a group of islands.

Diffraction

When waves strike an object, several things can happen. The waves can bounce off, or be reflected. If the object is transparent, light waves can be refracted as they pass through it. Sometimes the waves may be both reflected and refracted. If you look into a glass window, sometimes you can see your reflection in the window, as well as objects behind it. Light is passing through the window and is also being reflected at its surface.

Waves also can behave another way when they strike an object. The waves can bend around the object. **Figure 18** shows how ocean waves change direction and bend after they strike an island. **Diffraction** occurs when an object causes a wave to change direction and bend around it. Diffraction and refraction both cause waves to bend. The difference is that refraction occurs when waves pass through an object, while diffraction occurs when waves pass around an object.

Figure 19 When water waves pass through a small opening in a barrier, they diffract and spread out after they pass through the hole.

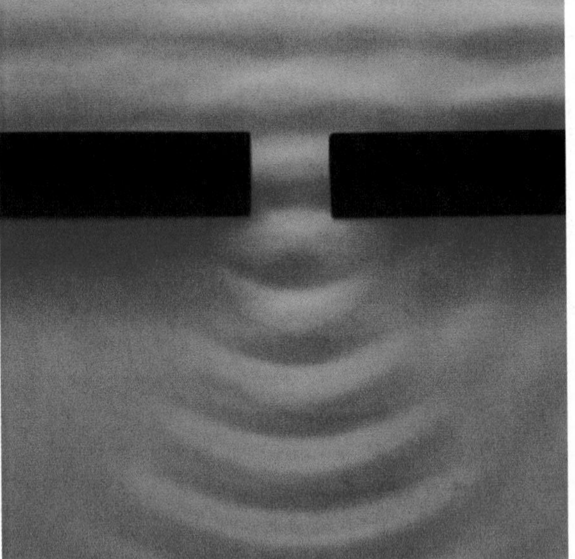

Reading Check *How do diffraction and refraction differ?*

Waves also can be diffracted when they pass through a narrow opening, as shown in **Figure 19.** After they pass through the opening, the waves spread out. In this case the waves are bending around the corners of the opening.

306 CHAPTER 10 Waves

Diffraction and Wavelength How much does a wave bend when it strikes an object or an opening? The amount of diffraction that occurs depends on how big the obstacle or opening is compared to the wavelength, as shown in **Figure 20.** When an obstacle is smaller than the wavelength, the waves bend around it. But if the obstacle is larger than the wavelength, the waves do not diffract as much. In fact, if the obstacle is much larger than the wavelength, almost no diffraction occurs. The obstacle casts a shadow because almost no waves bend around it.

Hearing Around Corners For example, you're walking down the hallway and you can hear sounds coming from the lunchroom before you reach the open lunchroom door. However, you can't see into the room until you reach the doorway. Why can you hear the sound waves but not see the light waves while you're still in the hallway? The wavelengths of sound waves are similar in size to a door opening. Sound waves diffract around the door and spread out down the hallway. Light waves have a much shorter wavelength. They are hardly diffracted at all by the door. So you can't see into the room until you get close to the door.

Diffraction of Radio Waves Diffraction also affects your radio's reception. AM radio waves have longer wavelengths than FM radio waves do. Because of their longer wavelengths, AM radio waves diffract around obstacles like buildings and mountains. The FM waves with their short wavelengths do not diffract as much. As a result, AM radio reception is often better than FM reception around tall buildings and natural barriers such as hills.

Science Online

Topic: Diffraction
Visit gpscience.com for Web links to information about diffraction.

Activity Research the wave lengths of several types of waves. For each wave type, give an example of an object that could cause diffraction to occur.

Figure 20 The diffraction of waves around an obstacle depends on the wavelength and the size of the obstacle.

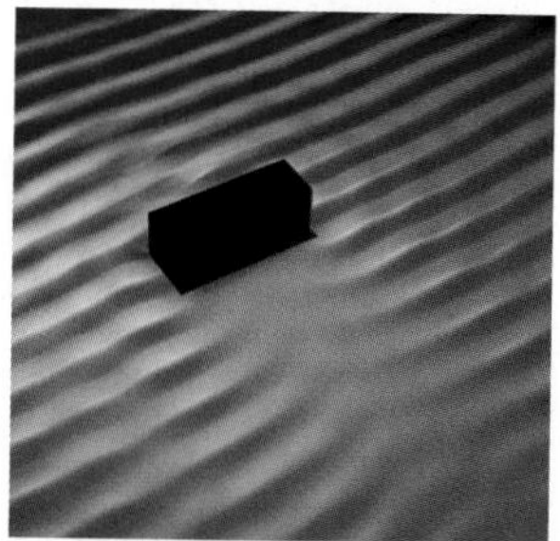

Less diffraction occurs if the wavelength is smaller than the obstacle.

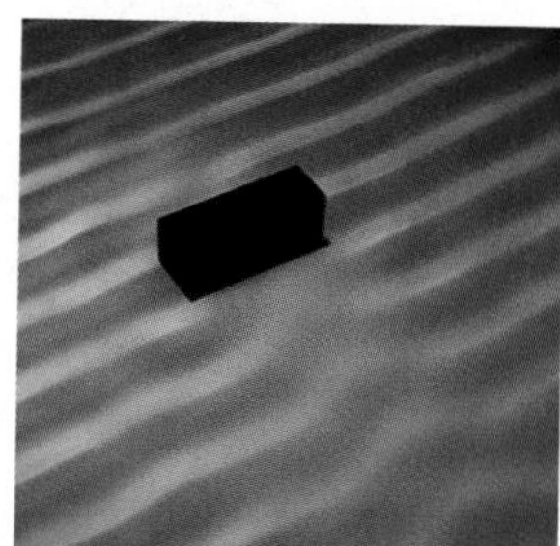

More diffraction occurs if the wavelength is the same size as the obstacle.

Teacher FYI

X Rays Because the wavelengths of X rays are about the same size as the distances between atoms in crystals, X rays are diffracted by crystals. This phenomenon is exploited in X ray crystallography, in which crystals are bombarded from different angles by X rays, and the crystal structure is determined by the diffraction of the X rays. This method has been used to determine the structure of thousands of organic, inorganic, organometallic, and biological compounds.

Discussion

Television Reception TV reception from antennas tends to be poor in mountainous regions. Based on what you read here, what type of radio waves would you guess delivers television signals? Why? FM waves. Due to their short wavelengths, they do not bend around natural obstacles like mountains. L2

Curriculum Connection

Art Have students use reflection, refraction, and diffraction to create artwork. The art could be as simple as sketching how refraction distorts objects viewed through water or as involved as photographing the diffraction patterns of light waves. Students may wish to research and experiment with how the surface of a CD diffracts light. Have students explain the phenomenon at work in their art. L2 ELL P IS **Visual-Spatial**

Fun Fact

When we listen to an orchestra, sound waves produced by all the instruments combine and hit our eardrums at the same time. The waves that reach our ears have the amplitude and frequency that result from adding together all of the waves produced by the individual instruments. Our brains and ears, however, are able to separate the wave into its components, and we hear the sounds made by the original instruments.

Caption Answer

Figure 21 the sum of the amplitudes of the original waves

Interference

Suppose two waves are traveling toward each other on a long rope as in **Figure 21A.** What will happen when the two waves meet? If you did this experiment, you would find that the two waves pass right through each other, and each one continues to travel in its original direction, as shown in **Figure 21B** and **Figure 21C.** If you look closely at the waves when they meet each other in **Figure 21B,** you see a wave that looks different than either of the two original waves. When the two waves arrive at the same place at the same time, they combine to form a new wave. When two or more waves overlap and combine to form a new wave, the process is called **interference.** This new wave exists only while the two original waves continue to overlap. The two ways that the waves can combine are called constructive interference and destructive interference.

Figure 21 Interference occurs while two waves are overlapping. Then the waves combine to form a new wave. Two waves traveling on a rope can interfere with each other.

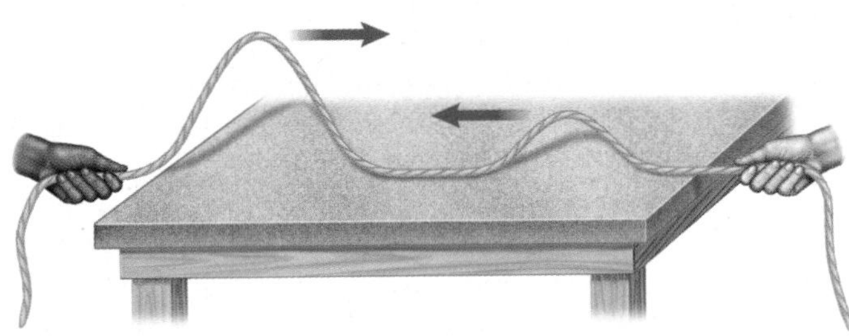

A Two waves move toward each other on a rope.

B As the waves overlap, they interfere to form a new wave. **Identify** *What is the amplitude of the new wave?*

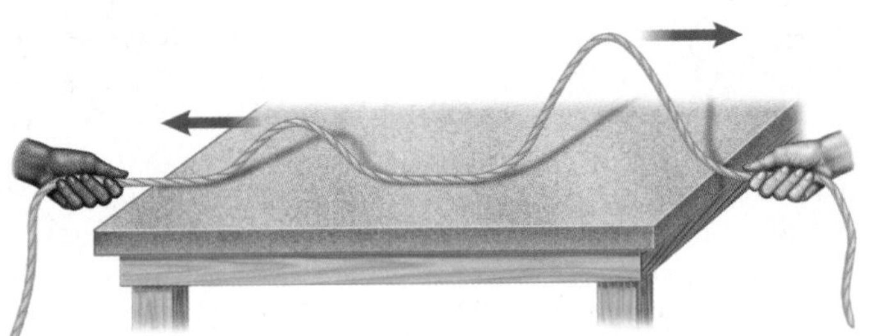

C While the two waves overlap, they continue to move right through each other. Afterward, they continue moving unchanged, as if they had never met.

Cultural Diversity

Mayan Echoes If you clap your hands in the Mayan temple of Kukulkan at Chichén Itzá in Mexico, you're greeted with a piercing echo. Many believe this echo sounds like the call of a quetzal bird. The bird is native to the region and prized for its bright colors and long tail. Archaeologists are studying the architecture of the temple to determine whether the Maya built it with this effect in mind. The shrieking, birdlike echo is produced by sound waves being diffracted by the gaps in the steps of one of the large staircases. The sound's amplification comes from waves interfering at just the right places.

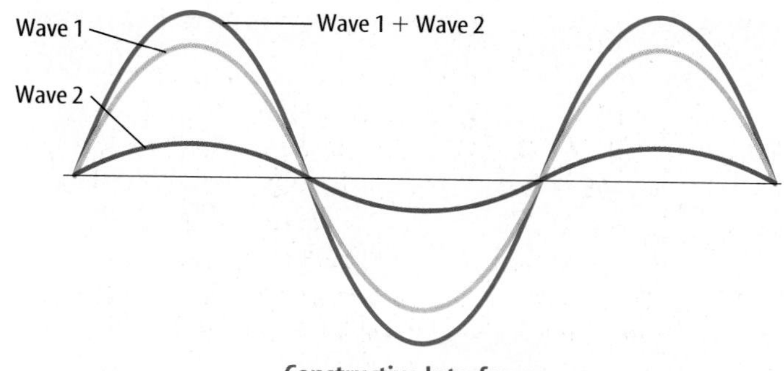

A If Wave 1 and Wave 2 overlap, they constructively interfere and form the green wave. Wave 1 and Wave 2 are in phase.

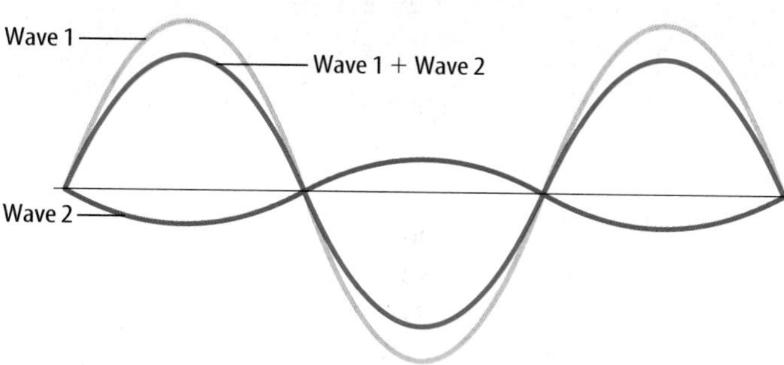

B If Wave 1 and Wave 2 overlap, they destructively interfere and form the green wave. Wave 1 and Wave 2 are out of phase.

Figure 22 When waves interfere with each other, constructive and destructive interference can occur. **Infer** *how the energy carried by each wave changes when interference occurs.*

Constructive Interference In constructive interference, shown in **Figure 22A,** the waves add together. This happens when the crests of two or more transverse waves arrive at the same place at the same time and overlap. The amplitude of the new wave that forms is equal to the sum of the amplitudes of the original waves. Constructive interference also occurs when the compressions of different compressional waves overlap. If the waves are sound waves, for example, constructive interference produces a louder sound. Waves undergoing constructive interference are said to be in phase.

Destructive Interference In destructive interference, the waves subtract from each other as they overlap. This happens when the crests of one transverse wave meet the troughs of another transverse wave, as shown in **Figure 22B.** The amplitude of the new wave is the difference between the amplitudes of the waves that overlapped. With compressional waves, destructive interference occurs when the compression of one wave overlaps with the rarefaction of another wave. The compressions and rarefactions combine and form a wave with reduced amplitude. When destructive interference happens with sound waves, it causes a decrease in loudness. Waves undergoing destructive interference are said to be out of phase.

Noise Damage People who are exposed to constant loud noises, such as those made by airplane engines, can suffer hearing damage. Special ear protectors have been developed that use destructive interference to cancel damaging noise. With a classmate, list all the jobs you can think of that require ear protectors.

Activity

Creating Interference Position a student at each end of a jump rope, and have them make different interference patterns in the rope. Challenge the students to create both constructive and destructive interference. L2 ELL

COOP LEARN LS **Kinesthetic**

Quick Demo

Interference Effects

Materials two or more musical instruments

Estimated Time 10 minutes

Procedure Ask students who play instruments to bring them in and demonstrate what happens when two notes that have almost the same pitch are played at the same time. Students should be able to hear the beats produced by the interference between the two notes. These pulses of sound disappear when the pitches become equal, so they are used by musicians as they tune their instruments. L2 LS **Auditory-Musical**

Noise Damage The use of destructive interference to cancel out noise is called active noise control. In active noise control, sounds are generated that exactly cancel out the unwanted sounds. Jobs requiring ear protection include rock concert sound mixer, airport runway worker, and factory worker.

Research Have students research the various types of hearing-protection devices that are available. Have students give a brief oral report to the class describing the various types.

Curriculum Connection

History Scientists first knew that light had wave properties when it could be shown that it produced interference patterns when passed through a slit. Have students find out whose experiments first showed this, and when. Thomas Young in 1801

L3 LS **Linguistic**

Caption Answer

Figure 22 destructive interference results in less energy carried; constructive interference results in more energy carried than each wave carried independently

Caption Answer

Figure 23 The nodes of a standing wave form where the waves traveling in opposite directions cancel out.

Purpose Students observe resonance and the conditions under which it can occur. L2 ELL

LS **Auditory-Musical**

Materials three tuning forks, two of which are at the same frequency, mallet

Teaching Strategy Demonstrate for students the best way to set a tuning fork vibrating. You don't have to hit it hard, but you do have to hit it sharply.

Analysis

The second tuning fork started vibrating, but the third one did not. The natural frequency of the second tuning fork is the same as the frequency of the waves that were hitting it from the first tuning fork, so it resonated. The natural frequency of the third tuning fork is different, so it did not resonate.

Assessment

Process Have students take the tuning forks to different areas of the classroom and see if they can find anything else that resonates with them. Use **Performance Assessment in the Science Classroom,** p. 97.

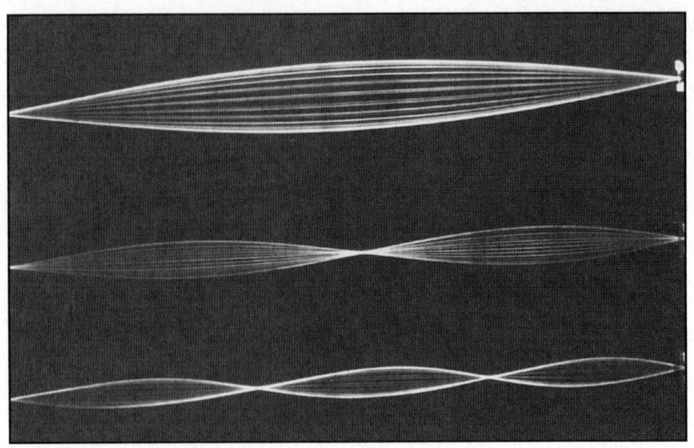

Figure 23 Standing waves form a wave pattern that seems to stay in the same place.
Explain *how nodes form in a standing wave.*

Standing Waves

When you make transverse waves with a rope, you might shake one end while your friend holds the other end still. What would happen if you both shook the rope continuously to create identical waves moving toward each other? As the two waves travel in opposite directions down the rope, they continually pass through each other. Interference takes place as the waves from each end overlap along the rope. At any point where a crest meets a crest, a new wave with a larger amplitude forms. But at points where crests meet troughs, the waves cancel each other and no motion occurs.

The interference of the two identical waves makes the rope vibrate in a special way, as shown in **Figure 23.** The waves create a pattern of crests and troughs that do not seem to be moving. Because the wave pattern stays in one place, it is called a standing wave. A **standing wave** is a special type of wave pattern that forms when waves equal in wavelength and amplitude, but traveling in opposite directions, continuously interfere with each other. The places where the two waves always cancel are called nodes. The nodes always stay in the same place on the rope. Meanwhile, the wave pattern vibrates between the nodes.

Standing Waves in Music When the string of a violin is played with a bow, it vibrates and creates standing waves. The standing waves in the string help produce a rich, musical tone. Other instruments also rely on standing waves to produce music. Some instruments, like flutes, create standing waves in a column of air. In other instruments, like drums, a tightly stretched piece of material vibrates in a special way to create standing waves. As the material in a drum vibrates, nodes are created on the surface of the drum.

Visual Learning

Figure 23 Provide pairs of students with jump ropes, and ask them to create standing waves similar to those shown in **Figure 23.** L2
LS **Kinesthetic**

Resonance

You might have noticed that bells of different sizes and shapes create different notes. When you strike a bell, the bell vibrates at certain frequencies called the natural frequencies. All objects have their own natural frequencies of vibration that depend on the object's size, shape, and the material it is made from.

There is another way to make something vibrate at its natural frequencies. Suppose you have a tuning fork that has a single natural frequency of 440 Hz. Imagine that a sound wave of the same frequency strikes the tuning fork. Because the sound wave has the same frequency as the natural frequency of the tuning fork, the tuning fork will vibrate. The process by which an object is made to vibrate by absorbing energy at its natural frequencies is called **resonance.**

Sometimes resonance can cause an object to absorb a large amount of energy. Remember that the amplitude of a wave increases as the energy it carries increases. In the same way, an object vibrates more strongly as it continues to absorb energy at its natural frequencies. If enough energy is absorbed, the object can vibrate so strongly that it breaks apart.

Experimenting with Resonance

Procedure

1. Strike a **tuning fork** with a **mallet.**
2. Hold the vibrating tuning fork near a **second tuning fork** that has the same frequency.
3. Strike the tuning fork again. Hold it near a **third tuning fork** that has a different frequency.

Analysis

What happened when you held the vibrating tuning fork near each of the other two? Explain.

section 3 review

Summary

Reflection and Refraction

- When reflection of a wave occurs, the angle of incidence equals the angle of reflection.
- Refraction occurs when a wave changes direction as it moves from one medium to another.

Diffraction

- Diffraction occurs when a wave changes direction by bending around an obstacle.
- The effects of diffraction are greatest when the wavelength is nearly the obstacle size.

Interference and Resonance

- Interference occurs when two or more waves overlap and form a new wave.
- Interference between two waves with the same wavelength and amplitude, but moving in opposite directions, produces a standing wave.
- Resonance occurs when an object is made to vibrate by absorbing energy from vibrations at its natural frequencies.

Self Check

1. **Compare** the loudness of sound waves that are in phase when they interfere with the loudness of sound waves that are out of phase when they interfere.
2. **Describe** how the reflection of light waves enables you to see your image in a mirror.
3. **Describe** the energy transformations that occur when one tuning fork makes another tuning fork resonate.
4. **Think Critically** Suppose the speed of light was greater in water than in air. Draw a diagram to show whether an object underwater would seem deeper or closer to the surface than it really is.

Applying Math

5. **Use Percentages** You aim a flashlight at a window. The radiant energy in the reflected beam is two fifths of the energy in the incident beam. What percentage of the incident beam energy passed through the window?
6. **Calculate Angle of Incidence** The angle between a flashlight beam that strikes a mirror and the reflected beam is 80 degrees. What is the angle of incidence?

gpscience.com/self_check_quiz

3 Assess

DAILY INTERVENTION

Check for Understanding

Visual-Spatial Have students create illustrated diagrams of the following wave behaviors: reflection, refraction, diffraction, interference, and standing wave. Have students label each drawing using the correct term.

Reteach

Wave Patterns Give pairs of students pieces of yarn and construction paper. Ask them to glue the yarn to the paper to show wave patterns. Students should identify the amplitude, wavelength, and frequency of the waves and point out any nodes. L2 COOP LEARN LS **Kinesthetic**

Assessment

Performance Have students make up songs describing the reflection, refraction, diffraction, and interference of waves. Use **Performance Assessment in the Science Classroom,** p. 151. L1

section 3 review

1. Sound waves that are in phase will be louder than the two waves are individually. Sound waves that are out of phase will be softer.
2. The light strikes your face and bounces off. The reflected light off your face strikes the mirror and is reflected into your eyes.
3. tuning fork vibrates forming a sound wave—mechanical energy to sound energy; sound waves strike tuning fork and make it vibrate—sound energy to mechanical energy
4. Students' drawings should show objects deeper than they actually are.
5. 60 percent
6. 40 degrees

Real-World Question

Purpose Students will generate transverse waves with a long spring and measure the speed and frequency of the waves. L2

Process Skills Observe, measure, recognize cause and effect, make and use tables, interpret data.

Time Required 45 minutes

Procedure

Safety Precautions Caution students to keep a firm hold on the spring so it doesn't fly off and hit someone.

Teaching Strategy Suggest to students that they practice the procedures for making and counting waves described in steps 2, 3, and 6 several times before they make their measurements.

Troubleshooting Make sure the spring has no kinks or rough places in it, as this will make it difficult for students to produce consistent waves.

Differentiated Instruction

Learning Disabled Have these students work in groups with students proficient in the lab. As students do the activity, have them take turns illustrating for each other the wavelength, frequency, and amplitude of waves they generate. Ask them to also create compressional waves, and compare and contrast them with transverse waves. L1 IS **Linguistic**

Measuring Wave Properties

Goals
- **Measure** the speed of a transverse wave.
- **Create** waves with different amplitudes.
- **Measure** the wavelength of a transverse wave.

Materials
long spring, rope, or hose
meterstick
stopwatch

Safety Precautions

Real-World Question

Some waves travel through space; others pass through a medium such as air, water, or earth. Each wave has a wavelength, speed, frequency, and amplitude. How can the speed of a wave be measured? How can the wavelength be determined from the frequency?

Procedure

1. With a partner, stretch your spring across an open floor and measure the length of the spring. Record this measurement in the data table. Make sure the spring is stretched to the same length for each step.
2. Have your partner hold one end of the spring. Create a single wave pulse by shaking the other end of the spring back and forth.
3. Have a third person use a stopwatch to measure the time needed for the pulse to travel the length of the spring. Record this measurement in the *Wave Time* column of your data table.
4. Repeat steps 2 and 3 two more times.
5. **Calculate** the speed of waves 1, 2, and 3 in your data table by using the formula:

   speed = distance/time

   Average the speeds of waves 1, 2, and 3 to find the speed of waves on your spring.
6. **Create** a wave with several wavelengths. You make one wavelength when your hand moves left, right, and left again. Count the number of wavelengths that you generate in 10 s. Record this measurement for wave 4 in the *Wavelength Count* column in your data table.
7. **Repeat** step 6 two more times. Each time, create a wave with a different wavelength by shaking the spring faster or slower.

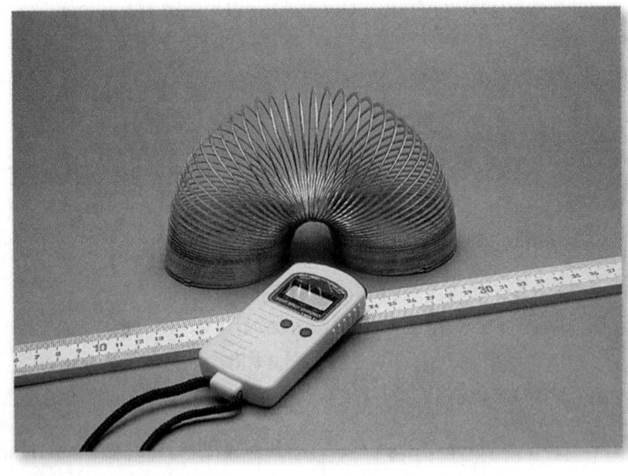

Alternative Inquiry Lab

Waves and Boundaries To extend this Lab into an Inquiry Lab, have students observe wave behavior at a boundary. To simulate waves traveling between two media, attach a hose and a rope, or two other materials, end to end and create a pulse. Try starting the pulse from the other end. Compare transmitted pulse to reflected pulse. Interested students can research coated optics (such as antiglare coating on glasses and camera lenses) or other uses for these wave properties.

Analyze Your Data

1. **Calculate** the frequency of waves 4, 5, and 6 by dividing the number of wavelengths by 10 s.
2. Calculate the wavelength of waves 4, 5, and 6 using the formula
   wavelength = wave speed/frequency
   Use the average speed calculated in step 5 for the wave speed.

Wave Property Measurement

	Spring Length	Wave Time	Wave Speed
Wave 1	Results will vary depending on the springs used.		
Wave 2			
Wave 3			
	Wavelength Count	**Frequency**	**Wavelength**
Wave 4	Results will vary depending on the springs used.		
Wave 5			
Wave 6			

Conclude and Apply

1. Was the wave speed different for the three different pulses you created? Why or why not?
2. Why would you average the speeds of the three different pulses to calculate the speed of waves on your spring?
3. How did the wavelength of the waves you created depend on the frequency of the waves?

Ask your teacher to set up a contest between the groups in your class. Have each group compete to determine who can create waves with the longest wavelength, the highest frequency, and the largest wave speed. Record the measurements of each group's efforts on the board.

Analyze Your Data

Expected Outcome Wave times measured in steps 3 and 4 should be similar.

Answers to Questions

1. Answers will vary.
2. Answers will vary.

Error Analysis Have groups compare their data with other students and discuss possible reasons for errors. As they compare their data, make sure students understand that wave times and wave speeds will be different for different springs.

Conclude and Apply

1. Accept all reasonable responses. Wave speed probably varies because it would be difficult to shake the spring exactly the same way each time.
2. to compensate for errors in measurement
3. Wavelength decreased as frequency increased. Wavelength = wave speed/frequency

Assessment

Performance Ask students to repeat the activity, but this time to generate compressional waves. Use **Performance Assessment in the Science Classroom**, p. 97.

Active Reading

Reflective Journal Have students divide pieces of paper into several columns. Have them record their thoughts under headings such as *What I did*, *What I learned*, *Questions I have*, and *Surprises I experienced.* Have students write a Reflective Journal entry for this activity. L2

Help students analyze the data on the board to determine whether there was any relationship between the amplitude, frequency, wavelength, and wave speed of the winning waves.

TIME

Content Background

The speed of sound in water was first calculated in 1822. Unlike light or radio waves, sound waves can travel long distances underwater.

Piezoelectric crystals discovered in the late 1800s made modern sonar feasible. When compressed, they produce an electrical charge. This enabled the development of transducers that could change the mechanical energy of sound waves into electrical signals.

Sonar enables the detection of silent objects by bouncing a sound wave from the object and listening for the echo. Today, sonar is used to inspect metals for flaws, monitor oceanic temperatures, and determine the health of unborn babies.

Historical Significance

The development of sonar tremendously increased the safety of shipping. Sonic fathometers allow deep drafted vessels to safely navigate previously hazardous channels. The ability to detect icebergs lengthens the shipping season in the high latitudes. In wartime sonar was a key element in the protection of commercial convoys.

Sonar and related technologies have improved the search for oil, made it possible to locate sunken objects, and have improved the quality of medical diagnostics and the integrity of structural materials.

TIME **SCIENCE AND HISTORY** SCIENCE CAN CHANGE THE COURSE OF HISTORY!

MAKING WAVES

Sonar Helps Create Deep-Sea Pictures and Save Lives

This machine houses side-scan sonar. It was used to help locate the wreck of the *Titanic*.

What is sonar?

Sonar is a device that uses sound waves to locate and measure the distance to underwater objects. Its name is a shortened version of SOund NAvigation and Ranging.

How does sonar work?

Sonar sends out a ping sound that reflects back when it hits an underwater object. Since sound travels through water at a known speed (about 1,500 m/s), scientists measure how long the sound takes to return, then calculate the distance.

Why was it invented?

Sonar was developed by scientists in the early twentieth century as a way to detect icebergs and prevent boating disasters. Its technical advancement was hurried by the Allies' need to detect German submarines in World War I. By 1918, the United States and Britain had developed an active sonar system placed in submarines sent to attack other subs.

By World War II, sonar allowed ships to defend themselves effectively from enemy subs. Their strategy was to use sonar to find subs and then fire depth charges at them from a safe distance. After the war, sonar-absorbing hulls and quiet engines and machinery ensured that subs could partly shield themselves from sonar.

Sonar is now used to help fishermen and scientists find schools of fish. Oceanographers also use it to map ocean and lake floors. Sonar has been vital, too, in the discovery of downed airplanes and ships, including the *Titanic*—the passenger liner that sank in 1912.

In 1985, a French and American team used a new type of sonar device called the side-scan sonar to locate the *Titanic*. This kind of sonar projects a tight beam of sound to create detailed images of the sea bed. Members of the expedition towed this sonar device about 170 m above the seabed across a section of the Atlantic Ocean where the *Titanic* went down. Weeks later, video cameras finally spotted the wreck.

The *Titanic* was found thanks to sonar.

Report **Research how sonar was used by navies in World War I and World War II. Did sonar affect each war's outcome? How did it save lives? What uses can you think of for sonar if it could be used in everyday life?**

For more information, visit gpscience.com/time

Report Have students research the modern uses of acoustic technology and make a "Family Tree" chart of all the products and equipment they can discover that perform their primary function through the use or detection of sounds, both audible and inaudible. Through class discussion, determine which are directly related to sonar and its basic principles. L2

Resources for Teachers and Students

Center for Bioacoustics, Texas A&M University-Corpus Christi, Natural Resources Center 3404, 6300 Ocean Drive, Corpus Christi, Texas 78412

National Sonar Association, 40414 Yardley Court, Temecula, CA 92591

Reviewing Main Ideas

Section 1 The Nature of Waves

1. Waves are rhythmic disturbances that transfer energy through matter or space.
2. Waves transfer only energy, not matter.

3. Mechanical waves need matter to travel through. Mechanical waves can be compressional or transverse.
4. When a transverse wave travels in a medium, matter in the medium moves at right angles to the direction the wave travels.
5. When a compressional wave travels in a medium, matter moves back and forth along the same direction as the wave travels.

Section 2 Wave Properties

1. The movement of high points in a medium called crests and low points called troughs forms a transverse wave.
2. The movement of more-dense regions called compressions and less-dense regions called rarefactions forms a compressional wave.
3. Transverse and compressional waves can be described by their wavelengths, frequencies, periods, and amplitudes. As frequency increases, wavelength always decreases.
4. The greater a wave's amplitude is, the more energy it carries.

5. A wave's velocity can be calculated by multiplying its frequency times its wavelength.

Section 3 The Behavior of Waves

1. For all waves, the angle of incidence equals the angle of reflection.
2. A wave is bent, or refracted, when it changes speed as it enters a new medium.

3. When two or more waves overlap, they combine to form a new wave. This process is called interference.

FOLDABLES Use the Foldable that you made at the beginning of this chapter to help you review transverse and compressional waves.

Science Online gpscience.com/interactive_tutor

Identifying Misconceptions

Assess

After students have done the activity at the beginning of this chapter, have them perform this activity.

Materials corks, pan of water, eyedropper

Procedure Have students work in groups and use the materials provided to design an experiment to see how water waves move corks. Use the dropper to create the waves.

Expected Outcome Students will realize that the corks are not displaced by the waves. Students should realize that the medium does not travel with the waves. L2

chapter 10 Study Guide

Reviewing Main Ideas

Summary statements can be used by students to review the major concepts of the chapter.

Science Online

Visit gpscience.com
/self_check_quiz
/interactive_tutor
/vocabulary_puzzlemaker
/chapter_review
/standardized_test

Assessment Transparency

For additional assessment questions, use the *Assessment Transparency* located in the transparency book.

Assessment

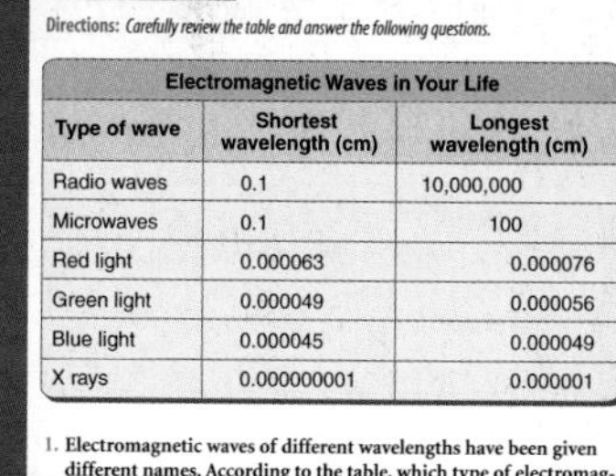

Assessment Transparency **Waves**

Directions: *Carefully review the table and answer the following questions.*

Electromagnetic Waves in Your Life		
Type of wave	Shortest wavelength (cm)	Longest wavelength (cm)
Radio waves	0.1	10,000,000
Microwaves	0.1	100
Red light	0.000063	0.000076
Green light	0.000049	0.000056
Blue light	0.000045	0.000049
X rays	0.000000001	0.000001

1. Electromagnetic waves of different wavelengths have been given different names. According to the table, which type of electromagnetic wave can have a wavelength greater than 5 m?
A Radio waves
B Microwaves
C Red light
D Blue light
2. According to the table, which type of electromagnetic wave can have a wavelength of 0.000046 cm?
F Radio waves
G Microwaves
H Red light
J Blue light
3. If a device were emitting an electromagnetic wave of 0.00000001 cm, what kind of device would it be?
A Radio
B Microwave oven
C Flashlight
D X-ray machine

L2

Waves

FOLDABLES Have students use their Foldables to review the content of the chapter. How would the differences between light waves and sound waves become apparent if you were visiting the Moon? Explain. L2

chapter 10 Review

Using Vocabulary

1. Reflection and refraction both involve waves contacting a surface and changing direction. In reflection, waves bounce off a surface, whereas refraction occurs when waves enter a new medium at an angle, change speed, and are bent.
2. Standing waves have nodes that do not move.
3. The rarefaction of a compressional wave has the lowest density.
4. Refraction and diffraction describe the bending of a wave.
5. When waves overlap, they interfere and form a new wave.
6. The amplitude of any transverse wave is the distance from the crest or trough to the rest position of the medium.
7. Frequency measures how many wavelengths pass a fixed point each second.
8. A mechanical wave always travels through a medium.

Checking Concepts

9. B
10. A
11. D
12. A
13. B
14. A
15. C
16. D
17. D

Interpreting Graphics

18. Check student's concept maps.

chapter 10 Review

Using Vocabulary

amplitude p. 300	rarefaction p. 296
compressional wave p. 292	refraction p. 304
crest p. 296	resonance p. 311
diffraction p. 306	standing wave p. 310
frequency p. 297	transverse wave p. 292
interference p. 308	trough p. 296
medium p. 291	wave p. 290
period p. 297	wavelength p. 297

Answer the following questions using complete sentences.

1. Compare and contrast reflection and refraction.
2. Which type of wave has points called nodes that do not move?
3. Which part of a compressional wave has the lowest density?
4. Find two words in the vocabulary list that describe the bending of a wave.
5. What occurs when waves overlap?
6. What is the relationship among amplitude, crest, and trough?
7. What does frequency measure?
8. What does a mechanical wave always travel through?

Checking Concepts

Choose the word or phrase that best answers the question.

9. Which of the following do waves carry?
   A) matter **C)** matter and energy
   B) energy **D)** the medium
10. What is the formula for calculating wave speed?
    A) $v = \lambda f$ **C)** $v = \lambda / f$
    B) $v = f - \lambda$ **D)** $v = \lambda + f$
11. When a compressional wave travels through a medium, which way does matter in the medium move?
    A) backward
    B) forward
    C) perpendicular to the rest position
    D) along the same direction the wave travels
12. What is the highest point of a transverse wave called?
    A) crest **C)** wavelength
    B) compression **D)** trough
13. If the frequency of the waves produced by a vibrating object increases, how does the wavelength of the waves produced change?
    A) It stays the same. **C)** It vibrates.
    B) It decreases. **D)** It increases.
14. If the amplitude of a wave changes, which of the following changes?
    A) wave energy **C)** wave speed
    B) frequency **D)** refraction
15. Which term describes the bending of a wave around an object?
    A) resonance **C)** diffraction
    B) interference **D)** reflection
16. What is equal to the angle of reflection?
    A) refraction angle **C)** bouncing angle
    B) normal angle **D)** angle of incidence

Use the table below to answer question 17.

Speed of Sound in Air

Temperature (°C)	Sound Speed (m/s)
0	331.4
10	337.4
20	343.4

17. Based on the data in the table above, which of the following would be the speed of sound in air at 30°C?
    A) 340.4 m/s **C)** 353.4 m/s
    B) 346.4 m/s **D)** 349.4 m/s

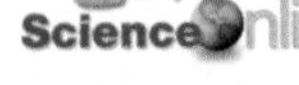
Science Online gpscience.com/vocabulary_puzzlemaker

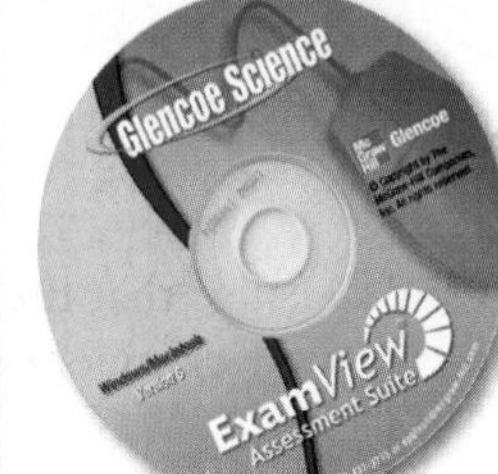

Use the *ExamView® Assessment Suite* CD-ROM to:

- create multiple versions of tests
- create modified tests with one mouse click for inclusion students
- edit existing questions and add your own questions
- build tests aligned with state standards using built-in State Curriculum Tags
- change English tests to Spanish with one mouse click and vice versa

Interpreting Graphics

18. Copy and complete the following concept map on waves.

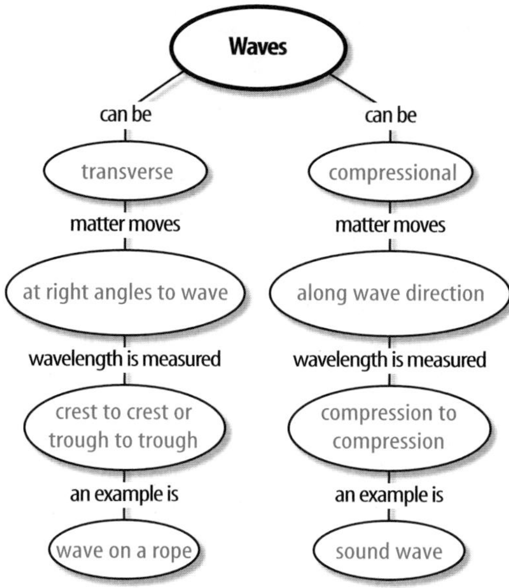

Thinking Critically

19. **Explain** An earthquake on the ocean floor produces a tsunami that hits a remote island. Is the water that hits the island the same water that was above the earthquake on the ocean floor?

20. **Compare** Suppose waves with different amplitudes are produced by a vibrating object. How do the frequencies of the waves with different amplitudes compare?

21. **Explain** Use the law of reflection to explain why you see only a portion of the area behind you when you look in a mirror.

22. **Explain** why you can hear a fire engine coming around a street corner before you can see it.

23. **Describe** the objects or materials that vibrated to produce three of the sounds you've heard today.

24. **Form a Hypothesis** In 1981, people dancing on the balconies of a Kansas City, Missouri, hotel caused the balconies to collapse. Use what have you learned about wave behavior to form a hypothesis that explains why this happened.

25. **Make and Use Tables** Find information in newspaper articles or magazines describing five recent earthquakes. Construct a table that shows for each earthquake the date, location, magnitude, and whether the damage caused by each earthquake was light, moderate, or heavy.

26. **Concept Map** Design a concept map that shows the characteristics of transverse waves. Include the terms *crest, trough, medium, wavelength, frequency, period,* and *amplitude.*

Applying Math

27. **Calculate Wavelength** Calculate the wavelength of a wave traveling on a spring if the wave moves at 0.2 m/s and has a period of 0.5 s.

28. **Calculate Wavespeed** The microwaves produced inside a microwave oven have a wavelength of 12.0 cm and a frequency of 2,500,000,000 Hz. At what speed do the microwaves travel in units of m/s?

29. **Calculate Frequency** Water waves on a lake travel toward a dock with a speed of 2.0 m/s and a wavelength of 0.5 m. How many wave crests strike the dock each second?

Science Online gpscience.com/chapter_review

Assessment Resources

Reproducible Masters

Chapter *Fast File* Resources
Chapter Review, pp. 37–38
Chapter Tests, pp. 39–42
Assessment Transparency Activity, p. 51

Glencoe Science Web site
Chapter Review Test
Standardized Test Practice

Glencoe Technology
Assessment Transparency
ExamView® Assessment Suite
MindJogger Videoquiz
Interactive Chalkboard

Thinking Critically

19. No; the water that hits the island is water that already was near the island. Through the wave, it has received energy from the earthquake miles away.
20. frequency is independent of amplitude
21. In a mirror, you can see only objects located at an angle such that their reflected beam bounces toward your eyes.
22. Sound waves have a longer wavelength than light waves. They can diffract around the street corner, but light waves cannot.
23. Possible answers: vocal cords, bell, car engine
24. The dancers created vibrations at the resonant frequency of the balcony. The vibrations of the balcony increased as it absorbed energy at its resonant frequency until its amplitude of vibration was large enough to cause the balcony to break.
25. Check students' work. Make sure magnitude is given in the same scale for all earthquakes.
26. Check students' work.

Applying Math

National Math Standards

1, 2, 9

27. $f = \frac{1}{period}; = \frac{1}{0.5_s} = 2\text{ Hz};$

$\lambda = \frac{v}{f} = \frac{(0.2\text{ m/s})}{2\text{ Hz}}$

$= 0.1\text{ m}$

28. $v = \lambda f$

$= (0.12\text{ m})(2.5 \times 10^9\text{ Hz})$

$= 3.0 \times 10^8\text{ m/s}$

29. $f = \frac{v}{\lambda} = \frac{(2.0\text{ m/s})}{(0.5\text{ m})} = 4\text{ Hz}$

Answer Sheet A practice answer sheet can be found at gpscience.com/answer_sheet.

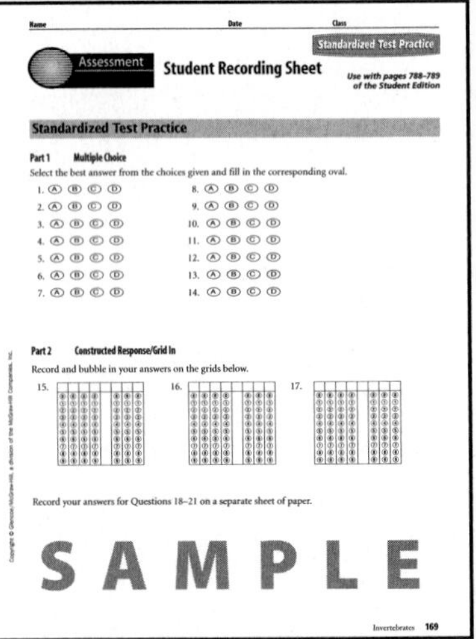
Name Date Class
Standardized Test Practice
Assessment Student Recording Sheet
Use with pages 788–789 of the Student Edition

Standardized Test Practice

Part 1 Multiple Choice
Select the best answer from the choices given and fill in the corresponding oval.

1. Ⓐ Ⓑ Ⓒ Ⓓ 8. Ⓐ Ⓑ Ⓒ Ⓓ
2. Ⓐ Ⓑ Ⓒ Ⓓ 9. Ⓐ Ⓑ Ⓒ Ⓓ
3. Ⓐ Ⓑ Ⓒ Ⓓ 10. Ⓐ Ⓑ Ⓒ Ⓓ
4. Ⓐ Ⓑ Ⓒ Ⓓ 11. Ⓐ Ⓑ Ⓒ Ⓓ
5. Ⓐ Ⓑ Ⓒ Ⓓ 12. Ⓐ Ⓑ Ⓒ Ⓓ
6. Ⓐ Ⓑ Ⓒ Ⓓ 13. Ⓐ Ⓑ Ⓒ Ⓓ
7. Ⓐ Ⓑ Ⓒ Ⓓ 14. Ⓐ Ⓑ Ⓒ Ⓓ

Part 2 Constructed Response/Grid In
Record and bubble in your answers on the grids below.
15. 16. 17.

Record your answers for Questions 18–21 on a separate sheet of paper.

SAMPLE

Invertebrates 169

Part 1 Multiple Choice

1. C	7. A
2. A	8. C
3. D	9. D
4. D	10. A
5. C	11. C
6. C	12. D

Part 2 Short Response

13. Water waves do not move the medium through which they travel. They only move energy.
14. A: Amp. = 0.5 m; λ = 1.0 m; B: Amp. = 0.4 m; λ = 2.0 m; C: Amp. = 0.6 m; λ = 2.0 m;
15. A, 2 Hz; B, 1 Hz; C, 1 Hz
16. $v = \lambda f = (1.32\text{ m})(256\text{ Hz}) = 338$ m/s
17. $f = \frac{v}{\lambda} = \frac{(330\text{ m/s})}{(15\text{ m})} = 22\text{ Hz}$
18. $\lambda = \frac{v}{f} = \frac{(345\text{ m/s})}{(2050\text{ Hz})} = 0.168\text{ m}$

chapter 10 Standardized Test Practice

Part 1 Multiple Choice

Record your answers on the answer sheet provided by your teacher or on a sheet of paper.

1. When a transverse wave travels through a medium, which way does matter in the medium move?
   A. backward
   B. all directions
   C. at right angles to the direction the wave travels
   D. in the same direction the wave travels

Use the illustration below to answer questions 2 and 3.

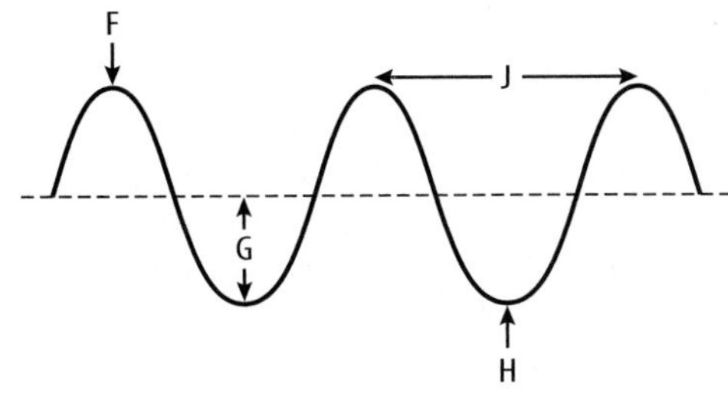

2. What wave property is shown at G?
   A. amplitude **C.** crest
   B. wavelength **D.** trough
3. What property of the wave is shown at H?
   A. amplitude **C.** crest
   B. wavelength **D.** trough
4. What is the number of waves that pass a point in a certain time called?
   A. wavelength **B.** wave amplitude
   C. wave intensity **D.** wave frequency
5. The period of a wave can be directly calculated from which of the following?
   A. troughs **C.** frequency
   B. amplitude **D.** wavelength
6. What is the energy of a wave related to?
   A. frequency **C.** amplitude
   B. wave speed **D.** refraction
7. What is the bending of a wave as it enters a new material called?
   A. refraction **C.** reflection
   B. diffraction **D.** interference
8. When the crests of two identical waves meet, what is the amplitude of the resulting wave?
   A. three times the amplitude of each wave
   B. half the amplitude of each wave
   C. twice the amplitude of each wave
   D. four times the amplitude of one of the original waves

Use the illustration below to answer questions 9 and 10.

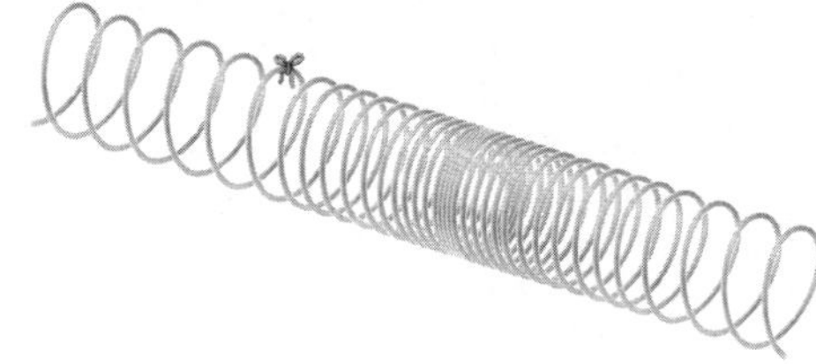

9. What kind of wave is shown?
   A. mechanical **C.** transverse
   B. compressional **D.** both A and B
10. What happens to the yarn tied to the coil?
    A. It moves back and forth as the wave passes.
    B. It moves up and down as the wave passes.
    C. It does not move as the wave passes.
    D. It moves to the next coil as the wave passes.
11. Through which of the following can sound waves NOT travel?
    A. water **C.** outer space
    B. wood **D.** air
12. What property of a wave is measured in hertz?
    A. amplitude **C.** speed
    B. wavelength **D.** frequency

Part 3 Open Ended

19. A standing wave forms when waves equal in wavelength and amplitude, but traveling in opposite directions, continuously interfere with each other. The places where the two waves always cancel are called nodes.
20. Light waves from the object under water bend away from the normal as they pass from water to air making the object appear closer to the surface than it really is.
21. Diffraction and refraction both cause waves to bend. The difference is that refraction occurs when waves change speed in moving from one material to another, while diffraction occurs when waves pass around an object.
22. No, sound waves must have a medium to travel through. Sound waves would not travel through outer space. They would see the explosion because light waves do not require a medium to travel.

Part 2 Short Response/Grid In

Record your answers on the answer sheet provided by your teacher or on a sheet of paper.

13. Explain why water waves traveling toward a swimmer on a float do not move the float forward.

Use the illustration below to answer questions 14 and 15.

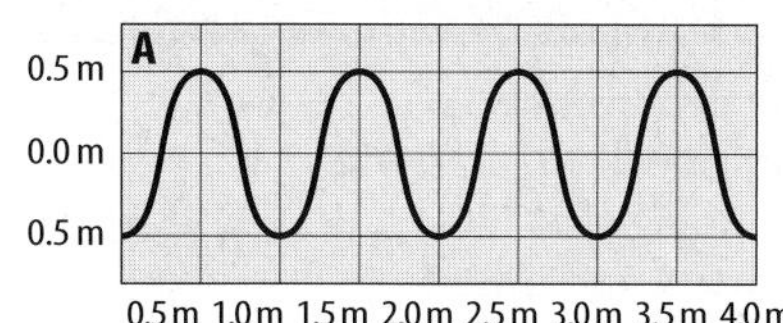

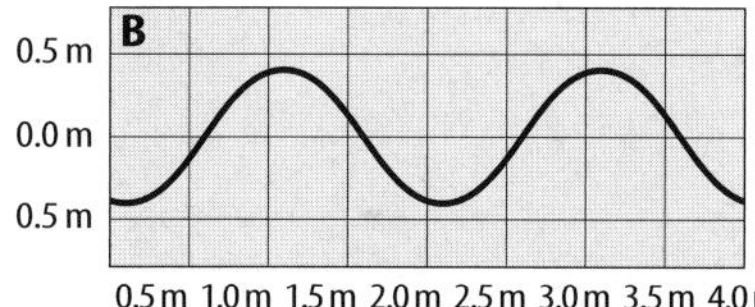

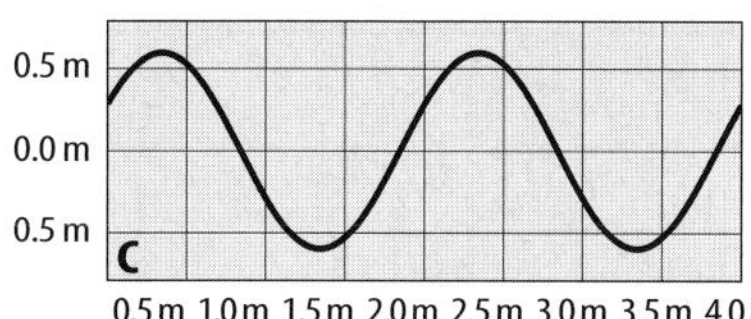

14. Determine the amplitudes and the wavelengths of each of the three waves.

15. If the length of the x-axis on each diagram represents 2 s of time, what is the frequency of each wave?

16. A tuning fork vibrates at a frequency of 256 Hz. The wavelength of the sound produced by the tuning fork is 1.32 m. What is the speed of the wave?

17. A sound wave has a speed in air of 330 m/s. If it has a wavelength of 15 m, what is the frequency of the wave?

18. A wave has a speed of 345 m/s and its frequency is 2050 Hz. What is its wavelength?

Part 3 Open Ended

Record your answers on a sheet of paper.

19. Describe how a standing wave forms and why it has nodes.

20. Explain why objects that are underwater seem to be closer to the surface than they really are.

21. Compare and contrast refraction and diffraction of waves.

22. In a science fiction movie, a huge explosion occurs on the surface of a planet. People in a spaceship heading toward the planet see and hear the explosion. Is this realistic? Explain.

23. Would you expect better reception from AM or FM radio stations on your car radio when the car was traveling in a mountainous area? Explain.

Use the illustration below to answer questions 24 and 25.

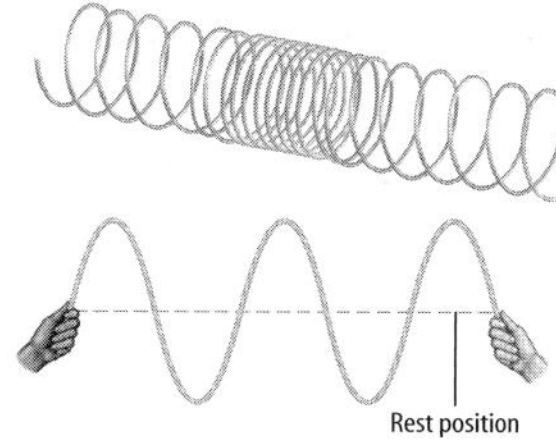

24. Describe how the amplitude of each of the two waves shown is defined.

25. Describe how you would change both drawings to show waves that carry more energy.

Test-Taking Tip

Answer every question Never leave any open ended answer blank. Answer each question as best you can. You can receive partial credit for partially correct answers.

Question 19 Before you answer the question, list what you know about standing waves.

23. The reception would be better from AM radio stations because the wavelengths are longer and will diffract around large obstacles such as mountains.

24. The wavelength of the compressional wave is the distance from compression to compression or rarefaction to rarefaction. The wavelength of the transverse wave is the distance from crest to crest or trough to trough.

25. For the compressional wave, make the spring coil farther apart in the rarefactions and closer together in the compressions. For the transverse wave, make the crests higher and the troughs deeper.

Rubrics

The following rubrics are sample scoring devices for short response and open-ended questions.

Short Response

Points	Description
2	The student demonstrates a thorough understanding of the science of the task. The response may contain minor flaws that do not detract from the demonstration of a thorough understanding.
1	The student has provided a response that is only partially correct.
0	The student has provided a completely incorrect solution or no response at all.

Open Ended

Points	Description
4	The student demonstrates a thorough understanding of the science of the task. The response may contain minor flaws that do not detract from the demonstration of a thorough understanding.
3	The student demonstrates an understanding of the science of the task. The response is essentially correct and demonstrates an essential but less than thorough understanding of the science.
2	The student demonstrates only a partial understanding of the science of the task. Although the student may have used the correct approach to a solution or may have provided a correct solution, the work lacks an essential understanding of the underlying science concepts.
1	The student demonstrates a very limited understanding of the science of the task. The response is incomplete and exhibits many flaws.
0	The student provides a completely incorrect solution or no response at all.

Sound

BIG Idea **Sound waves are compressional waves produced by something that vibrates.**

	Content Standards	Learning Objectives	Resources to Assess Mastery
Section 1	**5–8:** UCP.1–3, 5; A.1, 2 **9–12:** UCP.1–3, 5; A.1, 2	**The Nature of Sound** 1. **Explain** how sound travels through different mediums. 2. **Identify** what influences the speed of sound. 3. **Describe** how the ear enables you to hear. ***Main Idea*** Sound waves are compressional waves that can only travel through matter.	Formative Assessment Reading Check, pp. 323, 325 Section Review, p. 326 Summative Assessment *ExamView® Assessment Suite*
Section 2	**5–8:** UCP.1–3, 5; A.1, 2 **9–12:** UCP.1–3, 5; A.1, 2	**Properties of Sound** 4. **Recognize** how amplitude, intensity, and loudness are related. 5. **Describe** how sound intensity is measured and what levels can damage hearing. 6. **Explain** the relationship between frequency and pitch. 7. **Discuss** the Doppler effect. ***Main Idea*** The loudness of a sound depends on its intensity and its pitch depends on its frequency.	Formative Assessment Reading Check, pp. 329, 331 Section Review, p. 332 Summative Assessment *ExamView® Assessment Suite*
Section 3	**5–8:** UCP.1–3, 5; A.1, 2 **9–12:** UCP.1–3, 5; A.1, 2	**Music** 8. **Distinguish** between noise and music. 9. **Describe** why different instruments have different sound qualities. 10. **Explain** how string, wind, and percussion instruments produce music. 11. **Describe** the formation of beats. ***Main Idea*** A musical instrument produces combinations of frequencies that determine how the instrument sounds.	Formative Assessment Reading Check, pp. 334, 336, 337 Section Review, p. 337 Summative Assessment *ExamView® Assessment Suite*
Section 4	**5–8:** UCP.1–3, 5; A.1, 2; F.1 **9–12:** UCP.1–3, 5; A.1, 2; F.1 See pp. 16T–17T for a Key to Standards.	**Using Sound** 12. **Recognize** some of the factors that determine how a concert hall or theater is designed. 13. **Describe** how some animals use sound waves to hunt and navigate. 14. **Discuss** the uses of sonar. 15. **Explain** how ultrasound is useful in medicine. ***Main Idea*** Sound waves are used to locate objects, form images, and to treat medical problems.	Formative Assessment Reading Check, pp. 341, 342 Section Review, p. 343 Summative Chapter Asĺsessment MindJogger, Ch. 11 *ExamView® Assessment Suite* Leveled Chapter Test Test A L1 Test B L2 Test C L3 Test Practice, pp. 350–351

<table>
<tr><th colspan="5">Suggested Pacing</th></tr>
<tr><th>Period</th><th>Instruction</th><th>Labs</th><th>Review & Assessment</th><th>Total</th></tr>
<tr><td>Single</td><td>4 days</td><td>2.5 days</td><td>2.5 days</td><td>9 days</td></tr>
<tr><td>Block</td><td>2 blocks</td><td>1.25 blocks</td><td>1.25 blocks</td><td>4.5 blocks</td></tr>
</table>

<table>
<tr><th rowspan="2">Core Instruction</th><th rowspan="2">Leveled Resources</th><th rowspan="2">Leveled Labs</th><th colspan="3">Pacing</th></tr>
<tr><th>Period</th><th></th><th>Block</th></tr>
<tr><td rowspan="2">Student Text, pp. 320–326
Section Focus Transparency, Ch. 11, Section 1
Teaching Transparency, Ch. 11, Section 1
Interactive Chalkboard, Ch. 11, Section 1
Identifying Misconceptions, p. 324
Differentiated Instruction, pp. 323, 325</td><td rowspan="2">Chapter Fast File Resources
Directed Reading for Content Mastery, p. 18 [L1]
Note-taking Worksheet, pp. 33–35
Reinforcement, p. 25 [L2]
Enrichment, p. 29 [L3]
Reading Essentials, p. 174 [L1] [ELL]
Science Notebook, p. 117 [ELL]</td><td rowspan="2">Launch Lab, p. 321: thin metric ruler 5 min [L2]

MiniLAB, p. 323: metal object, string, chair or table 10 min [L2]</td><td>1</td><td>Section 1, pp. 321–323 (includes MiniLAB and Launch Lab)</td><td rowspan="2">1</td></tr>
<tr><td>2</td><td>Section 1, pp. 324–326 (includes Section Review)</td></tr>
<tr><td rowspan="2">Student Text, pp. 327–332
Section Focus Transparency, Ch. 11, Section 2
Interactive Chalkboard, Ch. 11, Section 2
Differentiated Instruction, pp. 329, 330</td><td rowspan="2">Chapter Fast File Resources
Directed Reading for Content Mastery, p. 18 [L1]
Note-taking Worksheet, pp. 33–35
Reinforcement, p. 26 [L2]
Enrichment, p. 30 [L3]
Reading Essentials, p. 179 [L1] [ELL]
Science Notebook, p. 121 [ELL]</td><td rowspan="2">MiniLAB, p. 330: radio, thick cloth 10 min [L2]</td><td>3</td><td>Section 2, pp. 327–329 (includes MiniLAB)</td><td rowspan="2">2</td></tr>
<tr><td>4</td><td>Section 2, pp. 330–332 (includes Section Review)</td></tr>
<tr><td rowspan="2">Student Text, pp. 333–338
Section Focus Transparency, Ch. 11, Section 3
Interactive Chalkboard, Ch. 11, Section 2
Differentiated Instruction, pp. 335, 336</td><td rowspan="2">Chapter Fast File Resources
Directed Reading for Content Mastery, p. 19 [L1]
Note-taking Worksheet, pp. 33–35
Reinforcement, p. 27 [L2]
Enrichment, p. 31 [L3]
Reading Essentials, p. 185 [L1] [ELL]
Science Notebook, p. 124 [ELL]</td><td rowspan="2">*Lab, p. 338: test tubes, test-tube rack 30 min [L1] [L2] [L3] [Video Lab]</td><td>5</td><td>Section 3, pp. 333–337 (includes Section Review)</td><td rowspan="2">3</td></tr>
<tr><td>6</td><td>Lab:Making Music, p. 338</td></tr>
<tr><td rowspan="3">Student Text, pp. 339–345
Section Focus Transparency, Ch. 11, Section 3
Interactive Chalkboard, Ch. 11, Section 2
Visualizing Bat Echolocation, p. 340
Applying Math, p. 342
Differentiated Instruction, pp. 340, 342
Chapter Study Guide, p. 347</td><td rowspan="3">Chapter Fast File Resources
Directed Reading for Content Mastery, pp. 19, 20 [L1]
Note-taking Worksheet, pp. 33–35
Reinforcement, p. 28 [L2]
Enrichment, p. 32 [L3]
Reading Essentials, p. 190 [L1] [ELL]
Science Notebook, p. 127 [ELL]</td><td rowspan="3">*Lab, pp. 344–345: radio, CD player, horn, drum, or other loud noise source; shrubs, trees, concrete walls, brick wall, stone wall, wooden fences, parked car, or hanging laundry; sound meter; meterstick or metric tape measure 45 min (2 weeks outside of class) [L1] [L2] [L3]

*Lab version A [L1]
version B [L2] [L3]</td><td>7</td><td>Section 4, pp. 339–343 (includes Section Review)</td><td rowspan="2">4</td></tr>
<tr><td>8</td><td>Lab:Blocking Noise Pollution, pp. 344–345</td></tr>
<tr><td>9</td><td>Study Guide, Chapter Review, and Test Practice, pp. 347–351</td><td>4.5</td></tr>
</table>

[Video Lab icon] Video Lab

Transparencies

Section Focus

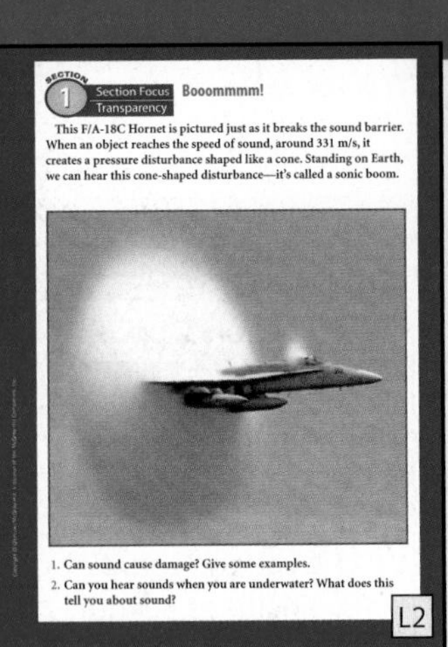

SECTION 1 Section Focus Transparency **Booommmm!**

This F/A-18C Hornet is pictured just as it breaks the sound barrier. When an object reaches the speed of sound, around 331 m/s, it creates a pressure disturbance shaped like a cone. Standing on Earth, we can hear this cone-shaped disturbance—it's called a sonic boom.

1. Can sound cause damage? Give some examples.
2. Can you hear sounds when you are underwater? What does this tell you about sound?

L2

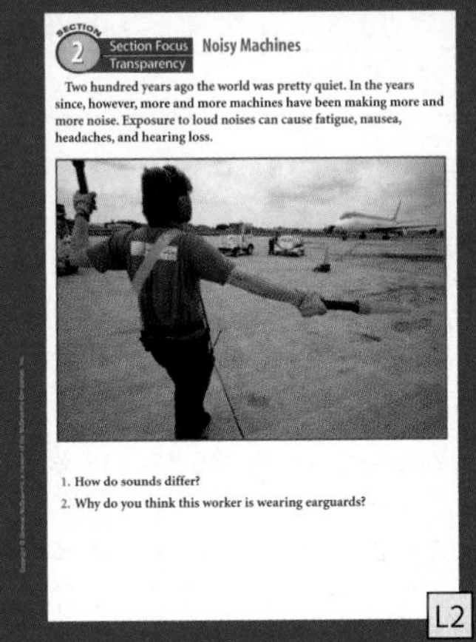

SECTION 2 Section Focus Transparency **Noisy Machines**

Two hundred years ago the world was pretty quiet. In the years since, however, more and more machines have been making more and more noise. Exposure to loud noises can cause fatigue, nausea, headaches, and hearing loss.

1. How do sounds differ?
2. Why do you think this worker is wearing earguards?

L2

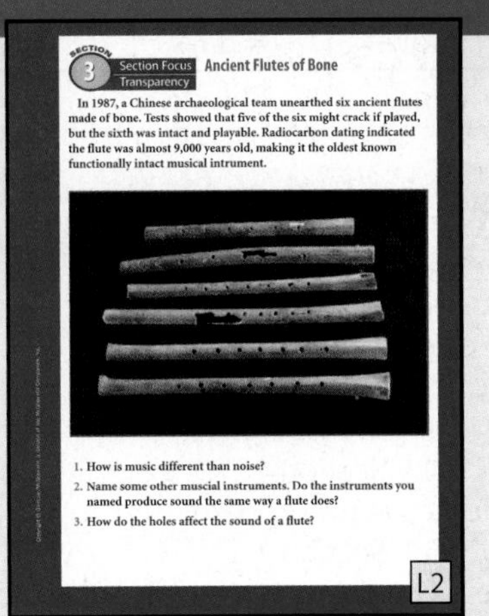

SECTION 3 Section Focus Transparency **Ancient Flutes of Bone**

In 1987, a Chinese archaeological team unearthed six ancient flutes made of bone. Tests showed that five of the six might crack if played, but the sixth was intact and playable. Radiocarbon dating indicated the flute was almost 9,000 years old, making it the oldest known functionally intact musical intrument.

1. How is music different than noise?
2. Name some other muscial instruments. Do the instruments you named produce sound the same way a flute does?
3. How do the holes affect the sound of a flute?

L2

This is a representation of key blackline masters available in the Teacher Classroom Resources. See Resource Manager boxes within the chapter for additional information.

Key to Teaching Strategies

The following designations will help you decide which activities are appropriate for your students.

- L1 Level 1 activities should be appropriate for students with learning difficulties.
- L2 Level 2 activities should be within the ability range of all students.
- L3 Level 3 activities are designed for above-average students.
- ELL ELL activities should be within the ability range of English Language Learners.
- COOP LEARN Cooperative Learning activities are designed for small group work.
- LS Multiple Learning Styles logos, as described on page 12T, are used throughout to indicate strategies that address different learning styles.
- P These strategies represent student products that can be placed into a best-work portfolio.
- PBL Problem-Based Learning activities apply real-world situations to learning.

Assessment

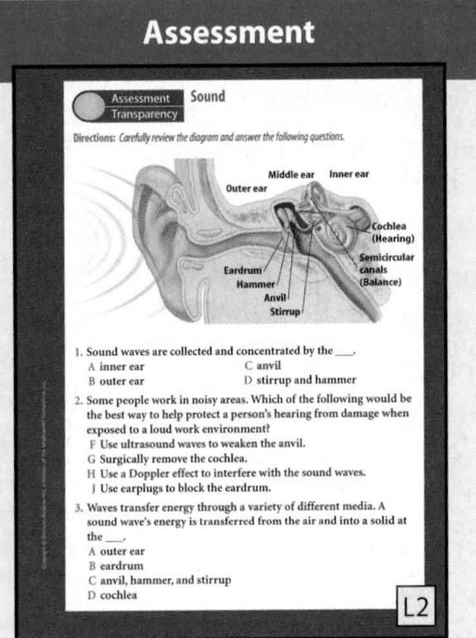

Assessment Transparency **Sound**

Directions: Carefully review the diagram and answer the following questions.

1. Sound waves are collected and concentrated by the ___.
   A inner ear
   B outer ear
   C anvil
   D stirrup and hammer
2. Some people work in noisy areas. Which of the following would be the best way to help protect a person's hearing from damage when exposed to a loud work environment?
   F Use ultrasound waves to weaken the anvil.
   G Surgically remove the cochlea.
   H Use a Doppler effect to interfere with the sound waves.
   J Use earplugs to block the eardrum.
3. Waves transfer energy through a variety of different media. A sound wave's energy is transferred from the air and into a solid at the ___.
   A outer ear
   B eardrum
   C anvil, hammer, and stirrup
   D cochlea

L2

Teaching

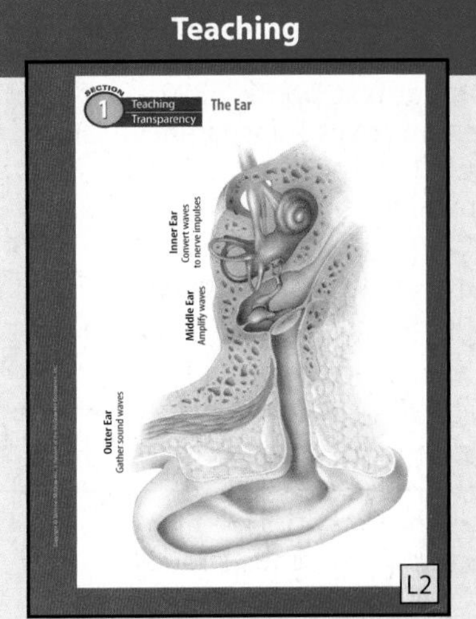

SECTION 1 Teaching Transparency **The Ear**

L2

Hands-on Activities

Student Text Lab Worksheet

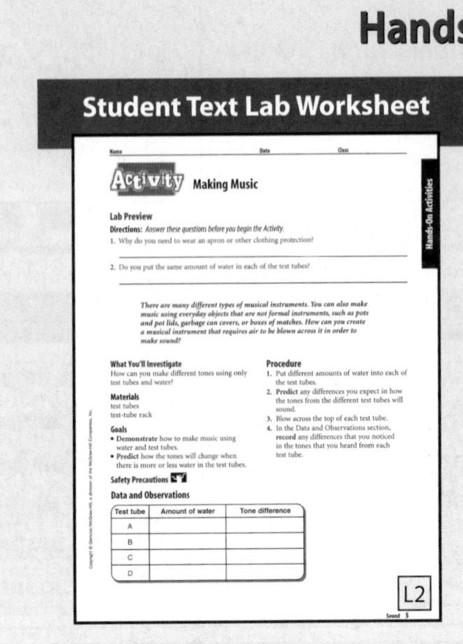

Name Date Class

Activity **Making Music**

Hands-On Activities

Lab Preview

Directions: *Answer these questions before you begin the Activity.*

1. Why do you need to wear an apron or other clothing protection?
2. Do you put the same amount of water in each of the test tubes?

There are many different types of musical instruments. You can also make music using everyday objects that are not formal instruments, such as pots and pot lids, garbage can covers, or boxes of matches. How can you create a musical instrument that requires air to be blown across it in order to make sound?

What You'll Investigate

How can you make different tones using only test tubes and water?

Materials

test tubes
test-tube rack

Goals

- **Demonstrate** how to make music using water and test tubes.
- **Predict** how the tones will change when there is more or less water in the test tubes.

Safety Precautions

Procedure

1. Put different amounts of water into each of the test tubes.
2. **Predict** any differences you expect in how the tones from the different test tubes will sound.
3. Blow across the top of each test tube.
4. In the Data and Observations section, **record** any differences that you noticed in the tones that you heard from each test tube.

Data and Observations

Test tube	Amount of water	Tone difference
A		
B		
C		
D		

L2

Sound 5

Laboratory Activities

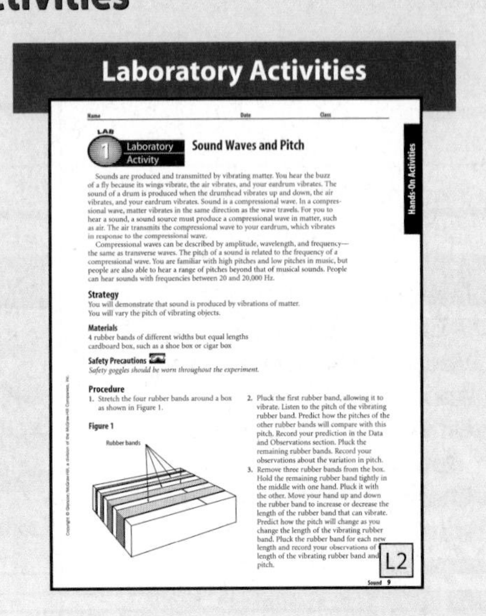

Name Date Class

LAB 1 Laboratory Activity **Sound Waves and Pitch**

Hands-On Activities

Sounds are produced and transmitted by vibrating matter. You hear the buzz of a fly because its wings vibrate, the air vibrates, and your eardrum vibrates. The sound of a drum is produced when the drumhead vibrates up and down, the air vibrates, and your eardrum vibrates. Sound is a compressional wave. In a compressional wave, matter vibrates in the same direction as the wave travels. For you to hear a sound, a sound source must produce a compressional wave in matter, such as air. The air transmits the compressional wave to your eardrum, which vibrates in response to the compressional wave.

Compressional waves can be described by amplitude, wavelength, and frequency—the same as transverse waves. The pitch of a sound is related to the frequency of a compressional wave. You are familiar with high pitches and low pitches in music, but people are also able to hear a range of pitches beyond that of musical sounds. People can hear sounds with frequencies between 20 and 20,000 Hz.

Strategy

You will demonstrate that sound is produced by vibrations of matter.
You will vary the pitch of vibrating objects.

Materials

4 rubber bands of different widths but equal lengths
cardboard box, such as a shoe box or cigar box

Safety Precautions

Safety goggles should be worn throughout the experiment.

Procedure

1. Stretch the four rubber bands around a box as shown in Figure 1.

Figure 1

Rubber bands

2. Pluck the first rubber band, allowing it to vibrate. Listen to the pitch of the vibrating rubber band. Predict how the pitches of the other rubber bands will compare with this pitch. Record your prediction in the Data and Observations section. Pluck the remaining rubber bands. Record your observations about the variation in pitch.
3. Remove three rubber bands from the box. Hold the remaining rubber band tightly in the middle with one hand. Pluck it with the other. Move your hand up and down the rubber band to increase or decrease the length of the rubber band that can vibrate. Predict how the pitch will change as you change the length of the vibrating rubber band. Pluck the rubber band for each new length and record your observations of the length of the vibrating rubber band and pitch.

L2

Sound 9

Meeting Different Ability Levels

Content Outline

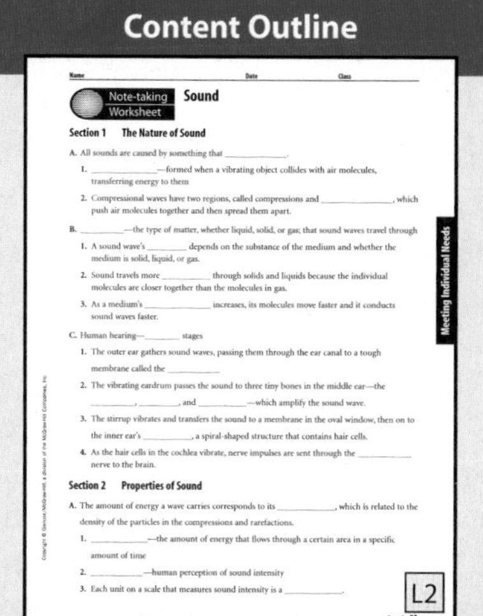

Note-taking Worksheet — Sound

Section 1 The Nature of Sound

Section 2 Properties of Sound

L2

Reinforcement

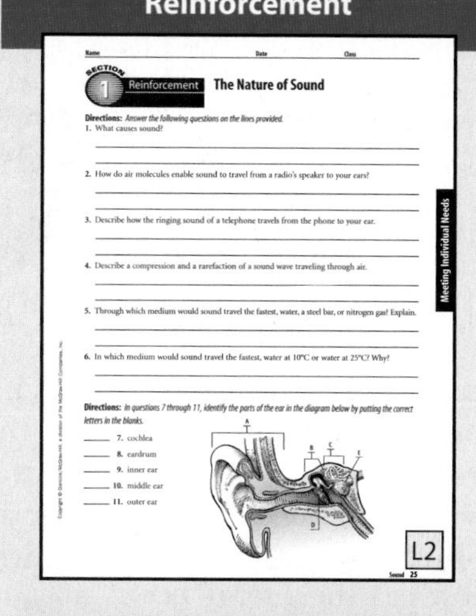

Reinforcement — The Nature of Sound

L2

Enrichment

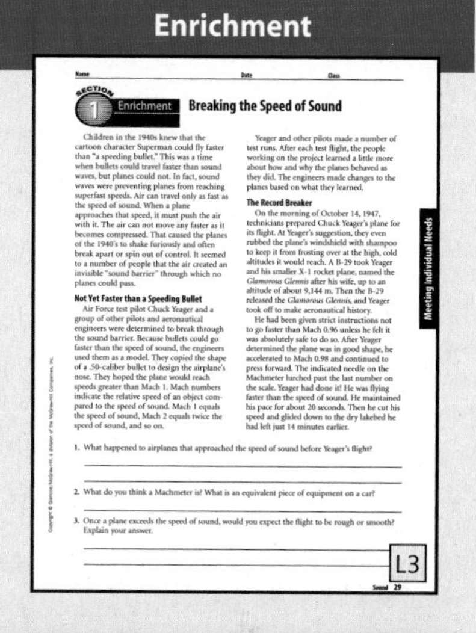

Enrichment — Breaking the Speed of Sound

L3

Directed Reading (English/Spanish)

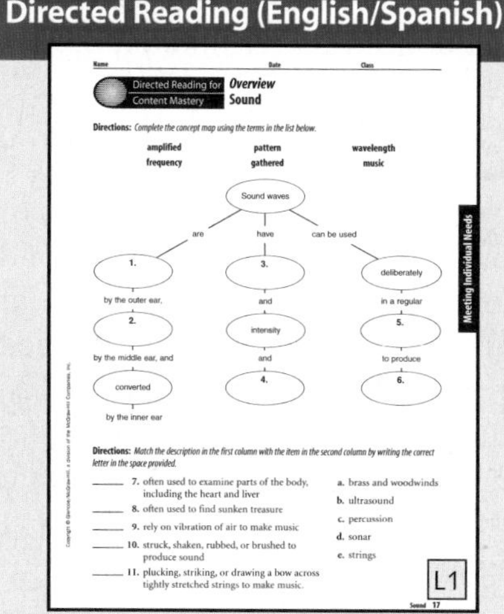

Directed Reading for Content Mastery — Overview — Sound

L1

Study Guide

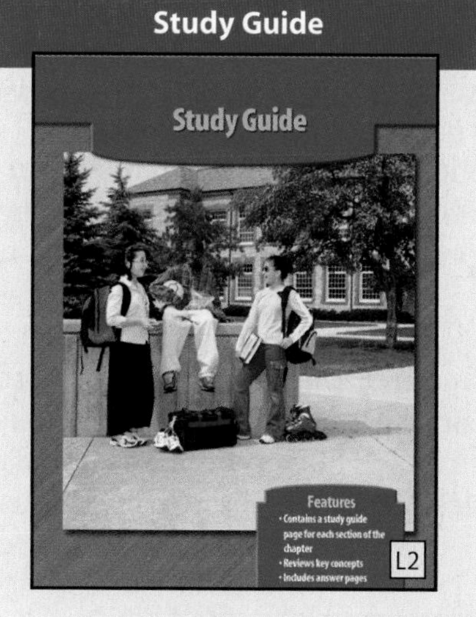

Study Guide
Features
• Contains a study guide page for each section of the chapter
• Reviews key concepts
• Includes answer pages

L2

Reading Essentials

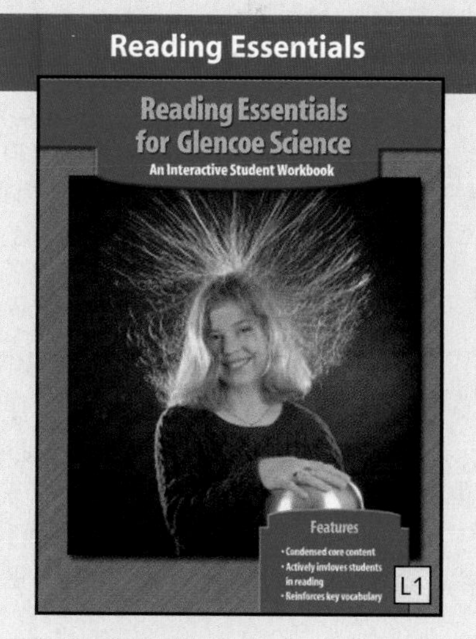

Reading Essentials for Glencoe Science
An Interactive Student Workbook
Features
• Condensed core content
• Actively involves students in reading
• Reinforces key vocabulary

L1

Assessment

Test Practice Workbook

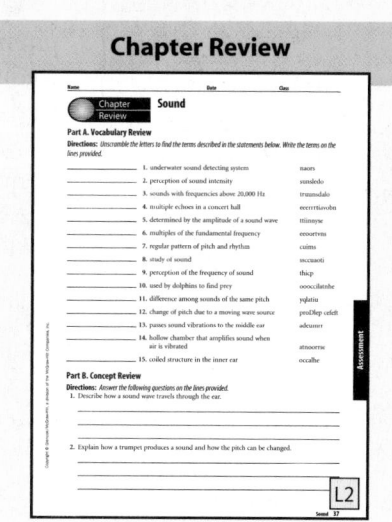

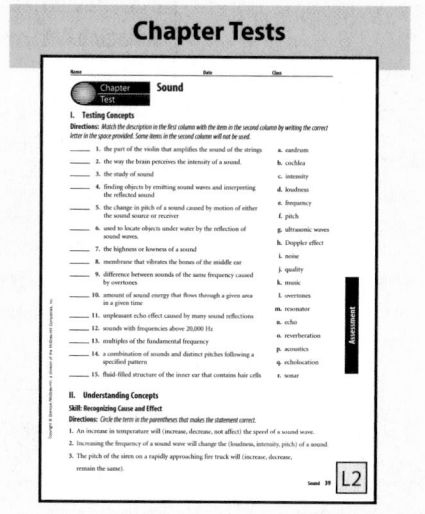

Chapter Test — Chapter 11 Sound

L2

Chapter Review

Chapter Review — Sound

Part A. Vocabulary Review

Part B. Concept Review

L2

Chapter Tests

Chapter Test — Sound

I. Testing Concepts

II. Understanding Concepts

L2

Science Content Background

section 1

The Nature of Sound

Sound Waves

A sound wave is a type of mechanical wave called a compressional or longitudinal wave. The compressions and rarefactions produced cause temporary changes in the pressure of the medium the waves travel through. Our ears respond to this changing pressure and interpret it as sound.

Moving Through Mediums

The speed of sound is how fast the energy carried by sound waves travels through a medium. This is quite different from the frequency of a sound wave, which is how often the particles of the medium vibrate back and forth. The approximate speed of sound through air at room temperature is 347 m/s, or 776 miles/hour. Although this is fast, light travels about 900,000 times faster. This explains why we see lightning before we hear thunder.

Sound travels about three times faster in helium than it does in air. The more dense the gas, the slower sound travels. This is because dense gases have particles with more mass that resist moving.

Teacher to Teacher

Erin Peters
Lead Science Teacher
Williamsburg Middle School
Arlington, VA

"I use a wind-up music box apparatus to demonstrate how sound waves travel through different mediums. Hold the apparatus in the air, wind the arm, and listen to the sound that it makes. The sound should be very quiet. Now wind the arm and put the apparatus on the desk. It should sound like the music box. Sound waves travel better when the vibrating particles are closer together."

Erin Peters

Properties of Sound

Intensity and Loudness

Sound intensity is how much energy passes through a given area in a given amount of time. Because sound waves spread out as they travel, the intensity of a sound decreases as it travels and is proportional to the inverse square of the distance from the source. This means that if the distance from the source doubles, the intensity of sound is one fourth as large. Humans can detect very low levels of sound. This threshold is defined as 0 dB. A sound of 0 dB will move our eardrums as little as one-billionth of a centimeter, but we can still hear it.

The Doppler Effect

When an airplane going faster than the speed of sound passes over us, it produces a very loud noise called a sonic boom. This is an example of the Doppler effect. The sound waves are pushed closer together as the high-speed airplane continues to produce sound waves. The plane goes so fast that the waves to pile up on each other. Then the wave energy reaches the listener all at once, producing a loud noise.

Music

What is music?

The sounds produced by different frequencies are referred to as pitch. People with well-trained ears can detect frequency differences of as little as 3 Hz. Some frequencies sound better together than others do. For example, sounds that are separated by a frequency ratio of 2 to 1 are pleasing. In music these frequencies are said to be separated by an octave.

Sound Quality

Timbre is the musical term to describe sounds with the same frequencies that are perceived differently by our ears.

section 4

Using Sound

Acoustics

A large number of echoes makes for a very noisy room. Theaters, music halls, and even restaurants are designed to absorb sound energy rather than reflect it.

Another important task of good acoustics is to make sure that the arrangement of the sound system in a room does not cause destructive interference. Speakers have to be placed in the appropriate positions so that this does not occur.

Echolocation

We can use echolocation to estimate the distance to large objects such as a building. Give a yell and time how long it takes to hear the echo. Because this time represents a round trip journey for the sound waves, you must divide the time by two, and then multiply this number by the speed of sound. For example, if it takes 3 seconds to hear the echo bounce off a building, the distance to the building is 1.5 s × 347 m/s = 520 m.

chapter content resources

Internet Resources

For additional content background, visit **gpscience.com** to:

- access your book online
- find references to related articles in popular science magazines
- access Web links with related content background
- access current events with science journal topics

Print Resources

Acoustics: Basic Physics Theory and Methods, edited by P. Filippi and others, Academic Press, 1999

The Physics of Musical Instruments, by Neville H. Fletcher and Thomas D. Rossing, Springer Verlag, 1998

Hands-On Physics Activities with Real-Life Applications: Easy-to-Use Labs and Demonstrations for Grades 8–12, by James Cunningham and Norman Herr, Jossey-Bass, 2002

Crandall/The Image Works

About the Photo

Sonic Boom This airplane is producing a shock wave as it moves faster than the speed of sound. As the plane approaches the speed of sound, the Doppler effect causes fronts of sound waves emitted by the plane to pile up in front of it. These wave fronts form a cone-shaped shock wave when they overlap as the plane reaches the speed of sound. An observer on the ground hears a loud boom or crack when the shock wave passes them.

Science Journal Student responses will vary. Students might want to know the wave types, how fast they travel, and how they might harm hearing.

BIG Idea

Sound Waves and Pressure Changes A sound wave produces an alternating series of compressions and rarefactions as it moves in a material. The density of the material is increased in the compressions and decreased in the rarefactions. In a gas, these density variations cause pressure variations, with higher pressure in the compressions. It is these pressure changes that cause the eardrum to vibrate. However, even for very loud sounds that humans can hear without pain, these pressure variations are small, being only about 30 Pa, or 0.03 percent of atmospheric pressure.

Introduce the Chapter Have students describe the differences in the sound of their voices in a gymnasium, an empty room with no furnishings, and a furnished room. Have students hypothesize why their voices sound different. Ask students how the gymnasium could be modified so voices sound more normal.

chapter 11

Sound

BIG Idea Sound waves are compressional waves produced by something that vibrates.

11.1 The Nature of Sound

MAIN Idea Sound waves are compressional waves that can only travel through matter.

11.2 Properties of Sound

MAIN Idea The loudness of a sound depends on its intensity and its pitch depends on its frequency.

11.3 Music

MAIN Idea A musical instrument produces combinations of frequencies that determine how the instrument sounds.

11.4 Using Sound

MAIN Idea Sound waves are used to locate objects, form images, and to treat medical problems.

Cracking the Sound Barrier

Have you ever heard the crack of a sonic boom? A sonic boom occurs when a plane exceeds the speed of sound. Sound waves create a cone-shaped shock wave coming from the aircraft. Behind the cone are low-pressure regions that can cause water vapor to condense, forming the cloud you see here.

Science Journal Write three things you would like to learn about sound.

320

Interactive Chalkboard

This CD-ROM is an editable Microsoft® PowerPoint® presentation that includes:

- an editable presentation for every chapter
- additional chapter questions
- animated graphics
- image bank
- links to gpscience.com

Start-Up Activities

What sound does a ruler make?

Think of the musical instruments you've seen and heard. Some have strings, some have hollow tubes, and others have keys or pedals. Musical instruments come in many shapes and sizes and are played with various techniques. These differences give each instrument a unique sound. What would an instrument made from a ruler sound like?

1. Hold one end of a thin ruler firmly down on a desk, allowing the free end to extend beyond the edge of the desk.
2. Gently pull up on and release the end of the ruler. What do you see and hear?
3. Vary the length of the overhanging portion and repeat the experiment several times.
4. **Think Critically** In your Science Journal, write instructions for playing a song with the ruler. Explain how the length of the overhanging part of the ruler affects the sound.

Science Online | Preview this chapter's content and activities at gpscience.com

FOLDABLES™ Study Organizer

Sound Make the following Foldable to help identify what you already know, what you want to know, and what you learned about sound.

STEP 1 **Fold** a vertical sheet of paper from side to side. Make the front edge about 1.25 cm shorter than the back edge.

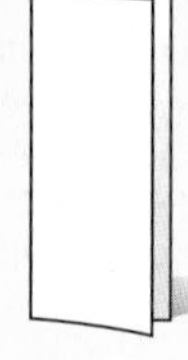

STEP 2 **Turn** lengthwise and **fold** into thirds.

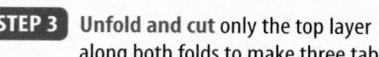

STEP 3 **Unfold and cut** only the top layer along both folds to make three tabs.

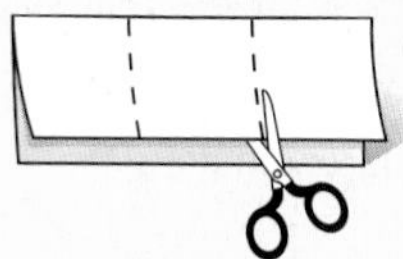

STEP 4 **Label** each tab as shown.

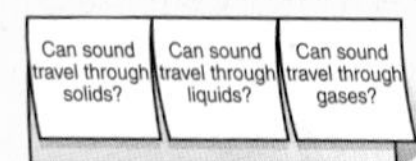

Identify Questions As you read the chapter, write what you learn about sound traveling through solids under the left tab of your Foldable, what you learn about sound traveling through liquids under the center tab, and what you learn about sound traveling through gases under the right tab.

321

Additional Chapter Media

- Virtual Lab: *How is an oscilloscope used to tune a musical instrument?*
- Video Lab: *Making Music*

Launch LAB

Purpose Use the Launch Lab to introduce students to musical pitches. Explain that as they read the chapter, they will be learning what sound is and what makes sounds different. L1 ELL

Materials thin ruler

Teaching Strategy Suggest that students work in pairs. Have one student describe and record the sounds heard while the other student adjusts and plays the ruler.

Think Critically

The longer the extending segment of the ruler, the deeper the pitch.

Assessment

Content Have students listen to the tones that occur at different lengths and then try to play a simple song.

FOLDABLES™ Study Organizer **Dinah Zike Study Fold**

Student preparation materials for this Foldable are available in the **Chapter *FAST FILE* Resources.**

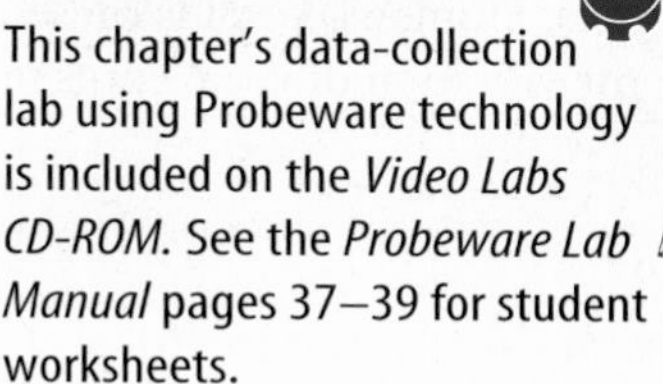

This chapter's data-collection lab using Probeware technology is included on the *Video Labs CD-ROM.* See the *Probeware Lab Manual* pages 37–39 for student worksheets.

section 1

1 Motivate

Bellringer

Section Focus Transparencies also are available on the Interactive Chalkboard CD-ROM.

L2 

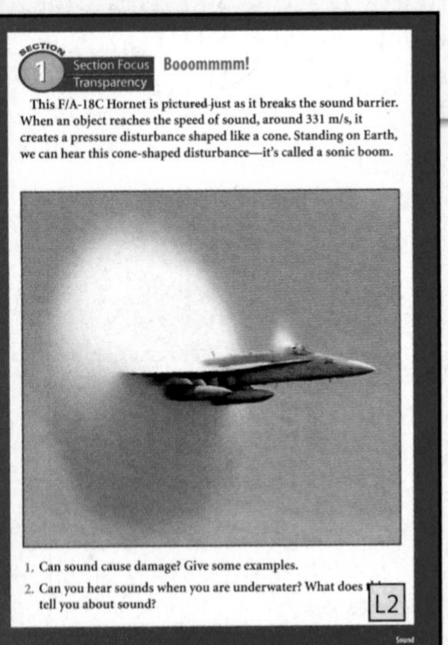

Section 1 Section Focus Transparency **Booommmm!**

This F/A-18C Hornet is pictured just as it breaks the sound barrier. When an object reaches the speed of sound, around 331 m/s, it creates a pressure disturbance shaped like a cone. Standing on Earth, we can hear this cone-shaped disturbance—it's called a sonic boom.

1. Can sound cause damage? Give some examples.
2. Can you hear sounds when you are underwater? What does this tell you about sound?

L2

Tie to Prior Knowledge

Sounds Ask students to name sounds they have heard today. Can they identify what made each sound? Tell them that all sounds are made by vibrating objects. Human speech is caused by the vibration of vocal cords in the larynx.

The Nature of Sound

Reading Guide

***What* You'll Learn**

- **Explain** how sound travels through different mediums.
- **Identify** what influences the speed of sound.
- **Describe** how the ear enables you to hear.

***Why* It's Important**

The nature of sound affects how you hear and interpret sounds.

Review Vocabulary

vibration: rhythmic back-and-forth motion

New Vocabulary

- eardrum
- cochlea

What causes sound?

An amusement park can be a noisy place. With all the racket of carousel music and booming loudspeakers, it can be hard to hear what your friends say. These sounds are all different, but they do have something in common—each sound is produced by an object that vibrates. For example, your friends' voices are produced by the vibrations of their vocal cords, and music from a carousel and voices from a loudspeaker are produced by vibrating speakers. All sounds are created by something that vibrates.

Figure 1 The vibration of a speaker produces compressional waves.

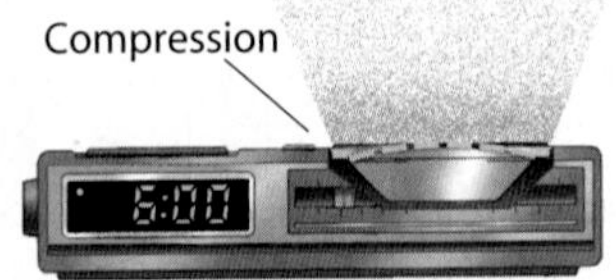

When the speaker vibrates outward, molecules in the air next to it are pushed together to form a compression.

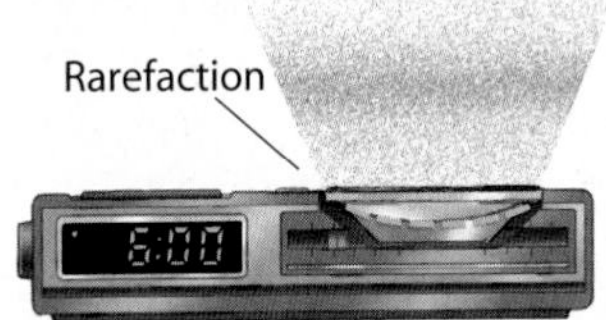

When the speaker vibrates inward, the molecules spread apart to form a rarefaction.

Sound Waves

When an object like a radio speaker vibrates, it collides with nearby molecules in the air, transferring some of its energy to them. These molecules then collide with other molecules in the air and pass the energy on to them. The energy originally transferred by the vibrating object continues to pass from one molecule to another. This process of collisions and energy transfer forms a sound wave.

Sound waves are compressional waves. Remember that a compressional wave is made up of two types of regions called compressions and rarefactions. If you look at **Figure 1,** you'll see that when a radio speaker vibrates outward, the nearby molecules in the air are pushed together to form compressions. As the figure shows, when the speaker moves inward, the nearby molecules in the air have room to spread out, and a rarefaction forms. As long as the speaker continues to vibrate back and forth, compressions and rarefactions are formed.

Section 1 Resource Manager 

Chapter *Fast File* Resources

MiniLAB, p. 3
Transparency Activity, pp. 44, 49–50
Note-taking Worksheets, pp. 33–35
Reinforcement, p. 25
Enrichment, p. 29
Directed Reading for Content Mastery, pp. 17, 18

Traveling as a Wave Compressions and rarefactions move away from the speaker as molecules in the air collide with their neighbors. As the speaker continues to vibrate, more molecules in the air are alternately pushed together and spread apart. A series of compressions and rarefactions forms that travels from the speaker to your ear. This sound wave is what you hear.

The Speed Of Sound

Most sounds you hear travel through air to reach your ears. However, if you've ever been swimming underwater and heard garbled voices, you know that sound also travels through water. In fact, sound waves can travel through any type of matter—solid, liquid, or gas. The matter that a wave travels through is called a medium. Sound waves create compressions and rarefactions in any medium they travel through.

What would happen if no matter existed to form a medium? Could sound be transmitted without particles of matter to compress, expand, and collide? On the Moon, which has no atmosphere, the energy in sound waves cannot be transmitted from particle to particle because no particles exist. Sound waves cannot travel through empty space. Astronauts must talk to each other using electronic communication equipment.

The Speed of Sound in Different Materials The speed of a sound wave through a medium depends on the substance the medium is made of and whether it is solid, liquid, or gas. For example, **Table 1** shows that at room temperature, sound travels at 347 m/s through air, at 1,498 m/s through water, and at 4,877 m/s through aluminum. In general, sound travels the slowest through gases, faster through liquids, and even faster through solids.

Reading Check *What are two things that affect the speed of sound?*

Sound travels faster in liquids and solids than in gases because the individual molecules in a liquid or solid are closer together than the molecules in a gas. When molecules are close together, they can transmit energy from one to another more rapidly. However, the speed of sound doesn't depend on the loudness of the sound. Loud sounds travel through a medium at the same speed as soft sounds.

Table 1 Speed of Sound in Different Mediums

Medium	Speed of Sound (in m/s)
Air	347
Cork	500
Water	1,498
Brick	3,650
Aluminum	4,877

Mini LAB

Listening to Sound Through Different Materials

Procedure

1. Tie the middle of a length of **string** onto a **metal object,** such as a wire hanger or a spoon, so that the string has two long ends.
2. Wrap each string end around a finger on each hand.
3. Gently placing your fingers in your ears, swing the object until it bumps against the edge of a **chair** or **table.** Listen to the sound.
4. Take your fingers out of your ears and listen to the sound made by the collisions.

Analysis

1. Compare and contrast the sounds you hear when your fingers are and are not in your ears.
2. Do sounds travel better through air or the string?

Mini LAB

Purpose Students listen to sound through different mediums. L1 ELL IS **Auditory-Musical**

Materials metal object such as a spoon, 1.5 m of string, chair or table

Teaching Strategy Suggest students try a variety of metal objects to obtain different sounds.

Analysis

1. Possible answer: Objects sound deeper and more muffled when your fingers are in your ears.
2. through the string

Assessment

Content Why does sound travel better through string than air? The molecules are closer to one another. Use **Performance Assessment in the Science Classroom,** p. 89.

Discussion

Mediums Look at the information in **Table 1** and explain why sound travels at different speeds through these mediums. Sound travels slower through a gas because the particles are farther apart. Sound travels slowly through cork because of the air pockets. Sound travels faster through water because it is a liquid and the particles are closer together. Brick and aluminum are solids, so sound will travel the fastest through them.

Reading Check

Answer the substance the medium is made of, and the state of the medium

Differentiated Instruction

Hearing Impaired For many of the activities in this chapter, these students can learn about the sound produced by feeling the vibrations. When they do the MiniLAB, have students feel the vibrations transmitted through the string to their fingers. Using different types of string and metal objects, they can feel how the vibrations differ for various materials. IS **Kinesthetic** L1

IDENTIFYING Misconceptions

Moving Molecules When looking at the pictures of compressions and rarefactions of sound waves, students may think that the molecules travel away from the sound source. Explain that the molecules push on their neighbors and then return to their original position. Only the energy is transported.

Caption Answer

Figure 2 Cork is less rigid than steel. Also, cork is filled with air holes, and sound waves travel more slowly through air because the particles are farther apart. LS **Logical-Mathematical**

Fun Fact

The speed of sound in air is called Mach 1. An object at Mach 2 is traveling at twice the speed of sound.

Use Science Words

Word Meaning Have students find out why the spiral-shaped structure in the inner ear is called the cochlea. The word *cochlea* comes from the Greek word *kochlias,* meaning "snail shell." L2
LS **Linguistic**

Activity

Vocal Cords Have students place their hands on their throats while talking to feel the vibrations caused by their vocal cords.
L2 ELL LS **Kinesthetic**

Figure 2 A line of people passing a bucket is a model for molecules transferring the energy of a sound wave.

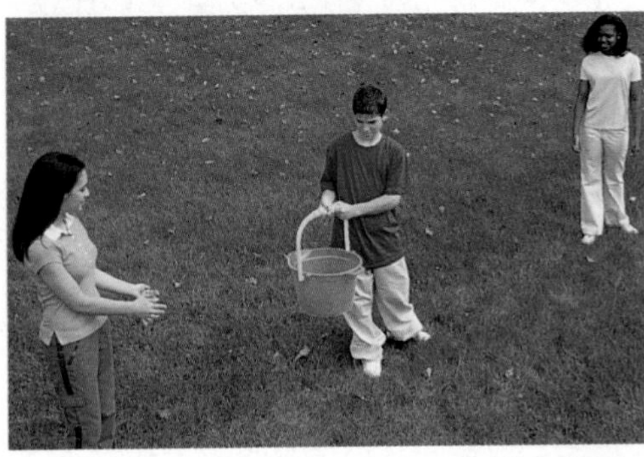

When the people are far away from each other, like the molecules in a gas, it takes longer to transfer the bucket of water from person to person.

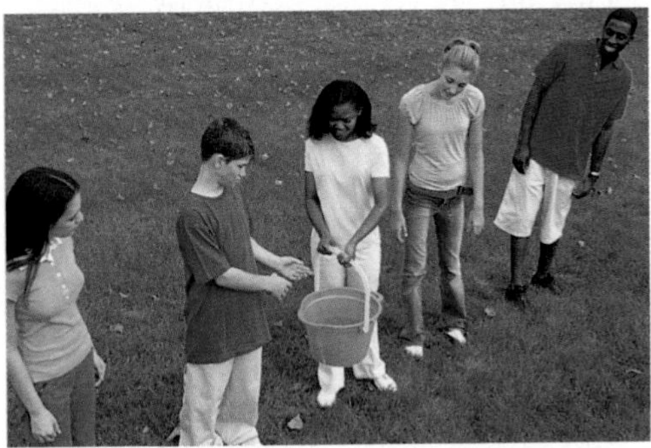

The bucket travels quickly down the line when the people stand close together.
Explain *why sound would travel more slowly in cork than in steel.*

A Model for Transmitting Sound You can understand why solids and liquids transmit sound well by picturing a large group of people standing in a line. Imagine that they are passing a bucket of water from person to person. If everyone stands far apart, each person has to walk a long distance to transfer the bucket, as in the top photo of **Figure 2.** However, if everyone stands close together, as in the bottom photo of **Figure 2,** the bucket quickly moves down the line.

The people standing close to each other are like particles in solids and liquids. Those standing far apart are like gas particles. The closer the particles, the faster they can transfer energy from particle to particle.

Temperature and the Speed of Sound The speed of sound waves also depends on the temperature of a medium. As the temperature of a substance increases, its molecules move faster. This makes them more likely to collide with each other. Remember that sound waves depend on the collisions of particles to transfer energy through a medium. If the particles in a medium are colliding with each other more often, more energy can be transferred in a shorter amount of time. Then sound waves move faster. For example, when the temperature is 0°C, sound travels through the air at only 331 m/s, but at a temperature of 20°C, it speeds up to 343 m/s.

Human Hearing

INTEGRATE Life Science

Think of the last conversation you had. Vocal cords and mouths move in many different ways to produce various kinds of compressional waves, but you were somehow able to make sense of these different sound waves. Your ears and brain work together to turn the compressional waves caused by speech, music, and other sources into something that has meaning. Making sense of these waves involves four stages. First, the ear gathers the compressional waves. Next, the ear amplifies the waves. In the ear, the amplified waves are converted to nerve impulses that travel to the brain. Finally, the brain decodes and interprets the nerve impulses.

Teacher FYI

Sound Speed The speed with which sound travels through a material depends on the elasticity of the material as well as on the material's density. Elasticity is the ability of the material to resume its previous shape after being acted on by a force. For example, steel is dense and has high elasticity, so sound travels quickly through steel.

Active Reading

Bubble Map Using a bubble map helps students start ideas flowing about a given topic. Words are clustered to describe a topic or idea that is studied. Students can use a bubble map for a prewriting, to generate ideas before writing in their Journals, or to review for a test. Have students design a bubble map for the concepts about sound discussed in this section. L2 P

324 CHAPTER 11 Sound

Gathering Sound Waves—The Outer Ear When you think of your ear, you probably picture just the fleshy, visible, outer part. But, as shown in **Figure 3,** the human ear has three sections called the outer ear, the middle ear, and the inner ear.

The visible part of your ear, the ear canal, and the eardrum make up the outer ear. The outer ear is where sound waves are gathered. The gathering process starts with the outer part of your ear, which is shaped to help capture and direct sound waves into the ear canal. The ear canal is a passageway that is 2-cm to 3-cm long and is a little narrower than your index finger. The sound waves travel along this passageway, which leads to the eardrum. The **eardrum** is a tough membrane about 0.1 mm thick. When incoming sound waves reach the eardrum, they transfer their energy to it and it vibrates.

Reading Check *What makes the eardrum vibrate?*

Amplifying Sound Waves—The Middle Ear When the eardrum vibrates, it passes the sound vibrations into the middle ear, where three tiny bones start to vibrate. These bones are called the hammer, the anvil, and the stirrup. They make a lever system that multiplies the force and pressure exerted by the sound wave. The bones amplify the sound wave. The stirrup is connected to a membrane on a structure called the oval window, which vibrates as the stirrup vibrates.

Audiology Some types of hearing loss involve damage to the inner ear. The use of a hearing aid often can improve hearing. Audiologists diagnose and treat people with hearing loss. Research the field of audiology. Find out what education is required for people to gain certification as audiologists, and the settings in which they work.

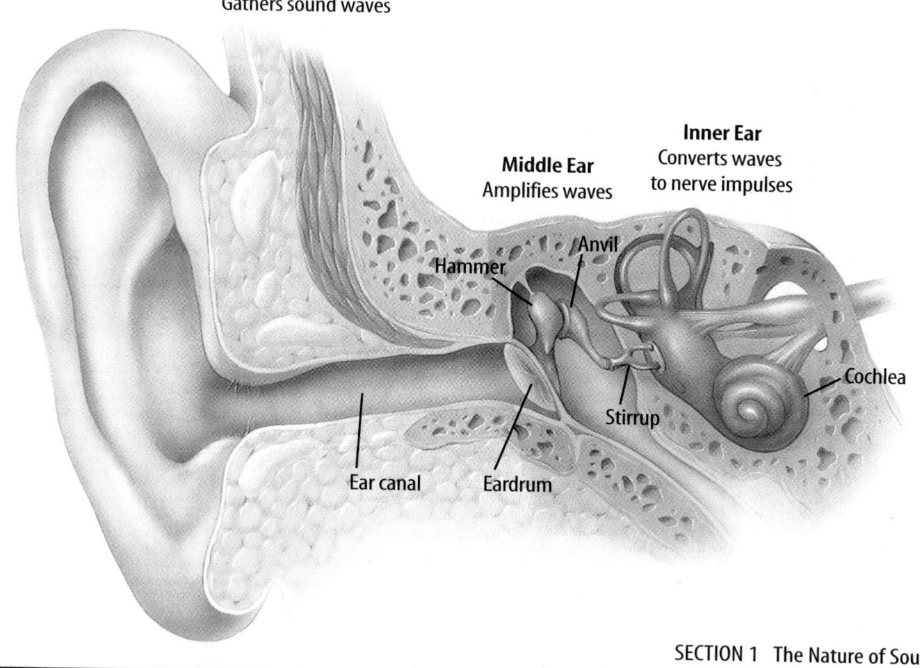

Figure 3 The ear has three regions that perform specific functions in hearing.

Audiology Hearing loss can result from disease, trauma, or long-term exposure to medications or loud noise. It affects 17 people per thousand in those younger than 18; 314 people per thousand in those older than 65. Students will find that four years of specialized study beyond a Bachelor's degree is required for certification as an audiologist. Upon certification, audiologists can work in private practices or hospital settings.

Research Have students investigate the employment outlook for audiologists in the future. Have students identify locations in their community that hire audiologists. L2

Fun Fact

The eardrum is also known as the tympanic membrane, from the Latin word tympanum, meaning "drum."

Reading Check

Answer energy from sound waves

Activity

Catching Waves Have students cup their hands around the backs of their ears to see how they can catch more sound waves. L2

LS **Kinesthetic**

Use an Analogy

Piano Strings The hair cells in the cochlea are like the strings of a piano. Like the thicker, looser low strings on a piano, cells in the wide, flexible part of the cochlea respond more to low-frequency sounds. Like the thinner, stiffer, shorter strings on a piano, the cells in the thin, stiffer part of the cochlea respond more to high-frequency sounds.

Differentiated Instruction

Challenge Have students do research on medical devices or techniques that are used to help those that are hearing impaired or deaf. Have students give an oral presentation to the class using the information they have found. L3

Visual Learning

Figure 3 The cochlea is divided down the middle into side-by-side canals. The membrane between these canals contains hair cells. Vibrations in the fluid travel in opposite directions in these canals. The shape of the cochlea determines how hair cells are displaced, enabling you to discern different frequencies. What happens if the vibration is too strong? Hair cells can be damaged. L2 LS **Visual-Spatial**

3 Assess

DAILY INTERVENTION

Check for Understanding

Kinesthetic Have students use their hands to demonstrate the motion of particles when sound waves pass through them. Ask them to show the movement of sound waves through air, then through aluminum. L2

Reteach

Sound on the Moon Model an alarm clock ringing on the moon. Place a ringing alarm clock under a bell jar on the pad of a vacuum pump. What happens as you begin to pump the air out of the jar? The ringing gets quieter. What happens as you slowly let air back into the jar? The ringing returns to normal loudness.

Assessment

Process Strike a tuning fork and place its handle against various surfaces, such as a wooden desk, a book, a metal surface, and a wall. For each surface, have students explain why the amplified sound is loud or soft. Sounds will be louder for larger, denser, and stiffer surfaces. Use **Performance Assessment in the Science Classroom,** p. 89. L2

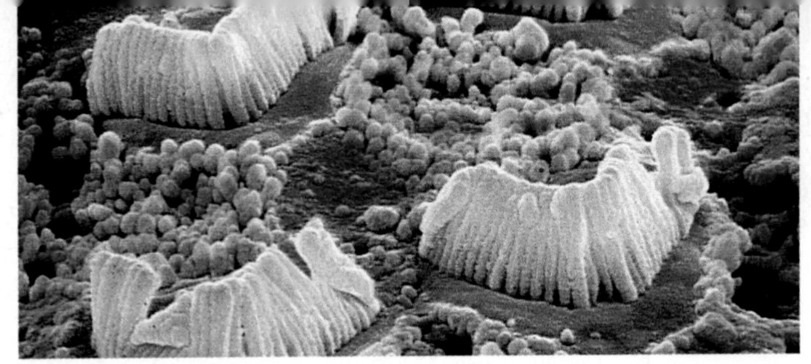

Figure 4 These hair cells in the human ear send nerve impulses to the brain when sound waves cause them to vibrate. In this photo the hair cells are magnified 3,900 times.

Converting Sound Waves—The Inner Ear When the membrane in the oval window vibrates, the sound vibrations are transmitted into the inner ear. The inner ear contains the **cochlea** (KOH klee uh), which is a spiral-shaped structure that is filled with liquid and contains tiny hair cells like those shown in **Figure 4.** When these tiny hair cells in the cochlea begin to vibrate, nerve impulses are sent through the auditory nerve to the brain. It is the cochlea that converts sound waves to nerve impulses.

When someone's hearing is damaged, it's usually because the tiny hair cells in the cochlea are damaged or destroyed, often by loud sounds. New research suggests that these hair cells may be able to repair themselves.

section 1 review

Summary

Sound Waves and Their Causes

- Sound results from compressional waves emanating from vibrating objects.
- The compressions and rarefactions of sound waves transfer energy.

Moving Through Materials

- Sound waves can travel through any matter.
- Sound travels fastest through solids, slower through liquids, and slowest through gases.
- Sound travels faster in warmer mediums.

Human Hearing

- The outer ear gathers sound waves and directs them to the eardrum.
- The middle ear contains three tiny bones that multiply the force and pressure of the vibrating eardrum.
- The inner ear's cochlea converts sound waves to nerve impulses.

Self Check

1. **Explain** how sound travels from your vocal cords to your friend's ears when you talk.
2. **Summarize** the physical reasons that sound waves travel at different speeds through liquids and gases.
3. **Explain** why sound speeds up when the temperature rises.
4. **Describe** in detail each section of the human ear and its role in hearing.
5. **Think Critically** Some people hear ringing in their ears, called tinnitus, even in the absence of sound. Form a hypothesis to explain why this occurs.

Applying Math

6. **Calculate Time** How long would it take a sound wave from a car alarm to travel 1 km if the temperature were 0°C?
7. **Calculate Time** How long would it take the same wave to travel 1 km if the temperature were 20°C?

Science Online gpscience.com/self_check_quiz

section 1 review

1. Your vocal cords create compressions and rarefactions in air molecules that travel out in all directions.
2. Sound travels faster in liquids than in gas because the molecules in a liquid are closer to one another than are the molecules in gas.
3. Increased temperature makes the molecules within the medium move faster, which makes them collide more frequently with other molecules.
4. The outer ear collects sound waves. Bones in the middle ear amplify sound waves and vibrate the oval window. This causes hairs in the cochlea of the middle ear to vibrate. The cochlea sends information about the vibrations as nerve impulses to the brain.
5. Possible answers: hair cells vibrate even when no sound is present, damage to nerve cells
6. $1{,}000 \text{ m}/(331 \text{ m/s}) = 3.02 \text{ s}$
7. $1{,}000 \text{ m}/(343 \text{ m/s}) = 2.92 \text{ s}$

section 2

Properties of Sound

Reading Guide

What **You'll Learn**

- **Recognize** how amplitude, intensity, and loudness are related.
- **Describe** how sound intensity is measured and what levels can damage hearing.
- **Explain** the relationship between frequency and pitch.
- **Discuss** the Doppler effect.

Why **It's Important**

Each property of a sound wave affects how things sound to you—from your blaring CD player to someone's whisper.

Review Vocabulary

potential energy: energy that is stored in an object's position

New Vocabulary

- intensity
- loudness
- decibel
- pitch
- ultrasonic
- Doppler effect

Intensity and Loudness

If the phone rings while you're listening to a stereo, you might have to turn down the volume on the stereo to be able to hear the person on the phone. What happens to the sound waves from your radio when you adjust the volume? The notes sound the same as when the volume was higher, but something about the sound changes. The difference is that quieter sound waves do not carry as much energy as louder sound waves do.

Recall that the amount of energy a wave carries corresponds to its amplitude. For a compressional wave, amplitude is related to the density of the particles in the compressions and rarefactions. Look at **Figure 5.** For a sound wave that carries less energy and has a lower amplitude, particles in the medium are less compressed in the compressions and less spread out in the rarefactions. For a sound wave that has a higher amplitude, particles in the medium are closer together, or more compressed, in the compressions and more spread out in the rarefactions.

To produce a wave that carries more energy, more energy is transferred from the vibrating object to the medium. More energy is transferred to the medium when the particles of the medium are forced closer together in the compressions and spread farther apart in the rarefactions.

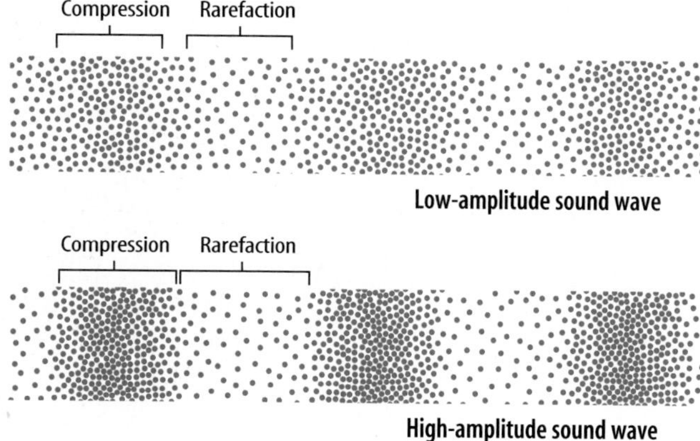

Figure 5 The amplitude of a sound wave depends on how tightly packed molecules are in the compressions and rarefactions.

Section 2 Resource Manager

Chapter *Fast File* Resources

Transparency Activity, p. 45

Enrichment, p. 30

Directed Reading for Content Mastery, p. 18

MiniLAB, p. 4

Reinforcement, p. 26

Lab Activity, pp. 9–10

Physical Science Critical Thinking/Problem Solving, p. 4

1 Motivate

Bellringer

Section Focus Transparencies also are available on the Interactive Chalkboard CD-ROM.

L2 

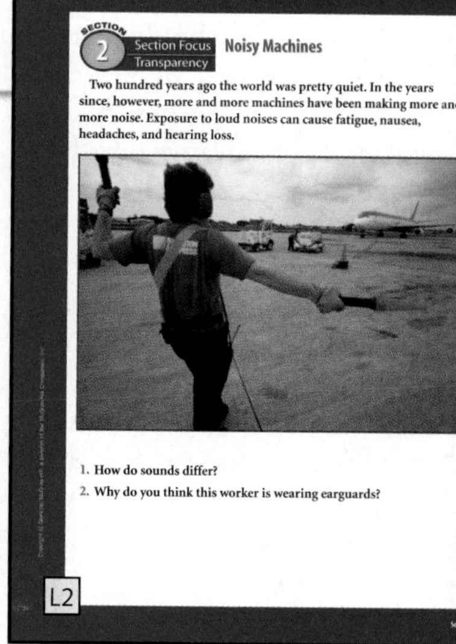

Section Focus Transparency 2
Noisy Machines
Two hundred years ago the world was pretty quiet. In the years since, however, more and more machines have been making more and more noise. Exposure to loud noises can cause fatigue, nausea, headaches, and hearing loss.
1. How do sounds differ?
2. Why do you think this worker is wearing earguards?
L2
Sound

Tie to Prior Knowledge

Different Sounds Ask volunteers to make a soft sound, then a loud sound. Can they make a high-pitched sound? How about a low-pitched sound? Tell students that in this section they will learn what causes these differences in sounds.

Inquiry Lab

Build a Muffler

Purpose Students will compete with each other to build shoebox mufflers.

Possible Materials shoe box, packing material, corks, wax paper, cardboard dividers, aluminum foil, sound meter, radio or stereo

Estimated Time two class periods

Teaching Strategies

- Each lab group of students needs a shoebox and cardboard dividers. They should make a hole in each end of the cardboard box. Noise goes in one end, and gets measured with the sound meter at the other end.
- Encourage students to test different materials and designs of mufflers. Interested students will easily find several automobile muffler designs online. You could tell students to make a mazelike passage for the sound waves to travel through. Allow students to bring extra materials from home.
- Encourage competition. Who can make the most effective muffler? Who can record the best comparative results for a few different designs?

For additional inquiry activities, see *Science Inquiry Labs*.

Caption Answer

Figure 6 It would be less.

Intensity Imagine sound waves moving through the air from your radio to your ear. If you held a square loop between you and the radio, as in **Figure 6,** and could measure how much energy passed through the loop in 1 s, you would measure intensity. **Intensity** is the amount of energy that flows through a certain area in a specific amount of time. When you turn down the volume of your radio, you reduce the energy carried by the sound waves, so you also reduce their intensity.

Intensity influences how far away a sound can be heard. If you and a friend whisper a conversation, the sound waves you create have low intensity and do not travel far. You have to sit close together to hear each other. However, when you shout to each other, you can be much farther apart. The sound waves made by your shouts have high intensity and can travel far.

Intensity Decreases With Distance Intensity influences how far a wave will travel because some of a wave's energy is converted to other forms of energy when it is passed from particle to particle. Think about what happens when you drop a basketball. The ball has potential energy as you hold it above the ground. This potential energy is converted into energy of motion as the ball falls. When the ball hits the ground and bounces up, a small amount of that energy has been transferred to the ground. The ball no longer has enough energy to bounce back to the original level. The ball transfers a small amount of energy with each bounce, until finally the ball has no more energy. If you held the ball higher above the ground, it would have more energy and would bounce for a longer time before it came to a stop. In a similar way, a sound wave of low intensity loses its energy more quickly, and travels a shorter distance than a sound wave of higher intensity.

Figure 6 The intensity of the sound waves from the CD player is related to the amount of energy that passes through the loop in a certain amount of time.
Describe *how the intensity would change if the loop were 10 m away from the radio.*

Teacher FYI

Sound Intensity The intensity of sound decreases as it travels away from a source not only because the waves transfer energy to matter, but also because they radiate out from the source. Sound intensity decreases as $1/r^2$, where r is the distance from the source. For example, the intensity of a sound 100 m from its source is about one-fourth the intensity of the same sound 50 m from its source.

Loudness When you hear different sounds, you do not need special equipment to know which sounds have greater intensity. Your ears and brain can tell the difference. **Loudness** is the human perception of sound intensity. Sound waves with high intensity carry more energy. When sound waves of high intensity reach your ear, they cause your eardrum to move back and forth a greater distance than sound waves of low intensity do. The bones of the middle ear convert the increased movement of the eardrum into increased movement of the hair cells in the inner ear. As a result, you hear a loud sound. As the intensity of a sound wave increases, the loudness of the sound you hear increases.

Reading Check *How are intensity and loudness related?*

Topic: Sound Intensity
Visit gpscience.com for Web links to information about sound as well as a list of sounds and their intensities in decibels.

Activity Make a table that lists some sounds you heard today, in order from loudest to quietest. In another column, write the intensity level of each sound.

The Decibel Scale It's hard to say how loud too loud is. Two people are unlikely to agree on what is too loud, because people vary in their perception of loudness. A sound that seems fine to you may seem earsplitting to your teacher. Even so, the intensity of sound can be described using a measurement scale. Each unit on the scale for sound intensity is called a **decibel** (DE suh bel), abbreviated dB. On this scale, the faintest sound that most people can hear is 0 dB. Sounds with intensity levels above 120 dB may cause pain and permanent hearing loss. During some rock concerts, sounds reach this damaging intensity level. Wearing ear protection, such as earplugs, around loud sounds can help protect against hearing loss. **Figure 7** shows some sounds and their intensity levels in decibels.

Figure 7 The decibel scale measures the intensity of sound. **Identify** *where a normal speaking voice would fall on the scale.*

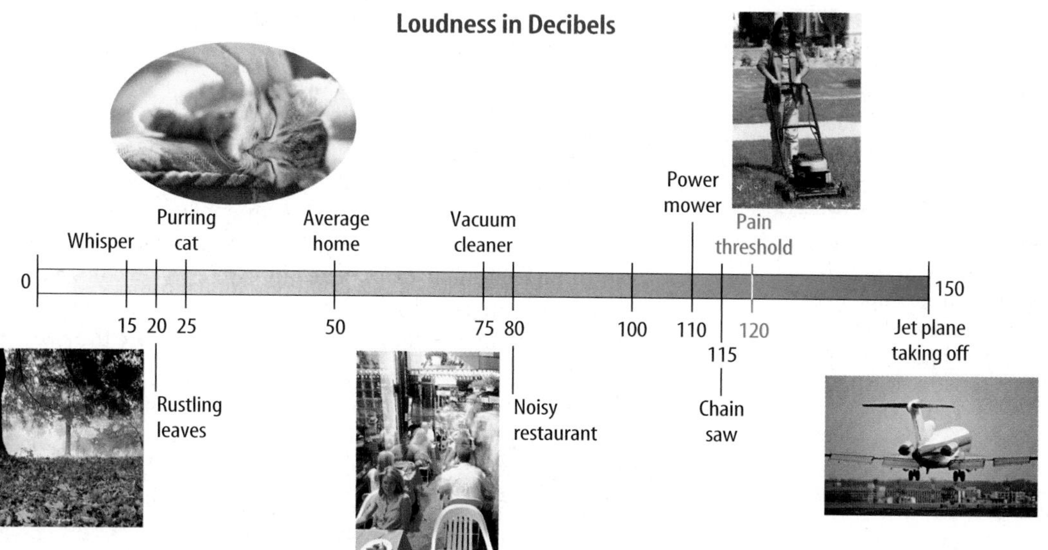

Activity

Ranking Volume Have students bring in various whistles. Have them blow the whistles and rank them from loudest to softest. Afterwards, have students examine the whistles to find out what produced the vibration and what feature caused one whistle to be louder than another. L2 ELL
LS **Auditory-Musical**

Reading Check

Answer Intensity is the amount of energy in sound waves that flows through a certain area in a specific amount of time. Loudness is the human perception of this intensity.

Discussion

Accurate Terms Why do you think scientists make a distinction between intensity and loudness? Intensity can be measured and agreed upon by everyone. Loudness is experienced differently by different people. A sound that is too loud for one person may be fine for another person. L2
LS **Logical-Mathematical**

Caption Answer

Figure 7 Between an average home and a vacuum cleaner; people normally speak at about 60 dB.

Fun Fact

A decibel is one-tenth of a bel, named in honor of Alexander Graham Bell.

Visual Learning

Figure 6 Have students analyze the photograph and the diagram in this figure while you read aloud the description from the text at the top of the page. Then ask a volunteer to explain the concept the figure is illustrating. Intensity of sound decreases as distance from the sound source increases. L2
LS **Auditory-Musical**

Differentiated Instruction

Challenge Many careers involve workplaces with dangerously high noise levels. Have students research such a career and find out what is done to protect the employees hearing. Have students find out what government agency regulates workplace conditions. Occupational Safety & Health Administration. L3

Quick Demo

Relating Frequency and Pitch

Materials oscilloscope with attached microphone; small band instrument

Estimated Time 10 minutes

Procedure Demonstrate the relationship between frequency and pitch by using the oscilloscope. Have a student volunteer play various pitches on the band instrument. Observe the corresponding waveforms on the oscilloscope.

Caption Answer

Figure 8 As frequency increases, pitch becomes higher.

Purpose Students will observe and interpret how hearing loss changes the sounds we hear. L1 ELL COOP LEARN

LS **Auditory-Musical**

Materials radio, thick cloth

Teaching Strategy If students use cloth to muffle their hearing, suggest that they gradually increase the volume of the radio until it is clear, and then take the cloth away from their ears and hear how loud the sound is.

Analysis

1. High pitches are harder to hear. Consonant sounds are harder to hear than vowel sounds.
2. People with hearing loss should be spoken to face-to-face, at a steady, unrushed pace with a slight emphasis on consonant sounds.

Assessment

Performance Have students hypothesize how these results would be affected if the bass were minimized and the treble maximized. Have them test their hypotheses. Sound would be clearer. Use **Performance Assessment in the Science Classroom,** p. 93.

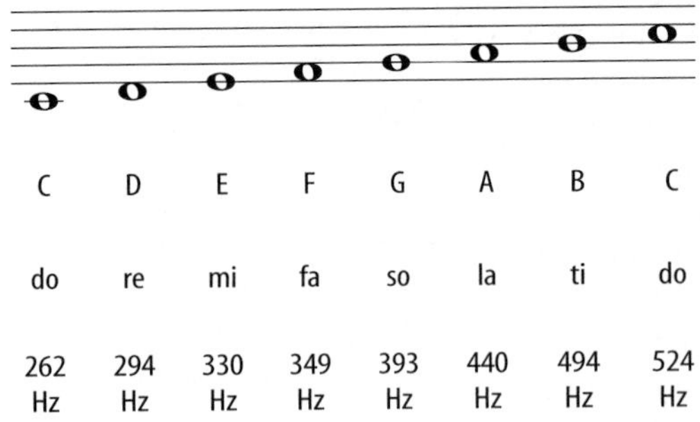

Figure 8 Every note has a different frequency, which gives it a distinct pitch.
Describe *how pitch changes when frequency increases.*

Simulating Hearing Loss

Procedure

1. Tune a **radio** to a news station. Turn the volume down to the lowest level you can hear and understand.
2. Turn the bass to maximum and the treble to minimum. If the radio does not have these controls, hold thick wads of **cloth** over your ears.
3. Observe which sounds are hardest and easiest to hear.

Analysis

1. Are high or low pitches harder to hear? Are vowel or consonant sounds harder to hear?
2. How could you help a person with hearing loss understand what you say?

Try at Home

Pitch

If you have ever taken a music class, you are probably familiar with the musical scale do, re, mi, fa, so, la, ti, do. If you were to sing this scale, your voice would start low and become higher with each note. You would hear a change in **pitch,** which is how high or low a sound seems to be. The pitch of a sound is related to the frequency of the sound waves.

Frequency and Pitch Frequency is a measure of how many wavelengths pass a particular point each second. For a compressional wave, such as sound, the frequency is the number of compressions or the number of rarefactions that pass by each second. Frequency is measured in hertz (Hz)—1 Hz means that one wavelength passes by in 1 s.

When a sound wave with high frequency hits your ear, many compressions hit your eardrum each second. The wave causes your eardrum and all the other parts of your ear to vibrate more quickly than if a sound wave with a low frequency hit your ear. Your brain interprets these fast vibrations caused by high-frequency waves as a sound with a high pitch. As the frequency of a sound wave decreases, the pitch becomes lower. **Figure 8** shows different notes and their frequencies. For example, a whistle with a frequency of 1,000 Hz has a high pitch, but low-pitched thunder has a frequency of less than 50 Hz.

A healthy human ear can hear sound waves with frequencies from about 20 Hz to 20,000 Hz. The human ear is most sensitive to sounds in the range of 440 Hz to about 7,000 Hz. In this range, most people can hear much fainter sounds than at higher or lower frequencies.

Ultrasonic and Infrasonic Waves Most people can't hear sound frequencies above 20,000 Hz, which are called **ultrasonic** waves. Dogs can hear sounds with frequencies up to about 35,000 Hz, and bats can detect frequencies higher than 100,000 Hz. Even though humans can't hear ultrasonic waves, they use them for many things. Ultrasonic waves are used in medical diagnosis and treatment. They also are used to estimate the size, shape, and depth of underwater objects.

Infrasonic, or subsonic, waves have frequencies below 20 Hz—too low for most people to hear. These waves are produced by sources that vibrate slowly, such as wind, heavy machinery, and earthquakes. Although you can't hear infrasonic waves, you may feel them as a rumble inside your body.

Science Journal

Feeling Pitch Have students place their hands gently over their necks and sing the musical scale, "do re mi fa so la ti do." Have them write their observations in their Science Journals. They should be able to tell that their vocal cords vibrate differently as they go up the scale. L2

LS **Kinesthetic**

Differentiated Instruction

Learning Disabled Have a student that plays a musical instrument bring their instrument to class and play the scales on this page. Students can assume that it is bass or treble clef as needed. If the student cannot bring the instrument to class have the student bring a tape of themselves playing the musical scale.

330 CHAPTER 11 Sound

The Doppler Effect

Imagine that you are standing at the side of a racetrack with race cars zooming past. As they move toward you, the different pitches of their engines become higher. As they move away from you, the pitches become lower. The change in pitch or wave frequency due to a moving wave source is called the **Doppler effect.** **Figure 9** shows how the Doppler effect occurs.

Reading Check *What is the Doppler effect?*

Moving Sound As a race car moves, it sends out sound waves in the form of compressions and rarefactions. In **Figure 9A,** the race car creates a compression, labeled A. Compression A moves through the air toward the flagger standing at the finish line. By the time compression B leaves the race car in **Figure 9B,** the car has moved forward. Because the car has moved since the time it created compression A, compressions A and B are closer together than they would be if the car had stayed still. Because the compressions are closer together, more compressions pass by the flagger each second than if the car were at rest. As a result, the flagger hears a higher pitch. You also can see from **Figure 9B** that the compressions behind the moving car are farther apart, resulting in a lower frequency and a lower pitch after the car passes and moves away from the flagger.

Red Shift The Doppler effect can also be observed in light waves emanating from moving sources—although the sources must be moving at tremendous speeds. Astronomers have learned that the universe is expanding by observing the Doppler effect in light waves. Research the phenomenon known as red shift and explain in your Science Journal how it relates to the Doppler effect.

Figure 9 The Doppler effect occurs when the source of a sound wave is moving relative to a listener.

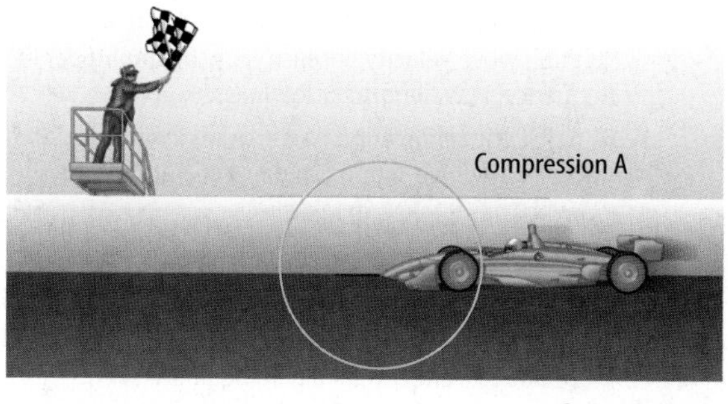

A The race car creates compression A.

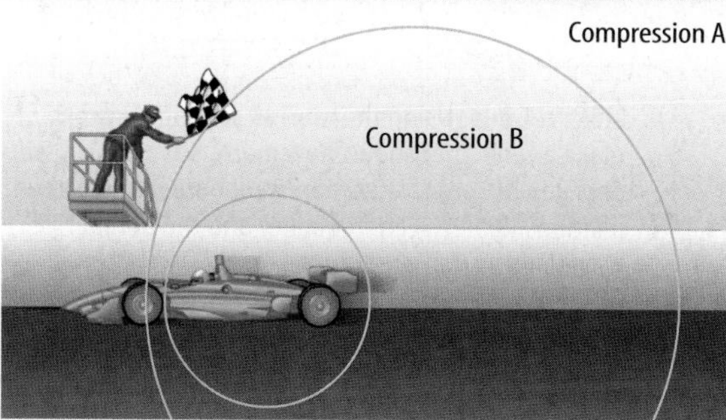

B The car is closer to the flagger when it creates compression B. Compressions A and B are closer together in front of the car, so the flagger hears a higher-pitched sound.

Red Shift The light from most galaxies is shifted toward the red end of the spectrum because, as these galaxies are moving away from Earth, their light waves become "stretched out." This is known as red shift. The stretching of the light waves is caused by the Doppler effect.

Reading Check

Answer the change in pitch or wave frequency due to a moving wave source

Quick Demo

The Doppler Effect

Materials sponge ball; small electric buzzer; battery; tape.

Estimated Time 15 minutes

Procedure Cut a small opening in the side of the sponge ball. Place the small electric buzzer connected to the batter inside the opening and tape the opening shut. Throw the ball from the front to the back of the room. The increased and decreased pitches caused by the Doppler effect should be audible.

Visual Learning

Figure 9 Remind students that the sound waves emitted by the car in the figure don't change. It is only the frequency at which they reach the flagger that changes. The car's driver hears no change in pitch at all. Have students draw circles representing sound waves to show how the Doppler effect increases if the speed of the sound source increases. L2 IS **Visual-Spatial**

Curriculum Connection

History When a jet travels faster than the speed of sound, the sound waves it produces trail behind as a cone of pressure disturbances in the air. This Mach cone might be heard as a loud sonic boom as the jet passes by. Have students research the first human-made sonic boom. Chuck Yeager was the first person to break the sound barrier and cause a sonic boom. He did this on October 14, 1947. L2

3 Assess

DAILY INTERVENTION

Check for Understanding

Logical-Mathematical Have each student work with a partner to produce a small diagram showing the composition of a sound wave. Ask them to label all parts of their diagrams. L1

Reteach

Sound Wave Properties Place a clear, shallow container of water on top of an overhead projector to demonstrate various properties of waves. For example, touch the water with vibrating tuning forks to show low and high frequencies. Move the vibrating tuning fork along the surface to show the Doppler effect. L2

Assessment

Portfolio Have students make posters showing pictures of things that produce sound at different frequencies. The pictures should include ultrasonic, infrasonic, and audible frequencies. Use **Performance Assessment in the Science Classroom,** p. 145. P L2

Figure 10 Doppler radar can show the movement of winds in storms, and, in some cases, can detect the wind rotation that leads to the formation of tornadoes, like the one shown here. This can help provide early warning and reduce the injuries and loss of life caused by tornadoes.

A Moving Observer You also can observe the Doppler effect when you are moving past a sound source that is standing still. Suppose you were riding in a school bus and passed a building with a ringing bell. The pitch would sound higher as you approached the building and lower as you rode away from it. The Doppler effect happens any time the source of a sound is changing position compared with the observer. It occurs no matter whether it is the sound source or the observer that is moving. The faster the change in position, the greater the change in frequency and pitch.

Using the Doppler Effect The Doppler effect also occurs for other waves besides sound waves. For example, the frequency of electromagnetic waves, such as radar waves, changes if an observer and wave source are moving relative to each other. Radar guns use the Doppler effect to measure the speed of cars. The radar gun sends radar waves toward a moving car. The waves are reflected from the car and their frequency is shifted, depending on the speed and direction of the car. From the Doppler shift of the reflected waves, the radar gun determines the car's speed. Weather radar also uses the Doppler shift to show the movement of winds in storms, such as the tornado in **Figure 10.**

section 2 review

Summary

Intensity and Loudness

- Tight, dense compressions in a sound wave mean high intensity, loudness, and more energy.
- Sound intensity is measured in decibels.

Pitch

- High frequency sound waves have closer compressions and rarefactions and higher pitch than those of low frequency.
- Ultrasonic waves are too high for people to hear, but are useful for medical purposes.

The Doppler Effect

- The Doppler effect occurs when a moving object emits sounds that change pitch as the object moves past you.
- Police radar uses the Doppler effect to detect speeding cars.

Self Check

1. **Determine** which will change if you turn up a radio's volume: wave velocity, intensity, pitch, amplitude, frequency, wavelength, or loudness.
2. **Describe** the range of human hearing in decibels, and the level at which sound can damage human ears.
3. **Contrast** frequency and pitch.
4. **Draw and label** a diagram that explains the Doppler effect.
5. **Think Critically** Why would a passing race car display more Doppler effect than a passing police siren?

Applying Math

6. **Make a Table** Using the musical scale in **Figure 8,** make a table that shows how many wavelengths will pass you in 1 min for each musical note. What is the relationship between frequency and the number of wavelengths that pass you in 1 min?

gpscience.com/self_check_quiz

section 2 review

1. intensity; amplitude, loudness
2. range of human hearing: 0 db and above; level damaging to human ears: 120 dB
3. Frequency is a measure of how many wavelengths pass a point each second. Pitch is how high or low a sound seems to be. As frequency increases, pitch gets higher.
4. Sketches should show that the wavelength of compressions decreases as a moving object comes near and increases as the moving object moves away.
5. The race car is moving faster so the Doppler shift is greater.
6. Check students' tables; the higher the frequency the greater the number of wavelengths that pass you in a second.

section 3

Music

Reading Guide

What You'll Learn

- **Distinguish** between noise and music.
- **Describe** why different instruments have different sound qualities.
- **Explain** how string, wind, and percussion instruments produce music.
- **Describe** the formation of beats.

Why It's Important

Music makes life more enjoyable, but noise pollution is unpleasant.

Review Vocabulary

frequency: the number of vibrations occurring in 1 s

New Vocabulary

- music
- sound quality
- overtone
- resonator

What is music?

To someone else, your favorite music might sound like a jumble of noise. Music and noise are caused by vibrations—with some important differences, as shown in **Figure 11.** Noise has random patterns and pitches. **Music** is made of sounds that are deliberately used in a regular pattern.

Natural Frequencies Every material or object has a particular set of frequencies at which it vibrates. This set of frequencies are its natural frequencies. When you pluck a guitar string the pitch you hear depends on the string's natural frequencies. Each string on a guitar has a different set of natural frequencies. The natural frequencies of a guitar string depend on the string's thickness, its length, the material it is made from, and how tightly it is stretched. Musical instruments contain strings, membranes, or columns of air that vibrate at their natural frequencies to produce notes with different pitches.

Piano

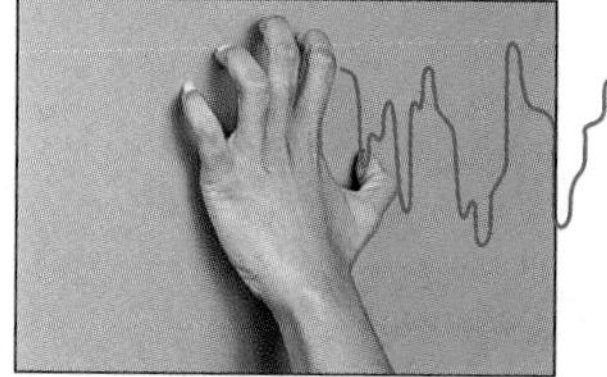

Scraping fingernails

Resonance The sound produced by musical instruments is amplified by resonance. Recall that resonance occurs when a material or an object is made to vibrate at its natural frequencies by absorbing energy from something that is also vibrating at those frequencies. The vibrations of the mouthpiece or the reed in a wind instrument cause the air inside the instrument to absorb energy and vibrate at its natural frequencies. The vibrating air makes the sound of the instrument louder.

Section 3 Resource Manager

Chapter FAST FILE Resources

Transparency Activity, p. 46
Directed Reading for Content Mastery, p. 19
Enrichment, p. 31
Lab Worksheet, pp. 5–6
Lab Activity, pp. 11–14
Reinforcement, p. 27
Cultural Diversity, p. 61

1 Motivate

Bellringer

Section Focus Transparencies also are available on the Interactive Chalkboard CD-ROM. L2 

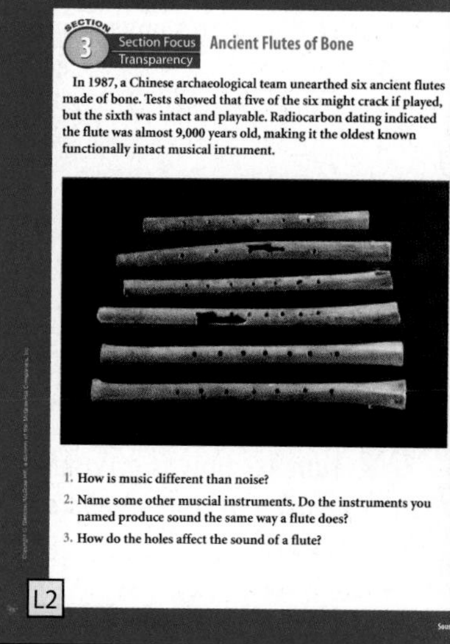

Section 3 Section Focus Transparency — Ancient Flutes of Bone

In 1987, a Chinese archaeological team unearthed six ancient flutes made of bone. Tests showed that five of the six might crack if played, but the sixth was intact and playable. Radiocarbon dating indicated the flute was almost 9,000 years old, making it the oldest known functionally intact musical intrument.

1. How is music different than noise?
2. Name some other muscial instruments. Do the instruments you named produce sound the same way a flute does?
3. How do the holes affect the sound of a flute?

L2

Tie to Prior Knowledge

Musical Student Ask students to name a musical instrument they play. Tell them that this section explains the science of music.

Caption Answer

Figure 11 the sound waves produced by the piano

2 Teach

Discussion

Overtones If a guitar string vibrates at a fundamental frequency of 294 Hz, what is the frequency of the first overtone? $294\text{ Hz} \times 2 = 588\text{ Hz}$

Reading Check

Answer Sound quality describes the differences among sounds of the same pitch and loudness. The specific combination of frequencies produced by a musical instrument gives the instrument its distinctive sound quality.

Caption Answer

Figure 12 at four times the fundamental frequency

Virtual Labs

Tune It *How is an oscilloscope used to tune a musical instrument?*

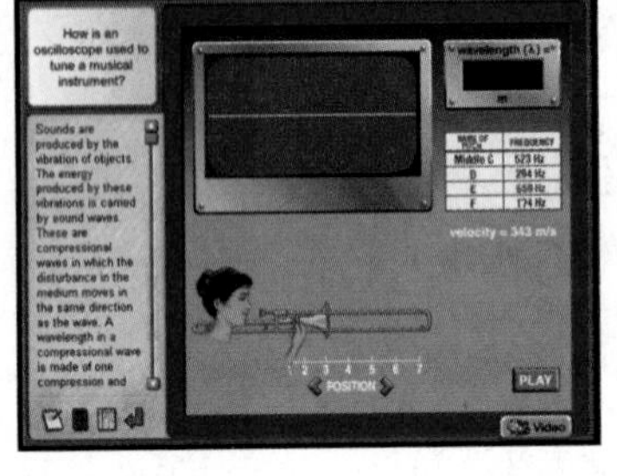

Science Online
Topic: Noise Pollution
Visit gpscience.com for Web links to information about noise pollution.

Activity Identify sources of noise pollution that you can help eliminate. Write your findings in your Science Journal.

Sound Quality

Suppose your classmate played a note on a flute and then a note of the same pitch and loudness on a piano. Even if you closed your eyes, you could tell the difference between the two instruments. Their sounds wouldn't be the same. Each of these instruments has a unique sound quality. **Sound quality** describes the differences among sounds of the same pitch and loudness. Objects can be made to vibrate at other frequencies besides their natural frequency. This produces sound waves with more than one frequency. The specific combination of frequencies produced by a musical instrument is what gives it a distinctive quality of sound.

Reading Check *What does sound quality describe and how is it created?*

Overtones Even though an instrument vibrates at many different frequencies at once, you still hear just one note. All of the frequencies are not at the same intensity. The main tone that is played and heard is called the fundamental frequency. On a guitar, for example, the fundamental frequency is produced by the entire string vibrating back and forth, as in **Figure 12.** In addition to vibrating at the fundamental frequency, the string also vibrates to produce overtones. An **overtone** is a vibration whose frequency is a multiple of the fundamental frequency. The first two guitar-string overtones also are shown in **Figure 12.** These overtones create the rich sounds of a guitar. The number and intensity of overtones vary with each instrument. These overtones produce an instrument's distinct sound quality.

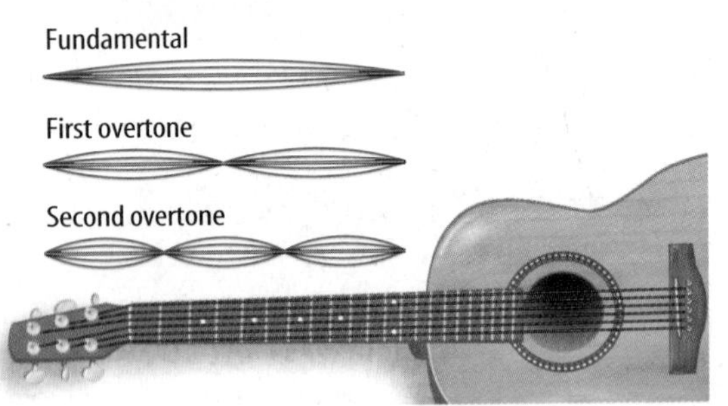

Figure 12 A guitar string can vibrate at more than one frequency at the same time. Here the guitar string vibrations produce the fundamental frequency, and first and second overtones are shown.
Infer *how the string would vibrate to produce the third overtone.*

Musical Instruments

A musical instrument is any device used to produce a musical sound. Violins, cello, oboes, bassoons, horns, and kettledrums are musical instruments that you might have seen and heard in your school orchestra. These familiar examples are just a small sample of the diverse assortment of instruments people play throughout the world. For example, Australian Aborigines accompany their songs with a woodwind instrument called the didgeridoo (DIH juh ree dew). Caribbean musicians use rubber-tipped mallets to play steel drums, and a flutelike instrument called the nay is played throughout the Arab world.

LAB DEMONSTRATION

Purpose to observe the relationship between resonant wavelength and cavity size

Materials water, 100-mL graduated cylinder, rubber hammer, 440-Hz tuning fork

Procedure Place 20 mL of water in the cylinder. Tap the fork with a rubber hammer and place it horizontally above the cylinder so students can hear the resonant sound produced. Repeat with 40, 60, 80, and 100 mL of water.

Expected Outcome Resonance can't occur if a cavity is less than $\frac{1}{4}$ wavelength long. The wavelength at 440 Hz is about 79 cm, so resonance doesn't occur if the length of the column of air is less than about 20 cm.

Assessment

What was the minimum height of the column of air for which resonance occurred? about 20 cm

Strings Soft violins, screaming electric guitars, and elegant harps are types of string instruments. In string instruments, sound is produced by plucking, striking, or drawing a bow across tightly stretched strings. Because the sound of a vibrating string is soft, string instruments usually have a resonator, like the violin in **Figure 13.** A **resonator** (RE zuh nay tur) is a hollow chamber filled with air that amplifies sound when the air inside of it vibrates. For example, if you pluck a guitar string that is stretched tightly between two nails on a board, the sound is much quieter than if the string were on a guitar. When the string is attached to a guitar, the guitar frame and the air inside the instrument begin to vibrate as they absorb energy from the vibrating string. The vibration of the guitar body and the air inside the resonator makes the sound of the string louder and also affects the quality of the sound.

Figure 13 The air inside the violin's resonator vibrates when the string is played. The vibrating air amplifies the string's sound.
Explain *what causes the air to vibrate.*

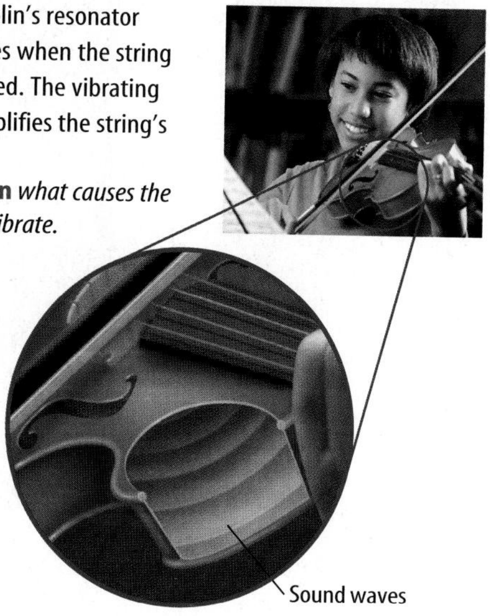

Sound waves

Brass and Woodwinds Brass and woodwind instruments rely on the vibration of air to make music. The many different brass and wind instruments—such as horns, oboes, and flutes—use various methods to make air vibrate inside the instrument. For example, brass instruments have cone-shaped mouthpieces like the one in **Figure 14.** This mouthpiece is inserted into metal tubing, which is the resonator in a brass instrument. As the player blows into the instrument, his or her lips vibrate against the mouthpiece. The air in the resonator also starts to vibrate, producing a pitch. On the other hand, to play a flute, a musician blows a stream of air against the edge of the flute's mouth hole. This causes the air inside the flute to vibrate.

In brass and wind instruments, the length of the vibrating tube of air determines the pitch of the sound produced. For example, in flutes and trumpets, the musician changes the length of the resonator by opening and closing finger holes or valves. In a trombone, however, the tubing slides in and out to become shorter or longer.

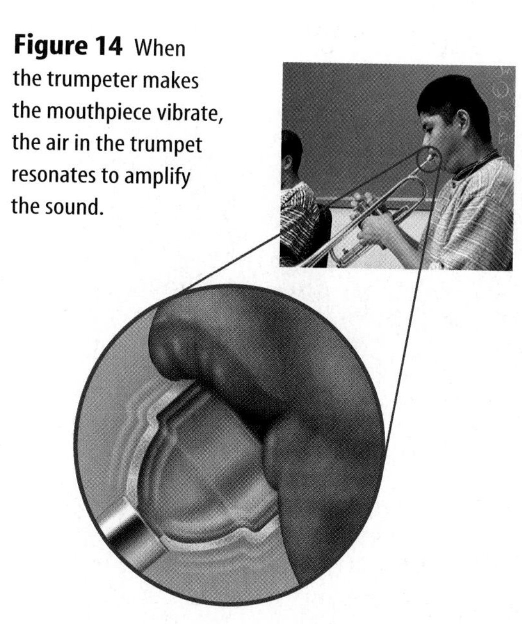

Figure 14 When the trumpeter makes the mouthpiece vibrate, the air in the trumpet resonates to amplify the sound.

Caption Answer

Figure 13 It absorbs energy from the vibrating string.

Make a Model

Creating Resource Students can learn more about the importance of resonators by creating a model. Have them cut a circle about 5 cm wide out of the top of a small box. First, they should pluck a stretched rubber band to hear the sound it makes. Next, they should put the rubber band around the box so that it crosses the hole. The rubber band will make a much louder sound when plucked over the hole. L2 ELL
LS **Auditory-Musical**

Activity

Sound Production Have students work in small groups to examine or research how instruments produce sound. Each group should choose one instrument and examine what vibrates and how it produces a change in pitch. Have groups share their findings with the class. L1 LS **Visual-Spatial**

Teacher FYI

String Length Vibrations in many string instruments, such as the violin (a bowed instrument), are altered by pressing on part of the string. This effectively shortens the length of the vibrating string, so the pitch is higher. Other instruments have fixed string lengths that correspond to different pitches. Examples of this are the harp (a plucked instrument) and the piano (a hammered instrument).

Cultural Diversity

Slack-key Guitar Musicians in Hawaii have a unique way of using a guitar to reflect the spirit and beauty of the island. The *ki ho´alu*, or slack-key guitar music, is named for the way the strings are loosened and tuned to various pitches. Play recorded slack-key guitar music and have students describe how the sound quality differs from that of other guitar music they have heard. L2
LS **Auditory-Musical**

Differentiated Instruction

English-Language Learners Have students create study cards to learn the vocabulary in this chapter. Have students write a vocabulary word on one side of an index card and the definition on the other. Students may add illustrations or definitions in their native language to the cards to help learn the words.

Caption Answer

Figure 15 The vibrating drum membrane causes the air inside the resonator to vibrate at the same frequency, thereby amplifying the sound.

Activity

Good Vibrations Obtain some percussion instruments. If possible, include a snare drum, a kettledrum, and a bass drum, as well as a tambourine and cymbals. Scatter some dry rice on a snare drum's membrane and hit the drum with a drumstick so students can see the vibration. If a kettledrum is available, show students that by pressing on the pedal you can tighten or loosen the membrane and alter the drum's pitch. For each of the different types of drums, have students explore the pitch produced and the way sound is amplified. L2 LS **Auditory-Musical**

Reading Check

Answer to send signals, accompany rituals, and entertain

Caption Answer

Figure 16 Each size resonates at a different frequency.

Quick Demo

Hearing Beats

Materials two identical tuning forks, rubber band, rubber hammer

Estimated Time 10 minutes

Procedure Wrap a rubber band around the tines of a tuning fork to alter its pitch slightly. Hit it and an identical unwrapped fork with a rubber hammer and touch the handles to a desk to amplify the sound. Because the frequencies interfere, students will hear beats.

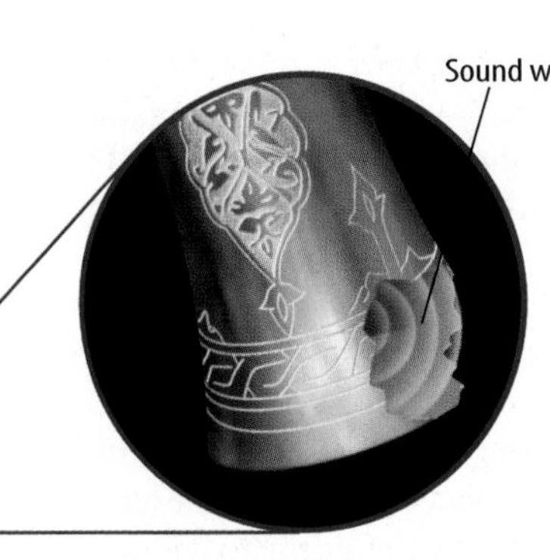

Figure 15 The air inside the resonator of the drum amplifies the sound created when the musician strikes the membrane's surface. **Describe** *how the natural frequency of the air in the drum affects the sound it creates.*

Percussion Does the sound of a bass drum make your heart start to pound? Since ancient times, people have used drums and other percussion instruments to send signals, accompany important rituals, and entertain one another. Percussion instruments are struck, shaken, rubbed, or brushed to produce sound. Some, such as kettledrums or the drum shown in **Figure 15,** have a membrane stretched over a resonator. When the drummer strikes the membrane with sticks or hands, the membrane vibrates and causes the air inside the resonator to vibrate. The resonator amplifies the sound made when the membrane is struck. Some drums have a fixed pitch, but others have a pitch that can be changed by tightening or loosening the membrane.

Caribbean steel drums were developed in the 1940s in Trinidad. As many as 32 different striking surfaces hammered from the ends of 55-gallon oil barrels create different pitches of sound. The side of a drum acts as the resonator.

Reading Check *How have people used drums?*

The xylophone shown in **Figure 16** is another type of percussion instrument. It has a series of wooden bars, each with its own tube-shaped resonator. The musician strikes the bars with mallets, and the type of mallet affects the sound quality. Hard mallets make crisp sounds, while softer rubber mallets make duller sounds. Other types of percussion instruments include cymbals, rattles, and even old-fashioned washboards.

Figure 16 Xylophones are made with many wooden bars that each have their own resonator tubes. **Explain** *why the resonators and bars on a xylophone are different sizes.*

Science Journal

Sound Effects Several singers, such as Ella Fitzgerald and Enrico Caruso, have reportedly broken crystal glasses by loudly singing a note at a specific frequency. Have students write their speculations about how this happens. The frequency of the singer's voice matches the natural frequency of the glass, causing it to resonate. If the glass vibrates intensely, it will shatter. L2 LS **Logical-Mathematical**

Differentiated Instruction

Challenge Have students study the history of musical instruments. Have students answer these questions: What were the first musical instruments? How did the trade routes change the musical instruments that were available? When were the first brass instruments made? Have students report their findings to the class. L3 P

Beats

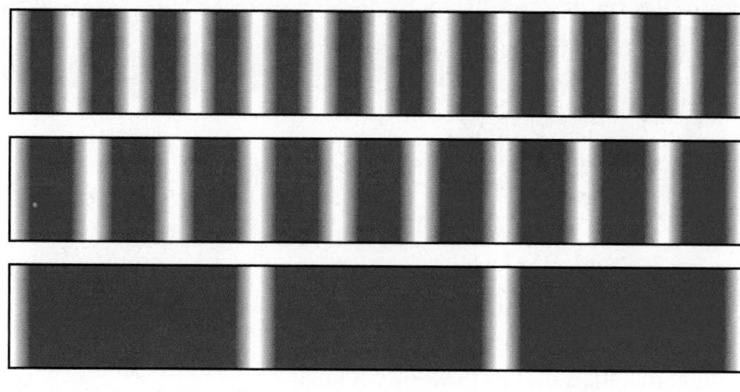

Have you ever heard two flutes play the same note when they weren't properly tuned? The sounds they produce have slightly different frequencies. You may have heard a pulsing variation in loudness, called beats.

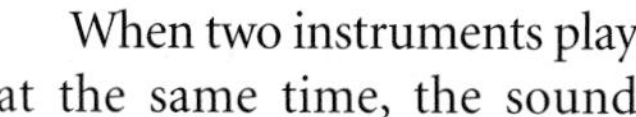

When two instruments play at the same time, the sound waves produced by each instrument interfere. The amplitudes of the waves add together when compressions overlap and rarefactions overlap, causing an increase in loudness. When compressions and rarefactions overlap each other, the loudness decreases. Look at **Figure 17.** If two waves of different frequencies interfere, a new wave is produced that has a different frequency. The frequency of this wave is actually the difference in the frequencies of the two waves. The frequency of the beats that you hear decreases as the two waves become closer in frequency. If two flutes that are in tune play the same note, no beats are heard.

Figure 17 Beats can occur when sound waves of different frequencies, shown in the top two panels, combine. These sound waves interfere with each other, forming a wave with a lower frequency, shown in the bottom panel. This wave causes a listener to hear beats.

Reading Check *How are beats produced?*

section 3 review

Summary

Nature of Music

- Music is sound used in regular patterns.
- Every material has a set of natural frequencies at which it will vibrate.
- Resonance helps amplify the sound produced by musical instruments.

Sound Quality

- Quality of sound describes the differences among sounds of the same pitch and loudness.
- Sound quality results from specific combinations of frequencies produced in various musical instruments.

Beats

- The interference of two waves with different frequencies produces beats.

Self Check

1. **Compare and contrast** music and noise.
2. **Explain** how an instrument's overtones contribute to its sound quality.
3. **Explain** how a flute, violin, and kettledrum produce sound.
4. **Describe** what occurs when two out-of-tune instruments play the same note.
5. **Think Critically** Why do musical instruments vary in different regions of the world?

Applying Math

6. **Calculate Frequencies** A string on a guitar vibrates with a frequency of 440 Hz. Two beats are heard when this string and a string on another guitar are played at the same time. What are the possible frequencies of vibration of the second string?

gpscience.com/self_check_quiz

Fun Fact

Our ears are capable of hearing beats only if the difference in the frequency of the two notes played is less than 7 Hz.

3 Assess

DAILY INTERVENTION

Check for Understanding

Logical-Mathematical Figure 17 depicts how beats form due to constructive and destructive interference. Ask students to work with partners to produce diagrams depicting the formation of beats. Have them write accompanying explanations of their diagrams. L2

Reteach

Music in Action Have students bring in musical instruments and show how they are played, how pitched can be changed, and how they amplify sound. L2

Assessment

Process Show students pictures of various musical instruments. Have them classify each one as a string, brass, woodwind, or percussion instrument. L2

Reading Check

Answer by the interference of two waves with slightly different frequencies

section 3 review

1. Music has definite pitches and sound qualities used in a set pattern. Noise does not.
2. An instrument vibrates at its fundamental frequency and at multiples of that frequency giving each instrument a distinctive sound quality.
3. The musician blows air against the flute's mouth hole. The flute acts as a resonator to amplify the sound. A bow rubs across a violin string causing it to vibrate. The body of the violin acts as a resonator. A kettledrum has a membrane that is stretched over a resonator. When the membrane is struck, the air inside the resonator vibrates.
4. The instruments create a pulsing variation in loudness due to the slightly differing frequencies.
5. Musical instruments were made from materials that were available in each particular region.
6. 442 H_2 and 438 H_2

Real-World Question

Purpose Students analyze resonance in air columns. L2 LS **Auditory-Musical**

Process Skills observe, infer, compare and contrast, recognize cause and effect, predict, communicate

Time Required 30 minutes

Alternate Materials Soda bottles can be used instead of test tubes.

Procedure

Teaching Strategies Be sure students understand to blow across the top of the tubes instead of directly into them.

Conclude and Apply

1. A longer column of water produces a higher pitch.
2. As the water height increases, the length of the air column decreases, and the wavelength of the fundamental becomes shorter, resulting in a higher pitch.
3. The length of the air column varied in each test tube giving the test tubes different tones.
4. When you blow across the top of the test tube, the column of air above the water begins to vibrate amplifying the sound.
5. Shorter air columns have higher frequencies than longer air columns.
6. Both produce sound when air is blown across an opening. The flute is an open-ended resonator. Its air column can be shortened or lengthened by opening or closing finger holes.

Making Music

There are many different types of musical instruments. Early instruments were made from materials that were easily obtained such as clay, shells, skins, wood, and reeds. These materials were fashioned into various instruments that produced pleasing sounds. In this lab, you are going to create a musical instrument using materials that are available to you—just as your ancestors did.

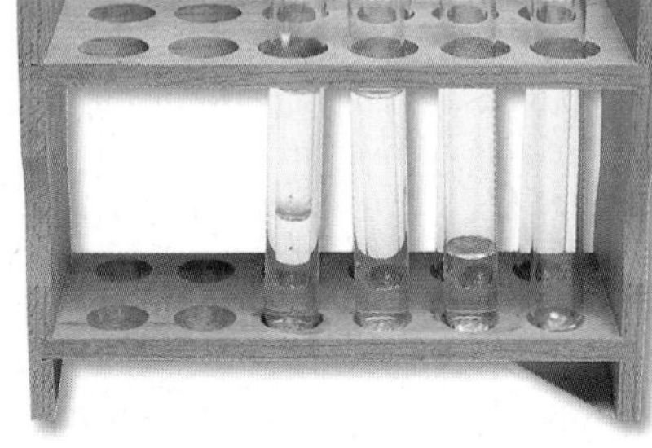

Real-World Question

How can you make different tones using only test tubes and water?

Goals

- **Demonstrate** how to make music using water and test tubes.
- **Predict** how the tones will change when there is more or less water in a test tube.

Materials

test tubes
test-tube rack

Safety Precautions

Procedure

1. Put different amounts of water into each of the test tubes.
2. **Predict** any differences you expect in how the tones from the different test tubes will sound.
3. Blow across the top of each test tube.
4. **Record** any differences that you notice in the tones that you hear from each test tube.

Conclude and Apply

1. **Describe** how the tones change depending on the amount of water in the test tube.
2. **Explain** why the pitch depends on the height of the water.
3. **Summarize** why each test tube produces a different tone.
4. **Explain** how resonance amplifies the sound from a test tube.
5. **Explain** how the natural frequencies of the air columns in each of the tubes differ.
6. **Compare and contrast** the way the test tubes make music with the way a flute makes music.

Communicating Your Data

When you are listening to music with family or friends, describe to them what you have learned about how musical instruments produce sound.

338 CHAPTER 11 Sound

Communicating Your Data

Have students draw sketches to show why the sound emerging from the test tubes will have wavelengths that are multiples of $\frac{1}{4}$ the length of the air column.

Assessment

Oral Ask students how the wavelength of a resonator differs if both ends of the cavity, rather than one as in the test tubes, is opened. If the cavity has only one open end, the sound will have wavelengths in multiples of $\frac{1}{4}$ the length of the tube. If both ends are open, the wavelengths will be multiples of $\frac{1}{2}$ the length of the tube. Use **Performance Assessment in the Science Classroom,** p. 89.

section 4

Using Sound

Reading Guide

What You'll Learn

- **Recognize** some of the factors that determine how a concert hall or theater is designed.
- **Describe** how some animals use sound waves to hunt and navigate.
- **Discuss** the uses of sonar.
- **Explain** how ultrasound is useful in medicine.

Why It's Important

Sound waves have many uses, from discovering sunken treasures to diagnosing and treating diseases.

Review Vocabulary

echo: the reflection of a sound from a surface

New Vocabulary

- acoustics
- echolocation
- sonar

Acoustics

When an orchestra stops playing, does it seem as if the sound of its music lingers for a couple of seconds? The sounds and their reflections reach your ears at different times, so you hear echoes. This echoing effect produced by many reflections of sound is called reverberation (rih vur buh RAY shun).

During an orchestra performance, reverberation can ruin the sound of the music. To prevent this problem, scientists and engineers who design concert halls must understand how the size, shape, and furnishings of the room affect the reflection of sound waves. These scientists and engineers specialize in **acoustics** (uh KEW stihks), which is the study of sound. They know that soft, porous materials can reduce excess reverberation, so they might recommend that the walls of concert halls be lined with carpets and draperies. **Figure 18** shows a concert hall that has been designed to create a good listening environment.

Figure 18 This concert hall uses cloth drapes to help reduce reverberations.
Explain *how the drapes absorb or reflect sound waves.*

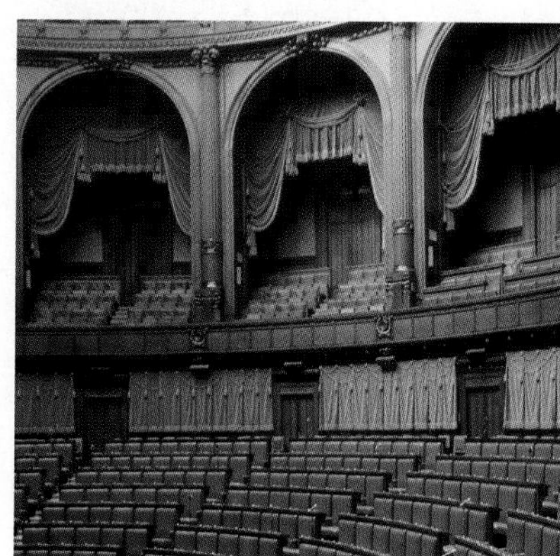

Echolocation

At night, bats swoop around in darkness without bumping into anything. They even manage to find insects and other prey in the dark. Their senses of sight and smell help them navigate. Many species of bats also depend on echolocation. **Echolocation** is the process of locating objects by emitting sounds and interpreting the sound waves that are reflected back. Look at **Figure 19** to learn how echolocation works.

Section 4 Resource Manager

Chapter *Fast File* Resources

Transparency Activity, p. 47
Directed Reading for Content Mastery, pp. 19, 20
Enrichment, p. 32
Reinforcement, p. 28
Lab Worksheet, pp. 7–8

Cultural Diversity, p. 51
Mathematics Skill Activities, p. 9
Reading and Writing Skill Activities, p. 7

1 Motivate

Bellringer

Section Focus Transparencies also are available on the Interactive Chalkboard CD-ROM. L2 ELL

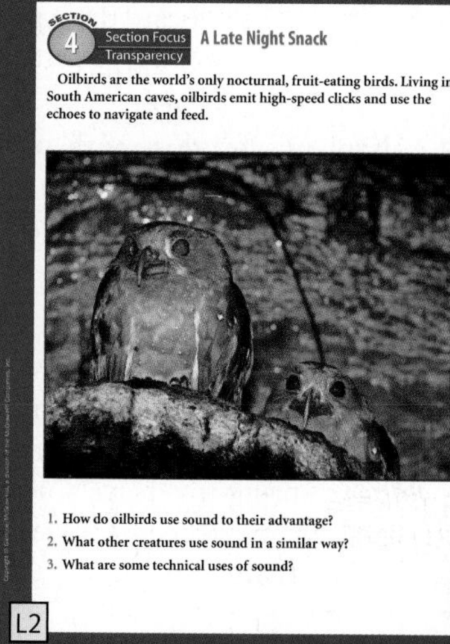
4 Section Focus Transparency **A Late Night Snack**

Oilbirds are the world's only nocturnal, fruit-eating birds. Living in South American caves, oilbirds emit high-speed clicks and use the echoes to navigate and feed.

1. How do oilbirds use sound to their advantage?
2. What other creatures use sound in a similar way?
3. What are some technical uses of sound?

L2

Tie to Prior Knowledge

Echolocation Ask students if they have ever used sounds to figure out where they were. Tell them that in this lesson they will learn how animals use sound to determine location.

Caption Answer

Figure 18 Draperies are soft materials that absorb sound waves instead of reflecting them.

NATIONAL GEOGRAPHIC

Visualizing Bat Echolocation

Have students examine the pictures and read the captions. Then ask the following questions.

What type of wave is the bat emitting, transverse or longitudinal? longitudinal waves

What is the medium in which this wave is traveling? air

How do bats locate their prey? by sensing the wave that is reflected off of the prey

Explain why this moth would be an easy prey to locate. This moth has a large surface area that will reflect the ultrasonic waves.

Activity

Have pairs of students simulate the compression wave of the bat using a spring toy. Have students watch for the reflected wave. L2 LS **Kinesthetic**

Figure 19

Many bats emit ultrasonic—very high-frequency—sounds. The sound waves bounce off objects, and bats locate prey by using the returning echoes. Known as echolocation, this technique is also used by dolphins, which produce clicking sounds as they hunt. The diagrams below show how a bat uses echolocation to capture a flying insect.

A Sound waves from a bat's ultrasonic cries spread out in front of it.

B Some of the waves strike a moth and bounce back to the bat.

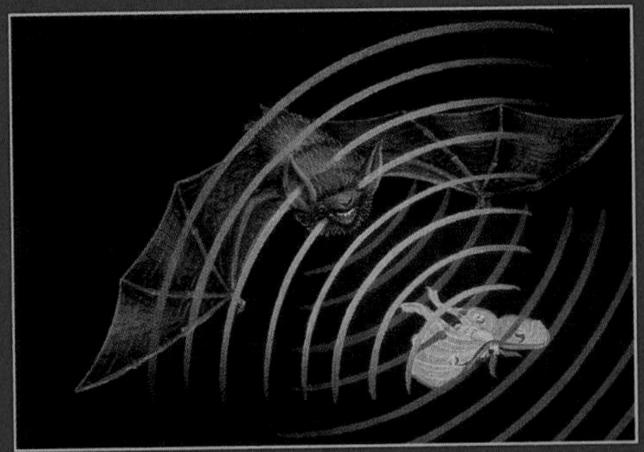

C The bat determines the moth's location by continuing to emit cries, then changes its course to catch the moth.

D By emitting a continuous stream of ultrasonic cries, the bat homes in on the moth and captures its prey.

Differentiated Instruction

Challenge Echolocation is very similar to sonar and radar. Have students research these methods that are used by humans to locate objects. Students should prepare posters outlining how these methods work and present their posters to the class. L3 LS **Visual-Spatial** P

Sonar

More than 140 years ago, a ship named the *Central America* disappeared in a hurricane off the coast of South Carolina. In its hold lay 21 tons of newly minted gold coins and bars that would be worth $1 billion or more in today's market. When the shipwreck occurred, there was no way to search for the ship in the deep water where it sank. The *Central America* and its treasures lay at the bottom of the ocean until 1988, when crews used sonar to locate the wreck under 2,400 m of water. **Sonar** is a system that uses the reflection of underwater sound waves to detect objects. First, a sound pulse is emitted toward the bottom of the ocean. The sound travels through the water and is reflected when it hits something solid, as shown in **Figure 20.** A sensitive underwater microphone called a hydrophone picks up the reflected signal. Because the speed of sound in water is known, the distance to the object can be calculated by measuring how much time passes between emitting the sound pulse and receiving the reflected signal.

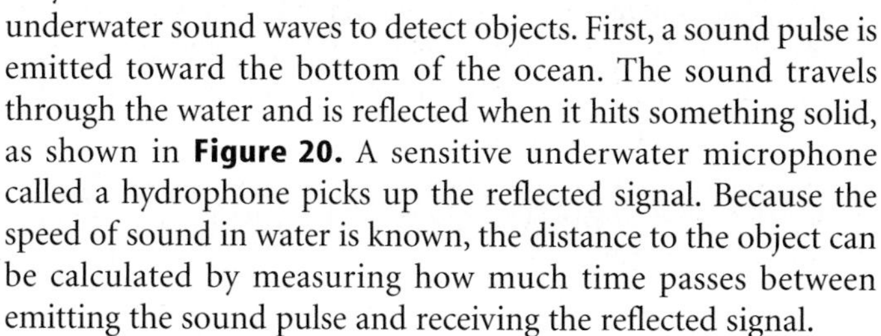

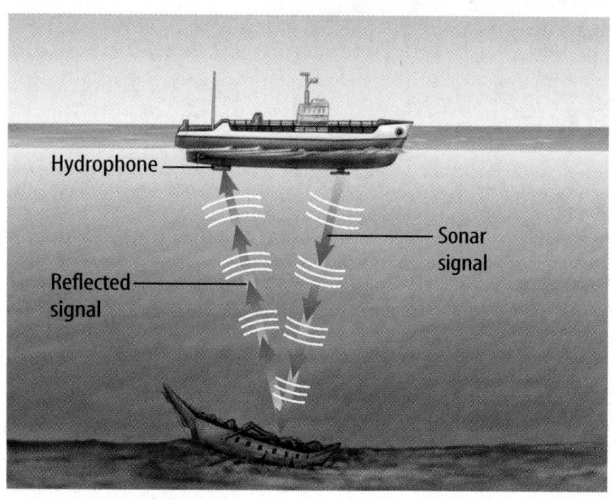

Figure 20 Sonar uses sound waves to find objects that are underwater.
Describe *how sonar is like echolocation.*

Reading Check *How does sonar detect underwater objects?*

The idea of using sonar to detect underwater objects was first suggested as a way of avoiding icebergs, but many other uses have been developed for it. Navy ships use sonar for detecting, identifying, and locating submarines. Fishing crews also use sonar to find schools of fish, and scientists use it to map the ocean floor. More detail can be revealed by using sound waves of high frequency. As a result, most sonar systems use ultrasonic frequencies.

Ultrasound in Medicine

High-frequency sound waves are used in more than just echolocation and sonar. Ultrasonic waves also are used to break up and remove dirt buildup from jewelry. Chemists sometimes use ultrasonic waves to clean glassware. One of the important uses of ultrasonic waves, though, is in medicine. Using special instruments, medical professionals can send ultrasonic waves into a specific part of a patient's body. Reflected ultrasonic waves are used to detect and monitor conditions such as pregnancy, certain types of heart disease, and cancer.

2 Teach

Use Science Words

Word Origin Have students find what the letters of the word *sonar* stand for and explain why this is an accurate description. Sonar stands for sound navigation and ranging. This is accurate because sonar is used to navigate and determine the distance or range to objects. L2

Caption Answer

Figure 20 Both use reflection of sound waves to detect objects.

Teacher FYI

There are three types of sonar systems. An active sonar system sends sound waves toward a target and analyzes the reflected waves. A passive sonar system doesn't emit sound waves; it simply listens for and analyzes sounds made by a target. Sonar systems can also be used for communication.

Reading Check

Answer by emitting a sound pulse and measuring the time for the pulse to travel to the object and return

Fun Fact

Ultrasounds are produced by using an electrical signal to induce vibration in a piezoelectric crystal.

Visual Learning

Figure 20 Remind students that the sound waves produced by the sonar signal and the reflected signal spread out in all directions. L2 LS **Visual-Spatial**

SECTION 4 Using Sound 341

Discussion

Ultrasound How does a patient benefit from ultrasound technology? Physicians are able to look at internal structures without having to perform exploratory surgery.

Answer Waves are reflected off of targeted organs and tissues. The reflected waves produce electrical signals that are converted by a computer into video images.

Ultrasound An ultrasound technician directs the sound waves with a hand-held transducer. The transducer emits an array of ultrasound pulses that vary with time. The density of the target determines the intensity of the pulse that is reflected back to the transducer.

Sonar Equation

National Math Standards

Correlation to Mathematics Objectives

1, 2, 9

Teaching Strategy

Follow the steps in the example problem.

Answer to Practice Problems

1. 1. 1,500 m/s

2. 5 s

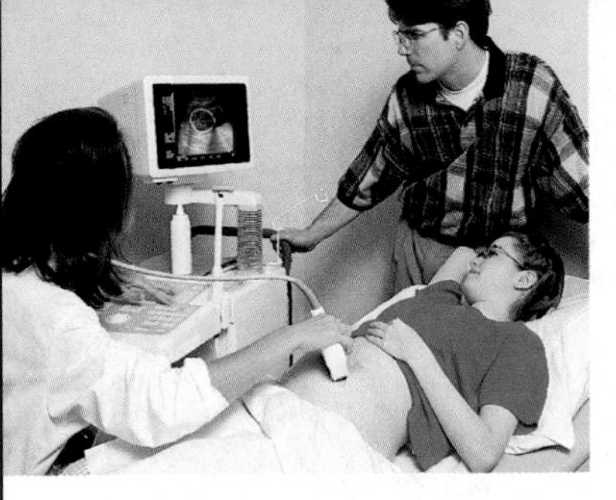

Figure 21 Ultrasonic waves are directed into a pregnant woman's uterus to form images of her fetus.

Ultrasound Imaging Like X rays, ultrasound can be used to produce images of internal structures. A medical ultrasound technician directs the ultrasound waves toward a target area of a patient's body. The sound waves reflect off the targeted organs or tissues, and the reflected waves are used to produce electrical signals. A computer program converts these electrical signals into video images, called sonograms. Physicians trained to interpret sonograms can use them to detect a variety of medical problems.

Reading Check *How does ultrasound imaging use reflected waves?*

Medical professionals use ultrasound to examine many parts of the body, including the heart, liver, gallbladder, pancreas, spleen, kidneys, breast, and eye. Ultrasound also is used to monitor the development of a fetus, as shown in **Figure 21.** However, ultrasound does not produce good images of the bones and lungs, because hard tissues and air absorb the ultrasonic waves instead of reflecting them.

Sonar Equation

Solve for depth A sonar pulse takes 3.00 s to return from a sunken ship directly below. Find the depth of the sunken ship if the speed of the pulse is 1,440 m/s. Hint: the sonar pulse travels a total distance equal to twice the depth of the sunken ship. Use the equation $d = st/2$ to find the depth, where s is the speed of the pulse and t is the time for the pulse to return.

1. **This is what you know:** speed of pulse: $s = 1{,}440$ m/s; time for pulse to return: $t = 3.00$ s
2. **This is what you need to find:** depth: d
3. **Use this formula:** $d = \frac{st}{2}$
4. **Substitute:** the values of t and s into the formula, multiply and divide by 2. $d = \frac{(1{,}440)(3.00)}{2} = 2{,}160$
5. **Determine the units:** units of d = (units of s) × (units of t) $= \frac{\text{m}}{\text{s}} \times \text{s} = \frac{\text{m}}{\text{s}} \times \text{s} = \text{m}$

Answer: The depth of the sunken ship is 2,160 m.

Science Online
For more practice problems, go to page 834, and visit gpscience.com/extra_problems.

Practice Problems

1. A wave traveling in water has a frequency of 500.0 Hz and a wavelength of 3.00 m. What is the speed of the wave?
2. **Challenge** How long will it take a sonar pulse that travels at a speed of 1,500 m/s to return from a sunken ship that is at a depth of 3,750 m?

Science Journal

Ultrasound Ask students to write in their Science Journals the answer to the following question: If ultrasound can be used to break up kidney stones, why won't it harm a developing fetus? The intensity of the sound waves is much higher when ultrasound is used to break up kidney stones.

Differentiated Instruction

Learning Disabled Go through the Applying Math feature step-by-step. Make sure the student understands the reason for each step in the problem. Watch the student perform the calculations to make sure the student is doing them correctly.

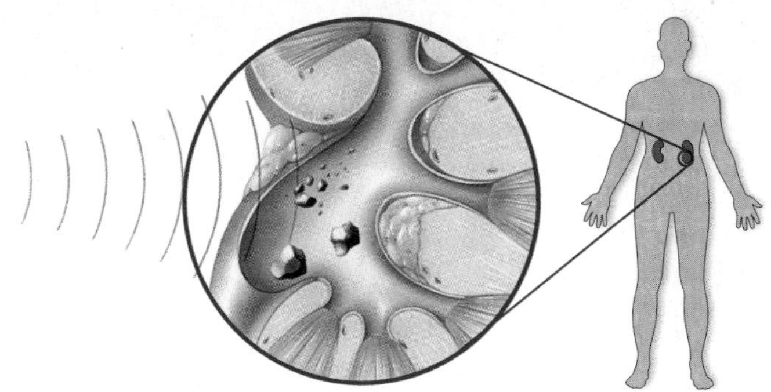

Figure 22 Ultrasonic waves can be used to break up kidney stones. **Explain** *why ultrasound therapy is beneficial for treating kidney stones.*

Treating with Ultrasound High-frequency sound waves can be used to treat certain medical problems. For example, sometimes small, hard deposits of calcium compounds or other minerals form in the kidneys, making kidney stones. In the past, physicians had to perform surgery to remove kidney stones. But now ultrasonic treatments are commonly used to break them up instead. Bursts of ultrasound create vibrations that cause the stones to break into small pieces, as shown in **Figure 22.** These fragments then pass out of the body with the urine. A similar treatment is available for gallstones. Patients who are treated successfully with ultrasound recover more quickly than those who must have surgery.

Doppler Waves Physicians can measure blood flow by studying the Doppler effect in ultrasonic waves. Brainstorm how the Doppler-shifted waves could help doctors diagnose diseases of the arteries and monitor their healing.

section 4 review

Summary

Acoustics

- Acoustics is a field in which scientists and engineers work to control the quality of sound in spaces.

Echolocation

- Bats locate objects by emitting sounds and then interpreting their reflected sound waves.

Sonar

- Humans using sonar can interpret reflected sound to locate objects underwater.

Ultrasound in Medicine

- High-frequency sound waves are useful for detecting and monitoring certain medical conditions.
- Medical ultrasound is also used to cure problems like kidney stones and gallstones.

Self Check

1. **Describe** some differences between a gym and a concert hall that might affect the amount of reverberation in each.
2. **Explain** how echolocation helps bats to find food and avoid obstacles.
3. **Explain** how sound waves can be used to find underwater objects.
4. **Describe** at least three uses of ultrasonic technology in medicine.
5. **Think Critically** How is sonar technology useful in locating deposits of oil and minerals?

Applying Math

6. **Calculate Distance** Sound travels at about 1,500 m/s in seawater. How far will a sonar pulse travel in 45 s?
7. **Calculate Time** How long will it take for an undersea sonar pulse to travel 3 km?

Science Online gpscience.com/self_check_quiz

Caption Answer

Figure 22 avoiding surgery, faster recovery time

Doppler Waves Doctors measure the Doppler effect on ultrasonic waves directed toward the arteries and calculate the rate of blood flow. If blood flow slows down somewhere, there may be problems with the arteries at that point.

3 Assess

DAILY INTERVENTION

Check for Understanding

Linguistic Have students prepare reports or have a class discussion about how concert halls or the music rooms in the school are designed or furnished to provide good acoustics.

Reteach

Ultrasound Illustrate the effect of sound waves on solids by using an ultrasonic cleaner on various substances (jewelry, loosely cemented rocks, dirty or clogged glassware).

Assessment

Process Have students examine X rays and ultrasound photos of the same body parts and then compare and contrast the films by listing what they see and identify. Ultrasounds show soft tissue structures better; X rays show bones better. Use **PASC**, p. 99.

section 4 review

1. Possible answer: The concert hall will have carpet and draperies to absorb sound and a gym will have bare floors and walls.
2. Bats emit sound pulses that bounce off prey or obstacles and return to the bat. From the echoes, the bat can determine the size and location of the object.
3. A sound pulse is emitted toward the bottom of the ocean. The sound reflects off solid objects, and the reflected signal is detected by an underwater microphone. Using the speed of sound in water, the location of the object can be determined.
4. Possible answers: producing sonograms of a developing fetus, breaking up kidney stones, breaking up gall stones
5. Sonar waves could be reflected from oil deposits. They also would travel with a different speed in oil and mineral deposits.
6. $(1{,}500 \text{ m/s}) \times (45 \text{ s}) = 67{,}500 \text{ m}$
7. $3{,}000 \text{ m} \div 1{,}500 \text{ m/s} = 2 \text{ s}$

Real-World Question

Purpose Students will test various sound barriers for effectiveness. L2 LS **Auditory-Musical**

Process Skills form a hypothesis, predict, test a hypothesis, identify and manipulate variables, collect data, interpret data

Time Required 2 weeks outside of class time

Materials Many of these barriers are not normally located around a school. Students may need to be provided with a sound meter and a meterstick or metric tape measure to perform this lab outside of class.

Safety Precautions Students should have some adult supervision when collecting their data.

Form a Hypothesis

Possible Hypothesis Most students' hypotheses will reflect that thick concrete walls or thick stone walls are the best sound barriers, and hanging laundry is the least effective.

Test Your Hypothesis

Possible Procedures Students should choose a sound that will remain constant for each sound barrier tested such as a radio or CD player at a constant volume. At the location of the sound barrier, students should record the level of the sound using the sound meter at the same distance from the source to the meter both behind the sound barrier and bypassing the sound barrier. These conditions will provide a test with only one variable.

Design Your Own

Blocking Noise Pollution

Goals
- **Design** an experiment that tests the effectiveness of various types of barriers and materials for blocking out noise pollution.
- **Test** different types of materials and barriers to determine the best noise blockers.

Possible Materials
radio, CD player, horn, drum, or other loud noise source
shrubs, trees, concrete walls, brick walls, stone walls, wooden fences, parked cars, or hanging laundry
sound meter
meterstick or metric tape measure

Real-World Question

What loud noises do you enjoy, and which ones do you find annoying? Most people enjoy a music concert performed by their favorite artist, booming displays of fireworks on the Fourth of July, and the roar of a crowd when their team scores a goal or touchdown. Although these are loud noises, most people enjoy them for short periods of time. Most people find certain loud noises, such as traffic, sirens, and loud talking, annoying. Constant, annoying noises are called noise pollution. What can be done to reduce noise pollution? What types of barriers best block out loud noises? What types of barriers will best block out noise pollution?

Form a Hypothesis

Based on your experiences with loud noises, form a hypothesis that predicts the effectiveness of different types of barriers at blocking out noise pollution.

Test Hypothesis

Make a Plan

1. **Decide** what type of barriers or materials you will test.
2. **Describe** exactly how you will use these materials.

344

Alternative Inquiry Lab

Real-World Connection Students have been asked by the school administration to test the sound levels in various parts of their school. They should make a chart of the sound levels and then consider which areas need sound barriers (e.g., in the band room, around the playground, in the cafeteria, and so forth). Have students investigate the most appropriate barriers for those areas that would fit a budget provided by the administration.

3. **Identify** the controls and variables you will use in your experiment.
4. **List** the steps you will use and describe each step precisely.
5. **Prepare** a data table in your Science Journal to record your measurements.
6. **Organize** the steps of your experiment in logical order.

Follow Your Plan

1. Ask your teacher to approve your plan and data table before you start.
2. **Conduct** your experiment as planned.
3. **Test** each barrier two or three times.
4. **Record** your test results in your data table in your Science Journal.

Analyze Your Data

1. **Identify** the barriers that most effectively reduced noise pollution.
2. **Identify** the barriers that least effectively reduced noise pollution.
3. **Compare** the effective barriers and identify common characteristics that might explain why they reduced noise pollution.
4. **Compare** the natural barriers you tested with the artificial barriers. Which type of barrier best reduced noise pollution?
5. **Compare** the different types of materials the barriers were made of. Which type of material best reduced noise pollution?

Conclude and Apply

1. **Evaluate** whether your results support your hypothesis.
2. **Predict** how your results would differ if you use a louder source of noise such as a siren.
3. **Infer** from your results how people living near a busy street could reduce noise pollution.
4. **Identify** major sources of noise pollution in or near your home. How could this be reduced?
5. **Research** how noise pollution can be unhealthy.

Communicating Your Data

Draw a poster illustrating how builders and landscapers could use certain materials to better insulate a home or office from excess noise pollution.

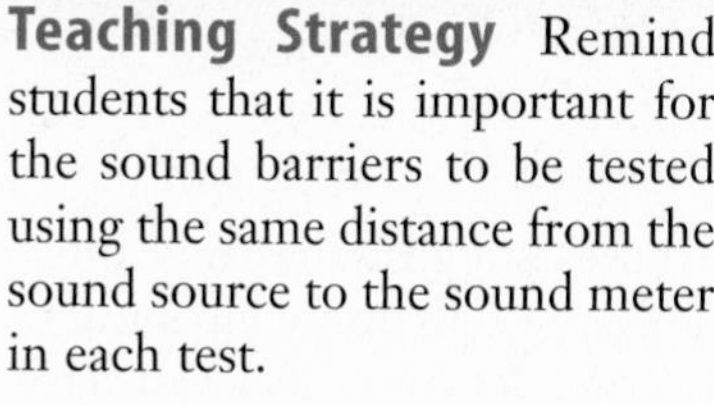

Teaching Strategy Remind students that it is important for the sound barriers to be tested using the same distance from the sound source to the sound meter in each test.

Expected Outcome Most results will show that thick concrete walls or thick stone walls are the best sound barriers.

Analyze Your Data

Answers to Questions

1. Answers may vary but may include concrete and stone walls.
2. Answers will vary but may be similar to hanging laundry.
3. The effective barriers are thick and dense structures.
4. Answers will vary.
5. Answers will vary.

Error Analysis Have students compare their results and their hypotheses and explain why differences occurred.

Conclude and Apply

1. Answers will vary.
2. The ranking of sound barriers will be the same.
3. People could build some type of sound barrier between the house and the street.
4. Answers will vary.
5. Answers should include eardrum damage.

Assessment

Process Have students write up their procedures and their results for this activity in lab reports. Suggest they include diagrams or photographs of their setups. Use **Performance Assessment in the Science Classroom,** p. 119. L2

Communicating Your Data

A gardening book from your local library will be helpful in choosing plants to use in the landscape design.

TIME

Content Background

Studies suggest that unwanted noise not only can contribute to hearing loss but also can have other adverse health effects. Unwanted sounds, even when they are not too loud, can cause stress, which can lead to digestive disorders, hypertension, abnormal sleep patterns, and a weakened immune system.

Children are at especially high risk. Reports indicate that school performance is affected when children are exposed to high noise levels. The World Health Organization advises that in order to hear and be heard in a classroom, background noise levels should not exceed 35 dB and playground noise from the environment around the playground should not exceed 55 dB.

Studies also indicate that the intensity, frequency and duration of noise have an effect on the performance of both children and adults. Noises that are unpredictable and random tend to distract people more than continuous noise. High-frequency or high-pitched noises have similar effects on concentration. Poor performances on reading tests and aural problem solving have been linked to excess noise in the classroom.

Investigate the Issue

Tell students that sounds can be classified according to various features, such as pitch, loudness, and duration. Knowing these characteristics enables people to identify harmful noises. Tell students that pitch has to do with bass and treble sounds, loudness involves volume or intensity, and duration relates to length of time.

TIME SCIENCE AND Society

SCIENCE ISSUES THAT AFFECT YOU!

Noise Pollution and Hearing Loss

Now hear this: More than 28 million Americans have hearing loss. Twelve million more people have a condition called tinnitus (TIN uh tus), or ringing in the ears. In at least 10 million of the 28 million cases mentioned above, hearing loss could have been prevented, because it was caused by noise pollution.

People take their music very seriously in the United States. And a lot of people like it loud. So loud, in fact, that it can damage their hearing. The medical term is *auditory overstimulation.* You may have experienced a high-pitched ringing in your ears for days after standing too close to a loudspeaker at a concert. That's how hearing loss starts.

Music isn't the only cause of hearing loss caused by noise pollution. Other kinds of environmental noise can be strong enough to damage the ears, too. Intense, short-duration noise, like the sound of a gunshot or even a thunderclap, can cause some hearing loss. All of the structures of the inner ear can be damaged this way.

A less intense but longer duration noise, like the sound of a lawn mower, a low-flying plane, or a drill blasting away at cement, can possibly damage the ear, as well.

All the Better to Hear You

There are 20,000 to 30,000 sensory receptors, or hair cells, located in the inner ear, or the cochlea. When vibrations reach these hair cells, electrical impulses are triggered.

The impulses send messages to the auditory center of the brain. But the human ear was not made to withstand all the very loud sounds of the modern world. Once hair cells are damaged, they don't grow back.

What can you do to avoid hearing damage? Well, the first thing is to turn the volume down on the stereo and TV. And keep the volume low when you've got your earphones on, no matter how tempting it is to blast it. Also, if you go to a rock concert, you can wear earplugs to muffle the sound. You'll still hear everything, but you won't damage your ears. And earplugs are now small enough that they're pretty much undetectable. So enjoy all that music and the street sounds of urban life, but mind your ears.

Test **Put on a blindfold and have a friend test your hearing. Have your friend choose several noise-making objects. (Not too loud, please, and make sure you have your teacher's permission.) Guess what object is making each sound.**

For more information, visit gpscience.com/time

Test Tell students to think about the three sound characteristics while they are blindfolded. Is the sound high-pitched or low pitched? Loud or soft? Long or short? Ask them whether the size of the object used to make the sound has an effect on its volume or intensity. L2

Resources for Teachers and Students

National Association of Noise Control Officials
53 Cubberly Rd.
Trenton, NJ 08690-3400
www.arcat.com

Noise Control Association
104 Cresta Verde Dr.
Rolling Hills Est., CA 90274

Reviewing Main Ideas

Section 1 The Nature of Sound

1. Sound is a compressional wave created by something that is vibrating.
2. Sound travels fastest through solids and slowest through gases. You see the flash of lightning before you hear the clap of thunder because light travels faster than sound.

3. The human ear can be divided into three sections—the outer ear, the middle ear, and the inner ear. Each section plays a specific role in hearing.
4. Hearing involves four stages: gathering sound waves, amplifying them, converting them to nerve impulses, and interpreting the signals in the brain.

Section 2 Properties of Sound

1. Intensity is a measure of how much energy a wave carries. Humans interpret the intensity of sound waves as loudness.
2. The pitch of a sound becomes higher as the frequency increases.
3. The Doppler effect is a change in frequency that occurs when a source of sound is moving relative to a listener.

Section 3 Music

1. Music is made of sounds used deliberately in a regular pattern.
2. Instruments, such as this flute, use a variety of methods to produce and amplify sound waves.
3. When sound waves of similar frequencies overlap, they interfere with each other to form beats.

Section 4 Using Sound

1. Acoustics is the study of sound. This gym is great for playing basketball, but the sound quality would be poor for a concert.
2. Sonar uses reflected sound waves to detect objects.
3. Ultrasound waves can be used for imaging body tissues or treating medical conditions.

FOLDABLES Use the Foldable that you made at the beginning of this chapter to help you review sound.

gpscience.com/interactive_tutor

Reviewing Main Ideas

Summary statements can be used by students to review the major concepts of the chapter.

Science Online

Visit gpscience.com
/self_check_quiz
/interactive_tutor
/vocabulary_puzzlemaker
/chapter_review
/standardized_test
/field_guide

Assessment Transparency

For additional assessment questions, use the *Assessment Transparency* located in the transparency book.

Assessment

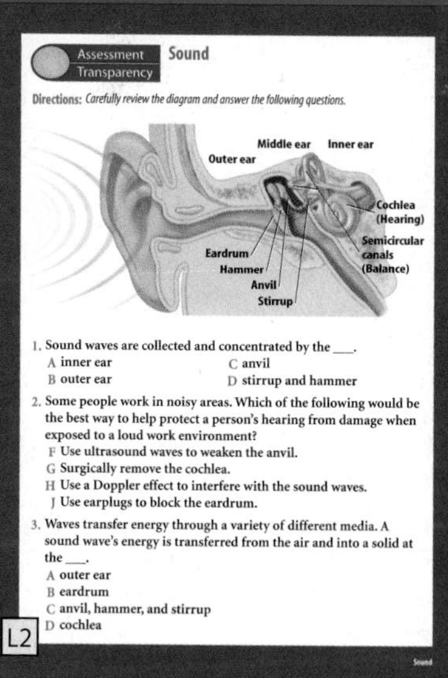

Assessment Transparency **Sound**

Directions: *Carefully review the diagram and answer the following questions.*

1. Sound waves are collected and concentrated by the ___.
   A inner ear
   B outer ear
   C anvil
   D stirrup and hammer
2. Some people work in noisy areas. Which of the following would be the best way to help protect a person's hearing from damage when exposed to a loud work environment?
   F Use ultrasound waves to weaken the anvil.
   G Surgically remove the cochlea.
   H Use a Doppler effect to interfere with the sound waves.
   J Use earplugs to block the eardrum.
3. Waves transfer energy through a variety of different media. A sound wave's energy is transferred from the air and into a solid at the ___.
   A outer ear
   B eardrum
   C anvil, hammer, and stirrup
   D cochlea

L2

Sound

FOLDABLES Have students use their Foldables to review the content of the chapter. On the back of the paper, have students write a paragraph describing why sound waves travel at different speeds through solids, liquids, and gases.

chapter 11 Review

Using Vocabulary

1. cochlea
2. acoustics
3. doppler effect
4. music
5. sound quality
6. loudness
7. decibel

Checking Concepts

8. B
9. D
10. B
11. D
12. A
13. C
14. C
15. C
16. A
17. C

Interpreting Graphics

18. See student page.
19. 14 h

chapter 11 Review

Using Vocabulary

acoustics p. 339	music p. 333
cochlea p. 326	overtone p. 334
decibel p. 329	pitch p. 330
Doppler effect p. 331	resonator p. 335
eardrum p. 325	sonar p. 341
echolocation p. 339	sound quality p. 334
intensity p. 328	ultrasonic p. 330
loudness p. 329	

Fill in the blanks with the correct vocabulary word or words.

1. The ________ is filled with fluid and contains tiny hair cells that vibrate.
2. ________ is the study of sound.
3. A change in pitch or wave frequency due to a moving wave source is called ________.
4. ________ is a combination of sounds and pitches that follows a specified pattern.
5. Differences among sounds of the same pitch and loudness are described as ________.
6. ________ is how humans perceive the intensity of sound.
7. ________ is a scale for sound intensity.

Checking Concepts

Choose the word or phrase that best answers the question.

8. For a sound with a low pitch, what else is always low?
   A) amplitude **C)** wavelength
   B) frequency **D)** wave velocity
9. Sound intensity decreases when which of the following decreases?
   A) wave velocity **C)** quality
   B) wavelength **D)** amplitude
10. When specific pitches and sounds are put together in a pattern, what are they called?
    A) overtones **C)** white noise
    B) music **D)** resonance
11. Sound can travel through all but which of the following?
    A) solids **C)** gases
    B) liquids **D)** empty space
12. What is the term for variations in the loudness of sound caused by wave interference?
    A) beats
    B) standing waves
    C) pitch
    D) forced vibrations
13. What does the outer ear do to sound waves?
    A) scatter them **C)** gather them
    B) amplify them **D)** convert them
14. Which of the following occurs when a sound source moves away from you?
    A) The sound's velocity decreases.
    B) The sound's loudness increases.
    C) The sound's frequency decreases.
    D) The sound's frequency increases.
15. Sounds with the same pitch and loudness traveling in the same medium may differ in which of these properties?
    A) frequency **C)** quality
    B) amplitude **D)** wavelength
16. What part of a musical instrument amplifies sound waves?
    A) resonator **C)** mallet
    B) string **D)** finger hole
17. What is the name of the method used to find objects that are underwater?
    A) sonogram
    B) ultrasonic bath
    C) sonar
    D) percussion

gpscience.com/vocabulary_puzzlemaker

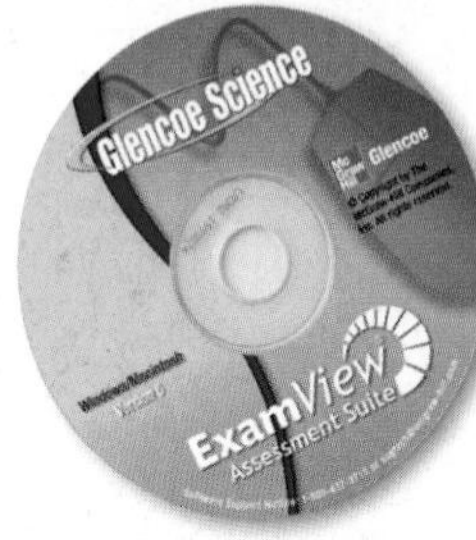

Use the *ExamView® Assessment Suite* CD-ROM to:
- create multiple versions of tests
- create modified tests with one mouse click for inclusion students
- edit existing questions and add your own questions
- build tests aligned with state standards using built-in State Curriculum Tags
- change English tests to Spanish with one mouse click and vice versa

Interpreting Graphics

18. Copy and complete the following table on musical instruments.

Characteristics of Musical Instruments			
	Guitar	Flute	Bongo Drum
How Played	plucked	blown into	struck
Role of Resonator	amplifies sound	amplifies sound	amplifies sound
Type of Instrument	string	wind	percussion

Use the table below to answer question 19.

Federally Recommended Noise Exposure Limits	
Sound Level (dB)	Time Permitted (hours per day)
90	8
95	4
100	2
105	1
110	0.5

19. You use a lawn mower with a sound level of 100 dB. Using the table above, determine the maximum number of hours a week you can safely work mowing lawns without ear protection.

Thinking Critically

20. **Infer** A car comes to a railroad crossing. The driver hears a train's whistle and its pitch becomes lower. What can be assumed about how the train is moving?

21. **Form Hypotheses** Sound travels slower in air at high altitudes than at low altitudes. Form a hypothesis to explain this.

22. **Apply** Acoustic scientists sometimes do research in rooms that absorb all sound waves. How could such a room be used to study how bats find their food?

23. **Explain** why windows might begin to rattle when an airplane flies overhead.

24. **Communicate** Some people enjoy using snowmobiles. Others object to the noise that they make. Write a proposal for a policy that seems fair to both groups for the use of snowmobiles in a state park.

Applying Math

Use the wave speed equation $v = f\lambda$ to answer questions 25–27.

25. **Calculate Frequency** A sonar pulse has a wavelength of 3.0 cm. If the pulse has a speed in water of 1,500 m/s, calculate its frequency.

26. **Calculate Wavelength** What is the wavelength of a sound wave with a frequency of 440 Hz if the speed of sound in air is 340 m/s?

27. **Calculate Wave Speed** An earthquake produces a seismic wave that has a wavelength of 650 m and a frequency of 10 Hz. How fast does the wave travel?

28. **Calculate Distance** The sound of thunder travels at a speed of 340 m/s and reaches you in 2.6 s. How far away is the storm?

29. **Calculate Time** The shipwrecked Central America was discovered lying beneath 2,400 m of water. If the speed of sound in seawater is 1,500 m/s, how long will it take a sonar pulse to travel to the shipwreck and return?

chapter 11 Review

Thinking Critically

20. The train is moving away.
21. The air is less dense and air molecules are farther apart at high altitudes, so the wave energy is not transferred as quickly.
22. Possible answer: The room would eliminate any sound reflections except those coming directly from the bat's food.
23. The windows are made to resonate by the sound waves emitted by the airplane.
24. Proposals might suggest limiting the use of snowmobiles to certain times of the day or to certain areas that are more isolated.

Applying Math

National Math Standards

1, 2, 5, 9

25. 500 Hz
26. 0.77 m
27. 6,500 m/s
28. 131 m
29. 3.2 s

Assessment Resources

Reproducible Masters

Chapter *Fast File* Resources
Chapter Review, pp. 37–38
Chapter Tests, pp. 39–42
Assessment Transparency Activity, p. 51

Glencoe Science Web site
Chapter Review Test
Standardized Test Practice

Glencoe Technology
Assessment Transparency
ExamView® Assessment Suite
MindJogger Videoquiz
Interactive Chalkboard

Answer Sheet A practice answer sheet can be found at gpscience.com/answer_sheet.

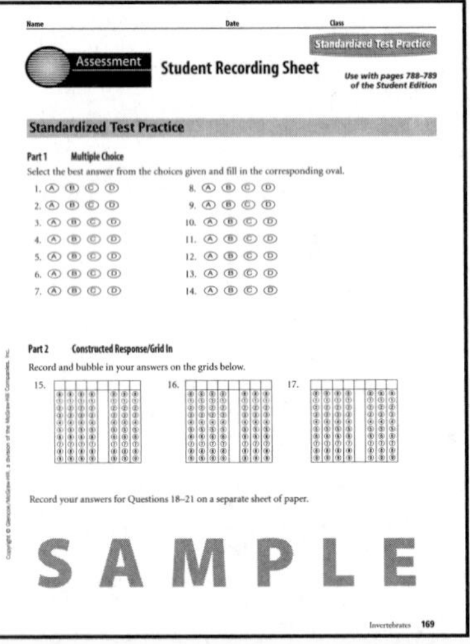

Part 1 Multiple Choice

1. A
2. D
3. B
4. D
5. D
6. D
7. B
8. C
9. A
10. D

Part 2 Short Response

11. 0.021 s
12. 0.43 s
13. 0.10 s
14. Placing your hand on the bell stops the bell from vibrating and thus stops the sound.
15. When different musical instruments play the same note, each instrument produces a different combination of frequencies.

chapter 11 Standardized Test Practice

Part 1 Multiple Choice

Record your answers on the answer sheet provided by your teacher or on a sheet of paper.

1. What does a sound's frequency determine?
A. pitch **C.** intensity
B. amplitude **D.** energy

2. Which medium does sound travel fastest through?
A. empty space **C.** gases
B. liquids **D.** solids

Use the table below to answer questions 3 and 4.

Sound	Loudness (dB)
Jet taking off	150
Pain threshold	120
Chain saw	115
Power mower	110
Vacuum cleaner	75
Average home	50
Purring cat	25

3. Which of the following would sound the loudest?
A. vacuum cleaner
B. chain saw
C. power mower
D. purring cat

4. Which of the following statements is true about a sound of 65 decibels?
A. It causes intense pain.
B. It can cause permanent hearing loss.
C. It cannot be heard by anyone.
D. It can be heard without discomfort or damage.

5. To which group of instruments does a clarinet belong?
A. electronic **C.** stringed
B. percussion **D.** wind

6. Which of the following will lower the pitch of the sound made by a guitar string?
A. shortening the vibrating string
B. tightening the string
C. plucking the string harder
D. loosening the string

Use the illustration below to answer questions 7 and 8.

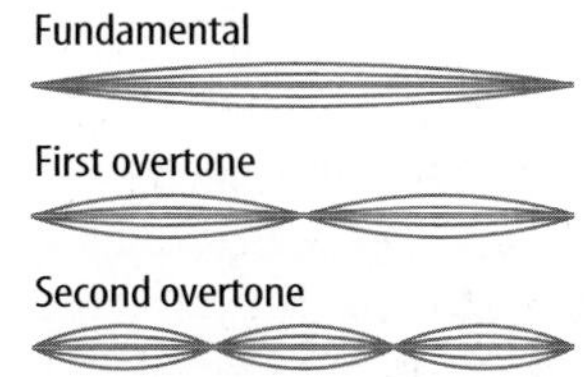

7. If the fundamental frequency of a guitar string is 262 Hz, what is the frequency of the first overtone?
A. 262 Hz **C.** 786 Hz
B. 524 Hz **D.** 1048 Hz

8. What is the frequency of the second overtone if the fundamental frequency is 294 Hz?
A. 294 Hz **C.** 882 Hz
B. 588 Hz **D.** 1176 Hz

9. If you were on a moving train, what would happen to the pitch of the bell at a crossing as you approached and then passed by the crossing?
A. pitch would increase and then decrease
B. pitch would remain the same
C. pitch would decrease and then increase
D. pitch would keep decreasing

10. On what does a guitar string's natural frequency depend?
A. thickness **C.** length
B. tightness **D.** all of these

Part 3 Open Ended

16. The noise level is above that of the loudest sound the ear can hear without pain. It is also above the noise level of sounds that can cause damage to hearing. The sound insulator in the ear muffs decreases the noise level near jet runways for those workers.
17. Sound waves are gathered by the outer ear and travel down the ear canal and cause the eardrum to vibrate. The vibrations are passed along through the hammer, anvil, and stirrup to the oval window in the inner ear. The fluid in the inner ear passes along vibrations to tiny hair cells in the cochlea which send nerve impulses along the auditory nerve to the brain.
18. Sounds waves traveling through the outer ear would be slower, since they are traveling through air. In the inner ear, the vibrations are traveling through a liquid and

Part 2 Short Response/Grid In

Record your answers on the answer sheet provided by your teacher or on a sheet of paper.

Use the table below to answer questions 11–13.

Medium	Speed of Sound (m/s)
Air	347
Water	1,498
Iron	5,103

11. A "fishfinder" sends out a pulse of ultrasound and measures the time needed for the sound to travel to a school of fish and back to the boat. If the fish are 16 m below the surface, how long would it take sound to make the round trip in the water?

12. Suppose you are sitting in the bleachers at a baseball game 150 m from home plate. How long after the batter hits the ball do you hear the "crack" of the ball and bat?

13. Suppose a friend is 500 m away along a railroad track while you have your ear to the track. He drops a stone on the tracks. How long will the sound take to reach your ear?

14. Explain why placing your hand on a bell that has just been rung will stop the sound immediately.

15. Why do different musical instruments have different sound qualities?

Test-Taking Tip

Make Sure the Units Match Read carefully and make note of the units used in any measurement.

Question 11 Compare the units given in the table with those in the problem. If the units do not match, you will have to do unit conversions.

Part 3 Open Ended

Record your answers on a sheet of paper.

16. Explain why people who work on the ground near jet runways wear big ear muffs filled with a sound insulator.

Use the illustration below to answer questions 17 and 18.

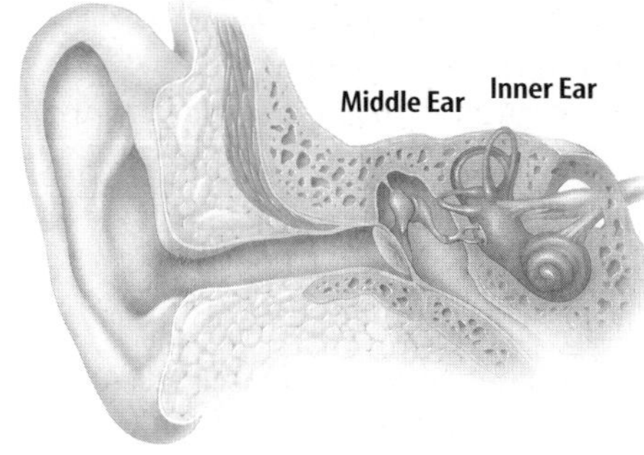

17. Describe the path of sound from the time it enters the ear until a message reaches the brain.

18. Would sound waves traveling through the outer ear travel faster or slower that those traveling through the inner ear? Explain.

19. Science-fiction movies often show battles in space where an enemy spaceship explodes with a very loud sound. Explain whether or not this scenario is accurate.

20. Compare the way a violin, a flute, and drum produce sound waves. What acts as a resonator in each instrument?

21. How can interference produce a sound with decreased loudness? How can interference produce a sound with increased loudness?

22. Imagine you have been hired by a school to reduce the amount of reverberation that occurs in the classrooms. What recommendations would you make?

sound travels faster through a liquid than through air.

19. It is not accurate. Sound waves need a medium through which to travel. Because there is no air or other medium through which sound waves could travel, explosions in space would be silent.

20. A violin produces sound by drawing a bow across tightly stretched strings to make the strings vibrate. The hollow frame of the violin and the air inside it act as a resonator. A flute produces sound when a player blows a stream of air against the edge of the flute's mouth hole. This causes the air inside the flute to vibrate. The metal tube containing the air is the resonator. A drum produces sound when the head is struck and vibrates. The body of the drum and the air inside it are the resonator.

21. If the rarefactions from one source overlap the compressions from another source, the loudness decreases. If the compressions and the rarefactions from both sources overlap, the loudness increases.

22. Some possible recommendations include installing carpeting, drapes, and rough-textured ceiling tiles.

Rubrics

For more help evaluating open-ended assessment questions, see the rubric on p. 10T.

Electromagnetic Waves

BIG Idea Electromagnetic waves can transfer energy through matter and space.

	Content Standards	Learning Objectives	Resources to Assess Mastery
Section 1	**5–8:** UCP.1–3, 5; A.1, 2; B.1–3; G.3 **9–12:** UCP.1–3, 5; A.1, 2; B.2, 4, 6; G.3	**What are electromagnetic waves?** **1. Describe** how electric and magnetic fields form electromagnetic waves. **2. Explain** how vibrating charges produce electromagnetic waves. **3. Describe** properties of electromagnetic waves. ***Main Idea*** Electromagnetic waves are transverse waves that can be produced by vibrating electric charges.	Formative Assessment Reading Check, pp. 356, 358 Section Review, p. 359 Summative Assessment *ExamView® Assessment Suite*
Section 2	**5–8:** UCP.1–3, 5; A.1, 2; B.1–3; D.1 **9–12:** UCP.1–3, 5; A.1, 2; B.2, 4, 6; D.1	**The Electromagnetic Spectrum** **4. Describe** the waves in the different regions of the electromagnetic spectrum. **5. Compare** the properties of different electromagnetic waves. **6. Identify** uses for different types of electromagnetic waves. ***Main Idea*** Each type of electromagnetic wave has a certain range of frequencies and wavelengths.	Formative Assessment Reading Check, pp. 361, 364 Section Review, p. 365 Summative Assessment *ExamView® Assessment Suite*
Section 3	**5–8:** UCP.1–3, 5; A.1, 2; B.1–3; G.3 **9–12:** UCP.1–3, 5; A.1, 2; B.2, 4, 6; G.3 See pp. 16T–17T for a Key to Standards.	**Radio Communication** **7. Explain** how modulating carrier waves enables information to be transmitted by radio waves. **8. Distinguish** between amplitude modulation and frequency modulation. **9. Identify** various ways of communicating using radio waves. ***Main Idea*** Signals and information can be transmitted using radio waves.	Formative Assessment Reading Check, pp. 370, 371 Section Review, p. 373 Summative Chapter Assessment MindJogger, Ch. 12 *ExamView® Assessment Suite* Leveled Chapter Test Test A L1 Test B L2 Test C L3 Test Practice, pp. 380–381

Suggested Pacing				
Period	**Instruction**	**Labs**	**Review & Assessment**	**Total**
Single	3.5 days	3.5 days	2 days	9 days
Block	1.75 blocks	1.75 blocks	1 block	4.5 blocks

Core Instruction	Leveled Resources	Leveled Labs	Pacing: Period		Pacing: Block
Student Text, pp. 352–359 Section Focus Transparency, Ch. 12, Section 1 Interactive Chalkboard, Ch. 12, Section 1 Identifying Misconceptions, p. 355 Differentiated Instruction, pp. 355, 358, 359 Applying Math, p. 357	**Chapter *Fast File* Resources** Directed Reading for Content Mastery, p. 20 L1 Note-taking Worksheet, pp. 33–35 Reinforcement, p. 27 L2 Enrichment, p. 30 L3 **Reading Essentials,** p. 194 L1 ELL **Science Notebook,** p. 131 ELL	**Launch Lab,** p. 353: construction paper (red) *15 min* L2 **MiniLAB,** p. 356: TV with remote control, glass, book, paper, metal pan *15 min* L2	**1**	Section 1, pp. 353–356 (includes Launch Lab)	**1**
			2	Section 1, pp. 356–359 (includes MiniLAB and Section Review)	
Student Text, pp. 360–366 Section Focus Transparency, Ch. 12, Section 2 Teaching Transparency, Ch. 12, Section 2 Interactive Chalkboard, Ch. 12, Section 2 Differentiated Instruction, pp. 361, 362	**Chapter *Fast File* Resources** Directed Reading for Content Mastery, p. 21 L1 Note-taking Worksheet, pp. 33–35 Reinforcement, p. 28 L2 Enrichment, p. 31 L3 **Reading Essentials,** p. 200 L1 ELL **Science Notebook,** p. 135 ELL	**MiniLAB,** p. 361: microwave oven, small beakers or baby food jars (2), dry sand, water, thermometer *15 min* L2 ***Lab,** p. 366: flashlight, several books, aluminum foil, small bowl *30 min* L1 L2 L3 (Video Lab)	**3**	Section 2, pp. 360–362 (includes MiniLAB)	**2**
			4	Section 2, pp. 363–365 (includes Section Review)	
			5	Lab: The Shape of Satellite Dishes, p. 366	**3**
Student Text, pp. 367–375 Section Focus Transparency, Ch. 12, Section 3 Interactive Chalkboard, Ch. 12, Section 3 Visualizing Radio Broadcasts, p. 369 Identifying Misconceptions, p. 368 Differentiated Instruction, pp. 368, 369 Chapter Study Guide, p. 377	**Chapter *Fast File* Resources** Directed Reading for Content Mastery, pp. 21, 22 L1 Note-taking Worksheet, pp. 33–35 Reinforcement, p. 29 L2 Enrichment, p. 32 L3 **Reading Essentials,** p. 206 L1 ELL **Science Notebook,** p. 138 ELL	***Lab,** pp. 274–275: Internet access *90 min* L1 L2 L3 *Lab version A L1 version B L2 L3	**6**	Section 4, pp. 367–373 (includes Section Review)	
			7	Lab: Radio Frequencies, pp. 274–275	**4**
			8	Lab: Radio Frequencies, pp. 274–275	
			9	Study Guide, Chapter Review, and Test Practice, pp. 377–381	**4.5**

(Video Lab icon) Video Lab

Transparencies

Section Focus

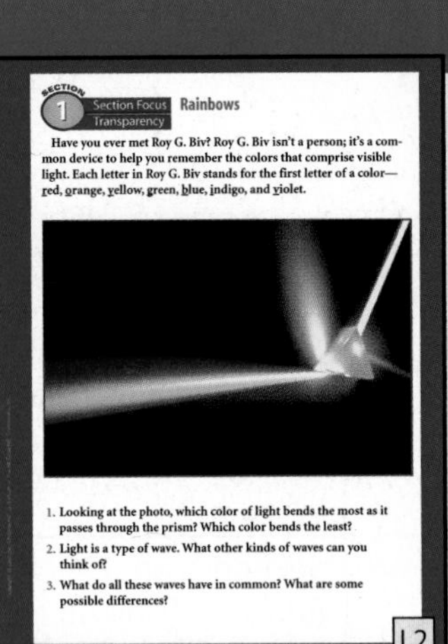

Section 1 Section Focus Transparency **Rainbows**

Have you ever met Roy G. Biv? Roy G. Biv isn't a person; it's a common device to help you remember the colors that comprise visible light. Each letter in Roy G. Biv stands for the first letter of a color—red, orange, yellow, green, blue, indigo, and violet.

1. Looking at the photo, which color of light bends the most as it passes through the prism? Which color bends the least?
2. Light is a type of wave. What other kinds of waves can you think of?
3. What do all these waves have in common? What are some possible differences?

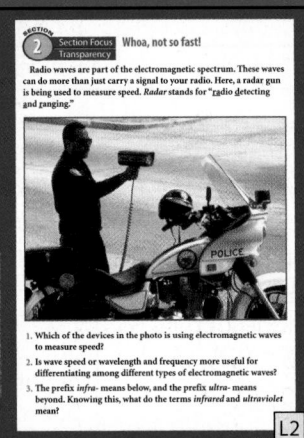

L2

Section 2 Section Focus Transparency **Whoa, not so fast!**

Radio waves are part of the electromagnetic spectrum. These waves can do more than just carry a signal to your radio. Here, a radar gun is being used to measure speed. *Radar* stands for "radio detecting and ranging."

1. Which of the devices in the photo is using electromagnetic waves to measure speed?
2. Is wave speed or wavelength and frequency more useful for differentiating among different types of electromagnetic waves?
3. The prefix *infra-* means below, and the prefix *ultra-* means beyond. Knowing this, what do the terms *infrared* and *ultraviolet* mean?

L2

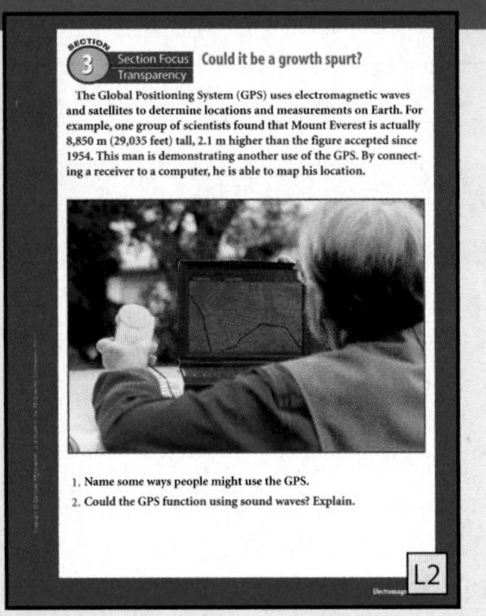

Section 3 Section Focus Transparency **Could it be a growth spurt?**

The Global Positioning System (GPS) uses electromagnetic waves and satellites to determine locations and measurements on Earth. For example, one group of scientists found that Mount Everest is actually 8,850 m (29,035 feet) tall, 2.1 m higher than the figure accepted since 1954. This man is demonstrating another use of the GPS. By connecting a receiver to a computer, he is able to map his location.

1. Name some ways people might use the GPS.
2. Could the GPS function using sound waves? Explain.

L2

This is a representation of key blackline masters available in the Teacher Classroom Resources. See Resource Manager boxes within the chapter for additional information.

Assessment

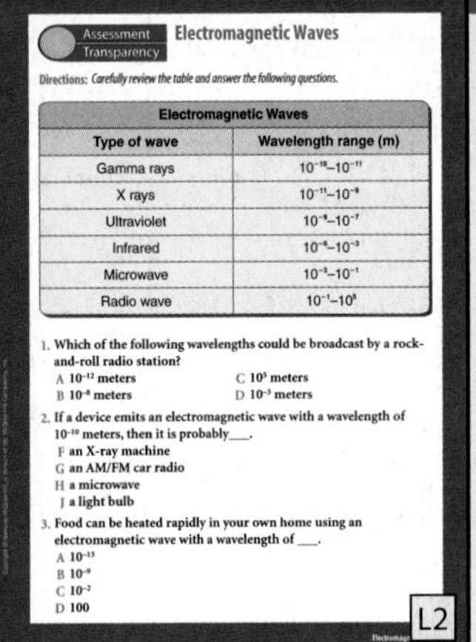

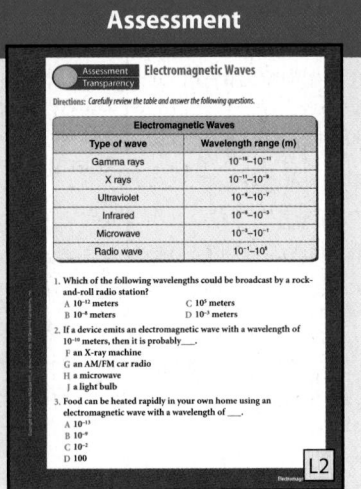

Assessment Transparency **Electromagnetic Waves**

Directions: *Carefully review the table and answer the following questions.*

Electromagnetic Waves	
Type of wave	**Wavelength range (m)**
Gamma rays	10^{-15}–10^{-11}
X rays	10^{-11}–10^{-8}
Ultraviolet	10^{-8}–10^{-7}
Infrared	10^{-6}–10^{-3}
Microwave	10^{-3}–10^{-1}
Radio wave	10^{-1}–10^{5}

1. Which of the following wavelengths could be broadcast by a rock-and-roll radio station?
   A 10^{-12} meters
   B 10^{-8} meters
   C 10^{5} meters
   D 10^{-3} meters
2. If a device emits an electromagnetic wave with a wavelength of 10^{-10} meters, then it is probably____.
   F an X-ray machine
   G an AM/FM car radio
   H a microwave
   J a light bulb
3. Food can be heated rapidly in your own home using an electromagnetic wave with a wavelength of ____.
   A 10^{-13}
   B 10^{-9}
   C 10^{-2}
   D 100

L2

Teaching

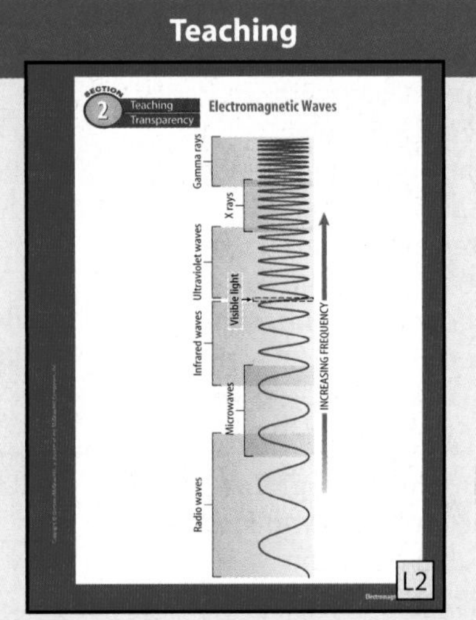

Section 2 Teaching Transparency **Electromagnetic Waves**

Key to Teaching Strategies

The following designations will help you decide which activities are appropriate for your students.

L1 Level 1 activities should be appropriate for students with learning difficulties.

L2 Level 2 activities should be within the ability range of all students.

L3 Level 3 activities are designed for above-average students.

ELL ELL activities should be within the ability range of English Language Learners.

COOP LEARN Cooperative Learning activities are designed for small group work.

LS Multiple Learning Styles logos, as described on page 12T, are used throughout to indicate strategies that address different learning styles.

P These strategies represent student products that can be placed into a best-work portfolio.

PBL Problem-Based Learning activities apply real-world situations to learning.

Hands-on Activities

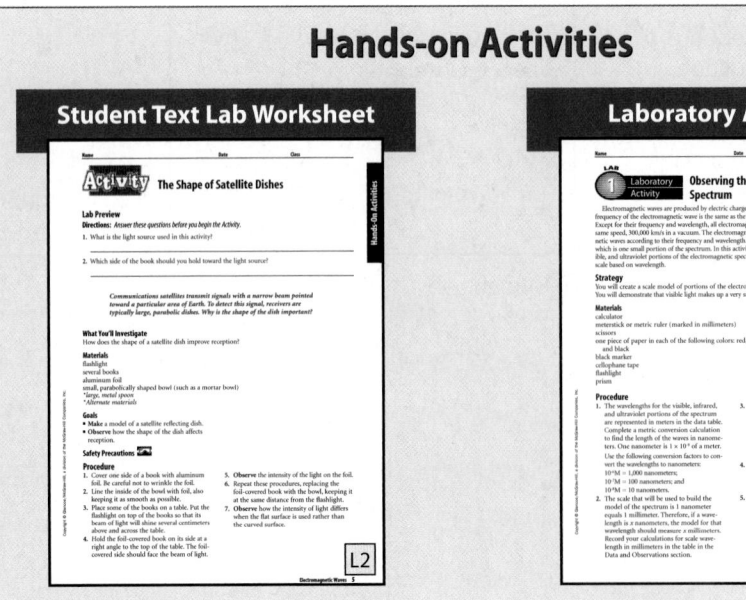

Student Text Lab Worksheet

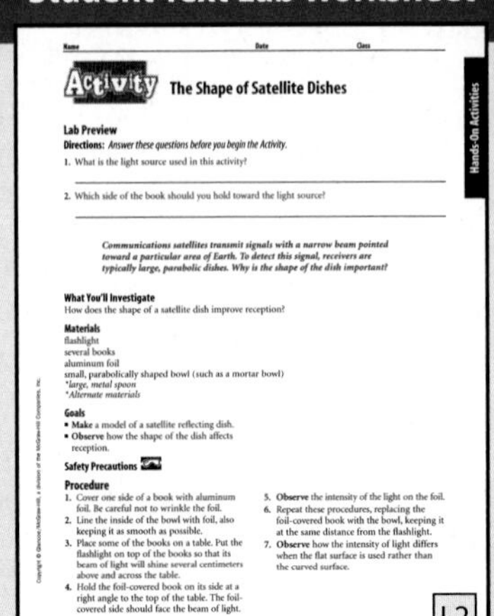

Name Date Class

Activity **The Shape of Satellite Dishes**

Hands-On Activities

Lab Preview

Directions: *Answer these questions before you begin the Activity.*

1. What is the light source used in this activity?
2. Which side of the book should you hold toward the light source?

Communications satellites transmit signals with a narrow beam pointed toward a particular area of Earth. To detect this signal, receivers are typically large, parabolic dishes. Why is the shape of the dish important?

What You'll Investigate

How does the shape of a satellite dish improve reception?

Materials

flashlight
several books
aluminum foil
small, parabolically shaped bowl (such as a mortar bowl)
**large, metal spoon*
**Alternate materials*

Goals

- **Make** a model of a satellite reflecting dish.
- **Observe** how the shape of the dish affects reception.

Safety Precautions

Procedure

1. Cover one side of a book with aluminum foil. Be careful not to wrinkle the foil.
2. Line the inside of the bowl with foil, also keeping it as smooth as possible.
3. Place some of the books on a table. Put the flashlight on top of the books so that its beam of light will shine several centimeters above and across the table.
4. Hold the foil-covered book on its side at a right angle to the top of the table. The foil-covered side should face the beam of light.
5. **Observe** the intensity of the light on the foil.
6. Repeat these procedures, replacing the foil-covered book with the bowl, keeping it at the same distance from the flashlight.
7. **Observe** how the intensity of light differs when the flat surface is used rather than the curved surface.

L2

Electromagnetic Waves 5

Laboratory Activities

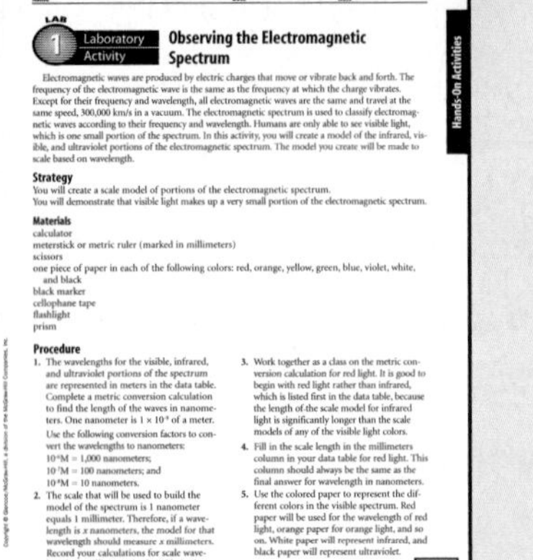

Name Date Class

LAB 1 Laboratory Activity **Observing the Electromagnetic Spectrum**

Hands-On Activities

Electromagnetic waves are produced by electric charges that move or vibrate back and forth. The frequency of the electromagnetic wave is the same as the frequency at which the charge vibrates. Except for their frequency and wavelength, all electromagnetic waves are the same and travel at the same speed, 300,000 km/s in a vacuum. The electromagnetic spectrum is used to classify electromagnetic waves according to their frequency and wavelength. Humans are only able to see visible light, which is one small portion of the spectrum. In this activity, you will create a model of the infrared, visible, and ultraviolet portions of the electromagnetic spectrum. The model you create will be made to scale based on wavelength.

Strategy

You will create a scale model of portions of the electromagnetic spectrum.
You will demonstrate that visible light makes up a very small portion of the electromagnetic spectrum.

Materials

calculator
meterstick or metric ruler (marked in millimeters)
scissors
one piece of paper in each of the following colors: red, orange, yellow, green, blue, violet, white, and black
black marker
cellophane tape
flashlight
prism

Procedure

1. The wavelengths for the visible, infrared, and ultraviolet portions of the spectrum are represented in meters in the data table. Complete a metric conversion calculation to find the length of the waves in nanometers. One nanometer is 1×10^{-9} of a meter.
   Use the following conversion factors to convert the wavelengths to nanometers:
   10^{-6}M = 1,000 nanometers;
   10^{-7}M = 100 nanometers; and
   10^{-8}M = 10 nanometers.
2. The scale that will be used to build the model of the spectrum is 1 nanometer equals 1 millimeter. Therefore, if a wavelength is *x* nanometers, the model for that wavelength should measure *x* millimeters. Record your calculations for scale wavelength in millimeters in the table in the Data and Observations section.
3. Work together as a class on the metric conversion calculation for red light. It is good to begin with red light rather than infrared, which is listed first in the data table, because the length of the scale model for infrared light is significantly longer than the scale models of any of the visible light colors.
4. Fill in the scale length in the millimeters column in your data table for red light. This column should always be the same as the final answer for wavelength in nanometers.
5. Use the colored paper to represent the different colors in the visible spectrum. Red paper will be used for the wavelength of red light, orange paper for orange light, and so on. White paper will represent infrared, and black paper will represent ultraviolet.

L2

Electromagnetic Waves 9

Resource Manager

Meeting Different Ability Levels

Content Outline

Note-taking Worksheet — Electromagnetic Waves

L2

Reinforcement

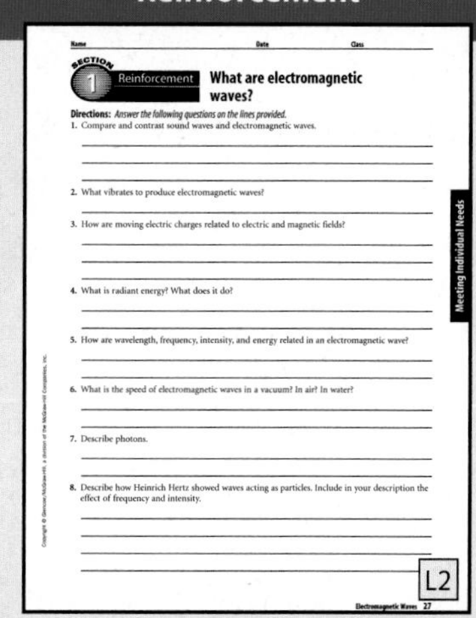
Reinforcement — What are electromagnetic waves?

L2

Enrichment

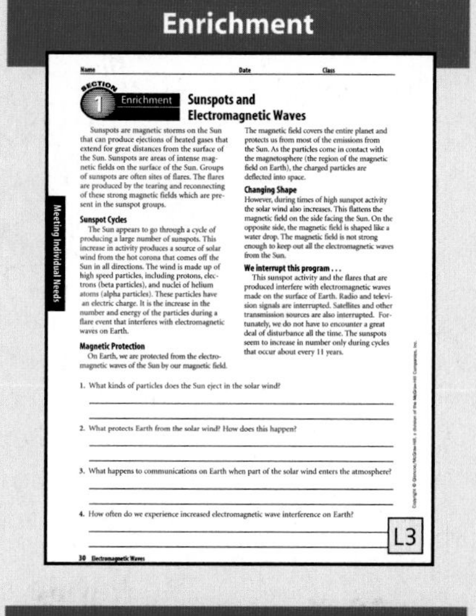
Enrichment — Sunspots and Electromagnetic Waves

L3

Directed Reading (English/Spanish)

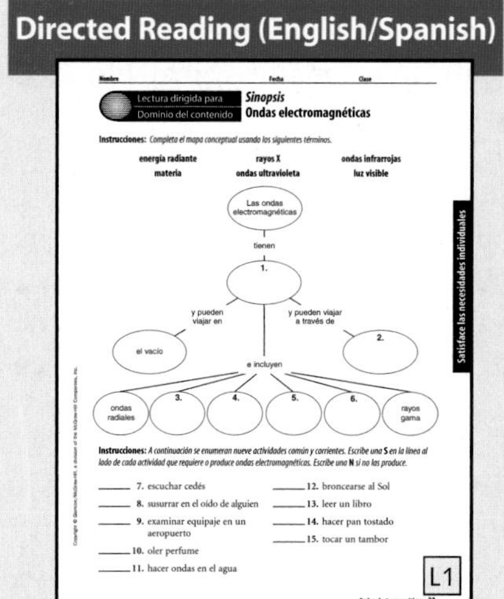
Lectura dirigida para Dominio del contenido — Sinopsis — Ondas electromagnéticas

L1

Study Guide

Study Guide
Features
• Contains a study guide page for each section of the chapter
• Reviews key concepts
• Includes answer pages

L2

Reading Essentials

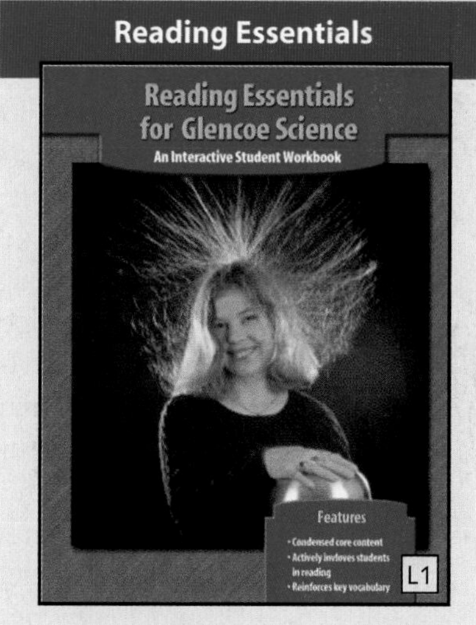
Reading Essentials for Glencoe Science
An Interactive Student Workbook
Features
• Condensed core content
• Actively involves students in reading
• Reinforces key vocabulary

L1

Assessment

Test Practice Workbook

Chapter Test — Chapter 13 Electromagnetic Waves

L2

Chapter Review

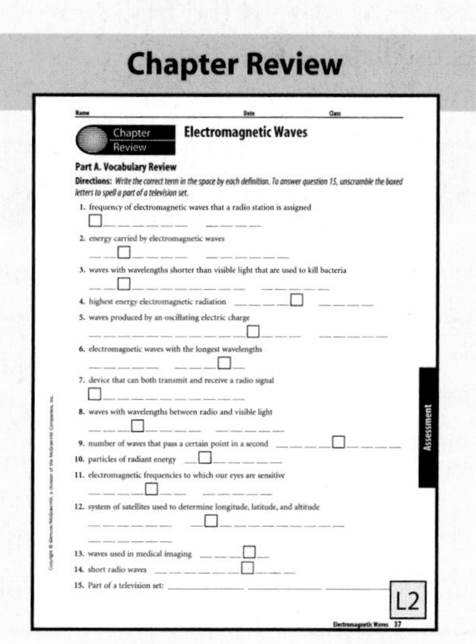
Chapter Review — Electromagnetic Waves

L2

Chapter Tests

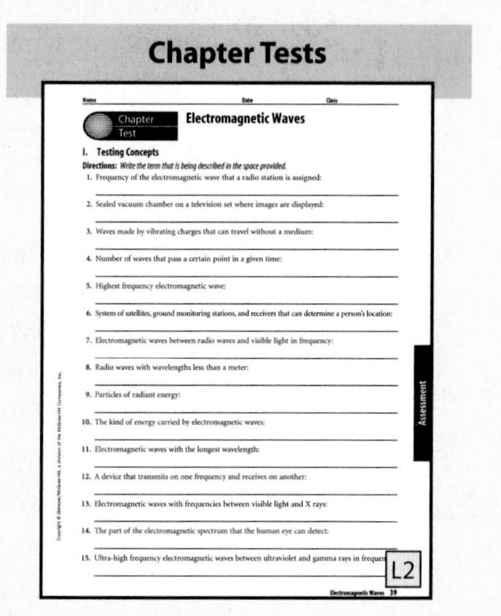
Chapter Test — Electromagnetic Waves

L2

Science Content Background

section 1 What are electromagnetic waves?

Waves in Space

Throughout history, people have learned about the universe from the visible light that reached their eyes. For the past 100 years, people have been able to detect other types of electromagnetic radiation as well. Instruments such as radio telescopes and ultraviolet detectors have made this possible.

The Nature of Electromagnetic Waves

Electricity and magnetism are related. For example, a moving electric charge produces a magnetic field. James Clerk Maxwell in the 1860s realized that a changing electric field can produce a magnetic field. He also realized that because changing electric and magnetic fields can create each other, an electromagnetic wave that consisted only of oscillating electric and magnetic fields could exist.

An electromagnetic wave can be produced by an electric charge that is moving back and forth. The oscillating charge produces a changing electric field. The changing electric field produces a changing magnetic field, which produces a changing electric field and so on. In this way, the electric and magnetic fields oscillate in time and induce each other.

The two fields oscillate perpendicular to each other and perpendicular to the direction the wave is traveling. The frequency of the wave is the frequency at which the fields oscillate.

section 2 The Electromagnetic Spectrum

Infrared Waves

All objects emit electromagnetic waves. The warmer an object is, the more radiation it emits. Infrared waves are emitted by heat lamps at fast-food restaurants to keep food warm. Remote control devices use infrared waves to send signals that control TVs, VCRs and stereo equipment.

Snakes in the pit viper family, which includes rattlesnakes, have "pits" in their heads that allow them to detect infrared radiation. They use this ability when hunting small, warm-blooded mammals in dark tunnels.

Ultraviolet Waves

Skin cells contain melanocytes, which form the pigment melanin when exposed to UV rays. Melanin causes people to tan, and it blocks some UV radiation. Some insects, such as bees, can see UV radiation.

X Rays and Gamma Rays

Radiation detectors use the tendency of X rays and gamma rays to ionize atoms as a means for detection. Workers who may be exposed to these types of radiation often wear radiation badges. The badges are periodically developed to determine the total amount of radiation the worker has been exposed to.

chapter content resources

Internet Resources

For additional content background, visit **gpscience.com** to:

- access your book online
- find references to related articles in popular science magazines
- access Web links with related content background
- access current events with science journal topics

Print Resources

Waves: The Electromagnetic Universe, by Gloria Skurzynski, National Geographic Society, 1996

The Visual Dictionary of Physics, Eyewitness Visual Dictionaries, Dorling Kindersley, 1995

Understanding Science—Atoms and Molecules, by Phil Roxbee and Max Parsonage, Usborne Publishing, 1992

section 3 Radio Communication

Radio Transmission

Although Guglielmo Marconi was given credit for inventing radio, much of the credit should be given to Nikola Tesla. Tesla invented the means to turn electrical energy into radio waves.

Antennas are made of materials that are good conductors of electricity, so they allow easy movement of electrons. Electrons accelerating up and down a vertical antenna produce radio waves. If an antenna is aligned vertically, incoming radio waves cause the electrons to accelerate up and down the antenna. For a 1.5 million Hz AM radio wave, the electrons move up and down 1.5 million times per second.

AM radio has a relatively small frequency range of 1.165 MHz, and FM has a range of 20 MHz. The AM band is fine for voices, but the FM band is better for listening to music because it produces a richer sound.

On some nights you can pick up AM stations several hundred miles from where they are broadcast. This is because AM radio waves reflect off the ionosphere. FM radio waves are not reflected by the ionosphere and need to travel in a straight line to reach a receiver. This limits their range.

Teacher to Teacher

Dr. Judith Doyle, Retired Teacher
Newark High School
Newark, Ohio

"To demonstrate how microwaves impact water molecules, place a marshmallow on a paper plate into a microwave and cook for two minutes at 50%-60% power. The marshmallow will expand rapidly, deflate slightly during off cycles, and then inflate more each time power resumes. (Microwaves vary, so test different power levels beforehand to determine best visual effect.) Microwaves cause the water molecules in the marshmallow to flip billions of times per second which in turn causes them to bump into each other and warm up, so as the marshmallow warms up, it expands."

Dr. Judith Doyle

Image Credit

chapter 12

About the Photo

The VLA These receiver dishes are part of the Very Large Array (VLA) radio telescope, located near Socorro, New Mexico. The 27 separate receivers together gather radio waves emitted by stars, galaxies, and other deep-space objects. Images are formed from the data that show details of the radio wave emission from the objects being studied.

Science Journal Student responses will vary, but may include: TV, tanning beds, stove, lightbulbs, toaster.

BIG Idea

Energy and Frequency Electromagnetic (EM) waves have a dual nature. In some situations, EM waves can behave like a beam of massless particles, called photons. Each photon has an energy that is proportional to the wave's frequency. Then the energy carried by a beam of EM waves is the number of photons in the beam times the energy per photon. To say, for example, that X rays carry more energy than infrared waves means that X-ray photons have more energy than infrared photons. However, it doesn't mean that all X-ray beams are more energetic than all infrared beams.

Introduce the Chapter Obtain a small, portable transistor radio. Tell students that the radio receives radio waves traveling through the air and converts them to sound waves. Wrap the radio in different materials, such as foil, paper, plastic wrap, and cloth, and compare the differences in reception. Ask students which materials are transparent to radio waves. Then ask students which materials are transparent to light waves.

chapter 12

Electromagnetic Waves

BIG Idea Electromagnetic waves can transfer energy through matter and space.

12.1 What are electromagnetic waves?

MAIN Idea Electromagnetic waves are transverse waves that can be produced by vibrating electric charges.

12.2 The Electromagnetic Spectrum

MAIN Idea Each type of electromagnetic wave has a certain range of frequencies and wavelengths.

12.3 Radio Communication

MAIN Idea Signals and information can be transmitted using radio waves.

How's the reception?

These giant 25-m dishes aren't picking up TV signals. Instead, they are part of a group of 27 antennas that detect radio waves coming from distant stars and galaxies. Radio waves, like microwaves and light waves, are electromagnetic waves. All objects, including you, emit electromagnetic waves.

Science Journal List six objects around you that emit light or feel warm.

352

Interactive Chalkboard

This CD-ROM is an editable Microsoft® PowerPoint® presentation that includes:
- an editable presentation for every chapter
- additional chapter questions
- animated graphics
- image bank
- links to gpscience.com

Start-Up Activities

Can electromagnetic waves change materials?

You often hear about the danger of the Sun's ultraviolet rays, which can damage the cells of your skin. When the exposure isn't too great, your cells can repair themselves, but too much at one time can cause a painful sunburn. Repeated overexposure to the Sun over many years can damage cells and cause skin cancer. In the lab below, observe how energy carried by ultraviolet waves can cause changes in other materials.

1. Cut a sheet of red construction paper in half.
2. Place one piece outside in direct sunlight. Place the other in a shaded location.
3. Keep the construction paper in full sunlight for at least 45 min. If possible, allow it to stay there for 3 h or more before taking it down. Be sure the other piece remains in the shade.
4. **Think Critically** In your Science Journal, describe any differences you notice in the two pieces of construction paper. Comment on your results.

Electromagnetic Waves Make the following Foldable to help you understand electromagnetic waves.

STEP 1 **Fold** a vertical sheet of paper in half from top to bottom.

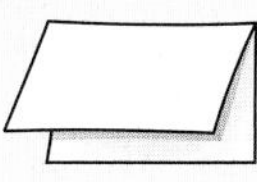

STEP 2 **Fold** in half from side to side with the fold at the top.

STEP 3 **Unfold** the paper once. **Cut** only the fold of the top flap to make two tabs.

STEP 3 **Write** on the front tabs as shown.

How do electromagnetic waves travel through space?

How do electromagnetic waves transfer energy to matter?

Identify Questions As you read the chapter, write answers to the questions on the back of the appropriate tabs.

Preview this chapter's content and activities at gpscience.com

353

Additional Chapter Media

- Virtual Lab: *What is the electromagnetic spectrum?*
- Video Lab: *The Shape of Satellite Dishes*

Purpose Students observe how electromagnetic waves from the Sun affect the dye in colored paper. L1 ELL IS **Visual-Spatial**

Materials Although any color of construction paper will work for this activity, red will show the most dramatic results. Be sure to use construction paper that has not previously been exposed to sunlight.

Teaching Strategies

- Construction paper that is exposed to sunlight through a window will fade much slower than construction paper in direct sunlight. The glass blocks much of the ultraviolet light.
- The construction paper should be exposed to sunlight for as long as possible. If time permits, allow students to observe the effects after different time intervals.

Think Critically

The color of the construction paper exposed to the Sun is faded compared to that of the paper left in the shade. Ultraviolet waves from the Sun have broken down some of the dye molecules.

Assessment

Process Ask students to compare how the ultraviolet waves affected the construction paper with what happens to their skin when they stay out too long in the Sun. Use **Performance Assessment in the Science Classroom,** p. 89.

Dinah Zike Study Fold

Student preparation materials for this Foldable are available in the Chapter *Fast File* Resources.

Probeware Labs

This chapter's data-collection lab using Probeware technology is included on the *Video Labs CD-ROM*. See the *Probeware Lab Manual* pages 45–47 for student worksheets.

1 Motivate

Bellringer

Section Focus Transparencies also are available on the Interactive Chalkboard CD-ROM. L2 ELL

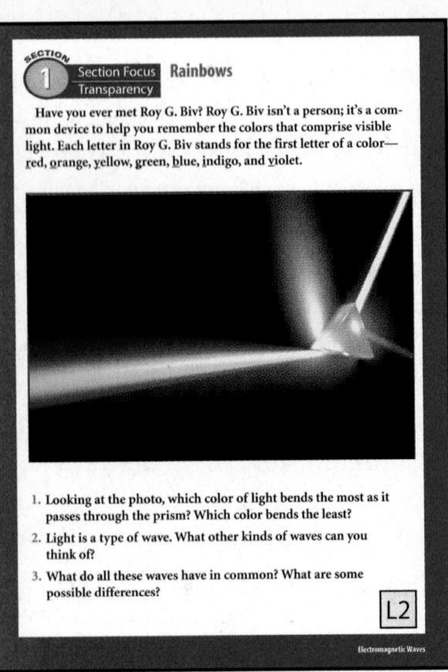

SECTION 1 Section Focus Transparency **Rainbows**

Have you ever met Roy G. Biv? Roy G. Biv isn't a person; it's a common device to help you remember the colors that comprise visible light. Each letter in Roy G. Biv stands for the first letter of a color—red, orange, yellow, green, blue, indigo, and violet.

1. **Looking at the photo, which color of light bends the most as it passes through the prism? Which color bends the least?**
2. **Light is a type of wave. What other kinds of waves can you think of?**
3. **What do all these waves have in common? What are some possible differences?**

L2

Electromagnetic Waves

Tie to Prior Knowledge

Magnets Show students how a magnet pulls on a nearby paper clip, even if they are not touching. Remind students that this is because a magnetic field surrounds the magnet. Tell students that in this section they will learn about magnetic fields and electric fields, and how vibrating electric and magnetic fields create electromagnetic waves.

section 1

What are electromagnetic waves?

Reading Guide

What **You'll Learn**

- **Describe** how electric and magnetic fields form electromagnetic waves.
- **Explain** how vibrating charges produce electromagnetic waves.
- **Describe** properties of electromagnetic waves.

Why **It's Important**

You, and all the objects and materials around you, are radiating electromagnetic waves.

Review Vocabulary

Hertz: the SI unit of frequency, abbreviated Hz; 1 Hz equals one vibration per second

New Vocabulary

- electromagnetic wave
- radiant energy
- photon

Waves in Space

Stay calm. Do not panic. As you are reading this sentence, no matter where you are, you are surrounded by electromagnetic waves. Even though you can't feel them, some of these waves are traveling right through your body. They enable you to see. They make your skin feel warm. You use electromagnetic waves when you watch television, talk on a cordless phone, or prepare popcorn in a microwave oven.

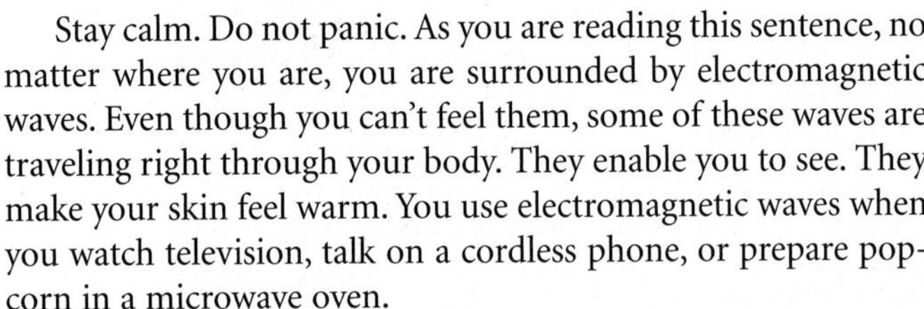

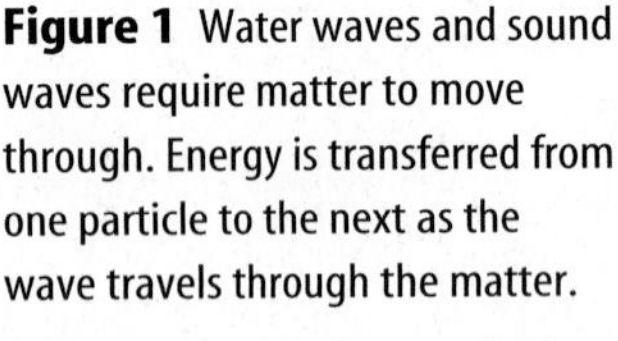

Figure 1 Water waves and sound waves require matter to move through. Energy is transferred from one particle to the next as the wave travels through the matter.

Sound and Water Waves Waves are produced by something that vibrates, and they carry energy from one place to another. Look at the sound wave and the water wave in **Figure 1.** Both waves are moving through matter. The sound wave is moving through air and the water wave through water. These waves travel because energy is transferred from particle to particle. Without matter to transfer the energy, they cannot move.

Electromagnetic Waves However, electromagnetic waves do not require matter to transfer energy. **Electromagnetic waves** are made by vibrating electric charges and can travel through space where matter is not present. Instead of transferring energy from particle to particle, electromagnetic waves travel by transferring energy between vibrating electric and magnetic fields.

Section 1 Resource Manager

Chapter *FAST FILE* Resources
Transparency Activity, p. 44
Directed Reading for Content Master, p. 20
Note-taking Worksheet, pp. 33–35
Enrichment, p. 30
MiniLAB, p. 3
Reinforcement, p. 27

Science Inquiry Labs, pp. 41–42
Performance Assessment in the Science Classroom, p. 35
Mathematics Skill Activities, p. 1

354 CHAPTER 12 Electromagnetic Waves

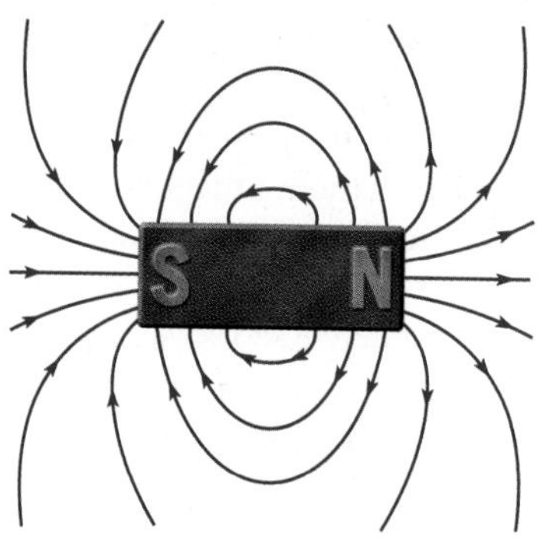

A magnetic field surrounds all magnets.

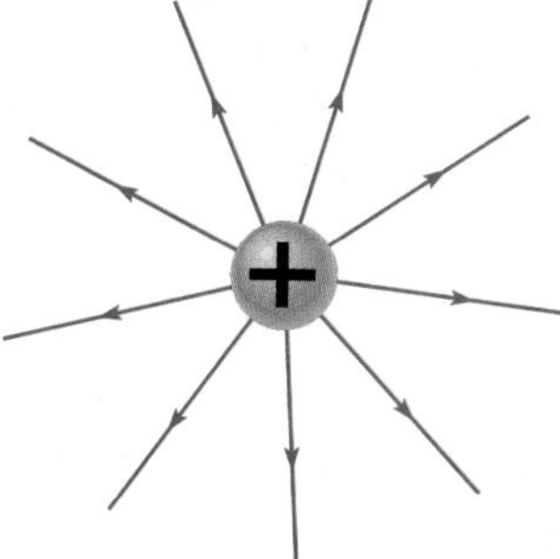

An electric field surrounds all charges.

Figure 2 Fields enable magnets and charges to exert forces at a distance. These fields extend throughout space.
Explain *how you could detect a magnetic field.*

Electric and Magnetic Fields

When you bring a magnet near a metal paper clip, the paper clip moves toward the magnet and sticks to it. The paper clip moved because the magnet exerted a force on it. The magnet exerted this force without having to touch the paper clip. The magnet exerts a force without touching the paper clip because all magnets are surrounded by a magnetic field, as shown in **Figure 2.** Magnetic fields exist around magnets even if the space around the magnet contains no matter.

Just as magnets are surrounded by magnetic fields, electric charges are surrounded by electric fields, also shown in **Figure 2.** An electric field enables charges to exert forces on each other even when they are far apart. Just as a magnetic field around a magnet can exist in empty space, an electric field exists around an electric charge even if the space around it contains no matter.

Magnetic Fields and Moving Charges Electric charges also can be surrounded by magnetic fields. An electric current flowing through a wire is surrounded by a magnetic field, as shown in **Figure 3.** An electric current in a wire is the flow of electrons in a single direction. It is the motion of these electrons that creates the magnetic field around the wire. In fact, any moving electric charge is surrounded by a magnetic field, as well as an electric field.

Figure 3 Electrons moving in a wire are surrounded by a magnetic field.
Describe *how you would confirm that a magnetic field exists around a current-carrying wire.*

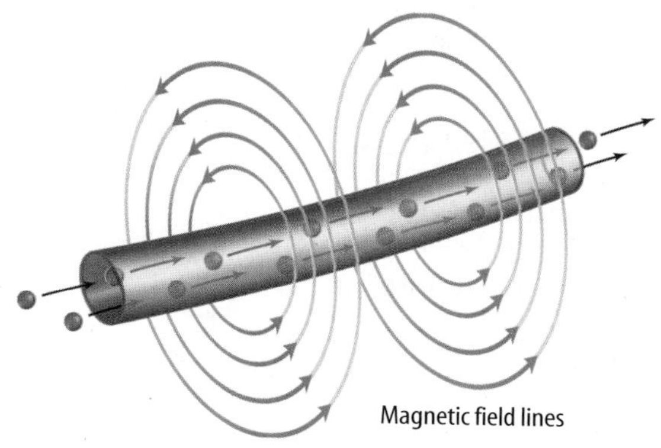

2 Teach

Caption Answers

Figure 2 Place a magnet where the field exists and see if there is a force exerted on the magnet.

Figure 3 Bring a compass near the wire.

Quick Demo

Seeing Magnetic Fields

Materials iron filings, iron bar magnet, plexiglass (optional: overhead projector, plastic wrap)

Estimated Time ten minutes

Procedure If using overhead, wrap writing surface with plastic wrap to protect. Place bar magnet on overhead or other flat surface. Lay plexiglass on top of magnet, and lightly sprinkle with iron filings above magnet. Point out how magnetic field drops off rapidly as distance from magnet increases. L2 IS **Visual-Spatial**

IDENTIFYING Misconceptions

No Magnetic Charge Students may believe that, since an electric field surrounds an electric charge, a magnetic field surrounds a magnetic charge. Explain that there is no magnetic charge. Magnetism is caused by moving electric charges. This is true even for magnetic materials. Electrons in all atoms move in a way that induces a small magnetic field. In most materials, these fields cancel, but in magnetic materials the atoms are arranged so that the fields combine to form a macroscopic field.

Differentiated Instruction

Challenge Have students research scientists who did early investigations on the relationship between electricity and magnetism, such as Oersted, Faraday, and Henry. Have students select an early experiment to demonstrate. L3

Teacher FYI

Affecting Matter The fields of an electromagnetic wave have different effects on matter. Usually, the electric field has a greater effect on matter.

Purpose Students investigate the behavior of electromagnetic waves. L2 ELL IS **Kinesthetic**

Materials television with remote control, glass, book, paper, metal pan

Teaching Strategy Suggest that students hold the objects both very close to the receiver and farther away from it. This will enable them to observe how the beam spreads out and can travel around objects.

Analysis

1. No (for most), because the infrared beam spreads out as it leaves its source.
2. The signal will travel through transparent or translucent materials.

Assessment

Process Some receivers are more sensitive and require the remote to be aimed directly at them. Ask students to suggest ways to control such a television without pointing the remote directly at the receiver. Possible answer: Aim the remote at an object in such a way that the reflected ray will hit the receiver. Use **Performance Assessment in the Science Classroom,** p. 93.

Try at Home

Answer an electric charge moving back and forth

Caption Answers

Figure 4 a transverse wave

Investigating Electromagnetic Waves

Procedure

1. Point your **television remote control** in different directions and observe whether it will still control the **television.**
2. Place various materials in front of the infrared receiver on the television and observe whether the remote still will control the television. Some materials you might try are **glass, a book, your hand, paper,** and a **metal pan.**

Analysis

1. Was it necessary for the remote to be pointing exactly toward the receiver to control the television? Explain.
2. Did the remote continue to work when the various materials were placed between it and the receiver? Explain why or why not.

Try at Home

Changing Electric and Magnetic Fields A changing magnetic field creates a changing electric field. For example, in a transformer, changing electric current in the primary coil produces a changing magnetic field. This changing magnetic field then creates a changing electric field in the secondary coil that produces current in the coil. The reverse is also true—a changing electric field creates a changing magnetic field.

Making Electromagnetic Waves

Waves such as sound waves are produced when something vibrates. Electromagnetic waves also are produced when something vibrates—an electric charge that moves back and forth.

Reading Check *What produces an electromagnetic wave?*

When an electric charge vibrates, the electric field around it changes. Because the electric charge is in motion, it also has a magnetic field around it. This magnetic field also changes as the charge vibrates. As a result, the vibrating electric charge is surrounded by changing electric and magnetic fields.

How do the vibrating electric and magnetic fields around the charge become a wave that travels through space? The changing electric field around the charge creates a changing magnetic field. This changing magnetic field then creates a changing electric field. This process continues, with the magnetic and electric fields continually creating each other. These vibrating electric and magnetic fields are perpendicular to each other and travel outward from the moving charge, as shown in **Figure 4.** Because the electric and magnetic fields vibrate at right angles to the direction the wave travels, an electromagnetic wave is a transverse wave.

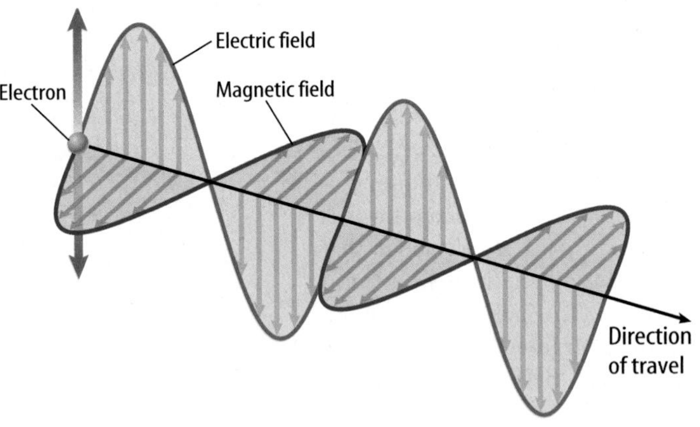

Figure 4 A vibrating electric charge creates an electromagnetic wave that travels outward in all directions from the charge. The wave in only one direction is shown here.
Determine *whether an electromagnetic wave is a transverse wave or a compressional wave.*

Visual Learning

Figure 4 The electromagnetic wave is shown in one direction to make it easier to visualize. In reality, a vibrating charge produces electromagnetic waves that travel in almost all directions. The wave shown here is vertically polarized: the electric field oscillates up and down, and the magnetic field oscillates right and left. In a horizontally polarized wave, the electric field oscillates right and left and the magnetic field oscillates up and down. Ask students to describe how the amplitude, frequency, and wavelength of the electric and magnetic fields are related. When the amplitude of the electric field is maximum, the amplitude of the magnetic field is maximum. The frequencies and wavelengths of the fields are the same.

Properties of Electromagnetic Waves

All matter contains charged particles that are always in motion. As a result, all objects emit electromagnetic waves. The wavelengths of the emitted waves become shorter as the temperature of the material increases. As an electromagnetic wave moves, its electric and magnetic fields encounter objects. These vibrating fields can exert forces on charged particles and magnetic materials, causing them to move. For example, electromagnetic waves from the Sun cause electrons in your skin to vibrate and gain energy, as shown in **Figure 5.** The energy carried by an electromagnetic wave is called **radiant energy.** Radiant energy makes a fire feel warm and enables you to see.

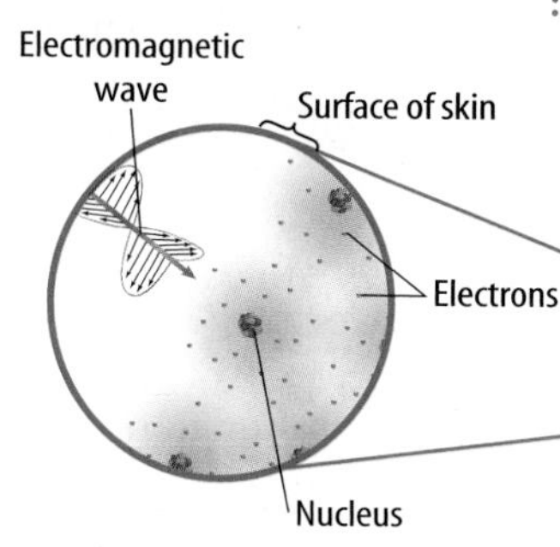

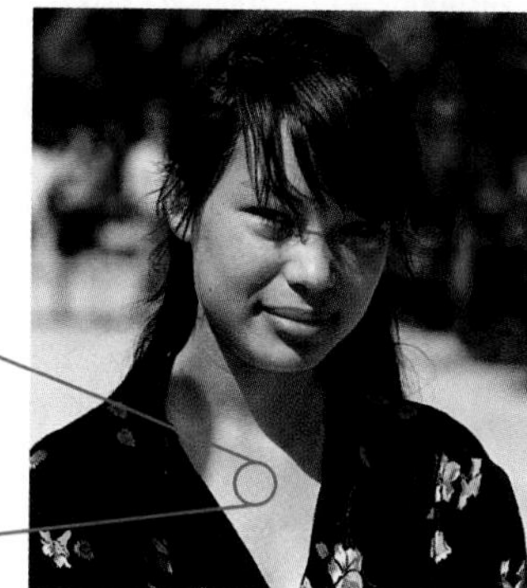

Figure 5 As an electromagnetic wave strikes your skin, electrons in your skin gain energy from the vibrating electric and magnetic fields.

Applying Science

THE SPEED OF LIGHT IN WATER The speed of light in water is 226,000 km/s. Write this number in scientific notation.

IDENTIFY known values and the unknown value

Identify the known values:

The speed of light in water is 226,000 km/s.

Identify the unknown value:

the number 226,000 written in scientific notation

SOLVE the problem

A number written in scientific notation has the form $M \times 10^N$. N is the number of places the decimal point in the number has to be moved so that the number M that results has only one digit to the left of the decimal point.

Write the number in scientific notation form:	$226{,}000. \times 10^N$
Move the decimal point five places to the left:	2.26000×10^N
The decimal point was moved 5 places, so N equals 5:	2.26000×10^5
Delete remaining zeroes at the end of the number.	2.26×10^5

CHECK your answer

Add zeroes to the end of the number and move the decimal point in the opposite direction five places. The result should be the original number.

Practice Problem

Write the following numbers in scientific notation: 433; 812,000,000; 73,000,000,000; 84,500.

For more practice problems go to page 834, and visit gpscience.com/extra_problems.

Quick Demo

Waves

Materials coiled metal spring toy

Estimated Time 5–10 minutes

Procedure Have two volunteers hold each end of the spring so that it is parallel with the floor. Demonstrate a transverse wave (a wave for which the medium moves at right angles to the direction the wave travels) by moving one end of the spring up and down. Demonstrate a longitudinal wave (a wave for which the medium moves along the same direction the wave travels) by holding both ends still, then gathering coils together and releasing them.

Applying Science

National Math Standards

Correlation to Mathematics Objectives

1

Answers to Practice Problems

$433 = 4.33 \times 10^2$

$812{,}000{,}000 = 8.12 \times 10^8$

$73{,}000{,}000{,}000 = 7.3 \times 10^{10}$

$84{,}500 = 8.45 \times 10^4$

Fun Fact

By 1800, many scientists suspected a relationship between electricity and magnetism but could not prove it. Then, in 1820, Hans Christian Oersted accidentally brought a wire carrying direct current near a compass needle while teaching class. The compass needle moved, demonstrating that the current-carrying wire was surrounded by a magnetic field.

Science Journal

Radiant Energy Warm objects emit more radiant energy than cool objects do. Have students investigate this topic and each write a paragraph summarizing what he/she learns. All objects contain charged particles, such as electrons, that are always moving. These charged particles emit electromagnetic waves whose frequency depends on the frequency of vibration of the charges. As the temperature of the object increases, these charged particles move faster. Their frequency of vibration increases and the frequency of the electomagnetic radiation they emit increases. L3 LS **Logical-Mathematical**

Activity

Drawing Waves To help students understand how frequency and wavelength are related, have one student draw a series of waves across the board, end to end, each having a similar wavelength. Have another student draw a series of waves with a much longer wavelength below the first set. The drawings should demonstrate that over the same distance, there are more waves with shorter wavelengths and fewer waves with longer wavelengths. L2

LS **Visual-Spatial**

Teacher FYI

Light History There is a rich scientific history leading to the idea that light has both particle and wave nature. In the fifth century B.C., the Pythagoreans thought streams of light were emitted by the eye. Newton formed a particle theory of light in the early eighteenth century, around the same time Huygens concluded that light was a wave. In 1905, Einstein proposed that electromagnetic waves can also behave as particles.

Reading Check

Answer 300,000 km/s in a vacuum

Virtual Labs

Wavelength *What is the electromagnetic spectrum?*

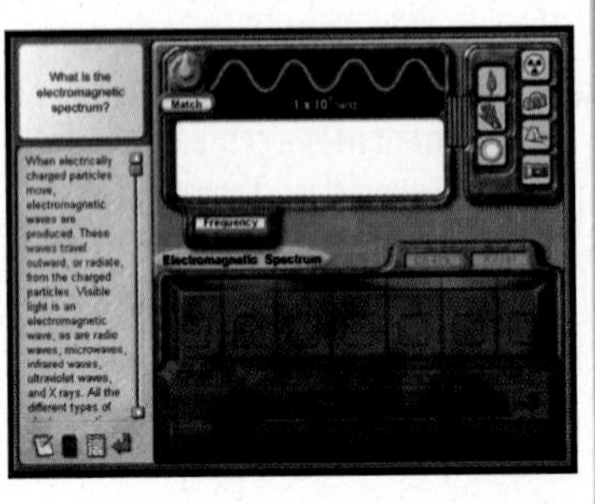

Table 1 Speed of Visible Light

Material	Speed (km/s)
Vacuum	300,000
Air	slightly less than 300,000
Water	226,000
Glass	200,000
Diamond	124,000

Wave Speed All electromagnetic waves travel at 300,000 km/s in the vacuum of space. Because light is an electromagnetic wave, the speed of electromagnetic waves in space is usually called the "speed of light." The speed of light is nature's speed limit—nothing travels faster than the speed of light. In matter, the speed of electromagnetic waves depends on the material they travel through. Electromagnetic waves usually travel the slowest in solids and the fastest in gases. **Table 1** lists the speed of visible light in various materials.

Reading Check *What is the speed of light?*

Wavelength and Frequency Like all waves, electromagnetic waves can be described by their wavelength and frequency. The wavelength of an electromagnetic wave is the distance from one crest to another, as shown in **Figure 6.**

The frequency of any wave is the number of wavelengths that pass a point in 1 s. The frequency of an electromagnetic wave also equals the frequency of the vibrating charge that produces the wave. This frequency is the number of vibrations, or back and forth movements, of the charge in one second. The frequency and wavelength of electromagnetic waves are related. As the frequency increases, the wavelength becomes smaller.

Waves and Particles

The difference between a wave and a particle might seem obvious—a wave is a disturbance that carries energy, and a particle is a piece of matter. However, in reality the difference is not so clear.

Waves as Particles In 1887, Heinrich Hertz found that by shining light on a metal, electrons were ejected from the metal. Hertz found that whether or not electrons were ejected depended on the frequency of the light and not the amplitude. Because the energy carried by a wave depends on its amplitude and not its frequency, this result was mysterious. Years later, Albert Einstein provided an explanation—electromagnetic waves can behave as a particle, called a **photon,** whose energy depends on the frequency of the waves.

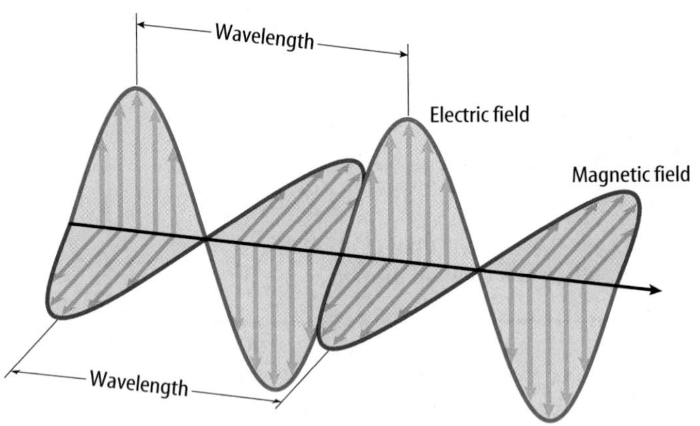

Figure 6 The wavelength of an electromagnetic wave is the distance between the crests of the vibrating electric field or magnetic field.

Active Reading

Metacognition Journal In this strategy, each student analyzes his or her own thought processes. Have students divide the paper in half. On the left, have them record what they have learned about a topic. On the right, have them record the reason they learned it. Have students write a Metacognition Journal about electromagnetic waves.

Differentiated Instruction

Behavioral Disorder Have students draw two waves on a piece of paper, each 5 cm long. Count the wavelengths in each wave. Discuss which wave has the highest frequency. For review, label resting point, amplitude, crest, trough, wavelength.

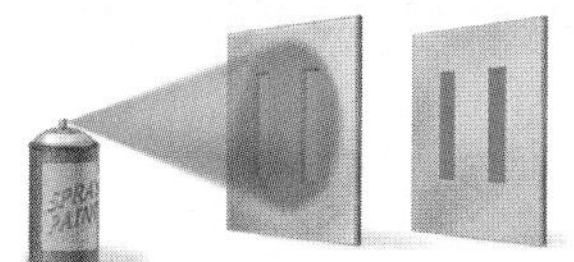

Particles of paint sprayed through two slits coat only the area behind the slits.

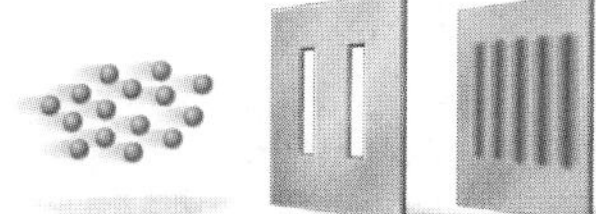

Electrons fired at two closely-spaced openings form a wave-like interference pattern.

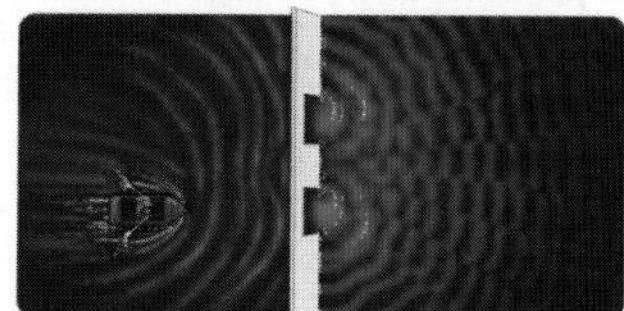

Water waves produce an interference pattern after passing through two openings.

Figure 7 When electrons are sent through two narrow slits, they behave as a wave.

Particles as Waves Because electromagnetic waves could behave as a particle, others wondered whether matter could behave as a wave. If a beam of electrons were sprayed at two tiny slits, you might expect that the electrons would strike only the area behind the slits, like the spray paint in **Figure 7.** Instead, it was found that the electrons formed an interference pattern. This type of pattern is produced by waves when they pass through two slits and interfere with each other, as the water waves do in **Figure 7.** This experiment showed that electrons can behave like waves. It is now known that all particles, not only electrons, can behave like waves.

section 1 review

Summary

Making Electromagnetic Waves

- Moving electric charges are surrounded by an electric field and a magnetic field.
- A vibrating electric charge produces an electromagnetic wave.
- An electromagnetic wave consists of vibrating electric and magnetic fields that are perpendicular to each other and travel outward from the vibrating electric charge.

Properties of Electromagnetic Waves

- Electromagnetic waves carry radiant energy.
- In empty space electromagnetic waves travel at 300,000 km/s—the speed of light.
- Electromagnetic waves travel slower in matter, with a speed that depends on the material.

Waves and Particles

- Electromagnetic waves can behave as particles that are called photons.
- In some circumstances, particles, such as electrons can behave as waves.

Self Check

1. **Explain** why an electromagnetic wave is a transverse wave and not a compressional wave.
2. **Compare** the frequency of an electromagnetic wave with the frequency of the vibrating charge that produces the wave.
3. **Describe** how electromagnetic waves transfer radiant energy to matter.
4. **Explain** why an electromagnetic wave can travel through empty space that contains no matter.
5. **Think Critically** Suppose a moving electric charge was surrounded only by an electric field. Infer whether or not a vibrating electric charge would produce an electromagnetic wave.

Applying Math

6. **Calculate Time** How many minutes does it take an electromagnetic wave to travel 150,000,000 km?
7. **Use Scientific Notation** Calculate the distance an electromagnetic wave in space would travel in one day. Express your answer in scientific notation.

Science Online gpscience.com/self_check_quiz

section 1 review

1. The vibrating electric and magnetic fields that create electromagnetic waves are perpendicular to the direction the wave travels. A compressional wave causes a disturbance that moves back and forth along the direction the wave travels.
2. They're equal.
3. by causing charged particles within objects to move
4. An electromagnetic wave is made of vibrating electric and magnetic fields that continually produce each other; matter is not needed for this to occur.
5. No, an electromagnetic wave would not be produced. Both a vibrating electric and magnetic field are needed to produce an electromagnetic wave that travels away from the vibrating charge.
6. 500 s = 8.33 min
7. 2.592×10^{10} km

3 Assess

DAILY INTERVENTION

Check for Understanding

Logical-Mathematical Using two columns, chart the characteristics of sound waves and electromagnetic waves comparing and contrasting the properties of each.

Reteach

Seeing Waves Radio waves are long-wavelength, low-frequency electromagnetic waves, and gamma rays are short-wavelength, high-frequency waves. Have students model the relationship between wavelength and frequency of waves by vertically shaking a rope attached to a door handle. First, they can shake it with low frequency to see long wavelengths, then with higher frequency to see shorter wavelengths. L2 ELL IS **Kinesthetic**

Assessment

Portfolio Have students write several paragraphs that describe how electric and magnetic fields together form electromagnetic waves, and how these waves vary in frequency and wavelength. Use **Performance Assessment in the Science Classroom,** p. 159. 

Differentiated Instruction

Challenge Ask students to research the early discoveries of Hertz, Planck, and Einstein on the quantum theory, black body radiation, and the photoelectric affect. Have students create a time line illustrating key concepts and experiments. L3

1 Motivate

Bellringer

Section Focus Transparencies also are available on the Interactive Chalkboard CD-ROM.

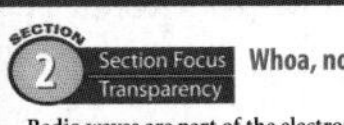

Whoa, not so fast!

Radio waves are part of the electromagnetic spectrum. These waves can do more than just carry a signal to your radio. Here, a radar gun is being used to measure speed. *Radar* stands for "radio detecting and ranging."

1. Which of the devices in the photo is using electromagnetic waves to measure speed?
2. Is wave speed or wavelength and frequency more useful for differentiating among different types of electromagnetic waves?
3. The prefix *infra-* means below, and the prefix *ultra-* means beyond. Knowing this, what do the terms *infrared* and *ultraviolet* mean?

L2

Electromagnetic Waves

Tie to Prior Knowledge

X Rays Ask students if they have ever had an X-ray image taken by an X-ray technician. X rays are one form of electromagnetic waves that they will be studying in this section.

Fun Fact

While working with radar in the 1940's, Percy Spencer discovered that the candy in his pockets had melted. He also discovered that directing the radar toward popcorn caused the kernels to pop. From these observations, Spencer went on to develop the microwave oven.

section 2

The Electromagnetic Spectrum

Reading Guide

What You'll Learn

- **Describe** the waves in the different regions of the electromagnetic spectrum.
- **Compare** the properties of different electromagnetic waves.
- **Identify** uses for different types of electromagnetic waves.

Why It's Important

Every day, waves in different regions of the electromagnetic spectrum are used in many ways.

Review Vocabulary

spectrum: a continuous sequence arranged by a particular property

New Vocabulary

- radio wave
- microwave
- infrared wave
- visible light
- ultraviolet wave
- X ray
- gamma ray

A Range of Frequencies

Electromagnetic waves can have a wide variety of frequencies. They might vibrate once each second or trillions of times each second. The entire range of electromagnetic wave frequencies is known as the electromagnetic spectrum, shown in **Figure 8.** Various portions of the electromagnetic spectrum interact with matter differently. As a result, they are given different names. The electromagnetic waves that humans can detect with their eyes, called visible light, are a small portion of the entire electromagnetic spectrum. However, various devices have been developed to detect the other frequencies. For example, the antenna of your radio detects radio waves.

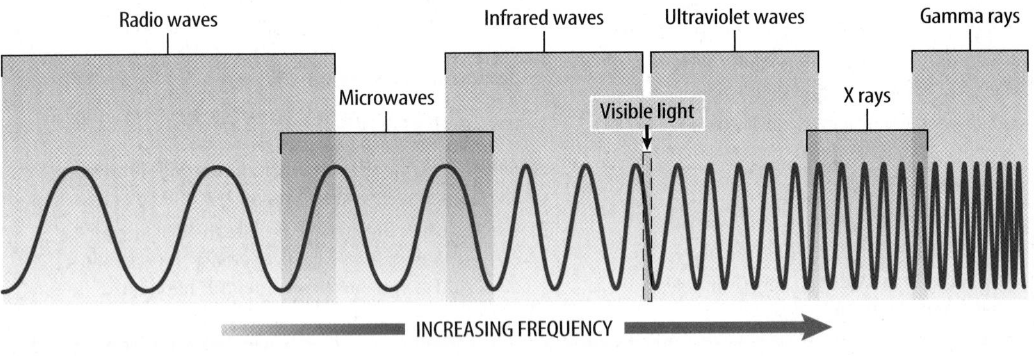

Figure 8 Electromagnetic waves are described by different names depending on their frequency and wavelength.

Section 2 Resource Manager

Chapter *FAST FILE* Resources

Transparency Activity, p. 45, 46
Directed Reading for Content Mastery, pp. 21, 22
MiniLAB, p. 4
Enrichment, p. 31
Lab Activity, pp. 9–12
Reinforcement, p. 51
Activity Worksheets, pp. 5–6
Earth Science Critical Thinking/Problem Solving, p. 13

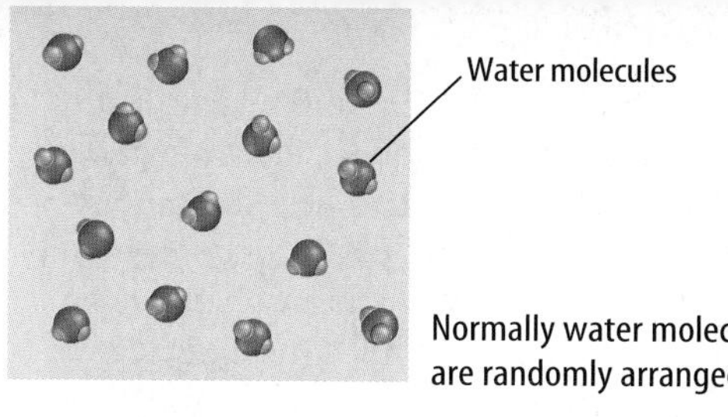
Water molecules
Normally water molecules are randomly arranged.

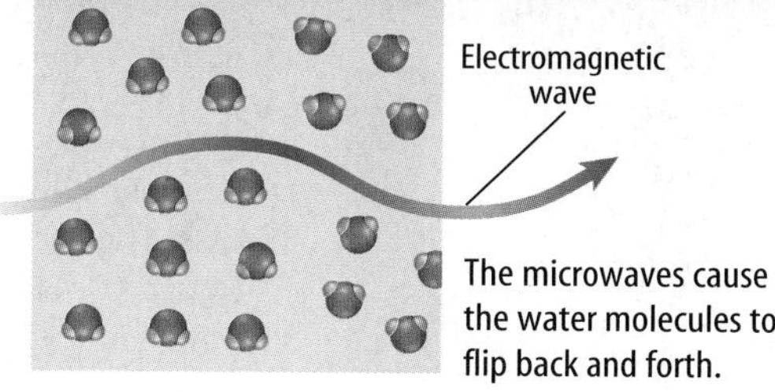
Electromagnetic wave
The microwaves cause the water molecules to flip back and forth.

Figure 9 Microwave ovens use electromagnetic waves to heat food.

Radio Waves

Stop and look around you. Even though you can't see them, radio waves are moving everywhere you look. Some radio waves carry an audio signal from a radio station to a radio. However, even though these radio waves carry information that a radio uses to create sound, you can't hear radio waves. You hear a sound wave when the compressions and rarefactions the sound wave produces reach your ears. A radio wave does not produce compressions and rarefactions as it travels through air.

Microwaves **Radio waves** are low-frequency electromagnetic waves with wavelengths longer than about 1 mm. Radio waves with wavelengths of less than about 30 cm are called **microwaves.** Microwaves with wavelengths of about 1 cm to 20 cm are widely used for communication, such as for cellular telephones and satellite signals. You are probably most familiar with microwaves because of their use in microwave ovens.

Reading Check *What is the difference between a microwave and a radio wave?*

Microwave ovens heat food when microwaves interact with water molecules in food, as shown in **Figure 9.** Each water molecule is positively charged on one side and negatively charged on the other side. The vibrating electric field inside a microwave oven causes water molecules in food to rotate back and forth billions of times each second. This rotation causes a type of friction between water molecules that generates thermal energy. It is the thermal energy produced by the interactions between the water molecules that causes your food to cook.

Radar Another use for radio waves is to find the position and movement of objects by a method called radar. Radar stands for **RA**dio **D**etecting **A**nd **R**anging. With radar, radio waves are transmitted toward an object. By measuring the time required for the waves to bounce off the object and return to a receiving antenna, the location of the object can be found. Law enforcement officers use radar to measure how fast a vehicle is moving. Radar also is used for tracking the movement of aircraft, watercraft, and spacecraft.

Heating with Microwaves

Procedure
1. Obtain two small **beakers or baby-food jars.** Place 50 mL of **dry sand** into each. To one of the jars, add 20 mL of **room-temperature water** and stir well.
2. Record the temperature of the sand in each jar.
3. Together, **microwave** both jars of sand for 10 s and immediately record the temperature again.

Analysis
1. Compare the initial and final temperatures of the wet and dry sand.
2. Infer why there was a difference.

2 Teach

Make a Model

Water Waves Have students use a pan of water to model how altering the frequency of a vibrating object in the water creates waves with different frequencies. L1 ELL LS **Kinesthetic**

Purpose Students observe how microwave ovens heat food. L2 ELL LS **Kinesthetic**

Materials microwave oven, two small beakers or baby food jars, dry sand, water, thermometer

Safety Precautions Be sure students do not overheat the sand.

Analysis
1. Wet sand becomes much hotter than dry sand.
2. The microwaves interact with the water molecules in the wet sand, increasing their kinetic energy. The water molecules transfer some of this energy to the surrounding sand.

Assessment

Process Ask students to infer why the inside of a microwave oven doesn't get hot. It is made of materials that don't absorb the energy carried by microwaves. Use **Performance Assessment in the Science Classroom,** p. 89.

Reading Check

Answer Microwaves are radio waves with wavelengths of less than a meter.

Differentiated Instruction

Learning Disabled Draw a diagram on the board or on a 6 ft. piece of paper similar to the one on p. 360. As each type of wave is discussed, tape examples of things that use that type of wave under the correct heading.

Visual Learning

Figure 9 Point out to students that water molecules are polar. The side with the hydrogen atoms has a slightly positive charge and the side with the oxygen atom has a slightly negative charge. Because of this polarity, the molecules tend to align themselves with an electric field. The changing electric field in microwaves causes the water molecules to rotate. L2 LS **Visual-Spatial**

Teacher FYI

Infared Radiation in Space Various celestial objects, including planets, stars, nebulae, and galaxies, give off infrared radiation. The Infrared Astronomical Satellite (IRAS), equipped with an infrared telescope sensitive to wavelengths of 8 to 100 micrometers, was launched in January 1983 to study space objects. The IRAS discovered clouds of solid debris around Vega, Fomalhaut, and several other stars. Scientists hypothesize these clouds may indicate the formation of planetary systems around these stars.

Use Science Words

Word Meanings Ask students to find the meaning of the prefix infra- and explain why it is appropriate for describing infrared waves. Infra- means "below." It is appropriate because infrared waves have frequencies just below that of red light. L2 LS **Linguistic**

Quick Demo

Visible Light Waves

Materials prism, light source, white screen

Estimated Time five minutes

Procedure Shine light onto white screen. Refract light using prism to show colors of light. Point out how each frequency refracted to a different degree with violet refracting the most and red the least.

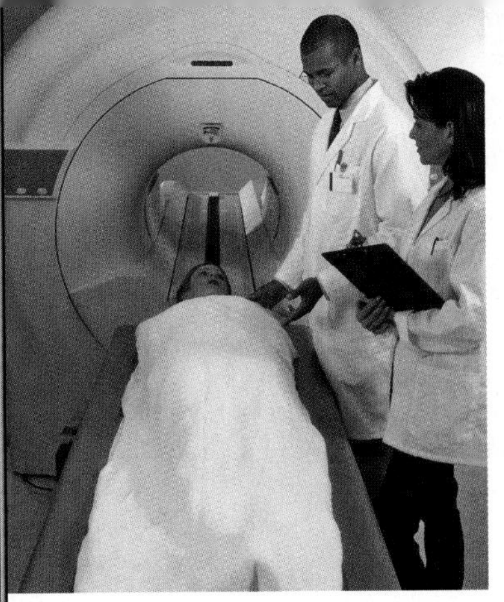

Figure 10 Magnetic resonance imaging technology uses radio waves as an alternative to X-ray imaging.

Magnetic Resonance Imaging (MRI) In the early 1980s, medical researchers developed a technique called Magnetic Resonance Imaging, which uses radio waves to help diagnose illness. The patient lies inside a large cylinder, like the one shown in **Figure 10.** Housed in the cylinder is a powerful magnet, a radio wave emitter, and a radio wave detector. Protons in hydrogen atoms in bones and soft tissue behave like magnets and align with the strong magnetic field. Energy from radio waves causes some of the protons to flip their alignment. As the protons flip, they release radiant energy. A radio receiver detects this released energy. The amount of energy a proton releases depends on the type of tissue it is part of. The released energy detected by the radio receiver is used to create a map of the different tissues. A picture of the inside of the patient's body is produced painlessly.

Infrared Waves

Most of the warm air in a fireplace moves up the chimney, yet when you stand in front of a fireplace, you feel the warmth of the blazing fire. Why do you feel the heat? The warmth you feel is thermal energy transmitted to you by **infrared waves,** which are a type of electromagnetic wave with wavelengths between about 1 mm and about 750 billionths of a meter.

You use infrared waves every day. A remote control emits infrared waves to control your television. A computer uses infrared waves to read CD-ROMs. In fact, every object emits infrared waves. Hotter objects emit more infrared waves than cooler objects emit. The wavelengths emitted also become shorter as the temperature increases. Infrared detectors can form images of objects from the infrared radiation they emit. Infrared sensors on satellites can produce infrared images that can help identify the vegetation over a region. **Figure 11** shows how cities appear different from surrounding vegetation in infrared satellite imagery.

Figure 11 Infrared images and visible light images can provide different types of information.

This visible light image of the region around San Francisco Bay in California was taken from an aircraft at an altitude of 20,000 m.

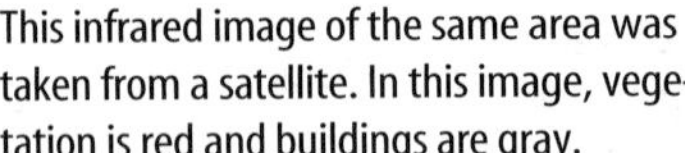

This infrared image of the same area was taken from a satellite. In this image, vegetation is red and buildings are gray.

362

Differentiated Instruction

Challenge Have students investigate other uses of infrared radiation, such as infrared spectroscopy and Forward-Looking Infrared Systems. Have them create informative posters conveying the various uses. L3

Science Journal

Imaging Safety Have students write short paragraphs in their Science Journals explaining why Magnetic Resonance Imaging is safer than X rays. The radio waves used for Magnetic Resonance Imaging have much lower energy than X rays, and they do not harm the body. L2 LS **Linguistic**

Visible Light

Visible light is the range of electromagnetic waves that you can detect with your eyes. Light differs from radio waves and infrared waves only by its frequency and wavelength. Visible light has wavelengths around 750 billionths to 400 billionths of a meter. Your eyes contain substances that react differently to various wavelengths of visible light, so you see different colors. These colors range from short-wavelength blue to long-wavelength red. If all the colors are present, you see the light as white.

Ultraviolet Waves

Ultraviolet waves are electromagnetic waves with wavelengths from about 400 billionths to 10 billionths of a meter. Ultraviolet waves are energetic enough to enter skin cells. Overexposure to ultraviolet rays can cause skin damage and cancer. Most of the ultraviolet radiation that reaches Earth's surface are longer-wavelength UVA rays. The shorter-wavelength UVB rays cause sunburn, and both UVA and UVB rays can cause skin cancers and skin damage such as wrinkling. Although too much exposure to the Sun's ultraviolet waves is damaging, some exposure is healthy. Ultraviolet light striking the skin enables your body to make vitamin D which is needed for healthy bones and teeth.

Useful UVs A useful property of ultraviolet waves is their ability to kill bacteria on objects such as food or medical supplies. When ultraviolet light enters a cell, it damages protein and DNA molecules. For some single-celled organisms, damage can mean death, which can be a benefit to health. Ultraviolet waves are also useful because they make some materials fluoresce (floor ES). Fluorescent materials absorb ultraviolet waves and reemit the energy as visible light. As shown in **Figure 12,** police detectives sometimes use fluorescent powder to show fingerprints when solving crimes.

CT Scans In certain situations, doctors will perform a CT scan on a patient instead of a traditional X ray. Research to find out more about CT scans. Compare and contrast CT scans with X rays. What are the advantages and disadvantages of a CT scan? Write a paragraph about your findings in your Science Journal.

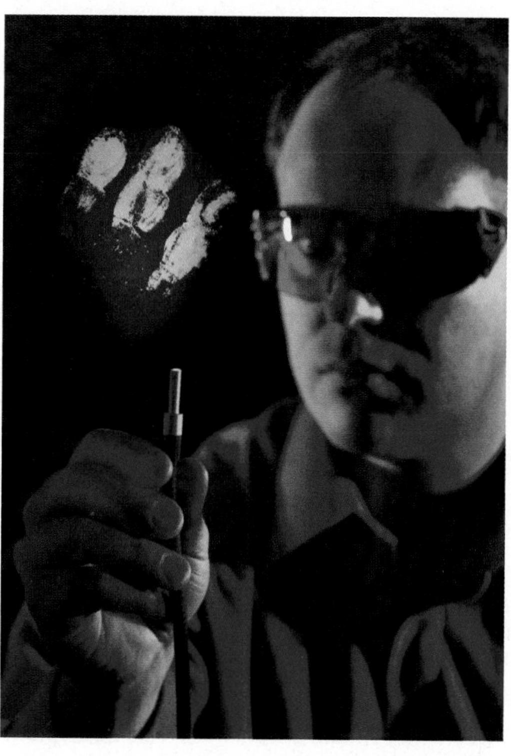

Figure 12 The police detective in this picture is shining ultraviolet light on a fingerprint dusted with fluorescent powder.

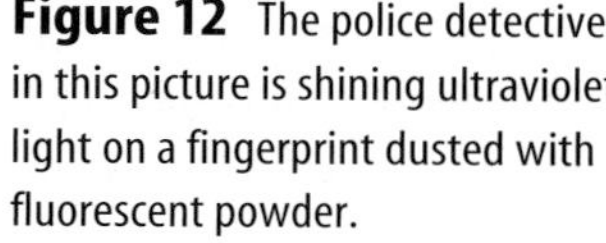

Fun Fact

Humans are able to see certain wavelengths of electromagnetic waves because cells called cones and rods in the retina of the human eye absorb those particular wavelengths.

CT scans In both traditional X ray imaging and CT (computerized tomography, also known as CAT, computerized axial tomography) scanning, X rays are passed through the body to provide an inside view. Traditional X-ray images are not appropriate for some purposes because they show only dense body parts. CT scans provide much clearer cross-sectional images made by rotating an X-ray beam around the patient. CT scans are more expensive.

Research Have students research specific uses for X rays and CT scans, and explain why each is best suited for that use.

LAB DEMONSTRATION

Purpose to demonstrate fluorescence L2
ELL LS **Kinesthetic**

Materials ultraviolet lamp; fluorescent rock kit or samples of calcite, fluorite, or opal; dry laundry detergent containing whiteners

Procedure In a darkened room, shine the UV lamp on the rocks and laundry detergent. Turn the lamp on and off comparing the affect of UV vs. visible light. Shine the light on clothing to check for fluorescent whiteners.

WARNING: *Be careful not to shine ultraviolet light in anyone's eyes.*

Expected Outcome Students will observe the materials fluoresce.

Assessment

Why do the materials fluoresce? When ultraviolet light strikes the materials, the electrons absorb the energy, then reemit it as light at a lower frequency.

Use Science Words

Word Origins Have students find out where the word *ozone* comes from. The word *ozone* comes from the Greek word *ozein* meaning "to smell." Point out that ozone can be formed when electricity or ultraviolet rays pass through oxygen. Its sharp smell can often be detected near electrical machinery or during a thunderstorm. L2 LS **Linguistic**

Answer it absorbs harmful UV waves

Investigating Infrared Photographs

Purpose To investigate the uses of infrared photography and conduct a simple investigation using an infrared photograph.

Possible Materials internet access, infrared photographs

Estimated Time 3–4 class sessions

Teaching Strategies

- Have students research uses of infrared photography and select one use to investigate in more detail. Examples: geology, vegetation health, environmental pollution, land use.
- Have students obtain a photograph related to their area of research, form a question and hypothesis that could be answered with the photo, and then answer the question.
- Students can present their findings to the class.
- U.S. Department of the Interior/U.S. Geological Survey has a fact sheet and a list of contacts. For more information go to gpscience.com and follow the links to your chapter.

For additional inquiry activities, see *Science Inquiry Labs*.

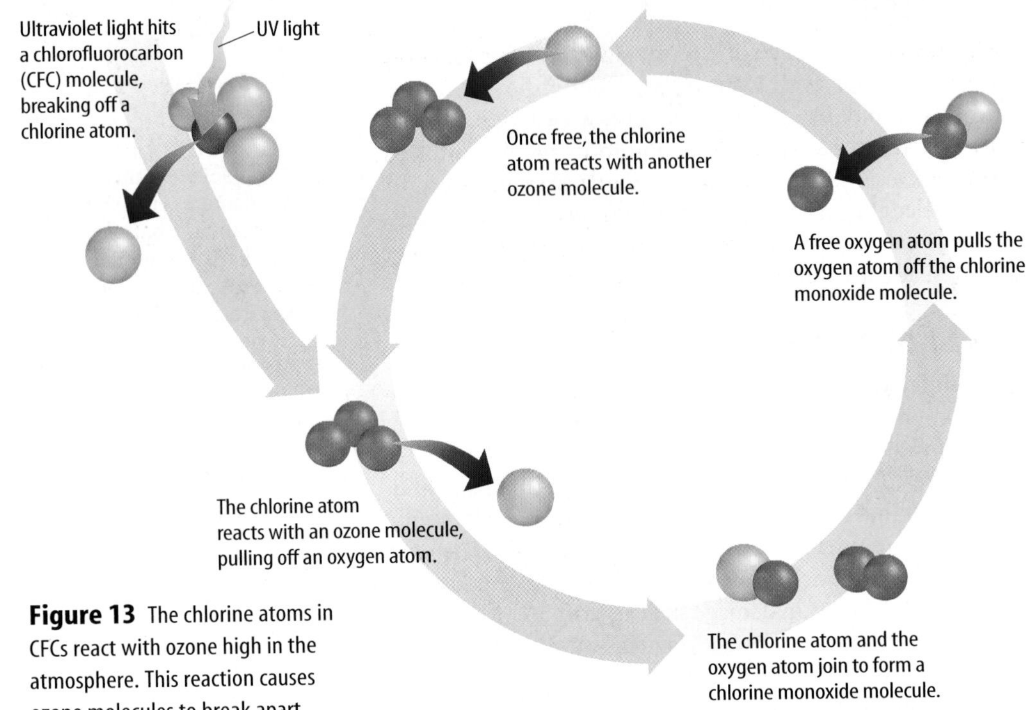

Figure 13 The chlorine atoms in CFCs react with ozone high in the atmosphere. This reaction causes ozone molecules to break apart.

The Ozone Layer About 20 to 50 km above Earth's surface in the stratosphere is a region called the ozone layer. Ozone is a molecule composed of three oxygen atoms. It is continually being formed and destroyed by ultraviolet waves high in the atmosphere. The ozone layer is vital to life on Earth because it absorbs most of the Sun's harmful ultraviolet waves. However, over the past few decades the amount of ozone in the ozone layer has decreased. Averaged globally, the decrease is about three percent, but is greater at higher latitudes.

Reading Check *Why is the ozone layer vital to life on Earth?*

INTEGRATE Environment The decrease in ozone is caused by the presence of certain chemicals, such as CFCs, high in Earth's atmosphere. CFCs are chemicals called chlorofluorocarbons that have been widely used in air conditioners, refrigerators, and cleaning fluids. When CFC molecules reach the ozone layer, they react chemically with ozone molecules as shown in **Figure 13.** One chlorine atom from a CFC molecule can break apart thousands of ozone molecules. As a result, many countries are reducing the use of CFCs and other ozone-depleting chemicals.

Curriculum Connection

Health Ozone in the stratosphere is necessary to protect life on Earth, but ozone near the ground is harmful. Ozone is a major component in smog produced by chemical pollutants from factories. Ozone also contributes to the greenhouse effect by trapping heat. Have students prepare posters showing useful and harmful effects of ozone. L3 LS **Visual-Spatial** P

X Rays and Gamma Rays

The electromagnetic waves with the shortest wavelengths and highest frequencies are X rays and gamma rays. Both X rays and gamma rays are high energy electromagnetic waves. **X rays** have wavelengths between about ten billionths of a meter and ten trillionths of a meter. Doctors and dentists use low doses of X rays to form images of internal organs, bones, and teeth, like the image shown in **Figure 14.** X rays also are used in airport screening devices to examine the contents of luggage.

Electromagnetic waves with wavelengths shorter than about 10 trillionths of a meter are gamma rays. These are the highest-energy electromagnetic waves and can penetrate through several centimeters of lead. Gamma rays are produced by processes that occur in atomic nuclei. Both X rays and gamma rays are used in a technique called radiation therapy to kill diseased cells in the human body. A beam of X rays or gamma rays can damage the biological molecules in living cells, causing both healthy and diseased cells to die. However, by carefully controlling the amount of X ray or gamma ray radiation received by the diseased area, the damage to healthy cells can be reduced.

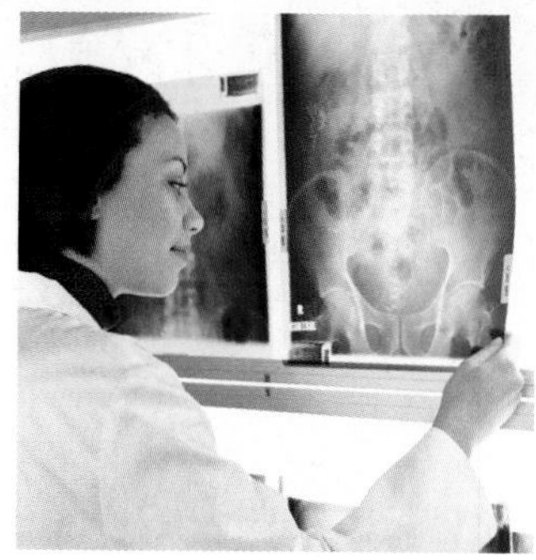

Figure 14 Bones are more dense than surrounding tissues and absorb more X rays. The image of a bone on an X ray is the shadow cast by the bone as X rays pass through the soft tissue.

section 2 review

Summary

Radio Waves and Infrared Waves

- Radio waves are electromagnetic waves with wavelengths longer than about 1 mm.
- Microwaves are radio waves with wavelengths between about 1 mm and 1 m.
- Infrared waves have wavelengths between about 1 mm and 750 billionths of a meter.

Visible Light and Ultraviolet Waves

- Visible light waves have wavelengths between about 750 and 400 billionths of a meter.
- Ultraviolet waves have wavelengths between about 400 and 40 billionths of a meter.
- Most of the harmful ultraviolet waves emitted by the Sun are absorbed by the ozone layer.

X Rays and Gamma Rays

- X rays and gamma rays are the most energetic electromagnetic waves.
- Gamma rays have wavelengths less than 10 trillionths of a meter and are produced in the nuclei of atoms.

Self Check

1. **Explain** A mug of water is heated in a microwave oven. Explain why the water gets hotter than the mug.
2. **Describe** why you can see visible light waves, but not other electromagnetic waves.
3. **List** the beneficial effects and the harmful effects of human exposure to ultraviolet rays.
4. **Identify** three objects in a home that produce electromagnetic waves and describe how the electromagnetic waves are used.
5. **Think Critically** What could an infrared image of their house reveal to the homeowners?

Applying Math

6. **Use Scientific Notation** Express the range of wavelengths corresponding to visible light, ultraviolet waves, and X rays in scientific notation.
7. **Convert Units** A nanometer, abbreviated nm, equals one billionth of a meter, or 10^{-9} meters. Express the range of wavelengths corresponding to visible light, ultraviolet waves and X rays in nanometers.

 gpscience.com/self_check_quiz

Discussion

Upper Limit Ask students whether or not they believe there is an upper limit to the energy of electromagnetic waves. Gamma rays with energies greater than a trillion electron volts (Tev) have been detected. By comparison, photons of visible light have energies of only a few electron volts. Astronomers believe that gamma rays with energies a thousand times greater should be emitted by certain galaxies, and have built instruments to detect these high-energy gamma rays. L3 LS **Logical-Mathematical**

3 Assess

DAILY INTERVENTION

Check for Understanding

Auditory-Musical Divide the class into six groups, assigning each one segment of the electromagnetic spectrum. Have groups write poems or rap songs highlighting key features of their segment.

Reteach

Wave Displays Divide the class into six groups. Ask each group to discuss and make a poster showing various properties and uses of one type of electromagnetic waves. Posters can be displayed in the classroom for reference. L2 COOP LEARN

LS **Visual-Spatial**

Assessment

Process Ask students to write paragraphs comparing and contrasting MRI and X-ray imaging. Both provide an inside view of a patient. MRI uses radio waves and is safer but more expensive. X-ray imaging uses potentially harmful X rays, but is less expensive. MRI provides clearer images. Use **Performance Assessment in the Science Classroom,** p. 157.

section 2 review

1. The molecules of which the mug is made do not absorb the energy carried by microwaves; water molecules do absorb microwave energy.
2. Human eyes contain chemical compounds that absorb the energy carried by visible light waves.
3. beneficial effects: production of Vitamin D in human body; harmful affects: damage protein and DNA molecules in cells, can damage skin and cause skin cancer
4. answers will vary
5. Possible answer: where heat is escaping from the house, and where insulation would be needed to reduce heat loss.
6. visible light = 7.5 to 4.0×10^{-7} m, ultraviolet = 40 to 1.0×10^{-8} m, X rays = 1.0×10^{-8} m to 1.0×10^{-11} m
7. visible light = 750 to 400 nm, ultraviolet = 400 to 10 nm, X rays = 10 to 0.01 nm

Real-World Question

Purpose Students learn how the shape of a satellite dish affects reception. L2 ELL
LS **Kinesthetic**

Process Skills observe and infer, communicate, compare and contrast, recognize cause and effect, make models

Time Required 30 minutes

Procedure

Alternate Materials Any small parabolic object can be used.

Teaching Strategy For accurate comparison, be sure students have the flashlight at the same distance from the receptor for all measurements.

Conclude and Apply

1. The light on the flat surface is spread out, but the light on the curved surface is mostly an intense spot in the middle.
2. The light from the flashlight spreads out as it leaves the flashlight. When it hits a flat surface, this light remains spread out. When it hits a curved surface, the light is reflected to the center, forming the intense spot.
3. This activity uses visible light as a model for the microwaves used in satellite communication. A curved satellite dish focuses the signal so that reception is much better.

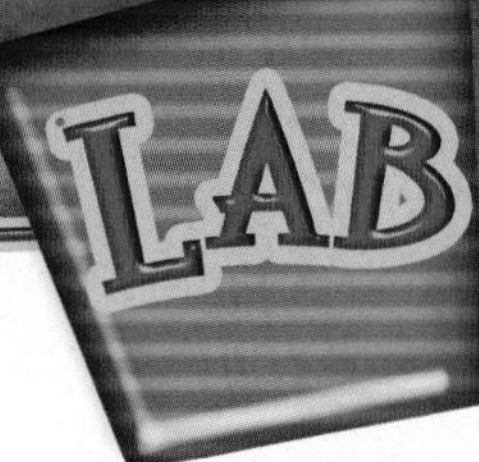

The Shape of Satellite Dishes

Communications satellites transmit signals with a narrow beam pointed toward a particular area of Earth. To detect this signal, receivers are typically large, parabolic dishes.

Real-World Question

How does the shape of a satellite dish improve reception?

Goals

- **Make** a model of a satellite reflecting dish.
- **Observe** how the shape of the dish affects reception.

Materials

flashlight	small bowl
several books	**large, metal spoon*
aluminum foil	**Alternate materials*

Safety Precautions

Procedure

1. Cover one side of a book with aluminum foil. Be careful not to wrinkle the foil.
2. Line the inside of the bowl with foil, also keeping it as smooth as possible.
3. Place some of the books on a table. Put the flashlight on top of the books so that its beam of light will shine several centimeters above and across the table.
4. Hold the foil-covered book on its side at a right angle to the top of the table. The foil-covered side should face the beam of light.
5. **Observe** the intensity of the light on the foil.
6. Repeat steps 4 and 5, replacing the foil-covered book with the bowl.

Conclude and Apply

1. **Compare** the brightness of the light reflected from the two surfaces.
2. **Explain** why the light you see from the curved surface is brighter.
3. **Infer** why bowl-shaped dishes are used to receive signals from satellites.

Communicating Your Data

Compare your conclusions with those observed by other students in your class. **For more help, refer to the** Science Skill Handbook.

Communicating Your Data

Have students use a computer graphics program to prepare sketches of the models they created in this activity. The sketches should show how the light is reflected directly back from a flat surface, but is reflected toward the center of a curved surface. Have students compare their sketches.

Assessment

Oral After students have completed the activity, ask them to explain why focusing a satellite signal is important. Focusing increases the intensity of the satellite signal. Use **Performance Assessment in the Science Classroom,** p. 89.

section 3

Radio Communication

Reading Guide

What You'll Learn

- **Explain** how modulating carrier waves enables information to be transmitted by radio waves.
- **Distinguish** between amplitude modulation and frequency modulation.
- **Identify** various ways of communicating using radio waves.

Why It's Important

Every day you use radio waves to communicate.

Review Vocabulary

modulate: to vary the amplitude or frequency of a wave in order to transmit information

New Vocabulary

- carrier wave
- cathode-ray tube
- transceiver
- Global Positioning System (GPS)

Radio Transmission

When you listen to the radio, you hear music and words that are produced at a distant location. The music and words are sent to your radio by radio waves. The metal antenna of your radio detects radio waves. As the electromagnetic waves pass by your radio's antenna, the electrons in the metal vibrate, as shown in **Figure 15.** These vibrating electrons produce a changing electric current that contains the information about the music and words. An amplifier boosts the current and sends it to speakers, causing them to vibrate. The vibrating speakers create sound waves that travel to your ears. Your brain interprets these sound waves as music and words

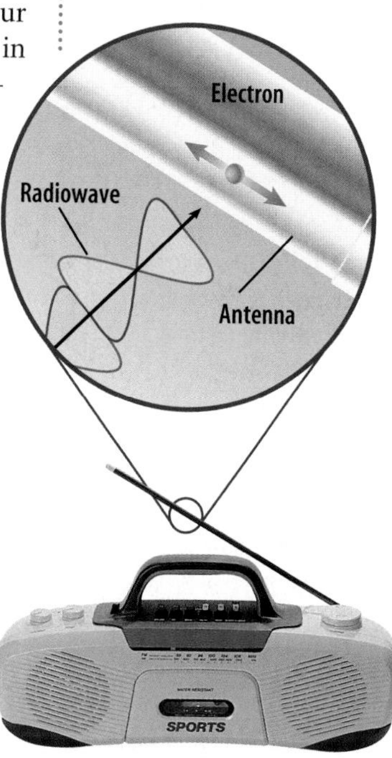

Figure 15 Radio waves exert a force on the electrons in an antenna, causing the electrons to vibrate.

Dividing the Radio Spectrum Each radio station is assigned to broadcast at one particular radio frequency. Turning the tuning knob on your radio allows you to select a particular frequency to listen to. The specific frequency of the electromagnetic wave that a radio station is assigned is called the **carrier wave.**

The radio station must do more than simply transmit a carrier wave. The station has to send information about the sounds that you are to receive. This information is sent by modifying the carrier wave. The carrier wave is modified to carry information in one of two ways, as shown in **Figure 16.**

Section 3 Resource Manager

Chapter *FAST FILE* Resources

Transparency Activity, p. 46
Enrichment, p. 32
Directed Reading for Content Mastery, pp. 21, 22
Reinforcement, p. 29
Activity Worksheet, pp. 7–8

Earth Science Critical Thinking/ Problem Solving, p. 5

1 Motivate

Bellringer

Section Focus Transparencies also are available on the Interactive Chalkboard CD-ROM. L2 ELL

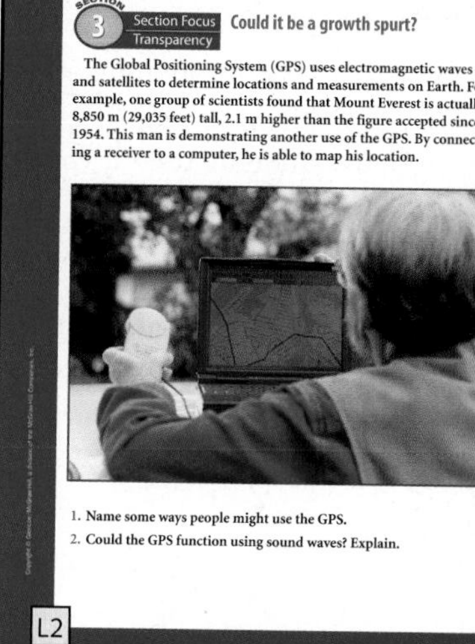

SECTION 3 Section Focus Transparency **Could it be a growth spurt?**

The Global Positioning System (GPS) uses electromagnetic waves and satellites to determine locations and measurements on Earth. For example, one group of scientists found that Mount Everest is actually 8,850 m (29,035 feet) tall, 2.1 m higher than the figure accepted since 1954. This man is demonstrating another use of the GPS. By connecting a receiver to a computer, he is able to map his location.

1. Name some ways people might use the GPS.
2. Could the GPS function using sound waves? Explain.

L2

Electromagnetic Waves

Tie to Prior Knowledge

Communication Ask students to name different forms of electronic communication. They might mention radio, television, telephone, or the Internet. Tell them that much communication relies on the use of radio waves.

2 Teach

Use an Analogy

Boat's Sail Having a larger sail on a boat increases the amount of wind you catch, so the boat moves faster. Similarly, lengthening a radio's antenna frequently improves reception because a larger area of the electromagnetic field is intercepted.

Quick Demo

Favorite Frequencies

Materials AM/FM radio

Estimated Time ten minutes

Procedure Bring a radio to class and have students tune it to AM and FM stations. Stress that radios are tuned in by the frequency of the carrier wave. List students' favorite radio stations on the board in order of increasing frequency. L2

LS **Auditory-Musical**

Wave Frequency Students might assume that AM stations broadcast with higher-frequency carrier waves than FM stations. For example, a station at 620 AM might seem to have a higher frequency than a station at 98 FM because 620 is greater than 98. Explain that the AM frequencies are in thousands of vibrations per second, while the FM frequencies are in millions of vibrations per second.

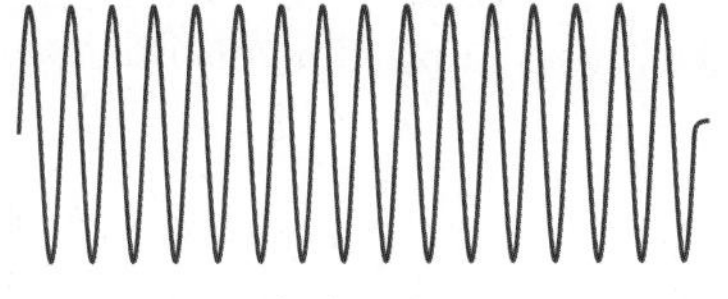
Carrier wave

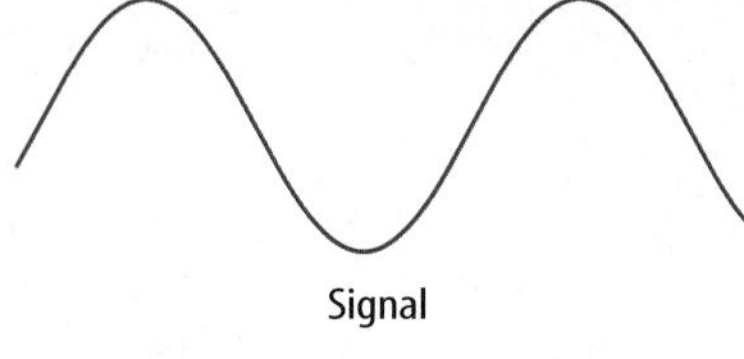
Signal

Amplitude modulation

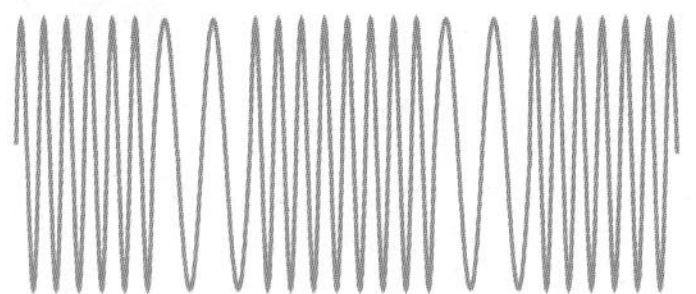
Frequency modulation

Figure 16 A carrier wave broadcast by a radio station can be altered in one of two ways to transmit a signal: amplitude modulation (AM) or frequency modulation (FM).

AM Radio An AM radio station broadcasts information by varying the amplitude of the carrier wave, as shown in **Figure 16.** Your radio detects the variations in amplitude of the carrier wave and produces a changing electric current from these variations. The changing electric current makes the speaker vibrate. AM carrier wave frequencies range from 540,000 to 1,600,000 Hz.

FM Radio Electronic signals are transmitted by FM radio stations by varying the frequency of the carrier wave, as in **Figure 16.** Your radio detects the changes in frequency of the carrier wave. Because the strength of the FM waves is kept fixed, FM signals tend to be more clear than AM signals. FM carrier frequencies range from 88 million to 108 million Hz. This is much higher than AM frequencies, as shown in **Figure 17. Figure 18** shows how radio signals are broadcast.

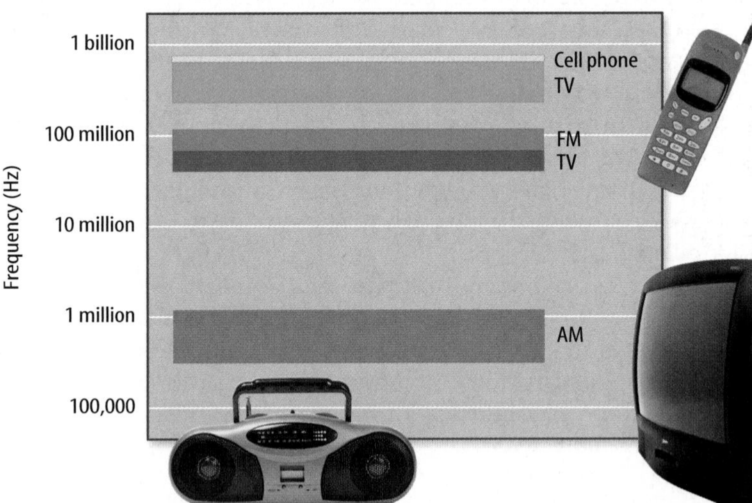

Figure 17 Cell phones, TVs, and radios broadcast at frequencies that range from more than 500,000 Hz to almost 1 billion Hz.

Differentiated Instruction

English-Language Learners To help students understand the meaning of *frequency* and *hertz*, have a student draw high-frequency waves on one end of the board and low-frequency waves on the other. When you list radio stations, write each radio station near the appropriate picture. Point to the pictures often as you use the terms *frequency*, *vibrations per second*, and *hertz*. L1 ELL

Curriculum Connection

Math The frequencies of AM radio stations are in kilohertz and those of FM stations are in megahertz. Have students use the equation wavelength = c/f to determine the wavelengths of the signals transmitted by local radio stations. (c = 300,000,000 m/s) Possible answer: For 98.6 FM, the wavelength is λ = 300,000,000 m/s/ 98,600,000 Hz = 3.04 m L3 LS **Logical-Mathematical**

NATIONAL GEOGRAPHIC VISUALIZING RADIO BROADCASTS

Figure 18

You flick a switch, turn the dial, and music from your favorite radio station fills the room. Although it seems like magic, sounds are transmitted over great distances by converting sound waves to electromagnetic waves and back again, as shown here.

Ⓐ At the radio station, musical instruments and voices create sound waves by causing air molecules to vibrate. Microphones convert these sound waves to a varying electric current, or electronic signal.

Ⓑ This signal then is added to the station's carrier wave. If the station is an AM station, the electronic signal modifies the amplitude of the carrier wave. If the station is a FM station, the electronic signal modifies the frequency of the carrier wave.

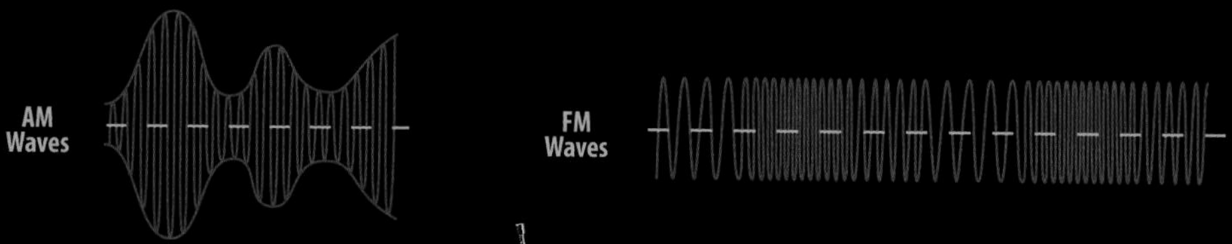

AM Waves

FM Waves

Ⓒ The modified carrier wave is used to vibrate electrons in the station's antenna. These vibrating electrons create a radio wave that travels out in all directions at the speed of light.

Ⓓ The radio wave from the station makes electrons in your radio's antenna vibrate. This creates an electric current. If your radio is tuned to the station's frequency, the carrier wave is removed from the original electronic signal. This signal then makes the radio's speaker vibrate, creating sound waves that you hear as music.

Visualizing Radio Broadcasts

Have students examine the pictures and read the captions. Then ask the following questions.

Compare and contrast how electromagnetic waves are modified to create AM and FM radio signals. Both signals are made by modifying electromagnetic waves and adding them to a carrier wave. The amplitude of the AM carrier wave is modified. The frequency of the FM carrier wave is modified.

Explain the roles of antennas in radio transmission and reception. In transmission, electrons in an antenna are caused to vibrate, sending the electromagnetic wave out in all directions at the speed of light. In reception, the electromagnetic wave makes electrons in an antenna vibrate. The vibrating electrons in the antenna form an electric current that is detected by a receiver.

Activity

Wave Skit Have students write and perform a skit about the life of a radio wave from birth (original sound wave) to death (final conversion back to a sound wave and then dampened). L2

LS **Kinesthetic**

Fun Fact

Radio had only been in use for a few years when the *Titanic* sent its distress calls in 1912. Although radio is credited in aiding *Titanic's* survivors, it was the lack of radio communication with the ship *Californian* that sealed the fate of many who perished.

Differentiated Instruction

Challenge Ask students to find out how radio frequencies are assigned in the United States and how the Federal Communications Commission (FCC) regulates the industry. Have them present their findings to the class. L3

Use an Analogy

Jigsaw Puzzle The tiny rectangles or lines on a television or computer screen form a complete image the same way pieces of a jigsaw puzzle do. Individually the pieces seem meaningless, but when put together they form a picture.

Astronomers Learning about objects in distant space requires observing the universe with the entire range of electromagnetic waves. The Compton Gamma Ray Observatory, for example, detected gamma rays to look for pulsars at the centers of galaxies. The Chandra X-ray Observatory detects X rays to search for binary stars and black holes. The Hubble Space Telescope detects electromagnetic waves from ultraviolet to infrared to look at stars and galaxies.

Career Have students investigate what an astronomer does during a typical work day and the type of challenges they face. Present findings to the class.

Teacher FYI

Display Options To avoid large cathode-ray tubes, flat-screen televisions and the displays on laptop computers use liquid crystal displays or gas-plasma displays.

Reading Check

Answer a sealed vacuum tube in which one or more beams of electrons are produced

Astronomers Do you ever look up at the stars at night and wonder how they were formed? With so many stars and so many galaxies, life might be possible on other planets. Research ways that astronomers use electromagnetic waves to investigate the universe. Choose one project astronomers currently are working on that interests you, and write about it in your Science Journal. Discuss the benefits of a career in astronomy.

Television

What would people hundreds of years ago have thought if they had seen a television? They might seem like magic, but not if you know how they work. Television and radio transmissions are similar. At the television station, sound and images are changed into electronic signals. These signals are broadcast by carrier waves. The audio part of television is sent by FM radio waves. Information about the color and brightness is sent at the same time by AM signals.

Cathode-Ray Tubes In many television sets, images are displayed on a cathode-ray tube (CRT), as shown in **Figure 19.** A **cathode-ray tube** is a sealed vacuum tube in which one or more beams of electrons are produced. The CRT in a color TV produces three electron beams that are focused by a magnetic field and strike a coated screen. The screen is speckled with more than 100,000 rectangular spots that are of three types. One type glows red, another glows green, and the third type glows blue when electrons strike it. The spots are grouped together with a red, green, and blue spot in each group.

An image is created when the three electron beams of the CRT sweep back and forth across the screen. Each electron beam controls the brightness of each type of spot, according to the information in the video signal from the TV station. By varying the brightness of each spot in a group, the three spots together can form any color so that you see a full-color image.

Reading Check *What is a cathode-ray tube?*

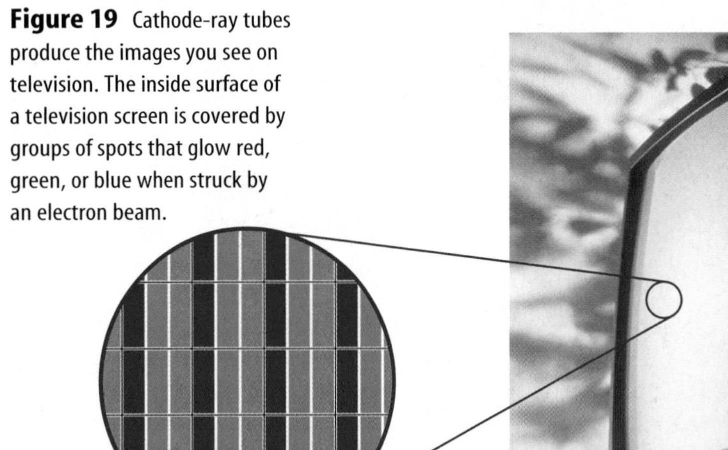

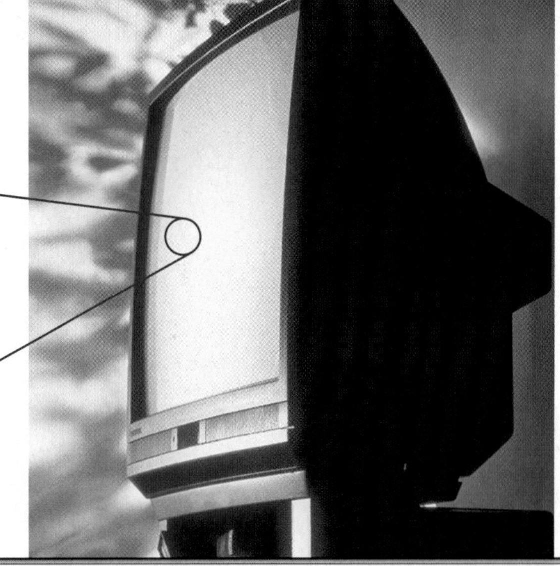

Figure 19 Cathode-ray tubes produce the images you see on television. The inside surface of a television screen is covered by groups of spots that glow red, green, or blue when struck by an electron beam.

Cultural Diversity

Television As a young boy, Kenjito Takayanagi was a slow learner in school, but hard work enabled him to overcome his difficulties. In 1926, he transmitted the first television signal in Japan. Today he is honored as the founder of Japanese television. Have students make a class time line showing this and other contributions to the invention of television.

Visual Learning

Figure 19 The tiny rectangular spots on a television screen are colored red, green, and blue because these are the primary colors of light. Our eyes combine these into different colors, depending on the intensity of each rectangle. To demonstrate this idea, allow students to experiment with additive color filters or paddles. L2 LS **Visual-Spatial**

Telephones

Until about 1950, human operators were needed to connect many calls between people. Just 20 years ago you never would have seen someone walking down the street talking on a telephone. Today, cell phones are seen everywhere. When you speak into a telephone, a microphone converts sound waves into an electrical signal. In cell phones, this current is used to create radio waves that are transmitted to and from a microwave tower, as shown in **Figure 20.** A cell phone uses one radio signal for sending information to a tower at a base station. It uses another signal for receiving information from the base station. The base stations are several kilometers apart. The area each one covers is called a cell. If you move from one cell to another while using a cell phone, an automated control station transfers your signal to the new cell.

Figure 20 The antenna at the top of a microwave tower receives signals from nearby cell phones. **Determine** *whether any microwave towers are located near your school or home. Describe their locations.*

Reading Check *What are the cells in a cell phone system?*

Cordless Telephones Like a cellular telephone, a cordless telephone is a transceiver. A **transceiver** transmits one radio signal and receives another radio signal from a base unit. Having two signals at different frequencies allows you to talk and listen at the same time. Cordless telephones work much like cell phones. With a cordless telephone, however, you must be close to the base unit. Another drawback is that when someone nearby is using a cordless telephone, you could hear that conversation on your phone if the frequencies match. For this reason, many cordless phones have a channel button. This allows you to switch your call to another frequency.

Pagers Another method of transmitting signals is a pager, which allows messages to be sent to a small radio receiver. A caller leaves a message at a central terminal by entering a callback number through a telephone keypad or by entering a text message from a computer. At the terminal, the message is changed into an electronic signal and transmitted by radio waves. Each pager is given a unique number for identification. This identification number is sent along with the message. Your pager receives all messages that are transmitted in the area at its assigned frequency. However, your pager responds only to messages with its particular identification number. Newer pagers can send data as well as receive them.

Topic: Radio Wave Technology

Visit gpscience.com for Web links to information about advances in radio wave technology.

Activity List the advances you find, and write about the significance of each one in your Science Journal.

Discussion

Cell Limit Why is there a limit to the number of people who can talk on cell phones in a particular cell at the same time? Each phone uses a different frequency of electromagnetic waves. If all of the assigned frequencies are being used, no other phones can be used at that time. L2

LS **Logical-Mathematical**

Caption Answer

Figure 20 Students should be encouraged to look for microwave towers on both freestanding towers and on other tall objects, such as buildings or water towers.

Discussion

Building Block Why is it difficult to talk on a cell phone if you are inside a metal building? The metal reflects the incoming and outgoing microwaves. L2

LS **Logical-Mathematical**

Answer The area that can receive signals from a base station

Science Journal

Telephones of the Future Technology associated with telephones is changing rapidly, and the difference between computers and telecommunication devices is becoming less distinct. Have students write in their Science Journals descriptions of what they think telephones will be like in ten years. L2 LS P **Linguistic**

Use Science Words

Word Origin The word *satellite* has many meanings. Ask students to look up the origin of the word *satellite* and list various types of *satellites*. For each one, they should describe why the word satellite is an appropriate term. *Satellite* comes from the Latin word *satelles* meaning "attendant." Possible types: moons, satellite countries.

Activity

GEO v. GPS Most communication satellites follow a geostationary equatorial orbit (GEO), also called a geosynchronous orbit. This is not the case with satellites for the Global Positioning System (GPS). Have students research the difference between a GEO and a GPS orbit. In a GEO, the satellite orbits Earth directly above the equator once every 24 hours, so that it is always above the same point on the equator. It maintains an altitude of about 35,800 km. In contrast, each of the 24 GPS satellites follows a different, circular orbit, circling Earth every 12 hours at an altitude of about 20,000 km. L2 LS **Linguistic**

Figure 21 Communications satellites, like the one shown here, use solar panels to provide the electrical energy they need to communicate with receivers on Earth. The solar panels are the structures on either side of the central body of the satellite.

Communications Satellites

Since satellites were first developed, thousands have been launched into Earth's orbit. Many of these, like the one in **Figure 21,** are used for communication. A station broadcasts a high-frequency microwave signal to the satellite. The satellite receives the signal, amplifies it, and transmits it to a particular region on Earth. To avoid interference, the frequency broadcast by the satellite is different than the frequency broadcast from Earth.

Satellite Telephone Systems If you have a mobile telephone, you can make a phone call when sailing across the ocean. To call on a mobile telephone, the telephone transmits radio waves directly to a satellite. The satellite relays the signal to a ground station, and the call is passed on to the telephone network. Satellite links work well for one-way transmissions, but two-way communications can have an annoying delay caused by the large distance the signals travel to and from the satellite.

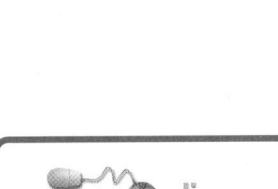

Topic: Satellite Communication

Visit gpscience.com for Web links to information about ways satellites are used for communication.

Activity Write a paragraph describing the advantages of placing a communications satellite in a geosynchronus orbit. Include a diagram.

Television Satellites The satellite-reception dishes that you sometimes see in yards or attached to houses are receivers for television satellite signals. Satellite television is used as an alternative to ground-based transmission. Communications satellites use microwaves rather than the longer-wavelength radio waves used for normal television broadcasts. Short-wavelength microwaves travel more easily through the atmosphere. The ground receiver dishes are rounded to help focus the microwaves onto an antenna.

372 CHAPTER 12 Electromagnetic Waves

The Global Positioning System

Getting lost while hiking is not uncommon, but if you are carrying a Global Positioning System receiver, it is much less likely to happen. The **Global Positioning System (GPS)** is a system of satellites, ground monitoring stations, and receivers that determine your exact location at or above Earth's surface. The 24 satellites necessary for 24-hour, around-the-world coverage became fully operational in 1995. GPS satellites are owned and operated by the United States Department of Defense, but the microwave signals they send out can be used by anyone. As shown in **Figure 22,** signals from four satellites are needed to determine the location of an object using a GPS receiver. Today GPS receivers are used in airplanes, ships, cars, and even by hikers.

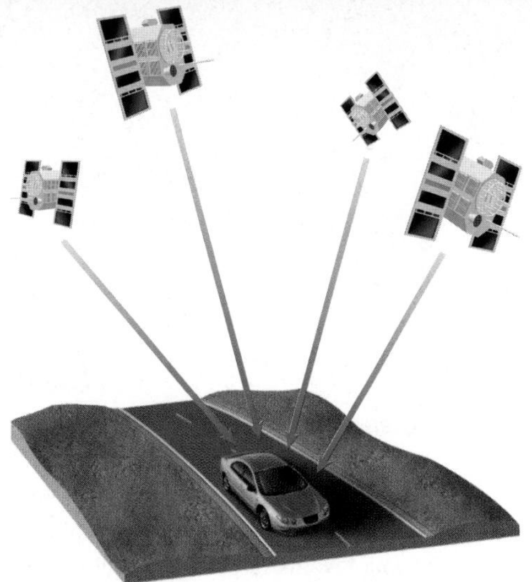

Figure 22 A GPS receiver uses signals from orbiting satellites to determine the receiver's location.

section 3 review

Summary

Radio Transmission

- Radio stations transmit electromagnetic waves that receivers convert to sound waves.
- Each AM radio station is assigned a carrier wave frequency and varies the amplitude of the carrier waves to transmit a signal.
- Each FM radio station is assigned a carrier wave frequency and varies the frequency of the carrier waves to transmit a signal.

Television

- TV sets use cathode-ray tubes to convert electronic signals from TV stations into both sound and images.

Telephones

- Telephones contain transceivers that convert sound waves into electrical signals and also convert electrical signals into sound waves.
- Wires, microwave towers, and satellites are used to transmit and receive telephone signals.

Global Positioning System

- The Global Positioning System uses a system of satellites to determine your exact position.

Self Check

1. **Explain** the difference between AM and FM radio. Make a sketch of how a carrier wave is modulated in AM and FM radio.
2. **Define** a cathode-ray tube, and explain how it is used in a television.
3. **Describe** what happens if you are talking on a cell phone while riding in a car and you travel from one cell to another cell.
4. **Explain** some of the uses of a Global Positioning System. Why might emergency vehicles all be equipped with GPS receivers?
5. **Think Critically** Why do cordless telephones stop working if you move too far from the base unit?

Applying Math

6. **Calculate a Ratio** A group of red, green and blue spots on a TV screen is a pixel. A standard TV has 460 pixels horizontally and 360 pixels vertically. A high-definition TV has 1,920 horizontal and 1,080 vertical pixels. What is the ratio of the number of pixels in a high-definition TV to the number in a standard TV?

Science Online gpscience.com/self_check_quiz

3 Assess

DAILY INTERVENTION

Check for Understanding

Visual-Spatial In pairs or small groups, have students create diagrams that illustrate the steps required for a radio, television, telephone, or satellite to transmit a message.

Reteach

How it Works Bring a radio or television into your classroom. Have students demonstrate the use of each device with proper physics explanations. They should include explanations about how the radio waves are picked up and what happens when you change the channel. L2 IS **Kinesthetic**

Assessment

Performance Have students work in pairs to make posters that show how one form of radio communication described in this section works. Posters can be displayed in the classroom to help students remember what they have studied. Use **Performance Assessment in the Science Classroom,** p. 145. L2 COOP LEARN IS **Visual-Spatial**

section 3 review

1. For AM, amplitude is modulated. For FM, frequency is modulated. Check students' sketches.
2. A sealed vacuum tube in which beams of electrons are produced. The electron beams hit dots on a coated screen, causing them to glow.
3. A central controller transfers your signal to the base station in the new cell.
4. GPS is used by hikers, airplanes, ships, cars, and others to identify their location on Earth. Emergency vehicles have GPS receivers to help them find places quickly.
5. The radio waves broadcast by the base unit become too weak for the handset to detect.
6. 12.5 to 1

Real-World Question

Purpose

Internet Students will use Internet sites that can be accessed through gpscience.com/internet_lab. They will investigate AM and FM radio station transmission frequencies and ranges.

Non-Internet Sources Contact the Federal Communications Commission (FCC) for information about station transmission frequencies and ranges.

Time Required two days

Make a Plan

Preparation Access gpscience.com/internet_lab to run through the steps that the students will follow.

Non-Internet Sources Organize FCC information about local radio stations by frequency and range.

Follow Your Plan

Teaching Strategy Remind students that AM stations broadcast at a lower frequency. These signals reflect off the ionosphere, providing a greater range. FM signals must travel by line of sight, so their range is less.

Use the Internet

Radio Frequencies

Goals

- **Research** which frequencies are used by different radio stations.
- **Observe** the reception of your favorite radio station.
- **Make** a chart of your findings and communicate them to other students.

Data Source

Visit gpscience.com/internet_lab for more information on radio frequencies, different frequencies of radio stations around the country, and the ranges of AM and FM broadcasts.

Real-World Question

The signals from many radio stations broadcasting at different frequencies are hitting your radio's antenna at the same time. When you tune to your favorite station, the electronics inside your radio amplify the signal at the frequency broadcast by the station. The signal from your favorite station is broadcast from a transmission site that may be several miles away.

You may have noticed that if you're listening to a radio station while driving in a car, sometimes the station gets fuzzy and you'll hear another station at the same time. Sometimes you lose the station completely. How far can you drive before that happens? Does the distance vary depending on the station you listen to? What are the ranges of radio stations? Form a hypothesis about how far you think a radio station can transmit? Which type of signal, AM or FM, has a greater range? Form a hypothesis about the range of your favorite radio station.

Make a Plan

1. **Research** what frequencies are used by AM and FM radio stations in your area and other areas around the country.
2. **Determine** these stations' broadcast locations.
3. **Determine** the broadcast range of radio stations in your area.
4. **Observe** how frequencies differ. What is the maximum difference between frequencies for FM stations in your area? AM stations?

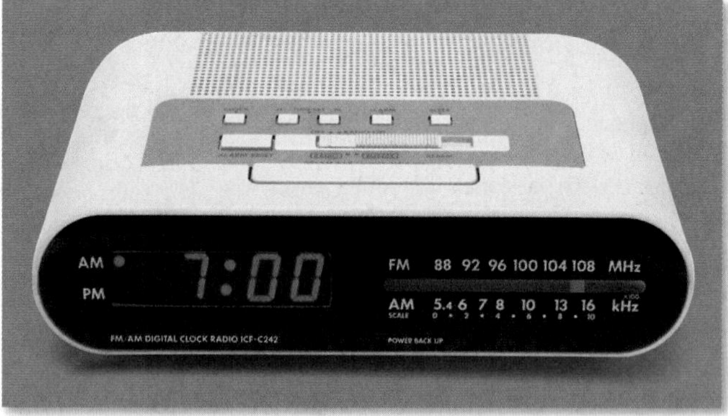

Alternative Inquiry Lab

Student Investigation To make this Lab an Inquiry Lab, have students design a way to compare the reception of local AM and FM stations under various conditions, such as day/night or clear/cloudy.

374 CHAPTER 12 Electromagnetic Waves

Follow Your Plan

1. **Make** sure your teacher approves your plan before you start.
2. Visit the link shown below for links to different radio stations.
3. **Compare** the different frequencies of the stations and the locations of the broadcasts.
4. **Determine** the range of radio stations in your area and the power of their broadcast signal in watts.
5. **Record** your data in your Science Journal.

Analyze Your Data

1. **Make** a map of the radio stations in your area. Do the ranges of AM stations differ from FM stations?
2. **Make** a map of different radio stations around the country. Do you see any patterns in the frequencies for stations that are located near each other?
3. **Write** a description that compares how close the frequencies of AM stations are and how close the frequencies of FM stations are. Also compare the power of their broadcast signals and their ranges.
4. **Share** your data by posting it at the link shown below.

Conclude and Apply

1. **Compare** your findings to those of your classmates and other data that was posted at the link shown below. Do all AM stations and FM stations have different ranges?
2. **Observe** your map of the country. How close can stations with similar frequencies be? Do AM and FM stations appear to be different in this respect?
3. **Infer** The power of the broadcast signal also determines its range. How does the power (wattage) of the signals affect your analysis of your data?

Find this lab using the link below. Post your data in the table provided. **Compare** your data to that of other students. Then combine your data with theirs and make a map for your class that shows all of the data.

Science Online
gpscience.com/internet_lab

Analyze Your Data

1. AM stations have longer ranges than FM stations. AM signals are reflected by the ionosphere, which enables the signals to travel farther. The higher frequency FM signals are not reflected.
2. If two stations' transmitters are close to each other, their stations' frequencies will not be the same.
3. AM stations are spaced no closer than 10 kHz. FM stations are spaced no closer than 200 kHz.
4. Students can compare radio stations' ranges and frequencies in different locations around the country.

Conclude and Apply

1. AM stations and FM stations have different ranges. Broadcast range depends on a station's transmitter power.
2. Station transmitters with similar frequencies cannot be very close together because their signals would interfere with one another. AM stations differ from FM stations in how close their transmitters can be, because AM stations have a greater broadcast range than FM stations.
3. Students should use information about signal power and frequency to determine the ranges of radio stations.

Assessment

Performance Show radio station transmitter locations on a map of your area. Have students draw each station's range on the map to understand how reception and interference can affect the ability to receive a station's signal. Use **Performance Assessment in the Science Classroom,** p. 127.

Use a spreadsheet program to collect information about radio stations. Include the station's call letters, locations of transmitters, frequency, and power.

TIME

Content Background

By the nineteenth century, it was widely believed that because light was a wave, it required a medium in which to travel, just as sound travels through air. The medium was called the ether, and was believed to be stationary. As a result, the ether provided an absolute reference system to which measurements in all other reference systems could be compared.

Several attempts were made to detect the ether, but failed. In 1887, Albert Michelson and Edward Morley attempted to measure the motion of Earth through the ether. To their surprise, they found no effects on the speed of light due to Earth's motion through the ether.

Einstein's paper on the special theory of relativity appeared in 1905. It postulated in any reference frame that is not accelerating, physical laws have the same form and that the speed of light is a constant. It was soon realized that the special theory could account for the results of the Michelson-Morley experiment, which was now seen as proving that the ether did not exist.

Discussion

Resisting Change Why are new theories often met with resistance? Possible answer: When theories are first proposed, they may not supported by enough experimental evidence to convince people of their validity.

Historical Significance

Additional Ideas Einstein's theory of special relativity led to the idea that matter and energy are equivalent ($E=mc^2$). The theory also provides a more accurate description of phenomena involving objects moving near the speed of light than was provided by Newton's laws of motion.

TIME SCIENCE AND HISTORY

SCIENCE CAN CHANGE THE COURSE OF HISTORY!

Einstein and the Special Theory of Relativity

Catch a Wave

At age sixteen, Albert Einstein wondered "What would it be like to ride a beam of light?" He imagined what might happen if he turned on a flashlight while riding a light beam. Because the flashlight was already traveling at the speed of light, would light from the flashlight travel at twice the speed of light?

What's so special?

Einstein thought about this problem and in 1905 he published the special theory of relativity. This theory stated that the speed of light measured by any observer that moves with a constant speed always would be the same. The measured speed of light would not depend on the speed of the observer or on how fast the source of light was moving. Einstein answered the question he asked himself when he was sixteen. He had found the universal speed limit that can't be broken.

It Doesn't Add Up

According to Einstein, electromagnetic waves like light waves behave very differently from other waves. For example, sound waves from the siren of an ambulance moving toward you move faster than they would if the ambulance were not moving. The speed of the ambulance adds to the speed of the sound waves. However, for light waves, the speed of a light source doesn't add to the speed of light.

Very Strange But True

Einstein's special theory of relativity makes other strange predictions. According to this theory, no object can travel faster than the speed of light. Another prediction is that the measured length of a moving object is shorter than when the object is at rest. Also, moving clocks should run slower than when they are at rest. These predictions have been confirmed by experiments. Measurements have shown, for example, that a moving clock does run slower.

Communicate Research the life of Albert Einstein and make a timeline showing important events in his life. Also include on your timeline major historical events that occurred during Einstein's lifetime.

For more information, visit gpscience.com/time

Communicate Encourage students to include international events; examine how these events impacted Einstein's research. Also, there are many visual metaphors and cartoons available to explain Einstein's theories in simple terms. Go to gpscience.com for more information.

Resources for Teachers and Students

Albert Einstein: Physicist and Genius by Joyce Goldenstern, Enslow Publishers, Inc., 1994

Einstein's Universe by Nigel Calder, Random House Value Publishing, Inc., 1990

Reviewing Main Ideas

Section 1 What are electromagnetic waves?

1. Electromagnetic waves consist of vibrating electric and magnetic fields, and are produced by vibrating electric charges.

2. Electromagnetic waves carry radiant energy and can travel through a vacuum or through matter.
3. Electromagnetic waves sometimes behave like particles called photons.

Section 2 The Electromagnetic Spectrum

1. Electromagnetic waves with the longest wavelengths are called radio waves. Radio waves have wavelengths greater than about 1 mm. Microwaves are radio waves with wavelengths between about 1 m and 1 mm.
2. Infrared waves have wavelengths between about 1 mm and 750 billionths of a meter. Warmer objects emit more infrared waves than cooler objects.
3. Visible light rays have wavelengths between about 750 and 400 billionths of a meter. Substances in your eyes react with visible light to enable you to see.
4. Ultraviolet waves have frequencies between about 400 and 10 billionths of a meter. Excessive exposure to ultraviolet waves can damage human skin.
5. X rays and gamma rays are high-energy electromagnetic waves with wavelengths less than 10 billionths of a meter. X rays are used in medical imaging.

Section 3 Radio Communication

1. Modulated radio waves are used often for communication. AM and FM are two forms of carrier wave modulation.
2. Television signals are transmitted as a combination of AM and FM waves.
3. Cellular telephones, cordless telephones, and pagers use radio waves to transmit signals. Communications satellites are used to relay telephone and television signals over long distances.
4. The Global Positioning System enables an accurate position on Earth to be determined.

FOLDABLES™ Use the Foldable that you made at the beginning of this chapter to help you review electromagnetic waves.

gpscience.com/interactive_tutor

Reviewing Main Ideas

Summary statements can be used by students to review the major concepts of the chapter.

Visit gpscience.com
/self_check_quiz
/interactive_tutor
/vocabulary_puzzlemaker
/chapter_review
/standardized_test

Assessment Transparency

For additional assessment questions, use the *Assessment Transparency* located in the transparency book.

Assessment

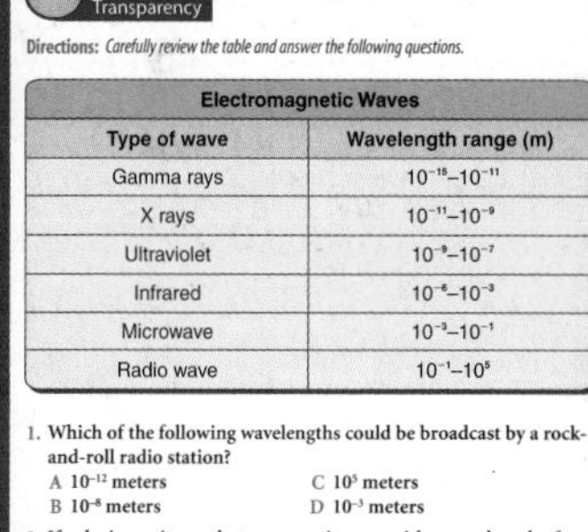

Assessment Transparency **Electromagnetic Waves**

Directions: *Carefully review the table and answer the following questions.*

Electromagnetic Waves	
Type of wave	**Wavelength range (m)**
Gamma rays	10^{-15}–10^{-11}
X rays	10^{-11}–10^{-9}
Ultraviolet	10^{-9}–10^{-7}
Infrared	10^{-6}–10^{-3}
Microwave	10^{-3}–10^{-1}
Radio wave	10^{-1}–10^{5}

1. Which of the following wavelengths could be broadcast by a rock-and-roll radio station?
   A 10^{-12} meters
   B 10^{-8} meters
   C 10^{5} meters
   D 10^{-3} meters
2. If a device emits an electromagnetic wave with a wavelength of 10^{-10} meters, then it is probably____.
   F an X-ray machine
   G an AM/FM car radio
   H a microwave
   J a light bulb
3. Food can be heated rapidly in your own home using an electromagnetic wave with a wavelength of ____.
   A 10^{-13}
   B 10^{-9}
   C 10^{-2}
   D 100

L2

Electromagnetic Waves

FOLDABLES™ Have students use their Foldables to review the content of the chapter. On the back of the paper, have students explain how they would likely make use of each type of electromagnetic wave in the course of their day.

Using Vocabulary

1. radio waves
2. infrared waves
3. radiant energy
4. ultraviolet waves
5. carrier waves
6. cathode ray tube
7. electromagnetic waves

Checking Concepts

8. A
9. C
10. B
11. A
12. C
13. B
14. D
15. A
16. C

Interpreting Graphics

17. see student page.
18. see student page.

Thinking Critically

19. They have enough energy to pass through the body's soft tissue but still be blocked by hard tissue. This causes a shadow image of the hard tissue to be formed on photographic film.
20. No, because the electric field must be changing to produce the magnetic field and the magnetic field must be changing to produce the electric field.
21. Visible light has a very high frequency, on the order of 10^{15} Hz. The magnetic field in visible light changes direction much too rapidly for the compass needle to respond.
22. Answers will vary.
23. Possible answer: Ultraviolet waves would be absorbed by Earth's ozone layer.

chapter 12 Review

Using Vocabulary

carrier wave p. 367	microwaves p. 361
cathode-ray tube p. 370	photon p. 358
electromagnetic wave p. 354	radiant energy p. 357
gamma rays p. 365	radio waves p. 361
Global Positioning System p. 373	transceiver p. 371
infrared waves p. 362	ultraviolet waves p. 363
	visible light p. 363
	X rays p. 365

Complete each statement using the correct word or words from the vocabulary list above.

1. ________ are the type of electromagnetic waves often used for communication.
2. A remote control uses ________ to communicate with a television set.
3. Electromagnetic waves carry ________ .
4. If you stay outdoors too long, your skin might be burned by exposure to ________ from the Sun.
5. A radio station broadcasts radio waves called ________ that have the specific frequency assigned to the station.
6. The image on a television screen is produced by a ________.
7. Transverse waves that are produced by vibrating electric charges and consist of vibrating electric and magnetic fields are ________.

Checking Concepts

Choose the word or phrase that best answers the question.

8. Which type of electromagnetic wave is the most energetic?
   A) gamma rays
   B) ultraviolet waves
   C) infrared waves
   D) microwaves
9. Electromagnetic waves can behave like what type of particle?
   A) electrons **C)** photons
   B) molecules **D)** atoms
10. Which type of electromagnetic wave enables skin cells to produce vitamin D?
    A) visible light
    B) ultraviolet waves
    C) infrared waves
    D) X rays
11. Which of the following describes X rays?
    A) short wavelength, high frequency
    B) short wavelength, low frequency
    C) long wavelength, high frequency
    D) long wavelength, low frequency
12. Which of the following is changing in an AM radio wave?
    A) speed **C)** amplitude
    B) frequency **D)** wavelength
13. Which type of electromagnetic wave has wavelengths greater than about 1 mm?
    A) X rays **C)** gamma rays
    B) radio waves **D)** ultraviolet waves
14. What is the name of the ability of some materials to absorb ultraviolet light and re-emit it as visible light?
    A) modulation **C)** transmission
    B) handoff **D)** fluorescence
15. Which of these colors of visible light has the shortest wavelength?
    A) blue **C)** red
    B) green **D)** white
16. Which type of electromagnetic wave has wavelengths slightly longer than humans can see?
    A) X rays
    B) ultraviolet waves
    C) infrared waves
    D) gamma rays

Science Online gpscience.com/vocabulary_puzzlemaker

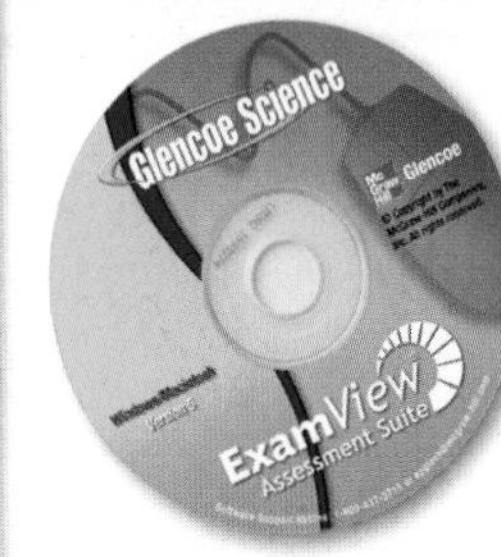

Use the *ExamView® Assessment Suite* CD-ROM to:
- create multiple versions of tests
- create modified tests with one mouse click for inclusion students
- edit existing questions and add your own questions
- build tests aligned with state standards using built-in State Curriculum Tags
- change English tests to Spanish with one mouse click and vice versa

Interpreting Graphics

17. Copy and complete the following table about the electromagnetic spectrum.

Uses of Electromagnetic Waves	
Type of Electromagnetic Waves	Examples of How Electromagnetic Waves Are Used
radio waves	radio, TV transmission
Infrared waves	remote control transmitters
Visible light	vision
ultraviolet light	fluorescent materials
X rays	medical imaging
gamma rays	destroying harmful cells

18. Copy and complete the following events chain about the destruction of ozone molecules in the ozone layer by CFC molecules.

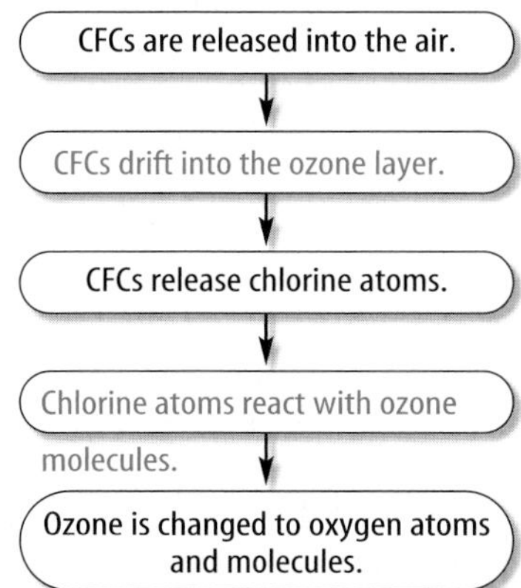

CFCs are released into the air.
CFCs drift into the ozone layer.
CFCs release chlorine atoms.
Chlorine atoms react with ozone molecules.
Ozone is changed to oxygen atoms and molecules.

Thinking Critically

19. **Explain** why X rays are used in medical imaging.

20. **Predict** whether an electromagnetic wave would travel through space if its electric and magnetic fields were not changing with time. Explain your reasoning.

21. **Infer** Electromagnetic waves consist of vibrating electric and magnetic fields. A magnetic field can make a compass needle. Why doesn't a compass needle move when visible light strikes the compass?

22. **Classify** Look around your home, school, and community. Make a list of the different devices that use electromagnetic waves. Beside each device, write the type of electromagnetic wave the device uses.

23. **Form a hypothesis** to explain why communications satellites don't use ultraviolet waves to receive information and transmit signals to Earth's surface.

24. **Compare** the energy of photons corresponding to infrared waves with the energy of photons corresponding to ultraviolet waves.

25. **Determine** whether or not all electromagnetic waves always travel at the speed of light. Explain.

Applying Math

26. **Use Fractions** When visible light waves travel in ethyl alcohol, their speed is three fourths of the speed of light in air. What is the speed of light in ethyl alcohol?

27. **Use Scientific Notation** The speed of light in a vacuum has been determined to be 299, 792, 458 m/s. Express this number to four significant digits using scientific notation.

28. **Calculate Wavelength** A radio wave has a frequency of 540,000 Hz and travels at a speed of 300,000 km/s. Use the wave speed equation to calculate the wavelength of the radio wave. Express your answer in meters.

24. Photons corresponding to electromagnetic waves with higher frequencies have greater energy; photons corresponding to ultraviolet waves will have greater energy than infrared photons.

25. No. They travel at their maximum speed in a vacuum. When moving through matter their speed is slower.

Applying Math

National Math Standards

1, 2, 9

26. 225,000 km/s

27. 2.998×10^8 km/s

28. $v = f\lambda$, so $\lambda = v/f = \frac{(300{,}000 \text{ km/s})}{(540{,}000 \text{ Hz})} = 0.55 \text{ km} = 550 \text{ m}$

Assessment Resources

Reproducible Masters

Chapter *Fast File* Resources
Chapter Review, pp. 37–38
Chapter Tests, pp. 39–42
Assessment Transparency Activity, p. 49

Glencoe Science Web site
Chapter Review Test
Standardized Test Practice

Glencoe Technology

Assessment Transparency
ExamView® Assessment Suite
MindJogger Videoquiz
Interactive Chalkboard

Answer Sheet A practice answer sheet can be found at gpscience.com/answer_sheet.

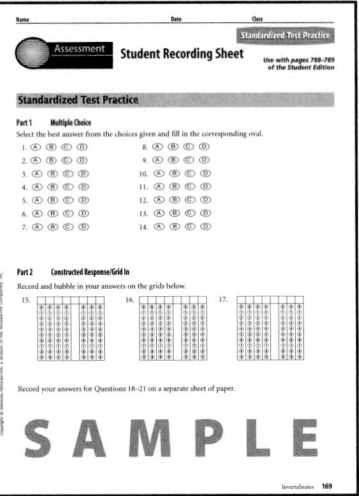

Name Date Class

Assessment Student Recording Sheet

Standardized Test Practice

Use with pages 788–789 of the Student Edition

Standardized Test Practice

Part 1 Multiple Choice

Select the best answer from the choices given and fill in the corresponding oval.

1. Ⓐ Ⓑ Ⓒ Ⓓ 8. Ⓐ Ⓑ Ⓒ Ⓓ
2. Ⓐ Ⓑ Ⓒ Ⓓ 9. Ⓐ Ⓑ Ⓒ Ⓓ
3. Ⓐ Ⓑ Ⓒ Ⓓ 10. Ⓐ Ⓑ Ⓒ Ⓓ
4. Ⓐ Ⓑ Ⓒ Ⓓ 11. Ⓐ Ⓑ Ⓒ Ⓓ
5. Ⓐ Ⓑ Ⓒ Ⓓ 12. Ⓐ Ⓑ Ⓒ Ⓓ
6. Ⓐ Ⓑ Ⓒ Ⓓ 13. Ⓐ Ⓑ Ⓒ Ⓓ
7. Ⓐ Ⓑ Ⓒ Ⓓ 14. Ⓐ Ⓑ Ⓒ Ⓓ

Part 2 Constructed Response/Grid In

Record and bubble in your answers on the grids below.

15. 16. 17.

Record your answers for Questions 18–21 on a separate sheet of paper.

SAMPLE

Part 1 Multiple Choice

1. A
2. D
3. B
4. C
5. A
6. C
7. B
8. D

Part 2 Short Response

9. carrier wave
10. AM, amplitude modulation
11. Hertz, the number of wavelengths that pass a point per second
12. Ultraviolet waves
13. radiant energy
14. A changing electric field creates a changing magnetic field, and a changing magnetic field creates a changing electric field.
15. FM

chapter 12 Standardized Test Practice

Part 1 Multiple Choice

Record your answers on the answer sheet provided by your teacher or on a sheet of paper.

1. Which of the following produces electromagnetic waves?
   A. vibrating charge
   B. direct current
   C. static charge
   D. constant magnetic field

Use the photograph below to answer questions 2 and 3.

2. A television image is produced by three electron beams. What device inside a television set produces the electron beams?
   A. transceiver **C.** antenna
   B. transmitter **D.** cathode-ray tube

3. What colors are the three types of glowing spots that are combined to form the different colors in the image on the screen?
   A. red, yellow, blue
   B. red, green, blue
   C. cyan, magenta, yellow
   D. cyan, magenta, blue

Test-Taking Tip

Marking on Tests Be sure to ask if it is okay to write on the test booklet when taking the test, but make sure you mark all answers on your answer sheet.

4. Which of the following explains how interference is avoided between the signals communications satellites receive and the signals they broadcast?
   A. The signals travel at different speeds.
   B. The signals have different amplitudes.
   C. The signals have different frequencies.
   D. The signals are only magnetic.

5. Which of the following people explained how light can behave as a particle, called a photon, whose energy depends on the frequency of light?
   A. Einstein **C.** Newton
   B. Hertz **D.** Galileo

Use the table below to answer questions 6 and 7.

Regions of the Electromagnetic Spectrum		
Infrared waves	Radio waves	Gamma rays
X rays	Visible light	Ultraviolet waves

6. If you arranged the list of electromagnetic waves shown above in order from shortest to longest wavelength, which would be first on the list?
   A. radio waves **C.** gamma rays
   B. X rays **D.** visible light

7. Which region of the electromagnetic spectrum listed in the table above includes microwaves?
   A. gamma rays **C.** ultraviolet waves
   B. radio waves **D.** infrared waves

8. The warmth you feel when you stand in front of a fire is thermal energy transmitted to you by what type of electromagnetic waves?
   A. X rays **C.** ultraviolet waves
   B. microwaves **D.** infrared waves

Part 3 Open Ended

16. The music is converted into a varying electric current. This current alters the carrier wave, which causes electrons to vibrate in the station's antenna, broadcasting a modulated carrier wave.
17. by causing charged particles within objects to vibrate.
18. A decrease in ozone allows more of the sun's harmful ultraviolet waves reach the earth. Other electromagnetic waves would not be affected.
19. Radio signals cause electron beams to vary the brightness of red, green, and blue spots. Varying the brightness of the three spots enables any color to be produced at any place on the screen.

Part 2 Short Response/Grid In

Record your answers on the answer sheet provided by your teacher or on a sheet of paper.

Use the illustrations below to answer questions 9 and 10.

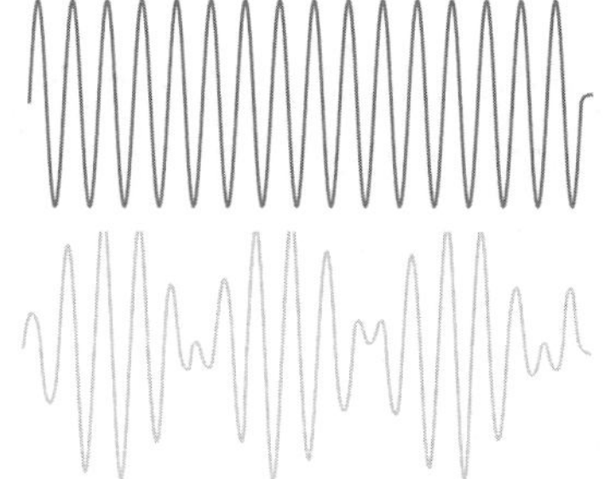

9. The illustration above shows two radio waves broadcast by a radio station. What is the upper, unmodulated wave called?

10. The lower figure shows the same wave that has been modulated to carry sound information. What type of modulation does it show?

11. The frequency of electromagnetic waves is measured in what units? What does this unit mean?

12. Even on a cloudy day, you can get sunburned outside. However, inside a glass greenhouse, you won't get sunburned. Which type of electromagnetic waves will pass through clouds, but not glass?

13. What term refers to the energy carried by an electromagnetic wave?

14. The following sentence is *not* true: A magnetic field creates an electric field, and an electric field creates a magnetic field. Rewrite the sentence so that it is true.

15. Which type of radio station transmits radio waves that have a higher frequency, AM stations or FM stations?

Part 3 Open Ended

Record your answers on a sheet of paper.

16. A CD player converts the musical information on a CD to a varying electric current. Describe how the varying electric current produced by a CD player in a radio station is converted into radio waves.

17. Explain how an electromagnetic wave that strikes a material transfers radiant energy to the atoms in the material.

18. How would changing the amount of ozone in the ozone layer affect the amount of the different types of electromagnetic waves emitted by the Sun that reach Earth's surface?

19. Explain how the cathode-ray tube in a television is able to produce all the colors that you see in an image on a television screen, using just three electron beams.

20. If all atoms contain electric charges, and if all atoms are constantly in motion, explain why all objects should emit electromagnetic waves.

Use the illustration below to answer questions 21 and 22.

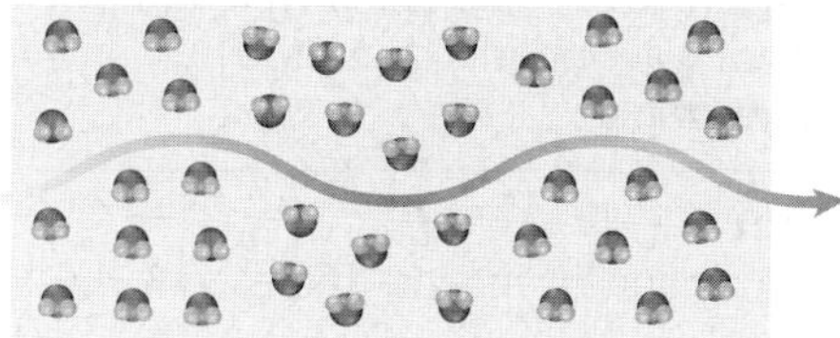

21. The illustration above shows microwaves interacting with water molecules in food. How does the electric field in microwaves affect water molecules?

22. Describe how thermal energy inside food is produced by microwaves interacting with water molecules.

20. Atoms in motion contain moving electrons which produce changing electric fields; changing electric fields create changing magnetic fields; vibrating electric and magnetic fields create electromagnetic waves

21. causes water molecules to rotate back and forth

22. The friction that occurs as rotating water molecules interact with each other is converted into thermal energy.

Rubrics

The following rubrics are sample scoring devices for short response and extended response questions.

Short Response

Points	Description
2	The student demonstrates a thorough understanding of the science of the task. The response may contain minor flaws that do not detract from the demonstration of a thorough understanding.
1	The student has provided a response that is only partially correct.
0	The student has provided a completely incorrect solution or no response at all.

Extended Response

Points	Description
4	The student demonstrates a thorough understanding of the science of the task. The response may contain minor flaws that do not detract from the demonstration of a thorough understanding.
3	The student demonstrates an understanding of the science of the task. The response is essentially correct and demonstrates an essential but less than thorough understanding of the science.
2	The student demonstrates only a partial understanding of the science of the task. Although the student may have used the correct approach to a solution or may have provided a correct solution, the work lacks an essential understanding of the underlying science concepts.
1	The student demonstrates a very limited understanding of the science of the task. The response is incomplete and exhibits many flaws.
0	The student provides a completely incorrect solution or no response at all.

chapter 13 Instructional Planner

Light

BIG Idea Visible light waves are electromagnetic waves that can be detected by the human eye.

	Content Standards	Learning Objectives	Resources to Assess Mastery
Section 1	**5–8:** UCP.1–3, 5; A.1, 2; B.1 **9–12:** UCP.1–3, 5; A.1, 2; B.2, 6	**The Behavior of Light** 1. **Describe** how light waves interact with matter. 2. **Explain** the difference between regular and diffuse reflection. 3. **Define** the index of refraction of a material. 4. **Explain** why a prism separates white light into different colors. ***Main Idea*** Light waves change direction when they are reflected or when they change speed.	**Formative Assessment** Reading Check, pp. 385, 386 Section Review, p. 388 **Summative Assessment** *ExamView® Assessment Suite*
Section 2	**5–8:** UCP.1–3, 5; A.1, 2; B.1; C.1 **9–12:** UCP.1–3, 5; A.1, 2; B.2, 6; C.6	**Light and Color** 4. **Explain** how you see color. 5. **Describe** the difference between light color and pigment color. 6. **Predict** what happens when different colors are mixed. ***Main Idea*** Light waves of different wavelengths or combinations of wavelengths cause the human eye to detect different colors.	**Formative Assessment** Reading Check, pp. 389, 390, 392 Section Review, p. 393 **Summative Assessment** *ExamView® Assessment Suite*
Section 3	**5–8:** UCP.1–3, 5; A.1, 2; B.1 **9–12:** UCP.1–3, 5; A.1, 2; B.2	**Producing Light** 7. **Explain** how incandescent and fluorescent lightbulbs work. 8. **Analyze** the advantages and disadvantages of different lighting devices. 9. **Explain** how a laser produces coherent light. 10. **Describe** various uses of lasers. ***Main Idea*** Heating a tungsten filament or passing a current through a gas are common ways of producing light.	**Formative Assessment** Reading Check, pp. 394, 395, 396 Section Review, p. 399 **Summative Assessment** *ExamView® Assessment Suite*
Section 4	**5–8:** UCP.1–3, 5; A.1, 2; B.1, 3 **9–12:** UCP.1–3, 5; A.1, 2; B.2, 6 See pp. 16T–17T for a Key to Standards.	**Using Light** 11. **Distinguish** polarized light from unpolarized light. 12. **Explain** how a hologram is made. 13. **Determine** when total internal reflection occurs. 14. **Describe** the uses of optical fibers. ***Main Idea*** Light can be used to form three-dimensional images and to transmit information in optical fibers.	**Formative Assessment** Reading Check, pp. 401, 402 Section Review, p. 404 **Summative Chapter Assessment** MindJogger, Ch. 13 *ExamView® Assessment Suite* Leveled Chapter Test Test A L1 Test B L2 Test C L3 Test Practice, pp. 412–413

Suggested Pacing				
Period	**Instruction**	**Labs**	**Review & Assessment**	**Total**
Single	4 days	3 days	2 days	9 days
Block	2 blocks	1.5 blocks	1 block	4.5 blocks

<table>
<tr><th rowspan="2">Core Instruction</th><th rowspan="2">Leveled Resources</th><th rowspan="2">Leveled Labs</th><th colspan="3">Pacing</th></tr>
<tr><th>Period</th><th></th><th>Block</th></tr>
<tr><td rowspan="2">Student Text, pp. 382–388
Section Focus Transparency, Ch. 13, Section 1
Teaching Transparency, Ch. 13, Section 1
Interactive Chalkboard, Ch. 13, Section 1
Identifying Misconceptions, p. 385
Differentiated Instruction, pp. 387</td><td rowspan="2">Chapter Fast File Resources
Directed Reading for Content Mastery, p. 20 [L1]
Note-taking Worksheet, pp. 35–37
Reinforcement, p. 27 [L2]
Enrichment, p. 31 [L3]
Reading Essentials, p. 212 [L1] ELL
Science Notebook, p. 143 ELL</td><td rowspan="2">Launch Lab, p. 383: prism, flashlight, bowl or pan, water dishwashing liquid, compact disc 10 min [L2]

MiniLAB, p. 387: penny, table, opaque cup, water 10 min [L2]</td><td>1</td><td>Section 1, pp. 383–386 (includes Launch Lab)</td><td rowspan="2">1</td></tr>
<tr><td>2</td><td>Section 1, pp. 386–388 (includes MiniLAB and Section Review)</td></tr>
<tr><td>Student Text, pp. 389–393
Section Focus Transparency, Ch. 13, Section 2
Interactive Chalkboard, Ch. 13, Section 2
Identifying Misconceptions, p. 390
Differentiated Instruction, pp. 391, 392</td><td>Chapter Fast File Resources
Directed Reading for Content Mastery, p. 20 [L1]
Note-taking Worksheet, pp. 35–37
Reinforcement, p. 28 [L2]
Enrichment, p. 32 [L3]
Reading Essentials, p. 217 [L1] ELL
Science Notebook, p. 147 ELL</td><td></td><td>3</td><td>Section 2, pp. 389–393 (includes Section Review)</td><td rowspan="2">2</td></tr>
<tr><td rowspan="2">Student Text, pp. 394–399
Section Focus Transparency, Ch. 13, Section 3
Interactive Chalkboard, Ch. 13, Section 3
Visualizing Lasers, p. 397
Identifying Misconceptions, p. 398
Differentiated Instruction, pp. 395, 398</td><td rowspan="2">Chapter Fast File Resources
Directed Reading for Content Mastery, p. 21 [L1]
Note-taking Worksheet, pp. 35–37
Reinforcement, p. 29 [L2]
Enrichment, p. 33 [L3]
Reading Essentials, p. 222 [L1] ELL
Science Notebook, p. 150 ELL</td><td rowspan="2">MiniLAB, p. 395: fluorescent and incandescent bulbs (same wattage), thermometer, polystyrene foam cup, stopwatch, plastic food wrap, power source) 25 min [L2] [Video Lab]</td><td>4</td><td>Section 3, pp. 394–396 (includes MiniLAB)</td></tr>
<tr><td>5</td><td>Section 3, pp. 396–399 (includes Section Review)</td><td rowspan="2">3</td></tr>
<tr><td rowspan="4">Student Text, pp. 400–407
Section Focus Transparency, Ch. 13, Section 4
Interactive Chalkboard, Ch. 13, Section 4
Identifying Misconceptions, p. 402, 403
Differentiated Instruction, pp. 401, 403
Chapter Study Guide, p. 409</td><td rowspan="4">Chapter Fast File Resources
Directed Reading for Content Mastery, pp. 21, 22 [L1]
Note-taking Worksheet, pp. 35–37
Reinforcement, p. 30 [L2]
Enrichment, p. 34 [L3]
Reading Essentials, p. 227 [L1] ELL
Science Notebook, p. 153 ELL</td><td rowspan="4">*Lab, p. 405: light source, unsharpened pencil, clear rectangular container, water, modeling clay 40 min [L1] [L2] [L3]

*Lab, pp. 406–407: polarizing filters (3), lamp or flashlight 40 min [L1] [L2] [L3]

*Lab version A [L1]
version B [L2] [L3]</td><td>6</td><td>Section 4, pp. 400–404 (includes Section Review)</td></tr>
<tr><td>7</td><td>Lab: Making a Light Bender, p. 405</td><td rowspan="2">4</td></tr>
<tr><td>8</td><td>Lab: Polarizing Filters, pp. 406–407</td></tr>
<tr><td>9</td><td>Study Guide, Chapter Review, and Test Practice, pp. 409–413</td><td>4.5</td></tr>
</table>

[Video Lab icon] Video Lab

Transparencies

Section Focus

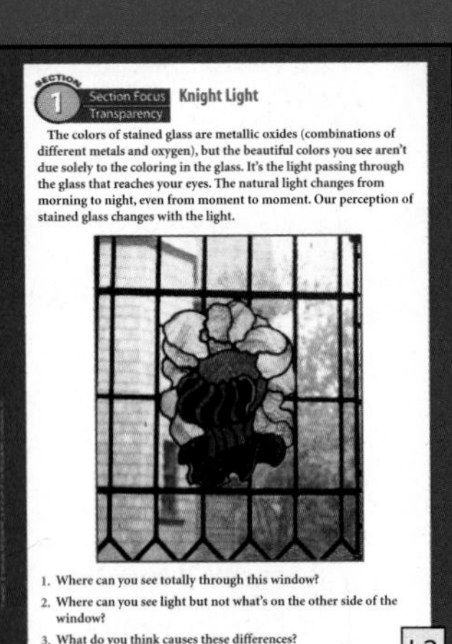

Section 1 Section Focus Transparency **Knight Light**

The colors of stained glass are metallic oxides (combinations of different metals and oxygen), but the beautiful colors you see aren't due solely to the coloring in the glass. It's the light passing through the glass that reaches your eyes. The natural light changes from morning to night, even from moment to moment. Our perception of stained glass changes with the light.

1. Where can you see totally through this window?
2. Where can you see light but not what's on the other side of the window?
3. What do you think causes these differences?

L2

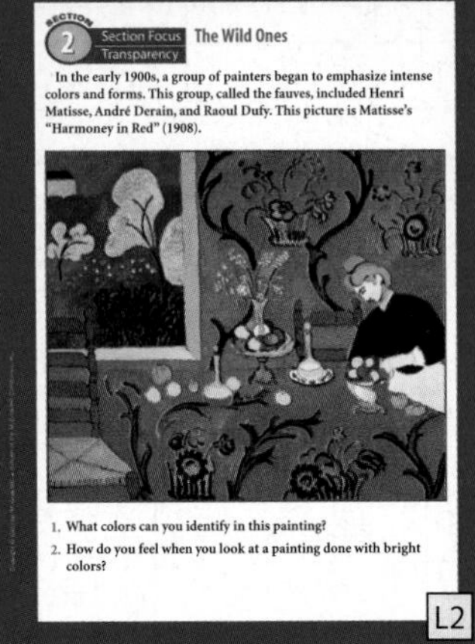

Section 2 Section Focus Transparency **The Wild Ones**

In the early 1900s, a group of painters began to emphasize intense colors and forms. This group, called the fauves, included Henri Matisse, André Derain, and Raoul Dufy. This picture is Matisse's "Harmony in Red" (1908).

1. What colors can you identify in this painting?
2. How do you feel when you look at a painting done with bright colors?

L2

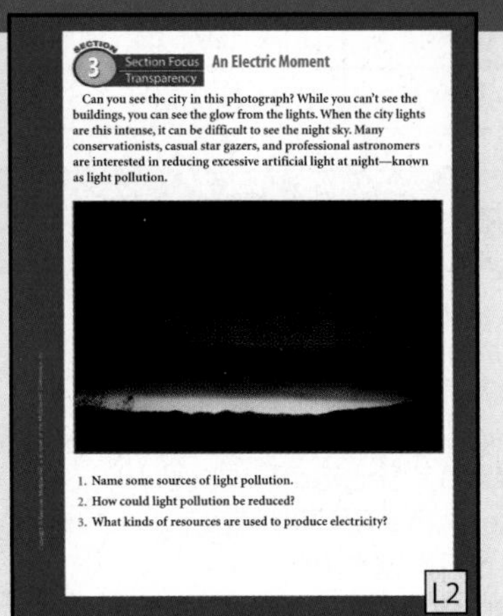

Section 3 Section Focus Transparency **An Electric Moment**

Can you see the city in this photograph? While you can't see the buildings, you can see the glow from the lights. When the city lights are this intense, it can be difficult to see the night sky. Many conservationists, casual star gazers, and professional astronomers are interested in reducing excessive artificial light at night—known as light pollution.

1. Name some sources of light pollution.
2. How could light pollution be reduced?
3. What kinds of resources are used to produce electricity?

L2

This is a representation of key blackline masters available in the Teacher Classroom Resources. See Resource Manager boxes within the chapter for additional information.

Assessment

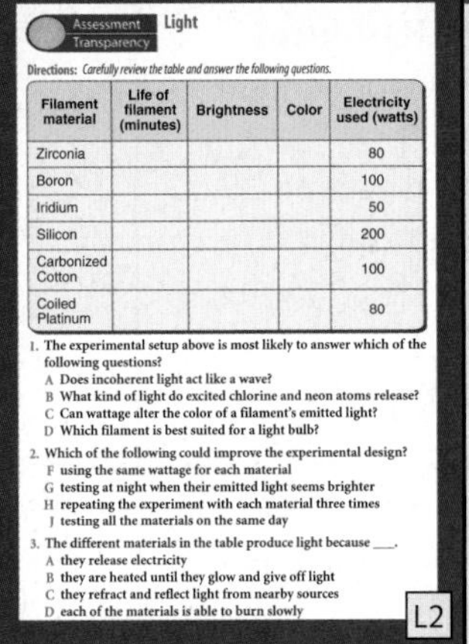

Assessment Transparency **Light**

Directions: Carefully review the table and answer the following questions.

Filament material	Life of filament (minutes)	Brightness	Color	Electricity used (watts)
Zirconia				80
Boron				100
Iridium				50
Silicon				200
Carbonized Cotton				100
Coiled Platinum				80

1. The experimental setup above is most likely to answer which of the following questions?
   - A Does incoherent light act like a wave?
   - B What kind of light do excited chlorine and neon atoms release?
   - C Can wattage alter the color of a filament's emitted light?
   - D Which filament is best suited for a light bulb?
2. Which of the following could improve the experimental design?
   - F using the same wattage for each material
   - G testing at night when their emitted light seems brighter
   - H repeating the experiment with each material three times
   - J testing all the materials on the same day
3. The different materials in the table produce light because ___.
   - A they release electricity
   - B they are heated until they glow and give off light
   - C they refract and reflect light from nearby sources
   - D each of the materials is able to burn slowly

L2

Teaching

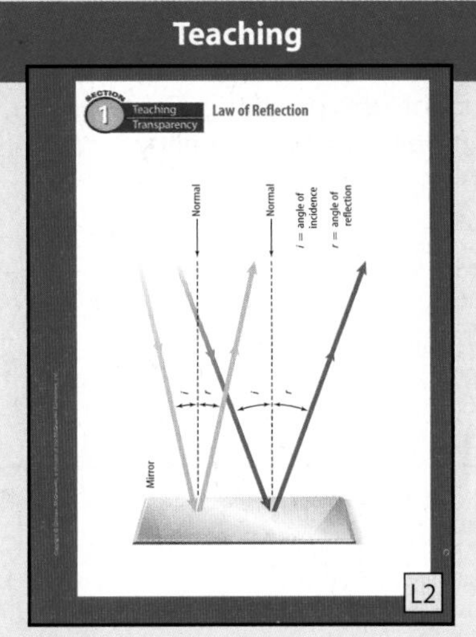

Section 1 Teaching Transparency **Law of Reflection**

L2

Key to Teaching Strategies

The following designations will help you decide which activities are appropriate for your students.

- **L1** Level 1 activities should be appropriate for students with learning difficulties.
- **L2** Level 2 activities should be within the ability range of all students.
- **L3** Level 3 activities are designed for above-average students.
- **ELL** ELL activities should be within the ability range of English Language Learners.
- **COOP LEARN** Cooperative Learning activities are designed for small group work.
- **LS** Multiple Learning Styles logos, as described on page 12T, are used throughout to indicate strategies that address different learning styles.
- **P** These strategies represent student products that can be placed into a best-work portfolio.
- **PBL** Problem-Based Learning activities apply real-world situations to learning.

Hands-on Activities

Student Text Lab Worksheet

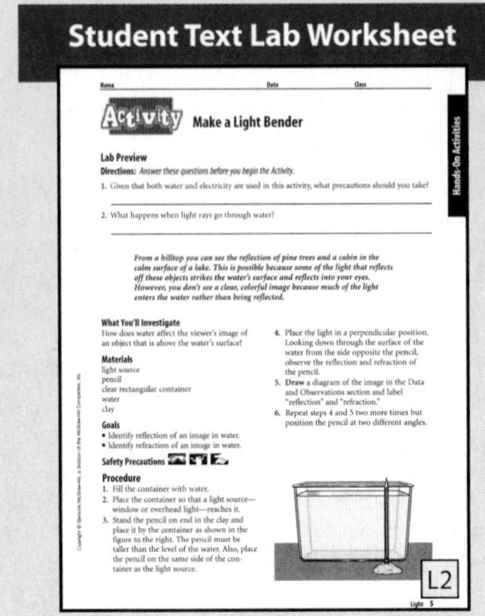

Name ____ Date ____ Class ____

Activity **Make a Light Bender**

Hands-On Activities

Lab Preview

Directions: *Answer these questions before you begin the Activity.*

1. Given that both water and electricity are used in this activity, what precautions should you take?
2. What happens when light rays go through water?

From a hilltop you can see the reflection of pine trees and a cabin in the calm surface of a lake. This is possible because some of the light that reflects off these objects strikes the water's surface and reflects into your eyes. However, you don't see a clear, colorful image because much of the light enters the water rather than being reflected.

What You'll Investigate

How does water affect the viewer's image of an object that is above the water's surface?

Materials

light source
pencil
clear rectangular container
water
clay

Goals

- Identify reflection of an image in water.
- Identify refraction of an image in water.

Safety Precautions

Procedure

1. Fill the container with water.
2. Place the container so that a light source—window or overhead light—reaches it.
3. Stand the pencil on end in the clay and place it by the container as shown in the figure to the right. The pencil must be taller than the level of the water. Also, place the pencil on the same side of the container as the light source.
4. Place the light in a perpendicular position. Looking down through the surface of the water from the side opposite the pencil, observe the reflection and refraction of the pencil.
5. **Draw** a diagram of the image in the Data and Observations section and label "reflection" and "refraction."
6. Repeat steps 4 and 5 two more times but position the pencil at two different angles.

L2

Light 5

Laboratory Activities

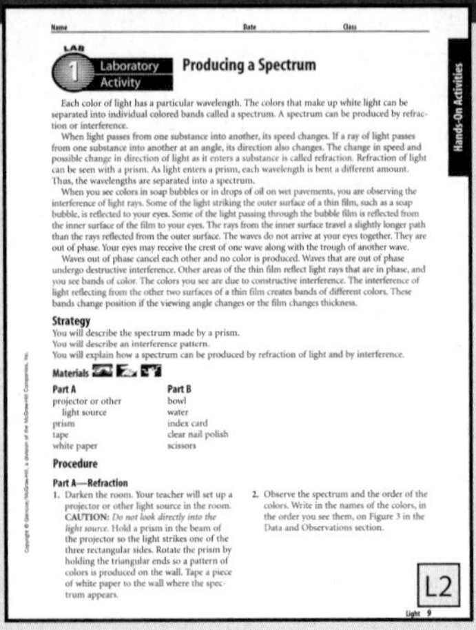

Name ____ Date ____ Class ____

Lab 1 Laboratory Activity **Producing a Spectrum**

Hands-On Activities

Each color of light has a particular wavelength. The colors that make up white light can be separated into individual colored bands called a spectrum. A spectrum can be produced by refraction or interference.

When light passes from one substance into another, its speed changes. If a ray of light passes from one substance into another at an angle, its direction also changes. The change in speed and possible change in direction of light as it enters a substance is called refraction. Refraction of light can be seen with a prism. As light enters a prism, each wavelength is bent a different amount. Thus, the wavelengths are separated into a spectrum.

When you see colors in soap bubbles or in drops of oil on wet pavements, you are observing the interference of light rays. Some of the light striking the outer surface of a thin film, such as a soap bubble, is reflected to your eyes. Some of the light passing through the bubble film is reflected from the inner surface of the film to your eyes. The rays from the inner surface travel a slightly longer path than the rays reflected from the outer surface. The waves do not arrive at your eyes together. They are out of phase. Your eyes may receive the crest of one wave along with the trough of another wave.

Waves out of phase cancel each other and no color is produced. Waves that are out of phase undergo destructive interference. Other areas of the thin film reflect light rays that are in phase, and you see bands of color. The colors you see are due to constructive interference. The interference of light reflecting from the other two surfaces of a thin film creates bands of different colors. These bands change position if the viewing angle changes or the film changes thickness.

Strategy

You will describe the spectrum made by a prism.
You will describe an interference pattern.
You will explain how a spectrum can be produced by refraction of light and by interference.

Materials

Part A	Part B
projector or other light source	bowl
prism	water
tape	index card
white paper	clear nail polish
	scissors

Procedure

Part A—Refraction

1. Darken the room. Your teacher will set up a projector or other light source in the room. **CAUTION:** *Do not look directly into the light source.* Hold a prism in the beam of the projector so the light strikes one of the three rectangular sides. Rotate the prism by holding the triangular ends so a pattern of colors is produced on the wall. Tape a piece of white paper to the wall where the spectrum appears.
2. Observe the spectrum and the order of the colors. Write in the names of the colors, in the order you see them, on Figure 3 in the Data and Observations section.

L2

Light 9

Meeting Different Ability Levels

Content Outline

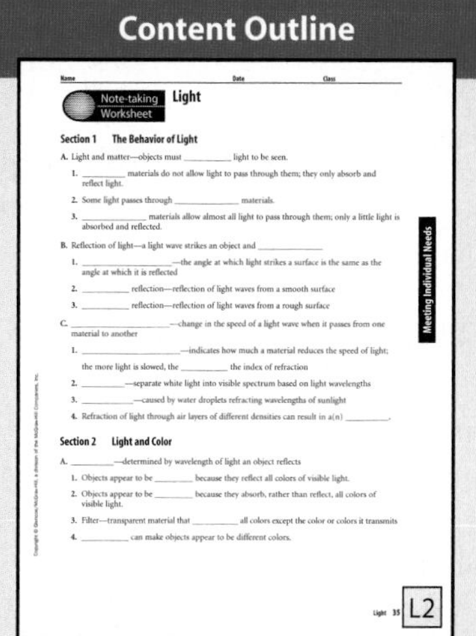

Name Date Class

Note-taking Worksheet **Light**

Section 1 The Behavior of Light

A. Light and matter—objects must __________ light to be seen.

1. __________ materials do not allow light to pass through them; they only absorb and reflect light.
2. Some light passes through __________ materials.
3. __________ materials allow almost all light to pass through them; only a little light is absorbed and reflected.

B. Reflection of light—a light wave strikes an object and __________

1. __________—the angle at which light strikes a surface is the same as the angle at which it is reflected
2. __________ reflection—reflection of light waves from a smooth surface
3. __________ reflection—reflection of light waves from a rough surface

C. __________—change in the speed of a light wave when it passes from one material to another

1. __________—indicates how much a material reduces the speed of light; the more light is slowed, the __________ the index of refraction
2. __________—separate white light into visible spectrum based on light wavelengths
3. __________—caused by water droplets refracting wavelengths of sunlight
4. Refraction of light through air layers of different densities can result in a(n) __________.

Section 2 Light and Color

A. __________—determined by wavelength of light an object reflects

1. Objects appear to be __________ because they reflect all colors of visible light.
2. Objects appear to be __________ because they absorb, rather than reflect, all colors of visible light.
3. Filter—transparent material that __________ all colors except the color or colors it transmits
4. __________ can make objects appear to be different colors.

Light 35 L2

Reinforcement

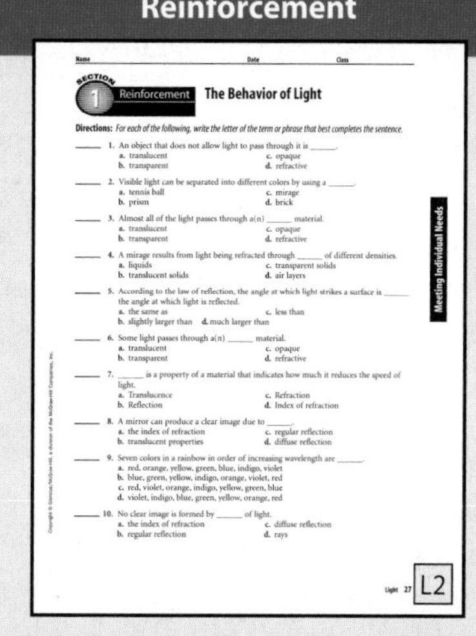

Name Date Class

Section 1 Reinforcement **The Behavior of Light**

Directions: *For each of the following, write the letter of the term or phrase that best completes the sentence.*

1. An object that does not allow light to pass through it is ______. a. translucent b. transparent c. opaque d. refractive
2. Visible light can be separated into different colors by using a ______. a. tennis ball b. prism c. mirage d. brick
3. Almost all of the light passes through a(n) ______ material. a. translucent b. transparent c. opaque d. refractive
4. A mirage results from light being refracted through ______ of different densities. a. liquids b. translucent solids c. transparent solids d. air layers
5. According to the law of reflection, the angle at which light strikes a surface is ______ the angle at which light is reflected. a. the same as b. slightly larger than c. less than d. much larger than
6. Some light passes through a(n) ______ material. a. translucent b. transparent c. opaque d. refractive
7. ______ is a property of a material that indicates how much it reduces the speed of light. a. Translucence b. Reflection c. Refraction d. Index of refraction
8. A mirror can produce a clear image due to ______. a. the index of refraction b. translucent properties c. regular reflection d. diffuse reflection
9. Seven colors in a rainbow in order of increasing wavelength are ______. a. red, orange, yellow, green, blue, indigo, violet b. blue, green, yellow, indigo, orange, violet, red c. red, violet, orange, indigo, yellow, green, blue d. violet, indigo, blue, green, yellow, orange, red
10. No clear image is formed by ______ of light. a. the index of refraction b. regular reflection c. diffuse reflection d. rays

Light 27 L2

Enrichment

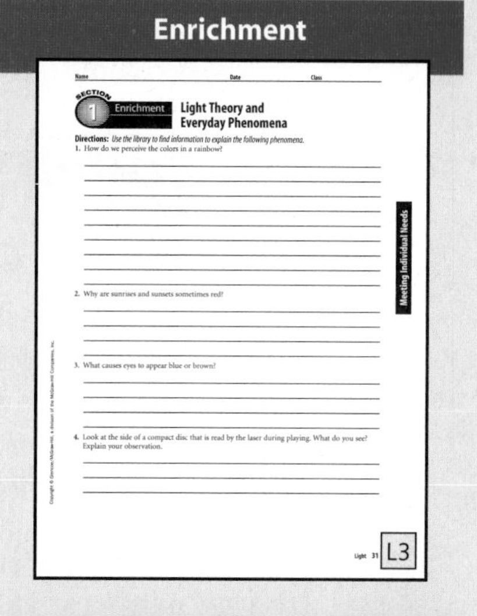

Name Date Class

Section 1 Enrichment **Light Theory and Everyday Phenomena**

Directions: *Use the library to find information to explain the following phenomena.*

1. How do we perceive the colors in a rainbow?
2. Why are sunrises and sunsets sometimes red?
3. What causes eyes to appear blue or brown?
4. Look at the side of a compact disc that is read by the laser during playing. What do you see? Explain your observation.

Light 31 L3

Directed Reading (English/Spanish)

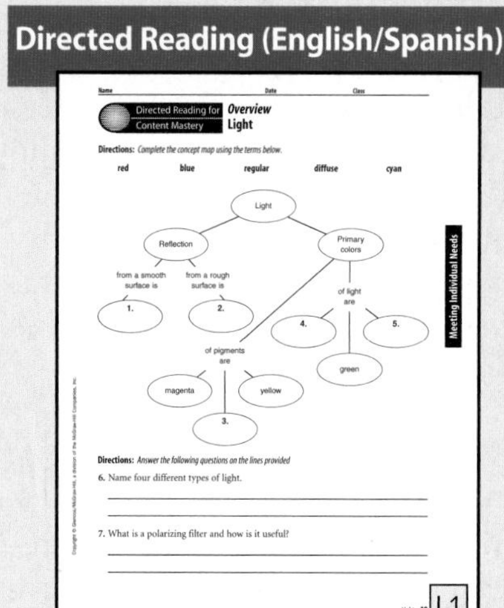

Name Date Class

Directed Reading for Content Mastery *Overview* **Light**

Directions: *Complete the concept map using the terms below.*

red blue regular diffuse cyan

Light
Reflection
Primary colors
from a smooth surface is
from a rough surface is
of light are
of pigments are
magenta
yellow
green

Directions: *Answer the following questions on the lines provided.*

6. Name four different types of light.
7. What is a polarizing filter and how is it useful?

Light 19 L1

Study Guide

Study Guide
Features
• Contains a study guide page for each section of the chapter
• Reviews key concepts
• Includes answer pages
L2

Reading Essentials

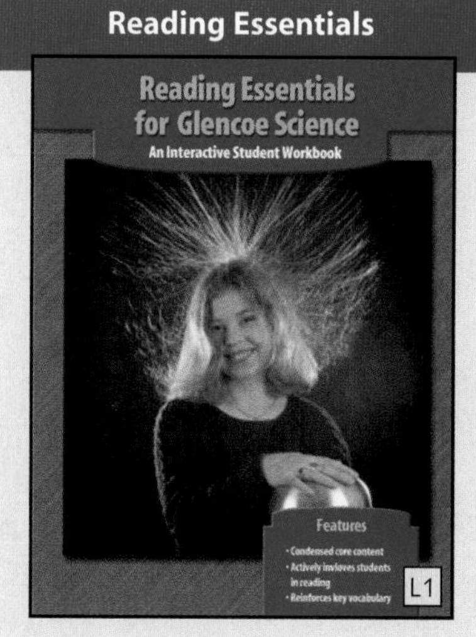

Reading Essentials for Glencoe Science
An Interactive Student Workbook
Features
• Condensed core content
• Actively involves students in reading
• Reinforces key vocabulary
L1

Assessment

Test Practice Workbook

Name: Date: Class:

Chapter Test *Chapter 14 Light*

DIRECTIONS

Read each question and choose the best answer. Then fill in the correct answer on your answer document.

Optic fiber	Length of optic fiber (cm)	Amount of light entering fiber	Amount of light emitted at end of fiber	Weight of optic fiber (g)	Color of optic fiber
1	20				
2	20				

1 The table above was set up to record data for an experiment. Which of these is the most likely hypothesis supported by this experiment?

A Optical fibers filter different wavelengths of light.
B Optical fibers have total internal reflection.*
C An optic fiber's weight affects its light transmission.
D An optic fiber's color affects its translucence.

Laser Emitter — Mirror — Partially Reflective Mirror

2 This device is able to emit a coherent beam of light because —

F helium and neon react chemically and release heat
G it captures and stores sunlight
H the coherent light transfers energy to the atoms in the chamber
J the mirror on the left lets some light through*

3 Which of the following processes is occurring in both pictures?

A Polarization of light
B Total internal reflection
C Refraction of light*
D Light becoming coherent

60 GO ON Energy on the Move L2

Chapter Review

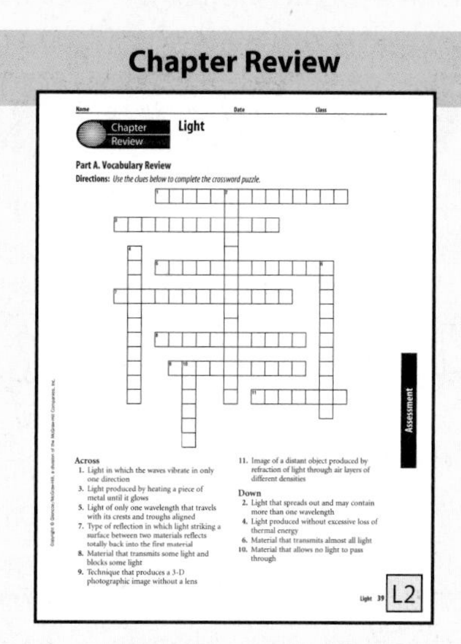

Name Date Class

Chapter Review **Light**

Part A. Vocabulary Review

Directions: *Use the clues below to complete the crossword puzzle.*

Across

1. Light in which the waves vibrate in only one direction
3. Light produced by heating a piece of metal until it glows
5. Light of only one wavelength that travels with its crests and troughs aligned
7. Type of reflection in which light striking a surface between two materials reflects totally back into the first material
8. Material that transmits some light and blocks some light
9. Technique that produces a 3-D photographic image without a lens
11. Image of a distant object produced by refraction of light through air layers of different densities

Down

2. Light that spreads out and may contain more than one wavelength
4. Light produced without excessive loss of thermal energy
6. Material that transmits almost all light
10. Material that allows no light to pass through

Light 39 L2

Chapter Tests

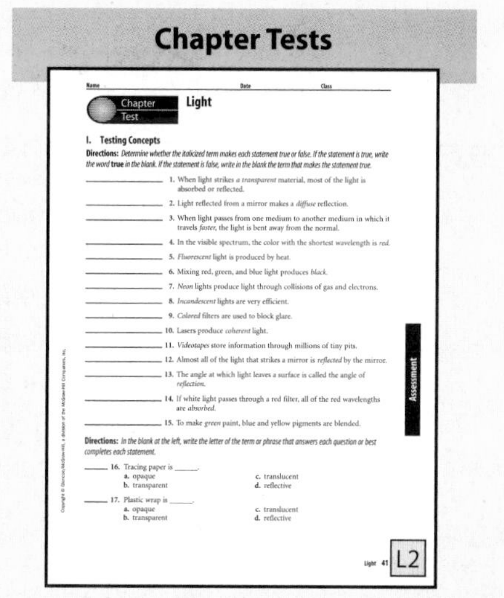

Name Date Class

Chapter Test **Light**

I. Testing Concepts

Directions: *Determine whether the italicized term makes each statement true or false. If the statement is true, write the word* **true** *in the blank. If the statement is false, write in the blank the term that makes the statement true.*

1. When light strikes a *transparent* material, most of the light is absorbed or reflected.
2. Light reflected from a mirror makes a *diffuse* reflection.
3. When light passes from one medium to another medium in which it travels *faster*, the light is bent away from the normal.
4. In the visible spectrum, the color with the shortest wavelength is *red*.
5. *Fluorescent* light is produced by heat.
6. Mixing red, green, and blue light produces *black*.
7. *Neon* lights produce light through collisions of gas and electrons.
8. *Incandescent* lights are very efficient.
9. *Colored* filters are used to block glare.
10. *Lasers* produce coherent light.
11. *Videotapes* store information through millions of tiny pits.
12. Almost all of the light that strikes a mirror is *reflected* by the mirror.
13. The angle at which light leaves a surface is called the angle of *reflection*.
14. If white light passes through a red filter, all of the red wavelengths are *absorbed*.
15. To make *green* paint, blue and yellow pigments are blended.

Directions: *In the blank at the left, write the letter of the term or phrase that answers each question or best completes each statement.*

16. Tracing paper is ______. a. opaque b. transparent c. translucent d. reflective
17. Plastic wrap is ______. a. opaque b. transparent c. translucent d. reflective

Light 41 L2

Science Content Background

section 1 The Behavior of Light

Reflection of Light

The reason we can see objects is that they either emit or reflect light. Most materials don't produce their own light, so almost everything we see is reflecting light. The reflected light travels to the retina of our eyes, where an image is received and sent to the brain.

Retroreflectors, such as those used on bicycle reflectors, reflect light of all angles back to its source. An example of a retroreflector is three mirrors arranged at right angles to form a corner. Light strikes one mirror and bounces around, and it returns in the direction of the incident rays. A bike's reflector is composed of many of these little "corners." Apollo 11 astronauts set up retroreflectors on the moon so laser beams would bounce back to their senders.

Refraction of Light

For refraction to occur, light must pass at an angle other than 90° into another material with a different index of refraction. When light slows down as it moves from one material to another, it is refracted toward the normal. When it speeds up, it is refracted away from the normal.

When most people swim underwater without goggles, their vision is not as good. Normally light is refracted when it goes from air into the eye, and this is necessary in order to see clearly. Because water has a higher index of refraction than air, light is not refracted enough. Wearing goggles puts air in front of the eye and restores normal vision.

section 2 Light and Color

Mixing Colors

Three types of color dots—red, blue, and green—are repeated throughout the screen of a color TV set. By varying the light intensity emitted by each, all the colors are achieved.

section 3 Producing Light

Fluorescent Lights

Molecules in black-light posters absorb ultraviolet radiation and then emit light in the visible spectrum. In a similar way, chemicals added to some laundry detergents contain molecules that absorb ultraviolet light and emit blue light. This blue makes white clothes look even whiter.

section 4 Using Light

Polarized Light

Three-dimensional movies are created by having two cameras record a scene and then two projectors play the recordings back. Through the use of special Polaroid or color lenses, one eye sees the movie from one camera and the other eye sees the movie from the other camera. This creates a very real 3D effect.

chapter content resources

Internet Resources

For additional content background, visit gpscience.com to:

- access your book online
- find references to related articles in popular science magazines
- access Web links with related content background
- access current events with science journal topics

Print Resources

Visual Perception, by Steven H. Schwartz, McGraw-Hill/Appleton and Lange, 1998

Light Science: Physics and the Visual Arts, by Thomas Rossing, and Christopher Chiaverina, Springer Verlag, 1999

The Magic Wand and Other Bright Experiments on Light and Color, by Paul Doherty, Don Rothjen, and The Exploratorium Teacher Institute, John Wiley and Sons, 1995

IDENTIFYING Misconceptions

Find Out What Students Think

Students may think that . . .

Only special materials reflect light.

Students are aware that mirrors and shiny metals reflect light. It is not as obvious that other materials also reflect light. Students may not be aware that we can see objects such as trees, rocks, walls, people, moons, and planets because they reflect light. This may seem obvious to most adults, but if a student is not aware of this, it will hinder learning other concepts about light.

Discussion

Write the following question on the board.

Which of the following materials ordinarily reflect light?

(a) mirror (b) blue poster paper
(c) aluminum foil (d) white cotton sheet

Ask students to answer the question individually, then have students discuss the question among themselves and attempt to agree upon the answer.

Promote Understanding

Activity

Tell students that they will now have the opportunity to test the materials listed in the question above to see for themselves which ones do or do not reflect light.

Organize the class into groups. Give each group the following:

- a flashlight
- a sheet of white paper
- a mirror
- a sheet of light blue paper
- a piece of aluminum foil
- a section of a white cotton sheet

- Tell students that you will darken the room for the investigations, but that first they must determine how they will conduct their investigations and write down their procedures.
- Procedures will vary but probably most students will shine the flashlight at the material and look for the reflection of light. The white paper can be used to detect the reflected light, especially from the white sheet and the blue paper.
- After students have finished their investigations, have one student from each group write the group's results on the board. Then discuss the results as a class. Make sure students realize that all of the materials tested reflect light.

Assess

After completing the chapter, see *Identifying Misconceptions* in the Study Guide at the end of the chapter.

About the Photo

Bioluminescence The photo shows a Market squid, which is a small squid about 16 cm long that lives in the Eastern Pacific Ocean. At night, these squid feed near the ocean surface. Bioluminescence makes Market squid harder to see by predators that are looking upward into the brighter surface layers. This defense strategy is called counterillumination.

Science Journal Possible answers include: mushrooms, bacteria, fireflies, firefly larvae (glow worms), millipedes, worms, and several other marine organisms

The BIG Idea

Light and Color The three types of cone cells in the human retina have their greatest sensitivity at about 560 (yellow-green), 530 (green), and 424 (blue) nanometers. Each cone cell contains a pigment that absorbs light, causing a series of chemical reactions that results in the transmittal of a nerve impulse to the brain. The nature of this impulse depends on the intensity and wavelengths of the light that interacts with the cell. The color that is seen depends on the signals from all three types of cone cells. As a result, different combinations of wavelengths can produce the same color sensation.

Introduce the Chapter Ask students to imagine they are in a closed room with an overhead lightbulb. Have them explain why objects in the room can no longer be seen when the lightbulb is turned off.

chapter 13

Light

BIG Idea
Visible light waves are electromagnetic waves that can be detected by the human eye.

13.1 The Behavior of Light
MAIN Idea Light waves change direction when they are reflected or when they change speed.

13.2 Light and Color
MAIN Idea Light waves of different wavelengths or combinations of wavelengths cause the human eye to detect different colors.

13.3 Producing Light
MAIN Idea Heating a tungsten filament or passing a current through a gas are common ways of producing light.

13.4 Using Light
MAIN Idea Light can be used to form three-dimensional images and to transmit information in optical fibers.

That Inner Glow

Some organisms, like this squid, can produce light. The production of light by organisms is called bioluminescence and results from a chemical reaction. Bioluminescent organisms glow to lure prey, to attract a mate, to coordinate group movements, and to evade predators.

Science Journal
Find other examples of living organisms that give off light.

Interactive Chalkboard

This CD-ROM is an editable Microsoft® PowerPoint® presentation that includes:

- an editable presentation for every chapter
- additional chapter questions
- animated graphics
- image bank
- links to gpscience.com

Start-Up Activities

Rainbows of Light

Light passing through a prism can produce exciting patterns of color. Imagine what your surroundings would look like now if humans could see only shades of gray instead of distinct colors. The ability to see color depends on the cells in your eyes that are sensitive to different wavelengths of light. What color is the light produced by a flashlight or the Sun?

1. In a darkened room, shine a flashlight through a glass prism. Project the resulting colors onto a white wall or ceiling.
2. In a darkened room, shine a flashlight over the surface of some water with dishwashing liquid bubbles in it. What do you see?
3. Aim a flashlight at the surface of a compact disc.
4. **Think Critically** How did your observations in each case differ? Explain where you think the colors came from.

Preview this chapter's content and activities at gpscience.com

Light Transmission Make the following Foldable to help identify the characteristics of opaque, translucent, and transparent objects.

STEP 1 **Fold** a vertical sheet of paper from side to side. Make the front edge about 1.25 cm shorter than the back edge.

STEP 2 **Turn** lengthwise and fold into thirds.

STEP 3 **Unfold** and cut only the top layer along both folds to make three tabs.

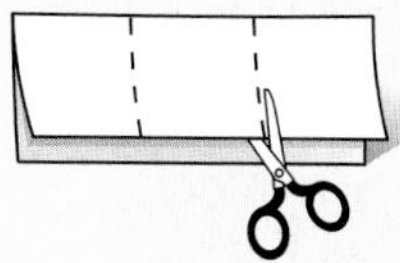

STEP 4 **Label** each tab as shown.

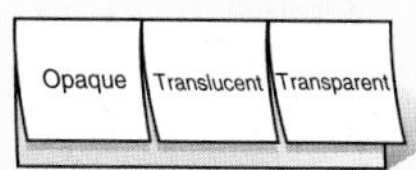

Find Main Ideas As you read this chapter, list the characteristics of opaque, translucent, and transparent objects.

383

Purpose The Launch Lab introduces students to the reflection and refraction of light. L2 ELL LS **Visual-Spatial**

Preparation Agitate the water and dishwashing liquid to form bubbles.

Materials prism, flashlight, bowl or pan, water, dishwashing liquid, compact disc

Teaching Strategy Darkening the room will make it easier for students to see the colors from the prism, dishwashing liquid, and compact disc.

Think Critically

In all three observations the student will see colors. The prism refracts the light, which separates it into colors that can be seen on the white wall or ceiling. The thin film on the soap bubbles and the closely spaced pits on the compact disc cause interference between light waves, causing the colors students observe on their surfaces.

Assessment

Portfolio Have students prepare a poster that accurately illustrates the light source, how light reached their eye, and color observations in each of the three steps of the Launch Lab. Use **Performance Assessment in the Science Classroom,** p. 145.

Dinah Zike Study Fold

Student preparation materials for this Foldable are available in the Chapter *Fast File* Resources.

Additional Chapter Media

- What's Science Got to Do With It?: *Crime Scene Investigation*
- BrainPOP *Color*
- Virtual Lab: *How are colors created?*
- Video Lab: *Discovering Energy Waste in Light*

section 1

The Behavior of Light

1 Motivate

Bellringer

Section Focus Transparencies also are available on the Interactive Chalkboard CD-ROM.

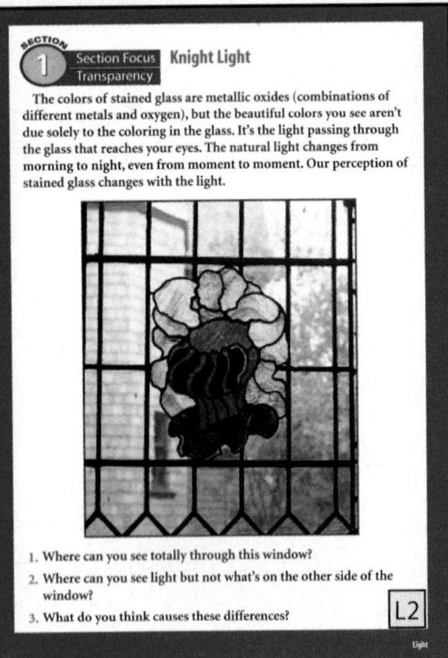
SECTION 1 Section Focus Transparency **Knight Light**

The colors of stained glass are metallic oxides (combinations of different metals and oxygen), but the beautiful colors you see aren't due solely to the coloring in the glass. It's the light passing through the glass that reaches your eyes. The natural light changes from morning to night, even from moment to moment. Our perception of stained glass changes with the light.

1. Where can you see totally through this window?
2. Where can you see light but not what's on the other side of the window?
3. What do you think causes these differences?

L2

Tie to Prior Knowledge

Water Distortion Ask students how their feet appear if they look at them while their heads are out of the water when they are standing in a swimming pool. They probably will say that they look distorted. This is because the speed of light in water is different from the speed of light in air, causing light to refract, which distorts the image.

Reading Guide

What You'll Learn

- **Describe** how light waves interact with matter.
- **Explain** the difference between regular and diffuse reflection.
- **Define** the index of refraction of a material.
- **Explain** why a prism separates white light into different colors.

Why It's Important

The images you see every day are due to the behavior of light waves.

Review Vocabulary

visible light: an electromagnetic wave with wavelengths between about 400 and 750 billionths of a meter

Vocabulary

- opaque
- translucent
- transparent
- index of refraction
- mirage

Figure 1 These candleholders have different light-transmitting properties.

A Opaque

B Translucent

C Transparent

Light and Matter

Look around your darkened room at night. After your eyes adjust to the darkness, you begin to recognize some familiar objects. You know that some of the objects are brightly colored, but they look gray or black in the dim light. Turn on the light, and you clearly can see all the objects in the room, including their colors. What you see depends on the amount of light in the room and the color of the objects. For you to see an object, it must reflect some light back to your eyes.

Opaque, Transparent, and Translucent Objects can absorb light, reflect light, and transmit light—allow light to pass through them. The type of matter in an object determines the amount of light it absorbs, reflects, and transmits. For example, the **opaque** (oh PAYK) material in the candleholder in **Figure 1A** only absorbs and reflects light—no light passes through it. As a result, you cannot see the candle inside. Materials that allow some light to pass through them, like the material of the candleholder in **Figure 1B,** are described as **translucent** (trans LEW sunt). You cannot see clearly through translucent materials.

Transparent materials like the candleholder in **Figure 1C** transmit almost all the light striking them, so you can see objects clearly through them. Only a small amount of light is absorbed and reflected.

Section 1 Resource Manager

Chapter *Fast File* Resources

Transparency Activity, pp. 46, 51-52
Note-taking Worksheets, pp. 35-37
Enrichment, p. 31
MiniLAB, p. 3
Directed Reading for Content Mastery, pp. 19-20
Reinforcement, p. 27
Lab Activity, pp. 9-12

Reflection of Light

Just before you left for school this morning, did you take a glance in a mirror to check your appearance? For you to see your reflection in the mirror, light had to reflect off you, hit the mirror, and reflect off the mirror into your eye. Reflection occurs when a light wave strikes an object and bounces off.

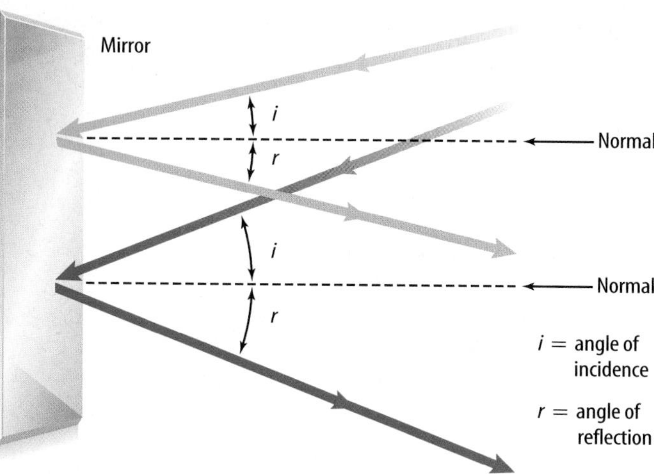

Figure 2 According to the law of reflection, light is reflected so that the angle of incidence always equals the angle of reflection.

The Law of Reflection

Because light behaves as a wave, it obeys the law of reflection, as shown in **Figure 2.** According to the law of reflection, the angle at which a light wave strikes a surface is the same as the angle at which it is reflected. Light reflected from any surface—a mirror or a sheet of paper—follows this law.

Regular and Diffuse Reflection Why can you see your reflection in a store window but not in a brick wall? The answer has to do with the smoothness of the surfaces. A smooth, even surface like that of a pane of glass produces a sharp image by reflecting parallel light waves in only one direction. Reflection of light waves from a smooth surface is regular reflection. A brick wall has an uneven surface that causes incoming parallel light waves to be reflected in many directions, as shown in **Figure 3.** Reflection of light from a rough surface is diffuse reflection.

Reading Check *What are some more examples of objects that produce regular or diffuse reflection?*

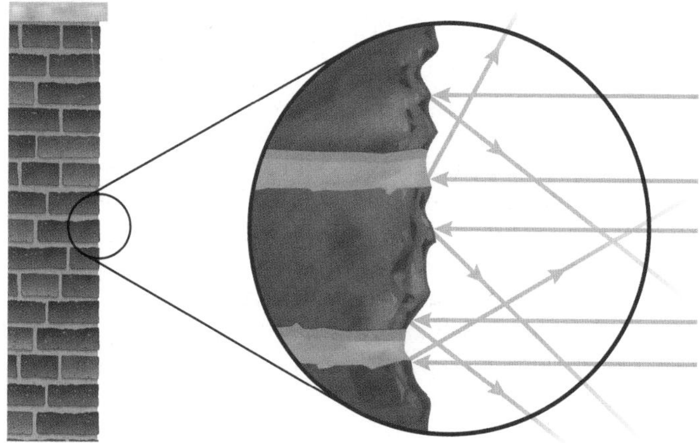

Figure 3 This brick wall has an uneven surface, so it produces a diffuse reflection.
Explain *Use the law of reflection to explain why a rough surface causes parallel light waves to be reflected in many directions.*

2 Teach

Use Science Words

Word Usage The words *opaque*, *transparent*, and *translucent* describe how well light passes through a material. Have students use these words in sentences that reflect their meanings. Possible answer: I can see through a transparent window, but I can't see through an opaque wall. I can see light but not images through waxed paper, which is translucent. L2 ELL IS **Linguistic**

IDENTIFYING Misconceptions

Reflecting Light Some students may think that only special materials reflect light. See page F at the beginning of this chapter for teaching strategies that address this misconception.

Activity

Reflective Foil Distribute two pieces of aluminum foil to small groups of students being careful not to wrinkle them. Have students crumple and then flatten one of their pieces of aluminum foil. Have students discuss which had a more regular reflection and why. The unwrinkled foil; it had smaller bumps L1

Reading Check

Answer Possible answers: regular reflection seen on surface of still water, shiny car, shiny plastic surface; diffuse reflection produced by sheet of paper, wood surface, painter wall

Caption Answer

Figure 3 The bumps and dips on a rough surface slope in many directions. Light rays that strike each bump or dip are reflected according to the law of reflection. Because the bumps and dips slope in many direction, parallel light rays are reflected from the surface in many directions.

Curriculum Connection

Language Arts Have students write fictitious short stories about why the sky is blue. Then have them research and write the true reason. The short-wavelength violet and blue portions of sunlight interact with molecules that make up air and are scattered, causing the sky to appear blue. We see the blue light rather than the violet because our eyes are more sensitive to blue. L3 P
IS **Linguistic**

Teacher FYI

Transparency Materials that are transparent to visible light are not necessarily transparent to other wavelengths. For example, clear glass transmits long-wavelength ultraviolet rays but blocks most short-wavelength ultraviolet rays. This is why you are not likely to get a sunburn through a window.

Use an Analogy

Bouncing Ball Tell students that reflecting light is similar to a ball bouncing off a wall. If you roll the ball directly toward the wall, it will bounce straight back toward you. If you roll it at an angle, it will bounce so that the angle between the incoming ball and the wall equals the angle between the outgoing ball and the wall. Allow students to roll a ball at a wall from different angles. L2 ELL LS **Kinesthetic**

Reading Check

Answer Refraction occurs as a light wave changes speed as it passes from one material to another.

Teacher FYI

The Index of Refraction The index of refraction of a material is the ratio of the speed of light in a vacuum to the speed of light in the material. The higher the index of refraction, the more slowly light travels through the material. The indices of refraction (n) in some common materials are: water, $n = 1.33$; glass, $n = 1.52$; diamond, $n = 2.42$.

LS **Logical-Mathematical**

Quick Demo

Toy Cars

Materials toy car, pamphlet

Estimated Time five minutes

Procedure Use a toy car to model how light bends when it moves from one medium to another. Place a thin pamphlet on a desk or table. Roll the toy car toward the pamphlet at a 90° angle and then at a 45° angle. Ask students to observe what happens as the car encounters the pamphlet.

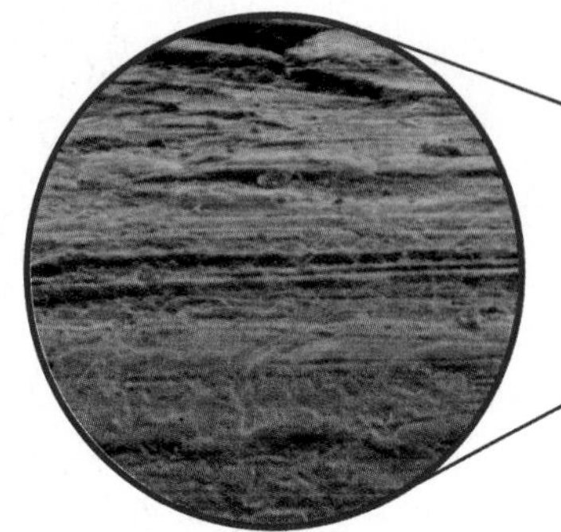

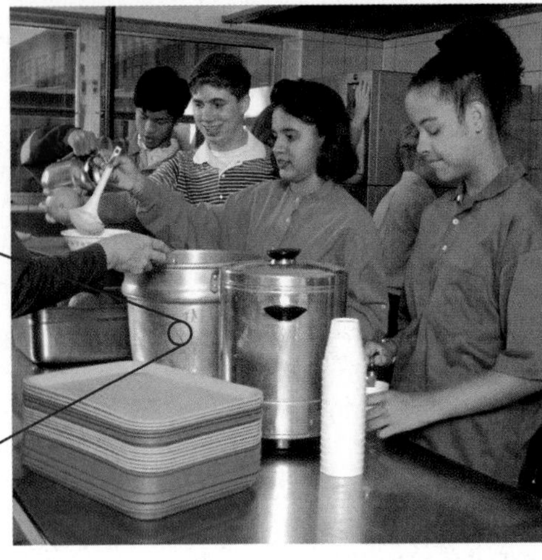

Figure 4 Although the surface of this pot may seem smooth, it produces a diffuse reflection. At high magnification, the surface is seen to be rough.

Roughness of Surfaces Even a surface that appears to be smooth can be rough enough to cause diffuse reflection. For example, a metal pot might seem smooth, but at high magnification, the surface shows rough spots, as shown in **Figure 4.** To cause a regular reflection, the roughness of the surface must be less than the wavelengths it reflects.

Refraction of Light

What occurs when a light wave passes from one material to another—from air to water, for example? Refraction is caused by a change in the speed of a wave when it passes from one material to another. If the light wave is traveling at an angle and the speed that light travels is different in the two materials, the wave will be bent, or refracted.

Reading Check *How does refraction occur?*

The Index of Refraction The amount of bending that takes place depends on the speed of light in both materials. The greater the difference is, the more the light will be bent as it passes at an angle from one material to the other. **Figure 5** shows an example of refraction. Every material has an **index of refraction**—a property of the material that indicates how much the speed of light in the material is reduced.

The larger the index of refraction, the more light is slowed down in the material. For example, because glass has a larger index of refraction than air, light moves more slowly in glass than air. Many useful devices like eyeglasses, binoculars, cameras, and microscopes form images using refraction.

Figure 5 The spoon looks bent because light waves are refracted as they change speed when they pass from the water to the air.

Visual Learning

Figure 5 Emphasize that the spoon appears to be broken because of the different paths the light takes as it comes toward your eyes. Light from the spoon in water is bent more than light from the spoon in air, so the light that goes through the water to reach your eyes comes from a different place than it appears. Have students sketch the paths light takes in this picture. L2 LS **Visual-Spatial**

Science Journal

Flattened Sun Late in the afternoon, just as the Sun approaches the horizon, it appears to have a flattened bottom. Have students apply what they have learned about refraction of light to write a paragraph in their Science Journals explaining this phenomenon. Light rays that pass closer to Earth's surface are refracted more. L3 LS **Logical-Mathematical**

Prisms A sparkling glass prism hangs in a sunny window, refracting the sunlight and projecting a colorful pattern onto the walls of the room. How does the bending of light create these colors? It occurs because the amount of bending usually depends on the wavelength of the light. Wavelengths of visible light range from the longer red waves to the shorter violet waves. White light, such as sunlight, is made up of this whole range of wavelengths.

Figure 6 Refraction causes a prism to separate a beam of white light into different colors.

Figure 6 shows what occurs when white light passes through a prism. The triangular prism refracts the light twice—once when it enters the prism and again when it leaves the prism and reenters the air. Because the longer wavelengths of light are refracted less than the shorter wavelengths are, red light is bent the least. As a result of these different amounts of bending, the different colors are separated when they emerge from the prism. Which color of light would you expect to bend the most?

Rainbows Does the light leaving the prism in **Figure 6** remind you of a rainbow? Like prisms, rain droplets also refract light. The refraction of the different wavelengths can cause white light from the Sun to separate into the individual colors of visible light, as shown in **Figure 7.** In a rainbow, the human eye usually can distinguish only about seven colors clearly. In order of decreasing wavelength, these colors are red, orange, yellow, green, blue, indigo, and violet.

Figure 7 As white light passes through the water droplet, different wavelengths are refracted by different amounts. This produces the separate colors seen in a rainbow.

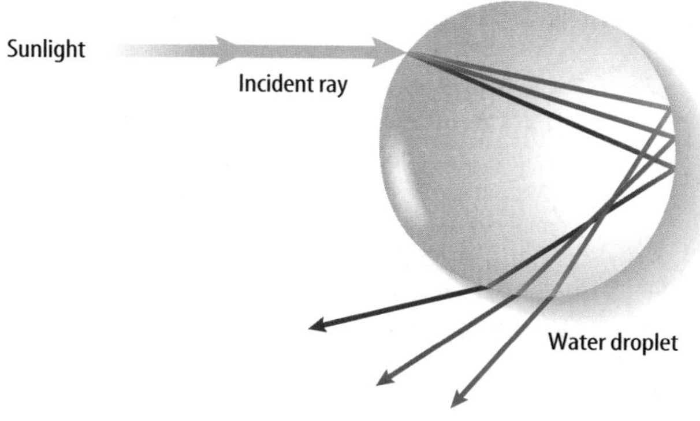

Observing Refraction in Water

Procedure

1. Place a **penny** at the bottom of a **short, opaque cup.** Set it on a **table** in front of you.
2. Have a partner slowly slide the cup away from you until you can't see the penny.
3. Without disturbing the penny or the cup and without moving your position, have your partner slowly pour **water** into the cup until you can see the penny.
4. Reverse roles and repeat the experiment.

Analysis

1. What did you observe? Explain how this is possible.
2. In your **Science Journal,** sketch the light path from the penny to your eye after the water was added.

Text Question Answer

violet

Purpose Students investigate how water bends light. L1 LS Visual-Spatial

Materials penny, table, opaque cup, water

Teaching Strategy Have students make a prediction about what may happen as the cup is filled with water.

Analysis

1. The penny became visible as water was added because the light from the penny was bent at the surface of the water.
2. Viewed from the side of the cup, a light ray travels diagonally upward from the penny to the surface of the water. At the surface, the ray is refracted more toward the horizontal.

Assessment

Oral Have students use the results of this MiniLAB to describe what a person sees when underwater in a swimming pool, wearing a mask and looking upward. objects are shifted above their true location Use **Performance Assessment in the Science Classroom,** p. 89.

Try at Home

Fun Fact

Rainbows are formed when sunlight is refracted by water droplets in the air. If light traveled at the same speed in water and air, there would be no rainbows.

Differentiated Instruction

Visually Impaired Suggest that visually impaired students work with sighted partners for the MiniLAB. The sighted student should clearly describe what can be seen at each step as the visually impaired student slides the cup away and feels the level of water in the cup. L2 ELL LS **Visual-Spatial**

Challenge Have students stand in front of a window where the other side of the window can be darkened (like a window between two rooms or from the outside). Darken the other side of the window and ask students why they saw their reflection when the other side was darkened. When the other room is lighted, the reflected light can't be easily seen because of all the light that is transmitted through the window. L3

Discussion

Mirages Why are mirages likely to appear in the desert? In a desert you can see a long distance over the surface and the air at ground level is much hotter than the air above it.

3 Assess

DAILY INTERVENTION

Check for Understanding

Visual-Spatial Draw different surfaces on the board and light rays approaching them. Make some rough and some smooth. Have the students copy the surfaces and draw light diagrams.

Reteach

Ray Diagrams Ask students to draw ray diagrams showing light coming from a flashlight, being refracted as it moves from air to water, being refracted off an object in the water, and being refracted as it moves from the water to air, and then hitting an observer's eye. L2

LS **Visual-Spatial**

Assessment

Process Show the class various materials and have students classify them as opaque, transparent, or translucent.

Figure 8 Mirages result when air near the ground is much warmer or cooler than the air above. This causes some light-waves reflected from the object to refract, creating one or more additional images.

Mirages You might have seen what looks like a pool of water on the road ahead. As you get closer, the water seems to disappear. You saw a **mirage,** an image of a distant object produced by the refraction of light through air layers of different densities. Mirages result when the air at ground level is much warmer or cooler than the air above it, as **Figure 8** shows. The density of air increases as air cools. Light waves travel slower as the density of air increases, so that light travels slower in cooler air. As a result, light waves refract as they pass through air layers with different temperatures.

section 1 review

Summary

Light and Matter

- When light waves strike an object, the light can be absorbed, reflected, and transmitted.
- The amount of light that is absorbed, reflected, or transmitted depends on the material an object is made from.

Reflection of Light

- Light waves always obey the law of reflection—the angle of incidence equals the angle of reflection.
- Regular reflection occurs when the roughness of a surface is less than the wavelengths reflected.
- Diffuse reflection causes parallel light waves to be reflected in many directions.

Refraction of Light

- Refraction occurs if a light wave changes speed in moving from one material to another.
- The index of refraction of a material indicates how much light slows down in the material.
- In a material, different wavelengths of light can be refracted by different amounts.

Self Check

1. **Compare and contrast** opaque, transparent, and translucent materials. Give at least one example of each.
2. **Discuss** why you can see your reflection in a smooth piece of aluminum foil but not in a crumpled ball of foil.
3. **Explain** why you are more likely to see a mirage on a hot day than on a mild day.
4. **Infer** what happens to white light when it passes through a prism.
5. **Think Critically** Decide whether the lens of your eye, a fingernail, your skin, and your tooth are opaque, translucent, or transparent. Explain.

Applying Math

6. **Find an Angle** A light ray strikes a mirror at an angle of 42° from the surface of the mirror. What angle does the reflected ray make with the normal?
7. **Find an Angle** A ray of light hits a mirror at 27° from the normal. What is the angle between the reflected ray and the normal?

Science Online gpscience.com/self_check_quiz

section 1 review

1. Transparent materials (clear glass) transmit all light, opaque materials (a wall) transmit no light, and translucent materials (waxed paper) transmit some light.
2. Smooth surfaces reflect parallel rays in one direction; rough surfaces reflect parallel rays in many directions.
3. Mirages are caused by refraction of light through air layers of different densities. On a hot day, air near the ground is warmer and less dense than air above it.
4. The different wavelengths of light in it are bent different amounts, causing a rainbow effect.
5. The lens is transparent, the fingernail and skin are translucent, the tooth is opaque.
6. 48°
7. 27°

section 2

Light and Color

Reading Guide

What **You'll Learn**
- **Explain** how you see color.
- **Describe** the difference between light color and pigment color.
- **Predict** what happens when different colors are mixed.

Why **It's Important**

From traffic lights to great works of art, color plays an important role in your world.

Review Vocabulary

retina: inner layer of the eye containing cells that convert light images into electrical signals

New Vocabulary
- pigment

Colors

Why do some apples appear red, while others look green or yellow? An object's color depends on the wavelengths of light it reflects. You know that white light is a blend of all colors of visible light. When a red apple is struck by white light, it reflects red light back to your eyes and absorbs all of the other colors. **Figure 9** shows white light striking a green leaf. Only the green light is reflected to your eyes.

Although some objects appear to be black, black isn't a color that is present in visible light. Objects that appear black absorb all colors of light and reflect little or no light back to your eye. White objects appear to be white because they reflect all colors of visible light.

Reading Check *Why does a white object appear white?*

Figure 9 This green leaf absorbs all wavelengths of visible light except green.

Colored Filters Wearing tinted glasses changes the color of almost everything you look at. If the lenses are yellow, the world takes on a golden glow. If they are rose colored, everything looks rosy. Something similar would occur if you placed a colored, clear plastic sheet over this white page. The paper would appear to be the same color as the plastic. The plastic sheet and the tinted lenses are filters. A filter is a transparent material that transmits one or more colors of light but absorbs all others. The color of a filter is the color of the light that it transmits.

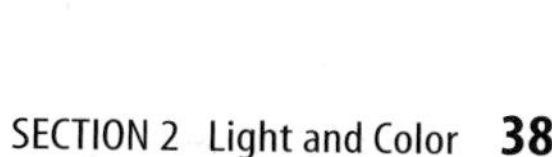

Section 2 Resource Manager

Chapter *Fast File* Resources
- Transparency Activity, p. 47
- Enrichment, p. 32
- Directed Reading for Content Mastery, p 20
- Reinforcement, p. 27
- **Physical Science Critical Thinking/Problem Solving,** p. 4

1 Motivate

Bellringer

Section Focus Transparencies also are available on the Interactive Chalkboard CD-ROM. L2 ELL

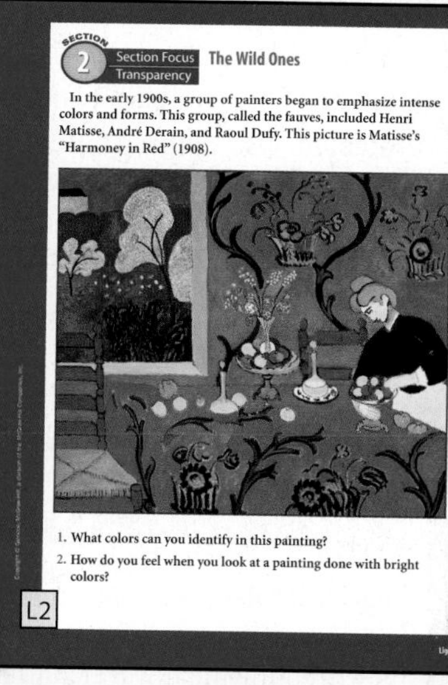

Tie to Prior Knowledge

Object Color Ask students to find something in the classroom that is red. Do this for orange, yellow, green, blue, and violet also. Tell students that in this section they will learn that the color of an object depends on how it absorbs or reflects light.

Reading Check

Answer It reflects all colors of visible light.

2 Teach

Discussion

Lightbulb Filter How is a colored lightbulb a filter? The color of the glass on the outside of the bulb determines which color of light is transmitted. The colored glass absorbs the other colors from the white light given off by the filament. L2 IS **Logical-Mathematical**

Quick Demo

Colored Filters

Materials colored filters and a colored object

Estimated Time five minutes

Procedure Use colored filters to demonstrate the effects shown in **Figure 10** with a colorful object in the classroom IS **Visual-Spatial**

IDENTIFYING Misconceptions

Individual Colors Students might assume that red, green, and blue are individual wavelengths of light. Explain that each of these is a range of wavelengths that has strongest reflection at a certain wavelength.

Reading Check

Answer The cooler absorbs the red light so no color is reflected back to your eyes.

Discussion

Black Pupils Why do the pupils of our eyes appear black? Almost all of the light that enters our eyes through the pupils is absorbed by the retina. IS **Logical-Mathematical**

Figure 10 The color of this cooler seems to change under different lighting conditions.

A The blue cooler is shown in white light.

B The cooler appears blue when viewed through a blue filter.

C The cooler appears black through a red filter.

Looking Through Colored Filters **Figure 10** shows what happens when you look at a colored object through various colored filters. In the white light in **Figure 10A,** a blue cooler looks blue because it reflects only the blue light in the white light striking it. It absorbs the light of all other colors. If you look at the cooler through a blue filter as in **Figure 10B,** the cooler still looks blue because the filter transmits the reflected blue light. **Figure 10C** shows how the cooler looks when you examine it through a red filter.

Reading Check *Why does the blue cooler appear black through a red filter?*

Seeing Color

As you approach a busy intersection, the color of the traffic light changes from green to yellow to red. On the cross street, the color changes from red to green. At a busy intersection, traffic safety depends on your ability to detect immediate color changes. How do you see colors?

Light and the Eye In a healthy eye, light enters and is focused on the retina, an area on the inside of your eyeball, as shown in **Figure 11A.** The retina is made up of two types of cells that absorb light, as shown in **Figure 11B.** When these cells absorb light energy, chemical reactions convert light energy into nerve impulses that are transmitted to the brain. One type of cell in the retina, called a cone, allows you to distinguish colors and detailed shapes of objects. Cones are most effective in daytime vision.

Curriculum Connection

Theater Arts Plan a trip to your school auditorium or to a theater. Show students what kind of colored lighting is used to illuminate the stage. Investigate the special effects that can be created with lighting. L1 ELL IS **Visual-Spatial**

Cultural Diversity

Names of Colors It may seem obvious to say that the sky is blue and grass is green, but the Mayan people of Mexico have no words that clearly define the two colors. Many other cultures distinguish between colors differently, also. Even in English differences in colors are often difficult to define. Have students bring samples of such colors to class.

Figure 11 Light enters the eye and focuses on the retina. The two types of light-detecting cells that make up the retina are called rods and cones.

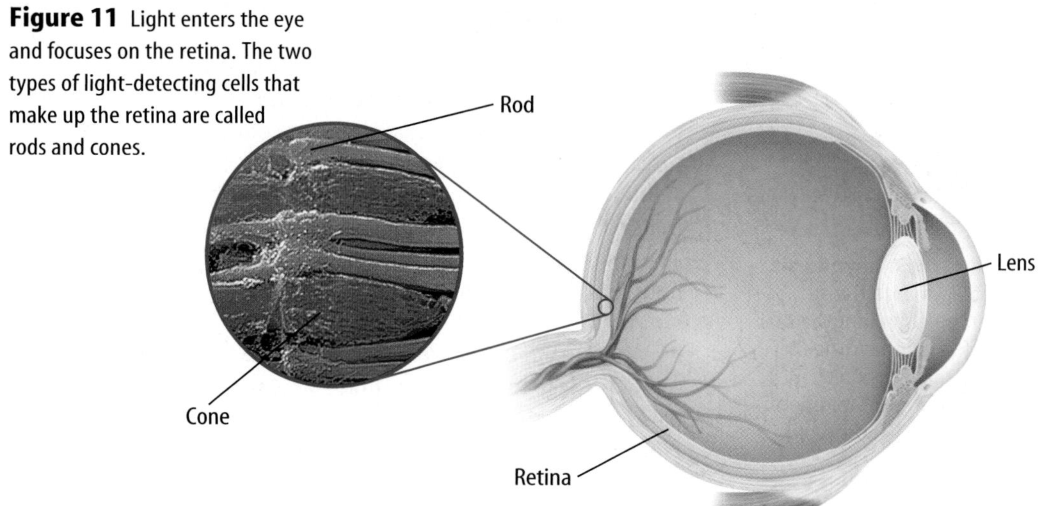

Cones and Rods Your eyes have three types of cones, each of which responds to a different range of wavelengths. Red cones respond to mostly red and yellow, green cones respond to mostly yellow and green, and blue cones respond to mostly blue and violet. The second type of cell, called a rod, is sensitive to dim light and is useful for night vision.

INTEGRATE Life Science

Interpreting Color Why does a banana look yellow? The light reflected by the banana causes the cone cells that are sensitive to red and green light to send signals to your brain. Your brain would get the same signal if a mixture of red light and green light reached your eye. Again, your red and green cones would respond, and you would see yellow light because your brain can't perceive the difference between incoming yellow light and yellow light produced by combining red and green light. The next time you are at a play or a concert, look at the lighting above the stage. Watch how the colored lights combine to produce effects onstage.

Figure 12 Color blindness is an inherited sex-linked condition in which certain cones do not function properly.
Identify *what number you see in the dots.*

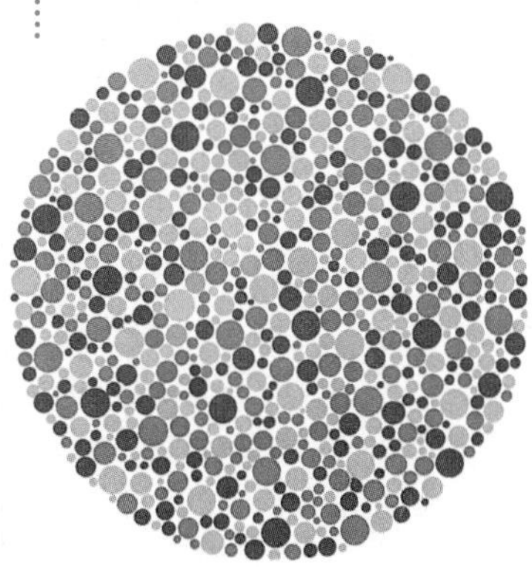

Color Blindness If one or more of your sets of cones did not function properly, you would not be able to distinguish between certain colors. About eight percent of men and one-half percent of women have a form of color blindness. Most people who are said to be color-blind are not truly blind to color, but they have difficulty distinguishing between a few colors, most commonly red and green. **Figure 12** shows a page of a color blindness test. Because these two colors are used in traffic signals, drivers and pedestrians must be able to identify them.

Teacher FYI

Section of Spectrum Visible light is a very small part of the electromagnetic spectrum. Imagine the distance between Earth and the Sun compared to the width of your thumb. Your thumb is a much larger percentage of the distance between earth and the sun, than the percentage of the electromagnetic spectrum that is visible light.

Caption Answer

Figure 12 Students who are not red-green deficient will see the number eight.

Discussion

Colors in the Dark Are objects still colored in a dark room? Some students may say no because color results from light reflection. Others may say yes, because the property that makes the object a certain color is still present whether or not the lights are on. L2 IS **Logical-Mathematical**

Inquiry Lab

Combining Colors

Materials flashlights covered in red, orange, yellow, green, blue and purple cellophane

Estimated Time 30 minutes

Procedure Have students work in groups to determine which combinations of colored light produce which colors including white light. Have them make a table of their discoveries.

For additional inquiry activities, see *Science Inquiry Labs.*

Visual Learning

Figure 11 Point out the position of the retina. Behind the retina is the optic nerve, which takes information from the rods and cones and sends it to the brain. Humans have many more rod cells than cone cells. Ask students to infer the number of rods in the eyes of nocturnal animals. They have far more rod cells than humans so they can see well at night.

Differentiated Instruction

Learning Disabled If students have trouble remembering which type of nerve cells of the retina interpret color and which interpret black and white, tell them to remember that the word *cone* starts with the same letter as the word *color*. To practice using this mnemonic, name some different things they might see and have them identify which type of retinal nerve cells would be used.

Color for Photosynthesis Carotenoids, yellow and orange pigments that include xanthophyll, are always present in green plants. These pigments absorb light in the blue and green wavelengths, which aids plants, especially those growing in low-light conditions, to absorb enough light to make food.

Research Flowers are many colors. Have students research to learn the primary pigment responsible for blue, lavender, and purple flowers. anthocyanins

Reading Check

Answer red, green, and blue

Activity

Filter Combinations Provide groups of students with red, green, and blue color filters (or colored transparency film) and an overhead projector. Have them use different combinations of filters to produce the colors yellow, magenta, and cyan. Ask them to write down the combination of filters they used to produce each color. Red and green produce yellow. Red and blue produce magenta. Green and blue produce cyan.

L2 ELL IS **Visual-Spatial** P

Virtual Labs

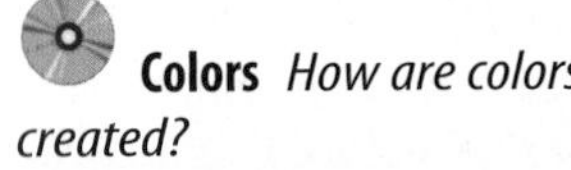
Colors *How are colors created?*

Color for Photosynthesis Plant pigments determine the wavelengths of light for photosynthesis. Leaves usually look green due to the pigment chlorophyll. Chlorophyll absorbs most wavelengths of visible light except green, which it reflects. But not all plants are green. Research different plant pigments to find how they allow plant species to survive in diverse habitats.

Mixing Colors

If you have ever browsed through a paint store, you have probably seen displays where customers can select paint samples of almost every imaginable color. The colors are a result of mixtures of pigments. For example, you might have mixed blue and yellow paint to produce green paint. A **pigment** is a colored material that is used to change the color of other substances. The color of a pigment results from the different wavelengths of light that the pigment reflects.

Mixing Colored Lights From the glowing orange of a sunset to the deep blue of a mountain lake, all the colors you see can be made by mixing three colors of light. These three colors—red, green, and blue—are the primary colors of light. They correspond to the three different types of cones in the retina of your eye. When mixed together in equal amounts, they produce white light, as **Figure 13** shows. Mixing the primary colors in different proportions can produce the colors you see.

Reading Check *What are primary colors?*

Paint Pigments If you were to mix equal amounts of red, green, and blue paint, would you get white paint? If mixing colors of paint were like mixing colors of light, you would, but mixing paint is different. Paints are made with pigments. Paint pigments usually are made of chemical compounds such as titanium oxide, a bright white pigment, and lead chromate, which is used for painting yellow lines on highways.

Figure 13 White light is produced when the three primary colors of light are mixed.

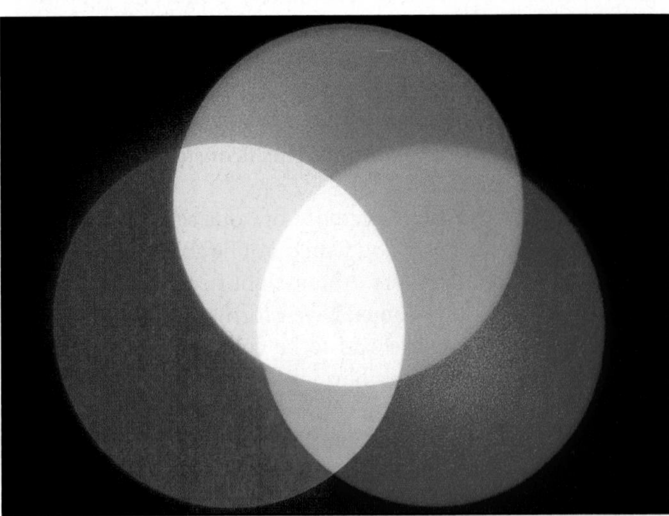

Active Reading

Cause and Effect Chart This strategy is used to focus on cause-effect relationships. Have students write *Mixing Colors.* On the left, instruct them to write combinations of the primary colors of light, followed by combinations of the primary pigments. On the right side, have students record the color that will result from each combination.

Differentiated Instruction

Challenge Have students stare at a red object for 20 seconds and then look at a white wall. They should see a faint blue/green after image of the object on the wall. Ask them to explain why they think this happens based on how our eyes see color. Their red cones lose sensitivity. When they look at the white wall, the part of their retinas that stared at the red object have only blue and green cones that are sensitive. L3

Mixing Pigments You can make any pigment color by mixing different amounts of the three primary pigments—magenta (bluish red), cyan (greenish blue), and yellow. In fact, color printers use those pigments to make full-color prints like the pages in this book. However, color printers also use black ink to produce a true black color. A primary pigment's color depends on the color of light it reflects. Actually, pigments both absorb and reflect a range of colors in sending a single color message to your eye. For example, in white light, the yellow pigment appears yellow because it reflects yellow, red, orange, and green light but absorbs blue and violet light. The color of a mixture of two primary pigments is determined by the primary colors of light that both pigments reflect.

Look at **Figure 14.** The area in the center where the colors all overlap appears to be black because the three blended primary pigments absorb all the primary colors of light. Recall that the primary colors of light combine to produce white light. They are called additive colors. However, the primary pigment colors combine to produce black. Because black results from the absence of reflected light, the primary pigments are called subtractive colors.

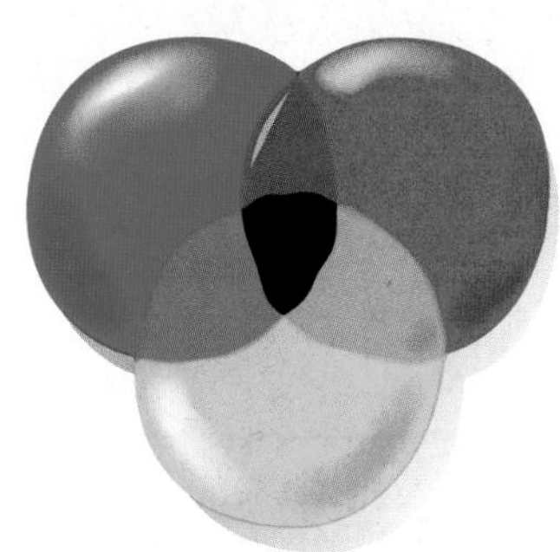

Figure 14 The three primary colors of pigment appear to be black when they are mixed.

section 2 review

Summary

Colors

- The color of an object is determined by the wavelengths of light it reflects.
- The color of a filter is the color of the light the filter transmits.

Seeing Color

- Rod and cone cells are light-sensitive cells found in the retina of the human eye.
- Rod cells are sensitive to dim light. Cone cells enable the human eye to see colors.
- There are three types of cone cells. One type responds to red light, another to green light, and another to blue light.

Mixing Colors

- Red, green and blue are the primary light colors. Any color can be created by mixing these primary light colors.
- Any pigment color can be formed by mixing the primary pigment colors—magenta, cyan, and yellow.

Self Check

1. **Identify** what colors are reflected and what colors are absorbed if a white light shines on a red shirt.
2. **Discuss** how the primary colors of light differ from the primary pigment colors.
3. **Explain** why a color-blind person can distinguish among some colors but not others.
4. **Determine** why a white fence appears to be white instead of multicolored if all colors are present in white light.
5. **Think Critically** Light reflected from an object passes through a green filter, then a red filter, and finally a blue filter. What color will the object seem to be?

Applying Math

6. **Use Percentages** In the human eye there are about 120,000,000 rods. If 90,000,000 rods trigger at once, what percentage of the total number of rods triggered?
7. **Convert Units** The wavelengths of a color are measured in nanometers (nm) which is 0.000001 mm. Find the wavelength in mm of a light wave that has a wavelength of 690 nm.

gpscience.com/self_check_quiz

section 2 review

1. red is reflected and all others are absorbed
2. Primary colors of light are red, green, and blue. Primary colors of pigment are magenta, cyan, and yellow. Primary colors of light transmit the color you see, while primary colors of pigment reflect the color you see.
3. not all of their cone cells function properly
4. The fence reflects all colors of visible light. Since all the cones in your eyes are stimulated, you see white.
5. It will appear black.
6. 75%
7. 0.00069 mm

Fun Fact

Have you ever noticed that brown is not in the rainbow? Brown is actually dark yellow.

3 Assess

DAILY INTERVENTION

Check for Understanding

Kinesthetic Create some color samples with combinations of magenta, cyan, and yellow paints. Provide students with sets of magenta, cyan, and yellow paint. Have students match the color samples with the paint you have provided.

Reteach

Pigments Have students work in groups to combine small amounts of various primary pigment paints to make other colors. For each color, have them describe which colors are reflected and which are absorbed. Be sure they mix all three primary pigments to produce black. Point out that black pigment absorbs all light and reflects none. L2 ELL

COOP LEARN IN **Kinesthetic**

Assessment

Oral Assess students' understanding of colors by asking them to explain why black and white are not true colors. Black is a lack of color that occurs when all light is absorbed. White occurs when all colors are reflected. Use **Performance Assessment in the Science Classroom,** p. 89.

Producing Light

1 Motivate

Bellringer

Section Focus Transparencies also are available on the Interactive Chalkboard CD-ROM.

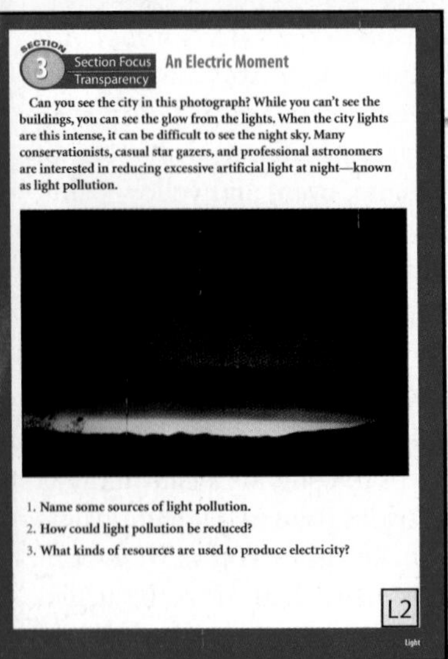

Section 3 Section Focus Transparency An Electric Moment

Can you see the city in this photograph? While you can't see the buildings, you can see the glow from the lights. When the city lights are this intense, it can be difficult to see the night sky. Many conservationists, casual star gazers, and professional astronomers are interested in reducing excessive artificial light at night—known as light pollution.

1. Name some sources of light pollution.
2. How could light pollution be reduced?
3. What kinds of resources are used to produce electricity?

L2

Tie to Prior Knowledge

Laser Light Show Ask students if they have ever seen a laser light show. Explain that lasers have a very intense, narrow beam of light because of the way the light is produced. In this section students will learn how lasers and other light sources produce light.

Answer More than 90% of the energy it gives off is heat.

Caption Answer

Figure 15 They absorb ultraviolet light and re-emit it as visible light.

Reading Guide

***What* You'll Learn**

- **Explain** how incandescent and fluorescent lightbulbs work.
- **Analyze** the advantages and disadvantages of different lighting devices.
- **Explain** how a laser produces coherent light.
- **Describe** various uses of lasers.

***Why* It's Important**

Knowing how different lighting devices work will help you choose the right one for your needs.

Review Vocabulary

electron: negatively charged particle found in an atom

New Vocabulary

- incandescent light
- fluorescent light
- coherent light
- incoherent light

Incandescent Lights

Most of the lightbulbs in your house probably produce **incandescent light**, which is generated by heating a piece of metal until it glows. Inside an incandescent lightbulb is a small wire coil, called a filament, that usually is made of tungsten metal. When an electric current flows in the filament, the electric resistance of the metal causes the filament to become hot enough to give off light. However, about 90% of the energy given off by an incandescent bulb is in the form of thermal energy.

Reading Check *Why does an incandescent lightbulb get hot?*

Fluorescent Lights

Your house also may have fluorescent (floo RE sunt) lights. A fluorescent bulb, like the one shown in **Figure 15,** is filled with a gas at low pressure. The inside of the bulb is coated with phosphors that emit visible light when they absorb ultraviolet radiation. The tube also contains electrodes at each end. Electrons are given off when the electrodes are connected in a circuit. When these electrons collide with the gas atoms, ultraviolet radiation is emitted. The phosphors on the inside of the bulb absorb this radiation and give off visible light.

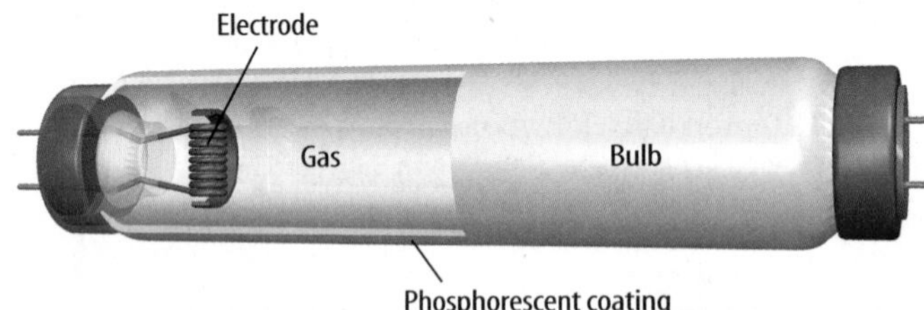

Figure 15 Fluorescent lightbulbs do not use filaments. **Determine** *what property of phosphors makes them useful in fluorescent bulbs.*

Section 3 Resource Manager

Chapter *FAST FILE* Resources

Transparency Activity, p. 48
MiniLAB, p. 4
Enrichment, p. 33
Directed Reading for Content Mastery, p. 21
Reinforcement, p. 29
Mathematics Skill Activities, p. 47

Efficient Lighting A **fluorescent light** uses phosphors to convert ultraviolet radiation to visible light. Fluorescent lights use as little as one fifth the electrical energy to produce the same amount of light as incandescent bulbs. Fluorescent bulbs also last much longer than incandescent bulbs. This higher efficiency can mean lower energy costs over the life of the bulb. Reduced energy usage could reduce the amount of fossil fuels burned to generate electricity, which also decreases the amount of carbon dioxide and pollutants released into Earth's atmosphere.

Fluorescent bulbs are used widely in hospitals, office buildings, schools, and factories. Compact fluorescent bulbs, which can be screwed into traditional lightbulb sockets, have been developed for use in homes.

Neon Lights

The vivid, glowing colors of neon lights, such as those shown in **Figure 16,** make them a popular choice for signs and eye-catching decorations on buildings. These lighting devices are glass tubes filled with gas, typically neon, and work similarly to fluorescent lights. When an electric current flows through the tube, electrons collide with the gas molecules. In this case, however, the collisions produce visible light. If the tube contains only neon, the light is bright red. Different colors can be produced by adding other gases to the tube.

Reading Check *What causes the color in a neon light?*

Mini LAB

Discovering Energy Waste in Lightbulbs

Procedure

1. Obtain an **incandescent bulb** and a **fluorescent bulb** of identical wattage.
2. Make a heat collector by covering the top of a **foam cup** with a piece of **plastic food wrap** to make a window. Carefully make a small hole (diameter less than the thermometer's) in the side of the cup. Push a **thermometer** through the hole.
3. Measure the temperature of the air inside the cup. Then, hold the window of the tester 1 cm from one of the lights for 2 min and measure the temperature.
4. Cool the heat collector and thermometer. Repeat step 3 using the second bulb.

Analysis

1. What was the temperature for each bulb?
2. Which bulb appears to give off more heat? Explain why this occurs.

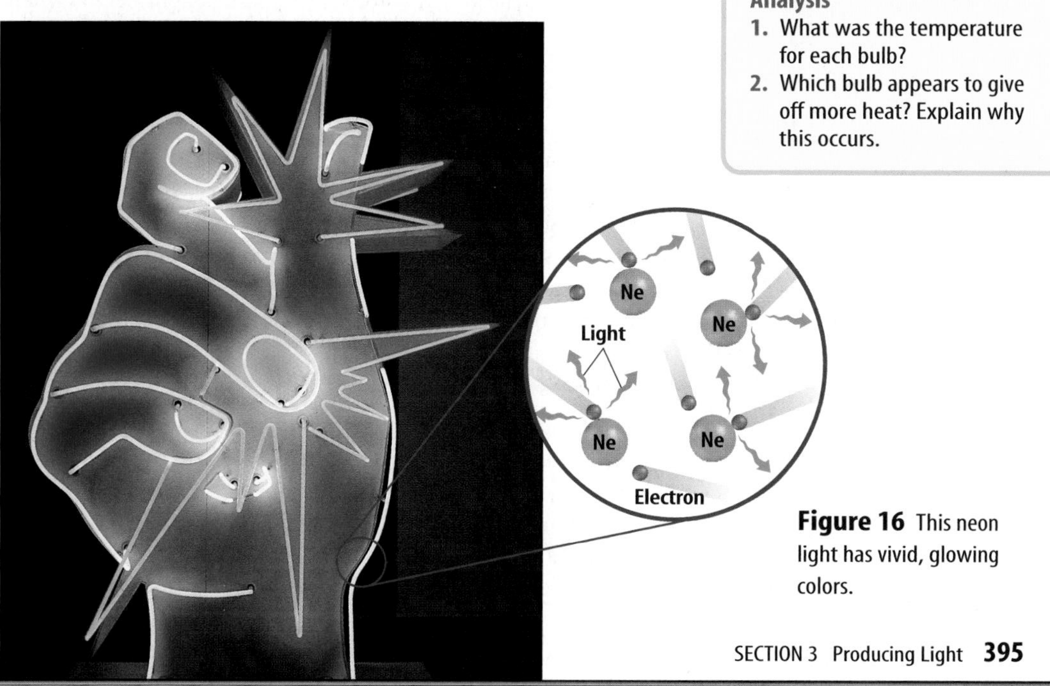

Figure 16 This neon light has vivid, glowing colors.

2 Teach

Purpose Students observe energy wasted by bulbs. L1 COOP LEARN IS Kinesthetic

Materials fluorescent and incandescent bulbs of same wattage, thermometer, polystyrene foam cup, stopwatch, plastic food wrap, power source for the bulbs

Safety Precautions Caution students not to touch or to allow their heat collectors to touch hot bulbs.

Analysis

1. The temperature should be higher for the incandescent bulb.
2. Incandescent bulb; it produces light by heating a tungsten filament.

Assessment

Oral Ask students which bulb emits high levels of infrared radiation. the incandescent bulb Use **Performance Assessment in the Science Classroom,** p. 89.

Reading Check

Answer electrons colliding with gas molecules

Discussion

Efficiency What make some light sources more efficient than others? Some light sources use some of their energy to produce heat or to move slightly rather than using a larger portion of their energy to produce light.

Teacher FYI

Fluorescent Bulbs Standard 60- to 75-watt incandescent bulbs can be replaced by 18-watt compact fluorescent bulbs. These bulbs use about 75 percent less electricity to produce the same amount of light.

Differentiated Instruction

English-Language Learners Have students who speak a different language translate the types of lighting they are familiar with into their native language. Have the students use flash cards to learn the English names for the different types of lighting L2 ELL

Activity

Light Sources Ask students to look around the community at night to find examples of various light sources. Explain that sodium-vapor lights are considered by many to be a good option for decreasing city light pollution. L2 ELL LS **Visual-Spatial**

Use Science Words

Word Meaning Laser stands for *L*ight *A*mplification by *S*timulated *E*mission of *R*adiation. Have students explain why this is an appropriate name. A laser amplifies, or magnifies, light by stimulating, or exciting, atoms. This results in the emission of radiation from the atoms as they de-excite. L2 LS **Linguistic**

Reading Check

Answer The partially reflective mirror reflects most of the light. As the light waves travel back and forth, they stimulate other atoms to emit identical light waves, which produces a beam of laser light.

Fun Fact

Police can't easily tell if there is a puddle of oil or blood in a parking lot lit by sodium-vapor lighting because there is so little red in the light that sodium-vapor lights give off.

Figure 17 Sodium-vapor lights emit mostly yellow light. Half of this photo was taken under sunlight and half was taken under sodium-vapor lighting.

Sodium-Vapor Lights

Sodium-vapor lights often are used for streetlights and other outdoor lighting. Inside a sodium-vapor lamp is a tube that contains a mixture of neon gas, a small amount of argon gas, and a small amount of sodium metal. When the lamp is turned on, the gas mixture becomes hot. The hot gases cause the sodium metal to turn to vapor, and the hot sodium vapor emits a yellow-orange glow, as shown in **Figure 17.**

Tungsten-Halogen Lights

Tungsten-halogen lights sometimes are used to create intensely bright light. These lights have a tungsten filament inside a quartz bulb or tube. The tube is filled with a gas that contains one of the halogen elements, such as fluorine or chlorine. The presence of this gas enables the filament to become much hotter than the filament in an ordinary incandescent bulb. As a result, the light is much brighter and also lasts longer. Tungsten-halogen lights sometimes are used on movie sets and in underwater photography.

Lasers

From laser surgery to a laser light show, lasers have become a large part of the world you live in. A laser's light begins when a number of light waves are emitted at the same time. To achieve this, a number of identical atoms each must be given the same amount of energy. When they release their energy, each atom sends off an identical light wave. This light wave is reflected between two facing mirrors at opposite ends of the laser. One of the mirrors is coated only partially with reflective material, so it reflects most light but allows some to get through. Some emitted light waves travel back and forth between the mirrors many times, stimulating other atoms to emit identical light waves also. **Figure 18** shows how this process produces a beam of laser light.

Reading Check *How do mirrors help in creating lasers?*

Lasers can be made with many different materials, including gases, liquids, and solids. One of the most common is the helium-neon laser, which produces a beam of red light. A mixture of helium and neon gases sealed in a tube with mirrors at both ends is excited by a flashtube. The excited atoms then lose their excess energy by emitting coherent light waves.

Science Online

Topic: Light Pollution

Visit gpscience.com for Web links to information about sodium vapor lights and light pollution.

Activity Research light pollution and how it affects astronomers. Determine which types of outdoor lights create more and which create less light pollution.

Visual Learning

Figure 17 Point out that the sodium-vapor lighting shown on the right enables more detail to be seen than white lights show. The yellow-orange light is in the range of wavelengths that our eyes see best. Sodium-vapor lighting also produces less glare than conventional lighting. L2 ELL LS **Visual-Spatial**

NATIONAL GEOGRAPHIC VISUALIZING LASERS

Figure 18

Lasers produce light waves that have the same wavelength. Almost all of these waves travel in the same direction and are in phase. As a result, beams of laser light can be made more intense than ordinary light. In modern eye surgery, shown at the right, lasers are often used instead of a traditional scalpel.

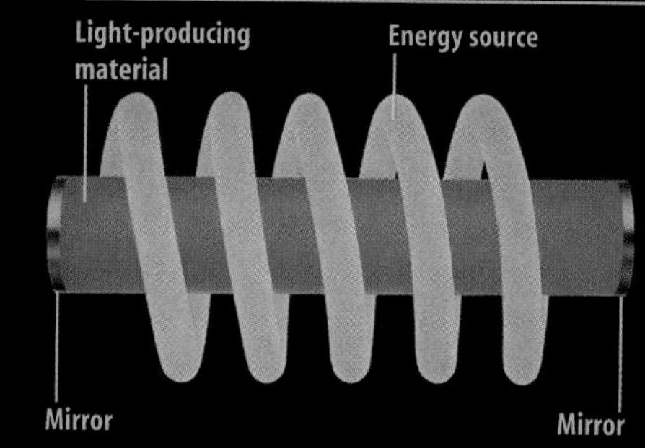

Ⓐ The key parts of a laser include a material that can be stimulated to produce light, such as a ruby rod, and an energy source. In this example, the energy source is a lightbulb that spirals around the ruby rod and emits an intense light.

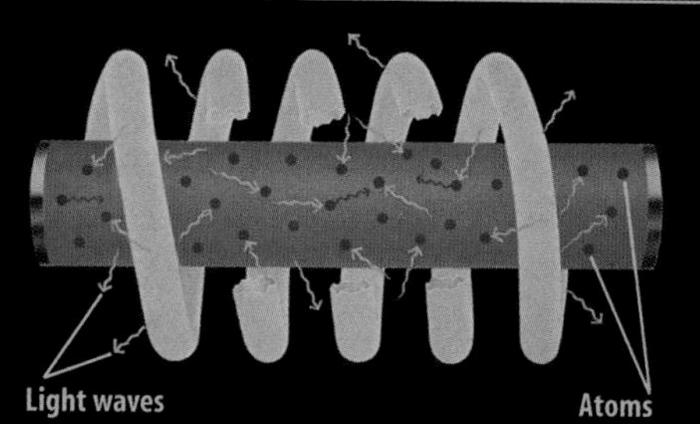

Ⓑ When the lightbulb is turned on, energy is absorbed by the atoms in the rod. These atoms then re-emit that energy as light waves that are in phase and have the same wavelength.

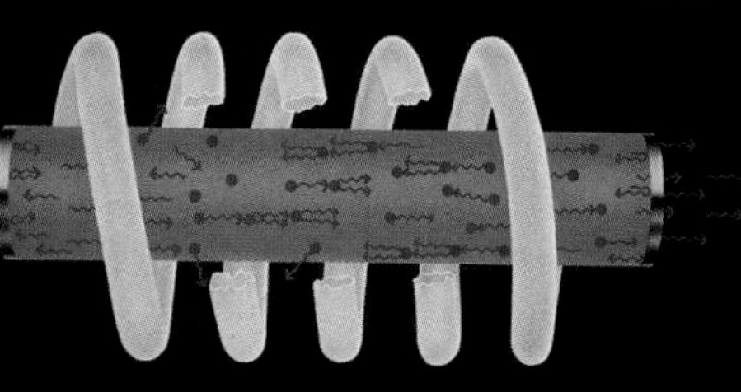

Ⓒ Most of these waves are reflected between the mirrors located at each end of the laser. One of the mirrors, however, is only partially reflective, allowing one percent of the light waves to pass through it and form a beam.

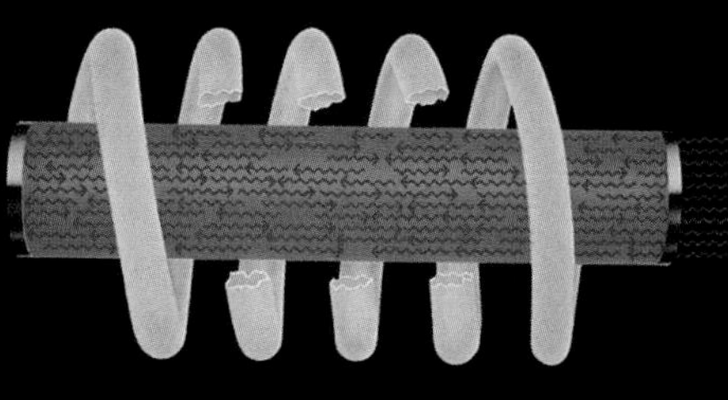

Ⓓ As the waves travel back and forth between the mirrors, they stimulate other atoms in the ruby rod to emit light waves. In a fraction of a second, billions of identical waves are bouncing between the mirrors. The waves are emitted from the partially reflective mirror in a stream of laser light.

397

NATIONAL GEOGRAPHIC

Visualizing Lasers

Have students examine the pictures and read the captions. Then ask the following questions.

In a laser, what is the purpose of the energy source? It provides the energy to stimulate the ruby rod to emit light waves that are of the same wavelength and in phase.

What is the effect of allowing only 1% of the light waves through the partially reflective mirror? The light waves remaining inside the ruby rod stimulate other atoms in the ruby rod to emit light waves, so the energy of the light increases.

Why does a laser beam transfer more energy than ordinary light? The light waves all have the same wavelength and are in phase.

Quick Demo

Laser Light

Materials laser pointer and chalk dust

Estimated Time five minutes

Procedure Use the laser pointer to show a beam of laser light. Remind students that because the beam is coherent, it spreads out very little and produces an intense spot of light on a faraway wall. You can't see the light until it strikes the wall. If you scatter fine powder, such as chalk dust, in the air, the light scatters off the dust particles and you can see the beam. **WARNING:** *A laser pointer should never be pointed toward someone's eyes.* ELL

LS **Visual-Spatial**

IDENTIFYING Misconceptions

Lasers The laser is often thought of as a very powerful and efficient energy source. The typical classroom laser will not burn a hole through your skin, as some students may think, but it should never be directed toward anyone's eyes. Classroom lasers are a very inefficient light source; they are often less than 1% efficient.

Use Science Words

Word Origin The word *coherent* has the prefix *co-*, meaning "together," and the Latin word *haerere*, meaning "to stick." Have each student write a sentence that explains how this definition applies to coherent light. Possible answer: Waves of coherent light have the same wavelength, and they travel together with crests and troughs aligned. L2 LS **Linguistic**

Figure 19 Light waves can be either coherent or incoherent.

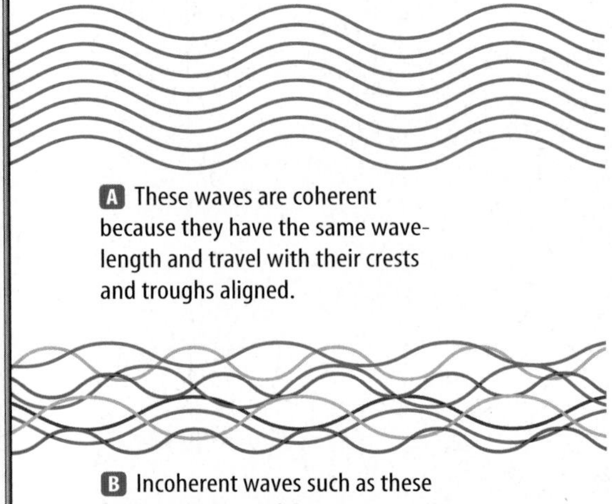

A These waves are coherent because they have the same wavelength and travel with their crests and troughs aligned.

B Incoherent waves such as these can contain more than one wavelength, and do not travel with their crests and troughs aligned.

Coherent Light Lasers produce the narrow beams of light that zip across the stage and through the auditorium during some rock concerts. Beams of laser light do not spread out because laser light is coherent. **Coherent light** is light of only one wavelength that travels with its crests and troughs aligned. The beam does not spread out because all the waves travel in the same direction, as shown in **Figure 19A.** As a result, the energy carried by the beam remains concentrated over a small area.

Incoherent Light Light from an ordinary lightbulb is incoherent. **Incoherent light** can contain more than one wavelength, and its electromagnetic waves are not aligned, as in **Figure 19B.** The waves don't travel in the same direction, so the beam spreads out. The energy carried by the light waves is spread over a large area, so the intensity of the light is much less than that of the laser beam.

Using Lasers

Compact disc players, surgical tools, and many other useful devices take advantage of the unique properties of lasers. A laser beam is narrow and does not spread out as it travels over long distances. So lasers can apply large amounts of energy to small areas. In industry, powerful lasers are used for cutting and welding materials. Surveyors and builders use lasers for measuring and leveling. To measure the moon's orbit with great accuracy, scientists use laser light reflected from mirrors placed on the Moon's surface. Information also can be coded in pulses of light from lasers. This makes them useful for communications. In telephone systems, pulses of laser light transmit conversations through long glass fibers called optical fibers.

Lasers in Medicine Lasers are routinely used to remove cataracts, reshape the cornea, and repair the retina. In the eye and other parts of the body, surgeons can use lasers in place of scalpels to cut through body tissues. The energy from the laser seals off blood vessels in the incision and reduces bleeding. Because most lasers do not penetrate deeply through the skin, they can be used to remove small tumors or birthmarks on the surface without damaging deeper tissues. By sending laser light into the body through an optical fiber, physicians can also treat conditions such as blocked arteries.

Science Journal

New Uses for Lasers Have each student write a paragraph describing several situations in which lasers are used. Ask them to include new uses that might be found for lasers in the future. Answers might include surgery, surveying, and welding. L2 LS **Linguistic**

Differentiated Instruction

Challenge Have students use colored pencils to draw three sketches of light waves. The first sketch should show incoherent light waves (different wavelengths with crests and troughs not aligned). The second should show light of one wavelength with crests and troughs not aligned. The third should show coherent light (one wavelength with crests and troughs aligned). L3 ELL LS **Visual-Spatial**

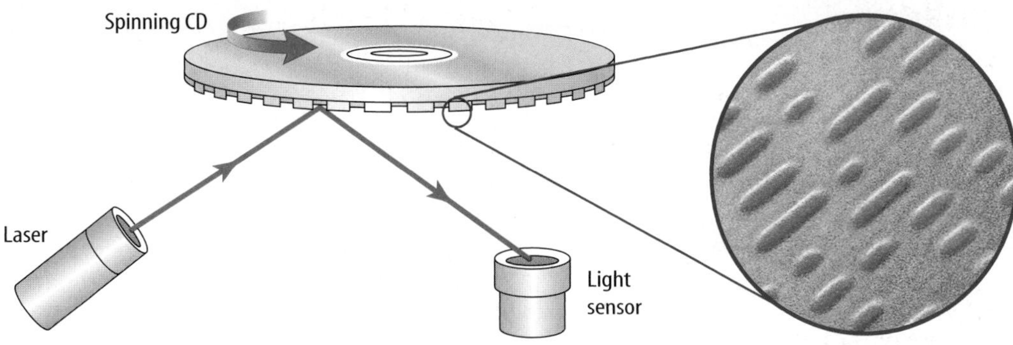

Figure 20 The blowup shows the pits (blue) on the bottom surface of a CD. A CD player uses a laser to convert the information on the CD to an electric signal.

Compact Discs Compact discs are plastic discs with reflective surfaces used to store sound, images, and text in digital form. When a CD is produced, the information is burned into the surface of the disc with a laser. The laser creates millions of tiny pits in a spiral pattern that starts at the center of the disc and moves out to the edge. A CD player, shown in **Figure 20,** also uses a laser to read the disc. As the laser beam strikes a pit or flat spot, different amounts of light are reflected to a light sensor. The reflected light is converted to an electric signal that the speakers use to create sound.

section 3 review

Summary

Incandescent and Fluorescent Lights

- In an incandescent bulb, an electric current heats a tungsten filament so that it glows.
- The phosphorescent coating on the inside of a fluorescent bulb absorbs ultraviolet light and emits visible light.

Other Light Sources

- In a neon tube, red light is produced when electrons collide with atoms of neon gas.
- In a sodium-vapor light, sodium metal is vaporized and emits a yellow-orange glow.
- A tungsten-halogen bulb is brighter and hotter than an ordinary incandescent bulb.

Lasers

- Laser light is produced when identical atoms are stimulated to emit coherent light.
- A laser beam does not spread, so energy carried by the beam can be concentrated in a small area.

Self Check

1. **Explain** how light is produced in an ordinary incandescent bulb.
2. **Discuss** the advantages of using a fluorescent bulb instead of an incandescent bulb.
3. **Describe** the difference between coherent and incoherent light.
4. **Think Critically** Which type of lighting device would you use for each of the following needs: an economical light source in a manufacturing plant, an eye-catching sign that will be visible at night, and a baseball stadium? Explain.

Applying Math

5. **Calculate Efficiency** A 25-W fluorescent light emits 5.0 J of thermal energy each second. What is the efficiency of the fluorescent light?
6. **Use Percentages** If 90 percent of the energy emitted by an incandescent bulb is thermal energy, how much thermal energy is emitted by a 60-W bulb each second?

3 Assess

DAILY INTERVENTION

Check for Understanding

Linguistic Have students write a description of the types of light sources they learned about in the section and explain how one object might appear differently under different light sources.

Reteach

Rhythm To reinforce the idea of coherent light, first have students all clap their hands in their own individual rhythms. The sound is scattered and jumbled. Now have everyone clap on the number as you count "one and two and three and . . ." The sound is coherent, or together, and more intense. L1 ELL LS **Auditory-Musical**

Assessment

Portfolio Have each student write a letter to the editor explaining why people should or should not switch to using fluorescent rather than incandescent light bulbs in their homes. Students should support their opinions with facts. Use **Performance Assessment in the Science Classroom,** p. 139. P

section 3 review

1. Electric charge flows through the filament, causing it to heat up and give off light.
2. The fluorescent bulb lasts longer and uses less energy to produce the same amount of light as an incandescent bulb.
3. Coherent light has only one wavelength and travels with its crests and troughs aligned; incoherent light can contain more than one wavelength, and the waves are not aligned.
4. Manufacturing plant—fluorescent lights; sign at night—neon; baseball stadium—tungsten halogen
5. 80%
6. 54 J

section 4

Using Light

1 Motivate

Bellringer

Section Focus Transparencies also are available on the Interactive Chalkboard CD-ROM. L2 

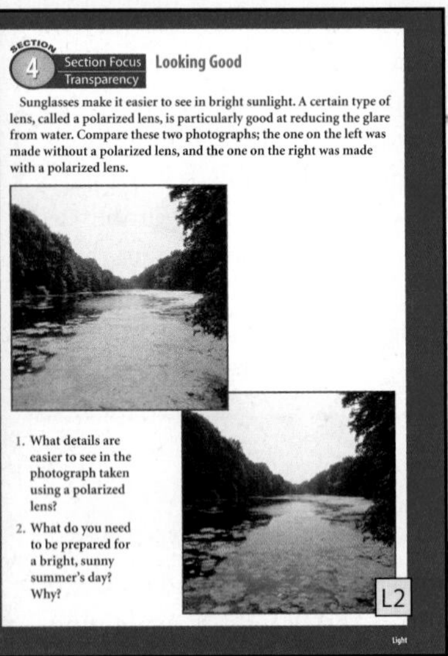

Tie to Prior Knowledge

Polarized Sunglasses Ask students if they have ever worn polarized sunglasses. Ask students who have to describe the difference between what they see through regular sunglasses and what they see through polarized sunglasses. Explain that in this section they will learn what polarized light is and how it can be used.

Reading Guide

What You'll Learn

- **Distinguish** polarized light from unpolarized light.
- **Explain** how a hologram is made.
- **Determine** when total internal reflection occurs.
- **Describe** the uses of optical fibers.

Why It's Important

Light waves were used to transmit a TV program you watched today, or to send a telephone call to a friend.

Review Vocabulary

interference: occurs when two or more waves overlap and form a new wave

New Vocabulary

- polarized light
- holography
- total internal reflection

Polarized Light

You may have a pair of sunglasses with a sticker on them that says "polarized." Do you know what makes them different from other sunglasses? The difference has to do with the vibration of light waves that pass through the lenses. You can make transverse waves in a rope vibrate in any direction—horizontal, vertical, or anywhere in between. Light also is a transverse wave and can vibrate in any direction. In **polarized light,** however, the waves vibrate in only one direction.

Polarizing Filters If the light passes through a special polarizing filter, the light becomes polarized. A polarizing filter acts like a group of parallel slits. Only light waves vibrating in the same direction as the slits can pass through. If a second polarizing filter is lined up with its slits at right angles to those of the first filter, no light can pass through, as **Figure 21** shows.

Polarized lenses are useful for reducing glare without interfering with your ability to see clearly. When light is reflected from a horizontal surface, such as a lake or a shiny car hood, it becomes partially horizontally polarized. The lenses of polarizing sunglasses have vertical polarizing filters that block out the reflected light that has been polarized horizontally.

Figure 21 Slats in a fence behave like a polarizing filter for a transverse wave on a rope.

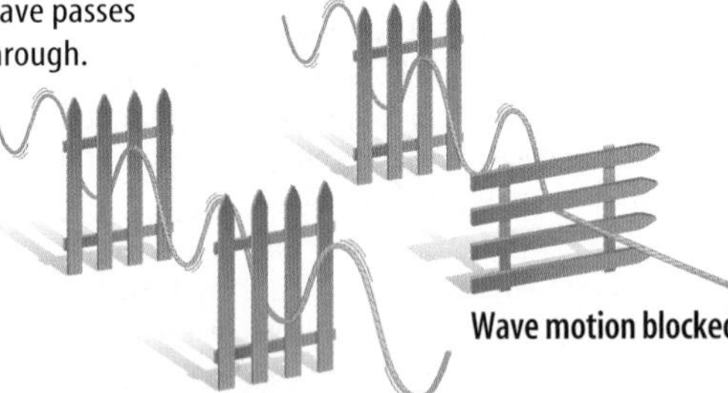

Section 4 Resource Manager 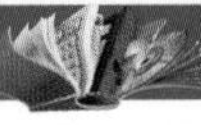

Chapter *FAST FILE* Resources

Transparency Activity, p. 49
Enrichment, p. 34
Directed Reading for Content Mastery, pp. 21-22
Lab Activity, pp. 13-16
Lab Worksheet, pp. 5-6, 7-8
Reinforcement, p. 30

Figure 22 Lasers can be used to make holograms like this one.

Holography

Science museums often have exhibits where a three-dimensional image seems to float in space, like the one shown in **Figure 22.** You can see the image from different angles, just as you would if you viewed the real object. Three-dimensional images on credit cards are produced by holography. **Holography** is a technique that produces a hologram—a complete three-dimensional photographic image of an object.

Making Holograms Illuminating objects with laser light produces holograms. Laser light reflects from the object onto photographic film. At the same time, a second beam split from the laser also is directed at the film. The light from the two beams creates an interference pattern on the film. The pattern looks nothing like the original object, but when laser light shines on the pattern on the film, a holographic image is produced.

Information in Light An ordinary photographic image captures only the brightness or intensity of light reflected from an object's surface, but a hologram records the intensity as well as the direction. As a result, it conveys more information to your eye than a conventional two-dimensional photograph does, but it also is more difficult to copy. Holographic images are used on credit cards, identification cards, and on the labels of some products to help prevent counterfeiting. Using X-ray lasers, scientists can produce holographic images of microscopic objects. It may be possible to create three-dimensional views of biological cells.

Reading Check *How are holographic images produced?*

Topic: Holograms
Visit gpscience.com for Web links to information about holograms.

Activity Make an events-chain concept map of how a hologram is produced.

2 Teach

Make a Model

Polarizing Filters Have students work in pairs to make model polarizing filters. Using the illustrations below as a guide, have students make two squares of craft sticks, and then glue several sticks in rows inside the square with small spaces between them. Have them use these squares to demonstrate polarized light by attaching a string to a door, running the string through the filters, and moving the string up and down to produce waves. If both filters are aligned vertically, the vibrating string models polarization. If the filters are at right angles, as shown below, the wave motion of the string is stopped, modeling the cancellation of light waves. L2

LS **Kinesthetic**

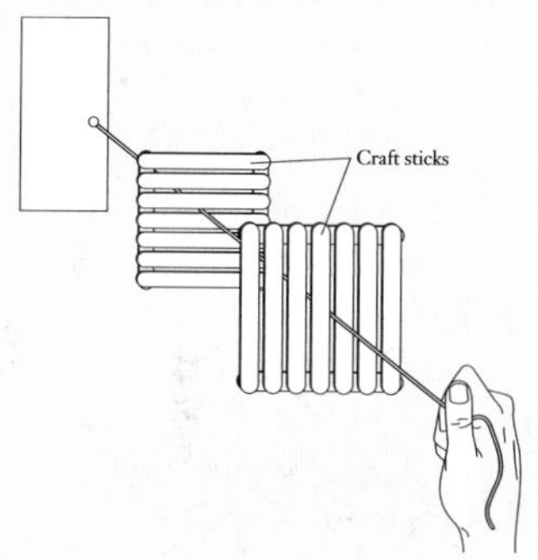

Reading Check

Answer A laser light is reflected from an object onto photographic film. At the same time, a second beam split from the laser is directed at the film. This creates an interference pattern on the film, which produces the holographic image when laser light shines on it.

Differentiated Instruction

Visually Impaired Suggest that visually impaired students work with sighted partners for the Make a Model Activity. The sighted student should allow the visually impaired student to feel the craft sticks before and after the model is made and feel the string lightly while it is being vibrated. L2

Teacher FYI

Sparkling Diamonds Internal reflection causes diamonds to sparkle. The critical angle for diamond is 24.5° and is smaller than for any other material.

Activity

Optical Fibers Have a physician visit your class to discuss the uses of optical fibers in medical procedures. After the presentation, have students write paragraphs describing one of the procedures. L3 LS **Auditory**

Semiconductor Size Students might imagine that the lasers used to transmit telephone or television signals through optical fibers are large. In fact, semiconductor diode lasers smaller than a speck of dust are used.

Reading Check

Answer It occurs when light traveling from one medium to another is completely reflected at the boundary between the two materials. This can occur only when light travels from one medium to another medium in which it moves faster.

Optical Fibers

When laser light must travel long distances or be sent into hard-to-reach places, optical fibers often are used. These transparent glass fibers can transmit light from one place to another. A process called total internal reflection makes this possible.

Total Internal Reflection Remember what happens when light speeds up as it travels from one medium to another. For example, when light travels from water to air the direction of the light ray is bent away from the normal, as shown in **Figure 23.** If the underwater light ray makes a larger angle with the normal, the light ray in the air bends closer the surface of the water. At a certain angle, called the critical angle, the refracted ray has been bent so that it is traveling along the surface of the water, as shown in **Figure 23.** For a light ray traveling from water into air, the critical angle is about 49°.

Figure 23 shows what happens if the underwater light ray strikes the boundary between the air and water at an angle larger than the critical angle. There is no longer any refraction, and the light ray does not travel in the air. Instead, the light ray is reflected at the boundary, just as if a mirror were there. This behavior of light is called total internal reflection. **Total internal reflection** occurs when light traveling from one medium to another is completely reflected at the boundary between the two materials. Then the light ray obeys the law of reflection. For total internal reflection to occur, light must travel slower in the first medium, and must strike the boundary at an angle greater than the critical angle.

Reading Check *How does total internal reflection occur?*

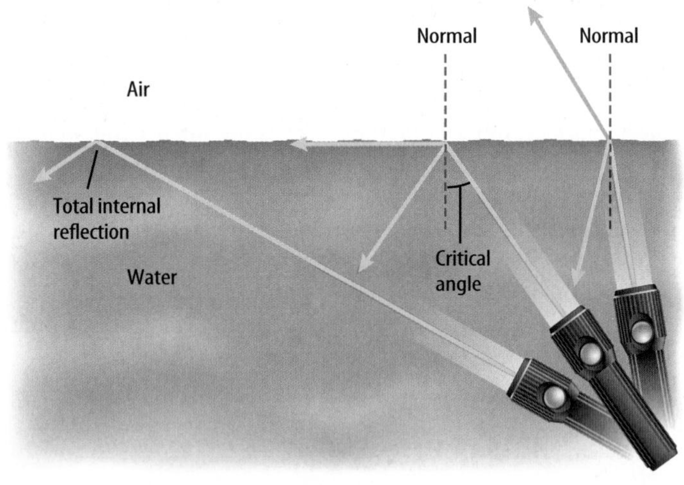

Figure 23 A light wave is bent away from the normal as it passes from water to air. At the critical angle, the refracted wave is traveling along the water surface. At angles greater than the critical angle, total internal reflection occurs.

LAB DEMONSTRATION

Purpose to show how total internal reflection can occur in an optical fiber

Materials laser pointer, 6 plane mirrors with stands (or clay to anchor mirrors), paper

Preparation Make two rows of side-by side mirrors. The lines should be about 5 cm apart. The mirrors should be facing each other. Tape the paper at the end of the row.

Procedure Darken the room. Shine the laser at an angle on the first mirror so that a series of reflections sends the beam from mirror to mirror through the "fiber" and allows the spot of light to be focused onto the paper at the end of the row.

Expected Outcome Light is reflected and shines on the paper.

Assessment

What happens if light striking the inner surface of the fiber is not totally reflected? The light loses intensity.

Figure 24 Optical fibers make use of total internal reflection.

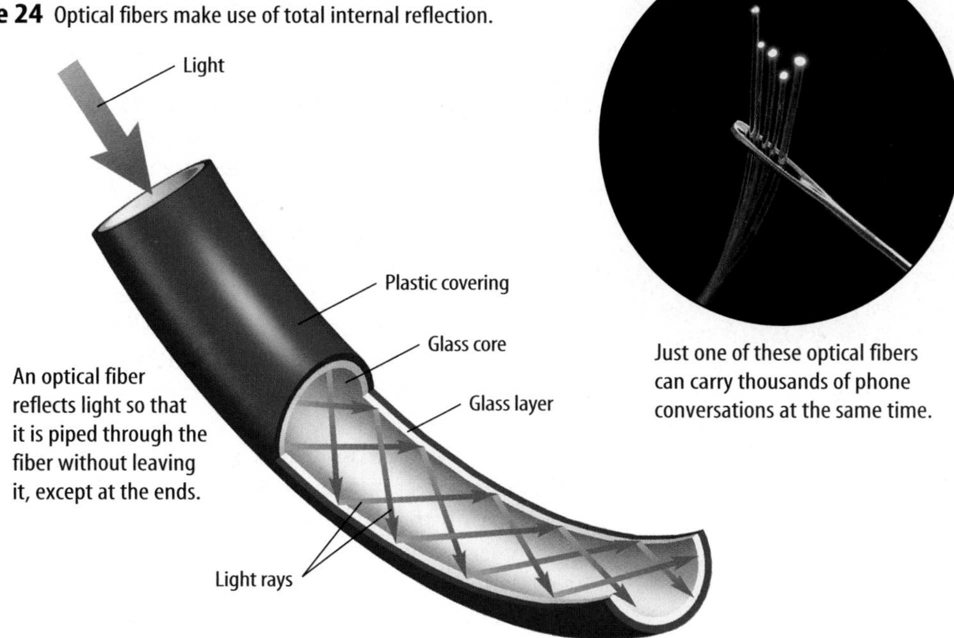

Light
Plastic covering
Glass core
Glass layer
An optical fiber reflects light so that it is piped through the fiber without leaving it, except at the ends.
Light rays

Just one of these optical fibers can carry thousands of phone conversations at the same time.

Light Pipes Total internal reflection makes light transmission in optical fibers possible. As shown in **Figure 24,** light entering one end of the fiber is reflected continuously from the sides of the fiber until it emerges from the other end. Like water moves through a pipe, almost no light is lost or absorbed in optical fibers.

Using Optical Fibers Optical fibers are most often used in communications. Telephone conversations, television programs, and computer data can be coded in light beams. Signals can't leak from one fiber to another and interfere with other messages, so the signal is transmitted clearly. To send telephone conversations through an optical fiber, sound is converted into digital signals consisting of pulses of light by a light-emitting diode or a laser. Some systems use multiple lasers, each with its own wavelength, to fit multiple signals into the same fiber. You could send a million copies of the play *Romeo and Juliet* in one second on a single fiber. **Figure 24** shows the size of typical optical fibers.

Optical fibers also are used to explore the inside of the human body. One bundle of fibers transmits light, while another carries the reflected light back to the doctor.

INTEGRATE
History

Wire Communication At one time telegraph and telephone communications were transmitted only through wire lines. Today, optical fibers sometimes are used instead of wires to transmit communications. Research the history of wire communication. Create a time line of what you learn.

Fun Fact

You could send a million copies of the play *Romeo and Juliet* in one second on a single optical fiber.

IDENTIFYING Misconceptions

Flexible Fibers Students might assume that because optical fibers are made of glass they are very fragile. Explain that because the fibers are so slender and because the glass core is so pure, optical fibers are instead very flexible. The plastic covering also protects the fibers from damage by preventing them from being bent too sharply.

Quick Demo

Feeling Fibers

Materials optical fibers (available from many scientific supply companies and novelty stores)

Estimated Time five minutes

Procedure Bring in fibers for students to see. Have students feel how thin and durable the fibers are. Shine a flashlight near the end of a fiber. Notice how the light doesn't exit through the sides of the fiber. Instead, you see a bright spot of light at the other end of the fiber. ELL

LS **Kinesthetic**

INTEGRATE
History

Wire Communication Some important dates: 1837, Samuel Morse patents the electric telegraph; 1844 first telegraph line between Washington D.C. and Baltimore; 1858, first transatlantic cable is laid; 1876, Alexander Graham Bell invents the telephone.

Differentiated Instruction

Challenge Have each student use a prism (preferably right-angle) and a laser pointer to demonstrate the concept of total internal reflection. Students should be able to explain how the light behaves as it goes through different sides of the prism depending on the angle of the incident light. Caution students never to look directly into the laser light or point it toward anyone else. L3 LS **Visual-Spatial**

Visual Learning

Figure 24 To achieve total internal reflection as shown by the arrows, the core of the optical fibers must have a higher index of refraction than the coating. The fiber core must be extremely pure, and the interface between the core and the glass layer must be smooth. What happens if there is a bubble of air in the core? The light is scattered. L3

LS **Visual-Spatial**

Discussion

Bar Codes Why do you think bar codes are typically black and white? This provides maximum contrast between dark and light areas so the sequence can be read reliably. LS **Logical-Mathematical**

Check for Understanding

Interpersonal Have students take turns explaining to a partner how total internal reflection makes optical fibers possible and describe some uses for optical fibers.

Reteach

Bar Codes Have each student make a concept map for how an optical scanner reads a bar code. The scanner reflects light off the bar code and detects its pattern. The pattern is translated into a digital signal that is compared with a computer database, providing information about the item. L2 P LS **Logical-Mathematical**

Assessment

Process Have students work in small groups to hypothesize ways holograms might be used in the future. Use **Performance Assessment in the Science Classroom,** p. 93.

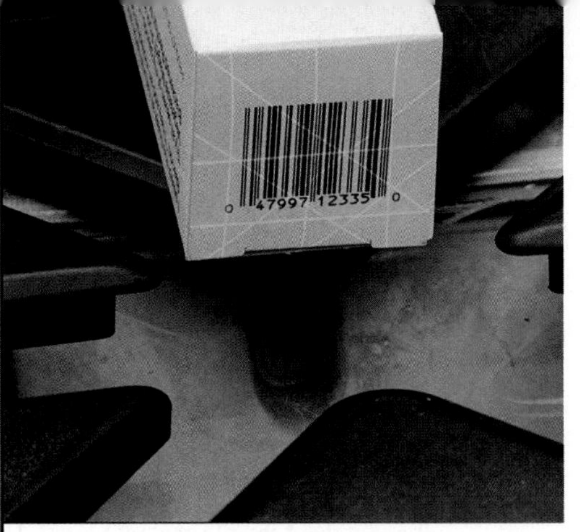

Figure 25 Optical scanners like this one use lasers to find the price of various products.

Optical Scanners

In supermarkets and many other kinds of stores, a cashier passes your purchases over a glass window in the checkout counter or holds a handheld device up to each item, like the one in **Figure 25.** In an instant, the optical scanner beeps and the price of the item appears on a screen. An optical scanner is a device that reads intensities of reflected light and converts the information to digital signals. You may have noticed that somewhere on each item the cashier scans is a pattern of thick and thin stripes called a bar code. An optical scanner detects the pattern and translates it into a digital signal, which goes to a computer. The computer searches its database for a matching item, finds its price, and sends the information to the cash register.

You may have used another type of optical scanner to convert pictures or text into forms you can use in computer programs. With a flatbed scanner, for example, you lay a document or picture facedown on a sheet of glass and close the cover. An optical scanner passes underneath the glass and reads the pattern of colors. The scanner converts the pattern to an electronic file that can be stored on a computer.

section 4 review

Summary

Polarized Light

- Polarized light has light waves that vibrate in only one direction.
- Polarizing filters block light waves that vibrate at right angles to the direction of the filter.

Holography

- A hologram is produced by interference between laser light reflected from an object and a second laser beam.

Optical Fibers

- Total internal reflection occurs when light is completely reflected at the boundary between two materials.
- Total internal reflection will occur when the angle between the light beam and the normal is equal to, or greater than, the critical angle.
- Optical fibers use total internal reflection to transmit light waves over long distances.

Self Check

1. **Explain** why polarized sunglasses can reduce the glare from light reflected from lakes and ponds.
2. **Describe** why a holographic image is considered to be three-dimensional.
3. **List** all the conditions that are necessary for total internal reflection to occur.
4. **Discuss** how optical fibers are used to transmit telephone conversations.
5. **Think Critically** On a sunny day you are looking at the surface of a lake through polarized sunglasses. How could you use your sunglasses to tell if the light reflected from the lake is polarized?

Applying Math

6. **Calculate Number of Fibers** An optical fiber has a diameter of 0.3 mm. How many fibers would be needed to form a cable with a square cross section, if the cross section was 1.5 cm on a side?

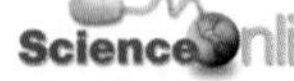

gpscience.com/self_check_quiz

section  review

1. Light reflected from lakes and ponds is partially horizontally polarized. Sunglasses with lenses that pass only vertically polarized light will filter out some of the reflected light.
2. Different parts of the image are seen when looking at the image from different sides.
3. Light must travel slower in the first medium and must strike the boundary at an angle greater than the critical angle.
4. The changing electric signal corresponding to the sound of a voice that is produced by a telephone is changed into a digital signal consisting of pulses of light. These light pulses then travel through the optical fiber, and then are converted back into an electric signal at the receiving end. The electric signal is converted back into sound in a telephone.
5. If the brightness of the light reflected from the lake increases when you remove your polarized sunglasses, then the light reflected from the lake's surface is polarized.
6. Fifty fibers have a total width of 1.5 cm, so the cable would have $50 \times 50 = 2{,}500$ fibers.

404 CHAPTER 13 Light

Make a Light Bender

From a hilltop you can see the reflection of pine trees and a cabin in the calm surface of a lake. This is possible because some of the light that reflects off these objects strikes the water's surface and reflects into your eyes. However, you don't see a clear, colorful image because much of the light enters the water rather than being reflected.

Real-World Question

How does water affect the viewer's image of an object that is above the water's surface?

Goals

- **Identify** reflection of an image in water.
- **Identify** refraction of an image in water.

Materials

light source
unsharpened pencil
clear rectangular container
water
clay

Safety Precautions

Procedure

1. Fill the container with water.
2. Place the container so that a light source—window or overhead light—reaches it.
3. Stand the pencil on end in the clay and place it by the container as shown in the figure above. The pencil must be taller than the level of the water. Also, place the pencil on the same side of the container as the light source.

4. Looking down through the surface of the water from the side opposite the pencil, observe the reflection and refraction of the image of the pencil.
5. **Draw** a diagram of the image and label *Reflection* and *Refraction*.
6. Repeat steps 4 and 5 two more times, but position the pencil at two different angles.

Conclude and Apply

1. **Discuss** how the image you see would change or be different if the surface of the water were a mirror.
2. **Predict** how the angles of reflection or refraction would change if the surface of the container were curved. Explain.

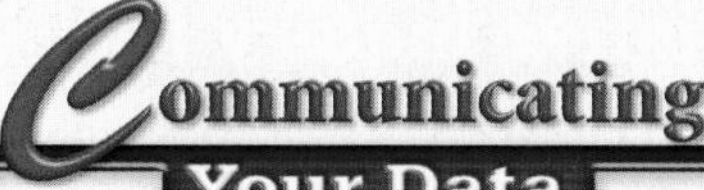

Communicating Your Data

Make a poster of your diagrams and use it to explain reflection and refraction of light waves to your class. For more help, refer to your Science Skill Handbook.

BENCH TESTED

Real-World Question

Purpose Students observe how light will reflect and refract. L1 ELL COOP LEARN

LS **Interpersonal**

Process Skills experiment, predict

Time Required 40 minutes

Procedure

Alternate Materials A clear baking dish can replace the rectangular container.

Safety Precautions If a standard 120-V AC wall light source is used, caution students about dangerous voltages and shock hazard. Light bulbs can become hot.

Teaching Strategy The light source should be taped so it can't move. The pencil must stand straight up.

Conclude and Apply

1. Only the top of the pencil would be visible, as the mirror would block light rays from entering the water, and would reflect them at the same angle as they hit the mirror.
2. For an individual light ray, the angles would not change. For groups of rays, images would be distorted.

Assessment

Oral Ask students to use data they gathered in this experiment to predict and then test to see if they would get the same results if a different clear liquid, such as alcohol or mineral oil, were in the box. The angles of reflected light would change. Use **Performance Assessment in the Science Classroom**, p. 105.

Communicating Your Data

Have students use computer graphics software to demonstrate this activity, especially noting the angles of reflection and refraction of the light waves.

Design Your Own

Polarizing Filters

Goals

- **Demonstrate** when light does and does not shine through a pair of polarizing filters.
- **Predict** what will happen when you add a third polarizing filter.

Possible Materials

polarizing filters (3)
lamp or flashlight

Safety Precautions

WARNING: *Never look directly at the Sun, even with a polarizing filter.*

Real-World Question

Polarizing filters cause light waves to vibrate only in one direction. Wearing polarized sunglasses can help reduce glare while allowing you to see clearly. If you have two polarizing filters on top of one another, when will light shine through and when will it not? What might happen if you added a third filter in between the first two?

Form a Hypothesis

Form a hypothesis about how two polarizing filters that are placed on top of one another must be oriented for light to shine through and for no light to shine through.

Test Your Hypothesis

Make a Plan

1. Using a pair of polarizing filters, choose at least three orientations of the filters to test your hypothesis.
2. When the two filters are oriented to allow the maximum amount of light to shine through, predict how a third filter placed between the two must be oriented for the same results.

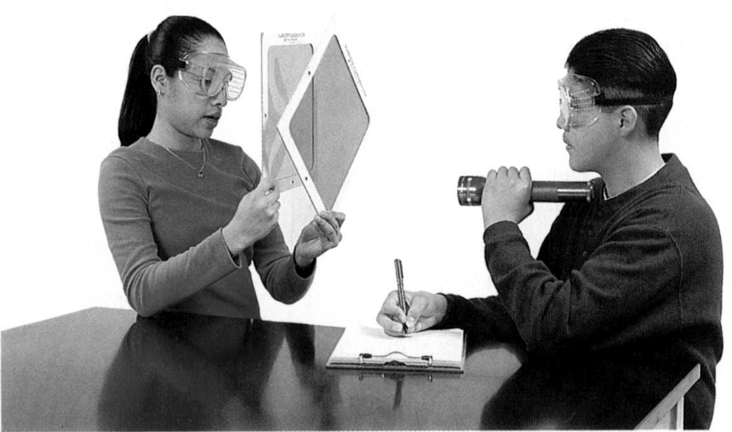

Real-World Question

Purpose Students will observe the effects of polarizing filters on the passage of light for two then three filters. L2 LS **Visual-Spatial**

Process Skills form a hypothesis, predict, recognize cause and effect, draw conclusions

Time Required 40 minutes

Materials polarizing light filters (3), lamp or flashlight

Form a Hypothesis

Possible Hypothesis For light to pass through the two polarizing filters, the polarizing axes of the filters must be parallel. When the polarizing axes are parallel, only the light that is vibrating parallel to the slits can pass through. As the polarizing axes become more perpendicular from parallel, less and less light can get through as less light of different orientations can pass through. For no light to pass through, the two polarizing axes must be perpendicular. When any two polarizing axes are perpendicular, all light is canceled out because the light can't vibrate in any direction. If the polarizing axes of three filters are parallel, light will pass through. If any two of the axes of the three filters are perpendicular, then no light will pass through.

Test Your Hypothesis

Possible Procedures Align two polarizing filters various ways and record observations. Add a third polarizing filter and again record observations.

Alternative Inquiry Lab

Extend the Activity Make this Lab an Inquiry Lab by having students theorize why polarized lenses would nearly eliminate glare from objects reflecting light, but not eliminate the rest of the light. If time allows, have them explore their ideas. Light that reflects from a regular surface mostly reflects polarized, so a polarizing lens can block most of the reflection or glare out.

Assessment

Oral Have students explain to a partner how much light will pass through the polarizing filters at various orientations and why. Transverse waves of light that are parallel to the polarizing axis of the filter can pass through. If the axes of two filters are perpendicular, no waves can pass through. If the filters are in any other orientation, the amount of light that passes through will vary.

3. Repeat step 2 but allow no light to shine through.
4. Make sure that your teacher approves your plan before you start.

Follow Your Plan

1. Using an appropriate light source, test when light does and does not shine through a pair of polarizing filters. Test each of the orientations you planned in step 1. Record the results.
2. Test three orientations of the third filter for allowing the maximum amount of light to pass through. Record the results.
3. Repeat step 2 but allow no light to shine through. Record the results.

Analyze Your Data

1. **Describe** how the pair of polarizing filters were oriented when light did and did not shine through. In cases where light did shine through, was it always the same amount of light? Or did the amount of light change in different orientations?
2. In each case, describe what happened when you added a third filter between the first two. How did the three orientations of the third filter change the amount of light that passed through? Explain.

Conclude and Apply

1. **Explain** why light did or did not shine through two polarizing filters in the various orientations.
2. **Evaluate** why or why not your hypothesis was supported.
3. **Infer** why light did or did not shine through various orientations of three polarizing filters.
4. **Analyze** whether or not your predictions were correct.
5. **Discuss** what you can conclude about the polarization of reflected light if a polarizing filter reduces the brightness of light reflected from the surface of a lake.

Communicating Your Data

The next time you see a family member or friend wearing sunglasses, explain to them how polarizing lenses can reduce problems of glare.

Expected Outcome Students are expected to discover the orientation that the polarizing filters must be in to allow light through and to block it.

Analyze Your Data

Answers to Questions

1. Parallel: light passes through; perpendicular: light is blocked; the light intensity gradually decreases as the filter is rotated.
2. If the polarizing axes of all three filters are parallel, light will pass through. If any two of the axes of the three filters are perpendicular, then no light will pass through.

Error Analysis Have students compare their results and their hypotheses and explain why differences occurred.

Conclude and Apply

1. If the polarizing axis of the filter is parallel to the transverse wave, the light can pass through. If the axes of two filters are perpendicular, the waves parallel to the first filter will not pass through the second filter. They cannot pass through the second filter, because they are perpendicular to the polarizing axis. If the filters are in any other orientation, the amount of light that passes through will vary.
2. Answers will vary
3. If the polarizing axes of any two adjacent filters are perpendicular, no light will pass through.
4. Answers will vary
5. That part of the reflected light had the same axis as the polarizing filter.

Assessment

Content Have students make posters explaining how polarizing filters work. Students should present their posters to their class. Use **Performance Assessment in the Science Classroom,** p. 145.

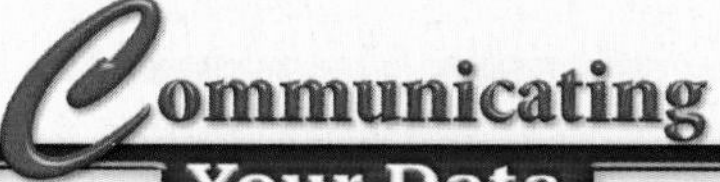

Suggest students use their poster to help explain to family members how polarizing filters work.

Understanding Literature

Japanese Haiku Because Haiku uses few words, the reader must use imagination to complete the picture or message.

Respond to the Reading

1. Possible answer: it helps the reader picture the season.
2. Possible answer: lingering indicates that the sun remains longer in the sky each day during spring.
3. **Linking Science and Writing** Suggest students pay attention to the mood they want to convey with their poems, and use color and properties of light appropriately.

Color The perception of color can effect the human body. The color red causes physiologic changes in the body. Studies show that upon seeing red, a person's blood pressure increases, breathing becomes more rapid, taste buds become more sensitive and the sense of smell is heightened.

Seeing the color blue slows down the pulse, lowers the body temperature, and reduces the appetite. Yellow is the first color a person distinguishes when he or she sees something. Studies show that yellow prepares a person for flight or fight, that children are more apt to cry in a yellow room, and allergies flare up more frequently in yellow surroundings. Green, on the other hand, has been shown to help decrease allergic reactions.

Science and Language Arts

A Haiku Garden:

The Four Seasons in Poems and Prints

by Stephen Addiss with Fumiko and Akira Yamamoto

Withered by winter
the sound of the wind—
one-color world
Basho

Lingering
in every pool of water—
spring sunlight
Issa

Understanding Literature

Japanese Haiku A haiku is a verse that consists of three lines and 17 syllables in the Japanese language. The first and third lines have five syllables each, and the middle line has seven syllables. Why is imagination important in reading Haiku?

Respond to the Reading

1. How do the illustrations help the reader better understand the poems?
2. What do you think is meant by the word *lingering* in the Haiku about spring sunlight?
3. **Linking Science and Writing** Write one haiku about summer and another about fall. In one poem, use color to help you describe the season. In the other, use light or some property of light to help describe the season.

INTEGRATE Physics Research has determined that there is a connection between color and mood. Warm colors have longer wavelengths, and can be more stimulating. Cool colors, which have shorter wavelengths, tend to have a calming or soothing effect on people. Light and color have long been used as literary symbols. Does the use of color change what you imagine when you read the haiku?

Resources for Teachers and Students

The Essential Haiku, ed. and trans. Robert Hass, The Ecco Press, 1994

The Power of Color, Dr. Morton Walker, Avery Publishing Group, 1991

408 CHAPTER 13 Light

Reviewing Main Ideas

Section 1 The Behavior of Light

1. When light interacts with matter, some light can be absorbed, some can be transmitted, and some can be reflected.
2. When light waves are reflected, they obey the law of reflection—the angle of incidence equals the angle of reflection.

3. Light waves are refracted, or bent, when a light wave changes speed as it travels from one material to another.

Section 2 Light and Color

1. You see color when light is reflected off objects and into your eyes.
2. Specialized cells in your eyes called cones allow you to distinguish colors and shapes of objects. Other cells, called rods, allow you to see in dim light.
3. Red, blue, and green are the three primary colors of light and can be mixed to form all other colors.
4. The color of a pigment is due to the wavelengths of the light reflected from the pigment. The primary pigment colors are magenta, cyan, and yellow.

Section 3 Producing Light

1. Incandescent bulbs produce light by heating a tungsten filament until it glows brightly.
2. Fluorescent bulbs give off light when ultraviolet radiation produced inside the bulb causes the phosphor coating inside the bulb to glow.
3. Neon lights contain a gas that glows when electric current passes through it.
4. A laser produces coherent light by emitting a beam of light waves that have only one wavelength, have their crests and troughs aligned, and are moving in a single direction.

Section 4 Using Light

1. Polarized light consists of transverse waves that vibrate along only one plane.
2. Total internal reflection occurs when a light wave strikes the boundary between two materials at an angle greater than the critical angle.
3. Optical scanners sense reflected light and convert the information to digital signals.

FOLDABLES™ Use the Foldable that you made at the beginning of this chapter to help you review light transmission.

chapter 13 Study Guide

Reviewing Main Ideas

Summary statements can be used by students to review the major concepts of the chapter.

Visit gpscience.com
/self_check_quiz
/interactive_tutor
/vocabulary_puzzlemaker
/chapter_review
/standardized_test

Assessment Transparency

For additional assessment questions, use the *Assessment Transparency* located in the transparency book.

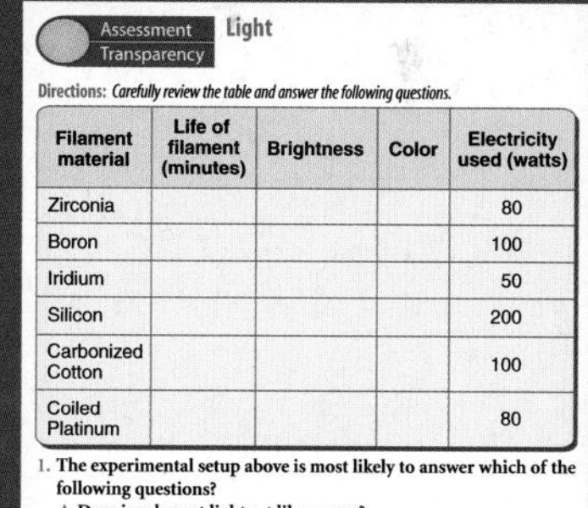

Assessment

Assessment Transparency **Light**

Directions: *Carefully review the table and answer the following questions.*

Filament material	Life of filament (minutes)	Brightness	Color	Electricity used (watts)
Zirconia				80
Boron				100
Iridium				50
Silicon				200
Carbonized Cotton				100
Coiled Platinum				80

1. The experimental setup above is most likely to answer which of the following questions?
   A Does incoherent light act like a wave?
   B What kind of light do excited chlorine and neon atoms release?
   C Can wattage alter the color of a filament's emitted light?
   D Which filament is best suited for a light bulb?
2. Which of the following could improve the experimental design?
   F using the same wattage for each material
   G testing at night when their emitted light seems brighter
   H repeating the experiment with each material three times
   J testing all the materials on the same day
3. The different materials in the table produce light because ___.
   A they release electricity
   B they are heated until they glow and give off light
   they refract and reflect light from nearby sources
   each of the materials is able to burn slowly

L2

Light

FOLDABLES™ Have students use their Foldables to review the content of the chapter. On the back of the paper, have students write a paragraph about the nature of the forces between magnets.

chapter 13 Review

Using Vocabulary
1. incandescent light
2. holography
3. transparent
4. total internal reflection
5. mirage
6. polarized light

Checking Concepts
7. B
8. C
9. D
10. A
11. B
12. A
13. D
14. C
15. C
16. B

Interpreting Graphics
17. See student page.
18. See student page.

chapter 13 Review

Using Vocabulary

coherent light p. 398	opaque p. 384
fluorescent light p. 395	pigment p. 392
holography p. 401	polarized light p. 400
incandescent light p. 394	total internal reflection p. 402
incoherent light p. 398	translucent p. 384
index of refraction p. 386	transparent p. 384
mirage p. 388	

Answer the following questions using complete sentences.

1. What type of light does heating a filament until it glows produce?
2. What process would you use to produce a complete three-dimensional image of an object?
3. How would you describe an object that you can see through?
4. What process makes it possible for optical fibers to transmit telephone conversations over long distances?
5. What is a false image of a distant object?
6. What type of light has light waves that vibrate in only one direction?

Checking Concepts

Choose the word or phrase that best answers the question.

7. Which word describes materials that absorb or reflect all light?
   A) translucent **C)** ultraviolet
   B) opaque **D)** diffuse
8. What is the term for the property of a material that indicates how much light slows down when traveling in the material?
   A) pigment **C)** index of refraction
   B) filter **D)** mirage
9. Which of the following explains why a prism separates white light into the colors of the rainbow?
   A) interference **C)** diffraction
   B) fluorescence **D)** refraction
10. What do you see when noting the color of an object?
   A) the light it reflects
   B) the light it absorbs
   C) polarization
   D) diffuse reflection
11. What do the phosphors inside fluorescent bulbs absorb to create a glow?
   A) incandescent light
   B) ultraviolet radiation
   C) halogens
   D) argon
12. What term describes objects that allow some light, but not all light to pass through them?
   A) translucent **C)** transparent
   B) reflective **D)** opaque
13. Which light waves are bent most when passing through a prism?
   A) red waves **C)** blue waves
   B) yellow waves **D)** violet waves
14. Which type of cells in your eyes allows you to see the color violet?
   A) red cones **C)** blue cones
   B) green cones **D)** rods
15. What color of light is produced when the three primary colors of light are combined in equal amounts?
   A) black **C)** white
   B) yellow **D)** cyan
16. Which of the following terms best describes laser light?
   A) incoherent **C)** incandescent
   B) coherent **D)** fluorescent

gpscience.com/vocabulary_puzzlemaker

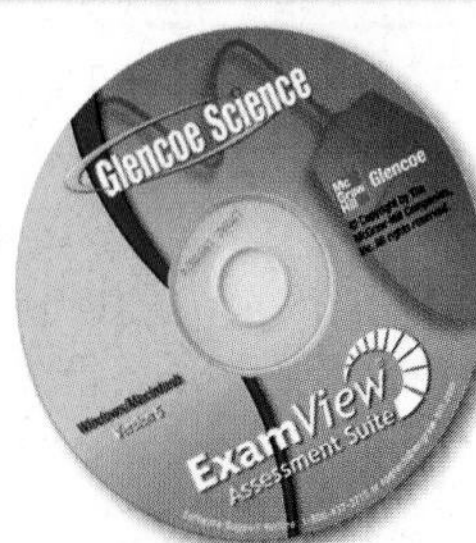

Use the *ExamView® Assessment Suite* CD-ROM to:
- create multiple versions of tests
- create modified tests with one mouse click for inclusion students
- edit existing questions and add your own questions
- build tests aligned with state standards using built-in State Curriculum Tags
- change English tests to Spanish with one mouse click and vice versa

Interpreting Graphics

17. **Concept Map** Copy and complete this concept map to show the steps in the production of fluorescent light.

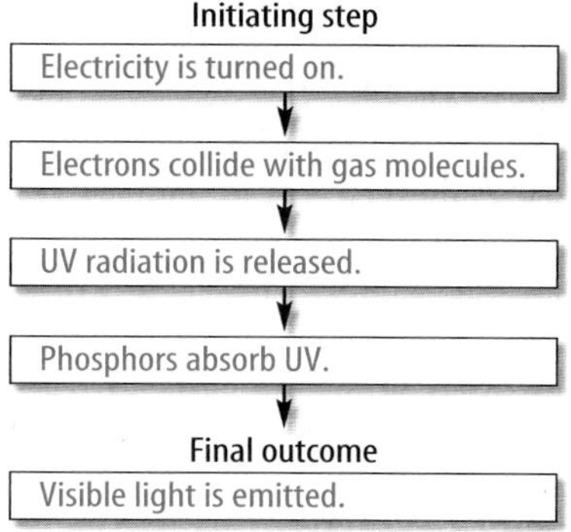

18. **Concept Map** Copy and complete the following concept map about producing light.

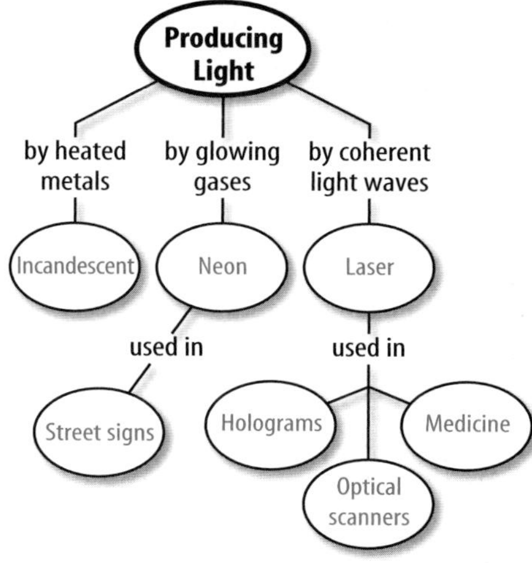

Thinking Critically

19. **Explain** how light is produced by an incandescent bulb. What is a disadvantage of these bulbs?

20. **Compare and contrast** the reflection of light from a white wall with a rough surface with the reflection of light from a mirror.

21. **Predict** what color a white shirt would appear to be if the light reflected from the shirt passed through a red filter and then through a green filter.

22. **Identify** the color of light that changes speed the most as it passes through a prism. Explain your reasoning.

23. **Infer** Most mammals, including dogs and cats, can't see colors. Infer how the retina of a cat's eye might be different from the retina of a human eye.

24. **Compare** White light passes through a translucent pane of glass, and shines on a shirt. Both the translucent glass and the shirt appear green. Compare the colors of light that are absorbed and transmitted by the glass and the shirt.

25. **Explain** The speed of light is greater in air than in glass. Explain whether or not internal reflection could occur when a light wave traveling in air strikes the glass.

Applying Math

26. **Calculate Angle of Incidence** A light ray is reflected from a mirror. If the angle between the incident ray and the reflected ray is 136 degrees, what is the angle of incidence?

27. **Calculate Speed** The index of refraction of a material equals the speed of light in a vacuum, which is 300,000 km/s, divided by the speed of light in the material. What is the speed of light in water if the index of refraction for water is 1.33?

chapter 13 Review

Thinking Critically

19. Heating a piece of metal until it glows produces incandescent light. A disadvantage of incandescent bulbs is that most of the electrical energy used is converted into heat.

20. Both reflect all the colors of light that hit them. Reflection from a white wall is diffuse while reflection from a mirror is regular.

21. The red filter transmits only the red light reflected from the shirt. This light would be absorbed completely by the green filter, and no light would be transmitted. The shirt would appear black.

22. Violet, because it is bent the most by a prism; the greater the difference in the speed of light in two different media, the more it is refracted.

23. Possible answer: A cat's eye does not have the cone nerve cells that a human's eye does.

24. The glass absorbs all colors except green, and transmits green light. The shirt absorbs all colors except green, and reflects green light.

25. No. For internal reflection to occur, light has to be moving toward a medium in which it will speed up.

Applying Math

National Math Standards

1, 4

26. 68 degrees

27. 225,000 km/s

Assessment Resources

Reproducible Masters

Chapter *Fast File* Resources

Chapter Review, pp. 39–40
Chapter Tests, pp. 41–44
Assessment Transparency Activity, p. 53

Glencoe Science Web site

Chapter Review Test
Standardized Test Practice

Glencoe Technology

Assessment Transparency
ExamView® Assessment Suite
MindJogger Videoquiz
Interactive Chalkboard

FAST FILE

Answer Sheet A practice answer sheet can be found at gpscience.com/answer_sheet.

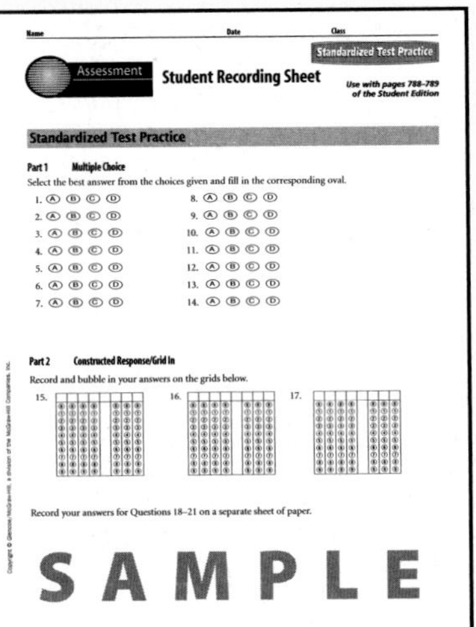
Name Date Class

Standardized Test Practice

Assessment Student Recording Sheet

Use with pages 788–789 of the Student Edition

Standardized Test Practice

Part 1 Multiple Choice

Select the best answer from the choices given and fill in the corresponding oval.

1. Ⓐ Ⓑ Ⓒ Ⓓ
2. Ⓐ Ⓑ Ⓒ Ⓓ
3. Ⓐ Ⓑ Ⓒ Ⓓ
4. Ⓐ Ⓑ Ⓒ Ⓓ
5. Ⓐ Ⓑ Ⓒ Ⓓ
6. Ⓐ Ⓑ Ⓒ Ⓓ
7. Ⓐ Ⓑ Ⓒ Ⓓ
8. Ⓐ Ⓑ Ⓒ Ⓓ
9. Ⓐ Ⓑ Ⓒ Ⓓ
10. Ⓐ Ⓑ Ⓒ Ⓓ
11. Ⓐ Ⓑ Ⓒ Ⓓ
12. Ⓐ Ⓑ Ⓒ Ⓓ
13. Ⓐ Ⓑ Ⓒ Ⓓ
14. Ⓐ Ⓑ Ⓒ Ⓓ

Part 2 Constructed Response/Grid In

Record and bubble in your answers on the grids below.

15. 16. 17.

Record your answers for Questions 18–21 on a separate sheet of paper.

SAMPLE

Part 1 Multiple Choice

1. B	5. A	9. D
2. A	6. B	10. B
3. C	7. C	11. B
4. B	8. B	

Part 2 Short Response

12. It is a prism and refracts each wavelength of white light a different amount. This refraction separates white light into a band of colors.
13. red, orange, yellow, green, blue, indigo, and violet
14. The green leaf would look black because a red filter transmits only red light. The green leaf absorbs all wavelengths of light except green. So the leaf would absorb the red light and reflect no light.
15. Diffuse reflection would cause the parallel rays to be reflected so that they were no longer parallel.
16. An object that appears black absorbs all the visible light rays that strike it. An object that appears white reflects all the visible light rays that strike it.
17. The black stripes still will appear black, and the white stripes will appear green.
18. In both cases, the current inside the fluorescent tube or the neon tube results in electrons colliding with gas atoms in the tube. In a fluorescent tube, the gas atoms give off ultraviolet radiation when the collisions occur. In the neon tube, the neon gas atoms give off visible light when the collisions occur.
19. The size of the bumps and dips on the surface must be less than the wavelengths of visible light.

Part 3 Open Ended

20. In bright light, cone cells in the retina are stimulated by visible light and produce the sensation of color. In dim light, these cells are not stimulated.
21. The beam of light from a laser does not spread out like the light beam from a flashlight. As a

chapter 13 Standardized Test Practice

Part 1 Multiple Choice

Record your answer on the answer sheet provided by your teacher or on a sheet of paper.

1. Which word describes materials that transmit almost all of the light that strikes them?
   A. translucent **C.** opaque
   B. transparent **D.** diffuse

Use the diagram below to answer questions 2 and 3.

2. How are the light waves shown described?
   A. coherent **C.** opaque
   B. incoherent **D.** translucent
3. What device produces these light waves?
   A. fluorescent light
   B. sodium-vapor light
   C. laser
   D. incandescent light
4. What happens when light traveling at an angle passes from one material into another?
   A. The light is reflected.
   B. The light is refracted.
   C. The light always speeds up.
   D. The light changes color.
5. Why does an apple look red?
   A. It reflects red light.
   B. It absorbs red light.
   C. It reflects all colors of light.
   D. It reflects all colors of light except red.
6. Which of the following processes is used in optical fibers to transmit light?
   A. diffuse reflection
   B. total internal reflection
   C. polarization
   D. incandescence
7. What part of the eye enables you see color in bright light?
   A. rods **C.** cones
   B. retina **D.** lens
8. What do the phosphors inside a fluorescent bulb absorb to make the bulb emit visible light?
   A. infrared radiation
   B. ultraviolet radiation
   C. electrons
   D. sodium vapor

Use the illustration below to answer questions 9–11.

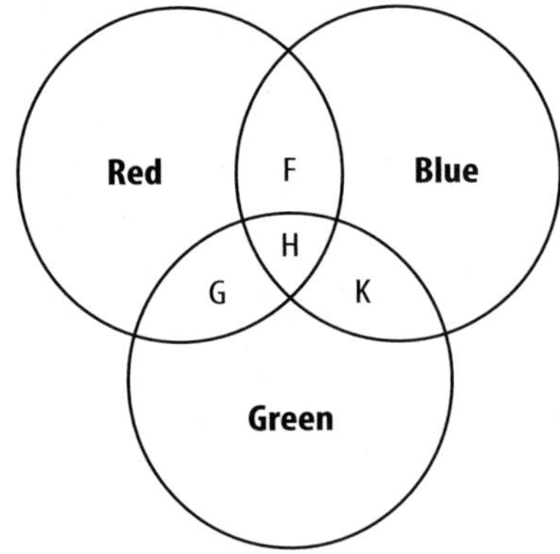

9. When the primary colors of light are added together, what color appears in area H?
   A. magenta **C.** cyan
   B. yellow **D.** white
10. What color appears in area G?
    A. magenta **C.** cyan
    B. yellow **D.** white
11. Which of the following light sources produces light by making a piece of metal hot enough to glow?
    A. fluorescent light **C.** neon light
    B. incandescent light **D.** laser light

Part 2 Short Response/Grid In

Record your answers on the answer sheet provided by your teacher or on a sheet of paper.

Use the illustration below to answer questions 12 and 13.

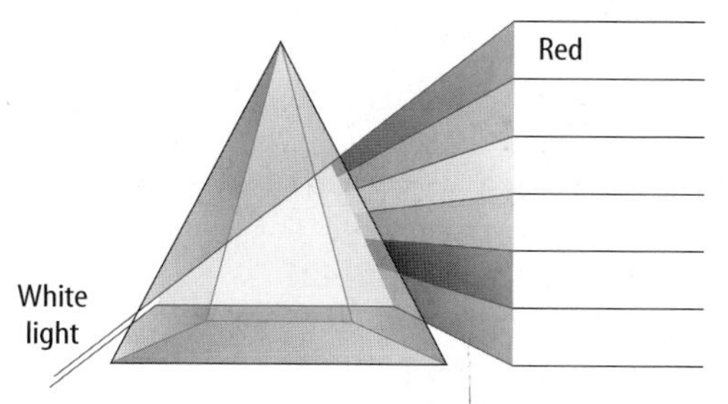

12. Identify the object shown in the figure and explain how it affects white light that passes through it.

13. Identify the colors that would be seen on the right side of the object, in order of decreasing wavelength.

14. Why would a green leaf appear to be black when you look at the leaf through a red filter?

15. Describe the effect that diffuse reflection would have on a beam of parallel light rays.

16. Describe the difference between an object that appears black and an object that appears white.

17. If green light shines on a black-and-white striped shirt, what colors will the stripes appear to be?

18. Why is an electric current needed to produce light in fluorescent lights and in neon lights?

19. For a regular reflection to occur, how must the roughness of a surface compare to the wavelengths of light it reflects?

Part 3 Open Ended

Record your answers on a sheet of paper.

20. Why can the human eye see colors better in bright light than in dim light?

21. Explain why, compared to the light from a lightbulb, a beam of laser light can deliver a large amount of energy to a small area.

22. Explain whether or not a large bottle made of green glass would be a suitable container in which to grow small plants.

Use the illustration below to answer questions 23 and 24.

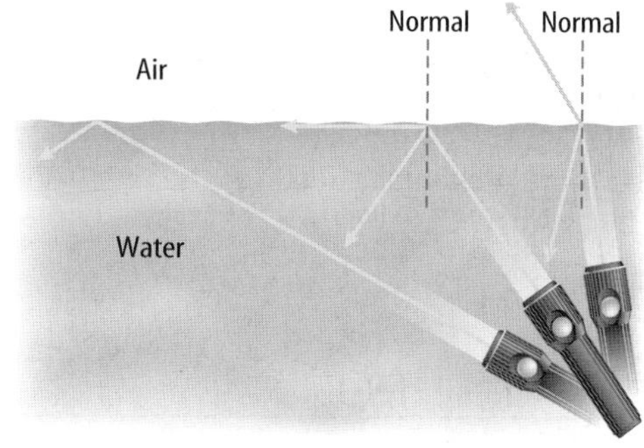

23. When a light wave traveling in water reaches the water's surface, under what circumstances will total internal reflection occur?

24. If the flashlight were in air and the direction of the light beams shown in the figure were reversed. Under what circumstances would total internal reflection occur? Explain.

Test-Taking Tip

Answer All Parts Make sure each part of a question is answered when listing discussion points. For example, if the question asks you to compare and contrast, make sure you list similarities and differences

Question 17 Be sure to describe the change in color of both the black and the white stripes.

Rubrics

The following rubrics are sample scoring devices for short response and open-ended questions.

Short Response

Points	Description
2	The student demonstrates a thorough understanding of the science of the task. The response may contain minor flaws that do not detract from the demonstration of a thorough understanding.
1	The student has provided a response that is only partially correct.
0	The student has provided a completely incorrect solution or no response at all.

Open Ended

Points	Description
4	The student demonstrates a thorough understanding of the science of the task. The response may contain minor flaws that do not detract from the demonstration of a thorough understanding.
3	The student demonstrates an understanding of the science of the task. The response is essentially correct and demonstrates an essential but less than thorough understanding of the science.
2	The student demonstrates only a partial understanding of the science of the task. Although the student may have used the correct approach to a solution or may have provided a correct solution, the work lacks an essential understanding of the underlying science concepts.
1	The student demonstrates a very limited understanding of the science of the task. The response is incomplete and exhibits many flaws.
0	The student provides a completely incorrect solution or no response at all.

result, the energy carried by the light beam remains concentrated over a small area.

22. No, it wouldn't be a suitable container. Plants absorb all visible light except wavelengths of green light. The wavelengths absorbed are used in the process of photosynthesis. A green bottle would transmit only green light, which the plant reflects. The green light could not be used by the plant for photosynthesis.

23. Total internal reflection will occur if the angle the beam makes with the normal is equal to or greater than the critical angle.

24. Total internal reflection would not occur for any incident angle. For total internal reflection to occur, light has to traveling into a medium in which it will speed up.

Mirrors and Lenses

BIG Idea Mirrors and lenses form images by causing light rays to change direction.

	Content Standards	Learning Objectives	Resources to Assess Mastery
Section 1	**5–8:** UCP.1–3, 5; A.1, 2; B.1 **9–12:** UCP.1–3, 5; A.1, 2; B.2	**Mirrors** **1. Describe** how an image is formed in three types of mirrors. **2. Explain** the difference between real and virtual images. **3. Identify** examples and uses of plane, concave, and convex mirrors. ***Main Idea*** Light rays change direction when they are reflected by a mirror.	**Formative Assessment** Reading Check, pp. 417, 421 Section Review, p. 422 **Summative Assessment** *ExamView® Assessment Suite*
Section 2	**5–8:** UCP.1–3, 5; A.1, 2; B.1; F.1 **9–12:** UCP.1–3, 5; A.1, 2; B.2	**Lenses** **4. Describe** the shapes of convex and concave lenses. **5. Explain** how convex and concave lenses form images. **6. Explain** how lenses are used to correct vision problems. ***Main Idea*** Light rays are bent when they pass through a lens.	**Formative Assessment** Reading Check, p. 428 Section Review, p. 431 **Summative Assessment** *ExamView® Assessment Suite*
Section 3	**5–8:** UCP.1–3, 5; A.1, 2; G.3 **9–12:** UCP.1–3, 5; A.1, 2; G.3 See pp. 16T–17T for a Key to Standards.	**Optical Instruments** **7. Compare** refracting and reflecting telescopes. **8. Explain** why a telescope in space would be useful. **9. Describe** how a microscope uses lenses to magnify small objects. **10. Explain** how a camera creates an image. ***Main Idea*** Lenses and mirrors are used to make objects easier to see.	**Formative Assessment** Reading Check, pp. 433, 434 Section Review, p. 437 **Summative Chapter Assessment** MindJogger, Ch. 14 *ExamView® Assessment Suite* Leveled Chapter Test Test A [L1] Test B [L2] Test C [L3] Test Practice, pp. 444–445

Suggested Pacing				
Period	**Instruction**	**Labs**	**Review & Assessment**	**Total**
Single	4 days	3 days	2 days	9 days
Block	2 blocks	1.5 blocks	1 block	4.5 blocks

Core Instruction	Leveled Resources	Leveled Labs	Pacing Period		Pacing Block
Student Text, pp. 414–423 Section Focus Transparency, Ch. 14, Section 1 Interactive Chalkboard, Ch. 14, Section 1 Differentiated Instruction, pp. 419, 421	**Chapter *Fast File* Resources** Directed Reading for Content Mastery, p. 20 L1 Note-taking Worksheet, pp. 33–35 Reinforcement, p. 27 L2 Enrichment, p. 30 L3 **Reading Essentials,** p. 232 L1 ELL **Science Notebook,** p. 157 ELL	**Launch Lab**, p. 415: plastic wrap, printed text, water, dropper *10 min* L2 **MiniLAB**, p. 419: shiny spoon, bright light source, white poster board (10-cm × 10-cm) *15 min* L2 **Lab**, p. 423: plane mirrors (2), masking tape, protractor, paper clip *45 min* L1 L2 L3 [disc icon]	1	Section 1, pp. 415–418 (includes Launch Lab)	1
			2	Section 1, pp. 419–422 (includes MiniLab and Section Review)	
			3	Lab: Reflections of Reflections, p. 423 [insert disc icon]	2
Student Text, pp. 424–431 Section Focus Transparency, Ch. 14, Section 2 Teaching Transparency, Ch. 14, Section 2 Interactive Chalkboard, Ch. 14, Section 2 Identifying Misconceptions, pp. 427, 429 Applying Science, p. 426 Differentiated Instruction, pp. 427, 430 Visualizing The Silicon Retina, p. 430	**Chapter *Fast File* Resources** Directed Reading for Content Mastery, p. 20 L1 Note-taking Worksheet, pp. 33–35 Reinforcement, p. 28 L2 Enrichment, p. 31 L3 **Reading Essentials,** p. 240 L1 ELL **Science Notebook,** p. 161 ELL		4	Section 2, pp. 424–428	
			5	Section 2, pp. 429–431 (includes Section Review)	3
Student Text, pp. 432–439 Section Focus Transparency, Ch. 14, Section 3 Interactive Chalkboard, Ch. 14, Section 3 Differentiated Instruction, pp. 433, 435 Chapter Study Guide, p. 441	**Chapter *Fast File* Resources** Directed Reading for Content Mastery, pp. 21, 22 L1 Note-taking Worksheet, pp. 33–35 Reinforcement, p. 29 L2 Enrichment, p. 32 L3 **Reading Essentials,** p. 247 L1 ELL **Science Notebook,** p. 164 ELL	**MiniLab**, p. 435: glass test tube with stopper or lid, water, paper *10 min* L2 ***Lab**, pp. 438–439: objective lens, eyepiece lenses, cardboard tubes, modeling clay, scissors *45 min* L1 L2 L3 *Lab version A L1 version B L2 L3	6	Section 4, pp. 432–434	
			7	Section 4, pp. 435–437 (includes MiniLAB and Section Review)	4
			8	Lab: Making a Refracting Telescope, pp. 438–439	
			9	Study Guide, Chapter Review, and Test Practice, pp. 441–445	4.5

[disc icon] Video Lab

Transparencies

Section Focus

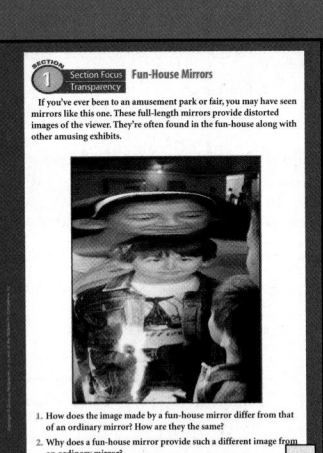

Section Focus Transparency
Fun-House Mirrors
If you've ever been to an amusement park or fair, you may have seen mirrors like this one. These full-length mirrors provide distorted images of the viewer. They're often found in the fun-house along with other amusing exhibits.
1. How does the image made by a fun-house mirror differ from that of an ordinary mirror? How are they the same?
2. Why does a fun-house mirror provide such a different image from an ordinary mirror?
L2

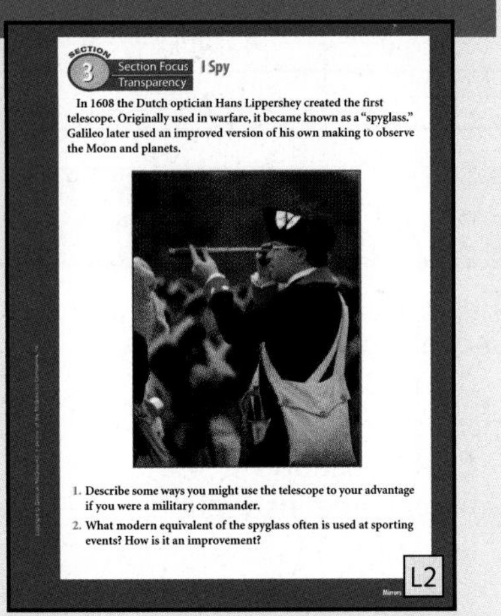

Section Focus Transparency
I Spy
In 1608 the Dutch optician Hans Lippershey created the first telescope. Originally used in warfare, it became known as a "spyglass." Galileo later used an improved version of his own making to observe the Moon and planets.
1. Describe some ways you might use the telescope to your advantage if you were a military commander.
2. What modern equivalent of the spyglass often is used at sporting events? How is it an improvement?
L2

This is a representation of key blackline masters available in the Teacher Classroom Resources. See Resource Manager boxes within the chapter for additional information.

Assessment

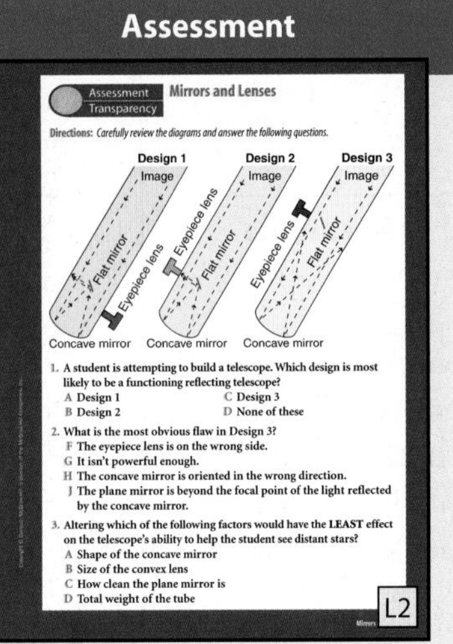

Assessment Transparency
Mirrors and Lenses
Directions: Carefully review the diagrams and answer the following questions.
Design 1
Design 2
Design 3
Image
Flat mirror
Eyepiece lens
Concave mirror
1. A student is attempting to build a telescope. Which design is most likely to be a functioning reflecting telescope?
A Design 1
B Design 2
C Design 3
D None of these
2. What is the most obvious flaw in Design 3?
F The eyepiece lens is on the wrong side.
G It isn't powerful enough.
H The concave mirror is oriented in the wrong direction.
J The plane mirror is beyond the focal point of the light reflected by the concave mirror.
3. Altering which of the following factors would have the LEAST effect on the telescope's ability to help the student see distant stars?
A Shape of the concave mirror
B Size of the convex lens
C How clean the plane mirror is
D Total weight of the tube
L2

Teaching

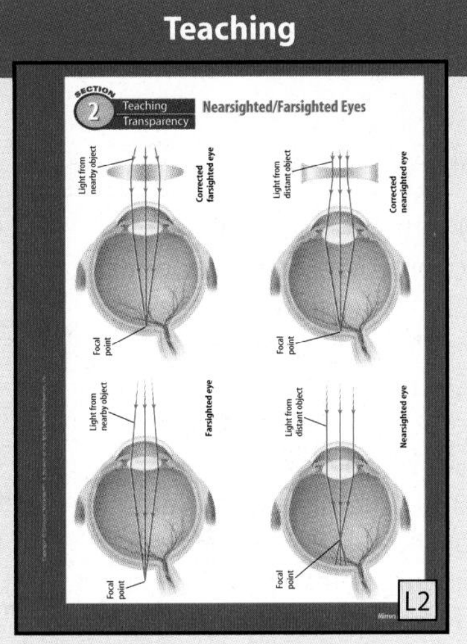

Key to Teaching Strategies

The following designations will help you decide which activities are appropriate for your students.

L1 Level 1 activities should be appropriate for students with learning difficulties.

L2 Level 2 activities should be within the ability range of all students.

L3 Level 3 activities are designed for above-average students.

ELL ELL activities should be within the ability range of English Language Learners.

COOP LEARN Cooperative Learning activities are designed for small group work.

LS Multiple Learning Styles logos, as described on page 12T, are used throughout to indicate strategies that address different learning styles.

P These strategies represent student products that can be placed into a best-work portfolio.

PBL Problem-Based Learning activities apply real-world situations to learning.

Hands-on Activities

Student Text Lab Worksheet

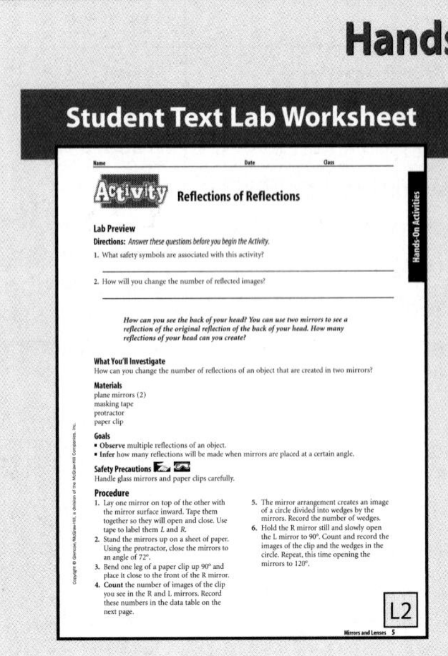

Activity
Reflections of Reflections
Lab Preview
1. What safety symbols are associated with this activity?
2. How will you change the number of reflected images?
L2

Laboratory Activities

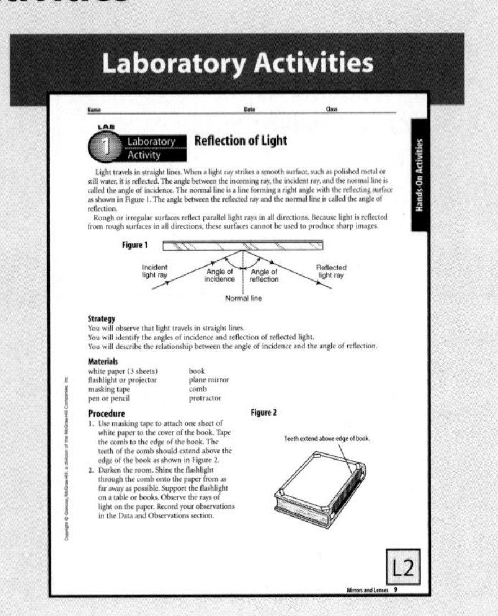

Meeting Different Ability Levels

Content Outline

Note-taking Worksheet — Mirrors and Lenses

Section 1 Mirrors

L2

Reinforcement

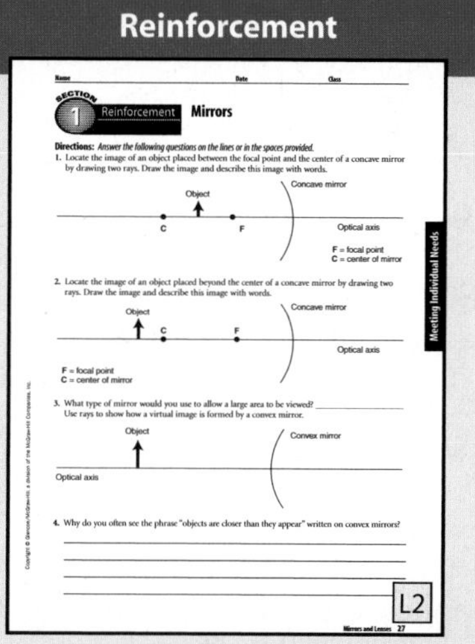

Section 1 Reinforcement — Mirrors

L2

Enrichment

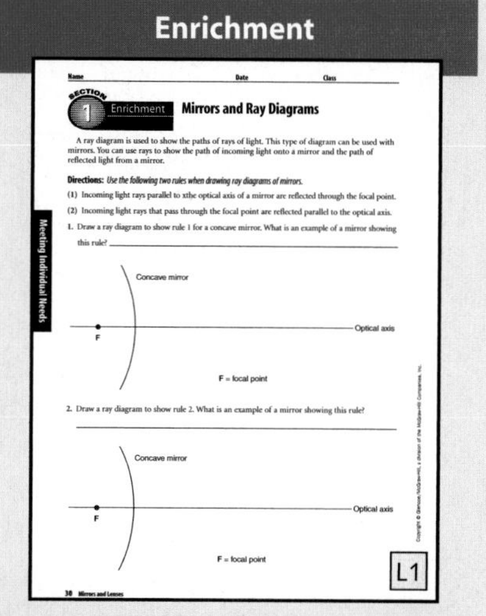

Section 1 Enrichment — Mirrors and Ray Diagrams

L1

Directed Reading (English/Spanish)

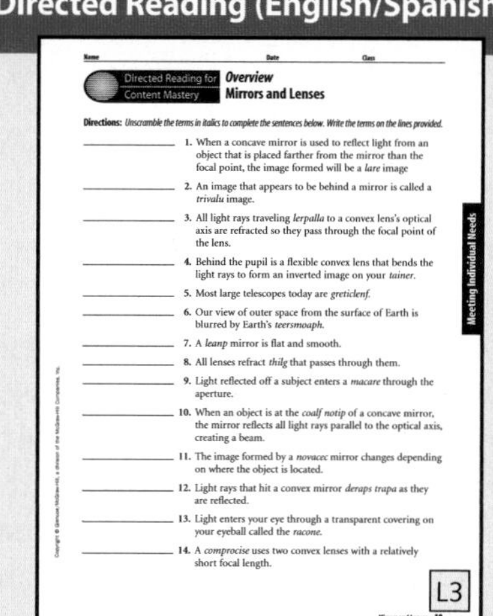

Directed Reading for Content Mastery — Overview: Mirrors and Lenses

L3

Study Guide

Study Guide
Features
• Contains a study guide page for each section of the chapter
• Reviews key concepts
• Includes answer pages

L2

Reading Essentials

Reading Essentials for Glencoe Science
An Interactive Student Workbook
Features
• Condensed core content
• Actively involves students in reading
• Reinforces key vocabulary

L1

Assessment

Test Practice Workbook

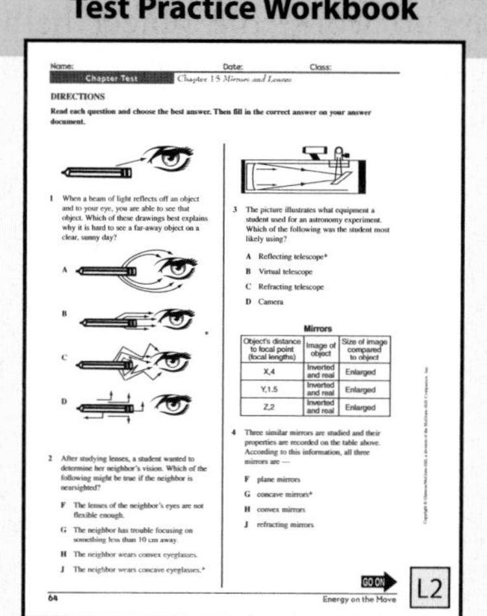

Chapter Test — Chapter 15 Mirrors and Lenses

L2

Chapter Review

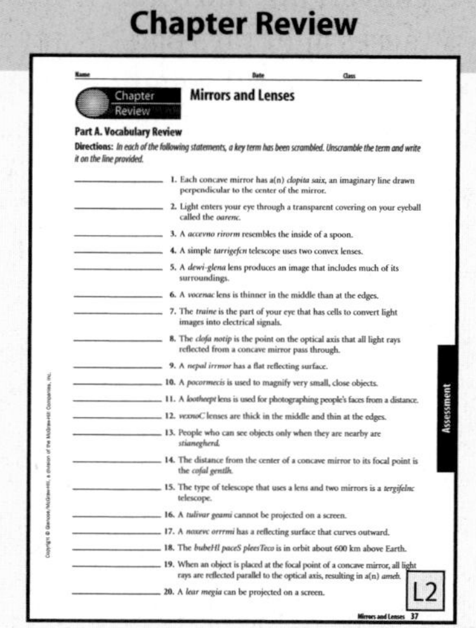

Chapter Review — Mirrors and Lenses

L2

Chapter Tests

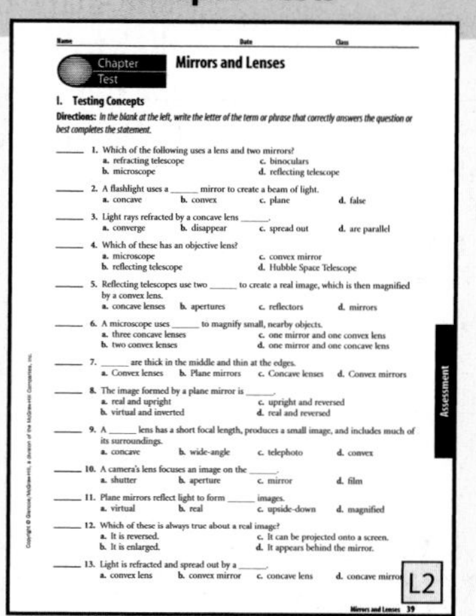

Chapter Test — Mirrors and Lenses

L2

Science Content Background

section 1 Mirrors

How do you use light to see?

You see objects that reflect light. Smooth surfaces such as mirrors produce clear reflections; rough surfaces produce disordered reflections because they scatter light in many directions.

Seeing with Plane Mirrors

The law of reflection applies whenever light is reflected. The angle of incidence is equal to the angle of reflection. To determine these angles, an imaginary reference line is drawn perpendicular to the reflecting surface. The angle between the incident ray and the reference line is the angle of incidence. The angle between the reflected ray and the reference line is the angle of reflection. The virtual image formed by a plane mirror is upright, but backward. The image appears to be the same distance behind the mirror as the object is in front of the mirror. The multiple images in some kaleidoscopes are produced by three plane mirrors positioned to form a triangle. Through the center of the triangle one can see the reflection of the moving pieces of colored plastic or glass forming the geometric images.

Concave Mirrors

The law of reflection also applies to curved mirrors. Concave mirrors are converging mirrors. The shape of these mirrors causes light rays parallel to the optical axis to be reflected through the focal point. Concave mirrors and convex lenses affect light rays in a similar way.

Teacher to Teacher
Nelson Farrier
Hamlin Middle School
Springfield, Oregon

"My students really enjoy making 'eyes' using a piece of black construction paper (their 'retina'), a lens and small votive candle. Cover your classroom windows and turn out the lights. By adjusting the lens between the candle and the construction paper, students will see a clear image of an upside down candle flame. This demo makes it easier for students to see and discuss how light bends and how the eye works."

Nelson Farrier

section 2 Lenses

What is a lens?

A lens is a curved, transparent device that bends light that passes through the lens. The bending, or refraction, of light requires two conditions: (a) light must pass from one material through another that has a different optical density, and (b) the light must enter the lens at an angle other than perpendicular.

Convex Lenses

When light passes through a convex lens, it bends toward the thicker part of the lens. For a magnifying glass to work, the object being magnified must be closer to the lens than the focal point of the lens.

Lenses and Eyesight

Eyes focus by a process called accommodation. In this process, muscles attached to the eye lens make the lens thinner or thicker to attain sharp focus. Most people with glasses or contact lenses wear concave lenses to correct myopia, or nearsightedness. This condition has various causes. For instance, a person may genetically have an eyeball that is too long, causing rays of light to be focused in front of, instead of on, the retina.

The use of corrective lenses has a long history. Lens-type objects, found in the ruins of Ancient Egypt, were used as long as 4,500 years ago. In the thirteenth century, magnifying glasses were used. Lenses for myopia were developed by the sixteenth century. In the late 1700s, Benjamin Franklin developed bifocal lenses. The first glass contact lenses were developed in the late 1800s by Adolf E. Fick.

section 3 Optical Instruments

Telescopes

Optical telescopes are popular for viewing the night sky. In order to get the best view of the Moon's craters and other features, look near the terminator. The terminator is the line the separates the lighted and dark portions of the Moon.

Cameras

In some cameras, a person moves the lens closer or further away from an object to focus the image. Disposable and other inexpensive cameras are often fixed-focus cameras—the lens does not move. It is set so that most images will be pretty well in focus. Automatic focusing cameras send out an infrared beam that is reflected from the subject. The camera then moves the lens to produce the optimal focus.

chapter content resources

Internet Resources

For additional content background, visit **gpscience.com** to:

- access your book online
- find references to related articles in popular science magazines
- access Web links with related content background
- access current events with science journal topics

Print Resources

Geometric, Physical, and Visual Optics, by Michael Keating, Butterworth-Heinemann, 2002

Seeing the Light, by David Falk, Dieter Brill, David Stork, John Wiley and Sons, 1985

Optics, by Eugene Hecht, Pearson Addison Wesley, 2001

Barry L. Runk/Grant Heilman Photography, Inc.

About the Photo

Distorted Reflections Even though the glass panes seem to be flat, the images they produce are distorted. The distortion is caused by panes that are slightly curved. Just as in a fun-house mirror, some panes are bent outward over some regions and inward over others. This causes the images they reflect to be distorted.

Science Journal Student responses may include checking personal appearance, looking for vehicles behind you while in a car or on a bicycle.

The BIG Idea

The Reflection of Light When light waves strike a material, the light waves interact with the atoms in the material. As a result, light waves of the same frequency are re-emitted from the material's surface, so that some of the incident wave energy is reflected. Each point on the surface of the material can be considered as a source of waves traveling away from the material. Alternatively, each point can also be considered as a source of light rays that travel in straight lines outward from the surface in all directions.

Introduce the Chapter Divide the class into small groups and give each group a magnifying lens. Have students look through the lens at a text page. Tell students to describe how the image of the text changes as the lens moves closer and farther from the page.

chapter 14

Mirrors and Lenses

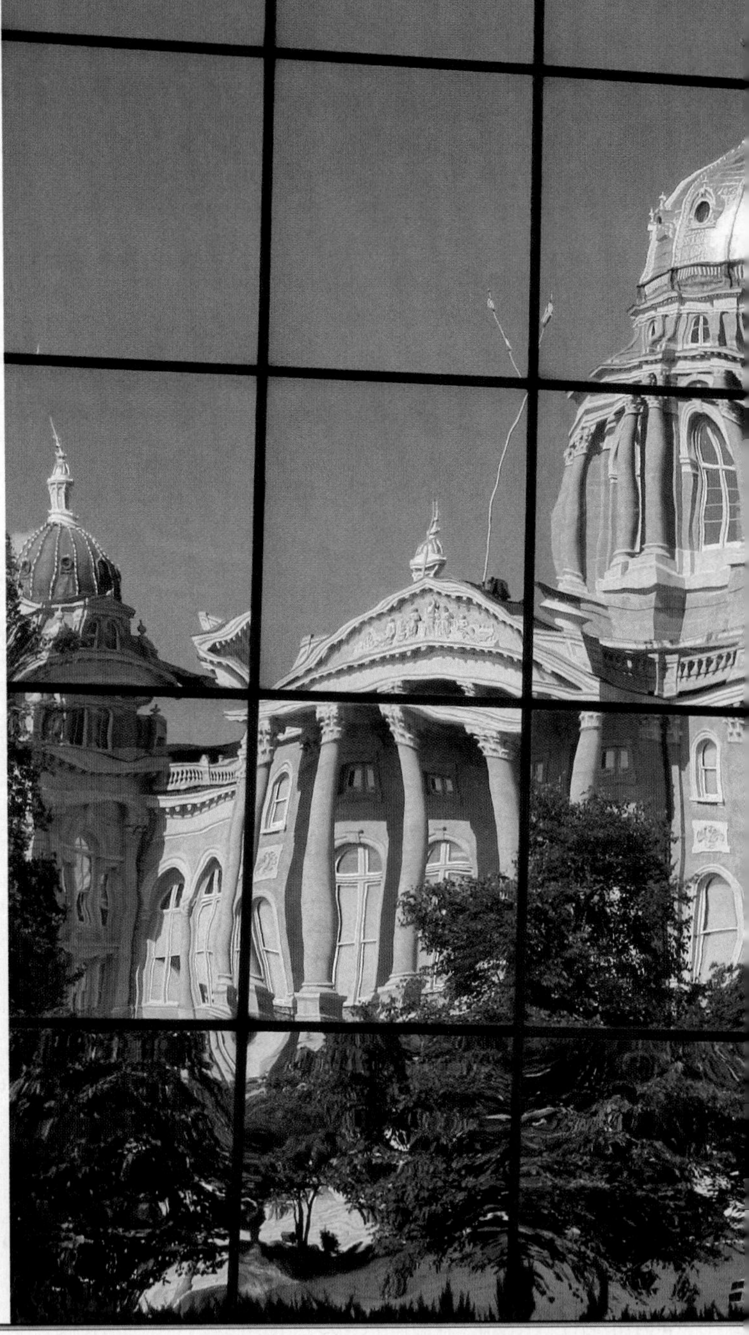

BIG Idea Mirrors and lenses form images by causing light rays to change direction.

14.1 Mirrors

MAIN Idea Light rays change direction when they are reflected by a mirror.

14.2 Lenses

MAIN Idea Light rays are bent when they pass through a lens.

14.3 Optical Instruments

MAIN Idea Lenses and mirrors are used to make objects easier to see.

Wavy Reflections

The dark-tinted glass panes of this office building are acting as mirrors. Depending on how the surface of a mirror is curved, a mirror can distort the image of an object and make it look larger or smaller.

Science Journal

Write a paragraph describing how you use mirrors every day.

414

Interactive Chalkboard

This CD-ROM is an editable Microsoft® PowerPoint® presentation that includes:

- an editable presentation for every chapter
- additional chapter questions
- animated graphics
- image bank
- links to gpscience.com

Start-Up Activities

Making a Water Lens

Have you ever used a magnifying glass, a camera, a microscope, or a telescope? If so, you were using a lens to create an image. A lens is a transparent material that bends rays of light and forms an image. In this activity, you will use water to create a lens.

1. Cut a 10-cm × 10-cm piece of plastic wrap. Set it on a page of printed text.
2. Place a small water drop on the plastic. Look at the text through the drop. What do you observe?
3. Make your water drop larger and observe the text through it again.
4. Carefully lift the piece of plastic wrap a few centimeters above the text and look at the text through the water drop again.
5. **Think Critically** Describe how the text looked in steps 2, 3, and 4. Why do you think water affects the way the text looks? What other materials might you use to change the appearance of the text?

Preview this chapter's content and activities at gpscience.com

Types of Mirrors Make the following Foldable to help identify the three different types of mirrors and their characteristics.

STEP 1 **Fold** a vertical sheet of paper from side to side. Make the front edge about 1.25 cm shorter than the back edge.

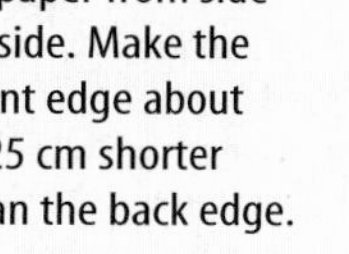

STEP 2 **Turn** lengthwise and fold into thirds.

STEP 3 **Unfold and cut** only the top layer along both folds to make three tabs.

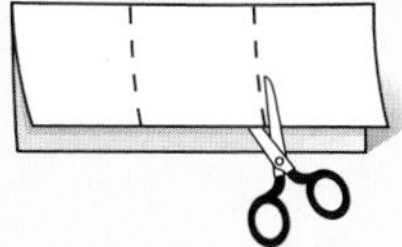

STEP 4 **Label** each tab as shown.

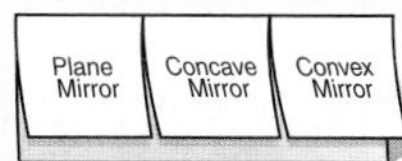

Read and Write As you read Section 1 of this chapter, write down important information under the appropriate tab about each type of mirror.

415

Additional Chapter Media

- Virtual Lab: *How are lenses used to correct vision?*
- Video Lab: *Reflections of Reflections*

Purpose Students observe the effects of the refraction of light through a drop of water, which acts as a convex lens. L2 ELL

LS **Visual-Spatial**

Preparation Bring to class samples of printed texts using different type sizes, including some that are very small, for students to observe.

Materials plastic wrap, printed text, water, dropper

Teaching Strategy Use an eyedropper to dispense drops of water.

Think Critically

In step 2 the text looked enlarged and upright. In step 3 it looked larger and still upright. In step 4 the text flipped and looked upside down. As the light reflected from the text moves from the water to the air it is refracted. Other possible materials include plastic, glass, and other transparent liquids and solids.

Assessment

Oral Ask students to make an events chain to describe the path of a light ray from the time it leaves a light source to the time it enters their eyes after passing through the drop of water. The ray moves straight through the air, hits the curved surface of the water and is refracted toward the normal, and passes through the water. It is refracted again, hits the printed page and is absorbed by the black print and reflected by the white page. The reflected light is refracted again as it enters the water, and is refracted again as it moves through the curved surface of the water drop, then moves straight to the students' eyes. Use **Performance Assessment in the Science Classroom,** p. 163.

Dinah Zike Study Fold

Student preparation materials for this Foldable are available in the **Chapter *Fast File* Resources.**

1 Motivate

Bellringer

Section Focus Transparencies also are available on the Interactive Chalkboard CD-ROM.

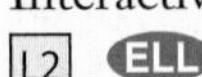 

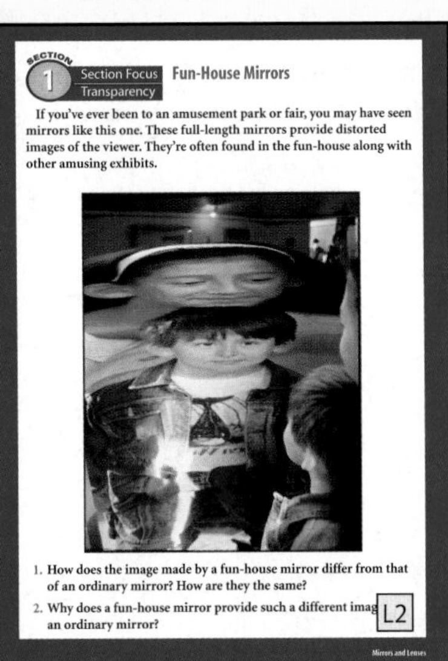

Section Focus Transparency 1 — Fun-House Mirrors

If you've ever been to an amusement park or fair, you may have seen mirrors like this one. These full-length mirrors provide distorted images of the viewer. They're often found in the fun-house along with other amusing exhibits.

1. How does the image made by a fun-house mirror differ from that of an ordinary mirror? How are they the same?
2. Why does a fun-house mirror provide such a different image from an ordinary mirror?

L2

Mirrors and Lenses

Tie to Prior Knowledge

Reflection Distortion Ask students whether they have ever looked at a rounded, shiny surface such as a doorknob and noticed that their reflection is distorted. In this section, students will learn how the shape of a mirror determines the type of reflection they see.

section 1

Mirrors

Reading Guide

What You'll Learn

- **Describe** how an image is formed in three types of mirrors.
- **Explain** the difference between real and virtual images.
- **Identify** examples and uses of plane, concave, and convex mirrors.

Why It's Important

Mirrors enable you to check your appearance, see objects behind you, and produce beams of light.

Review Vocabulary

reflection: occurs when waves change direction after striking a surface

New Vocabulary

- plane mirror
- virtual image
- concave mirror
- optical axis
- focal point
- focal length
- real image
- convex mirror

How do you use light to see?

Have you tried to read a book under the covers with only a small flashlight? Or have you ever tried to find an address number on a house or an apartment at night on a poorly lit street? It's harder to do those activities in the dark than it is when there is plenty of light. Your eyes see by detecting light, so anytime you see something, it is because light has come from that object to your eyes. Light is emitted from a light source, such as the Sun or a lightbulb, and then reflects off an object, such as the page of a book or someone's face. When light travels from an object to your eye, you see the object. Light can reflect more than once. For example, light can reflect off of an object into a mirror and then reflect into your eyes. When no light is available to reflect off of objects and into your eye, your eyes cannot see anything. This is why it is hard to read a book or see an address in the dark.

Figure 1 A light source, like a candle, sends out light rays in all directions.

Light Rays Light sources send out light waves that travel in all directions. These waves spread out from the light source just as ripples on the surface of water spread out from the point of impact of a pebble.

You also could think of the light coming from the source as being many narrow beams of light. Each narrow beam of light travels in a straight line and is called a light ray. **Figure 1** shows how a light source, such as a candle, gives off light rays that travel away from the source in all directions. Even though light rays can change direction when they are reflected or refracted, your brain interprets images as if light rays travel in a single direction.

Section 1 Resource Manager

Chapter *Fast File* Resources

Transparency Activity, p. 44
Note-taking Worksheets, pp. 33–35
Directed Reading for Content Mastery, pp. 19, 20
MiniLAB, p. 3
Enrichment, p. 30
Lab Activity, p. 9–12
Lab Worksheet, pp. 5–6
Reinforcement, p. 27

Performance Assessment in the Science Classroom, p. 52

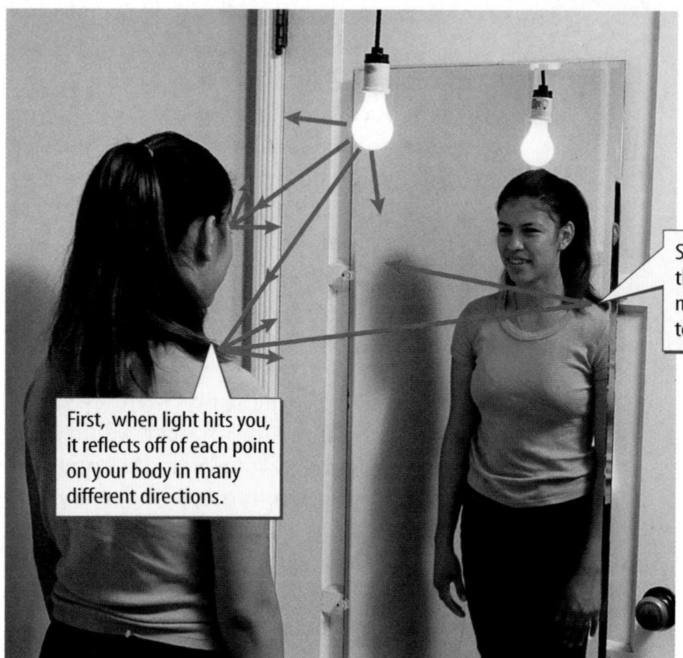
Some of the light rays then travel toward the mirror and reflect back toward your eyes.
First, when light hits you, it reflects off of each point on your body in many different directions.

Figure 2 Seeing an image of yourself in a mirror involves two sets of reflections.

Seeing Reflections with Plane Mirrors

Greek mythology tells the story of a handsome young man named Narcissus who noticed his image in a pond and fell in love with himself. Like pools of water, mirrors are smooth surfaces that reflect light to form images. Just as Narcissus did, you can see yourself as you glance into a quiet pool of water or walk past a shop window. Most of the time, however, you probably look for your image in a flat, smooth mirror called a **plane mirror.**

Reading Check *What is a plane mirror?*

Reflection from Plane Mirrors What do you see when you look into a plane mirror? Your reflection appears upright. If you were 1 m from the mirror, your image would appear to be 1 m behind the mirror, or 2 m from you. In fact, your image is what someone standing 2 m from you would see. **Figure 2** shows how your image is formed by a plane mirror. First, light rays from a light source strike you. Every point that is struck by the light rays reflects these rays so they travel outward in all directions. If your friend were looking at you, these reflected light rays coming from you would enter her eyes so she could see you. However, if a mirror is placed between you and your friend, the light rays are reflected from the mirror back to your eyes.

INTEGRATE Life Science

Mirror Images Your left hand and right hand are mirror images of each other. Some of the molecules in your body exist in two forms that are mirror images. However, your body uses some molecules only in the left-handed form and other molecules only in the right-handed form. Using different colors of gumdrops and toothpicks, make a model of a molecule that has a mirror image.

2 Teach

INTEGRATE Life Science

Mirror Images Show students pictures of the L and D isomers of ibuprofen and ask students how they relate to each other. They look like mirror images of each other. Tell students that the D-isomer relieves pain and the L-isomer does not.

Visual Learning

Figure 2 Have students trace the path of light in the picture as you read each caption aloud. Ask students why light rays reflect off your body in many different directions. The surface of the body is rough. As rays of light hit the rough surface, they bounce off in different directions. L1 ELL LS **Visual-Spatial**

Reading Check

Answer a flat, smooth mirror

Use Science Words

Word Meaning Have students explain why a flat mirror is called a *plane* mirror. In mathematics, the word *plane* refers to a flat surface that extends infinitely in all directions, so the word *plane* is frequently used as a synonym for *flat*.

Curriculum Connection

Social Studies Psychologists sometimes secretly observe animals or people using a two-way mirror, a coated window that only partially transmits light. If one side is in a lighted room, and the other is in a darkened room, the window acts as a mirror on the lighted side and a window on the darkened side. Have students debate whether use of this technology is an invasion of privacy. L3 LS **Linguistic**

Caption Answer

Figure 3 your image is double the distance between you and the mirror

Use Science Words

Word Usage The word *virtual* means having the effect of something without being the thing. Ask students to use this definition to explain the term *virtual image*. When you look in a plane mirror, you see the image of an object, but the rays of light don't actually come together to form an image. The image is virtual, meaning that your brain interprets the light rays that enter your eyes as though they were coming from an image at that location. L2 LS **Linguistic**

Activity

Concave Mirrors Allow students to experiment with concave mirrors to observe how focusing the image depends on the object's distance from the mirror. Have them observe how the image varies as they move the mirror from side to side. L2 ELL LS **Visual-Spatial**

Quick Demo

The Law of Reflection

Materials laser pointer

Estimated Time five minutes

Purpose Use the laser pointer to show light reflecting from one mirror to another. Demonstrate how the incoming angle equals the outgoing angle. WARNING: *Never direct a laser pointer toward someone's eyes.* L2 ELL LS **Visual-Spatial**

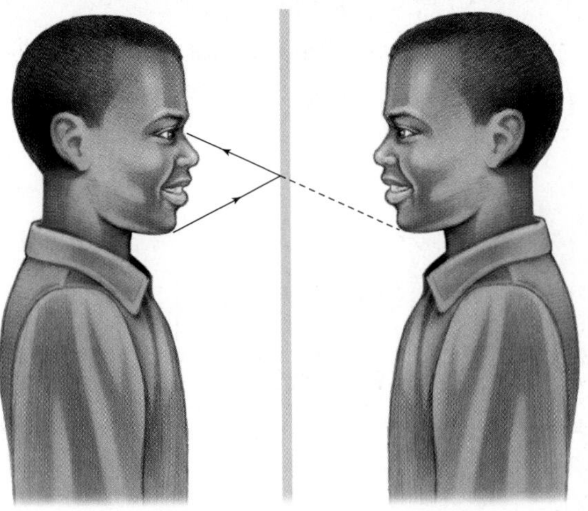

Figure 3 Your brain thinks that the light rays that reflect off of the mirror come from a point behind the mirror.
Infer *how the size of your image in a plane mirror depends on your distance from the mirror.*

Virtual Images You can understand how your brain interprets your reflection in a mirror by looking at **Figure 3.** The light waves that are reflected off of you travel in all directions. Light rays reflected from your chin strike the mirror at different places. Then, they reflect off of the mirror in different directions. Recall that your brain always interprets light rays as if they have traveled in a straight line. It doesn't realize that the light rays have been reflected and that they changed direction. If the reflected light rays were extended back behind the mirror, they would meet at a single point. Your brain interprets the rays that enter your eye as coming from this point behind the mirror. You seem to see the reflected image of your chin at this point. An image like this, which your brain perceives even though no light rays pass through it, is called a **virtual image.** The virtual image formed by a plane mirror is always upright and appears to be as far behind the mirror as the object is in front of it.

Concave Mirrors

Not all mirrors are flat like plane mirrors are. If the surface of a mirror is curved inward, it is called a **concave mirror.** Concave mirrors, like plane mirrors, reflect light waves to form images. The difference is that the curved surface of a concave mirror reflects light in a unique way.

Figure 4 A concave mirror has an optical axis and a focal point. When light rays travel toward the mirror parallel to the optical axis, they reflect through the focal point.

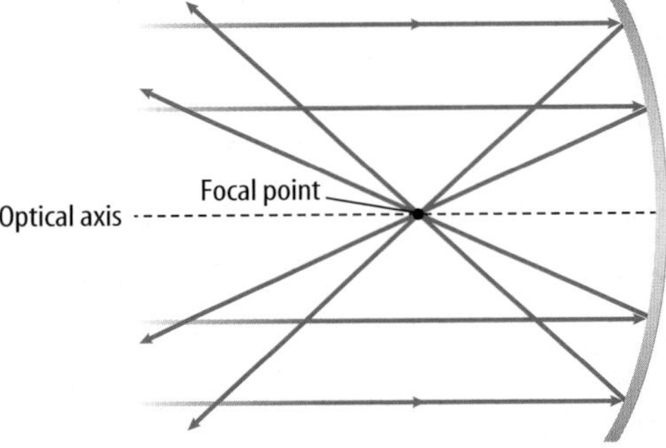

Features of Concave Mirrors A concave mirror has an optical axis. The **optical axis** is an imaginary straight line drawn perpendicular to the surface of the mirror at its center. Every light ray traveling parallel to the optical axis as it approaches the mirror is reflected through a point on the optical axis called the **focal point.** Using the focal point and the optical axis, you can diagram how some of the light rays that travel to a concave mirror are reflected, as shown in **Figure 4.** On the other hand, if a light ray passes through the focal point before it hits the mirror, it is reflected parallel to the optical axis. The distance from the center of the mirror to the focal point is called the **focal length.**

Science Journal

Convergence In biology, convergence is the tendency of different organisms to have some common characteristics when living in the same conditions. Concave mirrors converge light. Ask students to use this information to deduce a definition of *converge* and write it in their Science Journals. A definition from these contexts would be "to come together." L3 LS **Linguistic**

Visual Learning

Figure 4 Have students look at the diagram in **Figure 4.** Explain that one type of concave mirror is called a spherical mirror. In a spherical mirror, if the curve of the mirror extended around it would form a sphere. The center of this imaginary sphere is called the center of curvature. Is the mirror in this diagram a spherical mirror? yes L3 LS **Visual-Spatial**

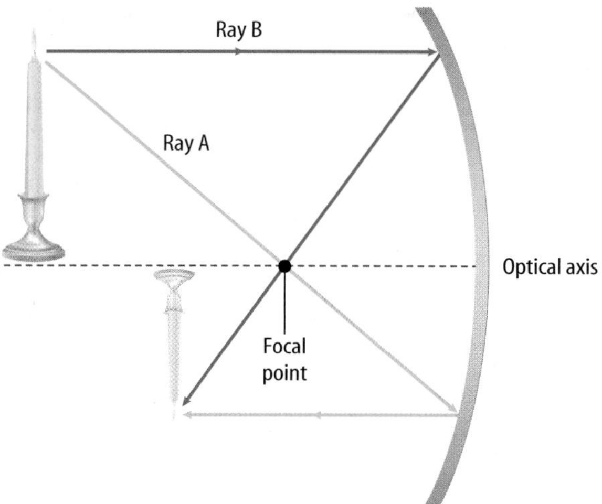

Figure 5 Rays A and B start from the same place on the candle, travel in different directions, and meet again on the reflected image.
Diagram *how other points on the image of the candle are formed.*

How a Concave Mirror Works The image that is formed by a concave mirror changes depending on where the object is located relative to the focal point of the mirror. You can diagram how an image is formed. For example, suppose that the distance between the object, such as the candle in **Figure 5,** and the mirror is a little greater than the focal length. Light rays bounce off of each point on the candle in all directions. One light ray, labeled Ray A, starts from a point on the flame of the candle and passes through the focal point on its way to the mirror. Ray A is then reflected so it travels parallel to the optical axis. Another ray, Ray B, starts from the same point on the candle's flame but travels parallel to the optical axis as it moves toward the mirror. When Ray B is reflected by the mirror, it passes through the focal point. The place where Ray A and Ray B meet after they are reflected forms a point on the flame of the reflected image.

More points on the reflected image can be located in this way. From each point on the candle, one ray can be drawn that passes through the focal point and is reflected parallel to the optical axis. Another ray can be drawn that travels parallel to the optical axis and passes through the focal point after it is reflected. The point where the two rays meet is on the reflected image.

Real Images The image that is formed by the concave mirror is not virtual. Rays of light pass through the location of the image. A **real image** is formed when light rays converge to form the image. You could hold a sheet of paper at the location of a real image and see the image projected on the paper. When an object is farther from a concave mirror than twice the focal length, the image that is formed is real, smaller, and upside down, or inverted.

Observing Images in a Spoon

Procedure

1. Look at the inside of a shiny **spoon**. Move it close to your face and then far away. The place where your image changes is the focal point.
2. Hold the inside of the spoon facing a bright **light,** a little farther away than the focal length of the spoon.
3. Place a piece of **poster board** between the light and the spoon without blocking all of the light.
4. Move the poster board between the spoon and the light until you see the reflected light on it.

Analysis

Which of the images you observed were real and which were virtual?

Try at Home

Differentiated Instruction

Challenge Have students set up a piece of black paper and a concave mirror with a known focal length so they are fixed more than two focal lengths apart. Have students hypothesize what types of images can be formed and where they are located. Then have students test their hypotheses.

Visual Learning

Figure 5 Have students work in pairs and take turns explaining to each other how rays from all parts of the candle are reflected off the concave mirror to form an image. L1 ELL IS **Visual-Spatial**

Caption Answer

Figure 5 Check your students' answers.

Teacher FYI

Spherical Aberration Spherical concave mirrors are unable to produce perfectly focused images because rays from the outer edges of the mirror focus slightly closer to the mirror than rays from the middle. This effect, known as spherical aberration, is especially troublesome for large mirrors. To avoid this, large mirrors typically have a parabolic shape, which allows all of the rays to converge at the same point.

Purpose Students observe real and virtual images in a spoon. L2 ELL IS **Visual-Spatial**

Materials shiny spoon, bright light source, 10-cm×10-cm square of white poster board

Teaching Strategy Folded index cards may be used instead of poster board.

Troubleshooting Shiny spoons produce clearer images.

Analysis

The up-close images were virtual. The faraway images were real.

Assessment

Oral Ask students why their images changed from upright to inverted. Up close, the student's distance from the mirror was less than the distance from the focal point to the mirror, so they saw a virtual, upright image. Past the focal point, they saw a real, inverted image. Use **Performance Assessment in the Science Classroom,** p. 89.

Caption Answer

Figure 6 The light source is located at the focal point.

Discussion

Rough Mirror How would the reflection of light from a concave mirror be different if the surface of the mirror were rough rather than smooth? At each individual point, the light rays would be reflected so that the angle of incidence equaled the angle of reflection. If the surface were rough, these angles would change from point to point, and the rays would be scattered. You would not see a clear image. L2 IS **Logical-Mathematical**

Activity

Flashlight Study Have students open the top of a flashlight to see the shape of the reflector. Explain that if the flashlight had a spherical mirror, the light rays coming out from it wouldn't be parallel. A parabolic reflector has a definite focal point for all rays, so it produces a straighter beam of light. L2 IS **Kinesthetic**

Caption Answer

Figure 7 The light rays diverge.

Quick Demo

Light Beams

Materials flashlight that has a rotating head to adjust the divergence of the light beam

Estimated Time 10 minutes

Procedure In a darkened room, show students that as you rotate the head, the beam spreads out. Explain that rotating the head moves the light bulb back and forth about the focal point of the reflecting mirror, varying the divergence of the beam. L3 IS **Visual-Spatial**

Figure 6 A flashlight uses a concave mirror to create a beam of light.
Explain *why the reflected rays of light in the diagram are parallel to each other.*

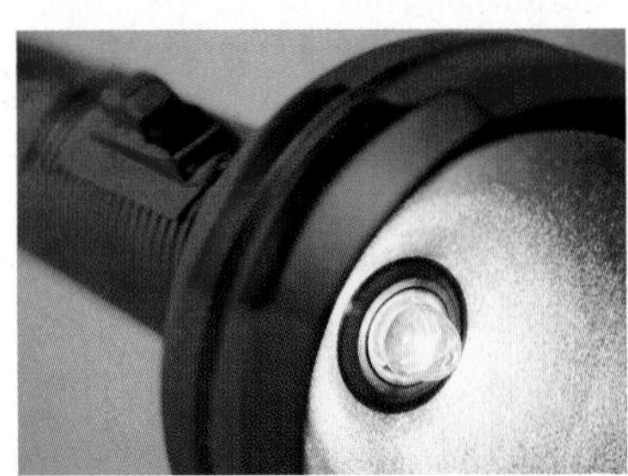

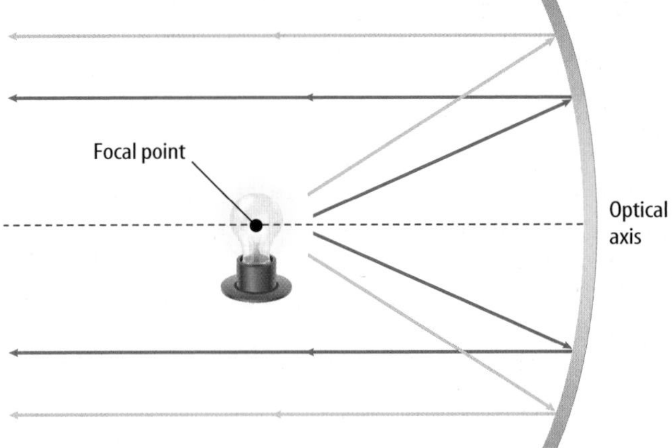

Creating Light Beams What happens if you place an object exactly at the focal point of the concave mirror? **Figure 6** shows that if the object is at the focal point, the mirror reflects all light rays parallel to the optical axis. No image forms because the rays never meet—not even if the rays are extended back behind the mirror. Therefore, a light placed at the focal point is reflected in a beam. Car headlights, flashlights, lighthouses, spotlights, and other devices use concave mirrors in this way to create concentrated light beams of nearly parallel rays.

Figure 7 If the candle is between the mirror and its focal point, the reflected image is enlarged and virtual.
Infer *why this image couldn't be projected on a screen.*

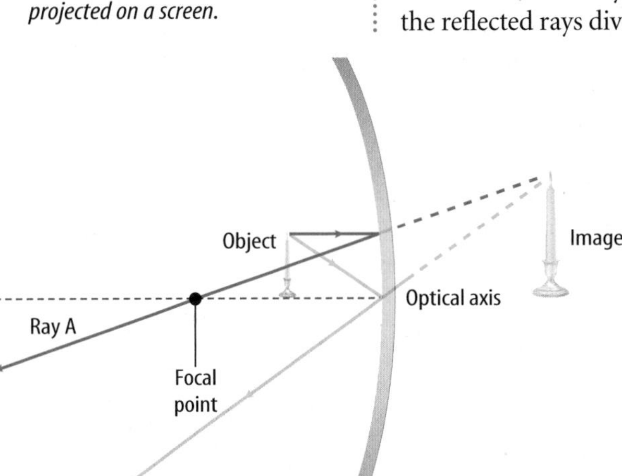

Mirrors That Magnify The image formed by a concave mirror changes again when you place an object between it and its focal point. The location of the reflected image again can be found by drawing two rays from each point. **Figure 7** shows that in this case, these rays never meet after they are reflected. Instead, the reflected rays diverge. Just as it does with a plane mirror, your brain interprets the diverging rays as if they came from one point behind the mirror. You can find this point by extending the rays behind the mirror until they meet. Because no light rays are behind the mirror where the image seems to be, the image formed is virtual. The image also is upright and enlarged.

Shaving mirrors and makeup mirrors are concave mirrors. They form an enlarged, upright image of a person's face so it's easier to see small details. The bowl of a shiny spoon also forms an enlarged, upright image of your face when it is placed close to your face.

Science Journal

Solar Furnace Concave mirrors are used in solar furnaces, in which sunlight heats objects. Have students describe in their Science Journals how they think a solar furnace works, and where the object to be heated must be located. At the focal point; the rays from the Sun that strike the mirror are parallel. By the law of reflection, the rays reflect to the focal point, which becomes intensely hot. L3 P IS **Logical-Mathematical**

Convex Mirrors

Why do you think the security mirrors in banks and stores are shaped the way they are? The next time you are in a store, look up to one of the back corners or at the end of an aisle to see if a large, rounded mirror is mounted there. You can see a large area of the store in the mirror. A mirror that curves outward like the back of a spoon is called a **convex mirror.** Light rays that hit a convex mirror diverge, or spread apart, after they are reflected. Look at **Figure 8** to see how the rays from an object are reflected to form an image. The reflected rays diverge and never meet, so the image formed by a convex mirror is a virtual image. The image also is always upright and smaller than the actual object is.

Reading Check *Describe the image formed by a convex mirror.*

Uses of Convex Mirrors Because convex mirrors cause light rays to diverge, they allow large areas to be viewed. As a result, a convex mirror is said to have a wide field of view. In addition to increasing the field of view in places like grocery stores and factories, convex mirrors can widen the view of traffic that can be seen in rearview or side-view mirrors of automobiles. However, because the image created by a convex mirror is smaller than the actual object, your perception of distance can be distorted. Objects look farther away than they truly are in a convex mirror. Distances and sizes seen in a convex mirror are not realistic, so most convex side mirrors carry a printed warning that says "Objects in mirror are closer than they appear."

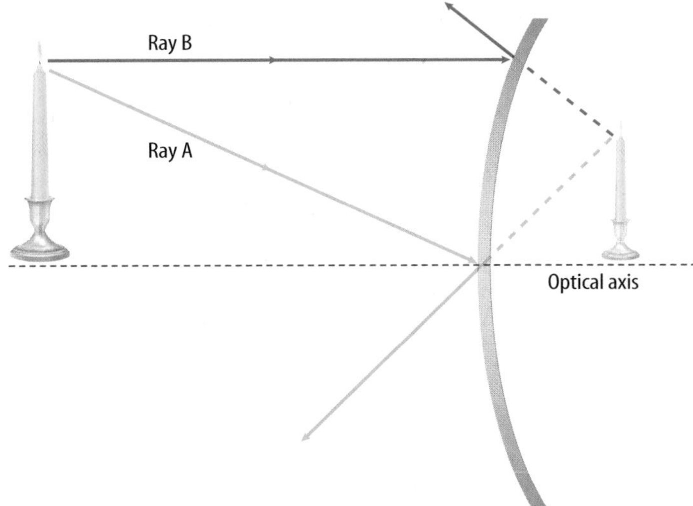

Figure 8 A convex mirror forms a reduced, upright, virtual image.

Reading Check

Answer upright, smaller, and virtual

Activity

Mirror Flash Cards Have students use the information in **Table 1** to make flash cards. Then have them work in pairs and, using their flash cards, quiz one another about the images formed by different types of mirrors. L2 LS **Interpersonal**

Inquiry Lab

Moving Light

Purpose Students will learn how to direct light using concave and plane mirrors.

Possible Materials flashlight, tape, several concave and plane mirrors

Estimated Time 30 min.

Teaching Strategies

- Tape a flashlight to a table, and make a target on a wall not facing the students. Darken the room. Using several concave and plane mirrors, have the students hold the mirrors (each student holding or placing a mirror) such that the beam of light is focused on the target.
- Encourage students to explore questions that arise during the experiment.

For additional inquiry activities, see *Science Inquiry Labs*.

Differentiated Instruction

Visually Impaired For all of the activities in this section, have visually impaired students work with sighted students. Make sure the visually impaired students have the opportunity to handle mirrors so they can identify their shapes. Have the sighted students describe in detail everything they do and see as they perform the activities.

3 Assess

DAILY INTERVENTION

Check for Understanding

Kinesthetic Place flashlights and various plane, convex, and concave mirrors on a table. Allow students to experiment with the different mirrors with the flashlights in a darkened room. Have the students write down an observation about what each mirror did with the beams of light.

Reteach

Real or Virtual Images Have a collection of plane, concave, and convex mirrors for students to experiment with. Ask them to predict for each one whether they will see upright, inverted, enlarged, or diminished images. Then have them look in the mirrors to find out whether they are correct. They should also tell whether the images they see are real or virtual. L2 LS **Visual-Spatial**

Assessment

Process Ask each student to draw a ray diagram that represents a person looking into a concave makeup or shaving mirror. Have them include the image seen by the person looking into the mirror. The person's face should be between the mirror and the focal point. The image should be enlarged, upright, and virtual (behind the mirror). They should use rays from the top and bottom of the face. Use **Performance Assessment in the Science Classroom,** p. 127.

Table 1 Images Formed by Mirrors

Mirror Shape	Position of Object	Virtual/Real	Image Created Upright/Upside Down	Size
Plane		virtual	upright	same as object
Concave	Object more than two focal lengths from mirror	real	upside down	smaller than object
	Object between one and two focal lengths	real	upside down	larger than object
	Object at focal point	none	none	none
	Object within focal length	virtual	upright	larger than object
Convex		virtual	upright	smaller than object

Mirror Images The different shapes of plane, concave, and convex mirrors cause them to reflect light in distinct ways. Each type of mirror has different uses. **Table 1** summarizes the images formed by plane, concave, and convex mirrors.

section 1 review

Summary

How do you use light to see?

- You see an object because your eyes detect the light reflected from that object.

Seeing with Plane Mirrors

- Plane mirrors are smooth and flat.
- A plane mirror forms upright, virtual images.
- No light rays pass through the location of a virtual image.

Concave Mirrors

- A concave mirror curves inward.
- The image formed by a concave mirror depends on the location of an object.

Convex Mirrors

- A convex mirror curves outward.
- Convex mirrors produce virtual, upright images that are smaller than the object.

Self Check

1. **Describe** how your image in a plane mirror changes as you move closer to the mirror.
2. **Diagram** how light rays from an object are reflected by a convex mirror to form an image.
3. **Describe** the image of an object that is 38 cm from a concave mirror that has a focal length of 10 cm.
4. **Infer** An object is less than one focal length from a concave mirror. How does the size of the image change as the object gets closer to the mirror?
5. **Think Critically** Determine whether or not a virtual image can be photographed.

Applying Math

6. **Calculate Angle of Reflection** A light ray from a flashlight strikes a plane mirror so that the angle between the mirror's surface and the light ray is 60°. What is the angle of reflection?

gpscience.com/self_check_quiz

section  review

1. Your image moves toward you and becomes larger.
2. Sketches should show light rays from a single point on the object diverging after being reflected from the mirror.
3. The object is more than two focal lengths from the mirror, so the image is real, smaller, and inverted.
4. The image gets smaller.
5. Yes, the virtual image formed by the convex mirror in Figure 8 has been photographed.
6. 30°

Reflections of Reflections

How can you see the back of your head? You can use two mirrors to view a reflection of a reflection of the back of your head.

Real-World Question

How many reflections can you see with two mirrors?

Goals

- **Infer** how the number of reflections depends on the angle between mirrors.

Materials

plane mirrors (2)
masking tape
protractor
paper clip

Safety Precautions

Handle glass mirrors and paper clips carefully.

Procedure

1. Lay one mirror on top of the other with the mirror surfaces inward. Tape them together so they will open and close. Use tape to label them *L* and *R*.
2. Stand the mirrors up on a sheet of paper. Using the protractor, close the mirrors to an angle of 72°.

Images and Wedges Seen in the Mirrors

Angle of Mirrors	Number of Paper Clip Images		Number of Wedges
	R	L	
72°	2	2	5
90°	2	1	4
120°	1	1	3

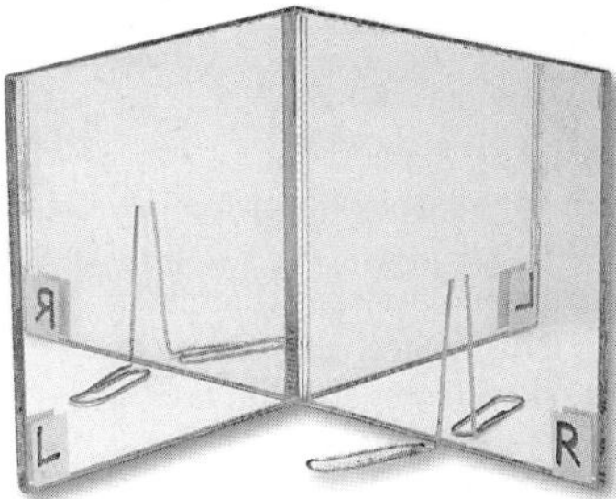

3. Bend one leg of a paper clip up 90° and place it close to the front of the R mirror.
4. Count the number of images of the clip you see in the *R* and *L* mirrors. Record these numbers in the data table.
5. The mirror arrangement creates an image of a circle divided into wedges by the mirrors. Record the number of wedges.
6. Hold the *R* mirror still and slowly open the *L* mirror to 90°. Count and record the images of the clip and the wedges in the circle. Repeat, this time opening the mirrors to 120°.

Conclude and Apply

1. **Infer** the relationship between the number of wedges and paper clip images you can see.
2. **Determine** the angle that would divide a circle into six wedges. Hypothesize how many images would be produced.

Communicating Your Data

Demonstrate for younger students the relationship between the angle of the mirrors and the number of reflections.

Real-World Question

Purpose Students will observe image formation by plane mirrors. L1 COOP LEARN IN **Visual-Spatial**

Process Skills measure, infer, recognize cause and effect, compare and contrast, form operational definitions

Time Required 45 minutes

Procedure

Teaching Strategies

- Use rectangular mirrors at least 5 cm across. Thin glass is better. Mirror tiles (hardware store) can be cut to size, but sharp edges must be ground or taped.
- Place a protractor on a copy machine and make lab worksheets upon which students can measure the appropriate angles.

Conclude and Apply

1. The number of paper clip images is one less than the number of wedges.
2. The angle producing six wedges is $\frac{360}{6} = 60°$. Five images will be produced.

Communicating Your Data

Have students draw circles divided into thirds (120°), quarters (90°), fifths (72°), and sixths (60°) and use the circles in their demonstrations to position the mirrors. Have them show younger students how the number of wedges seen relates to the angle between the mirrors.

Assessment

Performance Ask students to open the mirrors to an angle of 45° to each other. How many images of your face do you see? eight What about smaller angles? more images Larger angles? fewer images Explain. The number of reflections is determined by the angle. This number is 360 divided by the angle. Use **Performance Assessment in the Science Classroom,** p. 89.

section 2

Lenses

Reading Guide

What You'll Learn

- **Describe** the shapes of convex and concave lenses.
- **Explain** how convex and concave lenses form images.
- **Explain** how lenses are used to correct vision problems.

Why It's Important

Even if you don't wear eyeglasses or contacts, you still use lenses to see.

Review Vocabulary

transparent: a material that transmits almost all the light that strikes it

New Vocabulary

- convex lens
- concave lens
- cornea
- retina

What is a lens?

What do your eyes have in common with cameras, eyeglasses, and microscopes? Each of these things contains at least one lens. A lens is a transparent material with at least one curved surface that causes light rays to bend, or refract, as they pass through. The image that a lens forms depends on the shape of the lens. Like curved mirrors, a lens can be convex or concave.

Convex Lenses

A **convex lens** is thicker in the middle than at the edges. Its optical axis is an imaginary straight line that is perpendicular to the surface of the lens at its thickest point. When light rays approach a convex lens traveling parallel to its optical axis, the rays are refracted toward the center of the lens, as in **Figure 9.** All light rays traveling parallel to the optical axis are refracted so they pass through a single point, which is the focal point of the lens. The focal length of the lens depends on the shape of the lens. If the sides of a convex lens are less curved, light rays are bent less. As a result, lenses with flatter sides have longer focal lengths. **Figure 9** also shows that light rays traveling along the optical axis are not bent at all.

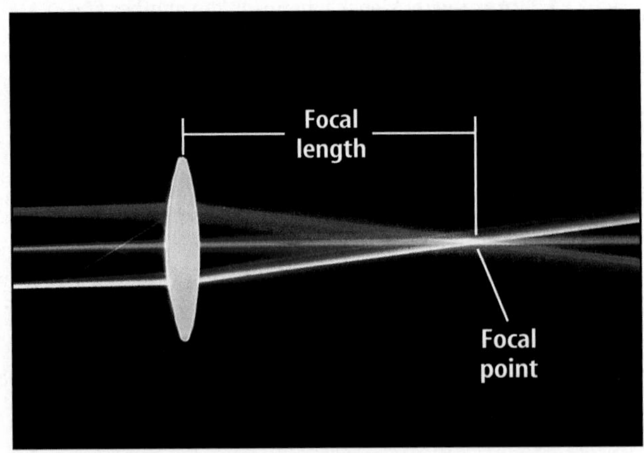

Figure 9 Convex lenses are thicker in the middle than at the edges. A convex lens focuses light rays at a focal point. A light ray that passes straight through the center of the lens is not refracted.

Section 2 Resource Manager

Chapter *FAST FILE* Resources
Transparency Activity, p. 45, 47–48
Directed Reading for Content Mastery, p. 20
Lab Activity, pp. 13–16
Enrichment, p. 31
Reinforcement, p. 28

Mathematics Skill Activities, p. 29
Science Inquiry Labs, pp. 39–40

1 Motivate

Bellringer

Section Focus Transparencies also are available on the Interactive Chalkboard CD-ROM.

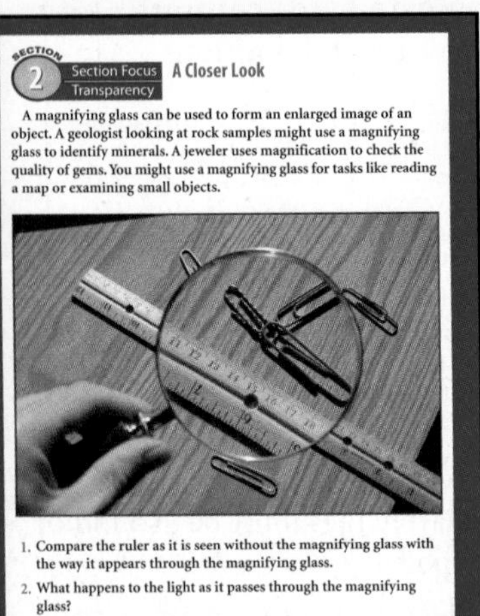
Section 2 Section Focus Transparency — A Closer Look

A magnifying glass can be used to form an enlarged image of an object. A geologist looking at rock samples might use a magnifying glass to identify minerals. A jeweler uses magnification to check the quality of gems. You might use a magnifying glass for tasks like reading a map or examining small objects.

1. Compare the ruler as it is seen without the magnifying glass with the way it appears through the magnifying glass.
2. What happens to the light as it passes through the magnifying glass?
3. How do people use lenses in their daily lives?

L2

Mirrors and Lenses

Tie to Prior Knowledge

Eyeglasses Many students wear corrective lenses, either as eyeglasses or contact lenses. Ask students what the eyeglasses do. They cause light rays to refract before they enter your eyes.

424 CHAPTER 14 Mirrors and Lenses

Figure 10 The image formed by a convex lens depends on the positions of the lens and the object.

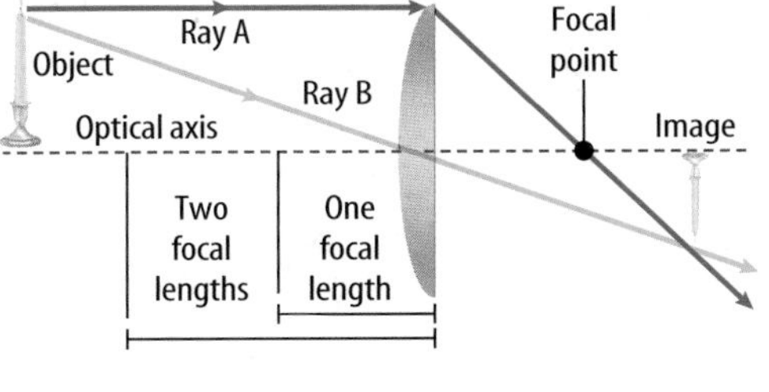

A When the candle is more than two focal lengths away from the lens, its image is real, reduced, and upside down.

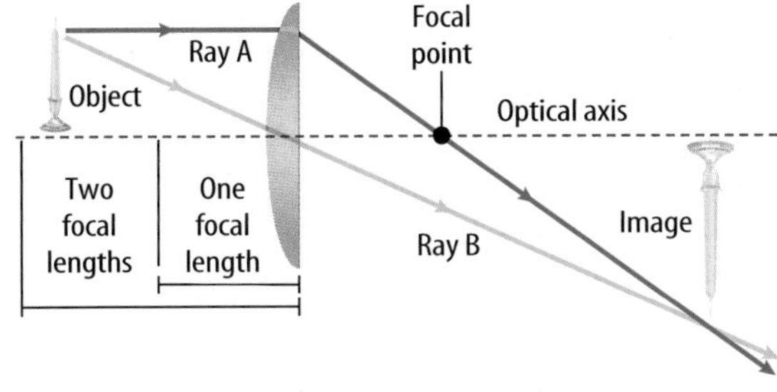

B When the candle is between one and two focal lengths from the lens, its image is real, enlarged, and upside down.

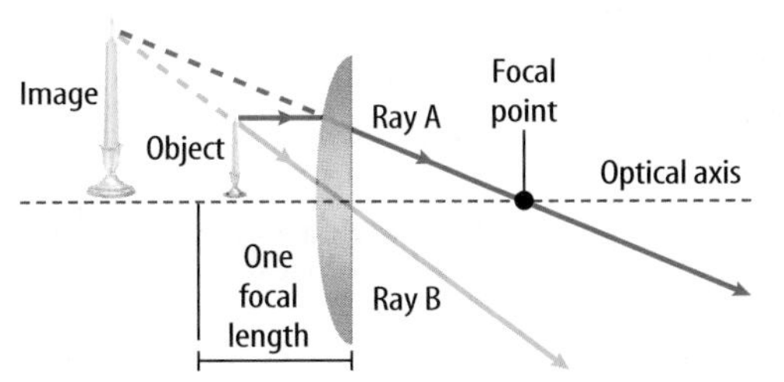

C When the candle is less than one focal length from the lens, its image is virtual, enlarged, and upright.

Forming Images with a Convex Lens The type of image a convex lens forms depends on where the object is relative to the focal point of the lens. If an object is more than two focal lengths from the lens, as in **Figure 10A,** the image is real, reduced, and inverted, and on the opposite side of the lens from the object.

As the object moves closer to the lens, the image gets larger. **Figure 10B** shows the image formed when the object is between one and two focal lengths from the lens. Now the image is larger than the object, but is still inverted.

When an object is less than one focal length from the lens, as in **Figure 10C,** the image becomes an enlarged, virtual image. The image is virtual because light rays from the object diverge after they pass through the lens. When you use a magnifying glass, you move a convex lens so that it is less than one focal length from an object. This causes the image of the object to be magnified.

2 Teach

Discussion

Lenses v. Mirrors What is the primary difference between lenses and mirrors? Mirrors reflect light and lenses transmit light.

Use Science Words

Word Origin Lenses were named because of the resemblance of an eye's lens to a small legume called a lentil. The Latin word for lentil is *lenticula.* Bring lentils to class so students can see the resemblance in shape. L2 LS **Visual-Spatial**

Activity

Convex Lenses Distribute to your class some convex lenses of varying focal lengths. Show students how to find the focal length of a lens by focusing the clearest possible image of an overhead light on a white piece of paper (held by a partner) and measuring the distance from the paper to the lens. L2 LS **Visual-Spatial**

Visual Learning

Figure 10 To help students understand **Figures 10A, 10B,** and **10C,** have them imagine that the candle in **Figure 10A** is moving toward the lens. As it does, the image gets larger. When it is at exactly $2f$ (where f is the focal length), the image is the same size as the candle. If the candle continues to move, the image becomes larger than the candle. To see this, trace a copy of **Figure 10A** with the candle at $2f$. Sketch rays to show how the image forms. L2 LS **Visual-Spatial**

Active Reading

Write-Draw-Discuss This strategy encourages students to actively participate in reading and lectures, assimilating content creatively. Have students write about an idea, clarify it, then make an illustration or drawing. Ask students to share responses with the class and display several examples. Have students Write-Draw-Discuss about convex and concave lenses.

Caption Answers

Figure 11 convex mirror; both cause light to diverge and produce virtual images

Use an Analogy

Prisms Convex lenses and concave lenses refract light much like two right-angle prisms joined together. When the prisms are joined at the base so that they are thick at the middle, a beam of light will be refracted downward by the upper prism and upward by the lower prism. This produces the effect of a converging convex lens. When they are joined at the apex, a beam of light will be refracted upward by the upper prism and downward by the lower prism, producing the effect of a diverging concave lens. L2 IS **Visual-Spatial**

Applying Science

Answers

1. Given the same focal length, as the object distance increases, the image distance decreases.
2. $\frac{1}{\text{image distance}} = \frac{1}{15.0} - \frac{1}{60} =$

   $0.067 - 0.017 = 0.05$

   $\text{image distance} = \frac{1}{0.05} = 20 \text{ cm}$

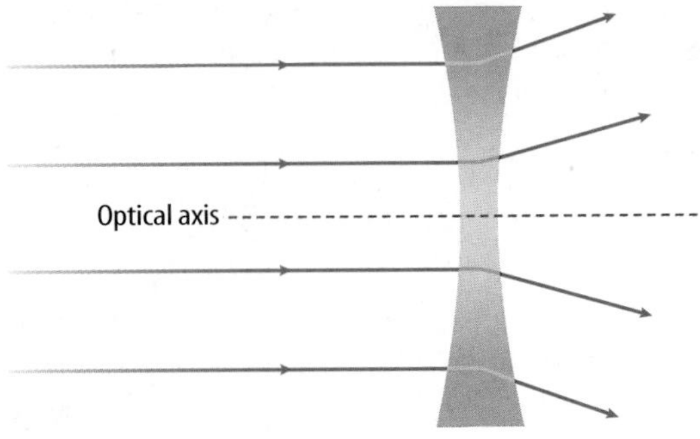

Figure 11 A concave lens refracts light rays so they spread out.
Classify *Is a concave lens most like a concave mirror or a convex mirror?*

Concave Lenses

A **concave lens** is thinner in the middle and thicker at the edges. As shown in **Figure 11,** light rays that pass through a concave lens bend outward away from the optical axis. The rays spread out and never meet at a focal point, so they never form a real image. The image is always virtual, upright, and smaller than the actual object is. Concave lenses are used in some types of eyeglasses and some telescopes. Concave lenses usually are used in combination with other lenses. A summary of the images formed by concave and convex lenses is shown in **Table 2** on the next page.

Applying Science

Comparing Object and Image Distances

The size and orientation of an image formed by a convex lens depends on the location of the object. What happens to the location of the image formed by a convex lens as the object moves closer to or farther from the lens? The distance from the lens to the object is the object distance, and the distance from the lens to the image is the image distance. How are the focal length, object distance, and image distance related to each other?

Object and Image Distances

Focal Length	Object Distance	Image Distance
15.0 cm	45.0 cm	22.5 cm
15.0 cm	30.0 cm	30.0 cm
15.0 cm	20.0 cm	60.0 cm

Identifying the Problem

A 5-cm-tall object is placed at different lengths from a double convex lens with a focal length of 15 cm. The table above lists the different object and image distances. How are these two measurements related?

Solving the Problem

1. What is the relationship between the object distance and the image distance?
2. The lens equation describes the relationship between the focal length and the image and object distances.
   1/focal length = 1/object distance + 1/image distance
   Using this equation, calculate the image distance of an object placed at a distance of 60.0 cm from the lens.

LAB DEMONSTRATION

Purpose to observe images with convex and concave lenses

Materials concave and convex lenses, optical bench with lens holders, tape, pencil

Preparation Place a convex lens in a holder on the bench. Using tape, mark one and two focal lengths.

Procedure Hold a pencil more than two focal lengths from the lens, between one and two focal lengths from the lens, and less than one focal length from the lens. At each position, have students look through the lens. Repeat using a concave lens.

Expected Outcome Students should see images, as shown in **Figures 10** and **11**.

Assessment

Ask students to explain why, when the convex lens is used, the image flips as the pencil moves closer to the lens. The light rays no longer converge.

Table 2 Images Formed by Lenses

Lens Shape	Location of Object	Type of Image		
		Virtual/Real	Upright/Inverted	Size
Convex	Object beyond 2 focal lengths from lens	real	inverted	smaller than object
	Object between 1 and 2 focal lengths	real	inverted	larger than object
	Object within 1 focal length	virtual	upright	larger than object
Concave	Object at any position	virtual	upright	smaller than object

Lenses and Eyesight

INTEGRATE Life Science What determines how well you can see the words on this page? If you don't need eyeglasses, the structure of your eye gives you the ability to focus on these words and other objects around you. Look at **Figure 12.** Light enters your eye through a transparent covering on your eyeball called the **cornea** (KOR nee uh). The cornea causes light rays to bend so that they converge. The light then passes through an opening called the pupil. Behind the pupil is a flexible convex lens. The lens helps focus light rays so that a sharp image is formed on your retina. The **retina** is the inner lining of your eye. It has cells that convert the light image into electrical signals, which are then carried along the optic nerve to your brain to be interpreted.

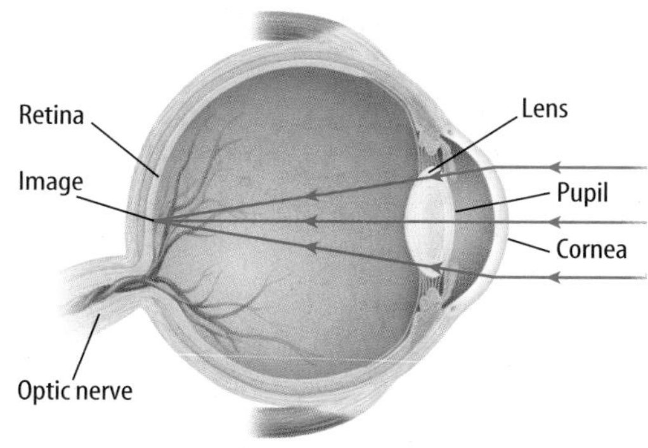

Figure 12 The cornea and lens in your eye focus light rays so that a sharp image is formed on the retina.

IDENTIFYING Misconceptions

Human Corneas Students might assume that rays of light pass through the cornea unaffected. In fact, the cornea does about two-thirds of the focusing and is responsible for most human vision problems. The flexible lens does the fine focusing.

Differentiated Instruction

Learning Disabled If students have trouble remembering which type of curved surface is concave and which is convex, tell them to remember that a concave surface is curved inward like a cave. To practice using this mnemonic, have them name some curved surfaces and identify them as concave or convex.

Teacher FYI

Animal Eyes Vertebrates, cephalopods, and some spiders have camera-like eyes with variable focusing. Worms, mollusks, and some crustaceans and insects have simple eyes that can distinguish light and dark. Most arthropods have compound eyes, with many separate lenses, each of which forms its own image.

SECTION 2 Lenses 427

Activity

Focusing Normally your eyes change from focusing on nearby objects to focusing on faraway objects without you being aware of it. It is possible, however, to feel the change. Have students hold a pencil about 10 cm directly in front of their eyes. Tell them to focus on the pencil for a few seconds and then, without moving the pencil, to look beyond it to a distant object. If they do this quickly several times, they will feel a slight strain as their eyes adjust focus.

Reading Check

Answer it becomes more convex

Quick Demo

Exploring an Eye

Materials model of a human eye

Estimated Time 30 minutes

Procedure Allow students to explore the model and observe the cornea, lens, and retina. Have students explain how light enters through the cornea and is refracted onto the retina. Point out the muscles that adjust the size of the lens, and note the optic nerve, which carries information about images to the brain. L2 IS **Visual-Spatial**

Science Online

Topic: Retina

Visit gpscience.com for Web links to information about diseases that affect the retina.

Activity Make a drawing of what an eye doctor sees when looking in your eyes.

Focusing on Near and Far How can your eyes focus both on close objects, like the watch on your wrist, and distant objects, like a clock across the room? For you to see an object clearly, its image must be focused sharply on your retina. However, the retina is always a fixed distance from the lens. Remember that the location of an image formed by a convex lens depends on the focal length of the lens and the location of the object. For example, look back at **Figure 10.** As an object moves farther from a convex lens, the position of the image moves closer to the lens.

For an image to be formed on the retina, the focal length of the lens needs to be able to change as the distance of the object changes. The lens in your eye is flexible, and muscles attached to it change its shape and its focal length. This is why you can see objects that are near and far away.

Look at **Figure 13.** As an object gets farther from your eye, the focal length of the lens has to increase. The muscles around the lens stretch it so it has a less convex shape. But when you focus on a nearby object, these muscles make the lens more curved, causing the focal length to decrease.

Reading Check *How does the shape of the lens in your eye change when you focus on a nearby object?*

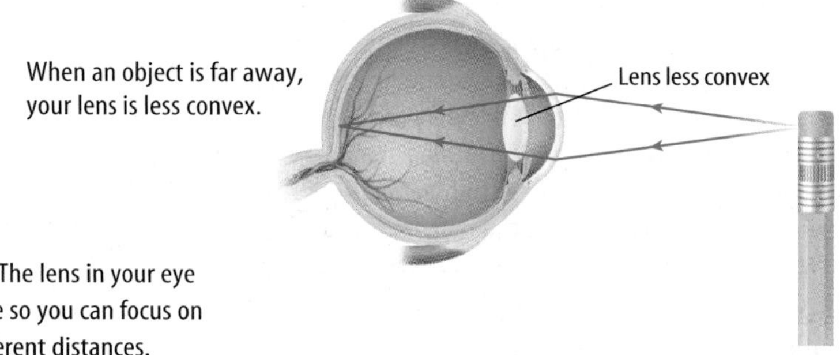
When an object is far away, your lens is less convex.
Lens less convex

Figure 13 The lens in your eye changes shape so you can focus on objects at different distances.

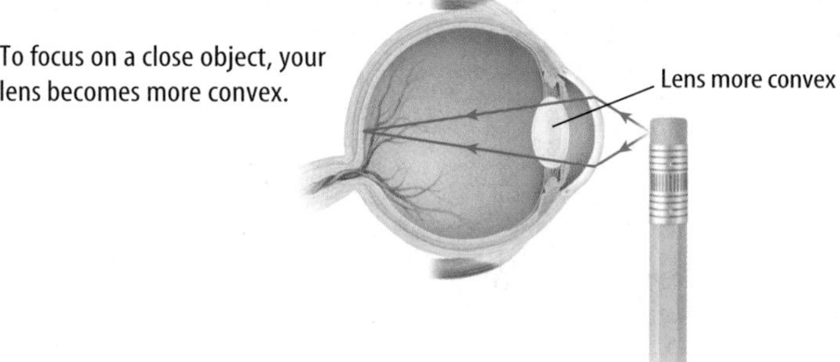
To focus on a close object, your lens becomes more convex.
Lens more convex

Cultural Diversity

Arabian Lights One of the greatest early physicists was an Arabian scientist named Abu Ali al-Hasan ibn al-Haytham, better known in the West as Alhazen. His book, *The Optical Thesaurus*, written around A.D. 1000, was unsurpassed until the appearance of Johannes Kepler's work 600 years later. Among Alhazen's contributions was the theory that vision is based on light coming from a source and being reflected from an object.

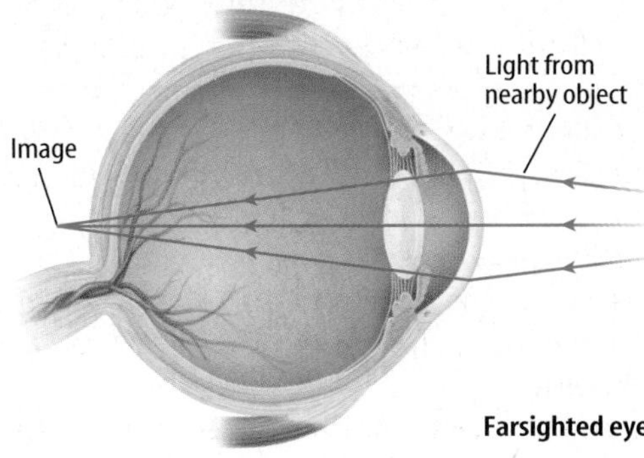

In a farsighted eye, light rays from nearby objects do not converge enough to form a sharp image on the retina.

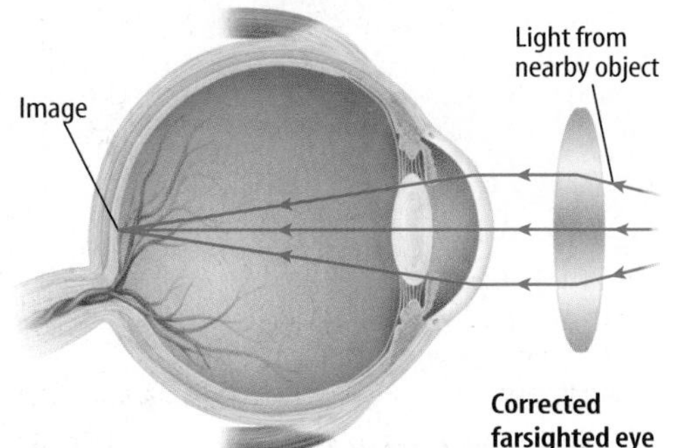

A convex lens makes light rays spread out less so that a sharp image can be formed on the retina.

Figure 14 Farsightedness can be corrected by a convex lens.

Vision Problems

People that have good vision can see objects clearly that are about 25 cm or farther away from their eyes. However, people with the most common vision problems see objects clearly only at some distances, or see all objects as being blurry.

Farsightedness A person who is farsighted can see distant objects clearly, but can't bring nearby objects into focus. Light rays from nearby objects do not converge enough after passing through the cornea and the lens to form a sharp image on the retina, as shown in **Figure 14.** The problem can be corrected by using a convex lens that bends light rays so they are less spread out before they enter the eye, as in **Figure 14.**

As many people age, their eyes develop a condition that makes them unable to focus on close objects. The lenses in their eyes become less flexible. The muscles around the lenses still contract as they try to change the shape of the lens. However, the lenses have become more rigid, and cannot be made curved enough to form an image on the retina. People who are more than 40 years old might not be able to focus on objects closer than 1 m from their eyes. Some vision problems are caused by diseases of the retina. **Figure 15** shows how using new technology allows people with diseased retinas to recover some vision.

Astigmatism Another vision problem, called astigmatism occurs when the surface of the cornea is curved unevenly. When people have astigmatism, their corneas are more oval than round in shape. Astigmatism causes blurry vision at all distances. Corrective lenses also have an uneven curvature, canceling out the effect of an uneven cornea.

INTEGRATE History

Eyeglasses and the Printing Press
Eyeglasses were first developed in Italy in the thirteenth century and were used mainly by nobles and the clergy. However, in 1456 the printing press was invented in Germany by Johannes Gutenberg. As books became more available, the demand for eyeglasses increased. In turn, the increasing availability of eyeglasses enabled more people to read. This helped increase the demand for books. Research the development of eyeglasses.

Fun Fact

Eyeglasses were used as early as the thirteenth century, and some crystals were used even earlier as natural magnifying glasses by the Greeks and Arabs.

The Invention of Spectacles The first eyeglasses seem to have been developed over 700 years ago in Italy. By the early fourteenth century, the Venetian Glassmakers Guild had imposed regulations forbidding the use of glass instead of quartz crystal to make spectacles. For hundreds of years eyeglasses were extremely expensive, but their use slowly became more widespread. By the middle of the twentieth century, plastic lenses had been developed, replacing the thick, heavy glass lenses that had been in use for centuries.

Using Science Words

Word Meaning Have students break the word *astigmatism* into its parts, then find out what each part means and what it contributes to the meaning of the whole word. *A-*, without; *stigma*, point; *-ism*, state, condition. Astigmatism is the condition of not having a point or a focus. L3 LS **Linguistic**

Identifying Misconceptions

Students might think because all eyeglass lenses round out in the front, that all of these lenses are convex. Show them two pairs of glasses with each type of lens. Help them to see that the convex are wider in the middle and the concave are thinner in the middle.

Curriculum Connection

Language Arts The manufacture of convex and concave lenses for eyeglasses and optical instruments requires high-precision measurements and the use of high-quality glass. Have students write a paper about this process. Students might mention cutting the glass, shaping the convex or concave surface, polishing, and grinding edges so the physical and optical centers match L2 P LS **Linguistic**

NATIONAL GEOGRAPHIC

Visualizing the Silicon Retina

Have students examine the pictures and read the captions. Then ask the following questions.

How do retinitis pigmentosa and macular degeneration affect vision differently? Retinitis pigmentosa causes a lack of peripheral vision, and macular degeneration initially affects central vision.

How might an artificial retina change a person's life? Possible answer: A person with improved vision could be more independent, could drive, and could work at jobs and enjoy hobbies and entertainment that rely on vision, such as reading, watching movies, or sewing.

Activity

Vision Technology Have small groups of students research other vision problems that can be helped by implants or other technologies. Have each group prepare a poster illustrating how the technology works. L2 LS **Visual-Spatial**

Virtual Labs

Vison *How are lenses used to correct vision?*

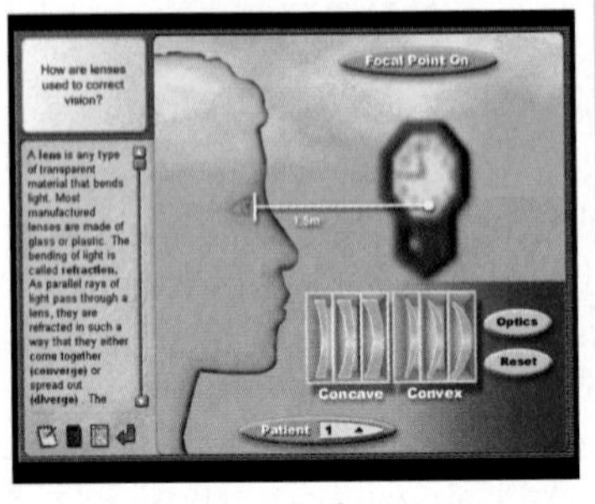

NATIONAL GEOGRAPHIC **VISUALIZING THE SILICON RETINA**

Figure 15

Millions of people worldwide suffer from vision problems associated with diseases of the retina. Until recently, such people had little hope of improving their eyesight. Now, however, scientists are developing specialized silicon chips that convert light into electrical pulses, mimicking the function of the retina. When implanted in the eye, these artificial silicon retinas may restore sight.

Viewed with normal vision

Viewed with retinitis pigmentosa

Viewed with macular degeneration

▲ These three photos show how normal vision can deteriorate as a result of diseases that attack the retina. Retinitis pigmentosa (ret uh NYE tis pig men TOE suh) causes a lack of peripheral vision. Macular degeneration can lead to total blindness.

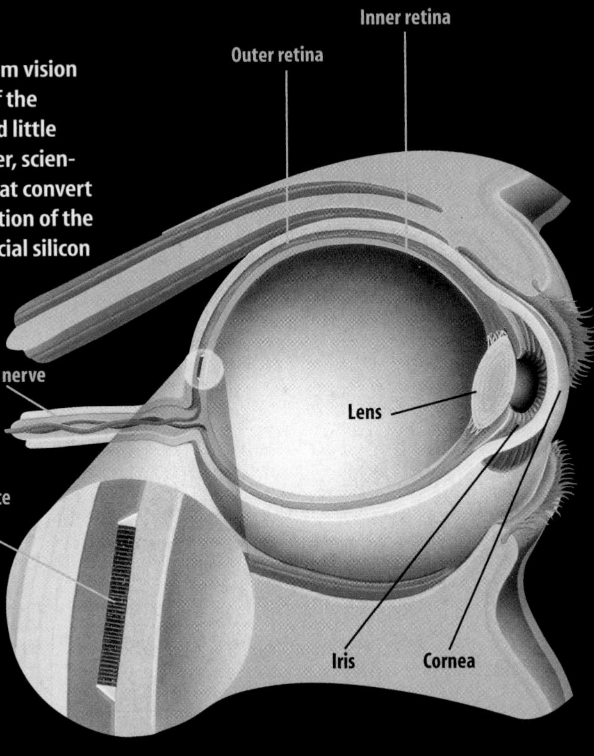

Inner retina

Outer retina

Optic nerve

Lens

Implant in the subretinal space

Iris

Cornea

▲ After making a number of incisions, surgeons implant the artificial silicon retina between the outer and inner retinal layers. Then they reseal the retina over the silicon chip.

▲ The artificial silicon retina, is thinner than a human hair and only 2 mm in diameter—the same diameter as the white dot on this penny.

430 CHAPTER 14 Mirrors and Lenses

Differentiated Instruction

Challenge Have students research how the silicon retina described in this feature differs from similar devices being developed in Germany and by Harvard Medical School and MIT. Ask students to present brief oral reports on what they learn. L3 LS **Linguistic**

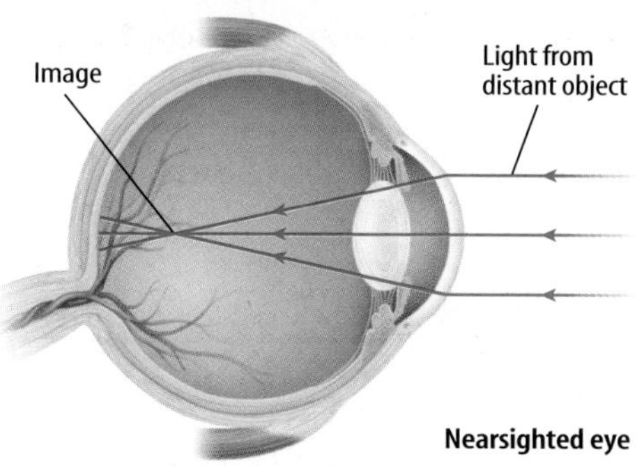

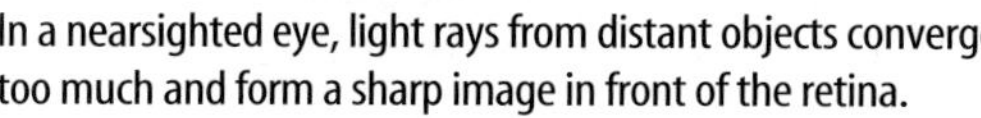

In a nearsighted eye, light rays from distant objects converge too much and form a sharp image in front of the retina.

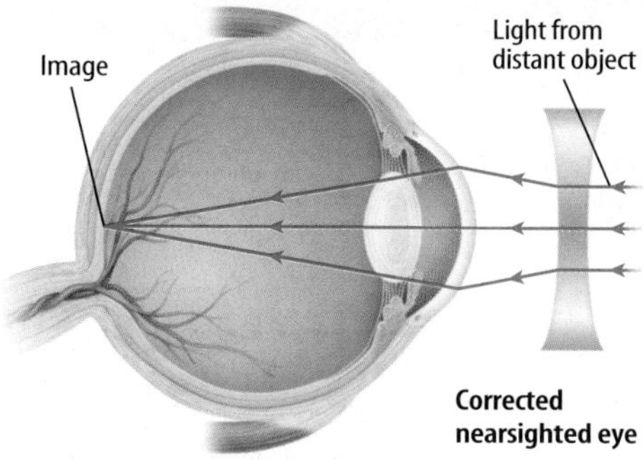

A concave lens makes the light rays more spread out, enabling a sharp image to be formed on the retina.

Figure 16 Nearsightedness can be corrected with a concave lens.

Nearsightedness A person who is nearsighted can see objects clearly only when they are nearby. Objects that are far away appear blurred. In a nearsighted eye, the cornea and the lens form a sharp image of a distant object in front of the retina, as shown in **Figure 16.** To correct this problem, a nearsighted person can wear concave lenses. **Figure 16** shows how a concave lens causes incoming light rays to diverge before they enter the eye. Then the light rays from distant objects can be focused by the eye to form a sharp image on the retina.

section 2 review

Summary

Convex Lenses

- A convex lens is thicker in the middle than at the edges. Light rays are refracted toward the optical axis.
- The image formed by a convex lens depends on the distance of the object from the lens.

Concave Lenses

- A concave lens is thinner in the middle and thicker at the edges. Light rays are refracted away from the optical axis.

The Eye and Vision Problems

- The eye contains a lens that changes shape to produce sharp images on the retina of objects that are at different distances.
- In a farsighted eye, the eye cannot form a sharp image of nearby objects on the retina. In a nearsighted eye, the eye cannot form a sharp image of distant objects on the retina.

Self Check

1. **Explain** how the focal length of a convex lens changes as the sides of the lens become less curved.
2. **Compare** the image of an object less than one focal length from a convex lens with the image of an object more than two focal lengths from the lens.
3. **Describe** the image formed by a concave lens.
4. **Explain** how the focal length of the lens in the eye changes to focus on a nearby object.
5. **Think Critically** If image formation by a convex lens is similar to image formation by a concave mirror, describe the image formed by a light source placed at the focal point of a convex lens.

Applying Math

6. **Calculate Object Distance** If you looked through a convex lens with a focal length of 15 cm and saw a real, inverted, enlarged image, what is the maximum distance between the lens and the object?

3 Assess

DAILY INTERVENTION

Check for Understanding

Visual-Spatial Have students draw a ray diagram of three rays: one near the top of a lens, one in the middle, and one near the bottom. Use several different combinations of concave and convex lenses.

Reteach

Eyeglass Exploration Compare eyeglasses that correct nearsightedness and farsightedness. Have students examine near and far objects through each type of lens and explain how each lens corrects vision problems. L2 ELL
LS **Visual-Spatial**

Assessment

Process Ask students to explain why the image you see with a magnifying glass is blurry if you hold the glass too far from the object. The object is more than one focal length from the lens, so that the image formed is real. To see the image clearly, the eye must be at the image's location. Use **Performance Assessment in the Science Classroom,** p. 89.

section 2 review

1. The focal length increases as the sides of the lens become less curved.
2. The image less than one focal length is enlarged, upright, and virtual. The image more than two focal lengths from the lens is reduced, inverted, and real.
3. The image formed by a concave lens is always reduced, upright, and virtual.
4. As the eye focuses on a nearby object, the lens in the eye becomes more curved, and its focal length decreases.
5. Light rays from the light source will be refracted by the lens so they travel parallel to the optical axis. A beam of light will be formed.
6. A real, inverted, enlarged image is formed if the object is between one and two focal lengths from the lens. So the maximum distance from the lens would be two focal lengths or 30 cm.

1 Motivate

Bellringer

Section Focus Transparencies also are available on the Interactive Chalkboard CD-ROM.

L2 ELL

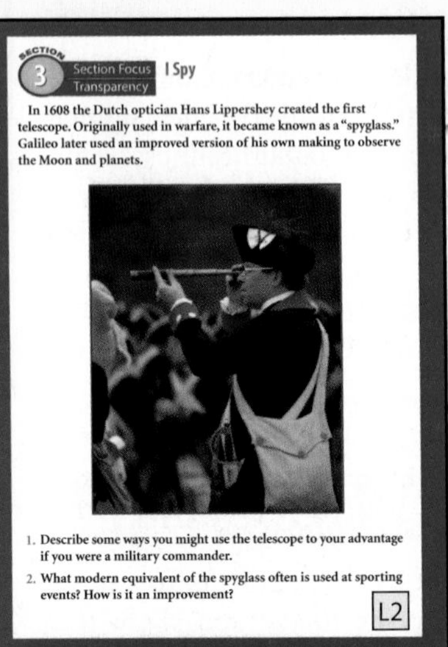
Section Focus Transparency — I Spy

In 1608 the Dutch optician Hans Lippershey created the first telescope. Originally used in warfare, it became known as a "spyglass." Galileo later used an improved version of his own making to observe the Moon and planets.

1. Describe some ways you might use the telescope to your advantage if you were a military commander.
2. What modern equivalent of the spyglass often is used at sporting events? How is it an improvement?

L2

Tie to Prior Knowledge

Blurry Pictures Ask students whether they have ever taken a blurry picture with a camera. Have them suggest why this might have happened. The camera or object might have moved, or the image might not have been focused on the film.

section 3

Optical Instruments

Reading Guide

What You'll Learn

- **Compare** refracting and reflecting telescopes.
- **Explain** why a telescope in space is useful.
- **Describe** how a microscope uses lenses to magnify small objects.
- **Explain** how a camera creates an image.

Why It's Important

Optical instruments, such as microscopes and telescopes, enable your eyes to see objects that otherwise would be too small or far away to see.

Review Vocabulary

refraction: the change in direction of a wave when it changes speed as it moves from one medium to another

New Vocabulary

- refracting telescope
- reflecting telescope
- microscope

Telescopes

You know from your experience that it's hard to see faraway objects clearly. When you look at an object, only some of the light reflected from its surface enters your eye. As the object moves farther away, the amount of light entering your eye decreases, as shown in **Figure 17.** As a result, the object appears dimmer and less detailed.

A telescope uses a lens or a concave mirror that is much larger than your eye to gather more of the light from distant objects. The largest telescopes can gather more than a million times more light than the human eye. As a result, objects such as distant galaxies appear much brighter. Because the image formed by a telescope is so much brighter, more detail can be seen when the image is magnified.

Figure 17 As the cup gets farther away, fewer light rays from any point on the cup enter the viewer's eye. The amount of light from an object that enters the eye decreases as the object gets farther away.

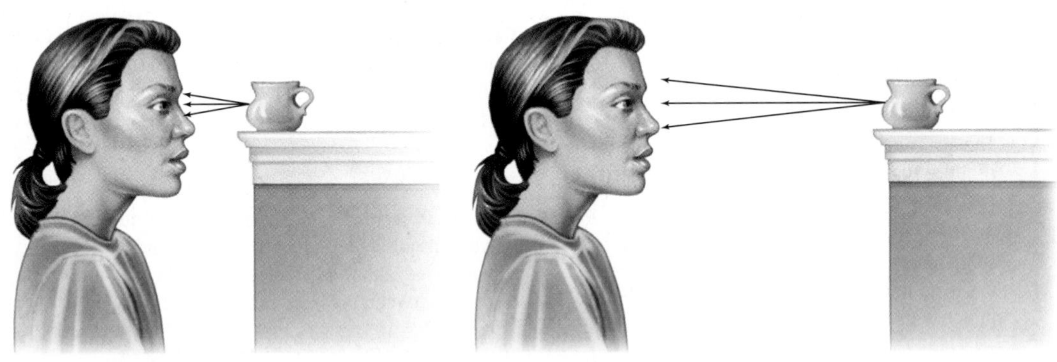

Section 3 Resource Manager

Chapter *FAST FILE* Resources
- Transparency Activity, p. 46
- Directed Reading for Content Mastery, pp. 21, 22
- MiniLAB, p. 4
- Enrichment, p. 32
- Reinforcement, p. 29
- Lab Worksheet, pp. 7–8

Cultural Diversity, p. 51

Physical Science Critical Thinking/Problem Solving, p. 4

Home and Community Involvement, p. 39

Refracting Telescopes One common type of telescope is the refracting telescope. A simple **refracting telescope,** shown in **Figure 18,** uses two convex lenses to gather and focus light from distant objects. Incoming light from distant objects passes through the first lens, called the objective lens. Because they are so far away, light rays from distant objects are nearly parallel to the optical axis of the lens. As a result, the objective lens forms a real image at the focal point of the lens, within the body of the telescope. The second convex lens, called the eyepiece lens, acts like a magnifying glass and magnifies this real image. When you look through the eyepiece lens, you see an enlarged, inverted, virtual image of the real image formed by the objective lens.

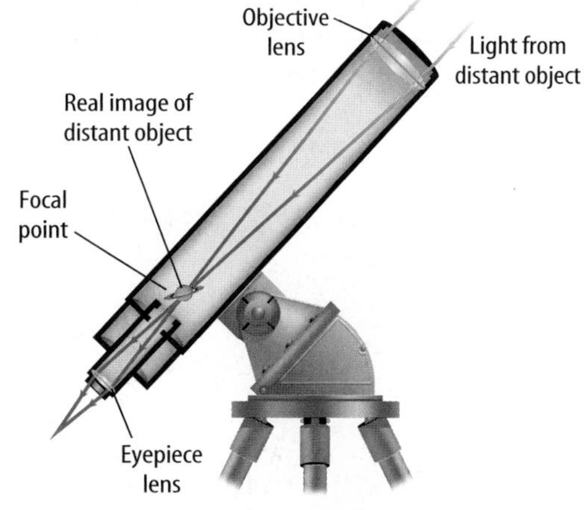

Figure 18 Light from a distant object passes through an objective lens and an eyepiece lens in a refracting telescope. The two lenses produce a large virtual image.

Reading Check *What type of image is formed by the objective lens in a refracting telescope?*

Several problems are associated with refracting telescopes. In order to form a detailed image of distant objects, such as planets and galaxies, the objective lens must be as large as possible. A large lens is heavy and can be supported in the telescope tube only around its edge. The lens can sag or flex due to its own weight, distorting the image it forms. Also, these heavy glass lenses are costly and difficult to make.

Reflecting Telescopes Due to the problems with making large lenses, most large telescopes today are reflecting telescopes. A **reflecting telescope** uses a concave mirror, a plane mirror, and a convex lens to collect and focus light from distant objects. **Figure 19** shows a reflecting telescope. Light from a distant object enters one end of the telescope and strikes a concave mirror at the opposite end. The light reflects off of this mirror and converges. Before it converges at a focal point, the light hits a plane mirror that is placed at an angle within the telescope tube. The light is reflected from the plane mirror toward the telescope's eyepiece. The light rays converge at the focal point, creating a real image of the distant object. Just as in a refracting telescope, a convex lens in the eyepiece then magnifies this image.

Figure 19 Reflecting telescopes use two mirrors to create a real image, which then is magnified by a convex lens.
Infer *whether the image produced by the eyepiece lens is real or virtual.*

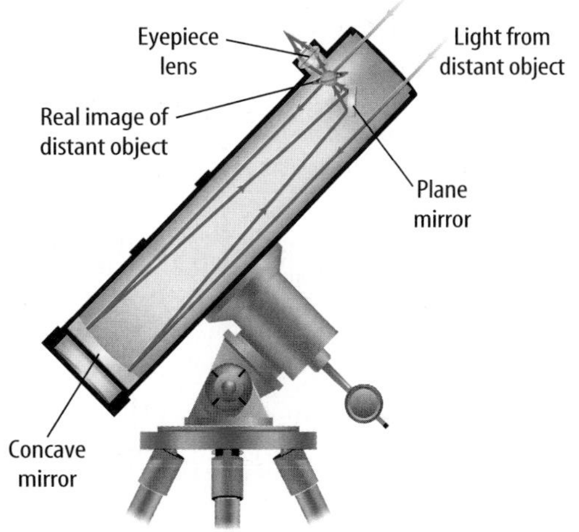

2 Teach

Teacher FYI

Telescope Inventors The identity of the inventor of the first true telescope is uncertain, but credit is often given to Hans Lippershey of Holland. Galileo heard of Lippershey's "looker" and made an improved version that he used to observe the heavens. Among Galileo's discoveries were sunspots, some moons of Jupiter, and the phases of Venus.

Reading Check

Answer real, reduced, upsidedown

Quick Demo

Telescopes

Materials refracting telescope, reflecting telescope

Estimated Time 30 minutes

Procedure Allow students to look through both a refracting telescope and a reflecting telescope at a faraway object. L2 IN **Visual-Spatial**

Fun Fact

A reflecting telescope is often called a Newtonian telescope after its inventor, Isaac Newton.

Differentiated Instruction

English-Language Learners At the beginning of this section have students who speak a different language translate the words telescope, microscope, and camera by picture or description into their native language. Have the students practice at home using these words in English.

Science Journal

Mystery Element The reflective coating on many mirrors used in telescopes used to be made of a valuable metallic element. This same element is found in the light-sensitive compounds used in photographic film. Have students write the name of the element, its chemical symbol, and its atomic number in their Science Journals. silver, Ag, atomic number 47 L3 IN **Logical-Mathematical**

Discussion

Telescope Locations What are some environmental factors that need to be considered when deciding where to build a new Earth-based telescope? Possible answers: weather, climate, atmospheric pollution, proximity to city lights, ground vibrations, geologic stability

L3 LS **Logical-Mathematical**

Make a Model

***Hubble* Model** Draw a line 2.4 m long to show the diameter of *Hubble's* primary mirror. The large size allows the telescope to capture much light so that faint, distant stars can be observed. Some of these stars cannot be seen from Earth. L1

LS **Visual-Spatial**

Quick Demo

Hubble Space Telescope

Materials area for a large drawing on the board

Estimated Time 10 minutes

Procedure Reinforce the idea that the *Hubble Space Telescope* needs to be above Earth's atmosphere by drawing on the board a circle to represent Earth and a shaded circle around it to represent the atmosphere. L2 ELL

LS **Visual-Spatial**

Fun Fact

The *Hubble Space Telescope* is 600 km above Earth and orbits it every 95 minutes.

Discussion

***Hubble* Knowledge** What kinds of knowledge might scientists gain from the *Hubble Space Telescope?* how the universe began and how old it is; how stars form; the dynamics of pulsars, quasars, and black holes; information about planets outside our solar system L2 LS **Logical-Mathematical**

Reading Check

Answer It is above Earth's atmosphere.

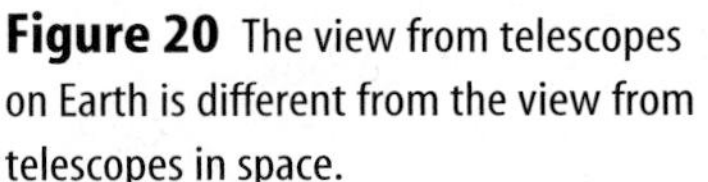
Figure 20 The view from telescopes on Earth is different from the view from telescopes in space.

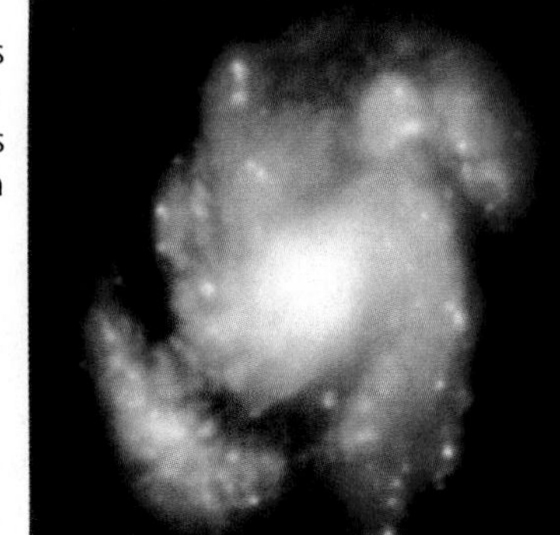
The distorting effects of Earth's atmosphere can cause telescopes on Earth to form blurry images.

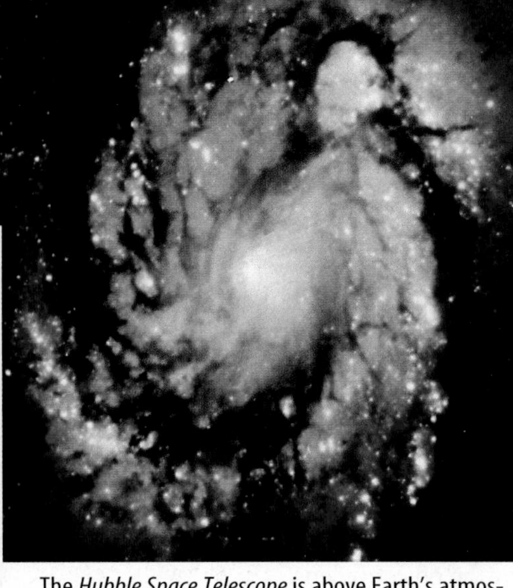
The *Hubble Space Telescope* is above Earth's atmosphere and forms clearer images of objects in space.

Telescopes In Space Imagine being at the bottom of a swimming pool and trying to read a sign by the pool's edge. The water in the pool would distort your view of any object beyond the water's surface. In a similar way, Earth's atmosphere blurs the view of objects in space. To overcome the blurriness of humans' view into space, the National Aeronautics and Space Administration (NASA) built a telescope called the *Hubble Space Telescope* to be placed into space high above Earth's atmosphere. On April 25, 1990, NASA used the space shuttle Discovery to launch this telescope into an orbit about 600 km above Earth. The *Hubble Space Telescope* has produced images much sharper and more detailed than the largest telescopes on Earth can. **Figure 20** shows the difference in the images produced by telescopes on Earth and the *Hubble* telescope. With the *Hubble Space Telescope,* scientists can detect visible light—as well as other types of radiation—that is affected by Earth's atmosphere from the planets, stars, and distant galaxies.

Science Online

Topic: *Hubble Space Telescope*

Visit gpscience.com for Web links to information and data about the *Hubble Space Telescope.*

Activity Prepare a speech to defend your opinion on whether or not the *Hubble Space Telescope* is useful and important. Hold a class debate.

Reading Check *Why is the* **Hubble Space Telescope** *able to produce clearer images than telescopes on Earth?*

The *Hubble* telescope is a type of reflecting telescope that uses two mirrors to collect and focus light to form an image. The primary mirror in the telescope is 2.4 m across. When the *Hubble* was first launched, a defect in this primary mirror caused the telescope to create blurry images. The telescope was repaired by astronauts in December 1993.

Science Journal

Binoculars Most binoculars are like two side-by-side refracting telescopes except that each side also contains two prisms. Have students find out what the prisms do, and in their Science Journals draw diagrams of the light path in binoculars. The prisms reflect the light, allowing the two objective lenses to be farther apart. This gives the viewer more depth perception.

L3 LS **Linguistic** P

Microscopes

A telescope would be useless if you were trying to study the cells in a butterfly wing, a sample of pond scum, or the differences between a human hair and a horse hair. You would need a microscope to look at such small objects. A **microscope** uses two convex lenses with relatively short focal lengths to magnify small, close objects. A microscope, like a telescope, has an objective lens and an eyepiece lens. However, it is designed differently because the objects viewed are close to the lens.

Figure 21 shows a simple microscope. The object to be viewed is placed on a transparent slide and illuminated from below. The light passes by or through the object on the slide and then travels through the objective lens. The objective lens is a convex lens. It forms a real, enlarged image of the object, because the distance from the object to the lens is between one and two focal lengths. The real image is then magnified again by the eyepiece lens (another convex lens) to create a virtual, enlarged image. This final image can be hundreds of times larger than the actual object, depending on the focal lengths of the two lenses.

Figure 21 A microscope uses two convex lenses to magnify small objects. **Explain** *where the object must be placed in relation to the objective lens's focal point.*

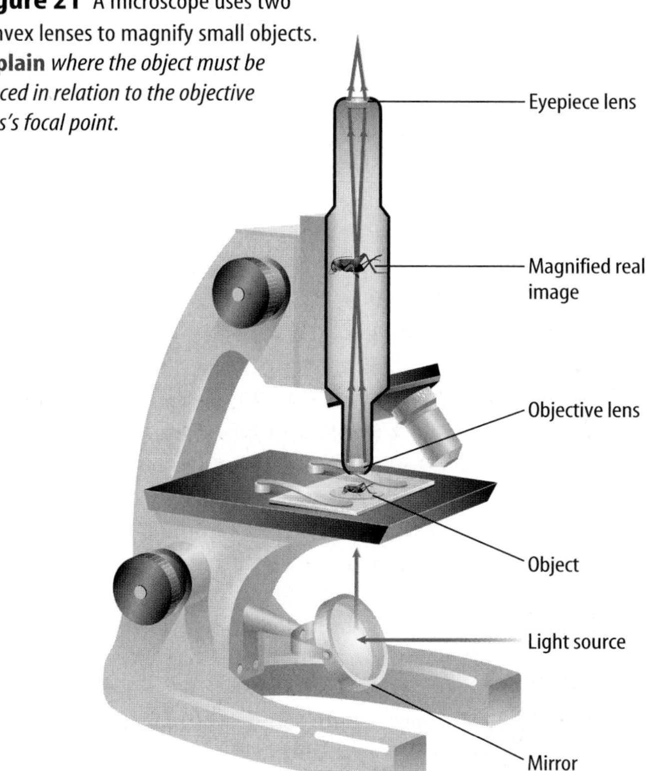

Mini LAB

Experimenting with Focal Lengths

Procedure

1. Fill a glass **test tube** with **water** and seal it with a **lid or stopper.**
2. Type or print the compound name *SULFUR DIOXIDE* in capital letters on a piece of **paper or a note card.**
3. Set the test tube horizontally over the words and observe them. What do you notice?
4. Hold the tube 1 cm over the words and observe them again. Record your observations. Repeat, holding the tube at several other heights above the words.

Analysis

1. What were your observations of the words at the different distances? How do you explain your observations?
2. Is the image you see at each height real or virtual?

Mini LAB

Purpose Students observe what happens when the distance from a lens to an object is changed. L1 ELL IS **Visual-Spatial**

Materials glass test tube with lid or stopper, water, paper

Teaching Strategy The words should be printed or typed in capital letters smaller than the test tubes. They can also be in two different colors.

Analysis

1. When the tube is on the paper, the words are slightly magnified. When the tube is about 1 cm above the words, SULFUR is upside down but DIOXIDE is unchanged because the letters are symmetrical. The whole image is inverted because the object is beyond the focal length of the lens.
2. The upright, magnified image is virtual. The inverted images are real.

Assessment

Content Ask students to explain whether a magnifying lens (a convex lens) could produce inverted images of the words. yes, if the glass were far enough from the words

Caption Answer

Figure 21 between one and two focal lengths away

Differentiated Instruction

Challenge Ask students to describe what you would have to do to change a microscope into a refracting telescope. You would have to make the objective lens bigger so it could gather more light. Having done that, you would have to lengthen the distance between the objective and the eyepiece to accommodate the longer focal distance of the larger objective lens. L2 IS **Logical-Mathematical**

Visual Learning

Figure 21 Point out that although the eyepiece performs as a single convex lens, it is typically a system of multiple lenses. Similarly, the objective is actually a combination of lenses that performs as a single convex lens. Although a single lens for each is possible, the combination of lenses provides clearer images.

Activity

Photographic Effects Have students find a book on photography and identify the variables in a camera that can be controlled to gain the desired effects in a photograph. Variables include aperture, shutter speed, lenses, film speed, and flashes. L3 LS **Linguistic**

Activity

Model Aperature A camera is easier to focus if it has a small aperture. To demonstrate this, have each student use a pencil to punch a small hole in an index card and look through the hole at a distant object. You can see better through a small opening, especially if you are nearsighted. L2 LS **Visual-Spatial**

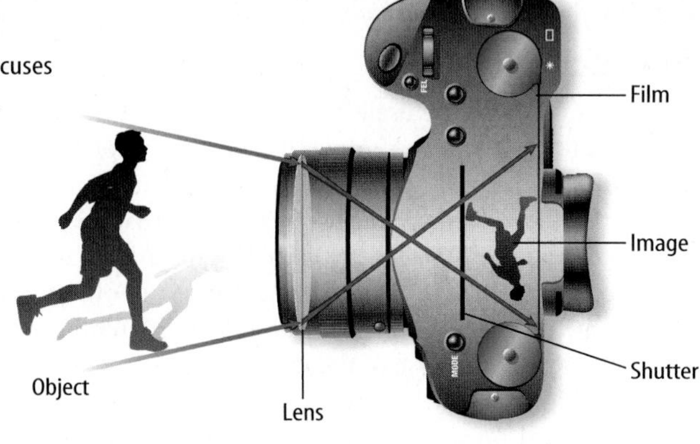

Figure 22 A camera's lens focuses an image on photographic film.

Cameras

Imagine swirls of lavender, gold, and magenta clouds sweeping across the sky at sunset. With the click of a button, you can capture the beautiful scene in a photo. How does a camera make a reduced image of a life-sized scene on film? A camera works by gathering and bending light with a lens. This lens then projects an image onto light-sensitive film to record a scene.

When you take a picture with a camera, a shutter opens to allow light to enter the camera for a specific length of time. The light reflected off your subject enters the camera through an opening called the aperture. It passes through the camera lens, which focuses the image on the film, as in **Figure 22.** The image is real, inverted, and smaller than the actual object. The size of the image depends upon the focal length of the lens and how close the lens is to the film.

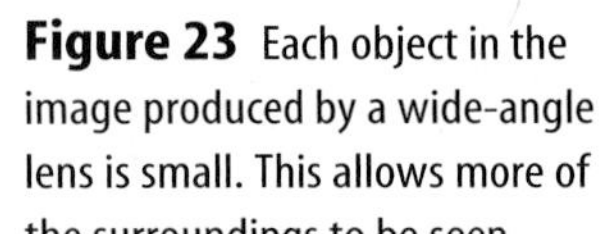

Figure 23 Each object in the image produced by a wide-angle lens is small. This allows more of the surroundings to be seen.

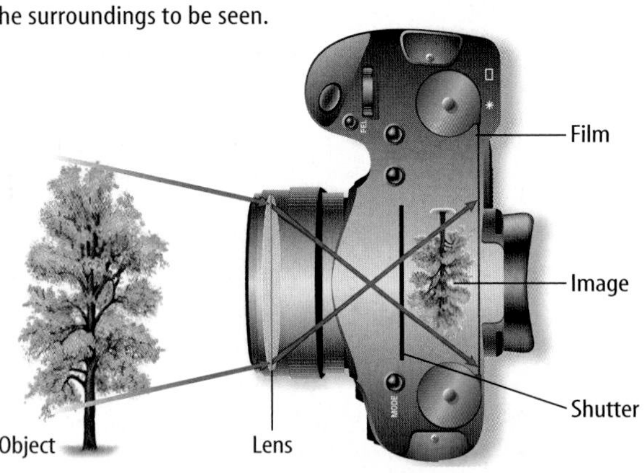

Wide-Angle Lenses Suppose you and a friend use two different cameras to photograph the same object at the same distance. If the cameras have different lenses, your pictures might look different. For example, some lenses have short focal lengths that produce a relatively small image of the object but have a wide field of view. These lenses are called wide-angle lenses, and they must be placed close to the film to form a sharp image with their short focal length. **Figure 23** shows how a wide-angle lens works. The photo in **Figure 23** was taken with a wide-angle lens.

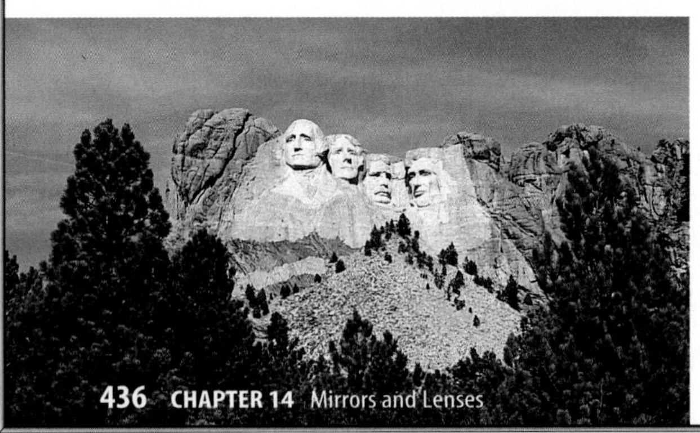

Curriculum Connection

Art Photographers have long used photography to produce art. Have students find out about early art photographers, their cameras, and some of the techniques they used to produce their photographs. Have them give multimedia presentations of their findings. Photographers include Edward Weston and Ansel Adams, who used large-format view cameras to produce black and white photographs. L3 LS **Linguistic**

Figure 24 A telephoto lens creates a larger image of an object than a wide-angle lens does.

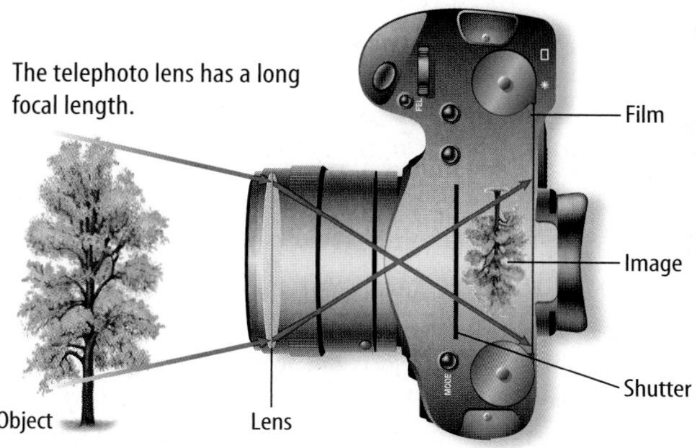

Less of the surroundings can be seen, though a close-up of one of the objects can be photographed.

Telephoto Lenses Telephoto lenses have longer focal lengths. **Figure 24** shows how a telephoto lens forms an image. The image through a telephoto lens seems enlarged and closer than it actually is. Telephoto lenses are easy to recognize because they usually protrude from the camera to increase the distance between the lens and the film.

section 3 review

Summary

Telescopes

- Refracting telescopes use two convex lenses to gather and focus light.
- Reflecting telescopes use a concave mirror, a plane mirror, and a convex lens to collect, reflect, and focus light.
- Placing a telescope in orbit avoids the distorting effects of Earth's atmosphere.

Microscopes

- A microscope uses two convex lenses with short focal lengths to magnify small, close objects.

Cameras

- A wide-angle lens has a short focal length that produces a wide field of view.
- Telephoto lenses have longer focal lengths and are located farther from the film than wide-angle lenses are.

Self Check

1. **Describe** the image formed by the objective lens in a microscope.
2. **Infer** how the amount of light that enters the eye from an object changes as the object moves closer.
3. **Identify** the advantage to making the objective lens larger in a refracting telescope.
4. **Explain** why the largest telescopes are reflecting telescopes instead of refracting telescopes.
5. **Think Critically** Which optical instrument—a telescope, a microscope, or a camera—forms images in a way most like your eye? Explain.

Applying Math

6. **Calculate Magnification** Suppose the objective lens in a microscope forms an image that is 100 times the size of an object. The eyepiece lens magnifies this image ten times. What is the total magnification?

Science Online gpscience.com/self_check_quiz

3 Assess

DAILY INTERVENTION

Check for Unerstanding

Interpersonal Students should look through a microscope and then discuss with a partner how the adjustments they made to the microscope affected the lenses inside and, in turn, what they saw.

Reteach

Camera Lenses Point to a distant object that can be seen apart from its surroundings. Ask students to imagine taking two photos of the object, one with a wide-angle lens and one with a telephoto lens. Have them sketch what they might see with each lens. Which lens has a longer focal length? telephoto L2 IS **Visual-Spatial**

Assessment

Process Show students sketches of the light paths of some optical instruments mentioned in this section. Have them identify the sketch as a refracting telescope, a reflecting telescope, or a microscope. For each, the student should describe the types of images formed. Use **Performance Assessment in the Science Classroom,** p. 89.

section 3 review

1. real, enlarged, inverted.
2. More light rays from each point on the object enter the eye as the object moves closer.
3. More light enters the lens, so that the images formed are brighter and more detailed.
4. It is easier to make very large concave mirrors than convex lenses, because mirrors need be polished only on one surface, and can be supported from the back so they don't bend under their own weight.
5. A camera; both adjust to focus on near and far objects, control the amount of light that enters, form real inverted images, and focus an image on a light-sensitive surface.
6. 1,000 ×

Real-World Question

Purpose Students build a model of a telescope, estimate the telescope's magnification, and compare the images formed with different types of lenses. L3 ELL IS **Kinesthetic**

Process Skills observe, use numbers, measure, compare and contrast, recognize cause and effect, formulate models

Time Required 45 minutes

Procedure

Alternate Materials Some gift-wrapping paper tubes will slide smoothly inside the tube from a roll of paper towels. Duct tape is flexible, but may be hard for students to handle, but small pieces could be cut. Cellophane tape is easier to handle, but may be harder to use to hold the lenses.

Safety Precautions Remind students not to look directly at the Sun with any telescope.

Teaching Strategies

- Have extra quantities of the smaller tube on hand for students who miscut their tubes.
- It may be easier to align the objective and eyepiece lenses if the lenses are slightly larger than the tubes, so they can be taped in place from the outside.
- Students should try to keep their fingerprints off the lenses as much as possible to get the sharpest image.

Model & Invent

Make a *Refracting* Telescope

Goals

- **Build** a simple telescope.
- **Estimate** the magnification of the telescope.
- **Compare** convex and concave eyepieces.

Possible Materials

objective lens—convex, 25 cm to 30 cm focal length, about 4 cm diameter
eyepiece lenses—one each convex and concave, 2 cm to 3 cm focal length, about 2.5 cm to 3 cm diameter
cardboard tubes—one with inside diameter of about 4 cm; one with inside diameter of about 3 cm. (The smaller tube should slide inside the larger one with a snug fit.)
clay to hold the lenses in place
**cellophane tape or duct tape*
scissors
**Alternate materials*

Safety Precautions

WARNING: *Do not look directly at the Sun through a telescope. Permanent eye damage can result.*

Real-World Question

Galileo used the telescope to enhance his eyesight. It enabled him to see planets and stars beyond the range of his eyes alone. By combining two lenses, distant objects can be magnified. A simple refracting telescope uses a small convex eyepiece lens and a larger convex objective lens at the other end. How do the lenses in a simple telescope form an image?

Procedure

1. Check that the smaller-diameter tube can slide in and out of the larger-diameter tube.
2. Hold the small concave eyepiece lens near your eye. Hold the objective lens in front of the eyepiece lens and move the objective lens away from you until a distant object is in focus. Estimate the distance between the two lenses.
3. Subtract half the length of the larger-diameter tube from the distance you estimated in step 2 to get the length needed for the smaller tube.
4. Cut the smaller-diameter tube to the length determined in step 3. Make two pieces this length.

Alternative Inquiry Lab

Have students explore ways to magnify images with lenses. Telescopes often use several lenses. With experimentation, students can increase magnification using more lenses. Check students' light diagrams for their plans before they carry them out.

5. Attach the objective lens with clay or tape to the end of the larger tube. Make sure that the lens is perpendicular to the sides of the tube.
6. Attach the convex eyepiece lens with clay or tape to the end of one of the smaller tubes. Make sure the lens is perpendicular to the sides of the tube.
7. Slide the smaller tube into the larger one and look through the eyepiece.
8. Move the smaller tube in and out of the larger tube until a distant object is focused clearly.

Analyze Your Data

1. Estimate how much larger the image seen through the eyepiece is than the image you see with your unaided eye. Describe the appearance of the image.
2. Attach the concave eyepiece to the second smaller tube that you cut.
3. Repeat your observations using the concave eyepiece. Describe the appearance of an object seen through the concave eyepiece.
4. How does the image produced using the convex and concave eyepiece lenses change when you look through the objective lens instead of the eyepiece lens?

Conclude and Apply

1. **Infer** the estimated magnification of your telescope.
2. **Discuss** how you could change the magnification of your telescope.
3. **Diagram** the path of light rays that pass through the telescope and then into your eye.
4. **Explain** how you could build a telescope with higher magnification than the one you constructed here.

Communicating Your Data

Compare your telescope and its operation with those of other members of your class. Try reading numbers or letters on a distant sign. Which telescope helps you see more detail?

Analyze Your Data

Expected Outcome The magnification of the telescope may be estimated by looking at an object alternately with the scope and with the unaided eye, and estimating the change in size of the object. The magnification can be accurately determined from the ratio of the focal lengths of the lenses.

Answers to Questions

1. The image size is about ten times larger than the object size and is inverted.
2. The image is upright.
3. The image is smaller
4. Concave eyepiece: image is smaller than object. Convex eyepiece: image size depends on the distance between the two lenses. As the distance between lenses decreases, the image becomes larger.

Conclude and Apply

1. The magnification should be about 10×.
2. The magnification depends on the focal lengths of the objective and eyepiece lenses, so the magnification can't be changed
3. See Figure 18.
4. Possible answers include: increase the focal length of the objective lens, decrease the focal length of the eyepiece lens

Assessment

Performance Have students draw two ray diagrams of their telescopes—one with a convex eyepiece and one with a concave eyepiece. Use **Performance Assessment in the Science Classroom,** p. 127.

Communicating Your Data

Have students use a spreadsheet program to put observations from class members' telescopes into a table.

TIME

Content Background

Surgery for cataracts was performed in India in 750 B.C. In 1906, a German surgeon successfully transplanted a human cornea but it was a last-resort procedure. Lasers developed in the 1960s and 70s enabled the removal of tumors and repair of torn retinas, but passed through the transparent cornea and worked by burning, which leaves scars. The ultraviolet "excimer laser" was developed in 1977 to cut transparent material. In 1981 it was found that the excimer leaves no scars in tissue and it was developed as a surgical tool. The first excimer technique was called PRK (photo refractive keratectomy). The procedure described in the article is called LASIK (laser in-situ keratomileusis) which reshapes the cornea but allows the epithelium to be replaced, reducing discomfort and shortening recovery time.

Discussion

Corneal Tissue How does removing tissue from the cornea reduce or eliminate the need for glasses? Possible answer: Reshaping the cornea in the proper way has the same light-bending effect as an artificial lens placed in front of the eye.

Investigate the Issue

Safety of Procedures There are still some concerns about the reliability of PRK and LASIK procedures. Students should research the statistics on these procedures to find the percentage of operations that are a complete success and the percentage of operations in which the patient is left worse than before. L2 LS **Linguistic**

TIME SCIENCE AND Society

SCIENCE ISSUES THAT AFFECT YOU!

Sight Lines

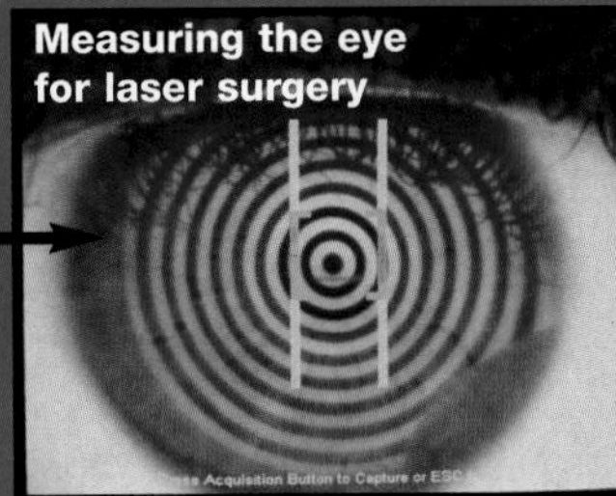
Measuring the eye for laser surgery

Lasers make it possible to throw away eyeglasses

Back in the 1970s, scientists developed a special kind of laser to make microscopic notches in computer chips. This laser is also perfect for eye surgery. It does not generate much heat, so it doesn't damage the delicate tissues of the eye. With this technology, most of the 160 million Americans who wear eyeglasses or contact lenses can kiss them goodbye forever.

The most common type of laser surgery used to correct poor vision is LASIK. This painless procedure takes only about five minutes per eye. The patient is awake the entire time and usually sees well immediately after the surgery.

The Cornea and Vision

The eyeball has two structures, the cornea and a flexible lens, that cause light to be focused on the retina. The cornea is a transparent structure at the front of the eye. Most of the bending of light rays occurs when they pass through the cornea. The lens fine-tunes the focus of light from objects by adjusting its shape so that a sharp image is formed on the retina. Unlike the lens, the shape of the cornea doesn't change.

How It Works:

The LASIK procedure fixes vision problems by reshaping the cornea. For farsighted eyes, the laser vaporizes a ring of tissue from the cornea. This makes the cornea more curved so that light rays are bent more. For nearsighted eyes, the laser vaporizes tissue from the center of the cornea, making it flatter.

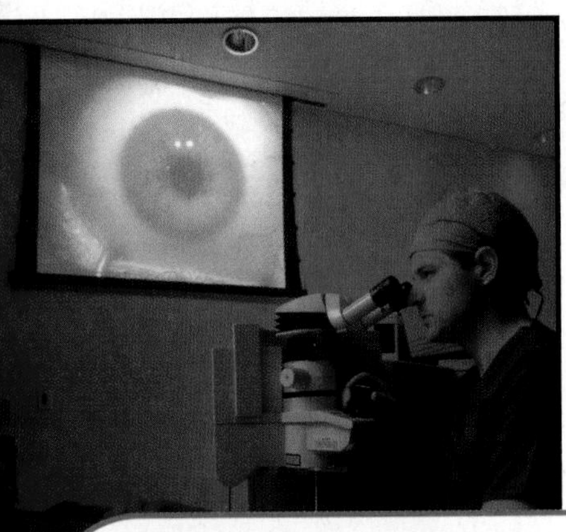

A microscope mounted on the laser gives the doctor a detailed view during the surgery. The screen allows others to view the surgery.

Interview **Ophthalmologists are medical doctors who specialize in healing eyes. Optometrists are doctors who specialize in correcting poor vision by prescribing glasses and contact lenses. Interview an optometrist or ophthalmologist to find out how he or she detects eye problems and how these problems can be corrected.**

For more information, visit gpscience.com/time

Interview Arrange to have an ophthalmologist or optometrist address the class after students have done research and can ask informed questions. Another option might be to compile questions from the class and submit them to an eye doctor who has agreed to correspond with the class.

Resources for Teachers and Students

Ophthalmic Surgery: Principles and Practice, by George L. Spaeth, Birk Cox, WB Saunders, 2003

The Complete Book of Laser Eye Surgery, by Steven G., Md. Slade, Richard N, Baker, Dorothy Brockman, Spencer P. Thornton, Bantam Books, 2002

Reviewing Main Ideas

Section 1 Mirrors

1. Plane mirrors reflect light to form upright, virtual images.
2. Concave mirrors can form various types of images, depending on where an object is relative to the focal point of the mirror. Concave mirrors can be used to magnify objects or create beams of light.
3. Convex mirrors spread out reflected light to form a reduced image. Convex mirrors allow you to see large areas.

Section 2 Lenses

1. Convex lenses converge light rays. Convex lenses can form real or virtual images, depending on the distance from the object to the lens.
2. Concave lenses diverge light rays to form virtual smaller, upright images. They often are used in combination with other lenses.

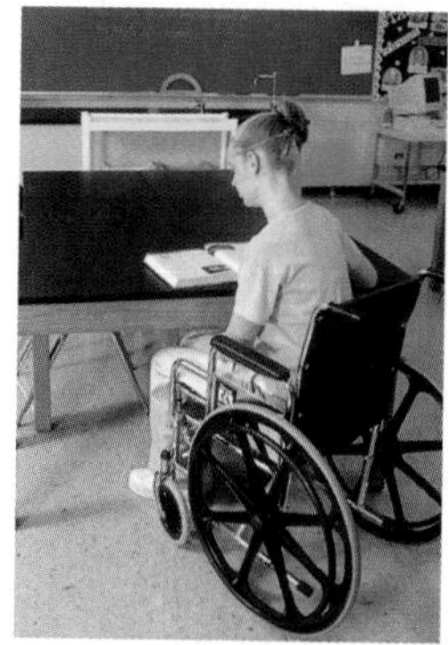

3. The human eye has a flexible lens that changes shape to focus an image on the retina.
4. People with imperfect vision can use corrective lenses to improve their vision. Farsighted people wear convex lenses, and nearsighted people wear concave lenses.

Section 3 Optical Instruments

1. A refracting telescope uses convex lenses to magnify distant objects.
2. A reflecting telescope uses concave and plane mirrors and a convex lens to magnify distant objects.
3. By avoiding atmospheric distortion, the *Hubble Space Telescope* produces sharper images than telescopes on Earth are able to produce.
4. A simple microscope uses a convex objective lens and eyepiece lens with short focal lengths to magnify small objects.

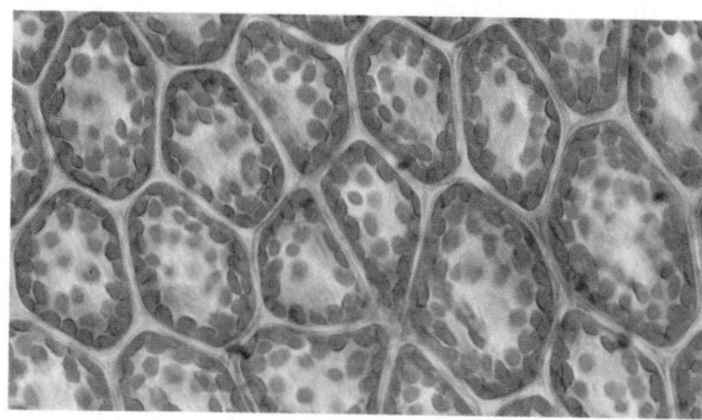

5. Light passing through the lens of a camera is focused on light-sensitive film inside the camera. The image on the film is inverted and reduced.

FOLDABLES™ Use the Foldable that you made at the beginning of the chapter to help you review image formation by mirrors.

Science Online gpscience.com/interactive_tutor

chapter Study Guide 14

Reviewing Main Ideas

Summary statements can be used by students to review the major concepts of the chapter.

Science Online

Visit gpscience.com
/self_check_quiz
/interactive_tutor
/vocabulary_puzzlemaker
/chapter_review
/standardized_test

Assessment Transparency

For additional assessment questions, use the *Assessment Transparency* located in the transparency book.

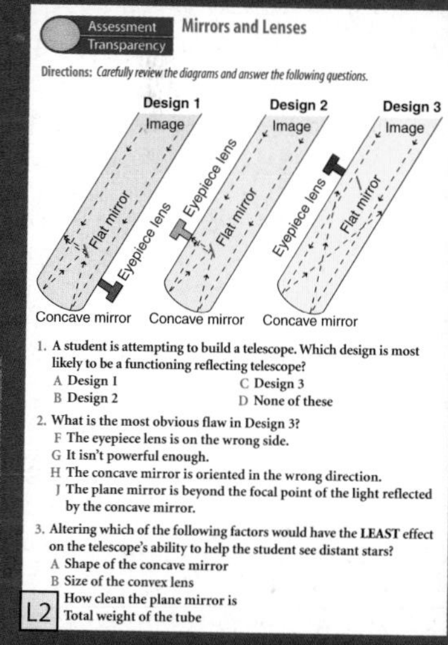

Assessment

Assessment Transparency **Mirrors and Lenses**

Directions: *Carefully review the diagrams and answer the following questions.*

1. A student is attempting to build a telescope. Which design is most likely to be a functioning reflecting telescope?
   A Design 1
   B Design 2
   C Design 3
   D None of these
2. What is the most obvious flaw in Design 3?
   F The eyepiece lens is on the wrong side.
   G It isn't powerful enough.
   H The concave mirror is oriented in the wrong direction.
   J The plane mirror is beyond the focal point of the light reflected by the concave mirror.
3. Altering which of the following factors would have the LEAST effect on the telescope's ability to help the student see distant stars?
   A Shape of the concave mirror
   B Size of the convex lens
   How clean the plane mirror is
   Total weight of the tube

L2

Mirrors and Lenses

FOLDABLES™ Have students use their Foldables to review the content of the chapter. Have students make a Foldables for convex and concave lenses.

Using Vocabulary

1. plane mirror
2. microscope
3. focal point
4. convex lens
5. retina

Checking Concepts

6. D
7. C
8. C
9. B
10. C
11. B
12. D
13. B
14. A
15. B

Interpreting Graphics

16. The candle moved away from the lens.
17. see table

chapter 14 Review

Using Vocabulary

concave lens p. 426	optical axis p. 418
concave mirror p. 418	plane mirror p. 417
convex lens p. 424	real image p. 419
convex mirror p. 421	reflecting telescope p. 433
cornea p. 427	refracting telescope p. 433
focal length p. 418	retina p. 427
focal point p. 418	virtual image p. 418
microscope p. 435	

Complete each sentence with the correct vocabulary word.

1. A flat, smooth surface that reflects light and forms an image is a(n) ________.
2. A(n) ________ uses two convex lenses to magnify small, close objects.
3. Every light ray that travels parallel to the optical axis before hitting a concave mirror is reflected such that it passes through the ________.
4. A(n) ________ is thicker in the middle than at the edges.
5. The inner lining of the eye that converts light images into electrical signals is called the ________.

Checking Concepts

Choose the word or phrase that best answers the question.

6. Which of the following best describes image formation by a plane mirror?
   A) A real image is formed in front of the mirror.
   B) A real image is formed behind the mirror.
   C) A virtual image is formed in front of the mirror.
   D) A virtual image is formed behind the mirror.

7. Which mirror can form an enlarged image?
   A) convex **C)** concave
   B) plane **D)** transparent

8. Which of the following is used in a headlight or a flashlight to create a beam of light?
   A) concave lens **C)** concave mirror
   B) convex lens **D)** convex mirror

9. What do lenses do?
   A) reflect light **C)** diffract light
   B) refract light **D)** interfere with light

10. Which way does a concave lens bend light?
    A) toward its optical axis
    B) toward its center
    C) toward its edges
    D) toward its focal point

11. What type of lens is used to correct farsightedness?
    A) flat lens **C)** concave lens
    B) convex lens **D)** plane lens

12. Which of the following is NOT part of a reflecting telescope?
    A) plane mirror **C)** convex lens
    B) concave mirror **D)** concave lens

13. Which of the following images do light rays never pass through?
    A) real **C)** enlarged
    B) virtual **D)** reduced

14. The image formed by a camera lens must always be which of the following?
    A) real **C)** virtual
    B) upright **D)** enlarged

15. What happens to a light ray traveling parallel to the optical axis of a convex lens that passes through the lens?
    A) It travels parallel to the optical axis.
    B) It passes through the focal point.
    C) It is bent away from the optical axis.
    D) It forms a virtual image.

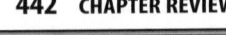

ScienceOnline gpscience.com/vocabulary_puzzlemaker

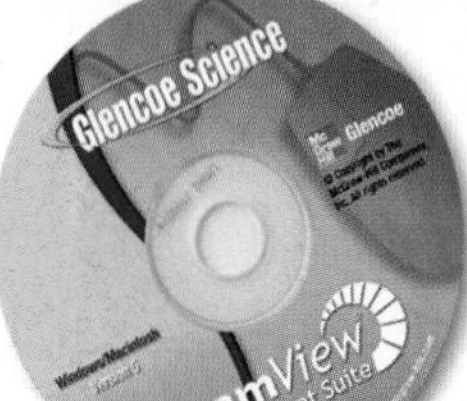

Use the *ExamView® Assessment Suite* CD-ROM to:

- create multiple versions of tests
- create modified tests with one mouse click for inclusion students
- edit existing questions and add your own questions
- build tests aligned with state standards using built-in State Curriculum Tags
- change English tests to Spanish with one mouse click and vice versa

Interpreting Graphics

Use the illustration below to answer question 16.

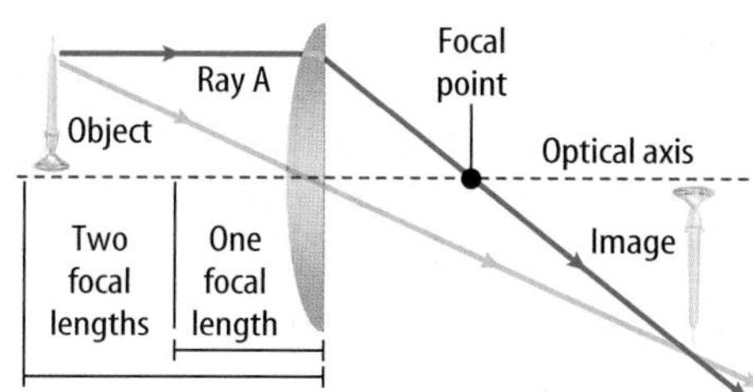

16. Suppose the image of the candle moves away from the focal point. How did the position of the candle change?

17. Copy and complete the following table on the image formation by lenses and mirrors.

Image Formation by Lenses and Mirrors

Type of Lens or Mirror	Position of Object	Type of Image
Concave lens	All positions of object	virtual, upright, reduced
Convex lens	closer than one focal length	virtual, upright, enlarged
	between one and two focal lengths	real, inverted, enlarged
	farther than two focal lengths	real, inverted reduced
Concave mirror	closer than one focal length	virtual, upright, enlarged
	object placed at focal point	no image is formed
	farther than two focal lengths	real, inverted, reduced
Convex mirror	All positions of object	virtual, upright, reduced

Thinking Critically

18. **Describe** how the shape of the lens in your eye changes when you look at a nearby object, and then a distant object.
19. **Compare and contrast** a refracting telescope and a microscope.
20. **Infer** why a convex mirror and a conccave lens can never produce a real image.
21. **Explain** why people often become far-sighted as they grow older.
22. **Infer** why it would be easier to make a concave mirror for a reflecting telescope than an objective lens of the same size for a refracting telescope.
23. **Determine** whether a convex lens could form an image that is enlarged, real, and upright.
24. **Compare** A concave lens made of plastic is placed in a liquid. Light rays traveling in the liquid are not refracted when they pass through the lens. Comare the speed of light in the plastic and in the liquid.

Applying Math

25. **Calculate Magnification** The magnification of a refracting telescope can be calculated by dividing the focal length of the objective lens by the focal length of the eyepiece lens. If an objective lens has a focal length of 1 m and the eyepiece has a focal length of 1 cm, what is the magnification of the telescope?
26. **Determine Object Distance** You hold an object in front of a concave mirror with a focal length of 30 cm. If you do not see a reflected image, how far from the mirror is the object?

 gpscience.com/chapter_review

chapter Review 14

Thinking Critically

18. The lens in your eye is more curved when you look at a nearby object, and then becomes flatter as you look at a distant object.
19. Both use two convex lenses to form an image. A refracting telescope forms images of distant objects, and uses a large objective lens. The object is more than two focal lengths away. A microscope forms images of all, nearby objects, and uses a small lens. The object is between one and two focal lengths from the lens.
20. Both a convex mirror and a concave lens cause light rays that strike them always to diverge.
21. As a person ages, the lens in the eye no longer is able to become curved enough to enable the eye to focus on nearby objects.
22. The concave mirror needs to be carefully polished on only one side instead of two. Also, the concave mirror can be made much thinner because it can be supported from the back, so less glass is required.
23. No. A convex lens forms an enlarged upright image that is virtual.
24. If no refraction occurs, the speed of light is the same in both materials.

Applying Math

National Math Standards

1, 4, 9

25. 1 m = 100 cm; magnification $= \frac{100 \text{ cm}}{1 \text{ cm}} = 100$
26. 30 cm

Assessment Resources

 **Reproducible Masters**

Chapter *Fast File* Resources
- Chapter Review, pp. 37–38
- Chapter Tests, pp. 39–42
- Assessment Transparency Activity, p. 49

Glencoe Science Web site
- Chapter Review Test
- Standardized Test Practice

Glencoe Technology
- Assessment Transparency
- *ExamView® Assessment Suite*
- MindJogger Videoquiz
- Interactive Chalkboard

Answer Sheet A practice answer sheet can be found at gpscience.com/answer_sheet.

Name Date Class

Assessment **Student Recording Sheet** Standardized Test Practice

Use with pages 788–789 of the Student Edition

Standardized Test Practice

Part 1 Multiple Choice

Select the best answer from the choices given and fill in the corresponding oval.

Part 2 Constructed Response/Grid In

Record and bubble in your answers on the grids below.

Record your answers for Questions 18–21 on a separate sheet of paper.

SAMPLE

chapter 14 Standardized Test Practice

Part 1 Multiple Choice

Record your answers on the answer sheet provided by your teacher or on a sheet of paper.

1. Which of the following describes the image formed by a convex mirror?

A. real
B. enlarged
C. inverted
D. virtual

Use the illustration below to answer questions 2 and 3.

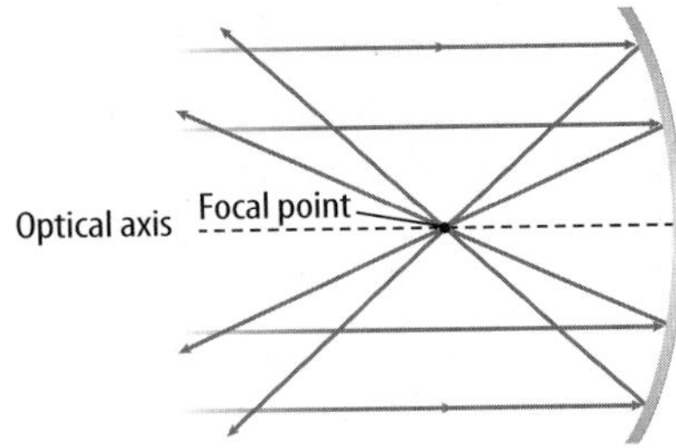

2. Which of the following describes a light ray that passes through the focal point and then is reflected by the mirror?

A. It travels parallel to the optical axis.
B. It forms a real image.
C. It is reflected back through the focal point.
D. It forms a virtual image

3. If the mirror becomes flatter and the focal point moves farther from the mirror, which of the following best describes the reflection of the parallel rays shown in the figure?

A. They pass through the old focal point.
B. They do not pass through either the old or the new focal point.
C. They pass through the new focal point.
D. They reverse direction.

Test-Taking Tip

Be Prepared Bring at least two sharpened No. 2 pencils and a good eraser to the test. Make sure the eraser erases completely.

4. How far is an object from a concave mirror if the image formed is upright?

A. one focal length
B. less than one focal length
C. more than two focal lengths
D. two focal lengths

5. What is an advantage to increasing the diameter of the concave mirror in a reflecting telescope?

A. Brighter images are formed.
B. The mirror forms larger images.
C. The mirror forms sharper images.
D. The focal length increases.

Use the table below to answer questions 6–8.

Image Magnification by a Convex Lens

Object Distance (cm)	Image Distance (cm)	Magnification
250.0	62.5	0.25
200.0	66.7	0.33
150.0	75.0	0.50
100.0	100.0	1.00
75.0	150.0	2.00

6. How does the image change as the object gets closer to the lens?

A. It gets larger.
B. It gets smaller
C. It gets closer.
D. It becomes real.

7. Which of the following is the best estimate of the magnification if the image is 225 cm from the lens?

A. 0.40
B. 1.25
C. 1.5
D. 0.3

8. What should the object distance be if the lens is to be used as a magnifying glass?

A. 150 cm
B. 100 cm
C. greater than 250 cm
D. less than 100 cm

Part 1 Multiple Choice

1. D
2. A
3. C
4. B
5. A
6. A
7. B
8. D

Part 2 Short Response

9. If the image can be formed on a screen or a piece of paper, it is a real image. If the image cannot be formed on a screen or a piece of paper, it is a virtual image.

10. $A = \pi r^2 = (3.14)(0.5\text{ m})^2 = (3.14)(0.25)\text{ m}^2 = 0.8\text{ m}^2$

11. $30 \times 20 = 600$ times.

12. The focal length decreases as the lens becomes more curved.

13. 5 cm

14. 10 cm

15. It is easier to make very large concave mirrors than very large convex lenses. Also, large lenses sag under their own weight, and produce distorted images. Large concave mirrors can be supported behind the reflecting surface, so they don't sag.

Part 3 Open Ended

16. This problem is farsightedness, which is the inability to focus on nearby objects. It occurs as people age and the lens in the eye is unable to become curved enough to produce a sharp image of nearby objects.

Part 2 | Short Response/Grid In

Record your answers on the answer sheet provided by your teacher or on a sheet of paper.

9. Describe how you could determine whether the image formed by a lens or mirror is a real image or a virtual image.

10. The largest refracting telescope has an objective lens with a diameter of 1.0 m. Calculate the area of this lens.

11. The objective lens in a microscope has a magnification of 30. What is the magnification of the microscope if the eyepiece lens has a magnification of 20?

12. Describe how the focal length of a convex lens changes as the lens becomes more curved.

Use the graph below to answer questions 13 and 14.

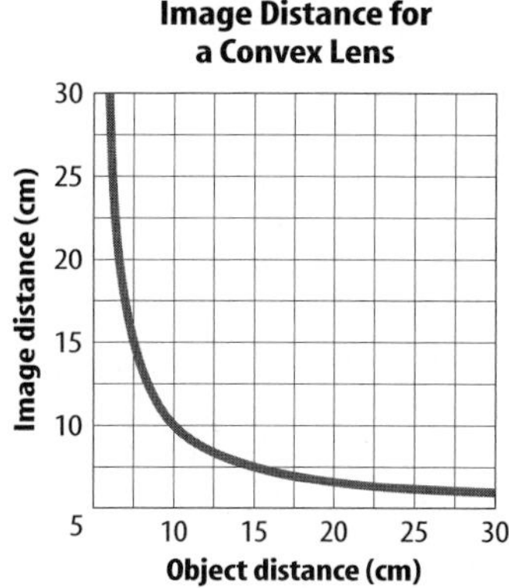

13. Determine how far the image is from the lens when the object is 15 cm from the lens.

14. At what object distance are the image distance and object distance equal?

15. Explain why the largest telescopes are reflecting telescopes instead of refracting telescopes.

Part 3 | Open Ended

Record your answers on a sheet of paper.

Use the illustration below to answer questions 16 and 17.

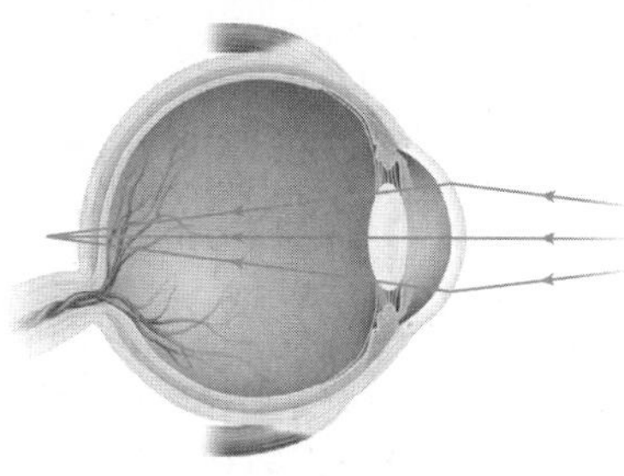

16. Describe the vision problem shown by the illustration. Why does this vision problem become more prevalent as people age?

17. Explain how the vision problem shown by the illustration can be corrected.

18. A convex lens is formed out of a transparent substance. Light travels with the same speed in this substance as in air. Explain why this lens would not cause light rays to converge.

19. Some cameras have zoom lenses that have a focal length that varies between 35 mm and 155 mm. Determine which focal length would correspond to a wide-angle lens and which would correspond to a telephoto lens.

20. Explain why side-view convex mirrors on the right side of cars have the printed warning "Objects in mirror are closer than they appear."

21. Describe the change in the lens in each of your eyes when you look at this book and then look out the window at a distant object.

22. Explain why objects become dimmer and less detailed as they move farther away.

Rubrics

The following rubrics are sample scoring devices for short response and open-ended questions.

Short Response

Points	Description
2	The student demonstrates a thorough understanding of the science of the task. The response may contain minor flaws that do not detract from the demonstration of a thorough understanding.
1	The student has provided a response that is only partially correct.
0	The student has provided a completely incorrect solution or no response at all.

Open Ended

Points	Description
4	The student demonstrates a thorough understanding of the science of the task. The response may contain minor flaws that do not detract from the demonstration of a thorough understanding.
3	The student demonstrates an understanding of the science of the task. The response is essentially correct and demonstrates an essential but less than thorough understanding of the science.
2	The student demonstrates only a partial understanding of the science of the task. Although the student may have used the correct approach to a solution or may have provided a correct solution, the work lacks an essential understanding of the underlying science concepts.
1	The student demonstrates a very limited understanding of the science of the task. The response is incomplete and exhibits many flaws.
0	The student provides a completely incorrect solution or no response at all.

17. A convex lens in front of the eye converges light rays so the lens in the eye is able to focus on nearby objects.

18. Refraction occurs when light rays change speed.

19. wide angle is 35 mm focal length, telephoto is 155 mm focal length

20. Objects in a convex mirror appear smaller than they really are, so they seem farther away than they are.

21. The lens in your eye becomes less convex as you look away from a close object to a more distant object.

22. Fewer light rays from each point on the object enter the eye as an object moves farther away. Because less light enters the eye, the object appears dimmer, and less detail can be seen.

unit 4

The Nature of Matter

Unit Contents

WebQuest *Art of Neon* is a motivating and challenging investigation of the chemistry of noble gases and how they are used in colorful neon signs and glowing sculptures. Students will research how the noble gases are inserted into bent tubing and made to glow. As a culminating activity, students will design a "blueprint" of their own neon sign, its components, colors, shape, size, and use.

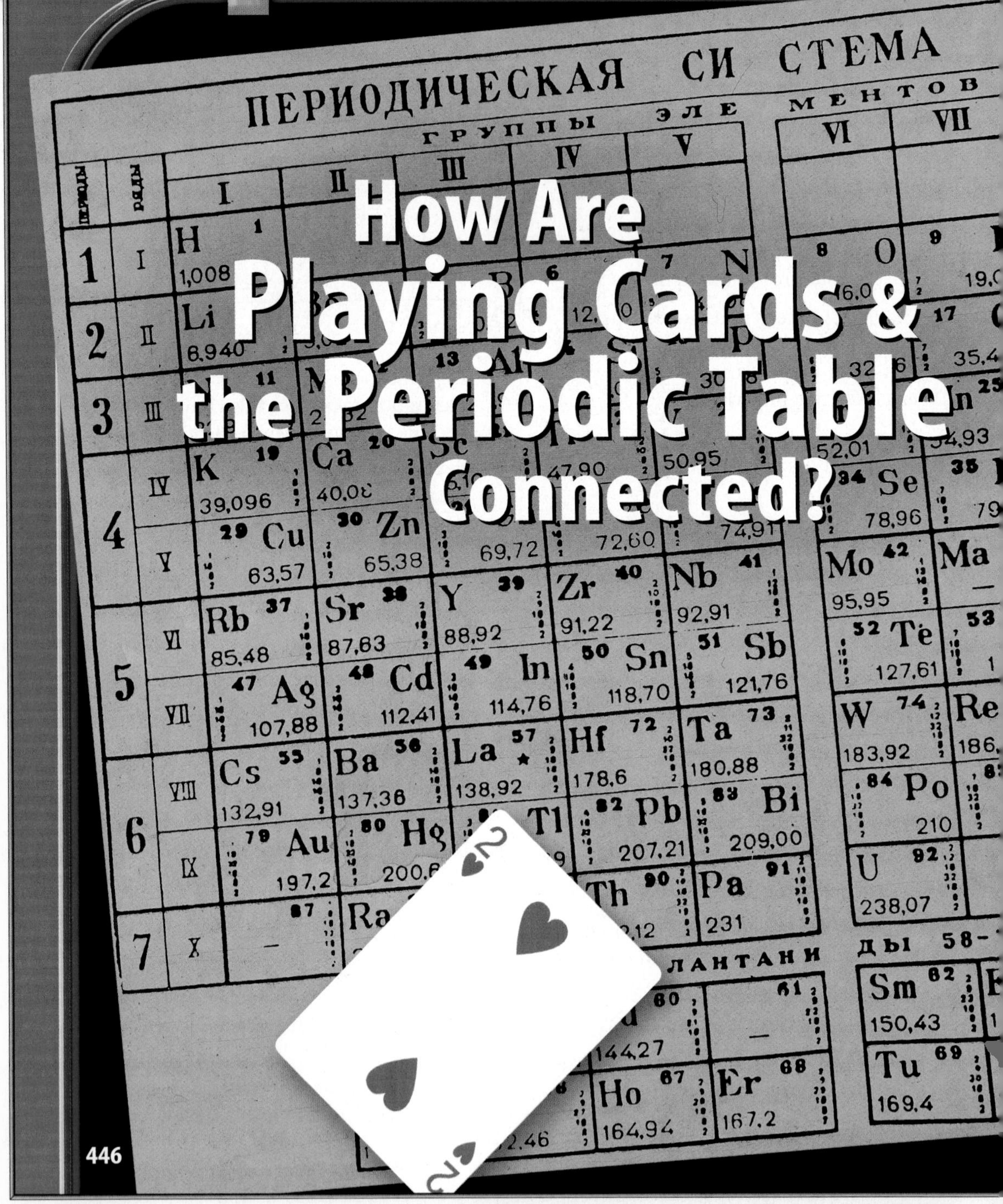

How Are Playing Cards & the Periodic Table Connected?

446

PROJECT CRISS[SM]

Study Skills

Discussion Several students are assigned to research each group on the periodic table or each collection of elements that belong together. After reading silently about the elements, the students take turns asking questions or making comments about the material until they have answers to the following questions: What elements are contained in the group? How many electrons are in the outer levels? How reactive is it? What properties do the elements share? Whole-class discussion follows.

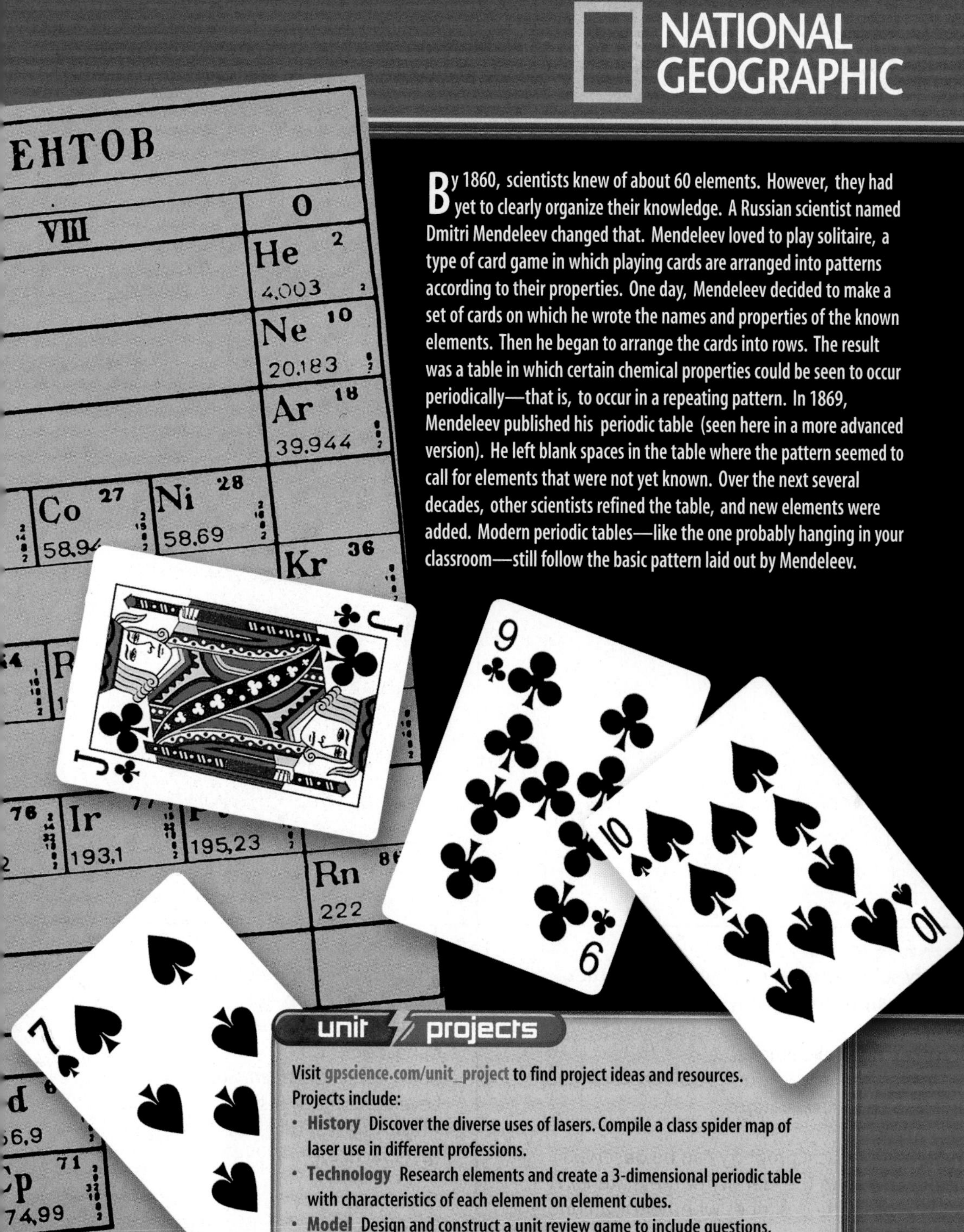

By 1860, scientists knew of about 60 elements. However, they had yet to clearly organize their knowledge. A Russian scientist named Dmitri Mendeleev changed that. Mendeleev loved to play solitaire, a type of card game in which playing cards are arranged into patterns according to their properties. One day, Mendeleev decided to make a set of cards on which he wrote the names and properties of the known elements. Then he began to arrange the cards into rows. The result was a table in which certain chemical properties could be seen to occur periodically—that is, to occur in a repeating pattern. In 1869, Mendeleev published his periodic table (seen here in a more advanced version). He left blank spaces in the table where the pattern seemed to call for elements that were not yet known. Over the next several decades, other scientists refined the table, and new elements were added. Modern periodic tables—like the one probably hanging in your classroom—still follow the basic pattern laid out by Mendeleev.

unit projects

Visit gpscience.com/unit_project to find project ideas and resources.
Projects include:

- **History** Discover the diverse uses of lasers. Compile a class spider map of laser use in different professions.
- **Technology** Research elements and create a 3-dimensional periodic table with characteristics of each element on element cubes.
- **Model** Design and construct a unit review game to include questions, answers, directions, playing pieces, and a creative box.

WebQuest *Art of Neon* is an investigation of the noble gases and how they are inserted into glass tubes to be used in art and signage.

NATIONAL GEOGRAPHIC How Are Playing Cards & the Periodic Table Connected?

- Tape a deck of cards sequentially on poster board. Ask students how all the cards in a row (period) are alike, and how all the cards in a column (family or group) are alike. They are all of one suit; the same card value is shown.
- Remind students that Mendeleev left blank spaces in his periodic table where elements seemed to be missing. Randomly remove several cards and ask students to identify the properties of the cards that belong in the empty spaces. Have them justify their answers and relate them to the empty spaces on Mendeleev's periodic table.

unit projects

Career Working in small groups, have students explore the diverse use of lasers in a variety of careers—medical, military, police, educational, or artistic light and sound shows. Students should investigate how electrical engineers are designing new equipment for each field to help technicians be more precise and efficient. As a class, design a spider map for lasers and compile each group's information into one large informative display.

Technology As a class, build a 3-D periodic table. Have students research an element, and then create a cube representing specific information about their element—name, symbol, atomic number, metal/nonmetal/metalloid, group, period, two physical properties, and two chemical properties. Have students refer to the link below to download a template for their element cube.

Model Ask students to design an entertaining and engaging game that will review concepts presented in this unit, giving them an opportunity to apply their new knowledge. Ideas might include card games, board games, trivia cards, dice, spinners, and game pieces, as well as complete directions, questions and answers, and a colorful intriguing container.

Additional Resources For more information, resources, and assessment rubrics, visit gpscience.com/unit_project

Classification of Matter

BIG Idea **Matter can be classified by what it is made of, by its physical properties, and by its chemical properties.**

	Content Standards	Learning Objectives	Resources to Assess Mastery
Section 1	**5–8:** UCP.1–3, 5; A.1, 2; B.1 **9–12:** UCP.1–3, 5; A.1, 2; B.2	**Composition of Matter** **1. Define** substances and mixtures. **2. Identify** elements and compounds. **3. Compare and contrast** solutions, colloids, and suspensions. ***Main Idea*** Matter can be either a pure substance (an element or a compound), or a mixture (either heterogeneous or homogeneous).	**Formative Assessment** Reading Check, pp. 452, 454, 455 Section Review, p. 456 **Summative Assessment** *ExamView® Assessment Suite*
Section 2	**5–8:** UCP.1, 3, 5; A.1, 2; B.1 **9–12:** UCP.1–3; B.2, 3, 6 See pp. 16T–17T for a Key to Standards.	**Properties of Matter** **4. Identify** substances using physical properties. **5. Compare and contrast** physical and chemical changes. **6. Identify** chemical changes. **7. Determine** how the law of conservation of mass applies to chemical changes. ***Main Idea*** A physical property can be observed without changing the identity of the material. A chemical property describes whether it can undergo a chemical change.	**Formative Assessment** Reading Check, pp. 460, 462, 465 Section Review, p. 465 **Summative Chapter Assessment** MindJogger, Ch. 15 *ExamView® Assessment Suite* Leveled Chapter Test Test A L1 Test B L2 Test C L3 Test Practice, pp. 472–473

Suggested Pacing				
Period	Instruction	Labs	Review & Assessment	Total
Single	2.5 days	3 days	1.5 days	7 days
Block	1.25 blocks	1.5 blocks	.75 block	3.5 blocks

Core Instruction	Leveled Resources	Leveled Labs	Pacing Period		Pacing Block
Student Text, pp. 448–457 Section Focus Transparency, Ch. 15, Section 1 Teaching Transparency, Ch. 15, Section 1 Interactive Chalkboard, Ch. 15, Section 1 Identifying Misconceptions, p. 452 Differentiated Instruction, pp. 451, 452, 455 Visualizing Elements, p. 451	**Chapter *Fast File* Resources** Directed Reading for Content Mastery, p. 20 L1 Note-taking Worksheet, pp. 31, 32 Reinforcement, p. 27 L2 Enrichment, p.29 L3 **Reading Essentials,** p. 252 L1 ELL **Science Notebook,** p. 169 ELL ***Active*Folders**: *Elements, Compounds, and Mixtures* L1 ELL	**Launch Lab**, p. 449: 200-mL beaker, water, food coloring (red), 100-mL graduated cylinder, evaporating dish, ice, tongs, white paper, hot plate *25 min* L2 (Video Lab)	**1**	Section 1, pp. 449–452 (includes Launch Lab)	**1**
		MiniLAB, p. 453: transparent-plastic gallon jar, soil, clay, sand, gravel, pebbles, water *15 min* L2	**2**	Section 1, pp. 453–456 (includes MiniLAB and Section Review)	
		***Lab**, p. 457: plastic freezer bag, copper wire, package of salt, pencil, aluminum foil, chalk, granite, sugar water, vial *25 min* L1 L2 L3	**3**	Lab: Elements, Compounds and Mixtures, p. 457	**2**
Student Text, pp. 458–467 Section Focus Transparency, Ch. 15, Section 2 Interactive Chalkboard, Ch. 15, Section 2 Identifying Misconceptions, p. 464 Applying Math, p. 463 Differentiated Instruction, p. 459 Chapter Study Guide, p. 469	**Chapter *Fast File* Resources** Directed Reading for Content Mastery, pp. 21, 22 L1 Note-taking Worksheet, pp. 31, 32 Reinforcement, p. 28 L2 Enrichment, p. 30 L3 **Reading Essentials,** p. 258 L1 ELL **Science Notebook,** p. 173 ELL ***Active*Folders**: *Chemical and Physical Changes* L1 ELL	**MiniLAB**, p. 460: water, potassium permanganate, sodium hydrogen sulfite, 250-mL beaker, stirring rod *15 min* L2	**4**	Section 2, pp. 458–461 (includes MiniLab)	
		***Lab**, pp. 466–467: baking soda, evaporating dish, magnifying lens, HCL (1M), 10-mL graduated cylinder, hot plate *45 min* L1 L2 L3	**5**	Section 2, pp. 461–465 (includes Section Review)	**3**
			6	Lab: Checking Out Chemical Changes, pp. 466–467	
		*Lab version A L1 version B L2 L3	**7**	Study Guide, Chapter Review, and Test Practice, pp. 469–473	**3.5**

(Video Lab icon) Video Lab

chapter  Classification of Matter

Transparencies

Section Focus

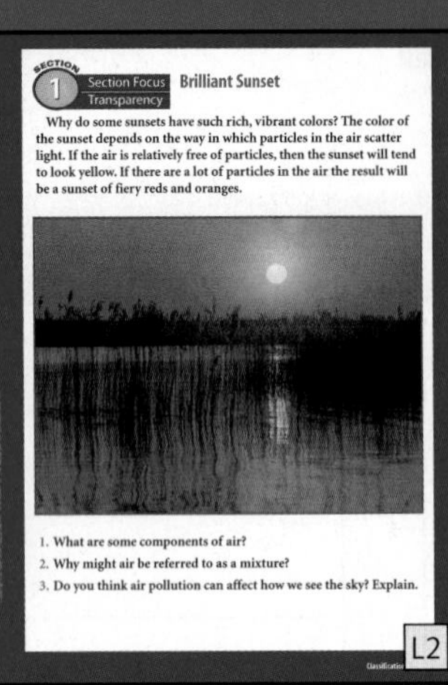
Section 1 Section Focus Transparency **Brilliant Sunset**

Why do some sunsets have such rich, vibrant colors? The color of the sunset depends on the way in which particles in the air scatter light. If the air is relatively free of particles, then the sunset will tend to look yellow. If there are a lot of particles in the air the result will be a sunset of fiery reds and oranges.

1. What are some components of air?
2. Why might air be referred to as a mixture?
3. Do you think air pollution can affect how we see the sky? Explain.

L2

Section 2 Section Focus Transparency **All that Glitters**

If you imagine a 19th century gold miner, you may think of someone standing in a river swirling water in a pan. Panning was a common technique used to separate gold from a mixture of sand and gravel.

1. What properties of gold allow it to be separated from sand and gravel by panning?
2. How does gold change from the time it is collected to the time it is ready to sell?

L2

This is a representation of key blackline masters available in the Teacher Classroom Resources. See Resource Manager boxes within the chapter for additional information.

Assessment

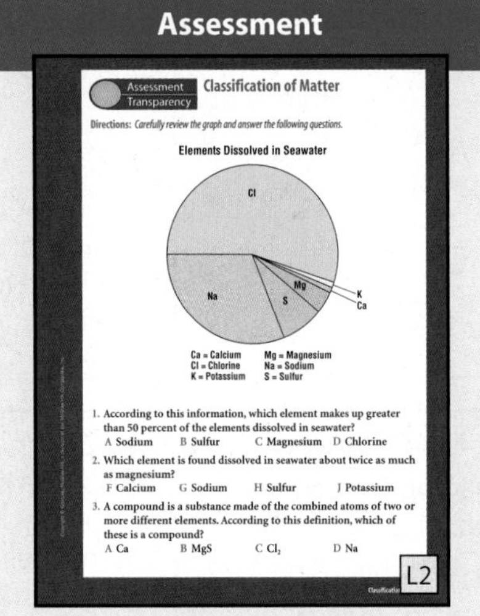
Assessment Transparency **Classification of Matter**

Directions: Carefully review the graph and answer the following questions.

Elements Dissolved in Seawater

1. According to this information, which element makes up greater than 50 percent of the elements dissolved in seawater?
A Sodium B Sulfur C Magnesium D Chlorine
2. Which element is found dissolved in seawater about twice as much as magnesium?
F Calcium G Sodium H Sulfur J Potassium
3. A compound is a substance made of the combined atoms of two or more different elements. According to this definition, which of these is a compound?
A Ca B MgS C Cl_2 D Na

L2

Teaching

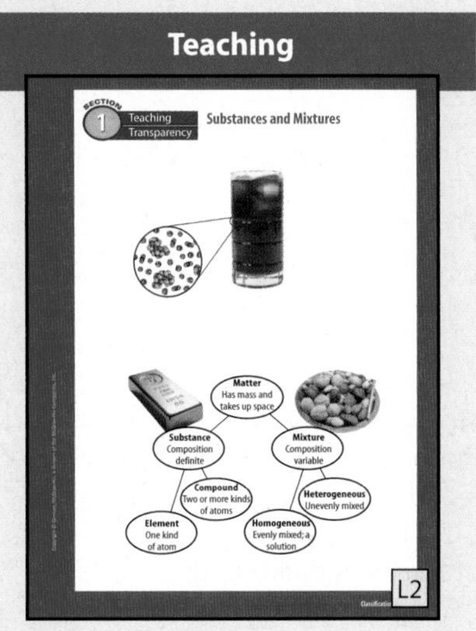
Section 1 Teaching Transparency **Substances and Mixtures**

L2

Key to Teaching Strategies

The following designations will help you decide which activities are appropriate for your students.

- **L1** Level 1 activities should be appropriate for students with learning difficulties.
- **L2** Level 2 activities should be within the ability range of all students.
- **L3** Level 3 activities are designed for above-average students.
- **ELL** ELL activities should be within the ability range of English Language Learners.
- **COOP LEARN** Cooperative Learning activities are designed for small group work.
- **LS** Multiple Learning Styles logos, as described on page 12T, are used throughout to indicate strategies that address different learning styles.
- **P** These strategies represent student products that can be placed into a best-work portfolio.
- **PBL** Problem-Based Learning activities apply real-world situations to learning.

Hands-on Activities

Student Text Lab Worksheet

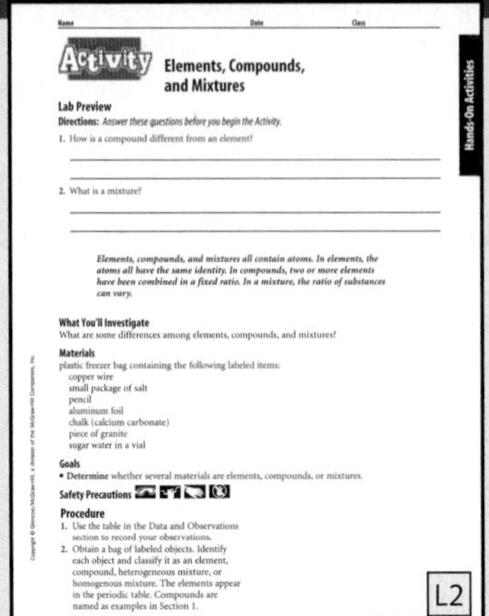
Activity **Elements, Compounds, and Mixtures**

Hands-On Activities

Lab Preview

Directions: Answer these questions before you begin the Activity.

1. How is a compound different from an element?
2. What is a mixture?

Elements, compounds, and mixtures all contain atoms. In elements, the atoms all have the same identity. In compounds, two or more elements have been combined in a fixed ratio. In a mixture, the ratio of substances can vary.

What You'll Investigate

What are some differences among elements, compounds, and mixtures?

Materials

plastic freezer bag containing the following labeled items: copper wire, small package of salt, pencil, aluminum foil, chalk (calcium carbonate), piece of granite, sugar water in a vial

Goals

- Determine whether several materials are elements, compounds, or mixtures.

Safety Precautions

Procedure

1. Use the table in the Data and Observations section to record your observations.
2. Obtain a bag of labeled objects. Identify each object and classify it as an element, compound, heterogeneous mixture, or homogeneous mixture. The elements appear in the periodic table. Compounds are named as examples in Section 1.

L2

Laboratory Activities

Lab 1 Laboratory Activity **Chromatography**

Hands-On Activities

Chromatography is a useful method for separating substances in a mixture. As you recall, the substances in a mixture are not chemically combined. Therefore, they can be separated. Chromatography can be used to separate the substances in certain mixtures because these substances dissolve at different rates.

Many mixtures, such as inks and food colorings, consist of two or more dyes. To separate the dyes, a small portion of the mixture is put on an absorbent material, such as filter paper. A liquid called a solvent is absorbed onto one end of the filter paper.

The solvent soaks the filter paper, dissolving the ink. If a dye in the ink dissolves well, it will move along the paper at the same rate as the solvent. If another dye in the ink doesn't dissolve as well, it will not move as far.

In a short time, a pattern of colors will appear on the filter paper. Each color will be a single dye that was in the ink. The distance that a component dye travels on the filter paper is a property of that dye. You can use this property to identify dyes that are found in inks of other colors.

Strategy

You will use chromatography to separate the substances in a mixture.
You will show differences in the physical properties of the substances that make up a mixture.

Materials

24-well microplate, filter paper, scissors, pencil, metric ruler, red, green, and black ink marking pens, plastic microtip pipette, ethanol, distilled water, masking tape, resealable plastic bag, paper towel

Procedure

1. Place the 24-well microplate on a flat surface. Arrange the plate so that the numbered columns are at the top and the lettered rows are at the left.
2. Cut three strips of filter paper so that each is approximately as long as the microplate and 1.5 cm wide.
3. Use a pencil to draw a line 1 cm from one end across each strip of filter paper.
4. Make a spot, using the red ink marking pen, in the middle of the pencil line on one of the strips of filter paper. After the ink has dried, apply more ink to the same spot. Allow the ink to dry. See Figure 1.

Figure 1

Pencil line — Ink spot — Filter paper strip

L2

Meeting Different Ability Levels

Content Outline

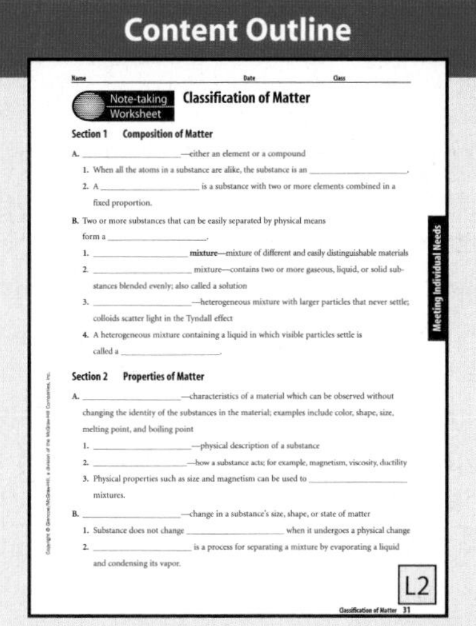

Name Date Class

Note-taking Worksheet **Classification of Matter**

Section 1 Composition of Matter

A. ____________________—either an element or a compound

1. When all the atoms in a substance are alike, the substance is an ____________________.
2. A ____________________ is a substance with two or more elements combined in a fixed proportion.

B. Two or more substances that can be easily separated by physical means form a ____________________.

1. ____________________ **mixture**—mixture of different and easily distinguishable materials
2. ____________________ mixture—contains two or more gaseous, liquid, or solid substances blended evenly; also called a solution
3. ____________________—heterogeneous mixture with larger particles that never settle; colloids scatter light in the Tyndall effect
4. A heterogeneous mixture containing a liquid in which visible particles settle is called a ____________________.

Section 2 Properties of Matter

A. ____________________—characteristics of a material which can be observed without changing the identity of the substances in the material; examples include color, shape, size, melting point, and boiling point

1. ____________________—physical description of a substance
2. ____________________—how a substance acts; for example, magnetism, viscosity, ductility
3. Physical properties such as size and magnetism can be used to ____________________ mixtures.

B. ____________________—change in a substance's size, shape, or state of matter

1. Substance does not change ____________________ when it undergoes a physical change
2. ____________________ is a process for separating a mixture by evaporating a liquid and condensing its vapor.

Meeting Individual Needs

Classification of Matter 31

L2

Reinforcement

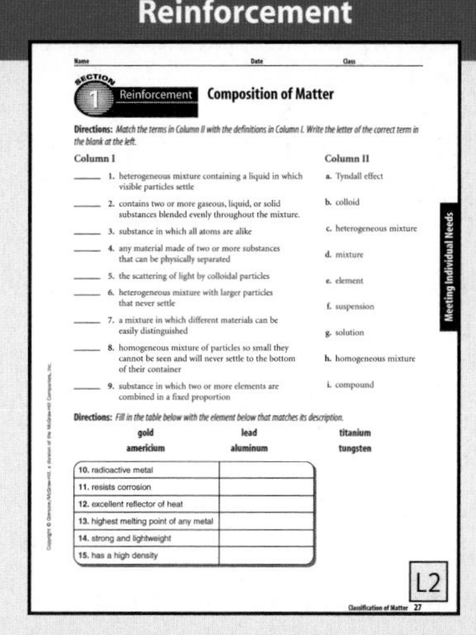

Name Date Class

SECTION 1 Reinforcement **Composition of Matter**

Directions: Match the terms in Column II with the definitions in Column I. Write the letter of the correct term in the blank at the left.

Column I

_____ 1. heterogeneous mixture containing a liquid in which visible particles settle
_____ 2. contains two or more gaseous, liquid, or solid substances blended evenly throughout the mixture
_____ 3. substance in which all atoms are alike
_____ 4. any material made of two or more substances that can be physically separated
_____ 5. the scattering of light by colloidal particles
_____ 6. heterogeneous mixture with larger particles that never settle
_____ 7. a mixture in which different materials can be easily distinguished
_____ 8. homogeneous mixture of particles so small they cannot be seen and will never settle to the bottom of their container
_____ 9. substance in which two or more elements are combined in a fixed proportion

Column II

a. Tyndall effect
b. colloid
c. heterogeneous mixture
d. mixture
e. element
f. suspension
g. solution
h. homogeneous mixture
i. compound

Directions: Fill in the table below with the element below that matches its description.

gold	lead	titanium
americium	aluminum	tungsten

10. radioactive metal	
11. resists corrosion	
12. excellent reflector of heat	
13. highest melting point of any metal	
14. strong and lightweight	
15. has a high density	

Meeting Individual Needs

Classification of Matter 27

L2

Enrichment

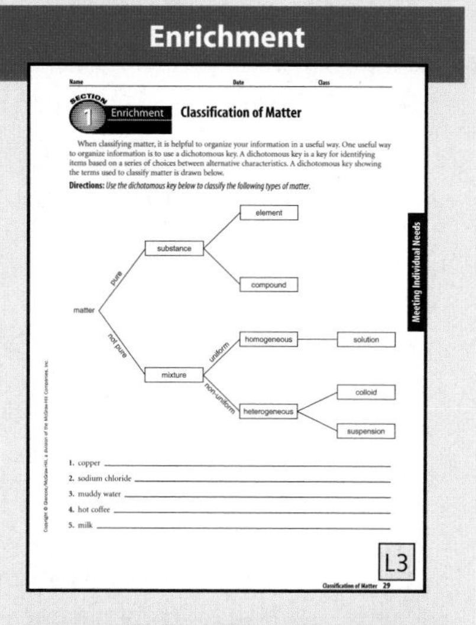

Name Date Class

SECTION 1 Enrichment **Classification of Matter**

When classifying matter, it is helpful to organize your information in a useful way. One useful way to organize information is to use a dichotomous key. A dichotomous key is a key for identifying items based on a series of choices between alternative characteristics. A dichotomous key showing the terms used to classify matter is drawn below.

Directions: Use the dichotomous key below to classify the following types of matter.

1. copper ____________________
2. sodium chloride ____________________
3. muddy water ____________________
4. hot coffee ____________________
5. milk ____________________

Meeting Individual Needs

Classification of Matter 29

L3

Directed Reading (English/Spanish)

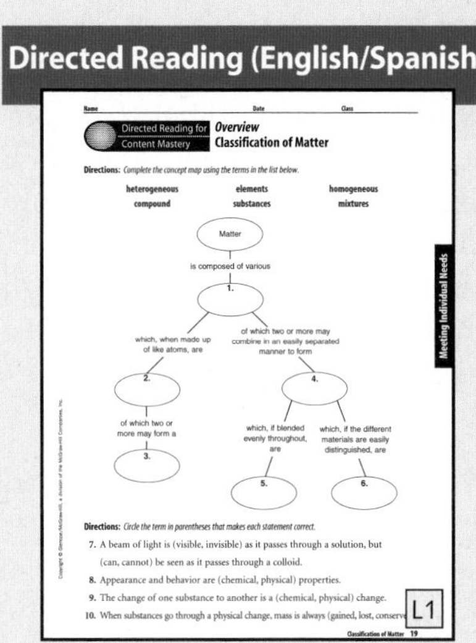

Name Date Class

Directed Reading for Content Mastery *Overview* **Classification of Matter**

Directions: Complete the concept map using the terms in the list below.

heterogeneous	elements	homogeneous
compound	substances	mixtures

Directions: Circle the term in parentheses that makes each statement correct.

7. A beam of light is (visible, invisible) as it passes through a solution, but (can, cannot) be seen as it passes through a colloid.
8. Appearance and behavior are (chemical, physical) properties.
9. The change of one substance to another is a (chemical, physical) change.
10. When substances go through a physical change, mass is always (gained, lost, conserv...

Meeting Individual Needs

Classification of Matter 19

L1

Study Guide

Reading Essentials

Assessment

Test Practice Workbook

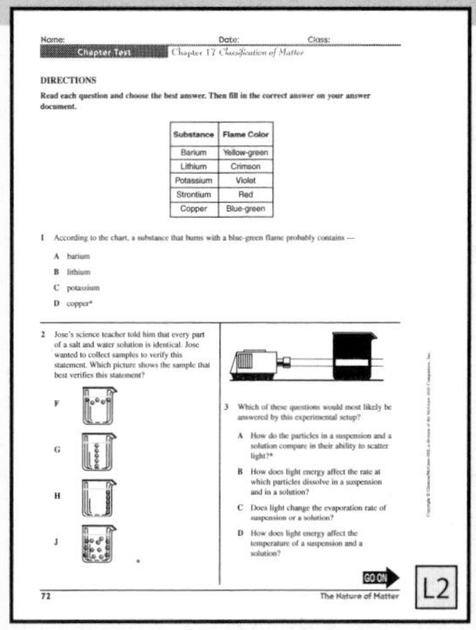

Name: Date: Class:

Chapter Test *Chapter 15 Classification of Matter*

DIRECTIONS

Read each question and choose the best answer. Then fill in the correct answer on your answer document.

Substance	Flame Color
Barium	Yellow-green
Lithium	Crimson
Potassium	Violet
Strontium	Red
Copper	Blue-green

1 According to the chart, a substance that burns with a blue-green flame probably contains —

A barium
B lithium
C potassium
D copper*

2 Jose's science teacher told him that every part of a salt and water solution is identical. Jose wanted to collect samples to verify this statement. Which picture shows the sample that best verifies this statement?

F
G
H
J

3 Which of these questions would most likely be answered by this experimental setup?

A How do the particles in a suspension and a solution compare in their ability to scatter light?*
B How does light energy affect the rate at which particles dissolve in a suspension and in a solution?
C Does light change the evaporation rate of suspension or a solution?
D How does light energy affect the temperature of a suspension and a solution?

GO ON

72 The Nature of Matter

L2

Chapter Review

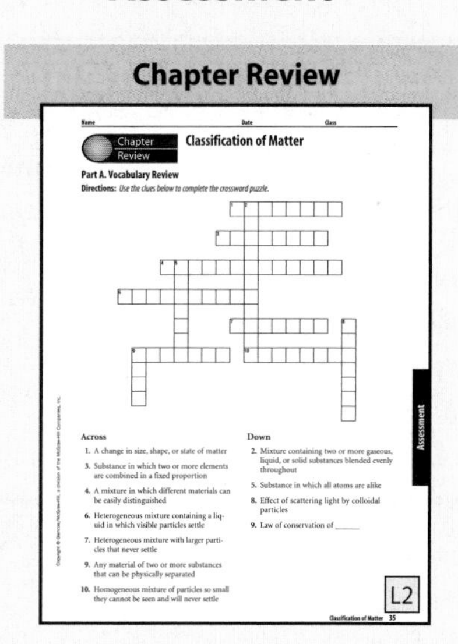

Name Date Class

Chapter Review **Classification of Matter**

Part A. Vocabulary Review

Directions: Use the clues below to complete the crossword puzzle.

Across

1. A change in size, shape, or state of matter
3. Substance in which two or more elements are combined in a fixed proportion
4. A mixture in which different materials can be easily distinguished
6. Heterogeneous mixture containing a liquid in which visible particles settle
7. Heterogeneous mixture with larger particles that never settle
9. Any material made of two or more substances that can be physically separated
10. Homogeneous mixture of particles so small they cannot be seen and will never settle

Down

2. Mixture containing two or more gaseous, liquid, or solid substances blended evenly throughout
5. Substance in which all atoms are alike
8. Effect of scattering light by colloidal particles
9. Law of conservation of ______

Assessment

Classification of Matter 35

L2

Chapter Tests

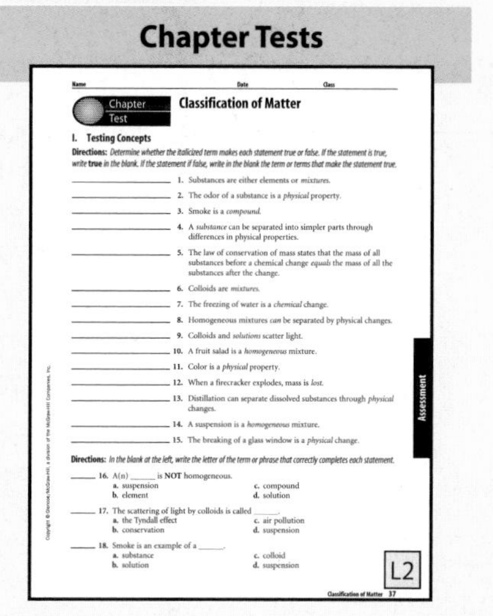

Name Date Class

Chapter Test **Classification of Matter**

I. Testing Concepts

Directions: Determine whether the italicized term makes each statement true or false. If the statement is true, write **true** *in the blank. If the statement if false, write in the blank the term or terms that make the statement true.*

_______ 1. Substances are either elements or *mixtures*.
_______ 2. The odor of a substance is a *physical* property.
_______ 3. Smoke is a *compound*.
_______ 4. A *substance* can be separated into simpler parts through differences in physical properties.
_______ 5. The law of conservation of mass states that the mass of all substances *before* a chemical change equals the mass of all the substances after the change.
_______ 6. Colloids are *mixtures*.
_______ 7. The freezing of water is a *chemical* change.
_______ 8. Homogeneous mixtures can be separated by physical changes.
_______ 9. Colloids and *solutions* scatter light.
_______ 10. A fruit salad is a *homogeneous* mixture.
_______ 11. Color is a *physical* property.
_______ 12. When a firecracker explodes, mass is *lost*.
_______ 13. Distillation can separate dissolved substances through *physical* changes.
_______ 14. A suspension is a *homogeneous* mixture.
_______ 15. The breaking of a glass window is a *physical* change.

Directions: In the blank at the left, write the letter of the term or phrase that correctly completes each statement.

_____ 16. A(n) _____ is NOT homogeneous.
a. suspension c. compound
b. element d. solution

_____ 17. The scattering of light by colloids is called _____.
a. the Tyndall effect c. air pollution
b. conservation d. suspension

_____ 18. Smoke is an example of a _____.
a. substance c. colloid
b. solution d. suspension

Assessment

Classification of Matter 37

L2

Science Content Background

section 1 Composition of Matter

Pure Substances

Matter can be divided into mixtures and pure substances. Pure substances can be described as either elements or chemical compounds. Mixtures can be either heterogeneous or homogeneous. Homogeneous mixtures are usually called solutions and have a constant composition. Heterogeneous mixtures have regions with visibly different compositions. Homogeneous liquid mixtures tend to be transparent, whereas heterogeneous liquid mixtures are often cloudy and separate on standing.

Elements

At this time there are at least 115 known elements. All the compounds found on Earth are formed when atoms of two or more different elements combine, creating new materials with new properties.

section 2 Properties of Matter

Physical Properties

The characteristics, or properties, that are used to describe matter can be classified in several ways. Physical properties are those that can be determined without changing the chemical composition of the sample, whereas chemical properties are those that do involve a chemical change in the sample. Intensive properties are those that have values that do not depend on the size of the sample. Extensive properties do depend on the size of the sample. Density, the intensive property that relates mass to volume, is an important and useful physical property. Knowing the density of a substance can be very useful, because it is often easier to measure the volume of a liquid than its mass.

Conservation of Mass

The law of conservation of matter states that matter is not created or destroyed but only converted from one form into another. Thus in a chemical reaction, the amount of matter before the reaction is the same as after the reaction. This is equally true for phase changes. Although a material may turn from a solid to a liquid to a gas, the amount of matter is conserved.

chapter content resources

Internet Resources

For additional content background, visit **gpscience.com** to:

- access your book online
- find references to related articles in popular science magazines
- access Web links with related content background
- access current events with science journal topics

Print Resources

Chemistry, The Molecular Nature of Matter and Change, Martin S. Silberberg, McGraw-Hill, 2003

Chemistry, Steve S. Zumdahl, Susan A. Zumdahl, Houghton Mifflin Company, 2003

IDENTIFYING Misconceptions

Find Out What Students Think

Students may think that . . .

Matter is not conserved in physical or chemical changes.

Perceptions are often more dominant than logic, and for students it may look as though matter simply vanishes when it turns into an invisible gas. When wood burns in a fire, it is obvious that only ashes remain, but it is not obvious what has happened to the bulk of the wood. For these reasons, students may not recognize the conservation of matter in physical or chemical changes.

Demonstration

Present Figure 1 to students. Tell them that the mass of the jar with everything in it is 500 g. Suppose the magnifying glass is used to light the candle, which then burns in the oxygen-enriched air for about one minute before going out. Ask students to describe any changes that have occurred in the jar. Is the mass of the jar and everything in it now less than, the same as, or greater than 500 g? The mass is still 500 g. L2 LS **Kinesthetic**

Light rays
Lid with seal
Glass jar
Wick
Oxygen-enriched air
Candle

Promote Understanding

Activity

Prior to class fill small plastic soda bottles two-thirds full of water, cap the bottles, and freeze.

On the day of the activity, provide each group of students with one frozen bottle and a paper towel. Then ask students in each group to

- dry the outside of the bottle and find its mass.
- predict what the mass of the bottle will be when the water melts.
- leave the bottles overnight so that the water inside them melts.

On the next day, have students dry the outside of the bottles and find their masses.

Make a table on the board with columns labeled *Mass of Bottle with Frozen Water* and *Mass of Bottle with Liquid Water* and a row for each group. Ask a member of each group to fill in the data for that group. With the class, analyze the data in the table. Discuss why the masses stayed the same. Help students realize that the bottles were closed so no mass was added to or subtracted from them. L2 LS **Visual-Spatial, Kinesthetic, Interpersonal**

Assess

After completing the chapter, see *Identifying Misconceptions* in the Study Guide at the end of the chapter.

chapter 15

About the Photo

Paints Although the solid colors look homogeneous, pigments are in a solvent or water-based solution to form a mixture called a suspension. Larger particles will settle out, while smaller particles remain in suspension and form a colloid. As paint dries, physical changes and chemical reactions occur, making the final properties of paint different from its original state.

Science Journal The physical change is that paint becomes a solid as it dries. Chemically, the paint forms a polymeric chain that link individual particles together.

The BIG Idea

Compounds and Molecules A substance is composed of individual atoms or molecules. Compounds are composed of molecules, in which atoms of various elements are bound together. For a given compound, all molecules are identical. As a result, a compound contains certain elements in definite proportions. For example, molecules of the gas ethane contain two carbon atoms and six hydrogen atoms. So any amount of ethane always contains three times as many hydrogen atoms as carbon atoms. When a physical change occurs, the molecules in a compound are not changed. When a chemical change occurs, the composition of the molecules in a compound changes.

Introduce the Chapter Ask students to list ten examples of changes to a material. Have students identify those examples in which the material itself didn't change. Ask them how the two categories of changes are different.

chapter 15

Classification of Matter

BIG Idea Matter can be classified by what it is made of, by its physical properties, and by its chemical properties.

15.1 Composition of Matter

MAIN Idea Matter can be either a pure substance (an element or a compound) or a mixture (either heterogeneous or homogeneous).

15.2 Properties of Matter

MAIN Idea A physical property can be observed without changing the identity of the material. A chemical property describes whether it can undergo a chemical change.

The Art of Mixtures

When painting, colors can be skillfully mixed to achieve a certain shade, or the artist can show several individual pigments in a single brush stroke. Paint undergoes physical and chemical changes with time that can make the artist's work endure.

Science Journal

Describe the changes that take place as the paint dries, particularly which changes are physical and which are chemical.

448

Interactive Chalkboard

This CD-ROM is an editable Microsoft® PowerPoint® presentation that includes:

- an editable presentation for every chapter
- additional chapter questions
- animated graphics
- image bank
- links to gpscience.com

Start-Up Activities

Demonstrate the Distillation of Water

Matter is classified according to the different properties that it exhibits. These differences in properties allow drinking water to be obtained from seawater. These properties could be very important to you if you were stranded on a desert island and needed drinking water. Purified water can be obtained through a process called distillation.

1. Place 75 mL of water in a 200-mL beaker and add 20 drops of red food coloring.
2. Place the beaker on a hot plate.
3. Add ice to an evaporating dish until the dish is half full. Add boiling chips. Place the evaporating dish on the beaker as shown in the photo.
4. Turn on the hot plate and slowly bring the water and food coloring solution to a boil.
5. After boiling the solution for five minutes, carefully remove the evaporating dish using heat-resistant gloves. Touch the drops of liquid on the bottom of the dish to a piece of white paper.
6. Observe the liquid on the paper.
7. **Think Critically** In your Science Journal, write a paragraph explaining where the liquid came from. What was in the beaker that is not in the liquid on the paper?

FOLDABLES Study Organizer

Classification of Matter Make the following Foldable to ensure that you have understood the content by defining the vocabulary terms from this chapter.

STEP 1 **Fold** a vertical sheet of paper from side to side. Make the front edge about 1.25 cm shorter than the back edge.

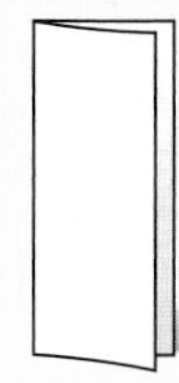

STEP 2 **Turn** lengthwise, with the fold on top, and **fold** into thirds.

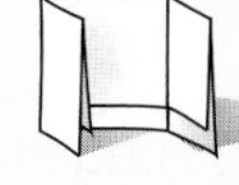

STEP 3 **Unfold and cut** only the top layer along both folds to make three tabs.

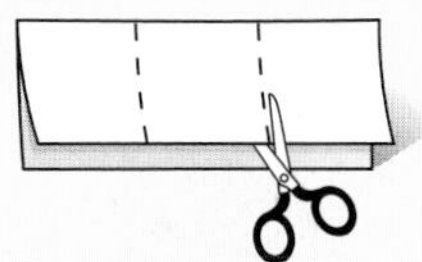

STEP 4 **Label** the tabs *Elements, Compounds,* and *Mixtures* as shown.

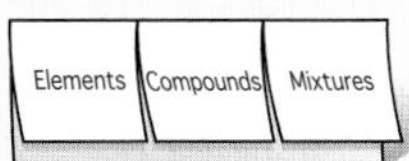

Define As you read the chapter, define each term and list examples of each under the appropriate tab.

Preview this chapter's content and activities at gpscience.com

Purpose Use this Launch Lab to demonstrate for students how water can be distilled and purified.

Preparation Set up a hotplate and acquire ice for each group.

Materials 200-mL beaker, water, food dye, 100-mL graduated cylinder, evaporating dish, ice, tongs, white paper, and a hot-plate for each group

Teaching Strategy To extend this activity, stage a contest to determine who can design an experiment that produces the maximum distillation rate.

Think Critically

Water droplets from the steam rising from the boiling water will condense on the evaporating dish. The water will be colorless. The distillation process will separate the water from the food dye.

Assessment

Content Have each group imagine they are marooned on a tropical island without supplies. Ask them what island materials or materials they are wearing they could use to construct an apparatus for distilling water. The lens of a pair of glasses could magnify sunlight on dried grass to produce a fire. Empty coconut shells could replace beakers and large tropical leaves could replace the evaporating dish.

Dinah Zike Study Fold

Student preparation materials for this Foldable are available in the **Chapter *Fast File* Resources.**

Additional Chapter Media

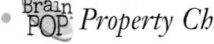

-  *Property Changes*
- Virtual Lab: *How can molecular models be built?*
- Video Lab: *Demonstrating the Distillation of Water*

section 1

Composition of Matter

Reading Guide

What You'll Learn

- **Define** substances and mixtures.
- **Identify** elements and compounds.
- **Compare and contrast** solutions, colloids, and suspensions.

Why It's Important

You can form a better picture of your world when you understand the concepts of elements and compounds.

Review Vocabulary

property: characteristic or essential quality

New Vocabulary

- substance
- element
- compound
- heterogeneous mixture
- homogeneous mixture
- solution
- colloid
- Tyndall effect
- suspension

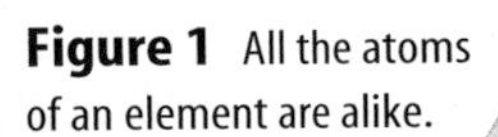

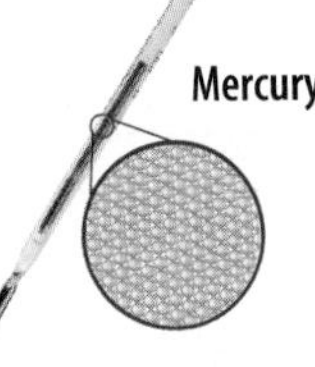

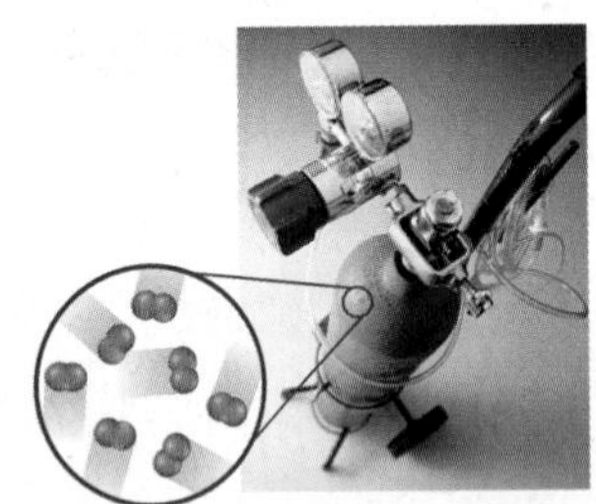

Figure 1 All the atoms of an element are alike.

Pure Substances

Have you ever seen a picture hanging on a wall that looked just like a real painting? Did you have to touch it to find out? If so, the rough or smooth surface told you which it was. Each material has its own properties. The properties of materials can be used to classify them into general categories.

Materials are made of a pure substance or a mixture of substances. A pure **substance,** or simply a substance, is a type of matter with a fixed composition. A substance can be either an element or a compound. Some substances you might recognize are helium, aluminum, water, and salt.

Elements All substances are built from atoms. If all the atoms in a substance have the same identity, that substance is an **element.** The graphite in your pencil point and the copper coating of most pennies are examples of elements. In graphite all the atoms are carbon atoms, and in a copper sample, all the atoms are copper atoms. The metal substance beneath the copper in the penny is another element—zinc. About 90 elements are found on Earth. More than 20 others have been made in laboratories, but most of these are unstable and exist only for short periods of time. Some elements you might recognize are shown in **Figure 1.** Some less common elements and their properties are shown in **Figure 2.**

1 Motivate

Bellringer

Section Focus Transparencies also are available on the Interactive Chalkboard CD-ROM. L2 ELL

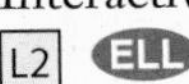

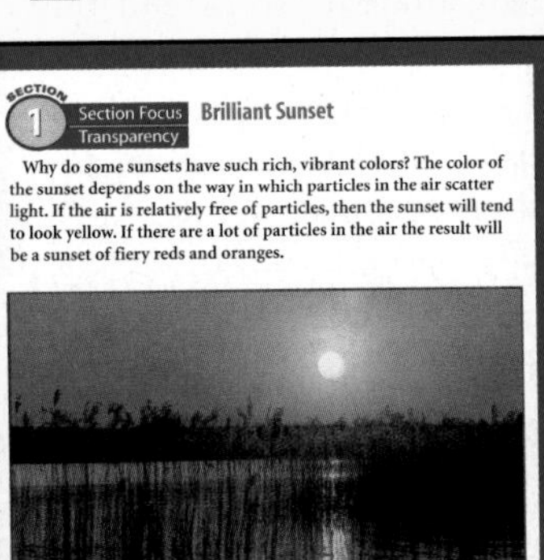

Section 1 Section Focus Transparency **Brilliant Sunset**

Why do some sunsets have such rich, vibrant colors? The color of the sunset depends on the way in which particles in the air scatter light. If the air is relatively free of particles, then the sunset will tend to look yellow. If there are a lot of particles in the air the result will be a sunset of fiery reds and oranges.

1. What are some components of air?
2. Why might air be referred to as a mixture?
3. Do you think air pollution can affect how we see the sky? Explain.

L2

Classification of Matter

Tie to Prior Knowledge

Ice Cream Sodas Ask students to describe the types of substances present in an ice cream soda. Possible answer: liquid and solid ice cream, liquid flavored syrup, liquid soda water, gas carbon dioxide, whipped cream, solid cherry Tell students that the whipped cream is a colloid—a heterogeneous mixture in which the particles are very small. L2

Section 1 Resource Manager

Chapter *Fast File* Resources

Transparency Activity, pp. 42, 45–46

Directed Reading for Content Mastery, pp. 19, 20

Note-taking Worksheets, pp. 31–32

MiniLAB, p. 3

Lab Activity, pp. 9–12

Lab Worksheet, pp. 5–6

Physical Science Critical Thinking/Problem Solving, p. 9

Cultural Diversity, p. 67

NATIONAL GEOGRAPHIC **VISUALIZING ELEMENTS**

Figure 2

Most of us think of gold as a shiny yellow metal used to make jewelry. However, it is an element that is also used in more unexpected ways, such as in spacecraft parts. On the other hand, some less common elements, such as americium (am uh REE see um), are used in everyday objects. Some elements and their uses are shown here.

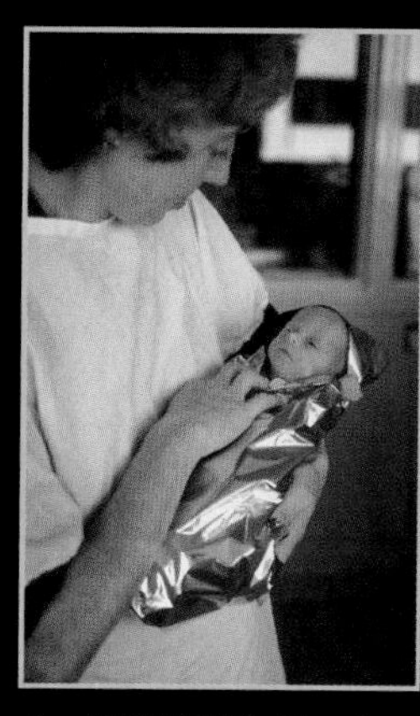

▲ ALUMINUM Aluminum is an excellent reflector of heat. Here, an aluminum plastic laminate is used to retain the body heat of a newborn baby.

▲ TUNGSTEN Although tungsten can be combined with steel to form a very durable metal, in its pure form it is soft enough to be stretched to form the filament of a lightbulb. Tungsten has the highest melting point of any metal.

▲ TITANIUM (tie TAY nee um) Parts of the exterior of the Guggenheim Museum in Bilbao, Spain, are made of titanium panels. Strong and lightweight, titanium is also used for body implants.

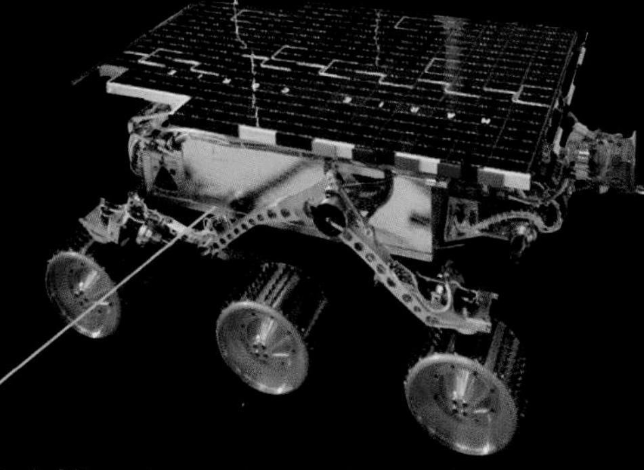

▲ GOLD Gold's resistance to corrosion and its ability to reflect infrared radiation make it an excellent coating for space vehicles. The electronic box on the six-wheel Sojourner Rover, above, part of NASA's Pathfinder 1997 mission to Mars, is coated with gold.

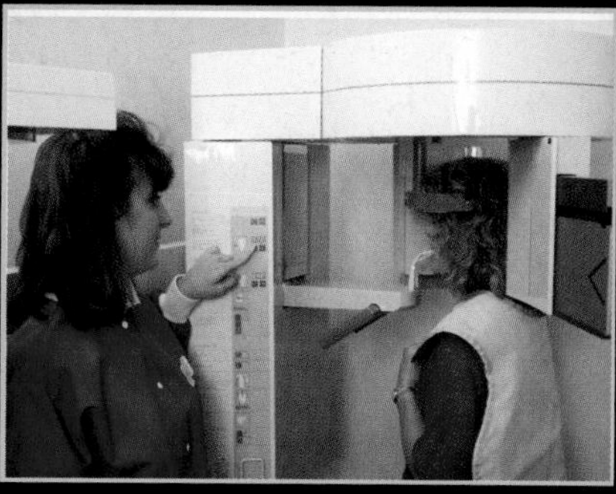

▲ LEAD Because lead has a high density, it is a good barrier to radiation. Dentists drape lead aprons on patients before taking X rays of the patient's teeth to reduce radiation exposure.

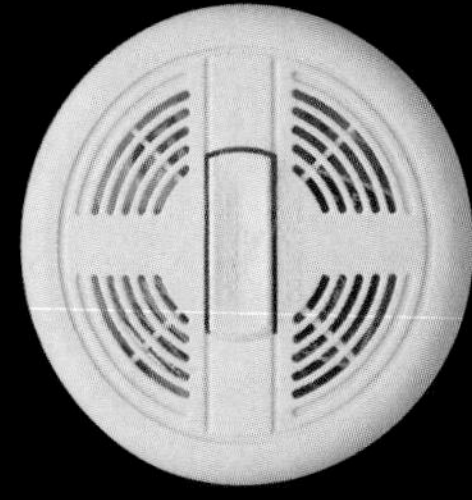

◀ AMERICIUM Named after America, where it was first produced, americium is a component of this smoke detector. It is a radioactive metal that must be handled with care to avoid contact.

NATIONAL GEOGRAPHIC

Visualizing Elements

Have students examine the pictures and read the captions. Then ask the following questions.

Why is pure tungsten used for the filaments of light bulbs? Because it is durable and stretchable, and has the highest melting point of any metal.

Why is it important to drape the trunk of your body during X rays? To avoid unnecessary radiation exposure to your vital organs.

Can you think of other ways that the reflective properties of aluminum are used? Answers will vary but may include some of the following: cooking, emergency blankets, and signaling mirrors.

Why would the Sojourner Rover need to reflect infrared radiation? To protect the equipment inside the box from excessive infrared radiation. L2 LS **Visual-Spatial**

Activity

Smoke Detectors Have students research and find out why americium is used in smoke detectors. Have the students report their findings to the class. L2

LS **Linguistic, Intrapersonal**

Differentiated Instruction

Challenge Have students find out why titanium is used for body implants and why it is used in aircraft landing gear. The students should report their findings to their class. L3

2 Teach

Discussion

Two Liquids Describe for students two liquids. Tell them that both liquids contain only hydrogen and oxygen, and both liquids are transparent and colorless. How can the two liquids have different identities? They have different combinations of atoms. One liquid is water, H_2O; the other is hydrogen peroxide, H_2O_2. L2

LS **Logical-Mathematical**

Definition of Compounds Students may think that elements made from more than one atom such as Cl_2, H_2, S_8, or P_4, are compounds. However, compounds must be made from combinations of different elements.

Use an Analogy

Pedal Power In pedal-powered vehicles, the ratio of one frame to one wheel makes a unicycle. One frame to two wheels forms a bicycle. One frame to three wheels produces a tricycle. Similarly, one carbon to one atom of oxygen makes carbon monoxide. One carbon to two oxygen atoms is carbon dioxide. These compounds do not have the same properties.

Reading Check

Answer Compounds contain two or more different elements.

Compounds Two or more elements can combine to form substances called compounds. A **compound** is a substance in which the atoms of two or more elements are combined in a fixed proportion. For example, water is a compound in which two atoms of the element hydrogen combine with one atom of the element oxygen. Chalk contains calcium, carbon, and oxygen in the proportion of one atom of calcium and carbon to three atoms of oxygen.

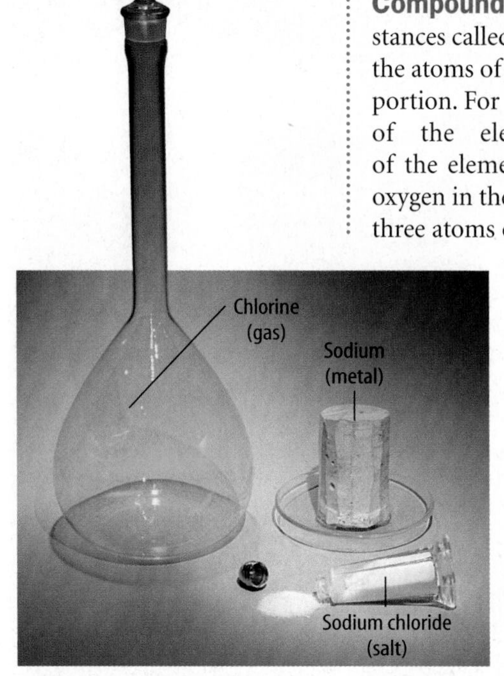

Figure 3 Chlorine gas and sodium metal combine dramatically in the ratio of one to one to form sodium chloride.

Reading Check *How are elements and compounds related?*

Can you imagine yourself putting something made from a silvery metal and a greenish-yellow, poisonous gas on your food? You might have shaken some on your food today—table salt is a chemical compound that fits this description. Even though it looks like white crystals and adds flavor to food, its components—sodium and chlorine—are neither white nor salty, as shown in **Figure 3.** Like salt, compounds usually look different from the elements in them.

Mixtures

Are pizza and a soft drink one of your favorite lunches? If so, you enjoy two foods that are classified as mixtures—but two different kinds of mixtures. A mixture, such as the pizza or soft drink shown in **Figure 4,** is a material made up of two or more substances that can be easily separated by physical means.

Figure 4 Pizza and soft drinks, like most foods, are mixtures.

Science Journal

Elements and Compounds Ask students to list in their Science Journals all the elements and chemical compounds they can think of without looking them up. Have them look up the chemical symbols for the elements and the chemical formulas for the compounds. Have them write the formulas next to the names of the substances.

L2 ELL P LS **Linguistic**

Differentiated Instruction

English-Language Learners Provide physical examples of various elements, compounds, and mixtures, and have them labelled to aid the students in developing their vocabulary.

452 CHAPTER 15 Classification of Matter

Heterogeneous Mixtures Unlike compounds, mixtures do not always contain the same proportions of the substances that make them up—the pizza chef doesn't measure precisely how much of each topping is sprinkled on. You easily can see most of the toppings on a pizza. A mixture in which different materials can be distinguished easily is called a **heterogeneous** (he tuh ruh JEE nee us) **mixture.** Granite, concrete, and dry soup mixes are other heterogeneous mixtures you can recognize.

You might be wearing another heterogeneous mixture—clothing made of permanent-press fabric like that seen in **Figure 5A.** Such fabric contains fibers of two materials—polyester and cotton. The amounts of polyester and cotton can vary from one article of clothing to another, as shown by the label. Though you might not be able to distinguish the two fibers just by looking at them with your naked eye, you probably could tell using a microscope, as shown in **Figure 5B.** Therefore, a permanent-press fabric is also a heterogeneous mixture.

Most of the substances you come in contact with every day are heterogeneous mixtures. Some components are easy to see, like the ingredients in pizza, but others are not. In fact, the component you see can be a mixture itself. For example, the cheese in pizza is also a mixture, but you cannot see the individual components. Cheese contains many compounds, such as milk proteins, butterfat, colorings, and other food additives.

Separating Mixtures

Procedure

1. Put equal amounts of **soil, clay, sand, gravel,** and **pebbles** in a **clear-plastic container.** Add **water** until the container is almost full. Wash your hands well after handling the materials.
2. Stir or shake the mixture thoroughly. Predict the order in which the materials will settle.
3. Observe what happens and compare your observations to your predictions.

Analysis

1. In what order did the materials settle?
2. Explain why the materials settled in the order they did.

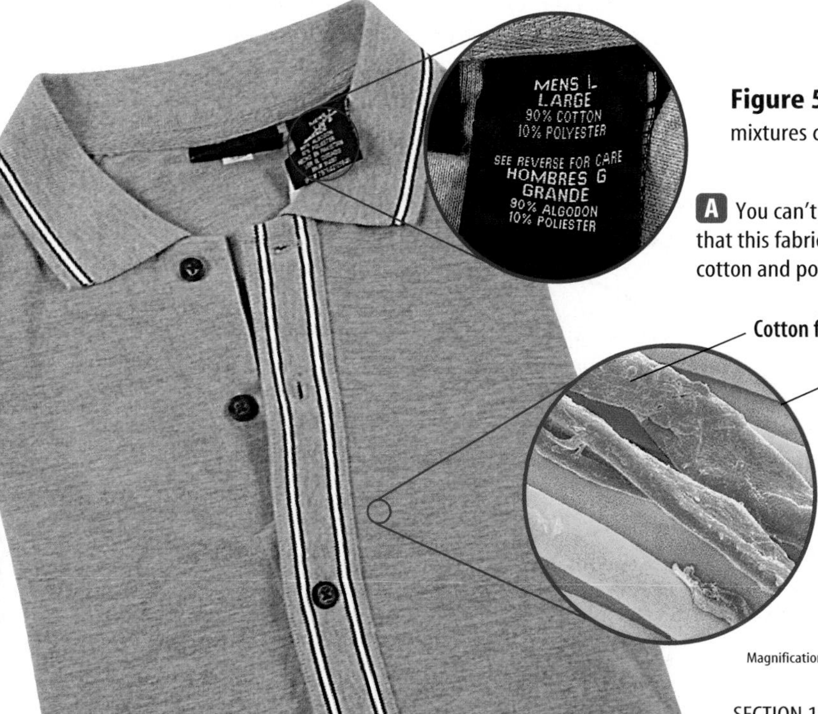

Figure 5 Heterogeneous mixtures can be hard to detect.

A You can't tell at a glance that this fabric is a mixture of cotton and polyester.

B With a microscope however, the difference between the two fibers is clear—the polyester fiber is perfectly smooth and the cotton is rough.

Purpose Students observe that heterogeneous mixtures have identifiable components that do not lose their identities while in the mixture. IS **Kinesthetic**

Materials transparent-plastic gallon jar, soil, clay, sand, gravel, small pebbles, water

Teaching Strategy Have students write down their predictions of the order of settling before they make the mixture.

Analysis

1. gravel, pebbles, sand, soil, clay
2. The materials settled out by particle size. L2 IS **Logical-Mathematical, Kinesthetic, Linguistic, Visual Spatial**

Assessment

Performance Have students devise a plan to separate the individual materials and then implement their plan. Use **Performance Assessment in the Science Classroom,** p. 95. L2 IS **Kinesthetic, Visual-Spatial**

Virtual Labs

Modeling *How can molecular models be built?*

Teacher FYI

Phases Heterogeneous mixtures contain more than one phase. A phase is a region with uniform properties that has a boundary between itself and other areas of uniform properties. For example, the structure, heat capacity, and density of floating ice vary from the liquid water in which it is floating.

Discussion

Homogeneous Mixtures Remind students that the components of a homogeneous mixture are blended evenly throughout the mixture. Tell students that an alloy can be a solid homogeneous mixture of metals. How can two solid metals mix homogeneously? The metals are melted, mixed as liquids, and then allowed to become solid again. L2 LS **Logical-Mathematical, Visual-Spatial**

Activity

Bag Project Bring four bags to class. Using large lettering, label the bags *Element*, *Compound*, *Homogeneous*, and *Heterogeneous*. Have students bring objects from home and place each one in the proper bag. After a week, empty the bags and discuss their contents and their classifications with the class. L2 ELL LS **Kinesthetic**

Visual Learning

Figure 7 Bring to class some aluminum foil, cereal with raisins, and liquid made from powdered, flavored drink mix dissolved in water. Have students classify these materials using the chart shown in **Figure 7.** Aluminum foil is an element; raisin cereal is a heterogeneous mixture; powdered, flavored drink mix dissolved in water is a homogeneous mixture. L2 LS **Visual-Spatial, Kinesthetic**

Answer a homogeneous mixture

Figure 6 A soft drink can be either heterogeneous or homogeneous. As carbon dioxide fizzes out it is a heterogeneous mixture.

The resulting flat soft drink is a homogeneous mixture of water, sugar, flavor, color, and some remaining carbon dioxide.

Homogeneous Mixtures Remember that soft drink you had with your pizza? Soft drinks contain water, sugar, flavoring, coloring, and carbon dioxide gas. **Figure 6** will help you to visualize these particles in a liquid soft drink.

Soft drinks in sealed bottles are examples of homogeneous mixtures. A **homogeneous** (hoh muh JEE nee us) **mixture** contains two or more gaseous, liquid, or solid substances blended evenly throughout. However, a soft drink in which you can see bubbles of carbon dioxide gas and ice cubes is a heterogeneous mixture.

Vinegar is another homogeneous mixture. It appears clear even though it is made up of particles of acetic acid mixed with water. Another name for homogeneous mixtures like vinegar and a cold soft drink is solution. A **solution** is a homogeneous mixture of particles so small that they cannot be seen with a microscope and will never settle to the bottom of their container. Solutions remain constantly and uniformly mixed. The differences between substances and mixtures are summarized in **Figure 7.**

Reading Check *What kind of mixture is a solution?*

Colloids Milk is an example of a specific kind of mixture called a colloid. It contains water, fats, and proteins in varying proportions. Like a solution, its components won't settle if left standing. A **colloid** (KAH loyd) is a type of mixture with particles that are larger than those in solutions but not heavy enough to settle out. The word *colloid* comes from a Greek word for glue. The first colloids studied were in gelatin, a source of some types of glue.

Paint is an example of a liquid with suspended colloid particles. Gases and solids can contain colloidal particles, too. For example, fog consists of particles of liquid water suspended in air, and smoke contains solids suspended in air.

Figure 7 All matter can be divided into substances and mixtures.

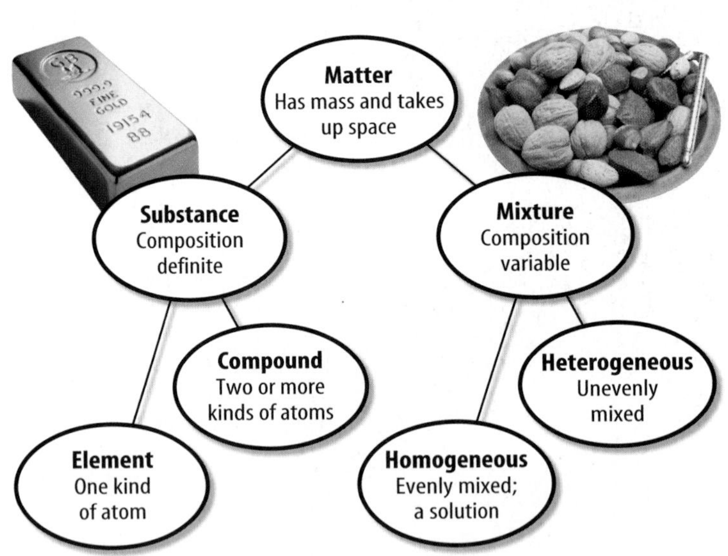

Curriculum Connection

Math Have students express the particle diameter given for solutions (0.000,000,001 m) in exponential notation. 1×10^{-9} m Then, ask them to convert the number to inches and to calculate how many particles it would take to go across one cm. 1×10^{-9} m $\times$ (100 cm/1 m) $= 1 \times 10^{-7}$ cm/particle, then 1 cm $\times$ (1 particle/1×10^{-7} cm) $= 1 \times 10^{7}$ or 10,000,000 particles. L3 LS **Logical-Mathematical**

454 CHAPTER 15 Classification of Matter

Figure 8 Fog is a colloid composed of water droplets suspended in air.

The light from the headlights is scattered by fog.

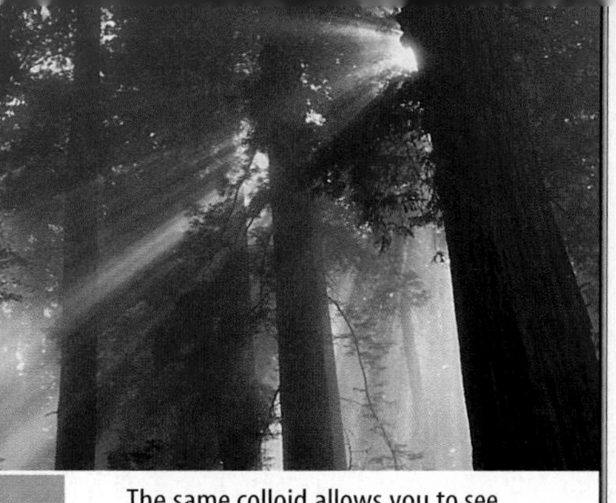

The same colloid allows you to see the sunlight as it streams through the trees.

Detecting Colloids One way to distinguish a colloid from a solution is by its appearance. Fog appears white because its particles are large enough to scatter light as shown in **Figure 8.** Sometimes it is not so obvious that a liquid is a colloid. For example, some shampoos and gelatins are colloids called gels that appear almost clear. You can tell for certain if a liquid is a colloid by passing a beam of light through it, as shown in **Figure 9.** A light beam is invisible as it passes through a solution, but can be seen readily as it passes through a colloid. This occurs because the particles in the colloid are large enough to scatter light, but those in the solution are not. This scattering of light by colloidal particles is called the **Tyndall effect.**

Reading Check *How can you distinguish a colloid from a solution?*

Figure 9 Because of the Tyndall effect, a light beam is scattered by the colloid suspension on the right, but passes invisibly through the solution on the left.

Use Science Words

Word Meaning Have students find out the names of colloids in which liquids contain liquids, liquids contain solids, and gases contain liquids or solids. Colloids of liquids in liquids are emulsions, colloids of solids in liquids are sols (once cooled, they are called gels), colloids of liquids or solids in gases are called aerosols. L3 LS **Linguistic**

Fun Fact

The Tyndall effect is named after Irish scientist John Tyndall, who first described the effect in the mid-1800s.

Reading Check

Answer Pass a beam of light through it and check for the Tyndall effect.

Active Reading

Learning Journal This strategy encourages students to interact with the reading, allowing personal responses. The left column entries can be research notes, lectures notes, or vocabulary terms. The right column entries are the student's response to, interpretation of, questions about, or analysis of the left column entries. L2 LS **Linguistic, Visual-Spatial**

Differentiated Instruction

Challenge Ask students to determine the connection between beautiful red sunsets and suspensions. The atmosphere around Earth has many suspended particles that scatter light. The more of these particles the light passes through, the redder the light appears. During a sunset, the Sun is low in the sky, so we see its light through a large number of scattering particles. Sunsets are particularly beautiful in years in which volcanic eruptions take place. L3 LS **Logical Mathematical**

Type Suspension Another type suspension is found in the meltwater of glaciers. This water has an opaque appearance caused by suspended soil and rock particles that eventually settle out. Ask students what size the particles in meltwater must be. greater than 100 nm

3 Assess

DAILY INTERVENTION

Check for Understanding

Kinesthetic Place red food coloring, sand, milk, water vinegar, and a clear drinking glass on a table. Allow students to mix these various substances in the order they choose. Have students write down observations and explain what qualities the mixtures exhibit after each addition of a new substance. L2 **LS Linguistic, Visual-Spatial**

Reteach

Compounds Place some NaCl and sand in a clear container and stir them together. Next, place some NaCl and water in a clear beaker and stir them together. Ask the class whether a new compound was formed in either process. no L2 **LS Visual-Spatial**

Assessment

Oral Burn a small sample of paper, and ask students to identify any elements, compounds, or mixtures. element: oxygen; compounds: carbon dioxide, the cellulose in the paper; mixtures: air, smoke particles in the air Use **Performance Assessment in the Science Classroom,** p. 89. L2 **Visually Impaired LS Visual-Spatial, Kinesthetic**

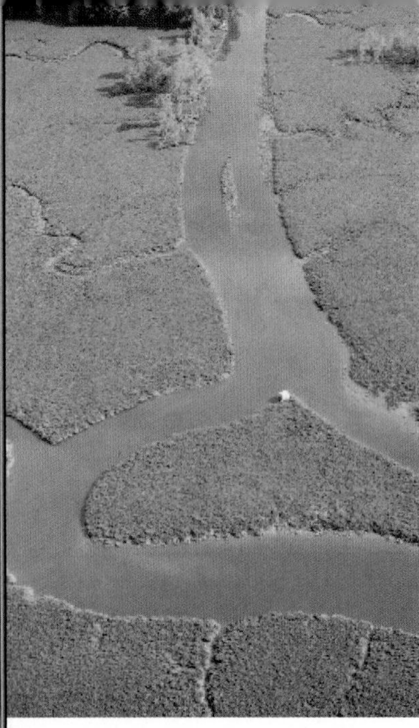

Figure 10 The mud deposited by the Mississippi River is said to be more than 10,000 m thick.

Table 1 Comparing Solutions, Colloids, and Suspensions

Description	Solutions	Colloids	Suspensions
Settle upon standing?	no	no	yes
Separate using filter paper?	no	no	yes
Particle size	0.1–1 nm	1–100 nm	>100 nm
Scatter light?	no	yes	yes

Suspensions Some mixtures are neither solutions nor colloids. One example is muddy pond water. If pond water stands long enough, some mud particles will fall to the bottom, and the water clears. Pond water is a **suspension,** which is a heterogeneous mixture containing a liquid in which visible particles settle. **Table 1** summarizes the properties of different types of mixtures.

River deltas are a large scale example of how a suspension settles. Rivers flow swiftly through narrow channels, picking up soil and debris along the way. As the river widens, it flows more slowly. Suspended particles settle forming deltas at the mouth, as shown in **Figure 10.**

section 1 review

Summary

Pure Substances

- An element is a substance in which all atoms have the same identity.
- A compound is a substance that has two or more elements combined in a fixed proportion.

Mixtures

- Heterogeneous mixtures are mixtures in which different materials can be distinguished easily.
- A homogeneous mixture contains two or more gaseous, liquid, or solid substances that are blended evenly throughout.
- Mixtures can be heterogeneous, homogeneous, colloids, or suspensions.

Self Check

1. **Describe** How is a compound similar to a homogeneous mixture? How is it different?
2. **Distinguish** between a substance and a mixture. Give two examples of each.
3. **Describe** the differences between colloids and suspensions.
4. **Think Critically** Why do the words "Shake well before using" indicate that the fruit juice is a suspension?

Applying Skills

5. **Compare and Contrast** In terms of suspensions and colloids, compare and contrast a glass of milk and a glass of fresh-squeezed orange juice.

gpscience.com/self_check

section 1 review

1. Both compounds and homogeneous mixtures are made of more than one element and are homogeneous. However, compounds must be made from elements in an exact ratio and involve chemical bonds between the elements in them.
2. A substance must be either an element or a compound. Mixtures can be made from combinations of compounds or elements.
3. Colloids do not settle out; suspensions eventually do settle out. Particles in colloids are smaller than particles in suspensions.
4. Because materials in suspensions settle out.
5. Milk is a colloid. Fat globules are small enough to keep from settling out. Orange juice is a suspension.

Elements, Compounds, and Mixtures

Elements, compounds, and mixtures all contain atoms. In elements, the atoms all have the same identity. In compounds, two or more elements have been combined in a fixed ratio. In mixtures, the ratio of substances can vary.

Real-World Question

What are some differences among elements, compounds, and mixtures?

Goals

- **Determine** whether several materials are elements, compounds, or mixtures.

Materials

plastic freezer bag containing the following labeled items:

copper wire
small package of salt
graphite from pencil
aluminum foil
chalk (calcium carbonate)
piece of granite
sugar water in a vial

Safety Precautions

Procedure

1. Copy the data table into your Science Journal and use it to record your observations.
2. Obtain a bag of objects. Identify each object and classify it as an element, compound, heterogeneous mixture, or homogeneous mixture. The elements appear in the periodic table. Compounds are named as examples in Section 1.

Conclude and Apply

1. If you know the name of a substance, how can you find out whether or not it is an element?
2. **Explain** how the appearance of the items is different. Which would you classify as a compound? Why? Which would you classify as a mixture? Why?
3. **Discuss** how chalk is different from the granite in relation to compounds and mixtures.

Classification of Objects

Object	Identity	Classification
1		
2		
3		
4		
5		
6		
7		

Communicating Your Data

Enter your data in the data table and compare your findings with those of your classmates. **For more help, refer to the** Science Skill Handbook.

Real-World Question

Purpose Students classify materials based on their appearance and chemical makeup. L2 LS **Logical Mathematical**

Process Skills observe, classify

Time Required 25 minutes

Procedure

Teaching Strategy Introduce formulas for the compounds or have students look them up.

Conclude and Apply

1. Check the periodic table.
2. Answers could include milk (mixture), water (compound), and soft drinks (mixture). Students will find few, if any, elements.
3. Milk is a heterogeneous mixture that is a colloid; uncarbonated soft drinks are homogeneous mixtures.

Assessment

Process Have students make homogeneous and heterogeneous mixtures and describe the mixtures and their components. Use **Performance Assessment in the Science Classroom**, p. 89. L2 LS **Kinesthetic, Visual-Spatial**

Communicating Your Data

As a class, discuss reasons for any differences in students' results. L2 LS **Logical-Mathematical**

section 2 Properties of Matter

1 Motivate

Bellringer

Section Focus Transparencies also are available on the Interactive Chalkboard CD-ROM. L2 

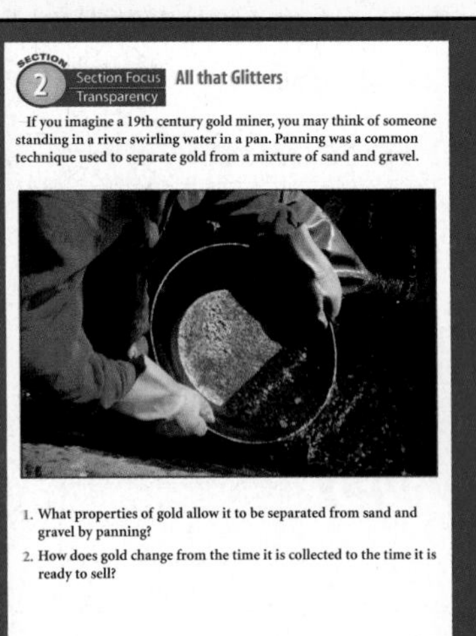
SECTION 2 Section Focus Transparency **All that Glitters**

If you imagine a 19th century gold miner, you may think of someone standing in a river swirling water in a pan. Panning was a common technique used to separate gold from a mixture of sand and gravel.

1. What properties of gold allow it to be separated from sand and gravel by panning?
2. How does gold change from the time it is collected to the time it is ready to sell?

L2

Tie to Prior Knowledge

Visiting Places Ask students to describe, without naming it, a place that they have visited. As others try to determine the site, remind students that any description, whether of matter or of a place, requires careful attention to important properties. L1 **Visual-Spatial**

Text Question Answer

size, shape, color, surface, density, mass

Text Question Answer

Mass could be measured with a balance.

Reading Guide

What You'll Learn

- **Identify** substances using physical properties.
- **Compare and contrast** physical and chemical changes.
- **Identify** chemical changes.
- **Determine** how the law of conservation of mass applies to chemical changes.

Why It's Important

Understanding chemical and physical properties can help you use materials properly.

Review Vocabulary

state of matter: one of three physical forms of matter—solid, liquid, or gas

New Vocabulary

- physical property
- physical change
- distillation
- chemical property
- chemical change
- law of conservation of mass

Physical Properties

You can stretch a rubber band, but you can't stretch a piece of string very much, if at all. You can bend a piece of wire, but you can't easily bend a matchstick. In each case, the materials change shape, but the identity of the substances—rubber, string, wire, wood—does not change. The abilities to stretch and bend are physical properties. Any characteristic of a material that you can observe without changing the identity of the substances that make up the material is a **physical property.** Examples of other physical properties are color, shape, size, density, melting point, and boiling point. What physical properties can you use to describe the items in **Figure 11?**

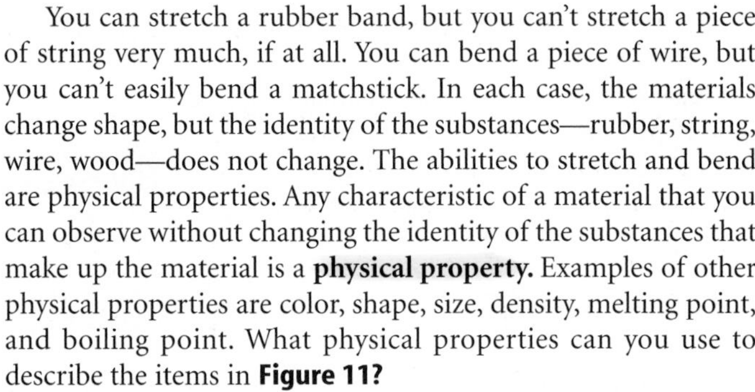

Figure 11 Appearance is the most obvious physical property. **Describe** *the appearance of these items.*

Appearance How would you describe a tennis ball? You could begin by describing its shape, color, and state of matter. For example, you might describe the tennis ball as a brightly colored, hollow sphere. You can measure some physical properties, too. For instance, you could measure the diameter of the ball. What physical property of the ball is measured with a balance?

To describe a soft drink in a cup, you could start by calling it a liquid with a brown color. You could measure its volume and temperature. Each of these characteristics is a physical property of that soft drink.

Section 2 Resource Manager 

Chapter *FAST FILE* Resources
- Transparency Activity, p. 43
- Directed Reading for Content Mastery, pp. 21, 22
- Lab Activity, pp. 13–16
- MiniLAB, p. 4
- Lab Worksheet, pp. 7–8

Home and Community Involvement, p. 43

Mathematics Skill Activities, p. 9

Physical Science Critical Thinking/Problem Solving, p. 10

Figure 12 The best way to separate substances depends on their physical properties. Size is the property used to separate poppy seeds from sunflower seeds in this example.

Behavior Some physical properties describe the behavior of a material or a substance. As you might know, objects that contain iron, such as a safety pin, are attracted by a magnet. Attraction to a magnet is a physical property of the substance iron. Every substance has a specific combination of physical properties that make it useful for certain tasks. Some metals, such as copper, can be drawn out into wires. Others, such as gold, can be pounded into sheets as thin as 0.1 micrometers (µm), about 4-millionths of an inch. This property of gold makes it useful for decorating picture frames and other objects. Gold that has been beaten or flattened in this way is called gold leaf.

Think again about your soft drink. If you knock over the cup, the drink will spread out over the table or floor. If you knock over a jar of molasses, however, it does not flow as easily. The ability to flow is a physical property of liquids.

Using Physical Properties to Separate Removing the seeds from a watermelon can be easily done based on the physical properties of the seeds compared to the rest of the fruit. **Figure 12** shows a mixture of poppy seeds and sunflower seeds. You can identify the two kinds of seeds by differences in color, shape, and size. By sifting the mixture, you can separate the poppy seeds from the sunflower seeds quickly because their sizes differ.

Now look at the mixture of iron filings and sand shown in **Figure 12.** You probably won't be able to sift out the iron filings because they are similar in size to the sand particles. What you can do is pass a magnet through the mixture. The magnet attracts only the iron filings and pulls them from the sand. This is an example of how a physical property, such as magnetic attraction, can be used to separate substances in a mixture. Something like this is done to separate iron for recycling.

Magnetism easily separates iron from sand.

Recycling and Physical Properties Recycling conserves natural resources. In some large recycling projects, aluminum metal must be separated from scrap iron. What physical properties of the two metals could be used to separate them?

2 Teach

Caption Answer

Figure 11 The ball is spherical, fuzzy, all one color, and has a curved line on it. The rock is rough, has many colors, has several dark straight lines, and has an irregular shape.

Recycling and Physical Properties Since metallic iron is magnetic and metallic aluminum is not, strong magnets could attract iron from a mixture of iron and aluminum.

Quick Demo

Chemical Change

Materials beaker, candle, matches

Estimated Time 4 minutes

Procedure Hold the bottom of a glass beaker directly over a burning candle for a few minutes. What clues indicate that a chemical change has taken place? Carbon deposits begin to form on the outside of the beaker caused by the breakdown of the hydrocarbon candle wax. Carbon is released from its bonds with other carbon and hydrogen atoms. L2 IS **Visual-Spatial, Kinesthetic**

Differentiated Instruction

Challenge Tell students that viscosity is a measure of a fluid's resistance to flow. Have students contact a service station or an auto parts store and ask about viscosity ratings of motor oils. Higher viscosity oils have more resistance to flow and are used in warm weather, while lower viscosity motor oils flow more easily and are used in cold temperatures. L3
IS **Logical-Mathematical**

Learning Disabled Bring a magnet and some iron filings to class. Prepare a mixture of the iron filings and sugar. Ask students how they know the mixture is not the result of a chemical change, and how the mixture can be separated. The mixture looks like the components from which it was made; add water to dissolve the sugar but not the iron, or use a magnet to separate the iron from the sugar particles. L1
IS **Kinesthetic, Visual-Spatial**

Reading Check

Answer No, the identity of the element or compound remains the same.

Purpose Students determine whether an observed change is chemical or physical. L2 IS Kinesthetic

Materials water, potassium permanganate, sodium hydrogen sulfite, 250-mL beaker, stirring rod

Teaching Strategy Have students wear safety goggles and use spatulas to manipulate chemicals.

Analysis

1. physical change
2. The change in color from purple to colorless indicated that new substances were being formed.

Assessment

Oral Ask students what other evidence of a chemical change they might look for. Answers may vary but could include the presence of a gas, the presence of a precipitate, or a change in odor. Use **Performance Assessment in the Science Classroom,** p. 91.

Identifying Changes

Procedure

WARNING: *Clean up any spills promptly. Potassium permanganate can stain clothing.*

1. Add **water** to a **250-mL beaker** until it is half-full.
2. Add a crystal of **potassium permanganate** to the water and observe what happens.
3. Add 1 g of **sodium hydrogen sulfite** to the solution and stir it until the solution becomes colorless.

Analysis

1. Is dissolving a chemical or a physical change?
2. What evidence of a chemical change did you see?

Physical Change

If you break a piece of chewing gum, you change some of its physical properties—its size and shape. However, you have not changed the identity of the materials that make up the gum.

The Identity Remains the Same When a substance freezes, boils, evaporates, or condenses, it undergoes physical changes. A change in size, shape, or state of matter is called a **physical change.** These changes might involve energy changes, but the kind of substance—the identity of the element or compound—does not change. Because all substances have distinct properties like densities, specific heats, and boiling and melting points, which are constant, these properties can be used to help identify them when a particular mixture contains substances which are not yet identified.

Reading Check *Does a change in state mean that a new substance has formed? Explain.*

Iron is a substance that can change states if it absorbs or releases enough energy—at high temperatures, it melts. However, in both the solid and liquid state, iron has physical properties that identify it as iron. Color changes can accompany a physical change, too. For example, when iron is heated it first glows red. Then, if it is heated to a higher temperature, it turns white, as shown in **Figure 13.**

Using Physical Change to Separate A cool drink of water is something most people take for granted, but in some parts of the world, drinkable water is scarce. Not enough drinkable water can be obtained from wells. Many such areas that lie close to the sea obtain drinking water by using physical properties of water to separate it from the salt. One of these methods, which uses the property of boiling point, is a type of distillation.

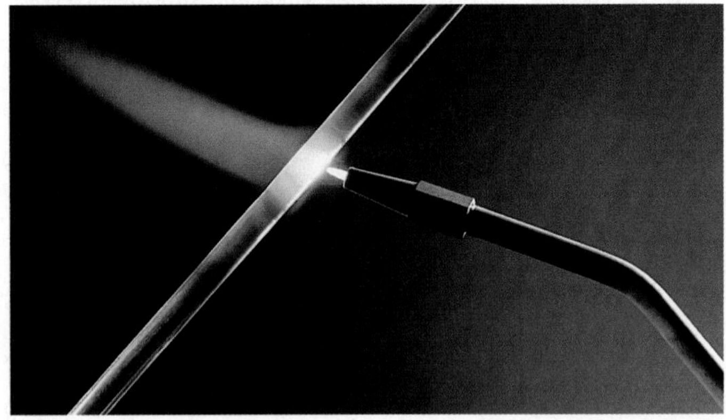

Figure 13 Heating iron raises its energy level and changes its color. These energy changes are physical changes because it is still iron.

LAB DEMONSTRATION

Purpose to separate a mixture by a physical property

Materials test tube, water, water-soluble black overhead marker, coffee filter, scissors

Preparation Place water in a test tube. Cut a strip of coffee filter that just fits into the tube. Use a marker to draw a line near the bottom of the strip.

Procedure Place the filter paper strip inside the tube. Make sure the ink line is slightly above the water level.

Expected Outcome Water will move up the paper and carry the ink with it. The dyes in the black ink will separate and other colors will become visible.

Assessment

What physical property of the dyes causes them to separate? solubility Are the dyes that move farther more or less soluble in water than the dyes that don't move as far? more soluble L2 IS **Visual-Spatial**

Distillation The process for separating substances in a mixture by evaporating a liquid and recondensing its vapor is **distillation.** It usually is done in the laboratory using an apparatus similar to that shown in **Figure 14.** As you can see, the liquid vaporizes and condenses, leaving the solid material behind.

Two liquids having different boiling points can be separated in a similar way. The mixture is heated slowly until it begins to boil. Vapors of the liquid with the lowest boiling point form first and are condensed and collected. Then, the temperature is increased until the second liquid boils, condenses, and is collected. Distillation is used often in industry. For instance, natural oils such as mint are distilled.

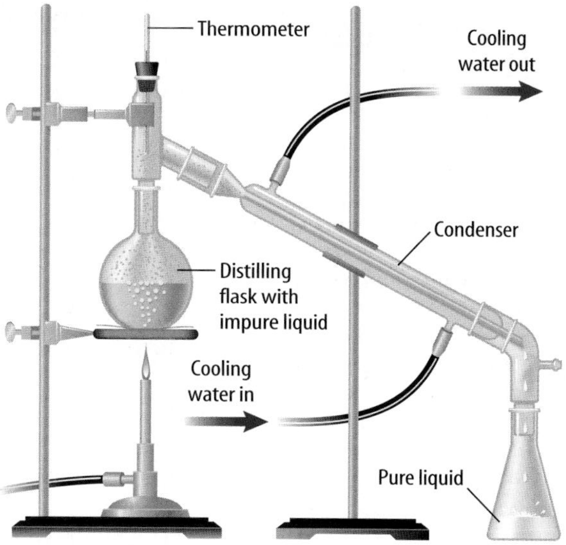

Figure 14 Distillation can easily separate liquids from solids dissolved in them. The liquid is heated until it vaporizes and moves up the column. Then, as it touches the water-cooled surface of the condenser, it becomes liquid again.

Chemical Properties and Changes

You probably have seen warnings on cans of paint thinners and lighter fluids for charcoal grills that say these liquids are flammable (FLA muh buhl). The tendency of a substance to burn, or its flammability, is an example of a chemical property because burning produces new substances during a chemical change. A **chemical property** is a characteristic of a substance that indicates whether it can undergo a certain chemical change. Many substances used around the home, such as lighter fluids, are flammable. Knowing which ones are flammable helps you to use them safely.

A less dramatic chemical change can affect some medicines. Look at **Figure 15.** You probably have seen bottles like this in a pharmacy. Many medicines are stored in dark bottles because they contain compounds that can change chemically if they are exposed to light.

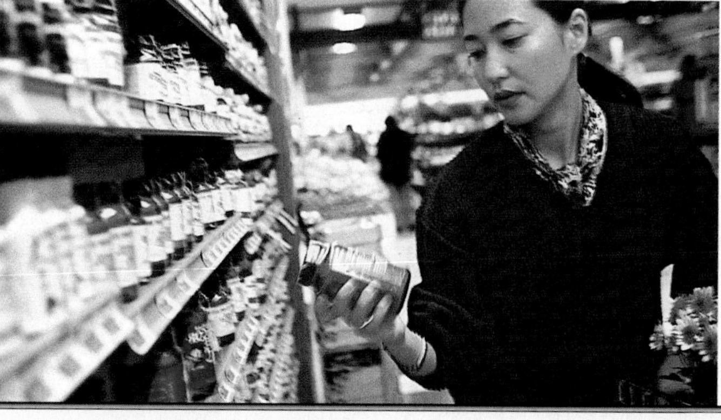

Figure 15 The brown color of these bottles tells you that these vitamins may react to light. Reaction to light is a chemical property.

Make a Model

Magnetism and Iron Turn a shoebox lid upside down and place iron filings and sand in the lid. Place a bar magnet underneath the lid and move it around while holding it against the bottom of the lid. Observe how the iron filings are both attracted and repulsed by the magnet depending upon the position of magnet. **Visual-Spatial**

Activity

Element Properties Ask students to pick a chemical element and use an encyclopedia or Internet source to make a list of its properties. Have them then divide the list into chemical and physical properties. L2 ELL
LS **Linguistic**

Discussion

Flammability What is involved in determining the flammability of a substance? Some of the factors used to determine flammability are temperature, vapor concentration, and ability to sustain combustion. Air is usually considered the oxidant in these measurements.

Fun Fact

Air or oxygen is not the only oxidant required for a substance to burn, there are also substances that will burn in fluorine gas.

Visual Learning

Figure 14 Review with students the distillation process, and ask a volunteer to trace the path of water through the apparatus shown in the figure. Explain that the distillate moves through the inner portion of the condenser, while cold water, which helps cool the distillate, runs through the outer portion. L2 LS **Visual-Spatial**

Curriculum Connection

History Compounds called nitrates played a major role in the history of Chile. Have students find out what chemical property makes nitrates important and what role they played in Chile. Nitrates are one component of explosives. Nitrates were Chile's largest export in the late 1800s, giving the country money for economic development. The nitrate market collapsed during World War I, when chemists discovered a way to synthesize nitrates. L3 LS **Linguistic**

SECTION 2 Properties of Matter 461

Reading Check

Answer a change of one substance to another

Alchemy Even though most people connect alchemy with the middle ages, alchemy started many years before that. References to alchemy can be found in Chinese, Egyptian, and Arabian histories.

Research Have students select and research a culture that has played a role in alchemy. Have students present their findings.

Career Meteorologists are scientists who study the earth's climate. They do more than just forecast the weather. Meteorologists are responsible for researching and analyzing weather patterns, air pollution, and global warming trends. They can work for the government, universities, or for private industries.

Inquiry Lab

Oxidation and Food

Purpose to demonstrate chemical reactions in common foods

Possible Materials potato, lemon juice, peach, pear, apple, bowls (2)

Teaching Strategies

- Cut the potato, peach, pear, and apple in half. Dip the exposed inner surface of one of the food items in the lemon juice, then place in bowl.
- Place the other half in another bowl and allow both items to sit for 30 minutes. Encourage students to explain the reactions that occurred and allow them to explore other questions that arise. L2 IS **Kinesthetic, Visual-Spatial**

For additional inquiry activities, see *Science Inquiry Labs*.

Alchemy In the Middle Ages, alchemy was an early form of chemistry devoted to the study of changing baser metals into gold and also to finding the elixir of perpetual youth. Based on what we know now about the properties of metals and biology, it is easy to understand why this field of study is no longer practiced.

Detecting Chemical Change

If you leave a pan of chili cooking unattended on the stove for too long, your nose soon tells you that something is wrong. Instead of a spicy aroma, you detect an unpleasant smell that alerts you that something is burning. This burnt odor is a clue telling you that a new substance has formed.

The Identity Changes The smell of rotten eggs and the formation of rust on bikes or car fenders are signs that a chemical change has taken place. A change of one substance to another is a **chemical change.** The foaming of an antacid tablet in a glass of water and the smell in the air after a thunderstorm are other signs of new substances being produced. In some chemical changes, a rapid release of energy—detected as heat, light, and sound—is a clue that changes are occurring.

Reading Check *What is a chemical change?*

Clues such as heat, cooling, or the formation of bubbles or solids in a liquid are helpful indicators that a reaction is taking place. However, the only sure proof is that a new substance is produced. Consider the following example. The heat, light, and sound produced when hydrogen gas combines with oxygen in a rocket engine are clear evidence that a chemical reaction has taken place. But no clues announce the reaction that takes place when iron combines with oxygen to form rust because the reaction takes place so slowly. The only clue that iron has changed into a new substance is the presence of rust. Burning and rusting are chemical changes because new substances form. You sometimes can follow the progress of a chemical reaction visually. For example, you can see lead nitrate forming in **Figure 16.**

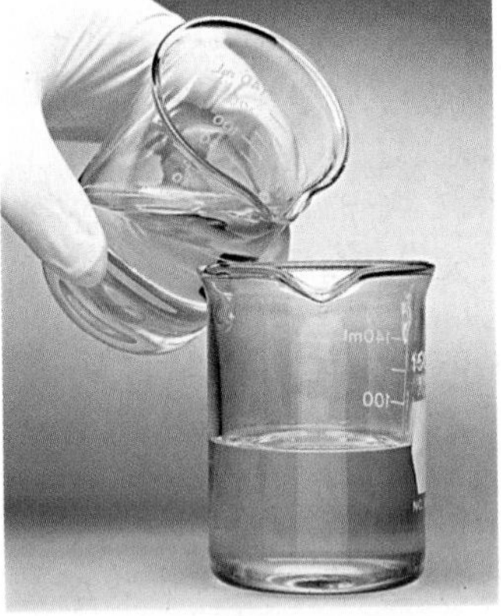

Figure 16 The solid forming from two liquids is another sign that a chemical reaction has taken place.

Science Journal

Chemical Changes in Daily Life Have students keep a log of chemical changes they encounter in a 24-hour period. The logs should describe each change and list clues that helped students conclude that the change was chemical. Answers could include: respiration—oxygen used, carbon dioxide released; combusting gasoline—carbon dioxide produced, heat released; cooking—an egg becomes white and solid. L2 P

IS **Linguistic, Visual-Spatial**

Using Chemical Change to Separate One case where you might separate substances using a chemical change is in cleaning tarnished silver. Tarnish is a chemical reaction between silver metal and sulfur compounds in the air which results in silver sulfide. It can be changed back into silver using a chemical reaction. This chemical reversal back to silver takes place when the tarnished item is placed in a warm water bath with baking soda and aluminum foil. You don't usually separate substances using chemical changes in the home. In industry and chemical laboratories, however, this kind of separation is common. For example, many metals are separated from their ores and then purified using chemical changes.

Law of Conservation of Mass

Calculating Total Mass of Product

When a chemical reaction takes place, the total mass of reactants equals the total mass of products. If 18 g of hydrogen react completely with 633 g of chlorine, how many grams of HCl are formed? The equation for this reaction is: $H_2 + Cl_2 \rightarrow 2HCl$

1. **This is what you know:** mass of H_2 = 18 g; mass of Cl_2 = 633 g
2. **This is what you need to find:** mass of HCl
3. **Use this formula:** total mass of reactants = total mass of products; mass of H_2 + mass of Cl_2 = mass of HCl
4. **Substitute:** 18 g + 633 g = 651 g
5. **Determine the units:** units of H_2 + units of Cl_2 = g + g = g

Answer: The mass of the product, HCl, is 651g.

Science Online

For more practice problems, go to page 834, and visit gpscience.com/extra_problems.

Practice Problems

1. In the following reaction, 24 g of CH_4 (methane) react completely with 96 g of O_2 to form 66 g of CO_2. How many grams of H_2O are formed? $CH_4 + 2O_2 \rightarrow CO_2 + 2H_2O$
2. **Challenge** In the following equation, 54.0 g of Al react completely with 409.2 g of $ZnCl_2$ to form 196.2 g of Zn metal. How many grams of $AlCl_3$ are formed? $2Al + 3ZnCl_2 \rightarrow 3Zn + 2AlCl_3$

Quick Demo

Chemical Properties

Materials beakers, pennies, file, 50 mL of 1*M* hydrochloric acid

Estimated Time 10 minutes

Safety Precautions

Procedure Obtain two relatively new pennies. Carefully file away the copper covering from the edge of one. Place both pennies in separate small beakers. Pour about 50 mL of 1*M* hydrochloric acid over both pennies. Point out the filed edge exposing the zinc metal that makes up the inside of a penny. Ask the class to report their observations of any interaction between the pennies and the acid. The exposed zinc reacts with the acid to form a gas, hydrogen. The other penny has only copper exposed to the acid and shows no reaction. Point out that this difference in chemical properties could be used to separate copper from zinc. L2 LS **Visual-Spatial, Kinesthetic**

Law of Conservation of Mass

National Math Standards

Correlation to Mathematics Objectives

1, 2, 9

Teaching Strategy

Have students count the atoms of each type of element. The number is the same on both sides of the equation. The total number of atoms of reactants will equal the total number of atoms of products. In the example, there are a total of four atoms: two hydrogens on each side. L2 LS **Logical-Mathematical**

Answers to Practice Problems

1. ($24\ g\ CH_4 + 96\ gO_2$) = ($66\ g\ CO_2 + x\ g\ H_2O$)
   $120\ g - 66\ g = 54\ g\ H_2O$
2. ($54\ g\ Al + 409.2\ g\ ZnCl_2$) = ($196.2\ g\ Zn + x\ g\ AlCl_3$)
   $463.2\ g = 196.2\ g + 267\ g\ AlCl_3$

Cultural Diversity

Chinese Chemistry The Chinese used chemical reactions to separate silver from lead and other impurities. In a process known as cupellation, they used high temperatures and blasts of air to oxidize the lead and other impurities, leaving pure silver behind.

Quick Demo

Physical and Chemical Changes

Materials chalk, file, dilute hydrochloric acid

Estimated Time five minutes

Safety Precautions

WARNING: *Wear goggles, gloves, and an apron. Avoid direct contact with the acid.*

Procedure A piece of chalk can be used to show the physical and chemical changes discussed in the text. Have students observe the chalk and note its size, appearance, and color. Next, file the chalk to show bits of it breaking away and reducing its size and form. This illustrates physical changes such as those produced by wind, geological movements, or cracking. Now take the same chalk, and place it in dilute hydrochloric acid. A noticeable gas-producing reaction ensues. This is a chemical change that produces new products, including carbon dioxide gas. L2 ELL IS **Visual-Spatial, Kinesthetic**

Matter Conservation Students may think that matter is not conserved in physical or chemical changes. Refer to page F at the beginning of this chapter for teaching strategies that address this misconception.

Reading Check

Answer The mass of all substances present before a chemical change equals the mass of all the substances remaining after the change.

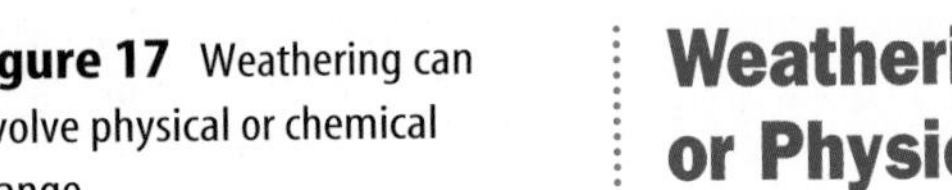

Flowing water shaped and smoothed these rocks in a physical process.

Both chemical and physical changes shaped the famous White Cliffs of Dover lining the English Channel.

Figure 17 Weathering can involve physical or chemical change.

Topic: Caves
Visit gpscience.com for Web links to information about cave formations.

Activity Describe the formation of stalactites and stalagmites. Explain the differences between the two and whether they are the result of a physical and/or chemical process.

Weathering—Chemical or Physical Change?

The forces of nature continuously shape Earth's surface. Rocks split, deep canyons are carved out, sand dunes shift, and curious limestone formations decorate caves. Do you think these changes, often referred to as weathering, are physical or chemical? The answer is both. Geologists, who use the same criteria that you have learned in this chapter, say that some weathering changes are physical and some are chemical.

Physical Large rocks can split when water seeps into small cracks, freezes, and expands. However, the smaller pieces of newly exposed rock still have the same properties as the original sample. This is a physical change. Streams can cut through softer rock, forming canyons, and can smooth and sculpt harder rock, as shown at left in **Figure 17.** In each case, the stream carries rock particles far downstream before depositing them. Because the particles are unchanged, the change is a physical one.

Chemical In other cases, the change is chemical. For example, solid calcium carbonate, a compound found in limestone, does not dissolve easily in water. However, when the water is even slightly acidic, as it is when it contains some dissolved carbon dioxide, calcium carbonate reacts. It changes into a new substance, calcium hydrogen carbonate, which does dissolve in water. This change in limestone is a chemical change because the identity of the calcium carbonate changes. The White Cliffs of Dover, shown at right in **Figure 17,** are made of limestone and undergo such chemical changes, as well as physical changes. A similar chemical change produces caves and the icicle-shaped rock formations that often are found in them.

Teacher FYI

Changing Limestone The weathering of Dover's white cliffs involves the breakdown of limestone into soluble compounds. The formation of stalactites in caves involves the precipitation of limestone from water solutions. Thus, the formation of stalactites is the reverse of the weathering of the cliffs of Dover.

The Conservation of Mass

Wood is combustible, or burnable. As you just learned, this is a chemical property. Suppose you burn a large log in the fireplace, as shown in **Figure 18,** until nothing is left but a small pile of ashes. Smoke, heat, and light are given off and the changes in the appearance of the log confirm that a chemical change took place. At first, you might think that matter was lost during this change because the pile of ashes looks much smaller than the log did. In fact, the mass of the ashes is less than that of the log. However, suppose that you could collect all the oxygen in the air that was combined with the log during the burning and all the smoke and gases that escaped from the burning log and measure their masses, too. Then you would find that no mass was lost after all.

Not only is no mass lost during burning, mass is not gained or lost during any chemical change. In other words, matter is neither created nor destroyed during a chemical change. According to the **law of conservation of mass,** the mass of all substances that are present before a chemical change equals the mass of all the substances that remain after the change.

Figure 18 This reaction appears to be destroying these logs. When it is over, only ashes will remain. Yet you know that no mass is lost in a chemical reaction.
Explain *why this is so.*

Reading Check *Explain what is meant by the law of conservation of mass.*

section 2 review

Summary

Physical Properties

- You can observe physical properties without changing the identity of a substance.

Physical Change

- Change in the size, shape, or state of matter is a physical change.

Chemical Properties and Changes

- A chemical property is a characteristic of a substance that indicates whether it can undergo a certain chemical change.
- A change of one substance to another is a chemical change.
- Many metals are separated from their ores and purified using chemical changes.

Self Check

1. **Explain** why evaporation of water is a physical change and not a chemical change.
2. **List** four physical properties you could use to describe a liquid.
3. **Describe** why flammability is a chemical property rather than a physical property.
4. **Explain** how the law of conservation of mass applies to chemical changes.
5. **Think Critically** How might you demonstrate this law of conservation of mass for melting ice and distillation of water?

Applying Math

6. **Calculate** In the following equation, 417.96 g of Bi (bismuth) react completely with 200 g of F (fluorine). How many grams of BiF_3 (bismuth fluoride) are formed? $2\ Bi + 3\ F_2 \longrightarrow 2\ BiF_3$

Science Online gpscience.com/self_check_quiz

section 2 review

1. The makeup of the water units is unchanged.
2. color, odor, volume, temperature
3. Because the original materials are changed into new substances.
4. The mass of all substances present before a chemical change equals the mass of all the substances remaining after the change.
5. Let the ice melt on a balance, and show that the balance doesn't move. Find the mass of the liquid water, boil it and collect the condensed vapor and any solids. Find the mass of the condensed vapor and solids.
6. 617.96 g

Caption Answer

Figure 18 Some of the log's components combine with oxygen to form gases.

3 Assess

DAILY INTERVENTION

Check for Understanding

Kinesthetic Have a student light a match and allow it to burn. Also, place an ice cube in a glass container and allow it to melt. Have students explain what type of changes took place with each item and describe the final properties of each. L2 LS **Visual-Spatial**

Reteach

Mass Place a small, open vial of dilute silver nitrate solution carefully inside a large flask containing a dilute solution of sodium chloride. Determine the mass of the entire assembly. Then tip the flask to intentionally spill the contents of the small vial. A white precipitate will quickly form. Re-mass the assembly. Ask students what law is demonstrated when the two masses are in agreement. law of conservation of mass L2 ELL LS **Visual-Spatial, Kinesthetic**

Assessment

Oral Display several similar but slightly different candles. Have a student describe each candle using a minimum number of physical properties. Other students must identify the candle from its physical properties. Use **Performance Assessment in the Science Classroom,** p. 89. L1

Real-World Question

Purpose Students design and carry out an experiment that shows evidence of a chemical change.

Process Skills observe and infer, hypothesize, recognize cause and effect, interpret data, and make and use tables

Time Required 45 minutes

Procedure

Materials Prepare dilute HCl (1*M*) by adding 15 mL of HCl (12*M*) to 165 mL of distilled water in a well-ventilated area.

Safety Precautions **WARNING:** *Students should avoid direct contact with HCl, immediately flushing any contacted area with water. They should also avoid inhaling HCl fumes.*

Form a Hypothesis

Possible Hypothesis Mixing baking soda and HCL solution will cause a chemical change, and a new substance will be detected.

Test Your Hypothesis

Possible Procedures Place 2 g of baking soda in an evaporating dish. Add 2 mL of dilute HCl. Observe. Allow residue to dry. Add an additional 1 mL of the acid to residue to see whether the material will react, and compare to the original reaction.

Checking Out Chemical Changes

Goals
- **Observe** the results of adding dilute hydrochloric acid to baking soda.
- **Infer** that the production of new substances indicates that a chemical change has occurred.
- **Design** an experiment that allows you to compare the activity of baking soda with that of a product formed when baking soda reacts.

Possible Materials
baking soda
small evaporating dish
magnifying lens
1*M* hydrochloric acid (HCl)
10-mL graduated cylinder
electric hot plate

Safety Precautions

Real-World Question

Mixing materials together does not always produce a chemical change. You must find evidence of a new substance with new properties being produced before you can conclude that a chemical change has taken place. Try this lab and use your observation skills to deduce what kind of change has occurred. What evidence indicates a chemical change?

Form a Hypothesis

Think about what happens when small pieces of limestone are mixed with sand. What happens when limestone is mixed with an acid? Based on these thoughts, form a hypothesis about how to determine when mixing substances together produces a chemical change.

Test Your Hypothesis

Make a Plan

1. As a group, agree upon a hypothesis and decide how to test it. Write the hypothesis statement.
2. To test your hypothesis, devise a plan to compare two different mixtures. The first mixture consists of 3 mL of hydrochloric acid and 0.5 g of baking soda. The second mixture is 3 mL of hydrochloric acid and the solid product of the first mixture. Describe exactly what you will do at each step.

Limestone

Sand

Alternative Inquiry Lab

Open It Up Make this Lab an Inquiry Lab by allowing students to choose their own materials. As a class, make a list of other safe materials they would like to test. Have those materials on hand the day of the Lab. Ask students to predict the results before they conduct the experiments. Have students record their observations and list any "I wonder" or "What if" questions they had during the experiment. If time allows, permit students to explore these additional questions.

3. Make a list of the materials needed to complete your experiment.
4. **Design** a table for data and observations in your Science Journal so that it is ready to use as your group observes what happens.

Follow Your Plan

1. Make sure your teacher approves your plan before you start.
2. Read over your entire experiment to make sure that all steps are in logical order.
3. **Identify** any constants and the variables of the experiment.
4. Should you run any test more than once? How will observations be summarized?
5. Assemble your materials and carry out the experiment according to your plan. Be sure to record your results as you work.

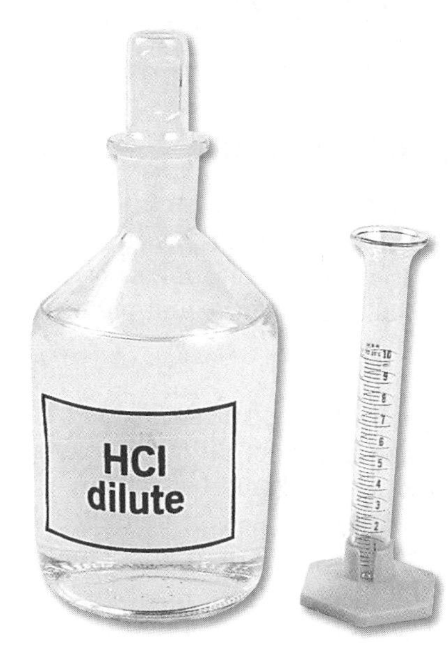

Analyze Your Data

1. **Observe** what happened to the baking soda. Did anything happen to the product formed from the first mixture? Explain why this occurred.
2. **Describe** What different properties of any new substances did you observe after adding hydrochloric acid to the baking soda?

Conclude and Apply

1. Did the results support your hypothesis? Explain.
2. If you had used vinegar, which contains acetic acid, as the acid, do you think a new susbstance would have formed? How could you test this?

Communicating Your Data

Write a description of your observations in your Science Journal. **Compare** your results with those of other groups. **Discuss** your conclusions.

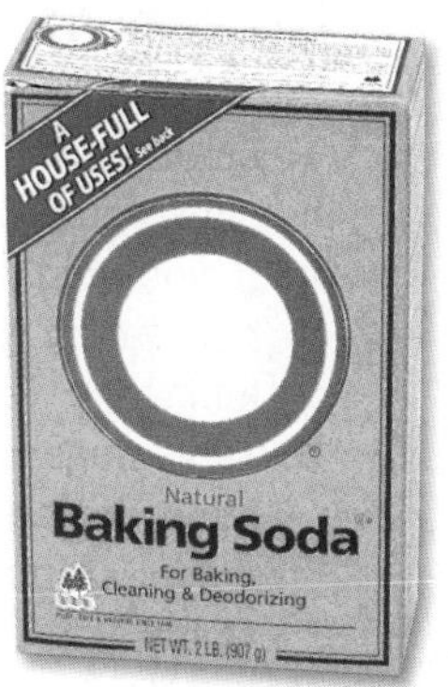

Assessment

Performance Have students draw a carbon atom, three oxygen atoms, two hydrogen atoms, a sodium atom and a chlorine atom. Then, have them use scissors to cut apart the atoms and reassemble the atoms as the products of the chemical change. Use **Performance Assessment in the Science Classroom,** p. 127. L2 IS **Visual-Spatial**

Communicating Your Data

Have students write down their observations about chemical changes in their Science Journals. Ask them to include descriptions of clues that led them to believe they witnessed a chemical change. Students can then compare their written notes with those of other students. P L2 IS **Linguistic**

Teaching Strategies

- The solution should be dried at a low enough temperature to avoid spattering.
- Tell students that baking soda is sodium hydrogen carbonate, $NaHCO_3$.

Expected Outcome Baking soda will react to produce carbon dioxide gas and, after drying, a white residue will be found. The chemical reaction is $NaHCO_3 + HCl \rightarrow H_2O + CO_2 + NaCl$. The NaCl will not react further with HCl.

Analyze Your Data

Answers to Questions

1. The baking soda reacted with the HCl solution to form bubbles of carbon dioxide. The product from the first mixture didn't react further because it was a different substance than $NaHCO_3$.
2. The white residue had a different physical appearance, and the new white residue did not react with HCl.

Error Analysis If too much $NaHCO_3$ or too little HCl is added, the acid may not completely react with the baking soda and the residue may contain some NaCl and some unreacted $NaHCO_3$.

Conclude and Apply

1. If the hypothesis was that the HCl and $NaHCO_3$ would react to form new substances, then, the hypothesis is supported.
2. Vinegar contains an acid, so it will react with baking soda to form carbon dioxide. However, the other product of the reaction will be different. Compare the properties of the reactants and products.

SCIENCE Stats

Content Background

Scientists constantly attempt to create or discover new elements. Recently discovered elements do not exist in nature but have been synthesized by bombarding existing elements with high-speed particles. The element seaborgium was synthesized by bombarding the element californium by highly accelerated oxygen nuclei.

Discussion

Oxygen The element oxygen makes up 46 percent of Earth's crust, yet it makes up only 21 percent of Earth's atmosphere. Most oxygen is contained in compounds. For example, sand is silicon dioxide, SiO_2.

Answers

1. 33,333 mg
2. 0.29 g
3. H-66 atoms; 0-33 atoms

Activity

Changing Elements Unless an element is radioactive and its nucleus changes, each atom remains the same element. However, elements change form and location. Provide students with the following statements. Have them draw an illustration that uses arrows and the statements to show how the element nitrogen is cycled on Earth. Statements:

- Plants obtain nitrogen from the soil.
- Bacteria on certain plants change atmospheric nitrogen to a useful form.
- Animals eat plants.
- Animals and plants die and decompose.

L2 IN **Visual-Spatial, Logical-Mathematical**

SCIENCE Stats

Intriguing Elements

Did you know...

... Silver-white cobalt, which usually is combined with other elements in nature, is used to create rich paint pigments. It can be used to form powerful magnets, treat cancer patients, build jet engines, and prevent disease in sheep.

... Gold is the most ductile (stretchable) of all the elements. Just 29 g of gold—about ten wedding bands—can be pulled into a wire 100 km long. That's long enough to stretch from Toledo, Ohio, to Detroit, Michigan, and beyond.

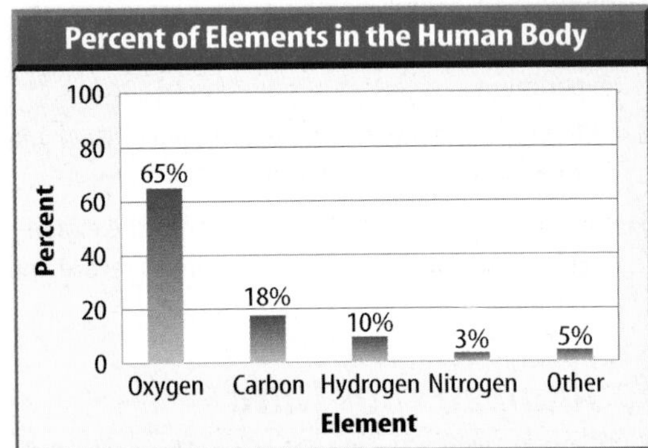

... Zinc makes chewing gum taste better. Up to 0.3 mg of zinc acetate can be added per 1,000 mg of chewing gum to provide a tart, zingy flavor.

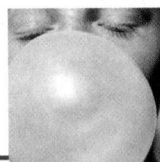

Applying Math

1. Zinc acetate is approximately 35% zinc. How many grams of chewing gum would be needed to provide a total of 10.0 mg of zinc?
2. If you wanted to produce a gold wire as mentioned in our example, how many grams would be needed to make a wire one kilometer in length?
3. Table sugar has the chemical formula $C_{12}H_{22}O_{11}$. If you were going to build a scale model of sucrose (table sugar) and you had 36 carbon model atoms, how many of each of the others (hydrogen and oxygen) would you need to build an accurate, complete sucrose model?

468 CHAPTER 15 Classification of Matter

Visual Learning

Have students use the bar graph to create a circle graph that depicts the composition of the human body. Have them multiply the percentages shown on the bar graph by 360° the number of degrees in a circle. The resulting products will provide the number of degrees of the circle represented by each element. Students can use a protractor to divide the circle into the correct number of degrees for each element. Student results should closely agree with the following figures: oxygen, 234°; carbon, 67°; hydrogen, 34°; nitrogen, 12°; and other, 13°. As a check for accuracy, have students be sure their percentages total 100% and their calculated degrees total 360°. L3 IN **Visual-Spatial, Logical-Mathematical**

Reviewing Main Ideas

Section 1 Composition of Matter

1. Elements and compounds are substances. A mixture is composed of two or more substances.
2. You can distinguish between the different materials in a heterogeneous mixture using either your unaided eye or a microscope.
3. Colloids and suspensions are two types of mixtures. The particles in a suspension will settle eventually. Particles of a colloid will not. Milk is an example of a colloid.
4. In a homogeneous mixture, the particles are distributed evenly and are not visible, even when using a microscope. Homogeneous mixtures can be composed of solids, liquids, or gases.
5. A solution is another name for a homogeneous mixture that remains constantly and uniformly mixed.

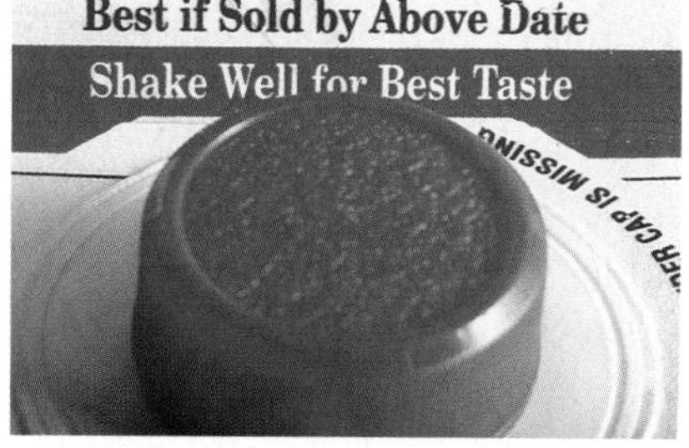

This is a clear indication that this is a suspension.

Section 2 Properties of Matter

1. Physical properties are characteristics of materials that you can observe without changing the identity of the substance.
2. Chemical properties indicate what chemical changes substances can undergo. Many medicines are stored in dark bottles because they react with light.

3. In physical changes, the identities of substances remain unchanged.
4. In chemical changes, the identities of substances change—new substances are formed. There is a visible chemical change that takes place when rust is cleaned with bleach.

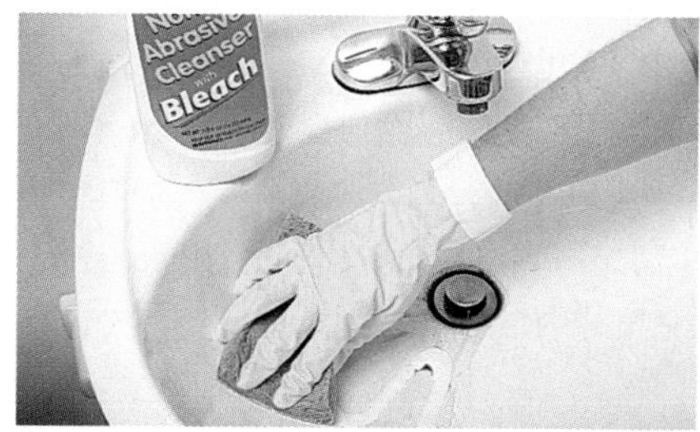

5. The law of conservation of mass states that during any chemical change, matter is neither created nor destroyed.

FOLDABLES Use the Foldable that you made at the beginning of the chapter to help you review the classifications of matter.

Identifying Misconceptions

Assess

Materials photograph of a sealed terrarium that contains a plant, an animal, and food for the animal

Procedure Show students the photograph. Explain that the terrarium is completely sealed. Suppose we measure the mass of this terrarium today, leave it for three months in a place where the plant gets enough light, and then measure the mass again. What is the terrarium's mass? L2 **Visual-Spatial**

Expected Outcome Students should realize that the mass of the terrarium would stay the same because it is a closed system.

chapter 15 Study Guide

Reviewing Main Ideas

Summary statements can be used by students to review the major concepts of the chapter.

Visit gpscience.com
/self_check_quiz
/interactive_tutor
/vocabulary_puzzlemaker
/chapter_review
/standardized_test

Assessment Transparency

For additional assessment questions, use the *Assessment Transparency* located in the transparency book.

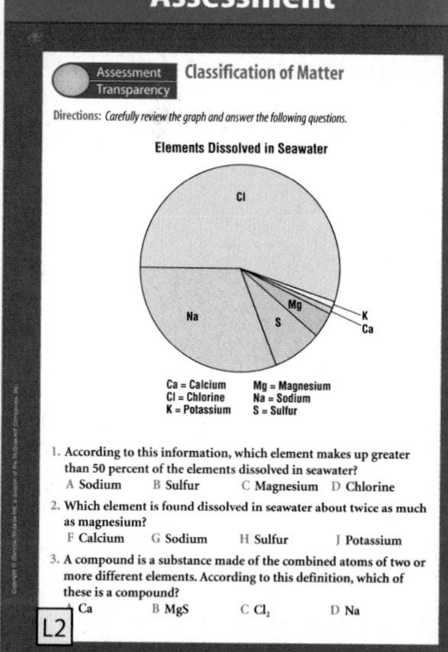
Assessment

Assessment Transparency — Classification of Matter

Directions: Carefully review the graph and answer the following questions.

1. According to this information, which element makes up greater than 50 percent of the elements dissolved in seawater?
   A Sodium B Sulfur C Magnesium D Chlorine
2. Which element is found dissolved in seawater about twice as much as magnesium?
   F Calcium G Sodium H Sulfur J Potassium
3. A compound is a substance made of the combined atoms of two or more different elements. According to this definition, which of these is a compound?
   A Ca B MgS C Cl_2 D Na

L2

FOLDABLES Have students use their Foldables to review the content of the chapter. On the back of the paper, have students write a paragraph about the nature of the forces between magnets.

chapter 15 Review

Using Vocabulary

1. compounds
2. suspension
3. physical change
4. law of conservation of mass
5. heterogeneous mixture
6. elements
7. physical change

Checking Concepts

8. B
9. A
10. B
11. A
12. D
13. D
14. D
15. B
16. B
17. B
18. A

Interpreting Graphics

19. compound
    sodium chloride
    element
    gold
    mixture
    heterogeneous
    breakfast cereal
    apple juice
20. smoke, marshmallow, paint and fog

chapter 15 Review

Using Vocabulary

chemical change p. 462
chemical property p. 461
colloid p. 454
compound p. 452
distillation p. 461
element p. 450
heterogeneous mixture p. 453
homogeneous mixture p. 454
law of conservation of mass p. 465
physical change p. 460
physical property p. 458
solution p. 454
substance p. 450
suspension p. 456
Tyndall effect p. 455

Complete each sentence with the correct vocabulary word or words.

1. Substances formed from atoms of two or more elements are called ________.
2. A(n) ________ is a heterogeneous mixture in which visible particles settle.
3. Freezing, boiling, and evaporation are all examples of ________.
4. According to the ________, matter is neither created nor destroyed during a chemical change.
5. A mixture in which different materials are easily identified is ________.
6. Compounds are made from the atoms of two or more ________.
7. Distillation is a process that can separate two liquids using ________.

Checking Concepts

Choose the word or phrase that best answers the question.

8. Bending a copper wire is an example of what type of property?
   A) chemical **C)** conservation
   B) physical **D)** element
9. Which of the following is NOT an element?
   A) water **C)** oxygen
   B) carbon **D)** hydrogen
10. Which of the following is an example of a chemical change?
    A) boiling **C)** evaporation
    B) burning **D)** melting
11. What type of substance is gelatin?
    A) colloid **C)** substance
    B) compound **D)** suspension
12. A visible sunbeam is an example of which of the following?
    A) an element **C)** a compound
    B) a solution **D)** the Tyndall effect
13. You start to eat some potato chips from an open bag you found in your locker and notice that they taste unpleasant. What do you think might cause this unpleasant taste?
    A) combustion **C)** physical change
    B) melting **D)** chemical change
14. How would you classify the color of a rose?
    A) chemical change **C)** chemical property
    B) physical change **D)** physical property
15. How would you describe the process of evaporating water from seawater?
    A) chemical change **C)** chemical property
    B) physical change **D)** physical property
16. Which of these warnings refers to a chemical property of the material?
    A) Fragile **C)** Handle with Care
    B) Flammable **D)** Shake Well
17. Which of the following is a substance?
    A) colloid **C)** mixture
    B) element **D)** solution
18. Which of these properties can be used to help identify an unknown substance?
    A) specific heat **C)** temperature
    B) combustion **D)** Tyndall effect

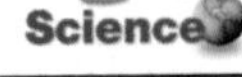

gpscience.com/vocabulary_puzzlemaker

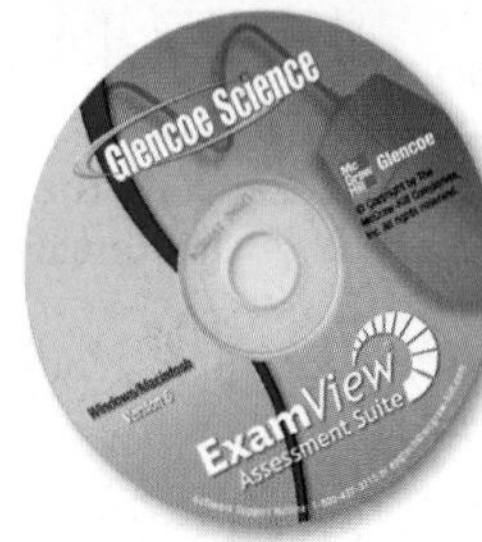

Use the *ExamView® Assessment Suite* CD-ROM to:

- create multiple versions of tests
- create modified tests with one mouse click for inclusion students
- edit existing questions and add your own questions
- build tests aligned with state standards using built-in State Curriculum Tags
- change English tests to Spanish with one mouse click and vice versa

Interpreting Graphics

19. Copy and complete the concept map below about matter.

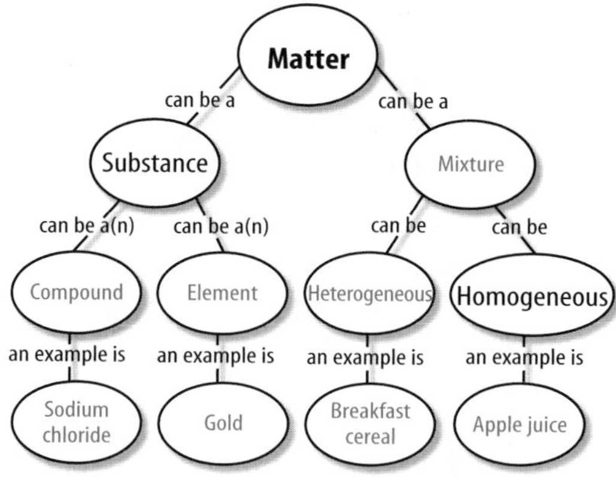

Use the table below to answer question 20.

Common Colloids

Colloid	Example
Solid in a liquid	Gelatin
Solid in a gas	
Gas in a solid	
Solid in a liquid	
Liquid in a gas	

20. Different colloids can involve different states. For example, gelatin is formed from solid particles in a liquid. Complete this table using these colloids: *smoke, marshmallow, fog,* and *paint.*

Thinking Critically

21. **Describe** the contents of a carton of milk using at least four physical properties.

22. **Explain** Carbon and the gases hydrogen and oxygen combine to form sugar. How do you know sugar is a compound?

23. **Explain** The word *colloid* means "gluelike." Why was this term chosen to name certain mixtures?

24. **Use** a nail rusting in air to explain the law of conservation of mass.

25. **Explain** Mai says that ocean water is a solution. Tom says that it's a suspension. Can they both be correct? Explain.

26. **Use Variables, Constants, and Controls** Marcos took a 100-cm^3 sample of a suspension, shook it well, and poured equal amounts into four different test tubes. He placed one test tube in a rack, one in hot water, one in warm water, and the fourth in ice water. He then observed the time it took for each suspension to settle. What was the variable in the experiment? What was one constant?

27. **Concept Map** Make a network tree to show types of liquid mixtures. Include these terms: *homogeneous mixtures, heterogeneous mixtures, solutions, colloids,* and *suspensions.*

Applying Math

28. **Interpret Data** Hannah started with a 25-mL sample of pond water. Without shaking the sample, she poured 5 mL through a piece of filter paper. She repeated this with four more pieces of filter paper. She dried each piece of filter paper and measured the mass of the sediment. Why did the last sample have a higher mass than did the first sample?

29. **Use Numbers** In the following equation, 243.5 g of Sb (antimony) react completely with 1000 g of I_2 (iodine) to form 1004.9 g of SbI_3 (antimony triiodide). How many grams of I_2 were consumed in the reaction? $2\ Sb + 3\ I_2 \rightarrow 2\ SbI_3$

Thinking Critically

21. Possible description: It is white. It is a liquid at room temperature. It is wet. The volume is a quart or one-half gallon. It is a colloid.
22. It can't be separated by physical means; it looks different from the elements that make it up.
23. Some of the first colloids studied were in gelatin, which is a source of glue.
24. The combined mass of the oxygen and the iron before the reaction is equal to the mass of the rust after the reaction.
25. Since ocean water contains dissolved salts it is a saltwater solution. Some ocean water also contains loose sand and other materials in suspension.
26. The variable was temperature. One constant was the amount of suspension put into each tube.
27. Mixtures include homogeneous mixtures, which are solutions, and heterogeneous mixtures, which include colloids or suspensions.

Applying Math

National Math Standards

2, 6, 9

28. The pond water was a suspension in which material had begun to settle out. The first 5 mL came from the top of the water sample, from which much of the suspension had settled out. The last 5 mL came from the bottom and contained settled material.
29. 238.6 g

Assessment Resources

Reproducible Masters

Chapter *Fast File* Resources
- Chapter Review, pp. 35–36
- Chapter Tests, pp. 37–40
- Assessment Transparency Activity, p. 47

Glencoe Science Web site
- Chapter Review Test
- Standardized Test Practice

Glencoe Technology
- Assessment Transparency
- *ExamView® Assessment Suite*
- MindJogger Videoquiz
- Interactive Chalkboard

Answer Sheet A practice answer sheet can be found at gpscience.com/answer_sheet.

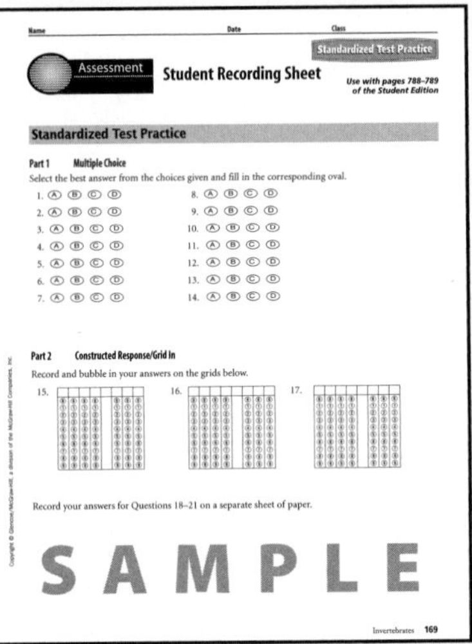

Part 1 Multiple Choice

1. B
2. C
3. D
4. A
5. B
6. B
7. D

Part 2 Short Response

8. Physical properties of these minerals include color, shape, magnetism, density, melting point, and boiling point.
9. Rocks and minerals undergo physical weathering as frozen water splits them apart or moving water or wind breaks them into smaller pieces. Some rocks and minerals weather chemically through contact with acidic water.
10. The chemicals in some medicines react to light. This chemical reaction results in the formation of a new substance, with different properties than the original medicine.
11. Tungsten can be stretched and shaped without breaking. It can be combined with steel to create a strong metal, and it has the highest melting point of any metal. Tungsten is used to make the filaments in light bulbs.
12. Gold has the ability to reflect infrared radiation, and is resistant to corrosion. Both of these properties provide protection for space vehicles.
13. Both are made up of two or more substances which can be separated by physical means. In heterogeneous mixtures, different materials can be distinguished and are not evenly mixed. In homogeneous mixtures, or solutions, the particles are evenly mixed, and are so small that they cannot be distinguished.
14. Add water to the mixture. Stir until all the salt is dissolved, then pour the water/salt solution off of the sand/iron mixture. Use a magnet to separate the iron and sand.

Part 3 Open Ended

15. Heat and light are produced, an odor is given off, and a new substance is created.
16. The experiment should include these components: Design an enclosure to trap all solid and gas products of the reaction. With the enclosure covering the reactants, measure the total mass (enclosure

Part 1 Multiple Choice

Record your answers on the answer sheet provided by your teacher or on a sheet of paper.

1. Which statement about elements is FALSE?
   A. All atoms in an element are alike.
   B. There are about 1,000 elements found in nature.
   C. Some elements have been made in laboratories.
   D. Zinc, copper, and iron are elements.

2. $CaCO_3$ is an example of which type of material?
   A. element
   B. mixture
   C. compound
   D. colloid

Use the graph below to answer questions 3 and 4.

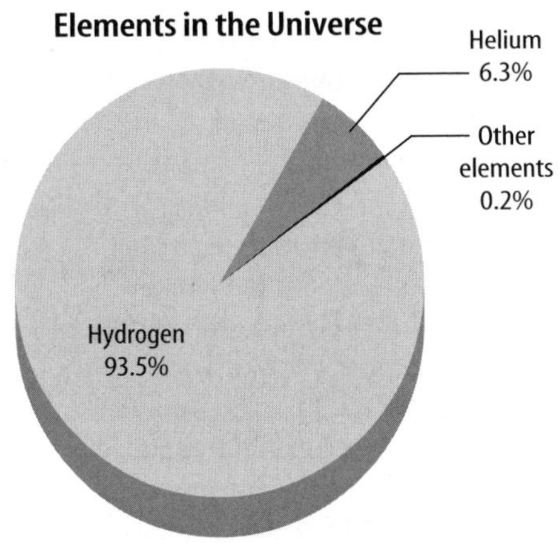

3. What percentage do the elements hydrogen and helium account for in the universe?
   A. 100%
   B. 99.9%
   C. 98%
   D. 99.8%

Test-Taking Tip

Directions and Instructions Listen carefully to the instructions from the teacher and read the directions and each question carefully.

4. The most plentiful element in the universe readily burns in air. What is this chemical property called?
   A. flammability
   B. ductility
   C. density
   D. boiling point

Use the graph below to answer questions 5 and 6.

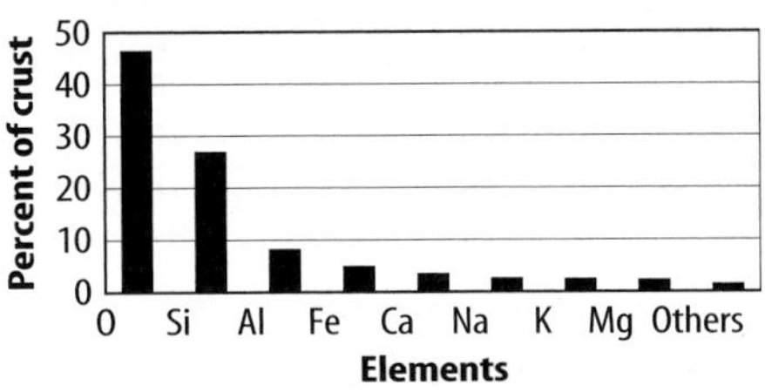

5. Which element makes up 8 percent of Earth's crust?
   A. iron
   B. aluminum
   C. silicon
   D. oxygen

6. Which element has the physical property of magnetism?
   A. sodium
   B. iron
   C. oxygen
   D. calcium

7. Which statement best decribes the law of conservation of mass?
   A. The mass of the products is always greater than the mass of the materials which react in a chemical change.
   B. The mass of the products is always less than the mass of the materials which react in a chemical change.
   C. A certain mass of material must be present for a reaction to occur.
   D. Matter is neither lost nor gained during a chemical change.

Part 2 | Short Response/Grid In

Record your answers on the answer sheet provided by your teacher or on a sheet of paper.

Use the illustrations below to answer questions 8 and 9.

8. What physical properties could be used to identify these minerals?
9. Describe some ways these minerals, or rocks which contain these minerals, are weathered in nature.
10. Why are some medicines stored in dark bottles?
11. Describe the properties of tungsten which make it a useful material. How do you use this element daily?
12. What physical and chemical properties of gold make it useful as a coating for space vehicles?
13. Compare and contrast the properties of heterogeneous and homogeneous mixtures. What is another name for a homogeneous mixture?
14. You are given a mixture of iron filings, sand, and salt. Describe how to separate this mixture.

Part 3 | Open Ended

Record your answers on a sheet of paper.

Use the illustration below to answer questions 15 and 16.

15. What indicates that more than just a physical change is taking place as the wood burns?
16. Design an experiment which shows that this type of chemical change is governed by the law of conservation of mass.
17. Illustrate and describe the process of distillation of sea water using a multi-step process. On what physical property is this process based?
18. Explain the statement "Everything on Earth is made from 90 elements." Does this surprise you? Why or why not?
19. What type of mixture is a salad dressing made with oil, vinegar, and herbs? How do you know?
20. Choose an object in the room and describe its physical properties as completely as possible. Use available tools to describe measurable properties of the object.
21. Describe how a compound is a combination of elements in a fixed proportion. Give two examples.

19. This mixture is a suspension. It is a heterogeneous mixture; different compounds, two of which are liquids, can be distinguished. The solid herb component settles to the bottom. This mixture must be shaken to redistribute its components.
20. Answers will vary. Descriptions of the objects may include color and shape, as well as length, mass, volume and density measurements.
21. By definition, a compound is a substance made from two or more elements. All compounds are fixed in the proportions of that compound. If the ratio of the elements changes, then a new compound is formed. Examples are: water, carbon dioxide, salt, and sugar. Accept answers that students may provide as long as they are compounds.

Rubrics

For more help evaluating open-ended assessment questions, see the rubric on p. 10T.

plus all reactants to be burned.) With enclosure in place, start the reaction. Once burning is complete, measure the total mass again. The initial and final masses will be equal.

17. Distillation is based on boiling point. A liquid mixture is heated. The gas from the liquid with the lowest boiling point is collected, cooled, and condensed back into liquid form. Liquids with successively higher boiling points can be separated from the mixture in the same way.
18. There are only 90 naturally occurring elements, which means that everything on Earth is made from some combination of these substances. Answers will vary.

Solids, Liquids, and Gases

BIG Idea **Many physical properties of matter can be described by the motion of its particles.**

	Content Standards	Learning Objectives	Resources to Assess Mastery
Section 1	**5–8:** UCP.1–3, 5; A.1, 2; B.1–3; G.3 **9–12:** UCP.1–3, 5; A.1, 2; B.2, 5, 6; G.3	**Kinetic Theory** **1. Explain** the kinetic theory of matter. **2. Describe** particle movement in the four states of matter. **3. Explain** particle behavior at the melting and boiling points. ***Main Idea*** Solids, liquids, and gases differ by the amount of thermal energy their particles have.	**Formative Assessment** Reading Check, pp. 477, 478, 479, 480, 482 Section Review, p. 483 **Summative Assessment** *ExamView® Assessment Suite*
Section 2	**5–8:** UCP.1–3, 5; A.1, 2; B.1–3; G.3 **9–12:** UCP.1–3, 5; A.1, 2; B.2, 4; G.3	**Properties of Fluids** **4. Explain** Archimedes' principle. **5. Explain** Pascal's principle. **6. Explain** Bernoulli's principle and explain how we use it. ***Main Idea*** An object will float in a fluid if the buoyant force exerted by a fluid is equal to the object's weight.	**Formative Assessment** Reading Check, pp. 485, 488, 489 Section Review, p. 489 **Summative Assessment** *ExamView® Assessment Suite*
Section 3	**5–8:** UCP.1–5; A.1, 2; B.1–3; G.3 **9–12:** UCP.1–3, 5; A.1, 2; B.2, 4, 5; G.3 See pp. 16T–17T for a Key to Standards.	**Behavior of Gases** **7. Explain** how a gas exerts pressure on its container. **8. Explain** how a gas is affected when pressure, temperature, or volume is changed. ***Main Idea*** The pressure, volume, and temperature of a gas are each affected by the other two properties.	**Formative Assessment** Reading Check, pp. 490, 493, 495 Section Review, p. 495 **Summative Chapter Assessment** MindJogger, Ch. 16 *ExamView® Assessment Suite* Leveled Chapter Test Test A L1 Test B L2 Test C L3 Test Practice, pp. 502–503

Suggested Pacing				
Period	Instruction	Labs	Review & Assessment	Total
Single	4 days	3 days	2 days	9 days
Block	2 blocks	1.5 blocks	1 block	4.5 blocks

Core Instruction	Leveled Resources	Leveled Labs	Pacing Period		Pacing Block
Student Text, pp. 474–484 Section Focus Transparency, Ch. 16, Section 1 Teaching Transparency, Ch. 16, Section 1 Interactive Chalkboard, Ch. 16, Section 1 Identifying Misconceptions, pp. 478, 480 Differentiated Instruction, p. 477	**Chapter *Fast File* Resources** Directed Reading for Content Mastery, p. 22 L1 Note-taking Worksheet, pp. 35–37 Reinforcement, p. 29 L2 Enrichment, p. 32 L3 **Reading Essentials,** p. 264 L1 ELL **Science Notebook,** p. 177 ELL ***Active*Folders**: *States of Matter* L1 ELL	**Launch Lab**, p. 475: balloon, tape measure, large beaker, hot plate, water *15 min* L2 ***Lab**, p. 484: beakers (2), ring stand, ring clamp, wire mesh, ice, thermometer, hot plate *40 min* L1 L2 L3	1	Section 1, pp. 475–478 (includes Launch Lab)	1
			2	Section 1, pp. 479–483 (includes Section Review)	
			3	Lab: Thermal Energy Changes in Matter, p. 484	2
Student Text, pp. 485–489 Section Focus Transparency, Ch. 16, Section 2 Interactive Chalkboard, Ch. 16, Section 2 Applying Math, p. 487 Differentiated Instruction, pp. 487, 488	**Chapter *Fast File* Resources** Directed Reading for Content Mastery, p. 22 L1 Note-taking Worksheet, pp. 35–37 Reinforcement, p. 30 L2 Enrichment, p. 33 L3 **Reading Essentials,** p. 272 L1 ELL **Science Notebook,** p. 181 ELL ***Active*Folders**: *Principles of Gases and Liquids* L1 ELL	**MiniLAB**, p. 486: 100-mL beakers (2), graduated cylinder, stirring rod, corn syrup, water, vegetable oil, food coloring, aluminum foil, steel nut, peppercorn *20 min* L2	4	Section 2, pp. 485–486 (includes MiniLAB)	
			5	Section 2, pp. 486–489 (includes Section Review)	3
Student Text, pp. 490–497 Section Focus Transparency, Ch. 16, Section 3 Interactive Chalkboard, Ch. 16, Section 3 Visualizing Atmospheric Layers, p. 491 Identifying Misconceptions, p. 494 Differentiated Instruction, pp. 491, 492, 493 Chapter Study Guide, p. 499	**Chapter *Fast File* Resources** Directed Reading for Content Mastery, pp. 23, 24 L1 Note-taking Worksheet, pp. 35–37 Reinforcement, p. 31 L2 Enrichment, p. 34 L3 **Reading Essentials,** p. 276 L1 ELL **Science Notebook,** p. 184 ELL	**MiniLAB**, p. 494: balloon, beaker, ice water *15 min* L2 ***Lab**, pp. 496–497: household liquids, spheres, 100-mL graduated cylinders, 150-mL beaker, metric ruler, stopwatch *45 min* L1 L2 L3 (Video Lab) *Lab version A L1 version B L2 L3	6	Section 3, pp. 490–493	
			7	Section 3, pp. 494–495 (includes MiniLAB and Section Review)	4
			8	Lab: Testing the Viscosity of Common Liquids, pp. 496–497	
			9	Study Guide, Chapter Review, and Test Practice, pp. 499–503	4.5

Video Lab

Transparencies

Section Focus

Section 1 Section Focus Transparency — Water Works

Sculptors use a variety of materials to create their works of art. Those who sculpt marble or wood expect their work to last for many years. Ice sculptors, on the other hand, know that the Sun will soon turn their intricate works into pools of water.

1. What happens to molecules of water as ice melts?
2. Why does snow melt when you hold it in your hand?
3. What happens when water boils?

L2

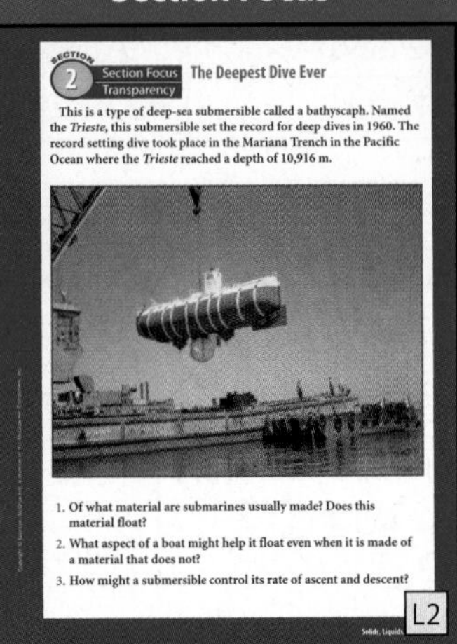
Section 2 Section Focus Transparency — The Deepest Dive Ever

This is a type of deep-sea submersible called a bathyscaph. Named the *Trieste*, this submersible set the record for deep dives in 1960. The record setting dive took place in the Mariana Trench in the Pacific Ocean where the *Trieste* reached a depth of 10,916 m.

1. Of what material are submarines usually made? Does this material float?
2. What aspect of a boat might help it float even when it is made of a material that does not?
3. How might a submersible control its rate of ascent and descent?

L2

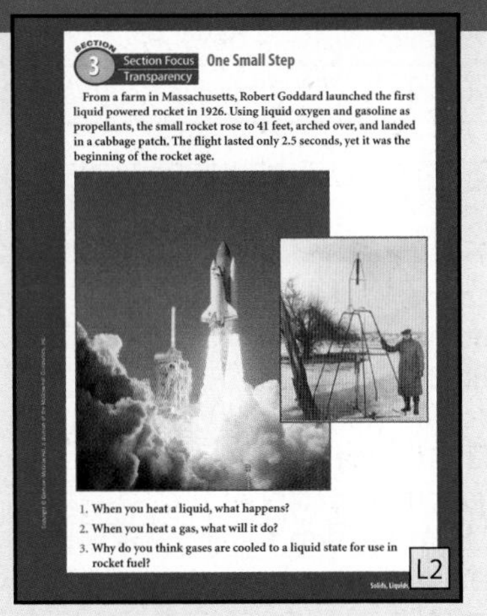
Section 3 Section Focus Transparency — One Small Step

From a farm in Massachusetts, Robert Goddard launched the first liquid powered rocket in 1926. Using liquid oxygen and gasoline as propellants, the small rocket rose to 41 feet, arched over, and landed in a cabbage patch. The flight lasted only 2.5 seconds, yet it was the beginning of the rocket age.

1. When you heat a liquid, what happens?
2. When you heat a gas, what will it do?
3. Why do you think gases are cooled to a liquid state for use in rocket fuel?

L2

This is a representation of key blackline masters available in the Teacher Classroom Resources. See Resource Manager boxes within the chapter for additional information.

Assessment

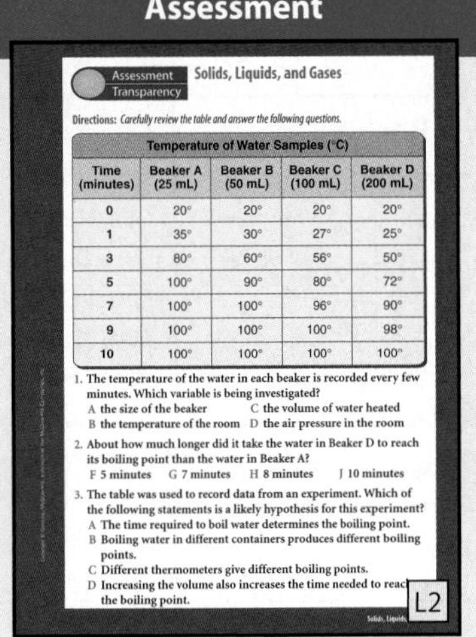
Assessment Transparency — Solids, Liquids, and Gases

Directions: *Carefully review the table and answer the following questions.*

Temperature of Water Samples (°C)				
Time (minutes)	Beaker A (25 mL)	Beaker B (50 mL)	Beaker C (100 mL)	Beaker D (200 mL)
0	20°	20°	20°	20°
1	35°	30°	27°	25°
3	80°	60°	56°	50°
5	100°	90°	80°	72°
7	100°	100°	96°	90°
9	100°	100°	100°	98°
10	100°	100°	100°	100°

1. The temperature of the water in each beaker is recorded every few minutes. Which variable is being investigated?
   A the size of the beaker C the volume of water heated
   B the temperature of the room D the air pressure in the room
2. About how much longer did it take the water in Beaker D to reach its boiling point than the water in Beaker A?
   F 5 minutes G 7 minutes H 8 minutes J 10 minutes
3. The table was used to record data from an experiment. Which of the following statements is a likely hypothesis for this experiment?
   A The time required to boil water determines the boiling point.
   B Boiling water in different containers produces different boiling points.
   C Different thermometers give different boiling points.
   D Increasing the volume also increases the time needed to reach the boiling point.

L2

Teaching

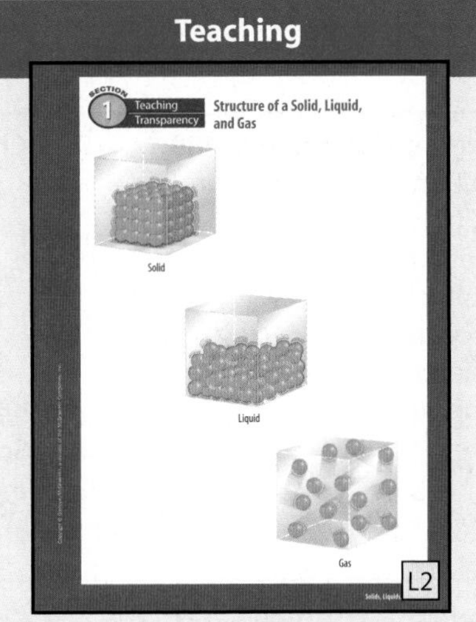
Section 1 Teaching Transparency — Structure of a Solid, Liquid, and Gas

L2

Key to Teaching Strategies

The following designations will help you decide which activities are appropriate for your students.

- L1 Level 1 activities should be appropriate for students with learning difficulties.
- L2 Level 2 activities should be within the ability range of all students.
- L3 Level 3 activities are designed for above-average students.
- ELL ELL activities should be within the ability range of English Language Learners.
- COOP LEARN Cooperative Learning activities are designed for small group work.
- LS Multiple Learning Styles logos, as described on page 12T, are used throughout to indicate strategies that address different learning styles.
- P These strategies represent student products that can be placed into a best-work portfolio.
- PBL Problem-Based Learning activities apply real-world situations to learning.

Hands-on Activities

Student Text Lab Worksheets

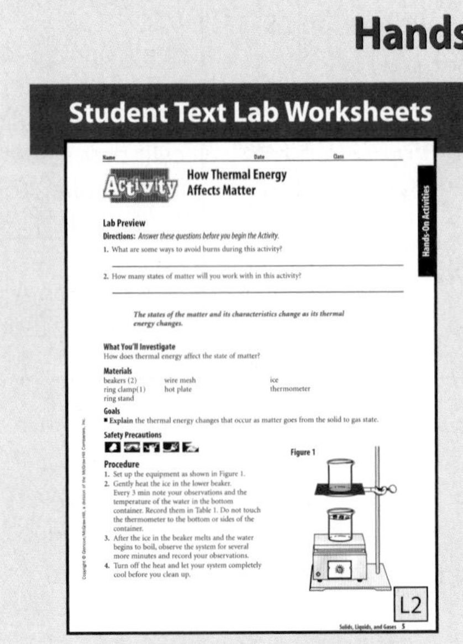
Name Date Class

Activity — How Thermal Energy Affects Matter

Lab Preview

Directions: *Answer these questions before you begin the Activity.*

1. What are some ways to avoid burns during this activity?
2. How many states of matter will you work with in this activity?

The states of the matter and its characteristics change as its thermal energy changes.

What You'll Investigate

How does thermal energy affect the state of matter?

Materials

beakers (2), ring clamp(1), ring stand, wire mesh, hot plate, ice, thermometer

Goals

- **Explain** the thermal energy changes that occur as matter goes from the solid to gas state.

Safety Precautions

Procedure

1. Set up the equipment as shown in Figure 1.
2. Gently heat the ice in the lower beaker. Every 3 min note your observations and the temperature of the water in the bottom container. Record them in Table 1. Do not touch the thermometer to the bottom or sides of the container.
3. After the ice in the beaker melts and the water begins to boil, observe the system for several more minutes and record your observations.
4. Turn off the heat and let your system completely cool before you clean up.

Figure 1

L2

Solids, Liquids, and Gases 5

Laboratory Activities

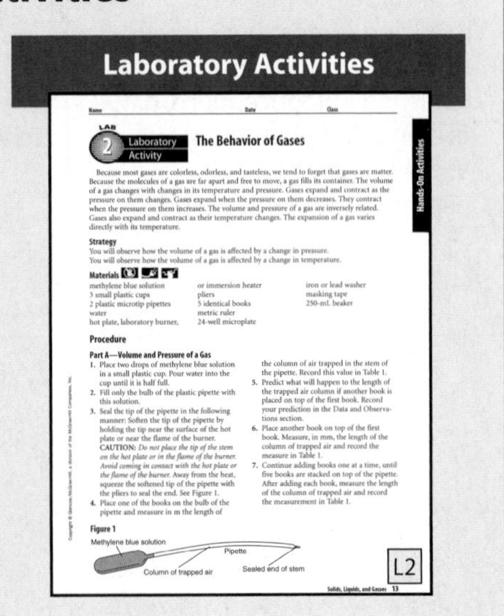
Name Date Class

Lab 2 Laboratory Activity — The Behavior of Gases

Because most gases are colorless, odorless, and tasteless, we tend to forget that gases are matter. Because the molecules of a gas are far apart and free to move, a gas fills its container. The volume of a gas changes with changes in its temperature and pressure. Gases expand and contract as the pressure on them changes. Gases expand when the pressure on them decreases. They contract when the pressure on them increases. The volume and pressure of a gas are inversely related. Gases also expand and contract as their temperature changes. The expansion of a gas varies directly with its temperature.

Strategy

You will observe how the volume of a gas is affected by a change in pressure.
You will observe how the volume of a gas is affected by a change in temperature.

Materials

methylene blue solution, 3 small plastic cups, 2 plastic microtip pipettes, water, hot plate, laboratory burner, or immersion heater, pliers, 5 identical books, metric ruler, 24-well microplate, iron or lead washer, masking tape, 250-mL beaker

Procedure

Part A—Volume and Pressure of a Gas

1. Place two drops of methylene blue solution in a small plastic cup. Pour water into the cup until it is half full.
2. Fill only the bulb of the plastic pipette with this solution.
3. Seal the tip of the pipette in the following manner: Soften the tip of the pipette by holding the tip near the surface of the hot plate or near the flame of the burner. CAUTION: *Do not place the tip of the stem on the hot plate or in the flame of the burner. Avoid coming in contact with the hot plate or the flame of the burner.* Away from the heat, squeeze the softened tip of the pipette with the pliers to seal the end. See Figure 1.
4. Place one of the books on the bulb of the pipette and measure in m the length of the column of air trapped in the stem of the pipette. Record this value in Table 1.
5. Predict what will happen to the length of the trapped air column if another book is placed on top of the first book. Record your prediction in the Data and Observations section.
6. Place another book on top of the first book. Measure, in mm, the length of the column of trapped air and record the measure in Table 1.
7. Continue adding books one at a time, until five books are stacked on top of the pipette. After adding each book, measure the length of the column of trapped air and record the measurement in Table 1.

Figure 1

L2

Solids, Liquids, and Gases 13

Meeting Different Ability Levels

Content Outline

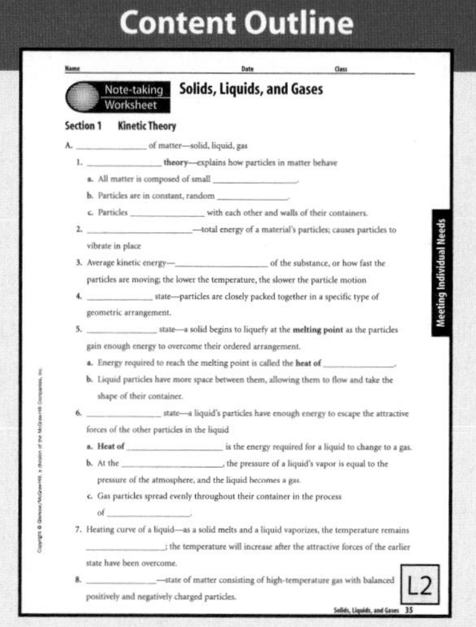

Note-taking Worksheet — Solids, Liquids, and Gases

L2

Reinforcement

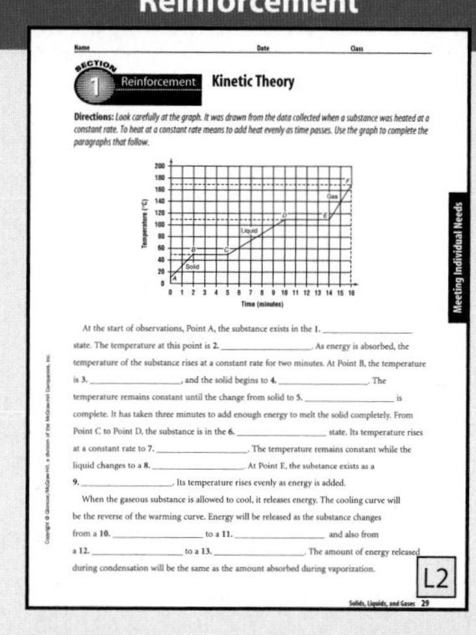

Reinforcement — Kinetic Theory

L2

Enrichment

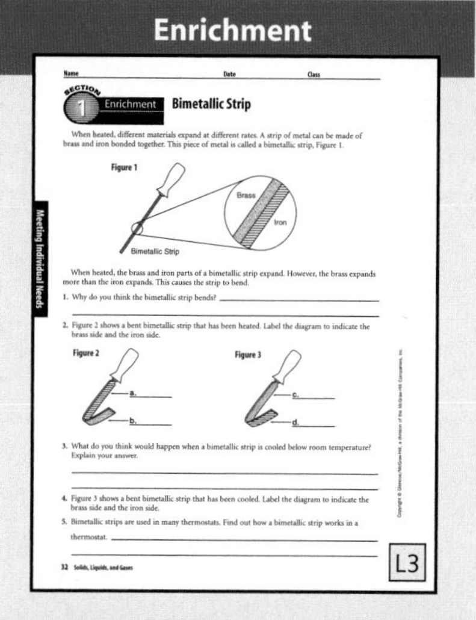

Enrichment — Bimetallic Strip

L3

Directed Reading (English/Spanish)

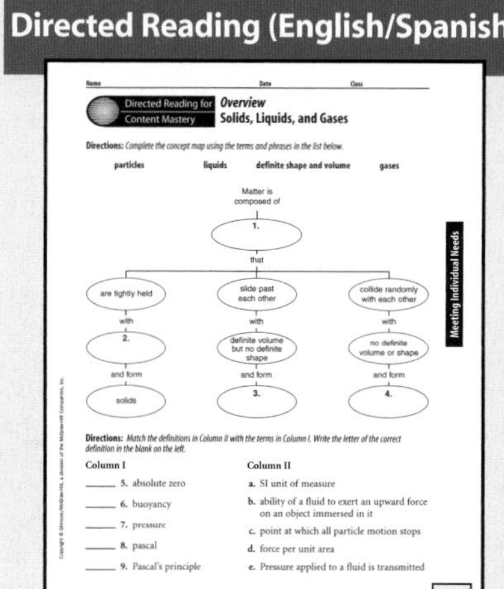

Directed Reading for Content Mastery — Overview: Solids, Liquids, and Gases

L1

Study Guide

Study Guide
Features
• Contains a study guide page for each section of the chapter
• Reviews key concepts
• Includes answer pages

L1

Reading Essentials

Reading Essentials for Glencoe Science
An Interactive Student Workbook
Features
• Condensed core content
• Actively involves students in reading
• Reinforces key vocabulary

L1

Assessment

Test Practice Workbook

Chapter Test — Chapter 16 Solids, Liquids, and Gases

L2

Chapter Review

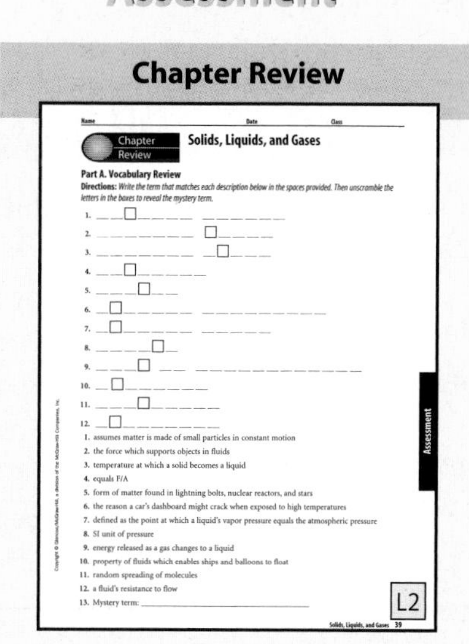

Chapter Review — Solids, Liquids, and Gases

L2

Chapter Tests

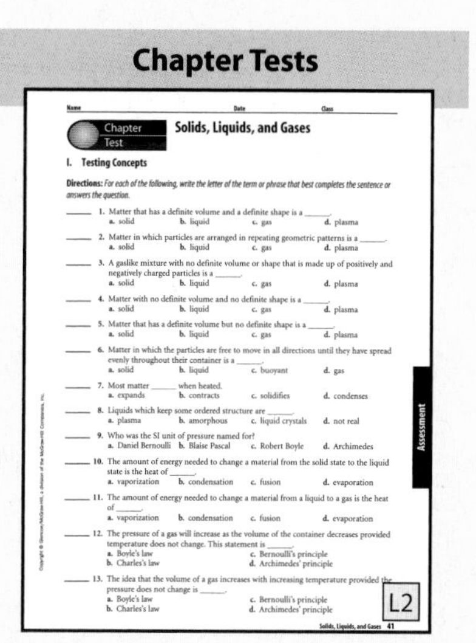

Chapter Test — Solids, Liquids, and Gases

L2

Science Content Background

section 1 Kinetic Theory

States of Matter

The Kelvin temperature scale begins at absolute zero, or 0 K. Scientists believe that at 0 K matter has the lowest possible amount of thermal energy. Each degree on the Kelvin scale is the same magnitude as a degree on the Celsius scale. The freezing point of water on the Celsius scale is 0 degrees; the freezing point of water on the Kelvin scale is 273 K. The average kinetic energy of the particles that make up a substance is directly proportional to the Kelvin temperature.

Matter is made of tiny particles separated by distances with nothing between the particles. The particles are in motion. In gases, the separation of the particles is the greatest because these particles are moving the fastest. The amount of space between the particles varies with temperature, volume, and pressure.

section 2 Properties of Fluids

Bernoulli's Principle

Daniel Bernoulli was born to a family of renowned Swiss mathematicians. Over the course of his career, he worked not only in mathematics but in a number of other disciplines, such as medicine, biology, physiology, mechanics, physics, astronomy, and oceanography. It was for his work in mathematics, however, that Bernoulli was best known. In 1738 he discovered that the pressure in a fluid decreases as the velocity of the fluid increases. That work, called Bernoulli's Principle, remains the basis today for many engineering applications, such as aircraft-wing design. Between 1725 and 1749, Bernoulli won 10 prizes from the Paris Academy of Sciences for his work in astronomy, gravity, tides, magnetism, ocean currents, and the behavior of ships at sea.

section 3 Behavior of Gases

Pressure

The work of Boyle, Charles, and others led to the formulation of a general theory to explain the behavior and properties of gases. This theory is called the kinetic-molecular theory. It ranks with the atomic theory as one of the greatest generalizations of modern science.

The kinetic-molecular theory is based on the motion of gas molecules. A gas that behaves exactly as outlined by the theory is known as an ideal gas. No ideal gases exist, but under certain conditions of temperature and pressure, real gases approach ideal behavior, or at least show only small deviations from it.

chapter content resources

Internet Resources

For additional content background, visit **gpscience.com** to:

- access your book online
- find references to related articles in popular science magazines
- access Web links with related content background
- access current events with science journal topics

Print Resources

Thermodynamics and the Kinetic Theory of Gases, by Wolfgang Pauli and Charles P. Enz, Dover Publishing Company, 2000

The Properties of Gases and Liquids, by Bruce E. Poling, John M. Prausnitz, and John P. O'Connell, McGraw-Hill Professional, 2000

Experiments with Solids, Liquids, and Gases, Salvatore Tocci, Children's Book Press, 2002

IDENTIFYING Misconceptions

Find Out What Students Think

Students may think that . . .

Gases are made of special substances that are not composed of particles like other matter.
Since students cannot see gases, they sometimes find it difficult to understand that gas particles exist, and that they are the same kinds of particles that make up solids and liquids.

Discussion

Draw Figure 1 on an overhead. Explain that the box is filled with a gas and that the pump removes some of the gas. Have students choose from Figure 2 the diagram that best represents what the setup looks like before and after the gas is removed. Have students discuss their ideas in small groups.

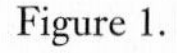

Figure 1.

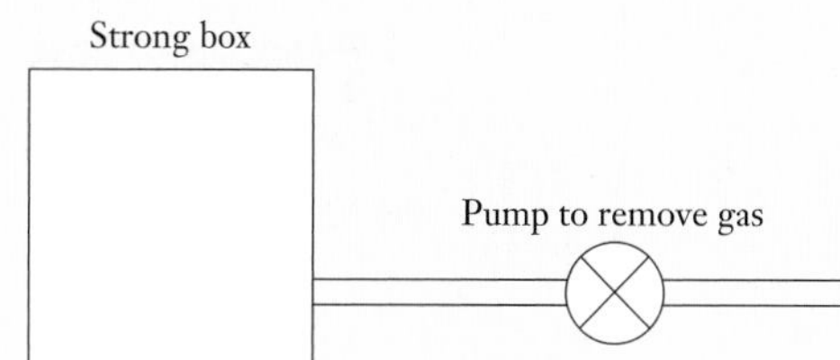

Figure 2.

Before After

A.

B.

C.

D.

E.

Promote Understanding

Demonstration

Show students a bottle of vanilla. Open the bottle, and place it on a desk in the front of the room. Have students raise their hands when they can smell the vanilla. When most students can smell the vanilla, ask the following questions: What did you smell? Did you smell a liquid or a gas? How did the vanilla extract go from being a liquid to being a gas? Explain that the particles of vanilla that were in the liquid are the same particles that are now in the gas. Ask students to draw liquid vanilla in the bottle as particles, represented by dots. The dots in the bottle should be very close. Then have them draw vanilla as a gas. The dots should be far apart.

Follow up by having students draw the activity and its results as a cartoon strip. Suggest that the first frame show the bottle when it was first opened, the second frame show the scene when the first row of students started to smell the vanilla, and the third frame show the scene when the whole class smelled the vanilla.

Assess

After completing the chapter, see *Identifying Misconceptions* in the Study Guide at the end of the chapter.

About the Photo

Mount Cook The photo shows Mount Cook, which is 3,754 m above sea level and is located on New Zealand's South Island. Mount Cook is also known by its native Maori name *Aoraki.*

Science Journal Student responses will vary, but may include: solid—desk; liquid—water; gas—air.

The BIG Idea

Particles in Matter All matter is made of particles, atoms, or molecules, in continual, random motion. These particles exert electrical forces on each other that depend on the distance between particles. As particles become farther apart, the strength of the forces between them decreases. In solids and liquids, the distance between particles is on the order of 10^{-10} m. As a result, for most materials the densities of the solid and liquid states are similar. In gases at atmospheric pressure and room temperature, the distance between particles is typically about 1,000 times greater.

Introduce the Chapter Provide students a number of pennies or small disc-shaped candies. Have students distribute the pennies evenly between two parallel rulers about 20 cm apart. Tell students to move the rulers toward each other until they are about 10 cm apart. Ask students how the distance between pennies has changed. Then have students move the rulers toward each other until they are as close as possible. Ask students how the arrangement of pennies has changed. If the pennies represent gas molecules, how has the density of the gas changed?

Solids, Liquids, and Gases

BIG Idea
Many physical properties of matter can be described by the motion of its particles.

16.1 Kinetic Theory
MAIN Idea Solids, liquids, and gases differ by the amount of thermal energy their particles have.

16.2 Properties of Fluids
MAIN Idea An object will float in a fluid if the buoyant force exerted by a fluid is equal to the object's weight.

16.3 Behavior of Gases
MAIN Idea The pressure, volume, and temperature of a gas are each affected by the other two properties.

Surrounded by Science

Driving down this road, you can't help but notice the scenery. Now look at this photo through a scientist's eyes. Can you find three states of water? The solid is present as snow on the mountaintops. The liquid is found as water in the lake. The gas is present in the atmosphere as water vapor.

Science Journal

Identify examples of a solid, a liquid, and a gas in your classroom.

474

Interactive Chalkboard

This CD-ROM is an editable Microsoft® PowerPoint® presentation that includes:

- an editable presentation for every chapter
- additional chapter questions
- animated graphics
- image bank
- links to gpscience.com

Start-Up Activities

The Expansion of a Gas

Why does the mercury in a themometer rise? Why do sidewalks, streets, and bridges have cracks? Many substances expand when heated and contract when cooled, as you will see during this lab.

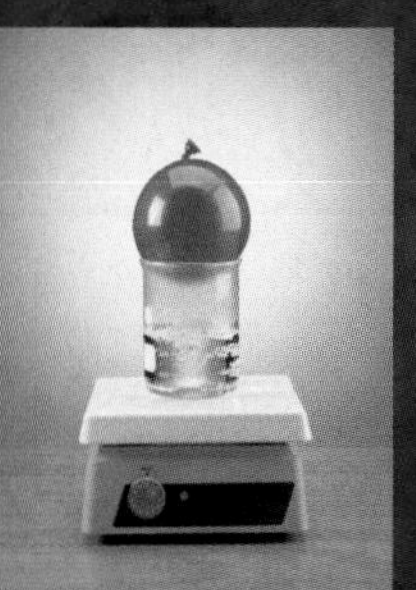

1. Blow up a balloon until it is half filled. Use a tape measure to measure the circumference of the balloon.
2. Pour water into a large beaker until it is half full. Place the beaker on a hot plate and wait for the water to boil.
3. Set the balloon on the mouth of the beaker and observe for five minutes. Be careful not to allow the balloon to touch the hot plate. Measure the circumference of the balloon.
4. **Think Critically** Write a paragraph in your Science Journal describing the changing size of the balloon's circumference. Infer why the balloon's circumference changed.

Solids, Liquids, and Gases The matter that surrounds you is either a solid, liquid, or gas. Make the following Foldable to help you organize information about solids, liquids, and gases.

STEP 1 **Fold** a sheet of paper in half lengthwise. Make the back edge about 5 cm longer than the front edge.

STEP 2 **Turn** the paper so the fold is on the bottom. Then **fold** it into thirds.

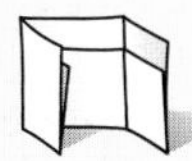

STEP 3 **Unfold and cut** only the top layer along both folds to make three tabs.

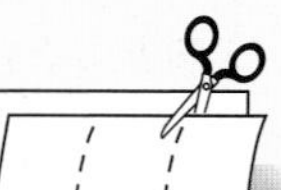

STEP 4 **Label** the Foldable as shown.

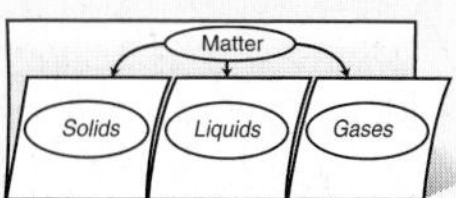

Read for Main Ideas As you read the chapter, list the characteristics of solids, liquids, and gases under the appropriate tab. List some examples of each under the tab also.

Preview this chapter's content and activities at gpscience.com

475

Purpose Use the Launch Lab to introduce students to the fact that matter changes as temperature changes.

Preparation Before students do this activity, obtain metric tape measures.

Materials balloon, tape measure, large beaker, hot plate, water

Teaching Strategy Help students set up data tables in which to record their measurements.

Think Critically

The balloon expanded when placed over the boiling water. The heat of the steam increased the energy of the air molecules in the balloon, causing them to move faster and make the balloon expand.

Assessment

Process Ask students how the results of this activity would have been different if they had put water in the balloon instead of air. The balloon would not have expanded much when it was heated. Use **Performance Assessment in the Science Classroom,** p. 89.

Dinah Zike Study Fold

Student preparation materials for this Foldable are available in the **Chapter *Fast File* Resources.**

Additional Chapter Media

- What's Science Got to Do With It?: *Under Pressure*
- BrainPOP *States of Matter*
- Virtual Lab: *What factors affect the pressure of gas in a container?*
- Video Lab: *Testing the Viscosity of Common Liquids*

1 Motivate

Bellringer

Section Focus Transparencies also are available on the Interactive Chalkboard CD-ROM.

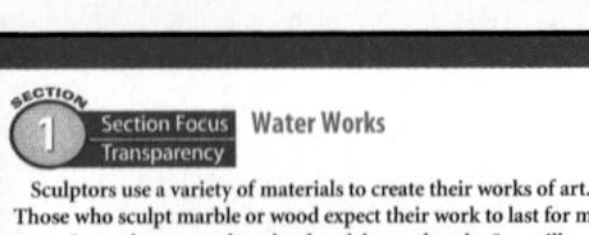

Section Focus Transparency 1 — Water Works

Sculptors use a variety of materials to create their works of art. Those who sculpt marble or wood expect their work to last for many years. Ice sculptors, on the other hand, know that the Sun will soon turn their intricate works into pools of water.

1. What happens to molecules of water as ice melts?
2. Why does snow melt when you hold it in your hand?
3. What happens when water boils?

L2

Solids, Liquids, and Gases

Tie to Prior Knowledge

Temperature and Fuel Ask students if they have ever heard of fuel line freeze-up or vapor lock. With vapor lock, which usually happens in the summer, fuel vaporizes at a hot spot, causing a fuel line to partially fill with vapor. This causes problems for a car's fuel pump, which is designed to pump a liquid, not a vapor. In winter, water from condensation in the gasoline tank can freeze and block the fuel line. Discuss with students how temperature affects the state of matter of the fuel.

Text Question Answer

They are alike because they are both composed of water molecules. They differ in the amount of kinetic energy the molecules contain and the distance between the particles.

section 1

Kinetic Theory

Reading Guide

What **You'll Learn**

- **Explain** the kinetic theory of matter.
- **Describe** particle movement in the four states of matter.
- **Explain** particle behavior at the melting and boiling points.

Why **It's Important**

You can use energy that is lost or gained when a substance changes from one state to another.

Review Vocabulary

kinetic energy: energy in the form of motion

New Vocabulary

- kinetic theory
- melting point
- heat of fusion
- boiling point
- heat of vaporization
- diffusion
- plasma
- thermal expansion

States of Matter

You probably do not think of the states of matter as you do everyday activities. An everyday activity such as eating lunch may include solids, liquids, and gases. Look at **Figure 1.** Can you identify the states of matter present? The boiling soup on the stove and the visible steam above the boiling soup is in the liquid state. The ice cube dropped into the soup to cool it, is in the solid state. How are these states alike and different?

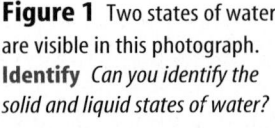

Figure 1 Two states of water are visible in this photograph.
Identify *Can you identify the solid and liquid states of water?*

Kinetic Theory The **kinetic theory** is an explanation of how particles in matter behave. To explain the behavior of particles, it is necessary to make some basic assumptions. The three assumptions of the kinetic theory are as follows:

1. All matter is composed of small particles (atoms, molecules, and ions).
2. These particles are in constant, random motion.
3. These particles are colliding with each other and the walls of their container.

Particles lose some energy during collisions with other particles. But the amount of energy lost is very small and can be neglected in most cases.

To visualize the kinetic theory, think of each particle as a tiny table-tennis ball in constant motion. These balls are bouncing and colliding with each other. Mentally visualizing matter in this way can help you understand the movement of particles in matter.

476 CHAPTER 16 Solids, Liquids, and Gases

Section 1 Resource Manager

Chapter *FAST FILE* Resources

Transparency Activity, p. 46, 49–50
Directed Reading for Content Mastery, pp. 21, 22
Note-taking Worksheets, pp. 35–37
Enrichment, p. 32
Lab Worksheet, pp. 5–6
Reinforcement, p. 29

Reading and Writing Skill Activities, p. 33
Science Inquiry Lab, pp. 47–48
Cultural Diversity, p. 55

Thermal Energy Think about the ice cube in the soup. Does the ice cube appear to be moving? How can a frozen, solid ice cube have motion? Remember to focus on the particles. Atoms in solids are held tightly in place by the attraction between the particles. This attraction between the particles gives solids a definite shape and volume. However, the thermal energy in the particles causes them to vibrate in place. Thermal energy is the total energy of a material's particles, including kinetic—vibrations and movement within and between the particles—and potential—resulting from forces that act within or between particles. When the temperature of the substance is lowered, the particles will have less thermal energy and will vibrate more slowly.

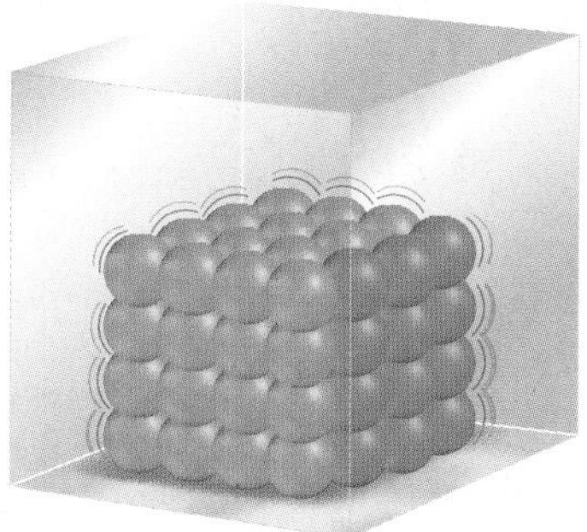
Solid

Figure 2 The particles in a solid are packed together tightly and are constantly vibrating in place.

 ***What is thermal energy?***

Average Kinetic Energy Temperature is the term used to explain how hot or cold an object is. In science, temperature means the average kinetic energy of particles in the substance, or how fast the particles are moving. On average, molecules of frozen water at 0°C will move slower than molecules of water at 100°C. Therefore, water molecules at 0°C have lower average kinetic energy than the molecules at 100°C. Molecules will have kinetic energy at all temperatures, including absolute zero. Scientists theorize that at absolute zero, or –273.15°C, particle motion is so slow that no additional thermal energy can be removed from a substance.

Reading Check ***How are kinetic energy and temperature related?***

Solid State An ice cube is an example of a solid. The particles of a solid are closely packed together, as shown in **Figure 2.** Most solid materials have a specific type of geometric arrangement in which they form when cooled. The type of geometric arrangement formed by a solid is important. Chemical and physical properties of solids often can be attributed to the type of geometric arrangement that the solid forms. **Figure 3** shows the geometric arrangement of solid water. Notice that the hydrogen and oxygen atoms are alternately spaced in the arrangement.

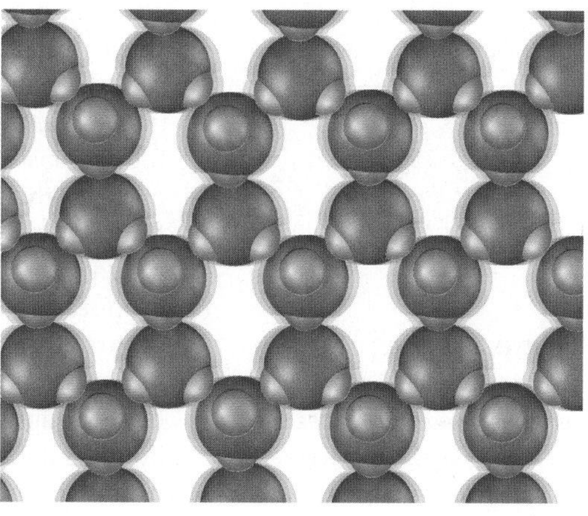

Figure 3 The particles in solid water align themselves in an ordered geometric pattern. Even though a solid ice cube doesn't look like it is moving, its molecules are vibrating in place.

2 Teach

Caption Answer

Figure 1 The water in the soup is liquid. The ice cube in the soup is solid.

Reading Check

Answer the total energy of a material's particles, including both kinetic and potential energy

Quick Demo

Observing Salt Crystals

Materials salt crystals, microscope or magnifying lens

Estimated Time 10 minutes

Procedure Have students observe the regular, cubic shape of salt crystals under a microscope or with a magnifying lens.

Reading Check

Answer Temperature is the average kinetic energy of the particles of a substance.

Use an Analogy

Sporting Event States of matter are like the crowd at a sporting event. When seated, people are like particles in a solid. They can move in place but don't go anywhere. The people in the aisles are like particles in a liquid. They move past each other but aren't free to move far apart. Upon reaching the parking lot, the people are free to move randomly, as are particles in a gas.

Differentiated Instruction

English-Language Learners Have students make vocabulary study cards out of index cards. Have students write a vocabulary word in both languages on one side of the card. On the other side of the card, write the definition of the word in both languages. Make a card for each vocabulary word in the chapter. Use the cards to study before quizzes and tests.

Challenge Investigate the concept of absolute zero. Find out what the concept of absolute zero means. How do real and ideal gases behave at absolute zero? Which two widely used temperature scales are absolute temperature scales? Prepare a report of your research findings about absolute zero and share it with your class. Kelvin and Rankine are absolute temperature scales.

Reading Check

Answer the amount of energy required to change a substance from the solid state to the liquid state at its melting point

Steam Students may think that steam is water in the gaseous state. Actually, steam is liquid water droplets that have condensed from gaseous water in the air.

Reading Check

Answer The particles have gained enough kinetic energy to partially escape the attractive forces in the solid.

Activity

Altitude and Cooking Have students examine the labels of foods such as cake mixes. On Earth, air pressure decreases as altitude increases. Have students determine the effect of altitude on cooking time and temperature for these items. L2 IS **Linguistic**

Caption Answer

Figure 6 Evaporation is vaporization that occurs at the surface of a liquid. It can occur at temperatures below the liquid's boiling point. Boiling is vaporization that occurs throughout the liquid at a specific temperature depending on the pressure at the surface of the liquid.

Figure 4 The particles in a liquid are moving more freely than the particles in a solid. They have enough kinetic energy to slip out of the ordered arrangement of a solid.

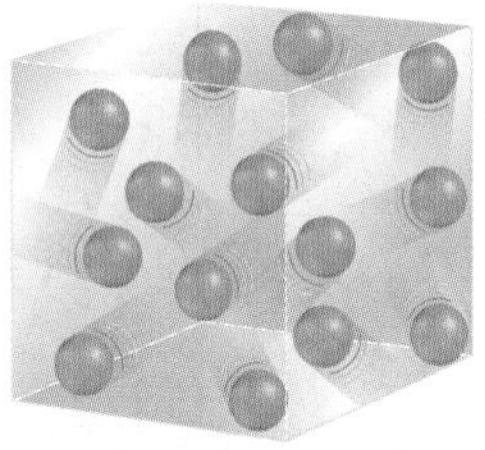

Figure 5 In gases, the particles are far apart and the attractive forces between the particles are overcome. Gases do not have a definite volume or shape.

Liquid State What happens to a solid when thermal energy or heat is added to it? Think about the ice cube in the hot soup. The particles in the hot soup are moving fast and colliding with the vibrating particles in the ice cube. The collisions of the particles transfer energy from the soup to the ice cube. The particles on the surface of the ice cube vibrate faster. These particles collide with and transfer energy to other ice particles. Soon the particles of ice have enough kinetic energy to overcome the attractive forces. The particles of ice gain enough kinetic energy to slip out of their ordered arrangement and the ice melts. This is known as the **melting point,** or the temperature at which a solid begins to liquefy. Energy is required for the particles to slip out of the ordered arrangement. The amount of energy required to change a substance from the solid phase to the liquid phase at its melting point is known as the **heat of fusion.**

Reading Check *What is heat of fusion?*

Liquids Flow Particles in a liquid, shown in **Figure 4,** have more kinetic energy than particles in a solid. This extra kinetic energy allows particles to partially overcome the attractions to other particles. Thus, the particles can slide past each other, allowing liquids to flow and take the shape of their container. However, the particles in a liquid have not completely overcome the attractive forces between them. This causes the particles to cling together, giving liquids a definite volume.

Reading Check *Why do liquids flow?*

Gas State Particles in the gas state are shown in **Figure 5.** Gas particles have enough kinetic energy to overcome the attractions between them. Gases do not have a fixed volume or shape. Instead, gas particles spread out so that they fill whatever container they are in. How does a liquid become a gas? The particles in a liquid are constantly moving. Some particles are moving faster and have more kinetic energy than others. The particles that are moving fast enough can escape the attractive forces of other particles and enter the gas state. This process is called vaporization. Vaporization can occur in two ways—evaporation and boiling. Evaporation is vaporization that occurs at the surface of a liquid and can occur at temperatures below the liquid's boiling point. To evaporate, particles must have enough kinetic energy to escape the attractive forces of the liquid. They must be at the liquid's surface and traveling away from the liquid.

LAB DEMONSTRATION

Purpose to demonstrate the movement of gas particles.

Materials a balloon, 5 drops of vanilla flavoring, dropper

Procedure Use a dropper to put 5 drops of vanilla into a balloon. Close the bottle of vanilla flavoring so that a minimum amount of odor is released. Blow up the balloon, tie it closed, then smell near the surface of the balloon.

Expected Outcome Students will detect the aroma of vanilla as it evaporates inside the balloon.

Assessment

Ask the students why they can smell the vanilla near the surface of the balloon. The moving particles of vanilla passed between the molecules of the stretched balloon.

478 CHAPTER 16 Solids, Liquids, and Gases

Figure 6 Boiling occurs throughout a liquid when the pressure of the vapor in the liquid equals the pressure of the vapor on the surface of the liquid. **Explain** *the difference between boiling and evaporation.*

Boiling Point A second way that a liquid can vaporize is by boiling. Unlike evaporation, boiling occurs throughout a liquid at a specific temperature depending on the pressure on the surface of the liquid. Boiling is shown in **Figure 6.** The **boiling point** of a liquid is the temperature at which the pressure of the vapor in the liquid is equal to the external pressure acting on the surface of the liquid. This external pressure is a force pushing down upon a liquid, keeping particles from escaping. Particles require energy to overcome this force. **Heat of vaporization** is the amount of energy required for the liquid at its boiling point to become a gas.

Reading Check *How does external pressure affect the boiling point of a liquid?*

Gases Fill Their Container What happens to the attractive forces between the particles in a gas? The gas particles are moving so quickly and are so far apart that they have overcome the attractive forces between them. Because the attractive forces between them are overcome, gases do not have a definite shape or a definite volume. The movement of particles and the collisions between them cause gases to diffuse. **Diffusion** is the spreading of particles throughout a given volume until they are uniformly distributed. Diffusion occurs in solids and liquids but occurs most rapidly in gases. For example, if you spray air freshener in one corner of a room, it's not long before you smell the scent all over the room. The particles of gas have moved, collided, and "filled" their container—the room. The particles have diffused. Gases will fill the container that they are in even if the container is a room. The particles continue to move and collide in a random motion within their container.

Topic: States of Matter
Visit gpscience.com for Web links to information about states of matter.

Activity Create a slide presentation about the states of matter using the computer and presentation software.

Reading Check

Answer At greater atmospheric pressure (lower elevation) the boiling point is a higher temperature than at less atmospheric pressure (higher elevation).

Inquiry Lab

Preserving a Solid State

Question How should you pack and transport a fragile chocolate sculpture that must be shipped to a warm, tropical climate?

Possible Materials resource materials, paper and pencils, sample packaging materials, resources and pricing information from shipping companies

Estimated Time 1 week outside class time

Teaching Strategies

- Students packaging design must keep the chocolate from melting, breaking, and getting wet.
- The sculpture must arrive at its destination within 3 days.
- Students should brainstorm how they should pack their sculpture.
- The packaging and shipping should be moderately priced and affordable for a manufacturer and a customer.
- Students should draw their design and supply estimated costs for shipping the sculpture.
- Allow students to explore other questions that arise.

For additional inquiry activities, see *Science Inquiry Labs*.

Cultural Diversity

Sharing Languages In English-speaking countries, the three states of water are called *ice*, *water*, and *water vapor*. In Spanish-speaking countries the words are *hielo*, *aqua*, and *vapor*. If you have students in your class that speak other languages, ask them to share the terms they know with the class.

Curriculum Connection

Art Have students visit shopping malls and observe how different states of matter are used to decorate the mall and make shopping more pleasant. Have them write about what they see. Items seen may include fountains (liquid), helium-filled balloons (gas), marble floors (solid), and fluorescent and neon lighting (gases). L2 IS **Visual-Spatial** P

IDENTIFYING Misconceptions

Volume Remind students that even though gases fill the volume of their container, almost all of the volume of the container is empty space. The volume of a container of gas is much greater than the total volume of the gas particles.

Reading Check

Answer The particles are gaining energy and are in the process of changing state.

Use Science Words

Word Meaning Have students find the meaning of the word *plasma* as it is used by biologists and compare that to the meaning as used by physicists. To a biologist, plasma is the colorless fluid part of blood, i.e., blood stripped of red blood cells. To a physicist, plasma is matter in which electrons have been stripped away from the protons and neutrons. L2

LS **Linguistic**

Fun Fact

Unlike most gases, plasmas conduct electricity well and are affected by magnetic fields. Also, while the particles that make up gases move randomly, sometimes the electrons and ions that make up plasmas move together in a wavelike motion.

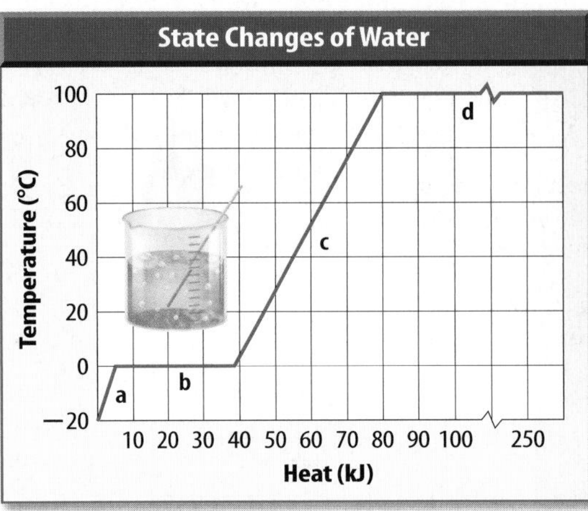

Figure 7 This graph shows the heating curve of water. At **a** and **c** the water is increasing in kinetic energy. At **b** and **d** the added energy is used to overcome the bonds between the particles.

Heating Curve of a Liquid A graph of water being heated from –20°C to 100°C is shown in **Figure 7.** This type of graph is called a heating curve because it shows the temperature change of water as thermal energy, or heat, is added. Notice the two areas on the graph where the temperature does not change. At 0°C, ice is melting. All of the energy put into the ice at this temperature is used to overcome the attractive forces between the particles in the solid. The temperature remains constant during melting. After the attractive forces are overcome, particles move more freely and their average kinetic energy, or temperature, increases. At 100°C, water is boiling or vaporizing and the temperature remains constant again. All of the energy that is put into the water goes to overcoming the remaining attractive forces between the water particles. When all of the attractive forces in the water are overcome, the energy goes to increasing the temperature of the particles.

Reading Check *What is occurring at the two temperatures on the heat curve where the graph is a flat line?*

Plasma State So far, you've learned about the three familiar states of matter—solids, liquids, and gases. But none of these is the most common state of matter in the universe. Scientists estimate that much of the matter in the universe is plasma. **Plasma** is matter consisting of positively and negatively charged particles. Although this matter contains positive and negative particles, its overall charge is neutral because equal numbers of both charges are present. Recall that on average, particles of matter move faster as the matter is heated to higher temperatures. The faster the particles move the greater the force is with which they collide. The forces produced from high-energy collisions are so great that electrons from the atom are stripped off. This state of matter is called plasma. All of the observed stars including the Sun, shown in **Figure 8,** consist of plasma. Plasma also is found in lightning bolts, neon and fluorescent tubes, and auroras.

Figure 8 Stars including the Sun contain matter that is in the plasma phase. Plasma exists where the temperature is extremely high. **Describe** *the plasma phase.*

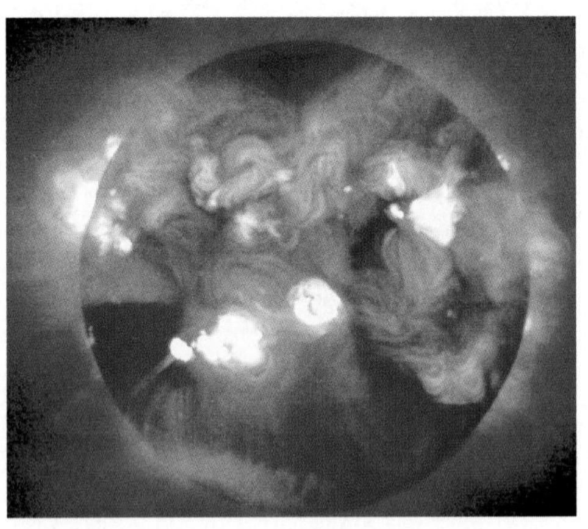

Reading Check *What is plasma?*

Reading Check

Answer matter consisting of positively and negatively charged particles

Teacher FYI

Effects of Pressure At 1 atm, water freezes at 0°C and boils at 100°C. At different pressures, water goes through these changes at different temperatures. In fact, when the pressure is 0.61 kPA and the temperature is 0.01°C, water can exist as a solid, a liquid, and a gas. This is called the triple point.

Visual Learning

Figure 7 Ask a volunteer to read aloud the section of the SE text that describes the graph while the rest of the students follow the graph with their fingers. Discuss with students the effect of adding heat to water at different temperatures. L1

ELL LS **Auditory-Musical**

Thermal Expansion

You have learned how the kinetic theory is used to explain the behavior of particles in different states of matter. The kinetic theory also explains other characteristics of matter in the world around you. Have you noticed the seams in a concrete driveway or sidewalk? A gap often is left between the sections to clearly separate them. These separation lines are called expansion joints. When concrete absorbs heat, it expands. Then when it cools, it contracts. If expansion joints are not used, the concrete will crack when the temperature changes.

Figure 9 As the thermometer is heated, the column of liquid in the thermometer expands. As the temperature cools, the liquid in the thermometer contracts.

Expansion of Matter The kinetic theory can be used to explain this behavior in concrete. Recall that particles move faster and separate as the temperature rises. This separation of particles results in an expansion of the entire object, known as thermal expansion. **Thermal expansion** is an increase in the size of a substance when the temperature is increased. The kinetic theory can be used to explain the contraction in objects, too. When the temperature of an object is lowered, particles slow down. The attraction between the particles increases and the particles move closer together. The movements of the particles closer together result in an overall shrinking of the object, known as contraction.

Expansion in Liquids Expansion and contraction occur in most solids, liquids, and gases. A common example of expansion in liquids occurs in thermometers, as shown in **Figure 9.** The addition of energy causes the particles of the liquid in the thermometer to move faster. The particles in the liquid in the narrow thermometer tube start to move farther apart as their motion increases. The liquid has to expand only slightly to show a large change on the temperature scale.

Expansion in Gases An example of thermal expansion in gases is shown in **Figure 10.** Hot-air balloons are able to rise due to thermal expansion of air. The air in the balloon is heated, causing the distance between the particles in the air to increase. As the hot-air balloon expands, the number of particles per cubic centimeter decreases. This expansion results in a decreased density of the hot air. Because the density of the air in the hot-air balloon is lower than the density of the cooler air outside, the balloon will rise.

Figure 10 Heating the air in this hot-air balloon causes the particles in the air to move apart, creating a lower density inside the balloon.

Quick Demo

Thermal Expansion

Materials two identical jars with lids that are difficult to open

Estimated Time 10 minutes

Procedure Have a student attempt to open one of the jars. Place the other lid in hot water for a few minutes. Have the same student attempt to open that jar. Warming the jar lid causes thermal expansion, making the jar easier to open. L2 ELL IN **Kinesthetic**

Discussion

Food Preservation Sealing food containers is important to preserve freshness and prevent spoilage. What are two reasons a lid put on a food container when it is warm might become tight as the food cools? Inside the container, warm gases gradually cool, causing the pressure inside the container to drop. Then the pressure outside the container is greater than the pressure inside the container, and the lid has a tighter seal. Also, when the lid placed on the warm container begins to cool, it contracts slightly, causing it to fit more tightly on the container. L3 IN **Logical-Mathematical**

Caption Answer

Figure 8 Plasma is matter that contains particles with high energy. The particles experience high-energy collisions which strip electrons off of the atoms. Because of these collisions, the matter consists of positively and negatively charged particles. The overall charge of the plasma is neutral because equal numbers of both charges are present.

Visual Learning

Figure 9 Most thermometers contain either alcohol or mercury. Ask students how the design of a thermometer may depend on the liquid used in it. The size of the bulb and tube are determined by the rate of expansion of the liquid used in the particular thermometer. L2 IN **Logical-Mathematical**

Science Journal

Weathering Soils form from the breaking down of rocks. Have students find out and write in their Science Journals the role played by thermal expansion in the weathering of rocks. Rocks are often broken down, or weathered, when water enters cracks in the rocks and then freezes. The expansion of the water as it freezes breaks up the rock. L2 IN **Linguistic**

Visual Learning

Figure 11 Explain to students that the charged parts of the water molecules do not have as much charge as an electron or proton. To show a partial charge, the lowercase Greek letter delta (δ) is used with a sign to show positive (δ^+) or negative (δ^-) charge. Have students draw a picture of a water molecule with partial charges shown. Drawings should show two hydrogen atoms connected to one oxygen atom with a (δ^-) by the oxygen atom, and a (δ^+) by each of the hydrogen atoms. L2 IS **Visual-Spatial**

Understanding Unusual Behavior The work of Pierre-Gilles de Gennes led to a better understanding of the properties of liquid crystals. Today many common products use liquid crystals. Bring to class several devices that use liquid crystals such as thermometers, digital watches, calculators, miniature television sets, or portable computers. Ask what advantage liquid crystal thermometers have over mercury thermometers. They eliminate the danger of mercury, which is poisonous. Ask what advantage the liquid crystal displays may have over other types of displays. Liquid crystal displays are sharper and use less power than other types of displays.

Answer glass and plastics

Caption Answer

Figure 11 Water expands when going from a liquid to a solid state. Solid ice is less dense than water-so it floats.

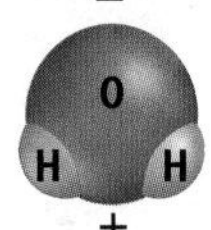

Figure 11 The positively and negatively charged regions on a water molecule interact to create empty spaces in the crystal lattice. These interactions cause water to expand when it is in the solid phase. **Explain** *why ice floats on water.*

The Strange Behavior of Water Normally, substances expand as the temperature rises, because the particles move farther apart. An exception to this rule, however, is water. Water molecules are unusual in that they have highly positive and highly negative areas. **Figure 11** is a diagram of the water molecule showing these charged regions. These charged regions affect the behavior of water. As the temperature of water drops, the particles move closer together. The unlike charges will be attracted to each other and line up so that only positive and negative zones are near each other. Because the water molecules orient themselves according to charge, empty spaces occur in the structure. These empty spaces are larger in ice than in liquid water, so water expands when going from a liquid to a solid state. Solid ice is less dense than liquid water. That is why ice floats on the top of lakes in the winter.

Solid or a Liquid?

Other substances also have unusual behavior when changing states. Amorphous solids and liquid crystals are two classes of materials that do not react as you would expect when they are changing states.

Amorphous Solids Ice melts at 0°C, gold melts at 1,064°C, and lead melts at 327°C. But not all solids have a definite temperature at which they change from solid to liquid. Some solids merely soften and gradually turn into a liquid over a temperature range. There is not an exact temperature like a boiling point where the phase change occurs. These solids lack the highly ordered structure found in crystals. They are known as amorphous solids from the Greek word for "without form."

You are familiar with two amorphous solids—glass and plastics. The particles that make up amorphous solids are typically long, chainlike structures that can get jumbled and twisted instead of being neatly stacked into geometric arrangements. Interactions between the particles occur along the chain, which gives amorphous solids some properties that are very different from crystalline solids.

Liquids do not have an orderly arrangement of particles. Some amorphous solids form when liquid matter changes to solid matter too quickly for an orderly structure to form. One example of this is obsidian—a volcanic glass. Obsidian forms when lava, made of molten rock, cools quickly, such as when it spills into water.

Understanding Unusual Behavior Pierre-Gilles de Gennes, a French physicist, was awarded the 1991 Nobel Prize for Physics for his discoveries about the behavior of molecules in liquid crystals and polymers (plastics). His discoveries led to a better understanding about the behavior and control of these substances.

Reading Check *What are two examples of amorphous solids?*

Science Journal

Dry Ice At atmospheric pressure, a few materials, such as iodine and carbon dioxide, change directly from solid to gas without going through a liquid state. Use the kinetic theory to explain what happens when heat is added to solid carbon dioxide (dry ice). The particles increase in energy enough to go from vibrating in place to escaping from the surface of the dry ice. L2 IS **Logical-Mathematical**

Liquid Crystals Liquid crystals are another group of materials that do not change states in the usual manner. Normally, the ordered geometric arrangement of a solid is lost when the substance goes from the solid state to the liquid state. Liquid crystals start to flow during the melting phase similar to a liquid, but they do not lose their ordered arrangement completely, as most substances do. Liquid crystals will retain their geometric order in specific directions.

Liquid crystals are placed in classes depending upon the type of order they maintain when they liquefy. They are highly responsive to temperature changes and electric fields. Scientists use these unique properties of liquid crystals to make liquid crystal displays (LCD) in the displays of watches, clocks, and calculators, as shown in **Figure 12.**

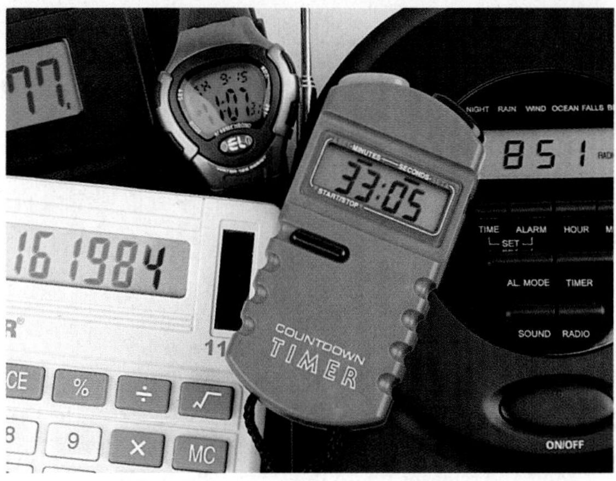

Figure 12 Liquid crystals are used in the displays of watches, clocks, calculators, and some notebook computers because they respond to electric fields.

section 1 review

Summary

States of Matter

- The kinetic theory is an explanation of how particles in matter move.
- Thermal energy is the total energy of a material's particles, including kinetic and potential energy.
- Temperature is the average kinetic energy of a substance.
- In most substances, as temperature increases the kinetic energy and disorder of the particles increase.

Thermal Expansion

- Some materials undergo thermal expansion when heated.
- Water expands when it changes from a liquid to a solid.

Solid or a Liquid?

- Amorphous solids have no definite melting point. They liquefy over a temperature range.
- Liquid crystals maintain some geometric order in the liquid state.

Self Check

1. **List** the three basic assumptions of the kinetic theory.
2. **Describe** the movement of the particles in solids, liquids, and gases.
3. **Describe** the movement of the particles at the melting point of a substance.
4. **Describe** the movement of the particles at the boiling point of a substance.
5. **Think Critically** Would the boiling point of water be higher or lower on the top of a mountain peak? How would the boiling point be affected in a pressurized boiler system? Explain.

Applying Math

6. **Interpret Data** Using the graph in **Figure 7,** describe the energy changes that are occurring when water goes from −15°C to 100°C.
7. **Make and Use Graphs** The melting point of acetic acid is 16.6°C and the boiling point is 117.9°C. Draw a graph similar to the graph in **Figure 7** showing the phase changes for acetic acid. Clearly mark the three phases, the boiling point, and the melting point on the graph.

Science Online gpscience.com/self_check_quiz

3 Assess

DAILY INTERVENTION

Check for Understanding

Visual-Spatial Have students make an illustration showing how solid, liquid, and gas particles behave and interact.

Reteach

Demonstrating the States of Matter Have students make a snow globe to model the behavior of solids, liquids, and gases. Have students use a small jar with a lid as the container. Fill the jar with enough glitter to cover the bottom of the jar a depth of 1 cm. Fill the jar with water, mineral oil, or baby oil. The particles will move slower in oil. Have students use their snow globe to model the behavior of solids, liquids, and gases.

Assessment

Process Ask students to draw diagrams illustrating what determines the boiling point of a liquid. At the boiling point, the pressure from molecules leaving the liquid to become gas is equal to the atmospheric pressure above them. Use **Performance Assessment in the Science Classroom,** p. 127.

section 1 review

1. All matter is composed of small particles; the particles are in constant motion; these particles are constantly colliding.
2. solid: vibrate in place; liquid: slide past each other; gas: move freely and randomly and collide with one another
3. The particles gain enough kinetic energy to slip out of their ordered arrangement.
4. The particles in the liquid overcome the downward pressure and escape from the liquid.
5. lower, because atmosphere pressure is lower; higher, the appliance creates a higher pressure above the liquid
6. From −15°C to 0°C, solid water absorbs energy. At 0°C, additional energy breaks attractions in the solid. After the solid melts, the temperature rises until it reaches 100°C. The temperature does not rise again until all the liquid has become gas.
7. Graphs should show the temperature rising until it reaches 16.6°C, where it plateaus. Then it rises to 117.9°C, where it again plateaus. Finally, it rises once more.

Real-World Question

Purpose Students will heat ice and graph the temperature changes over time. L2 LS **Kinesthetic**

Process Skills collect data, make and use tables, record observations, make and use graphs

Time Required 40 minutes

Procedure

Safety Precautions Caution students not to use the thermometers as stirring rods and not to allow the thermometers to rest on the bottom of the beaker.

Teaching Strategy Remind students that temperature is defined as the average kinetic energy of a substance.

Conclude and Apply

1. Check students' drawings. Encourage them to make the drawings as complete as possible.
2. The gaseous state on the drawing has the greatest amount of thermal energy and the solid state has the least amount.
3. Check students' graphs

Thermal Energy Changes in Matter

Thermal energy changes in matter are important in your home, but you may not realize it. Your refrigerator removes thermal energy from warm food and releases it into the room. This process keeps food from spoiling by decreasing the temperature of the food.

Real-World Question

Can a study of thermal energy changes lead to better understanding of matter and energy?

Goals

- **Explain** the thermal energy changes that occur as matter goes from the solid to gas state.

Materials

beakers (2)
ring clamp
ring stand
wire mesh
ice
thermometer
hot plate

Safety Precautions

Procedure

1. Set up the equipment as pictured. Prepare a data table in your Science Journal.
2. Gently heat the ice in the lower beaker. Every 3 min record your observations and the temperature of the water in the bottom container. Do not touch the thermometer to the bottom or sides of the container.
3. After the ice in the beaker melts and the water begins to boil, observe the system for several more minutes and record your observations.
4. Turn off the heat and let your system completely cool before you clean up.

Conclude and Apply

1. **Draw** a picture of the system used in this lab in your Science Journal. Label the state the water started at in the lower beaker, the state it changed into in the lower beaker, the state above the lower beaker, and the state on the outside of the upper beaker.
2. **Find** the location on the diagram that has the greatest thermal energy and which has the least amount of thermal energy.
3. **Draw** a time-temperature graph using your data from your Science Journal.

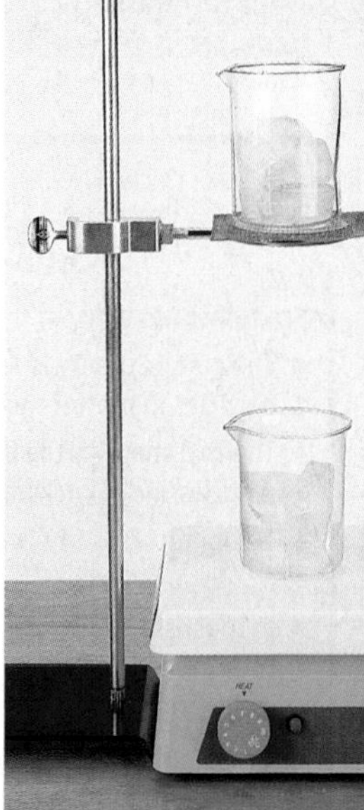

Compare your results with other groups in the lab. **For more help, refer to the** Science Skill Handbook.

Assessment

Process Have students write summaries of their graphs. Make sure they include descriptions of any areas where the temperature did not change quickly or did not change at all. Use **Performance Assessment in the Science Classroom,** p. 113.

Students should discuss why their conclusions did or did not agree.

section 2

Properties of Fluids

Reading Guide

What You'll Learn
- **Explain** Archimedes' principle.
- **Explain** Pascal's principle.
- **Explain** Bernoulli's principle and explain how we use it.

Why It's Important
Properties of fluids determine the design of ships, airplanes, and hydraulic machines.

Review Vocabulary
density: mass per unit volume of a material

New Vocabulary
- buoyancy
- pressure
- viscosity

How do ships float?

Some ships are so huge that they are like floating cities. For example, aircraft carriers are large enough to allow airplanes to take off and land on their decks. Despite their weight, these ships are able to float. This is because a greater force pushing up on the ship opposes the weight—or force—of the ship pushing down. What is this force? This supporting force is called the buoyant force. **Buoyancy** is the ability of a fluid—a liquid or a gas—to exert an upward force on an object immersed in it. If the buoyant force is equal to the object's weight, the object will float. If the buoyant force is less than the object's weight, the object will sink.

Archimedes' Principle In the third century B.C., a Greek mathematician named Archimedes made a discovery about buoyancy. Archimedes found that the buoyant force on an object is equal to the weight of the fluid displaced by the object. For example, if you place a block of wood in water, it will push water out of the way as it begins to sink—but only until the weight of the water displaced equals the block's weight. When the weight of water displaced—the buoyant force—becomes equal to the weight of the block, it floats. If the weight of the water displaced is less than the weight of the block, the object sinks. **Figure 13** shows the forces that affect an object in a fluid.

Reading Check *Why do rocks sink and rubber balls float in a swimming pool?*

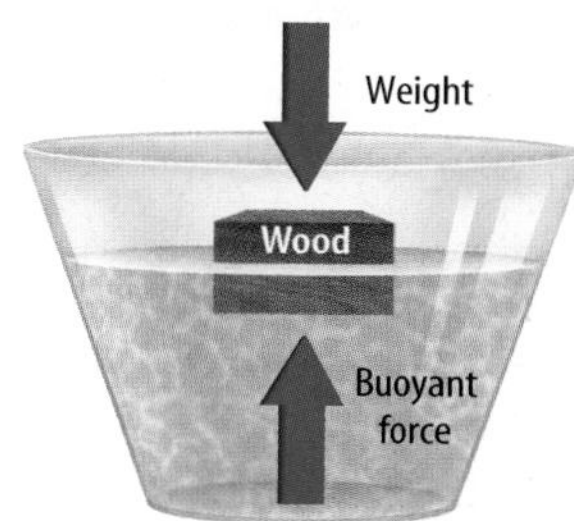

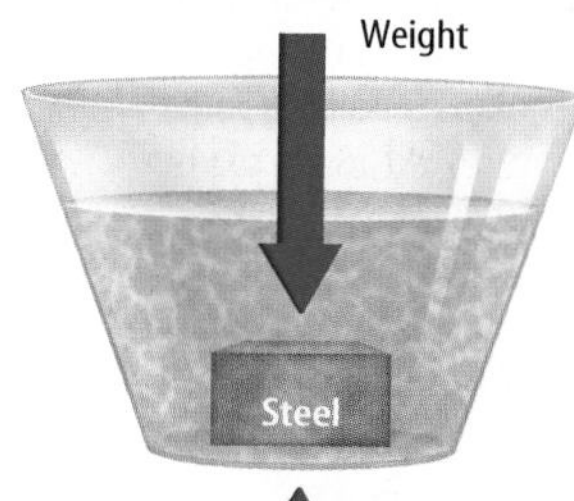

Figure 13 If the buoyant force of the fluid is equal to the weight of the object, the object floats. If the buoyant force of the fluid is less than the weight of the object, the object sinks.

Section 2 Resource Manager

Chapter *Fast File* Resources
- Transparency Activity, p. 47
- Directed Reading for Content Mastery, p. 22
- MiniLAB, p. 3
- Enrichment, p. 33
- Reinforcement, p. 30
- Lab Activity, pp. 9–11

1 Motivate

Bellringer

Section Focus Transparencies also are available on the Interactive Chalkboard CD-ROM. L2 

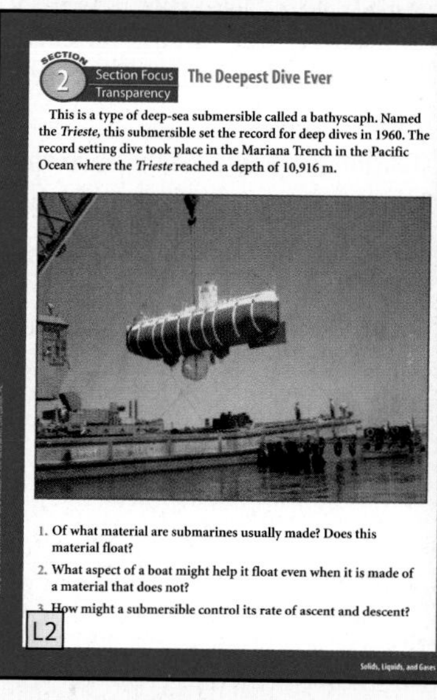
SECTION 2 Section Focus Transparency — The Deepest Dive Ever

This is a type of deep-sea submersible called a bathyscaph. Named the *Trieste*, this submersible set the record for deep dives in 1960. The record setting dive took place in the Mariana Trench in the Pacific Ocean where the *Trieste* reached a depth of 10,916 m.

1. Of what material are submarines usually made? Does this material float?
2. What aspect of a boat might help it float even when it is made of a material that does not?
3. How might a submersible control its rate of ascent and descent?

L2

Solids, Liquids, and Gases

Tie to Prior Knowledge

Sink or Float Ask students to name objects they know that sink or float in water. Have students form a hypothesis about why something as heavy as a boat will float.

Reading Check

Answer Rocks sink because the weight of the rock is greater than the buoyant force. Rubber balls float because the buoyant force of the water is greater than the weight of the ball.

2 Teach

Mini LAB

Purpose Students investigate the properties of density and buoyancy. L2 LS **Kinesthetic**

Materials 100-mL beakers (2); graduated cylinder; stirring rod; 10 mL each corn syrup, water, and vegetable oil; food coloring; 0.5-cm × 0.5-cm piece of aluminum foil; steel nut; peppercorn

Teaching Strategy Make sure students dispose of steel nuts, aluminum foil, and peppercorns in a trash can, not in the sink.

Safety Precautions Students should wear goggles and a lab apron for this activity.

Analysis

1. The corn syrup (highest density) went to the bottom, the water (medium density) was in the middle, and the oil (lowest density) was on top.
2. The weight of the foil was less than the buoyant force of the displaced oil, so it floated on top of the oil. The weight of the peppercorn was less than the buoyant force of the displaced water and more than the buoyant force of the oil. The weight of the steel nut was more than the buoyant force of any of the liquids, so it sank to the bottom.

Assessment

Process Have students make drawings showing the layers in their beaker. Clearly label each section and item in the drawing. Use **Performance Assessment in the Science Classroom**, p. 127.

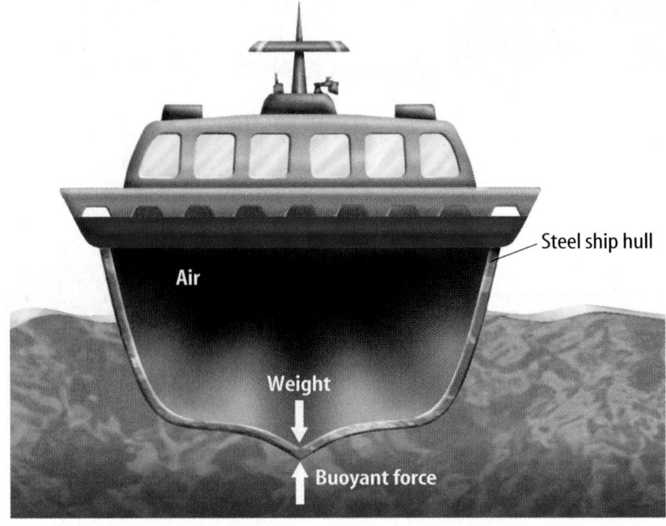

Figure 14 An empty hull of a ship contains mostly air. Its density is much lower than the density of a solid-steel hull. The lower density of the steel and air combination is what allows the ship to float in water. **Explain** *why a boat that takes in water will sink.*

Mini LAB

Observing Density and Buoyancy of Substances

Procedure

1. Pour 10 mL of **corn syrup** into a 100-mL beaker. In another **beaker,** add 3 to 4 drops of **food coloring** to 10 mL of **water.** Pour the dyed water into the 100-mL beaker containing corn syrup. Add 10 mL of **vegetable oil** to the beaker.
2. Drop a 0.5-cm square piece of **aluminum foil,** a **steel nut,** and a **whole peppercorn** into the 100-mL beaker.

Analysis

1. Using the concept of density, explain why the contents of the beaker separated into layers.
2. Using the concept of buoyancy, explain why the foil, steel nut, and peppercorn settled in their places.

Density Would a steel block the same size as a wood block float in water? They both displace the same volume and weight of water when submerged. Therefore, the buoyant force on the blocks is equal. Yet the steel block sinks and the wood block floats. What is different? The volume of the blocks and the volume of the water displaced each have different masses. If the three equal volumes have different masses, they must have different densities. Remember that density is mass per unit volume. The density of the steel block is greater than the density of water. The density of the wood block is less than the density of water. An object will float if its density is less than the density of the fluid it is placed in.

Suppose you formed the steel block into the shape of a hull filled with air, as in **Figure 14.** Now the same mass takes up a larger volume. The overall density of the steel boat and air is less than the density of water. The boat will now float.

Pascal's Principle

If you are underwater, you can feel the pressure of the water all around you. **Pressure** is force exerted per unit area, or $P=F/A$. Do you realize that Earth's atmosphere is a fluid? Earth's atmosphere exerts pressure all around you.

Blaise Pascal (1623–1662), a French scientist, discovered a useful property of fluids. According to Pascal's principle, pressure applied to a fluid is transmitted throughout the fluid. For example, when you squeeze one end of a balloon, the balloon expands out on the other end. When you squeeze one end of a toothpaste tube, toothpaste emerges from the other end. The pressure has been transmitted through the fluid toothpaste.

Active Reading

Bubble Map Using a bubble map helps students start ideas flowing about a given topic. Words are clustered to describe a topic or idea that is studied. Students can use a bubble map for a prewriting, to generate ideas before writing in their Journals, or to review for a test. Have students design a Bubble Map for the properties of fluids discussed in this section. P

Applying the Principle Hydraulic machines are machines that move heavy loads in accordance with Pascal's principle. Maybe you've seen a car raised using a hydraulic lift in an auto repair shop. A pipe that is filled with fluid connects small and large cylinders as shown in **Figure 15.** Pressure applied to the small cylinder is transferred through the fluid to the large cylinder. Because pressure remains constant throughout the fluid, according to Pascal's principle, more force is available to lift a heavy load by increasing the surface area. With a hydraulic machine, you could use your weight to lift something much heavier than you are. Do the following activity to see how force, pressure, and area are related.

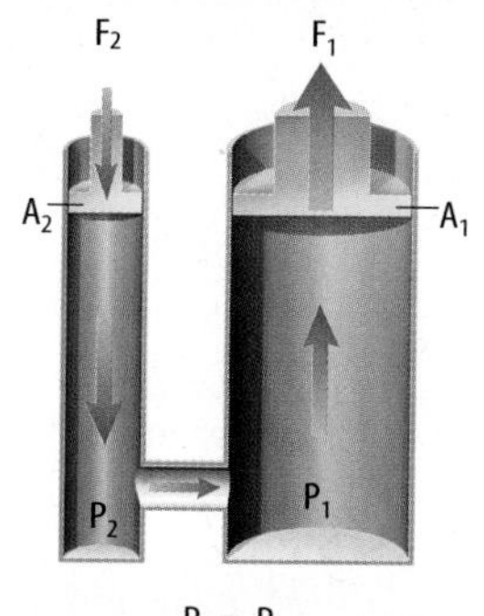

Figure 15 The pressure remains the same throughout the fluid in a hydraulic lift.

PRESSURE-FORCE EQUATION

Calculating Forces A hydraulic lift is used to lift a heavy machine that is pushing down on a 2.8-m² piston (A_1) with a force (F_1) of 3,700 N. What force (F_2) needs to be exerted on a 0.072 m² piston (A_2) to lift the machine?

1. **This is what you know:** $A_1 = 2.8\ m^2$ $\quad F_1 = 3{,}700\ N$ $\quad A_2 = 0.072\ m^2$
2. **This is what you need to find:** F_2
3. **Use this formula:** $P_1 = P_2$ $\quad \frac{F_1}{A_1} = \frac{F_2}{A_2}$
4. **Rearrange the equation and substitute:** $F_2 = \frac{F_1A_2}{A_1}$, then $F_2 = \frac{3700\ N \times 0.072\ m^2}{2.8\ m^2}$

   $F_2 = 95\ N$
5. **Determine the units:** units of $F_2 = \frac{\text{units } F_1 \times \text{units } A_2}{\text{units } A_1}$

   units of $F_2 = \frac{N \times \cancel{m^2}}{\cancel{m^2}}$

   units of $F_2 = N$

Answer: A force of 95 N is required to lift the machine.

Practice Problem

Challenge A heavy crate applied a force of 1,500 N on a 25-m² piston. What force needs to be exerted on the 0.80-m² piston to lift the crate?

Science Online
For more practice problems, go to page 834, and visit gpscience.com/extra_problems.

Visual Learning

Figure 15 Remind students that pressure is force per unit area. Review with them the pressure and area of each side of the hydraulic machine in this figure and the forces exerted on each side. L2 LS **Visual-Spatial**

Discussion

Mathematical Reasoning If the piston on the left in **Figure 15** moves down 10 cm, will the piston on the right move up 10 cm, less than 10 cm, or more than 10 cm? less than 10 cm L3 LS **Logical-Mathematical**

Use an Analogy

Moving Heavy Loads A hydraulic lift is analogous to a first-class lever in which the fulcrum is closer to the load than it is to the effort force. In both, a relatively small force is moved a long distance to move a heavy load a short distance.

PRESSURE-FORCE EQUATION

National Math Standards

Correlation to Mathematics Objectives

1, 2

Teaching Strategy

Follow the steps in the example problem.

Answer to Practice Problem

$F_2 = \frac{F_1A_2}{A_1} = 1{,}500\ N(0.80\ m^2)/25 m^2 = 48\ N$

Differentiated Instruction

Learning Disabled Review the arithmetic in Applying Math with these students slowly and carefully. Allow students to use calculators to work through the example problem. Check each number they enter into the calculator to make sure it is correct.

Teacher FYI

Narrow Spaces Fluids flow faster when forced to flow through narrow spaces. The resultant reduction in pressure in these spaces is a special case of Bernoulli's principle. When wind blows between rows of skyscrapers, the reduced air pressure outside of buildings can cause windows to pop out.

Reading Check

Answer pressure decreases

INTEGRATE
Earth Science

Magma and Viscosity A shield volcano is associated with lava that has low viscosity. Lava with higher viscosity produces cones with steeper slopes.

Research Find out more about magma and the types of cones that are produced. Make a poster showing how the different types of cones are produced.

Make a Model

Bernoulli's Principle Take a sheet of notebook paper and place it under your bottom lip, as shown in **Figure 16.** Blow across the top of the page. The fast moving air across the top of the page causes the paper to rise.

Activity

Paper Airplanes Allow students to make paper airplanes by folding notebook paper. Have a contest to see which airplane flies the farthest and the straightest. Have students compare the designs of the airplanes to determine which characteristics allowed the airplanes to fly the farthest and straightest.

Caption Answer

Figure 17 Bernoulli's principle states that as the velocity of a fluid increases, the pressure exerted by the fluid decreases.

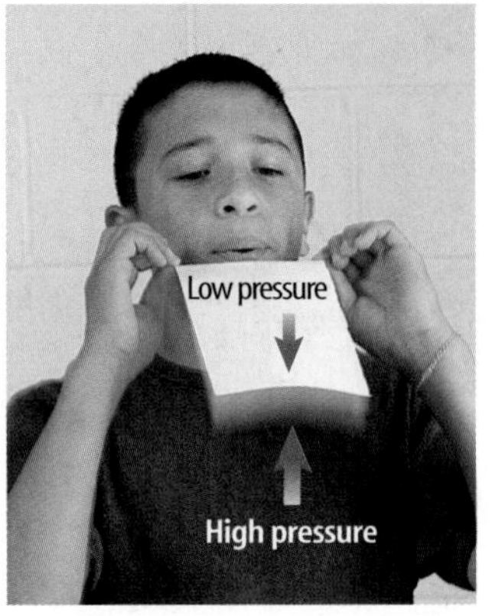

Low pressure
High pressure

Figure 16 The air above the sheet of paper is moving faster than the air under the paper, creating a low-pressure area above the paper, so the paper rises.

Bernoulli's Principle

Daniel Bernoulli (1700–1782) was a Swiss scientist who studied the properties of moving fluids such as water and air. He published his discovery in 1738. According to Bernoulli's principle, as the velocity of a fluid increases, the pressure exerted by the fluid decreases. One way to demonstrate Bernoulli's principle is to blow across the top surface of a sheet of paper, as in **Figure 16.** The paper will rise. The velocity of the air you blew over the top surface of the paper is greater than that of the quiet air below it. As a result, the air pressure pushing down on the top of the paper is lower than the air pressure pushing up on the paper. The net force below the paper pushes the paper upward. This principle is used today when designing aircraft wings and fluid-transporting piping systems.

Another application of Bernoulli's principle is the hose-end sprayer. This sprayer is used to apply fertilizers, herbicides, and insecticides to yards and gardens. To use this sprayer, a concentrated solution of the chemical that is to be applied is placed in the sprayer. The sprayer is attached to a garden hose, as shown in **Figure 17.** A strawlike tube is attached to the lid of the unit. The end of the tube is submerged into the concentrated chemical. The water to the garden hose is turned to a high flow rate. When you are ready to apply the chemicals to the lawn or plant area, you must push a trigger on the sprayer attachment. This allows the water in the hose to flow at a high rate of speed, creating a low pressure area above the strawlike tube. The concentrated chemical solution is sucked up through the straw and into the stream of water. The concentrated solution is mixed with water, reducing the concentration to the appropriate level and creating a spray that is easy to apply.

Reading Check ***How does pressure change as the velocity of a fluid increases?***

Figure 17 Bernoulli's principle was used in designing the hose-end sprayer.
Define *Bernoulli's principle.*

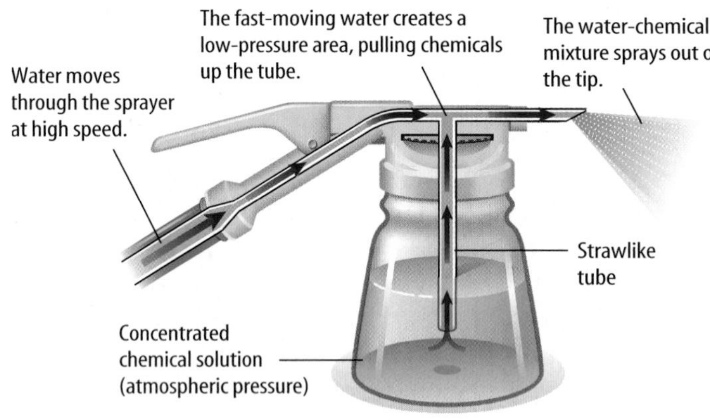

The fast-moving water creates a low-pressure area, pulling chemicals up the tube.
The water-chemical mixture sprays out of the tip.
Water moves through the sprayer at high speed.
Strawlike tube
Concentrated chemical solution (atmospheric pressure)

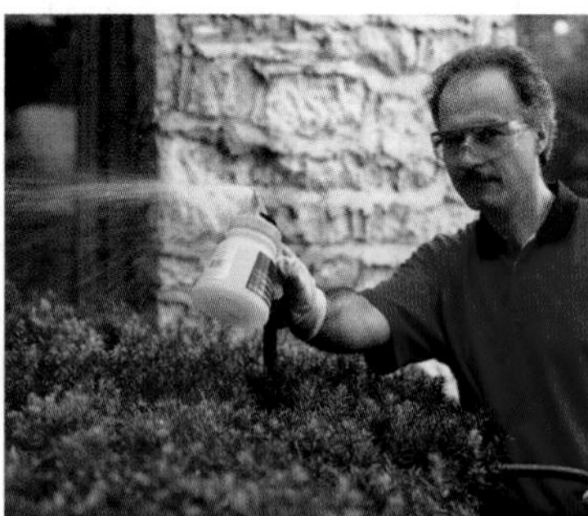

Differentiated Instruction

Challenge Tell students that the Venturi effect is a specific example of the Bernoulli principle. Ask them to find out what the Venturi effect is and build a model to demonstrate it. According to the Venturi effect, a fluid will speed up as it moves through a narrow passageway. Models could include a sand streambed with a narrow section. L3 LS **Kinesthetic**

Fluid Flow

Another property exhibited by fluid is its tendency to flow. The resistance to flow by a fluid is called **viscosity.** Fluids vary in their tendency to flow. For example, when you take syrup out of the refrigerator and pour it, the flow of syrup is slow. But if this syrup were heated, it would flow much faster. Water has a low viscosity because it flows easily. Cold syrup has a high viscosity because it flows slowly.

When a container of liquid is tilted to allow flow to begin, the flowing particles will transfer energy to the particles that are stationary. In effect, the flowing particles are pulling the other particles, causing them to flow, too. If the flowing particles do not effectively pull the other particles into motion, then the liquid has a high viscosity, or a high resistance to flow. If the flowing particles pull the other particles into motion easily, then the liquid has low viscosity, or a low resistance to flow.

How does temperature affect viscosity?

Magma and Viscosity Magma, or liquefied rock from a volcano, is an example of a liquid with varying viscosity. The viscosity of magma depends upon its composition. The viscosity of the magma flow determines the shape of the volcanic cone. In your Science Journal, infer the type of volcano cone that is created with high- and low-viscosity lava flows.

Answer Viscosity decreases as temperature increases.

3 Assess

DAILY INTERVENTION

Check for Understanding

Kinesthetic Have students blow up a balloon and observe Pascal's principle on the balloon. Have students gently squeeze one end and observe the effect on the balloon. Have students explain using the terms pressure and fluid what occurred when they gently squeezed the balloon.

Reteach

Buoyancy Have students test several objects that sink or float in water. Have students use density, volume, and weight to explain why each object sinks or floats. L2 ELL LS **Logical-Mathematical**

Assessment

Process Have each student form a hypothesis about what will happen if they blow air between two empty soft drink cans that are placed on their sides 2 cm apart. Have them test their hypotheses. The cans will move closer together. Use **Performance Assessment in the Science Classroom,** p. 93.

section 2 review

Summary

How do ships float?

- Buoyancy is the ability of a liquid or gas to exert an upward force on an object immersed in it.
- If the buoyant force is equal to the object's weight, the object will float. If the buoyant force is less than the object's weight, the object will sink.

Pascal's Principle

- Pascal's principle says that pressure applied to a fluid is transmitted throughout the fluid.

Bernoulli's Principle

- Bernoulli's principle says that as the velocity of a fluid increases, the pressure exerted by the fluid decreases.

Fluid Flow

- The resistance to flow by a fluid is called viscosity.
- Increasing the temperature increases the rate of energy transfer between the particles. This decreases the resistance to flow, or the viscosity.

Self Check

1. **Describe** the two opposing forces that are acting on an object floating in water.
2. **Explain** how a heavy boat floats on water.
3. **Explain** Use Pascal's principle to explain why squeezing a plastic mustard bottle forces mustard out the top.
4. **Describe,** using Bernoulli's principle, how roofs are lifted off buildings in tornados.
5. **Think Critically** If you fill a balloon with air, tie it off, and release it, it will fall to the floor. Why does it fall instead of float? What would happen if the balloon contained helium?

Applying Math

6. **Find Force** The density of water is 1.0 g/cm^3. How many kilograms of water does a submerged 120-cm^3 block displace? One kilogram has a force of 9.8 N. What is the buoyant force on the block?
7. **Solve an Equation** To lift an object weighing 20,000 N, how much force is needed on a small piston with an area of 0.072 m^2 if the large piston has an area of 2.8 m^2?

section 2 review

1. Weight is pushing down and buoyant force is pushing up.
2. Archimedes' principle says that the buoyant force on an object in a fluid is equal to the weight of the fluid displaced by the object. The overall density of an air-filled ship is less than that of water.
3. When you squeeze one end of a mustard container, the pressure is transmitted throughout the mustard, forcing mustard out the top.
4. The fast-moving winds in tornadoes create a low pressure area above the roof. The pressure under the roof is greater than the pressure above the roof, pushing the roof off.
5. The air in the balloon is compressed. Thus, its weight exceeds the buoyant force of the surrounding air. Helium is less dense than air, and the balloon would float.
6. The mass of water displaced is 120 cm^3 × 1.0 g/cm^3, or 120 g, which is 0.12 kg. The buoyant force is 0.12 kg × 9.8 N/kg, or 1.2 N.
7. $F_2 = \frac{F_1 A_2}{A_1} = \frac{(20{,}000\ \text{N})(0.072\ \text{m}^2)}{2.8\ \text{m}^2} = 514\ \text{N}$

section 3

Behavior of Gases

Reading Guide

What You'll Learn

- **Explain** how a gas exerts pressure on its container.
- **Explain** how a gas is affected when pressure, temperature, or volume is changed.

Why It's Important

Being able to explain and to predict the behavior of gases is useful because you live in a sea of air.

Review Vocabulary

temperature: a measure of the average kinetic energy of all the particles in an object

New Vocabulary

- pascal

Pressure

You learned from the kinetic theory that gas particles are constantly moving and colliding with anything in their path. The collisions of these particles in the air result in pressure. Pressure is the amount of force exerted per unit of area.

Often, gases are confined within containers. A balloon and a bicycle tire are considered to be containers. They remain inflated because of collisions the air particles have with the walls of their container, as shown in **Figure 18.** This collection of forces, caused by the collisions of the particles, pushes the walls of the container outward. If more air is pumped into the balloon, the number of air particles is increased. This causes more collisions with the walls of the container, which causes it to expand. Since the bicycle tire can't expand much, its pressure increases.

Pressure is measured in a unit called **pascal** (Pa), the SI unit of pressure. Because pressure is the amount of force divided by area, one pascal of pressure is one Newton per square meter or 1 N/m^2. This is a small pressure unit, so most pressures are given in kilopascals (kPa), or 1,000 pascals. At sea level, atmospheric pressure is 101.3 kPa. This means that at Earth's surface, the atmosphere exerts a force of about 101,300 N on every square meter—about the weight of a large truck. More information about the atmosphere is shown in **Figure 19.** Notice the temperature and pressure differences in the atmosphere as the distance from the surface of Earth increases.

Figure 18 The force created by the many particles in air striking the balloon's walls pushes the wall outward, keeping the balloon inflated.
Explain *why the term pressure can be used to describe these forces.*

How are force, area, and pressure related?

1 Motivate

Bellringer

Section Focus Transparencies also are available on the Interactive Chalkboard CD-ROM.

Section 3 Section Focus Transparency **One Small Step**

From a farm in Massachusetts, Robert Goddard launched the first liquid powered rocket in 1926. Using liquid oxygen and gasoline as propellants, the small rocket rose to 41 feet, arched over, and landed in a cabbage patch. The flight lasted only 2.5 seconds, yet it was the beginning of the rocket age.

1. When you heat a liquid, what happens?
2. When you heat a gas, what will it do?
3. Why do you think gases are cooled to a liquid state for use in rocket fuel?

L2

Solids, Liquids, and Gases

Tie to Prior Knowledge

Popping Ears Ask students if they have ever felt their ears pop as their altitude increased. Discuss the changes in pressure that cause this.

Answer Pressure is the amount of force exerted per unit of area.

Caption Answer

Figure 18 Pressure is force per unit of area. These particles are creating a force on the inside area of the balloon.

Section 3 Resource Manager

Chapter *Fast File* Resources

- Transparency Activity, p. 48
- Directed Reading for Content Mastery, pp. 23, 24
- Lab Activity, pp. 13–18
- Reinforcement, p. 31
- Enrichment, p. 34
- Lab Worksheet, pp. 7–8
- MiniLAB, p. 4

Lab Management and Safety, p. 44

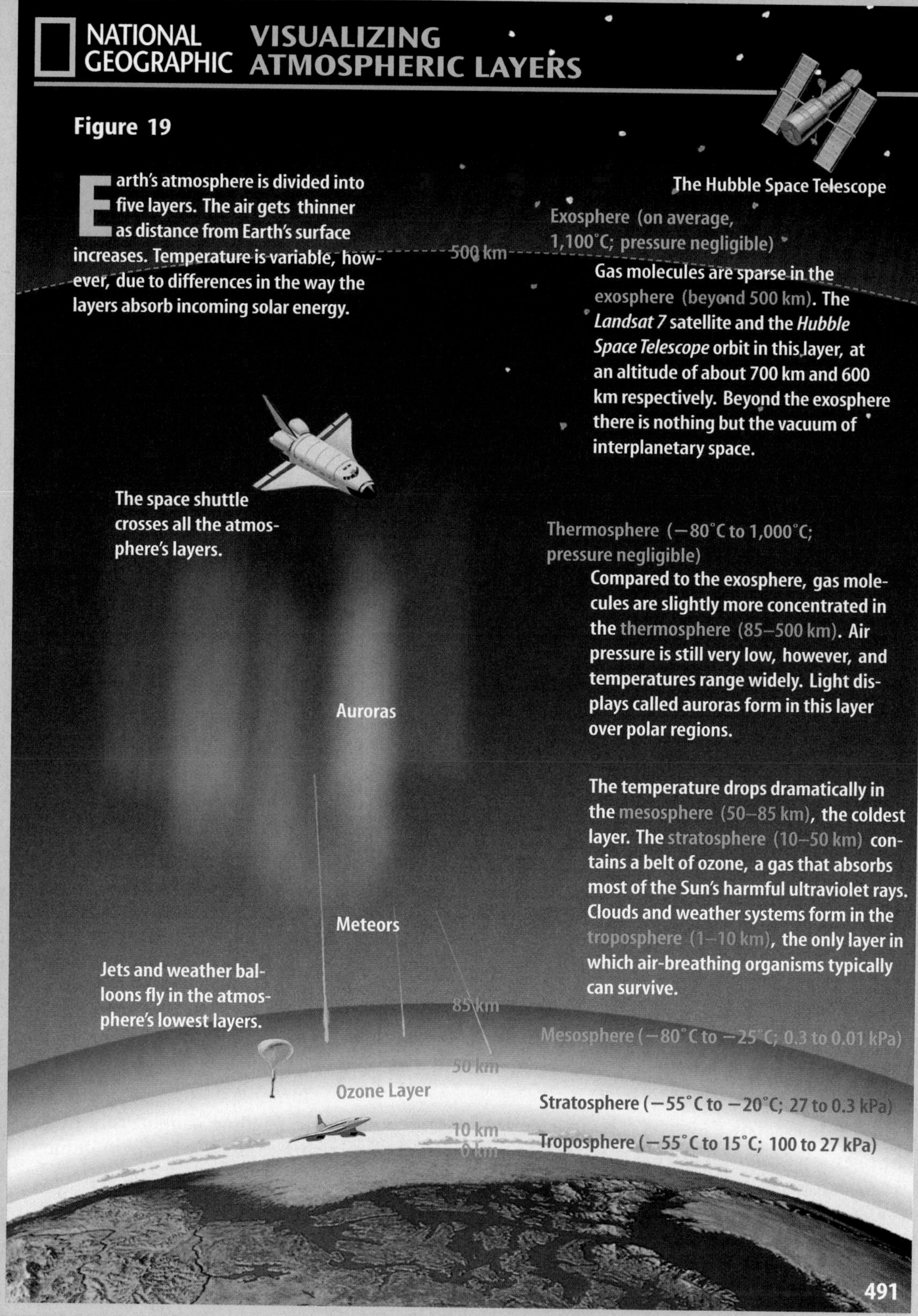

NATIONAL GEOGRAPHIC **VISUALIZING ATMOSPHERIC LAYERS**

Figure 19

Earth's atmosphere is divided into five layers. The air gets thinner as distance from Earth's surface increases. Temperature is variable, however, due to differences in the way the layers absorb incoming solar energy.

The Hubble Space Telescope
500 km
Exosphere (on average, 1,100°C; pressure negligible)
Gas molecules are sparse in the exosphere (beyond 500 km). The *Landsat 7* satellite and the *Hubble Space Telescope* orbit in this layer, at an altitude of about 700 km and 600 km respectively. Beyond the exosphere there is nothing but the vacuum of interplanetary space.
The space shuttle crosses all the atmosphere's layers.
Thermosphere (−80°C to 1,000°C; pressure negligible)
Compared to the exosphere, gas molecules are slightly more concentrated in the thermosphere (85–500 km). Air pressure is still very low, however, and temperatures range widely. Light displays called auroras form in this layer over polar regions.
Auroras
The temperature drops dramatically in the mesosphere (50–85 km), the coldest layer. The stratosphere (10–50 km) contains a belt of ozone, a gas that absorbs most of the Sun's harmful ultraviolet rays. Clouds and weather systems form in the troposphere (1–10 km), the only layer in which air-breathing organisms typically can survive.
Meteors
Jets and weather balloons fly in the atmosphere's lowest layers.
85 km
Mesosphere (−80°C to −25°C; 0.3 to 0.01 kPa)
50 km
Ozone Layer
Stratosphere (−55°C to −20°C; 27 to 0.3 kPa)
10 km
0 km
Troposphere (−55°C to 15°C; 100 to 27 kPa)

491

Visualizing Atmospheric Layers

Have students examine the pictures and read the captions. Then ask the following questions.

Why does the atmosphere get less dense as the distance from the Earth increases? because the gravitational pull on the molecules in the atmosphere is less

Why is the belt of ozone in the stratosphere important to organisms that live on Earth? the belt of ozone screens out harmful radiation from the Sun

Why does the *Hubble Space Telescope* orbit in the exosphere instead of closer to Earth? The exosphere has fewer molecules of gas and particles of dust that can limit the visibility of the telescope.

Activity

Atmosphere Game Have students design a game that involves answering questions about the layers of the atmosphere. L2 LS **Logical-Mathematical**

Differentiated Instruction

Challenge Have students make line graphs of the temperature and pressure gradients within each atmospheric level. Color-coding the graphs will make the graphs easier to read and understand. L3 LS **Visual-Spatial**

2 Teach

Activity

Barometer Bring a barometer to class. Have students measure and record the pressure and keep a log of weather conditions each day for several days. Ask them to search the data for correlations. They may observe that days of low pressure, tend to be cloudy with precipitation, while days of high pressure are more likely to be clear. L3 ELL

LS **Visual-Spatial**

Caption Answers

Figure 20 The balloon continues to expand until it ruptures.

Figure 21 500 L

Discussion

Pressurized Gases Why do you think gases used in industry are kept in pressurized containers? to reduce the volume they occupy, which makes them easier to store and transport

L2 LS **Logical-Mathematical**

Quick Demo

Changing Volume

Materials balloon, pin

Estimated Time 5 minutes

Procedure Inflate the balloon and knot the end. Ask students if the pressure is greater inside the balloon or outside. inside Ask the students what will happen if you prick the balloon with the pin and why. The pressure is greater on the inside of the balloon, so the air will flow from high pressure (inside balloon) to low pressure (outside balloon). The volume of the balloon decreases because the pressure decreases, when the balloon is pricked with the pin.

Figure 20 Balloons are used to measure the weather conditions at high altitudes. These balloons expand as they rise due to decreased pressure. **Describe** *what eventually happens to the balloon.*

Boyle's Law

You now know how gas creates pressure in a container. What happens to the gas pressure if you decrease the size of the container? You know that the pressure of a gas depends on how often its particles strike the walls of the container. If you squeeze gas into a smaller space, its particles will strike the walls more often—giving an increased pressure. The opposite is true, too. If you give the gas particles more space, they will hit the walls less often—gas pressure will be reduced. Robert Boyle (1627–1691), a British scientist, described this property of gases. According to Boyle's law, if you decrease the volume of a container of gas and hold the temperature constant, the pressure of the gas will increase. An increase in the volume of the container causes the pressure to drop, if the temperature remains constant.

The behavior of weather balloons, as shown in **Figure 20,** can be explained using Boyle's law. Rubber or neoprene weather balloons are used to carry sensing instruments to high altitudes to detect weather information. The balloons are inflated near Earth's surface with a low-density gas. As the balloon rises, the atmospheric pressure decreases. The balloon gradually expands to a volume of 30 to 200 times its original size. At some point the expanding balloon ruptures. Boyle's law states that as pressure is decreased the volume increases, as demonstrated by the weather balloon. The opposite also is true, as shown by the graph in **Figure 21.** As the pressure is increased, the volume will decrease.

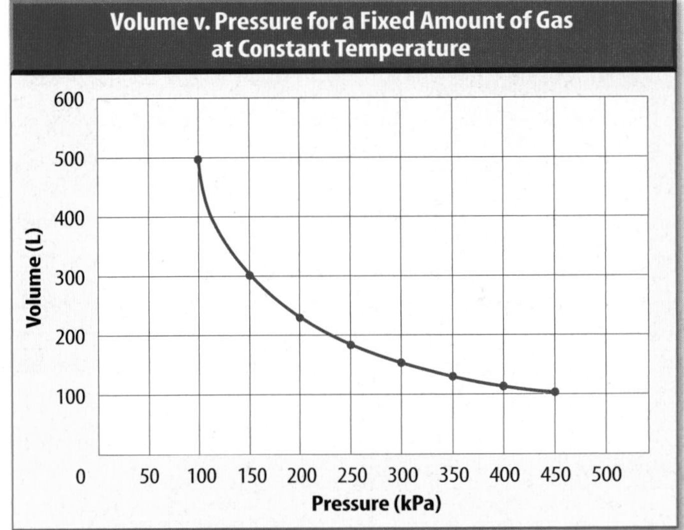

Figure 21 The graph shows that, as pressure increases, volume decreases; as pressure decreases, volume increases.
Use Graphs *What is the volume of the gas at 100 kPa?*

Fun Fact

At room temperature, oxygen gas molecules have an average speed of 1,700 km/h.

Differentiated Instruction

Challenge Remind students that 1 pascal is 1 N of force exerted over an area of 1 m^2. Ask them to convert this to find out how much force is exerted by 1 pascal on 1 cm^2. Then ask them to use their results to calculate the amount of force exerted by atmospheric pressure on 1 cm^2. 1 m^2 = 10,000 cm^2. Therefore, 1 pascal = 1N/10,000 cm^2 = 0.0001 N/cm^2. 1 kPa = 0.1 N/cm^2; therefore, 101.3 kPa exerts a force of 10.13 N/cm^2. L3 LS **Logical-Mathematical** P

492 CHAPTER 16 Solids, Liquids, and Gases

Boyle's Law in Action When Boyle's law is applied to a real life situation, we find that the pressure multiplied by the volume is always equal to a constant if the temperature is constant. As the pressure and volume change indirectly, the constant will remain the same. You can use the equations P_1V_1 = constant = P_2V_2 to express this mathematically. This shows us that the product of the initial pressure and volume—designated with the subscript 1—is equal to the product of the final pressure and volume—designated with the subscript 2. Using this equation, you can find one unknown value, as shown in the example problem below.

Reading Check *What is $P_1V_1 = P_2V_2$ known as?*

Topic: Compressed Gases
Visit gpscience.com for Web links to information about compressed gases.

Activity Make a brochure about the information that you learn. Share the brochure with your class.

Volume-Pressure Equation

Calculating Volume A balloon has a volume of 10.0 L at a pressure of 101 kPa. What will be the new volume when the pressure drops to 43.0 kPa?

1. **This is what you know:** $P_1 = 101$ kPa, $V_1 = 10.0$ L, $P_2 = 43.0$ kPa
2. **This is what you need to find:** V_2
3. **Use this formula:** $P_1V_1 = P_2V_2$
4. **Rearrange the equation and substitute:** $V_2 = \frac{P_1V_1}{P_2}$

   $$V_2 = \frac{(101 \text{ kPa})(10.0 \text{ L})}{43.0 \text{ kPa}} = 23.5 \text{ L}$$

5. **Determine the units:** Units of $V_2 = \frac{\text{units } P_1 \times \text{units } V_1}{\text{units } P_2}$

   Units of $V_2 = \frac{\cancel{\text{kPa}} \times \text{L}}{\cancel{\text{kPa}}} = \text{L}$

Answer: When the pressure drops to 43.0 kPa, the new volume is 23.5 L.

Science Online
For more practice problems, go to page 834, and visit gpscience.com/extra_problems.

Practice Problem

Challenge A volume of helium occupies 11.0 L at 98.0 kPa. What is the new volume if the pressure drops to 86.2 kPa?

Reading Check

Answer Boyle's law

Use Science Words

Word Origin The word *gas* comes from the Latin word *chaos*. Have students look up *chaos* in the dictionary and explain why it is an appropriate term to explain gases. Chaos is a situation of disorder. Gas particles are in disorder. L2

LS **Linguistic**

Volume-Pressure Equation

National Math Standards

Correlation to Mathematics Objectives

1, 2

Answer to Practice Problem

$V_2 = \frac{P_1V_1}{P_2} = 11.0 \text{ L } (98.0 \text{ kPa}) \div 86.2 \text{ kPa} = 12.5 \text{ L}$

Teacher FYI

Pressurized Tennis Balls When the gases in tennis balls are at a high pressure, the balls bounce higher. Tennis balls come in pressurized cans so that the gases contained in the balls do not escape. Once out of the can, the balls will lose gas pressure over time.

Virtual Labs

Boyle's Law *What factors influence the pressure of gas in a container?*

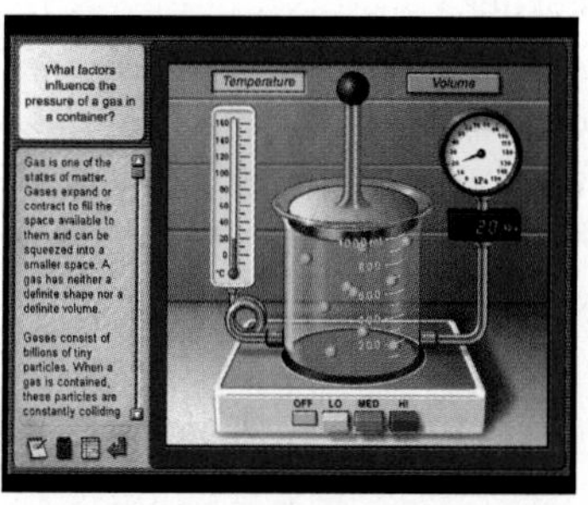

Differentiated Instruction

Learning Disabled Before they solve a gas law problem, have students make a prediction about the answer. After they solve the problem, have them compare their predictions with their answers. For example, when solving a Boyle's law problem in which pressure increases, students should predict that volume decreases. L1

LS **Logical-Mathematical**

Purpose to demonstrate Charles's law L2 LS **Kinesthetic**

Materials balloon, beaker, ice water

Teaching Strategy Students will need to leave balloons on the beakers for several minutes.

Troubleshooting The balloon will contract faster if it is in contact with the cold water.

Analysis

1. The molecules in the gas slowed down, putting less pressure on the balloon, so it contracted.
2. $V_2 = \frac{(0.5 L)(358 K)}{(298 K)} = 0.6 L$

Assessment

Process Have students allow the balloons to return to room temperature and record their observations. Use **Performance Assessment in the Science Classroom**, p. 97.

IDENTIFYING Misconceptions

Temperature Scales Students may not understand the relative sizes of temperature units. They may think that 1K=1°C =1°F. While the size of one kelvin unit of temperature does equal the size of one degree Celsius, the size of one degree Fahrenheit is much smaller.

Observing Pressure

Safety Precautions

Procedure

1. Blow up a **balloon** to about half its maximum size.
2. Place the balloon on a **beaker** filled with **ice water.**

Analysis

1. Explain what happened to the balloon when you placed it on the beaker.
2. If the volume of the half-filled balloon was 0.5 L at a temperature of 298 K, what would the volume of the balloon be if the temperature increased to 358 K?

Try at Home

The Pressure-Temperature Relationship

Have you ever read the words "keep away from heat" on a pressurized spray canister? What happens if you heat an enclosed gas? The particles of gas will strike the walls of the canister more often. Because this canister is rigid, its volume cannot increase. Instead, its pressure increases. If the pressure becomes greater than the canister can hold, it will explode. At a constant volume, an increase in temperature results in an increase in pressure.

Charles's Law

If you've watched a hot-air balloon being inflated, you know that gases expand when they are heated. Because particles in the hot air are farther apart than particles in the cool air, the hot air is less dense than the cool air. This difference in density allows the hot air balloon to rise. Jacques Charles (1746–1823) was a French scientist who studied gases. According to Charles's law, the volume of a gas increases with increasing temperature, as long as pressure does not change. As with Boyle's law, the reverse is true, also. The volume of a gas shrinks with decreasing temperature, as shown in **Figure 22.**

Charles's law can be explained using the kinetic theory of matter. As a gas is heated, its particles move faster and faster and its temperature increases. Because the gas particles move faster, they begin to strike the walls of their container more often and with more force. In the hot-air balloon, the walls have room to expand so instead of increased pressure, the volume increases.

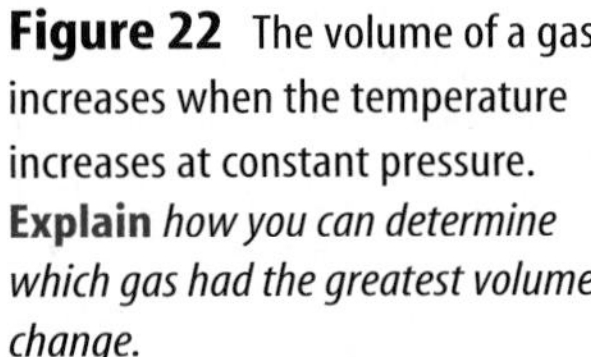

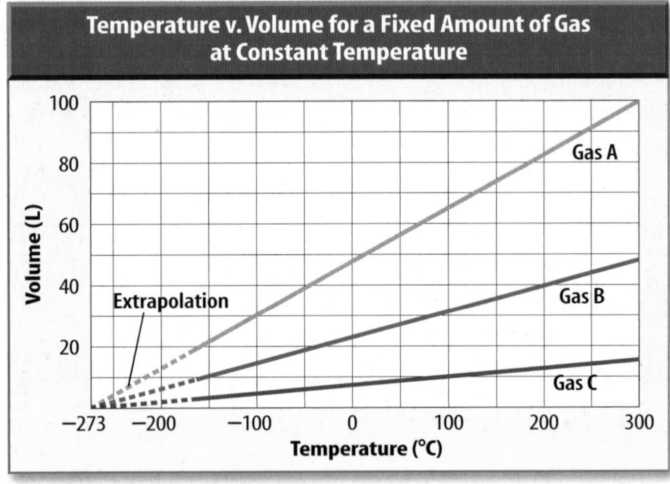

Figure 22 The volume of a gas increases when the temperature increases at constant pressure. **Explain** *how you can determine which gas had the greatest volume change.*

Visual Learning

Figure 22 Give students several different temperatures from the graph and have them read back to you the volume associated with each. L2 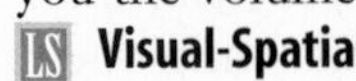 LS **Visual-Spatial**

Caption Answer

Figure 22 The gas with the greatest slope has the greatest volume change.

Using Charles's Law The formula that relates the variables of temperature to volume shows a direct relationship, $V_1/T_1 = V_2/T_2$, when temperature is given in kelvin. When using Charles's law, the pressure must be kept constant. What would be the resulting volume of a 2.0-L balloon at 25.0°C that was placed in a container of ice water at 3.0°C, as shown in **Figure 23?**

$$V_1 = 2.0\text{ L} \qquad T_1 = 25.0°\text{C} + 273 = 298\text{ K}$$

$$V_2 = ? \qquad T_2 = 3.0°\text{C} + 273 = 276\text{ K}$$

$$\frac{V_1}{T_1} = \frac{V_2}{T_2} = \frac{2.0\text{ L}}{298\text{ K}} = \frac{V_2}{276\text{ K}}$$

$$V_2 = \frac{(2.0\text{ L})(276\text{ K})}{298\text{ K}} = 1.9\text{ L}$$

As Charles's law predicts, the volume decreased as the temperature of the trapped gas decreased. This assumed no changes in pressure.

According to Charles's law, what happens to the volume of a gas if the temperature increases?

Figure 23 Charles's law states that as the temperature of a gas is lowered, the volume decreases.
Calculate *If the balloon in the text was placed in a freezer at 5°C, what would be the new volume?*

section 3 review

Summary

Pressure

- Pressure is the amount of force exerted per unit area.
- Pressure is measured in pascals.

Boyle's Law

- Boyle's law states that if the temperature is constant, as the volume of a gas decreases the pressure increases. It states also that at constant temperature, as the volume of a gas increases the pressure decreases.

The Pressure-Temperature Relationship

- This relationship describes how, at a constant volume, the pressure increases with increasing temperature.

Charles's Law

- Charles's law states that at constant pressure, the volume of a gas increases with increasing temperature.

Self Check

1. **Explain** why a gas has pressure.
2. **Describe** Earth's atmosphere at sea level. How does the pressure change as the distance from Earth increases?
3. **Explain**, using Boyle's law, the volume change of an inflated balloon that a diver takes to a pressure of 2 atm.
4. **Explain**, using Charles's law, the purpose of a gas burner on a hot-air balloon.
5. **Think Critically** Labels on cylinders of compressed gases state the highest temperature to which the cylinder may be exposed. Give a reason for this warning.

Applying Math

6. **Find Volume** A helium balloon has a volume of 2.00 L at 101 kPa. As the balloon rises the pressure drops to 97.0 kPa. What is the new volume?
7. **Solve One-Step Equations** If a 5-L balloon at 25°C was gently heated to 30°C, what new volume would the balloon have?

section 3 review

1. Gas particles move and collide with the sides of their container.
2. The pressure at sea level is 101.3 kPa; pressure decreases as the distance from Earth increases
3. The volume of the ballon will decrease because the pressure increased.
4. The gas burner heats the air in the ballon increasing the volume of the ballon and decreasing the air's density causing the ballon to rise.
5. As temperature increases, pressure increases. The cylinder might explode.
6. $V_2 = \frac{P_1V_1}{P_2} = \frac{(101\text{ kPa})(2.00\text{ L})}{(97.0\text{ kPa})} = 2.08\text{ L}$
7. $5\text{ L}(303\text{ K}/298\text{ K}) = 5.1\text{ L}$

Caption Answer

Figure 23 1.8 L

Answer The volume increases if pressure stays the same.

3 Assess

DAILY INTERVENTION

Check for Understanding

Visual-Spatial Put 20 mL of water into an empty aluminum soft-drink can, and place it on a hot plate to boil. After the can has filled with steam, grasp it with tongs or a hot pad and plunge the can inverted into ice water so that it contracts inward. From the results, have students infer the relationship among volume, temperature, and pressure. As temperature decreases, pressure and volume decrease. L2 IS **Visual-Spatial**

Reteach

Changing Volume Have students seal an air sample in a heavy-duty resealable plastic bag and place it in the freezer. Tell them to remove the bag the next day and, with the bag sealed, warm it with a hair dryer or warm water. Ask students to explain their observations. The volume of the air decreased in the freezer and increased as the temperature increased. L2 ELL IS **Visual-Spatial**

Assessment

Content Have students write questions about the behavior of gases. Have other students answer them. Check answers for accuracy. Use **Performance Assessment in the Science Classroom,** p. 91.

Real-World Question

Purpose Students observe and measure the movement of a solid through liquids of different viscosities L2 ELL IN **Kinesthetic**

Process Skills observe, measure, use numbers, make and use tables, make and use graphs, recognize cause and effect, control variables, interpret data

Time Required 45 minutes

Procedure

Materials Make sure you include materials with a variety of viscosities. Water, alcohol, and corn oil have relatively low viscosities while molasses has a relatively high viscosity.

Teaching Strategies

- This lab will be easier for students to do if they work in pairs.
- Some of these liquids will likely be spilled during the course of the lab. Make sure students clean up their work areas and wash their hands after doing this lab.
- Have your students make wise choices about reusing materials for each of their trials.

Testing the Viscosity of Common Liquids

Goals

- Observe and compare the viscosity of common liquids.

Materials

room temperature household liquids such as:
- dish detergent
- corn syrup
- pancake syrup
- shampoo
- vegetable oil
- vinegar
- molasses
- water

spheres such as glass marbles or steel balls
100-mL graduated cylinders
150-mL beaker
ruler
stopwatch

Safety Precautions

Dispose of wastes as directed by your teacher.

Real-World Question

The resistance to flow of a liquid is called viscosity, and it can be measured and compared. One example of the importance of a liquid's viscosity is motor oil in car engines. The viscosity of motor oil in your family car is important because it keeps the engine lubricated. It must cling to the moving parts and not run off, leaving the parts dry and unlubricated. If the engine is not properly lubricated, it will be damaged eventually. The motor oil must maintain its viscosity in all types of weather, from extreme heat in the summer to freezing cold in the winter. Can the study of viscosity lead to a better understanding of the properties of matter?

Procedure

1. Measure equal amounts of the liquids to be tested into the graduated cylinders.
2. Measure the depth of the liquid.
3. Copy the data chart into your Science Journal.
4. Place the sphere on the surface of the liquid. Using a stopwatch, measure and record how long it takes for it to travel to the bottom of the liquid.
5. Remove the sphere and repeat step 4 two more times for the same liquid.
6. Rinse and dry the sphere.
7. Repeat steps 4, 5, and 6 for two more liquids.

Alternative Inquiry Lab

Transporting Viscous Liquids To make this Lab an Inquiry Lab, have students brainstorm various types of industrial settings where the viscosity of a fluid must be controlled. For instance, would a railroad tanker car full of corn syrup be easy to unload if the temperature were 5°C? What could be done to make this job easier? How could engineers control the viscosity of corn syrup and design a pumping system that would pump the correct amount of corn syrup into vats of catsup during processing? Students may conduct experiments or draw diagrams to test or explain their ideas. By doing this lab, students will improve their problem-solving skills.

Viscosity of Common Liquids

Substance	Trial	Depth of Liquid (cm)	Time (s)	Speed (cm/s)
honey		6.0	9.65	0.62
shampoo #1		6.0	6.19	0.97
shampoo #2		6.0	4.01	1.50
hand soap		6.0	4.15	1.45
syrup		6.0	2.44	2.46
corn oil		6.0	0.21	28.13

Analyze Your Data

1. **Graph** the average speed of the sphere for each liquid on a bar graph.
2. **Interpret Data** In which liquid did the sphere move the fastest? Would that liquid have a high or low viscosity? Explain.

Conclude and Apply

1. **Infer** Would it matter if you dropped or threw the sphere into the liquid instead of placing it there? Explain your answer.
2. **Analyze Results** What effect does temperature play in the viscosity of a liquid? What would happen to the viscosity of your slowest liquid if you made it colder? Explain.
3. **Infer** If the temperature of the liquids is dropped to 10°C, would all of the liquids have an equivalent change in viscosity? Explain your answer.
4. **Explain** Would corn syrup, molasses, or pancake syrup make a good lubricant in a car engine? Explain your answer.

Compare your results with other groups and discuss differences noted. Why might these differences have occurred? **For more help, refer to the** Science Skill Handbook.

Troubleshooting Students may need to use hot water and soap to clean the sphere between liquids.

Analyze Your Data

Answers to Questions

1. Check students' work. Make sure they have graphed speed and not time.
2. Answers will vary depending on liquids used. The liquid in which the sphere moved fastest has a low viscosity.

Error Analysis Problems might occur if students drop or throw the sphere into the liquids or are not careful about observing and timing the sphere's movement.

Conclude and Apply

1. If you threw the sphere into the liquid it would move faster because the force of your throw gave it an initial velocity.
2. If you cooled the slowest liquid, its viscosity would increase because the particles in it would slow down.
3. No, the viscosities may vary because of differing intermolecular attractions between the particles.
4. No, the viscosities vary too much over a temperature range.

Assessment

Process Have students hypothesize how their results would have been different if they had used paper clips instead of spheres in the activity. Then have them test their hypotheses using one of the liquids. Use **Performance Assessment in the Science Classroom,** p. 93.

Active Reading

Reflective Journal In this strategy, students identify activities and what they learned and record responses to the activities. Have students divide pieces of paper into several columns. Have them record their thoughts under headings such as *What I learned, Questions I have,* and *Surprises I experienced.* Have each student write a Reflective Journal entry for this lab.

Have students use a computer spread sheet program to compile data from all students in the class and use it to produce class-average bar graphs for the liquids used.

SCIENCE Stats

Content Background

Chemical reactions, such as the burning of fuels, either release or absorb energy. The amount of energy released by a chemical reaction is small compared to the energy released during a nuclear reaction, such as those that occur during a supernova. A nuclear reaction involves the conversion of a small amount of mass into a tremendous amount of energy.

Discussion

Separating Air Oxygen and other gases are removed from liquid air by warming the liquid air until each component reaches its boiling point. At that point, the liquid becomes a gas and can be separated from the mixture. The boiling points for several components of air are: oxygen, −183° C; argon, −186° C; nitrogen, −196° C, and carbon dioxide, −78° C. In what order will these gases be removed from liquid air? nitrogen, argon, oxygen, carbon dioxide L2
LS **Logical-Mathematical**

Activity

Hot or Cold? Have students show that hot and cold are relative terms. Provide students with three bowls of water, one containing very warm water, one containing cold water, and one containing room-temperature water. Have each student place one hand in the warm water and one hand in the cold water for two minutes. Then have them place both hands in the room-temperature water and write a paragraph describing what they felt. L1 LS **Linguistic**

SCIENCE Stats

Hot and Cold

Did you know...

... The world's coldest substance, liquid helium, is about −269°C. It's used in cryogenics research, which is the study of extremely low temperatures. Cryogenics has enabled physicians to freeze and preserve body parts, such as corneas from human eyes. The freezing keeps cells alive until they are needed.

Cryogenics laboratory

Oxyacetylene torch

... The hottest known flame is made by burning a mixture of oxygen and acetylene. The flame of an oxyacetylene torch can become as hot as 3,300°C. That's more than two times hotter than the melting point of steel.

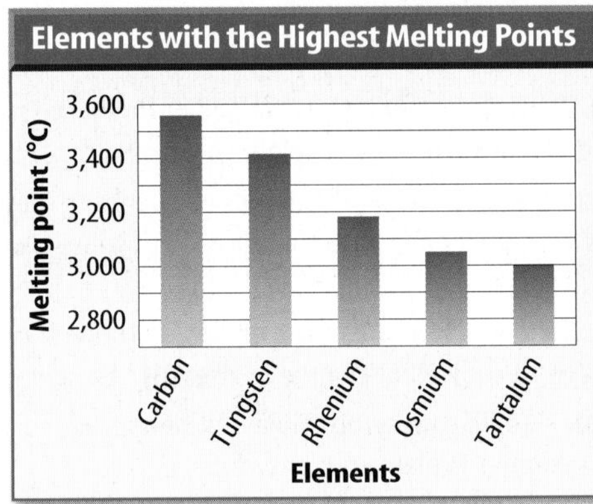

Applying Math

1. In 1983, the temperature dropped to −89°C in Vostok, Antarctica. How many more degrees Celsius would the temperature need to drop for the air to become a liquid?
2. Look at the graph above. List the elements that could be melted by an oxyacetylene torch.

Visual Learning

Melting Points Have students use the graph to answer the following questions. What is the difference between the melting points of tungsten and tantalum? approximately 400° C Carbon and tungsten are elements added to iron to make certain types of steel. How would adding one of these elements to iron affect its melting point? It would raise it.

Applying Math

1. about 1,650° C
2. rhenium, osmium, and tantalum

Reviewing Main Ideas

Section 1 Kinetic Theory

1. Four states of matter exist: solid, liquid, gas, and plasma.
2. According to the kinetic theory, all matter is made of constantly moving particles that collide without losing energy.
3. Most matter expands when heated and contracts when cooled. This expansion joint allows the concrete to expand and contract without damage.

4. Changes of state can be interpreted in terms of the kinetic theory of matter.

Section 2 Properties of Fluids

1. Archimedes' principle states that the buoyant force of an object in a fluid is equal to the weight of the fluid displaced. The buoyant force on this penny was less than its weight, so the penny sank.

2. Pascal's principle states that pressure applied to a fluid is transmitted unchanged throughout the fluid.
3. Bernoulli's principle states that the pressure exerted by a fluid decreases as its velocity increases.

Section 3 Behavior of Gases

1. Gas pressure results from moving particles colliding with the inside walls of the container.
2. The SI unit of pressure is the pascal (Pa). Because this is a small pressure unit, pressures often are given in kilopascals.
3. Boyle's law states that the volume of a gas decreases when the pressure increases at constant temperature.
4. Charles's law states that the volume of a gas increases when the temperature increases at constant pressure.
5. At constant volume, as the temperature of a gas increases, so does the pressure of a gas. The pressure in this cylinder will increase as the sun increases the temperature.

FOLDABLES Use the Foldable that you made at the beginning of this chapter to help you review solids, liquids, and gases.

Science Online gpscience.com/interactive_tutor

Identifying Misconceptions

Assess

Use this assessment as a follow-up to page F at the beginning of the chapter

Materials rubbing alcohol, cotton, wool, well-ventilated room

Procedure Using the cotton, dab the backs of students' hands with rubbing alcohol. Ask students to write and explain their observations.

Expected Outcome In the liquid, the particles were close together so students could see the alcohol. When it evaporated the particles became far apart, so students could no longer see it, but the particles were still alcohol particles.

chapter 16 Study Guide

Reviewing Main Ideas

Summary statements can be used by students to review the major concepts of the chapter.

Visit gpscience.com
/self_check_quiz
/interactive_tutor
/vocabulary_puzzlemaker
/chapter_review
/standardized_test

Assessment Transparency

For additional assessment questions, use the *Assessment Transparency* located in the transparency book.

Assessment

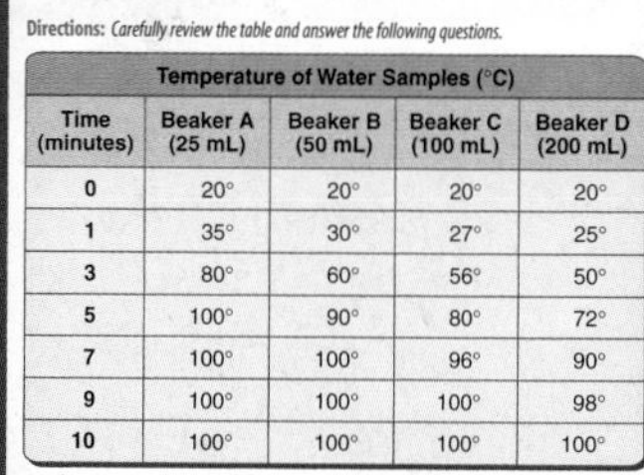

Assessment Transparency **Solids, Liquids, and Gases**

Directions: *Carefully review the table and answer the following questions.*

Temperature of Water Samples (°C)				
Time (minutes)	Beaker A (25 mL)	Beaker B (50 mL)	Beaker C (100 mL)	Beaker D (200 mL)
0	20°	20°	20°	20°
1	35°	30°	27°	25°
3	80°	60°	56°	50°
5	100°	90°	80°	72°
7	100°	100°	96°	90°
9	100°	100°	100°	98°
10	100°	100°	100°	100°

1. The temperature of the water in each beaker is recorded every few minutes. Which variable is being investigated?
   A the size of the beaker C the volume of water heated
   B the temperature of the room D the air pressure in the room
2. About how much longer did it take the water in Beaker D to reach its boiling point than the water in Beaker A?
   F 5 minutes G 7 minutes H 8 minutes J 10 minutes
3. The table was used to record data from an experiment. Which of the following statements is a likely hypothesis for this experiment?
   A The time required to boil water determines the boiling point.
   B Boiling water in different containers produces different boiling points.
   C Different thermometers give different boiling points.
   D Increasing the volume also increases the time needed to reach the boiling point.

L2

Solids, Liquids, and Gases

FOLDABLES Have students use their Foldables to review the content of the chapter. On the back of the paper, have students write a paragraph about the characteristics of solids, liquids, and gases.

Using Vocabulary

1. Viscosity is the resistance of a fluid to flow.
2. The SI unit of pressure is the pascal.
3. Pressure is the amount of force exerted per unit of area.
4. A solid begins to liquefy at its melting point.
5. The kinetic theory is used to explain the behavior of particles in matter.
6. Buoyancy is the ability of a fluid to exert an upward force on a body immersed in it.

Checking Concepts

7. A
8. D
9. C
10. B
11. A
12. A
13. C
14. A

Interpreting Graphics

15. a. Ice is warming to its melting point.
    b. Ice is absorbing energy and melting.
    c. Liquid water is warming.
    d. Liquid is absorbing energy and boiling.
16. See student page.

chapter 16 Review

Using Vocabulary

boiling point p. 479	melting point p. 478
buoyancy p. 485	pascal p. 490
diffusion p. 479	plasma p. 480
heat of fusion p. 478	pressure p. 486
heat of vaporization p. 479	thermal expansion p. 481
kinetic theory p. 476	viscosity p. 489

Answer the following questions using complete sentences.

1. What is the property of a fluid that represents its resistance to flow?
2. What is the SI unit of pressure?
3. What term is used to describe the amount of force exerted per unit of area?
4. What is the temperature when a solid begins to liquefy?
5. What theory is used to explain the behavior of particles in matter?
6. What is the ability of a fluid to exert an upward force on an object?

Checking Concepts

Choose the word or phrase that best answers the question.

7. What is the temperature at which all particle motion of matter ceases?
   A) absolute zero **C)** boiling point
   B) melting point **D)** heat of fusion
8. What is the most common state of matter in the universe?
   A) solid **C)** gas
   B) liquid **D)** plasma
9. Which of the following would be used to measure pressure?
   A) gram **C)** kilopascals
   B) newtons **D)** kilograms
10. Which of the following uses Pascal's principle?
    A) aerodynamics **C)** buoyancy
    B) hydraulics **D)** changes of state
11. Which of the following uses Bernoulli's principle?
    A) airplane **C)** skateboard
    B) piston **D)** snowboard
12. The particles in which of the following are farthest apart from each other?
    A) gas **C)** liquid
    B) solid **D)** plasma
13. What is the upward force in a liquid?
    A) pressure **C)** buoyancy
    B) kinetic theory **D)** diffusion
14. What is the amount of energy needed to change a solid to a liquid at its melting point called?
    A) heat of fusion
    B) heat of vaporization
    C) temperature
    D) absolute zero

Interpreting Graphics

Use the graph below to answer question 15.

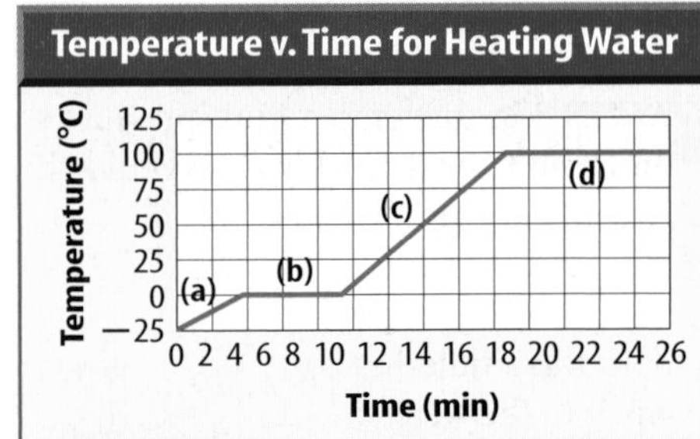

15. A group of students heated ice until it turned to steam. They measured the temperature each minute. Their graph is provided above. Explain what is happening at each letter (a, b, c, d) in the graph.

gpscience.com/vocabulary_puzzlemaker

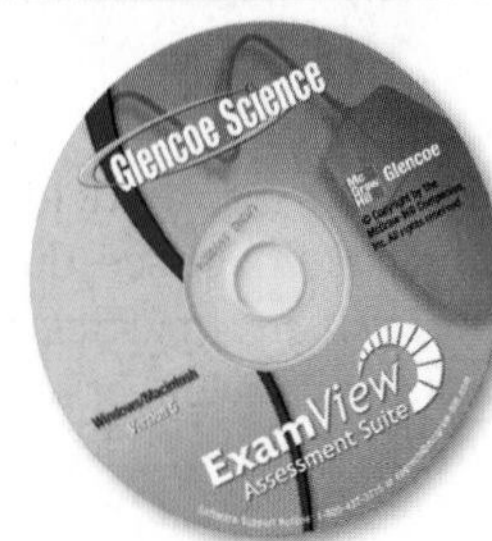

Use the *ExamView® Assessment Suite* CD-ROM to:

- create multiple versions of tests
- create modified tests with one mouse click for inclusion students
- edit existing questions and add your own questions
- build tests aligned with state standards using built-in State Curriculum Tags
- change English tests to Spanish with one mouse click and vice versa

16. Copy and complete this concept map.

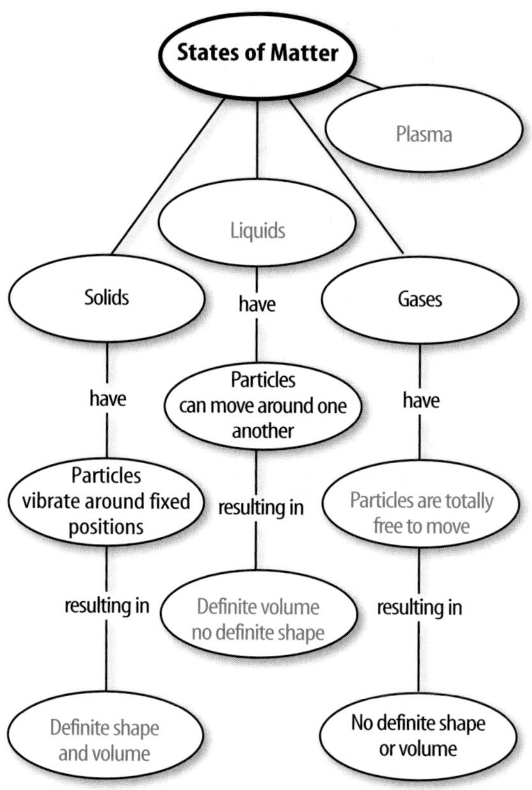

Thinking Critically

17. **Explain** Use the temperature-pressure relationship to explain why you should check your tire pressure when the temperature changes.

18. **Describe** the changes that occur inside a helium balloon as it rises from sea level.

19. **Explain** why aerosol cans have a "do not incinerate" warning.

20. **Explain** The Dead Sea is a solution that is so dense you float on it easily. Explain why you are able to float easily, using the terms *density* and *buoyant force.*

Applying Math

21. **Use Numbers** As elevation increases, boiling point decreases. List each of the following locations as *at sea level, above sea level,* or *below sea level.* (Boiling point of water is given in parenthesis.)

Death Valley (100.3°C), Denver (94°C), Madison (99°C), Mt. Everest (76.5°C), Mt. McKinley (79°C), New York City (100°C), Salt Lake City (95.6°C)

Use the illustration below to answer question 22.

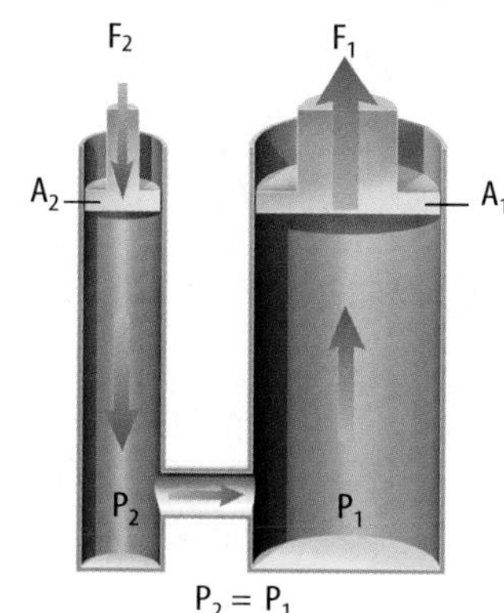

22. **Solve One-Step Equations** A hydraulic lift is used to lift a heavy box that is pushing down on a 3.0 m^2 piston (A_1) with a force (F_1) of 1,500 N. What force needs to be exerted on a 0.08 m^2 piston (A_2) to lift the machine?

23. **Calculate** What would be the resulting volume of a 1.5 L balloon at 25.0°C that was placed in a container of hot water at 90.0°C?

24. **Use Numbers** A balloon has a volume of 25.0 L at a pressure of 98.7 kPa. What will be the new volume when the pressure is 51.2 kPa?

Assessment Resources

Reproducible Masters

Chapter *Fast File* Resources
Chapter Review, pp. 39–40
Chapter Tests, pp. 41–44
Assessment Transparency Activity, p. 51

Glencoe Science Web site
Chapter Review Test
Standardized Test Practice

Glencoe Technology
Assessment Transparency
ExamView® Assessment Suite
MindJogger Videoquiz
Interactive Chalkboard

chapter Review 16

Thinking Critically

17. The temperature-pressure law states that if the volume of a gas sample remains constant, as the temperature increases, so does the pressure. When the temperature drops, so does the tire pressure. When the temperature rises, so does the tire pressure.

18. The pressure decreases outside of the balloon as the balloon rises, and the helium molecules force the walls of the balloon outward. At some point, the maximum pressure that the walls of the balloon can stand is reached and the balloon ruptures.

19. When the temperature increases, pressure increases if volume stays the same. If pressure increases enough, the can might explode.

20. The density of the water is greater than normal because of minerals dissolved in the water. Due to its increased density, the water is able to exert a greater buoyant force on the floating body.

Applying Math

National Math Standards

2, 6, 7

Answers to Practice Problems

21. above sea level: Denver, Madison, Mount Everest, Mount McKinley, Salt Lake City; at sea level: New York City; below sea level: Death Valley

22. $F_2 = \frac{(1{,}500\ N)(0.08\ m^2)}{3.0\ m^2} = 40\ N$

23. $V_2 = \frac{(1.5\ L)(363\ K)}{298\ K} = 1.8\ L$

24. $V_2 = \frac{(98.7\ KPa)(25.0L)}{51.2\ KPa} = 48.2\ L$

Answer Sheet A practice answer sheet can be found at gpscience.com/answer_sheet.

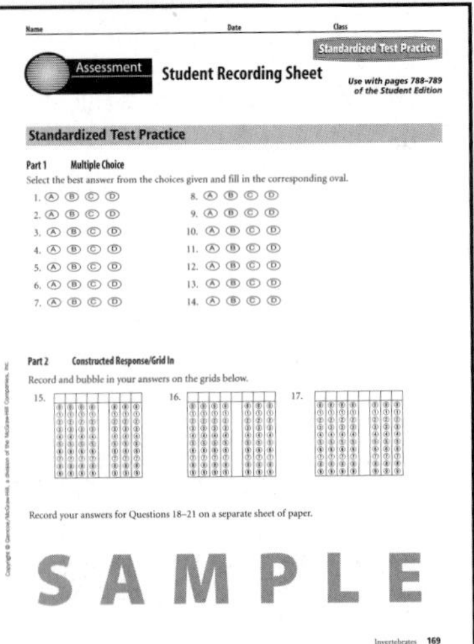

Part 1 Multiple Choice

1. A
2. C
3. B
4. D
5. A
6. B
7. A
8. C

Part 2 Short Response

9. The block that floats has a density less than water. The block that sinks has a greater than water.
10. The balloon rises because the gas inside the balloon has a lower density than the surrounding air.
11. Oil with a lower number would be better for cold-weather driving because it will still flow as the temperature drops.
12. Because the tanks are rigid, the volume of air in the tank cannot expand as it is heated. Its pressure could increase so much that the tank explodes.
13. 500 N

chapter 16 Standardized Test Practice

Part 1 Multiple Choice

Record your answers on the answer sheet provided by your teacher or on a sheet of paper.

1. Which state of matter would you expect to find water, at −25°C and 1 atm on Earth?
   A. solid **C.** gas
   B. liquid **D.** plasma

Use the graph below to answer questions 2 and 3.

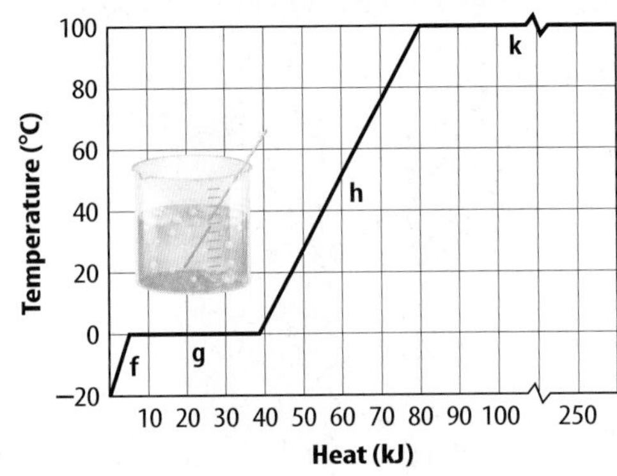

2. Which points on the graph is water increasing in kinetic energy?
   A. F and G **C.** F and H
   B. G and K **D.** H and K

3. On which points on the graph is the added energy used to overcome the bonds between particles?
   A. F and G **C.** F and H
   B. G and K **D.** H and K

4. Which of the following is unlikely to contain plasma?
   A. stars **C.** lightning
   B. neon lights **D.** water

Test-Taking Tip

Read Carefully Read all choices before answering the questions.

5. Which term is the amount of energy required for a liquid at its boiling point to become a gas?
   A. heat of vaporization
   B. diffusion
   C. heat of fusion
   D. thermal energy

6. In which state of matter do particles stay close together, yet are able to slide past each other?
   A. solid **C.** gas
   B. liquid **D.** plasma

Use the graph below to answer questions 7 and 8

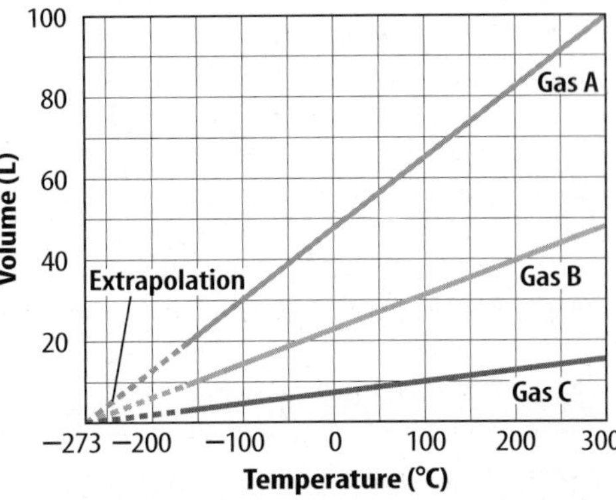

7. Which of the following statements is true?
   A. Gas A had the greatest increase in volume.
   B. Gas B had the greatest increase in volume.
   C. Gas C had the greatest increase in volume.
   D. The gases had the same increase in volume.

8. Approximately what temperature is the volume of Gas B about 40 L^3?
   A. 100°C **C.** 200°C
   B. 150°C **D.** 300°C

Part 3 Open Ended

14. Hot air causes the balloon to rise because of the thermal expansion of air. The air in the balloon has a lower density than the cooler air surrounding it. As long as the combined density of the balloon, basket, and people is less than the surrounding cool air, the balloon will float.
15. When the burner is turned off, the air in the balloon begins to cool and contract. This contraction causes the density of the air to increase. When the density of the balloon, basket, and people becomes greater than the density of the surrounding air, the balloon will begin to sink.
16. When the diver breathes in, the added air in the lungs slightly increases the diver's density, so the diver will rise slightly. When the diver exhales, the diver's density becomes slightly more, so the diver will sink slightly.

Part 2 Short Response/Grid In

Record your answers on the answer sheet provided by your teacher or on a sheet of paper.

9. If you place two wood blocks in water and one sinks while the other floats, what do you know about the densities of the blocks?

Use the illustration below to answer question 10.

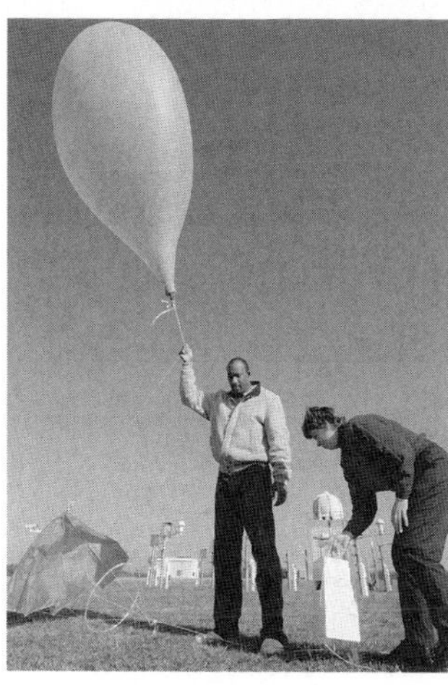

10. A weather balloon is inflated near Earth's surface with a low-density gas. Explain why the balloon rises when it is released.

11. Motor oil with a lower viscosity grade flows more easily than oil with a higher viscosity grade. Which grade of oil would be better for cold-weather driving? Explain.

12. The air in a scuba tank is under more than 200 times normal air pressure. Why should a filled scuba tank never be left in a hot car for an extended period of time?

13. A large crate applies a force of 2,500 N to a piston with an area of 25 m^2. What force must be applied to a piston with an area of 5.0 m^2 in order to lift the crate?

Part 3 Open Ended

Record your answers on a sheet of paper.

Use the illustration below to answer questions 14 and 15.

14. Explain why the hot-air balloon can still float in the air when it is carrying a basket filled with people.

15. Explain what will happen when the burner on the hot-air balloon is turned off when the balloon is in the air.

16. Scuba divers often add or remove air from their buoyancy vests to maintain neutral buoyancy. This means they will neither sink to the bottom, nor float to the surface. If the diver takes a deep breath, the diver will rise slightly. When the diver exhales, the diver will sink slightly. Explain why this happens.

17. A penny will sink in a beaker of water, but it will float in a beaker of mercury. Explain how this is possible.

18. Explain the difference between evaporation and boiling.

19. Use the kinetic theory to explain how the temperature and the pressure of a given amount of gas are related.

Science Online gpscience.com/standardized_test

17. For the penny to float, it must have a density that is less than the fluid it is placed in, so the density of mercury must greater than the density of the penny.

18. Evaporation is vaporization that occurs only at the surface of a liquid. It can occur at temperatures below the liquid's boiling point. Boiling occurs throughout a liquid at a specific temperature called the boiling point.

19. As the temperature of a gas increases, the particles gain kinetic energy and move faster. They strike the walls of the container more often, increasing in the pressure of the gas.

Rubrics

The following rubrics are sample scoring devices for short response and open-ended questions.

Short Response

Points	Description
2	The student demonstrates a thorough understanding of the science of the task. The response may contain minor flaws that do not detract from the demonstration of a thorough understanding.
1	The student has provided a response that is only partially correct.
0	The student has provided a completely incorrect solution or no response at all.

Open Ended Response

Points	Description
4	The student demonstrates a thorough understanding of the science of the task. The response may contain minor flaws that do not detract from the demonstration of a thorough understanding.
3	The student demonstrates an understanding of the science of the task. The response is essentially correct and demonstrates an essential but less than thorough understanding of the science.
2	The student demonstrates only a partial understanding of the science of the task. Although the student may have used the correct approach to a solution or may have provided a correct solution, the work lacks an essential understanding of the underlying science concepts.
1	The student demonstrates a very limited understanding of the science of the task. The response is incomplete and exhibits many flaws.
0	The student provides a completely incorrect solution or no response at all.

Properties of Atoms and the Periodic Table

BIG Idea The properties of an element are determined by the composition of its atoms.

	Content Standards	Learning Objectives	Resources to Assess Mastery
Section 1	**5–8:** UCP.1–3, 5; A.1, 2; B.1–3; G.3 **9–12:** UCP.1–3, 5; A.1, 2; B.2, 5, 6; G.3	**Structure of the Atom** 1. **Identify** the names and symbols of common elements. 2. **Identify** quarks as subatomic particles of matter. 3. **Describe** the electron cloud model of the atom. 4. **Explain** how electrons are arranged in an atom. ***Main Idea*** Protons and neutrons are located in an atom's nucleus, and electrons are located in an electron cloud surrounding the nucleus.	**Formative Assessment** Reading Check, pp. 507, 509 Section Review, p. 511 **Summative Assessment** *ExamView® Assessment Suite*
Section 2	**5–8:** UCP.1–3, 5; A.1, 2; B.1–3; G.3 **9–12:** UCP.1–3, 5; A.1, 2; B.2, 5, 6; G.3	**Masses of Atoms** 5. **Compute** the atomic mass and mass number of an atom. 6. **Identify** the components of isotopes. 7. **Interpret** the average atomic mass of an element. ***Main Idea*** All atoms of the same element have the same number of protons but can have different numbers of neutrons.	**Formative Assessment** Reading Check, pp. 512, 513, 514 Section Review, p. 515 **Summative Assessment** *ExamView® Assessment Suite*
Section 3	**5–8:** UCP.1–3, 5; A.1, 2; B.1; C.4; G.3 **9–12:** UCP.1–3, 5; A.1, 2; B.2, 5, 6; G.3 See pp. 16T–17T for a Key to Standards.	**The Periodic Table** 8. **Explain** the composition of the periodic table. 9. **Use** the periodic table to obtain information. 10. **Explain** what the terms *metal, nonmetal,* and *metalloid* mean. ***Main Idea*** Atoms of elements that are in the same group on the periodic table contain the same number of outer energy level electrons.	**Formative Assessment** Reading Check, pp. 517, 521, 522, 523 Section Review, p. 524 **Summative Chapter Assessment** MindJogger, Ch. 17 *ExamView® Assessment Suite* Leveled Chapter Test Test A [L1] Test B [L2] Test C [L3] Test Practice, pp. 532–533

Suggested Pacing				
Period	**Instruction**	**Labs**	**Review & Assessment**	**Total**
Single	3 days	4 days	2 days	9 days
Block	1.5 blocks	2 blocks	1 block	4.5 blocks

Core Instruction	Leveled Resources	Leveled Labs	Pacing: Period		Pacing: Block
Student Text, pp. 504–511 Section Focus Transparency, Ch. 17, Section 1 Teaching Transparency, Ch. 17, Section 1 Interactive Chalkboard, Ch. 17, Section 1 Differentiated Instruction, pp. 507, 509 Visualizing The Atomic Model, p. 510	**Chapter *Fast File* Resources** Directed Reading for Content Mastery, p. 20 L1 Note-taking Worksheet, pp. 33–35 Reinforcement, p. 27 L2 Enrichment, p. 30 L3 **Reading Essentials,** p. 282 L1 ELL **Science Notebook,** p. 189 ELL ***Active*Folders**: *Matter* L1 ELL	**Launch Lab,** p. 505: various dried beans, envelopes *10 min* L2 (Video Lab) **MiniLAB,** p. 509: paper (blue, orange, red), metric ruler, hole punch *15 min* L2	**1**	Section 1, pp. 505–508 (includes Launch Lab)	**1**
			2	Section 1, pp. 509–511 (includes MiniLAB and Section Review)	
Student Text, pp. 512–515 Section Focus Transparency, Ch. 17, Section 2 Interactive Chalkboard, Ch. 17, Section 2 Identifying Misconceptions, p. 514 Applying Science, p. 514 Differentiated Instruction, pp. 513, 514	**Chapter *Fast File* Resources** Directed Reading for Content Mastery, p. 20 L1 Note-taking Worksheet, pp. 33–35 Reinforcement, p. 28 L2 Enrichment, p. 31 L3 **Reading Essentials,** p. 288 L1 ELL **Science Notebook,** p. 193 ELL		**3**	Section 2, pp. 512–515 (includes Section Review)	**2**
Student Text, pp. 516–527 Section Focus Transparency, Ch. 17, Section 3 Interactive Chalkboard, Ch. 17, Section 3 Identifying Misconceptions, pp. 519, 521 Differentiated Instruction, pp. 519, 520, 521 Chapter Study Guide, p. 529	**Chapter *Fast File* Resources** Directed Reading for Content Mastery, pp. 21, 22 L1 Note-taking Worksheet, pp. 33–35 Reinforcement, p. 29 L2 Enrichment, p. 32 L3 **Reading Essentials,** p. 293 L1 ELL **Science Notebook,** p. 196 ELL ***Active*Folders**: *Periodic Table* L1 ELL	**MiniLAB,** p. 517: variety of objects *20 min* L2 ***Lab,** p. 525: paper (11 × 17), metric ruler, colored pencils or markers *45 min* L1 L2 L3 ***Lab,** pp. 526–527: Internet access *90 min* L1 L2 L3 *Lab version A L1 version B L2 L3	**4**	Section 3, pp. 516–519 (includes MiniLAB)	
			5	Section 3, pp. 520–524 (includes Section Review)	**3**
			6	Lab: A Periodic Table of Foods, p. 525	
			7	Lab: What's in a name?, pp. 526–527	**4**
			8	Lab: What's in a name?, pp. 526–527	
			9	Study Guide, Chapter Review, and Test Practice, pp. 529–533	**4.5**

(Video Lab icon) Video Lab

chapter  Properties of Atoms and the Periodic Table

Transparencies

Section Focus

SECTION 1 Section Focus Transparency — Subatomic Collision

An individual atom is so small that it would take 50 million of them lined up in a row to equal one centimeter! Atoms, however, can be divided into component parts, and, amazingly, some of these parts have particles that are tinier yet. Below is an image created by these subatomic particles taken in a device called a bubble chamber.

1. Why do you think scientists have only recently discovered these subatomic particles?
2. What might scientists learn by breaking apart atomic nuclei?

L2

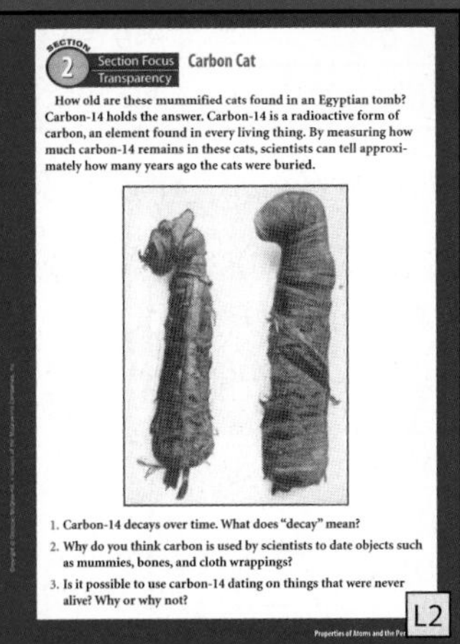
SECTION 2 Section Focus Transparency — Carbon Cat

How old are these mummified cats found in an Egyptian tomb? Carbon-14 holds the answer. Carbon-14 is a radioactive form of carbon, an element found in every living thing. By measuring how much carbon-14 remains in these cats, scientists can tell approximately how many years ago the cats were buried.

1. Carbon-14 decays over time. What does "decay" mean?
2. Why do you think carbon is used by scientists to date objects such as mummies, bones, and cloth wrappings?
3. Is it possible to use carbon-14 dating on things that were never alive? Why or why not?

L2

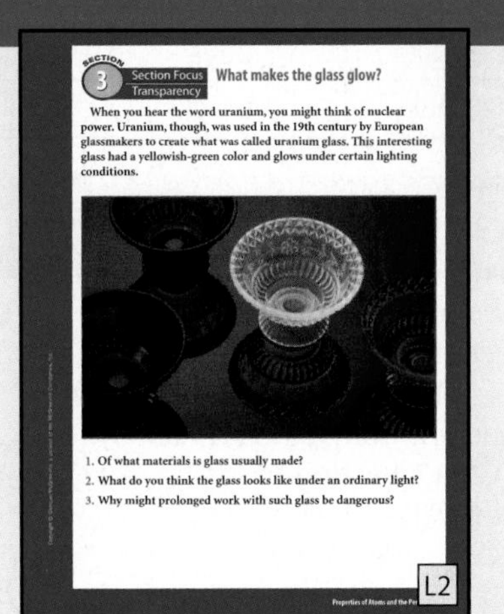
SECTION 3 Section Focus Transparency — What makes the glass glow?

When you hear the word uranium, you might think of nuclear power. Uranium, though, was used in the 19th century by European glassmakers to create what was called uranium glass. This interesting glass had a yellowish-green color and glows under certain lighting conditions.

1. Of what materials is glass usually made?
2. What do you think the glass looks like under an ordinary light?
3. Why might prolonged work with such glass be dangerous?

L2

This is a representation of key blackline masters available in the Teacher Classroom Resources. See Resource Manager boxes within the chapter for additional information.

Assessment

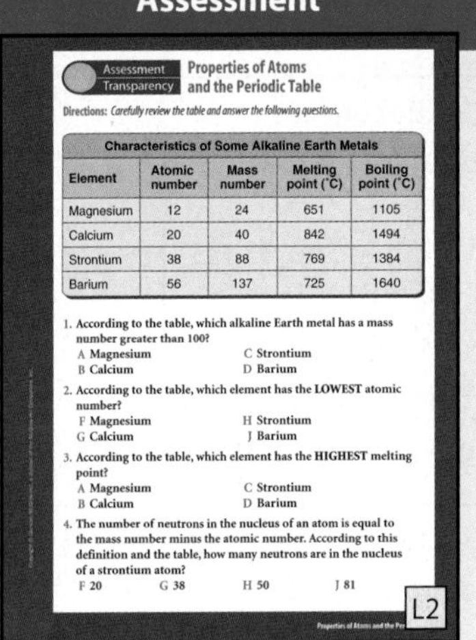
Assessment Transparency — Properties of Atoms and the Periodic Table

Directions: Carefully review the table and answer the following questions.

Characteristics of Some Alkaline Earth Metals

Element	Atomic number	Mass number	Melting point (°C)	Boiling point (°C)
Magnesium	12	24	651	1105
Calcium	20	40	842	1494
Strontium	38	88	769	1384
Barium	56	137	725	1640

1. According to the table, which alkaline Earth metal has a mass number greater than 100?
   A Magnesium C Strontium
   B Calcium D Barium
2. According to the table, which element has the LOWEST atomic number?
   F Magnesium H Strontium
   G Calcium J Barium
3. According to the table, which element has the HIGHEST melting point?
   A Magnesium C Strontium
   B Calcium D Barium
4. The number of neutrons in the nucleus of an atom is equal to the mass number minus the atomic number. According to this definition and the table, how many neutrons are in the nucleus of a strontium atom?
   F 20 G 38 H 50 J 81

L2

Teaching

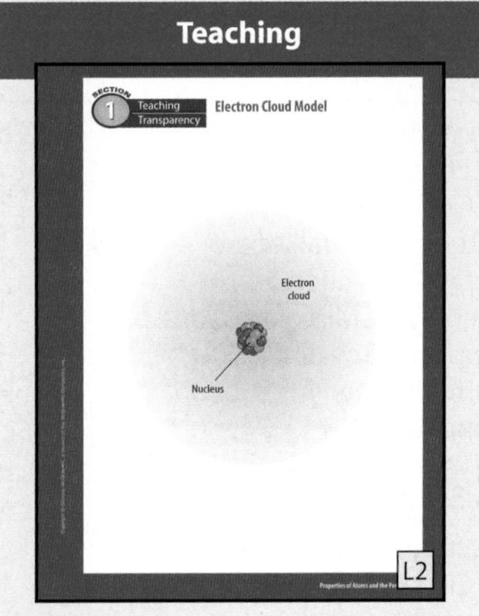
SECTION 1 Teaching Transparency — Electron Cloud Model

L2

Key to Teaching Strategies

The following designations will help you decide which activities are appropriate for your students.

L1 Level 1 activities should be appropriate for students with learning difficulties.

L2 Level 2 activities should be within the ability range of all students.

L3 Level 3 activities are designed for above-average students.

ELL ELL activities should be within the ability range of English Language Learners.

COOP LEARN Cooperative Learning activities are designed for small group work.

LS Multiple Learning Styles logos, as described on page 12T, are used throughout to indicate strategies that address different learning styles.

P These strategies represent student products that can be placed into a best-work portfolio.

PBL Problem-Based Learning activities apply real-world situations to learning.

Hands-on Activities

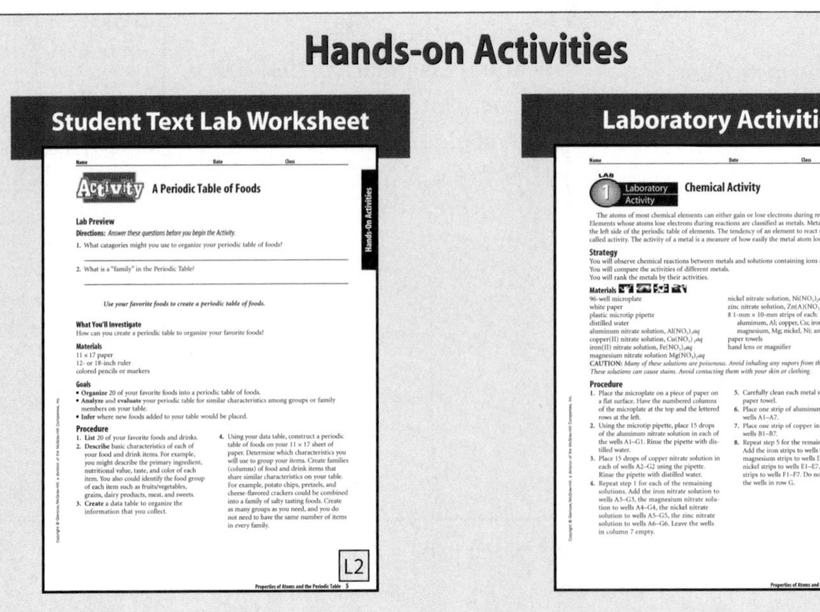

Student Text Lab Worksheet

Name Date Class

Activity — A Periodic Table of Foods

Lab Preview

Directions: *Answer these questions before you begin the Activity.*

1. What catagories might you use to organize your periodic table of foods?
2. What is a "family" in the Periodic Table?

Use your favorite foods to create a periodic table of foods.

What You'll Investigate

How can you create a periodic table to organize your favorite foods?

Materials

11 × 17 paper
12- or 18-inch ruler
colored pencils or markers

Goals

- **Organize** 20 of your favorite foods into a periodic table of foods.
- **Analyze** and **evaluate** your periodic table for similar characteristics among groups or family members on your table.
- **Infer** where new foods added to your table would be placed.

Procedure

1. **List** 20 of your favorite foods and drinks.
2. **Describe** basic characteristics of each of your food and drink items. For example, you might describe the primary ingredient, nutritional value, taste, and color of each item. You also could identify the food group of each item such as fruits/vegetables, grains, dairy products, meat, and sweets.
3. **Create** a data table to organize the information that you collect.
4. Using your data table, construct a periodic table of foods on your 11 × 17 sheet of paper. Determine which characteristics you will use to group your items. Create families (columns) of food and drink items that share similar characteristics on your table. For example, potato chips, pretzels, and cheese-flavored crackers could be combined into a family of salty tasting foods. Create as many groups as you need, and you do not need to have the same number of items in every family.

Hands-On Activities

L2

Properties of Atoms and the Periodic Table 5

Laboratory Activities

Name Date Class

LAB 1 Laboratory Activity — Chemical Activity

The atoms of most chemical elements can either gain or lose electrons during reactions. Elements whose atoms lose electrons during reactions are classified as metals. Metals are found on the left side of the periodic table of elements. The tendency of an element to react chemically is called activity. The activity of a metal is a measure of how easily the metal atom loses electrons.

Strategy

You will observe chemical reactions between metals and solutions containing ions of metals.
You will compare the activities of different metals.
You will rank the metals by their activities.

Materials

96-well microplate
white paper
plastic microtip pipette
distilled water
aluminum nitrate solution, $Al(NO_3)_3aq$
copper(II) nitrate solution, $Cu(NO_3)_2aq$
iron(II) nitrate solution, $Fe(NO_3)_2aq$
magnesium nitrate solution $Mg(NO_3)_2aq$
nickel nitrate solution, $Ni(NO_3)_2aq$
zinc nitrate solution, $Zn(A)(NO_3)_2aq$
8 1-mm × 10-mm strips of each: aluminum, Al; copper, Cu; iron, Fe; magnesium, Mg; nickel, Ni; and Zinc, Zn
paper towels
hand lens or magnifier

CAUTION: *Many of these solutions are poisonous. Avoid inhaling any vapors from the solutions. These solutions can cause stains. Avoid contacting them with your skin or clothing.*

Procedure

1. Place the microplate on a piece of paper on a flat surface. Have the numbered columns of the microplate at the top and the lettered rows at the left.
2. Using the microtip pipette, place 15 drops of the aluminum nitrate solution in each of the wells A1–G1. Rinse the pipette with distilled water.
3. Place 15 drops of copper nitrate solution in each of wells A2–G2 using the pipette. Rinse the pipette with distilled water.
4. Repeat step 1 for each of the remaining solutions. Add the iron nitrate solution to wells A3–G3, the magnesium nitrate solution to wells A4–G4, the nickel nitrate solution to wells A5–G5, the zinc nitrate solution to wells A6–G6. Leave the wells in column 7 empty.
5. Carefully clean each metal strip with a paper towel.
6. Place one strip of aluminum in each of the wells A1–A7.
7. Place one strip of copper in each of the wells B1–B7.
8. Repeat step 5 for the remaining metals. Add the iron strips to wells C1–C7, the magnesium strips to wells D1–D7, the nickel strips to wells E1–E7, and the zinc strips to wells F1–F7. Do not put strips in the wells in row G.

Hands-On Activities

L2

Properties of Atoms and the Periodic Table 9

Meeting Different Ability Levels

Content Outline

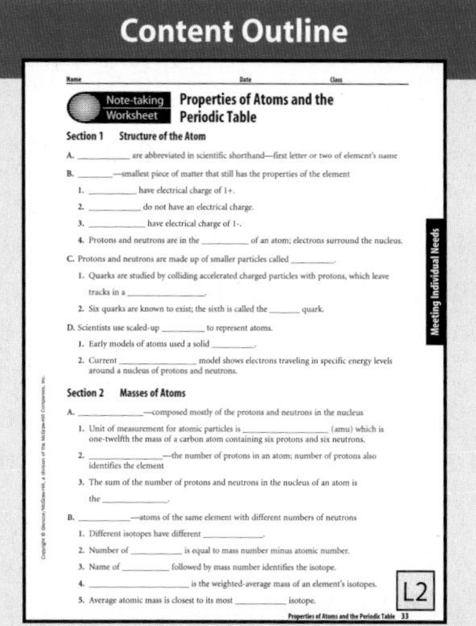
Note-taking Worksheet
Properties of Atoms and the Periodic Table
Section 1 Structure of the Atom
Section 2 Masses of Atoms
L2

Reinforcement

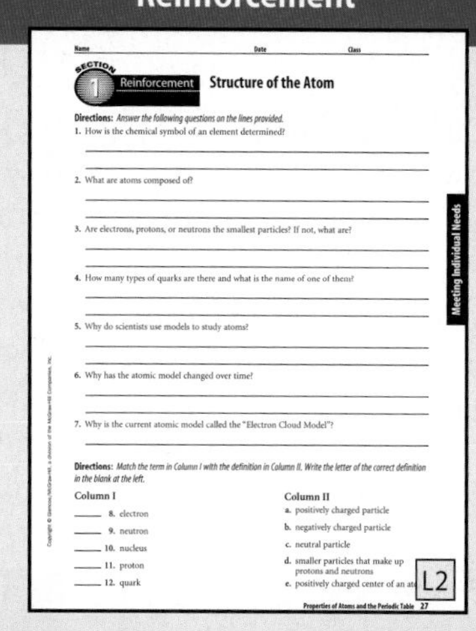
Section 1 Reinforcement
Structure of the Atom
L2

Enrichment

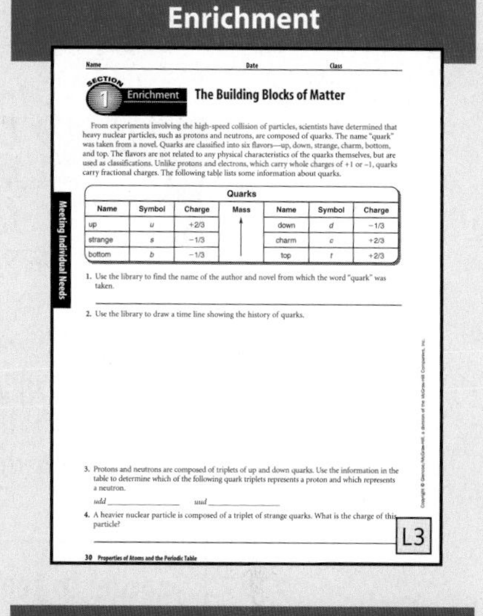
Section 1 Enrichment
The Building Blocks of Matter
L3

Directed Reading (English/Spanish)

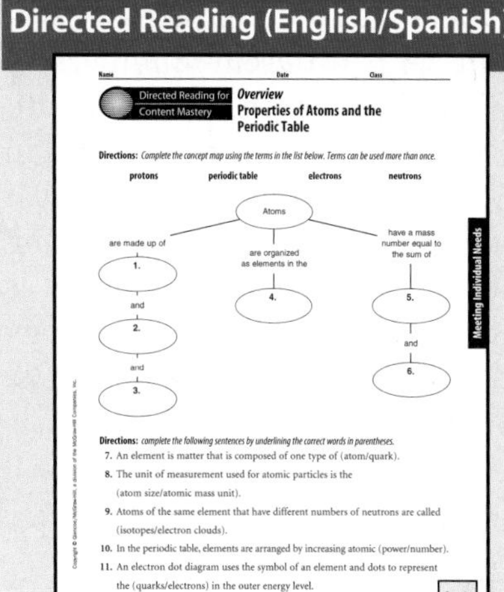
Directed Reading for Content Mastery
Overview
Properties of Atoms and the Periodic Table
L1

Study Guide

Study Guide
Features
• Contains a study guide page for each section of the chapter
• Reviews key concepts
• Includes answer pages
L2

Reading Essentials

Reading Essentials for Glencoe Science
An Interactive Student Workbook
Features
• Condensed core content
• Actively involves students in reading
• Reinforces key vocabulary
L1

Assessment

Test Practice Workbook

Chapter Test
Chapter 18 Properties of Atoms and the Periodic Table
L2

Chapter Review

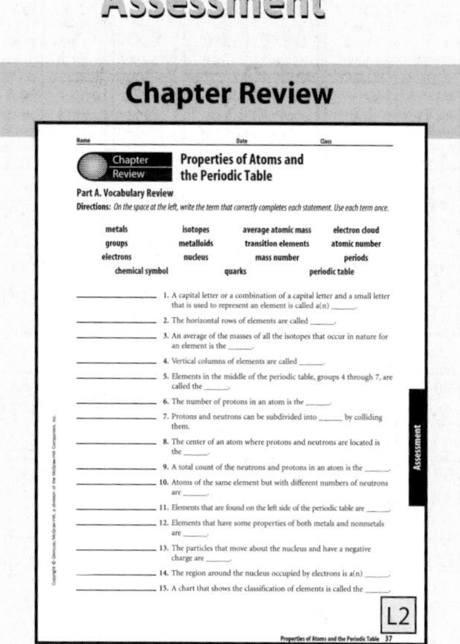
Chapter Review
Properties of Atoms and the Periodic Table
Part A. Vocabulary Review
L2

Chapter Tests

Chapter Test
Properties of Atoms and the Periodic Table
I. Testing Concepts
L2

Science Content Background

section 1 Structure of the Atom

Models—Tools for Scientists

In 1926, Austrian physicist Erwin Schrodinger (1887–1961) proposed the quantum mechanical model of the atom. The model was based on the wavelike properties of the electron. Electrons were no longer seen as small particles moving around the nucleus in a defined path. In fact, it was shown in 1927 by Werner Heisenberg (1901–1976), described in the Heisenberg Uncertainty Principle, that it is impossible to know precisely both an electron's position and momentum at a given time. Since that time, the location of electrons in an atom has been described as an electron cloud. An electron cloud is a volume of space where an electron with a certain amount of energy is most likely to be found.

Teacher to Teacher

Petrolia Moss, Teacher
North Heights Junior High
Texarkana, AR

"Multicolored modeling clay is an inexpensive and reusable material for middle school students to use to visualize science concepts. Students use their creativity to make 'atoms' that have touchable protons, neutrons, and electrons."

Petrolia Moss

section 2 Masses of Atoms

Isotopes

Isotopes are atoms of the same element with different numbers of neutrons. Many isotopes, such as carbon-14, occur naturally, and scientists have succeeded in producing many artificial isotopes. Isotopes that are radioactive are called radioisotopes. Among other applications, radioisotopes are used as tracers in medicine, geology, and biology research and are used to measure the thickness of materials in industry.

1 H 1.01																	2 He 4.00
3 Li 6.94	4 Be 9.01											5 B 10.8	6 C 12.0	7 N 14.0	8 O 16.0	9 F 19.0	10 Ne 20.2
11 Na 23.0	12 Mg 24.3											13 Al 27.0	14 Si 28.1	15 P 31.0	16 S 32.1	17 Cl 35.5	18 Ar 40.0
19 K 39.1	20 Ca 40.1	21 Sc 45.0	22 Ti 47.9	23 V 50.9	24 Cr 52.0	25 Mn 54.9	26 Fe 55.8	27 Co 58.9	28 Ni 58.7	29 Cu 63.5	30 Zn 65.4	31 Ga 69.7	32 Ge 72.6	33 As 74.9	34 Se 79.0	35 Br 79.9	36 Kr 83.8
37 Rb 85.5	38 Sr 87.6	39 Y 88.9	40 Zr 91.2	41 Nb 92.9	42 Mo 95.9	43 Tc 98	44 Ru 101	45 Rh 103	46 Pd 106	47 Ag 108	48 Cd 112	49 In 115	50 Sn 119	51 Sb 122	52 Te 128	53 I 127	54 Xe 131
55 Cs 133	56 Ba 137	57 La 139	72 Hf 178	73 Ta 181	74 W 184	75 Re 186	76 Os 190	77 Ir 192	78 Pt 195	79 Au 197	80 Hg 201	81 Tl 204	82 Pb 207	83 Bi 209	84 Po 210	85 At 210	86 Rn 222
87 Fr 223	88 Ra 226	89 Ac 227	104 Rf 227	105 Db 262	106 Sg 263	107 Bh 264	108 Hs 265	109 Mt 268	110 Ds 281	111 Uuu 269	112 Uub 277	113	114 Uuq 289	115	116	117	118
		58 Ce 140	59 Pr 141	60 Nd 144	61 Pm 147	62 Sm 150	63 Eu 152	64 Gd 157	65 Tb 159	66 Dy 163	67 Ho 165	68 Er 167	69 Tm 169	70 Yb 173	71 Lu 175		
		90 Th 232	91 Pa 231	92 U 238	93 Np 237	94 Pu 244	95 Am 243	96 Cm 247	97 Bk 247	98 Cf 251	99 Es 254	100 Fm 257	101 Md 258	102 No 255	103 Lr 256		

color code = light metals -brittle metals -ductile metals -low melting metals -non-metals -noble gases -lanthanides -actinides

section 3 The Periodic Table

Organizing the Elements

In 1817, the German chemist Johann Dobereiner found that he could arrange many elements into groups that he called triads. He noticed for example that lithium, sodium, and potassium react vigorously with water. Similar regularities were uncovered for calcium, strontium, and barium, and for fluorine, chlorine, and bromine.

Dobereiner's early work laid the groundwork for other chemists as they searched for an organizing principle by which to classify elements. In 1863, English chemist John Newlands proposed that when the known elements were arranged according to atomic mass, similarities in chemical properties occurred with every eighth element. He called this regularity the law of octaves. This regularity was also noticed by Dmitri Mendeleev. Mendeleev arranged the elements into a periodic table, which he published in 1869.

The modern periodic table didn't come into being until a Dutch physicist, Anton van den Broek, proposed that the elements should be arranged according to nuclear charge rather than atomic mass. Henry Mosely confirmed this hypothesis through studies of the X-ray spectra of a series of elements that had consecutive positions on the table. The change to ordering by atomic number resulted in the reversal of the positions of a few elements.

The Atom and the Periodic Table

The period in which an element appears in the periodic table indicates how many main electron energy levels that are in that atom. For example, oxygen is in the second period, so the oxygen atom has two main energy levels. The group number (for main group elements) indicates how many electrons are in the outermost energy level. Oxygen has six outer or valence electrons, so oxygen is in Group 6A. It is these outermost electrons that determine how an atom reacts.

For every principle quantum number (period or horizontal row), there are sublevels designated by letters, such as *s*, *p*, *d*, and *f*. In the sublevels, electron pairs are found in orbitals. There is a maximum of one *s* orbital, three *p* orbitals, five *d* orbitals, and seven *f* orbitals in an energy level. As you move across any period of the table, Groups 1 and 2 are filling *s* orbitals with two electrons. Groups 13–18 are filling *p* orbitals with six electrons. In periods 4 through 7, the transition elements, Groups 2–12, are filling five *d* orbitals with ten electrons. The inner transition elements, located below the periodic table, are filling the 4*f* and 5*f* orbitals with 14 electrons.

chapter content resources

Internet Resources

For additional content background, visit gpscience.com to:

- access your book online
- find references to related articles in popular science magazines
- access Web links with related content background
- access current events with science journal topics

Print Resources

Essential Elements: Atoms, Quarks, and the Periodic Table, by Matt Tweed, Walker and Company, 2003

Conceptual Chemistry: Understanding Our World of Atoms and Molecules, Second Edition, by John Suchocki, Pearson Benjamin Cummins, 2003

Fizz, Bubble, and Flash: Element Explorations and Atom Adventures (Williamson Kids Can! Series), by Anita Brandolini, Ph.D., Williamson Publishing, 2003

About the Photo

Atoms and Molecules The photo shows the city and harbor of Cabo San Lucas, Mexico, located at the southern tip of the Baja Peninsula. All the objects and materials that students can see in this photograph are composed of atoms. In most of these objects and materials, atoms are bound together with other atoms to form molecules.

Science Journal Student responses will vary, but may include information about the components that make up atoms or the methods of studying atoms.

The BIG Idea

Properties and Energy Levels In the periodic table, elements are arranged according to their atomic number—the number of protons in the atom's nucleus. The atomic number is also equal to the number of electrons in the atom. Elements in the same vertical column or group have similar physical and chemical properties. This is due to similarities in the way electrons are distributed in the various electronic energy levels. Atoms that have the same number of electrons in their highest, or outermost, available energy level tend to have similar chemical and physical properties.

Introduce the Chapter Have students write a description of what they think an atom is and what it is made of. Remind students that all atoms have a nucleus surrounded by electrons, and that protons and neutrons are found in the nuclei of atoms.

chapter 17

Properties of Atoms and the Periodic Table

BIG Idea The properties of an element are determined by the composition of its atoms.

17.1 Structure of the Atom
MAIN Idea Protons and neutrons are located in an atom's nucleus, and electrons are located in an electron cloud surrounding the nucleus.

17.2 Masses of Atoms
MAIN Idea All atoms of the same element have the same number of protons but can have different numbers of neutrons.

17.3 The Periodic Table
MAIN Idea Atoms of elements that are in the same group on the periodic table contain the same number of outer energy level electrons.

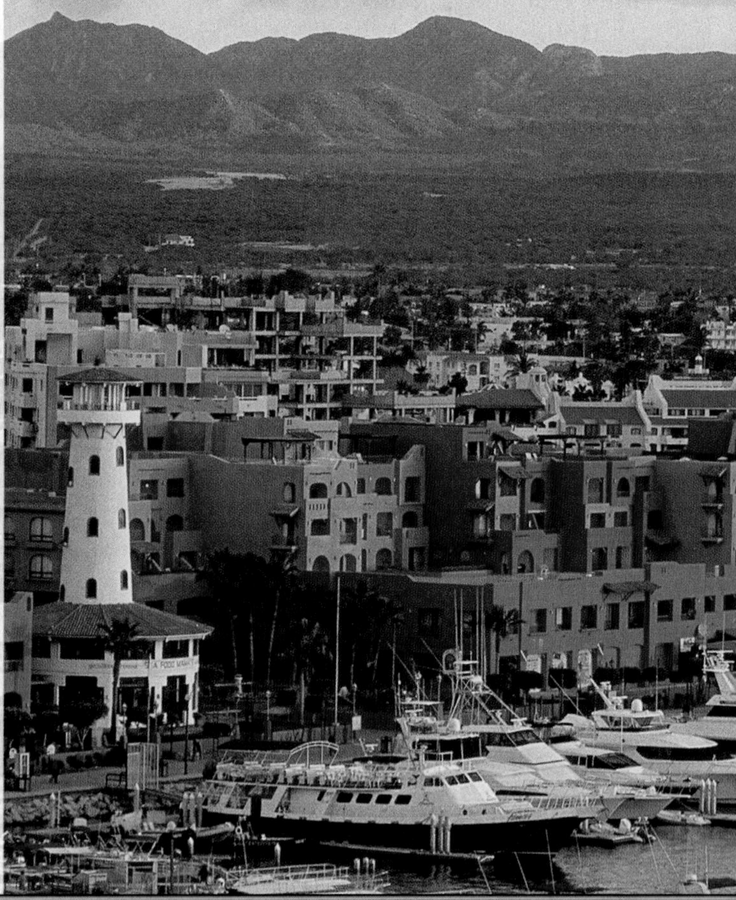

Atoms Compose All Things—Great and Small

Everything in this photo and the universe is composed of tiny particles called atoms. You will learn about atoms and their components—protons, neutrons, electrons, and quarks.

Science Journal

In your Science Journal, write a few paragraphs about what you know about atoms.

504

Interactive Chalkboard

This CD-ROM is an editable Microsoft® PowerPoint® presentation that includes:

- an editable presentation for every chapter
- additional chapter questions
- animated graphics
- image bank
- links to gpscience.com

Start-Up Activities

Inferring What You Can't Observe

How do detectives solve a crime when no witnesses saw it happen? How do scientists study atoms when they cannot see them? In situations such as these, techniques must be developed to find clues to answer the question. Do the lab below to see how clues might be gathered.

1. Take an envelope from your teacher.
2. Place an assortment of dried beans in the envelope and seal it. **WARNING:** *Do not eat any lab materials.*
3. Trade envelopes with another group.
4. Without opening the envelope, try to figure out the types and number of beans that are in the envelope. Record a hypothesis about the contents of the envelope in your Science Journal.
5. After you record your hypothesis, open the envelope and see what is inside.
6. **Think Critically** Describe the contents of your envelope. Was your hypothesis correct?

Preview this chapter's content and activities at gpscience.com

Atoms You have probably studied atoms before. Make the following Foldable to help identify what you already know, what you want to know, and what you learned about atoms.

STEP 1 **Fold** a vertical sheet of paper from side to side. Make the front edge about 1.25 cm shorter than the back edge.

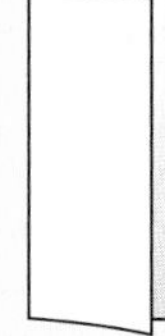

STEP 2 **Turn** lengthwise and **fold** into thirds.

STEP 3 **Unfold and cut** only the top layer along both folds to make three tabs.

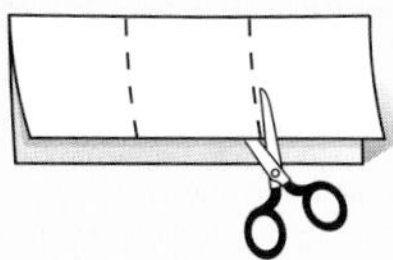

STEP 4 **Label** each tab as shown.

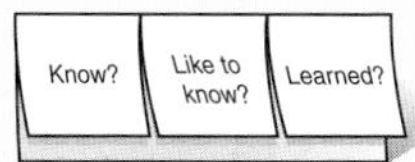

Identify Questions Before you read the chapter, write what you already know about atoms under the left tab of your Foldable, and write questions about what you'd like to know under the center tab. After you read the chapter, list what you learned under the right tab.

505

Additional Chapter Media

- BrainPOP: *Atomic Model*
- Virtual Lab: *How is the structure of an atom related to its position on the periodic table?*
- Video Lab: *Inferring What You Can't Observe*

Purpose Use the Launch Lab to show students how to use inference to describe something they cannot see. L2 IN **Kinesthetic**

Preparation Obtain several varieties of dried beans with different sizes and shapes.

Materials various dried beans, envelopes

Teaching Strategy Suggest that students

- lay a piece of thin paper over the sealed envelope and rub the side of a pencil over the beans.
- hold the envelope up to a bright light to see an outline of the beans.
- shake the envelope from side to side to see whether the beans are flat or round.

Think Critically

Answers will vary depending on the assortment of beans. The clues students find should be used in their conclusions. For example, aroma could help them identify coffee beans.

Assessment

Oral Ask students whether they have ever attempted to guess the contents of a wrapped gift. Have them explain how they used inference to get clues. Finally, ask them to explain how their gift-guessing might be similar to the reasoning used by atomic scientists to determine atomic structure. Use **Performance Assessment in the Science Classroom,** p. 89.

Dinah Zike Study Fold

Student preparation materials for this Foldable are available in the **Chapter *Fast File* Resources.**

Section 1: Structure of the Atom

1 Motivate

Bellringer

Section Focus Transparencies also are available on the Interactive Chalkboard CD-ROM. L2 

Section 1 Section Focus Transparency — Subatomic Collision

An individual atom is so small that it would take 50 million of them lined up in a row to equal one centimeter! Atoms, however, can be divided into component parts, and, amazingly, some of these parts have particles that are tinier yet. Below is an image created by these subatomic particles taken in a device called a bubble chamber.

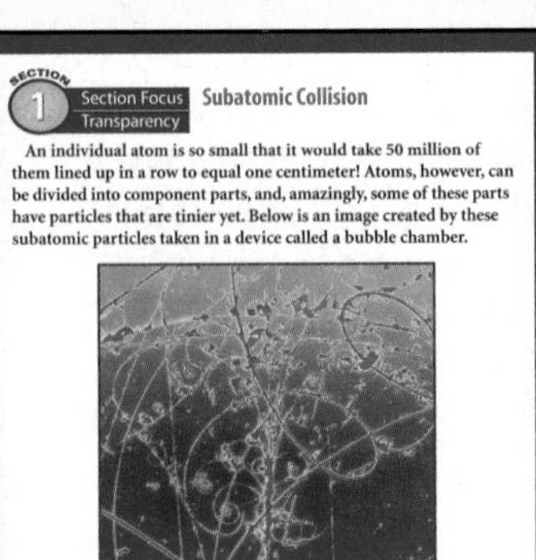

1. Why do you think scientists have only recently discovered these subatomic particles?
2. What might scientists learn by breaking apart atomic nuclei?

L2

Properties of Atoms and the Periodic Table

Tie to Prior Knowledge

Brainstorm Names Have students brainstorm a list of the names of elements that they know without referring to a periodic table. Record the list on the board or on chart paper. Make sure that things like brass or steel, which are mixtures of elements, are not accepted.

Reading Guide

What You'll Learn

- **Identify** the names and symbols of common elements.
- **Identify** quarks as subatomic particles of matter.
- **Describe** the electron cloud model of the atom.
- **Explain** how electrons are arranged in an atom.

Why It's Important

Everything that you see, touch, and breathe is composed of tiny atoms.

Review Vocabulary

element: substance with atoms that are all alike

New Vocabulary

- atom
- nucleus
- proton
- neutron
- electron
- quark
- electron cloud

Scientific Shorthand

Do you have a nickname? Do you use abbreviations for long words or the names of states? Scientists also do this. In fact, scientists have developed their own shorthand for dealing with long, complicated names.

Do the letters C, Al, Ne, and Ag mean anything to you? Each letter or pair of letters is a chemical symbol, which is a short or abbreviated way to write the name of an element. Chemical symbols, such as those in **Table 1,** consist of one capital letter or a capital letter plus one or two small letters. For some elements, the symbol is the first letter of the element's name. For other elements, the symbol is the first letter of the name plus another letter from its name. Some symbols are derived from Latin. For instance, *Argentum* is Latin for "silver." Elements have been named in a variety of ways. Some elements are named to honor scientists, for places, or for their properties. Other elements are named using rules established by an international committee. Regardless of the origin of the name, scientists derived this international system for convenience. It is much easier to write H for hydrogen, O for oxygen, and H_2O for dihydrogen oxide (water). Because scientists worldwide use this system, everyone understands what the symbols mean.

Table 1 Symbols of Some Elements

Element	Symbol	Element	Symbol
Aluminum	Al	Iron	Fe
Calcium	Ca	Mercury	Hg
Carbon	C	Nitrogen	N
Chlorine	Cl	Oxygen	O
Gold	Au	Potassium	K
Hydrogen	H	Sodium	Na

Section 1 Resource Manager

Chapter *FAST FILE* Resources

- Transparency Activity, pp. 44, 47–48
- Directed Reading for Content Mastery, pp. 19, 20
- Note-taking Worksheets, pp. 33–35
- Enrichment, p. 30
- MiniLAB, p. 3
- Reinforcement, p. 27

Reading and Writing Skill Activities, p. 43

Physical Science Critical Thinking/Problem Solving, p. 13

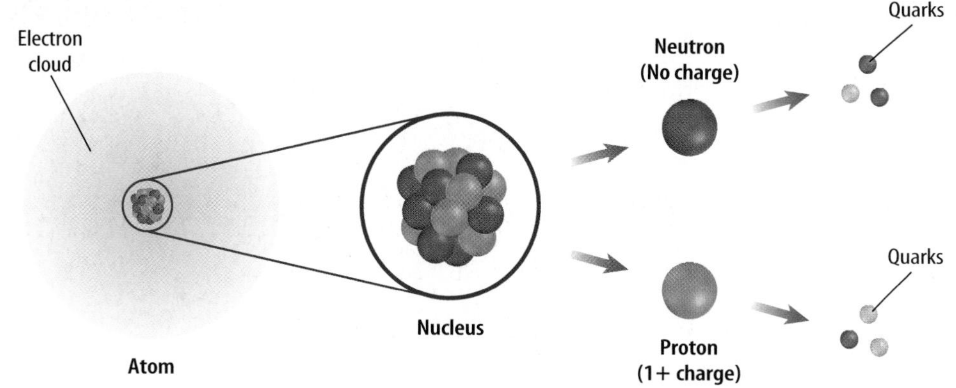

Figure 1 The nucleus of the atom contains protons and neutrons that are composed of quarks. The proton has a positive charge and the neutron has no charge. A cloud of negatively charged electrons surrounds the nucleus of the atom.

Atomic Components

An element is matter that is composed of one type of **atom,** which is the smallest piece of matter that still retains the property of the element. For example, the element silver is composed of only silver atoms and the element hydrogen is composed of only hydrogen atoms. Atoms are composed of particles called protons, neutrons, and electrons, as shown in **Figure 1.** Protons and neutrons are found in a small, positively-charged center of the atom called the **nucleus** that is surrounded by a cloud containing electrons. **Protons** are particles with an electrical charge of 1+. **Neutrons** are neutral particles that do not have an electrical charge. **Electrons** are particles with an electrical charge of 1−. Atoms of different elements differ in the number of protons they contain.

Reading Check *What are the particles that make up the atom and where are they located?*

Quarks—Even Smaller Particles

Are the protons, electrons, and neutrons that make up atoms the smallest particles that exist? Scientists hypothesize that electrons are not composed of smaller particles and are one of the most basic types of particles. Protons and neutrons, however, are made up of smaller particles called **quarks.** So far, scientists have confirmed the existence of six uniquely different quarks. Scientists theorize that an arrangement of three quarks held together with the strong nuclear force produces a proton. Another arrangement of three quarks produces a neutron. The search for the composition of protons and neutrons is an ongoing effort.

Topic: Particle Research
Visit gpscience.com for Web links to information about particle research at Fermi National Accelerator Laboratory.

Activity Write a paragraph describing the information that you found at the site.

Differentiated Instruction

English-Language Learners Have students use colored pencils to draw a diagram of an atom of the element lithium. Students should draw the correct numbers of protons, neutrons, and electrons. Students should color code the components and provide a key to their diagram. Have students use 3 protons, 4 neutrons, and 3 electrons in their diagram. L2 ELL

2 Teach

Use Science Words

Word Usage Have students compare and contrast the use of the word *nucleus* in biology and in physical science. In biology, *nucleus* refers to the cellular organelle where control of cell functions originates. It is in the interior of the cell, but not necessarily at the center. In physical science, the nucleus is also a sort of control area because the number of protons found in the nucleus determines the identity of the atom. The nucleus of an atom, however, is located at the center of the atom. L2 IN **Linguistic**

Reading Check

Answer Particles that make up atoms include protons and neutrons, which are located in the nucleus, and electrons, which are located in a cloud surrounding the nucleus.

Make a Model

Nesting Dolls Obtain a set of nesting dolls and place them in the front of the room. Ask students what they think is inside. After they respond, open the largest figure and reveal the smaller one. Continue this until you reach the last doll. How are the dolls similar to the search for smaller nuclear particles? Scientists thought several times that they had found the smallest particles, but each time they found even smaller particles. Now scientists would say that the last doll is like a quark. L2 IN **Visual-Spatial**

Discussion

Quarks Why are scientists having trouble determining the composition of protons and neutrons? Until recently, technology was not available to determine the existence of quarks. Subatomic particles are difficult to study because of their size.

2 Teach

Use an Analogy

Snow Tracks People walking in snow or skiing down a mountain leave their tracks behind. If there were no snow, tracks of activity would be much more difficult to see. When detecting quarks or other atomic particles, scientists create an environment that helps them see the tracks the moving particles leave behind. In a cloud chamber, a dense cloud condenses to an even denser track when a particle passes through. Just as skiers leave a different track than do snowboarders, an electron moving through the dense cloud leaves a different track than does a proton. L2

Caption Answer

Figure 2 to accelerate the particles so they will have enough energy to break each other apart when they collide

Quick Demo

Gathering Evidence

Materials one large sheet of poster board, various types of markers and pens, tape, magnifying lens

Estimated Time 10 minutes

Procedure Display a large poster in front of the class on which you have made several curved lines using different markers and pens. Tape the markers and pens to the poster board and provide a magnifying lens. Ask students to match the pen with the appropriate line by examining the pen tip with the lens. Next, ask what other method they could use to identify the lines. Make comparison marks with each pen or marker. Tell students that nuclear scientists use both predictions and matching techniques.

Figure 2 The Tevatron is a huge machine. The aerial photograph of Fermi National Accelerator Laboratory shows the circular outline of the Tevatron particle accelerator. The close-up photograph of the Tevatron gives you a better view of the tunnel.
Infer *Why is such a long tunnel needed?*

Finding Quarks To study quarks, scientists accelerate charged particles to tremendous speeds and then force them to collide with—or smash into—protons. This collision causes the proton to break apart. The Fermi National Accelerator Laboratory, a research laboratory in Batavia, Illinois, houses a machine that can generate the forces that are required to collide protons. This machine, the Tevatron, shown in **Figure 2,** is approximately 6.4 km in circumference. Electric and magnetic fields are used to accelerate, focus and collide the fast-moving particles.

The particles that result from the collision can be detected by various collection devises. Often, scientists use multiple collection devices to collect the most possible information about the particles created in a collision. Just as police investigators can reconstruct traffic accidents from tire marks and other clues at the scene, scientists are able to examine and gather information about the particles, as shown in **Figure 3.** Scientists use inference to identify the subatomic particles and to reveal information about each particle's inner structure.

Figure 3 Bubble chambers can be used by scientists to study the tracks left by subatomic particles.

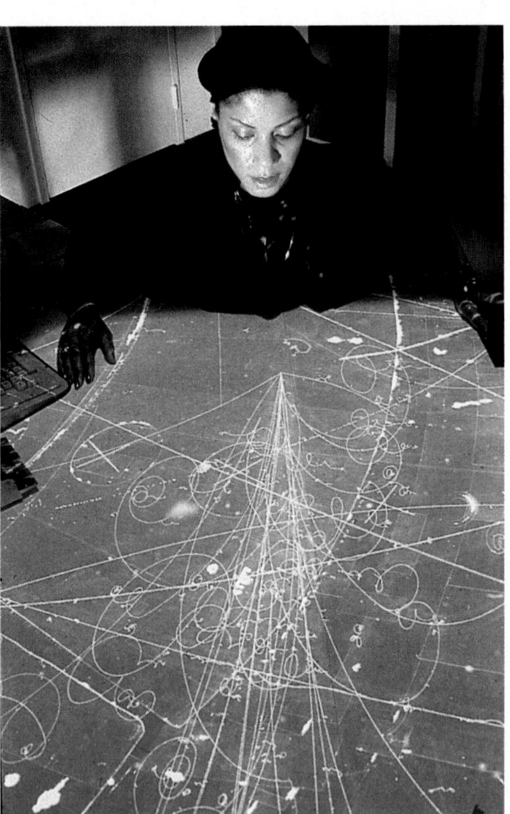

The Sixth Quark Finding evidence for the existence of the quarks was not an easy task. Scientists found five quarks and hypothesized that a sixth quark existed. However, it took a team of nearly 450 scientists from around the world several years to find the sixth quark. The tracks of the sixth quark were hard to detect because only about one billionth of a percent of the proton collisions performed showed the presence of a sixth quark—typically referred to as the *top* quark.

Teacher FYI

Cloud Chambers The first cloud chambers were developed near the beginning of the 1900s by C.T.R. Wilson, a Scottish physicist. He was trying to reproduce weather conditions in a closed chamber. Supersaturated vapor formed in the chamber and formed visible vapor trails when X rays passed through. This led to more sophisticated bubble chambers for detailed study of the vapor trails formed as beta and alpha particles passed through the supersaturated vapor.

Models—Tools for Scientists

Scientists and engineers use models to represent things that are difficult to visualize—or picture in your mind. You might have seen models of buildings, the solar system, or airplanes. These are scaled-down models. Scaled-down models allow you to see either something too large to see all at once, or something that has not been built yet. Scaled-up models are often used to visualize things that are too small to see. To give you an idea of how small the atom is, it would take about 24,400 atoms stacked one on top of the other to equal the thickness of a sheet of aluminum foil. To study the atom, scientists have developed scaled-up models that they can use to visualize how the atom is constructed. For the model to be useful, it must support all of the information that is known about matter and the behavior of atoms. As more information about the atom is collected, scientists change their models to include the new information.

Reading Check *Explain how models can simplify science.*

The Changing Atomic Model You know now that all matter is composed of atoms, but this was not always known. Around 400 B.C., Democritus proposed the idea that atoms make up all substances. However, another famous Greek philosopher, Aristotle, disputed Democritus's theory and proposed that matter was uniform throughout and was not composed of smaller particles. Aristotle's incorrect theory was accepted for about 2,000 years. In the 1800s, John Dalton, an English scientist, was able to offer proof that atoms exist.

Dalton's model of the atom, a solid sphere shown in **Figure 4,** was an early model of the atom. As you can see in **Figure 5,** the model has changed somewhat over time. Dalton's modernization of Aristotle's idea of the atom provided a physical explanation for chemical reactions. Scientists could then express these reactions in quantitative terms using chemical symbols and equations.

Mini LAB

Modeling an Aluminum Atom

Procedure

1. Arrange thirteen 3-cm circles cut from **orange paper** and fourteen 3-cm circles cut from **blue paper** on a **flat surface** to represent the nucleus of an atom. Each orange circle represents one proton, and each blue circle represents one neutron.
2. Position two holes punched from **red paper** about 20 cm from your nucleus.
3. Position eight punched holes about 40 cm from your nucleus.
4. Position three punched holes about 60 cm from your nucleus.

Analysis

1. How many protons, neutrons, and electrons does an aluminum atom have?
2. Explain how your circles model an aluminum atom.
3. Explain why your model does not accurately represent the true size and distances in an aluminum atom.

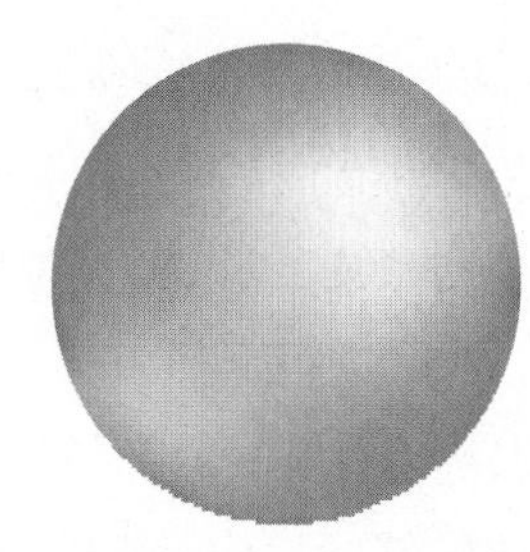

Figure 4 John Dalton's atomic model was a simple sphere.

Purpose to make a model showing the particles in an atom L2

Materials blue, orange, and red paper, metric ruler, hole punch

Teaching Strategy To save time, prepare the circles and the punched holes ahead of time.

Analysis

1. 13 protons, 14 neutrons, and 13 electrons
2. Like an aluminum atom, the model has 13 protons and 14 neutrons. It also has three energy levels with 2 electrons in the first level, 8 in the second, and 3 in the third.
3. In reality, protons and neutrons are more than 1,800 times larger than electrons. This activity does not attempt to model subatomic particle radii nor their exact locations in the cloud. It is merely modeling the grouping that occurs within the cloud.

Assessment

Process Have students use their materials to make models of atoms of as many different elements as they can. Ask them to make lists of the atoms they made, and draw a quick sketch of each one. Use **Performance Assessment in the Science Classroom,** p. 97.

Reading Check

Answer Models are less expensive to build than the actual item and they allow the study of things that are difficult to visualize or duplicate.

Differentiated Instruction

Challenge Have students research models that are used in other fields such as architecture, aerospace, or the automotive industry. Have students bring in a model of their choice and make a presentation to the class on how the models are used by scientists and engineers in their selected field. L3

Visual Learning

Figure 4 Tell students that the wooden sphere atom models that Dalton constructed are on display in the Science Museum in London. Many of his contemporaries ridiculed his idea of atoms simply on the basis that atoms could not be seen and, therefore, did not exist. What are some other things that exist but can't be seen? Possible answers: electromagnetic waves, air L2 IN **Visual-Spatial**

Visualizing The Atomic Model

Have students examine the pictures and read the captions. Then ask the following questions.

What significant changes occurred in the atomic model between **Figure 5A** and **Figure 5B?** Scientists found that the atom was not "uncuttable" but was composed of positive and negative particles.

What significant changes occurred in the atomic model between **Figure 5B** and **Figure 5C?** Scientists found that the mass of the atom was concentrated in the center instead of throughout the atom and that electrons orbit the nucleus.

What significant changes occurred in the atomic model between **Figure 5C** and **Figure 5D?** Scientists found that the orbits of the electrons are not random but are at fixed distances from the nucleus. Scientists also found that the nucleus is composed of protons and neutrons.

Activity

Rutherford Report Have students research and find out how Rutherford discovered that the mass of the atom is concentrated primarily in the center of the atom. Ask students to write brief reports in their Science Journals describing Rutherford's experiment. L2 LS **Linguistic**

Figure 5

The ancient Greek philosopher Democritus proposed that elements consisted of tiny, solid particles that could not be subdivided (A). He called these particles *atomos,* meaning "uncuttable." This concept of the atom's structure remained largely unchallenged until the 1900s, when researchers began to discover through experiments that atoms were composed of still smaller particles. In the early 1900s, a number of models for atomic structure were proposed (B-D). The currently accepted model (E) evolved from these ideas and the work of many other scientists.

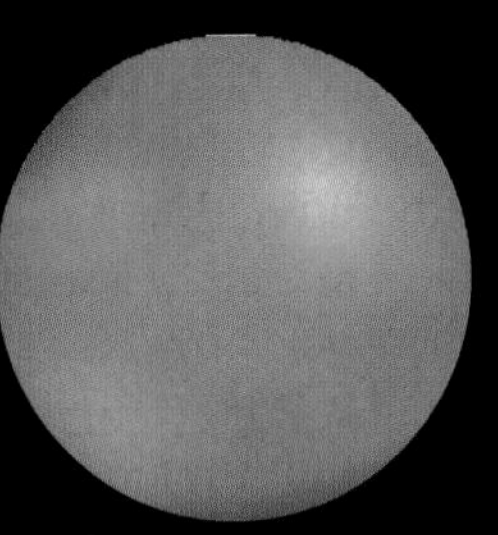

A DEMOCRITUS'S UNCUTTABLE ATOM

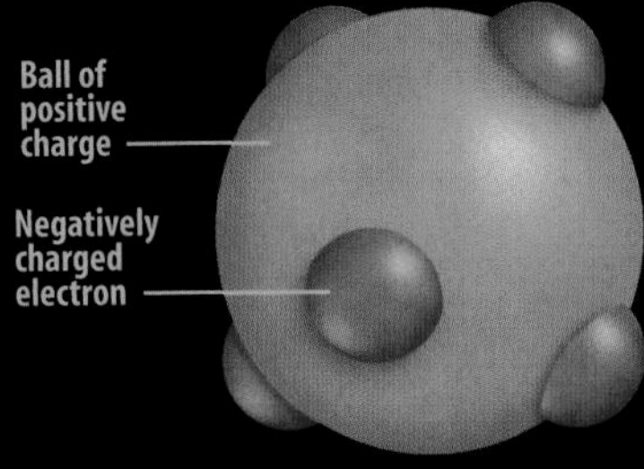

B THOMSON MODEL, 1904 **English physicist Joseph John Thomson inferred from his experiments that atoms contained small, negatively charged particles. He thought these "electrons" (in red) were evenly embedded throughout a positively charged sphere, much like chocolate chips in a ball of cookie dough.**

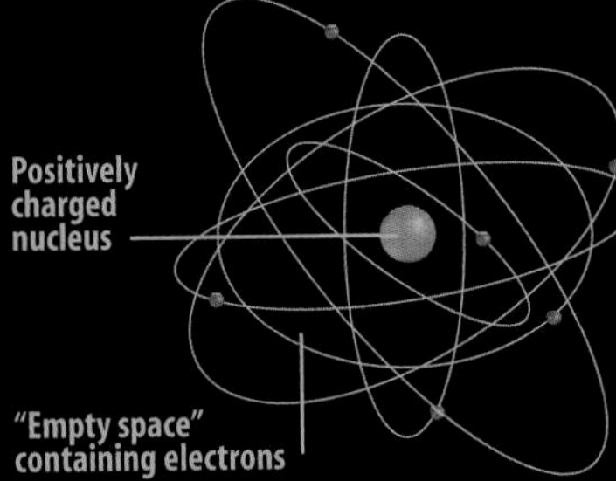

C RUTHERFORD MODEL, 1911 **Another British physicist, Ernest Rutherford, proposed that almost all the mass of an atom—and all its positive charges—were concentrated in a central atomic nucleus surrounded by electrons.**

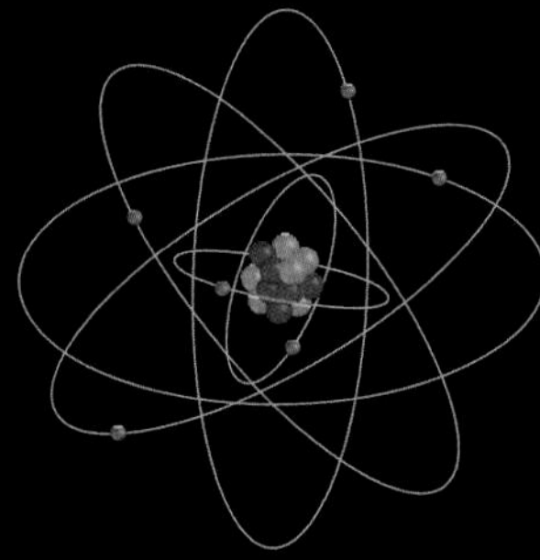

D BOHR MODEL, 1913 **Danish physicist Niels Bohr hypothesized that electrons traveled in fixed orbits around the atom's nucleus. James Chadwick, a student of Rutherford, concluded that the nucleus contained positive protons and neutral neutrons.**

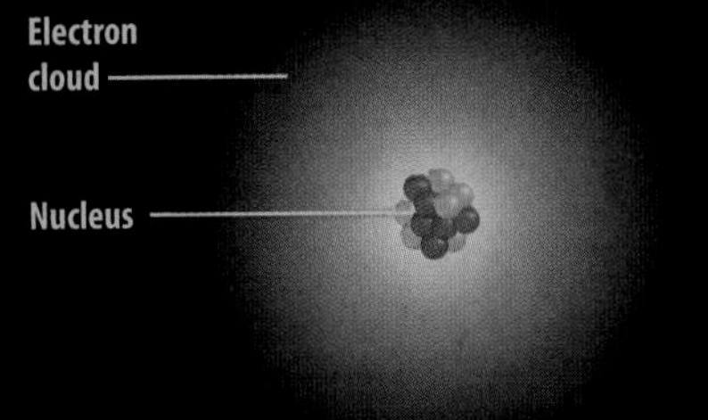

E ELECTRON CLOUD MODEL, CURRENT **According to the currently accepted model of atomic structure, electrons do not follow fixed orbits but tend to occur more frequently in certain areas around the nucleus at any given time.**

510 CHAPTER 17 Properties of Atoms and the Periodic Table

The Electron Cloud Model By 1926, scientists had developed the electron cloud model of the atom that is in use today. An **electron cloud** is the area around the nucleus of an atom where its electrons are most likely found. The electron cloud is 100,000 times larger than the diameter of the nucleus. In contrast, each electron in the cloud is much smaller than a single proton.

Because an electron's mass is small and the electron is moving so quickly around the nucleus, it is impossible to describe its exact location in an atom. Picture the spokes on a moving bicycle wheel. They are moving so quickly that you can't pinpoint any single spoke. All you see is a blur that contains all of the spokes somewhere within it. In the same way, an electron cloud is a blur containing all of the electrons of the atom somewhere within it. **Figure 6** illustrates what the electron cloud might look like.

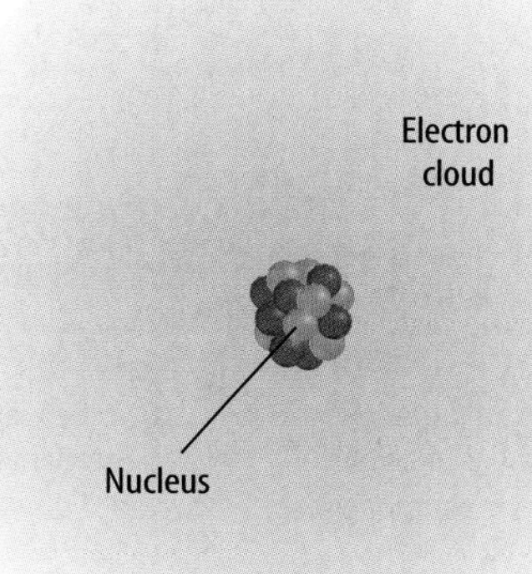

Figure 6 The electrons are located in an electron cloud surrounding the nucleus of the atom.

section 1 review

Summary

Scientific Shorthand

- Scientists use chemical symbols as shorthand when naming elements.

Atomic Components

- Atoms are composed of small particles that have known charges.
- The particles that make up the atom are located in predictable locations within the atom.

Quarks—Even Smaller Particles

- So far, scientists have confirmed the existence of six different quarks.

Models—Tools for Scientists

- Models are used by scientists to simplify the study of concepts and things.
- The current atomic model is an accumulation of over two hundred years of knowledge.
- The electron cloud model is the current atomic model.

Self Check

1. **List** the chemical symbols for the elements carbon, aluminum, hydrogen, oxygen, and sodium.
2. **Identify** the names, charges, and locations of three kinds of particles that make up an atom.
3. **Identify** the smallest particle of matter. How were they discovered?
4. **Describe** the electron cloud model of the atom.
5. **Think Critically** Explain how a rotating electric fan might be used to model the atom. Explain how the rotating fan is unlike an atom.

Applying Math

6. **Use Numbers** The mass of a proton is estimated to be 1.6726×10^{-24} g and the mass of an electron is estimated to be 9.1093×10^{-28} g. How many times larger is the mass of a proton compared to the mass of an electron?
7. **Calculate** What is the difference between the mass of a proton and the mass of an electron?

3 Assess

DAILY INTERVENTION

Check for Understanding

Linguistic Have students write a narrative describing the changes in the atomic model through time. L2 P

Reteach

Demonstrating Atoms Place some sesame seeds inside a balloon and carefully (do not breathe in any seeds) inflate and tie off the balloon. As you shake the balloon, ask students how this model could represent electrons in an atom. The seeds are small compared to the balloon, they are constantly moving, their locations are difficult to predict. Ask students how this model does not parallel the electrons in an atom. The balloon has a specific boundary beyond which the seeds cannot move. Electrons can move away from atoms. L2 LS **Visual-Spatial**

Assessment

Oral Tell students that a fundamental particle is one that cannot be divided into other particles. Ask whether protons, neutrons, or electrons are fundamental particles. Electrons are fundamental particles. Protons and neutrons are not. Use **Performance Assessment in the Science Classroom,** p. 89. L2

section 1 review

1. C; Al; H; O; Na
2. proton, +1, nucleus; neutron, 0, nucleus; electron, −1, electron cloud
3. quark; by accelerating protons and making them collide with so much force that they broke apart
4. This model says electrons are most likely to be found in a cloud surrounding the nucleus; it is 100,000 times larger than the diameter of the nucleus.
5. The blades on a rotating fan appear as a smooth metal surface around the center hub. The probability area for electrons in an atom also presents a solid appearance. The fan blades are different from electrons because they are much larger and, when the fan stops, can easily be seen.
6. 1,836 times larger
7. 1.6717×10^{-24}

section 2

Masses of Atoms

Reading Guide

What **You'll Learn**

- **Compute** the atomic mass and mass number of an atom.
- **Identify** the components of isotopes.
- **Interpret** the average atomic mass of an element.

Why **It's Important**

Some elements naturally exist in more than one form—radioactive and nonradioactive.

Review Vocabulary

mass: amount of matter in an object

New Vocabulary

- atomic number
- mass number
- isotope
- average atomic mass

Table 2 Subatomic Particle Masses

Particle	Mass (g)
Proton	1.6726×10^{-24}
Neutron	1.6749×10^{-24}
Electron	9.1093×10^{-28}

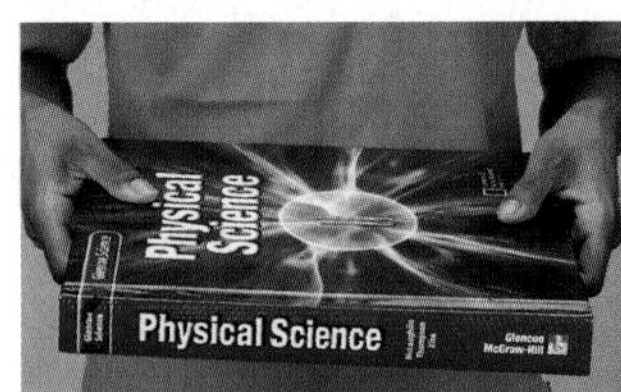

Figure 7 If you held a textbook and placed a paper clip on it, you wouldn't notice the added mass because the mass of a paper clip is small compared to the mass of the book. In a similar way, the masses of an atom's electrons are negligible compared to an atom's mass.

Atomic Mass

The nucleus contains most of the mass of the atom because protons and neutrons are far more massive than electrons. The mass of a proton is about the same as that of a neutron—approximately 1.6726×10^{-24} g, as shown in **Table 2.** The mass of each is approximately 1,836 times greater than the mass of the electron. The electron's mass is so small that it is considered negligible when finding the mass of an atom, as shown in **Figure 7.**

If you were asked to estimate the height of your school building, you probably wouldn't give an answer in kilometers. The number would be too cumbersome to use. Considering the scale of the building, you would more likely give the height in a smaller unit, meters. When thinking about the small masses of atoms, scientists found that even grams were not small enough to use for measurement. Scientists need a unit that results in more manageable numbers. The unit of measurement used for atomic particles is the atomic mass unit (amu). The mass of a proton or a neutron is almost equal to 1 amu. This is not coincidence—the unit was defined that way. The atomic mass unit is defined as one-twelfth the mass of a carbon atom containing six protons and six neutrons. Remember that the mass of the carbon atom is contained almost entirely in the mass of the protons and neutrons that are located in the nucleus. Therefore, each of the 12 particles in the nucleus must have a mass nearly equal to one.

Where is the majority of the mass of an atom located?

1 Motivate

Bellringer

Section Focus Transparencies also are available on the Interactive Chalkboard CD-ROM.

Section 2 Section Focus Transparency **Carbon Cat**

How old are these mummified cats found in an Egyptian tomb? Carbon-14 holds the answer. Carbon-14 is a radioactive form of carbon, an element found in every living thing. By measuring how much carbon-14 remains in these cats, scientists can tell approximately how many years ago the cats were buried.

1. Carbon-14 decays over time. What does "decay" mean?
2. Why do you think carbon is used by scientists to date objects such as mummies, bones, and cloth wrappings?
3. Is it possible to use carbon-14 dating on things that were never alive? Why or why not?

L2

Properties of Atoms and the Periodic Table

Tie to Prior Knowledge

Mass, Volume, and Weight Ask students to explain the differences between mass, weight, and volume. Mass is the amount of matter in an object, weight is a measure of the force of gravity on an object, and volume is the amount of space the object occupies. L2

Answer in the nucleus

Section 2 Resource Manager

Chapter *Fast File* Resources

- Transparency Activity, p. 45
- Directed Reading for Content Mastery, p. 20
- Lab Activity, pp. 9–12
- Reinforcement, p. 28
- Enrichment, p. 31

Mathematics Skill Activities, p. 7

Science Inquiry Labs, pp.49–50

Table 3 Mass Numbers of Some Atoms

Element	Symbol	Atomic Number	Protons	Neutrons	Mass Number	Average Atomic Mass*
Boron	B	5	5	6	11	10.81 amu
Carbon	C	6	6	6	12	12.01 amu
Oxygen	O	8	8	8	16	16.00 amu
Sodium	Na	11	11	12	23	22.99 amu
Copper	Cu	29	29	34	63	63.55 amu

*The atomic mass units are rounded to two decimal places.

Protons Identify the Element You learned earlier that atoms of different elements are different because they have different numbers of protons. In fact, the number of protons tells you what type of atom you have and vice versa. For example, every carbon atom has six protons. Also, all atoms with six protons are carbon atoms. Atoms with eight protons are oxygen atoms. The number of protons in an atom is equal to a number called the **atomic number.** The atomic number of carbon is six. Therefore, if you are given any one of the following—the name of the element, the number of protons in the element, or the atomic number of the element, you can determine the other two.

Reading Check *Which element is an atom with six protons in the nucleus?*

Mass Number The **mass number** of an atom is the sum of the number of protons and the number of neutrons in the nucleus of an atom. Look at **Table 3** and see if this is true.

If you know the mass number and the atomic number of an atom, you can calculate the number of neutrons. The number of neutrons is equal to the atomic number subtracted from the mass number.

$$\text{number of neutrons} = \text{mass number} - \text{atomic number}$$

Atoms of the same element with different numbers of neutrons can have different properties. For example, carbon with a mass number equal to 12, or carbon-12, is the most common form of carbon. Carbon-14 is present on Earth in much smaller quantities. Carbon-14 is radioactive and carbon-12 is not.

2 Teach

Reading Check

Answer carbon

Discussion

Atom Charge How many electrons are found in a neutral atom of carbon? six What would the charge be on the carbon atom if it lost four electrons? Explain. + 4; The atom now has 4 more protons than electrons. How does neutron count affect atomic charge? It has no effect. L2

Quick Demo

Modeling Atoms

Materials modeling clay, three different colors

Estimated Time 20 minutes

Procedure Create models of the atoms in **Table 3** using three different colors of modeling clay. Use small balls from two of the colors to create the protons and neutrons in the nucleus. Use the third color to represent the electrons.

Discussion

Atom Numbers Have students determine the number of neutrons, protons, and electrons in neon −20, potassium −39, and gold −197. Ne: 10 protons, 10 neutrons, 10 electrons; K: 19 protons, 20 neutrons, 19 electrons; Au: 79 protons, 118 neutrons, 79 electrons L3

LS **Logical-Mathematical**

Activity

Element Game Have students play the element game in pairs. One student should write down the name of an element on a piece of paper. This student gives the other student a hint about the name of the element. The student keeps giving hints until the other student guesses the element. L2

Teacher FYI

Isotopes Nearly all elements have isotopes, some of which are radioactive. The mass of an element listed on the periodic table is the weighted average of the masses of the isotopes of that element.

Differentiated Instruction

Visually Impaired If **Table 3** is difficult for some to read, use one type of object, such as small corks, to represent protons and another type, such as rubber stoppers, to represent neutrons. Have students assemble the right numbers of protons and neutrons for the atoms listed in **Table 3**. L2

IDENTIFYING Misconceptions

Protons v. Neutrons Students may think that since many of the lighter elements have the same number of protons as neutrons, all elements have this property. Remind them that this is not true. Large atoms have more neutrons than protons because neutrons play a role in stabilizing the repulsive forces between the protons in the nucleus.

Carbon Dating Archaeologists are most interested in carbon-13 and carbon-14 because these isotopes are radioactive. The longer a once-living organism has been dead, the less radioactive it will be per gram of carbon. This gives archaeologists a way to determine the approximate age of once-living organisms.

Answer 146 neutrons

Applying Science

Answers

1. 48,800 million years; 97,600 million years
2. 8,920 million years; lead-206

Carbon Dating Living organisms on Earth contain carbon. Carbon-12 makes up 99 percent of this carbon. Carbon-13 and carbon-14 make up the other one percent. Which isotopes are archaeologists most interested in when they determine the age of carbon-containing remains? Explain your answer in your Science Journal.

Isotopes

Not all the atoms of an element have the same number of neutrons. Atoms of the same element that have different numbers of neutrons are called **isotopes.** Suppose you have a sample of the element boron. Naturally occurring atoms of boron have mass numbers of 10 or 11. How many neutrons are in a boron atom? It depends upon the isotope of boron to which you are referring. Obtain the number of protons in boron from the periodic table. Then use the formula on the previous page to calculate the number of neutrons in each boron isotope. You can determine that boron can have five or six neutrons.

Reading Check *Uranium-238 has 92 protons. How many neutrons does it have?*

Applying Science

Radioactive Isotopes Help Tell Time

Atoms can be used to measure the age of bones or rock formations that are millions of years old. The time it takes for half of the radioactive atoms in a piece of rock or bone to change into another element is called its half-life. Scientists use the half-lives of radioactive isotopes to measure geologic time.

Half-Lives of Radioactive Isotopes

Radioactive Element	Changes to This Element	Half-Life
uranium-238	lead-206	4,460 million years
potassium-40	argon-40, calcium-40	1,260 million years
rubidium-87	strontium-87	48,800 million years
carbon-14	nitrogen-14	5,715 years

Identifying the Problem

The table above lists the half-lives of a sample of radioactive isotopes and into which elements they change. For example, it would take 5,715 years for half of the carbon-14 atoms in a rock to change into atoms of nitrogen-14. After another 5,715 years, half of the remaining carbon-14 atoms will change, and so on. You can use these radioactive clocks to measure different periods of time.

Solving the Problem

1. How many years would it take half of the rubidium-87 atoms in a piece of rock to change into strontium-87? How many years would it take for 75% of the atoms to change?
2. After a long period, only 25% of the atoms in a rock remained uranium-238. How many years old would you predict the rock to be? The other 75% of the atoms are now which radioactive element?

Visual Learning

Figure 8 Have students draw diagrams in their Science Journals of the nuclei of carbon-12, carbon-13, and carbon-14. Carbon-12 has 6 protons and 6 neutrons, carbon-13 has 6 protons and 7 neutrons, and carbon-14 has 6 protons and 8 neutrons. L2 LS **Visual-Spatial**

Differentiated Instruction

Challenge Have students research radioactive isotopes that are used in medicine. Have students give a presentation to the class about the types of isotopes used and what they are used for. L3

Identifying Isotopes Models of two isotopes of boron are shown in **Figure 8.** Because the numbers of neutrons in the isotopes are different, the mass numbers are also different. You use the name of the element followed by the mass number of the isotope to identify each isotope: boron-10 and boron-11. Because most elements have more than one isotope, each element has an average atomic mass. The **average atomic mass** of an element is the weighted-average mass of the mixture of its isotopes. For example, four out of five atoms of boron are boron-11, and one out of five is boron-10. To find the weighted-average or the average atomic mass of boron, you would solve the following equation:

$$\frac{4}{5}(11 \text{ amu}) + \frac{1}{5}(10 \text{ amu}) = 10.8 \text{ amu}$$

The average atomic mass of the element boron is 10.8 amu. Note that the average atomic mass of boron is close to the mass of its most abundant isotope, boron-11.

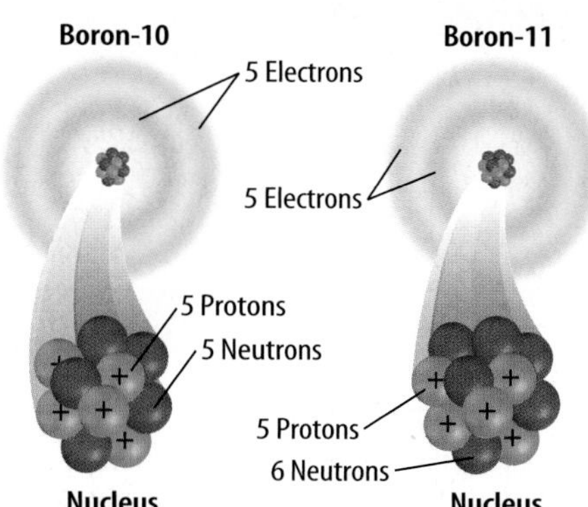

Figure 8 Boron-10 and boron-11 are two isotopes of boron. These two isotopes differ by one neutron.
Explain *why these atoms are isotopes.*

section 2 review

Summary

Atomic Mass

- The nucleus contains most of the mass of an atom.
- The mass of a proton and neutron are approximately equal.
- The mass of an electron is considered negligible when finding the mass of an atom.
- The unit of measurement for atomic particles is the atomic mass unit.
- The carbon-12 isotope was used to define the atomic mass unit.
- The number of protons identifies the element.

Isotopes

- Atoms of the same element with different numbers of neutrons are called isotopes.
- The average atomic mass of an element is the weighted-average mass of the mixture of isotopes.

Self Check

1. **Identify** the mass number and atomic number of a chlorine atom that has 17 protons and 18 neutrons.
2. **Explain** how the isotopes of an element are alike and how are they different.
3. **Explain** why the atomic mass of an element is an average mass.
4. **Explain** how you would calculate the number of neutrons in potassium-40.
5. **Think Critically** Chlorine has an average atomic mass of 35.45 amu. The two naturally occurring isotopes of chlorine are chlorine-35 and chlorine-37. Why does this indicate that most chlorine atoms contain 18 neutrons?

Applying Math

6. **Use Numbers** If a hydrogen atom has 2 neutrons and 1 proton, what is its mass number?
7. **Use Tables** Use the information in **Table 2** to find the mass in kilograms of each subatomic particle.

3 Assess

DAILY INTERVENTION

Check for Understanding

Visual-Spatial Have students use colored pencils to draw the electron cloud model for lithium. Students should include the correct number of protons and electrons. Tell students to include four neutrons in their drawing. L2

Reteach

Weighted Averages Have students calculate the weighted average of student quiz scores if the following results were obtained: 5 students scored 80%; 19 students scored 90%.

$$\left(\frac{5}{24} \times 80\right) + \left(\frac{19}{24} \times 90\right) = 88$$

L2 LS **Logical-Mathematical**

Assessment

Oral Place a small plastic container on a table. Have students count as you place colored marbles, representing protons, into the bowl. When you stop, ask them to identify the element. Then ask them to predict the number of neutrons needed for a particular isotope of that element, and add the correct number of a different color of marbles. Ask how many small cotton balls, representing electrons, you must lay around the outside of the container to make a neutral atom. Use **Performance Assessment in the Science Classroom,** p. 89. L2

section 2 review

1. Mass number = 35; atomic number = 17
2. Isotopes have the same number of protons but different numbers of neutrons.
3. Elements have several isotopes with different numbers of neutrons, and thus different masses. The average atomic mass is the weighted average of the masses of the element's isotopes.
4. Mass number − atomic number = number of neutrons = 40 − 19 = 21
5. The average of 35.45 lies closer to the 35 mass number than to the 37 mass number.
6. 3
7. proton = 1.6726×10^{-27} kg
   neutron = 1.6749×10^{-27} kg
   electron = 9.1093×10^{-31} kg

Caption Answer

Figure 8 These atoms are isotopes because they have the same number of protons, but differ in the number of neutrons.

section 3

The Periodic Table

Reading Guide

What You'll Learn

- **Explain** the composition of the periodic table.
- **Use** the periodic table to obtain information.
- **Explain** what the terms *metal, nonmetal,* and *metalloid* mean.

The periodic table is an organized list of the elements that compose all living and nonliving things that are known to exist in the universe.

Review Vocabulary

chemical property: any characteristic of a substance that indicates whether it can undergo a certain chemical change

New Vocabulary

- periodic table
- group
- electron dot diagram
- period

Figure 9 Mendeleev discovered that the elements had a periodic pattern in their chemical properties. Notice the question marks in his chart. These were elements that had not been discovered at that time.

Organizing the Elements

On a clear evening, you can see one of the various phases of the Moon. Each month, the Moon seems to grow larger, then smaller, in a repeating pattern. This type of change is periodic. *Periodic* means "repeated in a pattern." The days of the week are periodic because they repeat themselves every seven days. The calendar is a periodic table of days and months.

In the late 1800s, Dmitri Mendeleev, a Russian chemist, searched for a way to organize the elements. When he arranged all the elements known at that time in order of increasing atomic masses, he discovered a pattern. **Figure 9** shows Mendeleev's early periodic chart. Chemical properties found in lighter elements could be shown to repeat in heavier elements. Because the pattern repeated, it was considered to be periodic. Today, this arrangement is called a periodic table of elements. In the **periodic table,** the elements are arranged by increasing atomic number and by changes in physical and chemical properties.

1 Motivate

INTERACTIVE CHALKBOARD
PowerPoint® Presentations

Bellringer

Section Focus Transparencies also are available on the Interactive Chalkboard CD-ROM. L2 ELL

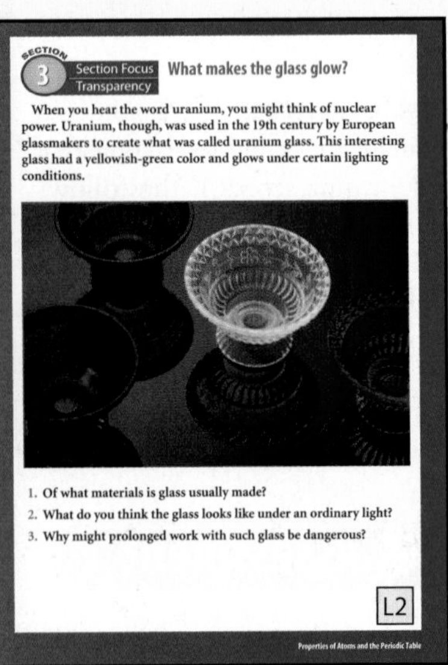

Section 3 Section Focus Transparency

What makes the glass glow?

When you hear the word uranium, you might think of nuclear power. Uranium, though, was used in the 19th century by European glassmakers to create what was called uranium glass. This interesting glass had a yellowish-green color and glows under certain lighting conditions.

1. Of what materials is glass usually made?
2. What do you think the glass looks like under an ordinary light?
3. Why might prolonged work with such glass be dangerous?

L2

Properties of Atoms and the Periodic Table

Tie to Prior Knowledge

Repeating Patterns Students are already familiar with the repeating pattern of the days of the week. Point out that just as a calendar illustrates the periodic pattern of the days of the week, the periodic table illustrates the periodic patterns of the chemical properties of chemical elements.

Section 3 Resource Manager

Chapter *FAST FILE* Resources
- Transparency Activity, p. 46
- MiniLAB, p. 4
- Lab Activity, pp. 13–15
- Directed Reading for Content Mastery, pp. 21, 22
- Enrichment, p.32
- Reinforcement, p. 29
- Lab Worksheet, pp. 5–6, 7–8

Reading and Writing Skill Activities, p. 47
Home and Community Involvement, p. 25
Cultural Diversity, p. 59

Table 4 Mendeleev's Predictions

Predicted Properties of Ekasilicon (Es)	Actual Properties of Germanium (Ge)
Existence Predicted—1871	*Actual Discovery—1886*
Atomic mass = 72	Atomic mass = 72.61
High melting point	Melting point = 938°C
Density = 5.5 g/cm^3	Density = 5.323 g/cm^3
Dark gray metal	Gray metal
Density of EsO_2 = 4.7 g/cm^3	Density of GeO_2 = 4.23 g/cm^3

Mendeleev's Predictions Mendeleev had to leave blank spaces in his periodic table to keep the elements properly lined up according to their chemical properties. He looked at the properties and atomic masses of the elements surrounding these blank spaces. From this information, he was able to predict the properties and the mass numbers of new elements that had not yet been discovered. **Table 4** shows Mendeleev's predicted properties for germanium, which he called ekasilicon. His predictions proved to be accurate. Scientists later discovered these missing elements and found that their properties were extremely close to what Mendeleev had predicted.

Reading Check *How did Mendeleev organize his periodic chart?*

Improving the Periodic Table Although Mendeleev's arrangement of elements was successful, it did need some changes. On Mendeleev's table, the atomic mass gradually increased from left to right. If you look at the modern periodic table, shown in **Table 5,** you will see several examples, such as cobalt and nickel, where the mass decreases from left to right. You also might notice that the atomic number always increases from left to right. In 1913, the work of Henry G.J. Moseley, a young English scientist, led to the arrangement of elements based on their increasing atomic numbers instead of an arrangement based on atomic masses. This new arrangement seemed to correct the problems that had occurred in the old table. The current periodic table uses Moseley's arrangement of the elements.

Reading Check *How is the modern periodic table arranged?*

Organizing a Personal Periodic Table

Procedure

1. Collect as many of the following items as you can find: **feather, penny, container of water, pencil, dime, strand of hair, container of milk, container of orange juice, square of cotton cloth, nickel, crayon, quarter, container of soda, golf ball, sheet of paper, baseball, marble, leaf, paper clip.**
2. Organize these items into several columns based on their similarities to create your own periodic table.

Analysis

1. Explain the system you used to group your items.
2. Were there any items on the list that did not fit into any of your columns?
3. Infer how your activity modeled Mendeleev's work in developing the periodic table of the elements.

Try at Home

2 Teach

Purpose Students classify objects that are very different. L2

LS **Logical-Mathematical**

Materials a variety of objects that can be sorted into several categories

Teaching Strategy A wide variety of objects will force the students to work harder to find common traits.

Analysis

1. Answers will vary but possible groups include metal objects, coins, organic items, spheres, liquids, and writing implements.
2. Answers will vary.
3. Just as Mendeleev searched for similarities and repeating patterns among the elements, students searched for commonalities among the objects to place them in groups.

Assessment

Performance Provide students with an assortment of bolts, screws, and nails. Have them build another periodic table using these items. Use **Performance Assessment in the Science Classroom,** p. 121.

Reading Check

Answer He arranged the elements by increasing atomic mass and aligned them in columns based on chemical and physical properties.

Answer by atomic number

Teacher FYI

Mendeleev's Predictions Mendeleev predicted several elements in addition to ekasilicon. These included successful predictions of ekaaluminum and ekaboron, which were later found to be gallium and scandium, and unsuccessful predictions of ekaniobium and ekacesium, which do not exist. The prefix *eka* is Sanskrit for the numeral one.

Teacher FYI

Nonmetallic The elements have an increasing nonmetallic characteristic as you read from left to right across the table. Along the stair-step line are metalloids, which have properties of both metals and nonmetals.

Use an Analogy

Orderly Classification Remind students that orderly classification allows them to enter a music store and quickly find a desired selection without examining every CD in the store. The periodic table gives chemists the same advantage when they are looking for elements with particular properties.

Fun Fact

Hydrogen, by its electron arrangement, is part of Group 1. However, because it has only one electron in an energy level that can hold two electrons, it has its own unique set of properties.

Activity

Atomic Mass Chart Have students list the elements in the first six periods that would be out of sequence if the chart were arranged by atomic mass. Ar and K, Co and Ni, Te and I L2 LS **Logical-Mathematical**

Visual Learning

Periodic Table Which element has an average mass greater than 75 but less than 79? selenium Is it possible to have more than one element that could fit that restriction? No; based on average masses, there are no missing atomic numbers from 33 to 34 to 35.

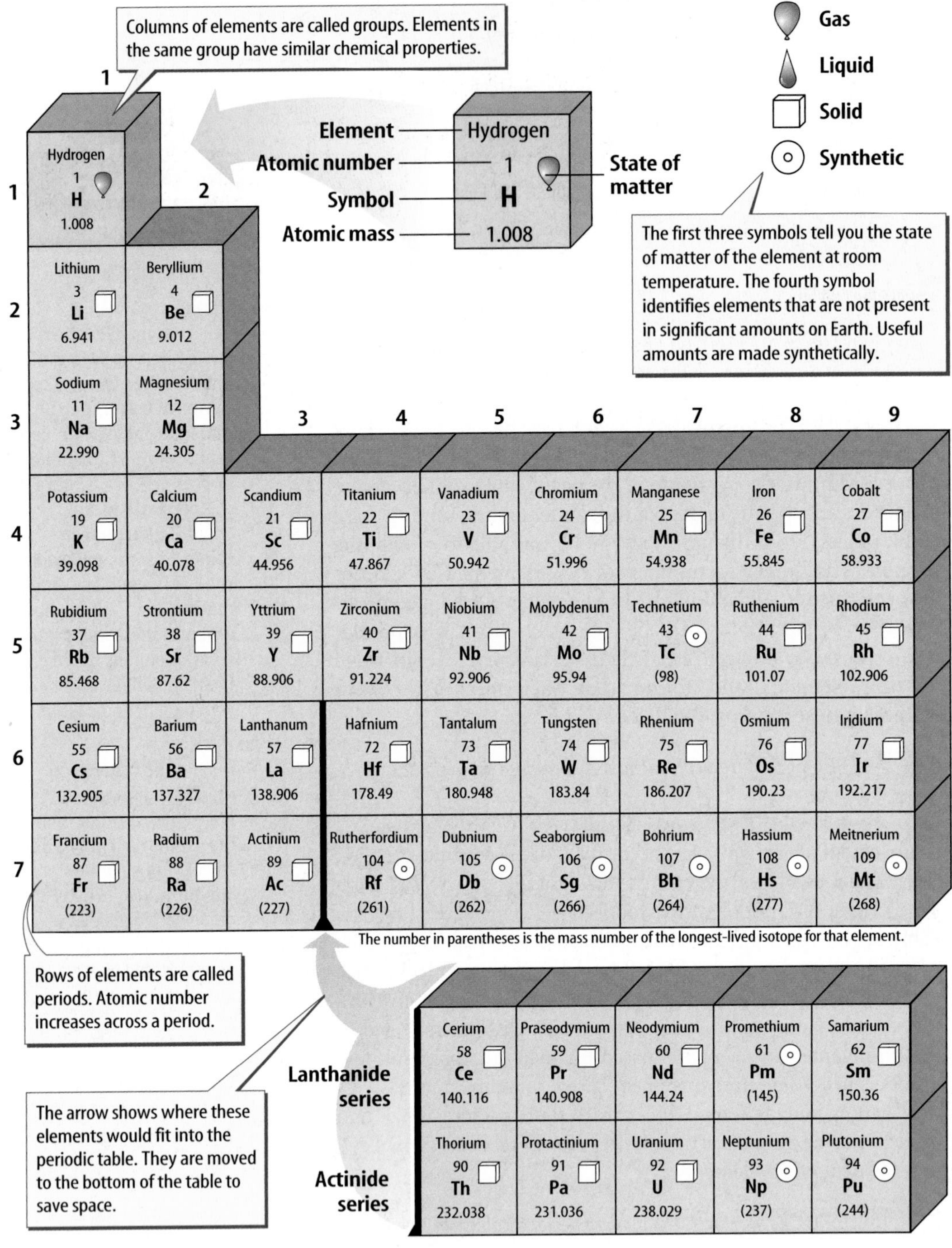

Curriculum Connection

Music In music, the syllables *do*, *re*, *mi*, *fa*, *sol*, *la*, *ti*, *do* give the pitches of the diatonic scale. Have students find out how this scale is similar to the periodic table. The scale *do, re, mi, fa, sol, la, ti, do* can be related to Li, Be, B, C, N, O, F, and Na in the periodic table. Na repeats the properties of Li just as the second *do* is one octave higher than the first *do*. L2 LS **Auditory-Musical**

518 CHAPTER 17 Properties of Atoms and the Periodic Table

Metal

Metalloid

Nonmetal

The color of an element's block tells you if the element is a metal, nonmetal, or metalloid.

Science Online

Topic: Periodic Table Updates

Visit gpscience.com for updates to the periodic table.

10	11	12	13	14	15	16	17	18
								Helium 2 **He** 4.003
			Boron 5 **B** 10.811	Carbon 6 **C** 12.011	Nitrogen 7 **N** 14.007	Oxygen 8 **O** 15.999	Fluorine 9 **F** 18.998	Neon 10 **Ne** 20.180
			Aluminum 13 **Al** 26.982	Silicon 14 **Si** 28.086	Phosphorus 15 **P** 30.974	Sulfur 16 **S** 32.065	Chlorine 17 **Cl** 35.453	Argon 18 **Ar** 39.948
Nickel 28 **Ni** 58.693	Copper 29 **Cu** 63.546	Zinc 30 **Zn** 65.409	Gallium 31 **Ga** 69.723	Germanium 32 **Ge** 72.64	Arsenic 33 **As** 74.922	Selenium 34 **Se** 78.96	Bromine 35 **Br** 79.904	Krypton 36 **Kr** 83.798
Palladium 46 **Pd** 106.42	Silver 47 **Ag** 107.868	Cadmium 48 **Cd** 112.411	Indium 49 **In** 114.818	Tin 50 **Sn** 118.710	Antimony 51 **Sb** 121.760	Tellurium 52 **Te** 127.60	Iodine 53 **I** 126.904	Xenon 54 **Xe** 131.293
Platinum 78 **Pt** 195.078	Gold 79 **Au** 196.967	Mercury 80 **Hg** 200.59	Thallium 81 **Tl** 204.383	Lead 82 **Pb** 207.2	Bismuth 83 **Bi** 208.980	Polonium 84 **Po** (209)	Astatine 85 **At** (210)	Radon 86 **Rn** (222)
Darmstadtium 110 **Ds** (281)	Roentgenium 111 **Rg** (272)	Ununbium * 112 **Uub** (285)		Ununquadium * 114 **Uuq** (289)				

* The names and symbols for elements 112 and 114 are temporary. Final names will be selected when the elements' discoveries are verified.

Europium 63 **Eu** 151.964	Gadolinium 64 **Gd** 157.25	Terbium 65 **Tb** 158.925	Dysprosium 66 **Dy** 162.500	Holmium 67 **Ho** 164.930	Erbium 68 **Er** 167.259	Thulium 69 **Tm** 168.934	Ytterbium 70 **Yb** 173.04	Lutetium 71 **Lu** 174.967
Americium 95 **Am** (243)	Curium 96 **Cm** (247)	Berkelium 97 **Bk** (247)	Californium 98 **Cf** (251)	Einsteinium 99 **Es** (252)	Fermium 100 **Fm** (257)	Mendelevium 101 **Md** (258)	Nobelium 102 **No** (259)	Lawrencium 103 **Lr** (262)

IDENTIFYING Misconceptions

A Disadvantage Mendeleev did not have the advantage of knowing atomic structure when he made his periodic chart. Electrons were not discovered until the late 1890s. His chart was based on mass and properties of the elements.

Differentiated Instruction

Challenge The chemical symbols for the following elements are not abbreviations of their English names. Have students use reference books to determine the symbols for the following elements and the names upon which the symbols are based: copper (Cu, cuprum); gold (Au, aurum); iron (Fe, ferrum); lead (Pb, plumbum); tin (Sn, stannum); mercury (Hg, hydrargyrum); silver (Ag, argentum); sodium (Na, natrium); potassium (K, kalium); antimony (Sb, stibium); tungsten (W, wolfram). Have students present their research results to their class. L3 LS **Linguistic**

LAB DEMONSTRATION

Purpose to choose a criterion for arranging items

Materials 5 clear plastic cups, water, blue food coloring

Preparation Add an equal amount of water to each cup. Add 1 drop of food coloring to cup 1, 2 drops to cup 2, and so on. Make one with $3\frac{1}{2}$ drops and put it aside.

Procedure Mix the order of the cups and display them. Have students place the cups in a sequence. Display the solution made with $3\frac{1}{2}$ drops of food coloring and ask them to place it in its proper location.

Expected Outcome The sequence may be from diluted to concentrated or the opposite.

Assessment

How does this activity demonstrate the thinking Mendeleev used for his chart? He made a sequence of chemical elements based on their properties and could tell where new discoveries fit in. L2

SECTION 3 The Periodic Table 519

Research Physicist The amount of energy an electron contains determines its behavior. Physicists can apply this knowledge to the fields of nuclear energy, electronics, optics, and communications.

Research Have students research who employs research physicists and what the future job outlook statistics are for this career.

Visual Learning

Figure 10 Point out to students that this diagram is not intended to represent relative sizes of the electrons, atom, or nucleus.

Differentiated Instruction

Challenge Each energy level contains sublevels, which in turn contain atomic orbitals. Have students find out more about the distribution of electrons in sublevels and atomic orbitals. Have students make a chart showing the information found about sublevels. The first energy level has only one sublevel, while the second level has two sublevels, and the third has three. The first sublevel in any level contains one *s* orbital, which can contain up to two electrons. The second sublevel in any level contains three *p* orbitals. Each *p* orbital can contain up to two electrons, so this sublevel can contain a maximum of six electrons. The third sublevel contains five *d* orbitals, each of which can contain up to two electrons, so this sublevel can contain up to ten electrons. The fourth sublevel contains seven *f* orbitals, each of which can contain up to two electrons, so this sublevel can contain up to fourteen electrons. L3

LS **Linguistic** P

Research Physicist The study of nuclear interactions is shared by chemists and physicists. Research physicists use their knowledge of the physical laws of nature to explain the behavior of the atom and its composition. Explain in your Science Journal why physicists would study the amount of energy that electrons contain.

The Atom and the Periodic Table

Objects often are sorted or grouped according to the properties they have in common. This also is done in the periodic table. The vertical columns in the periodic table are called **groups,** or families, and are numbered 1 through 18. Elements in each group have similar properties. For example, in Group 11, copper, silver, and gold have similar properties. Each is a shiny metal and a good conductor of electricity and heat. What is responsible for the similar properties? To answer this question, look at the structure of the atom.

Electron Cloud Structure You have learned about the number and location of protons and neutrons in an atom. But where are the electrons located? How many are there? In a neutral atom, the number of electrons is equal to the number of protons. Therefore, a carbon atom, with an atomic number of six, has six protons and six electrons. These electrons are located in the electron cloud surrounding the nucleus.

Scientists have found that electrons within the electron cloud have different amounts of energy. Scientists model the energy differences of the electrons by placing the electrons in energy levels, as in **Figure 10.** Energy levels nearer the nucleus have lower energy than those levels that are farther away. Electrons fill these energy levels from the inner levels (closer to the nucleus) to the outer levels (farther from the nucleus).

Elements that are in the same group have the same number of electrons in their outer energy level. It is the number of electrons in the outer energy level that determines the chemical properties of the element. It is important to understand the link between the location on the periodic table, chemical properties, and the structure of the atom.

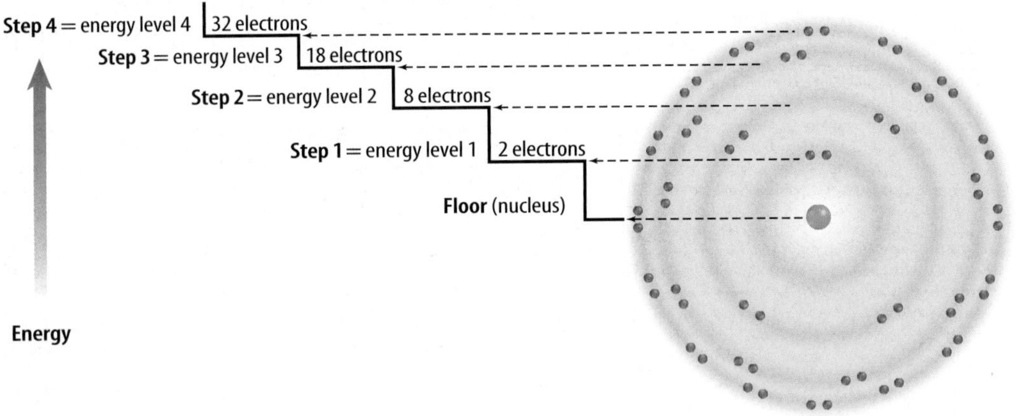

Figure 10 Energy levels in atoms can be represented by a flight of stairs. Each stair step away from the nucleus represents an increase in the amount of energy within the electrons. The higher energy levels contain more electrons.

Cultural Diversity

Culturally Diverse Elements Have students make a list of elements that are named after countries or cities. magnesium—Magnesia; scandium—Scandinavia; germanium—Germany; yttrium, ytterbium, terbium—town of Ytterby in Sweden; hafnium—Copenhagen; holmium—Stockholm; ruthenium—Russia; polonium—Poland; strontium—Strontian (Scotland); lutetium—Paris L3

Energy Levels These energy levels are named using numbers one to seven. The maximum number of electrons that can be contained in each of the first four levels is shown in **Figure 10.** For example, energy level one can contain a maximum of two electrons. Energy level two can contain a maximum of eight electrons. Notice that energy levels three and four contain several electrons. A complete and stable outer energy level will contain eight electrons. In elements in periods three and higher, additional electrons can be added to inner energy levels although the outer energy level contains only eight electrons.

Rows on the Table Remember that the atomic number found on the periodic table is equal to the number of electrons in an atom. Look at **Figure 11.** The first row has hydrogen with one electron and helium with two electrons both in energy level one. Because energy level one is the outermost level containing an electron, hydrogen has one outer electron. Helium has two outer electrons. Recall from **Figure 10** that energy level one can hold only two electrons. Therefore, helium has a full or complete outer energy level.

The second row begins with lithium, which has three electrons—two in energy level one and one in energy level two. Lithium has one outer electron. Lithium is followed by beryllium with two outer electrons, boron with three, and so on until you reach neon with eight outer electrons. Again, looking at **Figure 10,** energy level two can only hold eight electrons. Therefore, neon has a complete outer energy level. Do you notice how the row in the periodic table ends when an outer energy level is filled? In the third row of elements, the electrons begin filling energy level three. The row ends with argon, which has a full outer energy level of eight electrons.

Reading Check *How many electrons are needed to fill the outer energy level of sulfur?*

Science Online

Topic: Atomic Energy Level Structure

Visit gpscience.com for Web links to information about the structure of atomic energy levels.

Activity Draw a diagram that details how the energy levels are structured.

Hydrogen 1 **H**							Helium 2 **He**
Lithium 3 **Li**	Beryllium 4 **Be**	Boron 5 **B**	Carbon 6 **C**	Nitrogen 7 **N**	Oxygen 8 **O**	Fluorine 9 **F**	Neon 10 **Ne**
Sodium 11 **Na**	Magnesium 12 **Mg**	Aluminum 13 **Al**	Silicon 14 **Si**	Phosphorus 15 **P**	Sulfur 16 **S**	Chlorine 17 **Cl**	Argon 18 **Ar**

Figure 11 One proton and one electron are added to each element as you go across a period in the periodic table.
Explain *what the elements in the last column share in relation to their outer energy levels.*

Fun Fact

The maximum number of electrons in a level is $2n^2$, where n is the level number. For example, when $n = 3$ there can be a maximum of $2(3^2) = 18$ electrons.

Discussion

Row Questions In which row do you find the metalloid germanium? fourth row Which row contains the fewest elements? first row Which row probably contains the largest atoms on the periodic table? seventh row L2

LS **Visual-Spatial**

IDENTIFYING Misconceptions

Lanthenides and Actinides Students may be confused by the depiction of the last two rows of the periodic table below the rest of the table. These two rows, called the lanthanides and actinides, respectively, are shown below to allow the table to be displayed in a manner that is easy to read.

Caption Answer

Figure 11 Each element in the last column has a full outer-energy level.

Answer two additional electrons

Differentiated Instruction

Learning Disabled Obtain samples of several elements, such as tin, copper, sulfur, silver, and aluminum. Have students examine and record the characteristics of each element. They should look for such properties as color, hardness, texture, and brittleness. They can play a game in which one student lists the characteristics and another identifies the element. L1

Activity

Energy Levels With a periodic table prominently displayed, or while students look at the one in the text, select various elements by name and atomic number. Have students determine the correct number of outer level electrons and write the dot diagram on the board. Do not use the elements from Groups 3–12 for this activity. These groups, called the transition elements, have their new electrons added to a lower energy level. L2

LS **Visual-Spatial**

Use an Analogy

Wearing a Hat Remind students that when atoms gain or lose electrons, they become charged, negatively if they gain electrons and positively if they lose electrons, but the atoms retain their identity because the number of protons in the nucleus remains the same. This is analogous to the way a person can wear a hat and easily take it off without losing his or her identity. L2

Fun Fact

The elements in Group 18, known as the noble gases, had no recognized compounds until 1962 when xenon and fluorine were combined. Since then, other noble gas compounds have been formed. As recently as 2000, argon was found to combine. These are rare cases. In nature, noble gases are found uncombined.

Reading Check

Answer All members of a group have the same number of electrons in their outer energy level.

Figure 12 The elements in Group 1 have one electron in their outer energy level. This electron dot diagram represents that one electron.

H•

Li•

Na•

K•

Rb•

Cs•

Fr•

Electron Dot Diagrams Did you notice that hydrogen, lithium, and sodium have one electron in their outer energy level? Elements that are in the same group have the same number of electrons in their outer energy level. These outer electrons are so important in determining the chemical properties of an element that a special way to represent them has been developed. American chemist G. N. Lewis created this method while teaching a college chemistry class. An **electron dot diagram** uses the symbol of the element and dots to represent the electrons in the outer energy level. **Figure 12** shows the electron dot diagram for Group 1 elements. Electron dot diagrams are used also to show how the electrons in the outer energy level are bonded when elements combine to form compounds.

Same Group—Similar Properties The elements in Group 17, the halogens, have electron dot diagrams similar to chlorine, shown in **Figure 13.** All halogens have seven electrons in their outer energy levels. Since all of the members of a group on the periodic table have the same number of electrons in their outer energy level, group members will undergo chemical reactions in similar ways.

A common property of the halogens is the ability to form compounds readily with elements in Group 1. Group 1 elements have only one electron in their outer energy level. **Figure 13** shows an example of a compound formed by one such reaction. The Group 1 element, sodium, reacts easily with the Group 17 element, chlorine. The result is the compound sodium chloride, or NaCl—ordinary table salt.

Not all elements will combine readily with other elements. The elements in Group 18 have complete outer energy levels. This special configuration makes Group 18 elements relatively unreactive. You will learn more about why and how bonds form between elements in the later chapters.

Reading Check *Why do elements in a group undergo similar chemical reactions?*

Figure 13 Electron dot diagrams show the electrons in an element's outer energy level.

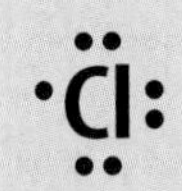

The electron dot diagram for Group 17 consists of three sets of paired dots and one single dot.

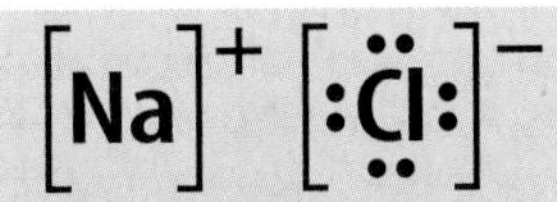

Sodium combines with chlorine to give each element a complete outer energy level in the resulting compound.

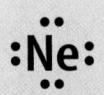

Neon, a member of Group 18, has a full outer energy level. Neon has eight electrons in its outer energy level, making it unreactive.

Active Reading

Jigsaw In this collaborative learning technique, individuals become experts on a portion of a text and share their expertise with a small group, called their home group. Everyone shares responsibility for learning the assigned reading. Assign each person in each home group an expert number. Have students gather into the expert groups that correspond to the numbers they were assigned. Have them read, discuss, and master chapter concepts and determine how best to teach them to their home groups. Have students return to their home groups and share the content they learned in their expert groups. Have students use this strategy to help them learn about the characteristics of elements and how they are grouped on the periodic table. L2

522 CHAPTER 17 Properties of Atoms and the Periodic Table

Regions on the Periodic Table

The periodic table has several regions with specific names. The horizontal rows of elements on the periodic table are called **periods.** The elements increase by one proton and one electron as you go from left to right in a period.

All of the elements in the blue squares in **Figure 14** are metals. Iron, zinc, and copper are examples of metals. Most metals exist as solids at room temperature. They are shiny, can be drawn into wires, can be pounded into sheets, and are good conductors of heat and electricity.

Those elements on the right side of the periodic table, in yellow, are classified as nonmetals. Oxygen, bromine, and carbon are examples of nonmetals. Most nonmetals are gases, are brittle, and are poor conductors of heat and electricity at room temperature. The elements in green are metalloids or semimetals. They have some properties of both metals and nonmetals. Boron and silicon are examples of metalloids.

Reading Check *What are the properties of the elements located on the left side of the periodic table?*

A Growing Family Scientists around the world are continuing their research into the synthesis of elements. In 1994, scientists at the Heavy-Ion Research Laboratory in Darmstadt, Germany, discovered element 111. As of 1998, only one isotope of element 111 has been found. This isotope had a life span of 0.002 s. In 1996, element 112 was discovered at the same laboratory. As of 1998, only one isotope of element 112 has been found. The life span of this isotope was 0.00048 s. Both of these elements are produced in the laboratory by joining smaller atoms into a single atom. The search for elements with higher atomic numbers continues. Scientists think they have synthesized elements 114 and 116. However, the discovery of these elements has not yet been confirmed.

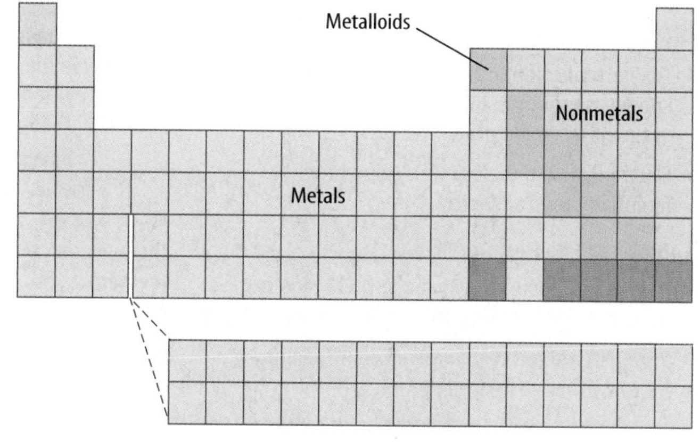

Figure 14 Metalloids are located along the green stair-step line. Metals are located to the left of the metalloids. Nonmetals are located to the right of the metalloids.

Science Online
Topic: New Elements
Visit gpscience.com for Web links to information about newly synthesized elements.

Activity Write a paragraph explaining how several new elements were synthesized and who synthesized them.

Reading Check

Answer The elements on the left side of the table are metals, which are solids at room temperature, shiny, and good conductors of heat and electricity. Hydrogen is an exception to these properties.

Virtual Labs

Periodic Table *How is the structure of an atom related to its position on the periodic table?*

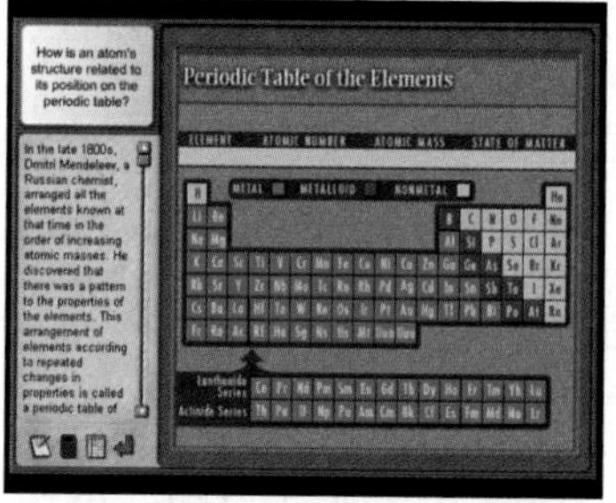

Inquiry Lab

Purpose to explore compounds that may form between elements

Possible Materials index cards or paper and markers

Estimated Time one class session

Teaching Strategies

- Students make cards with electron dot diagrams for elements in groups 1–2 and 13–17.
- Students will need more than one card for some elements.
- Students can predict compounds that will form between the elements using electron dot diagrams.
- Have students make a list of the compounds that may form.

For additional inquiry activities, see *Science Inquiry Labs.*

Fun Fact

As a general rule, elements with three or fewer electrons in the outer energy level are considered to be metals, and elements with five or more electrons in the outer energy level are considered to be nonmetals.

Science Journal

New Elements Have students research and identify the newest synthesized element. Have them write in their Science Journals the element's name, atomic number, isotope, half-life, and where the element was discovered. L2 IS **Linguistic**

3 Assess

DAILY INTERVENTION

Check for Understanding

Visual-Spatial Have students draw a generic dot diagram for elements in Groups 1, 2, and 13-18. L2

Reteach

Classifying Elements Using a poster-sized periodic table, point to various elements and ask students to identify the group number and period number of each element and classify it as a metal, nonmetal, or metalloid. L2 LS **Visual-Spatial**

Assessment

Performance Gather pens and pencils from the class and have students suggest ways to group them that place similar ones together. Then have students arrange the pens and pencils by approximate mass in a pencil-pen periodic table. Give students a new pen or pencil and ask them to decide where to place it in the table. How is this similar to Mendeleev's activities? He arranged chemical elements by mass and by properties and could predict and classify new elements. Use **Performance Assessment in the Science Classroom,** p. 121. L2

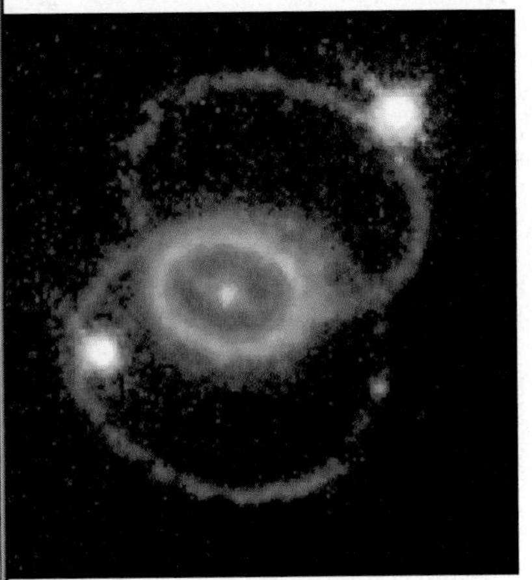

Figure 15 Scientists think that some elements are found in nature only within stars.

Elements in the Universe

INTEGRATE Astronomy Using the technology that is available today, scientists are finding the same elements throughout the universe. They have been able to study only a small portion of the universe, though, because it is so vast. Many scientists believe that hydrogen and helium are the building blocks of other elements. Atoms join together within stars to produce elements with atomic numbers greater than 1 or 2—the atomic numbers of hydrogen and helium. Exploding stars, or supernovas, shown in **Figure 15,** give scientists evidence to support this theory. When stars go supernova a mixture of elements, including the heavy elements such as iron, are flung into the galaxy. Many scientists believe that supernovas have spread the elements that are found throughout the universe. Promethium, technetium, and elements with an atomic number above 92 are rare or are not found on Earth. Some of these elements are found only in trace amounts in Earth's crust as a result of uranium decay. Others have been found only in stars.

section 3 review

Summary

Organizing the Elements

- Mendeleev organized the elements using increasing atomic mass and chemical and physical properties.
- Mendeleev left blank spaces in his table to allow for elements that were yet undiscovered.
- Moseley corrected the problems in the periodic table by arranging the elements in order of increasing atomic number.

The Atom and the Periodic Table

- The vertical columns in the periodic table are known as groups or families. Elements in a group have similar properties.
- Electrons within the electron cloud have different amounts of energy.

Regions of the Periodic Table

- The periodic table is divided into these regions: periods, metals, nonmetals, and metalloids.
- Scientists around the world are continuing to try to synthesize new elements.

Self Check

1. **Identify** Use the periodic table to find the name, atomic number, and average atomic mass of the following elements: N, Ca, Kr, and W.
2. **List** the period and group in which each of these elements is found: nitrogen, sodium, iodine, and mercury.
3. **Classify** each of these elements as a metal, a nonmetal, or a metalloid and give the full name of each: K, Si, Ba, and S.
4. **Think Critically** The Mendeleev and Mosely periodic charts have gaps for the as-then-undiscovered elements. Why do you think the chart used by Mosely was more accurate at predicting where new elements would be placed?

Applying Math

5. **Make a Graph** Construct a circle graph showing the percentage of elements classified as metals, metalloids, and nonmetals. Use markers or colored pencils to distinguish clearly between each section on the graph. Record your calculations in your Science Journal.

Science Online gpscience.com/self_check_quiz

section 3 review

1. N, nitrogen, 7,14.007; Ca ,calcium; 20, 40.078; Kr, krypton, 36, 83.798; W, tungsten, 74, 183.84
2. nitrogen, period 2, Group 15; sodium, period 3, Group 1; iodine, period 5, Group 17; mercury, period 6, Group 12
3. K, potassium, metal; Si, silicon, metalloid; Ba, barium, metal; S, sulfur, nonmetal
4. One could not be certain that the gaps in Mendeleev's chart would be filled by only one element. However, Moseley's chart was arranged by number of protons. Therefore, if the gap were between two elements differing by two protons, only one element could fit.
5. The graph should indicate that about 79% of the elements are metals; about 7% are metalloids, and about 14% are nonmetals.

A Periodic Table of Foods

Real-World Question

Mendeleev's task of organizing a collection of loosely related items probably seemed daunting at first. How will using your favorite foods to create your own periodic table be similar to the task that Mendeleev had?

Goals

- **Organize** 20 of your favorite foods into a periodic table of foods.
- **Analyze** and **evaluate** your periodic table for similar characteristics among groups or family members on your table.
- **Infer** where new foods added to your table would be placed.

Materials

11 × 17 paper
12- or 18-inch ruler
colored pencils or markers

Procedure

1. **List** 20 of your favorite foods and drinks.
2. **Describe** basic characteristics of each of your food and drink items. For example, you might describe the primary ingredient, nutritional value, taste, and color of each item. You also could identify the food group of each item such as fruits/vegetables, grains, dairy products, meat, and sweets.
3. **Create** a data table to organize the information that you collect.
4. Using your data table, construct a periodic table of foods on your 11 × 17 sheet of paper. Determine which characteristics you will use to group your items. Create families (columns) of food and drink items that share similar characteristics on your table.

For example, potato chips, pretzels, and cheese-flavored crackers could be combined into a family of salty tasting foods. Create as many groups as you need, and you do not need to have the same number of items in every family.

Conclude and Apply

1. **Evaluate** the characteristics you used to make the groups on your periodic table. Do the characteristics of each group adequately describe all the family members? Do the characteristics of each group distinguish its family members from the family members of the other groups?
2. **Analyze** the reasons why some items did not fit easily into a group.
3. **Infer** why chemists have not created a periodic table of compounds.

Communicating Your Data

Construct a bulletin board of the periodic tables of foods created by the class. How are the tables similar?

BENCH TESTED

Real-World Question

Purpose Students create a periodic table to organize foods. L2
LS **Logical-Mathematical**

Process Skills classify, compare and contrast, sequence, make and use tables

Procedure

Time Required 30 minutes

Teaching Strategies Have references available from which students can find the nutritional content of foods, such as fruits, that have no labels.

Conclude and Apply

1. Answers will vary, but food items containing several major ingredients such as pizza or ice cream cones often present classification problems.
2. Individual foods such as mangos or tuna are easily grouped into the major food groups, but when food ingredients are combined into items such as cakes or soups, classification becomes difficult.
3. There are about 115 elements, many with common characteristics. There are millions of compounds, which makes a table of compounds impractical to construct and apply.

Assessment

Process Have students repeat the activity using only unprocessed foods. Does this make it easier or more difficult to divide foods into families? Use **Performance Assessment in the Science Classroom,** p. 121.

Communicating Your Data

Students may want to use a spreadsheet program to determine the layout of the class periodic table of foods for the bulletin board.

Real-World Question

Internet Students use Internet sites that can be accessed at gpscience.com/internet_lab. Students can post their findings on the site and get information from other schools around the country.

Non-Internet Sources In its entry for an element, an encyclopedia often will give the history of the discovery and naming of that element. Find books about the history of science, including biographies of famous scientists and descriptions of important discoveries and inventions.

Time Required about two days

Make a Plan

Preparation

Internet To run through the steps that the students will follow, visit gpscience.com/internet_lab.

Non-Internet Sources Bring to class books on the history of chemistry and the history of science that describe how elements were discovered and named.

Use the Internet

What's in a name?

Goals

- **Research** the names and symbols of various elements.
- **Study** the methods that are used to name elements and how they have changed through time.
- **Organize** your data by making your own periodic table.
- **Study** the history of certain elements and their discoveries.
- **Create** a table of your findings and communicate them to other students.

Data Source

Science Online

Visit gpscience.com/internet_lab for more information on naming elements, elements' symbols, and the discovery of new elements, and for data from other students.

Real-World Question

The symbols used for different elements sometimes are easy to figure out. After all, it makes sense for the symbol for carbon to be C and the symbol for nitrogen to be N. However, some symbols aren't as easy to figure out. For example, the element silver has the symbol Ag. This symbol comes from the Latin word for silver, *Argentum.* How are symbols and names chosen for elements?

Make a Plan

1. Make a list of particular elements you wish to study.
2. **Compare and contrast** these elements' names to their symbols.
3. **Research** the discovery of these elements. Do their names match their symbols? Were they named after a property of the element, a person, their place of discovery, or a system of nomenclature? What was that system?

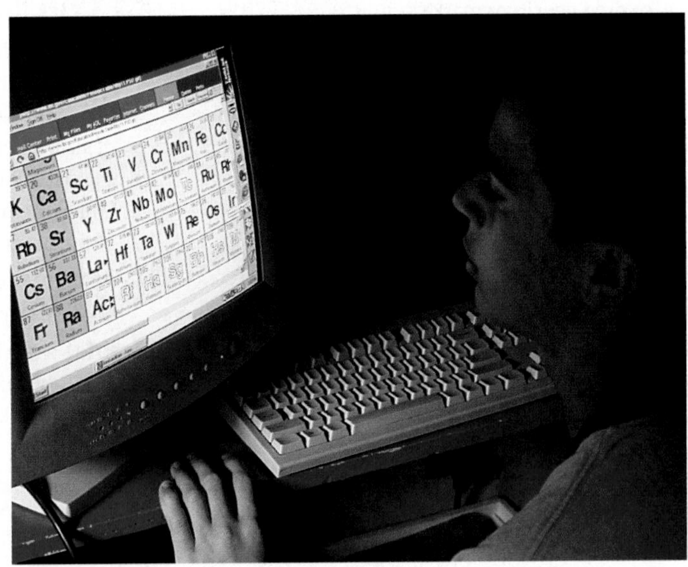

Alternative Inquiry Lab

Real-World Connection To make this Lab an Inquiry Lab, give the students more personal investment into the problem by connecting it to the real world. Tell the students that they must devise a system for naming new elements that are discovered. Have them devise a naming system that can be used by scientists world wide. After students have devised their system, have them compare and contrast their system to the system devised by the International Union of Pure and Applied Chemistry. L2

Follow Your Plan

1. Make sure your teacher approves your plan before you start.
2. Visit the Web site provided for links to different sites about elements, their history, and how they were named.
3. **Research** these elements.
4. Carefully record your data in your Science Journal.

Analyze Your Data

1. **Record** in your Science Journal how the symbols for your elements were chosen. What were your elements named after?
2. Make a periodic table that includes the research information on your elements that you found.
3. Make a chart of your class's findings. Sort the chart by year of discovery for each element.
4. How are the names and symbols for newly discovered elements chosen? Make a chart that shows how the newly discovered elements will be named.

Conclude and Apply

1. **Compare** your findings to those of your classmates. Did anyone's data differ for the same element? Were all the elements in the periodic table covered?
2. **Explain** the system that is used to name the newly discovered elements today.
3. **Explain** Some elements were assigned symbols based on their name in another language. Do these examples occur for elements discovered today or long ago?

Communicating Your Data

Find this lab using the link below. Post your data in the table provided. **Compare** your data to those of other students. Combine your data with those of other students to complete your periodic table with all of the elements.

gpscience.com/internet_lab

Follow Your Plan

Teaching Strategies

- Suggest that students include in their lists of elements to study some elements discovered long ago and some elements discovered more recently.
- Suggest that each student study at least ten elements.
- Have books on Greek and Roman mythology available so students can learn more about the characters from these myths for whom some of the elements are named.

Analyze Your Data

1. Students should report how the names and symbols of the elements were determined.
2. The student's periodic table should resemble the periodic table of the elements.
3. Answers will vary.
4. Different scientific organizations have created naming recommendations for newly discovered elements.

Conclude and Apply

1. Student data for the same element should not differ. Have students write their names next to the elements they researched to see if all the elements were investigated.
2. The International Union of Pure and Applied Chemistry has specific recommendations for giving names and symbols to newly-discovered elements.
3. elements discovered long ago

Communicating Your Data

Students can build an interactive periodic table of the elements. Have them use the computer and a Web page development program to display the periodic table. Suggest they design the table so that when an element is clicked, the computer will display information about the origin of the name and symbol for that element.

Assessment

Portfolio Ask students to prepare written reports of their findings about the way elements were named hundreds of years ago and the way they are named today. Have them include in their reports their original hypotheses and discussions of how the information they found proved or disproved their hypotheses. Use **Performance Assessment in the Science Classroom**, p. 157. P

TIME

Content Background

Air trapped in ice cores contains traces of whatever the lower atmosphere contained at the time the ice formed. Large increases in the concentration of sulfates indicate volcanic activity. Changes in types of pollen provide clues to general trends in temperature.

Discussion

Finding Clues Why do we know more about what caused the Greenland colony to vanish today than the people who discovered the colonists missing? Possible answer: The scientific knowledge and technology to extract and analyze ice cores did not exist until very recently. L2

Historical Significance

Climate change is not a relic of the past, but a continuing cyclical process. Obtain for the class a cross sectional slab of tree trunk or a large photo of one. The tree should be approximately three feet in diameter. Make sure you know where the tree grew and when. Have students determine how long the tree lived by counting the rings and then determine where and when it lived. With this knowledge, students can research local temperatures over the lifespan of the tree and plot them using small flags on pins placed at the appropriate rings. Discuss with students the relation between ring size and temperature. Discuss any anomalous variations in ring size and other possible environmental conditions that may have been responsible for them.

TIME SCIENCE AND HISTORY

SCIENCE CAN CHANGE THE COURSE OF HISTORY!

A CHILLING STORY

A scientist inspects an ice core sample from the Greenland Ice Sheet. The samples are stored in a freezer at −36°C.

Picture this: It's 1361. A ship from Norway arrives at a Norwegian settlement in Greenland. The ship's crew hopes to trade its cargo with the people living there. The crew gets off the ship. They look around. The settlement is deserted. More than 1,000 people had vanished!

New evidence has shed some light on the mysterious disappearance of the Norse settlers. The evidence came from a place on the Greenland Ice Sheet over 600 km away from the settlement. This part of Greenland is so cold that snow never melts. As new snow falls, the existing snow is buried and turns to ice. By drilling deep into this ice, scientists can recover an ice core.

Air bubbles and dirt trapped in ice provide clues to Earth's past climate.

The core is made up of ice formed from snowfalls going way, way back in time.

By measuring the ratio of oxygen isotopes in the ice core, scientists can estimate Greenland's past air temperatures. The cores provide a detailed climate history going back over 80,000 years. Individual ice layers can be dated much like tree rings to determine their age, and the air bubbles trapped within each layer are used to learn about climate variations. Dust and pollen trapped in the ice also yield clues to ancient climates.

A Little Ice Age

Based on their analysis, scientists think the Norse moved to Greenland during an unusually warm period. Then in the 1300s, the climate started to cool and a period known as the Little Ice Age began. The ways the Norse hunted and farmed were inadequate for survival in this long chill. Since they couldn't adapt to their colder surroundings, the settlers died out.

Research Report Evidence seems to show that Earth is warming. Rising temperatures could affect our lives. Research global warming to find out how Earth may change. Share your report with the class.

For more information, visit gpscience.com/time

Research Report Research periods of glaciation over the history of Earth and discuss the cycles in light of present climate conditions. You might want to construct a timeline for students showing Earth's average temperatures at different points in time and the percentage of Earth's surface covered with ice at those times. L2

Resources for Teachers and Students

U.S. National Ice Core Laboratory, United States Geological Survey, MS-975, Box 25046, DFC, Denver, CO 80225

"Core Values. (Samplings)." *Natural History*, March, 2003

Reviewing Main Ideas

Section 1 Structure of the Atom

1. A chemical symbol is a shorthand way of writing the name of an element.
2. An atom consists of a nucleus made of protons and neutrons surrounded by an electron cloud as shown in the figure to the right.

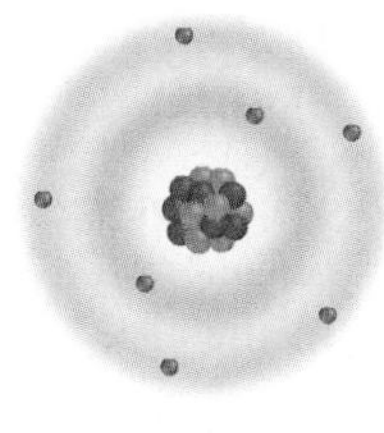

3. Quarks are particles of matter that make up protons and neutrons.
4. The model of the atom changes over time. As new information is discovered, scientists incorporate it into the model.

Section 2 Masses of Atoms

1. The number of neutrons in an atom can be computed by subtracting the atomic number from the mass number.
2. The isotopes of an element are atoms of that same element that have different numbers of neutrons. The figure below shows the isotopes of hydrogen.

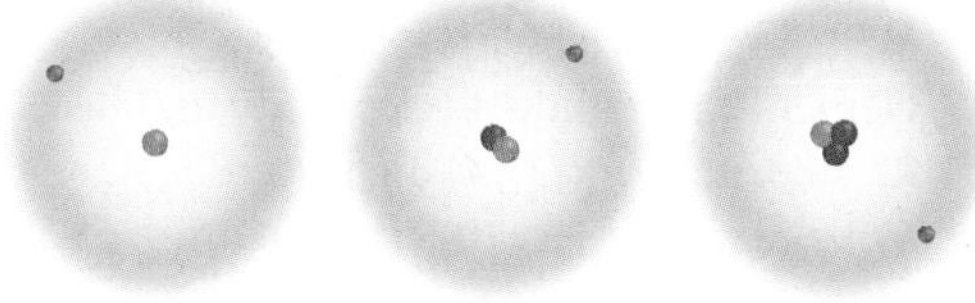

3. The average atomic mass of an element is the weighted-average mass of the mixture of its isotopes. Isotopes are named by using the element name, followed by a dash, and its mass number.

Section 3 The Periodic Table

1. In the periodic table, the elements are arranged by increasing atomic number resulting in periodic changes in properties. Knowing that the number of protons, electrons, and atomic number are equal gives you partial composition of the atom.
2. In the periodic table, the elements are arranged in 18 vertical columns, or groups, and seven horizontal rows, or periods.
3. Metals are found at the left of the periodic table, nonmetals at the right, and metalloids along the line that separates the metals from the nonmetals as shown below.

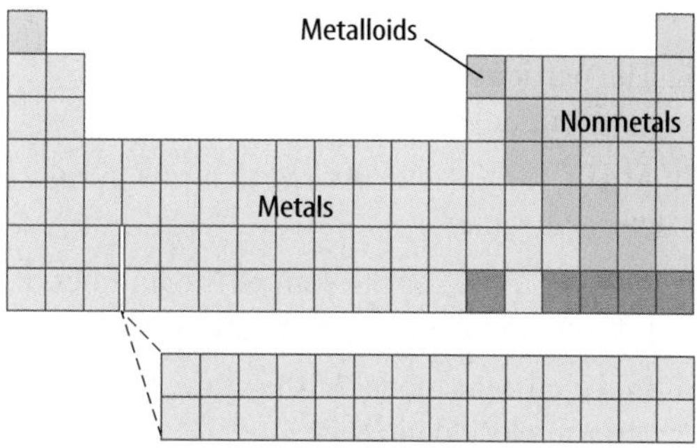

4. Elements are placed on the periodic table in order of increasing atomic number. A new row on the periodic table begins when the outer energy level of the element is filled.

FOLDABLES™ Use the Foldable that you made at the beginning of the chapter to help you review properties of atoms and the periodic table.

gpscience.com/interactive_tutor

chapter 17 Study Guide

Reviewing Main Ideas

Summary statements can be used by students to review the major concepts of the chapter.

Visit gpscience.com
/self_check_quiz
/interactive_tutor
/vocabulary_puzzlemaker
/chapter_review
/standardized_test

Assessment Transparency

For additional assessment questions, use the *Assessment Transparency* located in the transparency book.

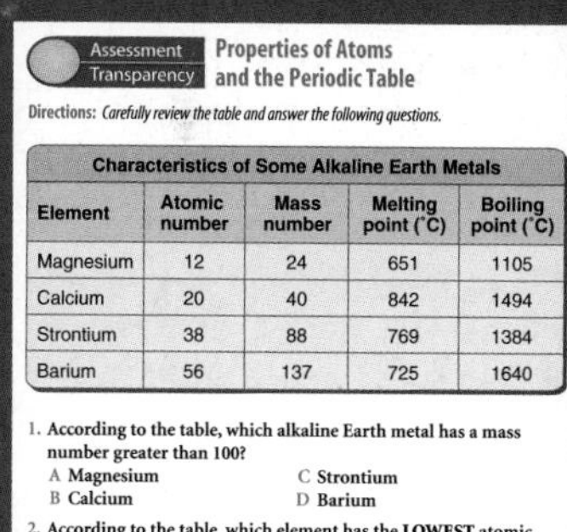

Assessment

Assessment Transparency **Properties of Atoms and the Periodic Table**

Directions: *Carefully review the table and answer the following questions.*

Characteristics of Some Alkaline Earth Metals				
Element	Atomic number	Mass number	Melting point (°C)	Boiling point (°C)
Magnesium	12	24	651	1105
Calcium	20	40	842	1494
Strontium	38	88	769	1384
Barium	56	137	725	1640

1. According to the table, which alkaline Earth metal has a mass number greater than 100?
   A Magnesium C Strontium
   B Calcium D Barium
2. According to the table, which element has the LOWEST atomic number?
   F Magnesium H Strontium
   G Calcium J Barium
3. According to the table, which element has the HIGHEST melting point?
   A Magnesium C Strontium
   B Calcium D Barium
4. The number of neutrons in the nucleus of an atom is equal to the mass number minus the atomic number. According to this definition and the table, how many neutrons are in the nucleus of a strontium atom?
   F 20 G 38 H 50 J 81

L2

Properties of Atoms and the Periodic Table

FOLDABLES™ Have students use their Foldables to review the content of the chapter. On the back of the paper, have students write a paragraph about how the atomic model looks today.

chapter 17 Review

Using Vocabulary

1. periodic table
2. isotopes
3. Average atomic mass
4. nucleus
5. quarks
6. period
7. mass number
8. electron cloud

Checking Concepts

9. D
10. C
11. B
12. B
13. A
14. C
15. D
16. A
17. D
18. B

chapter 17 Review

Using Vocabulary

atom p. 507
atomic number p. 513
average atomic mass p. 515
electron p. 507
electron cloud p. 511
electron dot diagram p. 522
group p. 520
isotope p. 514
mass number p. 513
neutron p. 507
nucleus p. 507
period p. 523
periodic table p. 516
proton p. 507
quark p. 507

Fill in the blanks with the correct word or words.

1. Mendeleev created an organized table of elements called the ________.
2. Two elements with the same number of protons but a different number of neutrons are called ________.
3. ________ is the weighted-average mass of all the known isotopes for an element.
4. The positively charged center of an atom is called the ________.
5. The particles that make up protons and neutrons are called ________.
6. A(n) ________ is a horizontal row in the periodic table.
7. The ________ is the sum of the number of protons and neutrons in an atom.
8. In the current model of the atom, the electrons are located in the ________.

Checking Concepts

Choose the word or phrase that best answers the question.

9. In which state of matter are most of the elements to the left of the stair-step line in the periodic table?
   A) gas **C)** plasma
   B) liquid **D)** solid
10. Which is a term for a pattern that repeats?
   A) isotopic **C)** periodic
   B) metallic **D)** transition
11. Which of the following is an element that would have similar properties to those of neon?
   A) aluminum **C)** arsenic
   B) argon **D)** silver
12. Which of the following terms describes boron?
   A) metal **C)** noble gas
   B) metalloid **D)** nonmetal
13. How many outer-level electrons do lithium and potassium have?
   A) 1 **C)** 3
   B) 2 **D)** 4
14. Which of the following is NOT found in the nucleus of an atom?
   A) proton **C)** electron
   B) neutron **D)** quark
15. The halogens are located in which group?
   A) 1 **C)** 15
   B) 11 **D)** 17
16. In which of the following states is nitrogen found at room temperature?
   A) gas **C)** metal
   B) metalloid **D)** liquid
17. Which of the elements below is a shiny element that conducts electricity and heat?
   A) chlorine **C)** hydrogen
   B) sulfur **D)** magnesium
18. The atomic number of Re is 75. The atomic mass of one of its isotopes is 186. How many neutrons are in an atom of this isotope?
   A) 75 **C)** 186
   B) 111 **D)** 261

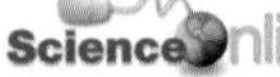

gpscience.com/vocabulary_puzzlemaker

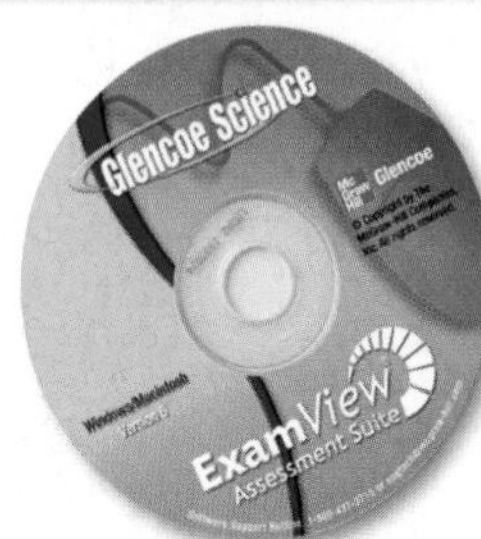

Use the *ExamView® Assessment Suite* CD-ROM to:

- create multiple versions of tests
- create modified tests with one mouse click for inclusion students
- edit existing questions and add your own questions
- build tests aligned with state standards using built-in State Curriculum Tags
- change English tests to Spanish with one mouse click and vice versa

Interpreting Graphics

19. As a star dies, it becomes more dense. Its temperature rises to a point where He nuclei are combined with other nuclei. When this happens, the atomic numbers of the other nuclei are increased by 2 because each gains the two protons contained in the He nucleus. For example, Cr fuses with He to become Fe. Copy and complete the concept map showing the first four steps in He fusion.

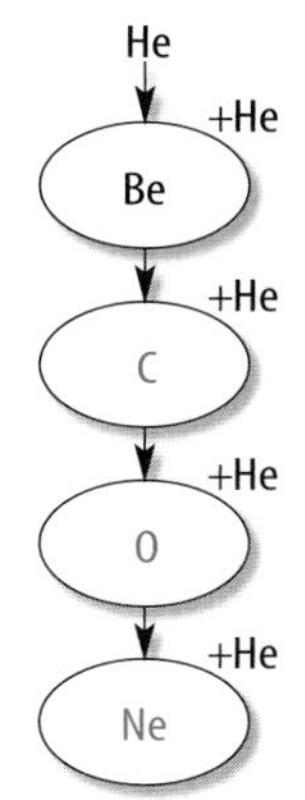

20. Copy and complete the concept map below.

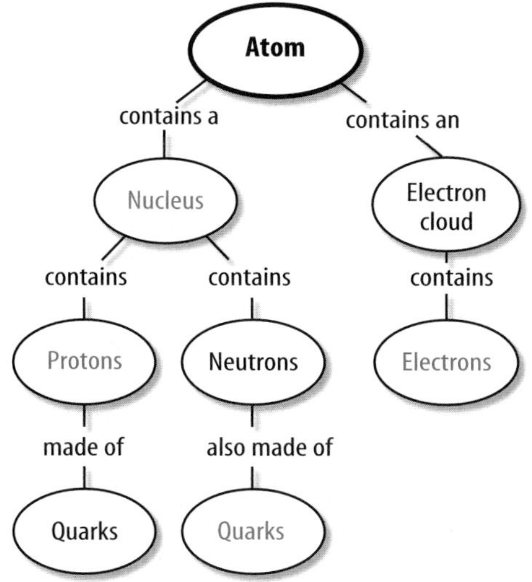

Thinking Critically

21. Infer Lead and mercury are two pollutants in the environment. From information about them in the periodic table, determine why they are called heavy metals.

22. Explain why it is necessary to change models as new information becomes available.

23. Infer Why did scientists choose carbon to base the atomic mass unit? Which isotope of carbon did they use?

24. Infer Ge and Si are used in making semiconductors. Are these two elements in the same group or the same period?

25. Explain Using the periodic table, predict how many outer level electrons will be in elements 114, 116, and 118. Explain your answer.

26. Infer Ca is used by the body to make bones and teeth. Sr-90 is radioactive. Ca is safe for people and Sr-90 is hazardous. Why is Sr-90 hazardous to people?

Applying Math

27. Solve One-Step Equations The atomic number of Yttrium is 39. The atomic mass of one of its isotopes is 89. How many neutrons are in an atom of this isotope?

Use the table below for question 28.

Electrons per Energy Level

Energy Level	Maximum Number of Electrons
1	2
2	8
3	8
4	0

28. Use Tables Use the information in **Figure 10** to determine how many electrons should be in the 2nd, 3rd, and 4th energy levels for Argon, atomic number 18. Copy and complete the table above with the number of electrons for each energy level.

 gpscience.com/chapter_review

chapter 17 Review

Interpreting Graphics

19. See student page.

20. See student page.

Thinking Critically

21. Compared to many metals, both lead and mercury have large average atomic masses.

22. Models must be updated to reflect the new information that is found. If the models are not updated, they are obsolete when the new information is found. The model would be useless.

23. Student answers may vary. It is possible that carbon was chosen because living organisms contain a significant amount of carbon. carbon-12

24. same group

25. 114-4; 116-6; 118-8; because these elements are in groups 14, 16, and 18 respectively

26. The radioactive nature of Sr can damage human cells.

Applying Math

National Math Standards

1, 5, 9

27. 50

28. See student page.

Assessment Resources

 **Reproducible Masters**

Chapter *Fast File* Resources
Chapter Review, pp. 37–38
Chapter Tests, pp. 39–42
Assessment Transparency Activity, p. 49

Glencoe Science Web site
Chapter Review Test
Standardized Test Practice

Glencoe Technology

Assessment Transparency
ExamView® Assessment Suite
MindJogger Videoquiz
Interactive Chalkboard

FAST FILE

Answer Sheet A practice answer sheet can be found at gpscience.com/answer_sheet.

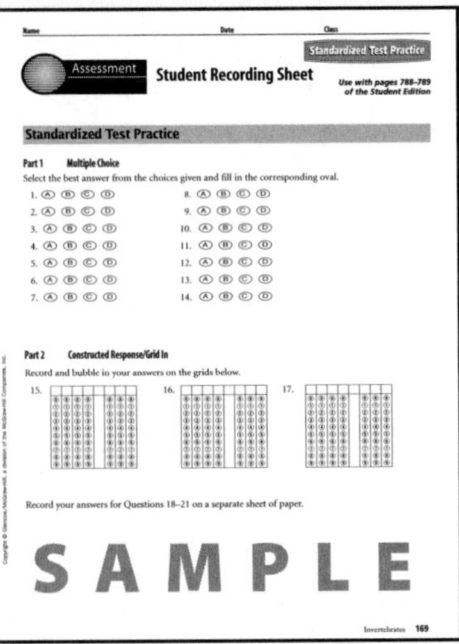
Name Date Class
Standardized Test Practice
Assessment
Student Recording Sheet
Use with pages 788–789 of the Student Edition
Standardized Test Practice
Part 1 Multiple Choice
Select the best answer from the choices given and fill in the corresponding oval.
Part 2 Constructed Response/Grid In
Record and bubble in your answers on the grids below.
Record your answers for Questions 18–21 on a separate sheet of paper.
SAMPLE

Part 1 Multiple Choice

1. C
2. D
3. B
4. A
5. C
6. C
7. C
8. A
9. C

Part 2 Short Response

10. 125
11. 35.5 amu
12. The + indicates that the sodium atom loses an electron, and the − indicates the chlorine atom gains an electron when the ionic bond forms.
13. The dots indicate that the chlorine atom has eight electrons in its outer energy level when it is part of the ionic compound sodium chloride.
14. The electron's mass is so much less than the masses of a proton and a neutron that it is negligible.

chapter 17 Standardized Test Practice

Part 1 Multiple Choice

Record your answers on the answer sheet provided by your teacher or on a sheet of paper.

1. Atoms of different elements are different because they have different numbers of what type of particle?
   A. electrons **C.** protons
   B. photons **D.** neutrons

2. Which group of elements on the periodic table do not combine readily with other elements?
   A. Group 1 **C.** Group 17
   B. Group 2 **D.** Group 18

Use the illustration below to answer questions 3 and 4.

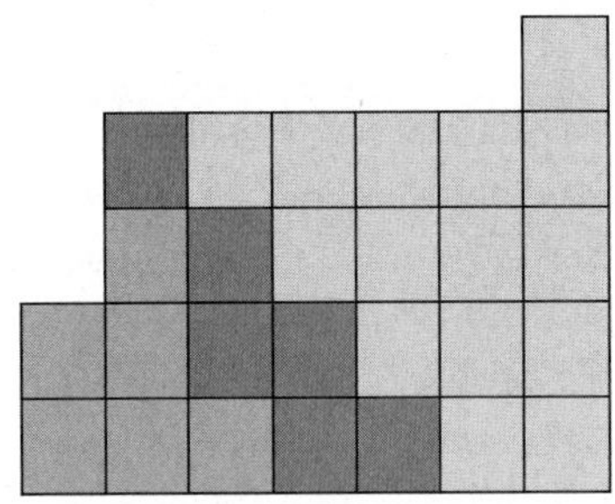

3. What is the name by which the elements along the stair-step line, darkly shaded on the periodic table shown above, are known?
   A. lanthanides **C.** metals
   B. metalloids **D.** nonmetals

4. Which of the regions shown on the periodic table contains mostly elements that are gases at room temperature?
   A. region 1 **C.** region 3
   B. region 2 **D.** region 4

5. Which scientist proposed the idea that atoms make up all substances?
   A. Aristotle **C.** Democritus
   B. Dalton **D.** Galileo

Use the table below to answer questions 6 and 7.

Element	Electrons in a Neutral Atom	Electrons in Outer Energy Level
Carbon	6	4
Oxygen	8	6
Neon	10	8
Sodium	11	1
Chlorine	17	7

6. The table above lists properties of some elements. Which element in the table has a complete outer energy level?
   A. carbon **C.** neon
   B. oxygen **D.** sodium

7. Which element would you expect to be located in Group 1 of the periodic table?
   A. oxygen **C.** sodium
   B. neon **D.** chlorine

8. How many quarks have been found to exist?
   A. six **C.** ten
   B. eight **D.** twelve

9. The element nickel has five naturally occurring isotopes. Which of the following describes the relationship of these isotopes?
   A. same mass, same atomic number
   B. same mass, different atomic number
   C. different mass, same atomic number
   D. different mass, different atomic number

Test-Taking Tip

Partial Credit Never leave any open ended answer blank. Answer each question as best as you can. Often, you can receive partial credit for partially correct answers.

Question 20 If you have some of the particles mixed up, try to write as much as you remember.

Part 2 Short Response

15. the number of electrons in the outer energy level
16. half-life
17. Yes, it is true. The atomic mass is the weighted-average mass of the mixture of different isotopes of the element.

Part 3 Open Ended

18. A cloud of negatively-charged electrons moves in an area around the nucleus of the atom.
19. Bohr hypothesized that electrons travel in fixed orbits around the atom's nucleus. In the electron cloud model of an atom, the electrons do not follow fixed orbits. Both models agree that the nucleus contains positively-charged protons and neutrons with no charge.
20. Scientists believe that electrons are not composed of smaller particles. Protons and neutrons are made up of smaller particles called quarks.

Part 2 Short Response/Grid In

Record your answers on the answer sheet provided by your teacher or on a sheet of paper.

10. According to the periodic table, an atom of lead has an atomic number of 82. How many neutrons does lead-207 have?

11. About three out of four chlorine atoms are chlorine-35, and about one out of four are chlorine-37. What is the average atomic mass of chlorine?

Use the illustration below to answer questions 12 and 13.

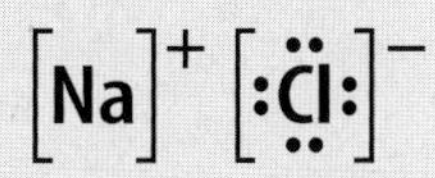

12. The electron dot diagram above shows how a sodium atom, Na, combines with a chlorine atom, Cl, to form sodium chloride. What do the + and the − symbols indicate in the diagram?

13. What do the dots around the chlorine atom indicate?

14. Why isn't the mass of the electron included in the mass of an atom on the periodic table?

15. What determines the chemical properties of an element?

16. What property of radioactive isotopes can scientists use to determine the age of bones or rock formations?

17. The atomic mass for silicon is listed as 28.09 amu on the periodic table. A student claims that no silicon atom has this atomic mass. Is this true? Explain why or why not.

Part 3 Open Ended

Record your answers on a sheet of paper.

Use the illustration below to answer questions 18 and 19.

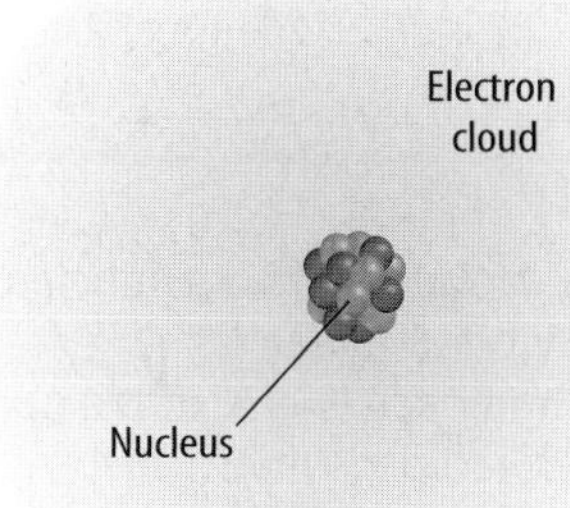

18. The illustration above shows the currently accepted model of atomic structure. Describe this model.

19. Compare and contrast the model shown above with Bohr's model of an atom.

20. Describe the composition of protons, neutrons, and electrons.

21. How can you use the periodic table to determine the average number of neutrons an element has, even though the number of neutrons is not listed?

22. Describe the concept of energy levels and how they relate to the placement of elements on the periodic table.

23. Explain the importance of the rows in the periodic table's organization of elements.

24. Describe how Dalton's modernization of the ancient Greek's ideas of element, atom, and compound provided a basis for understanding chemical reactions. Give an example.

21. You can determine the average number of neutrons by subtracting the atomic number from the average atomic mass.

22. Electrons close to the nucleus have lower energy than those farther away. Electrons fill the inner levels first, then the successively higher energy levels. On the periodic table, elements in the same group have the same number of electrons in their outer energy level.

23. The elements in each row have the same number of energy levels.

24. Dalton's model could be used to explain chemical reactions in quantitative terms. For example, chemists could explain that water was a combination of hydrogen atoms and oxygen atoms in a ratio of 2:1.

Rubrics

The following rubrics are sample scoring devices for short response and open-ended questions.

Short Response

Points	Description
2	The student demonstrates a thorough understanding of the science of the task. The response may contain minor flaws that do not detract from the demonstration of a thorough understanding.
1	The student has provided a response that is only partially correct.
0	The student has provided a completely incorrect solution or no response at all.

Open Ended

Points	Description
4	The student demonstrates a thorough understanding of the science of the task. The response may contain minor flaws that do not detract from the demonstration of a thorough understanding.
3	The student demonstrates an understanding of the science of the task. The response is essentially correct and demonstrates an essential but less than thorough understanding of the science.
2	The student demonstrates only a partial understanding of the science of the task. Although the student may have used the correct approach to a solution or may have provided a correct solution, the work lacks an essential understanding of the underlying science concepts.
1	The student demonstrates a very limited understanding of the science of the task. The response is incomplete and exhibits many flaws.
0	The student provides a completely incorrect solution or no response at all.

Radioactivity and Nuclear Reactions

BIG Idea Protons and neutrons are held together in a nucleus by the strong nuclear force.

	Content Standards	Learning Objectives	Resources to Assess Mastery
Section 1	**5–8:** UCP.1–3, 5; A.1, 2; B.1; G.3 **9–12:** UCP.1–3, 5; A.1, 2; B.1, 2; G.3	**Radioactivity** **1. Describe** the structure of an atom and its nucleus. **2. Explain** what radioactivity is. **3. Contrast** properties of radioactive and stable nuclei. **4. Discuss** the discovery of radioactivity. ***Main Idea*** The repulsive electrical force between protons causes some nuclei to be unstable.	**Formative Assessment** Reading Check, pp. 537, 539 Section Review, p. 540 **Summative Assessment** *ExamView® Assessment Suite*
Section 2	**5–8:** UCP.1–3, 5; A.1, 2; B.1 **9–12:** UCP.1–3, 5; A.1, 2; B.1, 2	**Nuclear Decay** **5. Compare and contrast** alpha, beta, and gamma radiation. **6. Define** the half-life of a radioactive material. **7. Describe** the process of radioactive dating. ***Main Idea*** Unstable nuclei can emit particles and energy when they decay.	**Formative Assessment** Reading Check, pp. 541, 544 Section Review, p. 545 **Summative Assessment** *ExamView® Assessment Suite*
Section 3	**5–8:** UCP.1–3, 5; A.1, 2; B.1; F.1 **9–12:** UCP.1–3, 5; A.1, 2; B.1, 2; F.1	**Detecting Radioactivity** **8. Describe** how radioactivity can be detected in cloud and bubble chambers. **9. Explain** how an electroscope can be used to detect radiation. **10. Explain** how a Geiger counter can measure nuclear radiation. ***Main Idea*** Nuclear radiation produces charged particles in matter than can be detected.	**Formative Assessment** Reading Check, pp. 546, 549 Section Review, p. 550 **Summative Assessment** *ExamView® Assessment Suite*
Section 4	**5–8:** UCP.1–3, 5; A.1, 2; B.1–3; F.1; G.3 **9–12:** UCP.1–3, 5; A.1, 2; B.1, 2, 4; F.1; G.3 See pp. 16T–17T for a Key to Standards.	**Nuclear Reactions** **11. Explain** nuclear fission and how it can begin a chain reaction. **12. Discuss** how nuclear fusion occurs in the Sun. **13. Describe** how radioactive tracers can be used to diagnose medical problems. **14. Discuss** how nuclear reactions can help treat cancer. ***Main Idea*** Nuclear fission splits nuclei apart and nuclear fusion joins nuclei together.	**Formative Assessment** Reading Check, pp. 551, 554 Section Review, p. 556 **Summative Chapter Assessment** MindJogger, Ch. 18 *ExamView® Assessment Suite* Leveled Chapter Test Test A L1 Test B L2 Test C L3 Test Practice, pp. 564–565

Suggested Pacing				
Period	**Instruction**	**Labs**	**Review & Assessment**	**Total**
Single	4 days	3 days	2 days	9 days
Block	2 blocks	1.5 blocks	1 block	4.5 blocks

Core Instruction	Leveled Resources	Leveled Labs	Pacing: Period		Pacing: Block
Student Text, pp. 534–540 Section Focus Transparency, Ch. 18, Section 1 Interactive Chalkboard, Ch. 18, Section 1 Identifying Misconceptions, p. 539 Differentiated Instruction, p. 539	**Chapter *Fast File* Resources** Directed Reading for Content Mastery, p. 20 L1 Note-taking Worksheet, pp. 35–37 Reinforcement, p. 27 L2 Enrichment, p. 31 L3 **Reading Essentials,** p. 300 L1 ELL **Science Notebook,** p. 201 ELL	**Launch Lab,** p. 535: meterstick, sugar, paper *10 min* L2 (Video Lab) **MiniLAB,** p. 539: small candies (15 yellow, 13 red, 2 green) *15 min* L2	1	Section 1, pp. 535–538 (includes Launch Lab)	1
			2	Section 2, pp. 538–540 (includes MiniLAB and Section Review)	1
Student Text, pp. 541–545 Section Focus Transparency, Ch. 18, Section 2 Teaching Transparency, Ch. 18, Section 2 Interactive Chalkboard, Ch. 18, Section 2 Differentiated Instruction, pp. 543, 544	**Chapter *Fast File* Resources** Directed Reading for Content Mastery, p. 20 L1 Note-taking Worksheet, pp. 35–37 Reinforcement, p. 28 L2 Enrichment, p. 32 L3 **Reading Essentials,** p. 306 L1 ELL **Science Notebook,** p. 205 ELL		3	Section 2, pp. 541–545 (includes Section Review)	2
Student Text, pp. 546–550 Section Focus Transparency, Ch. 18, Section 3 Interactive Chalkboard, Ch. 18, Section 3 Applying Math, p. 548 Identifying Misconceptions, p. 547 Differentiated Instruction, p. 549	**Chapter *Fast File* Resources** Directed Reading for Content Mastery, p. 21 L1 Note-taking Worksheet, pp. 35–37 Reinforcement, p. 29 L2 Enrichment, p. 33 L3 **Reading Essentials,** p. 312 L1 ELL **Science Notebook,** p. 208 ELL		4	Section 3, pp. 546–550 (includes Section Review)	2
Student Text, pp. 551–559 Section Focus Transparency, Ch. 18, Section 4 Interactive Chalkboard, Ch. 18, Section 4 Visualizing PET Scans, p. 555 Differentiated Instruction, pp. 552, 554 Chapter Study Guide, p. 561	**Chapter *Fast File* Resources** Directed Reading for Content Mastery, pp. 21, 22 L1 Note-taking Worksheet, pp. 35–37 Reinforcement, p. 30 L2 Enrichment, p. 34 L3 **Reading Essentials,** p. 317 L1 ELL **Science Notebook,** p. 211 ELL	***MiniLAB,** p. 552: marbles, beaker, modeling clay *15 min* L2 ***Lab,** p. 557: dominoes, stopwatch *40 min* L1 L2 L3 (Video Lab) ***Lab,** pp. 558–559: rice (brown, white), colored candies, dried beans, dried seeds, glue, poster board *45 min* L1 L2 L3 *Lab version A L1 version B L2 L3	5	Section 4, pp. 551–553 (includes MiniLAB)	3
			6	Section 4, pp. 554–556 (includes Section Review)	3
			7	Lab: Chain Reactions, p. 557	4
			8	Lab: Modeling Transmutations, pp. 558–559	4
			9	Study Guide, Chapter Review, and Test Practice, pp. 561–565	4.5

(Video Lab icon) Video Lab

chapter  Radioactivity and Nuclear Reactions

Transparencies

Section Focus

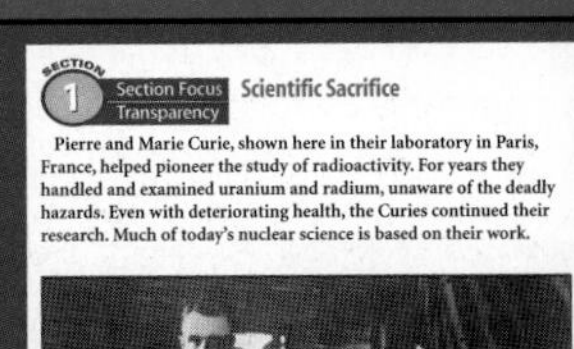

SECTION 1 Section Focus Transparency — Scientific Sacrifice

Pierre and Marie Curie, shown here in their laboratory in Paris, France, helped pioneer the study of radioactivity. For years they handled and examined uranium and radium, unaware of the deadly hazards. Even with deteriorating health, the Curies continued their research. Much of today's nuclear science is based on their work.

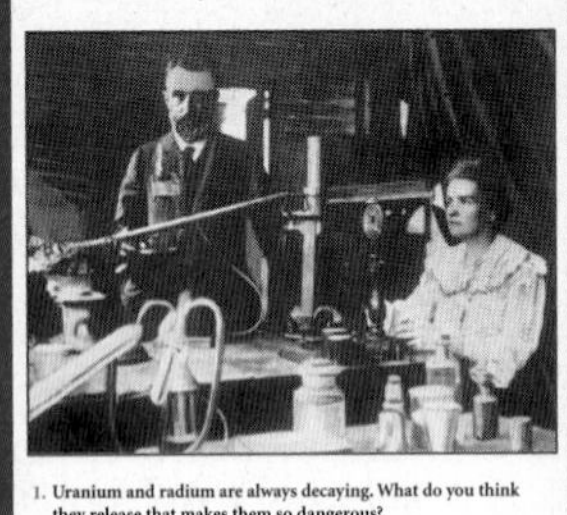

1. Uranium and radium are always decaying. What do you think they release that makes them so dangerous?
2. Name some present day uses of uranium.

L2

SECTION 2 Section Focus Transparency — A Distant Relative

In 1974, Donald Johanson and Tom Gray discovered the skeleton of the world's oldest human relative. Nicknamed Lucy, the remains were dated using the potassium-argon radioactive decay method. Lucy was determined to be 3.2 million years old.

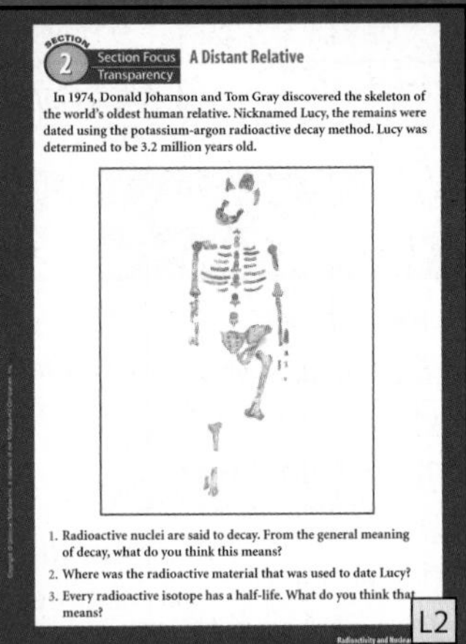

1. Radioactive nuclei are said to decay. From the general meaning of decay, what do you think this means?
2. Where was the radioactive material that was used to date Lucy?
3. Every radioactive isotope has a half-life. What do you think that means?

L2

SECTION 3 Section Focus Transparency — Home Safety

Radon is a radioactive gas that exists naturally in soil and rock. This odorless and colorless gas can seep through cracks into basements. At high levels, radon is a serious health risk. A home radon detector, like the one shown below, is a practical way to check radon levels.

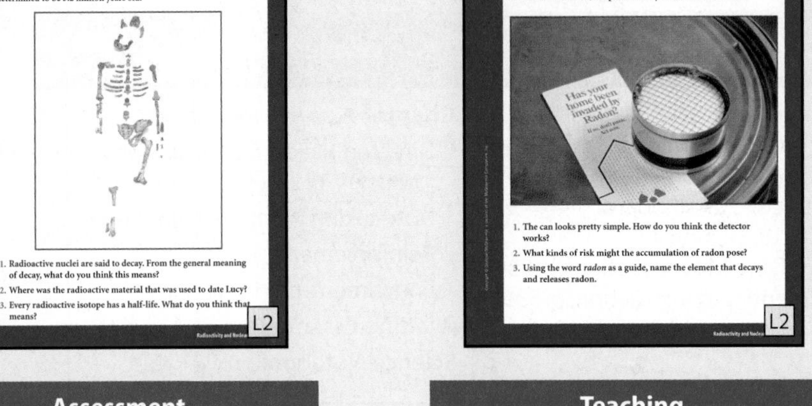

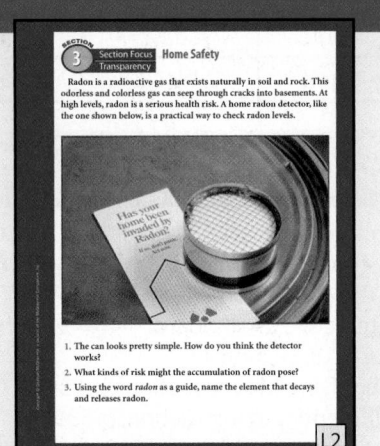

1. The can looks pretty simple. How do you think the detector works?
2. What kinds of risk might the accumulation of radon pose?
3. Using the word *radon* as a guide, name the element that decays and releases radon.

L2

This is a representation of key blackline masters available in the Teacher Classroom Resources. See Resource Manager boxes within the chapter for additional information.

Assessment

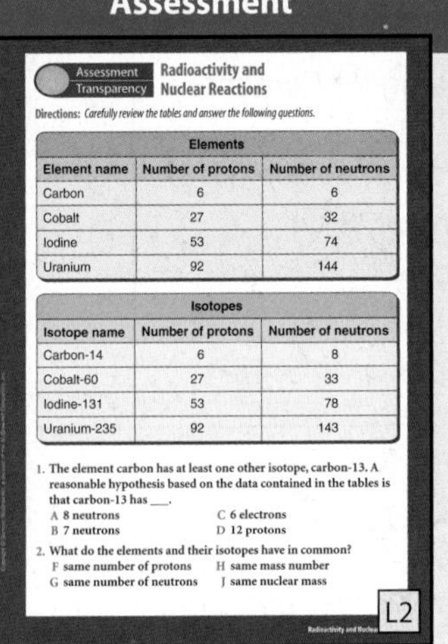

Assessment Transparency — Radioactivity and Nuclear Reactions

Directions: *Carefully review the tables and answer the following questions.*

Elements

Element name	Number of protons	Number of neutrons
Carbon	6	6
Cobalt	27	32
Iodine	53	74
Uranium	92	144

Isotopes

Isotope name	Number of protons	Number of neutrons
Carbon-14	6	8
Cobalt-60	27	33
Iodine-131	53	78
Uranium-235	92	143

1. The element carbon has at least one other isotope, carbon-13. A reasonable hypothesis based on the data contained in the tables is that carbon-13 has ___.
   A 8 neutrons C 6 electrons
   B 7 neutrons D 12 protons
2. What do the elements and their isotopes have in common?
   F same number of protons H same mass number
   G same number of neutrons J same nuclear mass

L2

Teaching

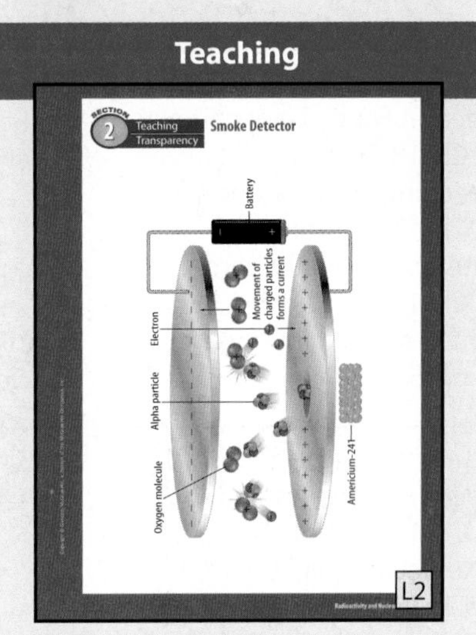

SECTION 2 Teaching Transparency — Smoke Detector

L2

Key to Teaching Strategies

The following designations will help you decide which activities are appropriate for your students.

- **L1** Level 1 activities should be appropriate for students with learning difficulties.
- **L2** Level 2 activities should be within the ability range of all students.
- **L3** Level 3 activities are designed for above-average students.
- **ELL** ELL activities should be within the ability range of English Language Learners.
- **COOP LEARN** Cooperative Learning activities are designed for small group work.
- **LS** Multiple Learning Styles logos, as described on page 12T, are used throughout to indicate strategies that address different learning styles.
- **P** These strategies represent student products that can be placed into a best-work portfolio.
- **PBL** Problem-Based Learning activities apply real-world situations to learning.

Hands-on Activities

Student Text Lab Worksheet

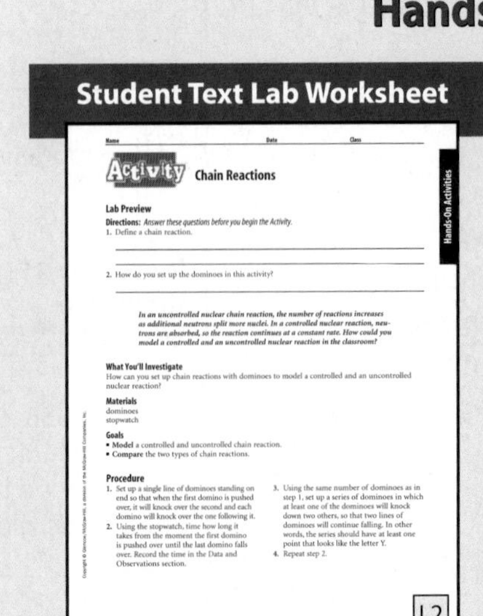

Name Date Class

Activity — Chain Reactions

Lab Preview

Directions: *Answer these questions before you begin the Activity.*

1. Define a chain reaction.
2. How do you set up the dominoes in this activity?

In an uncontrolled nuclear chain reaction, the number of reactions increases as additional neutrons split more nuclei. In a controlled nuclear reaction, neutrons are absorbed, so the reaction continues at a constant rate. How could you model a controlled and an uncontrolled nuclear reaction in the classroom?

What You'll Investigate

How can you set up chain reactions with dominoes to model a controlled and an uncontrolled nuclear reaction?

Materials

dominoes
stopwatch

Goals

- **Model** a controlled and uncontrolled chain reaction.
- **Compare** the two types of chain reactions.

Procedure

1. Set up a single line of dominoes standing on end so that when the first domino is pushed over, it will knock over the second and each domino will knock over the one following it.
2. Using the stopwatch, time how long it takes from the moment the first domino is pushed over until the last domino falls over. Record the time in the Data and Observations section.
3. Using the same number of dominoes as in step 1, set up a series of dominoes in which at least one of the dominoes will knock down two others, so that two lines of dominoes will continue falling. In other words, the series should have at least one point that looks like the letter Y.
4. Repeat step 2.

Hands-On Activities

Radioactivity and Nuclear Reactions L2

Laboratory Activities

Name Date Class

LAB 1 Laboratory Activity — The Effect of Radiation on Seeds

When seeds are exposed to nuclear radiation, many changes may be observed. Seeds contain genetic materials that determines the characteristics of the plants produced from them. Radiation can alter this genetic material. The type of seeds and the amount of radiation absorbed determine the extent of this alteration.

Strategy

You will grow plants from seeds that have been exposed to different amounts of nuclear radiation.
You will observe and record the growth patterns of the plants during a period of a week.
You will use the results of your experiment to discuss some of the possible effects of exposure to nuclear radiation.

Materials

seeds that have received different amounts of radiation
a few seeds that have not been irradiated
potting soil
boxes or containers for planting

Procedure

1. It is important that all seeds are planted and grown under the same conditions. Plant the seeds according to your teacher's instructions. Plant one container of untreated seeds. Label this container *1*. Carefully label each of the remaining containers. In Table 1, record the number of each container and the amount of radiation the seeds planted in it received.
2. Place the containers in a location away from drafts where they can receive as much light as possible. Keep the soil moist, but not wet, at all times.
3. As soon as the first seeds sprout, start recording your observations in Table 2. Observe the seeds at regular intervals for several weeks. If necessary, continue Table 2 on a separate sheet of paper. Watch for variations in sprouting and growth rates and differences in size, color, shape, number, and location of the stems and leaves. Remember, it is important to make an entry in the table for each container at every observation date, even if you report no change.
4. In the space provided in the Data and Observations section, make sketches of your plants and show any variation in growth patterns.

Data and Observations

Table 1

Container number	Amount of radiation
1	no radiation

Hands-On Activities

Radioactivity and Nuclear Reactions L2

Meeting Different Ability Levels

Content Outline

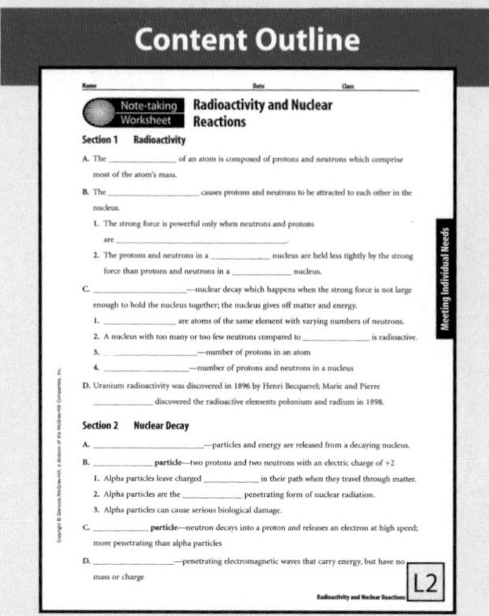

Note-taking Worksheet — Radioactivity and Nuclear Reactions

L2

Reinforcement

Radioactivity

L2

Enrichment

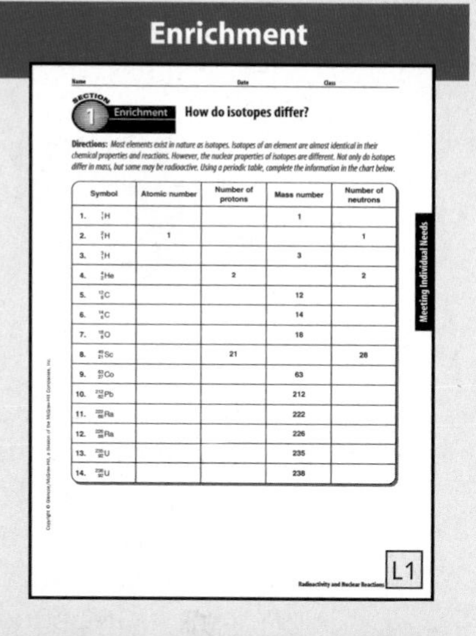

How do isotopes differ?

L1

Directed Reading (English/Spanish)

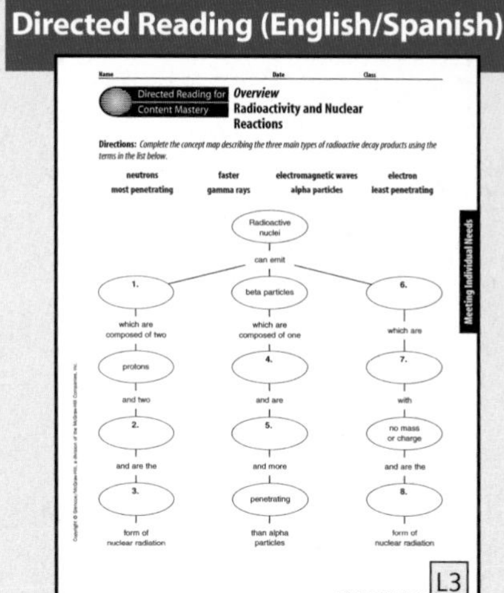

Directed Reading for Content Mastery — Overview: Radioactivity and Nuclear Reactions

L3

Study Guide

Study Guide

L2

Reading Essentials

Reading Essentials for Glencoe Science — An Interactive Student Workbook

L1

Assessment

Test Practice Workbook

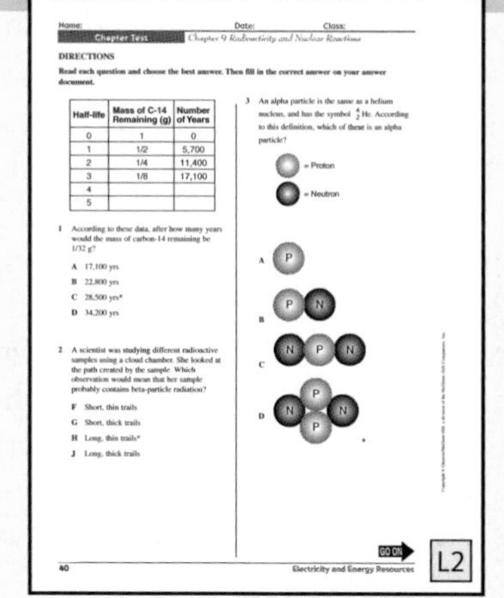

Chapter Test — Chapter 9 Radioactivity and Nuclear Reactions

L2

Chapter Review

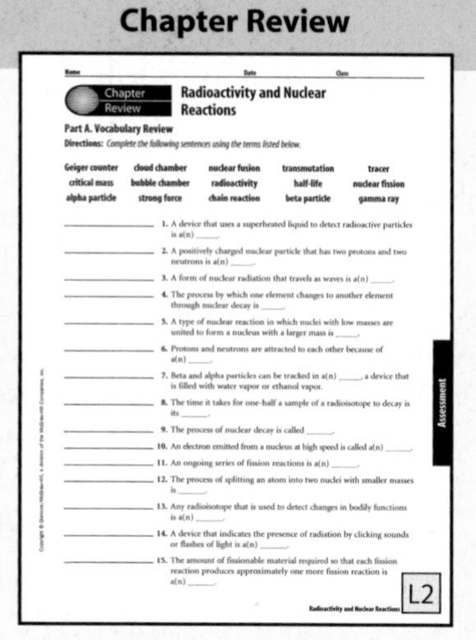

Chapter Review — Radioactivity and Nuclear Reactions

L2

Chapter Tests

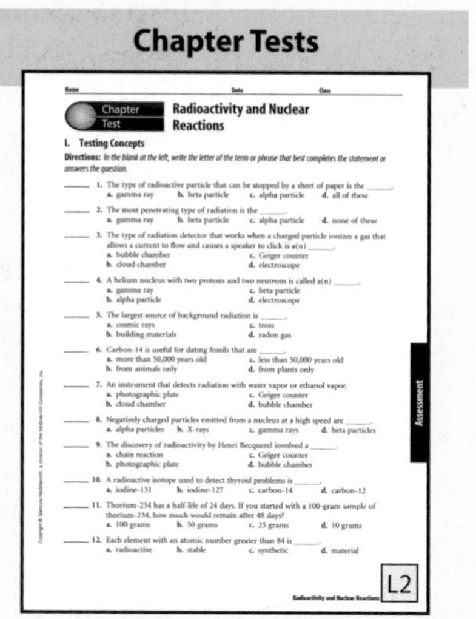

Chapter Test — Radioactivity and Nuclear Reactions

L2

Science Content Background

section 1 Radioactivity

The Nucleus

There are six "flavors" of quarks—the fundamental components of matter. The up, charm, and top quarks have a charge of +2/3. The down, strange, and bottom quarks have a charge of −1/3. Protons are made of two up quarks and one down quark. Neutrons are made of one up quark and two down quarks. Quarks are bound tightly together by the strong force so they are not observed as free particles.

In periodic tables the atomic mass of an element is usually not written as a whole number. For example, silicon is shown as having an atomic mass of 28.086. The atomic mass on the periodic table is the average of the masses of all of the isotopes of an element weighted by the relative occurrence of each isotope.

Carbon is the standard for the atomic mass of elements. It is defined as having a mass of 12 atomic mass units.

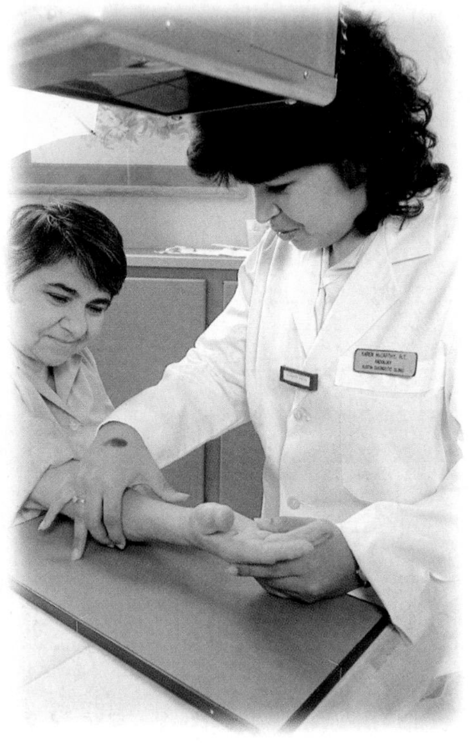

B. Daemmrich/The Image Works

Discovery of Radioactivity

Initial investigators of radioactivity were not aware of the long-term health risks associated with the handling of radioactive materials. Unfortunately this may have contributed to the death of Marie Curie due to leukemia in 1934.

chapter content resources

Internet Resources

For additional content background, visit gpscience.com to:

- access your book online
- find references to related articles in popular science magazines
- access Web links with related content background
- access current events with science journal topics

Print Resources

Contemporary College Physics, by Edwin R. Jones and Richard L. Childers, McGraw-Hill, 2001

How Things Work, 2nd Edition, Louis A. Bloomfield, John Wiley & Sons, 2001

section 2 Nuclear Decay

Gamma Rays

Gamma rays penetrate human tissue. Some cellular necrosis is not a problem as most cells can be replaced. The larger threat is from gamma rays that pass through tissues and change DNA. These changes can make a cell function less efficiently. When the cell reproduces, it produces more cells with less than optimal functioning. Aging is caused by the buildup of these kinds of cells. In rarer circumstances DNA is damaged in a way that results in a malfunction in the control of the growth of the cell, resulting in rapid cell growth and division—a condition known as cancer.

Teacher to Teacher
Cindy L. Marr
Frazier High School
Perryopolis, PA

"Use coated candies to simulate radioactive decay. Pour 60-100 candies on a paper plate. Each candy represents a radioactive atom. Candies with letters showing are "radioactive," and the others have "decayed". Count the radioactive atoms, record the number in a data table, and then remove the decayed atoms. Pour the remaining candies on the plate again. Repeat the procedure until all the "atoms" have "decayed". Plot the data (atoms left vs. trial number) and draw a smooth curve through the points. Obtain the half-life by selecting two values on the y-axis, one twice as large as the other, and finding the difference between corresponding values on the x-axis."

Cindy Marr

Putting food into sealed bags and exposing it to gamma rays can reduce the need for chemical preservatives or canning procedures. However, many people object to food irradiation. Some believe it will make food radioactive, which is not true. Others are concerned with the effects of eating foods that have been exposed to ionizing radiation.

section 3

Detecting Radioactivity

Measuring Radiation

Many radiation detectors use the tendency of radiation to ionize atoms as a means for detection. Ionization can be as simple as knocking an electron off an atom or it might involve the more complex breakup of a molecule into positive and negative pieces.

Health care workers who use X rays and people who work with radioactivity often wear radiation badges and carry pocket dosimeters. The badges are worn for periods of one to three months and then analyzed to assess how much radiation the person has received during that period. Pocket dosimeters tell the wearer how much radiation he or she has received in a shorter time period such as one day of work.

Background Radiation

Cosmic radiation in space is an obstacle that must be overcome before astronauts can spend longer periods in space. The majority of cosmic rays are protons, but heavier nuclei are common. Some cosmic rays are gamma rays.

section 4

Nuclear Reactions

Nuclear Fusion

Research is underway to develop reactors that use nuclear fusion to generate electricity. Unlike fission reactors, a fusion reactor would generate very little long-lived radioactive material. However, extremely high temperatures are needed for the fusion reactions to occur and the plasma created is difficult to confine under these conditions. One way to contain the plasma is to use strong magnetic fields that prevent the plasma from touching the inside surfaces of the reactor.

Telegraph Colour Library/FPG International

About the Photo

The photograph shows a giraffe herd in Etosha National Park in Namibia, Southern Africa. This park covers about 22,270 km^2 and was established in 1907. Part of the park is an ancient dry lake bed that holds water during heavy rains, when it attracts wading birds, such as pelicans. Numerous animal species inhabit the park, including about 2,500 giraffes.

Science Journal Student responses might include brightness, warmth and heat, intensity, and they feel more energetic on a sunny day.

The BIG Idea

The Range of the Strong Force In a nucleus, the strength of the attractive strong force among protons and neutrons depends on the distance between them. The range of the strong force exerted by a proton or a neutron is about 10^{-15} m, a distance called one fermi (fm). At distances greater than this, the strength of the strong force very quickly drops to zero. Because the size of a proton or a neutron is also about 1 fm, the strong force exists only over a very narrow region around a proton or a neutron. One model for the strong force is to imagine protons and neutrons as billiard balls surrounded by a thin, sticky layer, so that the balls must be very close before they stick together.

Introduce the Chapter Ask students how they might model an atom, including the nucleus. How would the nucleus be different from the rest of the atom? What materials might they use for the different parts of the atom?

chapter 18

Radioactivity and Nuclear Reactions

BIG Idea Protons and neutrons are held together in a nucleus by the strong nuclear force.

Planet Power

Although less than one-billionth of the energy emitted by the Sun falls on Earth, this energy powers the entire planet. Solar energy is produced inside the Sun by nuclear fusion-a nuclear reaction in which atomic nuclei are joined together..

Science Journal

In your Science Journal, write a paragraph describing your impressions of the sun.

534

Interactive Chalkboard

INTERACTIVE CHALKBOARD PowerPoint® Presentations

This CD-ROM is an editable Microsoft® PowerPoint® presentation that includes:

- an editable presentation for every chapter
- additional chapter questions
- animated graphics
- image bank
- links to gpscience.com

Start-Up Activities

The Size of a Nucleus

Do you realize you are made up mostly of empty space? Your body is made of atoms, and atoms are made of electrons whizzing around a small nucleus of protons and neutrons. The size of an atom is the size of the space in which the electrons move around the nucleus. In this lab, you'll find out how the size of an atom compares with the size of a nucleus.

1. Go outside and pour several grains of sugar onto a sheet of paper.
2. Choose one of the grains of sugar to represent the nuculeus of an atom.
3. Brush the rest of the sugar off the paper and place the sugar grain in the center of the paper.
4. Use a meterstick to measure a distance of 10 m from the sugar grain. This distance represents the radius of the electron cloud around an atom.
5. **Think Critically** In your Science Journal, explain why an atom contains mostly empty space. Use the fact that an electron is much smaller than the nucleus.

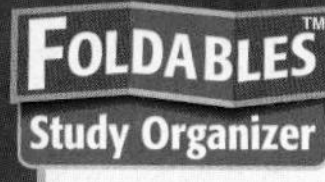

Radioactivity and Nuclear Reactions Make the following Foldable to help you understand radioactivity and nuclear reactions.

STEP 1 **Fold** a sheet of paper in half lengthwise.

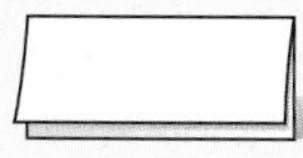

STEP 2 **Fold** paper down 2.5 cm from the top. (Hint: From the tip of your index finger to your middle knuckle is about 2.5 cm.)

STEP 3 **Open and draw** lines along the 2.5-cm fold. **Label** as shown.

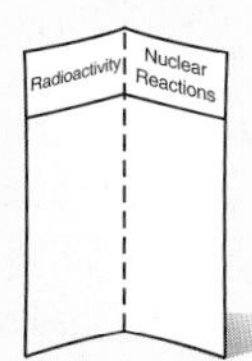

Summarize in a Table As you read the chapter, write what you learn about radioactivity in the left column, and what you learn about nuclear reactions in the right column.

Preview this chapter's content and activities at gpscience.com

535

Launch LAB

Purpose Use this Launch Lab to introduce students to what the interior of an atom is like.

Preparation Choose an outdoor location that will safely accommodate all the groups. To avoid confusion, assign a location for each group.

Materials A meterstick, sugar, sheet of paper for each group

Teaching Strategies Ask one student to be a group leader and assign the tasks of choosing and measuring the sugar grain and measuring the 10-m distance to group members.

Think Critically

The space in which the electrons move is much larger than the nucleus. Since the electron is much smaller than the nucleus, the space occupied by the electrons and the nucleus is much smaller than the space occupied by the atom.

Assessment

Content Sometimes it is said that an atom is mostly empty space. Ask students to write a paragraph discussing whether this statement is true. The sizes of the nucleus and electrons in an atom are much smaller than the size of the atom. However, electrons move throughout the space occupied by the atom. Use **Performance Assessment in the Science Classroom,** p. 89.

Dinah Zike Study Fold

Student preparation materials for this Foldable are available in the **Chapter *Fast File* Resources.**

Additional Chapter Media

-  *Isotopes*
- Virtual Lab: *How can you simulate the radioactive half-life of an element?*
- Video Lab: *Chain Reactions*

section 1 Radioactivity

1 Motivate

Bellringer

Section Focus Transparencies also are available on the Interactive Chalkboard CD-ROM.

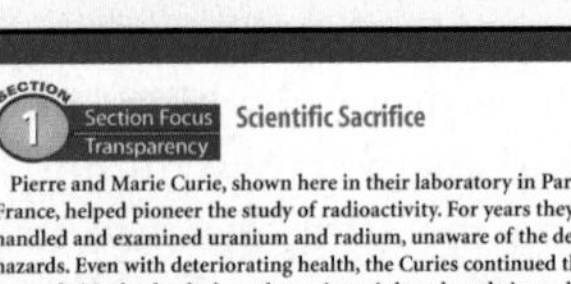

Section Focus Transparency 1 — Scientific Sacrifice

Pierre and Marie Curie, shown here in their laboratory in Paris, France, helped pioneer the study of radioactivity. For years they handled and examined uranium and radium, unaware of the deadly hazards. Even with deteriorating health, the Curies continued their research. Much of today's nuclear science is based on their work.

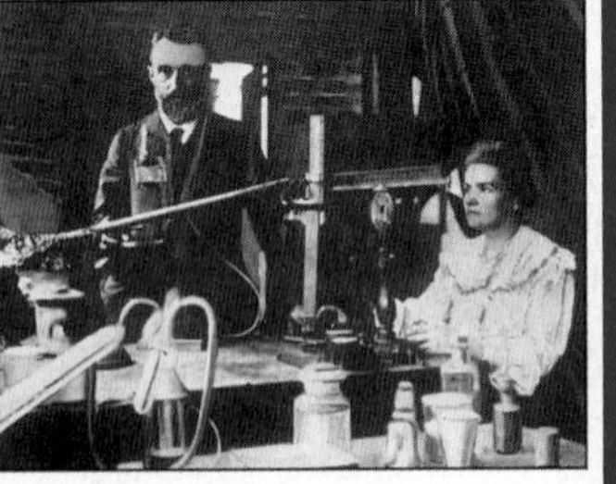

1. Uranium and radium are always decaying. What do you think they release that makes them so dangerous?
2. Name some present day uses of uranium.

L2

Radioactivity and Nuclear Reactions

Tie to Prior Knowledge

Parts of an Atom Ask students to recall the parts of an atom. Students are probably aware that an atom is composed of electrons swirling around a nucleus of protons and neutrons. In this section they will learn about the force that holds the nucleus together and why some nuclei are radioactive.

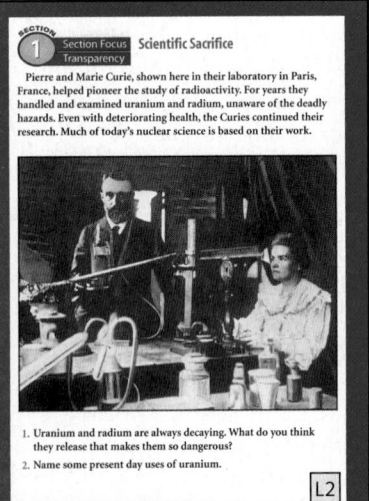

Reading Guide

What You'll Learn
- **Describe** the structure of an atom and its nucleus.
- **Explain** what radioactivity is.
- **Contrast** properties of radioactive and stable nuclei.
- **Discuss** the discovery of radioactivity.

Why It's Important
Radioactivity is everywhere because every element on the periodic table has some atomic nuclei that are radioactive.

Review Vocabulary
long-range force: a force that becomes weaker with distance, but never vanishes

New Vocabulary
- strong force
- radioactivity

The Nucleus

Every second you are being bombarded by energetic particles. Some of these particles come from unstable atoms in soil, rocks, and the atmosphere. What types of atoms are unstable? What type of particles do unstable atoms emit? The answers to these questions begin with the nucleus of an atom.

Recall that atoms are composed of protons, neutrons, and electrons. The nucleus of an atom contains the protons, which have a positive charge, and neutrons, which have no electric charge. The total amount of charge in a nucleus is determined by the number of protons, which also is called the atomic number. You might remember that an electron has a charge that is equal but opposite to a proton's charge. Atoms usually contain the same number of protons as electrons. Negatively charged electrons are electrically attracted to the positively charged nucleus and swarm around it.

Figure 1 The size of a nucleus in an atom can be compared to a marble sitting in the middle of an empty football stadium.

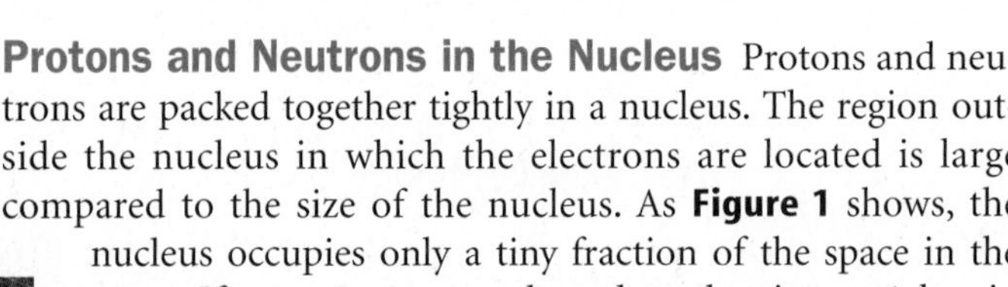

Protons and Neutrons in the Nucleus Protons and neutrons are packed together tightly in a nucleus. The region outside the nucleus in which the electrons are located is large compared to the size of the nucleus. As **Figure 1** shows, the nucleus occupies only a tiny fraction of the space in the atom. If an atom were enlarged so that it was 1 km in diameter, its nucleus would have a diameter of only a few centimeters. But the nucleus contains almost all the mass of the atom, because the mass of one proton or neutron is almost 2,000 times greater than the mass of an electron.

536

Section 1 Resource Manager

Chapter FAST FILE Resources
- Transparency Activity, p. 46
- Note-taking Worksheets, pp. 35–37
- Directed Reading for Content Mastery, pp. 19, 20
- Enrichment, p. 31
- Reinforcement, p.27
- **Science Inquiry Labs,** pp. 19–20

Figure 2 The particles in the nucleus are attracted to each other by the strong force.

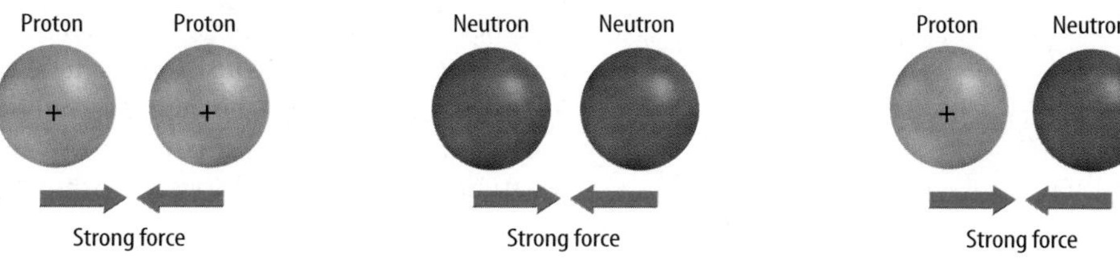

The Strong Force

How do you suppose protons and neutrons are held together so tightly in the nucleus? Positive electric charges repel each other, so why don't the protons in a nucleus push each other away? Another force, called the **strong force,** causes protons and neutrons to be attracted to each other, as shown in **Figure 2.**

The strong force is one of the four basic forces in nature and is about 100 times stronger than the electric force. The attractive forces between all the protons and neutrons in a nucleus keep the nucleus together. However, protons and neutrons have to be close together, like they are in the nucleus, to be attracted by the strong force. The strong force is a short-range force that quickly becomes extremely weak as protons and neutrons get farther apart. The electric force is a long-range force, so protons that are far apart still are repelled by the electric force, as shown in **Figure 3.**

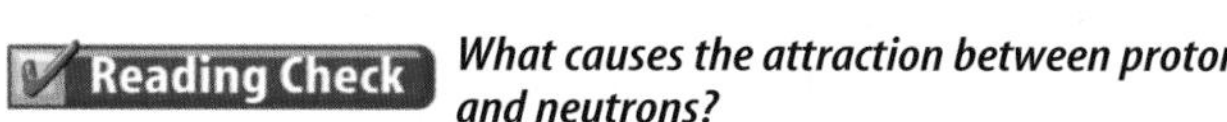

Reading Check *What causes the attraction between protons and neutrons?*

Figure 3 The total force between two protons depends on how far apart they are. **Infer** *whether the total force between two protons could become zero.*

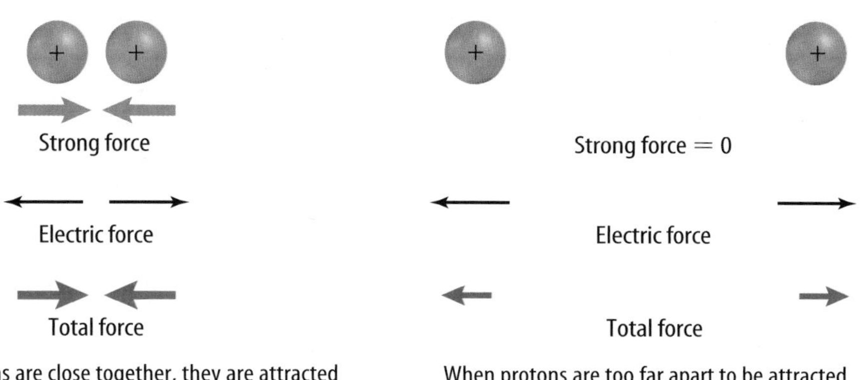

When protons are close together, they are attracted to each other. The attraction due to the short-range strong force is much stronger than the repulsion due to the long-range electric force.

When protons are too far apart to be attracted by the strong force, they still are repelled by the electric force between them. Then the total force between them is repulsive.

2 Teach

Activity

Atomic Structure To review atomic structure, display a periodic table. Have students choose an element and draw its structure on the board using different colors for protons, neutrons, and electrons. Tell students that physicists often refer to the number of protons (atomic number) as "Z." L1 ELL LS **Visual-Spatial**

Make a Model

The Nucleus The strong force is significant only for a distance that is less than the width of a few protons and neutrons. Have students model the nucleus of a nitrogen atom by drawing closely packed circles as nucleons. (Tracing around a penny works well.) Students should draw seven neutrons and seven protons, randomly placed and colored differently. By multiplying the diameter of a circle by three, they can see about how far the strong force can be felt. L2 ELL LS **Kinesthetic**

Reading Check

Answer the strong force

Fun Fact

There is another particle called a positron, which is an electron with a positive charge.

Caption Answer

Figure 3 Yes, if they were separated by a distance such that the attractive strong force was balanced by the repulsive electric force.

Teacher FYI

Four Fundamental Forces Scientists have identified four fundamental forces of nature. The strong force holds neutrons and protons together; the electromagnetic force acts between particles with electric charge; the weak force is involved in the neutron decay process; and the weakest force is gravity.

Visual Learning

Figure 4 Point out to students that in the large nucleus the protons near the center of the nucleus feel a slightly greater strong force than those near the edge of the nucleus. Protons near the edge have no neighbors on the outer side of the nucleus to pull on them. This can be a source of instability in the nucleus. L2 LS **Visual-Spatial**

Quick Demo

Strong Force v. Magnetism

Materials magnets

Estimated Time 2–5 min

Procedure Use magnets to review the concepts of repulsion and attraction. With magnetism, like poles repel and unlike poles attract. Similarly, two protons (both positively charged) repel each other. With the strong force, however, the charge doesn't matter; all protons and neutrons attract one another at very short distances. L2 ELL LS **Visual-Spatial**

Discussion

Periodic End Why is there an end to the periodic table? As the number of protons in the nucleus increases, the relative effect of the electromagnetic repulsion between protons increases, causing large nuclei to be unstable. Beyond a certain point, the electromagnetic repulsion makes large nuclei too unstable to exist. L3 LS **Logical-Mathematical**

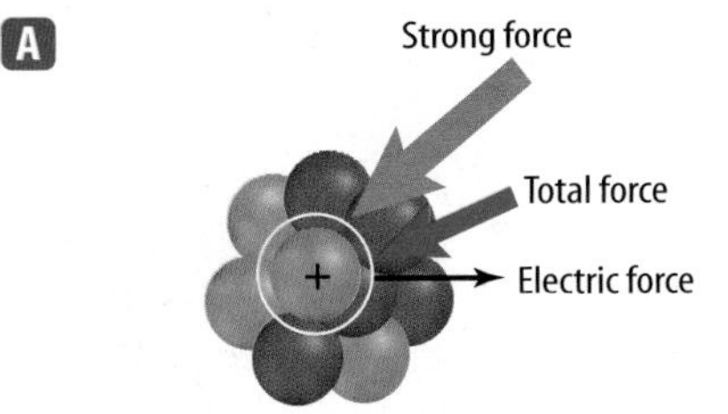

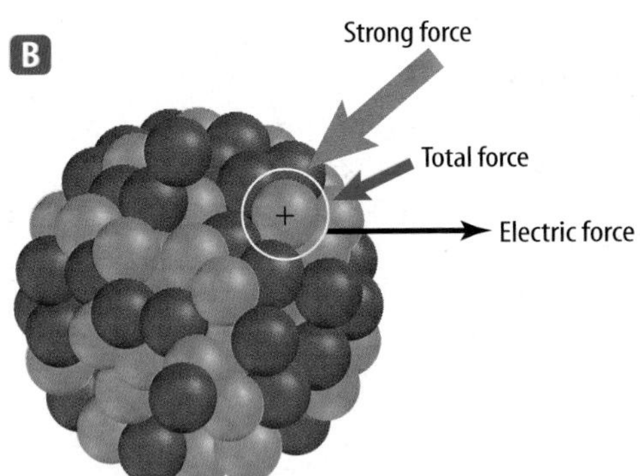

Figure 4 Protons and neutrons are held together less tightly in large nuclei. The circle shows the range of the attractive strong force. **A** Small nuclei have few protons, so the repulsive force on a proton due to the other protons is small. **B** In large nuclei, the attractive strong force is exerted only by the nearest neighbors, but all the protons exert repulsive forces. The total repulsive force is large.

Attraction and Repulsion Some atoms, such as uranium, have many protons and neutrons in their nuclei. These nuclei are held together less tightly than nuclei containing only a few protons and neutrons. To understand this, look at **Figure 4A.** If a nucleus has only a few protons and neutrons, they are all close enough together to be attracted to each other by the strong force. Because only a few protons are in the nucleus, the total electric force causing protons to repel each other is small. As a result, the overall force between the protons and the neutrons attracts the particles to each other.

Forces in a Large Nucleus However, if nuclei have many protons and neutrons, each proton or neutron is attracted to only a few neighbors by the strong force, as shown in **Figure 4B.** The other protons and neutrons are too far away. Because only the closest protons and neutrons attract each other in a large nucleus, the strong force holding them together is about the same as in a small nucleus. However, all the protons in a large nucleus exert a repulsive electric force on each other. Thus, the electric repulsive force on a proton in a large nucleus is larger than it would be in a small nucleus. Because the repulsive force increases in a large nucleus while the attractive force on each proton or neutron remains about the same, protons and neutrons are held together less tightly in a large nucleus.

Radioactivity

In many nuclei the strong force is able to keep the nucleus permanently together, and the nucleus is stable. When the strong force is not large enough to hold a nucleus together tightly, the nucleus can decay and give off matter and energy. This process of nuclear decay is called **radioactivity.**

Large nuclei tend to be unstable and can break apart or decay. In fact, all nuclei that contain more than 83 protons are radioactive. However, many other nuclei that contain fewer than 83 protons also are radioactive. Even some nuclei with only one or a few protons are radioactive.

Almost all elements with more than 92 protons don't exist naturally on Earth. They have been produced only in laboratories and are called synthetic elements. These synthetic elements are unstable, and decay soon after they are created.

Cultural Diversity

Hideki Yukawa In 1949 Japanese scientist Hideki Yukawa received the Nobel Prize in physics for his work on nuclear forces. In 1935 he predicted the existence of particles he called mesons, that would transfer energy between protons and neutrons and hold the nucleus together. His theory also stated that the nuclear force must be stronger than electromagnetic forces over short distances in order to overcome the repulsion between protons. The mesons Yukawa predicted, now known as pions, were discovered in 1937.

Isotopes The atoms of an element all have the same number of protons in their nuclei. For example, the nuclei of all carbon atoms contains six protons. However, naturally occurring carbon nuclei can have six, seven, or eight neutrons. Nuclei that have the same number of protons but different numbers of neutrons are called isotopes. The element carbon has three isotopes that occur naturally. The atoms of all isotopes of an element have the same number of electrons, and have the same chemical properties. **Figure 5** shows two isotopes of helium.

Stable and Unstable Nuclei The ratio of neutrons to protons is related to the stability of the nucleus. In less massive elements, an isotope is stable if the ratio is about 1 to 1. Isotopes of the heavier elements are stable when the ratio of neutrons to protons is about 3 to 2. However, the nuclei of any isotopes that differ much from these ratios are unstable, whether the elements are light or heavy. In other words, nuclei with too many or too few neutrons compared to the number of protons are radioactive.

Nucleus Numbers A nucleus can be described by the number of protons and neutrons it contains. The number of protons in a nucleus is called the atomic number. Because the mass of all the protons and neutrons in a nucleus is nearly the same as the mass of the atom, the number of protons and neutrons is called the mass number.

Reading Check *What is the atomic number of a nucleus?*

A nucleus can be represented by a symbol that includes its atomic number, mass number, and the symbol of the element it belongs to. The symbol for the nucleus of the stable isotope of carbon is shown below as an example.

$$\begin{array}{r} \text{mass number} \rightarrow \\ \text{atomic number} \rightarrow \end{array} {}^{12}_{6}\text{C} \leftarrow \text{element symbol}$$

This isotope is called carbon-12. The number of neutrons in the nucleus is the mass number minus the atomic number. So the number of neutrons in the carbon-12 nucleus is $12 - 6 = 6$. Carbon-12 has six protons and six neutrons. Now, compare the isotope carbon-12 to this radioactive isotope of carbon:

$$\begin{array}{r} \text{mass number} \rightarrow \\ \text{atomic number} \rightarrow \end{array} {}^{14}_{6}\text{C} \leftarrow \text{element symbol}$$

The radioactive isotope is carbon-14. How many neutrons does carbon-14 have?

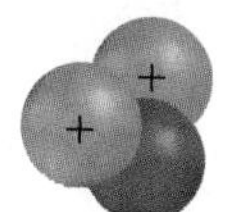

Helium-3

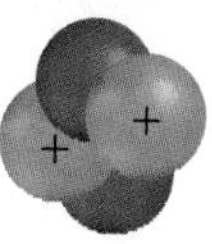

Helium-4

Figure 5 These two isotopes of helium each have the same number of protons, but different numbers of neutrons.
Identify *the ratio of protons to neutrons in each of these isotopes of helium.*

Modeling the Strong Force

Procedure

1. Gather **15 yellow candies** to represent neutrons and **13 red** and **2 green candies** to represent protons.
2. Model a small nucleus by placing 2 red protons and 3 neutrons around a green proton so they touch.
3. Model a larger nucleus by arranging the remaining candies around the other green proton so they are touching.

Analysis

1. Compare the number of protons and neutrons touching a green proton in both models.
2. Suppose the strong force on a green proton is due to protons and neutrons that touch it. Compare the strong force on a green proton in both models.

Try at Home

Differentiated Instruction

Challenge Have students determine the size of the nuclei of Helium, Neon, Argon, Krypton, Xenon, Radon, and Uranium. Calculate the ratio of the diameter of each nucleus to its atomic mass and graph using the atomic mass on the x-axis, and the ratio on the y-axis. Does the ratio remain constant as the size of the nucleus increases? Explain why this would be true. L3

Visually Impaired Allow visually impaired students to hold magnets and feel the attraction and repulsion to help them understand what happens when two protons are close together. Explain that the strong force is like your hands holding the repelling magnets close together.

Caption Answers

Figure 5 Helium-3: 2 to 1, Helium-4: 2 to 2

Radioactive Energy Students may think that radioactive materials glow. Explain that energy is given off, but not in the form of light. Radiation can, however, induce fluorescence in some materials.

Text Question Answer

8

Answer the number of protons

Purpose Students construct models to discover how the size of the nucleus affects the strong force on protons. L2 LS **Kinesthetic**

Materials small candies (15 yellow, 13 red, two green)

Analysis

1. About the same number touch the green proton in the larger nucleus, so the strong force is about the same.
2. The total number of protons and neutrons increases. The number nearby stays the same. The electromagnetic force on a proton increases, but the strong force stays the same, so the nucleus is less stable.

Assessment

Process Show students a drawing of a uranium nucleus and ask whether it is stable. It is too large to be stable. Use **PASC,** p. 89.

Activity

Radiation Time Line With students, make a class time line of the important events in nuclear radiation, beginning with Henri Becquerel's discovery of radioactivity. The time line could include contributions by Pierre and Marie Curie, Ernest Rutherford, Irène and Frédéric Joliot-Curie, Kasimir Fajans, Leo Szilard, Otto Hahn, Fritz Strassman, and Lise Meitner. L3 LS **Visual-Spatial**

DAILY INTERVENTION

Check for Understanding

Logical-Mathematical Why don't elements with atomic numbers greater than 92 exist naturally on Earth in significant quantities? because they are so unstable that if they are created, they decay almost immediately L3 LS

Reteach

Reviewing Isotopes Write on the board the chemical symbol, atomic mass, and atomic number of an isotope. Have students tell the number of protons and neutrons the element has and predict whether the isotope is radioactive. Do this for several isotopes. L2 ELL LS **Visual-Spatial**

✓ Assessment

Content Have students work in groups to create games that teach about radioactive elements. Games should reinforce the concept that unstable nuclei cause radioactivity. Use **Performance Assessment in the Science Classroom,** p. 169.

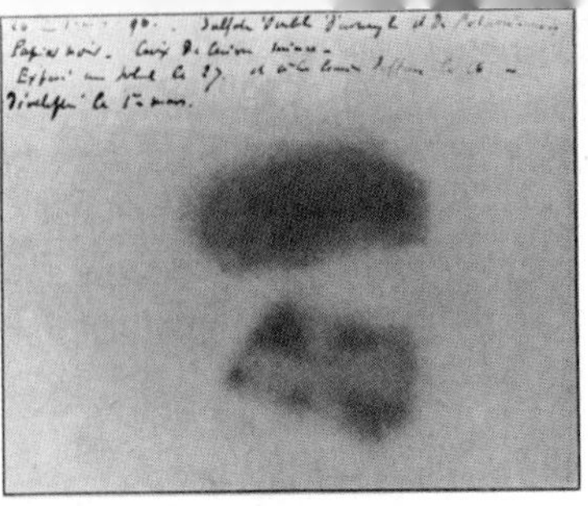

Figure 7 The dark spots on this photographic plate were made by the radiation emitted by radioactive uranium atoms. Uranium salt had been placed next to the plate by Henri Becquerel in 1896.

Science Online

Topic: Marie Curie

Visit gpscience.com for Web links to information about the life of Marie Curie.

Activity Create a timeline showing important events in the life of Marie Curie.

The Discovery of Radioactivity In 1896, Henri Becquerel left uranium salt in a desk drawer with a photographic plate. Later, when he developed the plate, shown in **Figure 6,** he found an outline of the clumps of the uranium salt. He hypothesized that the uranium salt had emitted some unknown invisible rays, or radiation, that had darkened the film.

Two years after Becquerel's discovery, Marie and Pierre Curie discovered two new elements, polonium and radium, that also were radioactive. To obtain a sample of radium large enough to be studied, they developed a process to extract radium from the mineral pitchblende. After more than three years, they were able to obtain about 0.1 g of radium from several tons of pitchblende. Years of additional processing gradually produced more radium that was made available to other researchers all over the world.

section 1 review

Summary

The Strong Force

- The short-ranged strong force causes neutrons and protons to be attracted to each other.
- The long-ranged electric force causes protons to repel each other.
- The combination of the strong and electric forces causes protons and neutrons in a large nucleus to be held together less tightly than in a small nucleus.

Radioactivity and Isotopes

- Radioactivity is the process of nuclear decay.
- Isotopes of an element have the same number of protons, but different numbers of neutrons.
- The atomic number is the number of protons in a nucleus. The mass number is the number of protons and neutrons in a nucleus.

Self Check

1. **Describe** the properties of the strong force.
2. **Compare** the strong force between protons and neutrons in a small nucleus and a large nucleus.
3. **Explain** why large nuclei are unstable.
4. **Identify** the contributions of the three scientists who discovered the first radioactive elements.
5. **Think Critically** What is the ratio of protons to neutrons in lead-214? Explain whether you would expect this isotope to be radioactive or stable.

Applying Math

6. **Calculate a Ratio** What is the ratio of neutrons to protons in a nucleus of radon-222?
7. **Use Percentages** A silicon rod contains 30.21 g of silicon-28, 1.53 g of silicon-29, and 1.02 g of silicon-30. Calculate the percentage of each isotope in the rod.

 Science Online gpscience.com/self_check_quiz

section 1 review

1. short range, attractive, exists between protons, neutrons, and protons and neutrons
2. The strong force is exerted by nearest neighbors, so it is nearly the same in both nuclei.
3. Large nuclei have so many protons that the strong force is unable to overcome the total electrical repulsion.
4. Becquerel found that uranium salt emitted radiation. Marie and Pierre Curie discovered polonium and radium.
5. 82/132 = 0.62; might be radioactive because the ratio of protons to neutrons differs from the 2-to-3 (0.67) ratio for stable heavy elements.
6. 86/136 = 0.63
7. total mass of rod = 32.76 g. Percentage of silicon-28 = 30.21/32.76 = 92.2%; silicon-29 = 1.53/32.76 = 4.7%; silicon-30 = 1.02/32.76 = 3.1%.

540 CHAPTER 18 Radioactivity and Nuclear Reactions

Nuclear Decay

Reading Guide

What You'll Learn
- **Compare and contrast** alpha, beta, and gamma radiation.
- **Define** the half-life of a radioactive material.
- **Describe** the process of radioactive dating.

Why It's Important
Nuclear decay produces nuclear radiation that can both harm people and be useful.

Review Vocabulary
electromagnetic wave: a transverse wave consisting of vibrating electric and magnetic fields

New Vocabulary
- alpha particle
- transmutation
- beta particle
- gamma ray
- half-life

Nuclear Radiation

When an unstable nucleus decays, particles and energy called nuclear radiation are emitted from it. The three types of nuclear radiation are alpha, beta (BAY tuh), and gamma radiation. Alpha and beta radiation are particles. Gamma radiation is an electromagnetic wave.

Alpha Particles

When alpha radiation occurs, an **alpha particle**—made of two protons and two neutrons, as shown in **Table 1**—is emitted from the decaying nucleus. An alpha particle is the same as the nucleus of a helium atom and has a charge of +2 and an atomic mass of 4. Its symbol is the same as the symbol of a helium nucleus, $^{4}_{2}He$.

Reading Check *What does an alpha particle consist of?*

Compared to beta and gamma radiation, alpha particles are much more massive. They also have the most electric charge. As a result, alpha particles lose energy more quickly when they interact with matter than the other types of nuclear radiation do. When alpha particles pass through matter, they exert an electric force on the electrons in atoms in their path. This force pulls electrons away from atoms and leaves behind charged ions. Alpha particles lose energy quickly during this process. As a result, alpha particles are the least penetrating form of nuclear radiation. Alpha particles can be stopped by a sheet of paper.

Table 1 Alpha Particles

Symbol	$^{4}_{2}He$
Mass	4
Charge	+2

1 Motivate

Bellringer

Section Focus Transparencies also are available on the Interactive Chalkboard CD-ROM.  

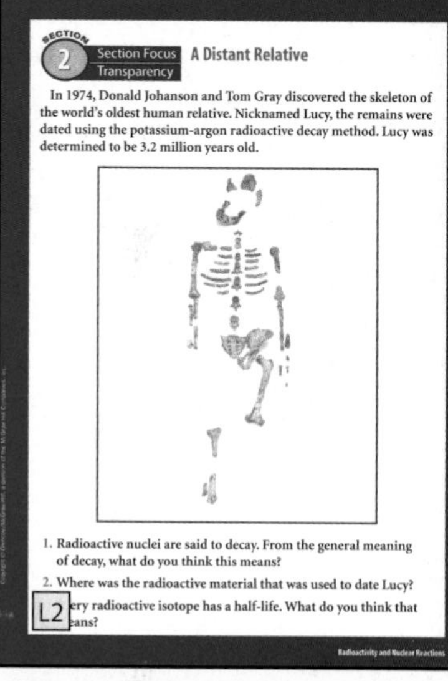

Section Focus Transparency
A Distant Relative
In 1974, Donald Johanson and Tom Gray discovered the skeleton of the world's oldest human relative. Nicknamed Lucy, the remains were dated using the potassium-argon radioactive decay method. Lucy was determined to be 3.2 million years old.
1. Radioactive nuclei are said to decay. From the general meaning of decay, what do you think this means?
2. Where was the radioactive material that was used to date Lucy?
L2
Radioactivity and Nuclear Reactions

Tie to Prior Knowledge

Gamma Radiation Tell students that gamma radiation is one kind of radiation emitted during radioactive decay.

Section 2 Resource Manager 

Chapter *Fast File* Resources
- Transparency Activity, p. 47, 51–52
- Lab Activity, pp. 9–12, 13–16
- Enrichment, p. 32
- MiniLAB, p. 3
- Reinforcement, p. 28
- **Mathematics Skill Activities,** p. 3

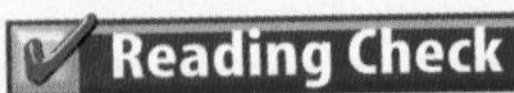

2 Teach

Reading Check

Answer two protons and two neutrons

Visual Learning

Figure 7 Point out to students that the metal plate of the ionization chamber serves as shielding for the radioactive source underneath. Bring in a smoke detector that uses americium-241. Light some flash paper or a candle to produce enough smoke to make the smoke detector beep. L2 ELL IS **Visual-Spatial**

Caption Answer

Figure 8 Yes

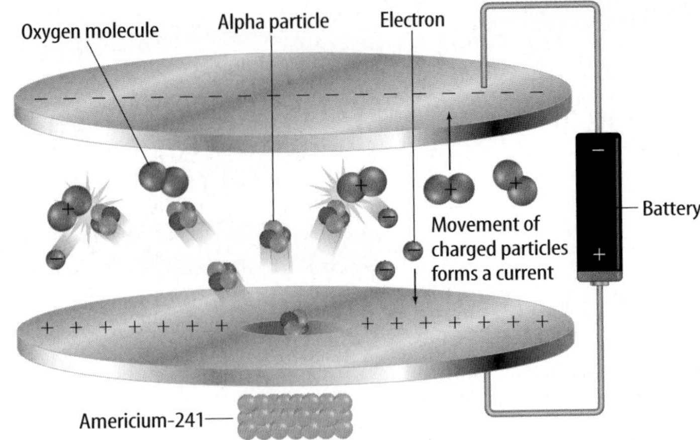

Figure 7 When alpha particles collide with molecules in the air, positively-charged ions and electrons result. The ions and electrons move toward charged plates, creating a current in the smoke detector.

Damage from Alpha Particles Alpha particles can be dangerous if they are released by radioactive atoms inside the human body. Biological molecules inside your body are large and easily damaged. A single alpha particle can damage many fragile biological molecules. Damage from alpha particles can cause cells not to function properly, leading to illness and disease.

Smoke Detectors Some smoke detectors give off alpha particles that ionize the surrounding air. Normally, an electric current flows through this ionized air to form a circuit, as in **Figure 7.** But if smoke particles enter the ionized air, they will absorb the ions and electrons. The circuit is broken and the alarm goes off.

Transmutation When an atom emits an alpha particle, it has two fewer protons, so it is a different element. **Transmutation** is the process of changing one element to another through nuclear decay. In alpha decay, two protons and two neutrons are lost from the nucleus. The new element has an atomic number two less than that of the original element. The mass number of the new element is four less than the original element. **Figure 8** shows a nuclear transmutation caused by alpha decay. The charge of the original nucleus equals the sum of the charges of the nucleus and the alpha particle that are formed.

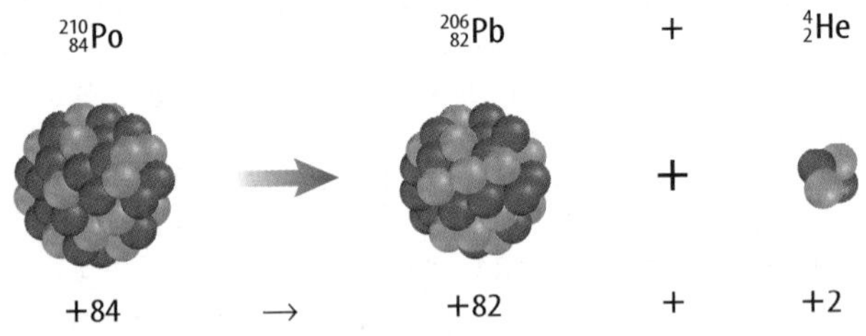

Figure 8 In this transmutation, polonium emits an alpha particle and changes into lead. **Determine** *whether the charges and mass numbers of the products equal the charge and mass number of the polonium nucleus.*

LAB DEMONSTRATION

Purpose to test the shielding of radiation

Materials Geiger counter; sources of α, β, and γ radiation; shielding (paper, aluminum foil, lead sheet)

Procedure Slowly bring the α source near, but not touching, the Geiger counter. Do this three more times, each time holding one type of radiation shielding between the detector and the source. Repeat the procedure for the β and γ sources.

Expected Outcome Students will observe how paper blocks alpha particles, foil blocks beta particles, and lead blocks gamma radiation.

Assessment

When you shield the Geiger counter from the radioactive sources, it continues to register, at a low rate. Why? It is detecting cosmic rays—high-energy particles from outer space.

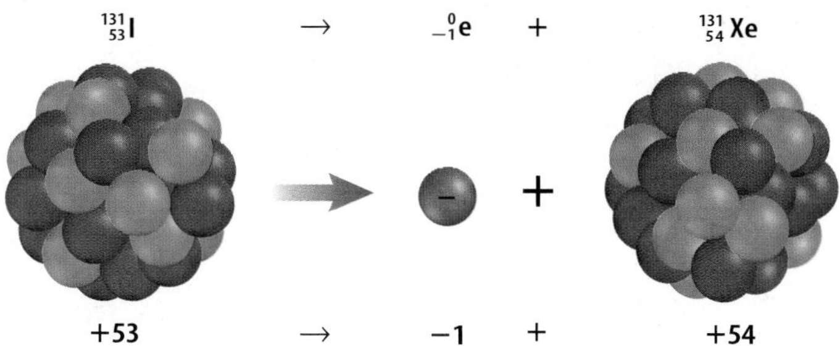

Figure 9 Nuclei that emit beta particles undergo transmutation. In beta decay shown here, iodine changes to xenon.
Compare *the total atomic number and mass number of the products with the atomic number and mass number of the iodine nucleus.*

Beta Particles

A second type of radioactive decay is called beta decay, which is summarized in **Table 2.** Sometimes in an unstable nucleus a neutron decays into a proton and emits an electron. The electron is emitted from the nucleus and is called a **beta particle.** Beta decay is caused by another basic force called the weak force.

Because the atom now has one more proton, it becomes the element with an atomic number one greater than that of the original element. Atoms that lose beta particles undergo transmutation. However, because the total number of protons and neutrons does not change during beta decay, the mass number of the new element is the same as that of the original element. **Figure 9** shows a transmutation caused by beta decay.

Damage from Beta Particles Beta particles are much faster and more penetrating than alpha particles. They can pass through paper but are stopped by a sheet of aluminum foil. Just like alpha particles, beta particles can damage cells when they are emitted by radioactive nuclei inside the human body.

Table 2 Beta Particles

Symbol	$^{0}_{-1}e$
Mass	0.0005
Charge	−1

Gamma Rays

The most penetrating form of nuclear radiation is gamma radiation. **Gamma rays** are electromagnetic waves with the highest frequencies and the shortest wavelengths in the electromagnetic spectrum. They have no mass and no charge and travel at the speed of light. They usually are emitted from a nucleus when alpha decay or beta decay occurs. The properties of gamma rays are summarized in **Table 3.**

Thick blocks of dense materials, such as lead and concrete, are required to stop gamma rays. However, gamma rays cause less damage to biological molecules as they pass through living tissue. Suppose an alpha particle and a gamma ray travel the same distance through matter. The gamma ray produces fewer ions because it has no electric charge.

Table 3 Gamma Rays

Symbol	γ
Mass	0
Charge	0

Caption Answer

Figure 9 The electron has a mass number of 0 and a charge of -1, so the mass number of the products equals 131, and the charge of the products equals +53.

Inquiry Lab

Electromagnetic Radiation

Purpose to demonstrate the penetration of electromagnetic radiation, using light

Possible Materials flashlight, blue plastic wrap, red plastic wrap, clear plastic wrap, white T-shirt, aluminum foil, and any other materials students choose.

Estimated Time 10–15 min

Teaching Stratiegies Have students shine a flashlight through various materials to observe if the light penetrates the material and hits the wall. Students can change the wavelength of the light by placing blue or red plastic wrap over the flashlight. If the light penetrates, measure how far back they can move from the wall and still see the light on the wall, then make a table summarizing their results. Repeat with any other materials they choose. Have them draw conclusions about the penetration of different wavelengths of light.

Discussion

Emitting Particles Have students summarize the effect on an atom's atomic mass (A) and atomic number (Z) if the atom emits an alpha particle, a beta particle, or a gamma ray. When an alpha particle is released, A decreases by four and Z decreases by two. When a beta particle is released, A is unchanged and Z increases by one. When gamma rays are released, A and Z are unchanged. L2 LS **Logical-Mathematical**

Differentiated Instruction

English Language-Learners Have ELL students draw three Lithium atoms with three electrons around the nucleus with a pencil. Have them erase one electron from each Lithium atom, and explain that an ion is a atom missing an electron, and that ions have the capacity to transfer electrons, which is electricity.

Science Journal

Radiation Have students find out who chose alpha, beta, and gamma to name different kinds of radiation, why, and when, and write this information in their journals. Ernest Rutherford gave these names to these types of radiation for, as he said, simplicity. He named alpha and beta radiation between 1895 and 1898 and gamma rays in 1903. L2 LS **Linguistic**

Fun Fact

The rate of radioactive decay seems to be impossible to change. Attempts to change it by alteration of temperature and pressure conditions, use of other chemical reactions, or exposure to electric and magnetic fields have been unsuccessful.

Caption Question Answer

Figure 10 one

Use an Analogy

Half-Lives Tell students to each hold up a large sheet of paper. Measure ten seconds, and have students tear their sheets of paper in half and place one half on their desks. During the next ten seconds, have them tear off half of the part that is left and place it on the desk. Continue counting ten-second intervals while students continue tearing their papers in half until they can no longer continue. Explain that, like the ever-smaller pieces of paper, the concentration of radioactive isotopes in a substance continuously decreases. L2

ELL IN **Kinesthetic**

Answer the nucleus left after the isotope decays

Discussion

Carbon in Bones Scientists find two bones. The first bone has half as much radioactive carbon as a new bone, and the second bone has one-fourth as much radioactive carbon. How old is each bone? The first is 5,730 years old; the second is 11,460 years old. L2

IN **Logical-Mathematical**

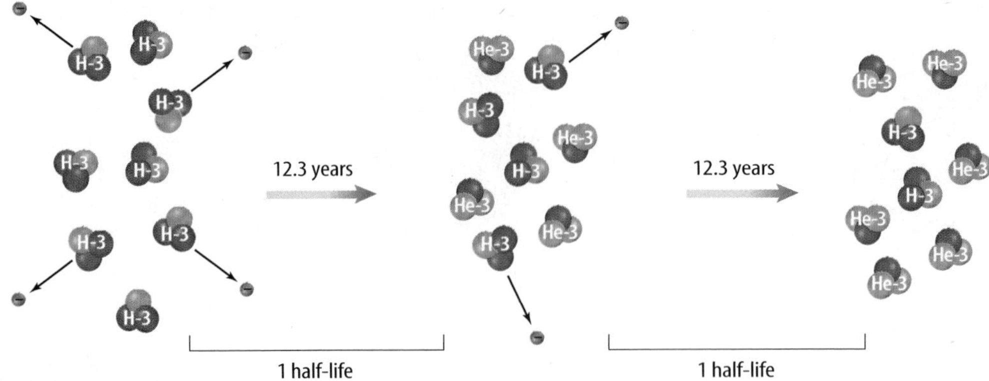

Figure 10 The half-life of $^{3}_{1}H$ is 12.3 years. During each half-life, half of the atoms in the sample decay into helium.
Infer *how many hydrogen atoms will be left in the sample after the next half-life.*

Radioactive Half-Life

If an element is radioactive, how can you tell when its atoms are going to decay? Some radioisotopes decay to stable atoms in less than a second. However, the nuclei of certain radioactive isotopes require millions of years to decay. A measure of the time required by the nuclei of an isotope to decay is called the half-life. The **half-life** of a radioactive isotope is the amount of time it takes for half the nuclei in a sample of the isotope to decay. The nucleus left after the isotope decays is called the daughter nucleus. **Figure 10** shows how the number of decaying nuclei decreases after each half-life.

Half-lives vary widely among the radioactive isotopes. For example, polonium-214 has a half-life of less than a thousandth of a second, but uranium-238 has a half-life of 4.5 billion years. The half-lives of some other radioactive elements are listed in **Table 4.**

Reading Check *What is a daughter nucleus?*

Table 4 Sample Half-Lives

Isotope	Half-Life
$^{3}_{1}H$	12.3 years
$^{212}_{82}Pb$	10.6 hr
$^{14}_{6}C$	5,730 years
$^{211}_{84}Po$	0.5 s
$^{235}_{92}U$	7.04×10^8 years
$^{131}_{53}I$	8.04 days

Radioactive Dating

Some geologists, biologists, and archaeologists, among others, are interested in the ages of rocks and fossils found on Earth. The ages of these materials can be determined using radioactive isotopes and their half-lives. First, the amounts of the radioactive isotope and its daughter nucleus in a sample of material are measured. Then, the number of half-lives that need to pass to give the measured amounts of the isotope and its daughter nucleus is calculated. The number of half-lives is the amount of time that has passed since the isotope began to decay. It is also usually the amount of time that has passed since the object was formed, or the age of the object. Different isotopes are useful in dating different types of materials.

Curriculum Connection

History Have students do research to learn how radioactive dating has been used to determine the ages of artifacts found in archaeological digs. Students might research Pompeii, China's terra-cotta army, or Easter Island. L3 IN **Linguistic**

Differentiated Instruction

Challenge Have students investigate the process scientists use to determine the levels of radioactive isotopes and daughter nuclei present in a sample when performing carbon or uranium dating. Put the process in a flow chart. L3

Carbon Dating The radioactive isotope carbon-14 often is used to estimate the ages of plant and animal remains. Carbon-14 has a half-life of 5,730 years and is found in molecules such as carbon dioxide. Plants use carbon dioxide when they make food, so all plants contain carbon-14. When animals eat plants, carbon-14 is added to their bodies.

The decaying carbon-14 in a plant or animal is replaced when an animal eats or when a plant makes food. As a result, the ratio of the number of carbon-14 atoms to the number of carbon-12 atoms in the organism remains nearly constant. But when an organism dies, its carbon-14 atoms decay without being replaced. The ratio of carbon-14 to carbon 12 then decreases with time. By measuring this ratio, the age of an organism's remains can be estimated. However, only material from plants and animals that lived within the past 50,000 years contains enough carbon-14 to be measured.

Uranium Dating Radioactive dating also can be used to estimate the ages of rocks. Some rocks contain uranium, which has two radioactive isotopes with long half-lives. Each of these uranium isotopes decays into a different isotope of lead. The amount of these uranium isotopes and their daughter nuclei are measured. From the ratios of these amounts, the number of half-lives since the rock was formed can be calculated.

section  review

Summary

Nuclear Radiation

- When an unstable nucleus decays it emits nuclear radiation that can be alpha particles, beta particles, or gamma rays.
- An alpha particle consists of two protons and two neutrons.
- A beta particle is an electron and is emitted when a neutron decays into a proton.
- Gamma rays are electromagnetic waves of very high frequency that usually are emitted when alpha decay or beta decay occurs.

Half-Life and Radioactive Dating

- The half-life of a radioactive isotope is the amount of time for half the nuclei in a sample of the isotope to decay.
- The amounts of a radioactive isotope and its daughter nucleus are needed to date materials.

Self Check

1. **Infer** how the mass number and the atomic number of a nucleus change when it emits a beta particle.
2. **Determine** the daughter nucleus formed when a radon-222 nucleus emits an alpha particle.
3. **Describe** how each of the three types of radiation can be stopped.
4. **Think Critically** Sample 1 contains nuclei with a half-life of 10.6 hr and sample 2 contains an equal number of nuclei with a half-life of 0.5 s. After 3 half-lives pass for each sample, which sample contains more of the original nuclei?

Applying Math

5. **Use Percentages** What is the percentage of radioactive nuclei left after 3 half-lives pass?
6. **Use Fractions** If the half-life of iodine 131 is 8 days, how much of a 5-g sample is left after 32 days?

Science Online gpscience.com/self_check_quiz

Quick Demo

Radiation Detection

Materials Geiger counter, different samples of rock and bone

Estimated Time five minutes

Procedure Use the Geiger counter to detect radiation in samples of rock and bone, and to confirm that all materials have some radioactive material.

3 Assess

DAILY INTERVENTION

Check for Understanding

Linguistic Have students find out more about the forces and radiation involved in beta decay. Beta decay involves the weak force and is accompanied by the release of particles called neutrinos, which have high energy but very little mass. L3

Reteach

Half-Life Have students tell how long it would take for three-fourths of a sample of each isotope in **Table 4** to decay. twice the listed half-life L2 LS **Logical-Mathematical**

Assessment

Have students make drawings illustrating how radioactive isotopes decay.

Virtual Labs

Half-life *How can you simulate the radioactive half-life of and element?*

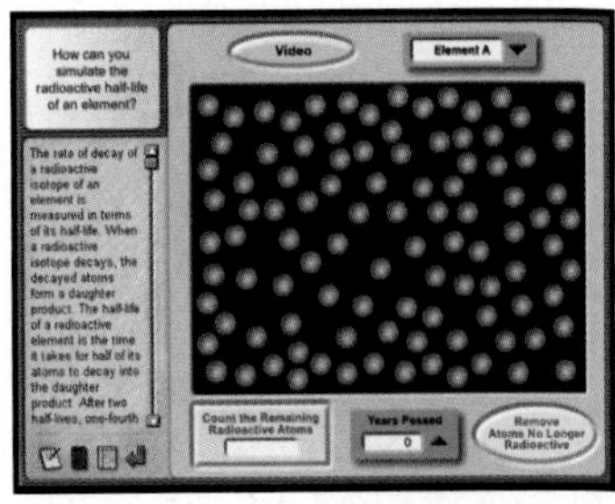

section  review

1. The atomic number increases by one and the mass number doesn't change.
2. $^{222}_{86}Rn \rightarrow ^{218}_{84}Po + ^{4}_{2}He$; polonium
3. alpha particles: sheet of paper; beta particles: sheet of metal foil; gamma rays: thick blocks of lead or concrete
4. They contain the same number. After three half lives, each sample contains one eighth of the original number of nuclei, which was the same for both samples.
5. 12.5%
6. 32 days = 4 half-lives = 1/16 of original number of nuclei left; 1/16 x 5 g = 0.3 g left

1 Motivate

Bellringer

Section Focus Transparencies also are available on the Interactive Chalkboard CD-ROM.

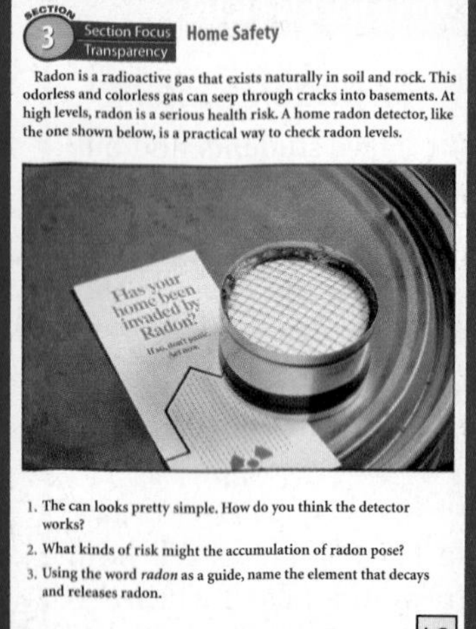

Section Focus Transparency 3 — Home Safety

Radon is a radioactive gas that exists naturally in soil and rock. This odorless and colorless gas can seep through cracks into basements. At high levels, radon is a serious health risk. A home radon detector, like the one shown below, is a practical way to check radon levels.

1. The can looks pretty simple. How do you think the detector works?
2. What kinds of risk might the accumulation of radon pose?
3. Using the word *radon* as a guide, name the element that decays and releases radon.

L2

Tie to Prior Knowledge

Detecting Radiation Our five senses allow us to see, hear, smell, taste, and feel, but none of our senses can tell us when we are being exposed to radioactivity. In this section, students will learn about four methods scientists have devised for detecting radiation.

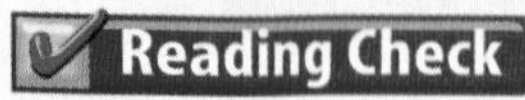

Answer The charged particles knock electrons off atoms in the air, leaving a trail of ions. The vapor condenses around these ions.

section 3

Detecting Radioactivity

Reading Guide

What You'll Learn

- **Describe** how radioactivity can be detected in cloud and bubble chambers.
- **Explain** how an electroscope can be used to detect radiation.
- **Explain** how a Geiger counter can measure nuclear radiation.

Why It's Important

Devices that detect and measure radioactivity are used to monitor exposure to humans.

Review Vocabulary

ion: an atom that has gained or lost electrons

New Vocabulary

- cloud chamber
- bubble chamber
- Geiger counter

Radiation Detectors

Because you can't see or feel alpha particles, beta particles, or gamma rays, you must use instruments to detect their presence. Some tools that are used to detect radioactivity rely on the fact that radiation forms ions in the matter it passes through. The tools detect these newly formed ions in several ways.

Cloud Chambers A **cloud chamber,** shown in **Figure 11,** can be used to detect alpha or beta particle radiation. A cloud chamber is filled with water or ethanol vapor. When a radioactive sample is placed in the cloud chamber, it gives off charged alpha or beta particles that travel through the water or ethanol vapor. As each charged particle travels through the chamber, it knocks electrons off the atoms in the air, creating ions. It leaves a trail of ions in the chamber. The water or ethanol vapor condenses around these ions, creating a visible path of droplets along the track of the particle. Beta particles leave long, thin trails, and alpha particles leave shorter, thicker trails.

Reading Check *Why are trails produced by alpha and beta particles seen in cloud chambers?*

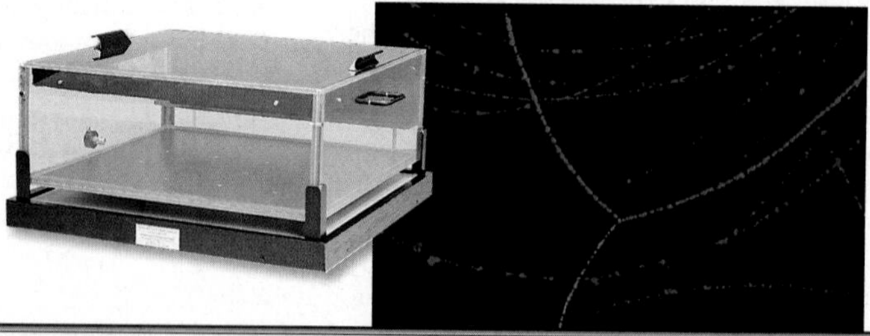

Figure 11 If a sample of radioactive material is placed in a cloud chamber, a trail of condensed vapor will form along the paths of the emitted particles.

546

Section 3 Resource Manager

Chapter *FAST FILE* Resources
- Transparency Activity, p. 48
- Directed Reading for Content Mastery, p. 21
- Enrichment, p. 33
- Reinforcement, p. 29
- **Mathematics Skill Activities,** p. 31

Bubble Chambers Another way to detect and monitor the paths of nuclear particles is by using a bubble chamber. A **bubble chamber** holds a superheated liquid, which doesn't boil because the pressure in the chamber is high. When a moving particle leaves ions behind, the liquid boils along the trail. The path shows up as tracks of bubbles, like the ones in **Figure 12.**

Figure 12 Particles of nuclear radiation can be detected as they leave trails of bubbles in a bubble chamber.

Electroscopes Do you remember how an electroscope can be used to detect electric charges? When an electroscope is given a negative charge, its leaves repel each other and spread apart, as in **Figure 13A.** They will remain apart until their extra electrons have somewhere to go and discharge the electroscope. The excess charge can be neutralized if it combines with positive charges. Nuclear radiation moving through the air can remove electrons from some molecules in air, as shown in **Figure 13B,** and cause other molecules in air to gain electrons. When this occurs near the leaves of the electroscope, some positively charged molecules in the air can come in contact with the electroscope and attract the electrons from the leaves, as **Figure 13C** shows. As these negatively charged leaves lose their charges, they move together. **Figure 13D** shows this last step in the process. The same process also will occur if the electroscope leaves are positively charged. Then the electrons move from negative ions in the air to the electroscope leaves.

Figure 13 Nuclear radiation can cause an electroscope to lose its charge.

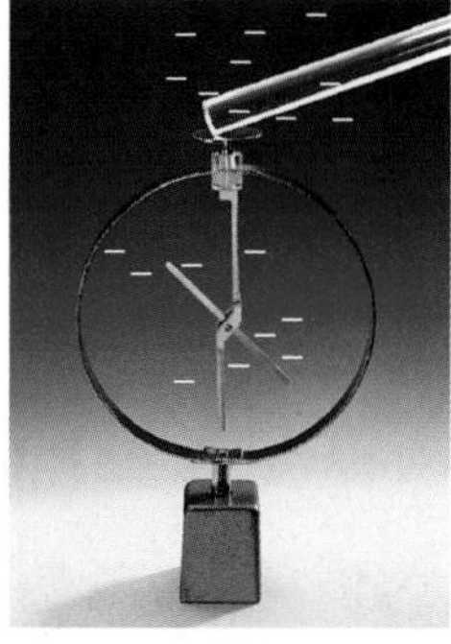

A The electroscope leaves are charged with negative charge.

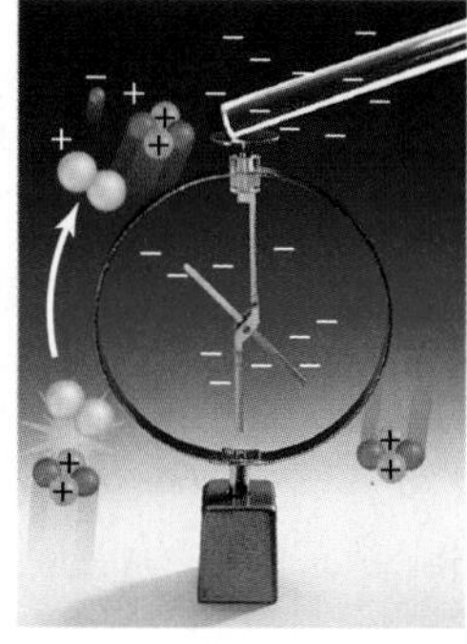

B Nuclear radiation, such as alpha particles, can create positive ions.

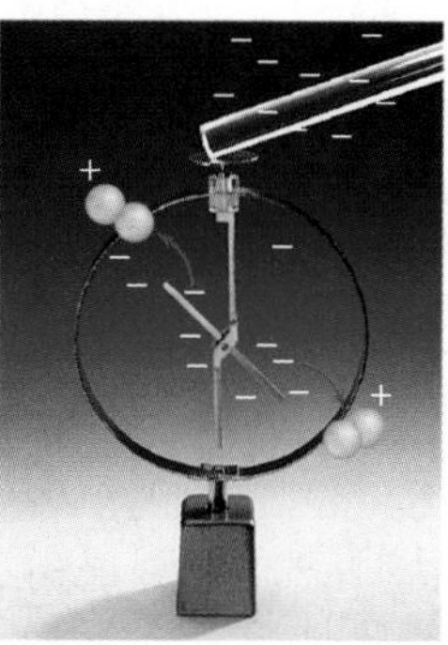

C Negative charges move from the leaves to positively charged ions.

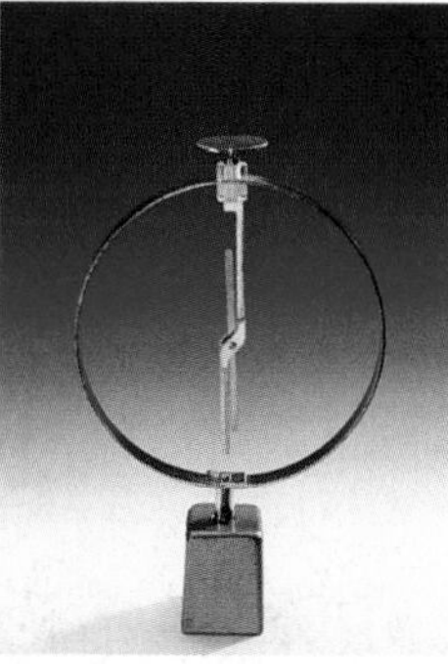

D The electroscope leaves lose their negative charge and come together.

2 Teach

Use an Analogy

Vapor Trails Tell students that the vapor trails sometimes seen behind jet airplanes are made up of water droplets that have condensed around the jet's exhaust fumes. Like the trails in cloud chambers, vapor trails provide a visual record of the path of the object that caused them.

Visual Learning

Figure 12 Point out to students that at the lower part of this bubble chamber photograph, particles collide and create a spray of charged particles. A magnetic field perpendicular to the page deflects the particles so that those curling to the left must have an opposite charge to those curling to the right. Note that only charged particles are visible.

IDENTIFYING Misconceptions

Fundamental Particles Students might assume that electrons, protons, and neutrons are the smallest possible particles. Explain that electrons are fundamental particles, but that protons and neutrons are composite particles made up of smaller particles called quarks.

Teacher FYI

Bubble Chamber The bubble chamber, developed in the 1950s, was used by scientists for many years to observe the particles in matter. It has since been replaced by newer, more complex detectors.

Quick Demo

Tracking Radiation Exposure

Materials Radiation film badge

Time Required 2–5 min

Procedure People whose work involves possible exposure to radiation are required to wear film badges that record the amount of radiation the person has received. You can obtain one of these badges from the radiation laboratory at a hospital. Explain to students that a small piece of film is encased in a plastic holder. The casing is light-tight so the film responds only to alpha, beta, and gamma radiation, not visible light. Every month, the film is removed and the amount of radiation it (and therefore the wearer) has received is measured. New film is then inserted in the holder. L3 LS **Visual-Spatial**

Calculating Rock Age

National Math Standards

Correlation to Mathematics Objectives

1, 2, 9,

Answers to Practice Problems

1. 4.19 billion years
2. 0.42 billion years
3. Half of the uranium-238 atoms have decayed, so there are equal numbers of uranium-238 atoms and lead-206 atoms, and the ratio is 1.0.

Measuring Radiation

It is important to monitor the amount of radiation a person is being exposed to because large doses of radiation can be harmful to living tissue. A **Geiger counter** is a device that measures the amount of radiation by producing an electric current when it detects a charged particle.

Calculating Rock Age

Measuring the Age of Rocks The nucleus uranium-238 has a half-life of 4.5 billion years and decays to produce the daughter nucleus lead-206. This decay can be used to date rocks. The age of a rock sample can be calculated from this equation:

$$age = (1.44 \times H) \ln[1 + \frac{N_L}{N_U}]$$

where H is the half-life of uranium 238, N_L is the number of lead-206 atoms in the sample, and N_U is the number of uranium-238 atoms. In the above equation, "ln" means the natural logarithm of the number $1 + N_L/N_U$ inside the brackets. Find the age of a sample in which the ratio N_L/N_U is measured to be 0.55.

1. **This is what you know:** half-life of uranium-238: H = **4.5 billion years**; lead-206 to uranium-238 ratio: $\frac{N_L}{N_U} = 0.55$
2. **This is what you need to find:** age of mineral sample: ***age***
3. **Use this formula:** $age = (1.44 \times H) \ln[1 + \frac{N_L}{N_U}]$
4. **Substitute:** the values of H and N_L/N_U into the formula.
   $age = (1.44 \times 4.5) \ln[1 + 0.55]$
   $= (6.48) \ln(1.55)$

   To calculate ln(1.55), enter 1.55 on your calculator and press the "ln" button. The result is 0.438. Substitute this value in the above equation:
   $age = (6.48)(0.438) = 2.84$
5. **Determine the units:** The logarithm of a number does not have any units.
   units of *age* = units of H = **billion years**

Answer: The age of the mineral sample is 2.84 billion years.

Practice Problems

1. In a mineral sample, the ratio of the number of lead-206 atoms to uranium-238 atoms is 0.91. What is the age of the sample?
2. In a certain mineral sample there are 750,000 uranium-238 atoms and 50,000 lead-206 atoms. What is the age of the sample?
3. **Challenge** What is the ratio of lead-206 atoms to uranium-238 atoms after one half-life?

Science Online

For more practice problems, go to page 834, and visit gpscience.com/extra_problems.

Teacher FYI

Radiation Units There are several units for measuring radiation. The curie and the becquerel are based on the number of disintegrations per second. The roentgen, the rad, and the gray measure the effect radiation has on the absorbing material. The rem is used to measure biological damage to humans.

Active Reading

Metacognition Journal In this strategy, each student analyzes his or her own thought processes. Have students divide a sheet of paper in half. On the left, have them record what they have learned about radiation detection. On the right, have them record the reason they learned it.

Figure 14 Electrons that are stripped off gas molecules in a Geiger counter move to a positively charged wire in the device. This causes current to flow in the wire. The current then is used to produce a click or a flash of light.

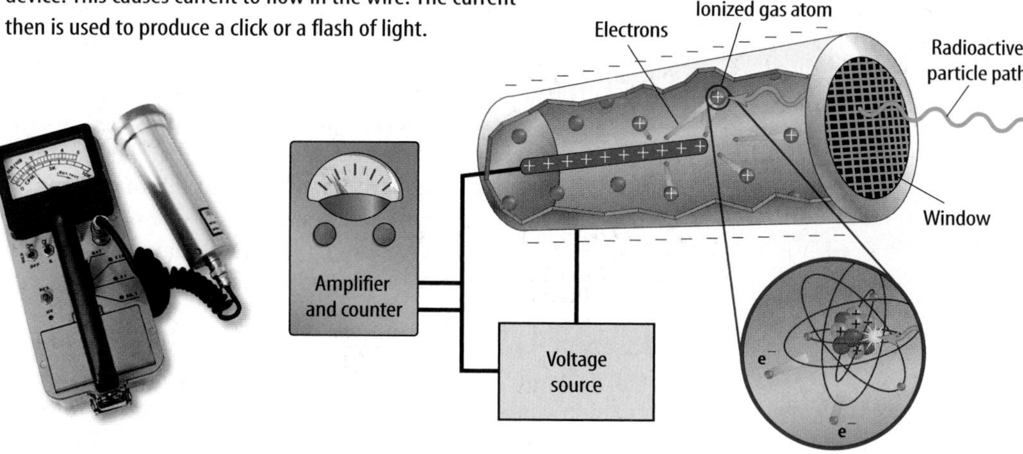

Geiger Counters A Geiger counter, shown in **Figure 14,** has a tube with a positively charged wire running through the center of a negatively charged copper cylinder. This tube is filled with gas at a low pressure. When radiation enters the tube at one end, it knocks electrons from the atoms of the gas. These electrons then knock more electrons off other atoms in the gas, and an "electron avalanche" is produced. The free electrons are attracted to the positive wire in the tube. When a large number of electrons reaches the wire, a short, intense current is produced in the wire. This current is amplified to produce a clicking sound or flashing light. The intensity of radiation present is determined by the number of clicks or flashes of light each second.

How does a Geiger counter indicate that radiation is present?

Background Radiation

It might surprise you to know that you are bathed in radiation that comes from your environment. This radiation, called background radiation, is not produced by humans. Instead it is low-level radiation emitted mainly by naturally occurring radioactive isotopes found in Earth's rocks, soils, and atmosphere. Building materials such as bricks, wood, and stones contain traces of these radioactive materials. Traces of naturally occurring radioactive isotopes are found in the food, water, and air consumed by all animals and plants. As a result, animals and plants also contain small amounts of these isotopes.

Artificial Rainmaking It may be possible to ease the health and economic hardships caused by severe droughts by artificially making rain. The formation of raindrops in a cloud is similar to the formation of droplets in a cloud chamber. Rain forms when cold droplets freeze around microscopic particles of dust, and then melt as they fall through warmer air. Research artificial rainmaking and report you findings to your class.

Artificial Rainmaking Scientists have tried three ways to make artificial rain. Have students research artificial rain to learn how the methods work. One method is spraying water into warm. clouds. Another method is to drop dry ice into clouds. The third method is to drop silver iodide crystals or similar crystals into clouds. None of these methods have been very successful.

Discussion

Detectors In addition to the instruments mentioned in the text, scientists use other detectors to observe high energy particles. One such detector is the Cherenkov detector, which is filled with perfluoro butane gas. Protons with energy above a certain threshold create "Cherenkov Light", which can be focused using mirrors and Winston cones to produce an electrical signal.

Reading Check

Answer by a clicking sound or flashing light

Activity

Background Radiation Have students do research to find out about sources of background radiation in their community. L2 LS **Linguistic**

Differentiated Instruction

Visually Impaired If you have a Geiger counter, let your visually impaired students hear the difference in the clicking between different materials. If you don't have a Geiger counter, do a web search for Geiger counter sounds and download a sound file for them to hear.

Teacher FYI

The G-M Counter The Geiger counter was invented by a German physicist named Hans Geiger. In 1928, Geiger, along with Walther Müller, improved the detector, so it is often called the Geiger-Müller counter, or simply the G-M counter.

SECTION 3 Detecting Radioactivity **549**

Visual Learning

Figure 15 According to this circle graph, how much of the background radiation received by an average person in the United States comes from natural sources outside the body? at least 89 percent

3 Assess

DAILY INTERVENTION

Check For Understanding

Visual-Spatial Ask students to draw sketches of pictures that might be obtained with a cloud chamber and a bubble chamber. For each sketch, have the students explain the lines they have drawn and which type of particle would cause that type of line. L2 IS P

Reteach

Natural Radioactivity Have students explain why radiation occurs naturally in the human body. Radioactive isotopes of elements used by the body occur in nature and are used in the same way as the stable isotopes of the same elements. L2 IS **Logical-Mathematical**

Assessment

Process Have students create a concept map for each of the four methods of radiation detection mentioned in this section. Use **Performance Assessment in the Science Classroom,** p. 161.

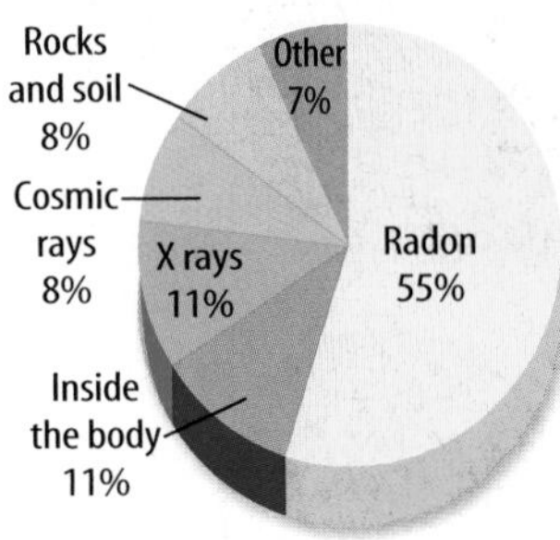

Figure 15 This circle graph shows the sources of background radiation received on average by a person living in the United States.

Sources of Background Radiation Background radiation comes from several sources, as shown in **Figure 15.** The largest source comes from the decay of radon gas. Radon is produced in Earth's crust by the decay of uranium-238 and emits an alpha particle when it decays. Radon gas can seep into houses and basements from the surrounding soil and rocks.

Some background radiation comes from high-speed nuclei, called cosmic rays, that strike Earth's atmosphere. They produce showers of particles, including alpha, beta, and gamma radiation. Most of this radiation is absorbed by the atmosphere. Higher up, there is less atmosphere to absorb this radiation, so the background radiation from cosmic rays increases with altitude.

Radiation in Your Body Some of the elements that are essential for life have naturally occurring radioactive isotopes. For example, about one out of every trillion carbon atoms is carbon-14, which emits a beta particle when it decays. With each breath, you inhale about 3 million carbon-14 atoms.

The amount of background radiation a person receives can vary greatly. The amount depends on the type of rocks underground, the type of materials used to construct the person's home, and the elevation at which the person lives, among other things. However, because it comes from naturally occurring processes, background radiation never can be eliminated.

section 3 review

Summary

Radiation Detectors

- Alpha and beta particles can be detected by the trail of ions they form when they pass through a cloud chamber or a bubble chamber.
- The presence of alpha or beta particles can cause an electroscope to become discharged.
- A Geiger counter produces a clicking sound or a flash of light when alpha or beta particles enter the Geiger counter tube, and is used to measure radiation levels.

Background Radiation

- Background radiation is low-level radiations emitted mainly by radioactive isotopes in Earth's rocks, soils, and atmosphere.
- The largest source of background radiation is from the alpha decay of radon gas.

Self Check

1. **Describe** why a charged electroscope will discharge when placed near a radioactive material.
2. **Compare and contrast** cloud and bubble chambers.
3. **Describe** that process that occurs in a Geiger counter when a click is produced.
4. **Explain** why background radiation never can be completely eliminated.
5. **Think Critically** If the radioactive isotope radon-222 has a half-life of only four days, how can radon gas be continually present inside houses?

Applying Math

6. **Use Percentages** The amount of radiation can be measured in units called millirems. If 25 millirems from cosmic rays is 8.0 percent of the average background radiation, what is the amount of the average background radiation in millirems?

Science Online gpscience.com/self_check_quiz

section 3 review

1. Nuclear radiation causes some molecules in air to become positively charged. Negative charges on the electroscope leaves move from the leaves to the positively charged ions.
2. Both show the paths of ions created by radiation. In bubble chambers a liquid boils along the trail of the ions. In cloud chambers, vapor condenses around the ions.
3. A charged particle strikes a gas molecule in the tube, knocking off electrons. These electrons are attracted to a positively charged wire in the tube, producing more electrons as they collide with gas molecules. The current is amplified to produce a click.
4. Natural sources of background radiation include the decay of radioactive materials in rocks and soil, and cosmic rays, which cannot be eliminated.
5. Radon gas is continually produced by the decay of the isotope uranium-238, which has a half-life of 4.5 billion years.
6. Set up a ratio: (25 millirem)/x = 0.08; so x = (25 millirem)/0.08 = 312 millirem.

section 4

Nuclear Reactions

Reading Guide

What You'll Learn

- **Explain** nuclear fission and how it can begin a chain reaction.
- **Discuss** how nuclear fusion occurs in the Sun.
- **Describe** how radioactive tracers can be used to diagnose medical problems.
- **Discuss** how nuclear reactions can help treat cancer.

Why It's Important

Almost all of the different atoms that you are made of were formed by the nuclear reactions inside ancient, distant stars.

Review Vocabulary

kinetic energy: energy of motion; increases as the mass or speed of an object increases

New Vocabulary

- nuclear fission
- chain reaction
- critical mass
- nuclear fusion
- tracer

Nuclear Fission

In the 1930s the physicist Enrico Fermi thought that by bombarding nuclei with neutrons, nuclei would absorb neutrons and heavier nuclei would be produced. However, in 1938, Otto Hahn and Fritz Strassmann found that when a neutron strikes a uranium-235 nucleus, the nucleus splits apart into smaller nuclei.

In 1939 Lise Meitner was the first to offer a theory to explain these results. She proposed that the uranium-235 nucleus is so distorted when the neutron strikes it that it divides into two smaller nuclei, as shown in **Figure 16.** The process of splitting a nucleus into several smaller nuclei is **nuclear fission.** The word *fission* means "to divide."

Reading Check *What initiates nuclear fission of a uranium-235 nucleus?*

Only large nuclei, such as the nuclei of uranium and plutonium atoms, can undergo nuclear fission. The products of a fission reaction usually include several individual neutrons in addition to the smaller nuclei. The total mass of the products is slightly less than the mass of the original nucleus and the neutron. This small amount of missing mass is converted to a tremendous amount of energy during the fission reaction.

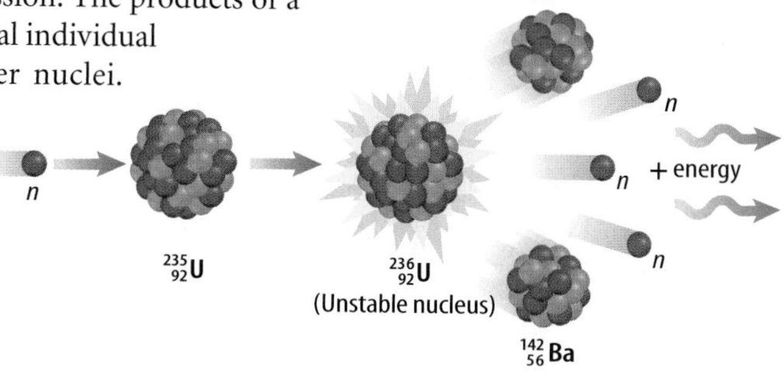

Figure 16 When a neutron hits a uranium-235 nucleus, the uranium nucleus splits into two smaller nuclei and two or three free neutrons. Energy also is released.

Section 4 Resource Manager

Chapter *Fast File* Resources

Transparency Activity, p. 49

MiniLAB, p. 4

Directed Reading for Content Mastery, pp. 21–22

Enrichment, p. 34

Lab Worksheet, pp. 5–6, 7–8

Reinforcement, p. 30

Home and Community Involvement, p. 37

Reading and Writing Skill Activities, p. 47

1 Motivate

Bellringer

Section Focus Transparencies also are available on the Interactive Chalkboard CD-ROM.

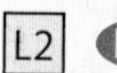
L2

ELL

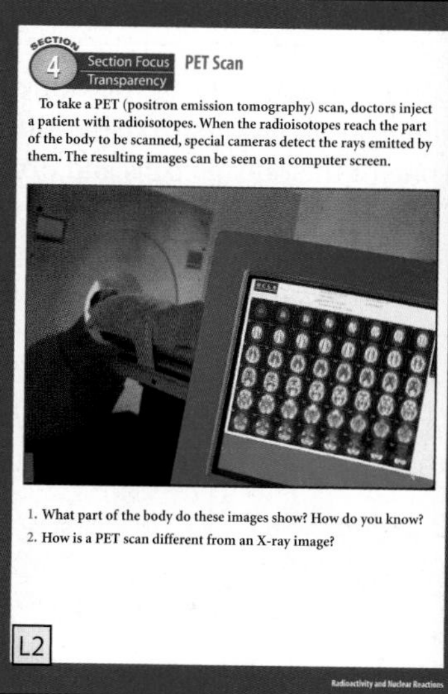

Tie to Prior Knowledge

Breaking and Combining Tell students that fission means breaking things apart and fusion means putting things together. Ask them to give examples of processes they know that fit these definitions. Tell them that in this section they will learn about nuclear fission and nuclear fusion.

Reading Check

Answer A neutron striking the nucleus causes it to split.

2 Teach

Quick Demo

Atomic Forces

Materials kinetic toy—several ball bearings suspended by two strings in contact with each other.

Time Required 1–3 min

Procedure Explain the forces at work in splitting an atom. The kinetic energy of a neutron is high enough to disrupt the strong force in the target nucleus, causing the atom to split into more stable configurations. At this point demonstrate the kinetic energy of the neutron by lifting one of the outside balls and dropping it to see the kinetic energy transmitted through the intermediary balls to the opposite outside ball and observe that ball flying out from the group.

Purpose Students model a nuclear reaction. L2 ELL

IS **Kinesthetic**

Materials marbles, beaker, modeling clay

Teaching Strategy Emphasize that the marbles taken out represent nuclei that decay but do not disappear; they change into nuclei of a different element.

Analysis

1. one minute
2. No. The waste products might be radioactive. They will not undergo fission.

Assessment

Oral What was the half-life of the marbles with clay? How many were left after 5 min? 1 min; one Use **PASC,** p. 101.

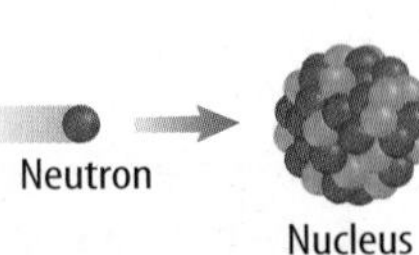

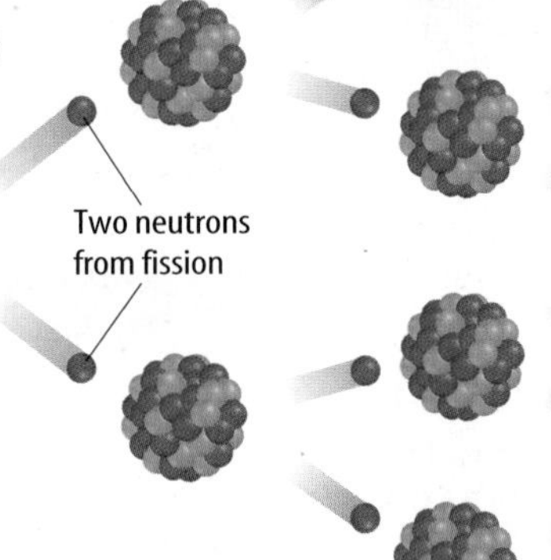

Figure 17 A chain reaction occurs when neutrons emitted from a split nucleus cause other nuclei to split and emit additional neutrons.

Modeling a Nuclear Reaction

Procedure

1. Put **32 marbles,** each with an attached lump of **clay,** into a large **beaker.** These marbles with clay represent unstable atoms.
2. During a 1-min period, remove half of the marbles and pull off the clay. Place the removed marbles into another beaker and place the lumps of clay into a pile. Marbles without clay represent stable atoms. The clay represents waste from the reaction—smaller atoms that still might decay and give off energy.
3. Repeat this procedure four more times.

Analysis

1. What is the half-life of this reaction?
2. Explain whether the waste products could undergo nuclear fission.

Mass and Energy Albert Einstein proposed that mass and energy were related in his special theory of relativity. According to this theory, mass can be converted to energy and energy can be converted to mass. The relation between mass and energy is given by this equation:

Mass-Energy Equation

Energy (joules) = mass (kg) × [speed of light (m/s)]^2

$$E = mc^2$$

A small amount of mass can be converted into an enormous amount of energy. For example, if one gram of mass is converted to energy, about 100 trillion joules of energy are released.

Chain Reactions When a nuclear fission reaction occurs, the neutrons emitted can strike other nuclei in the sample, and cause them to split. These reactions then release more neutrons, causing additional nuclei to split, as shown in **Figure 17.** The series of repeated fission reactions caused by the release of neutrons in each reaction is a **chain reaction.**

If the chain reaction is uncontrolled, an enormous amount of energy is released in an instant. However, a chain reaction can be controlled by adding materials that absorb neutrons. If enough neutrons are absorbed, the reaction will continue at a constant rate.

For a chain reaction to occur, a critical mass of material that can undergo fission must be present. The **critical mass** is the amount of material required so that each fission reaction produces approximately one more fission reaction. If less than the critical mass of material is present, a chain reaction will not occur.

Science Journal

Nuclear Energy? Advocates claim that nuclear reactors are a safe, clean method of producing electricity. Opponents argue that because of the danger from spent nuclear fuel and nuclear waste, reactors should be permanently shut down. Have students write their opinions on this issue in their Science Journals. L2 IS **Linguistic**

Differentiated Instruction

Physically Disabled Pair students who cannot manipulate the marbles with students who can. Have the disabled student in each pair calculate the number of marbles to be processed during each one-minute period, and keep track of the number of marbles processed.

Nuclear Fusion

Tremendous amounts of energy can be released in nuclear fission. In fact, splitting one uranium-235 nucleus produces about 30 million times more energy than chemically reacting one molecule of dynamite. Even more energy can be released in another type of nuclear reaction, called nuclear fusion. In **nuclear fusion,** two nuclei with low masses are combined to form one nucleus of larger mass. Fusion fuses atomic nuclei together, and fission splits nuclei apart.

Temperature and Fusion For nuclear fusion to occur, positively charged nuclei must get close to each other. However, all nuclei repel each other because they have the same positive electric charge. If nuclei are moving fast, they can have enough kinetic energy to overcome the repulsive electrical force between them and get close to each other.

Remember that the kinetic energy of atoms or molecules increases as their temperature increases. Only at temperatures of millions of degrees Celsius are nuclei moving so fast that they can get close enough for fusion to occur. These extremely high temperatures are found in the center of stars, including the Sun.

Nuclear Fusion and the Sun The Sun is composed mainly of hydrogen. Most of the energy given off by the Sun is produced by a process involving the fusion of hydrogen nuclei. This process occurs in several stages, and one of the stages is shown in **Figure 18.** The net result of this process is that four hydrogen nuclei are converted into one helium nucleus. As this occurs, a small amount of mass is changed into an enormous amount of energy. Earth receives a small amount of this energy as heat and light.

As the Sun ages, the hydrogen nuclei are used up as they are converted into helium. So far, only about one percent of the Sun's mass has been converted into energy. Eventually, no hydrogen nuclei will be left, and the fusion reaction that changes hydrogen into helium will stop. However, it is estimated that the Sun has enough hydrogen to keep this reaction going for another 5 billion years.

Topic: Fusion Reactors
Visit gpscience.com for Web links to information about the use of nuclear fusion as a future energy source.

Activity Write a paragraph describing the different types of fusion reactors that have been developed.

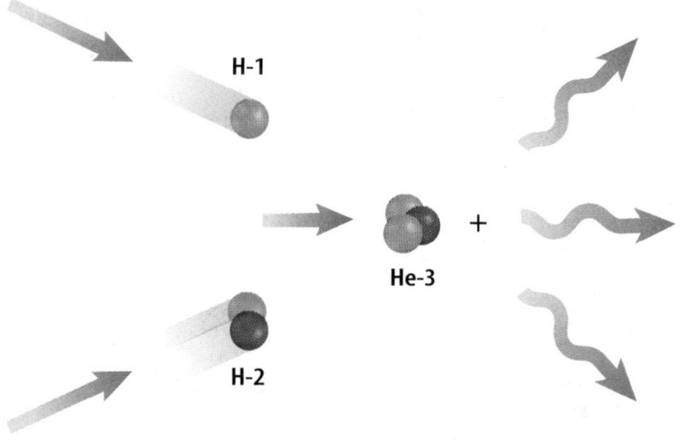

Figure 18 The fusion of hydrogen to form helium takes place in several stages in the Sun. One of these stages is shown here. An isotope of helium is produced when a proton and the hydrogen isotope H-2 undergo fusion.

Make a Model

Clay Nuclei Have students model fusion by using small balls of clay to show how two nuclei can join to become one larger nucleus. They should use different colors of clay to represent protons and neutrons. An easy reaction to model is the one in which a deuterium nucleus (hydrogen with one neutron) and a tritium nucleus (hydrogen with two neutrons) combine to form a helium nucleus and one neutron. Point out that when the number of protons changes, a nucleus of a new element is formed. L2
LS **Kinesthetic**

Teacher FYI

Hydrogen Bomb Scientists have been unable to achieve controlled fusion because the high temperature needed to initiate the reaction creates plasma that is difficult to contain. A hydrogen bomb, however, uses uncontrolled fusion. Inside the hydrogen bomb's casing, an atomic bomb uses fission to create the extreme temperatures needed to start the fusion reaction.

Use Science Words

Word Meaning Have students explain why the fusion of hydrogen nuclei on the Sun is called a thermonuclear reaction. *Thermo-* comes from a Greek word meaning "heat." Forcing hydrogen nuclei to fuse requires extreme heat. L3 LS **Linguistic**

Fun Fact

The submarines of the U.S. Navy are powered by nuclear reators.

Radioactive Decay Equations The atomic number of barium is 56 and the atomic number of krypton is 36. These add up to 92. Uranium-235 breaks into neodymium (atomic number 60) and germanium (atomic number 32).

Research Potassium-40 decays to form two other isotopes. Research to learn what these isotopes are. argon-40 and calcium 40

Discussion

Tracers How is the use of tracers similar to the use of radio collars in tracking wild animals? The collars emit an electromagnetic signal that can be detected with an antenna and receiver. This allows scientists to determine the movement of the animal. Similarly, a radioactive tracer emits radiation, which allows physicians to track its movement in the body. L2 LS **Logical-Mathematical**

Answer by detecting the radioactivity they emit

Caption Answer

Figure 19 Iodine is naturally taken up by the thyroid. Also, it allows doctors to determine how well the thyroid is functioning without having to actually look at it.

Radioactive Decay Equations A uranium-235 atom can fission, or break apart, to form barium and krypton. Use a periodic table to find the atomic numbers of barium and krypton. What do they add up to? A uranium-235 atom can fission in several other ways such as producing neodymium and another element. What is the other element?

Using Nuclear Reactions in Medicine

If you were going to meet a friend in a crowded area, it would be easier to find her if your friend told you that she would be wearing a red hat. In a similar way, scientists can find one molecule in a large group of molecules if they know that it is "wearing" something unique. Although a molecule can't wear a red hat, if it has a radioactive atom in it, it can be found easily in a large group of molecules, or even in a living organism. Radioactive isotopes can be located by detecting the radiation they emit.

When a radioisotope is used to find or keep track of molecules in an organism, it is called a **tracer.** Scientists can use tracers to follow where a particular molecule goes in your body or to study how a particular organ functions. Tracers also are used in agriculture to monitor the uptake of nutrients and fertilizers. Examples of tracers include carbon-11, iodine-131, and sodium-24. These three radioisotopes are useful tracers because they are important in certain body processes. As a result, they accumulate inside the organism being studied.

Reading Check *How are tracers located inside the human body?*

INTEGRATE Health

Iodine Tracers in the Thyroid The thyroid gland is located in your neck and produces chemical compounds called hormones. These hormones help regulate several body processes, including growth. Because the element iodine accumulates in the thyroid, the radioisotope iodine-131 can be used to diagnose thyroid problems. As iodine-131 atoms are absorbed by the thyroid, their nuclei decay, emitting beta particles and gamma rays. The beta particles are absorbed by the surrounding tissues, but the gamma rays penetrate the skin. The emitted gamma rays can be detected and used to determine whether the thyroid is healthy, as shown in **Figure 19.** If the detected radiation is not intense, then the thyroid has not properly absorbed the iodine-131 and is not functioning properly. This could be due to the presence of a tumor. **Figure 20** shows how radioactive tracers are used to study the brain.

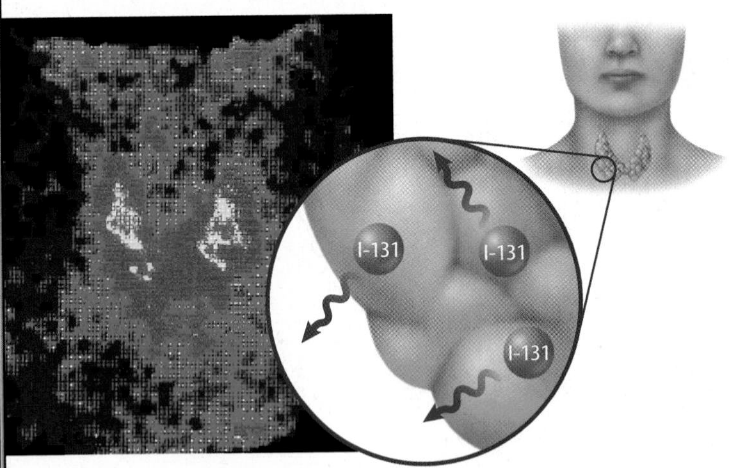

Figure 19 Radioactive iodine-131 accumulates in the thyroid gland and emits gamma rays, which can be detected to form an image of a patient's thyroid.
List *some advantages of being able to use iodine-131 to form an image of a thyroid.*

Differentiated Instruction

Challenge Have students investigate other ways that tracers are used in medicine and prepare a report on one method. If possible, they should interview a physician who uses tracers to find out drawbacks and benefits of the procedure. Possible topics are tracers used to detect problems with the heart, kidneys, or digestion. L3 LS **Linguistic**

Visual Learning

Figure 19 Point out that the picture to the left shows the thyroid after the person has ingested the iodine-131 tracer. The red and orange colors indicate areas in which the iodine is well absorbed. Have students each find his or her thyroid gland, which is located in the neck between the larynx and the trachea. L2 LS **Visual-Spatial**

NATIONAL GEOGRAPHIC VISUALIZING PET SCANS

Figure 20

The diagram below shows an imaging technique known as Positron Emission Tomography, or PET. Positrons are emitted from the nuclei of certain radioactive isotopes when a proton changes to a neutron. PET can form images that show the level of activity in different areas of the brain. These images can reveal tumors and regions of abnormal brain activity.

Ⓐ When positrons are emitted from the nucleus of an atom, they can hit electrons from other atoms and become transformed into gamma rays.

Ⓑ The radioactive isotope fluorine-18 emits positrons when it decays. Fluorine-18 atoms are chemically attached to molecules that are absorbed by brain tissue. These compounds are injected into the patient and carried by blood to the brain.

Ⓒ Inside the patient's brain, the decay of the radioactive fluorine-18 nuclei emits positrons that collide with electrons. The gamma rays that are released are sensed by the detectors.

Ⓓ A computer uses the information collected by the detectors to generate an image of the activity level in the brain. This image shows normal activity in the right side of the brain (red, yellow, green) but below-normal activity in the left (purple).

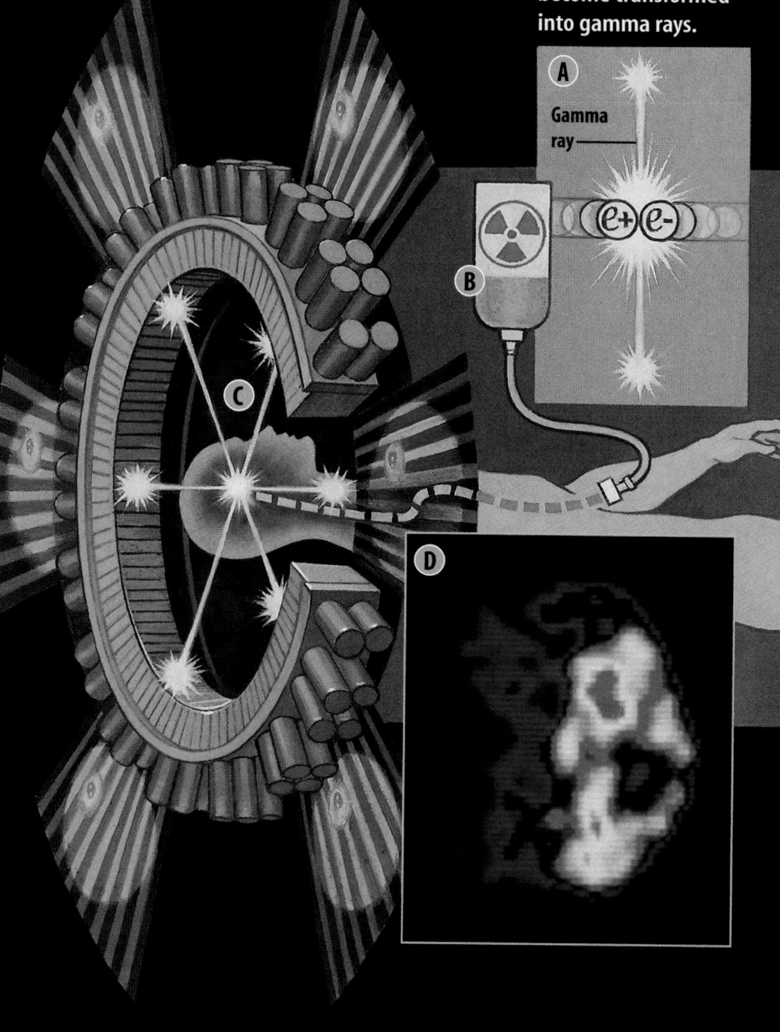

Visualizing PET Scans

Have students examine the pictures and read the captions. Then ask the following questions:

What is a positron? A positron has the same mass as an electron but a positive charge. It can be considered a positively charged electron.

What is formed when a positron and electron combine? gamma rays

Why is it important for the fluorine-18 to be chemically attached to substances that are normally absorbed by the brain? The fluorine-18 needs to be absorbed in the brain tissue because that is the area that is being studied.

Activity

Position Posters Have the students research how positrons are formed. Suggest students make posters illustrating their findings and present their posters to the class. L2 LS **Visual-Spatial** P

3 Assess

DAILY INTERVENTION

Check for Understanding

Logical-Mathematical Ask students to explain why chain reactions do not occur in naturally existing material. Fission occurs only for certain rare isotopes. The percentage of these isotopes in naturally existing material is so low that a chain reaction is unlikely. IS

Reteach

Chain Reactions Have students discuss why a critical mass is necessary to keep a fission reaction going but not to keep a fusion reaction going. In a fission reaction, a particle bombards a nucleus and splits it into two nuclei plus several neutrons. If these neutrons hit other fissionable nuclei, those nuclei will split and produce new particles. This chain reaction will continue as long as there is enough fissionable material nearby. The amount needed to keep the reaction going is the critical mass. A fusion reaction is not a chain reaction. L2 IS **Logical-Mathematical**

Assessment

Content Many benefits result from nuclear applications in medicine, but there are disadvantages, too. Ask students to write newspaper articles explaining how radiation can cause as well as treat cancer. Possible answers: It can cause mutations in cell structures, leading to tumor formation, or it can kill cancer cells. Use **PASC**, p. 141.

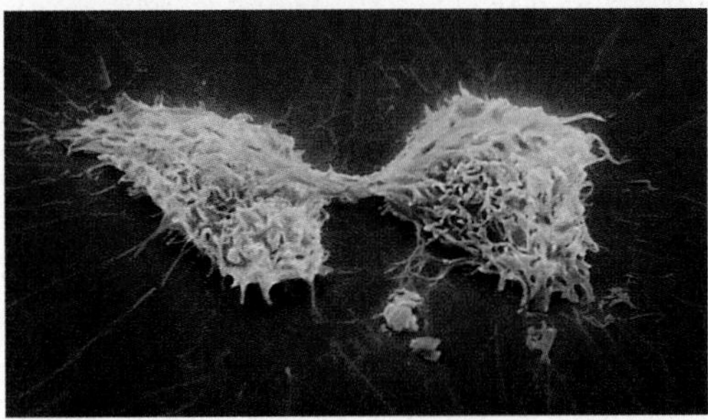

Figure 21 Cancer cells, such as the ones shown here, can be killed with carefully measured doses of radiation.

Treating Cancer with Radioactivity

When a person has cancer, a group of cells in that person's body grows out of control and can form a tumor. Radiation can be used to stop some types of cancerous cells from growing. Remember that the radiation that is given off during nuclear decay is strong enough to ionize nearby atoms. If a source of radiation is placed near cancer cells, such as those shown in **Figure 21,** atoms in the cells can be ionized. If the ionized atoms are in a critical molecule, such as the DNA or RNA of a cancer cell, then the molecule might no longer function properly. The cell then could die or stop growing.

When possible, a radioactive isotope such as gold-198 or iridium-192 is implanted within or near the tumor. Other times, tumors are treated from outside the body. Typically, an intense beam of gamma rays from the decay of cobalt-60 is focused on the tumor for a short period of time. The gamma rays pass through the body and into the tumor. How can physicians be sure that only the cancer cells will absorb radiation? Because cancer cells grow quickly, they are more susceptible to absorbing radiation and being damaged than healthy cells are. However, other cells in the body that grow quickly also are damaged, which is why cancer patients who have radiation therapy sometimes experience severe side effects.

section 4 review

Summary

Nuclear Fission

- Nuclear fission occurs when a neutron strikes a nucleus, causing it to split into smaller nuclei.
- A chain reaction requires a critical mass of fissionable material.

Nuclear Fusion

- Nuclear fusion occurs when two nuclei combine to form another nucleus.
- Nuclear fusion occurs at temperatures of millions of degrees, which occur inside the Sun.

Medical Uses of Radiation

- Radioactive isotopes are used as tracers to locate various atoms or molecules in organisms.
- Radiation emitted by radioactive isotopes is used to kill cancer cells.

Self Check

1. **Infer** whether mass is conserved in a nuclear reaction.
2. **Explain** why fusion reactions can occur inside stars.
3. **Explain** how a chain reaction can be controlled.
4. **Describe** two properties of a tracer isotope used for monitoring the functioning of an organ in the body.
5. **Think Critically** Explain why high temperatures are needed for fusion reactions to occur, but not for fission reactions to occur.

Applying Math

6. **Calculate Number of Nuclei** In a chain reaction, two neutrons are emitted by each nucleus that is split. If one nucleus is split in the first step of the reaction, how many nuclei will have been split after the fifth step?

section  review

1. No. Some of the mass in the initial nuclei is converted into energy.
2. Fusion reactions require extremely high temperatures to get started. These temperatures occur in the interior of stars.
3. By absorbing some of the neutrons emitted when fission occurs.
4. The isotope must be absorbed by the organ being studied, and must have a half-life sufficiently long for the study to be completed before it decays away.
5. For fusion to occur, positively charged nuclei must get close to each other for the strong force to act. The nuclei must be moving fast enough to overcome the electrical repulsion between the nuclei. Nuclei are moving at the necessary speeds only at very high temperatures. In nuclear fission, a neutron is not repelled by a positively charged nucleus, and doesn't have to be moving at a high speed to strike the nucleus.
6. 1st step = 1, 2nd step = 2, 3rd step = 4, 4th step = 8, 5th step = 16.

Chain Reactions

In an uncontrolled nuclear chain reaction, the number of reactions increases as additional neutrons split more nuclei. In a controlled nuclear reaction, neutrons are absorbed, so the reaction continues at a constant rate. How could you model a controlled and an uncontrolled nuclear reaction in the classroom?

Real-World Question

How can you use dominoes to model chain reactions?

Goals

- **Model** a controlled and uncontrolled chain reaction.
- **Compare** the two types of chain reactions.

Materials

dominoes
stopwatch

Procedure

1. Set up a single line of dominoes standing on end so that when the first domino is pushed over, it will knock over the second and each domino will knock over the one following it.
2. Using the stopwatch, time how long it takes from the moment the first domino is pushed over until the last domino falls over. Record the time.
3. Using the same number of dominoes as in step 1, set up a series of dominoes in which at least one of the dominoes will knock down two others, so that two lines of dominoes will continue falling. In other words, the series should have at least one point that looks like the letter Y.
4. Repeat step 2.

Conclude and Apply

1. **Compare** the amount of time it took for all of the dominoes to fall in each of your two arrangements.
2. **Determine** the average number of dominoes that fell per second in both domino arrangements.
3. **Identify** which of your domino arrangements represented a controlled chain reaction and which represented an uncontrolled chain reaction.
4. **Describe** how the concept of critical mass was represented in your model of a controlled chain reaction.
5. Assuming that they had equal amounts of material, which would finish faster—a controlled or an uncontrolled nuclear chain reaction? Explain.

Communicating Your Data

Explain to friends or members of your family how a controlled nuclear chain reaction can be used in nuclear power plants to generate electricity.

BENCH TESTED

Real-World Question

Purpose Students model controlled and uncontrolled chain reactions. L2 LS **Kinesthetic**

Process Skills collect data, make models, compare and contrast, draw conclusions

Time Required 40 min

Teaching Strategy Students can collect additional data by forming large groups and using all of their dominoes to form longer chains.

Conclude and Apply

1. The Y-shaped arrangement fell faster.
2. No, in the Y-shaped arrangement some places had two dominoes falling at once.
3. The straight arrangement represented a controlled reaction because any neutron that split off was absorbed. The Y-shaped arrangement represented an uncontrolled reaction.
4. Critical mass was represented because the reaction stopped when the fissionable material (dominoes) was used up.
5. An uncontrolled reaction would finish faster because a single reaction could produce two reactions which could produce four reactions and so on.

Assessment

Content Have students write and perform a skit that demonstrates controlled and uncontrolled reactions. Use **Performance Assessment in the Science Classroom,** p. 147.

Communicating Your Data

Students should prepare an illustration of a controlled and an uncontrolled reaction to help explain what is taking place.

Real-World Question

Purpose Students will model the decay of a uranium atom through the process of transmutation. L2 LS **Kinesthetic**

Process Skills making a model, comparing, constructing, identifying, and inferring

Time Required one 45-minute class period

Alternate Materials Students can use any small objects in place of the rice, beans, or candy. A strong bonding glue should be used when constructing the model.

Safety Precautions Never eat foods used in the lab.

Discussion

Radioactive Substances Ask students to think about radioactive substances such as uranium and plutonium. Have them consider the exposure to radiation some people have been exposed to such as after nuclear testing or the Chernobyl accident. Why is radiation dangerous? Where does radiation come from? What effects would come from having radioactive materials in their homes? What radioactive substance might be found in their basements (Radon)?

Model and Invent

Modeling Transmutations

Possible Materials

brown rice
white rice
colored candies
dried beans
dried seeds
glue
poster board

Safety Precautions

WARNING: *Never eat foods used in the lab.*

Data Source

Refer to your textbook for general information about transmutation.

Real-World Question

Imagine what would happen if the oxygen atoms around you began changing into nitrogen atoms. Without oxygen, most living organisms, including people, could not live. Fortunately, more than 99.9 percent of all oxygen atoms are stable and do not decay. Usually, when an unstable nucleus decays, an alpha or beta particle is thrown out of its nucleus, and the atom becomes a new element. A uranium-238 atom, for example, will undergo eight alpha decays and six beta decays to become lead. This process of one element changing into another element is called transmutation. How could you create a model of a uranium-238 atom and the decay process it undergoes during transmutation? What types of materials could you use to represent the protons and neutrons in a U-238 nucleus? How could you use these materials to model transmutation?

Make a Model

1. **Choose** two materials of different colors or shapes for the protons and neutrons of your nucleus model. Choose a material for the negatively charged beta particle.

Differentiated Instruction

Physically Challenged If students cannot manipulate the materials, have them design a model, and ask other students to work with them to make the model.

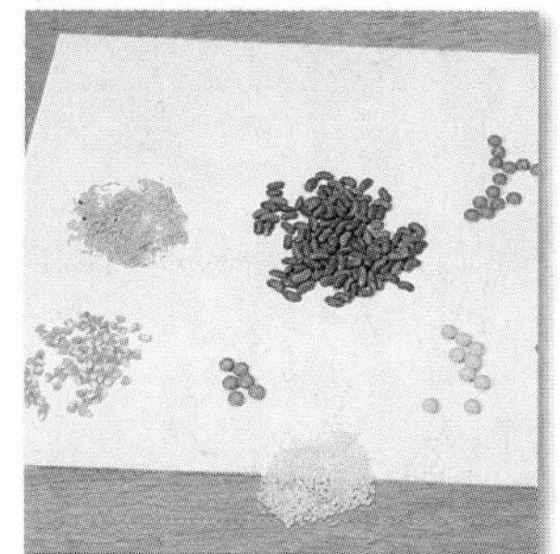

2. **Decide** how to model the transmutation process. Will you create a new nucleus model for each new element? How will you model an alpha or beta particle leaving the nucleus?
3. **Create** a transmutation chart to show the results of each transmutation step of a uranium-238 atom with the identity, atomic number, and mass number of each new element formed and the type of radiation particle emitted at each step. A uranium-238 atom will undergo the following decay steps before transmuting into a lead-206 atom: alpha decay, beta decay, beta decay, alpha decay, alpha decay, alpha decay, alpha decay, alpha decay, beta decay, beta decay, alpha decay, beta decay, beta decay, alpha decay.
4. **Describe** your model plan and transmutation chart to your teacher and ask how they can be improved.
5. **Present** your plan and chart to your class. Ask classmates to suggest improvements in both.
6. Construct your model of a uranium-238 nucleus showing the correct number of protons and neutrons.

Test Your Model

1. Using your nucleus model, demonstrate the transmutation of a uranium-238 nucleus into a lead-206 nucleus by following the decay sequence outlined in the previous section.
2. Show the emission of an alpha particle or beta particle between each transmutation step.

Analyze Your Data

1. **Compare** how alpha and beta decay change an atom's atomic number.
2. **Compare** how alpha and beta decay change the mass number of an atom.

Conclude and Apply

1. **Calculate** the ratio of neutrons to protons in lead-206 and uranium-238. In which nucleus is the ratio closer to 1.5?
2. **Identify** Alchemists living during the Middle Ages spent much time trying to turn lead into gold. Identify the decay processes needed to accomplish this task.

Show your model to the class and explain how your model represents the transmutation of U-238 into Pb-206.

Assessment

Process Ask students to make pamphlets identifying ways the transmutation of uranium and plutonium are used. nuclear power plant, nuclear weapons, nuclear submarines, and spacecraft Use **Performance Assessment in the Science Classroom**, p. 129.

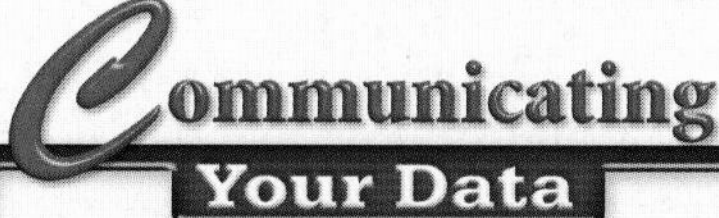

Encourage students to use electronically designed diagrams to accompany their models.

Make a Model

Possible Procedures

- Use white rice for protons and brown rice for neutrons
- Make a model of the nucleus of a Uranium-238 atom in the upper left corner of the poster board by gluing the appropriate rice to the board.
- Draw an arrow with the type of decay above it pointing to the resulting isotope.
- Repeat through all 14 steps of decay.
- Make rice model of Lead-206 nucleus in lower right corner.

Teaching Strategy Have references available for students to use that show the transmutation of uranium into lead.

Test Your Model

Expected Outcome Students will build a model that demonstrates the transmutation of uranium.

Analyze Your Data

1. Alpha decay decreases the atomic number by two; beta decay increases the atomic number by one.
2. Alpha decay decreases the mass number by four; beta decay causes no change in the mass number.

Conclude and Apply

1. For lead-206, the ratio is 1.51. For uranium-238, the ratio is 1.59. Lead-206 has a ratio closer to 1.5.
2. Two alpha decays and one beta decay would be required to turn an atom of lead into an atom of gold.

TIME

Content Background

After Henri Becquerel's discovery of radioactivity in 1896, no one as yet suspected that atoms were not indivisible. At first it was thought that radioactivity was the result of chemical processes that occurred in the atoms involved. However, in 1902, Ernest Rutherford and Frederick Soddy discovered that radioactive thorium produced other elements, and realized that thorium atoms were decaying.

In the early 1930s, Enrico Fermi started a series of experiments in which he bombarded nuclei of various elements with neutrons, in an attempt to produce artificial radioactivity. When uranium was bombarded with neutrons, several radioactive products were produced. In 1938, Otto Hahn and Fritz Strassmann announced that the products of the neutron bombardment of uranium were smaller nuclei. This was the first demonstration of nuclear fission.

Historical Significance

The discovery of radioactivity and the development of methods to control nuclear fission have resulted in techniques for using nuclear radiation to treat diseases, as well as nuclear power plants. However, the development of nuclear weapons has had a profound impact on relations between the United States and other countries.

TIME SCIENCE AND HISTORY

SCIENCE CAN CHANGE THE COURSE OF HISTORY!

The Nuclear Alchemists

The colored tracks are alpha particles emitted from a speck of radium salt placed on a special photographic plate.

For centuries, ancient alchemists tried in vain to convert common metals into gold. However, in the early 20th century, some scientists realized there was a way to convert atoms of some elements into other elements—nuclear fission.

A Startling Discovery

As the twentieth century dawned, most scientists thought atoms could not be broken apart. In 1902, a New Zealand physicist Ernest Rutherford and his colleague Frederick Soddy showed that heavy elements uranium and thorium decayed into slightly lighter elements, with the production of helium gas. "Don't call it transmutation. They'll have our heads off as alchemists!" Rutherford warned Soddy. In 1908, Rutherford showed that the alpha particles emitted in radioactive decay were the same as a helium nucleus.

Something's Missing

In 1938 in Germany, Otto Hahn and Fritz Strassmann found the uranium-235 nucleus would split if struck by a neutron. The process was called nuclear fission.

Enrico Fermi lead the development of the first nuclear reactor.

A year later, Austrian physicist Lise Meitner pointed out that the total mass of the particles produced when the uranium nucleus split was less than that of the original uranium nucleus. According to the special theory of relativity, this small amount of missing mass results in the release of a tremendous amount of energy when fission occurs. But is there any way this energy could be controlled?

Lise Meitner was the first to explain how nuclear fission occurs.

Controlling a Chain Reaction

Only a few years later, Italian physicist Enrico Fermi, working with colleagues in the United States, found the answer. Fermi realized that the neutrons released when fission occurs could lead to a chain reaction. However, materials that absorb neutrons could be used to control the chain reaction. In late 1942, Fermi and his colleagues built the first nuclear reactor by using cadmium rods to absorb neutrons and control the chain reaction. The tremendous energy released by nuclear fission could be controlled.

Research Find out more about the contributions these scientists made to understanding radioactivity and the nucleus. What other discoveries did Rutherford and Fermi make?

For more information, visit gpscience.com/time

Research Rutherford also discovered alpha rays and beta rays, the existence of the atomic nucleus, and predicted the existence of the neutron. Fermi discovered that neutron bombardment causes nuclear transformations, formulated the theory of beta decay, and predicted the existence of the neutrino.

Resources for Teachers and Students

How Do We Know the Nature of the Atom?, Natalie Goldstein, Rosen Publishing Group, Incorporated, 2001

Ernest Rutherford and the Atom, John L. Heilbron, Oxford, 2003

Reviewing Main Ideas

Section 1 Radioactivity

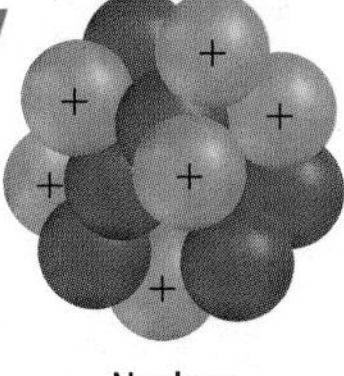

Nucleus

1. The protons and neutrons in an atomic nucleus, like the one to the right, are held together by the strong force.
2. The ratio of protons to neutrons indicates whether a nucleus will be stable or unstable. Large nuclei tend to be unstable.
3. Radioactivity is the emission of energy or particles from an unstable nucleus.
4. Radioactivity was discovered accidentally by Henri Becquerel about 100 years ago.

Section 2 Nuclear Decay

1. Unstable nuclei can decay by emitting alpha particles, beta particles, and gamma rays.
2. Alpha particles consist of two protons and two neutrons. A beta particle is an electron.
3. Gamma rays are the highest frequency electromagnetic waves.
4. Half-life is the amount of time in which half of the nuclei of a radioactive isotope will decay.
5. Because all living things contain carbon, the radioactive isotope carbon-14 can be used to date the remains of organisms that lived during the past 50,000 years, such as this skeleton.

6. Radioactive isotopes of uranium are used to date rocks.

Section 3 Detecting Radioactivity

1. Radioactivity can be detected with a cloud chamber, a bubble chamber, an electroscope, or a Geiger counter.
2. A Geiger counter measures the amount of radiation by producing electric current when it is struck by a charged particle.
3. Background radiation is low-level radiation emitted by naturally occurring isotopes found in Earth's rocks and soils, the atmosphere, and inside your body.

Section 4 Nuclear Reactions

1. When nuclear fission occurs, a nucleus splits into smaller nuclei. Neutrons and a large amount of energy are emitted.
2. Neutrons emitted when a nuclear fission reaction occurs can cause a chain reaction. A chain reaction can occur only if a critical mass of material is present.
3. Nuclear fusion occurs at high temperatures when light nuclei collide and form heavier nuclei, releasing a large amount of energy.
4. Radioactive tracers that are absorbed by specific organs can help diagnose health problems. Nuclear radiation is used to kill cancer cells.

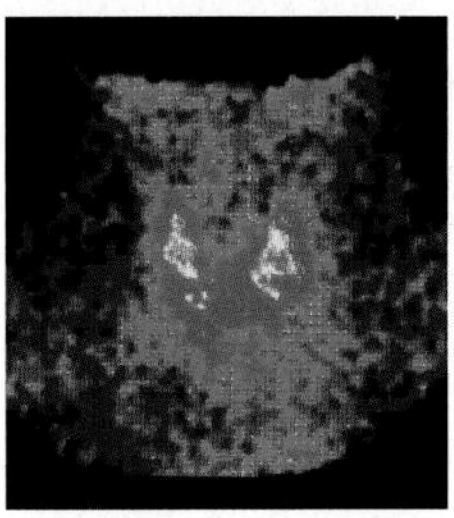

FOLDABLES™ Use the Foldable that you made at the beginning of this chapter to help you review advantages and disadvantages of using radioactive materials and nuclear reactions.

Science Online gpscience.com/interactive_tutor

chapter 18 Study Guide

Reviewing Main Ideas

Summary statements can be used by students to review the major concepts of the chapter.

Visit gpscience.com
/self_check_quiz
/interactive_tutor
/vocabulary_puzzlemaker
/chapter_review
/standardized_test

Assessment Transparency

For additional assessment questions, use the *Assessment Transparency* located in the transparency book.

Assessment

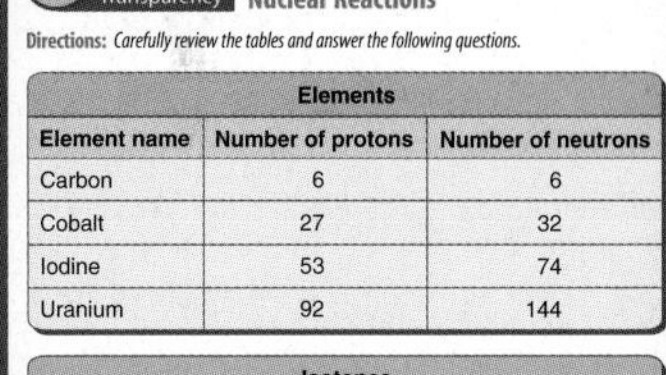

Assessment Transparency — Radioactivity and Nuclear Reactions

Directions: *Carefully review the tables and answer the following questions.*

Elements		
Element name	Number of protons	Number of neutrons
Carbon	6	6
Cobalt	27	32
Iodine	53	74
Uranium	92	144

Isotopes		
Isotope name	Number of protons	Number of neutrons
Carbon-14	6	8
Cobalt-60	27	33
Iodine-131	53	78
Uranium-235	92	143

1. The element carbon has at least one other isotope, carbon-13. A reasonable hypothesis based on the data contained in the tables is that carbon-13 has ___.
   A 8 neutrons
   B 7 neutrons
   C 6 electrons
   D 12 protons
2. What do the elements and their isotopes have in common?
   F same number of protons
   G same number of neutrons
   H same mass number
   J same nuclear mass

L2

Radioactivity and Nuclear Reactions

FOLDABLES™ Have students use their Foldables to review the content of the chapter. Is radioactivity necessarily a good thing or a bad thing? Explain why.

Using Vocabulary

1. Both are used to detect subatomic particles. In both, charged particles create ions. In a cloud chamber, vapor condenses around these ions. In a bubble chamber, a liquid boils along the trail of ions.
2. A chain reaction is an ongoing series of fission reactions. Critical mass is the minimum amount of fissionable material required for a fission chain to occur.
3. Nuclear fission is the splitting of a nucleus. Nuclear fusion is the combining of two nuclei.
4. Radioactivity is the emission of high-energy radiation or particles from the nucleus of a radioactive atom. Half-life is the time required for half of a sample of radioactive material to decay.
5. An alpha particle is made of two protons and two neutrons. A beta particle is a high-speed electron. A gamma ray is high-energy electromagnetic radiation. All are types of nuclear radiation.
6. A Geiger counter is a device that measures radioactivity by producing an electric current when radiation is present. A tracer is a radioactive isotope that can be detected as it moves in an organism.
7. Nuclear fission is the splitting of a nucleus. Transmutation is the process of changing one element to another.
8. An electroscope detects radiation by responding to ionization of the surrounding air, which causes its leaves to separate. In a Geiger counter, electric current is produced when the instrument detects radiation.
9. The strong force binds atomic nuclei together. Radioactivity occurs when a nucleus emits alpha, beta, or gamma radiation.

Checking Concepts

10. A	**14.** A	**18.** A
11. B	**15.** A	**19.** D
12. B	**16.** C	
13. A	**17.** A	

chapter 18 Review

Using Vocabulary

alpha particle p. 541
beta particle p. 543
bubble chamber p. 547
chain reaction p. 552
cloud chamber p. 546
critical mass p. 552
gamma ray p. 543
Geiger counter p. 548
half-life p. 544
nuclear fission p. 551
nuclear fusion p. 553
radioactivity p. 538
strong force p. 537
tracer p. 554
transmutation p. 542

Use what you know about the vocabulary words to explain the differences in the following sets of words. Then explain how the words are related.

1. cloud chamber—bubble chamber
2. chain reaction—critical mass
3. nuclear fission—nuclear fusion
4. radioactivity—half-life
5. alpha particle—beta particle—gamma ray
6. Geiger counter—tracer
7. nuclear fission—transmutation
8. electroscope—Geiger counter
9. strong force—radioactivity

Checking Concepts

Choose the word or phrase that best answers the question.

10. What keeps particles in a nucleus together?
A) strong force
B) repulsion
C) electrical force
D) atomic glue

11. Which device would be most useful for measuring the amount of radiation in a nuclear laboratory?
A) a cloud chamber
B) a Geiger counter
C) an electroscope
D) a bubble chamber

12. What is an electron that is produced when a neutron decays called?
A) an alpha particle
B) a beta particle
C) gamma radiation
D) a negatron

13. Which of the following describes an isotope's half-life?
A) a constant time interval
B) a varied time interval
C) an increasing time interval
D) a decreasing time interval

14. For which of the following could carbon-14 dating be used?
A) a bone fragment
B) a marble column
C) dinosaur fossils
D) rocks

15. Which term describes an ongoing series of fission reactions?
A) chain reaction
B) decay reaction
C) positron emission
D) fusion reaction

16. Which process is responsible for the tremendous energy released by the Sun?
A) nuclear decay
B) nuclear fission
C) nuclear fusion
D) combustion

17. Which radioisotope acts as an external source of ionizing radiation in the treatment of cancer?
A) cobalt-60
B) carbon-14
C) gold-198
D) technetium-99

18. Which of the following describes all nuclei with more than 83 protons?
A) radioactive
B) repulsive
C) synthetic
D) stable

19. Which of the following describes atoms with the same number of protons and a different number of neutrons?
A) unstable
B) synthetic
C) radioactive
D) isotopes

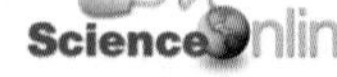

gpscience.com/vocabulary_puzzlemaker

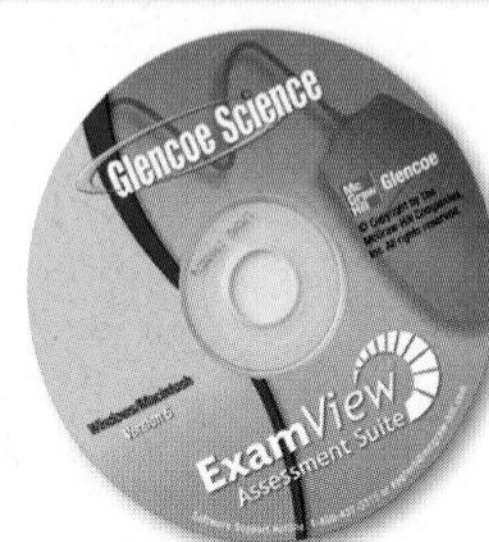

Use the *ExamView® Assessment Suite* CD-ROM to:
- create multiple versions of tests
- create modified tests with one mouse click for inclusion students
- edit existing questions and add your own questions
- build tests aligned with state standards using built-in State Curriculum Tags
- change English tests to Spanish with one mouse click and vice versa

Interpreting Graphics

20. Copy and complete the following concept map on radioactivity.

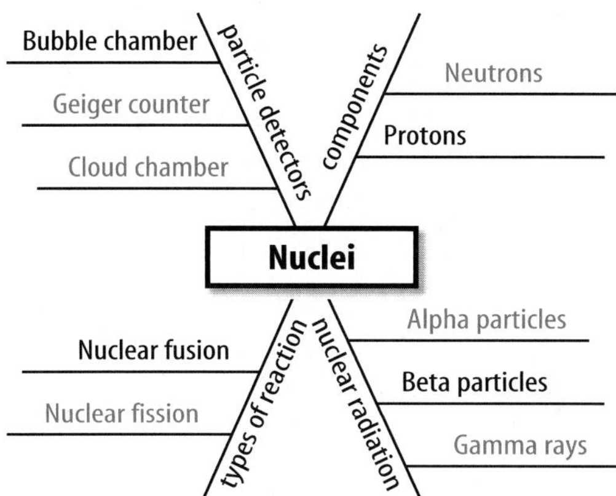

21. Make a table summarizing the use of radioactive isotopes or nuclear radiation in the following applications: radioactive dating, monitoring the thyroid gland, and treating cancer. Include a description of the radioactive isotope or radiation involved.

Use the data in the table below to answer question 22.

Isotope Half-Lives

Isotope	Mass Number	Half-Life
Radon-222	222	4 days
Thorium-234	234	24 days
Iodine-131	131	8 days
Bismuth-210	210	5 days
Polonium-210	210	138 days

22. Graph the data in the table above with the x-axis the mass number and the y-axis the half-life. Infer from your graph whether there is a relation between the half-life and the mass number. If so, how does half-life depend on mass number?

Thinking Critically

23. Explain why the amount of background radiation a person receives can vary greatly from place to place.

24. Infer how the atomic number of a nucleus changes when the nucleus emits only gamma radiation.

25. Identify the properties of alpha particles that make them harmful to living cells.

26. Determine the type of nuclear radiation that is emitted by each of the following nuclear reactions:
- a. uranium-238 to thorium-234
- b. boron-12 to carbon-12
- c. cesium-130 to cesium 130
- d. radium-226 to radon-222

27. Determine how the motion of an alpha particle is affected when it passes between a positively-charged electrode and a negatively charged electrode. How is the motion of a gamma ray affected?

28. Infer how the background radiation a person receives changes when they fly in a jet airliner.

Applying Math

29. Use a Ratio The mass of an alpha particle is 4.0026 mass units, and the mass of a beta particle is 0.000548 mass units. How many times larger is the mass of an alpha particle than the mass of a beta particle?

30. Calculate Number of Half-Lives How many half-lives have elapsed when the amount of a radioactive isotope in a sample is reduced to 3.125 percent of the original amount in the sample.

chapter 18 Review

Interpreting Graphics

20. Check students' work.

21. radioactive dating: carbon-14; monitoring the thyroid gland: iodine-131; treating cancer: gamma rays

22. Graphs should show that there is no relation between mass number and half-life.

Thinking Critically

23. The amount of background radiation a person receives depends on their elevation above sea level, the material their house is made from, and the type of minerals in the ground.

24. The atomic number doesn't change when gamma radiation is emitted.

25. Alpha particles have the most mass and the greatest charge, and cause more ions to be formed as they travel in matter.

26. a. alpha particle, b. beta particle, c. gamma radiation, d. alpha particle

27. The alpha particle is deflected toward the negative electrode; the gamma ray is not affected.

28. The background radiation increases, because there is less atmosphere at higher elevations to absorb cosmic rays.

Applying Math

National Math Standards

1, 6, 9

29. about 7,300 times larger

30. five half-lives

Assessment Resources

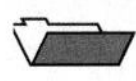

Reproducible Masters

Chapter *Fast File* Resources
- Chapter Review, pp. 39–40
- Chapter Tests, pp. 41–44
- Assessment Transparency Activity, p. 51

Glencoe Science Web site
- Chapter Review Test
- Standardized Test Practice

Glencoe Technology
- Assessment Transparency
- *ExamView® Assessment Suite*
- MindJogger Videoquiz
- Interactive Chalkboard

FAST FILE

Answer Sheet A practice answer sheet can be found at gpscience.com/answer_sheet.

Name Date Class

Standardized Test Practice

Assessment Student Recording Sheet *Use with pages 788–789 of the Student Edition*

Standardized Test Practice

Part 1 Multiple Choice

Select the best answer from the choices given and fill in the corresponding oval.

1. Ⓐ Ⓑ Ⓒ Ⓓ 8. Ⓐ Ⓑ Ⓒ Ⓓ
2. Ⓐ Ⓑ Ⓒ Ⓓ 9. Ⓐ Ⓑ Ⓒ Ⓓ
3. Ⓐ Ⓑ Ⓒ Ⓓ 10. Ⓐ Ⓑ Ⓒ Ⓓ
4. Ⓐ Ⓑ Ⓒ Ⓓ 11. Ⓐ Ⓑ Ⓒ Ⓓ
5. Ⓐ Ⓑ Ⓒ Ⓓ 12. Ⓐ Ⓑ Ⓒ Ⓓ
6. Ⓐ Ⓑ Ⓒ Ⓓ 13. Ⓐ Ⓑ Ⓒ Ⓓ
7. Ⓐ Ⓑ Ⓒ Ⓓ 14. Ⓐ Ⓑ Ⓒ Ⓓ

Part 2 Constructed Response/Grid In

Record and bubble in your answers on the grids below.

15. 16. 17.

Record your answers for Questions 18–21 on a separate sheet of paper.

SAMPLE

Assessment 169

Part 1 Multiple Choice

1. D
2. C
3. A
4. C
5. A
6. B
7. C
8. D
9. B

chapter 18 Standardized Test Practice

Part 1 Multiple Choice

Record your answers on the answer sheet provided by your teacher or on a sheet of paper.

1. If a radioactive material has a half-life of 10 y, what fraction of the material will remain after 30 y?
A. one half **C.** one fourth
B. one third **D.** one eighth

2. Which of the follow statements is true about all the isotopes of an element?
A. They have the same mass number.
B. They have different numbers of protons.
C. They have different numbers of neutrons.
D. They have the same number of neutrons.

3. How does the beta decay of a nucleus cause the nucleus to change?
A. The number of protons increases.
B. The number of neutrons increases.
C. The number of protons decreases.
D. The number of protons plus the number of neutrons decreases.

Use the illustration below to answer questions 4 and 5.

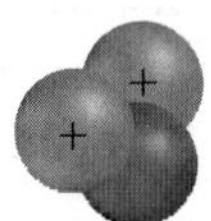
Helium-3

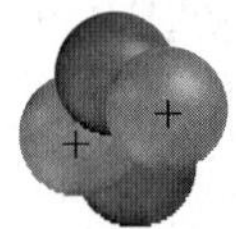
Helium-4

4. What does the illustration show?
A. nuclear fusion **C.** isotopes
B. nuclear decay **D.** half-lives

5. Which is a TRUE statement about the two nuclei?
A. They have the same atomic number.
B. They have the same mass number.
C. They have different numbers of electrons.
D. They have different numbers of protons.

6. What is the atomic number of a nucleus equal to?
A. the number of neutrons
B. the number of protons
C. the number of neutrons and protons
D. the number of neutrons minus the number of protons

Use the illustration below to answer questions 7 and 8.

$^{210}_{84}Po$ $^{206}_{82}Pb$ + $^{4}_{2}He$

7. What process is shown by this illustration?
A. nuclear fusion **C.** transmutation
B. chain reaction **D.** beta decay

8. How do the total charge and total mass number of the products compare to the charge and mass number of the polonium nucleus?
A. The charges are equal but the mass numbers are not equal.
B. The mass numbers are equal but the charges are not equal.
C. Neither the mass numbers or the charges are equal
D. The mass numbers and charges are equal.

9. Radioactive isotopes of which element are used to study the brain?
A. uranium **C.** carbon
B. fluorine **D.** lead

Test-Taking Tip

Understand the Question Be sure you understand the question before you read the answer choices. Make special note of words like NOT or EXCEPT. Read and consider all the answer choices before you mark your answer sheet.

Part 2 Short Response/Grid In

10. The decay of radon gas.
11. Alpha particles are more massive and have more charge.
12. 10 g
13. 3.84 billion years
14. iodine-131
15. Control rods absorb some of the neutrons produced by the fission reactions.
16. A nucleus undergoes fission and emits neutrons; some of these neutrons strike other nuclei, causing them to undergo fission and emit neutrons, and the process contains.
17. A 24-h period would be 12 half-lives of the isotope. Very little of the isotope would be left, and might not be detectable. The study would need an isotope with a longer half-life.
18. lithium-7

Part 2 Short Response/Grid In

Record your answers on the answer sheet provided by your teacher or on a sheet of paper.

10. What process contributes the most to the background radiation received by a person in the United States?

11. Explain why alpha particles tend to produce more ions than beta particles or gamma rays when they pass through matter.

Use the table below to answer questions 12–14.

Half-Lives of Isotopes	
Isotope	**Half-life**
Carbon-14	5,730 years
Potassium-40	1.28 billion years
Iodine-131	8.04 days
Radon-222	4 days

12. Calculate how much of an 80 g sample of carbon-14 will be left after 17,190 years.

13. Potassium-40 decays to argon-40. What is the age of a rock in which 87.5 percent of the atoms are argon-40?

14. A sample containing which radioactive isotope will have one-eighth of the isotope left after 24 days?

15. Explain how control rods are able to control a chain reaction.

16. Describe the sequence of events that must occur for a nuclear chain reaction to occur.

17. A radioactive tracer with a half-life of 2 h is used to study the accumulation of a compound in the kidneys. Explain whether this study could be done over a 24-h period.

18. When the boron isotope boron-10 is bombarded with neutrons, it absorbs a neutron, and then emits an alpha particle. Identify the isotope that is formed in this process.

Part 3 Open Ended

Record your answers on a sheet of paper.

19. Compare the strength of the strong force on a proton and the strength of the electric force on a proton in a small nucleus and a large nucleus.

20. Explain how the alpha particles emitted by the decay of the radioactive isotope americium-241 in a smoke detector produce an electric current between the charged plates of the smoke detector.

21. The geothermal heat that flows from inside Earth is produced by the decay of radioactive isotopes. Form a hypothesis about how the rate of geothermal heat production will change with time.

Use the illustration below to answer questions 22 and 23.

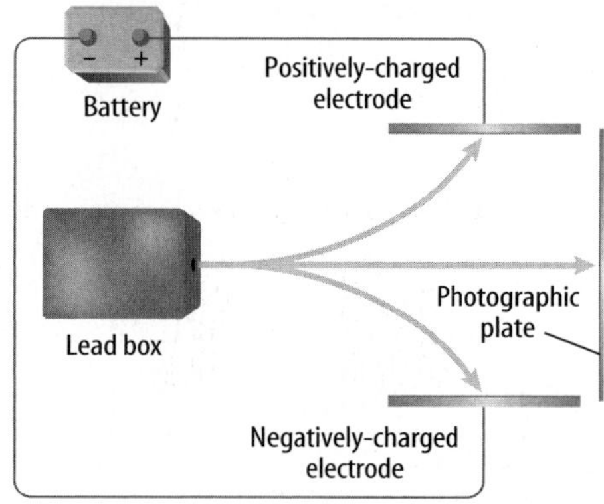

22. In the figure above, nuclear radiation is escaping from a small hole in the lead box. Which type of nuclear radiation is deflected toward the positively-charged electrode, and why is this radiation deflected toward this electrode?

23. Explain why the radiation that struck the photographic plate was not deflected by the electrodes.

Part 3 Open Ended

19. Compared to a small nucleus, in a large nucleus the repulsive electric force on a proton has increased more than the attractive strong force has increased.

20. The alpha particles collide with molecules in air, producing ions. The movement of these charged particles toward the oppositely charged plates forms an electric current.

21. As these isotopes decay over a long period of time, the rate of geothermal heat production will gradually decrease.

22. Beta particles are negatively charged, and because like charges repel and unlike charges attract, they are deflected away from the negatively charged electrode and toward the positively charged electrode.

23. Gamma rays have no charge and their motion is not affected by the charged electrodes.

Rubrics

The following rubrics are sample scoring devices for short response and open-ended questions.

Short Response

Points	Description
2	The student demonstrates a thorough understanding of the science of the task. The response may contain minor flaws that do not detract from the demonstration of a thorough understanding.
1	The student has provided a response that is only partially correct.
0	The student has provided a completely incorrect solution or no response at all.

Open Ended

Points	Description
4	The student demonstrates a thorough understanding of the science of the task. The response may contain minor flaws that do not detract from the demonstration of a thorough understanding.
3	The student demonstrates an understanding of the science of the task. The response is essentially correct and demonstrates an essential but less than thorough understanding of the science.
2	The student demonstrates only a partial understanding of the science of the task. Although the student may have used the correct approach to a solution or may have provided a correct solution, the work lacks an essential understanding of the underlying science concepts.
1	The student demonstrates a very limited understanding of the science of the task. The response is incomplete and exhibits many flaws.
0	The student provides a completely incorrect solution or no response at all.

Unit Contents

WebQuest While completing *Recycling Plastics,* sudents will investigate the history of plastics, what defines the seven classes of plastics and their uses, the chemistry behind plastics, and how they can be recycled–compared to paper, glass, and aluminum. Completing a table listing each type of plastic, its normal use, and into what it can be recycled may help students become more active, responsible, aware citizens.

unit 5 **Diversity of Matter**

How Are Billiards & Bottles Connected?

566

PROJECT CRISS[SM]

Study Skills

Active Reading Questions will arise in the students' minds as they read. Encourage students to write these questions in their Science Journals to aid in their understanding of the diversity of matter. Questions about elements, organic compounds, and newly-developed and versatile materials can be addressed in a whole-class discussion.

NATIONAL
GEOGRAPHIC
Billiards, a popular table game of the 1800s, used balls carved from ivory. In the 1860s, an ivory shortage prompted one billiard-ball manufacturer to offer a reward of $10,000 to anyone who could come up with a suitable substitute. In an attempt to win the prize, an inventor combined certain organic compounds, put them into a mold, and subjected them to heat and pressure. The result was a hard, shiny lump that sparked a major new industry—the plastics industry. By the mid-1900s, chemists had invented many different kinds of moldable plastic. Today, plastic is made into countless products—everything from car parts to soda bottles.
unit projects
Visit gpscience.com/unit_project to find project ideas and resources.
Projects include:
• History Construct a ceramics time line by exploring the history of ceramics and the way they meet advanced technological needs.
• Career Develop trivia cards on the life of Friedrich August Kekule, a chemist and theorist.
• Model Develop an original use for a new material, design "blueprints," conduct a patent search, and present your idea to fellow class scientists.
Recycling Plastics investigates the history of plastics, the seven classes of plastics, their chemistry, and how they can be recycled. Become a more active, aware, and responsible citizen.

unit projects

History Have students explore the use of ceramics in society. Have students construct a time line of 20 uses of this ancient material and how it is being used in new and creative ways with constantly changing technology.

Career Ask students to research Freidrich August Kekule and his contribution to chemistry and theory. Have students develop 12 interesting facts about Kekule and present them in a question-and-answer-trivia format.

Model Working with a partner, have students design a unique use for ceramics, polymers, alloys, or other new materials. Have students draw a "blueprint," conduct a patent search for similar devices, and then modify their design based on their research. Using visual aids, students may then host presentations of their new product to fellow class scientists.

Additional Resources For more information, resources, and assessment rubrics, visit gpscience.com/unit_project

NATIONAL GEOGRAPHIC How Are Billiards & Bottles Connected?

- Ask students how they can identify plastics. Have them write down their thoughts and revise them as they study more about different types of materials.
- Ask students to define the term *diverse.* Emphasize to students that matter is diverse, and different types of matter can be classified into even more diverse categories.
- Ask students how the plastic in a billiard ball differs from that in a bottle. Point out that the term *plastic* refers to a type of material, not a specific one.

Elements and Their Properties

BIG Idea **Elements can be classified into three main types—metals, nonmetals, and metalloids.**

	Content Standards	Learning Objectives	Resources to Assess Mastery
Section 1	**5–8:** UCP.1–3, 5; A.1, 2; B.1, 2 **9–12:** UCP.1–3, 5; A.1, 2; B.1, 2, 4	**Metals** 1. **Describe** the properties of a typical metal. 2. **Identify** the alkali metals and alkaline earth metals. 3. **Differentiate** among three groups of transition elements. ***Main Idea*** Metals are located on the left side of the periodic table and are generally shiny, good conductors, malleable, and ductile.	**Formative Assessment** Reading Check, pp. 571, 575 Section Review, p. 577 **Summative Assessment** *ExamView® Assessment Suite*
Section 2	**5–8:** UCP.1–3, 5; A.1, 2; B.1, 2 **9–12:** UCP.1–3, 5; A.1, 2; B.2, 4	**Nonmetals** 4. **Recognize** hydrogen as a nonmetal. 5. **Compare and contrast** properties of the halogens. 6. **Describe** properties and uses of the noble gases. ***Main Idea*** Nonmetals are located on the right side of the periodic table and are generally dull, poor conductors, and brittle.	**Formative Assessment** Reading Check, pp. 579, 581 Section Review, p. 582 **Summative Assessment** *ExamView® Assessment Suite*
Section 3	**5–8:** UCP.1–3, 5; A.1, 2; B.1, 2; F.1; G.3 **9–12:** UCP.1–3, 5; A.1, 2; B.2, 4; F.1; G.3 See pp. 16T–17T for a Key to Standards.	**Mixed Groups** 7. **Distinguish** among metals, nonmetals, and metalloids. 8. **Describe** the nature of allotropes. 9. **Recognize** the significance of differences in crystal structure in carbon. 10. **Understand** the importance of synthetic elements. ***Main Idea*** Some groups on the periodic table contain metalloids—elements that share some properties of both metals and nonmetals.	**Formative Assessment** Reading Check, pp. 585, 588 Section Review, p. 591 **Summative Chapter Assessment** MindJogger, Ch. 19 *ExamView® Assessment Suite* Leveled Chapter Test Test A L1 Test B L2 Test C L3 Test Practice, pp. 598–599

Suggested Pacing				
Period	Instruction	Labs	Review & Assessment	Total
Single	3.5 days	2.5 days	2 days	8 days
Block	1.75 blocks	1.25 blocks	1 block	4 blocks

Core Instruction	Leveled Resources	Leveled Labs	Pacing: Period		Pacing: Block
Student Text, pp. 568–577 Section Focus Transparency, Ch. 19, Section 1 Interactive Chalkboard, Ch. 19, Section 1 Identifying Misconceptions, p. 571 Differentiated Instruction, pp. 571, 573, 574, 575, 576	**Chapter *Fast File* Resources** Directed Reading for Content Mastery, p. 20 L1 Note-taking Worksheet, pp. 33–36 Reinforcement, p. 27 L2 Enrichment, p. 30 L3 **Reading Essentials,** p. 322 L1 ELL **Science Notebook,** p. 215 ELL	**Launch Lab,** p. 569: paper clips, tongs, sodium chloride, strontium chloride, copper (II) sulfate, gas burner, distilled water, small beakers *15 min* L2 **MiniLAB,** p. 574: tape, magnet, pencil, dry fortified cereal, plastic bag, deep bowl, water *15 min* L2	1	Section 1, pp. 569–573 (includes Launch Lab)	1
			2	Section 1, pp. 574–577 (includes Section Review)	
Student Text, pp. 578–583 Section Focus Transparency, Ch. 19, Section 2 Interactive Chalkboard, Ch. 19, Section 2 Differentiated Instruction, pp. 580, 581	**Chapter *Fast File* Resources** Directed Reading for Content Mastery, p. 20 L1 Note-taking Worksheet, pp. 33–36 Reinforcement, p. 28 L2 Enrichment, p. 31 L3 **Reading Essentials,** p. 328 L1 ELL **Science Notebook,** p. 219 ELL	**MiniLAB,** p. 580: dropper, graduated cylinder, NaCl, distilled water, silver nitrate *15 min* L2 ***Lab,** p. 583: Samples (C, Mg, Al, S, Sn), dishes, paper towels, conductivity tester, spatula, small hammer *30 min* L1 L2 L3	3	Section 2, pp. 579–582 (includes MiniLAB and Section Review)	2
			4	Lab: What type is it?, p. 583	
Student Text, pp. 584–593 Section Focus Transparency, Ch. 19, Section 3 Teaching Transparency, Ch. 19, Section 3 Interactive Chalkboard, Ch. 19, Section 3 Visualizing The Discovery of Elements, p. 591 Applying Math, p. 587 Differentiated Instruction, pp. 587, 588, 589, 590, 591 Chapter Study Guide, p. 595	**Chapter *Fast File* Resources** Directed Reading for Content Mastery, pp. 21, 22 L1 Note-taking Worksheet, pp. 33–36 Reinforcement, p. 29 L2 Enrichment, p. 32 L3 **Reading Essentials,** p. 332 L1 ELL **Science Notebook,** p. 222 ELL	***Lab,** pp. 592–593: thin spaghetti, small gumdrops, thin polystyrene sheets, flat cardboard, scissors *35 min* L1 L2 L3 (Video Lab) *Lab version A L1 version B L2 L3	5	Section 3, pp. 584–588	3
			6	Section 3, pp. 588–591 (includes Section Review)	
			7	Lab: Slippery Carbon, pp. 592–593	4
			8	Study Guide, Chapter Review and Test Practice, pp. 595–599	

Video Lab

Transparencies

Section Focus

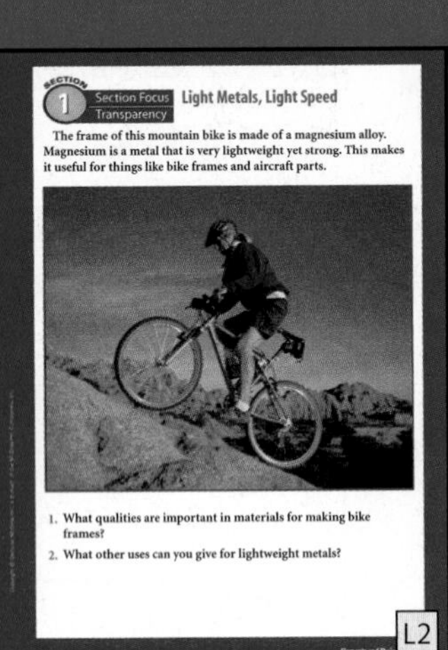
Section 1 Section Focus Transparency **Light Metals, Light Speed**

The frame of this mountain bike is made of a magnesium alloy. Magnesium is a metal that is very lightweight yet strong. This makes it useful for things like bike frames and aircraft parts.

1. What qualities are important in materials for making bike frames?
2. What other uses can you give for lightweight metals?

L2

Section 2 Section Focus Transparency **It's a Gas**

How many ways can you think of to fly? Planes and gliders use wings for lift, while hot air balloons use air. Blimps have a different way to get off the ground; they use helium gas.

1. Why was hydrogen replaced by helium for use in blimps?
2. Do you suspect helium is very reactive? Explain.
3. Give some differences between blimps and hot air balloons.

L2

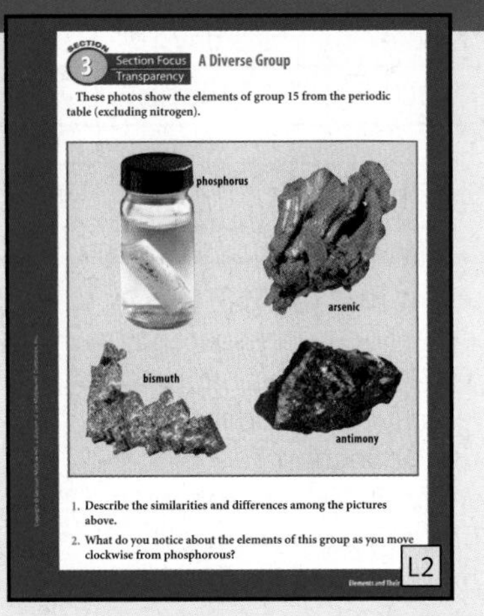

Section 3 Section Focus Transparency **A Diverse Group**

These photos show the elements of group 15 from the periodic table (excluding nitrogen).

1. Describe the similarities and differences among the pictures above.
2. What do you notice about the elements of this group as you move clockwise from phosphorous?

L2

This is a representation of key blackline masters available in the Teacher Classroom Resources. See Resource Manager boxes within the chapter for additional information.

Assessment

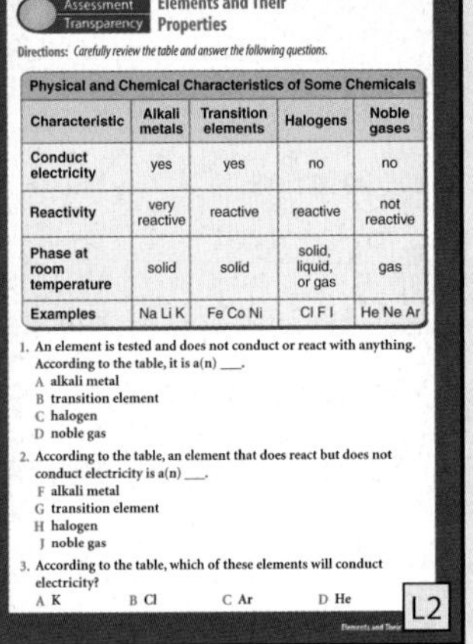
Assessment Transparency **Elements and Their Properties**

Directions: *Carefully review the table and answer the following questions.*

Physical and Chemical Characteristics of Some Chemicals

Characteristic	Alkali metals	Transition elements	Halogens	Noble gases
Conduct electricity	yes	yes	no	no
Reactivity	very reactive	reactive	reactive	not reactive
Phase at room temperature	solid	solid	solid, liquid, or gas	gas
Examples	Na Li K	Fe Co Ni	Cl F I	He Ne Ar

1. An element is tested and does not conduct or react with anything. According to the table, it is a(n) ___.
   A alkali metal
   B transition element
   C halogen
   D noble gas
2. According to the table, an element that does react but does not conduct electricity is a(n) ___.
   F alkali metal
   G transition element
   H halogen
   J noble gas
3. According to the table, which of these elements will conduct electricity?
   A K B Cl C Ar D He

L2

Teaching

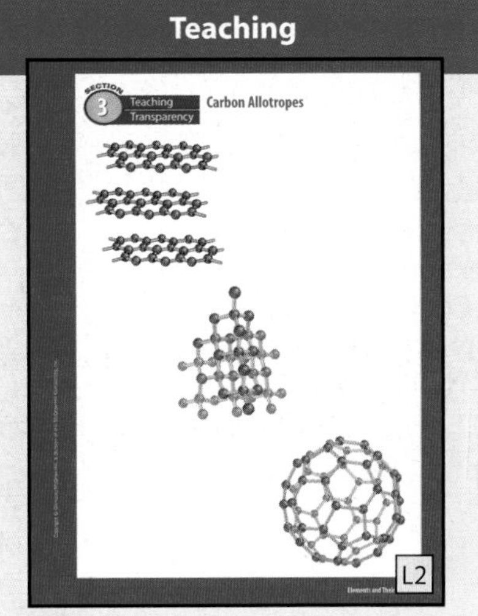
Section 3 Teaching Transparency **Carbon Allotropes**

L2

Key to Teaching Strategies

The following designations will help you decide which activities are appropriate for your students.

- L1 Level 1 activities should be appropriate for students with learning difficulties.
- L2 Level 2 activities should be within the ability range of all students.
- L3 Level 3 activities are designed for above-average students.
- ELL ELL activities should be within the ability range of English Language Learners.
- COOP LEARN Cooperative Learning activities are designed for small group work.
- LS Multiple Learning Styles logos, as described on page 12T, are used throughout to indicate strategies that address different learning styles.
- P These strategies represent student products that can be placed into a best-work portfolio.
- PBL Problem-Based Learning activities apply real-world situations to learning.

Hands-on Activities

Student Text Lab Worksheet

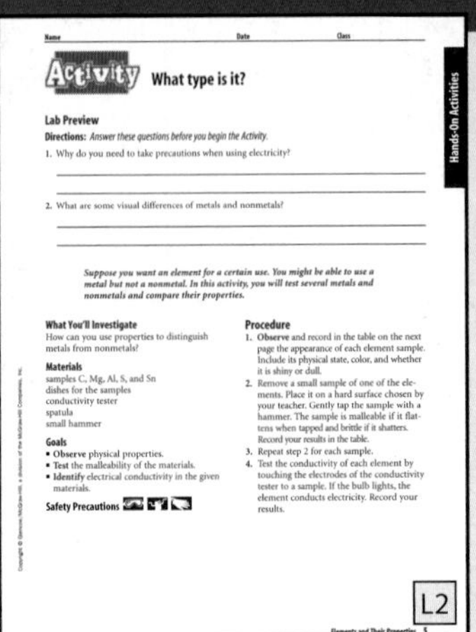
Name Date Class

Hands-On Activities

Activity What type is it?

Lab Preview

Directions: *Answer these questions before you begin the Activity.*

1. Why do you need to take precautions when using electricity?
2. What are some visual differences of metals and nonmetals?

Suppose you want an element for a certain use. You might be able to use a metal but not a nonmetal. In this activity, you will test several metals and nonmetals and compare their properties.

What You'll Investigate

How can you use properties to distinguish metals from nonmetals?

Materials

samples C, Mg, Al, S, and Sn
dishes for the samples
conductivity tester
spatula
small hammer

Goals

- **Observe** physical properties.
- **Test** the malleability of the materials.
- **Identify** electrical conductivity in the given materials.

Safety Precautions

Procedure

1. **Observe** and record in the table on the next page the appearance of each element sample. Include its physical state, color, and whether it is shiny or dull.
2. Remove a small sample of one of the elements. Place it on a hard surface chosen by your teacher. Gently tap the sample with a hammer. The sample is malleable if it flattens when tapped and brittle if it shatters. Record your results in the table.
3. Repeat step 2 for each sample.
4. Test the conductivity of each element by touching the electrodes of the conductivity tester to a sample. If the bulb lights, the element conducts electricity. Record your results.

L2

Elements and Their Properties 5

Laboratory Activities

Name Date Class

Hands-On Activities

LAB 1 Laboratory Activity **Preparation of Carbon Dioxide**

When you burn a material that contains carbon, such as paper or gasoline, carbon dioxide gas is produced. You also produce carbon dioxide when your body "burns" the food you eat. You don't burn the food with a flame, however. The cells of your body combine the carbon in the food you eat with the oxygen in a reaction called oxidation. When carbon compounds are oxidized, carbon dioxide gas is produced.

Carbon dioxide gas is colorless, odorless, and tasteless. It is necessary for photosynthesis, the process by which green plants produce oxygen and glucose.

Strategy

You will observe a reaction that produces carbon dioxide gas.
You will describe the reaction that produces carbon dioxide gas.
You will observe the chemical properties of carbon dioxide gas.

Materials

metric ruler	hydrochloric acid solution	forceps
distilled water	24-well microplate	marble chips
lime water	scissors	transparent tape
toothpicks	long stem plastic pipette	plastic microtip pipettes (4)
matches		

CAUTION: *Hydrochloric acid is corrosive. Avoid its contact with your skin or clothing. Rinse spills with water.*

Procedure

Part A—Preparing Carbon Dioxide Gas

1. Place the microplate on a flat surface. Have the numbered columns of the microplate at the top and the lettered rows at the left.
2. Use the scissors to trim the stem of the long stem pipette to a length of 2.5 cm.
3. Using the scissors, cut a small slit in the pipette as shown in Figure 1.

Figure 1

Cut
2.5 cm

4. Use the forceps to insert a small marble chip through the slit into the bulb of the pipette. Cover the slit with transparent tape to seal the bulb. Place the bulb of the pipette in well A1.
5. Make collector pipettes by cutting the stems of 2 of the microtip pipettes to lengths of 1 cm, as shown in Figure 2.

Figure 2

Collector pipettes
1 cm

6. Completely fill the two collector pipettes with water by holding each pipette under running water with its stem upward. Squeeze the bulb repeatedly until there is no more air in the pipette.
7. Stand the collector pipettes with their stems upward in wells C1 and C2.
8. Using an uncut microtip pipette, add about half a pipetteful of hydrochloric acid to well C3. Rinse the pipette with distilled water.
9. Take the pipette containing the marble chip from well A1 and invert it.

L2

Elements and Their Properties 9

Meeting Different Ability Levels

Content Outline

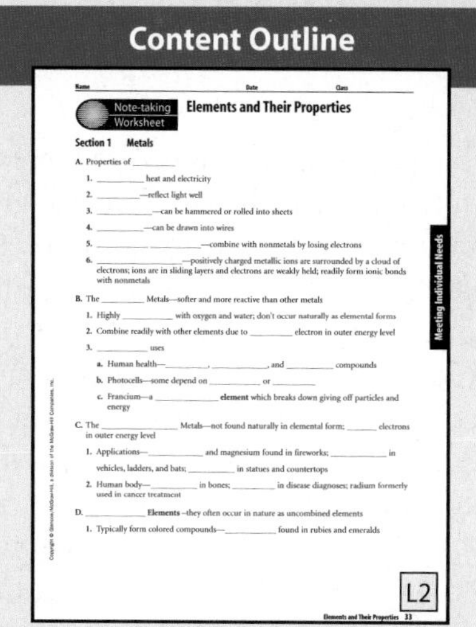

Note-taking Worksheet

Elements and Their Properties

Section 1 Metals

L2

Reinforcement

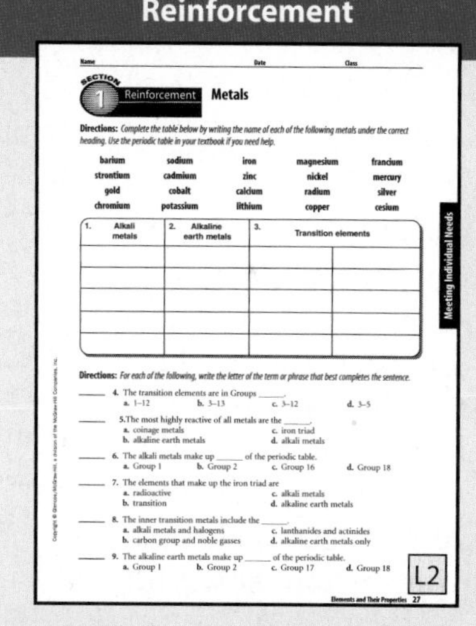

Section 1 Reinforcement

Metals

L2

Enrichment

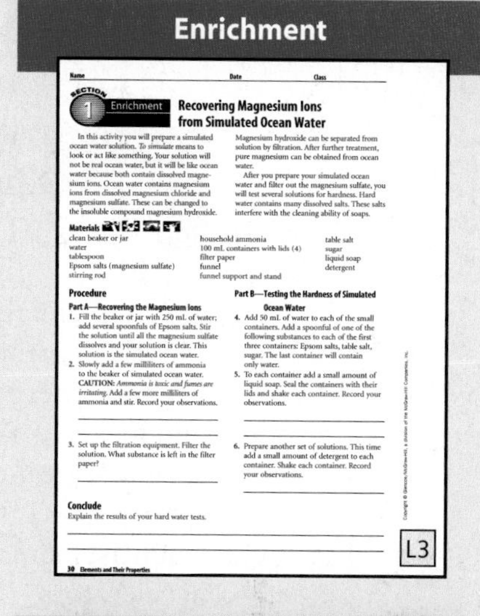

Section 1 Enrichment

Recovering Magnesium Ions from Simulated Ocean Water

L3

Directed Reading (English/Spanish)

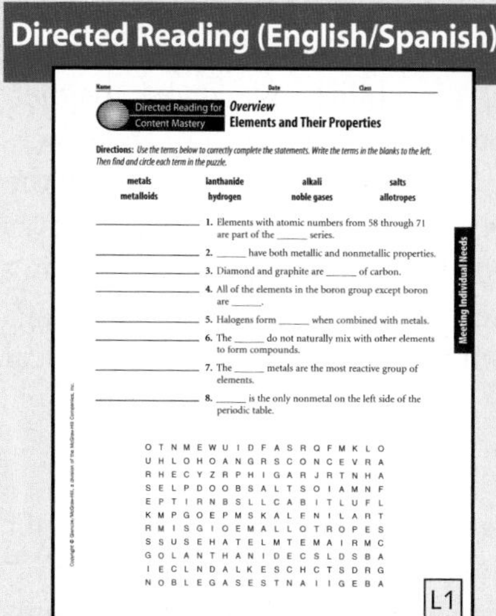

Directed Reading for Content Mastery

Overview

Elements and Their Properties

L1

Study Guide

Study Guide
Features
• Contains a study guide page for each section of the chapter
• Reviews key concepts
• Includes answer pages
L2

Reading Essentials

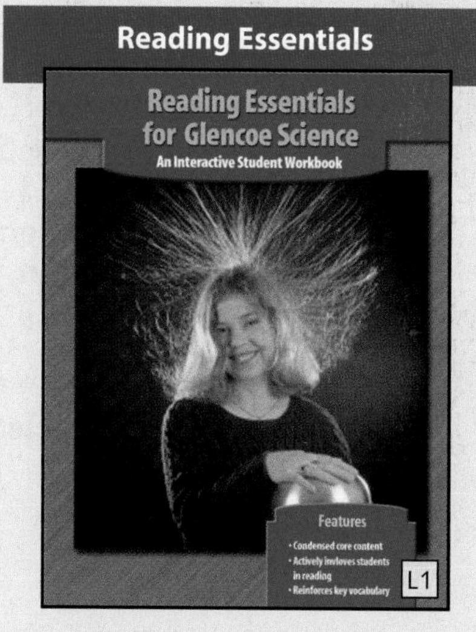

Reading Essentials for Glencoe Science
An Interactive Student Workbook
Features
• Condensed core content
• Actively involves students in reading
• Reinforces key vocabulary
L1

Assessment

Test Practice Workbook

Chapter Test

Chapter 19 Chemical Bonds

L2

Chapter Review

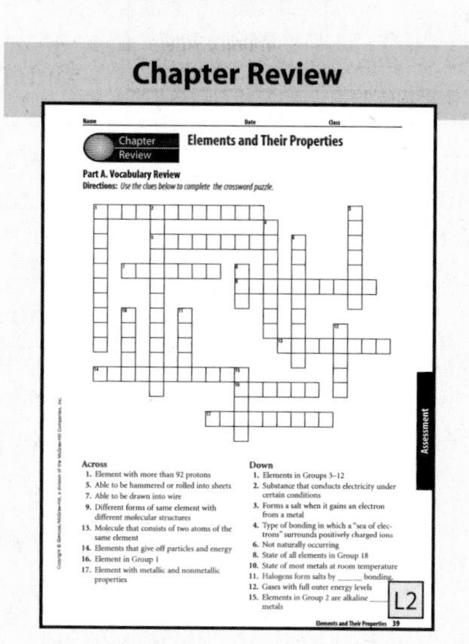

Chapter Review

Elements and Their Properties

Part A. Vocabulary Review

L2

Chapter Tests

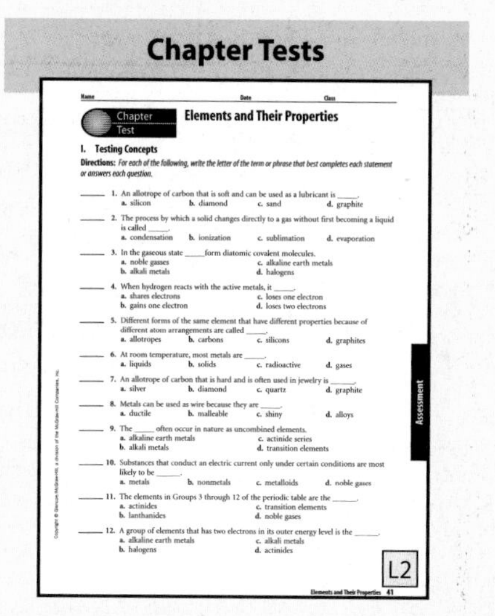

Chapter Test

Elements and Their Properties

I. Testing Concepts

L2

Science Content Background

section 1 Metals

Properties of Metals

The families of elements found on the left side of the periodic table are the metals. Elements whose atoms have identical arrangements of electrons in their highest energy levels have similar properties and make up a family of elements in the periodic table (vertical columns). The number of known elements, 115 at this time, changes each time scientists create a new one using powerful accelerators.

The sections of the periodic table reflect the electron configurations of the elements and the sublevels occupied by the electrons. It is the electron configuration of the atom that determines its chemical reactivity. Every principle quantum number (period, or horizontal row), contains one or more sublevels designated by letters s, p, d, and f, which contain electrons.

Teacher to Teacher
Monica Tatera,
Roy Public High School
Roy, Montana

"I wrap a dollar bill around a 2" diameter piece of solid metal. Then I wave a flame underneath the bill. After that, I leave the flame under the bill for several seconds, and it still will not burn."

Monica Tatera

Metallic Bonding

Metallic bonding is partly responsible for a metal's ability to conduct electricity. In recent years, much research has been done with superconductivity.

A superconductor is a material that loses all electrical resistance below a characteristic temperature called the superconducting transition temperature. This phenomenon was discovered in 1911 by the Dutch physicist Heike Kamerlingh Onnes, who found that mercury abruptly loses its electrical resistance when it is cooled with liquid helium to 4.2 K (−229 degrees Celsius). Below its superconducting transition temperature, a superconductor becomes a perfect conductor, and an electric current, once started, flows indefinitely without loss of energy.

Since 1911, scientists have been searching for materials that superconduct at higher temperatures, and hundreds of superconductors are now known.

One of the most amazing properties of a superconductor is its ability to levitate a magnet. When a magnet is lowered toward it, the superconductor and magnet repel each other, and the magnet hovers above the superconductor as though suspended in midair. Superconducting magnets are used in magnetic resonance imaging (MRI) instruments, widely used in medical diagnosis.

The Alkali Metals

The alkali metals have one electron in an outer s orbital. This single electron is in a higher energy level than any inner level of electrons, and the inner electrons shield it from the full attractive force of the nucleus. As a result, relatively little energy is needed to remove the electron, and thus ionize the atom to a 1+ ion. As you move down the alkali metal group, the outermost s electron is farther and farther from the nucleus and ionization becomes successively easier. As a result, the reactivity of the alkali metals increases down the family.

Alkaline Earth Metals

The alkaline earth metals have two electrons in an outer s orbital. The energy needed to remove both these electrons is low enough to make this group of elements almost as active as the alkali metals. The trend in reactivity for the oxygen group and the halogens is opposite that of Groups 1 and 2. Fluorine is the most active of the halogens, and activity decreases down the group.

section 2 Nonmetals

Properties of Nonmetals

The size of the elements' atoms is related to an element's position in the periodic table. The size of the atoms increases as you go down each column and decreases as you go from left to right. Since the nonmetals are on the right side of the periodic table, it follows that atoms of nonmetals are generally smaller than atoms of metals within a period.

Only seventeen of the known elements are classified as nonmetals. Of those seventeen elements, six belong to the family of noble gases and are considered inert, or nonreactive. As a result, discussions of the chemistry of the nonmetals usually focuses on hydrogen, carbon, nitrogen, oxygen, fluorine, phosphorus, sulfur, chlorine, selenium, bromine, and iodine.

section 3 Mixed Groups

Properties of Metalloids

Metalloids are elements that are neither true metals nor true nonmetals. They have some properties of each group. Metalloids are the elements that touch the line separating the metals from the nonmetals. Aluminum, a metal, is the only exception.

There are eight elements in this group: boron, silicon, germanium, arsenic, antimony, tellurium, polonium, and astatine. These elements often look like metals, but they tend to be brittle, and they are more likely to be semiconductors than conductors of electricity.

Some of the elements in this group are used as semiconductors. However, there are other applications in the field of composites and ceramics.

Known since ancient times, ceramics are inorganic, nonmetallic, non-molecular solids. The first ceramics were pottery and porcelain. Modern ceramic materials have high-tech engineering, electronic, and biomedical applications. In many respects, the properties of ceramics are superior to those of metals. Ceramics have higher melting points, and they are stiffer, harder, and more resistant to wear and corrosion. Because ceramics are less dense than steel, they are lightweight, high-temperature materials used for replacing metal components in aircraft, space vehicles, and automotive engines. However, ceramics are brittle.

Ceramics can be strengthened and toughened by mixing the ceramic with fibers of a second ceramic material, such as carbon, boron, or silicon carbide. The resulting hybrid material, called a ceramic composite, combines the advantageous properties of both components.

chapter content resources

Internet Resources

For additional content background, visit gpscience.com to:

- access your book online
- find references to related articles in popular science magazines
- access Web links with related content background
- access current events with science journal topics

Print Resources

Chemistry: The Molecular Nature of Matter and Change, by Martin S. Silberberg, McGraw-Hill, 2003

Nature's Building Blocks: An A-Z Guide to the Elements, by John Emsley, Oxford University Press, 2002

About the Photo

Properties of Elements Discuss some of the elements used in the aircraft and why some elements are more desirable than others. For example, Aluminum is used in many instances because it is light, strong, and resists corrosion. Iron would be a poor choice for many applications due to its susceptibility to oxidation and heavier weight.

Science Journal Student responses will vary, but help them to differentiate between elements and compounds, many will probably give examples of compounds.

BIG Idea

Metallic Behavior Metals tend to have moderate to high melting points; are good conductors of thermal energy and electric current; and are shiny, malleable, and ductile. Metallic behavior tends to decrease from left to right across a period and increase from top to bottom down a group. Metals generally have a few outer electrons surrounding filled inner energy levels. These filled inner levels tend to shield the outer electrons from the positive nuclear charge. As a result, compared to other elements, the outer electrons are not tightly held by the metal atom, and can move easily in the solid metal lattice.

Introduce the Chapter Have students make a list of elements they consider to be metals and elements they consider to be nonmetals. Ask students what properties they think the metals have and what properties the nonmetals have.

Elements and Their Properties

BIG Idea
Elements can be classified into three main types—metals, nonmetals, and metalloids.

19.1 Metals

MAIN Idea Metals are located on the left side of the periodic table and are generally shiny, good conductors, malleable, and ductile.

19.2 Nonmetals

MAIN Idea Nonmetals are located on the right side of the periodic table and are generally dull, poor conductors, and brittle.

19.3 Mixed Groups

MAIN Idea Some groups on the periodic table contain metalloids—elements that share some properties of both metals and nonmetals.

Stress and the Elements

It takes a combination of metals, nonmetals, and metalloids to construct an airplane and have a viable aircraft. It is necessary to understand the properties of each element and how they will work with each other.

Science Journal

Describe what some of the key elements are (which might be found in this picture) and the properties of these elements that make them so crucial.

568

Interactive Chalkboard

This CD-ROM is an editable Microsoft® PowerPoint® presentation that includes:

- an editable presentation for every chapter
- additional chapter questions
- animated graphics
- image bank
- links to gpscience.com

Start-Up Activities

Observe Colorful Clues

It is the distinct physical properties of each element that make it so that one element can be identified from another. In this lab, you will observe how the heated atoms of some elements absorb energy and then in a short time release the absorbed energy, which you see as colored light.

1. Wearing gloves and using tongs, carefully hold a clean paper clip in the hottest part of a lab burner flame for 45 seconds.
2. Dip the hot paper clip into a solution of copper(II) sulfate.
3. Using the tongs with the same paper clip, repeat step 1, observing any color change.
4. Repeat all three steps using solutions of strontium chloride and sodium chloride with clean tongs and new paper clips.
5. **Think Critically** Which element—chlorine or strontium—was responsible for the color observed when strontium chloride was placed in the flame? How do you know? Devise a plan to determine whether copper or sulfate was responsible for the color in step 2.

Groups Make the following Foldable to help classify and organize elements into groups based on their common features.

STEP 1 **Fold** a vertical sheet of paper in half from top to bottom.

STEP 2 **Fold** in half from side to side with the fold at the top.

STEP 3 **Unfold** the paper once. **Cut** only the fold of the top flap to make two tabs.

STEP 4 **Turn** the paper horizontally and **label** the tabs *Metals* and *Nonmetals* as shown.

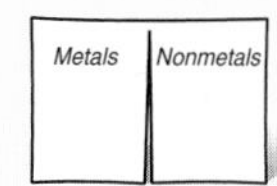

Illustrate and Label Before reading the chapter, list all of the metal and nonmetal elements you know under the appropriate tab. As you read the chapter, check your list and make changes as needed.

Preview this chapter's content and activities at gpscience.com

Additional Chapter Media

- Virtual Lab: *What properties do elements have?*
- Video Lab: *Slippery Carbon*

Purpose Students will observe that atoms of certain heated elements emit unique colors that can be used to identify the elements. L2 ELL COOP LEARN

LS **Logical-Mathematical**

Preparation Before class, make the three concentrated salt solutions. Be sure to use distilled water.

Materials paper clips, tongs, sodium chloride, strontium chloride, copper(II) sulfate, gas burner, distilled water, small beakers

Teaching Strategy It is important that the burner flame be adjusted to the palest blue color. Sodium compounds give a large yellow flame, strontium compounds give a red flame, and copper compounds give a green flame.

Safety Precautions Have students wear goggles and aprons and be cautious when working with open flames. The paper clip will become very hot.

Think Critically

1. Strontium; The strontium chloride and the sodium chloride both contain chlorine but produced different colors. Therefore, the color is due to the strontium.
2. Test a copper compound without sulfate and a sulfate compound without copper.

Assessment

Performance Repeat the procedure with a calcium chloride solution. A red-orange color (similar to the strontium color) will appear. Ask students to explain why flame tests may sometimes be unreliable. Use **Performance Assessment in the Science Classroom,** p. 89.

Dinah Zike Study Fold

Student preparation materials for this Foldable are available in the Chapter *Fast File* Resources.

section 1

Metals

1 Motivate

Bellringer

Section Focus Transparencies also are available on the Interactive Chalkboard CD-ROM. L2 

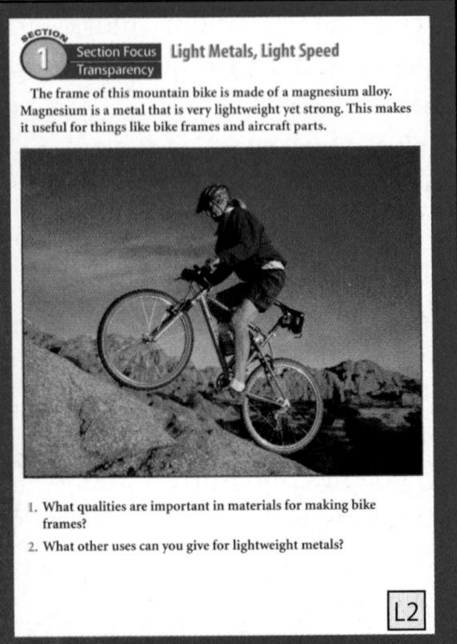

Tie to Prior Knowledge

Daily Metals Ask students to identify metals they come into contact with on a daily basis. aluminum foil, copper wire, titanium metal in bicycles, and iron in magnets

Caption Answers

Figure 1A Possible answers: shielding (lead), plating (gold), house siding (aluminum)

Figure 1B ductility

Reading Guide

What You'll Learn

- **Describe** the properties of a typical metal.
- **Identify** the alkali metals and alkaline earth metals.
- **Differentiate** among three groups of transition elements.

Why It's Important

Metals are a part of your everyday life—from electric cords to the cars you ride in.

Review Vocabulary

element: substance with atoms that are all alike

New Vocabulary

- metal
- malleable
- ductile
- metallic bonding
- radioactive element
- transition element

Properties of Metals

Figure 1 The various properties of metals make them useful.

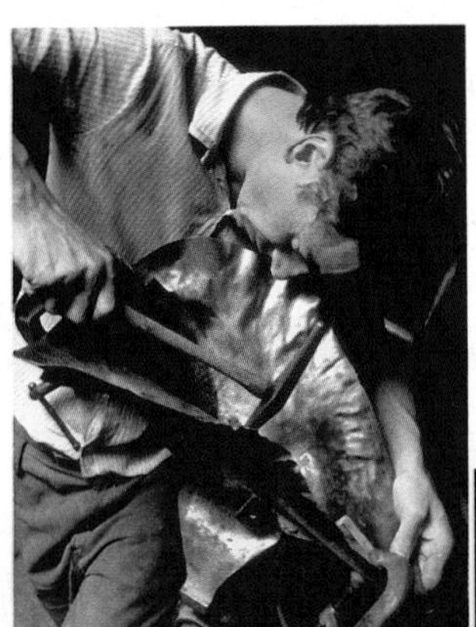

Metals, like the one shown, can be hammered into thin sheets.
Explain *one use for a sheet of metal.*

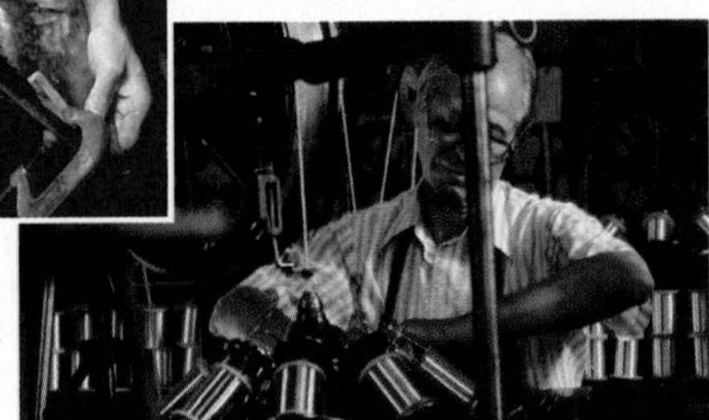

Metals can be drawn into wires, like the wire that is being used here.
Describe *what this property of metals is called.*

The first metal used about 6,000 years ago was gold. The use of copper and silver followed a few thousand years later. Then came tin and iron. Aluminum wasn't refined until the 1800s because it must go through a much more complicated refining process that earlier civilizations had not yet developed.

In the periodic table, metals are elements found to the left of the stair-step line. In the table on the inside back cover of your book, the metal element blocks are colored blue. **Metals** usually have common properties—they are good conductors of heat and electricity, and all but one are solid at room temperature. Mercury is the only metal that is not a solid at room temperature. Metals also reflect light. This is a property called luster. Metals are **malleable** (MAL yuh bul), which means they can be hammered or rolled into sheets, as shown in **Figure 1.** Metals are also **ductile,** which means they can be drawn into wires like the ones shown in **Figure 1.** These properties make metals suitable for use in objects ranging from eyeglass frames to computers to building structures.

Section 1 Resource Manager 

Chapter *Fast File* Resources

Transparency Activity, p. 46
Directed Reading for Content Mastery, pp. 19, 20
Note-taking Worksheets, pp. 33–36
Enrichment, p. 30
MiniLAB, p.3
Reinforcement, p. 27

Mathematics Skill Activities, p. 1
Physical Science Critical Thinking/Problem Solving, p. 1
Earth Science Critical Thinking/Problem Solving, p. 12
Science Inquiry Labs, p. 35–36
Cultural Diversity, p. 35

Ionic Bonding in Metals The atoms of metals generally have one to three electrons in their outer energy levels. In chemical reactions, metals tend to give up electrons easily because of the strength of charge of the protons in the nucleus. When metals combine with nonmetals, the atoms of the metals tend to lose electrons to the atoms of nonmetals, forming ionic bonds, as shown in **Figure 2.** Both metals and nonmetals become more chemically stable when they form ions. They take on the electron structure of the nearest noble gas.

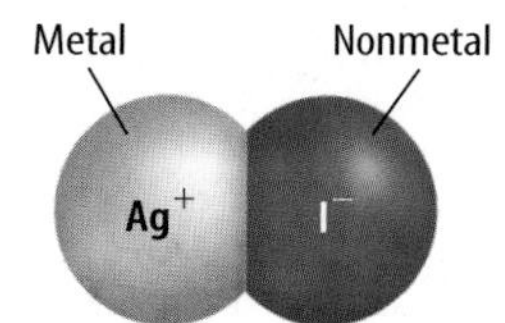

Figure 2 Metals can form ionic bonds with nonmetals.

Metallic Bonding Another type of bonding, neither ionic nor covalent, occurs among the atoms in a metal. In **metallic bonding,** positively charged metallic ions are surrounded by a cloud of electrons. Outer-level electrons are not held tightly to the nucleus of an atom. Rather, the electrons move freely among many positively charged ions. As shown in **Figure 3,** the electrons form a cloud around the ions of the metal.

The idea of metallic bonding explains many of the properties of metals. For example, when a metal is hammered into a sheet or drawn into a wire, it does not break because the ions are in layers that slide past one another without losing their attraction to the electron cloud. Metals are also good conductors of electricity because the outer-level electrons are weakly held.

Reading Check *Why do metals conduct electricity?*

Look at the periodic table inside the back cover of your book. How many of the elements in the table are classified as metals? All of the blue-shaded boxes represent metals. Except for hydrogen, all the elements in Groups 1 through 12 are metals, as well as the elements under the stair-step line in Groups 13 through 15. You will learn more about metals in some of these groups throughout this chapter.

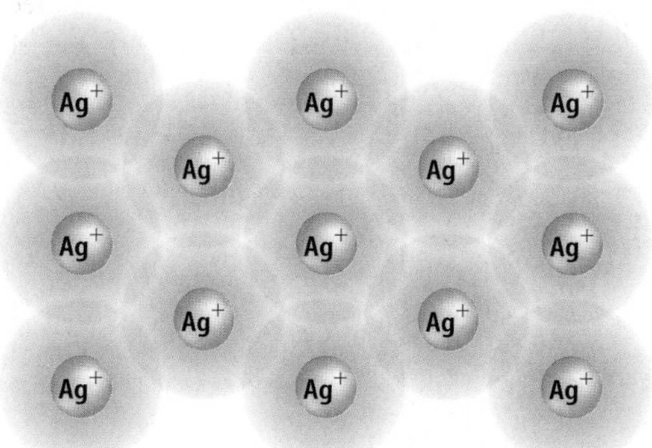

Figure 3 In metallic bonding, the electrons represented by the cloud are not attached to any one silver ion. This allows them to move and conduct electricity.

2 Teach

Use an Analogy

Potluck Supper The interactions between metal ions and electrons in metallic bonding are analogous to food at a potluck supper. You arrive with your food, as a metal atom arrives with its own electrons. Once people join for dinner, however, the food is shared by all, regardless of who brought which dish. In the same way, the outer electrons of metals are shared, and it matters little with which atom an electron arrived.

Conductivity and Temperature Students may think that electrical conductivity is independent of temperature or that it increases as temperature increases. Explain that in metals, conductivity generally increases as temperature decreases.

Reading Check

Answer because their outer-level electrons are weakly held

Visual Learning

Figure 3 Ask students how the metallic bonding shown in this figure is different from covalent bonding. In covalent bonding, electrons are shared between specific atoms, placing the atoms at defined angles, and uniting them into molecules containing a precise number of each atom. In metallic bonding, the atoms share all the valence electrons present, and the electrons are not restricted to specific atoms. This means that no specific molecules form. L3 LS **Visual-Spatial**

Differentiated Instruction

English-Language Learners Use a conductivity meter or an ohmmeter with an audible or visible signal to help demonstrate the conductive properties of metals. Use this same equipment to demonstrate that nonmetals are not good conductors of electricity. ELL

Curriculum Connection

History Have students find out which were the first metals to be used by humans, when they were first used, and how. Copper and bronze, an alloy of copper and tin, were the first metals used by humans. They were used in weapons and tools. The Bronze Age began in the Middle East by about 3500 B.C. L2 LS **Linguistic**

Quick Demo

Malleabililty

Materials clear plastic lid, BBs, ruler

Estimated Time five minutes

Procedure To show how metal atoms slide over each other to produce the property of malleability, place a clear plastic lid from a container on the overhead projector. Next, layer in metal shot (BBs) to form a layer of rows. Now, show how the rows can be moved from side to side with the movement of a ruler on one side of a layer. L2 LS **Visual-Kinesthetic**

Teacher FYI

Largest Atoms Some of the largest atoms on the periodic table are found in the alkali group because of their relatively weak attraction for their outer level electrons. Each atom has only one outer electron, which is held weakly because of repulsion by the underlying level of electrons. Therefore, these metals have relatively low melting points and a soft texture. Cesium melts at a temperature lower than that of the human body. Although it must be done with extreme caution, the metal can be sliced with a knife.

Discussion

Francium This element occurs in nature in uranium ore. Its most stable isotope, francium-223, has a half-life of about 22 minutes, and is formed from the radioactive decay of actinium-227. How do scientists know how much francium is in Earth's crust at one time? They know how much uranium ore is in Earth's crust, and they can calculate the percentage that is francium. L3 LS **Logical-Mathematical**

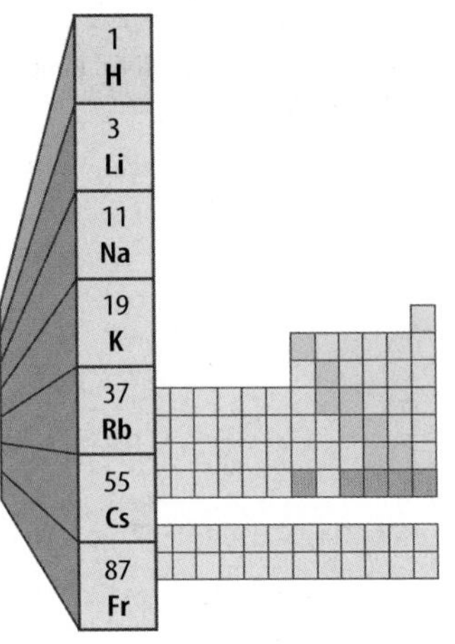

The Alkali Metals

The elements in Group 1 of the periodic table are the alkali (AL kuh li) metals. Like other metals, Group 1 metals are shiny, malleable, and ductile. They are also good conductors of heat and electricity. However, they are softer than most other metals. The alkali metals are the most reactive of all the metals. They react rapidly—sometimes violently—with oxygen and water, as shown in **Figure 4.** Because they combine so readily with other elements, alkali metals don't occur in nature in their elemental form and are stored in substances that are unreactive, such as an oil.

Each atom of an alkali metal has one electron in its outer energy level. This electron is given up when an alkali metal combines with another atom. As a result, the alkali metal becomes a positively charged ion in a compound such as sodium chloride, NaCl, or potassium bromide, KBr.

Alkali metals and their compounds have many uses. You and other living things need potassium and sodium compounds to stay healthy. Doctors sometimes use lithium compounds to treat bipolar disorder. The lithium keeps chemical levels that are important to mental health within a narrow range. The operation of some photocells depends upon rubidium or cesium compounds. Francium, the last element in Group 1, is extremely rare and radioactive. A **radioactive element** is one in which the nucleus breaks down and gives off particles and energy. Francium can be found in uranium minerals, but only 25 g to 30 g of francium are in all of Earth's crust at one time.

Figure 4 Alkali metals are very reactive.

Potassium reacts strongly in water.

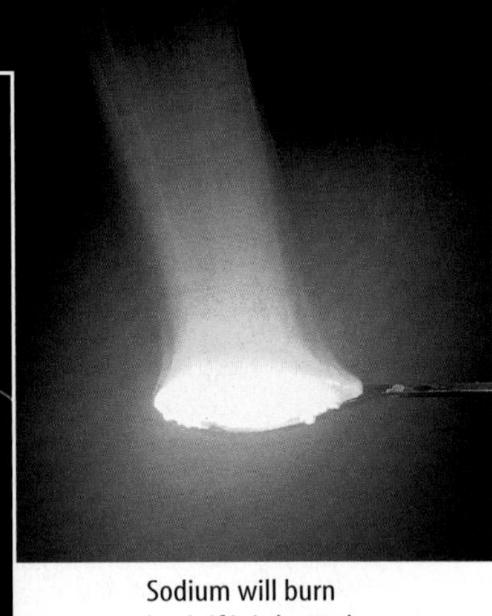

Sodium will burn in air if it is heated.

Curriculum Connection

Health When doctors prescribe a low-sodium diet, they typically recommend reducing the consumption of salt (NaCl). While some sodium is critical to good health, too much can cause problems. Have students find out why sodium is important to our diets. Na^+ helps conduct nerve impulses. Ask students to bring in labels from foods and drinks to compare sodium content. L2 LS **Linguistic**

Active Reading

Quickwrites This strategy, sometimes called freewrites, lets students use spontaneous writing to discover what they already know. Have students write a list of ideas about a topic, then share these ideas with the class. Next, have students write their ideas freely in a paragraph without worrying about punctuation, spelling, and grammar. L2

The Alkaline Earth Metals

The alkaline earth metals make up Group 2 of the periodic table. Like most metals, these metals are shiny, malleable, and ductile. They are also similar to alkali metals in that they combine so readily with other elements that they are not found as free elements in nature. Each atom of an alkaline earth metal has two electrons in its outer energy level. These electrons are given up when an alkaline earth metal combines with a nonmetal. As a result, the alkaline earth metal becomes a positively charged ion in a compound such as calcium fluoride, CaF_2.

Fireworks and Other Uses Magnesium metal is one of the metals used to produce the brilliant white color in fireworks like the ones in **Figure 5.** Compounds of strontium produce the bright red flashes. Magnesium's lightness and strength account for its use in cars, planes, and spacecraft. Magnesium also is used in compounds to make such things as household ladders and baseball and softball bats. Most life on Earth depends upon chlorophyll, a magnesium compound that enables plants to make food. Marble statues and some countertops are made of the calcium compound calcium carbonate.

The Alkaline Earth Metals and Your Body Calcium is seldom used as a free metal, but its compounds are needed for life. You may take a vitamin with calcium. Calcium phosphate in your bones helps make them strong.

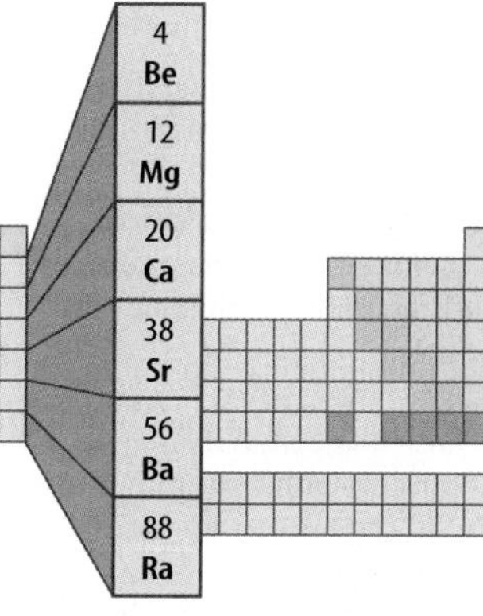

Figure 5 Alkaline earth metals make spectacular fireworks.

INTEGRATE Health The barium compound $BaSO_4$ is used to diagnose some digestive disorders because it absorbs X-ray radiation well. First, the patient swallows a barium compound. Next, an X ray is taken while the barium compound is going through the digestive tract. A doctor can then see where the barium is in the body. In this way, doctors can diagnose internal abnormalities in the body.

Radium, the last element in Group 2, is radioactive and is found associated with uranium. It was once used to treat cancers. Today, other radioactive elements that are more readily available are replacing radium in cancer therapy.

Quick Demo

Magnesium

Materials magnesium ribbon, flame source, tongs, gloves, metallic can, safety goggles

Estimated Time 10 minutes

Procedure Magnesium burns with an intensely bright white flame. To demonstrate this safely, hold a small strip of magnesium ribbon with tongs in a flame. **WARNING:** *Be sure to wear gloves and safety goggles.* When the Mg begins to burn, quickly plunge it into a large metallic can. The reflected glare will show students why magnesium has practical use in flares. Adding water to the white, powdery residue of magnesium oxide (MgO) produces a solution with alkaline properties (turns red litmus blue).

Use Science Words

Word Usage Elements that are radioactive often decay into other elements. Radium is radioactive. Have students find out what happens to radium during the decay process. Radium releases an alpha particle (helium nucleus) and changes into radon.

Teacher FYI

Group 2 Metals Like those in Group 1, the Group 2 metals in water produce hydroxide ions. The reaction (where M represents an alkaline earth metal) is $M + 2H_2O \rightarrow M(OH)_2 + H_2$. The Group 2 metals need two hydroxide ions. The Group 2 metals generally have a two + charge in compounds.

Differentiated Instruction

Challenge Ask students to find the characteristic colors of flames for some alkali and alkaline earth elements not used in the MiniLAB. Possible answers include K, lilac; Ca, red-orange; Ba, yellow-green L3

LS **Linguistic**

Challenge Successful farming depends on the ability of soil to provide crops with the nutrients they need. Have students find out how calcium helps this process. Farmers put CaO, called lime, in the soil. CaO reacts with water to form $Ca(OH)_2$, which neutralizes soil that is too acidic. Maintaining the proper acid level is critical to dissolving soil minerals needed for plant growth. L3

LS **Linguistic**

Purpose Students collect iron from breakfast cereal. L1 ELL IS **Kinesthetic**

Materials plastic bag, high-iron-content cereal, water, pencil, tape, small strong magnet, bowl

Teaching Strategy Provide research materials for students to answer the second question.

Analysis

1. iron
2. Iron is part of hemoglobin and is needed for producing blood.

Assessment

Oral Ask students why the metal collected is probably iron and not some other transition element. Most metals are not magnetic, and iron is.

Discovering What's in Cereal

Procedure

1. **Tape** a small, strong **magnet** to a **pencil** at the eraser end.
2. Place some **dry, fortified, cold cereal** in a **plastic bag.**
3. Thoroughly crush the cereal.
4. Pour the crushed cereal into a **deep bowl** and cover it with **water.**
5. Stir the mixture for about 10 min with your pencil/magnet. Stir slowly for the last minute.
6. Remove the magnet and examine it carefully. Record your observations.

Analysis

1. What common element is attracted to your magnet?
2. Why is this element added to the cereal?

Try at Home

Transition Elements

A titanium bike frame and a glowing tungsten lightbulb filament are examples of objects made from transition elements. **Transition elements** are those elements in Groups 3 through 12 in the periodic table. They are called transition elements because they are considered to be elements in transition between Groups 1 and 2 and Groups 13 through 18. Look at the periodic table inside the back cover of your book. Which elements do you think of as being typical metals? Transition elements are the most familiar because they often occur in nature as uncombined elements, unlike Group 1 and Group 2 metals which are less stable.

Transition elements often form colored compounds. The gems in **Figure 6** show brightly colored compounds containing chromium. Cadmium yellow and cobalt blue paints are made from compounds of transition elements. However, cadmium and cobalt paints are so toxic that their use is limited.

Iron, Cobalt, and Nickel The first elements in Groups 8, 9, and 10—iron, cobalt, and nickel—form a unique cluster of transition elements. These three sometimes are called the iron triad. All three elements are used in the process to create steel and other metal mixtures.

Iron—the main component of steel—is the most widely used of all metals. It is the second most abundant metallic element in Earth's crust after aluminum. Other metals are added to steel to give it various characteristics. Some steels contain cobalt or nickel. Nickel is added to some metals to give them strength. Also, nickel is used to give a shiny, protective coating to other metals.

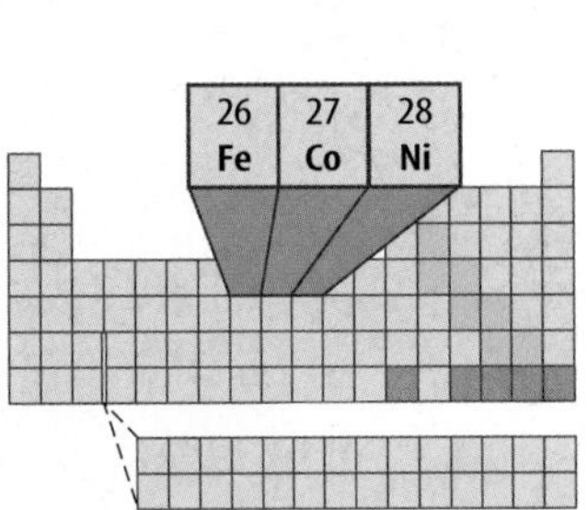

Figure 6 The colors of the ruby and emerald are due to the transition element chromium.

Differentiated Instruction

Challenge Other metals are often alloyed with steel to produce metals with particular properties. Have students identify some steel alloys and their uses. Aluminum added to steel makes it smooth and strong. Chromium steel has hardness, strength, and elasticity that make it useful for automobile and airplane parts. The most widely used alloy of steel is nickel steel, which is extremely strong. Nickel-chromium steel is shock resistant and is used for armor plate. L3 IS **Linguistic**

Science Journal

Transition Metals Ask students to list in their Science Journals metal objects they come in contact with in their daily lives, note the metals from which the objects are made, and put an asterisk beside each that contains transition metals. Possibilities include aluminum cans, iron in steel in an automobile, copper and zinc in brass ornaments, tin in cans, gold and silver in jewelry. L2 IS **Naturalist**

Figure 7 The coinage metals have many uses.

Because gold and silver are so expensive, copper is more common in coins.

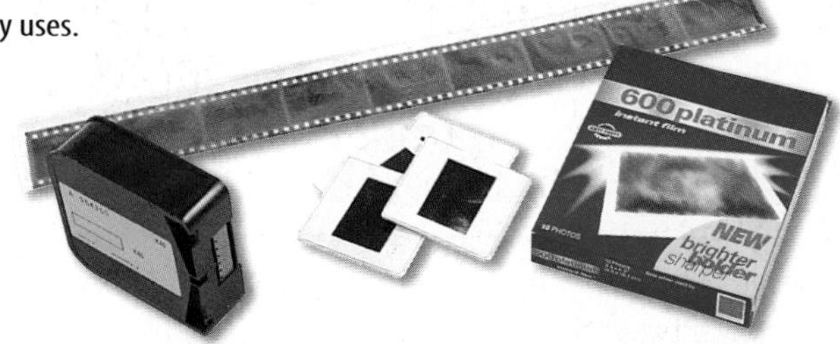

Silver is used in compounds to make photographic materials.

Gold frequently is used in jewelry.

Copper, Silver, and Gold The main metals in the objects in **Figure 7** are copper, silver, and gold—the three elements in Group 11. Because they are so stable and malleable and can be found as free elements in nature, these metals were once used widely to make coins. For this reason, they are known as the coinage metals. Because they are so expensive, silver and gold rarely are used in coins anymore. The United States stopped using gold in the production of its coins in 1933 and silver in 1964. Most coins now are made of nickel and copper.

Copper often is used in electrical wiring because of its superior ability to conduct electricity and its relatively low cost. Can you imagine a world without photographs and movies? Silver iodide and silver bromide break down when exposed to light, producing an image on paper. Consequently, these compounds are used to make photographic film and paper. Silver and gold are used in jewelry because of their attractive color, relative softness, resistance to corrosion, and rarity.

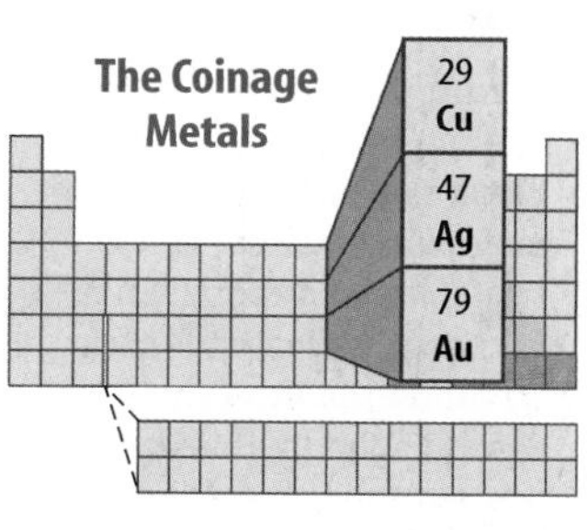

Why does gold's relative softness make it a good choice for jewelry?

Zinc, Cadmium, and Mercury Zinc, cadmium, and mercury are found in Group 12 of the periodic table. Zinc combines with oxygen in the air to form a thin, protective coating of zinc oxide on its surface. Zinc and cadmium often are used to coat, or plate, other metals such as iron because of this protective quality. Cadmium is used also in rechargeable batteries.

Mercury is a silvery, liquid metal—the only metal that is a liquid at room temperature. It is used in thermometers, thermostats, switches, and batteries. Mercury is poisonous and can accumulate in the body. People have died of mercury poisoning after eating fish that lived in mercury-contaminated water.

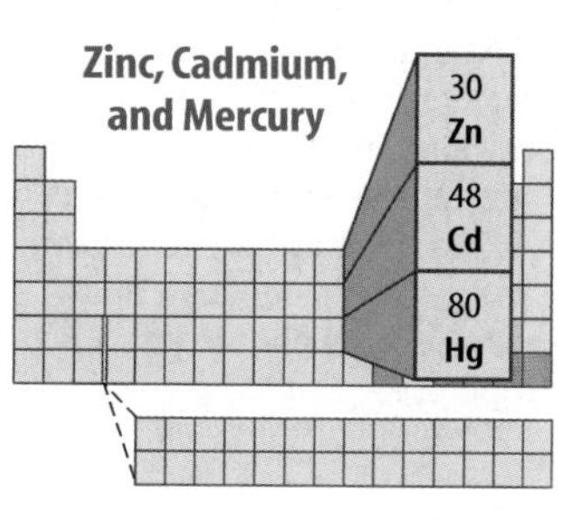

Reading Check

Answer Gold is soft enough to be delicately shaped.

Activity

Transition Elements Place a large sheet of butcher paper at the front of the room. On it, list the transition elements. Have students add to the list any uses of the elements, or examples of the elements, they encounter during the week. At the end of the week, decide why some elements appear on the sheet more often than others. Possible answers: rarity of the element, cost of manufacture, need for materials that match properties of the element L2 IS **Interpersonal**

Conductivity

Purpose teach students about conductivity through metal

Possible Materials flashlight bulb, batteries, various kinds of wire or metal bar (copper, aluminum, steel, and lead), and ohmmeter

Estimated Time 20 min

Teaching Strategies

- Have the students connect the flashlight bulb to the negative pole of the battery using one of the copper wires, then use one of each of the other wires or bars to connect to the positive pole of the battery.
- Use the ohmmeter to measure the resistance (milliamps) of the electricity conducting through the different wires. Record the measurements and have the students describe which metals were better conductors and why.
- Allow students to explore other questions that arise. L2

For additional inquiry activities, see Science Inquiry Labs.

Cultural Diversity

Forms of Money The use of metals for money began around the seventh century B.C. In the Middle East, bronze probably was used first, with gold and silver also exchanged. There is evidence that standard weight and value coins were developed in the area of modern Turkey around 650 B.C. Have students discuss characteristics that make a material useful as money. value, portability, rarity, availability, sturdiness L2 IS **Logical-Mathematical**

Differentiated Instruction

Challenge Have students find out which metal is used in the galvanizing process. zinc What is the main use of galvanizing? Zinc, when plated over iron containers, slows down the rusting process, because it oxidizes before the iron does and forms a protective coating. L3 IS **Linguistic**

Caption Answer

Figure 8 between Groups 3 and 4 in periods 6 and 7

Mining Engineer Besides processing ores into metals, mining engineers design open pits and the underground mines. They are also responsible for the safety of the workers and the environment. A large percentage of mining engineers work in the mining industry. Others work in the professional and technical service firms as consultants to the mining industry.

Discussion

Radioactive Elements Why are the elements beyond uranium radioactive? As the number of protons increases, so does the repulsive force within the nucleus; this can cause several types of nuclear rearrangements. L2 **Logical-Mathematical**

Virtual Labs

Elements *What properties do elements have?*

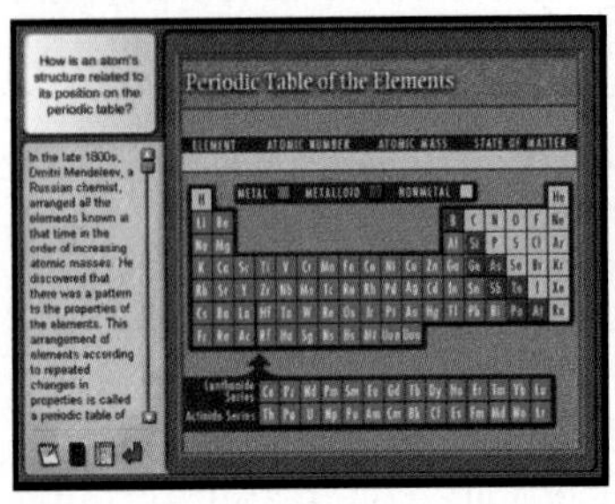

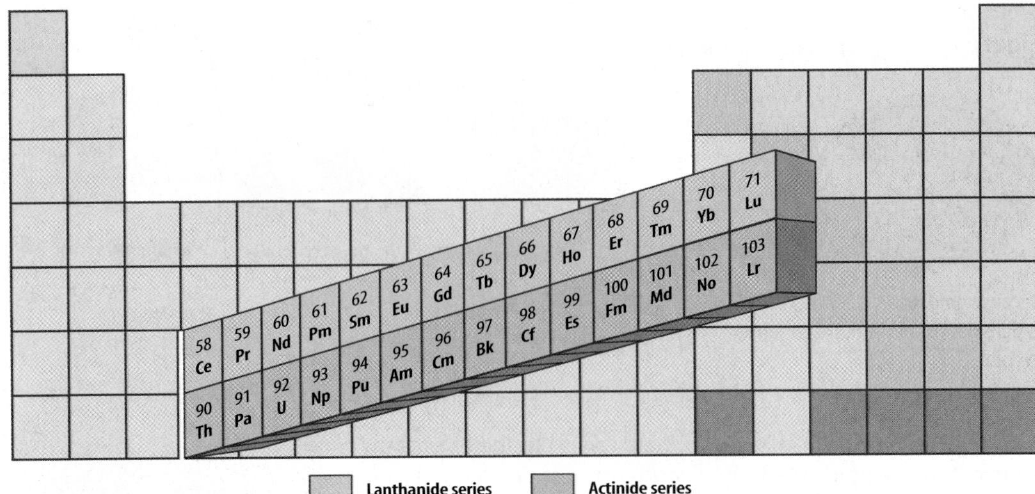

Figure 8 To save space, the periodic table usually isn't shown with the inner transition elements positioned where they should be. **Identify** *where the lanthanide and actinide series are found.*

Mining Engineer The processing of ores mined from Earth normally begins with metals in very low concentrations and generally not in the most desirable form. To refine the ores and concentrate the metal into the desired form, the mining engineer must develop a process that is economical and environmentally sound to be a viable process. Investigate some of the processes used to refine various metals and give examples of a process that is environmentally friendly but not cost effective and of a process that is just the opposite.

The Inner Transition Metals

The two rows of elements that seem to be disconnected from the rest on the periodic table are called the inner transition elements. They are called this because like the transition elements, they fit in the periodic table between Groups 3 and 4 in periods 6 and 7, as shown in **Figure 8.** To save room, they are listed below the table.

The Lanthanides The first row includes a series of elements with atomic numbers of 58 to 71. These elements are called the lanthanide series because they follow the element lanthanum.

Lanthanum, cerium, praseodymium, and samarium are used with carbon to make a compound that is used extensively by the motion picture industry. Europium, gadolinium, and terbium are used to produce the colors you see on your TV screen.

The Actinides The second row of inner transition metals includes elements with atomic numbers ranging from 90 to 103. These elements are called the actinide series because they follow the element actinium. All of the actinides are radioactive and unstable. Their unstable nature makes researching them difficult. Thorium and uranium are the actinides found in the Earth's crust in usable quantities. Thorium is used in making the glass for high-quality camera lenses because it bends light without much distortion. Uranium is best known for its use in nuclear reactors and in weapons applications, but one of its compounds has been used as photographic toner, as well.

Curriculum Connection

History Changing one element into another is called transmutation. Transmutation was one of the major goals of alchemists. Ask students to find out what alchemists hoped to transmute. They wanted to change base metals into gold. L3 **Linguistic**

Differentiated Instruction

Challenge When the number of protons changes, the identity of the element changes. Many of the actinides are formed by changing the number of protons in atoms of other elements. Have each student choose one of the actinides and find out how it is formed. Possible answer: When uranium-238 is bombarded with a neutron, it becomes U-239, then decomposes to neptunium-239 and an electron, or beta particle. L3 **Linguistic**

576 CHAPTER 19 Elements and Their Properties

Metals in the Crust

Earth's hardened outer layer, called the crust, contains many compounds and a few uncombined metals such as gold and copper. Metals must be mined and separated from their ores, as shown in **Figure 9.**

Most of the world's platinum is found in South Africa. Chromium is important because it is used to harden steel, to manufacture stainless steel, and to form other alloys. The United States imports most of its chromium from South Africa, the Philippines, and Turkey.

Figure 9 Copper is mined in the United States at the Bingham Canyon Copper Mine in Utah.

Ores: Minerals and Mixtures Metals in Earth's crust that combined with other elements are found as ores. Most ores consist of a metal compound, or mineral, within a mixture of clay or rock. After an ore is mined from Earth's crust, the rock is separated from the mineral. Then the mineral often is converted to another physical form. This step usually involves heat and is called roasting. Finally, the metal is refined into a pure form. Later it can be alloyed with other metals.

Removing the waste rock can be expensive. If the cost of removing the waste rock becomes greater than the value of the desired material, the mineral no longer is classified as an ore.

section 1 review

Summary

Properties of Metals

- Metals tend to form ionic and metallic bonds due to low numbers of electrons in their outer energy level.

Alkali and Alkaline Earth Metals

- Elements in Group 1 are called alkali metals.
- Elements in Group 2 are called alkaline earth metals.

Transition Elements and Inner Transition Metals

- Transition elements are elements in Groups 3–12 in the periodic table.
- Inner transition metals fit in the periodic table between Groups 3 and 4 in periods 6 and 7.

Self Check

1. **Describe** how to test palladium to see if it is a metal.
2. **Explain** how arrangement of the iron triad differs from arrangements of coinage metals.
3. **Identify** how metallic bonds differ from ionic and covalent bonds.
4. **Think Critically** If X stands for a metal, how can you tell from the following formulas—XCl and XCl_2—which compound contains an alkali metal and which contains an alkaline earth metal?

Applying Math

5. **Use Percentages** Pennies used to be made of copper and zinc, and weighed 3.11 g. Today, pennies are made of copper-plated zinc, and weighs 2.5 g. A new penny weighs what percent of an old penny?

3 Assess

DAILY INTERVENTION

Check for Understanding

Logical-Mathematical Ask students why metallic atoms generally obtain positive charges when combining with nonmetallic elements and have them give some examples. L2

Reteach

Groups Have students make flash cards with the symbol of a metallic element on one side of each card and the name of the element and whether it is an alkali metal, alkaline earth metal, transition element, or rare earth metal on the other. Have students form small groups and take turns using their cards to quiz the other students in the group. L2 COOP LEARN  **Interpersonal**

Assessment

Portfolio Ask each student to draw a diagram that shows how the atoms in a metal are bonded to each other. Diagrams should show a cloud of valence electrons with various nuclei in the cloud. Use **Performance Assessment in the Science Classroom,** p. 127. P L2

section 1 review

1. see if it conducts heat and electricity, reflects light, and is malleable and ductile
2. The iron triad is a horizontal arrangement while the others are vertical. The zinc group is vertical too.
3. Unlike covalent bonds, metallic bonds do not form separate molecules. Unlike ionic bonds, metallic bonds do not produce inflexible structures. Metallic bonds enable electrical conductivity in the solid state, unlike covalent or ionic bonds.
4. Cl carries a 1− charge when bonded to metals, so the metal in XCl must have a 1+ charge to balance it. This means the metal must be from Group 1. To balance the Cl_2 in XCl_2, the X must have a 2+ charge, which means it must be from Group 2.
5. The weight of a penny is 80% of the weight of an old penny.

section 2

Nonmetals

1 Motivate

Bellringer

Section Focus Transparencies also are available on the Interactive Chalkboard CD-ROM. L2 

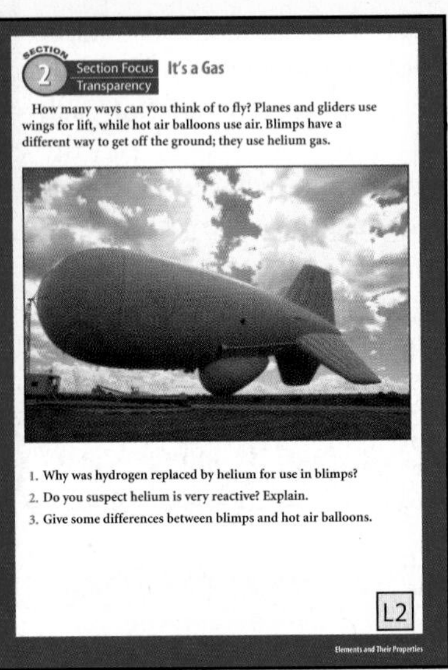

Section 2 Section Focus Transparency It's a Gas
How many ways can you think of to fly? Planes and gliders use wings for lift, while hot air balloons use air. Blimps have a different way to get off the ground; they use helium gas.
1. Why was hydrogen replaced by helium for use in blimps?
2. Do you suspect helium is very reactive? Explain.
3. Give some differences between blimps and hot air balloons.
L2

Tie to Prior Knowledge

Air Elements Ask students to name the most abundant elements found in the air they are breathing. nitrogen and oxygen What are the two most plentiful elements in the universe? hydrogen and helium Tell students that all of these gases are nonmetals, about which they will learn more in this section. L2

Activity

Elements in Body In **Figure 10** there is a reference to other elements as making up 2% of the body. Have students research what are some of these other elements. Have them pick one and collect information as to what purpose this particular element serves in the body. Have them make a poster to present the information that they have found. **Visual-Spatial** P

Reading Guide

What You'll Learn
- **Recognize** hydrogen as a nonmetal.
- **Compare and contrast** properties of the halogens.
- **Describe** properties and uses of the noble gases.

Why It's Important
Nonmetals are not only all around you, they are an essential part of your body.

Review Vocabulary
molecule: neutral particle formed when atoms share electrons

New Vocabulary
- nonmetal
- diatomic molecule
- salt
- sublimation

Properties of Nonmetals

Most of your body's mass is made of oxygen, carbon, hydrogen, and nitrogen, as shown in **Figure 10.** Calcium, a metal, and other elements make up the remaining four percent of your body's mass. Phosphorus, sulfur, and chlorine are among these other elements found in your body. These elements are classified as nonmetals. **Nonmetals** are elements that usually are gases or brittle solids at room temperature. Because solid nonmetals are brittle or powdery, they are not malleable or ductile. Most nonmetals do not conduct heat or electricity well, and generally they are not shiny.

Figure 10 As a percentage of mass, humans are made up of mostly nonmetals.

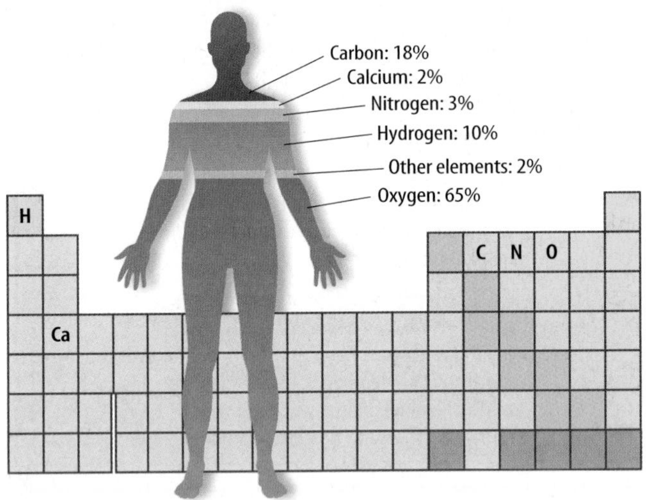

In the periodic table, all nonmetals except hydrogen are found at the right of the stair-step line. On the table in the inside back cover of your book, the nonmetal element blocks are colored yellow. The noble gases, Group 18, make up the only group of elements that are all nonmetals. Group 17 elements, except for astatine, are also nonmetals. Other nonmetals, found in Groups 13 through 16, will be discussed later.

Section 2 Resource Manager

Chapter *Fast File* Resources
Transparency Activity, p. 47
Directed Reading for Content Mastery, p. 20
MiniLAB, p. 4
Enrichment, p. 31
Reinforcement, p. 28
Lab Worksheet, pp. 5–6
Lab Activity, pp. 9–12

Science Inquiry Labs, pp. 35–36

Lead and sulfur bond ionically to form lead sulfide, PbS, also known as galena.

Carbon and oxygen can bond covalently to form carbon dioxide, CO_2.

Figure 11 Nonmetals form ionic bonds with metals and covalent bonds with other nonmetals.

Bonding in Nonmetals The electrons in most nonmetals are strongly attracted to the nucleus of the atom. So, as a group, nonmetals are poor conductors of heat and electricity.

Most nonmetals can form ionic and covalent compounds. Examples of these two kinds of compounds are shown in **Figure 11.**

When nonmetals gain electrons from metals, the nonmetals become negative ions in ionic compounds. An example of such an ionic compound is potassium iodide, KI, which often is added to table salt. KI is formed from the nonmetal iodine and the metal potassium. When bonded with other nonmetals, atoms of nonmetals usually share electrons to form covalent compounds. An example is ammonia, NH_3, the strong, unpleasant-smelling compound you notice when you open a bottle of some household cleaners.

Hydrogen

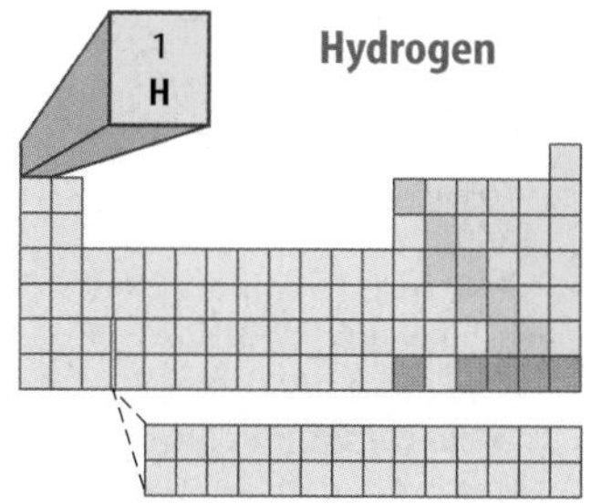

If you could count all the atoms in the universe, you would find that about 90 percent of them are hydrogen. Most hydrogen on Earth is found in the compound water. The word *hydrogen* is derived from the Greek term for "water forming." When water is broken down into its elements, hydrogen becomes a gas made up of diatomic molecules. A **diatomic molecule** consists of two atoms of the same element in a covalent bond.

Hydrogen is highly reactive. A hydrogen atom has a single electron, which the atom shares when it combines with other nonmetals. For example, hydrogen burns in oxygen to form water, H_2O, in which hydrogen shares electrons with oxygen.

Hydrogen can gain an electron when it combines with alkali and alkaline earth metals. The compounds formed are hydrides, such as sodium hydride, NaH.

Reading Check *What is a diatomic molecule?*

2 Teach

Visual Learning

Figure 11 Point out to students the diagrams showing ionic bonding and covalent bonding. Ask a volunteer to describe the similarities and differences between the two. In ionic bonding, electrons move from one atom to another. In covalent bonding, electrons are shared between atoms. In both types of bonding, the outer electron energy levels are filled. L2

LS **Visual-Spatial**

Teacher FYI

Liquid Elements Under normal pressures, nitrogen and oxygen do not become liquids until they reach the very cold temperatures of −196°C and −183°C, respectively.

Reading Check

Answer A diatomic molecule consists of two atoms of the same element joined by a covalent bond.

LAB DEMONSTRATION

Purpose to prepare a sample of hydrogen and examine its properties

Materials pea-sized sample of zinc metal; two large test tubes; one-holed rubber stopper fitted with 90° bent-glass tubing; 6*M* sulfuric acid

Procedure Place 4 mL of acid in one tube. Add zinc to the acid, and stopper the tube. Collect H_2 gas by inverting second tube over the upraised 90° glass bend. Carefully bring inverted tube containing H_2 near a burning wood splint so that H_2 ignites. **WARNING:** *Use an explosion shield and goggles. Never prepare more than this amount.*

Expected Outcome The reaction is $Zn + H_2SO_4 \rightarrow ZnSO_4 + H_2$. The H_2 then combines with O_2 to form water. L2

Assessment

What type of bond do hydrogen and oxygen make when they form water? covalent

Purpose Students determine the presence of chlorine compounds in drinking water. L2

LS **Kinesthetic**

Materials dropper; graduated cylinder; standard chloride comparison compound (0.10 g NaCl in 1 L of distilled water); silver nitrate testing solution (1.7 g $AgNO_3$ in 100 mL of distilled water)

Teaching Strategy

Safety Precaution Remind students to avoid contact with the silver nitrate testing solution.

Analysis

1. Standard chloride will show a white precipitate from the formation of AgCl. Distilled water showed no white precipitate.
2. If the drinking water contains a chlorine compound, it will show a white cloudiness similar to that of the standard but not as dense.

Assessment

Performance Have students test a sample of bottled water and determine whether it contains a chlorine compound. Read the label to verify results. Use **Performance Assessment in the Science Classroom,** p. 97.

Discussion

Chlorine This element is added to drinking water and to swimming pools. Explain to the students that chlorine is used to kill the bacteria and algae and make the water safe for human consumption. At the same time, chlorine gas in large enough concentrations can be deadly to humans. It is important to understand an element and its properties.

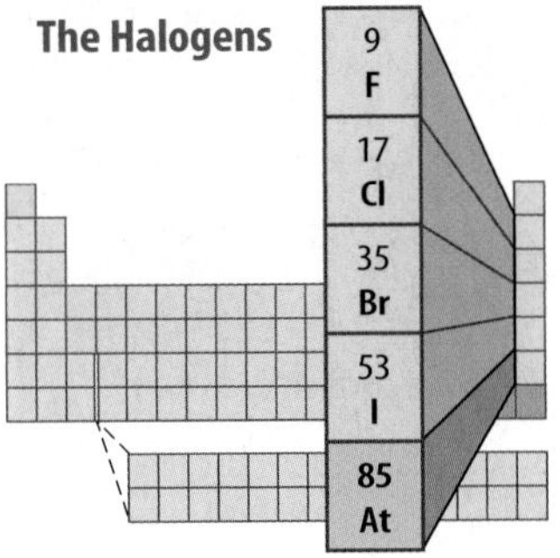

The Halogens

Halogen lights contain small amounts of bromine or iodine. These elements, as well as fluorine, chlorine, and astatine, are called halogens and are in Group 17. They are very reactive in their elemental form, and their compounds have many uses. As shown in **Figure 12,** fluorides are added to toothpastes and to city water systems to prevent tooth decay, and chlorine compounds are added to water to disinfect it.

Because an atom of a halogen has seven electrons in its outer energy level, only one electron is needed to complete this energy level. If a halogen gains an electron from a metal, an ionic compound, called a **salt,** is formed. An example of this is NaCl. In the gaseous state, the halogens form reactive diatomic covalent molecules and can be identified by their distinctive colors. Chlorine is greenish yellow, bromine is reddish orange, and iodine is violet.

Fluorine is the most chemically active of all elements. Hydrofluoric acid, a mixture of hydrogen fluoride and water, is used to etch glass and to frost the inner surfaces of lightbulbs and is also used in the fabrication of semiconductors.

Identifying Chlorine Compounds in Your Water

Procedure

1. In three labeled **test tubes,** obtain 2 mL of **chlorine standard solution, distilled water,** and **drinking water.**
2. Carefully add five drops of **silver nitrate solution** to each and stir. **WARNING:** *Avoid contact with the silver nitrate solution. Silver nitrate is a corrosive liquid that can stain skin and clothes.*

Analysis

1. Which solution will definitely show a presence of chlorine? How did this result compare to the result with distilled water?
2. Which result most resembled your drinking water?

Figure 12 The halogens have many uses.

Chlorine compounds are used in pools to disinfect the water.

Fluoride compounds are used in toothpaste to prevent tooth decay.

Teacher FYI

Halogens The term *halogen* means "salt former." When the atoms of halogens bond to each other, their electrons are shared to form diatomic molecules, such as Cl_2 and Br_2. When bonded to metals, however, they attract electrons so strongly that they form large negative ions.

Differentiated Instruction

Visually Impaired Provide these students with hand lenses to help them see the precipitate in the MiniLAB. L2

Figure 13 This ocean-salt recovery site uses evaporation to separate the halogen compounds from the water so the salts can be refined further.

Uses of Halogens The odor you sometimes smell near a swimming pool is chlorine. Chlorine compounds are used to disinfect water. Chlorine, the most abundant halogen, is obtained from seawater at ocean-salt recovery sites like the one in **Figure 13.** Household and industrial bleaches used to whiten flour, clothing, and paper also contain chlorine compounds.

Bromine, the only nonmetal that is a liquid at room temperature, also is extracted from compounds in seawater. Other bromine compounds are used as dyes in cosmetics.

Iodine, a shiny purple-gray solid at room temperature, is obtained from seawater. When heated, iodine changes directly to a purple vapor. The process of a solid changing directly to a vapor without forming a liquid is called **sublimation,** as shown in **Figure 14.** Iodine is essential in your diet for the production of the hormone thyroxin and to prevent goiter, an enlarging of the thyroid gland in the neck.

Reading Check *What is sublimation?*

Astatine is the last member of Group 17. It is radioactive and rare, but has many properties similar to those of the other halogens. There are no known uses due to its rarity.

INTEGRATE Environment

Chlorofluorocarbons Compounds called chlorofluorocarbons are used in refrigeration systems. If released, these compounds destroy ozone in the atmosphere. The ozone protects you from some of the harmful rays from the Sun. Find the advantages and disadvantages of these compounds. Write your answer in your Science Journal.

Figure 14 Frozen carbon dioxide, or dry ice, is used to make inexpensive, visible gas for theatrical productions. The carbon dioxide is brought out as a solid, then it sublimes as shown here.

INTEGRATE Environment

Chlorofluorocarbons Advantages: nontoxic, nonflammable, easily converted from liquid to gas and back, well-suited for many applications; disadvantages: can cause ozone depletion. Have students find the formula of freon and write the electron dot diagram for the molecule. CCl_2F_2 L2 LS **Logical-Mathematical** P

Career Meteorologists who research and study the atmosphere physical characteristics and the way it affects our environment are called atmospheric scientists. These scientists study trends in the Earth's climate. They may be researching global warming, ozone depletion, or severe storms. You can find these scientists working for the federal government, colleges and universities, media and the military.

Quick Demo

Sublimation

Materials dry ice, clear plastic sealable bag, gloves

Estimated Time 15 minutes

Procedure The process of sublimation can be demonstrated with dry ice. Carefully place a few small pieces of dry ice in a sealed plastic food bag. **WARNING:** *Wear gloves.* The phase change from solid to gas is observable as the CO_2 gas inflates the bag. Explain to students that solid iodine would do the same if gently heated. However, unlike CO_2 gas, iodine vapor is purple and is potentially harmful. L2

LS **Visual-Spatial**

Differentiated Instruction

Challenge Chlorofluorocarbons (CFCs) have been replaced as the major product to be used in refrigeration equipment. Have the students find out what is currently being used in its place and why. Currently hydrochlorofluorocarbons (HCFC) and hydrofluorocarbons (HFC)are being used to replace CFCs in refrigeration units. The advantage of using HCFCs is that the hydrogen reacts with tropospheric hydroxyl (OH), resulting in a shorter atmospheric lifetime. L3

Cultural Diversity

Seaweed in China The Chinese recognized very early that seaweed, which is high in iodine, could be used to treat goiter, an enlargement of the thyroid gland. The information was not brought to Europe until several centuries later. Have students find the recommended daily allowance for iodine. The RDA for iodine is 150 mcg. L1 LS **Linguistic**

Reading Check

Answer the process by which a solid changes directly to a gas without forming a liquid

Quick Demo

Noble Gases

Materials periodic table, laser pointer

Estimated Time five minutes

Procedure Bring a pencil-sized laser to class, and demonstrate its use. Have students locate on the periodic table the nonmetal noble gases helium and neon, which are typically used in these lasers. **WARNING:** *Do not point the laser beam directly into anyone's eyes.* L2 LS **Visual-Spatial**

3 Assess

DAILY INTERVENTION

Check for Understanding

Logical-Mathematical Ask students to use references to find the formulas of these common acids: hydrochloric HCl, nitric HNO_3, sulfuric H_2SO_4, hydrofluoric HF, and carbonic H_2CO_3. Then ask them to determine if the acids are typically formed with atoms of metals or nonmetals. nonmetals L2

Reteach

Applications Bring to class magazine, newspaper, and Internet photos of nonmetals in use. Ask students to name each nonmetal and locate it on the periodic table. Examples: lipstick (carbon), bleach (chlorine and oxygen), neon lights (neon). L2 LS **Visual-Spatial**

Assessment

Performance Point to two elements on the periodic table and ask students to predict the bond type that would form between them. If it is an ionic bond, ask them which element is likely to form a negative ion and which is likely to form a positive ion. For example, point to Na and F—ionic, Na is positive, F is negative. Point to sulfur and oxygen. The bond is covalent, and the formula is SO_2 or SO_3. Use **PASC,** p. 89 L2 LS **Logical-Mathematical**

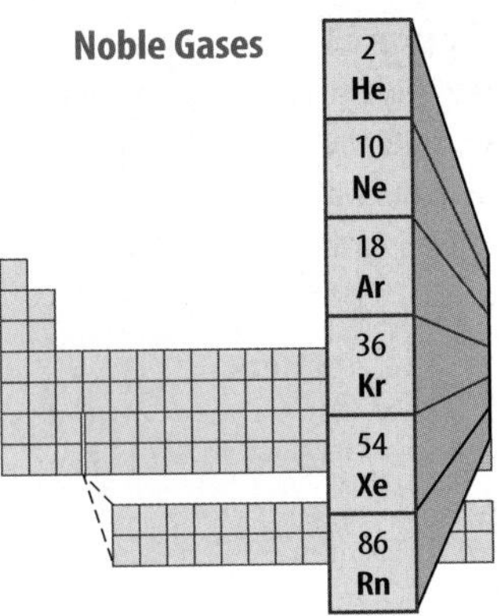

The Noble Gases

The noble gases exist as isolated atoms. They are stable because their outermost energy levels are full. No naturally occurring noble gas compounds are known, but several compounds of xenon and krypton with fluorine have been created in a laboratory.

The stability of noble gases is what makes them useful. In addition, the light weight of helium makes it useful in lighter-than-air blimps and balloons. Neon and argon are used in "neon lights" for advertising. Argon and krypton are used in electric lightbulbs to produce light in lasers, as seen in **Figure 15.**

Figure 15 Noble gases are used to produce spectacular laser light shows.

section 2 review

Summary

Properties of Nonmetals

- Nonmetals usually are gases or brittle solids that are not shiny and do not conduct heat or electricity.

Hydrogen

- Hydrogen makes up 90 percent of the atoms in the universe and is highly reactive.

Halogens

- Halogens are in Group 17 and are highly reactive in their elemental form.

The Noble Gases

- Noble gases exist only as isolated atoms because their outer energy levels are full.

Self Check

1. **Describe** two ways in which hydrogen combines with other elements.
2. **Rank** the following nonmetals from lowest number of electrons in the outer level to highest: *Cl^-, H^+, He, H.*
3. **Explain** how solid nonmetals are different from solid metals.
4. **Describe** how you can tell that a gas is a halogen.
5. **Think Critically** What is the process of a solid changing directly into a vapor? Which element undergoes this process at room temperature?

Applying Math

6. **Interpret data** by identifying the nonmetal with its oxidation number in these compounds: *MgO, NaH, $AlBr_3$,* and *FeS.*

Science Online gpscience.com/self_check_quiz

section 2 review

1. covalently with most nonmetals and ionically with active metals
2. H^+ (zero); H (one); He (two) Cl^- (eight).
3. Unlike solid metals, solid nonmetals typically are not ductile or malleable and do not conduct electricity.
4. By their colors: Cl_2 is greenish-yellow, Br_2 is reddish-orange, and I_2 is violet. Also, halogens will react readily with Group 1 and Group 2 metals.
5. sublimation; iodine
6. MgO: oxygen is 2−; NaH: H is 1−; $AlBr_3$: Br is 1−; FeS: S is 2−.

What Type is it?

Suppose you want an element for a certain use. You might be able to use a metal but not a nonmetal. In this lab, you will test several metals and nonmetals and compare their properties.

Real-World Question

How can you use properties to distinguish metals from nonmetals?

Goals

- **Observe** physical properties.
- **Test** the malleability of the materials.
- **Identify** electrical conductivity in the given materials.

Materials

samples of C, Mg, Al, S, and Sn
dishes for the samples
paper towels
conductivity tester
spatula
small hammer

Safety Precautions

Procedure

1. **Prepare** a table in your Science Journal like the one shown above.
2. **Observe** and record the appearance of each element sample. Include its physical state, color, and whether it is shiny or dull.
3. Remove a small sample of one of the elements. Gently tap the sample with a hammer. The sample is malleable if it flattens when tapped and brittle if it shatters. Clean the hammer between testing using a paper towel.
4. Repeat step 3 for each sample.
5. Test the conductivity of each element by touching the electrodes of the conductivity tester to a sample. If the bulb lights, the element conducts electricity.

Observing Properties

Element	Appearance	Malleable or Brittle	Electrical Conductivity	Shiny or Dull
Carbon	black solid	B	N	D
Magnesium	silver metal	M	Y	S
Aluminum	silver metal	M	Y	S
Sulfur	yellow solid	B	N	D
Tin	silver metal	M	Y	S

Conclude and Apply

1. **Compare and Contrast** Locate each element you used on the periodic table. Compare your results with what you would expect from an element in that location.
2. **Explain** Locate palladium, Pd, on the periodic table. Use the results you obtained during the activity to predict some of the properties of palladium.

Communicating Your Data

Compare your results with those of other students. **For more help, refer to the** Science Skill Handbook.

Real-World Question

Purpose Students will observe properties of metals and nonmetals and use their observations to classify the substances. L2 COOP LEARN IS **Kinesthetic**

Process Skills observe, interpret data, compare and contrast, classify

Time Required 30 min

Procedure

Safety Precautions Have students wear goggles and use caution when hammering.

Teaching Strategy Encourage the students to try and use as many of their senses as possible to describe the properties of each material.

Troubleshooting Test the conductivity tester before class. Use amorphous carbon such as charcoal, but not graphite, which is shiny and will conduct a current.

Conclude and Apply

1. Elements on the left side of the periodic table should show metallic properties, while those on the right should illustrate nonmetallic properties.
2. Predictions may include that it is shiny, malleable, and a conductor.

Assessment

Performance Provide a periodic table, and ask students to draw a circle around the metallic elements. Use **Performance Assessment in the Science Classroom,** p. 89. L2

Communicating Your Data

Have students display their data tables and share their results with the rest of the class

1 Motivate

Bellringer

Section Focus Transparencies also are available on the Interactive Chalkboard CD-ROM.

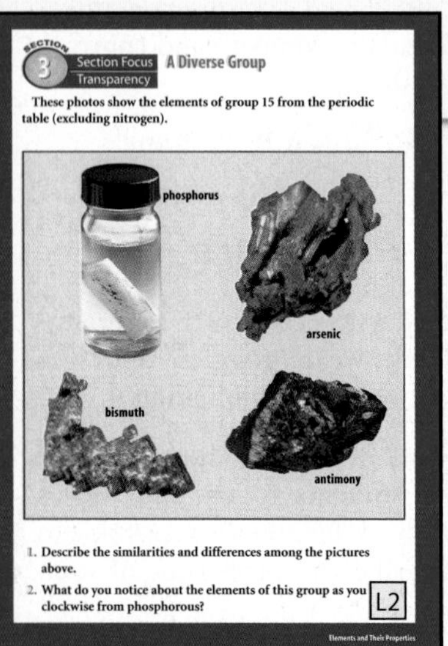

Section 3 Section Focus Transparency **A Diverse Group**

These photos show the elements of group 15 from the periodic table (excluding nitrogen).

phosphorus / arsenic / bismuth / antimony

1. Describe the similarities and differences among the pictures above.
2. What do you notice about the elements of this group as you move clockwise from phosphorous? L2

Elements and Their Properties

Tie to Prior Knowledge

Computers Ask students what element they typically associate with computers. silicon Where is this element located on the periodic table? between metals and nonmetals What type of properties would you expect silicon to have? Properties between those of metals and nonmetals; for example, while metals are conductors and nonmetals are nonconductors, silicon is a semiconductor. L2

section 3

Mixed Groups

Reading Guide

What You'll Learn

- **Distinguish** among metals, nonmetals, and metalloids.
- **Describe** the nature of allotropes.
- **Recognize** the significance of differences in crystal structure in carbon.
- **Understand** the importance of synthetic elements.

Why It's Important

The elements in mixed groups affect your life every day, because they are in everything from the computer you use to the air you breathe.

Review Vocabulary

substance: element or compound that cannot be broken down into simpler components

New Vocabulary

- metalloid
- allotrope
- semiconductor
- transuranium element

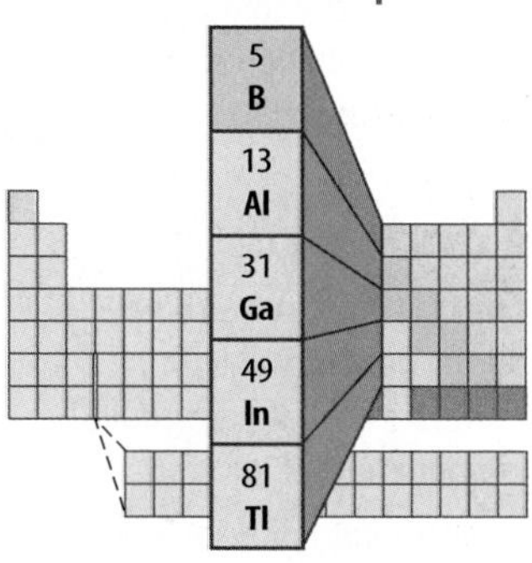

Properties of Metalloids

Can an element be a metal and a nonmetal? In a sense, some elements called metalloids are. Metalloids share unusual characteristics. **Metalloids** can form ionic and covalent bonds with other elements and can have metallic and nonmetallic properties. Some metalloids can conduct electricity better than most nonmetals, but not as well as some metals, giving them the name semiconductor. With the exception of aluminum, the metalloids are the elements in the periodic table that are located along the stair-step line. The mixed groups—13, 14, 15, 16, and 17—contain metals, nonmetals, and metalloids.

The Boron Group

Boron, a metalloid, is the first element in Group 13. If you look around your home, you might find two compounds of boron. One of these is borax, which is used in some laundry products to soften water. The other is boric acid, a mild antiseptic. Boron also is used as a grinding material and as boranes, which are compounds used for jet and rocket fuel.

Aluminum, a metal in Group 13, is the most abundant metal in Earth's crust. It is used in soft-drink cans, foil wrap, cooking pans, and as siding. Aluminum is strong and light and is used in the construction of airplanes such as the one in **Figure 16.**

Figure 16 Aluminum is used frequently in the construction of airplanes because it is light and strong.

Section 3 Resource Manager

Chapter *FAST FILE* Resources

Transparency Activity, pp. 48, 49–51
Directed Reading for Content Mastery, pp. 21, 22
Lab Activity, pp. 13–16
Enrichment, p. 32
Reinforcement, p. 29
Lab Worksheet, pp. 7–8

Life Science Critical Thinking/Problem Solving, p. 22
Mathematics Skill Activities, p. 5
Earth Science Critical Thinking/Problem Solving, p. 3
Physical Science Critical Thinking/Problem Solving, p. 13

584 CHAPTER 19 Elements and Their Properties

Silicon is used to make the chips that allow this computer to run.

Figure 17 Elements in Group 14 have many uses.

These tin cans are made of steel with a tin coating.

The Carbon Group

Each element in Group 14, the carbon family, has four electrons in its outer energy level, but this is where much of the similarity ends. Carbon is a nonmetal, silicon and germanium are metalloids, and tin and lead are metals. Carbon occurs as an element in coal and as a compound in oil, natural gas, and foods. Carbon in these materials can combine with oxygen to produce carbon dioxide, CO_2. In the presence of sunlight, plants utilize CO_2 to make food. Carbon compounds, many of which are essential to life, can be found in you and all around you. All organic compounds contain carbon, but not all carbon compounds are organic.

Silicon is second only to oxygen in abundance in Earth's crust. Most silicon is found in sand, SiO_2, and almost all rocks and soil. The crystal structure of silicon dioxide is similar to the structure of diamond. Silicon occurs as two allotropes. **Allotropes,** which are different forms of the same element, have different molecular structures. One allotrope of silicon is a hard, gray substance, and the other is a brown powder.

Reading Check *What are allotropes?*

Silicon is the main component in **semiconductors**—elements that conduct an electric current under certain conditions. Many of the electronics that you use every day, like the computer in **Figure 17,** need semiconductors to run. Germanium, the other metalloid in the carbon group, is used along with silicon in making semiconductors. Tin is used to coat other metals to prevent corrosion, like the tin cans in **Figure 17.** Tin also is combined with other metals to produce bronze and pewter. Lead was used widely in paint at one time, but because it is toxic, lead no longer is used.

The Carbon Group

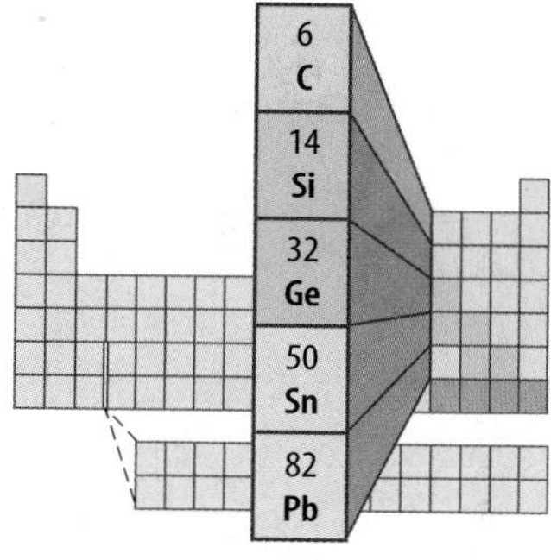

2 Teach

Teacher FYI

Conductivity When solids conduct, valence electrons move from their normal positions to a slightly higher energy level called a conducting band. In metals, the energy gap between the nonconducting band and the conducting band is slight, so metals conduct easily. In metalloids such as Si, the gap between the two states is also small but is larger than in metals. Hence, metalloids do not conduct as well as most metals.

Use Science Words

Word Origin Have students look up the roots of the word *allotrope* and explain how they combine to apply to elements. *Allotrope* comes from the Greek allo-, "other," and *tropos,* "turning or direction." Each allotrope of an element has another, or different, form. L2 LS **Linguistic**

Discussion

Gaining and Losing Typically, nonmetals gain electrons and a negative charge when reacting while metals lose electrons to obtain positive charges as they react. Ask students what they predict the charges will be for the carbon group. Plus or minus four. L2

Reading Check

Answer Allotropes are different forms of the same element.

Teacher FYI

Long Chains Another important property of carbon is its ability to connect with itself to form long chains. This is called catenation, and it enables carbon to make proteins and other large chain molecules. No other element comes close to carbon in this ability.

Make a Model

Tetrahedrons Draw an equilateral triangle 5 cm on a side. Make copies, and give each student four. Have each student cut out the triangles, leaving small tabs on each side, and tape the triangles together to form a tetrahedron. Ask students to stack several tetrahedrons to show how tetrahedrons support one another. This interlocking network represents the structure that carbon forms in diamonds.
L1 ELL IS P **Kinesthetic**

Fun Fact

Soft lead metal was once used for writing black marks on paper. Graphite mixed with clay is less toxic and has replaced lead in pencils for writing. The term *graphite* comes from the Greek word *graphein,* which means "to write."

Caption Answer

Figure 18 graphite, hexagons; diamond, tetrahedrons; buckminsterfullerene, soccer-ball-shaped, made from hexagons and pentagons

Topic: Buckminsterfullerene
Visit gpscience.com for Web links to information about this compound.

Activity Research this compound and describe some of the qualities that make it unique.

Allotropes of Carbon What do the diamond in a diamond ring and the graphite in your pencil have in common? They are both carbon. Diamond, graphite, and buckminsterfullerene, shown in **Figure 18,** are allotropes of an element.

A diamond is clear and extremely hard. In a diamond, each carbon atom is bonded to four other carbon atoms at the vertices, or corner points, of a tetrahedron. In turn, many tetrahedrons join together to form a giant molecule in which the atoms are held tightly in a strong crystalline structure. This structure accounts for the hardness of diamond.

Graphite is a black powder that consists of hexagonal layers of carbon atoms. In the hexagons, each carbon atom is bonded to three other carbon atoms. The fourth electron of each atom is bonded weakly to the layer next to it. This structure allows the layers to slide easily past one another, making graphite an excellent lubricant. In the mid-1980s, a new allotrope of carbon called buckminsterfullerene was discovered. This soccer-ball-shaped molecule, informally called a buckyball, was named after the architect-engineer R. Buckminster Fuller, who designed structures with similar shapes.

In 1991, scientists were able to use the buckyballs to synthesize extremely thin, graphitelike tubes. These tubes, called nanotubes, are about 1 billionth of a meter in diameter. That means you could stack tens of thousands of nanotubes just to get the thickness of one piece of paper. Nanotubes might be used someday to make computers that are smaller and faster and to make strong building materials.

Figure 18 Three allotropes of carbon are depicted here. **Identify** *the geometric shapes that make up each allotrope.*

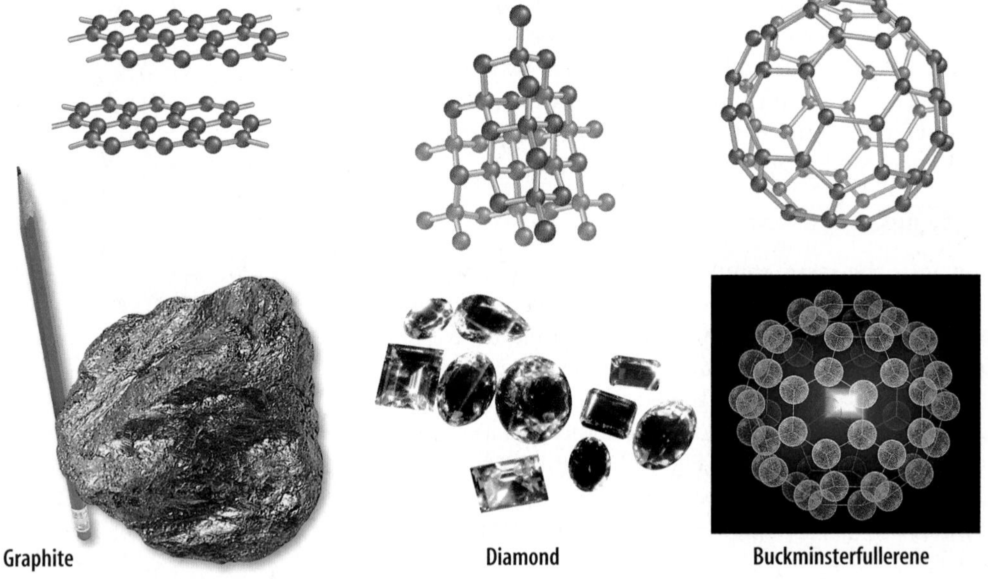

Visual Learning

Figure 18 Ask students to examine the structure of buckminsterfullerene and explain why some chemists call it a cage molecule. This molecule is hollow inside, like a cage. How could the molecule be used as a delivery system? A substance could be inserted into the cage, the cage could be put in the desired location and then opened, and the contents could be released.
L2 IS **Visual-Spatial**

Teacher FYI

Diamonds Diamonds are crystallized under tremendous heat and pressure, probably in regions of molten rock deep within Earth. Diamonds conduct heat well but are not good conductors of electricity. They are resistant to bases and acids, and burn at about 800°C to form carbon dioxide.

The Nitrogen Group

The nitrogen family makes up Group 15. Each element has five electrons in its outer energy level. These elements tend to share electrons and to form covalent compounds with other elements. Nitrogen often is used to make nitrates (which are compounds that contain the nitrate ion, NO_3^-) and ammonia, NH_3, both of which are used in fertilizers. Nitrogen is the fourth most abundant element in your body. Each breath you take is about 80 percent gaseous nitrogen in the form of diatomic molecules, N_2. Yet you and other animals and plants can't use nitrogen in its diatomic form. The nitrogen must be combined into compounds, such as amino acids.

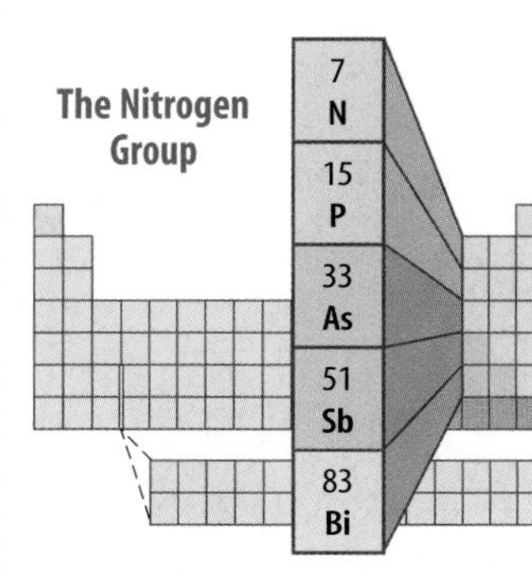

CIRCLE GRAPHS

Use Circle Graphs Oxygen, the predominant element in Earth's crust, makes up approximately 46.6 percent of the crust. If you were to show this information on a circle graph, how many degrees would represent oxygen?

1. **This is what you know:** % oxygen = 46.6%; total degrees in a circle = 360°
2. **This is what you need to find:** degrees of a circle that represent 46.6%
3. **Use this formula:** $\frac{\text{\% oxygen}}{\text{\% total}} = \frac{\text{degrees oxygen}}{\text{degrees total}}$
4. **Rearrange the equation and substitute:**

$$\text{degrees oxygen} = \frac{\text{\% oxygen} \times \text{degrees total}}{\text{\% total}}$$

$$\text{degrees oxygen} = \frac{46.6\% \times 360°}{100\%}$$

degrees oxygen = 167.76°, rounded to 168°

5. **Determine the units:** $\text{degrees} = \frac{\cancel{\text{percent}} \times \text{degrees}}{\cancel{\text{percent}}}$

Answer: In a circle graph, the number of degrees 46.6% of oxygen would represent is 168°.

Science Online
For more practice problems, go to page 834, and visit gpscience.com/extra_problems.

Practice Problems

1. The percentages of remaining elements in Earth's crust are: silicon, 27.7; aluminum, 8.1; iron, 5.0; calcium, 3.6; sodium, 2.8; potassium, 2.6; magnesium, 2.1; and other elements, 1.5. Find the number of degrees in a circle each percentage would represent.
2. **Challenge** Create a circle graph of the elements in Earth's crust.

Make a Model

Ballons The general composition of air can be modeled using balloons of two different colors. Have 80% of them one color to represent N_2 and 20% the other color to represent O_2. Bring the inflated and tied balloons to class, and position them in a corner of the room for students to observe. Explain that the balloons show the approximate ratio of nitrogen molecules to oxygen molecules in air. L2

LS **Visual-Spatial**

CIRCLE GRAPHS

National Math Standards

Correlation to Mathematics Objectives

1, 2, 9

Answers to Practice Problems

1. degrees of the circle needed for each element: O, 167.76; Si, 99.72; Al, 29.16; Fe, 18.00; Ca, 12.96; Na, 10.08; K, 9.36; Mg, 7.56; other, 5.4.
2. Check students' work

Differentiated Instruction

Learning Disabled To help students with the math in the Math Skills Activity, draw a circle on the board and divide it into fourths. Ask students how many degrees are in each of the angles between the divisions of the circle. 90° What percent of the area of the circle is in each division? 25% Once they see this relationship, work through the math with them: $\frac{25}{100} = \frac{x}{360}$; $x = (25 \times 360) \div 100 = 90$ L2

Challenge Have students make posters illustrating the process of phosphorylation in photosynthesis and in respiration. In both photosynthetic phosphorylation and respirational phosphorylation, a phosphate group is added to adenosine diphosphate (ADP) to form adenosine triphosphate (ATP). ATP is used by cells as a source of energy to power cell processes such as the synthesis of proteins. L3 P

LS **Logical-Mathematical**

Reading Check

Answer to lower the melting point of the plug that holds the water in, so heat from a fire will quickly activate the sprinkler

Use an Analogy

Futons A futon is a piece of furniture that can be used as a sofa or laid flat to be used as a bed. These various forms of the same piece of furniture are like the allotropes, or other forms, of the same element. L2

Fun Fact

Sulfur is one of the oldest known elements. Originally called *brimstone*, meaning "burning stone," it was used by ancient Greeks as a house fumigant. By itself it is odorless, but rotten eggs, skunks, and onions all owe their characteristic odors to compounds of sulfur. Sulfur's main use is in the manufacture of sulfuric acid, which is widely used in making fertilizers.

Uses of the Nitrogen Group Phosphorus is a nonmetal that has three allotropes. Phosphorous compounds can be used for many things from water softeners to fertilizers, match heads, and even in fine china. Antimony is a metalloid, and bismuth is a metal. Both elements are used with other metals to lower their melting points. Because of this property, the metal in automatic fire-sprinkler heads contains bismuth.

Reading Check *Why is bismuth used in fire-sprinkler heads?*

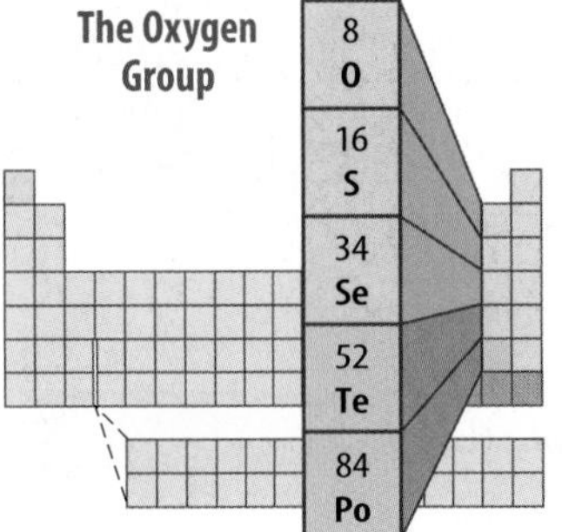

The Oxygen Group

Group 16 on the periodic table is the oxygen group. You can live for only a short time without oxygen, which makes up about 21 percent of air. Oxygen, a nonmetal, exists in the air as diatomic molecules, O_2. During electrical storms, some oxygen molecules, O_2, change into ozone molecules, O_3. Oxygen also has several uses in compound form, including the one shown at left in **Figure 19.**

Nearly all living things on Earth need O_2 for respiration. Living things also depend on a layer of O_3 around Earth for protection from some of the Sun's radiation.

The second element in the oxygen group is sulfur. Sulfur is a nonmetal that exists in several allotropic forms. It exists as different-shaped crystals and as a noncrystalline solid. Sulfur combines with metals to form sulfides of such distinctive colors that they are used as pigments in paints.

The nonmetal selenium and two metalloids—tellurium and polonium—are the other Group 16 elements. Selenium is the most common of these three. This element is one of several that you need in trace amounts in your diet. Many multivitamins contain this nonmetal as an ingredient. But selenium is toxic if too much of it gets into your system. Selenium also is used in photocopiers like the one in **Figure 19.**

Figure 19 Group 16 compounds have a variety of uses.

Solutions of hydrogen peroxide, H_2O_2, are used to clean minor wounds.

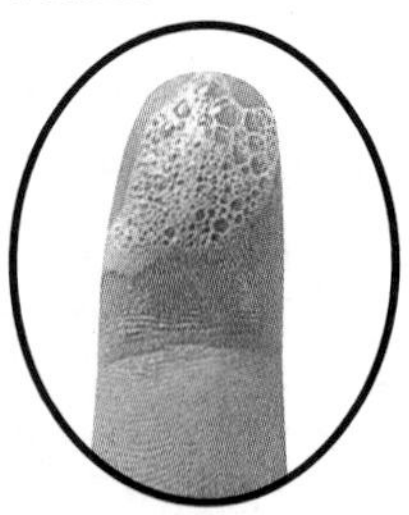

Selenium is used in xerography to make photocopies.

Differentiated Instruction

Challenge Polonium is in the area of the periodic table that might make it seem like a metalloid, yet it is often classified as a metal. Have students find out why. Like metals, polonium conducts electricity better when it is cooled. Metalloids conduct electricity better when they are heated. L3 LS **Logical-Mathematical**

Science Journal

Mystery Element Have students review the work done by the Curies to discover polonium and write about it in their Journals. Marie Curie noticed that samples of a uranium ore called pitchblende were more radioactive than could be accounted for by their uranium content. She theorized that another element was present in the ore. After reducing and purifying tons of the ore, the Curies succeeded in 1898 in isolating the element that is now called polonium . L3 LS **Linguistic**

Figure 20 The americium used in smoke detectors is a synthetic element that has saved lives.

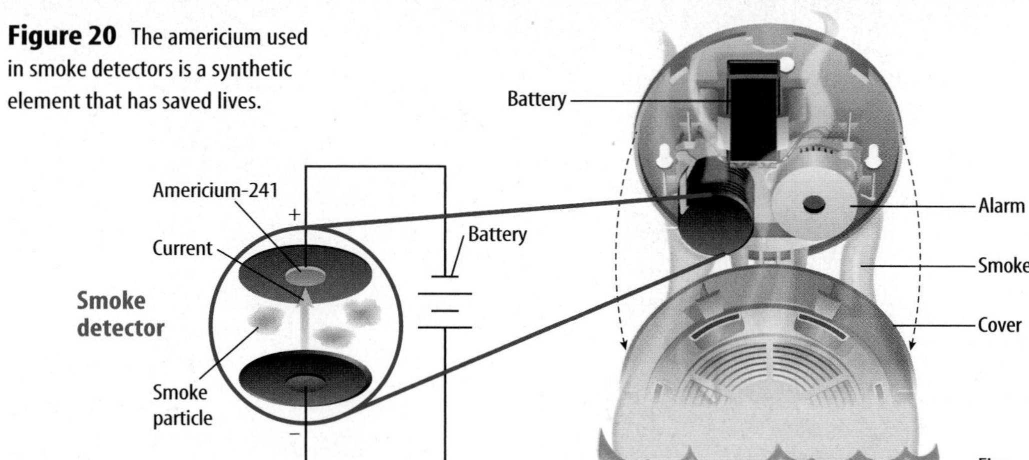

Synthetic Elements

If you made something that always fell apart, you might think you were not successful. However, nuclear scientists are learning to do just that. By smashing existing elements with particles accelerated in a heavy ion accelerator, they have been successful in creating elements not typically found on Earth. Except for technetium 43 and promethium 61, each synthetic element has more than 92 protons.

Bombarding uranium with neutrons can make neptunium, element 93. Half of the synthesized atoms of neptunium disintegrate in about two days. This may not sound useful, but when neptunium atoms disintegrate, they form plutonium. This highly toxic element has been produced in control rods of nuclear reactors and is used in bombs. Plutonium also can be changed to americium, element 95. This element is used in home smoke detectors such as the one in **Figure 20.** In smoke detectors, a small amount of americium emits charged particles. An electric plate in the smoke detector attracts some of these charged particles. When a lot of smoke is in the air, it interferes with the electric current, which immediately sets off the alarm in the smoke detector.

Transuranium Elements Elements having more than 92 protons, the atomic number of uranium, are called **transuranium elements.** These elements do not belong exclusively to the metal, nonmetal, or metalloid group. These are the elements toward the bottom of the periodic table. Some are in the actinide series, and some are on the bottom row of the main periodic table. All of the transuranium elements are synthetic and unstable, and many of them disintegrate quickly.

The Transuranium Elements

92
U

Activity

Synthetic Isotopes Assign each student one of the synthetic elements. Ask students to identify the isotopes of their assigned elements and the half-lives of the isotopes. Have students compile the information into a class table. L2 **Visual-Spatial**

Use Science Words

Word Origins Ask students to find the origins of the word *radioactive* and determine how the words *radio* and *radioactive* are related. The prefix *radi-* means "radiant energy or radiation," and comes from the Latin word *radius,* meaning "ray." A radio is a device that transmits or receives signals by means of electromagnetic radiation. When used this way, radio is short for radiotelegraphy. L3 **Linguistic**

Quick Demo

Smoke Detection

Materials paper, smoke detector, matches, or lighter

Estimated Time five minutes

Procedure Hold a detached smoke detector in one hand and light a piece of paper with a match and hold it underneath the smoke detector. The smoke detector will sound if the paper is generating enough smoke. What caused the smoke detector to go off? Explain to the students that the smoke interferes with the electrical current of charged particles emitted by a trace amount of americium to a charged plate in the smoke detector. When this flow of particles is interrupted, the alarm sounds.

Science Journal

The Newest Elements What is the newest element? Ask students to use internet sources to determine the current number of known chemical elements and to write their findings in their Science Journals. This could change at any time, as scientists worldwide continue attempting to synthesize new elements. L2 **Linguistic**

Differentiated Instruction

Challenge Technetium was predicted by the periodic table. Have students find out how and where technetium was first synthesized and the atomic number and half-life of its most stable isotope. Technetium was first found in 1937 in a sample of molybdenum bombarded with deuterons. Technetium-98 is the most stable isotope of technetium currently known. It has a half-life of 6.6 million years. L3 **Linguistic**

Visualizing the Discovery of Elements

Have students examine the pictures and read the captions. Then ask the following questions.

Why would gold be a useful material for people to use as early as the Stone Age? Answers will vary, but may be similar to the following response. Gold is soft and easy to process using primitive tools. It also has other desirable properties (namely luster) and is available in limited quantities—giving it monetary value. L2

Why were so few of the naturally occurring elements still undiscovered as late as 1776? Laboratory methods were still primitive and the technology was not yet available to separate and identify many of the individual elements. L2

Activity

Song Have the students write a song about elements and their uses. Have them perform their song for the class. L2

Discussion

Paint Paints are mixtures that can be designed for use in very specific environments and situations. There are paints that are designed to adhere well to metal surfaces and endure lengthy exposure to the Sun's ultraviolet rays and not fade, while there are others that are made to wash off easily with soap and water. All of these formulas had to be developed by people who understood the properties of each ingredient and combined them in the way that the product will perform as expected.

NATIONAL GEOGRAPHIC **VISUALIZING THE DISCOVERY OF ELEMENTS**

Figure 21

Some elements, such as gold, silver, tin, carbon, copper, and lead, have been known and used for thousands of years. Most others were discovered much more recently. Even at the time of the American Revolution in 1776, only 24 elements were known. The timeline below shows the dates of discovery of selected elements, ancient and modern.

Au - GOLD
Prized since the Stone Age

Ag - SILVER
Found in tombs dating to 4000 B.C.

A.D. 1774
Cl - CHLORINE
Pale green, toxic gas

A.D. 1700

1817
Cd - CADMIUM
Used to color yellow and red paint

1825
Al - ALUMINUM
Most abundant element in Earth's crust

1868
He - HELIUM
Lighter-than-air gas used to fill balloons

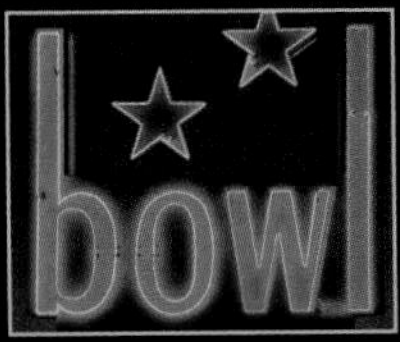

1898
Ne - NEON
Glows when electricity flows through it

1898
Po - POLONIUM and Ra - RADIUM
Radioactive elements discovered by Marie and Pierre Curie

A.D. 1800

1900
Rn - RADON
Radioactive gas that may cause cancer

1952
Es - EINSTEINIUM
Radioactive gas named after Albert Einstein

1981–1996
Bh- BOHRIUM, Ds - DARMSTADTIUM
Elements isolated by a heavy ion accelerator such as the UNILAC, below

A.D. 1900

A.D. 2000

Differentiated Instruction

Challenge Challenge students to research the life and work of Marie and Pierre Curie and their contributions to chemistry. Have them prepare a poster illustrating the important milestones in their careers. Students can share the information that they learn and their poster with the class. L3

Why make elements? **Figure 21** shows when some of the elements were discovered throughout history. The processes used to discover these elements have varied widely. The most recently discovered elements are synthetic. By studying how the synthesized elements form and disintegrate, you can gain an understanding of the forces holding the nucleus together. When these atoms disintegrate, they are said to be radioactive.

Radioactive elements can be useful. For example, technetium's radioactivity makes it ideal for many medical applications. At this time, many of the synthetic elements last only small fractions of seconds after they are constructed and can be made only in small amounts. However, the value of applications that might be discovered easily could offset their costs.

Seeking Stability Element 114, discovered in 1999, appears to be much more stable than most synthetic elements of its size. It lasted for 30 s before it broke apart. This may not seem like long, but it lasts 100,000 times longer than an atom of element 112. Perhaps this special combination of 114 protons and 175 neutrons allows the nucleus to hold together despite the enormous repulsion between the protons.

In the 1960s, scientists theorized that stable synthetic elements exist. Finding one might help scientists understand how the forces inside the atom work. Perhaps someday you'll read about some of the everyday uses this discovery has brought.

Topic: Synthetic Elements
Visit gpscience.com for Web links to information and an online update about synthetic elements.

Activity Find what some of the latest developments are in synthetic elements. Collect information on the one that interests you most and explain what you think is the most intriguing property of this element.

section 3 review

Summary

Properties of Metalloids

- Metalloids are elements that can form ionic and covalent bonds with other elements and can have metallic and nonmetallic properties.

Carbon Group

- The elements in Group 14 have four electrons in their outer energy levels.

Nitrogen Group

- The elements in Group 15 tend to share electrons and form covalent bonds.

Synthetic Elements

- Synthetic elements are elements that are not typically found on Earth.
- By synthesizing elements, scientists may understand how the forces inside the atom work.

Self Check

1. **Explain** why Groups 14 and 15 are better representatives of mixed groups than Groups 13 and Group 16.
2. **Describe** how allotropes of silicon differ in appearance.
3. **Explain** how an element is classified as a transuranium element.
4. **Describe** what type of structure a diamond has. How would you build a model of this?
5. **Think Critically** Graphite and a diamond are both made of the element carbon. Why is graphite a lubricant and diamond the hardest gem known?

Applying Math

6. **Calculate** Element 114 lasted 30s before falling apart. It lasted 100,000 times longer than element 112. How long did element 112 last?

 gpscience.com/self_check_quiz

3 Assess

DAILY INTERVENTION

Check for Understanding

Visual-Spatial Point to various groups on the periodic table and ask students to identify the name of that group and explain some of the generic qualities of that particular group. L2

Reteach

Charge Display a periodic table on the wall or by using an overhead projector. Point out an element near the bottom of Group 1 or 2. Ask students if the element would more likely have a negative or positive charge in compounds. positive L2

IS **Visual-Spatial**

Differentiated Instruction

Challenge Ask students to find out why scientists add small amounts of germanium and arsenic to silicon to make different types of computer chips. Arsenic has one more valence electron than silicon, and germanium has one less valence electron than silicon. When silicon is doped with small amounts of these elements, its ability to conduct electricity increases. Chips containing different combinations of these elements can control the current in a circuit. L3

IS **Logical-Mathematical**

Assessment

Content Give students blank outlines of the periodic table and have them label as many rows and columns as they can. Then ask them to fill in as many elements as they can. Ask them to include the lines separating the metals, nonmetals, and metalloids. L2

section 3 review

1. Groups 14 and 15 each contain metals, metalloids, and nonmetals while Group 13 contains metals and a metalloid, and Group 16 contains metalloids and nonmetals.
2. One is a hard gray substance, and the other is a brown powder.
3. The element has an atomic number higher than that of uranium.
4. Tetrahedrons joined in a crystal; answers will vary.
5. Diamond consists of interlocking tetrahedrons that provide support in all directions. Graphite has strong bonds in one direction and weak bonds between flat layers. The layers slide over each other as the weak bonds are easily broken under stress.
6. 0.0003 seconds

Real-World Question

Purpose Students will make a working model of the layered graphite structure and use the model to determine the cause-and-effect relationship of the bonding between carbon atoms in graphite and graphite's physical properties. L2 COOP LEARN LS **Kinesthetic**

Process Skills make and use models, communicate, classify, recognize cause and effect, form a hypothesis, design an experiment

Time Required 35 minutes

Procedure

Materials The polystyrene sheets can be cut from plastic report cover sheets.

Safety Precautions Advise students to use care when working with scissors, especially when making holes in any of the materials.

Form a Hypothesis

Possible Hypothesis The weak bonds between layers of graphite allow the layers to slide easily over each other, while the strong bonds within the layers keep the layers intact.

Test Your Hypothesis

Possible Procedures

1. Use scissors to cut hexagon shapes out of the thin polystyrene or cardboard sheets.
2. Carefully punch small holes near each corner of the hexagons. Insert gum drops in the small holes.
3. Draw lines between the gumdrops on the hexagon to represent bonds between hydrogen atoms.
4. Use the thin spaghetti to connect hexagons to each other by inserting both ends of the spaghetti through gumdrops on different hexagons.
5. Gently push on the connected hexagons to see what happens to the structure.

Design Your Own

Slippery Carbon

Goals

- **Make a model** that will demonstrate the molecular structure of graphite.
- **Compare and contrast** the strength of the different bonds in graphite.
- **Infer** the relationship between bonding and physical properties.

Possible Materials

thin spaghetti
small gumdrops
thin polystyrene sheets
flat cardboard
scissors

Safety Precautions

Use care when working with scissors and uncooked spaghetti.

Real-World Question

Often, a lubricant is needed when two metals touch each other. For example, a sticky lock sometimes works better with the addition of a small amount of graphite. What gives this allotrope of carbon the slippery property of a lubricant? Why do certain arrangements of atoms in a material cause the material to feel slippery?

Form a Hypothesis

Based on your understanding of how carbon atoms bond, form a hypothesis about the relationship of graphite's molecular structure to its physical properties.

Using Scientific Methods

Test Your Hypothesis

Make A Plan

1. As a group, agree upon a logical hypothesis statement.
2. As a group, sequence and list the steps you need to take to test your hypothesis. Be specific, describing exactly what you will do at each step to make a model of the types of bonding present in graphite.
3. Remember from **Figure 18** that graphite consists of rings of six carbons bonded in a flat hexagon. These rings are bonded to each other. In addition, the flat rings in one layer are weakly attached to other flat layers.
4. List possible materials you plan to use.
5. Read over the experiment to make sure that all steps are in logical order.
6. Will your model be constructed with materials that show weak and strong attractions?

Follow Your Plan

1. Make sure your teacher approves your plan before you start.
2. Have you selected materials to use in your model that demonstrate weak and strong attractions? Carry out the experiment as planned.
3. Once your model has been constructed, list any observations that you make and include a sketch in your Science Journal.

Analyze Your Data

1. **Compare** your model with designs and results of other groups.
2. How does your model illustrate two types of attractions found in the graphite structure?
3. How does the bonding of graphite that you explored in the lab explain graphite's lubricating properties? Write your answer in your Science Journal.

Conclude and Apply

1. **Describe** the results you obtained from your experiment. Did the results support your hypothesis?
2. **Describe** why graphite makes a good lubricant.
3. **Explain** what kinds of bonds you think a diamond has.

Explain to a friend why graphite makes a good lubricant and how the two types of bonds make a difference.

Teaching Strategy Have students compare lines made by pencils of various ratings (e.g. #2, #2.5). This shows how graphite slides and is sloughed off under applied pressure.

Analyze Your Data

Expected Outcome

- Models should represent six carbon atoms bonded together in a flat, six-sided structure that does not break under pressure. Two flat layers of these structures should be connected by easily broken objects representing the easily broken bonds between graphite layers.
- When pressure is applied to graphite, the weak bonds between layers break. This change causes the layers to slide over each other while the hexagons remain intact.

Answers to Questions

1. All should show two different strength bonds between carbon atoms.
2. Attractions within the flat layers are strong and resist change, while the attractions between layers are weak and break easily.
3. The layers of graphite slide easily over each other, so when graphite is placed between two surfaces, it slides between them.

Conclude and Apply

1. Answers will vary. The results should confirm a hypothesis that the weak bonds between layers of graphite molecules allow layers to slide easily over each other, while strong bonds keep the layers intact.
2. Good lubricants need to be fairly unreactive and be able to reduce friction between surfaces. Graphite has both properties.
3. covalent

Assessment

Oral Have students loosen and tighten a nut and bolt with and without graphite. Ask them to explain why the addition of graphite makes this mechanical movement easier. Use **Performance Assessment in the Science Classroom,** p. 89. L2

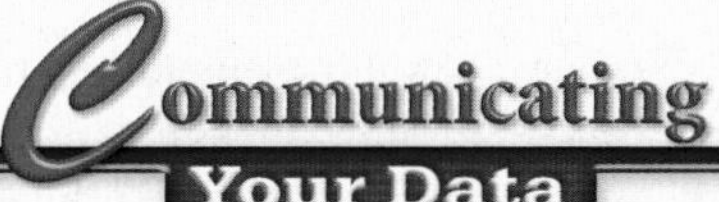

If feasible, have students take digital photos of their models before, during, and after the application of stress to their hexagonal structures. These photos can then be posted on the web, or printed out in a time-lapse presentation. L2

Content Background

Neon was discovered in 1898 by William Ramsay and Morris Travers. Earlier Ramsay had helped isolate argon and predicted the existence of neon. Travers and Ramsay were looking for the missing element. They were testing the products of air liquefaction by bombarding them with electrons in a low-pressure, sealed tube. At some point, one of the elements glowed with an intense red light that had not been seen before. Ramsay named the element neon after the Greek word for new.

Mixing argon and mercury with the neon gas produced color variations. Neon as decorative lighting was rediscovered by the art community in the 1970s. New fluorescent tube coatings and gas mixtures expanded the color range beyond what was available to the original sign makers.

Discussion

Noble Gases Have the students research the noble gases. Why do they emit light when stimulated by electricity? Possible answer: The stable gas atoms absorb the electrical energy, causing an excitation of one or more electrons in lower energy levels. These electrons temporarily move to higher, less stable energy levels. When the electrons move back to their original energy levels, they give off energy as light. L2

Historical Significance

Lighting Explain that, although neon is the best known of the noble gases, argon, helium, krypton, xenon, and radon are all important in modern tube technology.

Argon is very stable and is used in light bulbs to extend the life of tungsten filaments and to prevent the oxidation of metals during welding. Krypton and xenon are used extensively in gas lasers. Their uses range from delicate eye surgery to cutting the hardest synthetic materials.

TIME SCIENCE AND HISTORY

SCIENCE CAN CHANGE THE COURSE OF HISTORY!

The GAS that glows

A neon sign in the making. Workers carefully twist the light tubes into different shapes.

Neon has made the world a more colorful place

"Nothing in the world gave a glow such as we had seen." With these words, two British chemists recorded their discovery of neon in 1898. Neon is a noble gas that emits a spectacular red-orange glow when an electric current is passed through it. It also makes up a tiny portion of the air we breathe.

But neon's presence remained undetected until a technology called spectroscopy allowed the chemists to view that "blaze of crimson light" in their lab—a light that soon lit up the world in fantastical ways.

Signs of Change

Pink flamingos, cowboys on bucking broncos, deep-sea fish afloat in the air—neon signs make any building or billboard come alive in a kaleidoscope of colors. Barely a decade after neon was discovered, a chemist developed the first neon sign. The chemist took the air out of a glass tube and replaced it with neon gas. When the gas was jolted with electricity, it glowed like a fiery sunset. The chemist sold the light to a barber, who hung it over his storefront. By the 1920s, neon lights were used to advertise everything from cars to diners.

When a touch of mercury is added to neon, it glows a tropical blue. The other colors seen in "neon lights" actually come from other noble gases. Krypton, for instance, glows yellow. Xenon shines like a bluish-white star.

Other Uses for Neon

The vivid light emitted by neon can penetrate the densest fog, making it a natural choice for airplane beacons. Neon also is used to manufacture lasers and television tubes. Neon definitely helps light up our lives!

Identify As a group, brainstorm a new product or business, then design a neon sign to advertise your idea. See if other groups can correctly guess what your sign represents.

For more information, visit gpscience.com/time

Identity Students should evaluate each other's signs to see if their messages are clear. Did the use of color add to the effectiveness of the sign? How would the signs be designed differently if color were not available? L2

Resources for Teachers and Students

NEON TECHNIQUES: The 4th Edition of the Handbook of Neon Sign and Cold-Cathode Lighting, edited by Wayne Strattman, Cincinnati, Ohio: ST Publications, 1998

Reviewing Main Ideas

Section 1 Metals

1. A typical metal is a hard, shiny solid that, due to metallic bonding, is malleable, ductile, and a good conductor.

2. Groups 1 and 2 are the alkali and alkaline earth metals, which have some similar and some contrasting properties.
3. The iron triad, the coinage metals, and the elements in Group 12 are examples of transition elements.
4. The lanthanides and actinides have atomic numbers 58 through 71 and 90 through 103, respectively.

Section 2 Nonmetals

1. Nonmetals can be brittle and dull. They are also poor conductors of electricity.
2. As a typical nonmetal, hydrogen is a gas that forms compounds by sharing electrons with other nonmetals and by forming ionic bonds with metals.
3. All the halogens, Group 17, have seven outer electrons and form covalent and ionic compounds, but each halogen has some properties that are unlike each of the others in the group.
4. The noble gases, Group 18, are elements whose properties and uses are related to their chemical stability.

Section 3 Mixed Groups

1. Groups 13 through 16 include metals, nonmetals, and metalloids.

2. Allotropes are forms of the same element having different molecular structures.
3. The properties of three forms of carbon—graphite, diamond, and buckminsterfullerene—depend upon the differences in their crystal structures.
4. All synthetic elements are short-lived. Except for technetium-43 and promethium-61, they have atomic numbers greater than 92 and are referred to as transuranium elements. These elements are found toward the bottom of the periodic table.

FOLDABLES™ Use the Foldable that you made at the beginning of this chapter to help you review elements and their properties.

chapter 19 Study Guide

Reviewing Main Ideas

Summary statements can be used by students to review the major concepts of the chapter.

Science Online

Visit gpscience.com
/self_check_quiz
/interactive_tutor
/vocabulary_puzzlemaker
/chapter_review
/standardized_test

Assessment Transparency

For additional assessment questions, use the *Assessment Transparency* located in the transparency book.

Assessment

Assessment Transparency **Elements and Their Properties**

Directions: *Carefully review the table and answer the following questions.*

Physical and Chemical Characteristics of Some Chemicals				
Characteristic	Alkali metals	Transition elements	Halogens	Noble gases
Conduct electricity	yes	yes	no	no
Reactivity	very reactive	reactive	reactive	not reactive
Phase at room temperature	solid	solid	solid, liquid, or gas	gas
Examples	Na Li K	Fe Co Ni	Cl F I	He Ne Ar

1. An element is tested and does not conduct or react with anything. According to the table, it is a(n) ___.
   A alkali metal
   B transition element
   C halogen
   D noble gas
2. According to the table, an element that does react but does not conduct electricity is a(n) ___.
   F alkali metal
   G transition element
   H halogen
   J noble gas
3. According to the table, which of these elements will conduct electricity?
   A K B Cl C Ar D He

L2

Elements and Their Properties

FOLDABLES™ Have students use their Foldables to review the content of the chapter. On the back of the paper, have students write a paragraph about the nature of the forces between magnets. What does the forces between magnets depend on?

chapter 19 Review

Using Vocabulary

1. metals
2. allotropes
3. metallic bonding
4. diatomic molecule
5. transition elements

Checking Concepts

6. B
7. A
8. D
9. C
10. A
11. C
12. C
13. D

chapter 19 Review

Using Vocabulary

allotrope p. 585	radioactive element p. 572
diatomic molecule p. 579	salt p. 580
ductile p. 570	semiconductor p. 585
malleable p. 570	sublimation p. 581
metal p. 570	transition element p. 574
metallic bonding p. 571	transuranium element p. 589
metalloid p. 584	
nonmetal p. 578	

Complete each sentence with the correct vocabulary word(s).

1. The _________ are located to the left of the stair–step line on the periodic table.
2. Different structural forms of the same element are called _________.
3. Positively charged ions are surrounded by freely moving electrons in _________.
4. A(n) _________ is a molecule comprised of two atoms.
5. The _________ are in Groups 3 through 12 on the periodic table.

Checking Concepts

Choose the word or phrase that best answers the question.

6. When magnesium and fluorine react, what type of bond is formed?
   A) metallic **C)** covalent
   B) ionic **D)** diatomic
7. What type of bond is found in a piece of pure gold?
   A) metallic **C)** covalent
   B) ionic **D)** diatomic
8. Because electrons move freely in metals, which property describes metals?
   A) brittle **C)** dull
   B) hard **D)** conductors
9. Which set of elements makes up the most reactive group of all metals?
   A) iron triad
   B) coinage metals
   C) alkali metals
   D) alkaline earth metals
10. Which element is the most reactive of all nonmetals?
    A) fluorine **C)** hydrogen
    B) uranium **D)** oxygen
11. Which element is always found in nature combined with other elements?
    A) copper **C)** magnesium
    B) gold **D)** silver
12. Which elements are least reactive?
    A) metals **C)** noble gases
    B) halogens **D)** actinides
13. What element is formed when neptunium disintegrates?
    A) ytterbium **C)** americium
    B) promethium **D)** plutonium

Interpreting Graphics

14. Copy and complete the concept map using the following: *transition elements, hydrogen, metals, inner transition metals, noble gases.*

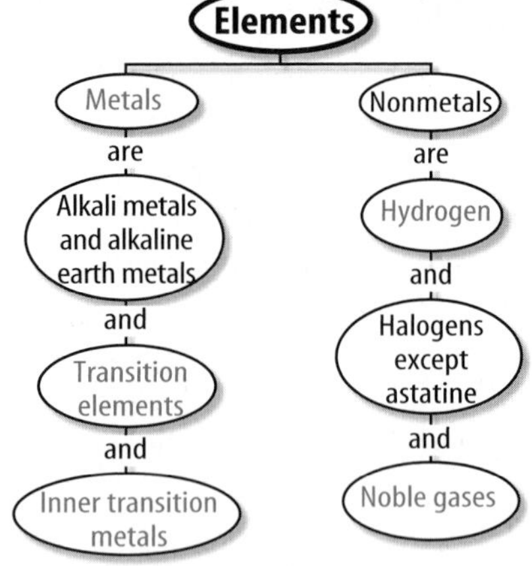

gpscience.com/vocabulary_puzzlemaker

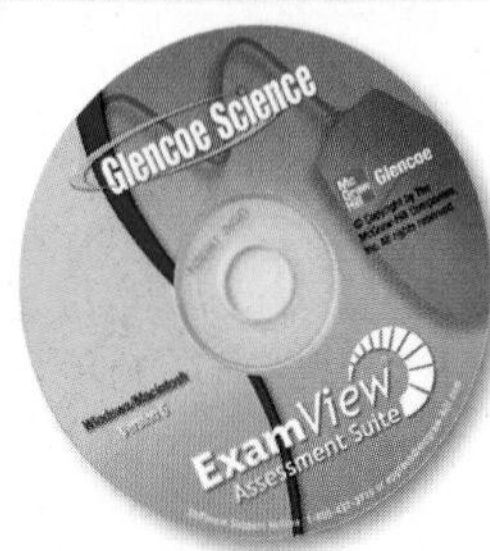

Use the *ExamView® Assessment Suite* CD-ROM to:

- create multiple versions of tests
- create modified tests with one mouse click for inclusion students
- edit existing questions and add your own questions
- build tests aligned with state standards using built-in State Curriculum Tags
- change English tests to Spanish with one mouse click and vice versa

Thinking Critically

15. **Concept Map** Copy and complete the concept map using the following: *Na, Fe, Actinides, Hg, Ba, Alkali, and Inner transition.*

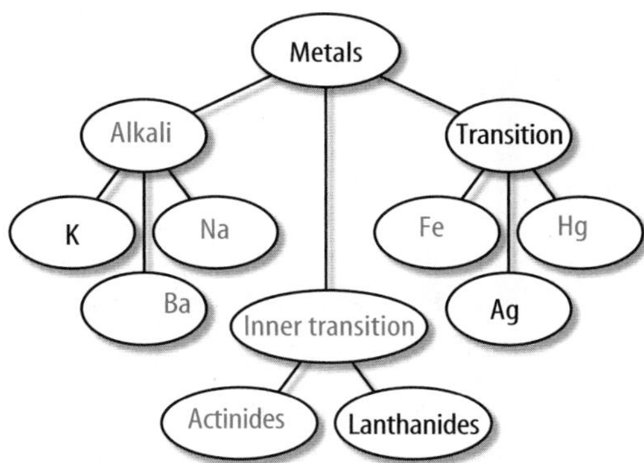

16. **Make and Use Tables** Use the periodic table to classify each of the following as a lanthanide or actinide: californium, europium, cerium, nobelium, terbium, and uranium.

17. **Explain** why mercury is rarely used in thermometers that take body temperatures.

18. **Explain** The density of hydrogen is lower than air and can be used to fill balloons. Why is helium used instead of hydrogen?

19. **Explain** Copper is a good choice for use in electrical wiring. What type of elements would not work well for this purpose? Why?

20. **Explain** why various silver compounds are used in photography.

21. **Describe** Like selenium, chromium is poisonous but is needed in trace amounts in your diet. How would you apply this information in order to use vitamin and mineral pills safely?

22. **Compare and Contrast** Explain why aluminum is a metal and carbon is not.

23. **Explain** What is metallic bonding? Explain how this affects conductivity.

24. **Describe** the geometric shapes of the carbon allotropes.

Applying Math

Use the following table to answer question 25.

Gas Analysis

Gas	Volume %
CO	6.8
H_2	47.3
CH_4	33.9
CO_2	2.2
N_2	6
Other	3.8

25. **Interpret Data** When coke-oven gas is burned in an industrial process, several gases are produced in the reaction. If 385 grams of coke-oven gas are consumed in this reaction, how many grams of CH_4 (methane) are produced?

26. **Use Percentage** Chloroform has the chemical formula, $CHCl_3$, and a molecular weight of 119.39 g. What is the percentage of Cl (chlorine) present in this compound?

27. **Use Numbers** Calculate the molecular weight of gallium bromide ($GaBr_3$).

Assessment Resources

Reproducible Masters

Chapter *Fast File* Resources
Chapter Review, pp. 39–40
Chapter Tests, pp. 41–44
Assessment Transparency Activity, p. 51

Glencoe Science Web site
Chapter Review Test
Standardized Test Practice

Glencoe Technology
Assessment Transparency
ExamView® Assessment Suite
MindJogger Videoquiz
Interactive Chalkboard

Interpreting Graphics

14. See student page.

Thinking Critically

15. See student page.
16. lanthanides: europium, cerium; terbium; actinides: californium, nobelium; uranium
17. Mercury is poisonous. It would poison the person using it if it broke or leaked.
18. Hydrogen is flammable whereas helium is inert.
19. Elements that are not solid or solid elements that are not ductile or conductors (nonmetals).
20. Some silver compounds change chemically when exposed to light.
21. Do not exceed recommended doses.
22. Carbon has four electrons in its outer energy level while aluminum has three. Aluminum holds on to its electrons less tightly than carbon does, so it can form metallic bonds.
23. In metallic bonding, the electrons are not attached to any one metallic ion. Because of this, metals have the ability to conduct heat and electricity.
24. In a diamond, each carbon atom is bonded to four other carbon atoms at the corner points of a tetrahedron. Graphite consists of hexagonal layers of carbon atoms. Each carbon atom is bonded to three other carbon atoms. The buckyball allotrope is a soccer-ball shaped molecule.

Applying Math

National Math Standards
1, 2, 5, 9

25. 130.5 g
26. 29.7%
27. 309.4 g

Answer Sheet A practice answer sheet can be found at gpscience.com/answer_sheet.

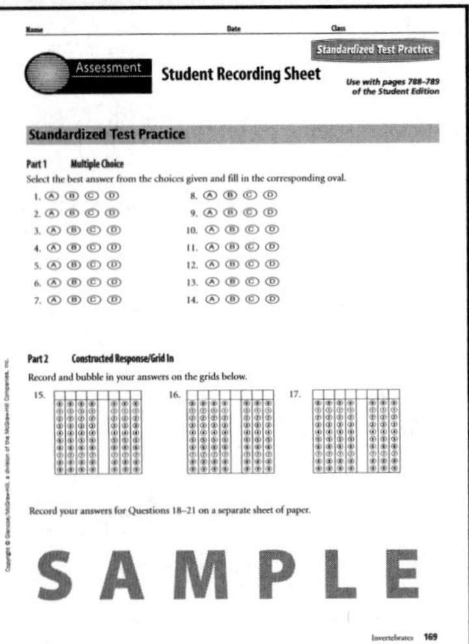

Part 1 Multiple Choice

1. A
2. A
3. D
4. C
5. B
6. A
7. D
8. A

Part 2 Short Response

9. Metals are good conductors of heat and electricity, and are typically solid at room temperature. They have luster, which means they reflect light. They are malleable, meaning they can be hammered or rolled into sheets, and they are ductile, meaning they can be drawn into wires.
10. Atoms of these elements have only one electron in the outer shell, making sodium and potassium highly reactive, particularly with members of the halogen group.
11. Allotropes are different forms of the same element which have different molecular structures. The carbon allotropes are graphite and diamond.
12. Graphite is composed of layers of carbon atoms which can slide easily past each other, making graphite a good lubricant. In diamond, carbon atoms are bonded in tetrahedrons, which join to form a tight, crystalline structure. This tight structure makes diamonds extremely hard.
13. Hydrogen makes up about 90 percent of the atoms in the universe. This highly reactive element occurs naturally as a diatomic molecule. Each hydrogen atom has a single electron.
14. Chlorine compounds are used to disinfect water, as well as to whiten flour, clothing, and paper. Bromine compounds are used as dyes in cosmetics. Iodine plays an essential role in certain body processes.
15. When a nonmetal gains electrons from a metal, the nonmetal becomes a negative ion and forms an ionic bond with the positively charged metal ion. When nonmetals bond with other nonmetals, they usually share electrons to form covalent bonds.

chapter 19 Standardized Test Practice

Part 1 Multiple Choice

Record your answers on the answer sheet provided by your teacher or on a sheet of paper.

1. Which of these elements is the main component of steel, and the most widely used of all metals?
   A. iron
   B. aluminum
   C. cadmium
   D. magnesium

2. What term describes the Group 1 elements lithium, sodium, and potassium?
   A. alkali metals
   B. radioactive elements
   C. lanthanides
   D. transition metals

Use the illustration below to answer questions 3 and 4.

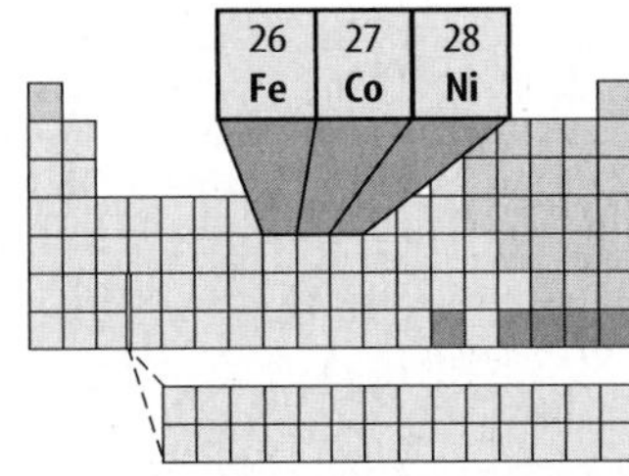

3. What name is given to these three elements which are used in processes that create steel and other metal mixtures?
   A. halogens
   B. the coin metals
   C. actinides
   D. the iron triad

4. To which major group do these elements belong?
   A. nonmetals
   B. noble gases
   C. transition elements
   D. alkali metals

Test-Taking Tip

Eliminate Choices If you don't know the answer to a multiple-choice question eliminate as many incorrect choices as possible.

Use the illustration below to answer questions 5 and 6.

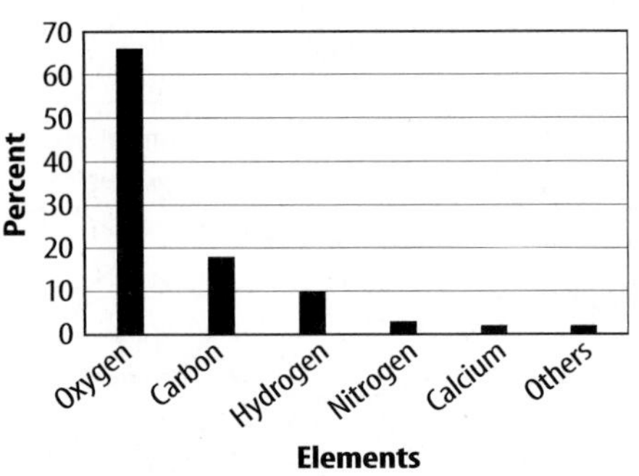

5. Which of these is a property of the elements that make up 98 percent of the human body?
   A. malleability
   B. poor electrical and heat conductivity
   C. shiny appearance
   D. ductility

6. In which of these phases does the element present in the highest percentage in the human body exist?
   A. gas
   B. solid
   C. liquid
   D. plasma

7. Which element is present in all organic compounds?
   A. silicon
   B. oxygen
   C. nitrogen
   D. carbon

8. Which of these is NOT a property of transuranium elements?
   A. occur naturally
   B. have greater than 92 protons
   C. are synthetic
   D. are unstable

Part 2 Short Response/Grid In

Record your answers on the answer sheet provided by your teacher or on a sheet of paper.

9. Define the general properties of metals which make them useful and versatile materials.
10. Use the electron configuration of the elements sodium and potassium to explain why these elements do not occur in nature in elemental form.

Use the illustrations below to answer questions 11 and 12.

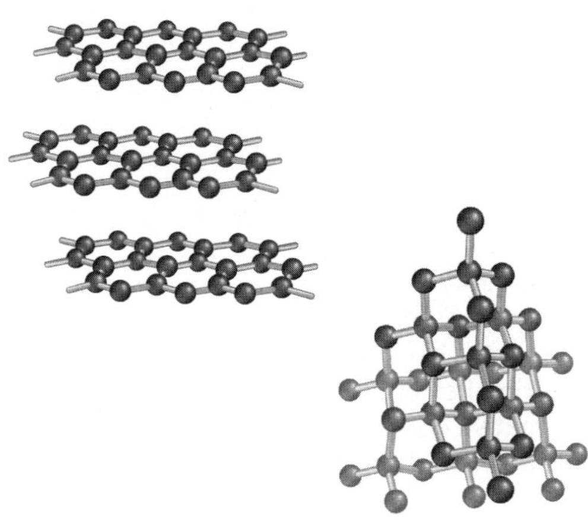

11. Define the term *allotrope*, and identify these allotropes of carbon.
12. Compare the structures of these carbon allotropes and relate the structures to the properties of these materials.
13. Describe some unique properties of hydrogen.
14. Identify and describe the uses of some of the halogens obtained from seawater.
15. Compare the two types of bonds which nonmetals can form.

Part 3 Open Ended

Record your answers on the answer sheet provided by your teacher or on a sheet of paper.

16. Recent Federal Drug Administration statements advise limiting consumption of tuna and salmon. Which transitional element is the source of the problem? Explain why this element poses a potential risk.
17. Use the properties of metallic bonds to explain why metal hammered into sheets does not break, as well as why metals conduct electricity.
18. Based on its electron configuration and position in the periodic table, explain why fluorine is the most chemically active of all elements.

Use the illustration below to answer question 19.

19. Identify the gas which enables this blimp to remain suspended in the atmosphere. Why would it be dangerous to use hydrogen for this purpose?
20. Explain the importance of organisms that convert nitrogen from its diatomic form into other compounds.

Part 3 Open Ended

16. Mercury is poisonous to both land and marine organisms. Over time, it can accumulate in organisms that live in contaminated water, then in organisms which consume them.
17. In a metallic bond, outer level electrons are loosely held, and thus can move freely and conduct electricity. The positive ions lie in layers that can slide past each other when the material is manipulated, resulting in a bendable material.
18. Fluorine is the first element in the halogen group. The seven electrons in its outer shell are closer to the nucleus than any other element in this group, giving it a greater ability to attract another electron in a chemical bond than any other element.
19. Helium is a chemically stable noble gas; it does not react with other elements. It is lighter than the other gases in the atmosphere. Though hydrogen is lighter, it is also highly reactive, making it a potential explosion and fire hazard.
20. Humans can not use nitrogen in diatomic form. Certain types of bacteria change diatomic nitrogen into a form in which it can be used in these life processes.

Rubrics

For more help evaluating open-ended assessment questions, see the rubric on p. 10T.

Chemical Bonds

BIG Idea **Just over 110 elements combine with chemical bonds to form a nearly infinite number of compounds.**

	Content Standards	Learning Objectives	Resources to Assess Mastery
Section 1	**5–8:** UCP.1–3, 5; A.1, 2; B.1–3 **9–12:** UCP.1–3, 5; A.1–2; B.2, 4, 6	**Stability in Bonding** 1. **Describe** how a compound differs from its component elements. 2. **Explain** what a chemical formula represents. 3. **Explain** that the electric forces between oppositely charged electrons and protons are essential to forming compounds. 4. **State** a reason why chemical bonding occurs. ***Main Idea*** When atoms form compounds, each atom is more stable in the compound than it was by itself.	Formative Assessment Reading Check, p. 603 Section Review, p. 606 Summative Assessment *ExamView® Assessment Suite*
Section 2	**5–8:** UCP.1–3, 5; A.1, 2; B.1–3; F.1 **9–12:** UCP.1–3, 5; A.1–2; B.2, 4, 6; F.1	**Types of Bonds** 5. **Describe** ionic bonds and covalent bonds. 6. **Identify** the particles produced by ionic bonding and by covalent bonding. 7. **Distinguish** between a nonpolar covalent bond and a polar covalent bond. ***Main Idea*** Atoms form ionic bonds by transferring electrons and form covalent bonds by sharing electrons.	Formative Assessment Reading Check, pp. 609, 614 Section Review, p. 614 Summative Assessment *ExamView® Assessment Suite*
Section 3	**5–8:** UCP.1–3, 5; A.1, 2; B.2, 3; G.3 **9–12:** UCP.1–3, 5; A.1–2; B.4, 6; G.3 See pp. 16T–17T for a Key to Standards.	**Writing Formulas and Naming Compounds** 8. **Explain** how to determine oxidation numbers. 9. **Write** formulas and names for ionic compounds. 10. **Write** formulas and names for covalent compounds. ***Main Idea*** The oxidation numbers of the ions in ionic compounds determine the formula of the compounds.	Formative Assessment Reading Check, p. 621 Section Review, p. 621 Summative Chapter Assessment MindJogger, Ch. 20 *ExamView® Assessment Suite* Leveled Chapter Test Test A L1 Test B L2 Test C L3 Test Practice, pp. 628–629

Suggested Pacing				
Period	Instruction	Labs	Review & Assessment	Total
Single	4 days	3 days	2 days	9 days
Block	2 blocks	1.5 blocks	1 block	4.5 blocks

Core Instruction	Leveled Resources	Leveled Labs	Pacing: Period		Pacing: Block
Student Text, pp. 600–607 Section Focus Transparency, Ch. 20, Section 1 Interactive Chalkboard, Ch. 20, Section 1 Differentiated Instruction, pp. 604, 605	**Chapter *Fast File* Resources** Directed Reading for Content Mastery, p. 20 L1 Note-taking Worksheet, pp. 33–35 Reinforcement, p. 27 L2 Enrichment, p. 30 L3 **Reading Essentials,** p. 338 L1 ELL **Science Notebook,** p. 227 ELL ***Active*Folders**: *Chemical Bonds* L1 ELL	**Launch Lab**, p. 601: 100-mL graduated cylinders (2), water, vegetable oil, rubbing alcohol, food coloring, dropper *15 min* L2 ***Lab**, p. 607: index cards (4-in x 6-in), periodic table *40 min* L1 L2 L3	1	Section 1, pp. 601–603 (includes Launch Lab)	1
			2	Section 1, pp. 604–606 (includes Section Review)	1
			3	Lab: Atomic Trading Cards, p. 607	2
Student Text, pp. 608–614 Section Focus Transparency, Ch. 20, Section 2 Interactive Chalkboard, Ch. 20, Section 2 Differentiated Instruction, pp. 609, 611, 612, 613 Visualizing Polar Molecules, p. 613	**Chapter *Fast File* Resources** Directed Reading for Content Mastery, p. 20 L1 Note-taking Worksheet, pp. 33–35 Reinforcement, p. 28 L2 Enrichment, p. 31 L3 **Reading Essentials,** p. 344 L1 ELL **Science Notebook,** p. 231 ELL ***Active*Folders**: *Chemical Bonds* L1 ELL	**MiniLAB**, p. 612: stream of water, balloon, wool or fur *15 min* L2	4	Section 2, pp. 608–611	2
			5	Section 2, pp. 612–614 (includes MiniLAB and Section Review)	3
Student Text, pp. 615–623 Section Focus Transparency, Ch. 20, Section 3 Teaching Transparency, Ch. 20, Section 3 Interactive Chalkboard, Ch. 20, Section 3 Identifying Misconceptions, p. 616 Applying Math, p. 617 Applying Science, p. 618 Differentiated Instruction, pp. 617, 619 Chapter Study Guide, p. 625	**Chapter *Fast File* Resources** Directed Reading for Content Mastery, pp. 21, 22 L1 Note-taking Worksheet, pp. 33–35 Reinforcement, p. 29 L2 Enrichment, p. 32 L3 **Reading Essentials,** p. 351 L1 ELL **Science Notebook,** p. 234 ELL	**MiniLAB**, p. 620: plaster of paris, water, small bowl, rubber hammer, hair dryer, paper towel *15 min* L2 (Video Lab) ***Lab**, pp. 622–623: samples (crushed ice, table salt, sugar), wire test-tube holder, test tubes, laboratory burner, stopwatch *45 min* L1 L2 L3 *Lab version A L1 version B L2 L3	6	Section 3, pp. 615–618	3
			7	Section 3, pp. 619–621 (includes MiniLAB and Section Review)	4
			8	Lab: Become a Bond Breaker, pp. 622–623	4
			9	Study Guide, Chapter Review, and Test Practice, pp. 625–629	4.5

(Video Lab icon) Video Lab

Transparencies

Section Focus

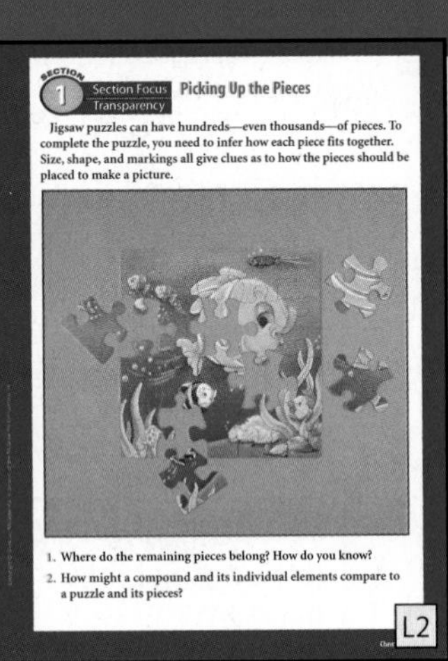
Section 1 Section Focus Transparency — Picking Up the Pieces

Jigsaw puzzles can have hundreds—even thousands—of pieces. To complete the puzzle, you need to infer how each piece fits together. Size, shape, and markings all give clues as to how the pieces should be placed to make a picture.

1. Where do the remaining pieces belong? How do you know?
2. How might a compound and its individual elements compare to a puzzle and its pieces?

L2

Section 2 Section Focus Transparency — A Crystal Nature

This picture shows salt crystals on the Dead Sea shore. When a salt crystal is pure, it is in the shape of a colorless cube. Impurities can make salt appear to be different colors, like white or gray. Table salt is a compound of sodium and chlorine.

1. Describe the appearance of the salt in the picture.
2. What happens to salt in water? How might you recover salt from ocean water?
3. How do people use salt?

L2

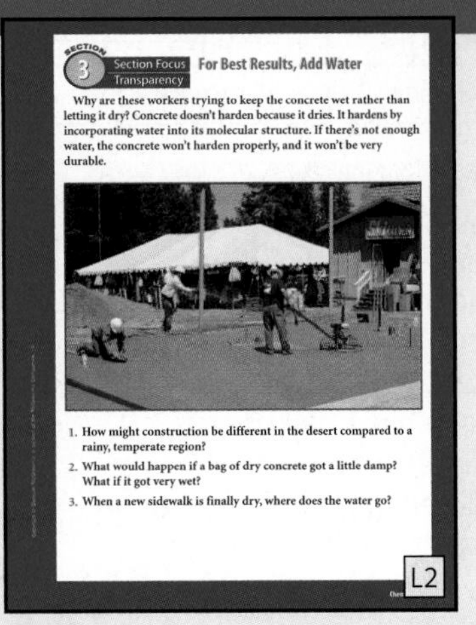
Section 3 Section Focus Transparency — For Best Results, Add Water

Why are these workers trying to keep the concrete wet rather than letting it dry? Concrete doesn't harden because it dries. It hardens by incorporating water into its molecular structure. If there's not enough water, the concrete won't harden properly, and it won't be very durable.

1. How might construction be different in the desert compared to a rainy, temperate region?
2. What would happen if a bag of dry concrete got a little damp? What if it got very wet?
3. When a new sidewalk is finally dry, where does the water go?

L2

This is a representation of key blackline masters available in the Teacher Classroom Resources. See Resource Manager boxes within the chapter for additional information.

Assessment

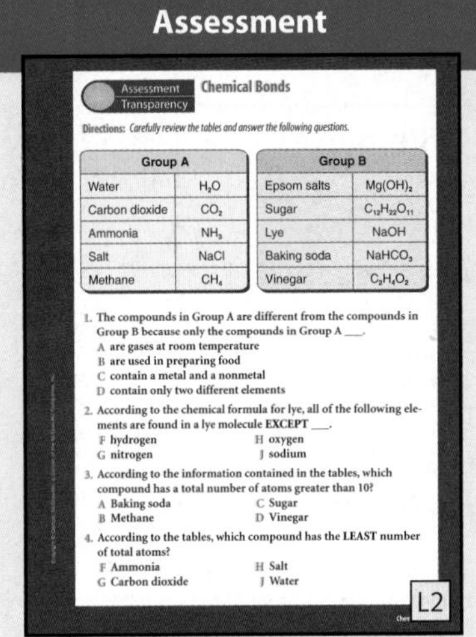
Assessment Transparency — Chemical Bonds

Directions: Carefully review the tables and answer the following questions.

Group A	
Water	H_2O
Carbon dioxide	CO_2
Ammonia	NH_3
Salt	NaCl
Methane	CH_4

Group B	
Epsom salts	$Mg(OH)_2$
Sugar	$C_{12}H_{22}O_{11}$
Lye	NaOH
Baking soda	$NaHCO_3$
Vinegar	$C_2H_4O_2$

1. The compounds in Group A are different from the compounds in Group B because only the compounds in Group A ___.
   A are gases at room temperature
   B are used in preparing food
   C contain a metal and a nonmetal
   D contain only two different elements
2. According to the chemical formula for lye, all of the following elements are found in a lye molecule EXCEPT ___.
   F hydrogen H oxygen
   G nitrogen J sodium
3. According to the information contained in the tables, which compound has a total number of atoms greater than 10?
   A Baking soda C Sugar
   B Methane D Vinegar
4. According to the tables, which compound has the LEAST number of total atoms?
   F Ammonia H Salt
   G Carbon dioxide J Water

L2

Teaching

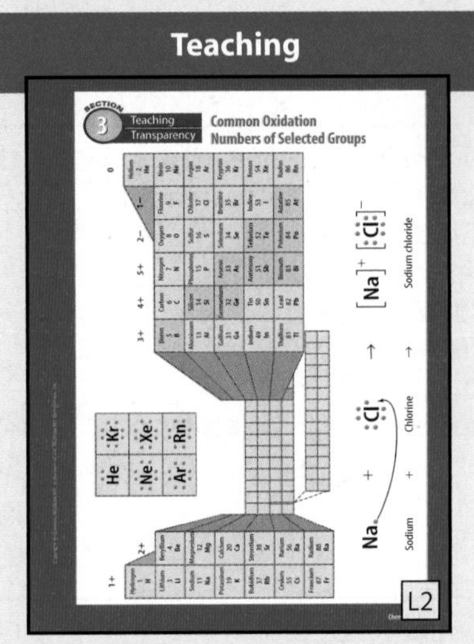
Section 3 Teaching Transparency — Common Oxidation Numbers of Selected Groups

L2

Key to Teaching Strategies

The following designations will help you decide which activities are appropriate for your students.

- L1 Level 1 activities should be appropriate for students with learning difficulties.
- L2 Level 2 activities should be within the ability range of all students.
- L3 Level 3 activities are designed for above-average students.
- ELL ELL activities should be within the ability range of English Language Learners.
- COOP LEARN Cooperative Learning activities are designed for small group work.
- LS Multiple Learning Styles logos, as described on page 12T, are used throughout to indicate strategies that address different learning styles.
- P These strategies represent student products that can be placed into a best-work portfolio.
- PBL Problem-Based Learning activities apply real-world situations to learning.

Hands-on Activities

Student Text Lab Worksheet

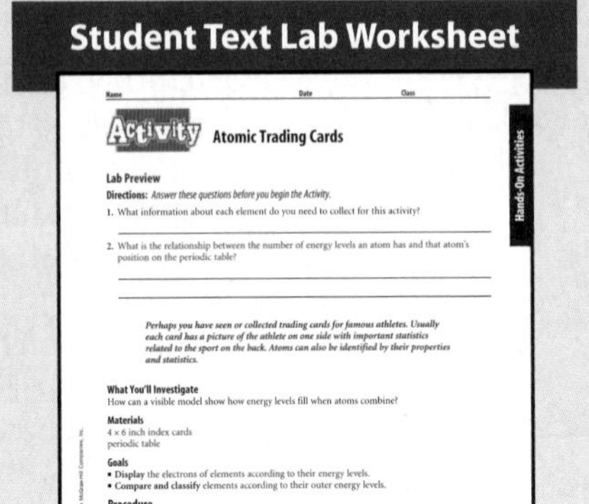
Activity — Atomic Trading Cards

Lab Preview

Directions: Answer these questions before you begin the Activity.

1. What information about each element do you need to collect for this activity?
2. What is the relationship between the number of energy levels an atom has and that atom's position on the periodic table?

What You'll Investigate

How can a visible model show how energy levels fill when atoms combine?

Materials

Goals

Procedure

L2

Laboratory Activities

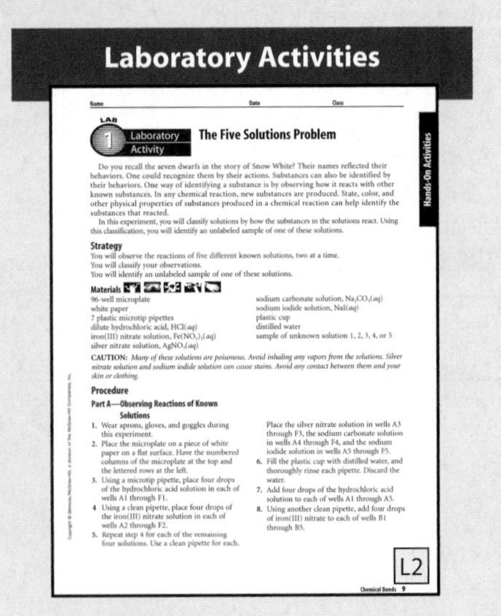
Lab 1 Laboratory Activity — The Five Solutions Problem

Strategy

Materials

CAUTION

Procedure

Part A—Observing Reactions of Known Solutions

L2

Meeting Different Ability Levels

Content Outline

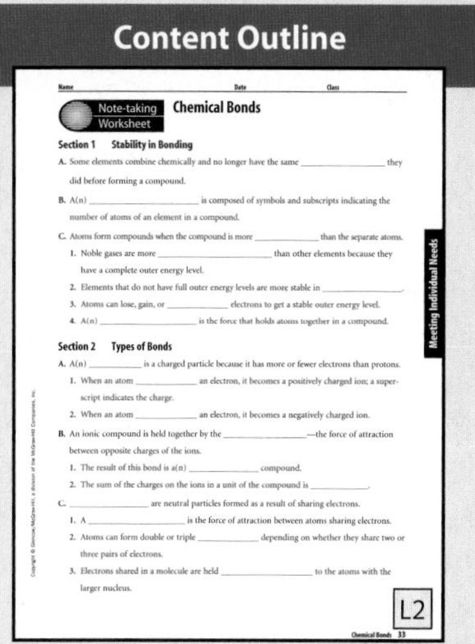

Name Date Class

Note-taking Worksheet **Chemical Bonds**

Section 1 Stability in Bonding

A. Some elements combine chemically and no longer have the same ________ they did before forming a compound.

B. A(n) ________ is composed of symbols and subscripts indicating the number of atoms of an element in a compound.

C. Atoms form compounds when the compound is more ________ than the separate atoms.
1. Noble gases are more ________ than other elements because they have a complete outer energy level.
2. Elements that do not have full outer energy levels are more stable in ________.
3. Atoms can lose, gain, or ________ electrons to get a stable outer energy level.
4. A(n) ________ is the force that holds atoms together in a compound.

Section 2 Types of Bonds

A. A(n) ________ is a charged particle because it has more or fewer electrons than protons.
1. When an atom ________ an electron, it becomes a positively charged ion; a superscript indicates the charge.
2. When an atom ________ an electron, it becomes a negatively charged ion.

B. An ionic compound is held together by the ________—the force of attraction between opposite charges of the ions.
1. The result of this bond is a(n) ________ compound.
2. The sum of the charges on the ions in a unit of the compound is ________.

C. ________ are neutral particles formed as a result of sharing electrons.
1. A ________ is the force of attraction between atoms sharing electrons.
2. Atoms can form double or triple ________ depending on whether they share two or three pairs of electrons.
3. Electrons shared in a molecule are held ________ to the atoms with the larger nucleus.

Meeting Individual Needs

L2

Chemical Bonds 33

Reinforcement

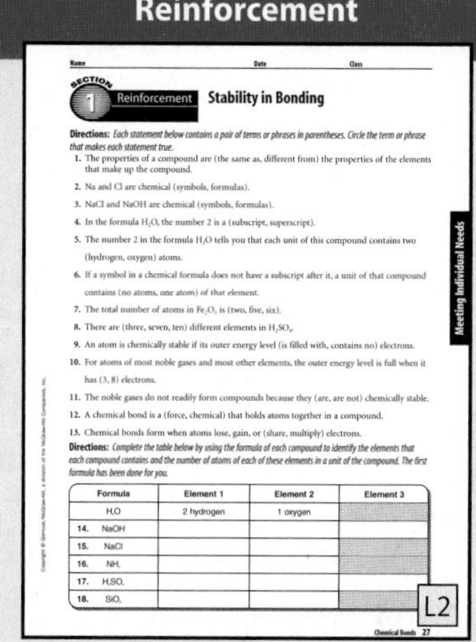

Name Date Class

Section 1 Reinforcement **Stability in Bonding**

Directions: Each statement below contains a pair of terms or phrases in parentheses. Circle the term or phrase that makes each statement true.

1. The properties of a compound are (the same as, different from) the properties of the elements that make up the compound.
2. Na and Cl are chemical (symbols, formulas).
3. NaCl and NaOH are chemical (symbols, formulas).
4. In the formula H_2O, the number 2 is a (subscript, superscript).
5. The number 2 in the formula H_2O tells you that each unit of this compound contains two (hydrogen, oxygen) atoms.
6. If a symbol in a chemical formula does not have a subscript after it, a unit of that compound contains (no atoms, one atom) of that element.
7. The total number of atoms in Fe_2O_3 is (two, five, six).
8. There are (three, seven, ten) different elements in H_2SO_4.
9. An atom is chemically stable if its outer energy level is (filled with, contains no) electrons.
10. For atoms of most noble gases and most other elements, the outer energy level is full when it has (3, 8) electrons.
11. The noble gases do not readily form compounds because they (are, are not) chemically stable.
12. A chemical bond is a (force, chemical) that holds atoms together in a compound.
13. Chemical bonds form when atoms lose, gain, or (share, multiply) electrons.

Directions: Complete the table below by using the formula of each compound to identify the elements that each compound contains and the number of atoms of each of these elements in a unit of the compound. The first formula has been done for you.

	Formula	Element 1	Element 2	Element 3
	H_2O	2 hydrogen	1 oxygen	
14.	NaOH			
15.	NaCl			
16.	NH_3			
17.	H_2SO_4			
18.	SiO_2			

Meeting Individual Needs

L2

Chemical Bonds 27

Enrichment

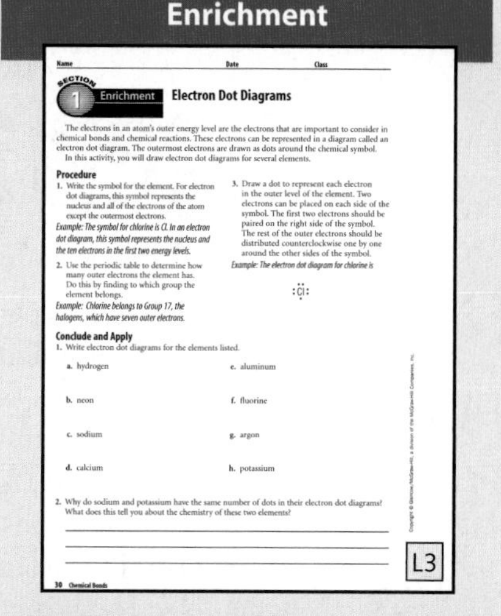

Name Date Class

Section 1 Enrichment **Electron Dot Diagrams**

The electrons in an atom's outer energy level are the electrons that are important to consider in chemical bonds and chemical reactions. These electrons can be represented in a diagram called an electron dot diagram. The outermost electrons are drawn as dots around the chemical symbol. In this activity, you will draw electron dot diagrams for several elements.

Procedure

1. Write the symbol for the element. For electron dot diagrams, this symbol represents the nucleus and all of the electrons of the atom except the outermost electrons. *Example: The symbol for chlorine is Cl. In an electron dot diagram, this symbol represents the nucleus and the ten electrons in the first two energy levels.*
2. Use the periodic table to determine how many outer electrons the element has. Do this by finding to which group the element belongs. *Example: Chlorine belongs to Group 17, the halogens, which have seven outer electrons.*
3. Draw a dot to represent each electron in the outer level of the element. Two electrons can be placed on each side of the symbol. The first two electrons should be paired on the right side of the symbol. The rest of the outer electrons should be distributed counterclockwise one by one around the other sides of the symbol. *Example: The electron dot diagram for chlorine is*

Conclude and Apply

1. Write electron dot diagrams for the elements listed.

a. hydrogen e. aluminum

b. neon f. fluorine

c. sodium g. argon

d. calcium h. potassium

2. Why do sodium and potassium have the same number of dots in their electron dot diagrams? What does this tell you about the chemistry of these two elements?

L3

30 Chemical Bonds

Directed Reading (English/Spanish)

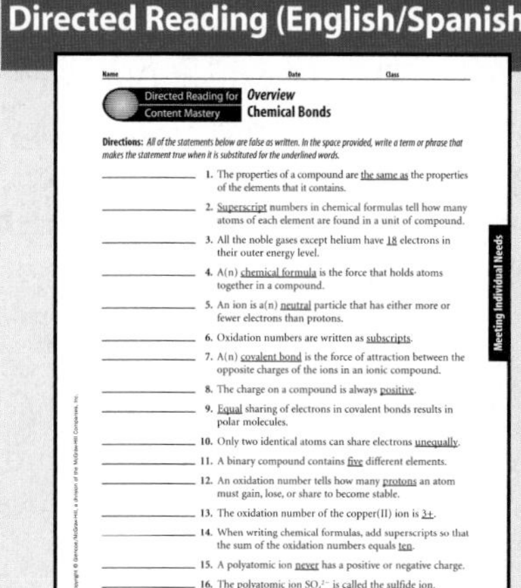

Name Date Class

Directed Reading for Content Mastery **Overview Chemical Bonds**

Directions: All of the statements below are false as written. In the space provided, write a term or phrase that makes the statement true when it is substituted for the underlined words.

1. The properties of a compound are the same as the properties of the elements that it contains.
2. Superscript numbers in chemical formulas tell how many atoms of each element are found in a unit of compound.
3. All the noble gases except helium have 18 electrons in their outer energy level.
4. A(n) chemical formula is the force that holds atoms together in a compound.
5. An ion is a(n) neutral particle that has either more or fewer electrons than protons.
6. Oxidation numbers are written as subscripts.
7. A(n) covalent bond is the force of attraction between the opposite charges of the ions in an ionic compound.
8. The charge on a compound is always positive.
9. Equal sharing of electrons in covalent bonds results in polar molecules.
10. Only two identical atoms can share electrons unequally.
11. A binary compound contains five different elements.
12. An oxidation number tells how many protons an atom must gain, lose, or share to become stable.
13. The oxidation number of the copper(II) ion is 3+.
14. When writing chemical formulas, add superscripts so that the sum of the oxidation numbers equals ten.
15. A polyatomic ion never has a positive or negative charge.
16. The polyatomic ion SO_4^{2-} is called the sulfide ion.

Meeting Individual Needs

L1

Chemical Bonds 19

Study Guide

Study Guide
Features
• Contains a study guide page for each section of the chapter
• Reviews key concepts
• Includes answer pages
L2

Reading Essentials

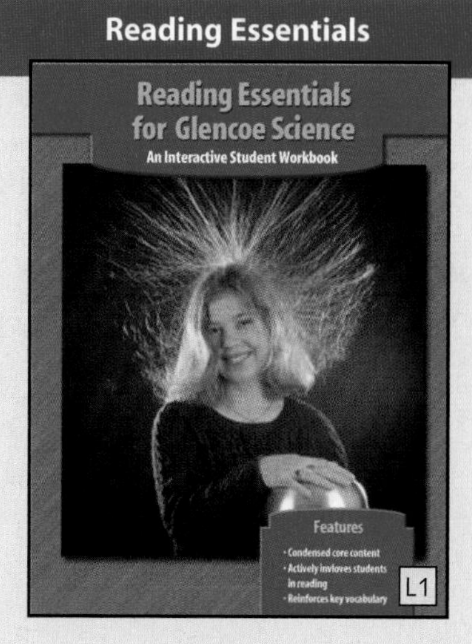
Reading Essentials for Glencoe Science
An Interactive Student Workbook
Features
• Condensed core content
• Actively involves students in reading
• Reinforces key vocabulary
L1

Assessment

Test Practice Workbook

Name: Date: Class:

Chapter Test Chapter 19 Chemical Bonds

DIRECTIONS

Read each question and choose the best answer. Then fill in the correct answer on your answer document.

Polyatomic Ions	Not Polyatomic Ions
NH_4^+	Cl^-
CO_3^{2-}	Na^+
OH^-	Ca^{2+}
PO_4^{3-}	O^{2-}

1 According to the diagrams, a polyatomic ion is a —

A group of ionically bonded atoms with a net charge of zero

B charged, covalently bonded group of atoms*

C group of covalently bonded atoms with a net charge of zero

D charged, ionically bonded group of atoms

2 According to the diagram, which statement best describes what happens to sodium and chlorine atoms when they combine to form sodium chloride?

F The sodium atom becomes a positive sodium ion, and the chlorine atom becomes a negative chloride ion.*

G The sodium atom becomes a negative sodium ion, and the chlorine atom becomes a positive chloride ion.

H The sodium atom becomes a positive chloride ion, and the chlorine atom becomes a negative sodium ion.

J The sodium atom becomes a negative chloride ion, and the chlorine atom becomes a positive sodium ion.

3 All of these atoms lend electrons and form positive ions EXCEPT —

A B C D

GO ON L2

80 The Nature of Matter

Chapter Review

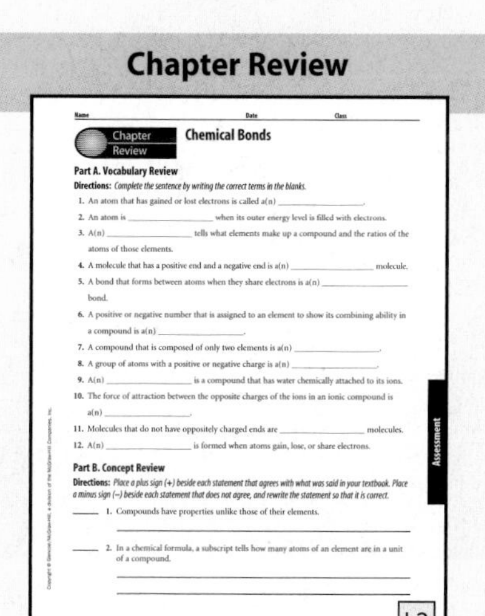

Name Date Class

Chapter Review **Chemical Bonds**

Part A. Vocabulary Review

Directions: Complete the sentence by writing the correct terms in the blanks.

1. An atom that has gained or lost electrons is called a(n) ________.
2. An atom is ________ when its outer energy level is filled with electrons.
3. A(n) ________ tells what elements make up a compound and the ratios of the atoms of those elements.
4. A molecule that has a positive end and a negative end is a(n) ________ molecule.
5. A bond that forms between atoms when they share electrons is a(n) ________ bond.
6. A positive or negative number that is assigned to an element to show its combining ability in a compound is a(n) ________.
7. A compound that is composed of only two elements is a(n) ________.
8. A group of atoms with a positive or negative charge is a(n) ________.
9. A(n) ________ is a compound that has water chemically attached to its ions.
10. The force of attraction between the opposite charges of the ions in an ionic compound is a(n) ________.
11. Molecules that do not have oppositely charged ends are ________ molecules.
12. A(n) ________ is formed when atoms gain, lose, or share electrons.

Part B. Concept Review

Directions: Place a plus sign (+) beside each statement that agrees with what was said in your textbook. Place a minus sign (–) beside each statement that does not agree, and rewrite the statement so that it is correct.

____ 1. Compounds have properties unlike those of their elements.

____ 2. In a chemical formula, a subscript tells how many atoms of an element are in a unit of a compound.

Assessment

L2

Chemical Bonds 37

Chapter Tests

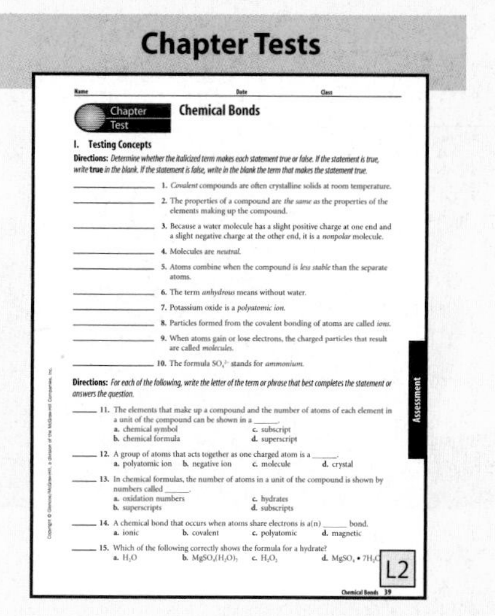

Name Date Class

Chapter Test **Chemical Bonds**

I. Testing Concepts

Directions: Determine whether the italicized term makes each statement true or false. If the statement is true, write **true** *in the blank. If the statement is false, write in the blank the term that makes the statement true.*

1. *Covalent* compounds are often crystalline solids at room temperature.
2. The properties of a compound are *the same as* the properties of the elements making up the compound.
3. Because a water molecule has a slight positive charge at one end and a slight negative charge at the other end, it is a *nonpolar* molecule.
4. Molecules are *neutral*.
5. Atoms combine when the compound is *less stable* than the separate atoms.
6. The term *anhydrous* means without water.
7. Potassium oxide is a *polyatomic ion*.
8. Particles formed from the covalent bonding of atoms are called *ions*.
9. When atoms gain or lose electrons, the charged particles that result are called *molecules*.
10. The formula SO_4^{2-} stands for *ammonium*.

Directions: For each of the following, write the letter of the term or phrase that best completes the statement or answers the question.

11. The elements that make up a compound and the number of atoms of each element in a unit of the compound can be shown in a ____.
a. chemical symbol c. subscript
b. chemical formula d. superscript

12. A group of atoms that acts together as one charged atom is a ____.
a. polyatomic ion b. negative ion c. molecule d. crystal

13. In chemical formulas, the number of atoms in a unit of the compound is shown by numbers called ____.
a. oxidation numbers c. hydrates
b. superscripts d. subscripts

14. A chemical bond that occurs when atoms share electrons is a(n) ____ bond.
a. ionic b. covalent c. polyatomic d. magnetic

15. Which of the following correctly shows the formula for a hydrate?
a. H_2O b. $MgSO_4(H_2O)_7$ c. H_2O_2 d. $MgSO_4 \cdot 7H_2O$

Assessment

L2

Chemical Bonds 39

Science Content Background

section 1 Stability in Bonding

Atomic Stability

Atoms undergo rearrangements of electrons to become more stable. This concept forms the basis for understanding chemical bonding. The most stable configuration of electrons is found in the noble gases. Atoms gain, lose, or share electrons, some more easily than others, so that they have the same electron configurations as the noble gases. For example, a chlorine atom gains an electron and attains an electron structure like the chemically stable noble gas argon (Cl^-). Sodium loses one of its 11 electrons to attain an electron structure like neon (Na^+). In general, metals tend to form positively charged ions (lose electrons) and nonmetals form negatively charged ions (gain electrons).

section 2 Types of Bonds

Electron Dot Structures

One of the most convenient ways to picture the sharing of electrons between atoms in covalent or polar covalent bonds is to use electron dot structures. Electron dot structures are often called Lewis structures, after American chemist G. N. Lewis (1875–1946), who invented this symbolism. Electron dot structures represent an atom's outer-level, or valence, electrons by dots. Atoms form covalent bonds by sharing electron pairs, with the resulting molecules drawn by assigning the correct number of valence electrons to each atom. Group 13 atoms have three valence electrons, Group 14 atoms have four valence electrons, and so on across the periodic table.

Group 18 elements, such as neon and argon, rarely form covalent bonds because they have a stable configuration of eight electrons in their outer energy levels. This is called the octet rule—representative elements react so that they attain eight electrons in their outer energy level.

Lewis dot structures can be used to model covalent bonding and predict the number of bonds between atoms in a compound. For example, in N_2, the atoms share three pairs of electrons. Each pair represents a bond, so N_2 has a triple bond. Multiple bonds are shorter and stronger than single bonds because there are more electrons holding the nuclei together.

Although Lewis dot structures are accurate models of bonding for most compounds, laboratory data from some compounds do not always agree with conclusions drawn from these models. This is the case with O_2. The Lewis dot structure predicts that O_2 will contain a double bond and four electron pairs. Bond length studies have shown that the O_2 bond length is consistent with that of a double bond. However, O_2 is known to be paramagnetic (it has unpaired electrons). This apparent discrepancy has been resolved by applying quantum-based molecular orbital (MO) theory.

Barry L. Runk/Grant Heilman Photography, Inc.

Electronegativity

When two different kinds of atoms share a pair of electrons, a bond forms in which electrons are shared unequally. The attractive force that an atom of an element has for shared electrons in a molecule is known as its electronegativity. Nobel laureate Linus Pauling (1901–1994) developed a scale of relative electronegativities, in which the most electronegative element, fluorine, is assigned a value of 4.0. The higher the electronegativity, the stronger an atom attracts electrons within a bond. Electronegativity generally increases from left to right across a period and decreases down a group for typical elements.

Teacher to Teacher
Mark Resch,
Ripon High School
Ripon, Wisconsin

"I balance an 8-inch piece of 2 × 4 lumber on a watch glass. Then, I induce a charge in an inflated balloon by rubbing it in my hair. I hold the charged balloon to the side near one end of the 2 × 4. The balloon will be attracted to the wood. I move the balloon to the other side to reverse direction. Unless the air is very humid, this will work."

Mark Resch

Polar or Nonpolar?

A general knowledge of electronegativities can be used to make predictions about bond polarity. A general guideline is that bonds between atoms with the same or similar values are nonpolar covalent, bonds between atoms whose values differ by more than 1.7 are substantially ionic, and bonds between atoms whose values differ by less than 1.7 are polar covalent. At the extreme, one or more electrons are actually transferred and an ionic bond results. It is important to realize that bonding is a continuum—the difference between ionic and covalent is a gradual change.

chapter content resources

Internet Resources
For additional content background, visit gpscience.com to:

- access your book online
- find references to related articles in popular science magazines
- access Web links with related content background
- access current events with science journal topics

Print Resources
Chemistry; The Molecular Nature of Matter and Change, by Martin S. Silberberg, McGraw-Hill, 2003
Structure and Bonding, by Jack Barrett and Eddie Abel, Wiley, John & Sons, Incorporated, 2002

section 3 Writing Formulas and Naming Compounds

Hydrates

The best-known hydrates are crystalline solids that lose their structure upon removal of their bound water. Although the number of molecules of water in a given hydrate is fixed, some substances can form several different hydrates. For example, there are four different hydrates of iron (II) sulfate, each with separate and unique physical properties.

About the Photo

Bond Strength Use the analogy of these skydivers gripping hands to associate bond strength with the formation of stable and unstable formations.

Science Journal Student responses will vary, but many should include references to outer electron energy levels.

BIG Idea

Covalent and Ionic Compounds In covalent compounds, atoms are bound together by covalent bonds and form molecules. Each molecule is identical in a covalent compound and behaves as an independent unit. The chemical formula for a covalent compound represents the number of atoms of each element in the molecule. In an ionic compound, there are no individual molecules. Instead, positive and negative ions usually form an ionic crystal—a three-dimensional array of ions arranged in a regularly repeating pattern. The chemical formula for an ionic compound represents the ratio of the different elements in the crystal.

Introduce the Chapter Have students work in groups. One student in each group chooses an element from Group 1, 2, 17, or 18. The other students then find the element on the periodic table and determine how many outer electrons the element has.

chapter 20

Chemical Bonds

BIG Idea Just over 110 elements combine with chemical bonds to form a nearly infinite number of compounds.

20.1 Stability in Bonding

MAIN Idea When atoms form compounds, each atom is more stable in the compound than it was by itself.

20.2 Types of Bonds

MAIN Idea Atoms form ionic bonds by transferring electrons and form covalent bonds by sharing electrons.

20.3 Writing Formulas and Naming Compounds

MAIN Idea The oxidation numbers of the ions in ionic compounds determine the formula of the compounds.

Elements Form Chemical Bonds

Just like these skydivers are linked together to make a stable formation, the atoms in elements can link together with chemical bonds to form a compound. You will read about how chemical bonds form and learn how to write chemical formulas and equations.

Science Journal Describe what makes some bonds more stable than others.

600

Interactive Chalkboard

This CD-ROM is an editable Microsoft® PowerPoint® presentation that includes:

- an editable presentation for every chapter
- additional chapter questions
- animated graphics
- image bank
- links to gpscience.com

Start-Up Activities

Chemical Bonds and Mixing

You have probably noticed that some liquids like oil and vinegar salad dressings will not stay mixed after the bottle is shaken. However, rubbing alcohol and water will mix. The compounds that make up the liquids are different. This lab will demonstrate the influence the types of chemical bonds have on how the compounds mix.

1. Pour 20 mL of water into a 100-mL graduated cylinder.
2. Pour 20 mL of vegetable oil into the same cylinder. Vigorously swirl the two liquids together, and observe for several minutes.
3. Add two drops of food dye and observe.
4. After several minutes, slowly pour 30 mL of rubbing alcohol into the cylinder.
5. Add two more drops of food dye and observe.
6. **Think Critically** In your Science Journal, write a paragraph describing how the different liquids mixed. Would your final results be different if you added the liquids in a different order? Explain.

Chemical Formulas Every compound has a chemical formula that tells exactly which elements are present in that compound and exactly how many atoms of each element are present in that compound. Make the following Foldable to help identify the chemical formulas from this chapter.

STEP 1 **Fold** a vertical sheet of notebook paper from side to side.

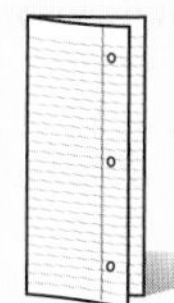

STEP 2 **Cut** along every third line of only the top layer to form tabs.

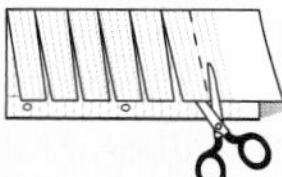

STEP 3 **Label** each tab.

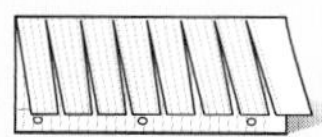

Read and Write Go through the chapter, find ten chemical formulas, and write them on the front of the tabs. As you read the chapter, write what compound each formula represents under the appropriate tab.

Preview this chapter's content and activities at gpscience.com

Purpose Use the Launch Lab to introduce students to the interaction between liquids with polar bonds and liquids with nonpolar bonds. L2 LS **Visual-Spatial**

Preparation Prepare small beakers of each liquid for each group.

Materials two 100-mL graduated cylinders, water, vegetable oil, rubbing alcohol, food dye, dropper

Teaching Strategy Explain that the molecules in water, food dye, and rubbing alcohol have polar chemical bonds, but the molecules in vegetable oil have nonpolar chemical bonds.

Think Critically

When the oil was added to the water and the cylinder was shaken, the oil formed bubbles that quickly separated from the water when the cylinder was allowed to sit. The oil then formed a layer on top of the water. The drops of food dye moved through the nonpolar oil as droplets. Once the drops of food dye passed through the oil/water boundary, they mixed with the water molecules, exploding with color. The alcohol, which is polar, remained on top of the oil, and the food dye dissolved in it immediately.

Assessment

Portfolio Ask students to draw a labeled diagram of their graduated cylinder filled with liquids. Use **Performance Assessment in the Science Classroom**, p. 127.

Dinah Zike Study Fold

Student preparation materials for this Foldable are available in the **Chapter *Fast File* Resources.**

Additional Chapter Media

- Virtual Lab: *How can you tell which elements form chemical bonds?*
- Video Lab: *Making a Hydrate*

section 1

Stability in Bonding

1 Motivate

Bellringer

Section Focus Transparencies also are available on the Interactive Chalkboard CD-ROM.

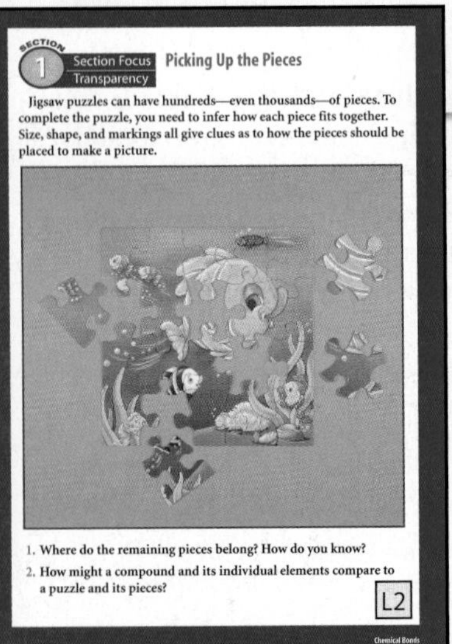
SECTION 1 Section Focus Transparency Picking Up the Pieces

Jigsaw puzzles can have hundreds—even thousands—of pieces. To complete the puzzle, you need to infer how each piece fits together. Size, shape, and markings all give clues as to how the pieces should be placed to make a picture.

1. Where do the remaining pieces belong? How do you know?
2. How might a compound and its individual elements compare to a puzzle and its pieces?

L2

Chemical Bonds

Tie to Prior Knowledge

Jigsaw Puzzle Have students consider how pieces of a jigsaw puzzle fit together in an orderly, exact way. Explain that it is possible to predict how atoms of different elements fit together in an exact way. As an example, discuss how water forms when two parts hydrogen combine with one part oxygen. The "parts" in this case are atoms that form chemical bonds with one another.

Reading Guide

What You'll Learn

- **Describe** how a compound differs from its component elements.
- **Explain** what a chemical formula represents.
- **Explain** that the electric forces between oppositely charged electrons and protons are essential to forming compounds
- **State** a reason why chemical bonding occurs.

Why It's Important

The millions of different kinds of matter around us are a result of chemical bonds.

Review Vocabulary

compound: substance formed from two or more elements in which the exact combination and proportion of elements is always the same

New Vocabulary

- chemical formula
- chemical bond

Figure 1 The difference between the elemental copper metal and the copper compound formed on the Statue of Liberty is striking.

Elemental copper

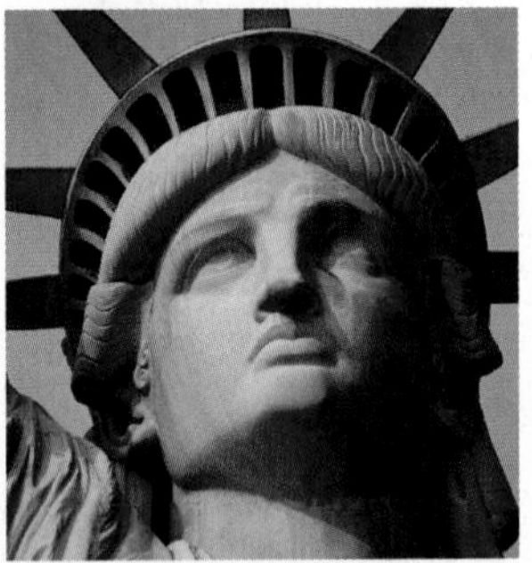
Surface coated with a copper compound

Combined Elements

Have you ever noticed the color of the Statue of Liberty? Why is it green? Did the sculptor purposely choose green? Why wasn't white, or tan, or even some other color like purple chosen? Was it painted that way? No, the Statue of Liberty was not painted. The Statue of Liberty is made of the metal copper, which is an element. Pennies, too, are made of copper. Wait a minute, you say. Copper isn't green—it's . . . well, copper colored.

You are right. Uncombined, elemental copper is a bright, shiny copper color. So again the question arises: Why is the Statue of Liberty green?

Compounds Some of the matter around you is in the form of uncombined elements such as copper, sulfur, and oxygen. But, like many other sets of elements, these three elements unite chemically to form a compound when the conditions are right. The green coating on the Statue of Liberty and some old pennies is a result of this chemical change. One compound in this coating, seen in contrast with elemental copper in **Figure 1,** is a new compound called copper sulfate. Copper sulfate isn't shiny and copper colored like elemental copper. Nor is it a pale-yellow solid like sulfur or a colorless, odorless gas like oxygen. It has its own unique properties.

Section 1 Resource Manager

Chapter *FAST FILE* Resources
- Transparency Activity, p. 44
- Directed Reading for Content Mastery, pp. 19, 20
- Note-taking Worksheets, pp. 33–35
- Lab Activity, pp. 9–12
- Enrichment, p. 30
- Reinforcement, p. 27
- Lab Worksheet, pp. 5–6

Cultural Diversity, p. 69

Physical Science Critical Thinking/Problem Solving, p. 1

New Properties One interesting observation you will make is that the compound formed when elements combine often has properties that aren't anything like those of the individual elements. Sodium chloride, for example, shown in **Figure 2,** is a compound made from the elements sodium and chlorine. Sodium is a shiny, soft, silvery metal that reacts violently with water. Chlorine is a poisonous greenish-yellow gas. Would you have guessed that these elements combine to make ordinary table salt?

Figure 2 Sodium is a soft, silvery metal that combines with chlorine, a greenish-yellow gas represented here as only one atom, to form sodium chloride, which is a white crystalline solid.
Describe *how the properties of table salt are different from those of sodium and chlorine.*

Formulas

The chemical symbols Na and Cl represent the elements sodium and chlorine. When written as NaCl, the symbols make up a formula, or chemical shorthand, for the compound sodium chloride. A **chemical formula** tells what elements a compound contains and the exact number of the atoms of each element in a unit of that compound. The compound that you are probably most familiar with is H_2O, more commonly known as water. This formula contains the symbols H for the element hydrogen and O for the element oxygen. Notice the subscript number 2 written after the H for hydrogen. *Subscript* means "written below." A subscript written after a symbol tells how many atoms of that element are in a unit of the compound. If a symbol has no subscript, the unit contains only one atom of that element. A unit of H_2O contains two hydrogen atoms and one oxygen atom.

Look at the formulas for each compound listed in **Table 1.** What elements combine to form each compound? How many atoms of each element are required to form each of the compounds?

Table 1 Some Familiar Compounds

Familiar Name	Chemical Name	Formula
Sand	Silicon dioxide	SiO_2
Milk of magnesia	Magnesium hydroxide	$Mg(OH)_2$
Cane sugar	Sucrose	$C_{12}H_{22}O_{11}$
Lime	Calcium oxide	CaO
Vinegar	Acetic acid	CH_3COOH
Laughing gas	Dinitrogen oxide	N_2O
Grain alcohol	Ethanol	C_2H_5OH
Battery acid	Sulfuric acid	H_2SO_4
Stomach acid	Hydrochloric acid	HCl

Describe what a chemical formula tells you.

2 Teach

Caption Answer

Figure 2 Table salt is a stable, white solid. Sodium is very reactive with water, silver in color, soft, and a metal. Chlorine is a poisonous, greenish-yellow gas.

Discussion

Similar Formulas Point out that H_2O and H_2O_2 have similar chemical formulas. Does this mean they are similar compounds? Explain. They are not similar compounds. The addition of one oxygen atom changes H_2O (water), a substance that is critical for life, into H_2O_2 (hydrogen peroxide), a substance that is used as a disinfectant and quickly reacts with many other compounds. L1 LS **Logical-Mathematical**

Text Question Answer

Sand: 1 atom of silicon (Si), 2 of oxygen (O); milk of magnesia: 1 atom of magnesium (Mg), 2 of oxygen (O), 2 of hydrogen (H); cane sugar: 12 atoms of carbon (C), 22 of hydrogen (H), 11 of oxygen (O); lime: 1 atom (ion) of calcium (Ca), 1 of oxygen (O); vinegar: 2 atoms of carbon (C), 2 of oxygen (O), and 4 of hydrogen (H); laughing gas: 2 atoms of nitrogen (N), 1 of oxygen (O); grain alcohol: 2 atoms of carbon (C), 6 of hydrogen (H), 1 of oxygen (O); battery acid: 2 atoms of hydrogen (H), 1 of sulfur (S), 4 of oxygen (O); stomach acid: 1 atom of hydrogen (H), 1 of chlorine (Cl). L2 LS **Logical-Mathematical**

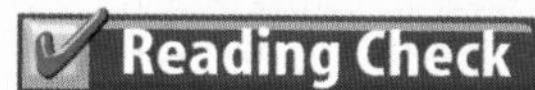

Answer Tells what elements are present in a compound and the exact number of the atoms of each element in a unit of that compound.

Teacher FYI

Ionic Compound NaCl is an ionic compound. This means that NaCl is not considered to be a molecule. Salt exists as an array of positive sodium ions attracted to negative chloride ions in a crystal lattice. The lattice has an equal number of sodium ions and chloride ions, so the formula for salt is given as NaCl.

Visual Learning

Figure 3 Have students predict whether each atom shown would more likely gain or lose electrons to form an octet. An atom with fewer than four electrons in the outer energy level tends to give up electrons, while those with more than four tend to gain electrons to form an octet. L1 **Visual-Spatial**

Use an Analogy

Gloves In a cold climate, each person would seek to have two gloves to keep his or her hands warm. Someone with fewer than two would try to get warm by gaining a glove or two. A person with more than two gloves might give up those not needed for warmth. Individuals with exactly two gloves would not be involved in any rearrangements. Similarly, some atoms give up electrons to have eight in their outer energy levels, while others must obtain electrons to have eight. An atom with exactly eight electrons in its outer level does not need to gain or lose electrons, so it does not participate in rearrangements of electrons between atoms. The atoms of all the nonreactive noble gases except helium have eight electrons in their outer energy levels. Helium's outer level is complete with two electrons.

Activity

Binary Compounds Have the students create binary compounds using the periodic chart. Then have the student research that compound and describe it to the other students.

Caption Answer

Figure 3 Group 16

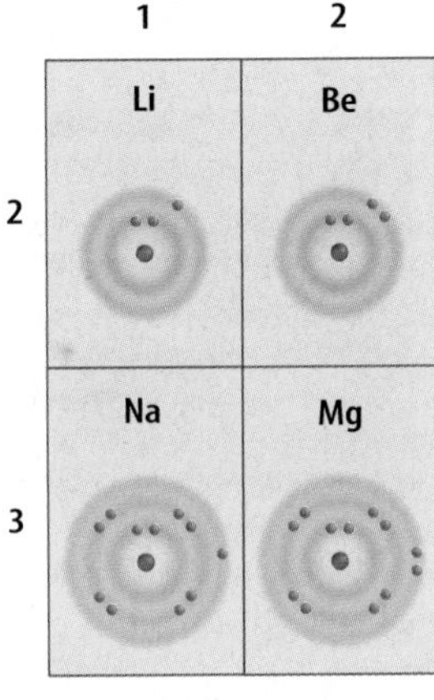

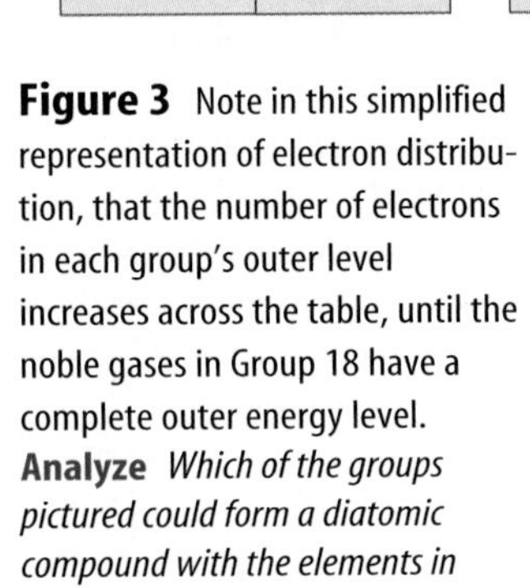

Figure 3 Note in this simplified representation of electron distribution, that the number of electrons in each group's outer level increases across the table, until the noble gases in Group 18 have a complete outer energy level.
Analyze *Which of the groups pictured could form a diatomic compound with the elements in Group 2?*

Figure 4 Electron dot diagrams of noble gases show that they all have a stable, filled outer energy level.

He	Kr
Ne	Xe
Ar	Rn

Atomic Stability

Why do atoms form compounds? The electric forces between oppositely charged electrons and protons hold atoms and molecules together, and thus are the forces that cause compounds to form. The periodic table on the inside back cover of your book lists the known elements, most of which can combine with other elements. However, the six noble gases in Group 18 seldom form compounds. Why is this so? Atoms of noble gases are unusually stable. Compounds of these atoms rarely form because they are almost always less stable than the original atoms.

The Unique Noble Gases To understand the stability of the noble gases, it is helpful to look at electron dot diagrams. Electron dot diagrams show only the electrons in the outer energy level of an atom. They contain the chemical symbol for the element surrounded by dots representing its outer electrons. How do you know how many dots to make? For Groups 1 and 2 and 13 through 18, you can use a periodic table or the portion of it shown in **Figure 3.** Look at the outer ring of each of the elements. Group 1 has one outer electron. Group 2 has two. Group 13 has three, Group 14, four, and so on to Group 18, the noble gases, which have eight.

Chemical Stability An atom is chemically stable when its outer energy level is complete. Recall that the outer energy levels of helium and hydrogen are stable with two electrons. The outer energy levels of all the other elements are stable when they contain eight electrons. The noble gases are stable because they each have a complete outer energy level. **Figure 4** shows electron dot diagrams of some of the noble gases. Notice that eight dots surround Kr, Ne, Xe, Ar, and Rn, and two dots surround He.

Teacher FYI

New Elements The number of known elements may change during your use of this text. Research teams in Dubna, Russia; Darmstadt, Germany; and Berkeley, California are working to synthesize new elements.

Differentiated Instruction

Challenge Some students will wonder why the text skips elements in Group 3 to Group 12 when talking about outer-level electrons. Encourage these students to research and write brief reports about why these transition metals are skipped. The outer energy levels of these elements are similar to those of elements in Groups 1 or 2. As electrons are added, they fill in incomplete lower electron energy levels. L3 IN **Linguistic**

604 CHAPTER 20 Chemical Bonds

Energy Levels and Other Elements How do the dot diagrams represent other elements, and how does that relate to their ability to make compounds? Hydrogen and helium, the elements in row one of the periodic table, can hold a maximum of two electrons in their outer energy levels. Hydrogen contains one electron in its lone energy level. A dot diagram for hydrogen has a single dot next to its symbol. This means that hydrogen's outer energy level is not full. It is more stable when it is part of a compound.

In contrast, helium's outer energy level contains two electrons. Its dot diagram has two dots—a pair of electrons—next to its symbol. Helium already has a full outer energy level by itself and is chemically stable. Helium rarely forms compounds but, by itself, the element is a commonly used gas.

When you look at the elements in Groups 13 through 17, you see that each of them falls short of having a stable energy level. Each group contains too few electrons for a stable level of eight electrons.

Outer Levels—Getting Their Fill As you just learned, hydrogen is an element that does not have a full outer energy level. How does hydrogen, or any other element, trying to become stable, gain or lose its outer electrons? Atoms with partially stable outer energy levels can lose, gain, or share electrons to obtain a stable outer energy level. They do this by combining with other atoms that also have partially complete outer energy levels. As a result, each achieves stability. **Figure 5** shows electron dot diagrams for sodium and chlorine. When they combine, sodium loses one electron and chlorine gains one electron. You can see from the electron dot diagram that chlorine now has a stable outer energy level similar to a noble gas. But what about sodium?

Topic: Dot Diagrams
Visit gpscience.com for Web links to information about using dot diagrams to represent outer energy level electrons.

Activity Draw a dot diagram of methane, CH_4.

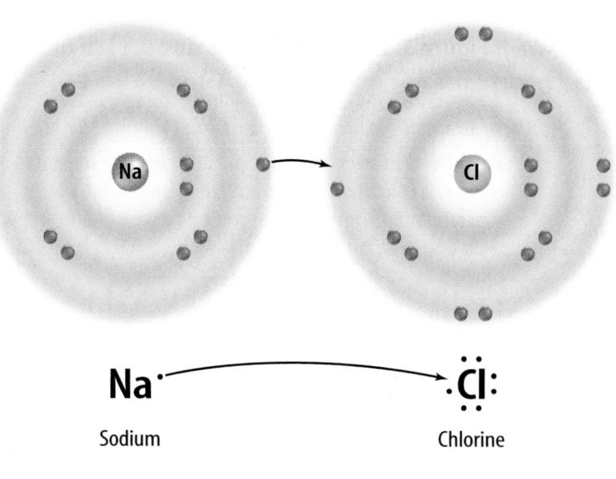

Figure 5 Each of these atoms has the potential of having a stable outer energy level by just adding or taking away one electron.

Quick Demo

Chemical Reactions

Materials calcium metal, 1 M HCl, beaker

Estimated Time 10 minutes

Safety Precautions

Procedure Place a pea-sized piece of calcium metal in a small amount of 1 M HCl. Have students note the production of bubbles as H_2 is given off. Carefully evaporate the liquid, leaving $CaCl_2$. On the board, write the dot diagram for the ions contained in this ionic compound. Both Ca^{2+} and Cl^- contain eight outer electrons. (If zinc metal is used instead of Ca, $ZnCl_2$ will form.) L2 ELL LS **Visual-Spatial**

Make a Model

Elements Have students use various colors of modeling clay to make spheres that represent metals and nonmetals. Tell them to use smaller spheres of a specific color to show electrons. Attach the correct number of electrons to each model sphere to represent the outer energy level of the selected atoms. Challenge students to use a periodic table to identify possible elements that each model represents. Then have them explain how the element in each model can obtain eight outer electrons through various combinations with other elements. L2 ELL LS **Kinesthetic**

Text Question Answer

Its outer level is filled, too.

Differentiated Instruction

Learning Disabled Prepare physical models of various atoms and have the students assemble them. Then they can see how the electrons are essential to forming stable chemical bonds between atoms.

Challenge Use dot diagrams with one carbon atom and two oxygen atoms to make an arrangement that gives the carbon and oxygen atoms an octet. Place carbon in the center and make double bonds between the carbon and oxygen atoms. In this arrangement, the carbon atom shares two electrons with one oxygen atom and two with the other. Each oxygen atom shares two electrons with the carbon atom. L3 LS **Visual-Spatial**

Fun Fact

The minimum amount of energy needed to remove the outermost (highest energy) electron from a neutral atom in the gaseous state is referred to as the first ionization potential.

3 Assess

DAILY INTERVENTION

Check for Understanding

Logical-Mathematical Have students review the periodic table and identify which groups would most likely form binary compounds with each other. Then have them give examples of some of the possible binary compounds and draw the dot diagrams of each one.

Reteach

Electron Distribution Remind students that giving up electrons can sometimes provide a new outer level of eight electrons. Make a poster with sodium's electron distribution written out—two in the first level, eight in the second. Loosely tape a page with the single electron in the third energy level written on it over the poster. Demonstrate that when the outer page is removed (losing the electron), the new outer level is shown to contain eight electrons. Point out that this can occur for several other metals as well. L1 ELL LS **Visual-Spatial**

Assessment

Performance Have students write out the dot diagrams for two atoms of aluminum and for three atoms of oxygen. Then have them show how this combination gives all atoms eight outer, shared electrons. Use **Performance Assessment in the Science Classroom**, p. 127. P

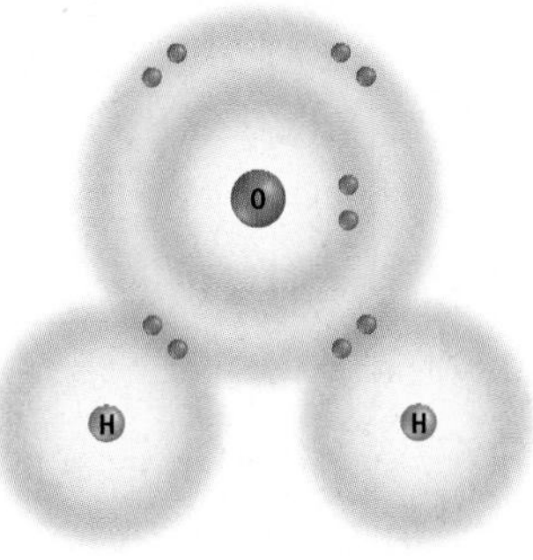

Figure 6 In water, hydrogen contributes one electron and oxygen contributes the other to each hydrogen-oxygen bond. The atoms share those electrons instead of giving them up.

Stability Is Reached Sodium had only one electron in its outer energy level, which it lost to combine with chlorine in sodium chloride. However, look back to the next, outermost energy level of sodium. This is now the new outer energy level, and it is stable with eight electrons. When the outer electron of sodium is removed, a complete inner energy level is revealed and now becomes the new outer energy level. Sodium and chlorine are stable now because of the exchange of an electron.

In the compound water, each hydrogen atom needs one electron to fill its outer energy level. The oxygen atom needs two electrons for its outer level to be stable with eight electrons. Hydrogen and oxygen become stable and form bonds in a different way than sodium and chlorine. Instead of gaining or losing electrons, they share them. **Figure 6** shows how hydrogen and oxygen share electrons to achieve a more stable arrangement of electrons.

When atoms gain, lose, or share electrons, an attraction forms between the atoms, pulling them together to form a compound. This attraction is called a chemical bond. A **chemical bond** is the force that holds atoms together in a compound. In Section 2 you will learn how these chemical bonds are formed.

section 1 review

Summary

Combined Elements

- When elements combine, the new compound has unique properties that are different from the original properties of the elements.

Formulas

- Chemical symbols and numbers are shorthand for the elements and their amounts in chemical formulas.

Atomic Stability

- The elements of Group 18, the noble gases, rarely combine with other elements.
- Electron dot diagrams show the electrons in the outer energy level of an atom.
- Most atoms need eight electrons to complete their outer energy level.
- Atoms form chemical bonds in three separate different ways to complete their outer energy levels.
- A chemical bond is the force that holds atoms together in a compound.

Self Check

1. **Compare and contrast** the properties of the individual elements that combine to make salt with the compound salt.
2. **Identify** what the formula BaF_2 tells you about this compound.
3. **Identify** the forces that hold atoms and molecules together at the atomic level. Give an example of how these forces are involved in a chemical reaction.
4. **Explain** why some elements are stable on their own while others are more stable in compounds.
5. **Describe** why chemical bonding occurs. Give two examples of how bonds can form.
6. **Think Critically** The label on a box of cleanser states that it contains CH_3COOH. What elements are in this compound? How many atoms of each element can be found in a unit of CH_3COOH?

Applying Math

7. **Use Percentages** Given that the molecular weight of $Mg(OH)_2$, magnesium hydroxide, is 58.32 g, what percentage of this compound is oxygen?

Science Online gpscience.com/self_check_quiz

section 1 review

1. Sodium, as an element, is a solid metal. Chlorine is a gas. When the two combine to form sodium chloride, they form a solid compound.
2. The compound ratio is made up of one barium ion and two floride ions. Also, since the compound is made up of a metal and a nonmetal, it is likely ionic.
3. Chemical bonds.
4. If an element has eight electrons in its outer electron energy level, it has a tendency not to react.
5. Electrons are either gained, lost, or shared between atoms.
6. Hydrogen, carbon, and oxygen are in the compound. Each unit contains four hydrogen, two carbon, and two oxygen atoms.
7. 54.86%

Atomic Trading Cards

Perhaps you have seen or collected trading cards for famous athletes. Usually each card has a picture of the athlete on one side with important statistics related to the sport on the back. Atoms can also be identified by their properties and statistics.

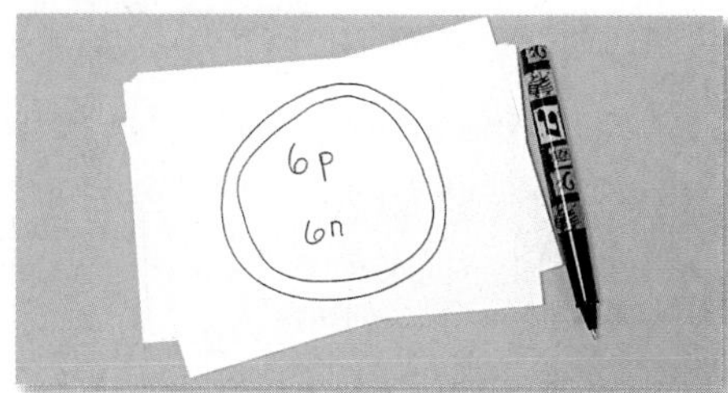

Real-World Question

How can a visible model show how energy levels fill when atoms combine?

Goals

- **Display** the electrons of elements according to their energy levels.
- **Compare and classify** elements according to their outer energy levels.

Materials

4-in × 6-in index cards
periodic table

Procedure

1. Get an assigned element from the teacher. Write the following information for your element on your index card: name, symbol, group number, atomic number, atomic mass, metal/nonmetal/metalloid.
2. On the other side of your index cards, show the number of protons and neutrons in the nucleus (e.g. *6p* for six protons and *6n* for six neutrons for carbon.)
3. Draw circles around the nucleus to represent the energy levels of your element. The number of circles you will need is the same as the row the element is in on the periodic table.
4. Draw dots on each circle to represent the electrons in each energy level. Remember, elements in row one become stable with two outer electrons while levels two and three become stable with eight electrons.
5. Look at the picture side only of four or five of your classmates' cards. Determine which element they have and to which group it belongs.

Conclude and Apply

1. As you classify the elements according to their group number, what pattern do you see in the number of electrons in the outer energy level?
2. Atoms that give up electrons combine with atoms that gain electrons in order to form compounds. In your Science Journal, predict some pairs of elements that would combine in this way.

Communicating Your Data

Make a graph that relates the groups to the number of electrons in their outer energy level. **For more help, refer to the Science Skill Handbook.**

BENCH TESTED

Real-World Question

Purpose Students make models showing the number of electrons in the outer energy levels of atoms of various elements and compare and classify those elements. L2 LS **Visual-Spatial**

Process Skills formulate models, classify, use numbers, compare and contrast, make and use graphs

Time Required 40 minutes

Procedure

Teaching Strategy To avoid confusion, assign elements from Groups 1, 2, and 13–18 only.

Troubleshooting Emphasize to students that the circles around the nucleus are only representations of the energy levels of electrons. Electrons do not actually move in circles.

Conclude and Apply

1. They are the same in each group.
2. Sodium and potassium give up the only electron in their respective outer energy levels to chlorine and iodine, forming the chemically stable compounds sodium chloride and potassium iodide.

Assessment

Oral Ask students to which group carbon and silicon belong and whether these two elements are more likely to gain electrons, lose electrons, or share electrons when they form compounds. **Group 14;** because they have four electrons in their outer energy levels they most likely share electrons. Use **Performance Assessment in the Science Classroom,** p. 89.

Communicating Your Data

Have students enter the number of electrons in the outer energy levels of atoms and the numbers of the groups to which the atoms belong in a computer spreadsheet. Then have them use the spreadsheet's graphing function to make the graph.

1 Motivate

Bellringer

Section Focus Transparencies also are available on the Interactive Chalkboard CD-ROM.

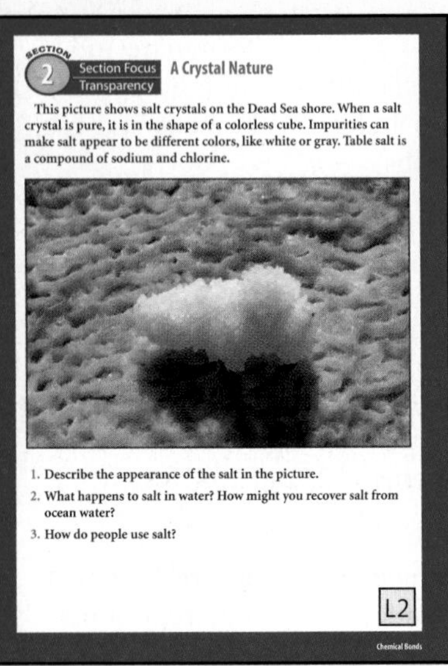

Section 2 Section Focus Transparency — A Crystal Nature

This picture shows salt crystals on the Dead Sea shore. When a salt crystal is pure, it is in the shape of a colorless cube. Impurities can make salt appear to be different colors, like white or gray. Table salt is a compound of sodium and chlorine.

1. Describe the appearance of the salt in the picture.
2. What happens to salt in water? How might you recover salt from ocean water?
3. How do people use salt?

L2

Chemical Bonds

Tie to Prior Knowledge

Electrolytes Ask students if they have ever consumed sports drinks. Explain that the electrolytes that are advertised to be in sports drinks are ions that are found naturally in human blood.

section 2

Types of Bonds

Reading Guide

What You'll Learn

- **Describe** ionic bonds and covalent bonds.
- **Identify** the particles produced by ionic bonding and by covalent bonding.
- **Distinguish** between a nonpolar covalent bond and a polar covalent bond.

Why It's Important

Bond type determines how compounds mix and interact with other compounds.

Review Vocabulary

atom: the smallest piece of matter that still retains the property of the element

New Vocabulary

- ion
- ionic bond
- covalent bond
- molecule
- polar molecule
- nonpolar molecule

Gain or Loss of Electrons

When you participate in a sport you might talk about gaining or losing an advantage. To gain an advantage, you want to have a better time than your opponent. It is important that you keep practicing because you don't want to lose that advantage. Gaining or losing an advantage happens as you try to meet a standard for your sport.

Atoms, too, lose or gain to meet a standard—a stable energy level. They do not lose or gain an advantage. Instead, they lose or gain electrons. An atom that has lost or gained electrons is called an ion. An **ion** is a charged particle because it now has either more or fewer electrons than protons. The positive and negative charges are not balanced. It is the electric forces between oppositely charged particles, such as ions, that hold compounds together.

Some of the most common compounds are made by the loss and gain of just one electron. These compounds contain an element from Group 1 on the periodic table and an element from Group 17. Some examples are sodium chloride, commonly known as table salt; sodium fluoride, an anticavity ingredient in some toothpastes; and potassium iodide, an ingredient in iodized salt.

Figure 7 Goiter, an enlargement of the thyroid gland in the neck, can be caused by iodine deficiency.

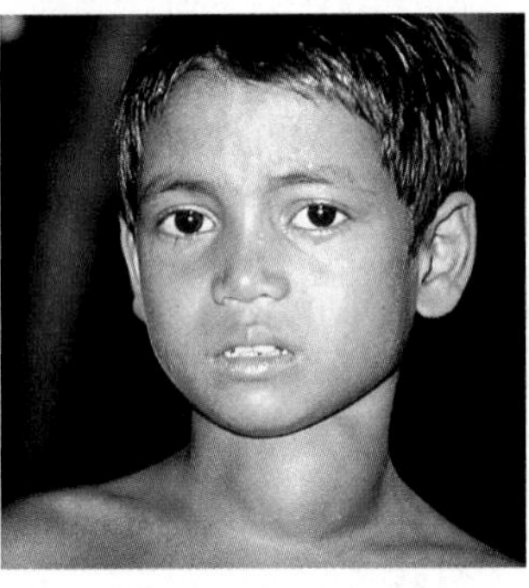

Why do people need iodine? A lack of iodine causes a wide range of problems in the human body. The most obvious is an enlarged thyroid gland, as shown in **Figure 7,** but the problems can include mental retardation, neurological disorders, and physical problems.

Section 2 Resource Manager

Chapter *FAST FILE* Resources
- Transparency Activity, p. 45
- Directed Reading for Content Mastery, p. 20
- Enrichment, p. 31
- MiniLAB, p. 3
- Lab Activity, pp. 13–16
- Reinforcement, p. 28

Science Inquiry Labs, pp. 43–44

Physical Science Critical Thinking/Problem Solving, p. 13

A Bond Forms What happens when potassium and iodine atoms come together? A neutral atom of potassium has one electron in its outer level. This is not a stable outer energy level. When potassium forms a compound with iodine, potassium loses one electron from its fourth level, and the third level becomes a complete outer level. However, the atom is no longer neutral. The potassium atom has become an ion. When a potassium atom loses an electron, the atom becomes positively charged because there is one electron less in the atom than there are protons in the nucleus. The 1+ charge is shown as a superscript written after the element's symbol, K^+, to indicate its charge. *Superscript* means "written above."

The iodine atom in this reaction undergoes change, as well. An iodine atom has seven electrons in its outer energy level. Recall that a stable outer energy level contains eight electrons. During the reaction with potassium, the iodide atom gains an electron, leaving its outer energy level with eight electrons. This atom is no longer neutral because it gained an extra negative particle. It now has a charge of 1− and is called an iodide ion, written as I^-. The compound formed between potassium and iodine is called potassium iodide. The dot diagrams for the process are shown in **Figure 8.**

Reading Check *What part of an ion's symbol indicates its charge?*

Another way to look at the electron in the outer shell of a potassium atom is as an advertisement to other atoms saying, "Available: One electron to lend." The iodine atom would have the message, "Wanted: One electron to borrow." When the two atoms get together, each becomes a stable ion. Notice that the resulting compound has a neutral charge because the positive and negative charges of the ions cancel each other.

Muscle Development
Ions are important in many processes in your body. The movement of muscles is just one of these processes. Muscle movement would be impossible without the movement of ions in and out of nerve cells.

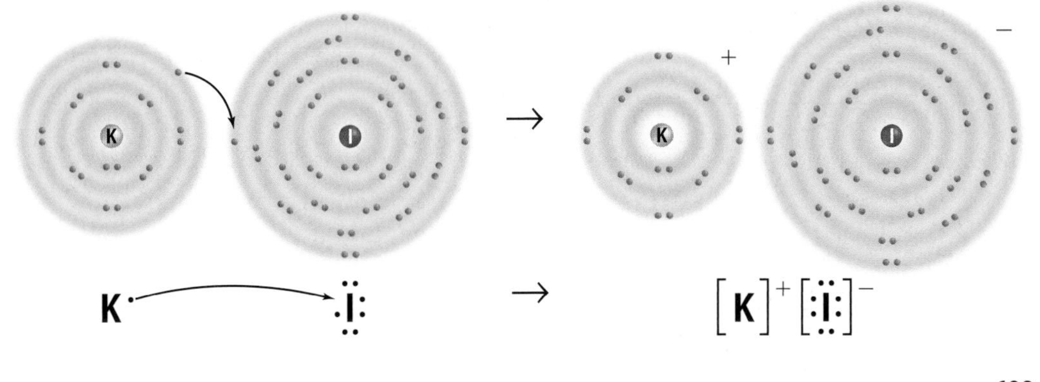

Figure 8 Potassium and iodine must perform a transfer of one electron. Potassium and iodine end up with stable outer energy levels.

2 Teach

Muscle Development The primary ions needed for nerve impulses are Na^+ and K^+. Remind students that the properties of an ion of an element are different from those of the neutral atom. For example, both sodium and potassium metals react violently with water, while their ions do not.

Discussion

Atom Identity How many protons and electrons are in an atom of chlorine? 17 protons and 17 electrons How many protons and electrons are in a common ion of Cl? 17 protons and 18 electrons Remind students that while atoms gain or lose electrons fairly easily, changing the number of protons changes the identity of the atom. L2 LS **Logical-Mathematical**

Reading Check

Answer the superscript written after the element's symbol

Virtual Labs

Bonding *How can you tell which elements form chemical bonds?*

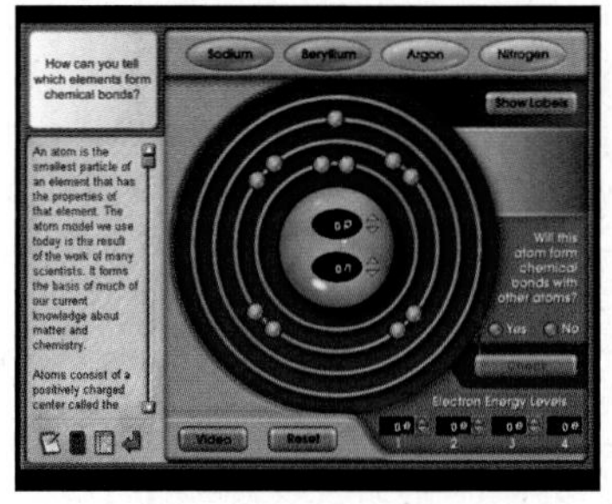

Visual Learning

Figure 8 Have students find potassium and iodine on the periodic table. How many electrons does potassium have? 19 How many does iodine have? 53 Have students count the electrons in each atom and ion in **Figure 8.** Explain that the first energy level in any atom can contain up to 2 electrons, the second level can contain up to 8 electrons, the third level can contain up to 18 electrons, and the fourth level can contain up to 32 electrons. L3 LS **Visual-Spatial**

Differentiated Instruction

Learning Disabled Provide students with two bar magnets. Have them use the magnets to determine that opposite ends (charges) of the magnets attract and like ends (charges) repel. Relate this concept to the attractions that bring opposite ions together. L1 LS **Kinesthetic**

Discussion

Electron Moves Explain to students that a metal may give up an electron when forming an ionic bond. What type of charge does the metal have after it loses an electron? positive L1 LS **Logical-Mathematical**

Activity

Ionic Bonds Using a classroom periodic table, or the one in the textbook, point out potassium (K) on the left of the table. Ask a volunteer to name a nonmetal that would likely form an ionic bond with that element. Possible answers: O or F (K_2O; KF) Repeat with barium (Ba). Possible answers: Cl or S ($BaCl_2$; BaS) Use this exercise to point out that the metals and nonmetals that form ionic bonds often are located far apart on the periodic table. L2 LS **Logical-Mathematical**

Fun Fact

Most ionic compounds are soluble in water, but are not soluble in nonpolar solvents.

Quick Demo

Conductivity in Salt

Materials 9-volt battery, two insulated copper wires, flashlight bulb, salt, distilled water, one beaker

Estimated Time 15 minutes

Procedure Pour distilled water into beaker. Connect one wire to positive pole of battery and put other end in one side of beaker into water. Run another wire from negative pole of battery to flashlight bulb and another wire from bulb to water at other end of beaker. After students see that bulb does not light up, add salt to beaker and stir water to dissolve salt, bulb should then light up if enough salt is added.

The Ionic Bond

When ions attract in this way, a bond is formed. An **ionic bond** is the force of attraction between the opposite charges of the ions in an ionic compound. In an ionic bond, a transfer of electrons takes place. If an element loses electrons, one or more elements must gain an equal number of electrons to maintain the neutral charge of the compound.

Now that you have seen how an ionic bond forms when one electron is involved, see how it works when more than one is involved. The formation of magnesium chloride, $MgCl_2$, is another example of ionic bonding. When magnesium reacts with chlorine, a magnesium atom loses two electrons and becomes a positively charged ion, Mg^{2+}. At the same time, two chlorine atoms gain one electron each and become negatively charged chloride ions, Cl^-. In this case, a magnesium atom has two electrons to lend, but a single chlorine atom needs to borrow only one electron. Therefore, it takes two chlorine atoms, as shown in **Figure 9,** to take the two electrons from the magnesium ion.

Science Online
Topic: Ionic Bonds
Visit gpscience.com for Web links to information about ionic bonding.

Activity Find out what a valence electron is and how it applies to an ionic bond.

Zero Net Charge The result of this bond is a neutral compound. The compound as a whole is neutral because the sum of the charges on the ions is zero. The positive charge of the magnesium ion is exactly equal to the negative charge of the two chloride ions. In other words, when atoms form an ionic compound, their electrons are shifted to other atoms, but the overall number of protons and electrons of the combined atoms remains equal and unchanged. Therefore, the compound is neutral.

Ionic bonds usually are formed by bonding between metals and nonmetals. Looking at the periodic table, you will see that the elements that bond ionically are often across the table from each other. Ionic compounds are often crystalline solids with high melting points.

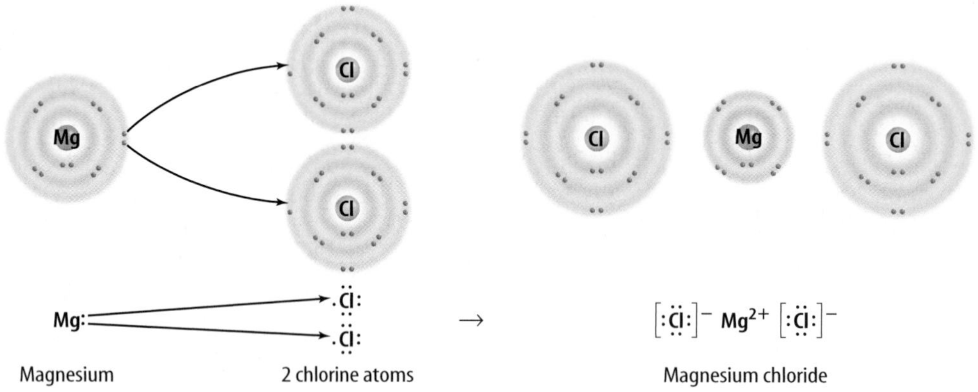

Figure 9 A magnesium atom gives an electron to each of two chlorine atoms to form $MgCl_2$.

Teacher FYI

Ion Attraction A positive ion is always smaller than its original neutral atom, and a negative ion is always larger than its original neutral atom. The charge on an ion acts as though it were located exactly in the center of the ion. Therefore, large ions have less attraction toward other ions; the center of charge is farther away. The more highly charged an ion is, the stronger the force around it. The strongest attractions take place between small, highly charged ions such as Al^{3+} and highly negative ions such as O^{2-}. Large, singly charged ions such as K^+ and I^- have less attractive force between them.

Sharing Electrons

Some atoms of nonmetals are unlikely to lose or gain electrons. For example, the elements in Group 14 of the periodic table have four electrons in their outer levels. They would have to either gain or lose four electrons in order to have a stable outer level. The loss of this many electrons takes a great deal of energy. Each time an electron is removed, the nucleus holds the remaining electrons even more tightly. Therefore, these atoms become more chemically stable by sharing electrons, rather than by losing or gaining electrons.

The attraction that forms between atoms when they share electrons is known as a **covalent bond.** A neutral particle that forms as a result of electron sharing is called a **molecule** as shown in **Figure 10.**

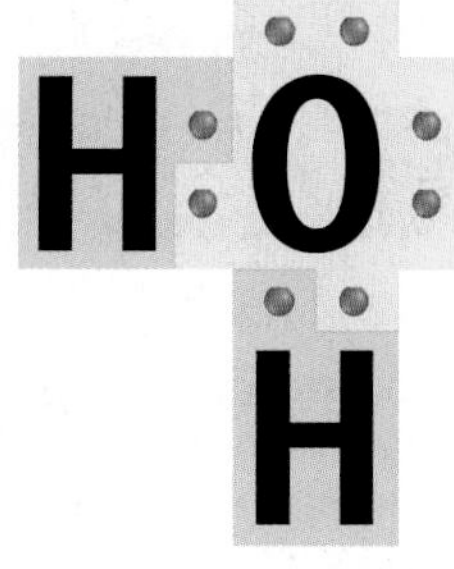

Figure 10 Each of the pairs of electrons between the two hydrogens and the oxygen is shared as each atom contributes one electron to the pair to make the bond.

Single Covalent Bonds A single covalent bond is made up of two shared electrons. Usually, one of the shared electrons comes from one atom in the bond and the other comes from the other atom in the bond. A water molecule contains two single bonds. In each bond, a hydrogen atom contributes one electron to the bond and the oxygen atom contributes the other. The two electrons are shared, forming a single bond. The result of this type of bonding is a stable outer energy level for each atom in the molecule. Each hydrogen atom is stable with two electrons, and the oxygen atom is stable with eight outer energy level electrons.

Multiple Bonds A covalent bond also can contain more than one pair of electrons. An example of this is the bond in nitrogen (N_2), shown in **Figure 11.** A nitrogen atom has five electrons in its outer energy level and needs to gain three electrons to become stable. It does this by sharing its three electrons with another nitrogen atom. The other nitrogen atom also shares its three electrons. When each atom contributes three electrons to the bond, the bond contains six electrons, or three pairs of electrons. Each pair of electrons represents a bond. Therefore, three pairs of electrons represent three bonds, or a triple bond. Each nitrogen atom is stable with eight electrons in its outer energy level. In a similar way, a bond that contains two shared pairs of electrons is a double bond. Carbon dioxide is an example of a molecule with double bonds.

Covalent bonds form between nonmetallic elements. These elements are close together in the upper right-hand corner of the periodic table. Many covalent compounds are liquids or gases at room temperature.

Figure 11 The dot diagram shows that the two nitrogen atoms in nitrogen gas share six electrons. **Explain** *which of these gases would require the most energy to react with another element to form a compound, H_2 or N_2.*

Activity

Bond Types Point out that in general the closer together reacting elements are on the periodic table, the more likely it is that they will share electrons with one another rather than form ionic bonds. Have students use this information to predict the type of bond that will form between carbon and oxygen. covalent Have them predict the type of bond formed between each of the following: sodium and oxygen, ionic; phosphorus and oxygen, covalent; magnesium and oxygen, ionic; aluminum and oxygen, ionic; chlorine and oxygen, covalent; sulfur and oxygen, covalent. L2 LS **Logical-Mathematical**

Inquiry Lab

Energy Levels

Purpose to familiarize students with the energy levels of elements

Possible Materials periodic table of elements

Estimated Time 30 minutes

Teaching Strategy Assign students to groups and give each group a different element from the periodic table. Then, have students sketch their element and its various energy levels to represent electrons making up those levels. Have students brainstorm questions about elements. Allow them to explore these questions as time allows.

For additional inquiry activities, see *Science Inquiry Labs.*

Caption Answer

Figure 11 N_2

Differentiated Instruction

English-Language Learners Use the dot diagrams to explain how atoms form covalent bonds in order to complete their outer electron energy level. Explain that the more covalent bonds that a compound has, the more energy that is required to separate the atoms with these bonds. **Visual-Spatial** ELL

Science Journal

Dot Diagrams Have students research the work of American chemist Gilbert N. Lewis and write short paragraphs in their Science Journals about his contribution to dot diagrams. The diagrams are called Lewis diagrams because he developed the idea as a way of explaining attractions besides ionic bonding between atoms. The dots allowed him to better explain bonding to his students. L2 LS **Linguistic**

SECTION 2 Types of Bonds 611

Purpose Students observe that water molecules are polar. L2 LS **Kinesthetic**

Materials water faucet, balloon, wool

Teaching Strategy Practice to determine the amount of static charge that can be built up on the balloon. High humidity reduces the buildup, causing a smaller deflection of the water stream.

Analysis

1. The balloon acquires a charge when rubbed against the wool. When brought near a thin stream of water, the charge attracts water, causing the stream to bend.
2. In both cases, opposites attract. A water molecule contains a negative region and a positive region that are similar to the opposite poles of a magnet.

Assessment

Oral Explain to students that pentane (C_5H_{12}) is a nonpolar molecule. Ask students to predict whether a stream of pentane would bend if they used the same procedure followed in the MiniLAB. No; pentane is nonpolar and therefore will not be attracted to the static charge on the balloon. Use **Performance Assessment in the Science Classroom,** p. 89. L2 LS **Logical-Mathmatical**

Observing Bond Type

Procedure

1. Turn on the faucet to produce a thin **stream of water.**
2. Rub an inflated **balloon** with **wool or fur.**
3. Bring the balloon near the stream of water, and describe what you see.

Analysis

1. Explain your observations.
2. Relate the attraction between the balloon and the water to the attraction between the north and south poles of two magnets. Why might water act like a magnet?

Try at Home

Unequal Sharing Electrons are not always shared equally between atoms in a covalent bond. The strength of the attraction of each atom to its electrons is related to the size of the atom, the charge of the nucleus, and the total number of electrons the atom contains. Part of the strength of attraction has to do with how far away from the nucleus the electron being shared is. For example, a magnet has a stronger pull when it is right next to a piece of metal rather than several centimeters away. The other part of the strength of attraction has to do with the size of the positive charge in the nucleus. Using a magnet as an example again, a strong magnet will hold the metal more firmly than a weak magnet.

One example of this unequal sharing is found in a molecule of hydrogen chloride, HCl. In water, HCl is hydrochloric acid, which is used in laboratories, in industry to clean metal, and is found in your stomach where it digests food. Chlorine atoms have a stronger attraction for electrons than hydrogen atoms do. As a result, the electrons shared in hydrogen chloride will spend more time near the chlorine atom than near the hydrogen atom, as shown in **Figure 12.** The chlorine atom has a partial negative charge represented by a lower case Greek symbol delta followed by a negative superscript, δ^-. The hydrogen atom has a partial positive charge represented by a δ^+.

Tug-of-War You might think of the bond as the rope in a tug-of-war, and the shared electrons as the knot in the center of the rope. **Figure 13** illustrates this concept. Each atom in the molecule attracts the electrons that they share. However, sometimes the atoms aren't the same size. The same thing happens in tug-of-war. Sometimes one team is larger or has stronger participants than the other.

When this is true, the knot in the middle of the rope ends up closer to the stronger team. Similarly, the electrons being shared in a molecule are held more closely to the atoms with the stronger pull or larger nucleus.

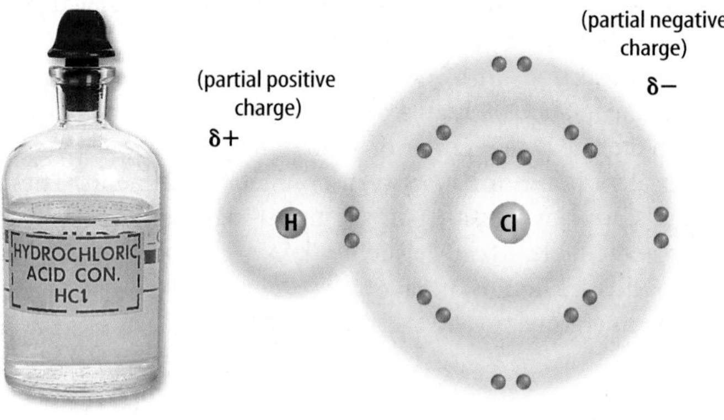

Figure 12 The chlorine atom exerts the greater pull on the electrons in hydrogen chloride which forms hydrochloric acid in water.

Differentiated Instruction

Challenge Have students research the electronegativity scale developed by Linus Pauling and relate the information they find to the formation of covalent, polar covalent, and ionic bonds. Pauling's electronegativity scale is a way of ranking the ability of an atom to attract electrons within a bond. Two atoms that have a small or no electronegativity difference form a covalent bond. Those with a great electronegativity difference form an ionic bond. If the difference is moderate, a polar covalent bond forms. Each element is given a numerical ranking, so simple subtraction gives the electronegativity difference. L3 LS **Linguistic**

VISUALIZING POLAR MOLECULES

Figure 13

When playing tug-of-war, if there are more—or stronger—team members on one end of the rope than the other, there is an unequal balance of power. The stronger team can pull harder on the rope and has the advantage. A similar situation exists in polar molecules, in which electrons are attracted more strongly by one type of atom in the molecule than another. Because of this unequal sharing of electrons, polar molecules have a slightly negative end and a slightly positive end, as shown below.

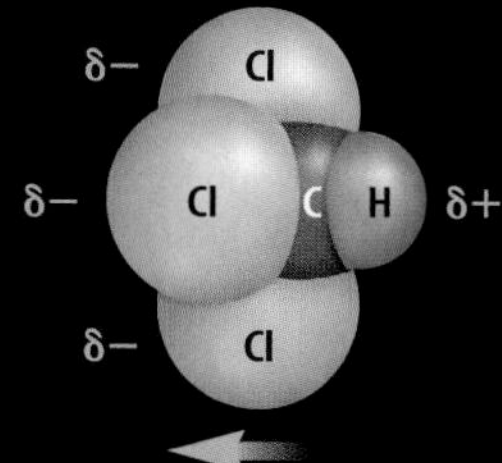

CHLOROFORM In a molecule of chloroform ($CHCl_3$), or trichloromethane (tri klor oh ME thayn), the three chlorine atoms attract electrons more strongly than the hydrogen atom does, creating a partial negative charge on the chlorine end of the molecule and a partial positive charge on the hydrogen end. This polar molecule is a clear, sweet-smelling liquid once widely used as an anesthetic in human and veterinary surgery.

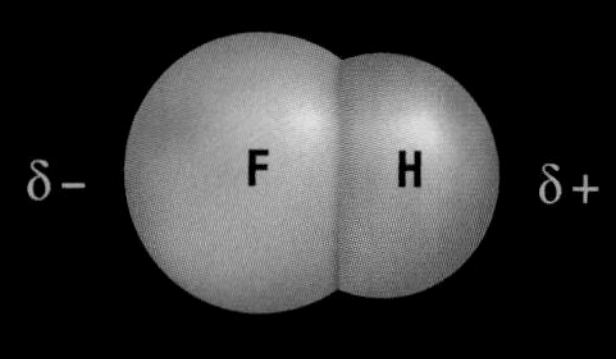

HYDROGEN FLUORIDE Hydrogen and fluorine react to form hydrogen fluoride (HF). In an HF molecule, the two atoms are bound together by a pair of electrons, one contributed by each atom. But the electrons are not shared equally because the fluorine atom attracts them more strongly than the hydrogen atom does. The result is a polar molecule with a slightly positive charge near the hydrogen end and a slightly negative charge near the fluorine end.

Visualizing Polar Molecules

Have students examine the pictures and read the captions. Then ask the following questions.

In your own words, describe why charge is distributed unevenly in chloroform molecules. Possible answer: The chlorine molecules have a stronger attraction for electrons than the hydrogen molecule.

Why are the hydrogen sides of both chloroform molecules and hydrogen fluoride molecules partially positive? The electrons have been pulled away, leaving an exposed proton in each hydrogen nucleus.

Activity

Electron Dot Diagrams Work together as a class to draw on the board the electron dot diagrams for both molecules. Students should easily see that the electrons are concentrated on one side of each molecule, which leads to a partial negative charge on that side. Have students draw these diagrams in their Science Journals. LS **Visual-Spatial**

Differentiated Instruction

Challenge Ask students to find out what an induced dipole is. Direct students to make posters showing examples of induced dipoles and explain their posters to the class. L3 LS **Visual-Spatial** P

Answer a molecule that has a slightly negative end and a slightly positive end

3 Assess

DAILY INTERVENTION

Check for Understanding

Interpersonal Assign students to groups and have them develop a brief presentation for the class explaining the differences between polar and nonpolar molecules.

Reteach

Identify Compounds List the formulas for HCl, H_2O, NaCl, and $MgCl_2$ on the board. Have students identify each compound as ionic or covalent. HCl, covalent; H_2O, covalent; NaCl, ionic; $MgCl_2$, ionic.

L2 LS **Logical-Mathematical**

Performance Have each student write the symbol of one of the first 30 elements on a sheet of paper. Now have the student use the periodic table to try to find an element that would form a covalent bond with the first element. Have students repeat the exercise for an ionic compound and explain their choices. Emphasize that both electron configuration and attraction for electrons determine whether two atoms will bond with each other. Use **Performance Assessment in the Science Classroom,** p. 93.

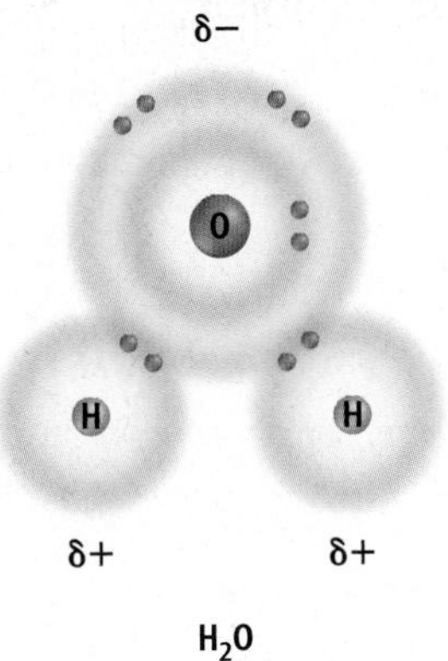

Figure 14 The polarity of water is responsible for many of its unique properties.

Polar or Nonpolar? For the molecule involved in this electron tug-of-war, there is another consequence. Again, look at the molecule of hydrogen chloride. This unequal sharing of electrons gives each chlorine atom a slight negative charge and each hydrogen atom a slight positive charge. The atom holding the electron more closely always will have a slightly negative charge. The charge is balanced but not equally distributed. This type of molecule is called polar. The term *polar* means "having opposite ends." A **polar molecule** is one that has a slightly positive end and a slightly negative end although the overall molecule is neutral. Water is an example of a polar molecule, as shown in **Figure 14.**

 *What is a polar molecule?*

Two atoms that are exactly alike can share their electrons equally, forming a nonpolar molecule. A **nonpolar molecule** is one in which electrons are shared equally in bonds. Such a molecule does not have oppositely charged ends. This is true of molecules made from two identical atoms or molecules that are symmetric, such as CCl_4.

section 2 review

Summary

Gain or Loss of Electrons

- An ion is a charged particle that has either fewer or more electrons than protons, resulting in a negative or positive charge.

Ionic Bond

- An ionic bond is the force or attraction between opposite charges of ions in an ionic bond.
- An ionic compound is neutral because the sum of the ion charges is zero.

Sharing Electrons

- Some atoms, like those in Group 4, share electrons instead of losing or gaining them.
- Covalent bonds can form single, double, or triple bonds.
- In a polar molecule the electrons are shared unequally in the bond. This results in slightly charged ends.
- Electrons are shared equally in a nonpolar molecule.

Self Check

1. **Explain** why an atom makes an ionic bond only with certain other atoms.
2. **Compare and contrast** the possession of electrons in ionic and covalent bonds.
3. **Name** the types of particles formed by covalent bonds.
4. **Think Critically** From the following list of symbols, choose two elements that are likely to form an ionic bond: O, Ne, S, Ca, K. Next, select two elements that would likely form a covalent bond. Explain.
5. **Concept Map** Using the following terms, make a network-tree concept map of chemical bonding: *ionic, covalent, ions, positive ions, negative ions, molecules, polar,* and *nonpolar.*

Applying Math

6. **Solve One-Step Equations** Aluminum oxide, Al_2O_3, can be produced during space shuttle launches. Show that the sum of the positive and negative charges in a unit of Al_2O_3 equals zero.

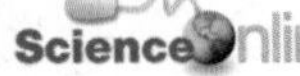 gpscience.com/self_check_quiz

section 2 review

1. In ionic bonds, one atom accepts electrons from another. This happens only among elements having large differences in their attractions for electrons.
2. In ionic bonds, one atom accepts an electron from another atom. In covalent bonds, electrons are shared, sometimes unequally.
3. Covalent bonding produces molecules.
4. Ionic: Ca–O and K–O, because K and Ca are metals far from O on the periodic table; covalent: S–O because S and O are nonmetals close to each other on the periodic table
5. Check students' work.
6. The charge on Al is +3 and the charge on O is [2 (+3)] + [3 (−2)] = 0.

Writing Formulas and Naming Compounds

Reading Guide

What You'll Learn
- **Explain** how to determine oxidation numbers.
- **Write** formulas and names for ionic compounds.
- **Write** formulas and names for covalent compounds.

Why It's Important
The name and the formula convey information about the compound.

Review Vocabulary
anion: a negatively charged ion

New Vocabulary
- binary compound
- oxidation number
- polyatomic ion
- hydrate

Binary Ionic Compounds

Does the table in **Figure 15** look like it has anything to do with chemistry? It is an early table of the elements made by alchemists—scientists who tried to make gold from other elements. The alchemist used symbols like these to write the formulas of substances. The first formulas of compounds you will write are for binary ionic compounds. A **binary compound** is one that is composed of two elements. Potassium iodide, the salt additive discussed in Section 2, is a binary ionic compound. However, before you can write a formula, you must have all the needed information at your fingertips. What will you need to know?

Are electrons gained or lost? You need to know which elements are involved and what number of electrons they lose, gain, or share in order to become stable. How can you determine this? Section 1 discussed the relationship between an element's position on the periodic table and the number of electrons it gains or loses. This is called the **oxidation number** of an element. An oxidation number tells you how many electrons an atom has gained, lost, or shared to become stable.

For ionic compounds the oxidation number is the same as the charge on the ion. For example, a sodium ion has a charge of 1+ and an oxidation number of 1+. A chloride ion has a charge of 1− and an oxidation number of 1−.

Figure 15 This old chart of the elements used pictorial symbols to represent elements.

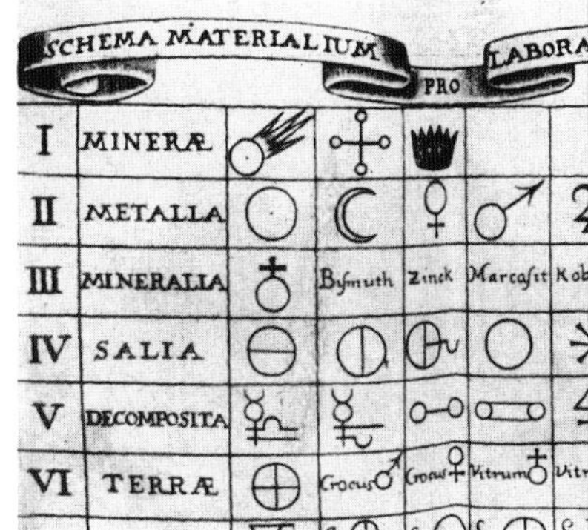

1 Motivate

Bellringer

Section Focus Transparencies also are available on the Interactive Chalkboard CD-ROM. L2 

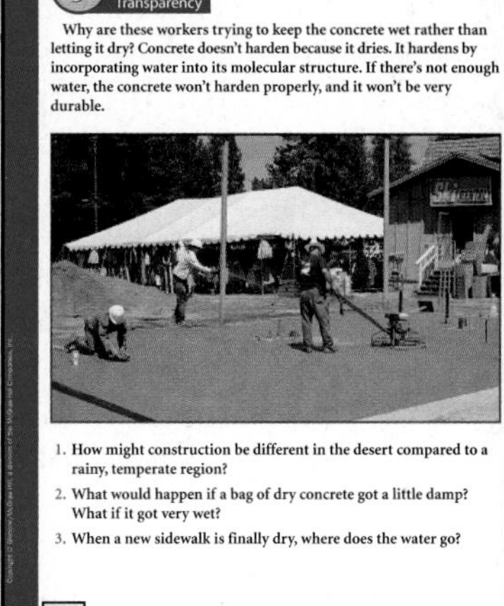

Section Focus Transparency
For Best Results, Add Water
Why are these workers trying to keep the concrete wet rather than letting it dry? Concrete doesn't harden because it dries. It hardens by incorporating water into its molecular structure. If there's not enough water, the concrete won't harden properly, and it won't be very durable.
1. How might construction be different in the desert compared to a rainy, temperate region?
2. What would happen if a bag of dry concrete got a little damp? What if it got very wet?
3. When a new sidewalk is finally dry, where does the water go?
L2

Tie to Prior Knowledge

Common Formulas Bring labels from common substances such as antacids that contain chemical formulas. Identify the substances shown by each formula. Then explain to students that in this section they will discover how to read and interpret such formulas and how to name the compounds they represent.

Section 3 Resource Manager

Chapter *FAST FILE* Resources
- Transparency Activity, pp. 46, 47–48
- Directed Reading for Content Mastery, pp. 21, 22
- Reinforcement, p. 29
- Enrichment, p. 32
- MiniLAB, p. 4
- Lab Worksheet, pp. 7–8

Home and Community Involvement, p. 46
Mathematics Skill Activities, p. 29
Reading and Writing Skill Activities, p. 41
Lab Management and Safety, p. 49

2 Teach

Quick Demo

Ion Charge

Materials cellophane tape

Estimated Time 5 minutes

Procedure Binary ionic compounds form when oppositely charged ions attract each other. Demonstrate the basic forces involved by placing two 25-cm pieces of cellophane tape side by side on a plastic surface. Pull both up at the same time. As they are brought close together they will repel. Explain that this happens because both pieces of tape have acquired the same charge. Place one piece of tape on the surface and a second piece directly on top of the first. Pull them off the table and separate them. They now attract each other. Why? They have acquired opposite charges, which causes them to attract each other. L1 **Visual-Spatial**

Roman Numerals The use of Roman numerals can be confusing. Copper(II) oxide is CuO, with one copper atom for each oxygen atom. The compound copper(I) oxide is written as Cu_2O, with two copper atoms for each oxygen atom. Remind students that the Roman numeral represents the charge on an atom, while Arabic subscript numbers, such as 2 and 3, show the number of atoms of each element.

1+	2+	3+	4+	3−	2−	1−	0
Hydrogen 1 H							Helium 2 He
Lithium 3 Li	Beryllium 4 Be	Boron 5 B	Carbon 6 C	Nitrogen 7 N	Oxygen 8 O	Fluorine 9 F	Neon 10 Ne
Sodium 11 Na	Magnesium 12 Mg	Aluminum 13 Al	Silicon 14 Si	Phosphorus 15 P	Sulfur 16 S	Chlorine 17 Cl	Argon 18 Ar
Potassium 19 K	Calcium 20 Ca	Gallium 31 Ga	Germanium 32 Ge	Arsenic 33 As	Selenium 34 Se	Bromine 35 Br	Krypton 36 Kr
Rubidium 37 Rb	Strontium 38 Sr	Indium 49 In	Tin 50 Sn	Antimony 51 Sb	Tellurium 52 Te	Iodine 53 I	Xenon 54 Xe
Cesium 55 Cs	Barium 56 Ba	Thallium 81 Tl	Lead 82 Pb	Bismuth 83 Bi	Polonium 84 Po	Astatine 85 At	Radon 86 Rn
Francium 87 Fr	Radium 88 Ra						

Figure 16 The number at the top of each column is the most common oxidation number of elements in that group.

Oxidation Numbers The numbers with positive or negative signs in **Figure 16** are the oxidation numbers for the elements in the columns below them. Notice how they fit with the periodic table groupings.

The elements in **Table 2** can have more than one oxidation number. When naming these compounds, the oxidation number is expressed in the name with a roman numeral. For example, the oxidation number of iron in iron(III) oxide is 3+.

Table 2 Special Ions

Name	Oxidation Number
Copper (I)	1+
Copper (II)	2+
Iron (II)	2+
Iron (III)	3+
Chromium (II)	2+
Chromium (III)	3+
Lead (II)	2+
Lead (IV)	4+

Compounds Are Neutral When writing formulas it is important to remember that although the individual ions in a compound carry charges, the compound itself is neutral. A formula must have the right number of positive ions and the right number of negative ions so the charges balance. For example, sodium chloride is made up of a sodium ion with a 1+ charge and a chloride ion with a 1− charge. One of each ion put together makes a neutral compound with the formula NaCl.

However, what if you have a compound like calcium fluoride? A calcium ion has a charge of 2+ and a fluoride ion has a charge of 1−. In this case you need to have two fluoride ions for every calcium ion in order for the charges to cancel and the compound to be neutral with the formula CaF_2.

Some compounds require more figuring. Aluminum oxide contains an ion with a 3+ charge and an ion with a 2− charge. You must find the least common multiple of 3 and 2 in order to determine how many of each ion you need. You need two aluminum ions and three oxygen ions in order to have a 6+ charge and a 6− charge and therefore, the neutral compound Al_2O_3.

Science Journal

Oxidation Number Have students use a periodic table to identify the oxidation numbers of the elements in Groups 1, 2, and 13–18. Ask students to make tables containing this information in their Science Journals. L1 LS **Visual-Spatial**

Active Reading

Reflective Journal Have students identify what they learned from activities. Then divide sheets of paper into several columns and record their thoughts under headings such as *What I did*, *What I learned*, *Questions I have*, *Surprises I experienced*, and *Overall response*. Have students write a Reflective Journal for writing formulas.

Writing Formulas After you've learned how to find the oxidation numbers and their least common multiple, you can write formulas for ionic compounds by using the following rules in this order.

1. Write the symbol of the element or polyatomic ion (ions containing more than one atom) that has the positive oxidation number or charge. Hydrogen, the ammonium ion (NH_4^+), and all metals have positive oxidation numbers.
2. Write the symbol of the element or polyatomic ion with the negative oxidation number. Nonmetals other than hydrogen and polyatomic ions other than NH_4^+ have negative oxidation numbers.
3. The charge (without the sign) of one ion becomes the subscript of the other ion. Reduce the subscripts to the smallest whole numbers that retain the ratio of ions.

Lime The use of compounds to enrich yield of crops has been developed through the ages. Farmers must sometimes add lime, which is calcium oxide, to soil in their fields. What is the formula of calcium oxide?

Applying Math

DETERMINING A CHEMICAL FORMULA What is the formula for lithium nitride?

IDENTIFY known values

Identify the known values:

Symbol and oxidation number of the positive element:

Lithium $\xrightarrow{\text{means}}$ Li^{1+}

Symbol and oxidation number of the negative element:

Nitrogen $\xrightarrow{\text{means}}$ N^{3-}

SOLVE the problem

The charge (without the sign) of one ion becomes the subscript of the other:

$Li^{1+}\ N^{3-}$ $\xrightarrow{\text{means}}$ Li_3N_1 or Li_3N

Reduce the subscripts to the smallest whole numbers that retain the ratios of ions.

CHECK the answer

Does your answer seem reasonable? Check your answer by determining if your compound is neutral.

Practice Problems

1. What is the formula for lead (IV) phosphide?
2. What is the formula for iron (III) oxide?

For more practice problems go to page 834, and visit gpscience.com/extra_problems.

Lime CaO

Research Have students identify other common fertilizers and the active ingredients that make them effective. Have them write the formulas for these compounds and explain the key function of each compound.

Applying Math

National Math Standards

Correlation to Mathematics Objectives

2, 6, 9

This is what you know: Write the symbol and oxidation number of the positive element: Lead (Pb) = 4+

Write the symbol and oxidation number of the negative element:

Phosphorus (P) = 3−

Least common multiple = 12

This is what you need to do:

Add subscripts so that the sum of the oxidation numbers is zero.

$3Pb = (3)(4+) = 12+$;

$4P = (4)(3-) = 12-$

Complete the formula.

Answers to Practice Problems

1. Pb_3P_4
2. Fe_2O_3

Activity

Ion Names Give students a list of compound names that consist of the various ions presented in this chapter. Have them write and balance the formula so that the net charge is zero.

Differentiated Instruction

Challenge Have the students inspect the ingredient list on the side of various containers and find five chemical formulas. Have them determine the oxidation numbers of the various elements in each of the five compounds and make a table to exhibit their findings. L3

Curriculum Connection

Language Arts The binary ionic compound Fe_3O_4 is the naturally magnetic mineral magnetite. Magnetite was used in the ancient world as a compass; it was called a *lodestone*. Ask students to find out where the name magnetite comes from. Magnetite was named by the ancient Greeks after the place it was originally found, Magnesia in what is now Turkey. L2

LS **Linguistic**

Activity

Compound Teams Organize the class into two teams. Have team one make a list of the names of compounds and write the names on the board. Team two must then write the correct formula next to each compound. Award one point for each correct answer. Then have team two make a list of compound formulas and write them on the board for team one to name. Alternate between the teams until one reaches a score of 10. L2 ELL COOP LEARN LS **Intrapersonal**

Visual Learning

Table 3 In a binary compound involving oxygen, what name is given to the second part of the compound? oxide L1 LS **Visual-Spatial**

Applying Science

Answers

1. copper (II) oxide
2. aluminum chloride

Table 3 Elements in Binary Compounds

Element	-ide Name
Oxygen	oxide
Phosphorus	phosphide
Nitrogen	nitride
Sulfur	sulfide

Writing Names You can name a binary ionic compound from its formula by using these rules.

1. Write the name of the positive ion.
2. Using **Table 2,** check to see if the positive ion is capable of forming more than one oxidation number. If it is, determine the oxidation number of the ion from the formula of the compound. To do this, keep in mind that the overall charge of the compound is zero and the negative ion has only one possible charge. Write the charge of the positive ion using roman numerals in parentheses after the ion's name. If the ion has only one possible oxidation number, proceed to step 3.
3. Write the root name of the negative ion. The root is the first part of the element's name. For chlorine the root is *chlor-*. For oxygen it is *ox-*.
4. Add the ending *-ide* to the root. **Table 3** lists several elements and their *-ide* counterparts. For example, BaF_2 is named barium fluoride.

Subscripts do not become part of the name for ionic compounds. However, subscripts can be used to help determine the charges of these metals that have more than one positive charge.

Applying Science

Can you name binary ionic compounds?

What would a chemist name the compound CuCl?

Identifying the Problem

There are four simple steps in naming binary ionic compounds.

1. Write the name of the positive ion in the compound. In CuCl, the name of the positive ion is copper.
2. Check **Table 2** to determine if copper is one of the elements that can have more than one oxidation number. Looking at **Table 2,** you can see that copper can have a 1+ or a 2+ oxidation number. You need to determine which to use. Looking at the compound, you see that there is one copper atom and one chlorine atom. You know that the overall charge of the compound is zero and that chlorine only forms a 1− ion. For the charge of the compound to be zero, the charge of the copper ion must be 1+. Write this charge using roman numerals in parentheses after the element's name, copper (I).
3. Write the root name of the negative ion. The negative ion is chlorine and its root is *chlor-*.
4. Add the ending *-ide* to the root, chloride.
5. The full name of the compound CuCl is copper (I) chloride.

Solving the Problem

1. What is the name of CuO?
2. What is the name of $AlCl_3$?

Teacher FYI

Hydrogen's Assignment Hydrogen is nearly always found with a +1 charge. However, when hydrogen combines with active metals such as those found in Groups 1 and 2, it is assigned a −1 charge. This assignment is made because of the ease with which those metals lose electrons to become + 1 ions. Examples include NaH and MgH_2. These compounds are called sodium hydride and magnesium hydride.

Compounds with Complex Ions

Not all compounds are binary. Baking soda—used in cooking, as a medicine, and for brushing your teeth—has the formula $NaHCO_3$. This is an example of an ionic compound that is not binary. Some compounds, including baking soda, are composed of more than two elements. They contain polyatomic ions. The prefix *poly-* means "many," so the term *polyatomic* means "having many atoms." A **polyatomic ion** is a positively or negatively charged, covalently bonded group of atoms. So the polyatomic ions as a whole contains two or more elements. The polyatomic ion in baking soda is the bicarbonate or hydrogen carbonate ion, HCO_3^-.

Table 4 Polyatomic Ions

Charge	Name	Formula
1+	ammonium	NH_4^+
1−	acetate	$C_2H_3O_2^-$
	chlorate	ClO_3^-
	hydroxide	OH^-
	nitrate	NO_3^-
2−	carbonate	CO_3^{2-}
	sulfate	SO_4^{2-}
3−	phosphate	PO_4^{3-}

Writing Names **Table 4** lists several polyatomic ions. To name a compound that contains one of these ions, first write the name of the positive ion. Use **Table 4** to find the name of a polyatomic ion. Then write the name of the negative ion. For example, K_2SO_4 is potassium sulfate. What is the name of $Sr(OH)_2$? Begin by writing the name of the positive ion, strontium. Then find the name of the polyatomic ion, OH^-. **Table 4** lists it as hydroxide. Thus the name is strontium hydroxide.

Writing Formulas To write formulas for these compounds, follow the rules for binary compounds, with one addition. When more than one polyatomic ion is needed, write parentheses around the polyatomic ion before adding the subscript. How would you write the formula of barium chlorate?

First, identify the symbol of the positive ion. Barium has a symbol of Ba and forms a 2+ ion, Ba^{2+}. Next, identify the negative chlorate ion. **Table 4** shows that it is ClO_3^-. Finally, you need to balance the charges of the ions to make the compound neutral. It will take two chlorate ions with a 1− charge to balance the 2+ charge of the barium ion. Because the chlorate ion is polyatomic, you use parentheses before adding the subscript. Therefore, the formula is $Ba(ClO_3)_2$. Another example of naming complex compounds is shown in **Figure 17.**

Figure 17 Naming Complex Compounds

How would a scientist write the chemical formula for ammonium phospate?
To write the formula, answer the following questions:

1. What is the positive ion and its charge?
   The positive ion is NH_4^{1+} and its charge 1^+.
2. What is the negative ion and its charge?
   The negative ion is PO_4^{3-} and its charge 3−.
3. Balance the charges to make the compound neutral.
   a) three NH_4^{1+} ions (+3) balances one PO_4^{3-} (3−) or
   b) The charge of one ion (without the sign) becomes the subscript of the other. Add parentheses for subscripts greater than one.
   NH_4^{1+} PO_4^{3-} gives $(NH_4)_3PO_4$

The chemical formula for ammonium phosphate is $(NH_4)_3PO_4$.

Discussion

Polyatomic Ions Provide practice using polyatomic ions by having students name each of the following compounds and determine the number of atoms of the underlined element in each: $Na_3P\underline{O}_4$, 4 oxygen atoms, sodium phosphate; $Al_2(\underline{C}O_3)_3$, 3 carbon atoms, aluminum carbonate; $Ca(C_2\underline{H}_3O_2)_2$, 6 atoms of hydrogen, calcium acetate L2 LS Logical-Mathematical

Fun Fact

Anhydrous compounds such as $CaCl_2$ are sometimes sold as products to reduce humidity. Anhydrous calcium chloride absorbs moisture to become a hydrate in a moist basement.

Cultural Diversity

Silicon Dioxide The binary covalent compound silicon dioxide, SiO_2, also known as quartz or rock crystal, has been revered in many cultures since ancient times. Have students report on some of the legends associated with SiO_2. Japanese, ancient Greek, Cherokee Indian, Burmese, Irish, and Scottish are some of the cultures that have legends surrounding SiO_2. P

Differentiated Instruction

Challenge Have students find the formulas, names, or charges of the following polyatomic ions: nitrite, NO_2^-; sulfite, SO_3^{2-}; MnO_4^-, permanganate; ClO_2^-, chlorite. L3 LS Logical-Mathematical

Use Science Words

Word Usage Have students use the word *hydrate* in a sentence in a way that describes its meaning. Possible answer: A hydrate forms when water molecules become attached to the ions of a compound. L1 IS **Linguistic**

Purpose Students will create their own hydrates.

Materials plaster of paris, water, small bowl, rubber hammer, hair dryer for each student

Teaching Strategy Ask students to show their final products to the class.

Analysis

1. The plaster should not crack when tapped before it is heated, but it becomes brittle and cracks easily after being heated.
2. Steam will rise from the plaster, and it will easily crumble and become powder. The heat removes water molecules from the hydrated gypsum causing the plaster to lose its strength.

Assessment

Performance Ask students to experiment with different proportions of water and plaster of paris to create hydrates with different heat and stress-resistant properties. Use **Performance Assessment in the Science Classroom,** p. 89.

Caption Answer

Figure 18 $CaSO_4$

Making a Hydrate

Procedure

1. Mix 150 mL of **plaster of paris** with 75 mL of **water** in a small **bowl.**
2. Let the plaster dry overnight and take the hardened plaster out of the bowl.
3. Lightly tap the plaster with a **rubber hammer.**
4. Heat the plaster with a **hair dryer** on the hottest setting and observe.
5. Place towel over the sample then lightly tap the plaster with the hammer after heating it.

Analysis

1. What happened to the plaster when you tapped it before and after heating it?
2. What did you observe happening to the plaster as you heated it? Explain.

Compounds with Added Water

Some ionic compounds have water molecules as part of their structure. These compounds are called hydrates. A **hydrate** is a compound that has water chemically attached to its ions and written into its chemical formula.

Common Hydrates The term *hydrate* comes from a word that means "water." When a solution of cobalt chloride evaporates, pink crystals that contain six water molecules for each unit of cobalt chloride are formed. The formula for this compound is $CoCl_2 \cdot 6H_2O$ and is called cobalt chloride hexahydrate.

You can remove water from these crystals by heating them. The resulting blue compound is called anhydrous, which means "without water." When anhydrous (blue) $CoCl_2$ is exposed to water, even from the air, it will revert back to its hydrated state.

The plaster of paris shown in **Figure 18** also forms a hydrate when water is added. It becomes calcium sulfate dihydrate, which is also known as gypsum. The water that was added to the powder became a part of the compound.

When writing a formula that contains a hydrate, the number is shown after a "·". Following the number 2 is the formula for water as shown below.

$$CaSO_4 \cdot 2\,H_2O$$

Naming Binary Covalent Compounds

Covalent compounds are those formed between elements that are nonmetals. Some pairs of nonmetals can form more than one compound with each other. For example, nitrogen and oxygen can form N_2O, NO, NO_2, and N_2O_5. In the system you have learned so far, each of these compounds would be called nitrogen oxide. You would not know from that name what the composition of the compound is.

Figure 18 The presence of water changes this powder into a material that can be used to create art.
Identify *the formula for this powder prior to the addition of water.*

LAB DEMONSTRATION

Purpose to observe the difference between a hydrated and a dehydrated compound

Materials copper(II) sulfate pentahydrate, test tube, Bunsen burner, water, dropper

Procedure Place a small amount of copper(II) sulfate pentahydrate in the tube and heat it in a flame. Have students observe the change. Let tube cool, then add a few drops of water.

Expected Outcome When heated, the deep blue copper(II) sulfate pentahydrate gradually changes into the white powder of the anhydrous compound. When water is added, the blue hydrate is restored.

Assessment

Write the formula for copper(II) sulfate pentahydrate. $CuSO_4 \cdot 5H_2O$ Was this a chemical change or a physical change? A chemical change; it changed the identity of the material.

Using Prefixes Scientists use the Greek prefixes in **Table 5** to indicate how many atoms of each element are in a binary covalent compound. The nitrogen and oxygen compounds N_2O, NO, NO_2, and N_2O_5 would be named dinitrogen oxide, nitrogen oxide, nitrogen dioxide, and dinitrogen pentoxide. Notice that the last vowel of the prefix is dropped when the second element begins with a vowel as in pentoxide. Often the prefix *mono-* is omitted, although it is used for emphasis in some cases. Carbon monoxide is one example.

Reading Check *What prefix would be used for seven atoms of one element in a covalent compound?*

These same prefixes are used when naming the hydrates previously discussed. The main ionic compound is named the regular way, but the number of water molecules in the hydrate is indicated by the Greek prefix.

You have learned how to write formulas of binary ionic compounds and of compounds containing polyatomic ions. Using oxidation numbers to write formulas, you can predict the ratio in which atoms of elements might combine to form compounds. You also have seen how hydrates have water molecules as part of their structures and formulas. Finally, you saw how to use prefixes in naming binary covalent compounds. As you continue to study, you will see many uses of formulas.

Table 5 Prefixes for Covalent Compounds

Number of Atoms	Prefix
1	*mono-*
2	*di-*
3	*tri-*
4	*tetra-*
5	*penta-*
6	*hexa-*
7	*hepta-*
8	*octa-*

section 3 review

Summary

Binary Ionic Compounds

- A binary compound is one composed of two elements.
- The oxidation number tells how many electrons an atom has gained, lost, or shared to become stable.
- The net charge of a compound is zero.

Compounds with Complex Ions

- A polyatomic ion is a positively or negatively charged, covalently bonded group of atoms.
- A hydrate is a compound that has water chemically attached to its ions.
- Greek prefixes are used to indicate how many atoms of each element are in a binary covalent compound.

Self Check

1. **Use Formulas** Write formulas for the following compounds: potassium iodide, magnesium hydroxide, aluminum sulfate, and chlorine heptoxide.
2. **Use Formulas** Write the names of these compounds: KCl, Cr_2O_3, $Ba(ClO_3)_2$, NH_4Cl, and PCl_3.
3. **Name** $Mg_3(PO_4)_2 \cdot 4H_2O$, and write the formula for calcium nitrate trihydrate.
4. **Think Critically** Explain why sodium and potassium will or will not react to form a bond with each other.

Applying Math

5. **Solve One-Step Equations** The overall charge on the polyatomic sulfate ion, found in some acids, is 2−. Its formula is SO_4^{2-}. If the oxygen ion has a 2− oxidation number, determine the oxidation number of sulfur in this polyatomic ion.

Text Question Answer

It will turn pink as the hydrate forms.

Answer *hepta-*

3 Assess

DAILY INTERVENTION

Check for Understanding

Logical-Mathematical Have students read the labels of various products and find five compounds that have names with the numeric prefixes. Have them write out the formula for each of these compounds.

Reteach

Prefix Ask students why calcium chloride ($CaCl_2$) is named without using the prefix system shown in **Table 5**, while carbon tetrachloride (CCl_4) does use a prefix to designate the number of chlorine atoms. The prefix system is used for covalent compounds between nonmetals. $CaCl_2$ is ionic. L2 LS **Logical-Mathematical**

Assessment

Performance The common name for $Na_2B_4O_5(OH)_4 \cdot 8H_2O$ is borax. It is used as an important source of boron and can also be used as a washing powder. Ask students to determine the number of oxygen atoms in the molecule. Use **Performance Assessment in the Science Classroom,** p.101.

section 3 review

1. KI; $Mg(OH)_2$; $Al_2(SO_4)_3$; Cl_2O_7
2. potassium chloride; chromium(III) oxide; barium chlorate; ammonium chloride; phosphorus trichloride
3. magnesium phosphate tetrahydrate; $Ca(NO_3)_2 \cdot 3H_2O$
4. Sodium and potassium will bond with atoms that are able to easily accept electrons. They would have a difficult time bonding with each other because both tend to lose electrons.
5. Oxygen contributes $4 \times -2 = -8$. The total charge is -2, so sulfur must contribute $+6$.

Real-World Question

Purpose Students design and carry out an experiment to show how the melting properties of a substance relate to the type of bonding found in the substance. L3 LS **Kinesthetic**

Process Skills observe, infer, compare, make and use tables, form a hypothesis, design an experiment, interpret data, measure

Time Required approximately 45 minutes

Safety Precautions Students should be careful around the hot burner and the heated materials.

Form a Hypothesis

Possible Hypothesis Students may hypothesize that the more easily a substance melts, the less attraction the particles in the substance have for each other.

Test Your Hypothesis

Possible Procedures Heat the same amount of each substance. One lab partner can watch for the first sign of melting while the other times the experiment. Students might also note the length of time between the first observable melting and total melting.

Teaching Strategies

- To avoid melting substances with low melting points too quickly, test tubes should be clean, dry, and at room temperature before starting the experiment.
- Review the chemical formulas of the substances being tested: sugar is $C_{12}H_{22}O_{11}$, water is H_2O, and salt is NaCl.

Data Table:

Substance	Ionic or Covalent	Time to Melt
Ice	Covalent	Melts 1st
Salt	Ionic	Doesn't Melt
Sugar	Covalent	Melts 2nd

Become a Bond Breaker

Goals

- **Observe** the effect of heat on melting points of selected substances.
- **Design** an experiment that allows you to make some inferences that relate ease of melting and forces of attraction between particles of a substance.

Possible Materials

small samples of crushed ice, table salt, and sugar
wire test-tube holder
test tubes
laboratory burner
stopwatch

Safety Precautions

WARNING: *Keep a safe distance from the open flame of the lab burner. Wear proper eye protection. Do not continue heating beyond 5 min.*

Real-World Question

The basic structural units of ionic compounds are ions. For covalent substances, molecules make up the basic units. By using controlled heat to melt substances, you can test various compounds to rate the attractive forces between their basic units. Would a substance that is difficult to melt have strong forces or weak forces holding its basic units together? How do the attractive forces between ions compare to the attractive forces between molecules?

Form a Hypothesis

Based on what you know about ions and molecules, state a hypothesis about which generally would have stronger attractions between their structural units.

Test Your Hypothesis

Make a Plan

1. As a group, agree upon and write a hypothesis statement.
2. As a group, write a detailed list of steps that are needed to test your hypothesis. Determine what your control will be.

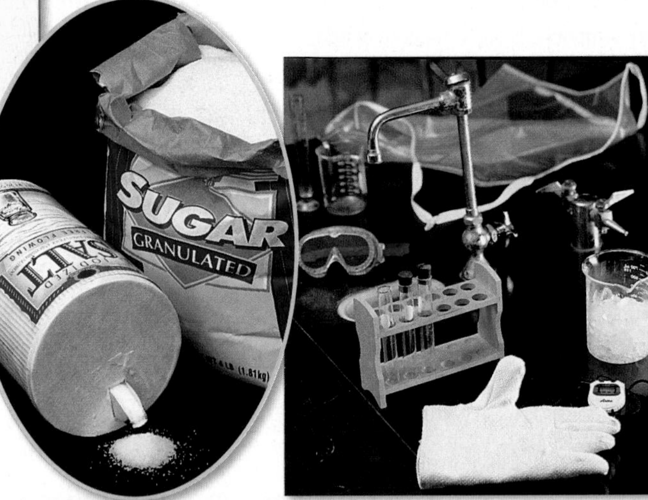

3. As you heat materials in a test tube, what variables are held constant?
4. How will you time the heating of the individual substances?
5. Will you run any tests more than one time?
6. Make a list of materials that you will need to complete your experiment.
7. **Design** a data table in your Science Journal to record your observations.
8. Make sure your teacher approves your plan before you start.

Follow Your Plan

1. Carry out the experiment exactly as planned.
2. While you are observing the heating of each substance, think about the movement of the particles. Which particles are held together by ionic bonds? Which are made up of covalent molecules? How does that affect their movement?
3. Be sure to write down exactly how long it takes to melt each tested substance.

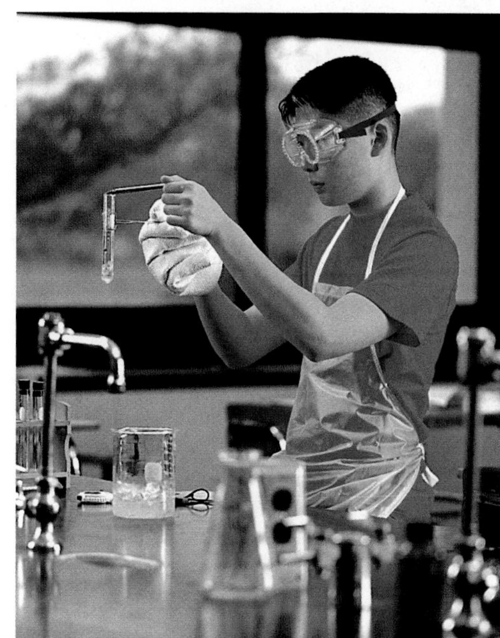

Analyze Your Data

1. **Compare** your results with those of other groups in the class.
2. **Classify** your tested substances as more likely ionic or covalent.
3. Which substances are generally more difficult to melt?
4. Did you have a control in this experiment? Variables?

Conclude and Apply

1. **Think Critically** How did the results of your experiment support or disprove your hypothesis?
2. **Infer** Sugar is known as a polar covalent compound. Knowing this, infer from your results how polarity affects melting point.

Communicating Your Data

Make a chart showing your results and pointing out ways to distinguish between the different kinds of bonds.

Expected Outcome The ice will melt first, followed by the sugar. NaCl will not melt at the temperatures reached by a typical burner.

Analyze Your Data

1. Results should be similar.
2. Ice, covalent; sugar, covalent; salt, ionic
3. Ionic substances are usually more difficult to melt because the network of attractions in an ionic crystal is difficult to break.
4. No, there was no control sample in this experiment. The controlled variables were the amount of the tested substances and constant position of the test tubes in the burner flame. The variable was the bonding of the substances being tested.

Error Analysis Sources of possible error include using different amounts of each substance and heating the substances differently.

Conclude and Apply

1. Answers will vary depending on student hypotheses.
2. Both sugar and water are polar covalent compounds. Salt is ionic. From the melting of water, sugar, and salt, the student can reach no conclusions about the effect of polarity on melting point.

Assessment

Oral Have students display their data tables and compare the results. Then have them decide where the compound KI would likely fit and what type of bonding it would have. KI is ionic, but has slightly lower melting point than NaCl. Use **Performance Assessment in the Science Classroom,** p. 99.

Suggest that students use a computer spreadsheet program for making their charts.

Oops! Accidents in SCIENCE

SOMETIMES GREAT DISCOVERIES HAPPEN BY ACCIDENT!

Content Background

Glue has been around for a long time. Egyptian carvings dating back 3,300 years show figures gluing thin pieces of veneer to sycamore planks. Throughout history, most glues came from a variety of natural sources, including beeswax, flour paste, egg whites, cheese, and extracts from animal horns and fish. Only in the recent century did synthetic glues become more prominent. Glues work because they are able to seep into the crevices of a surface and form chemical welds to the molecules on that surface. Strong polymer chains give glues their strength and flexibility.

Activity

Glue Experiment Let small groups of students experiment with their own glue. Give each group 15 mL of unflavored gelatin in a small beaker. Pour 25 mL of boiling water into the gelatin. **WARNING:** *Be careful with the hot water.* Have students stir the mixture until the gelatin dissolves. Let them use paintbrushes to apply the glue to various types of materials such as paper, wood, and plastic to see which kinds of materials the glue will bond together.

Analyze the Event

Explain to students that Louis Pasteur was a French scientist who discovered, among other things, the rabies vaccine and the pasteurization process for milk. Write the following quote of Pasteur's on the board: "In the field of observation, chance favors the prepared mind." Ask students to brainstorm what they think the quote means and how it applies to this feature. Possible answers: The first group of researchers didn't realize the possibilities of the discovery, but the later group did, so the later group had "prepared minds."

A Sticky Subject

In 1942, a research team was working on creating a new kind of glass. The group was working with some cyanoacrylate monomers (si uh noh A kruh layt • MAH nuh muhrz) which showed promise, but there was a problem that kept coming up. Everything the monomers touched stuck to everything else!

Cyanoacrylate is the chemical name for instant, super-type glues. The researcher was so focused on finding a different type of glass that at the time nobody recognized an important new adhesive. Not until a few years later.

In 1952, a member of the research team, working on new materials for jet plane canopies, made a similar complaint. The ethyl cyanoacrylate they were working with again made everything stick together. This time, the insight stuck to the scientists like, well, like GLUE! "I began gluing everything I could lay my hands on—glass plates, rubber stoppers, metal spatulas, wood, paper, plastic. Everything stuck to everything, almost instantly, and with bonds I could not break apart," recalls the head of the research group.

Super-type glues make it possible to perfectly repair broken objects.

Stick to It

Most adhesives, commonly called glues, are long chains of bonded molecules called polymers. Cyanoacrylate, however, exists as monomers—single molecules with double bonds. And it stays that way until it hits anything with moisture in it—like air. Yes, even the small amount of moisture in air and on the surfaces of most materials is enough to dissolve the double bonds in the monomers of cyanoacrylate, making them join together in long chains. The chains bond to surfaces as they polymerize.

The discovery of cyanoacrylates had an immediate impact on the automobile and airplane industries. And it soon "held" a spot in almost every household toolbox. Since the 1990s, however, cyanoacrylate glues are also finding a place in the doctor's office. A doctor can apply a thin layer of instant glue instead of putting stitches in a cut. This specially made medical glue was approved by the U.S. Food and Drug Administration in 1998.

Take Note **Visit a store and make a table of different kinds of glues. List their common names, their chemical names, what they are made of, how long it takes them to set, and the types of surfaces for which they are recommended. Note any safety precautions.**

For more information, visit gpscience.com/oops

Take Note Tell students to pay careful attention to the recommended uses for each type of glue. Ask students why one glue cannot meet all people's needs. (Possible answers: Some glues can be toxic and so wouldn't be useful for gluing drinking cups, as shown in the feature. Some glues might react chemically with paper or wood. Some glues aren't waterproof.)

Resources for Teachers and Students

"Adhesion," Encyclopedia Brittanica

The Encyclopedia of Modelmaking Techniques, by Christopher Payne and P. Quatro, 1996

The Crafter's Guide to Glues, by Tammy Young, Chilton Book Company, 1995

Sticky, Rigby Interactive Library, 1996

chapter 20 Study Guide

Reviewing Main Ideas

Section 1 Stability in Bonding

1. The properties of compounds are generally different from the properties of the elements they contain.
2. A chemical formula for a compound indicates the composition of a unit of the compound. This model of a water molecule shows the shape of the molecule and the relative size of the atoms.

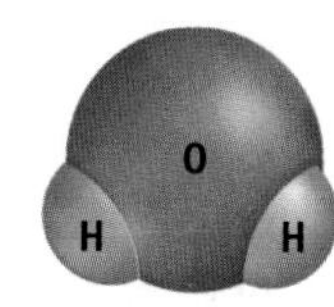

3. Chemical bonding occurs because atoms of most elements become more stable by gaining, losing, or sharing electrons in order to obtain a stable outer energy level.

Section 2 Types of Bonds

1. Ionic bonds between atoms are formed by the attraction between ions. Covalent bonds are formed by the sharing of electrons. Below is an example of an ionically bonded compound.

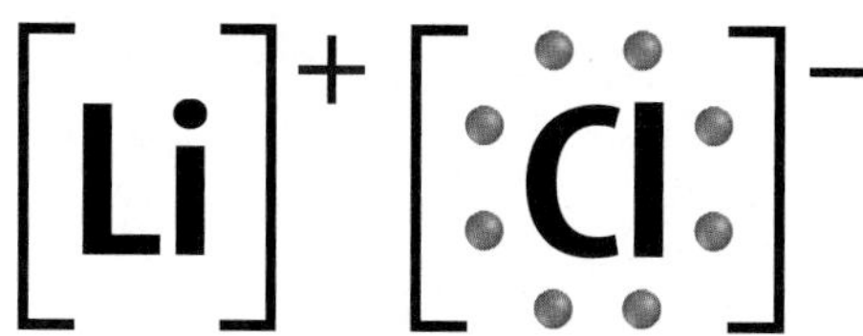

2. Ionic bonding occurs between charged particles called ions and produces ionic compounds. Covalent bonding produces units called molecules and occurs between nonmetallic elements.
3. The unequal sharing of electrons produces compounds that contain polar bonds, and the equal sharing of electrons produces nonpolar compounds.

Section 3 Writing Formulas and Naming Compounds

1. An oxidation number indicates how many electrons an atom has gained, lost, or shared when bonding with other atoms.
2. In the formula of an ionic compound, the element or ion with the positive oxidation number is written first, followed by the one with the negative oxidation number.
3. The name of a binary compound is derived from the names of the two elements that compose the compound. Salt is an example of a binary compound.

4. A hydrate is a compound that has water chemically attached to its ions and written into its formula.
5. Greek prefixes are used in the names of covalent compounds. These indicate the number of each atom present.

FOLDABLES™ Use the Foldable that you made at the beginning of this chapter to help you review chemical bonds.

Science Online gpscience.com/interactive_tutor

Reviewing Main Ideas

Summary statements can be used by students to review the major concepts of the chapter.

Visit gpscience.com
/self_check_quiz
/interactive_tutor
/vocabulary_puzzlemaker
/chapter_review
/standardized_test

Assessment Transparency

For additional assessment questions, use the *Assessment Transparency* located in the transparency book.

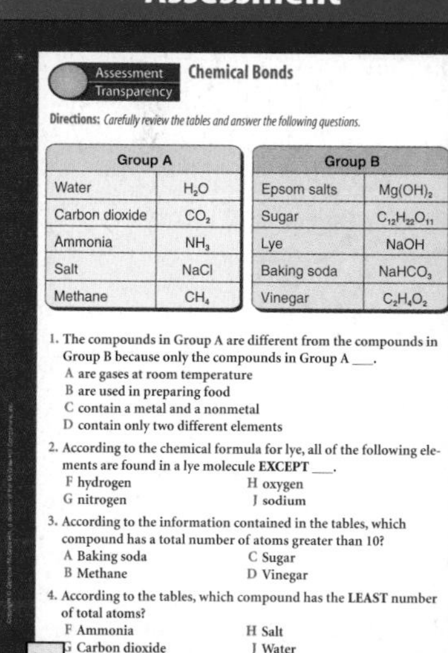

Assessment

Assessment Transparency **Chemical Bonds**

Directions: *Carefully review the tables and answer the following questions.*

Group A	
Water	H_2O
Carbon dioxide	CO_2
Ammonia	NH_3
Salt	NaCl
Methane	CH_4

Group B	
Epsom salts	$Mg(OH)_2$
Sugar	$C_{12}H_{22}O_{11}$
Lye	NaOH
Baking soda	$NaHCO_3$
Vinegar	$C_2H_4O_2$

1. The compounds in Group A are different from the compounds in Group B because only the compounds in Group A ___.
   A are gases at room temperature
   B are used in preparing food
   C contain a metal and a nonmetal
   D contain only two different elements
2. According to the chemical formula for lye, all of the following elements are found in a lye molecule **EXCEPT** ___.
   F hydrogen H oxygen
   G nitrogen J sodium
3. According to the information contained in the tables, which compound has a total number of atoms greater than 10?
   A Baking soda C Sugar
   B Methane D Vinegar
4. According to the tables, which compound has the **LEAST** number of total atoms?
   F Ammonia H Salt
   G Carbon dioxide J Water

L2

Chemical Bonds

FOLDABLES™ Use the Foldables that you made at the beginning of the chapter to help you review chemical formulas.

chapter 20 Review

Using Vocabulary

1. polyatomic ion
2. binary compound
3. polar molecule
4. ion
5. ionic bond
6. covalent bond
7. hydrate
8. molecule
9. oxidation number
10. chemical formula

Checking Concepts

11. B
12. C
13. A
14. D
15. B
16. B
17. A
18. D

Interpreting Graphics

19. More stable; Different from; Ionic; Gained and lost; Covalent; Shared; Oxidation number
20. hydrogen sulfide; H_2S
21. TeF_6, Na_2SO_4, CS_2, $BaCO_3$

chapter 20 Review

Using Vocabulary

binary compound p. 615	ionic bond p. 610
chemical bond p. 606	molecule p. 611
chemical formula p. 603	nonpolar molecule p. 614
covalent bond p. 611	oxidation number p. 615
hydrate p. 620	polar molecule p. 614
ion p. 608	polyatomic ion p. 619

Match each phrase with a vocabulary word.

1. a charged group of atoms
2. a compound composed of two elements
3. a molecule with partially charged areas
4. a positively or negatively charged particle
5. a chemical bond between oppositely charged ions
6. a bond formed from shared electrons
7. crystalline substance that contains water
8. a particle made of covalently bonded atoms
9. shows an element's combining ability
10. tells which elements are in a compound and their ratios.

Checking Concepts

Choose the word or phrase that best answers the question.

11. Which elements are least likely to react with other elements?
    A) metals **C)** nonmetals
    B) noble gases **D)** transition elements

12. What is the name of CuO?
    A) copper oxide
    B) copper(I) oxide
    C) copper(II) oxide
    D) copper(III) oxide

13. Which of the following formulas represents a nonpolar molecule?
    A) N_2 **C)** NaCl
    B) H_2O **D)** HCl

14. How many electrons are in the outer energy level of Group 17 elements?
    A) 1 **C)** 17
    B) 2 **D)** 7

15. Which is a binary ionic compound?
    A) O_2 **C)** H_2SO_4
    B) NaF **D)** $Cu(NO_3)_2$

16. Which of these is an example of an anhydrous compound?
    A) H_2O **C)** $CuSO_4 \cdot 5H_2O$
    B) $CaSO_4$ **D)** $CaSO_4 \cdot 2H_2O$

17. Which of the following is an atom that has gained an electron?
    A) negative ion **C)** polar molecule
    B) positive ion **D)** nonpolar molecule

18. Which of these is an example of a covalent compound?
    A) sodium chloride **C)** calcium chloride
    B) calcium fluoride **D)** sulfur dioxide

Interpreting Graphics

19. Copy and complete this concept map.

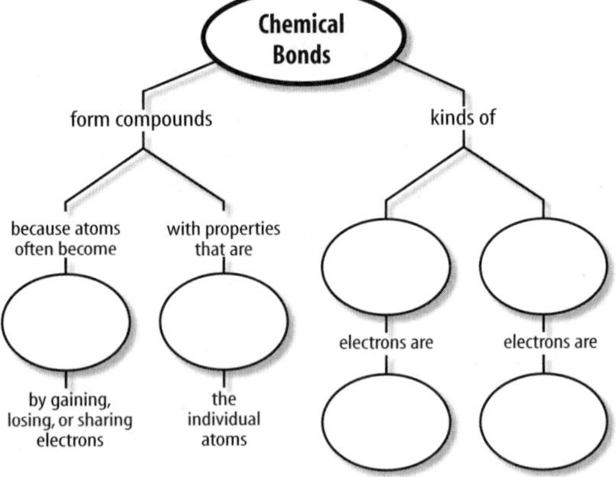

gpscience.com/vocabulary_puzzlemaker

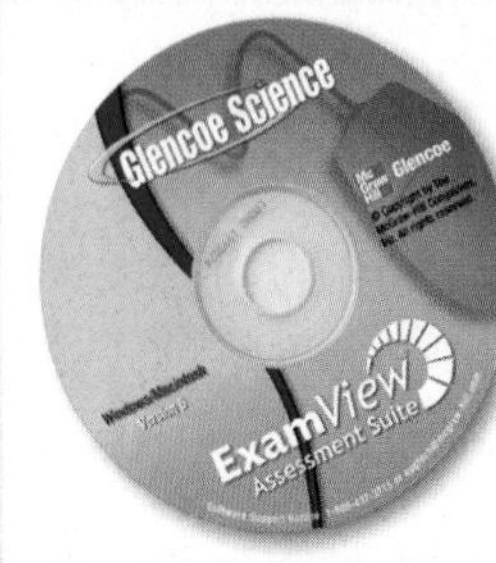

Use the *ExamView® Assessment Suite* CD-ROM to:

- create multiple versions of tests
- create modified tests with one mouse click for inclusion students
- edit existing questions and add your own questions
- build tests aligned with state standards using built-in State Curriculum Tags
- change English tests to Spanish with one mouse click and vice versa

20. Write the name and formula for the compound illustrated to the right.

Use the table below to answer question 21.

Which compounds exist?

Formula	Possible Compounds
SF_6	AlF_6 or TeF_6
K_2SO_4	Na_2SO_4 or Ba_2SO_4
CO_2	CCl_2 or CS_2
$CaCO_3$	OCO_3 or $BaCO_3$

21. Elements from one family (vertical column) of the periodic table generally combine with elements from another family and polyatomic ions in the same ratio. For example, one calcium atom combines with two chlorine atoms to give $CaCl_2$ (calcium chloride) as it does with two fluorine atoms to give CaF_2 (calcium fluoride). Using a periodic table as a guide, predict which of the two compounds on the right side of the table above is more likely to exist based upon the formula on the left side.

Thinking Critically

22. **Draw** Anhydrous magnesium chloride is used to make wood fireproof. Draw a dot diagram of magnesium chloride.

23. **Use Formulas** Artificial diamonds are made using thallium carbonate. If thallium has an oxidation number of 1+, what is the formula for the compound?

24. **Compare and contrast** polar and nonpolar molecules.

25. **Write** Baking soda, which is sodium hydrogen carbonate, and vinegar, which contains hydrogen acetate, can be used as household cleaners. Write the chemical formulas for these two compounds.

26. **Draw Conclusions** Ammonia gas and water react to form household ammonia, which contains NH_4^+ and OH^- ions. The formula for water is H_2O, what is the formula for ammonia gas?

27. **Draw Conclusions** The name of a compound called copper (II) sulfate is written on a bottle. What is the charge of the copper ion? What is the charge of the sulfate ion?

28. **Explain** what electric forces between oppositely charged electrons and protons have to do with chemical reactions.

29. **Name Compounds** Write the chemical name for the following compounds:
A) Fe_2S_3
B) $Cu(ClO_3)_2$
C) $Ca(PO_4)_2$
D) $(NH_4)_2SO_4$

30. **Model** One common form of phosphorus, white phosphorus, has the formula P_4 and is formed by four covalently bonded phosphorus atoms. Make a model of this molecule, showing that all four atoms are now chemically stable.

Applying Math

31. **Oxidation Number** What is the oxidation number of Fe in the compound Fe_2S_3?
A) 1^+
B) 2^+
C) 3^+
D) 4^+

32. **Chemical Formulas** Write the chemical formulas for the following compounds:
A) potassium chloride
B) calcium carbonate
C) copper sulfate
D) sodium oxide

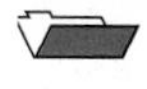
Science Online gpscience.com/chapter_review

chapter 20 Review

Thinking Critically

22. $[:\ddot{Cl}:]^- Mg^{2+} [:\ddot{Cl}:]^-$
23. Tl_2CO_3
24. A polar molecule has opposite charges (positive and negative) on each end because of an unequal sharing of electrons. A nonpolar molecule does not have oppositely charged ends because the electrons involved are shared equally.
25. $NaHCO_3$; $HC_2H_3O_2$
26. NH_3
27. Cu^{+2} SO_4^{-2}
28. In order to form an ionic charge, the quantity of electrons and protons are unequal. If one element loses electrons, another must gain in order to keep the neutral charge of the compound
29. **a.** iron sulfide
b. copper (II) chlorate
c. calcium phosphate
d. ammonium sulfate
30. :P::P:
:P::P:
Use **PASC,** p. 123

Applying Math

National Math Standards
2, 6, 9
31. +3
32. **a.** KCl
b. $CaCO_3$
c. $CuSO_4$
d. Na_2O

Assessment Resources

Reproducible Masters
Chapter *Fast File* Resources
Chapter Review, pp. 37–38
Chapter Tests, pp. 39–42
Assessment Transparency Activity, p. 49
Glencoe Science Web site
Chapter Review Test
Standardized Test Practice

Glencoe Technology
Assessment Transparency
ExamView® Assessment Suite
MindJogger Videoquiz
Interactive Chalkboard

FAST FILE

Answer Sheet A practice answer sheet can be found at gpscience.com/answer_sheet.

Assessment **Student Recording Sheet** Standardized Test Practice *Use with pages 788–789 of the Student Edition*

Standardized Test Practice

Part 1 Multiple Choice
Select the best answer from the choices given and fill in the corresponding oval.

Part 2 Constructed Response/Grid In
Record and bubble in your answers on the grids below.

Record your answers for Questions 18–21 on a separate sheet of paper.

SAMPLE

Part 1 Multiple Choice

1. B	**5.** A	**9.** B
2. D	**6.** D	**10.** B
3. A	**7.** C	**11.** A
4. D	**8.** C	

Part 2 Short Response

12. Beginning with neon and moving left across period 2 to nitrogen, the oxidation numbers decrease from 0 to −3.

13. Nitrogen and fluorine have oxidation numbers of −3 and −1, respectively. Nitrogen must gain three electrons to fill its outer energy level, while fluorine must gain one.

14. ·C̣· H· H:C:H (with H above and below C)

15. often crystalline solids with high melting points; usually formed when a metal and nonmetal react; $MgCl_2$, NaCl, and KBr

16. This is a hydrate, a compound which has water chemically attached to its ions. The name of this compound is magnesium sulfate heptahydrate.

17. the elements and the exact number of each which make up a compound

18. NaCl is an ionic bond. In an ionic bond, a transfer of electrons takes place. Because you have a + and a −, you get a zero net charge. $Na^+ + Cl^-$, which gives you a zero net charge.

chapter 20 Standardized Test Practice

Part 1 Multiple Choice

Record your answers on the answer sheet provided by your teacher or on a sheet of paper.

1. Which element is NOT part of the compound NH_4NO_3?
A. nitrogen **C.** oxygen
B. nickel **D.** hydrogen

2. When an atom is chemically stable, how many electrons are in its outer energy level?
A. 0 **C.** 4
B. 7 **D.** 8

Use the figure below to answer questions 3 and 4.

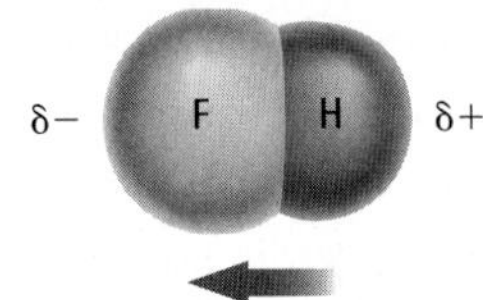

3. What type of bond holds the atoms of this molecule together?
A. covalent **C.** triple
B. ionic **D.** double

4. Which statement about this molecule is TRUE?
A. This is a nonpolar molecule.
B. The electrons are shared equally in the bonds of this molecule.
C. This molecule does not have oppositely charged ends.
D. This is a polar molecule.

Test-Taking Tip

Comprehension Be sure you understand the question before you read the answer choices. Make special note of words like NOT or EXCEPT. Read and consider all the answer choices before you mark your answer sheet.

Question 1 Try to identify each of the elements in the compound before reading the answer choices.

5. What do the group 7A elements become when they react with group 1A elements?
A. negative ions **C.** positive ions
B. neutral **D.** polyatomic ions

Use the illustration below to answer questions 6–8.

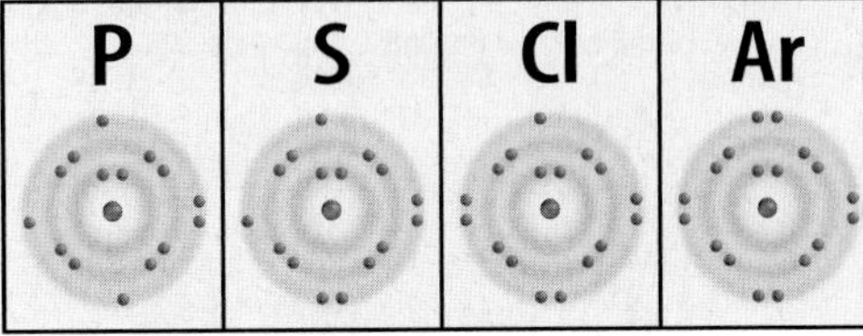

6. Which element is least likely to form an ionic bond with sodium?
A. phosphorous **C.** chlorine
B. sulfur **D.** argon

7. How many electrons are required to complete the outer energy level of a phosphorous atom?
A. 1 **C.** 3
B. 2 **D.** 4

8. How many electrons are in an argon atom?
A. 8 **C.** 18
B. 10 **D.** 26

9. What is the oxidation number of sodium in the compound Na_3PO_4?
A. −1 **C.** −3
B. +3 **D.** +1

10. What is the name of $KC_2H_3O_2$?
A. potassium carbide
B. potassium acetate
C. potassium hydroxide
D. potassium oxide

11. What is the chemical formula for lead (II) oxide?
A. PbO **C.** PbO_2
B. Pb_2O **D.** Pb_2O_2

Part 3 Open Ended

19. This is a covalent bond, formed from sharing of electrons. It is a triple bond, as three pairs of electrons are shared.

20. H:H :O::O: :F:F: :Cl:Cl: :Br:Br: :I:I:

21. These elements have four outer shell electrons. It would take a lot of energy to lose four electrons, because each time an electron was lost, the other electrons would be held even more tightly by the nucleus.

22. The size of the atom, the size of the positive charge in the nucleus, and the total number of electrons an atom has all affect the strength of the attraction between an atom and its electrons.

Part 2 Short Response/Grid In

Record your answers on the answer sheet provided by your teacher or on a sheet of paper.

Use the illustration below to answer questions 12 and 13.

Oxidation Numbers of Some Period 2 Elements

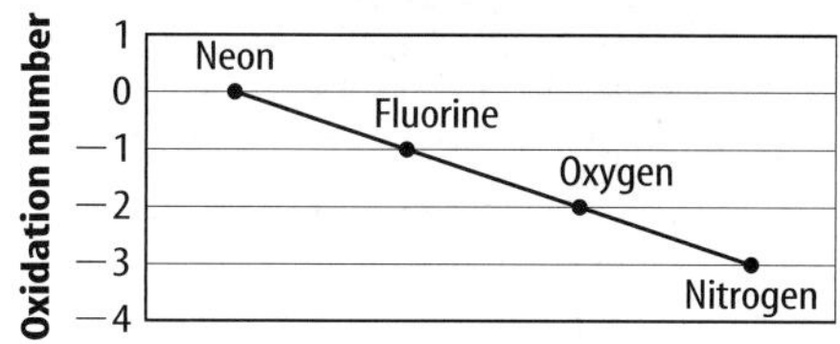

12. Describe the trend in the oxidation numbers of these period 2 elements.

13. Compare the oxidation numbers of nitrogen and fluorine. Why do they differ?

14. Draw electron dot diagrams for carbon and hydrogen. Draw a dot diagram for methane, CH_4, one of many compounds formed by these two elements.

15. Give several examples of ionic compounds. What are two properties often shared by these substances?

16. A compound has the formula $MgSO_4 \cdot 7H_2O$. Identify and define this type of compound. Using the appropriate prefix, write its name.

17. What information is given in a chemical formula?

18. The bonding of atoms and molecules is the result of oppositely charged electrons and protons being held together by electric forces within the atom. Using this information, explain the bonding of NaCl.

Part 3 Open Ended

Record your answers on a sheet of paper.

Use the illustration below to answer questions 19 and 20.

$\cdot\ddot{\underset{\cdot}{N}}\cdot \; + \; \cdot\ddot{\underset{\cdot}{N}}\cdot \; \rightarrow \; :N\vdots\vdots N:$

19. Describe the bond holding the nitrogen atoms together in this molecule.

20. Nitrogen occurs naturally as a diatomic molecule because N_2 molecules are more stable than nitrogen atoms. H_2, O_2, F_2, Cl_2, Br_2, and I_2 are other diatomic molecules. Draw dot diagrams for three of these molecules.

21. Explain why elements in Group 4A, which have four electrons in the outer energy level, are unlikely to lose all of the electrons in the outer energy level.

22. What factors affect how strongly an atom is attracted to its electrons?

23. Create a chart which compares the properties of polar and nonpolar molecules. Your chart should include several examples of each type of molecule.

24. Scientists have created a compound which combines xenon and fluorine. Why is this compound so unusual and difficult to create? Why is fluorine a good choice for scientists attempting to form a compound with xenon?

25. What is the difference between nitrogen oxide and dinitrogen pentoxide? Why are prefixes used in this situation?

26. KCl is an example of ionic bonding. HCl is an example of covalent bonding. Describe the difference in the bonds in terms of electrons and outer energy levels.

25. Nitrgen oxide is NO, while dinitrogen pentoxide is N_2O_5. Prefixes are used to identify the composition of compounds which are made of elements that can form more than one compound with each other.

26. HCL is an example of covalent bonding of unequal sharing. Chlorine atoms have a stronger attraction for electrons than hydrogen does. Therefore, the electrons shared in hydrogen chloride will spend more time near the chlorine atom than the hydrogen atom. The example of a tug-of-war with the knot being the electron shows how the bonding happens. Therefore the electron goes more with the chlorine which is bigger.

Ionic bonding is an equal sharing of electrons so that they equal 0. Potassium is a +1 and chlorine is a −1 which when you put +1 + −1 = 0.

Rubrics

For more help evaluating open-ended assessment questions, see the rubric on p. 10T.

23.

Polar Molecules	Nonpolar Molecules
Have covalent bonds	Have covalent bonds
Electrons are held more closely by one atom of the molecule	Electrons are shared equally
Have slightly positive and slightly negative ends	Do not have oppositely charged ends
Examples: NH_3, H_2O	Examples: CCl_4, CH_4

24. Xenon is a noble gas. Its complete outer energy level makes it highly unreactive. Fluorine is the most reactive of all elements. It has seven electrons in an outer energy level which is close to the nucleus, meaning the nucleus has a strong attraction for its electrons and a great affinity for acquiring more.

Chemical Reactions

BIG Idea A chemical reaction involves changing one or more substances into a different substance or substances.

	Content Standards	Learning Objectives	Resources to Assess Mastery
Section 1	**5–8:** UCP.1–5; A.1, 2; B.1, 3; G.3 **9–12:** UCP.1–3, 5; A.1, 2; B.2, 3; G.3	**Chemical Changes** **1. Identify** the reactants and products in a chemical reaction. **2. Determine** how a chemical reaction satisfies the law of conservation of mass. **3. Determine** how chemists express chemical changes using equations. ***Main Idea*** The rearrangement of atoms in a chemical change is described by a chemical equation.	Formative Assessment Reading Check, pp. 633, 634, 636 Section Review, p. 637 Summative Assessment *ExamView® Assessment Suite*
Section 2	**5–8:** UCP.1–3, 5; A.1, 2; B.1, 3 **9–12:** UCP.1–3, 5; A.1, 2; B.2, 3	**Chemical Equations** **4. Identify** what is meant by a balanced chemical equation. **5. Determine** how to write balanced chemical equations. ***Main Idea*** A balanced chemical equation contains the same numbers and types of atoms in the reactants as in the products.	Formative Assessment Reading Check, p. 639 Section Review, p. 640 Summative Assessment *ExamView® Assessment Suite*
Section 3	**5–8:** UCP.1–5; A.1, 2 **9–12:** UCP.1–3, 5; A.1, 2; B.2, 3, 6	**Classifying Chemical Reactions** **6. Identify** the five general types of chemical reactions. **7. Define** the terms *oxidation* and *reduction*. **8. Identify** redox reactions. **9. Predict** which metals will replace other metals in compounds. ***Main Idea*** Reactions can be classified based on how atoms are rearranged.	Formative Assessment Reading Check, pp. 642, 643 Section Review, p. 645 Summative Assessment *ExamView® Assessment Suite*
Section 4	**5–8:** UCP.1–5; A.1, 2; B.1, 3; G.1–3 **9–12:** UCP.1–3, 5; A.1, 2; B.2, 3; G.1–3 See pp. 16T–17T for a Key to Standards.	**Chemical Reactions and Energy** **10. Identify** the source of energy changes in chemical reactions. **11. Compare and contrast** exergonic and endergonic reactions. **12. Examine** the effects of catalysts and inhibitors on the speed of chemical reactions. ***Main Idea*** Exergonic reactions release energy and endergonic reactions absorb energy.	Formative Assessment Reading Check, pp. 648, 650 Section Review, p. 650 Summative Chapter Assessment MindJogger, Ch. 21 *ExamView® Assessment Suite* Leveled Chapter Test Test A L1 Test B L2 Test C L3 Test Practice, pp. 658–659

Suggested Pacing				
Period	Instruction	Labs	Review & Assessment	Total
Single	3 days	4 days	2 days	9 days
Block	1.5 blocks	2 blocks	1 block	4.5 blocks

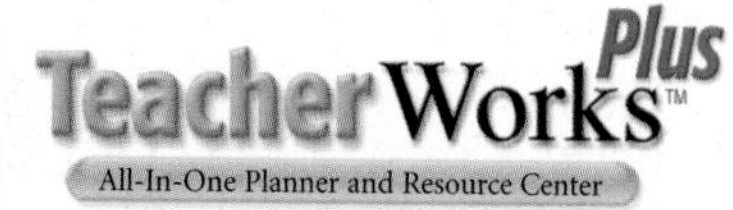

Core Instruction	Leveled Resources	Leveled Labs	Pacing Period		Pacing Block
Student Text, pp. 630–637 Section Focus Transparency, Ch. 21, Section 1 Teaching Transparency, Ch. 21, Section 1 Interactive Chalkboard, Ch. 21, Section 1 Identifying Misconceptions, p. 634 Differentiated Instruction, p. 634	**Chapter *Fast File* Resources** Directed Reading for Content Mastery, p. 20 [L1] Note-taking Worksheet, pp. 35–37 Reinforcement, p. 27 [L2] Enrichment, p. 31 [L3] **Reading Essentials,** p. 360 [L1] ELL **Science Notebook,** p. 239 ELL ***Active*Folders**: *Chemical Reactions* [L1] ELL	**Launch Lab,** p. 631: agar mixture, Petri dishes, aluminum nails, nail (iron or steel) *20 min (over 2 days)* [L2]	1	Section 1, pp. 631–634 (includes Launch Lab)	1
		MiniLab, p. 636: index cards (15) *15 min* [L2]	2	Section 1, pp. 635–637 (includes MiniLAB and Section Review)	
Student Text, pp. 638–640 Section Focus Transparency, Ch. 21 Section 2 Interactive Chalkboard, Ch. 21, Section 2 Differentiated Instruction, p. 639	**Chapter *Fast File* Resources** Directed Reading for Content Mastery, p. 20 [L1] Note-taking Worksheet, pp. 35–37 Reinforcement, p. 28 [L2] Enrichment, p. 32 [L3] **Reading Essentials,** p. 365 [L1] ELL **Science Notebook,** p. 243 ELL		3	Section 2, pp. 638–640	2
Student Text, pp. 641–645 Section Focus Transparency, Ch. 21, Section 3 Interactive Chalkboard, Ch. 21, Section 3 Applying Math, p. 644 Identifying Misconceptions, p. 644 Differentiated Instruction, pp. 643, 644	**Chapter *Fast File* Resources** Directed Reading for Content Mastery, p. 21 [L1] Note-taking Worksheet, pp. 35–37 Reinforcement, p. 29 [L2] Enrichment, p. 33 [L3] **Reading Essentials,** p. 369 [L1] ELL **Science Notebook,** p. 246 ELL		4	Section 3, pp. 641–645	
Student Text, pp. 646–653 Section Focus Transparency, Ch. 21, Section 4 Interactive Chalkboard, Ch. 21, Section 4 Visualizing Chemical Energy, p. 647 Differentiated Instruction, pp. 647 Chapter Study Guide, p. 655	**Chapter *Fast File* Resources** Directed Reading for Content Mastery, pp. 21, 22 [L1] Note-taking Worksheet, pp. 35–37 Reinforcement, p. 30 [L2] Enrichment, p. 34 [L3] **Reading Essentials,** p. 374 [L1] ELL **Science Notebook,** p. 249 ELL ***Active*Folders**: *Chemical Reactions* [L1] ELL	**MiniLab,** p. 648: water, test tube, $CuBr_2$ *15 min* [L2]	5	Section 4, pp. 646–650 (includes MiniLAB and Section Review)	3
		***Lab,** p. 651: test tubes (3), test-tube rack, H_2O_2 (3%), teaspoon, sand, hot plate, wooden splint, beaker, hot water, MnO_2 *30 min* [L1] [L2] [L3]	6	Lab: Catalyzed Reaction, p. 651	
		***Lab,** pp. 652–653: Internet access *90 min* [L1] [L2] [L3]	7	Lab: Fossil Fuels and Greenhouse Gases, pp. 652–653	4
			8	Lab: Fossil Fuels and Greenhouse Gases	
		*Lab version A [L1] version B [L2] [L3]	9	Study Guide, Chapter Review, and Test Practice, pp. 655–659	4.5

Chemical Reactions

Transparencies

Section Focus

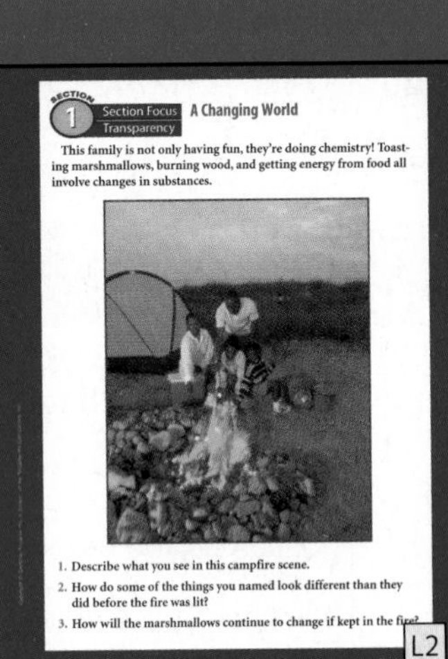
Section 1 Section Focus Transparency **A Changing World**

This family is not only having fun, they're doing chemistry! Toasting marshmallows, burning wood, and getting energy from food all involve changes in substances.

1. Describe what you see in this campfire scene.
2. How do some of the things you named look different than they did before the fire was lit?
3. How will the marshmallows continue to change if kept in the fire?

L2

Section 2 Section Focus Transparency **A Balanced Viewpoint**

Balances have been used for a very long time to compare the weights of different objects. Usually, an unknown weight is put in one pan and known weights are put in the other until the two pans are even. Chemical equations are balanced in a similar fashion.

1. How is the arrow in a chemical equation like the fulcrum of a balance?
2. If you could put all the reactants of a chemical reaction in one pan of a balance and all the products in the other pan, would the two pans be even? Explain.

L2

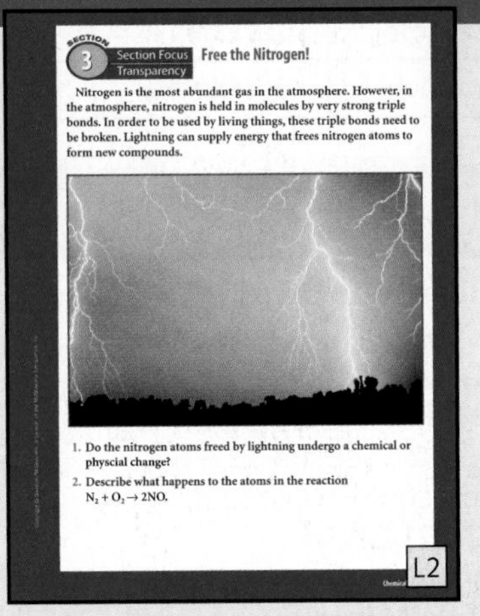
Section 3 Section Focus Transparency **Free the Nitrogen!**

Nitrogen is the most abundant gas in the atmosphere. However, in the atmosphere, nitrogen is held in molecules by very strong triple bonds. In order to be used by living things, these triple bonds need to be broken. Lightning can supply energy that frees nitrogen atoms to form new compounds.

1. Do the nitrogen atoms freed by lightning undergo a chemical or physical change?
2. Describe what happens to the atoms in the reaction $N_2 + O_2 \rightarrow 2NO$.

L2

This is a representation of key blackline masters available in the Teacher Classroom Resources. See Resource Manager boxes within the chapter for additional information.

Assessment

Assessment Transparency **Chemical Reactions**

Directions: Carefully review the diagrams and answer the following questions.

1. From the results of the experiment above, it is reasonable to assume that the production of ethene ___.
   - A has no effect on the rotting of a peach in its immediate area
   - B slows the rotting of a peach in its immediate area
   - C quickens the rotting of a peach in its immediate area
   - D slows the rotting process in the peach producing the gas
2. According to the information in the diagram, we can conclude that ethene consists of ___.
   - F hydrogen and helium
   - G carbon and hydrogen
   - H carbon and oxygen
   - J calcium and carbon
3. George wanted to use the peaches that he picked from the tree in his backyard to bake a pie. However, some were not quite ripe. George could best speed the ripening process by placing the peaches ___.
   - A in the refrigerator
   - B outside by the tree
   - C inside an enclosed space
   - D near a breezy window

L2

Teaching

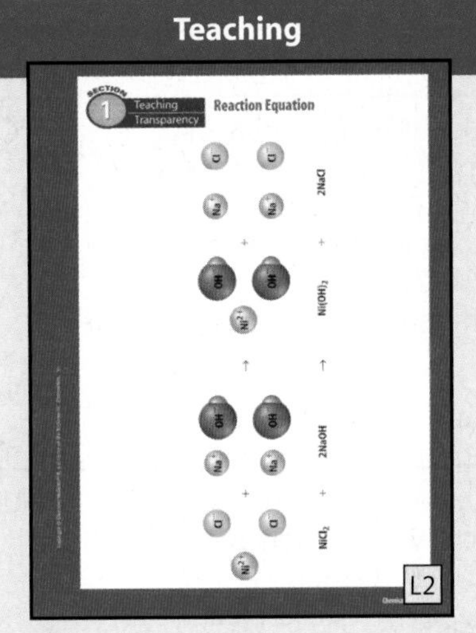
Section 1 Teaching Transparency **Reaction Equation**

L2

Key to Teaching Strategies

The following designations will help you decide which activities are appropriate for your students.

- L1 Level 1 activities should be appropriate for students with learning difficulties.
- L2 Level 2 activities should be within the ability range of all students.
- L3 Level 3 activities are designed for above-average students.
- ELL ELL activities should be within the ability range of English Language Learners.
- COOP LEARN Cooperative Learning activities are designed for small group work.
- LS Multiple Learning Styles logos, as described on page 12T, are used throughout to indicate strategies that address different learning styles.
- P These strategies represent student products that can be placed into a best-work portfolio.
- PBL Problem-Based Learning activities apply real-world situations to learning.

Hands-on Activities

Student Text Lab Worksheets

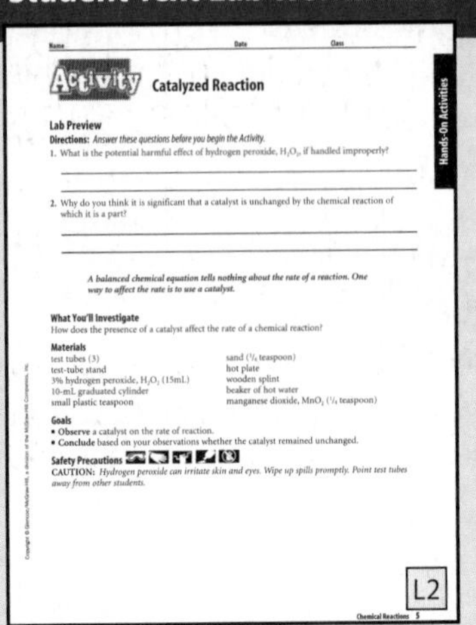
Name Date Class

Activity **Catalyzed Reaction**

Lab Preview

Directions: *Answer these questions before you begin the Activity.*

1. What is the potential harmful effect of hydrogen peroxide, H_2O_2, if handled improperly?
2. Why do you think it is significant that a catalyst is unchanged by the chemical reaction of which it is a part?

A balanced chemical equation tells nothing about the rate of a reaction. One way to affect the rate is to use a catalyst.

What You'll Investigate

How does the presence of a catalyst affect the rate of a chemical reaction?

Materials

test tubes (3)
test-tube stand
3% hydrogen peroxide, H_2O_2 (15mL)
10-mL graduated cylinder
small plastic teaspoon
sand (1/4 teaspoon)
hot plate
wooden splint
beaker of hot water
manganese dioxide, MnO_2 (1/4 teaspoon)

Goals

- **Observe** a catalyst on the rate of reaction.
- **Conclude** based on your observations whether the catalyst remained unchanged.

Safety Precautions

CAUTION: *Hydrogen peroxide can irritate skin and eyes. Wipe up spills promptly. Point test tubes away from other students.*

L2

Hands-On Activities

Chemical Reactions 5

Laboratory Activities

Name Date Class

LAB 1 Laboratory Activity **Conservation of Mass**

In a chemical reaction, the total mass of the substances formed by the reaction is equal to the total mass of the substances that reacted. This principle is called the law of conservation of mass, which states that matter is not created or destroyed during a chemical reaction.

In this experiment, sodium hydrogen carbonate, $NaHCO_3$ (baking soda), will react with hydrochloric acid, HCl. The substances formed by this reaction are sodium chloride, NaCl; water, H_2O; and carbon dioxide gas, CO_2.

Strategy

You will show that new substances are formed in a chemical reaction.
You will show the conservation of mass during a chemical reaction.

Materials

sealable plastic sandwich bag containing sodium hydrogen carbonate, $NaHCO_3$
hydrochloric acid, HCl
plastic pipette
paper towel
metric balance

Procedure

1. Obtain the plastic sandwich bag containing a small amount of sodium hydrogen carbonate.
2. Fill the pipette with the hydrochloric acid solution. Use a paper towel to wipe away any acid that might be on the outside of the pipette. Discard the paper towel. CAUTION: *Hydrochloric acid is corrosive. Handle with care.*
3. Carefully place the pipette in the bag. Press the bag gently to eliminate as much air as possible. Be careful not to press the bulb of the pipette. Seal the bag. See Figure 1.
4. Measure the mass of the sealed plastic bag using the metric balance. Record this value in the Data and Observations section.
5. Remove the plastic bag from the balance. Without opening the bag, direct the stem of the pipette into the sodium hydrogen carbonate. Press the bulb of the pipette and allow the hydrochloric acid to react with the sodium hydrogen carbonate. Make sure that all the acid mixes with the sodium hydrogen carbonate.
6. Observe the contents of the bag for several minutes. Record your observations in the Data and Observations section.
7. After several minutes, measure the mass of the sealed plastic bag and its contents. Record this value in the Data and Observations section.

Figure 1

Sodium hydrogen carbonate
Pipette filled with HCl

L2

Hands-On Activities

Chemical Reactions 9

Resource Manager

Meeting Different Ability Levels

Content Outline

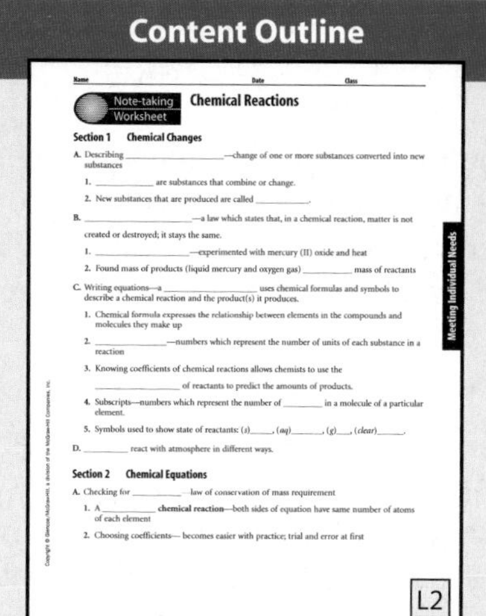

Name Date Class

Note-taking Worksheet — Chemical Reactions

Section 1 Chemical Changes

A. Describing ______________—change of one or more substances converted into new substances

1. __________ are substances that combine or change.
2. New substances that are produced are called __________.

B. ______________—a law which states that, in a chemical reaction, matter is not created or destroyed; it stays the same.

1. ______________—experimented with mercury (II) oxide and heat
2. Found mass of products (liquid mercury and oxygen gas) __________ mass of reactants

C. Writing equations—a ______________ uses chemical formulas and symbols to describe a chemical reaction and the product(s) it produces.

1. Chemical formula expresses the relationship between elements in the compounds and molecules they make up
2. ______________—numbers which represent the number of units of each substance in a reaction
3. Knowing coefficients of chemical reactions allows chemists to use the __________ of reactants to predict the amounts of products.
4. Subscripts—numbers which represent the number of ________ in a molecule of a particular element.
5. Symbols used to show state of reactants: (s)____, (aq)____, (g)____, (clear)____

D. __________ react with atmosphere in different ways.

Section 2 Chemical Equations

A. Checking for __________ law of conservation of mass requirement

1. A __________ chemical reaction—both sides of equation have same number of atoms of each element
2. Choosing coefficients— becomes easier with practice; trial and error at first

Meeting Individual Needs

L2

Chemical Reactions 35

Reinforcement

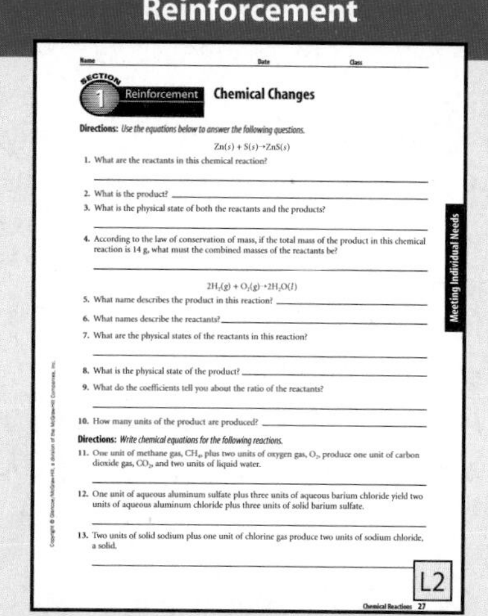

Name Date Class

Section 1 Reinforcement — Chemical Changes

Directions: Use the equations below to answer the following questions.

$Zn(s) + S(s) \rightarrow ZnS(s)$

1. What are the reactants in this chemical reaction?
2. What is the product?
3. What is the physical state of both the reactants and the products?
4. According to the law of conservation of mass, if the total mass of the product in this chemical reaction is 14 g, what must the combined masses of the reactants be?

$2H_2(g) + O_2(g) \rightarrow 2H_2O(l)$

5. What name describes the product in this reaction?
6. What names describe the reactants?
7. What are the physical states of the reactants in this reaction?
8. What is the physical state of the product?
9. What do the coefficients tell you about the ratio of the reactants?
10. How many units of the product are produced?

Directions: Write chemical equations for the following reactions.

11. One unit of methane gas, CH_4, plus two units of oxygen gas, O_2, produce one unit of carbon dioxide gas, CO_2, and two units of liquid water.
12. One unit of aqueous aluminum sulfate plus three units of aqueous barium chloride yield two units of aqueous aluminum chloride plus three units of solid barium sulfate.
13. Two units of solid sodium plus one unit of chlorine gas produce two units of sodium chloride, a solid.

Meeting Individual Needs

L2

Chemical Reactions 27

Enrichment

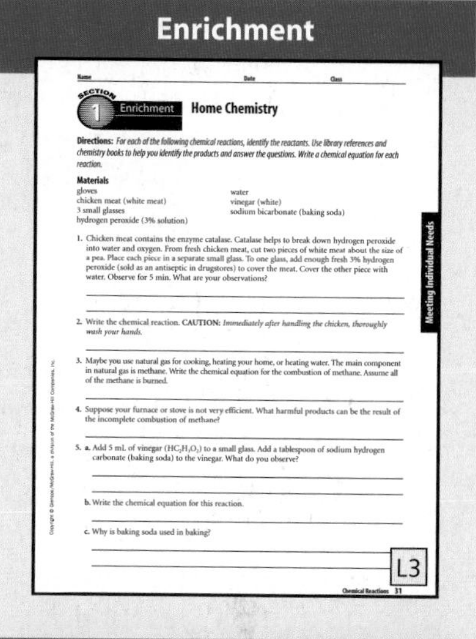

Name Date Class

Section 1 Enrichment — Home Chemistry

Directions: For each of the following chemical reactions, identify the reactants. Use library references and chemistry books to help you identify the products and answer the questions. Write a chemical equation for each reaction.

Materials

gloves; chicken meat (white meat); 3 small glasses; hydrogen peroxide (3% solution); water; vinegar (white); sodium bicarbonate (baking soda)

1. Chicken meat contains the enzyme catalase. Catalase helps to break down hydrogen peroxide into water and oxygen. From fresh chicken meat, cut two pieces of white meat about the size of a pea. Place each piece in a separate small glass. To one glass, add enough fresh 3% hydrogen peroxide (sold as an antiseptic in drugstores) to cover the meat. Cover the other piece with water. Observe for 5 min. What are your observations?
2. Write the chemical reaction. CAUTION: *Immediately after handling the chicken, thoroughly wash your hands.*
3. Maybe you use natural gas for cooking, heating your home, or heating water. The main component in natural gas is methane. Write the chemical equation for the combustion of methane. Assume all of the methane is burned.
4. Suppose your furnace or stove is not very efficient. What harmful products can be the result of the incomplete combustion of methane?
5. a. Add 5 mL of vinegar ($HC_2H_3O_2$) to a small glass. Add a tablespoon of sodium hydrogen carbonate (baking soda) to the vinegar. What do you observe?
   b. Write the chemical equation for this reaction.
   c. Why is baking soda used in baking?

Meeting Individual Needs

L3

Chemical Reactions 31

Directed Reading (English/Spanish)

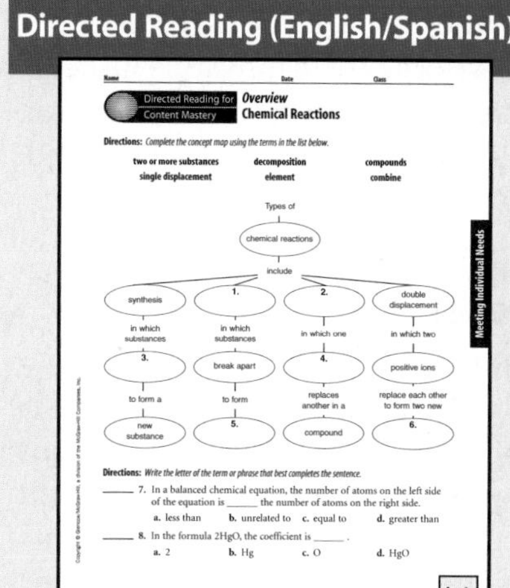

Name Date Class

Directed Reading for Content Mastery — Overview — Chemical Reactions

Directions: Complete the concept map using the terms in the list below.

two or more substances; decomposition; compounds; single displacement; element; combine

Types of — chemical reactions — include — synthesis; 1.; 2.; double displacement — in which substances 3. to form a new substance; in which substances break apart to form 5.; in which one 4. replaces another in a compound; in which two positive ions replace each other to form two new 6.

Directions: Write the letter of the term or phrase that best completes the sentence.

____ 7. In a balanced chemical equation, the number of atoms on the left side of the equation is _____ the number of atoms on the right side.
a. less than b. unrelated to c. equal to d. greater than

____ 8. In the formula 2HgO, the coefficient is _____.
a. 2 b. Hg c. O d. HgO

Meeting Individual Needs

L1

Chemical Reactions 19

Study Guide

Study Guide
Features
• Contains a study guide page for each section of the chapter
• Reviews key concepts
• Includes answer pages
L2

Reading Essentials

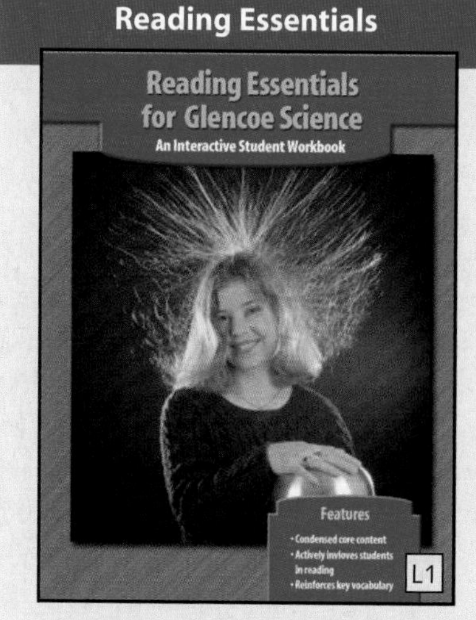

Reading Essentials for Glencoe Science
An Interactive Student Workbook
Features
• Condensed core content
• Actively involves students in reading
• Reinforces key vocabulary
L1

Assessment

Test Practice Workbook

Name: Date: Class:

Chapter Test — Chapter 24 Chemical Reactions

DIRECTIONS

Read each question and choose the best answer. Then fill in the correct answer on your answer document.

1 Antoine Lavoisier is credited with the discovery of the law of conservation of mass, which states that in a chemical reaction, matter is not created or destroyed, but preserved. Which of the following equations correctly expresses this law?

A $H_2 + Cl_2 \rightarrow 2HCl$*
B $H_2 + Cl_2 \rightarrow HCl$
C $H + Cl \rightarrow 2HCl$
D $2H_2 + Cl_2 \rightarrow 2HCl_2$

2 For which of the following reasons is a catalyst added to a chemical formula?

F To stabilize a substance
G To speed up a reaction*
H To produce a greater amount of the catalyst
J To prevent a compound from forming

3 A double-displacement reaction occurs if water, gas, or a precipitate (insoluble compound) forms when two ionic compounds in solution are combined. Which of the following is the generalized formula for this type of reaction?

A AB + CD → AD + CB*
B A + BC → AC + B
C D + BC → BD + C
D A + B → AB

$Mg(s) + O_2(g) \rightarrow 2MgO(s)$
Magnesium plus oxygen produces magnesium oxide

4 The equation above is not balanced. In order to balance the equation, a coefficient of 2 needs to be placed directly —

F after the symbol for magnesium on the left side of the equation
G before the symbol for oxygen on the left side of the equation
H after the symbol for oxygen on the left side of the equation
J before the symbol for magnesium on the left side of the equation*

GO ON

100 Interactions of Matter

L2

Chapter Review

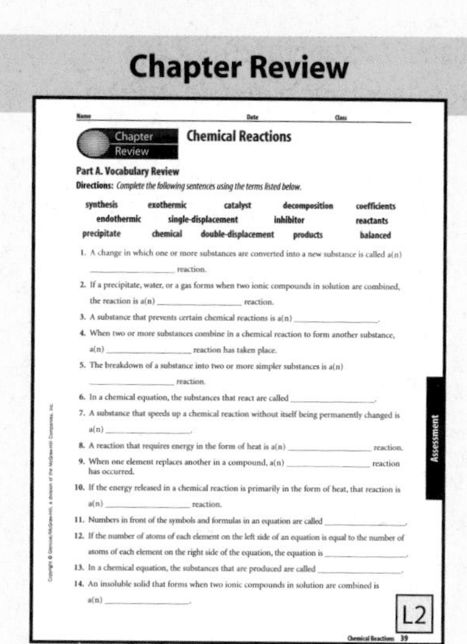

Name Date Class

Chapter Review — Chemical Reactions

Part A. Vocabulary Review

Directions: Complete the following sentences using the terms listed below.

synthesis; exothermic; catalyst; decomposition; coefficients; endothermic; single-displacement; inhibitor; reactants; precipitate; chemical; double-displacement; products; balanced

1. A change in which one or more substances are converted into a new substance is called a(n) __________ reaction.
2. If a precipitate, water, or a gas forms when two ionic compounds in solution are combined, the reaction is a(n) __________ reaction.
3. A substance that prevents certain chemical reactions is a(n) __________.
4. When two or more substances combine in a chemical reaction to form another substance, a(n) __________ reaction has taken place.
5. The breakdown of a substance into two or more simpler substances is a(n) __________ reaction.
6. In a chemical equation, the substances that react are called __________.
7. A substance that speeds up a chemical reaction without itself being permanently changed is a(n) __________.
8. A reaction that requires energy in the form of heat is a(n) __________ reaction.
9. When one element replaces another in a compound, a(n) __________ reaction has occurred.
10. If the energy released in a chemical reaction is primarily in the form of heat, that reaction is a(n) __________ reaction.
11. Numbers in front of the symbols and formulas in an equation are called __________.
12. If the number of atoms of each element on the left side of an equation is equal to the number of atoms of each element on the right side of the equation, the equation is __________.
13. In a chemical equation, the substances that are produced are called __________.
14. An insoluble solid that forms when two ionic compounds in solution are combined is a(n) __________.

Assessment

L2

Chemical Reactions 39

Chapter Tests

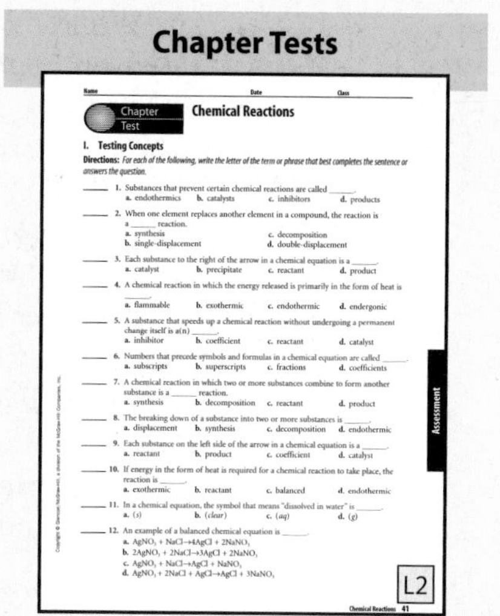

Name Date Class

Chapter Test — Chemical Reactions

I. Testing Concepts

Directions: For each of the following, write the letter of the term or phrase that best completes the sentence or answers the question.

____ 1. Substances that prevent certain chemical reactions are called _____.
a. endothermics b. catalysts c. inhibitors d. products

____ 2. When one element replaces another element in a compound, the reaction is a _____ reaction.
a. synthesis b. single-displacement c. decomposition d. double-displacement

____ 3. Each substance to the right of the arrow in a chemical equation is a _____.
a. catalyst b. precipitate c. reactant d. product

____ 4. A chemical reaction in which the energy released is primarily in the form of heat is _____.
a. flammable b. exothermic c. endothermic d. endergonic

____ 5. A substance that speeds up a chemical reaction without undergoing a permanent change itself is a(n) _____.
a. inhibitor b. coefficient c. reactant d. catalyst

____ 6. Numbers that precede symbols and formulas in a chemical equation are called _____.
a. subscripts b. superscripts c. fractions d. coefficients

____ 7. A chemical reaction in which two or more substances combine to form another substance is a _____ reaction.
a. synthesis b. decomposition c. reactant d. product

____ 8. The breaking down of a substance into two or more substances is _____.
a. displacement b. synthesis c. decomposition d. endothermic

____ 9. Each substance on the left side of the arrow in a chemical equation is a _____.
a. reactant b. product c. coefficient d. catalyst

____ 10. If energy in the form of heat is required for a chemical reaction to take place, the reaction is _____.
a. exothermic b. reactant c. balanced d. endothermic

____ 11. In a chemical equation, the symbol that means "dissolved in water" is _____.
a. (s) b. (clear) c. (aq) d. (g)

____ 12. An example of a balanced chemical equation is _____.
a. $AgNO_3 + NaCl \rightarrow 4AgCl + 2NaNO_3$
b. $2AgNO_3 + 2NaCl \rightarrow 3AgCl + 2NaNO_3$
c. $AgNO_3 + NaCl \rightarrow AgCl + NaNO_3$
d. $AgNO_3 + 2NaCl + AgCl \rightarrow AgCl + 3NaNO_3$

Assessment

L2

Chemical Reactions 41

Science Content Background

Chemical Changes

Conservation of Mass

For his work on conservation of mass, many consider eighteenth-century French scientist Antoine-Laurent Lavoisier to be the founder of modern chemistry. Lavoisier's work, done during the late 1700s, included some of the first quantitative chemical experiments ever performed. He showed that the quantity of matter is the same at the end of a chemical reaction as it is at the beginning of the reaction.

Teacher to Teacher
Jaime A. Sullivan,
South Caldwell High School
Hudson, NC

"One way to get a reaction out of the kids is to demonstrate with fire. In this case, I use a mixture of baking soda and vinegar to produce carbon dioxide, then I douse a lit candle in the CO_2. Now that they're wondering how the flame was put out, I explain that a chemical reaction took place and I show them the chemical formulas for vinegar (aqueous acetic acid, $C_2H_4O_2(aq)$) and baking soda (sodium hydrogen carbonate, $NaHCO_3$). I let them determine on their own (and they eventually will) that what is actually produced is $CO_2(g)$."

Jaime A. Sullivan

While most of Lavoisier's experiments centered on combustion, he also investigated the composition of water. In fact, he named the two components of water—hydrogen and oxygen. With the help of other scientists, he devised a chemical naming system that served as the basis of the modern system.

Lavoisier held many public offices in France, working in areas such as finance, agriculture, education, hygiene, and social welfare. In these capacities, he attempted to introduce various reforms, among them changes in the French monetary and tax systems, and also in farming methods. During the French Revolution, he and other influential French leaders fell out of favor. Lavoisier was arrested in 1793. On May 8, 1794, after a trial that lasted less than a day, Lavoisier and 27 others were beheaded.

section 2

Chemical Equations

Balanced Equations

A chemical equation must show the identities and relative amounts of the reactants and products. However, it can also indicate the physical states of the reactants and products, whether energy is released or absorbed, and whether a catalyst is used. A chemical equation is not accurate unless the formulas are correct and the equation is balanced.

section 3

Classifying Chemical Reactions

Types of Reactions

Most chemical reactions can be classified as one of five types of reactions: synthesis, decomposition, single-displacement, double-displacement, and combustion. In a double-displacement reaction, two elements replace one another in two different compounds. Double-displacement reactions occur only in solution and only if a precipitate, a gas, or water is formed.

Charles D. Winters/Photo Researchers

Chemical Reactions and Energy

Chemical Reaction—Energy Exchanges

Every reaction has a rate, or speed at which it proceeds. The study of reaction rates and reaction mechanisms is known as chemical kinetics. Temperature, concentration, particle size, catalysts, and the nature of the reactants determine the reaction rate. The rate of a reaction is not constant throughout the course of the reaction because the rate is proportional to reactant concentration. The concentration of reactants decreases as reactants are converted to products. In other words, as the reactants are used up to form products, the reactants cannot find one another as often as they could in the beginning of the reaction. This decreases the rate of reaction. To counteract this slowdown, an excess of one reactant is often used to keep the reaction from becoming impractically slow.

In 1888, the French chemist Henri Le Chatelier (1850–1936) set forth a simple important generalization on the behavior of equilibrium systems. This generalization, known as Le Chatelier's principle, states that if a stress is applied to a system at equilibrium, the system will shift to relieve that stress and restore equilibrium under a new set of conditions. The application of Le Chatelier's principle helps in predicting the effect of concentration, temperature, and volume on the rate of chemical reactions.

More Energy In

Catalysts are extremely important to industrial chemistry. Many industrial processes use catalysts to lower reaction temperatures, thus reducing energy costs. Once suitable catalysts are found, chemical reactions that are otherwise too slow to be of practical value may become cost-effective.

Enzymes are large proteins that act as catalysts for biological reactions. The enzyme amylase found in human digestive systems is able to catalyze the breakdown of starch to yield glucose but has no effect on cellulose, even though the two compounds are similar. This is why humans can digest a hamburger bun, but not the grass that fed the cow.

chapter content resources

Internet Resources

For additional content background, visit gpscience.com to:

- access your book online
- find references to related articles in popular science magazines
- access Web links with related content background
- access current events with science journal topics

Print Resources

Chemicals and Reactions, Jon Richards, Copper Beach Books, Brookfield, CT, 2000

Energy and Chemical Change, Brian J. Knapp, Grolier Educational, Danbury, CT, 1998

Oxidation and Reduction, Brian J. Knapp, Grolier Educational, Danbury, CT, 1998

Inquiry-Based Experiments in Chemistry, Valerie Lechtanski, Oxford University Press, 2000

John Paul Endress/The Stock Market

chapter 21

About the Photo

Fireworks All of the fireworks effects we enjoy, including the vibrant colors and the boom of the explosions, are the result of chemical reactions. The colors come from small amounts of metal ions-blue from copper, red from lithium, gold from sodium, and green from barium. The booms and bangs are the result of chemical reactions with oxygen.

Science Journal Most responses will be chemical reactions.

BIG Idea

Reaction Rate and Temperature For a chemical reaction to occur, the reactant atoms or molecules must collide. If these particles are moving fast enough, their collision can cause chemical bonds to break and new chemical bonds to form. At a given temperature, atoms and molecules are moving with a range of speeds. By increasing the temperature, these particles move faster on average, and more particles have enough kinetic energy to cause the reaction to occur when they collide. As a result, the reaction rate usually increases as temperature increases.

Introduce the Chapter Ask students to list the kinds of changes they think can occur during chemical reactions. Then ask students why they think chemical reactions occur or do not occur when wood or gasoline is burned and when food is cooked.

chapter 21

Chemical Reactions

BIG Idea A chemical reaction involves changing one or more substances into a different substance or substances.

21.1 Chemical Changes

MAIN Idea The rearrangement of atoms in a chemical change is described by a chemical equation.

21.2 Chemical Equations

MAIN Idea A balanced chemical equation contains the same numbers and types of atoms in the reactants as in the products.

21.3 Classifying Chemical Reactions

MAIN Idea Reactions can be classified based on how atoms are rearranged.

21.4 Chemical Reactions and Energy

MAIN Idea Exergonic reactions release energy and endergonic reactions absorb energy.

All-American Chemistry

Few things are as American as fireworks on the Fourth of July. Crowds everywhere enjoy the explosions of color and deafening booms. These sights and sounds are the results of chemical reactions.

Science Journal

Describe several events that might happen in your refrigerator. Later, decide which of the events are chemical reactions.

630

Interactive Chalkboard

This CD-ROM is an editable Microsoft® PowerPoint® presentation that includes:

- an editable presentation for every chapter
- additional chapter questions
- animated graphics
- image bank
- links to gpscience.com

Start-Up Activities

Rusting—A Chemical Reaction

Like exploding fireworks, rusting is a chemical reaction in which iron metal combines with oxygen. Other metals combine with oxygen, too—some more readily than others. In this lab, you will compare how iron and aluminum react with oxygen.

1. Place a clean iron or steel nail in a dish prepared by your teacher.
2. Place a clean aluminum nail in a second dish. These dishes contain agar gel and an indicator that detects a reaction with oxygen.
3. Observe both nails after one hour. Record any changes around the nails in your Science Journal.
4. Carefully examine both of the dishes the next day.
5. **Think Critically** Record any differences you noticed between the two dishes. Predict if a reaction occurred. How can you tell? What might have caused the differences you observed between the two nails. Explain.

Preview this chapter's content and activities at gpscience.com

FOLDABLES™ Study Organizer

Chemical Reactions Make the following Foldable to help you classify chemical reactions.

STEP 1 **Fold** a sheet of paper in half lengthwise.

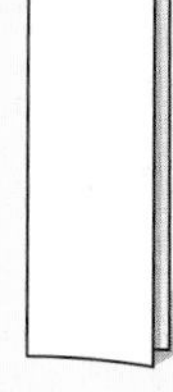

STEP 2 **Mark** four lines evenly spaced at even intervals down the page.

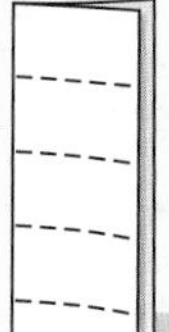

STEP 3 **Cut** only the top layer along the four marks to make five tabs.

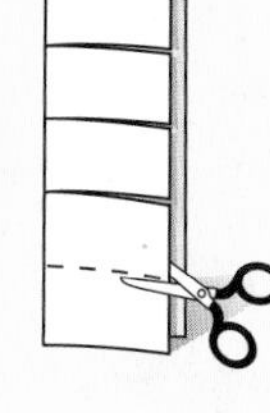

STEP 4 **Label** the tabs as shown.

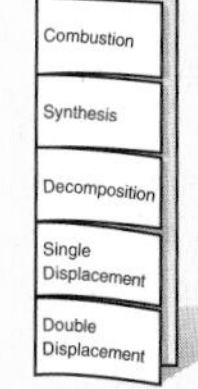

Classify As you read, record examples of each type of reaction from the book, then review the chapter and list other examples mentioned in the text or from classroom discussions.

Additional Chapter Media

- What's Science Got to Do With It?: *Arson Investigation*
- Virtual Lab: *What is a balanced chemical equation?*
- Video Lab: *Designing a Team Equation*

Purpose Use this Launch Lab to introduce students to chemical reactions and to the evidence that a chemical change has occurred. L2 ELL LS **Visual-Spatial**

Preparation Prepare agar by dissolving about ½ teaspoon of agar in about 240 mL of water. Heat just until boiling. Cool slightly and stir in 2 mL of 1% phenolphthalein (in alcohol) solution. Pour enough solution into the petri dishes to partly submerge the nails. Strips of aluminum cut from aluminum pie tins may be used in place of aluminum nails. **CAUTION:** aluminum strips may have sharp edges. For this lab, use only uncoated nails.

Materials agar mixture, petri dishes, aluminum nails, iron nails

Teaching Strategy Ask students how we know when a chemical change has taken place. evidence such as color changes

Think Critically

Rusting involves many chemical reactions. Among them is the formation of iron hydroxides, which cause the phenolphthalein to turn pink. The red-brown color that appears later indicates the formation of iron(III) oxide. Aluminum reacts slowly with oxygen, but this will not be visible here.

Assessment

Process Have students use colored markers to draw the two colors observed with the iron nail. Point out that these represent two different reactions. L2

Dinah Zike Study Fold

Student preparation materials for this Foldable are available in the Chapter *Fast File* Resources.

Chemical Changes

1 Motivate

Bellringer

Section Focus Transparencies also are available on the Interactive Chalkboard CD-ROM. L2 

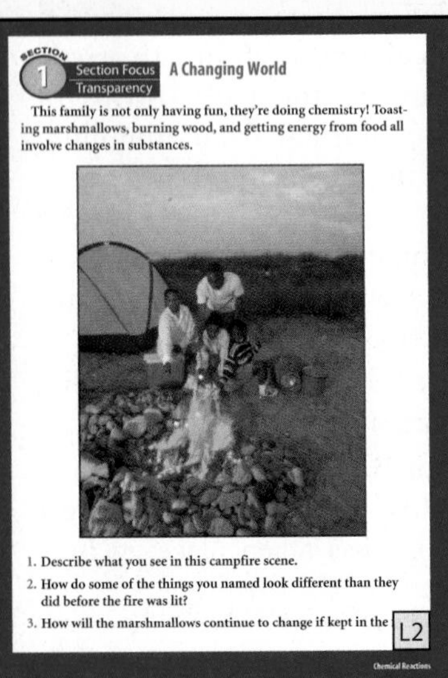
SECTION 1 Section Focus Transparency A Changing World

This family is not only having fun, they're doing chemistry! Toasting marshmallows, burning wood, and getting energy from food all involve changes in substances.

1. Describe what you see in this campfire scene.
2. How do some of the things you named look different than they did before the fire was lit?
3. How will the marshmallows continue to change if kept in the

L2

Chemical Reactions

Tie to Prior Knowledge

Observing Reactions Ask students to describe evidence they have observed of chemical reactions. Examples will vary but could include evolution of a gas (baking soda and vinegar); production of heat and light (burning a fuel); color change (cooking a hot dog over a fire); formation of a precipitate (spoiling of milk.) L2

Reading Guide

***What* You'll Learn**

- **Identify** the reactants and products in a chemical reaction.
- **Determine** how a chemical reaction satisfies the law of conservation of mass.
- **Determine** how chemists express chemical changes using equations.

***Why* It's Important**

Chemical reactions cook our food, warm our homes, and provide energy for our bodies.

Review Vocabulary

equation: a statement of the equality or equivalence of mathematical or logical quantities

New Vocabulary

- chemical reaction
- reactant
- product
- chemical equation
- coefficient

Describing Chemical Reactions

Dark mysterious mixtures react, gas bubbles up and expands, and powerful aromas waft through the air. Where are you? Are you in a chemical laboratory carrying out a crucial experiment? No. You are in the kitchen baking a chocolate cake. Nowhere in the house do so many chemical reactions take place as in the kitchen.

Actually, chemical reactions are taking place all around you and even within you. A **chemical reaction** is a change in which one or more substances are converted into new substances. The substances that react are called **reactants.** The new substances produced are called **products.** This relationship can be written as follows:

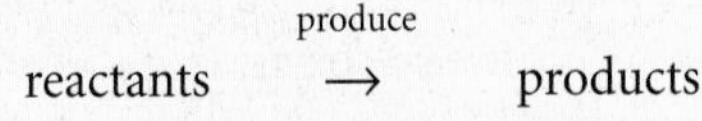

$$\text{reactants} \xrightarrow{\text{produce}} \text{products}$$

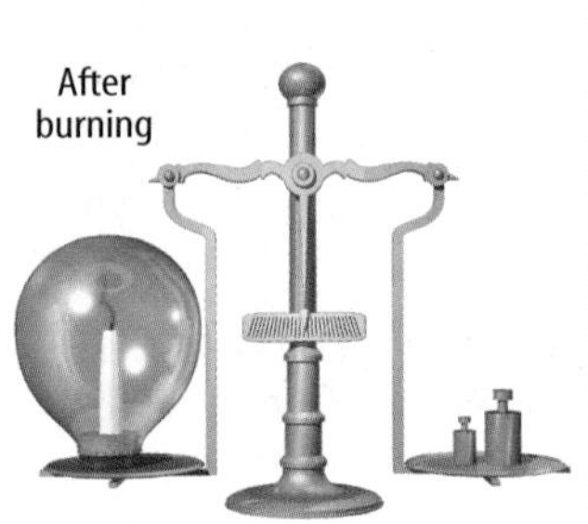

Figure 1 The mass of the candles and oxygen before burning is exactly equal to the mass of the remaining candle and gaseous products.

Conservation of Mass

By the 1770s, chemistry was changing from the art of alchemy to a true science. Instead of being satisfied with a superficial explanation of unknown events, scientists began to study chemical reactions more thoroughly. Through such study, the French chemist Antoine Lavoisier established that the total mass of the products always equals the total mass of the reactants. This principle is demonstrated in **Figure 1.**

Section 1 Resource Manager

Chapter *Fast File* Resources

Transparency Activity, pp. 46, 51–52
Directed Reading for Content Mastery, pp. 19, 20
Enrichment, p. 31
MiniLAB, p. 3
Reinforcement, p. 27

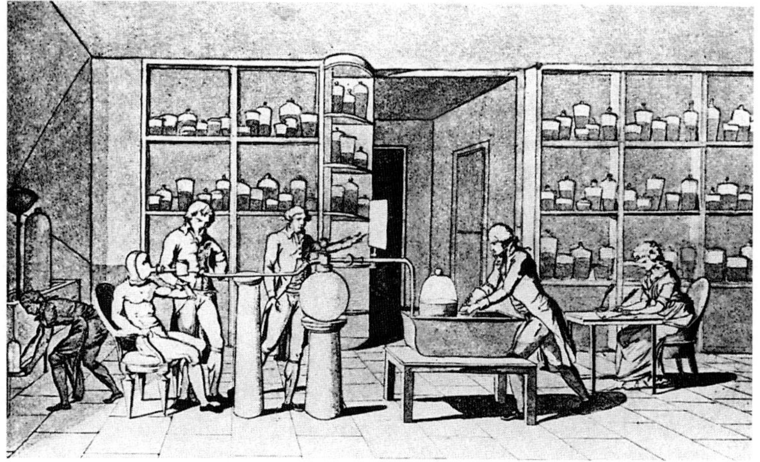

Figure 2 Antoine Lavoisier's wife, Marie-Anne, drew this view of Lavoisier in his laboratory performing studies on oxygen. She depicted herself at the right taking notes.

Lavoisier's Contribution One of the questions that motivated Lavoisier was the mystery of exactly what happened when substances changed form. He began to answer this question by experimenting with mercury. In one experiment, Lavoisier placed a carefully measured mass of solid mercury(II) oxide, which he knew as mercury calx, into a sealed container. When he heated this container, he noted a dramatic change. The red powder had been transformed into a silvery liquid that he recognized as mercury metal, and a gas was produced. When he determined the mass of the liquid mercury and gas, their combined masses were exactly the same as the mass of the red powder he had started with.

mercury(II) oxide		oxygen	plus	mercury
10.0 g	=	0.7 g	+	9.3 g

Lavoisier also established that the gas produced by heating mercury(II) oxide, which we call oxygen, was a component of air. He did this by heating mercury metal with air and saw that a portion of the air combined to give red mercury(II) oxide. He studied the effect of this gas on living animals, including himself. Hundreds of experiments carried out in his laboratory, as shown in **Figure 2,** confirmed that in a chemical reaction, matter is not created or destroyed, but is conserved. This principle became known as the law of conservation of mass. This means that the total starting mass of all reactants equals the total final mass of all products.

Reading Check *What does the law of conservation of mass state?*

Topic: Antoine Lavoisier
Visit gpscience.com for Web links to information about Antoine Lavoisier and his contributions to chemistry.

Activity In your Science Journal, write a brief biography of Antoine Lavoisier that includes some of his non-scientific activities and political interests, as well as his scientific contributions.

2 Teach

Use an Analogy

Balancing a Ledger Lavoisier's background included tax collecting and auditing. Balancing a ledger is somewhat like balancing a chemical equation. One must carefully consider what goes in and what comes out without losing anything. L2

Quick Demo

Conservation of Mass

Materials camera with removable flashcube; balance or scale

Estimated Time 15 minutes

Procedure In class, determine the mass of an unused flashcube. Attach the flashcube to the camera and snap a picture using the flash. Measure the mass of the flashcube after its use. Explain that the flash and the appearance of a whitish powder show that a chemical change has occurred. The fact that the mass of the flashcube remains constant indicates that mass is conserved. L2 ELL IS **Visual-Spatial**

Reading Check

Answer In a chemical reaction, matter is not created or destroyed.

Curriculum Connection

History Have students research and write a short report about the time period in France in which Lavoisier lived (mid- to late-eighteenth century). For comparison and perspective, have them relate the same period to the happenings in America. L2 P IS **Linguistic**

SECTION 1 Chemical Changes 633

Activity

Table of Elements Lavoisier was an early contributor to what became the periodic table of elements. Have students use the library or Internet to find the names of other scientists who helped shape and fill the table. L2

Nomenclature Students may think that there is only one form of nomenclature that serves all branches of science. Explain that different disciplines have different forms of specific nomenclature, but at the same time emphasize that nomenclature is consistent within each area. Also emphasize that guidelines are established to maintain consistency and uniformity and that the guidelines for nomenclature are often similar across disciplines. This makes it possible for scientists whose work crosses scientific boundaries to communicate effectively.

Reading Check

Answer He explained the theory of conservation of mass and was key in developing modern chemical nomenclature.

The Father of Modern Chemistry When Lavoisier demonstrated the law of conservation of mass, he set the field of chemistry on its modern path. In fact, Lavoisier is known today as the father of modern chemistry for his more accurate explanation of the conservation of mass and for describing a common type of chemical reaction called combustion, which you will learn about later in this chapter. Lavoisier also pioneered early experimentation on the biological phenomena of respiration and metabolism that contributed early milestones in the study of biochemistry, medicine, and even sports science.

Nomenclature Lavoisier's work led him to the conclusion that language and terminology would be critical to communicate novel scientific ideas. In his book *Elements of Chemistry* (1790), Lavoisier wrote, "…we cannot improve a science without improving the language or nomenclature which belongs to it…" With that recognition, Lavoisier began to develop the system of naming substances based on their composition that we still use today. In 1787, Lavoisier and several colleagues published *Méthode de Nomenclature Chimique* as one of the first sets of nomenclature guidelines. Since then, the guidelines have continued to evolve with scientific discovery, and in 1919 the International Union of Pure and Applied Chemistry (IUPAC) was formed. The primary mission of the IUPAC is to coordinate guidelines for naming chemical compounds systematically. Before a new element gets a permanent name, it has a IUPAC name. Element 110, which is now called darmstadium, was previously named ununnilium. **Figure 3** illustrates some of the early key events in nomenclature development.

Reading Check ***How did Lavoisier's contributions earn him the name Father of Modern Chemistry?***

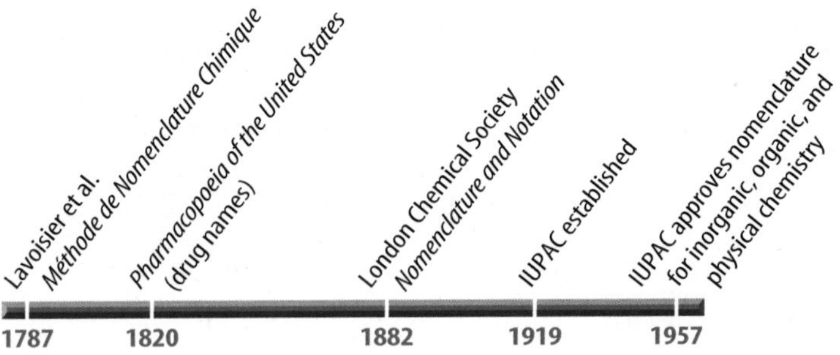

Figure 3 This time line of nomenclature development and publications does not end in 1957. In fact, today there are nomenclature organizations for almost every branch of scientific study, and the rules and guidelines for naming substances continue to evolve.

Differentiated Instruction

English-Language Learners Express to the class that scientists from many countries have made significant contributions to general science. Recount the scientific contributions of the Frenchman Lavoisier and have non-English language speakers read a chemical reaction so they can recognize that the formulas and notation are the same, regardless of the language of the scientist. L2 ELL

Challenge Photographs are made using a chemical reaction driven by exposure to light. Ask students to find out what metal is typically involved in the process. Silver ions in silver bromide (AgBr) can be changed to silver metal when exposed to light. L3 IN **Linguistic**

Writing Equations

If you wanted to describe the chemical reaction shown in **Figure 4,** you might write something like this:

Nickel(II) chloride, dissolved in water, plus sodium hydroxide, dissolved in water, produces solid nickel(II) hydroxide plus sodium chloride, dissolved in water.

This series of words is rather cumbersome, but all of the information is important. The same is true of descriptions of most chemical reactions. Many words are needed to state all the important information. As a result, scientists have developed a shorthand method to describe chemical reactions. A **chemical equation** is a way to describe a chemical reaction using chemical formulas and other symbols. Some of the symbols used in chemical equations are listed in **Table 1.**

The chemical equation for the reaction described above in words and shown in **Figure 4** looks like this:

$$NiCl_2(aq) + 2NaOH(aq) \rightarrow Ni(OH)_2(s) + 2NaCl(aq)$$

It is much easier to tell what is happening by writing the information in this form. Later, you will learn how chemical equations make it easier to calculate the quantities of reactants that are needed and the quantities of products that are formed.

Table 1 Symbols Used in Chemical Equations

Symbol	Meaning
$\rightarrow$	produces or forms
+	plus
(*s*)	solid
(*l*)	liquid
(*g*)	gas
(*aq*)	aqueous, a substance is dissolved in water
heat $\rightarrow$	the reactants are heated
light $\rightarrow$	the reactants are exposed to light
elec. $\rightarrow$	an electric current is applied to the reactants

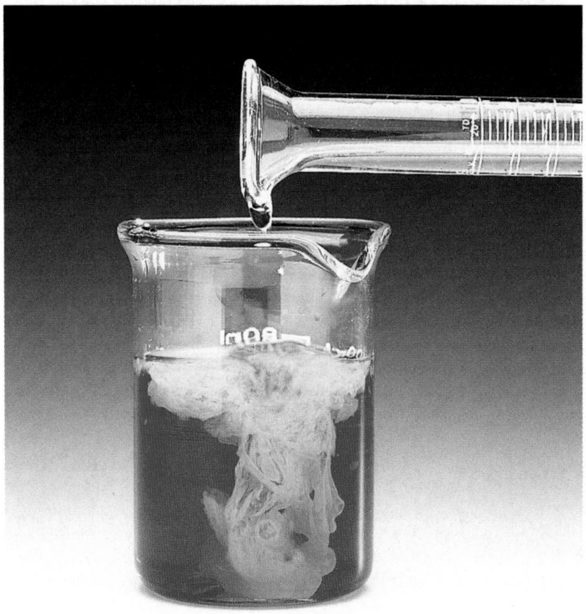

Figure 4 A white precipitate of nickel(II) hydroxide forms when sodium hydroxide is added to a green solution of nickel(II) chloride. Sodium chloride, the other product formed, is in solution.

Use an Analogy

Baseball Scores Have a baseball coach or interested student bring in a scorer's record book from a baseball game. The records are kept for each inning with accepted symbols for events such as strikeout (K), home run (HR), infield out made by throw from third to first base (5-3), etc. The symbols in baseball allow a great deal of information to be recorded accurately in a small space. Chemical equations do this as well. L2 LS **Logical-Mathematical**

Discussion

Burning Copper Burning a piece of copper in a flame will produce a product that has a greater mass than the original copper. Why doesn't this violate the law of conservation of mass? The mass of oxygen participating in the burning process must be included as part of the mass of the reactants. L2 LS **Logical-Mathematical**

Fun Fact

Lavoisier was an early advocate of the use of chemical equations. He used symbols to show both the identity and quantity of materials in reactions and thought that algebra was the best language for expressing scientific information. He wrote, "In order to show at a glance the results of what happens . . . I have constituted formulae of a kind that could at first be taken for algebraic formulae . . ."

Teacher FYI

Chemist Symbols Some chemists use the symbol (cr) to represent solids that are crystals and (amor) to represent amorphous solids, which have no definite structure.

Purpose Students see that coefficients are not conserved in a chemical equation but that mass is. L2 IN **Logical-Mathematical**

Materials 15 index cards per student, markers

Teaching Strategy Suggest students redo the activity, varying the composition of a team.

Analysis

1. G_2F_2C; 2 guards + 2 forwards + 1 center → 1 team
2. The equation uses coefficients like a chemical equation, and it shows conservation of mass. Only a specific number of each type of player can be used per team. Those left over sit on the bench (cannot be used).
3. The total number of cards at the beginning equals the number of leftover cards plus the cards being used for the team.

Assessment

Oral Ask students how many guards would be needed to make four teams. $4 \times 2 = 8$ How many complete teams could be made around 5 centers? $5 \times 1 = 5$ teams How many players would be left over when the following players assembled to make teams: 10 guards, 9 forwards, and 5 centers? $\frac{9}{2} = 4$ teams with 1 extra forward, 1 extra center, 2 extra guards Use **Performance Assessment in the Science Classroom,** p. 101.

Designing a Team Equation

Procedure

1. Obtain **15 index cards** and mark each as follows: five with *Guard,* five with *Forward,* and five with *Center.*
2. Group the cards to form as many complete basketball teams as possible. Each team needs two guards, two forwards, and one center.

Analysis

1. Write the formula for a team. Write the formation of a team as an equation. Use coefficients in front of each type of player needed for a team.
2. How is this equation like a chemical equation? Why can't you use the remaining cards?
3. How do the remaining cards illustrate the law of conservation of matter in this example?

Try at Home

Unit Managers

What do the numbers to the left of the formulas for reactants and products mean? Remember that according to the law of conservation of mass, matter is neither made nor lost during chemical reactions. Atoms are rearranged but never lost or destroyed. These numbers, called **coefficients,** represent the number of units of each substance taking part in a reaction. Coefficients can be thought of as unit managers.

Reading Check *What is the function of coefficients in a chemical equation?*

Imagine that you are responsible for making sandwiches for a picnic. You have been told to make a certain number of three kinds of sandwiches, and that no substitutions can be made. You would have to figure out exactly how much food to buy so that you had enough without any food left over. You might need two loaves of bread, four packages of turkey, four packages of cheese, two heads of lettuce, and ten tomatoes. With these supplies you could make exactly the right number of each kind of sandwich.

In a way, your sandwich-making effort is like a chemical reaction. The reactants are your bread, turkey, cheese, lettuce, and tomatoes. The number of units of each ingredient are like the coefficients of the reactants in an equation. The sandwiches are like the products, and the numbers of each kind of sandwich are like coefficients, also.

Knowing the number of units of reactants enables chemists to add the correct amounts of reactants to a reaction. Also, these units, or coefficients, tell them exactly how much product will form. An example of this is the reaction of one unit of $NiCl_2$ with two units of NaOH to produce one unit of $Ni(OH)_2$ and two units of NaCl. You can see these units in **Figure 5.**

Figure 5 Each coefficient in the equation represents the number of units of each type in this reaction.

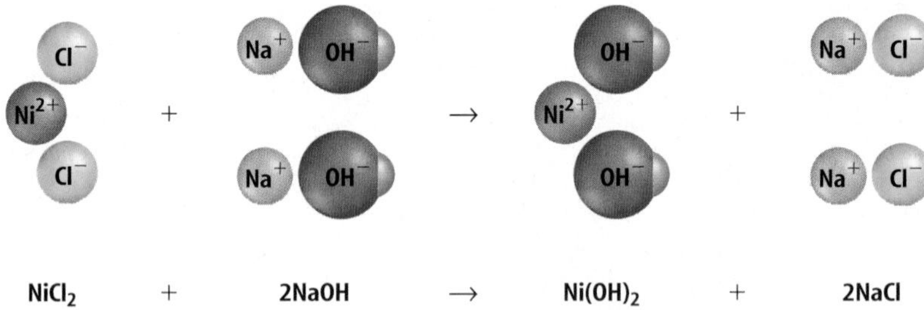

Reading Check

Answer They act as unit managers, representing the number of units of each substance taking part in a reaction.

Visual Learning

Figure 5 Have students count the atoms in the illustration and match them with the formulas in the equation. Point out which atoms combine to form each product. L2 IN **Visual-Spatial**

Science Journal

Soda Coefficients Have students calculate the total amount of soft drink in two 2-L bottles, three six-packs of 355-mL cans, and one case of 355-mL cans. Total = 4,000 + 6,390 + 8,520 = 18,910 mL. The coefficients in *2 bottles, 3 six-packs,* and *1 case* indicate the number of packaged units. Coefficients in a chemical equation indicate the number of units of atoms. L2

Metals and the Atmosphere

When iron is exposed to air and moisture, it corrodes or rusts, forming hydrated iron(III) oxide. Rust can seriously damage iron structures because it crumbles and exposes more iron to the air. This leads to more breakdown of the iron and eventually can destroy the structure. However, not all reactions of metals with the atmosphere are damaging like rust. Some are helpful.

Aluminum also reacts with oxygen in the air to form aluminum oxide. Unlike rust, aluminum oxide adheres to the aluminum surface, forming an extremely thin layer that protects the aluminum from further attack. You can see this thin layer of aluminum oxide on aluminum outdoor furniture. It makes the once shiny aluminum look dull.

Copper is another metal that corrodes when it is exposed to air, forming a blue-green coating called a patina. You can see this type of corrosion on many public monuments and also on the Statue of Liberty, shown in **Figure 6.**

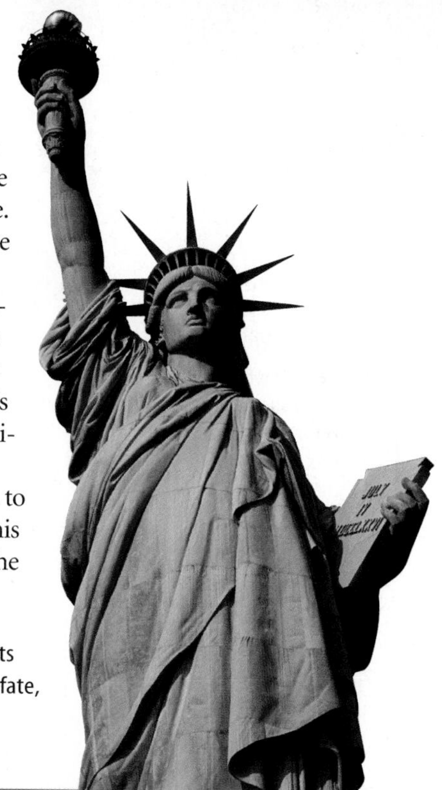

Figure 6 The blue-green patina that coats the Statue of Liberty contains copper(II) sulfate, among other copper corrosion products.

section 1 review

Summary

Describing Chemical Reactions

- A chemical reaction is a process that involves one or more reactants changing into one or more products.

Conservation of Mass

- A basic principle of chemistry is that matter, during a chemical change, can neither be created nor destroyed.
- Antoine Lavoisier is often considered to be "the father of modern chemistry" for his work in defining the law of conservation of mass.

Writing Equations

- Chemical equations describe the change of reactants to products and obey the law of conservation of mass.

Unit Managers

- Coefficients represent how many units of each substance are involved in a chemical reaction.

Self Check

1. **Identify** the reactants and the products in the following chemical equation.
   $Cd(NO_3)_2(aq) + H_2S(g) \longrightarrow CdS(s) + 2HNO_3(aq)$
2. **Identify** the state of matter of each substance in the following reaction.
   $Zn(s) + 2HCl(aq) \longrightarrow H_2(g) + ZnCl_2(aq)$
3. **Explain** why the reaction of oxygen with iron is a problem, but the reaction of oxygen with aluminum is not.
4. **Explain** the importance of the law of conservation of mass.
5. **Think Critically** Why do you think the copper patina was kept when the Statue of Liberty was restored?

Applying Math

6. **Solve One-Step Equations** When making soap, if 890 g of a specific fat react completely with 120 g of sodium hydroxide, the products formed are soap and 92 g of glycerin. Calculate the mass of soap formed to satisfy the law of conservation of mass.

Science Online gpscience.com/self_check_quiz

section 1 review

1. reactants: $Cd(NO_3)_2$ and H_2S; products: CdS and HNO_3
2. Zn is a solid, HCl is dissolved in water, H_2 is a gas, and $ZnCl_2$ is dissolved in water.
3. Iron and oxygen form a compound that flakes off and eventually destroys the iron structure. The aluminum-oxygen compound is resistant to further reaction and adheres to the original aluminum, forming a protective coat.
4. The law of conservation of mass explains why matter in the universe does not go away permanently.
5. It protects the statue.
6. 890 + 120 = 1,010 g of reactant, which must equal 1,010 g of product; 1,010 − 92 = 918 g of soap.

3 Assess

DAILY INTERVENTION

Check for Understanding

Chemistry Flashcards Create a set of chemistry flashcards by writing the chemical formulas for a variety of substances on standard index cards. Also write several forward-pointing arrows on some cards. Have students create basic chemical reactions demonstrating the concept of "reactants produce products". Remember when creating the flashcards to include appropriate product substances to pair with the reactants. L2

Reteach

Understanding Coefficients Show that the balanced equation for the decomposition of water is $2H_2O \rightarrow 2H_2 + O_2$. Ask students to use the coefficients to determine the number of hydrogen and oxygen atoms on each side of the equation. 4 hydrogens and 2 oxygens on the left side and 4 hydrogens and 2 oxygens on the right side L1 LS **Logical-Mathematical**

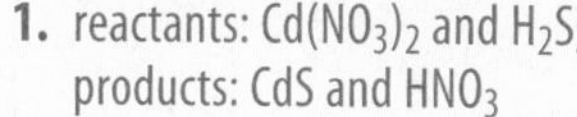

Assessment

Performance Have students examine this unbalanced equation for the rusting of iron ($Fe + O_2 + H_2O \rightarrow Fe_2O_3 \cdot 3H_2O$) to determine the products and reactants and use coefficients to balance the equation. The dot between Fe_2O_3 and $3H_2O$ shows that three water molecules are contained in the product. $4Fe + 3O_2 + 6H_2O \rightarrow 2Fe_2O_3 \cdot 3H_2O$
Use **Performance Assessment in the Science Classroom,** p. 101. L2

1 Motivate

Bellringer

Section Focus Transparencies also are available on the Interactive Chalkboard CD-ROM.

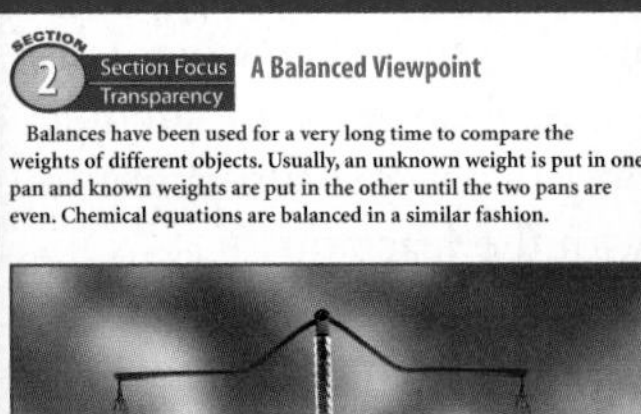

SECTION 2 Section Focus Transparency **A Balanced Viewpoint**

Balances have been used for a very long time to compare the weights of different objects. Usually, an unknown weight is put in one pan and known weights are put in the other until the two pans are even. Chemical equations are balanced in a similar fashion.

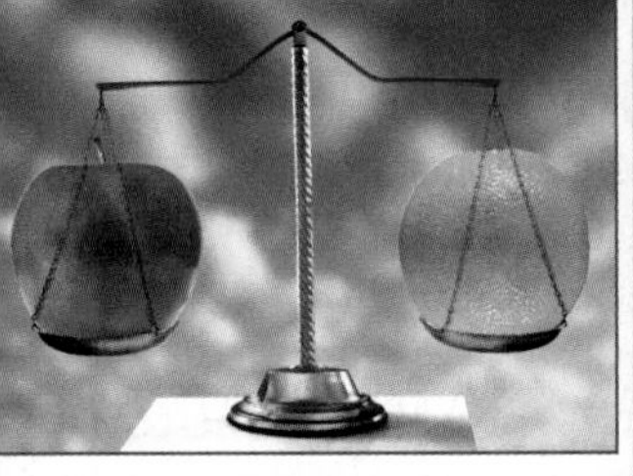

1. How is the arrow in a chemical equation like the fulcrum of a balance?
2. If you could put all the reactants of a chemical reaction in one pan of a balance and all the products in the other pan, would the two pans be even? Explain.

L2

Tie to Prior Knowledge

Building Blocks Ask students if they remember attachable plastic building blocks. Remind students that the structures could be disassembled to make different objects from the same blocks. In a similar way, a balanced chemical equation represents the rearrangement of a set of atoms into new compounds.

section 2

Chemical Equations

Reading Guide

What **You'll Learn**

- **Identify** what is meant by a balanced chemical equation.
- **Determine** how to write balanced chemical equations.

Why **It's Important**

Chemical equations are the language used to describe chemical change, which allow scientists to develop products for our world.

Review Vocabulary

subscript: in a chemical formula, a number below and to the right of a symbol indicating number of atoms

New Vocabulary

- balanced chemical equation

Balanced Equations

Lavoisier's mercury(II) oxide reaction, shown in **Figure 7**, can be written as:

$$HgO(s) \xrightarrow{\text{heat}} Hg(l) + O_2(g)$$

Notice that the number of mercury atoms is the same on both sides of the equation but that the number of oxygen atoms is not the same. One oxygen atom appears on the reactant side of the equation and two appear on the product side.

Atoms	HgO	→	Hg	+	O_2
Hg	1		1		
O	1				2

Figure 7 Mercury metal forms when mercury oxide is heated. Because mercury is poisonous, this reaction is never performed in a classroom laboratory.

But according to the law of conservation of mass, one oxygen atom cannot just become two. Nor can you simply add the subscript 2 and write HgO_2 instead of HgO. The formulas HgO_2 and HgO do not represent the same compound. In fact, HgO_2 does not exist. The formulas in a chemical equation must accurately represent the compounds that react.

Fixing this equation requires a process called balancing. Balancing an equation doesn't change what happens in a reaction—it simply changes the way the reaction is represented. The balancing process involves changing coefficients in a reaction to achieve a **balanced chemical equation,** which has the same number of atoms of each element on both sides of the equation.

Section 2 Resource Manager

Chapter *Fast File* Resources

- Transparency Activity, p. 47
- Directed Reading for Content Mastery, p. 20
- Lab Activity, pp. 13–16
- Reinforcement, p. 28
- Enrichment, p. 32

Home and Community Involvement, p. 46

638 CHAPTER 21 Chemical Reactions

Choosing Coefficients Finding out which coefficients to use to balance an equation is often a trial-and-error process. In the equation for Lavoisier's experiment, the number of mercury atoms is balanced, but one oxygen atom is on the left and two are on the right. If you put a coefficient of 2 before the HgO on the left, the oxygen atoms will be balanced, but the mercury atoms become unbalanced. To balance the equation, also put a 2 in front of mercury on the right. The equation is now balanced.

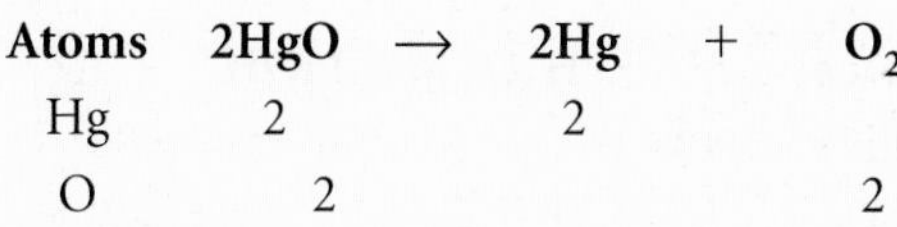

Atoms	$2HgO$	$\rightarrow$	$2Hg$	+	O_2
Hg	2		2		
O	2				2

Try Your Balancing Act Magnesium burns with such a brilliant white light that it is often used in emergency flares as shown in **Figure 8.** Burning leaves a white powder called magnesium oxide. To write a balanced chemical equation for this and most other reactions, follow these four steps.

Step 1 Write a chemical equation for the reaction using formulas and symbols. Recall that oxygen is a diatomic molecule.

$$Mg(s) + O_2(g) \rightarrow MgO(s)$$

Step 2 Count the atoms in reactants and products.

Atoms	Mg	+	O_2	$\rightarrow$	MgO
Mg	1				1
O			2		1

The magnesium atoms are balanced, but the oxygen atoms are not. Therefore, this equation isn't balanced.

Step 3 Choose coefficients that balance the equation. Remember, never change subscripts of a correct formula to balance an equation. Try putting a coefficient of 2 before MgO.

$$Mg(s) + O_2(g) \rightarrow 2MgO(s)$$

Step 4 Recheck the numbers of each atom on each side of the equation and adjust coefficients again if necessary. Now two Mg atoms are on the right side and only one is on the left side. So a coefficient of 2 is needed for Mg to balance the equation.

$$2Mg(s) + O_2(g) \rightarrow 2MgO(s)$$

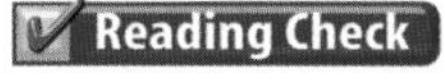

How can you balance a chemical equation using coefficients?

Topic: Balancing Chemical Equations
Visit gpscience.com for Web links to information about balancing chemical equations.

Activity Using the Web links, locate a website that offers practice problems for balancing chemical equations. Copy several of the unbalanced equations in your Science Journal and try to balance them. Check your work against the answers on the web site when you are done.

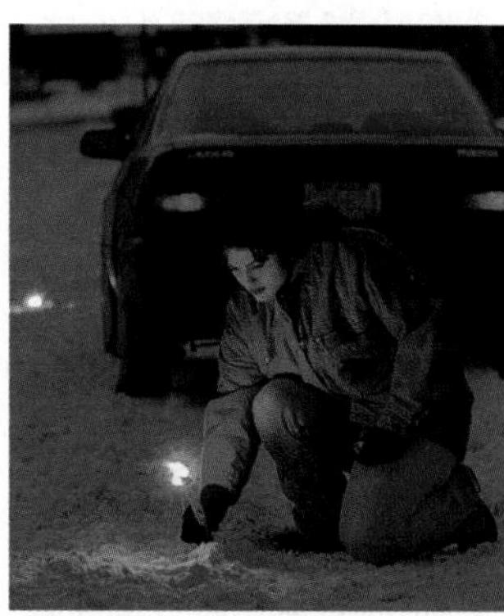

Figure 8 Magnesium combines with oxygen, giving an intense white light.

2 Teach

Teacher FYI

Calculating Fractions Fractions can be used to balance chemical equations. $Na + Cl_2 \rightarrow NaCl$ can be balanced as $2Na + Cl_2 \rightarrow 2NaCl$ or as $Na + \frac{1}{2}Cl_2 \rightarrow NaCl$. Fractions are used mainly when the calculations involve the formation of only one unit of a product.

Fun Fact

Air bags should really be called nitrogen bags. They are not filled with air, but with nitrogen.

Reading Check

Answer by a trial-and-error process, then by counting the number of atoms of reactant and product molecules

Virtual Labs

In Balance *What is a balanced chemical equation?*

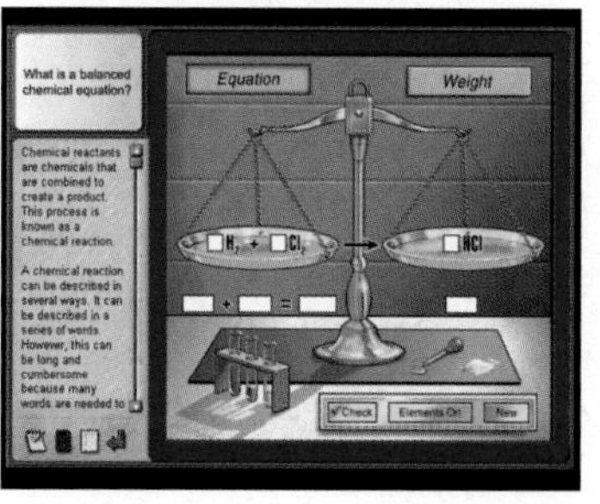

Discussion

Balancing Strategies Discuss with the class various techniques or strategies that might be helpful for students to visualize the number of atoms on each side of the equation and work through the process of assigning coefficients. Encourage students to share their individual processes.

Differentiated Instruction

Learning Disabled The concept of coefficients may be difficult for students to understand. Take time to relate the use of coefficients in chemical equations to the students' mathematics experience. In this instruction use simple, non-chemical examples to illustrate the concept of coefficients.

Challenge Safety air bags in automobiles depend on a chemical reaction to inflate. Have students supply the coefficients needed to balance the equation: $NaN_3(s) \rightarrow Na(g) + N_2(g)$ $2NaN_3(s) \rightarrow 2Na(s) + 3N_2(g)$ L3

3 Assess

DAILY INTERVENTION

Check for Understanding

Logical-Mathematical Bring a disposable butane lighter to class. Write the formula for butane, C_4H_{10}, on the chalkboard, and as you light the lighter, ask students to identify the chemical reaction taking place. Oxygen is combining with the carbon and hydrogen to produce water and carbon dioxide. Have them write and balance the equation for the reaction. $2C_4H_{10} + 13O_2 \rightarrow 8CO_2 + 10H_2O$ L3 LS

Reteach

Molecular View Using the style of **Figure 5,** draw on the chalkboard the structures of $Ca(OH)_2$, H_3PO_4, $Ca_3(PO_4)_2$, and H_2O. Tell students that calcium hydroxide reacts with hydrogen phosphate to produce calcium phosphate and water. Ask students to write the balanced chemical equation for this reaction. $3Ca(OH)_2 + 2H_3PO_4 \rightarrow Ca_3(PO_4)_2 + 6H_2O$ L2 LS **Visual-Spatial**

✓ Assessment

Performance Have students draw Venn diagrams to contrast the changes in chemical reactions with those in nuclear reactions. In a chemical change, the atoms do not change their basic identity. In nuclear changes, the identity of an atom is often changed. Use **Performance Assessment in the Science Classroom,** p. 167. P L3

Figure 9 When lithium metal is added to water, it reacts, producing a solution of lithium hydroxide and bubbles of hydrogen gas.

Polish Your Skill When lithium metal is treated with water, hydrogen gas and lithium hydroxide are produced, as shown in **Figure 9.**

Step 1 Write the chemical equation.

$$Li(s) + H_2O \rightarrow LiOH(aq) + H_2(g)$$

Step 2 Check for balance by counting the atoms.

Atoms	Li	+	H_2O	→	LiOH	+	H_2
Li	1				1		
H			2		1		2
O			1		1		

This equation is not balanced. There are three hydrogen atoms on the right and only two on the left. Complete steps 3 and 4 to balance the equation. After each step, count the atoms of each element. When equal numbers of atoms of each element are on both sides, the equation is balanced. The balanced chemical equation looks like this:

$$2Li + 2H_2O \rightarrow 2LiOH + H_2$$

This accurate statement tells chemists how much lithium metal to use to produce a certain amount of hydrogen gas.

section 2 review

Summary

Balanced Equations

- A chemical equation is a way to indicate reactants and products and relative amounts of each.
- A balanced chemical equation tells the exact number of atoms involved in the reaction.
- Balanced chemical equations must satisfy the law of conservation of matter; no atoms of reactant or product can be lost from one side to the other.
- Coefficients are used to achieve balance in a chemical equation.
- Chemical equations cannot be balanced by adjusting the subscript numerals in compound names because doing so would change the compounds.

Self Check

1. **Describe** two reasons for balancing chemical equations.
2. **Balance** this chemical equation: $Fe(s) + O_2(g) \rightarrow FeO(s)$.
3. **Explain** why oxygen gas must always be written as O_2 in a chemical equation.
4. **Infer** What coefficient is assumed if no coefficient is written before a formula in a chemical equation?
5. **Think Critically** Explain why the sum of the coefficients on the reactant side of a balanced equation does not have to equal the sum of the coefficients on the product side of the equation.

Applying Math

6. **Use Numbers** Balance the equation for the reaction $Fe(s) + Cl_2(g) \rightarrow FeCl_3(s)$.

Science Online gpscience.com/self_check_quiz

section 2 review

1. Conservation of mass requires that the number of atoms of an element on the left side equals the number of atoms on the right side. Balanced equations accurately depict chemical changes.
2. $2Fe + O_2 \rightarrow 2FeO$
3. Oxygen gas exists as a diatomic molecule.
4. 1
5. The coefficients represent the number of units of a compound, not the number of atoms.
6. $2Fe(s) + 3Cl_2(g) \rightarrow 2FeCl_3(s)$

section 3

Classifying Chemical Reactions

Reading Guide

What You'll Learn

- **Identify** the five general types of chemical reactions.
- **Define** the terms *oxidation* and *reduction*.
- **Identify** redox reactions.
- **Predict** which metals will replace other metals in compounds.

Why It's Important

Classifying chemical reactions helps to understand what is happening and predict the outcome of reactions.

Review Vocabulary

states of matter: the physical forms in which all matter naturally exists, most commonly solid, liquid, and gas

New Vocabulary

- combustion reaction
- synthesis reaction
- decomposition reaction
- single-displacement reaction
- double-displacement reaction
- precipitate
- oxidation
- reduction

Types of Reactions

You might have noticed that there are all sorts of chemical reactions. In fact, there are literally millions of chemical reactions that occur every day, and scientists have described many of them and continue to describe more. With all these reactions, it would be impossible to use the information without first having some type of organization. With this in mind, chemists have defined five main categories of chemical reactions: combustion, synthesis, decomposition, single displacement, and double displacement.

Combustion Reactions If you have ever observed something burning, you have observed a combustion reaction. As mentioned previously, Lavoisier was one of the first scientists to accurately describe combustion. He deduced that the process of burning (combustion) involves the combination of a substance with oxygen. Our definition states that a **combustion reaction** occurs when a substance reacts with oxygen to produce energy in the form of heat and light. Combustion reactions also produce one or more products that contain the elements in the reactants. For example, the reaction between carbon and oxygen produces carbon dioxide. Many combustion reactions also will fit into other categories of reactions. For example, the reaction between carbon and oxygen also is a synthesis reaction.

Figure 10 Rust has accumulated on the *Titanic* since it sank in 1912.

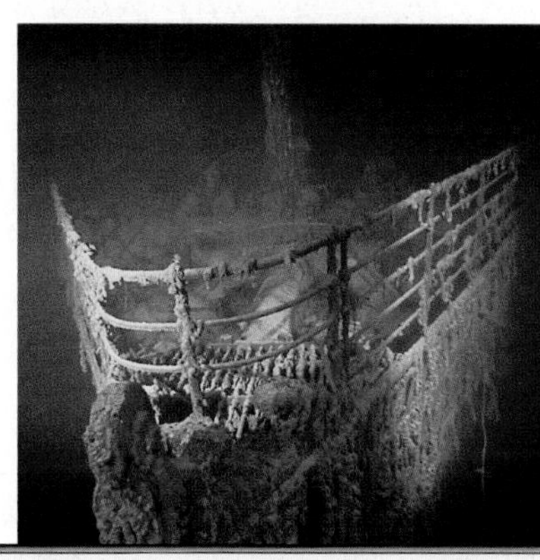

1 Motivate

Bellringer

Section Focus Transparencies also are available on the Interactive Chalkboard CD-ROM. L2 

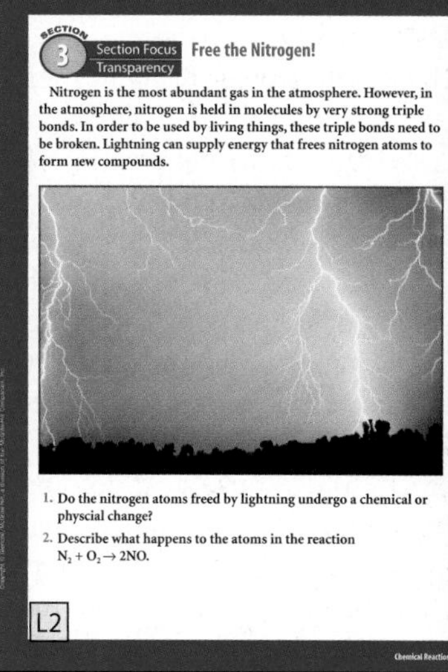

Section 3 Section Focus Transparency **Free the Nitrogen!**

Nitrogen is the most abundant gas in the atmosphere. However, in the atmosphere, nitrogen is held in molecules by very strong triple bonds. In order to be used by living things, these triple bonds need to be broken. Lightning can supply energy that frees nitrogen atoms to form new compounds.

1. Do the nitrogen atoms freed by lightning undergo a chemical or physcial change?
2. Describe what happens to the atoms in the reaction $N_2 + O_2 \rightarrow 2NO$.

L2

Chemical Reactions

Tie to Prior Knowledge

Chemical Reactions The five general types of chemical reactions are combustion, synthesis, decomposition, single displacement and double displacement. Ask students to think of situations they know in which these terms are used. Combustion—burning; Synthesis—bringing together carbon dioxide and water; decomposition—one substance converting to others as it falls apart, such as grass or leaves decomposing; single and double displacement —similar to collectors trading one or two souvenir pins with each other. L2

Section 3 Resource Manager

Chapter *FAST FILE* Resources

Transparency Activity, p. 48

Directed Reading for Content Mastery, p. 21

Enrichment, p. 33

Home and Community Involvement, p. 33

2 Teach

Caption Question Answer

Figure 11 There are twice as many molecules of hydrogen being produced than molecules of oxygen. The coefficient of hydrogen is 2 and the coefficient of oxygen is 1.

Reading Check

Answer One element replaces another in a compound.

Activity

Building Reactions Bring in a set of connecting, colored blocks and ask students to demonstrate the five types of chemical reactions using the blocks as the reactants and products. For example, they might combine a blue block with a red block to demonstrate a synthesis reaction or start with two blocks combined and separate them to demonstrate a decomposition reaction. Encourage capable students to use more than three or four blocks to demonstrate more complex reactions. L2

Quick Demo

Synthesis Reaction

Materials magnesium ribbon, Bunsen burner and lighter, tongs, crucible or glass catch plate

Estimated Time 15 minutes

Procedure Demonstrate the synthesis of magnesium oxide by burning magnesium ribbon in oxygen. Using tongs, position a small piece of magnesium ribbon in the flame of the Bunsen burner. *Hold the magnesium away from you and do NOT look directly into the flame.* Place the magnesium over a crucible or glass plate as it is burning to catch the ash (MgO). Reinforce the demonstration with the balanced chemical equation for the reaction: $2Mg_{(s)} + O2_{(g)} \rightarrow 2MgO_{(s)}$.

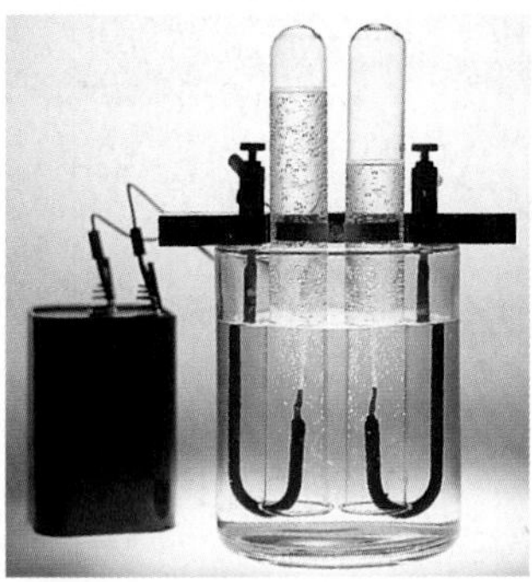

Figure 11 Water decomposes into hydrogen and oxygen when an electric current is passed through it. A small amount of sulfuric acid is added to increase conductivity. Notice the proportions of the gases collected. **Describe** *how this is related to the coefficients of the products in the equation.*

Synthesis Reactions One of the easiest reaction types to recognize is a synthesis reaction. In a **synthesis reaction,** two or more substances combine to form another substance. The generalized formula for this reaction type is as follows: $A + B \rightarrow AB$.

The reaction in which hydrogen burns in oxygen to form water is an example of a synthesis reaction.

$$2H_2(g) + O_2(g) \rightarrow 2H_2O(g)$$

This reaction is used to power some types of rockets. Another synthesis reaction is the combination of oxygen with iron in the presence of water to form hydrated iron(II) oxide or rust. This reaction is shown in **Figure 10.**

Decomposition Reactions A decomposition reaction is just the reverse of a synthesis. Instead of two substances coming together to form a third, a **decomposition reaction** occurs when one substance breaks down, or decomposes, into two or more substances. The general formula for this type of reaction can be expressed as follows: $AB \rightarrow A + B$.

Most decomposition reactions require the use of heat, light, or electricity. For example, an electric current passed through water produces hydrogen and oxygen as shown in **Figure 11.**

$$2H_2O(l) \xrightarrow{\text{elec.}} 2H_2(g) + O_2(g)$$

Figure 12 Copper in a wire replaces silver in silver nitrate, forming a blue-tinted solution of copper(II) nitrate.

Single Displacement When one element replaces another element in a compound, it is called a **single-displacement reaction.** Single-displacement reactions are described by the general equation $A + BC \rightarrow AC + B$. Here you can see that atom A displaces atom B to produce a new molecule AC. A single displacment reaction is illustrated in **Figure 12,** where a copper wire is put into a solution of silver nitrate. Because copper is a more active metal than silver, it replaces the silver, forming a blue copper(II) nitrate solution. The silver, which is not soluble, forms on the wire.

$$Cu(s) + 2AgNO_3(aq) \rightarrow Cu(NO_3)_2\,(aq) + 2Ag(s)$$

Reading Check *Describe a single-displacement reaction.*

Visual Learning

Figure 12 Ask students if the copper replacement of silver could have any practical use. It is a good way to retrieve silver for recycling. L2

LS **Logical-Mathematical**

Teacher FYI

Water Power Scientists are researching the possibility of using the synthesis of water to power automobiles. The reaction in a fuel cell is considered a clean reaction because the product is water instead of greenhouse gases or petroleum products.

642 CHAPTER 21 Chemical Reactions

Sometimes single-displacement reactions can cause problems. For example, if iron-containing vegetables such as spinach are cooked in aluminum pans, aluminum can displace iron from the vegetable. This causes a black deposit of iron to form on the sides of the pan. For this reason, it is better to use stainless steel or enamel cookware when cooking spinach.

We can predict which metal will replace another using the diagram shown in **Figure 13,** which lists metals according to how reactive they are. A metal will replace any less active metal. Notice that copper, silver, and gold are the least active metals on the list. That is why these elements often occur as deposits of the relatively pure element. For example, gold is sometimes found as veins in quartz rock, and copper is found in pure lumps known as native copper. Other metals occur as compounds.

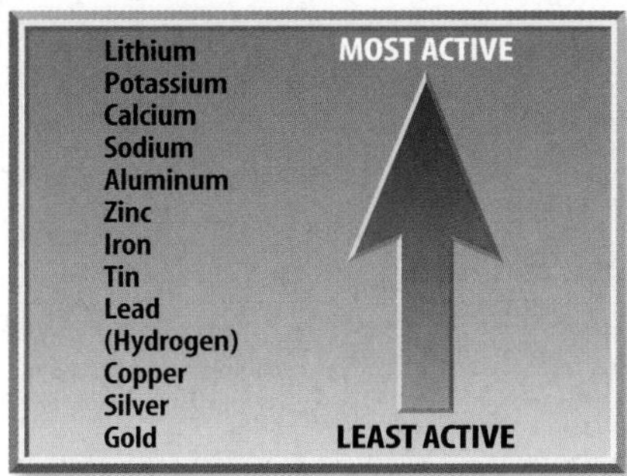

Figure 13 This figure shows the activity series of metals. A metal will replace any other metal that is less active.

Double Displacement In a **double-displacement reaction,** the positive ion of one compound replaces the positive ion of the other to form two new compounds. A double-displacement reaction takes place if a precipitate, water, or a gas forms when two ionic compounds in solution are combined. A **precipitate** is an insoluble compound that comes out of solution during this type of reaction. The generalized formula for this type of reaction is as follows: $AB + CD \rightarrow AD + CB$.

Reading Check *What type of reaction produces a precipitate?*

The reaction of barium nitrate with potassium sulfate is an example of this type of reaction. A precipitate—barium sulfate—forms, as shown in **Figure 14.** The chemical equation is as follows:

$$Ba(NO_3)_2(aq) + K_2SO_4(aq) \rightarrow BaSO_4(s) + 2KNO_3(aq)$$

These are a few examples of chemical reactions classified into types. Many more reactions of each type occur around you.

Figure 14 Solid barium sulfate is formed from the reaction of two solutions.
Observe *Has a chemical change occurred in this photo? How can you tell?*

Answer Double-displacement reactions frequently produce a precipitate.

Use an Analogy

Basketball Before a basketball game, the coach assembles the players and selects five to form the starting team. Which one of the four reactions does this resemble? synthesis One of the starting players on the basketball team fouls out of the game. The coach then substitutes a player from the bench into the game. Which one of the four reaction types does this resemble? single displacement L2

LS **Logical-Mathematical**

Inquiry Lab

Real-World Rust

Purpose To recognize that some chemical reactions have financial impacts, explain to students that when metal rusts, money must be spent to correct the problem and prevent further corrosion.

Possible Materials pencil and paper

Estimated Time 20 minutes

Teaching Strategies

- Start the brainstorming by giving an example of corrosion on a bridge support. Visit each group to be sure they are thinking of appropriate examples.
- Do not limit the brainstorming to the problem and solutions of rust. Accept and discuss other types of chemical reactions that may have financial impacts.
- Accept and discuss chemical reactions that can have real-world impacts on health or safety and encourage creative solutions to these types of situations.

For additional inquiry activities, see *Science Inquiry Labs.* L2

Differentiated Instruction

Learning Disabled Use visual learning techniques to describe the five main types of chemical reactions. Brightly colored blocks can be used to represent reactants products, and the reactions can be demonstrated physically in addition to the explanations in the text and teacher lectures. L1

Cultural Diversity

Japanese Chemistry In 1908, the Japanese chemist Kikunae Ikeda (1864–1936) used chemical reactions to make monosodium glutamate from hydrolyzed kelp protein. This synthesis became the foundation of Japan's chemical industry.

Discussion

Double-Displacement Reaction Refer to the Teacher to Teacher idea at the beginning of this chapter in which a chemical reaction created a gas that extinguished a candle. Discuss how this is a double-displacement reaction.

Make a Model

Electron Transfer Have students use themselves as model components to illustrate electron transfer in a redox reaction. Arrange several "electron" students around two nuclei, then have one or two of the "electrons" move over to the other atom. Describe how this model proves that a loss of electrons equals a gain of electrons somewhere else and that matter is neither created not destroyed when electrons move. L2

Applying Science

Answers to Practice Problems

1. $2HCl + Na_2CO_3 \rightarrow 2NaCl + H_2O + CO_2$
2. $2NaOH + CaBr_2 \rightarrow Ca(OH)_2 + 2NaBr$

Students may think that when the body of a car rusts away, leaving holes in the metal, that the law of conservation of matter is not obeyed. Explain that the corrosion of iron in the presence of water and oxygen in fact does obey the law, and reinforce this fact by introducing the chemical equation for the oxidation of iron: $4Fe(s) + 3O_2(g) \rightarrow 2Fe_2O_3(s)$.

Applying Science

BALANCING EQUATIONS A sample of barium sulfate is placed on a piece of paper, which is then ignited. Barium sulfate reacts with the carbon from the burned paper producing barium sulfide and carbon monoxide. Write a balanced chemical equation for this reaction.

IDENTIFY known values

We know the substances that are involved in the reaction. From this, we can write a chemical equation showing reactants and products.

$$BaSO_4(s) + C(s) \rightarrow BaS(s) + CO(g)$$

SOLVE the problem

The chemical equation above is not balanced. There are more oxygen atoms on the left side of the equation than there are on the right side. This must be corrected while keeping all other atom counts in balance. Begin to balance the equation by first counting and listing the atoms on the before and after the reaction.

Kind of Atom	Number of Atoms Before Reaction	Number of Atoms After Reaction
Ba	1	1
S	1	1
O	4	1
C	1	1

Next, adjust the coefficients until all atoms are balanced on the left and right sides of the arrow. Try putting a 4 in front of CO. Now you have 4 oxygen atoms on the right, which balances on both sides, but the carbon atoms become unbalanced. To fix this, add a 4 in front of the C in the reactants. The balanced equation looks like this:

$$BaSO_4(s) + 4C(s) \rightarrow BaS(s) + 4CO(g)$$

CHECK the answer

Review the number of atoms on each side of the equation and verify that they are equal.

Practice Problems

1. HCl is slowly added to aqueous Na_2CO_3 forming NaCl, H_2O, and CO_2. Follow the steps above to write a balanced equation for this reaction.
2. Balance this equation: $NaOH(aq) + CaBr_2(aq) \rightarrow Ca(OH)_2(s) + NaBr(aq)$.

For more practice problems, go to page 834 and visit gpscience.com/extra_problems.

Differentiated Instruction

Challenge Many single-displacement reactions involve oxidation and reduction. Challenge students to determine the importance of the two terms in determining the activity of a metal. Oxidation refers to losing electrons; reduction refers to gaining electrons. Chemical activity for metals usually involves the exchange of electrons. Active metals give up their electrons, or oxidize, easily. L3 P LS **Linguistic**

Oxidation-Reduction Reactions One characteristic that is common to many chemical reactions is the tendency of the substances to lose or gain electrons. Chemists use the term **oxidation** to describe the loss of electrons and the term **reduction** to describe the gain of electrons. Chemical reactions involving electron transfer of this sort often involve oxygen, which is very reactive, pulling electrons from metallic elements. Corrosion of metal is a visible result, as shown in **Figure 15.**

The cause and effect of oxidation and reduction can be taken one step further by describing the substances after the electron transfer. The substance that gains an electron or electrons obviously becomes more negative, so we say it is reduced. On the other hand, the substance that loses an electron or electrons then becomes more positive, and we say it is oxidized. The electrons that were pulled from one atom were gained by another atom in a chemical reaction called reduction. Reduction is the partner to oxidation; the two always work as a pair, which is commonly referred to as redox.

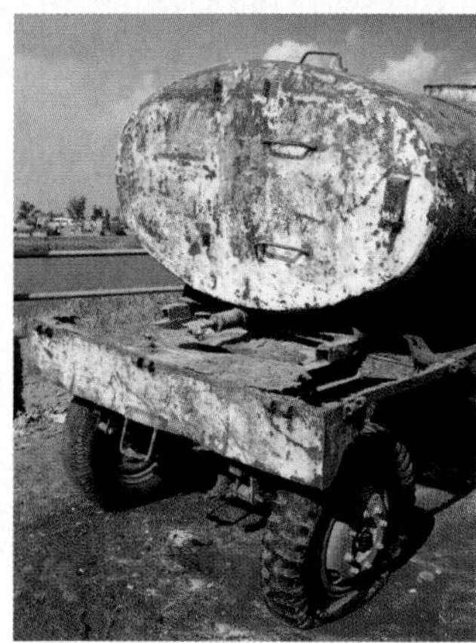

Figure 15 One of the results of all of these electrons moving from one place to another might show up on the metal body of a tanker.

section 3 review

Summary

Types of Reactions

- Chemical reactions are organized into five basic classes: combustion, synthesis, decomposition, single displacement, and double displacement.
- Lavoisier was one of the first scientists to accurately describe a combustion reaction.
- For single-displacement reactions, we can predict which metal will replace another by comparing the activity characteristic of each.
- Some reactions produce a solid called a precipitate when two ionic substances are combined.

Oxidation-Reduction Reactions

- Oxidation is the loss of electrons and reduction is the corresponding gain of electrons.
- Redox reactions often result in corrosion and rust.
- A substance that gains elections is reduced, and a substance that loses elections is oxidized.

Self Check

1. **Classify** each of the following reactions:
   a. $CaO(s) + H_2O \longrightarrow Ca(OH)_2\,(aq)$
   b. $Fe(s) + CuSO_4(aq) \longrightarrow FeSO_4(aq) + Cu(s)$
   c. $NH_4NO_3(s) \longrightarrow N_2O(g) + 2H_2O(g)$
2. **Describe** what happens in a combustion reaction.
3. **Explain** the difference between synthesis and decomposition reactions.
4. **Determine,** using **Figure 13,** if zinc will displace gold in a chemical reaction and explain why or why not.
5. **Think Critically** Describe one possible economic impact of redox reactions. How might that impact be lessened?

Applying Math

6. **Use Proportions** The following chemical equation is balanced, but the coefficients used are larger than necessary. Rewrite this balanced equation using the smallest coefficients.
   $9Fe(s) + 12H_2O(g) \longrightarrow 3Fe_3O_4(s) + 12H_2(g)$
7. **Use Coefficients** Sulfur trioxide, (SO_3), a pollutant released by coal-burning plants, can react with water in the atmosphere to produce sulfuric acid, H_2SO_4. Write a balanced equation for this reaction.

Science Online gpscience.com/self_check_quiz

Caption Question Answer

Figure 14 Yes; a precipitate (barium sulfate) forms as a result of the reaction.

3 Assess

DAILY INTERVENTION

Check for Understanding

Auditory-Musical With the class, come up with some mnemonic devices to remember the five types of chemical reactions. You may devise a poem or jingle. Have the students write the results in their Science Journals to reinforce the topic and for future study reference. L2

Reteach

Play Cards Ask students to review the following four kinds of chemical reactions by using colored note cards. Synthesis: Tape two different colored cards together. Decomposition: Two cards that are taped could be pulled apart. Single-displacement: Two different cards are taped together and a third colored card replaces one of them. Double-displacement: Two cards, from each of two sets of two different colored, taped cards are traded. L3 ELL

LS **Kinesthetic**

Assessment

Performance Have students complete and balance the following single-displacement reaction:

$K + AlCl_3 \rightarrow$ _____ + _____

$3K + AlCl_3 \rightarrow 3KCl + Al$

Use **Performance Assessment in the Science Classroom,** p. 101.

section 3 review

1. (a) synthesis (b) single displacement (c) decomposition
2. A substance combines with oxygen to produce energy.
3. Synthesis involves bringing elements or compounds together. Decomposition involves breaking compounds down.
4. Zinc will displace gold because zinc is more reactive than gold.
5. Answers may vary, but most will answer "rust." Rust can be prevented by coating a surface that is susceptible to rusting.
6. $3Fe(s) + 4H_2O(l) \longrightarrow Fe_3O_4(s) + 4H_2(g)$.
7. $SO_3 + H_2O \longrightarrow H_2SO_4$

SECTION 3 Classifying Chemical Reactions 645

1 Motivate

Bellringer

Section Focus Transparencies also are available on the Interactive Chalkboard CD-ROM. 

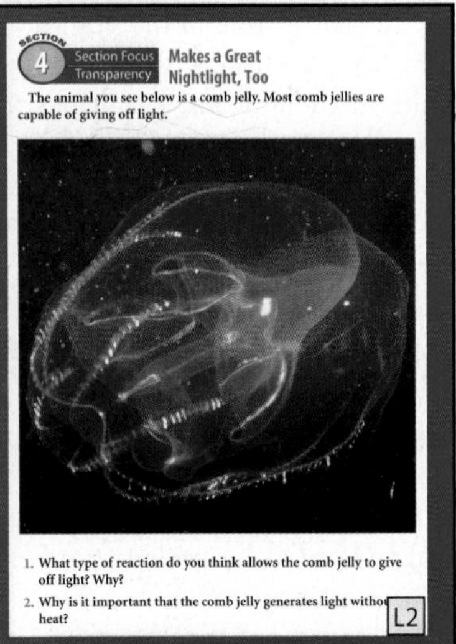

Section Focus Transparency 4 — Makes a Great Nightlight, Too

The animal you see below is a comb jelly. Most comb jellies are capable of giving off light.

1. What type of reaction do you think allows the comb jelly to give off light? Why?
2. Why is it important that the comb jelly generates light without heat?

L2

Chemical Reactions

Tie to Prior Knowledge

Eating Food Students realize that they obtain energy from eating food. Ask them how the energy is obtained from food. Chemical bonds in proteins, carbohydrates, and fats store energy. During digestion, those bonds are broken and new ones form. The energy required to break bonds is less than the energy released when new bonds form, so the net result is the release of energy. L2

section 4

Chemical Reactions and Energy

Reading Guide

What You'll Learn

- **Identify** the source of energy changes in chemical reactions.
- **Compare and contrast** exergonic and endergonic reactions.
- **Examine** the effects of catalysts and inhibitors on the speed of chemical reactions.

Why It's Important

Chemical reactions provide energy to cook your food, keep you warm, and transform the food you eat into substances you need to live and grow.

Review Vocabulary

chemical bond: the force that holds two atoms together

New Vocabulary

- exergonic reaction
- exothermic reaction
- endergonic reaction
- endothermic reaction
- catalyst
- inhibitor

Figure 16 When its usefulness is over, a building is sometimes demolished using dynamite. Dynamite charges must be placed carefully so that the building collapses inward, where it cannot harm people or property.

Chemical Reactions—Energy Exchanges

Often a crowd gathers to watch a building being demolished using dynamite. In a few breathtaking seconds, tremendous structures of steel and cement that took a year or more to build are reduced to rubble and a large cloud of dust. A dynamite explosion, as shown in **Figure 16,** is an example of a rapid chemical reaction.

Most chemical reactions proceed more slowly, but all chemical reactions release or absorb energy. This energy can take many forms, such as thermal energy, light, sound, or electricity. The thermal energy produced by a wood fire and the light emitted by a glow stick are examples of energy release.

Chemical bonds are the source of this energy. When most chemical reactions take place, some chemical bonds in the reactants are broken, which requires energy. In order for products to be produced, new bonds must form. Bond formation releases energy. Reactions such as dynamite combustion require much less energy to break chemical bonds than the energy released when new bonds are formed. The result is a release of energy and sometimes a loud explosion. Another release of energy is used to power rockets, as shown in **Figure 17.**

Section 4 Resource Manager

Chapter *FAST FILE* Resources

Transparency Activity, p. 49

Directed Reading for Content Mastery, pp. 21, 22

Enrichment, p. 34

MiniLAB, p. 4

Lab Worksheet, pp. 5–6, 7–8

Reinforcement, p. 30

Physical Science Critical Thinking/Problem Solving, p. 14

646 CHAPTER 21 Chemical Reactions

NATIONAL GEOGRAPHIC **VISUALIZING CHEMICAL ENERGY**

Figure 17

Rockets burn fuel to provide the thrust necessary to propel them upward. In 1926, engineer Robert Goddard used gasoline and liquid oxygen to propel the first ever liquid-fueled rocket. Although many people at the time ridiculed Goddard's space travel theories, his rockets eventually served as models for those that have gone to the Moon and beyond. A selection of rockets—including Goddard's—is shown here. The number below each craft indicates the amount of thrust—expressed in newtons (N)—produced during launch.

◀ SPACE SHUTTLE The main engines produce enormous amounts of energy by combining liquid hydrogen and oxygen. Coupled with solid rocket boosters, they produce over 32.5 million newtons (N) of thrust to lift the system's 2 million kg off the ground.

▶ JUPITER C This rocket launched the first United States satellite in 1958. It used a fuel called hydyne plus liquid oxygen.

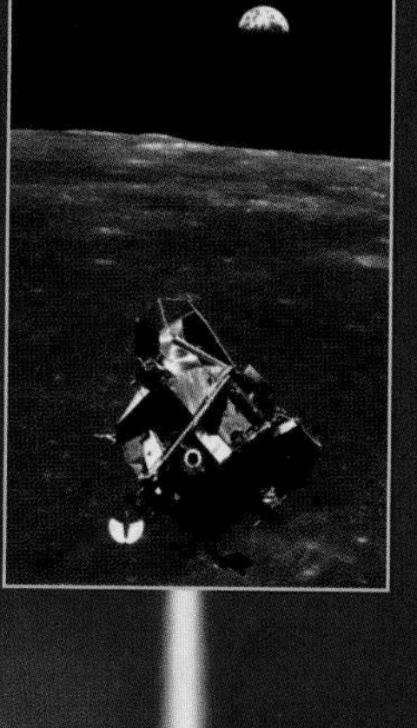

▼ LUNAR MODULE Smaller rocket engines, like those used by the Lunar Module to leave the Moon, use hydrazine-peroxide fuels. The number shown below indicates the fixed thrust from one of the module's two engines; the other engine's thrust was adjustable.

▼ GODDARD'S MODEL ROCKET Although his first rocket rose only 12.6 m, Goddard successfully launched 35 rockets in his lifetime. The highest reached an altitude of 2.7 km.

400 N

369,350 N

32,500,000 N

15,920 N

Differentiated Instruction

Visually Impaired If students cannot see the model rocket you demonstrated in the Quick Demo activity, organize the class into small groups and have each group make its own model rocket. Visually impaired students can work with others to accomplish the rocket design and they can provide the thrust for the craft.

Challenge Ask students to research new developments in rocket technology and the projected dates that the new technology will be used. Ask students to give short oral reports to the class describing what they learn. L3

Visualizing Chemical Energy

Have students examine the pictures and read the captions. Then ask the following questions.

How much more thrust did the Jupiter C rocket produce than Goddard's rocket? 369,350 N/400 N = 923.38 times more thrust

Why does the space shuttle require so much thrust to launch it into orbit? because it has so much mass

Activity

Rocket Technology Have students research the development of rocket technology throughout history and prepare time line posters showing the major milestones in this technology. L2

LS **Visual-Spatial**

Quick Demo

Model Rocket

Materials various tube materials such as straws, towel tubes, plastic tubing

Estimated Time 30 minutes

Procedure Make several small "rockets" and demonstrate the amount of force it takes to launch them. Rockets can be simple straws (small inside a large straw) propelled by your lungs or tube constructions launched by a hand pump. Relate to the class that to use a greater force to launch the rocket requires a heavier, sturdier rocket to withstand the force. Demonstrate different designs to aid the flight of the rocket. Explain that the design to fly is an important consideration inside Earth's atmosphere, but is inconsequential in space. L2

Purpose to observe evidence of a chemical reaction L2 ELL

LS **Visual Spatial**

Materials water, test tube, copper(II) bromide

Teaching Strategies The chemical reaction that occurs is

1. $CuBr_2 + 4H_2O \rightarrow Cu(H_2O)_4^{2+} + 2Br^-$
2. $Cu(H_2O)_4^{2+} + H_2O \rightarrow Cu(H_2O)_3OH^+ + H_3O^+$

Analysis

1. brown
2. blue
3. A chemical reaction occurred.

Assessment

Performance Have students repeat the activity and look for signs of energy absorbed or released by the reaction. Use **Performance Assessment in the Science Classroom**, p. 97.

Reading Check

Answer The energy given off by the reaction is primarily in the form of heat.

Visual Learning

Figure 19 Bring in several glow sticks and demonstrate the reaction. Be sure to quiet the class so they can hear the containers breaking inside the sticks. When the reaction is taking place, monitor how long it takes for the glow to be visible and how long it lasts.

Creating a Colorful Chemical Reaction

Procedure

1. Pour 5 mL of **water** into a **test tube.**
2. Sprinkle a few crystals of **copper(II) bromide** into the test tube and observe the color change of the crystals.
3. Slowly add more water and observe what happens.

Analysis

1. What color were the copper(II) bromide crystals after you added them to the test tube of water?
2. What color were they when you added more water?
3. What caused this color change?

More Energy Out

You have probably seen many reactions that release energy. Chemical reactions that release energy are called **exergonic** (ek sur GAH nihk) **reactions.** In these reactions less energy is required to break the original bonds than is released when new bonds form. As a result, some form of energy, such as light or thermal energy, is given off by the reaction. The familiar glow from the reaction inside a glow stick, shown in **Figure 18,** is an example of an exergonic reaction, which produces visible light. In other reactions however, the energy given off is thermal energy. This is the case with some heat packs that are used to treat muscle aches and other problems.

Thermal Energy Released When the energy given off is primarily in the form of thermal energy, the reaction is called an **exothermic reaction.** Wood burning and the explosion of dynamite are exothermic reactions. Iron rusting is also exothermic, but, under typical conditions, the reaction proceeds so slowly that it's difficult to detect any temperature change.

Reading Check *Why is a log fire considered to be an exothermic reaction?*

Exothermic reactions provide most of the power used in homes and industries. Fossil fuels that contain carbon, such as coal, petroleum, and natural gas, combine with oxygen to yield carbon dioxide gas and energy. Unfortunately impurities in these fuels, such as sulfur, burn as well, producing pollutants such as sulfur dioxide. Sulfur dioxide combines with water in the atmosphere, producing acid rain.

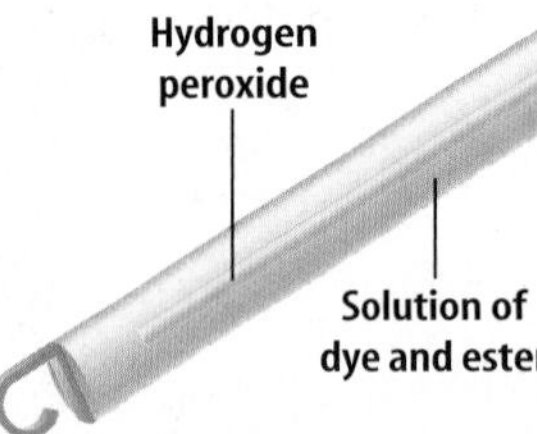

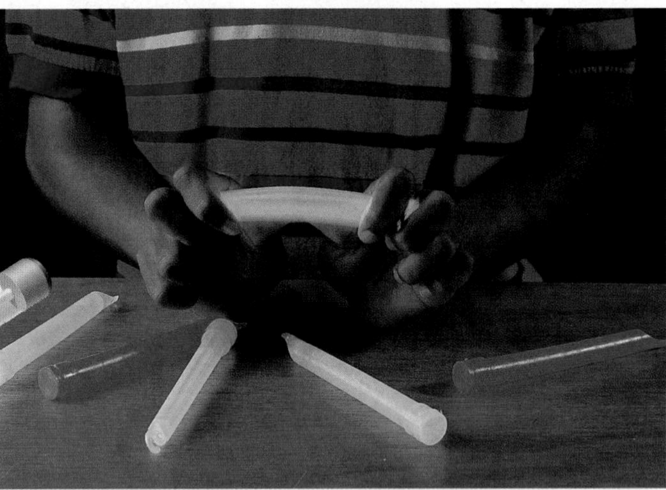

Figure 18 Glow sticks contain three different chemicals—an ester and a dye in the outer section and hydrogen peroxide in a center glass tube. Bending the stick breaks the tube and mixes the three components. The energy released is in the form of visible light.

LAB DEMONSTRATION

Purpose to demonstrate an exothermic process

Materials supersaturated solution of sodium acetate, sodium acetate crystal

Preparation Make a saturated solution of sodium acetate. Leave excess crystals in the bottom of the flask. Heat and stir until the crystals dissolve. Cool undisturbed to room temperature.

Procedure Drop an additional crystal of sodium acetate into the solution. Have students watch the solution and carefully feel the outside of the flask.

Expected Outcome The solution will crystallize, and the flask will become hot.

Assessment

Why did the solution release heat? The amount of energy required to break the bonds in the solution is less than the energy released when new crystals formed. The excess energy is released as heat. L2

More Energy In

Sometimes a chemical reaction requires more energy to break bonds than is released when new ones are formed. These reactions are called **endergonic reactions.** The energy absorbed can be in the form of light, thermal energy, or electricity.

Electricity is often used to supply energy to endergonic reactions. For example, electroplating deposits a coating of metal onto a surface, as shown in **Figure 19.** Also, aluminum metal is obtained from its ore using the following endergonic reaction.

$$2Al_2O_3(l) \xrightarrow{\text{elec.}} 4Al(l) + 3O_2(g)$$

In this case, electrical energy provides the energy needed to keep the reaction going.

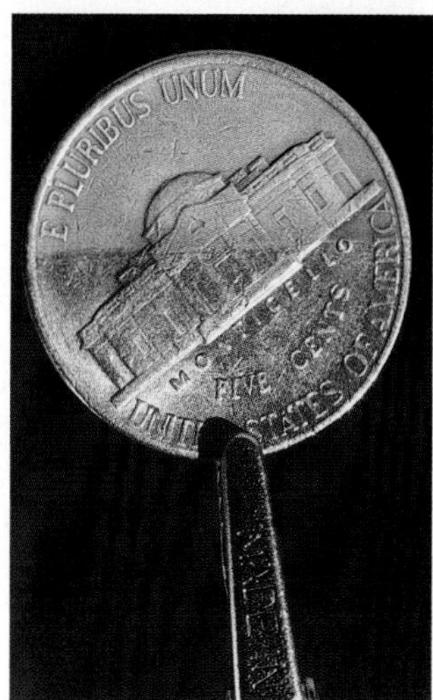

Figure 19 Electroplating of a metal is an endergonic reaction that requires electricity. A coating of copper was plated onto this coin.

Thermal Energy Absorbed When the energy needed is in the form of thermal energy, the reaction is called an **endothermic reaction.** The term *endothermic* is not just related to chemical reactions. It also can describe physical changes. The process of dissolving a salt in water is a physical change. If you ever had to soak a swollen ankle in an Epsom salt solution, you probably noticed that when you mixed the Epsom salt in water, the solution became cold. The dissolving of Epsom salt absorbs thermal energy. Thus, it is a physical change that is endothermic.

Some reactions are so endothermic that they can cause water to freeze. One such endothermic reaction is that of barium hydroxide $(BaOH)_2$ and ammonium chloride (NH_4Cl) in water, shown in **Figure 20.** Several drops of water were placed on the board, and when the reaction had taken place for several minutes, the temperature of the water in the beaker was cold enough to freeze the water drops and adhere the wood to the beaker. A cold pack, which contains ammonium nitrate crystals and water, is another example of an endothermic reaction.

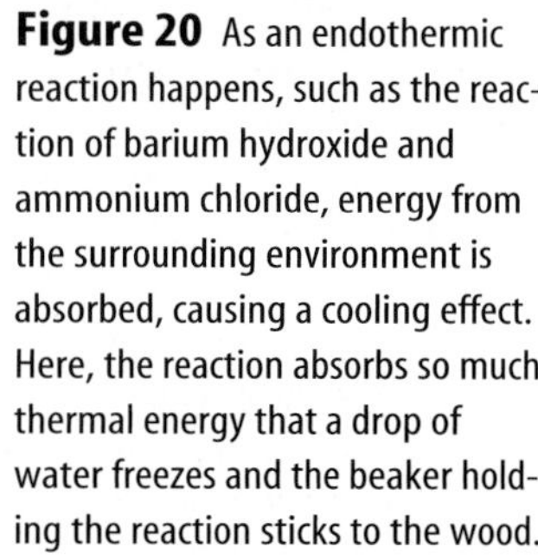

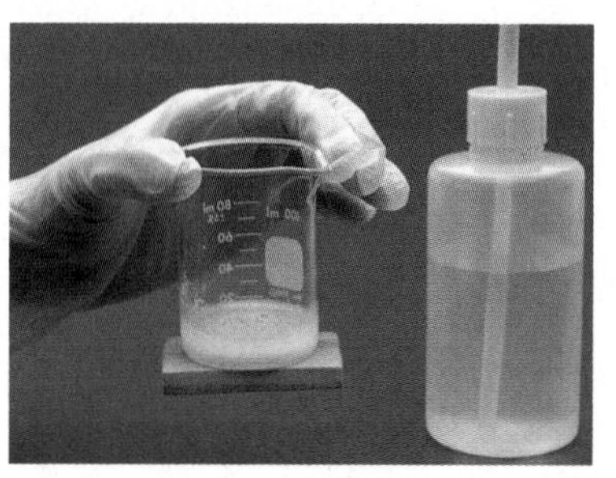

Figure 20 As an endothermic reaction happens, such as the reaction of barium hydroxide and ammonium chloride, energy from the surrounding environment is absorbed, causing a cooling effect. Here, the reaction absorbs so much thermal energy that a drop of water freezes and the beaker holding the reaction sticks to the wood.

Activity

Hand Warmers Obtain several packaged hand warmers used for outdoor activities from a sports supply store. Have students carefully follow the directions and observe the results. Place the hand warmers around a small beaker of water and measure the temperature change in the water. What causes heat to be released? Many such packaged devices have a sealed sample of iron that slowly combines with oxygen (rusts) after the seal is broken and releases more heat than is required to get the reaction started. L2

ELL IN **Kinesthetic**

Use Science Words

Word Meanings Ask students to break the words *endergonic* and *exergonic* down into parts, and find out what each part means. Have them then explain why the words are appropriate for describing chemical processes that release or require energy. Ex-ergon-ic: *ex-* out of, *ergon-* work, *-ic* - having the character of. End-ergon-ic: *end-* into, *ergon-* work, *-ic-* having the character of. An exergonic reaction produces energy that can do work. An endergonic reaction requires energy, or work, in order to occur. L2

IN **Linguistic**

Teacher FYI

Tracking Energy A cold pack absorbs heat as ammonium nitrate dissolves. The dissolving process usually is considered a physical change, not a chemical reaction. In most changes, the energy can be tracked as it moves from the surroundings to the system and vice versa. In the cold pack, the system is the chemical dissolving in water. The surroundings are the plastic bag, the air, any injured body area, etc.

Active Reading

Bubble Map Using a Bubble Map helps students start ideas flowing about a given topic. Words are clustered to describe a topic or idea that is studied. Students can use a bubble map for a prewriting, to generate ideas before writing in their Science Journals, or to review for a test. Have students design a Bubble Map for energy exchanges in chemical reactions. P L2

Catalysts The metals in exhaust catalysis help break down the unused hydrocarbon fuel molecules into less harmful compounds.

Research Have students research current trends in catalyst systems for automobiles and other vehicles that use fossil fuels. Findings can be noted in students' Science Journals.

Answer to speed up the reaction

DAILY INTERVENTION

Check for Understanding

Sounds of Chemistry Reiterate that the boom sounds from fireworks are also the results of chemical reactions. Have students name other sounds of chemical reactions. the backfire sound from a car or the pop sound from a toy cap gun L2

Reteach

Chemical Energy Write the following two equations on the board:

$A + B \rightarrow C + \text{heat}$

$X + Y + \text{heat} \rightarrow Z$

Which equation depicts an endothermic reaction? second one Which depicts an exothermic reaction? first one L2 LS **Logical-Mathematical**

Assessment

Oral Ask students to suppose that they are each holding a test tube that has a chemical change taking place inside. The tube is beginning to feel colder. Is the process in the tube endothermic or exothermic? Endothermic; the system is gaining energy from the surroundings—your hand. Use **PASC**, p. 89. L2

Catalysts Metals, such as platinum and palladium, are used as catalysts in the exhaust systems of automobiles. What reactions do you think they catalyze?

Catalysts and Inhibitors Some reactions proceed too slowly to be useful. To speed them up, a catalyst can be added. A **catalyst** is a substance that speeds up a chemical reaction without being permanently changed itself. When you add a catalyst to a reaction, the mass of the product that is formed remains the same, but it will form more rapidly. The catalyst remains unchanged and often is recovered and reused. Catalysts are used to speed many reactions in industry, such as polymerization to make plastics and fibers.

Reading Check *Why would a catalyst be needed for a chemical reaction?*

At times, it is worthwhile to prevent certain reactions from occurring. Substances called **inhibitors** are used to slow down a chemical reaction. The food preservatives BHT and BHA are inhibitors that prevent spoilage of certain foods, such as cereals and crackers.

One thing to remember when thinking about catalysts and inhibitors is that they do not change the amount of product produced. They only change the rate of production. Catalysts increase the rate and inhibitors decrease the rate. Other factors, including concentration, pressure, and temperature, also affect the rate of reaction and must be considered when catalyzing or inhibiting a reaction.

section 4 review

Summary

Chemical Reactions—Energy Exchanges

- Chemical reactions release or absorb energy as chemical bonds are broken and formed.
- The energy of chemical reactions can be in the form of thermal energy, light, sound, and/or electricity.
- Catalysts are used to increase the chemical reaction rate.

Chemical Energy

- Chemical reactions that release energy are called exergonic. Chemical reactions that absorb energy are called endergonic.
- Exothermic reactions give off thermal energy.
- Endothermic reactions absorb energy in the form of thermal energy.
- Exothermic reactions provide most of the power used in homes and industries.

Self Check

1. **Classify** the chemical reaction photosynthesis, which requires energy to proceed, as endergonic or exergonic.
2. **Explain** why a catalyst is not considered a reactant or product in a chemical reaction.
3. **Explain** why crackers containing BHT stay fresh longer than those without it.
4. **Classify** the reaction that makes a firefly glow in terms of energy input or output.
5. **Think Critically** To develop a product that warms people's hands, would you choose an exothermic or endothermic reaction to use? Why?

6. **Calculate** If an endothermic reaction begins at 26°C and loses 2°C per minute, how long will it take to reach 0°C?
7. **Use Graphs** Create a graph of the data in question 6. After 5 min, what is the temperature of the reaction?

Science Online gpscience.com/self_check_quiz

section  review

1. endergonic
2. A catalyst does not become permanently changed.
3. BHT is an inhibitor that slows spoilage of the cracker.
4. exergonic
5. Exothermic; it would release energy to warm people's hands.
6. 13 min
7. Check students' graphs. After 5 min, reaction is approximately 18°C.

650 CHAPTER 21 Chemical Reactions

CATALYZED Reaction

A balanced chemical equation tells nothing about the rate of a reaction. One way to affect the rate is to use a catalyst.

Real-World Question

How does the presence of a catalyst affect the rate of a chemical reaction?

Goals

- **Observe** the effect of a catalyst on the rate of reaction.
- **Conclude,** based on your observations, whether the catalyst remained unchanged.

Possible Materials

test tubes (3)
test-tube rack
3% hydrogen peroxide, H_2O_2 (15 mL)
10-mL graduated cylinder
small plastic teaspoon
sand (1/4 tsp)
hot plate
wooden splint
beaker of hot water
manganese dioxide, MnO_2 (1/4 tsp)

Safety Precautions

WARNING: *Hydrogen peroxide can irritate skin and eyes. Wipe up spills promptly. Point test tubes away from other students.*

Procedure

1. Label three test tubes and set them in a test-tube stand. Pour 5 mL of hydrogen peroxide into each tube.
2. Place about 1/4 teaspoon of sand in tube 2 and the same amount of MnO_2 in tube 3.
3. In the presence of a catalyst, H_2O_2 decomposes rapidly producing oxygen gas, O_2.

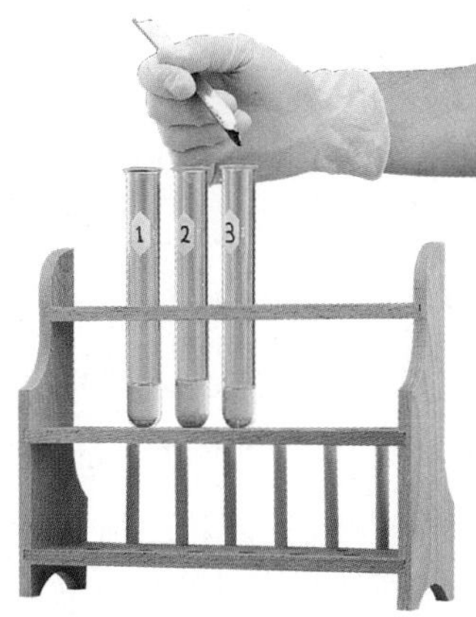

Test each tube by: Lighting a wooden splint, blowing out the flame, and inserting the glowing splint into the tube. The splint will relight if oxygen is present.

4. Place all three tubes in a beaker of hot water. Heat on a hot plate until all of the remaining H_2O_2 is driven away and no liquid remains.

Conclude and Apply

1. **Observe** the changes that happened when the solids were added to the tubes.
2. **Infer** which substance, sand or MnO_2, was the catalyst.
3. **Identify** what remained in each tube after the H_2O_2 was driven away.

Communicating Your Data

Compare your results with those of your classmates and discuss any differences observed. **For more help refer to the** Science Skill Handbook.

BENCH TESTED

Real-World Question

Purpose Students operationally define a catalyst and observe its action. L2 IS **Kinesthetic**

Process Skills observe, infer, form operational definitions, classify, recognize cause and effect

Time Required 30 minutes

Procedure

Safety Precautions Have students tie back long hair and keep clothing away from open flame.

Teaching Strategy Demonstrate the glowing splint test for students.

Troubleshooting To ensure that the splint will relight, be sure the splints still have some glowing ember when introduced into the test tube. A completely cold splint will not relight.

Conclude and Apply

1. There was no observable change from the addition of sand, but the MnO_2 increased the rate of oxygen production.
2. manganese dioxide
3. the sand in one tube, the MnO_2 in the other tube

Assessment

Performance Have students repeat the test with a small piece of liver instead of MnO_2. Ask what was in the liver to cause increased O_2 production. an enzyme Use **Performance Assessment in the Science Classroom,** p. 97.

Communicating Your Data

Have students draw illustrations showing each test tube at each step of the procedure.

Real-World Question

Purpose Students will understand what fossil fuels are and how they are used. They will also investigate the environmental effects of fossil fuels and consider whether their daily activities contribute to greenhouse gases.

Time Required about two days

Make a Plan

Internet To run through the steps the students will follow, visit gpscience.com/internet_lab.

Non-Internet Sources Collect information about greenhouse gases and how the burning of fossil fuels produces them.

Follow Your Plan

Teaching Strategy Have students work in small groups to brainstorm different activities that burn fossil fuels. Ask them to make a list of fossil fuels, which should include coal and oil.

Use the Internet

Fossil Fuels and Greenhouse Gases

Goals

- **Observe** how you use fossil fuels in your daily life.
- **Gather data** on the process of burning fossil fuels and how greenhouse gases are released.
- **Research** the chemical reactions that produce greenhouse gases.
- **Identify** the importance of fossil fuels and their effect on the environment.
- **Communicate** your findings to other students.

Data Source

Science Online

Visit gpscience.com/internet_lab for more information about fossil fuels, the chemical reactions that produce greenhouse gases, uses of fossil fuels, their effects on the environment, and data from other students.

Real-World Question

You've probably heard a lot about global warming and the greenhouse effect. According to one theory, certain gases in the atmosphere might be causing Earth's average global temperature to rise. The gases carbon dioxide, nitrous oxide, and methane, known as greenhouse gases, result from chemical reactions with oxygen when fossil fuels, such as coal, oil, and gas, are burned. What are some everyday activities that you do that might involve energy from fossil fuels? Form a hypothesis about how certain activities add greenhouse gases to our atmosphere.

Make a Plan

1. **Observe** the activities of your daily life. How are fossil fuels used each day?
2. **Develop** a way to categorize the different chemical reactions and the greenhouse gases they produce.
3. **Search** reference sources to learn which chemical reactions produce greenhouse gases.
4. **Identify** some activities and functions that do not use fossil fuels.
5. **Infer** if it is possible to never use fossil fuels.

Alternative Inquiry Lab

Expand the Focus Propose that there are other chemical reactions that affect our environment. Encourage students to use their knowledge of the types of chemical reactions to identify some of these reactions and describe their effects. Encourage students to think of positive effects as well as adverse effects. For example, students might consider the combustion reactions in a forest fire and conclude that some of the effects of those reactions might be beneficial. Students can brainstorm questions about these reactions and design a way to investigate their questions. Be sure to approve their plans before they begin. L2

Using Scientific Methods

Follow Your Plan

1. Make sure your teacher approves your plan before you start.
2. **Research** the chemical reactions that are commonly understood to produce greenhouse gases.
3. **Compare** the different reactions and their products.
4. **Record** your data in your Science Journal.

Analyze Your Data

1. **Record** in your Science Journal the activities that scientists believe contribute the greatest amount of greenhouse gases to our atmosphere.
2. **Analyze** the types of chemical reactions that produce greenhouse gases. What types of reactions are they?
3. **Compare** your results with other students. Do your results agree with those of environmental scientists? Why might you have identified different contributors to the greenhouse effect?
4. **Make a table** of your data.

Conclude and Apply

1. **Predict** How do you think your data would be affected if you had performed this experiment 100 years ago?
2. **Infer** What processes in nature might also contribute to the release of greenhouse gases? Compare their impact to that made by fossil fuels.

Communicating Your Data

Find this lab at the link below. Post your data in the table provided. Compare your data to that of other students. Combine your data with that of other students and write an entry in your Science Journal that explains how the production of greenhouse gases could be reduced.

Science Online
gpscience.com/internet_lab

Communicating Your Data

Have students make flowcharts showing how their everyday activities produce greenhouse gases. Flowcharts should include descriptions of the process and illustrations to show how the activities lead to greenhouse gas production.

Analyze Your Data

1. Answers may vary. Activities that result in the production of greenhouse gases include activities that use electricity or gasoline. Methane, which is also a greenhouse gas, is produced in the intestines of animals such as cows and termites.
2. Combustion reactions produce the largest amount of greenhouse gases in the atmosphere.
3. Carbon dioxide, methane, and water vapor are commonly released greenhouse gases. Student results and explanations of results will differ. Accept reasonable conclusions.
4. Students' tables should include information on the type of greenhouse gas, the chemical reaction that produces it, and activity that involves the chemical reaction.

Conclude and Apply

1. Accept all reasonable answers.
2. Respiration of plants and animals releases both carbon dioxide and water vapor into the air, but in smaller quantities than are released by the combustion of fossil fuels.

Assessment

Performance Have students write reports describing how the activity they investigated produces greenhouse gases. Make sure they include descriptions of the activity, the fossil fuel it burns, the chemical reaction that happens, and the gases that are produced. Use **Performance Assessment in the Science Classroom**, p. 157. L2

Oops! Accidents in SCIENCE

SOMETIMES GREAT DISCOVERIES HAPPEN BY ACCIDENT!

Content Background

When Chardonnet made his discovery in 1878, the French silk industry was in danger because something was causing the silkworms to die. Louis Pasteur was working to solve the mystery while, at the same time, Chardonnet was working to find a replacement for natural silk. He derived the solution from which he finally produced his artificial silk from the pulp of mulberry leaves, the natural food of silkworms. When he displayed the product at the Paris Exposition in 1889, he got backing for it immediately. It wasn't called rayon until about 1924.

Discussion

Learn from Mistakes Ask students why it might have been obvious to Chardonnet that his accident might lead to artificial silk. because he had been searching for an artificial silk anyway Discuss how this outcome might give students a new perspective on making mistakes. Remind students that we learn from mistakes and mistakes can often give a whole new outlook on a problem. L2

Analyze the Event

Eventually, the diseases striking silkworms were identified and controlled. Why do you think Chardonnet's artificial silk remained so popular? Possible answers: because now the amount of silk produced could be easily controlled. As much or as little fabric could be made as was necessary to meet demand. No longer did people have to worry about silkworms getting sick. L2

A Clumsy Move Pays Off

Hilaire de Chardonnet

Great scientific discoveries can happen in some very unlikely ways. Most people might not think that an accidental spill left uncleaned would become significant, but that's exactly what led a chemist named Hilaire de Chardonnet (hee LAYR • duh • shar doh NAY) to his discovery. In 1878, Chardonnet accidentally knocked over some nitrate chemicals. He put off cleaning up the mess and ended up inventing artificial silk.

Silk is produced naturally by silkworms. In the mid-1800s, though, silkworms were dying from disease and the silk industry was suffering. Businesses were going under and people were put out of work. Many scientists were working to develop a solution to this problem. Chardonnet had been searching for a silk substitute for years—he just didn't plan to find it by knocking it over!

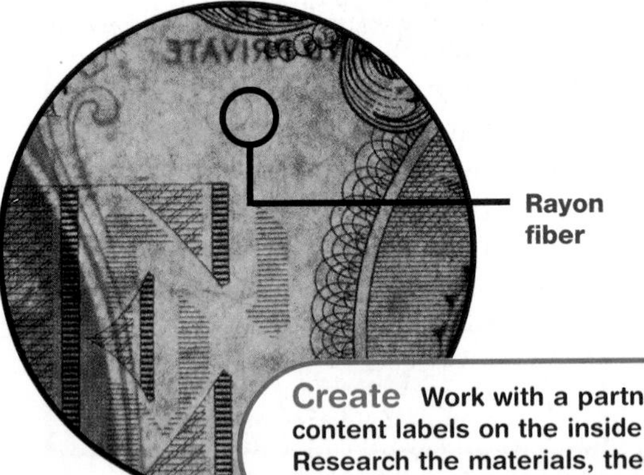

A Messy Discovery

Chardonnet was in his darkroom developing photographs when the accidental spill took place. He decided to clean up the spill later and finish what he was working on. By the time he returned to wipe up the spill, the chemical solution had turned into a thick, gooey mess. When he pulled the cleaning cloth away, the goop formed long, thin strands of fiber that stuck to the cloth. The chemicals had reacted with the cellulose in the wooden table and liquefied it. The strands of fiber looked just like the raw silk made by silkworms.

Within six years, Chardonnet had developed a way to make the fibers into an artificial silk. Other scientists extended his work, developing a fiber called rayon. Today's rayon is made from sodium hydroxide mixed with wood fibers, which is then stranded and woven into cloth.

Rayon has another real-world application. To help prevent counterfeiting, dollars are printed on paper that contains red and blue rayon fibers. If you can scratch off the red or blue, that means it's ink and your bill is counterfeit. If you can pick out the red or blue fiber with a needle, it's a real bill.

Create Work with a partner to examine the fabric content labels on the inside collars of your clothes. Research the materials, then make a data table that identifies their characteristics.

Science Online — For more information, visit gpscience.com/oops

What's the weather? Suggest students include in their tables information on the weather conditions for which each piece of clothing is used. Ask students to examine the textures and elasticity of the clothing and hypothesize how the polymers must be arranged. L2

Resources for Teachers and Students

Mistakes that Worked, by Charlotte Foltz Jones, Doubleday, 1994

They All Laughted . . . From Light Bulbs to Lasers, by Ira Flatlow, Perennial, 1993

Bright Ideas, by Sharon Dalgleish, Mason Crest Publishers, 2003

Reviewing Main Ideas

Section 1 Chemical Changes

1. In a chemical reaction, one or more substances are changed to new substances.
2. The substances that react are called reactants, and the new substances formed are called products. Charcoal, the reactant shown below, is almost pure carbon.

3. The law of conservation of mass states that in chemical reactions, matter is neither created nor destroyed, just rearranged.
4. Chemical equations efficiently describe what happens in chemical reactions.

Section 2 Chemical Equations

1. Balanced chemical equations give the exact number of atoms involved in the reaction.
2. A balanced chemical equation has the same number of atoms of each element on both sides of the equation. This satisfies the law of conservation of mass.
3. When balancing chemical equations, change only the coefficients of the formulas, never the subscripts. To change a subscript would change the compound.

Section 3 Classifying Chemical Reactions

1. In synthesis reactions, two or more substances combine to form another substance.
2. In single-displacement reactions, one element replaces another in a compound.
3. In double-displacement reactions, ions in two compounds switch places, often forming a gas or insoluble compound.
4. Using the activity series chart, scientists can determine which metal can replace another metal.

Section 4 Chemical Reactions and Energy

1. Energy in the form of light, thermal energy, sound or electricity is released from some chemical reactions known as exergonic reactions. This flame releases light and thermal energy.

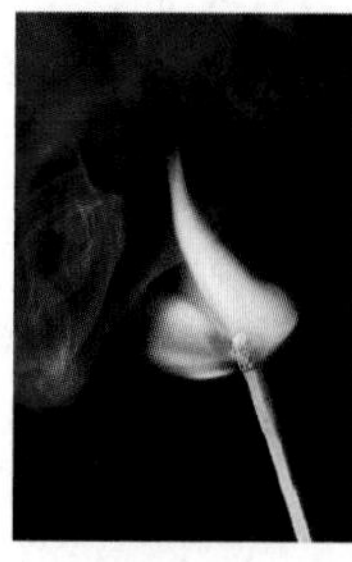

2. Reactions that absorb more energy than they release are called endergonic reactions.
3. Reactions may be sped up by adding catalysts and slowed down by adding inhibitors.
4. When energy is released in the form of thermal energy, the reaction is exothermic.

FOLDABLES™ Use the Foldable that you made at the beginning of this chapter to help you review chemical reactions.

chapter 21 Study Guide

Reviewing Main Ideas

Summary statements can be used by students to review the major concepts of the chapter.

Science Online

Visit gpscience.com
/self_check_quiz
/interactive_tutor
/vocabulary_puzzlemaker
/chapter_review
/standardized_test

Assessment Transparency

For additional assessment questions, use the *Assessment Transparency* located in the transparency book.

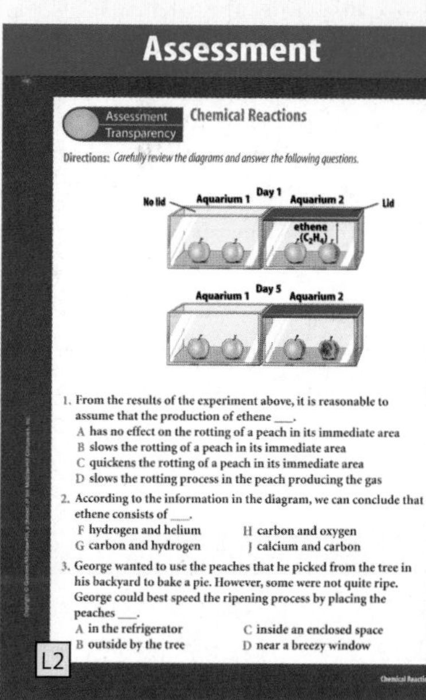

Assessment

Assessment Transparency — Chemical Reactions

Directions: *Carefully review the diagrams and answer the following questions.*

1. From the results of the experiment above, it is reasonable to assume that the production of ethene ___.
   A has no effect on the rotting of a peach in its immediate area
   B slows the rotting of a peach in its immediate area
   C quickens the rotting of a peach in its immediate area
   D slows the rotting process in the peach producing the gas
2. According to the information in the diagram, we can conclude that ethene consists of ___.
   F hydrogen and helium
   G carbon and hydrogen
   H carbon and oxygen
   J calcium and carbon
3. George wanted to use the peaches that he picked from the tree in his backyard to bake a pie. However, some were not quite ripe. George could best speed the ripening process by placing the peaches ___.
   A in the refrigerator
   B outside by the tree
   C inside an enclosed space
   D near a breezy window

L2

Chemical Reactions

FOLDABLES™ Have students use their Foldables to review the content of the chapter. Look at the reactions you've listed and for each type add one more.

Using Vocabulary

1. Coefficients are whole numbers used in front of chemical units to bring about a balanced chemical equation.
2. The two are opposite processes; in a synthesis reaction substances are put together and in a decomposition reaction they are taken apart.
3. In a chemical change, reactants change into products.
4. The two produce opposite outcomes; catalysts speed up chemical reactions, while inhibitors slow them down.
5. The two are opposite reactions; exothermic reactions release heat and endothermic reactions absorb heat.
6. Chemical reactions are processes in which new substances, called products, are formed.
7. Endergonic reactions absorb more energy than they give off. Exergonic reactions give off more energy than they take in.
8. In single-displacement reactions, only one element of one compound is replaced by another element. In double-displacement reactions, two elements in two compounds change places.
9. Not all chemical reactions are synthesis reactions, but all synthesis reactions are chemical reactions.
10. Both describe electron transfer; oxidation involves a loss of electrons and reduction involves a gain of electrons.

Checking Concepts

11. D
12. D
13. A
14. C
15. A
16. C
17. A
18. D
19. D
20. C

chapter 21 Review

Using Vocabulary

balanced chemical equation p. 638
catalyst p. 650
chemical equation p. 635
chemical reaction p. 632
coefficient p. 636
combustion reaction p. 641
decomposition reaction p. 642
double-displacement reaction p. 643
endergonic reaction p. 649
endothermic reaction p. 649
exergonic reaction p. 648
exothermic reaction p. 648
inhibitor p. 650
oxidation p. 645
precipitate p. 643
product p. 632
reactant p. 632
reduction p. 645
single-displacement reaction p. 642
synthesis reaction p. 642

For each set of vocabulary words below, explain the relationship that exists.

1. coefficient—balanced chemical equation
2. synthesis reaction—decomposition reaction
3. reactant—product
4. catalyst—inhibitor
5. exothermic reaction—endothermic reaction
6. chemical reaction—product
7. endergonic reaction—exergonic reaction
8. single-displacement reaction—double-displacement reaction
9. chemical reaction—synthesis reaction
10. oxidation—reduction

Checking Concepts

Choose the word or phrase that best answers the question.

11. Oxygen gas is always written as O_2 in chemical equations. What term is used to describe the "2" in this formula?
    A) product C) catalyst
    B) coefficient D) subscript
12. What law is based on the experiments of Lavoisier?
    A) coefficients C) chemical reaction
    B) gravity D) conservation of mass
13. What must an element be in order to replace another element in a compound?
    A) more reactive C) more inhibiting
    B) less reactive D) less inhibiting
14. How do you indicate that a substance in an equation is a solid?
    A) (l) C) (s)
    B) (g) D) (aq)
15. What term is used to describe the "4" in the expression 4 $Ca(NO_3)_2$?
    A) coefficient C) subscript
    B) formula D) symbol
16. What type of compound is the food additive BHA?
    A) catalyst C) inhibitor
    B) oxidized D) reduced
17. How do you show that a substance is dissolved in water when writing an equation?
    A) (aq) C) (g)
    B) (s) D) (l)
18. What word would you use to describe HgO in the reaction that Lavoisier used to show conservation of mass?
    A) catalyst C) product
    B) inhibitor D) reactant
19. When hydrogen burns, what is oxygen's role?
    A) catalyst C) product
    B) inhibitor D) reactant
20. What kind of chemical reaction involves one substance losing an electron and another substance gaining an electron?
    A) combustion C) redox
    B) decomposition D) synthesis

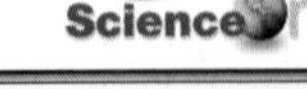

gpscience.com/vocabulary_puzzlemaker

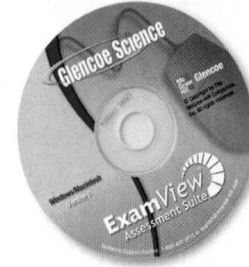

Interpreting Graphics

21. Copy and complete the concept map using the following terms: *oxidized, redox reactions, lost, reduced, oxidation, gained,* and *reduction.*

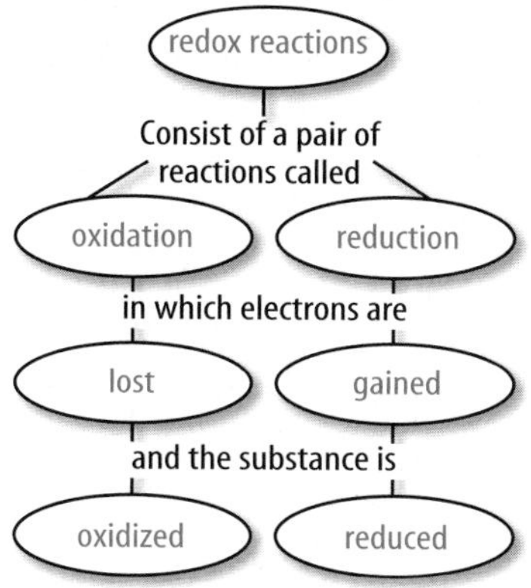

22. Sometimes a bond formed in a chemical reaction is weak and the product breaks apart as it forms. This is shown by a double arrow in chemical equations. Copy and complete the concept map, using the words *product(s)* and *reactant(s).* In the blank in the center, fill in the formulas for the substances appearing in the reversible reaction.

$$H_2(g) + I_2(g) \rightleftarrows 2HI(g)$$

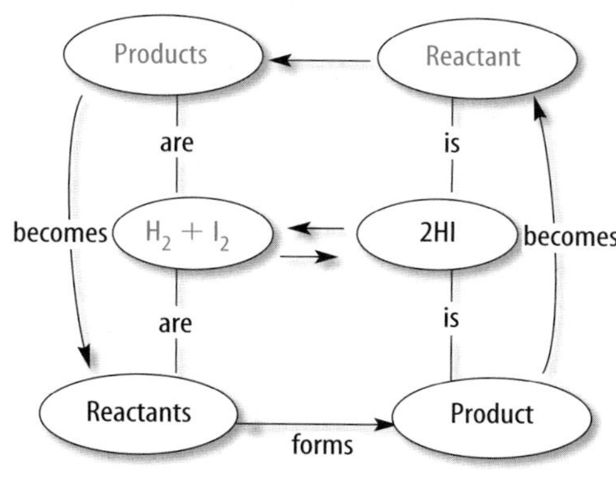

Thinking Critically

23. **Write a balanced chemical equation** for the reaction of propane $C_3H_8(g)$ burning in oxygen to form carbon dioxide and water vapor.

24. **Interpret** the balanced chemical equation from question 23 to explain the law of conservation of mass.

25. **Hypothesize** Zn is placed in a solution of $Cu(NO_3)_2$ and Cu is placed in a $Zn(NO_3)_2$ solution. In which of these will a reaction occur?

26. **Predict** what kind of energy process happens when lye, NaOH(*s*), is put in water and the water gets hot.

27. **Recognize Cause and Effect** Sucrose, or table sugar, is a disaccharide. This means that sucrose is composed of two simple sugars chemically bonded together. Sucrose can be separated into its components by heating it in an aqueous sulfuric acid solution. Research what products are formed by breaking up sucrose. What role does the acid play?

28. **Classify** Make an outline with the general heading *Chemical Reactions.* Include the five types of reactions, with a description and example of each.

Applying Math

29. **Interpret Data** When 46 g of sodium were exposed to dry air, 62 g of sodium oxide formed. How many grams of oxygen from the air were used?

30. **Calculate Mass** Chromium is produced by reacting its oxide with aluminum. If 76 g of Cr_2O_3 and 27 g of Al completely react to form 51 g of Al_2O_3, how many grams of Cr are formed?

Science Online gpscience.com/chapter_review

Assessment Resources

Reproducible Masters

Chapter *Fast File* Resources
- Chapter Review, pp. 39–40
- Chapter Tests, pp. 41–44
- Assessment Transparency Activity, p. 53

Glencoe Science Web site
- Chapter Review Test
- Standardized Test Practice

Glencoe Technology
- Assessment Transparency
- *ExamView®* *Assessment Suite*
- MindJogger Videoquiz
- Interactive Chalkboard

Interpreting Graphics

21. See student page.
22. See student page.

Thinking Critically

23. $C_3H_8(g) + 5O_2(g) \rightarrow 3CO_2(g) + 4H_2O(g)$
24. There are 3 atoms of carbon, 8 atoms of hydrogen, and 10 atoms of oxygen on both sides of the equation.
25. Zinc reacts in the solution of copper nitrate and displaces copper to form $Zn(NO_3)_2$. In the second solution, no reaction is observed.
26. exothermic
27. Fructose and glucose; the acid is a catalyst.
28. Chemical Reactions
    1. Combustion Reaction
       A substance reacts with oxygen to produce energy as heat or light.
    2. Synthesis Reaction
       Two or more elements or compounds combine.
    3. Decomposition
       A compound is broken down into its elements or other compounds.
    4. Single displacement
       An element in one compound is replaced by another element.
    5. Double displacement
       Two elements from two different compounds replace each other. Accept all reasonable examples.

Applying Math

National Math Standards
1, 2, 9, 10

29. $62\text{ g} - 46\text{ g} = 16\text{ g of } O_2$
30. 52 grams

FAST FILE

Answer Sheet A practice answer sheet can be found at gpscience.com/answer_sheet.

Assessment Student Recording Sheet

Standardized Test Practice

SAMPLE

Part 1 Multiple Choice

1. D
2. B
3. D
4. C
5. D
6. C
7. A

Part 2 Short Response

8. A synthesis reaction is a chemical reaction in which two or more substances combine to form another substance.
9. chemical bonds
10. $NiCl_2(aq) + 2NaOH(aq) \longrightarrow Ni(OH)_2(s) + 2NaCl(aq)$
11. The number of atoms of nickel, chlorine, sodium, oxygen, and hydrogen that are present before the reaction equals the number of each present after the reaction.
12. The symbol *s* means solid, *aq* means aqueous, *g* means gas, and *l* means liquid.

Part 1 Multiple Choice

Record your answers on the answer sheet provided by your teacher or on a sheet of paper.

Use the photograph below to answer questions 1 and 2.

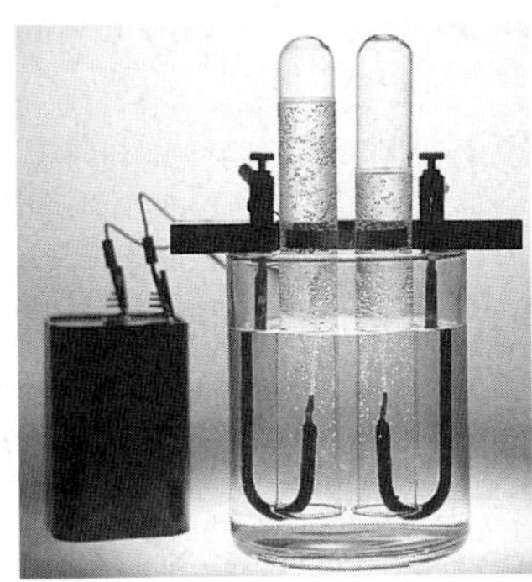

1. The photograph above shows a chemical reaction in which water decomposes into hydrogen gas and oxygen gas when an electric current is passed through it. Which of the following is the correct chemical equation for this reaction?
   A. $H_2O(l) \longrightarrow H_2(g) + O(g)$
   B. $H_2O(l) \longrightarrow 2H(g) + O(g)$
   C. $2H_2O(l) \longrightarrow 2H_2(g) + 2O(g)$
   D. $2H_2O(l) \longrightarrow 2H_2(g) + O_2(g)$

2. Which of the following is the correct classification for the chemical reaction shown in the photograph?
   A. synthesis
   B. decomposition
   C. single displacement
   D. double displacement

Test-Taking Tip

Missing Information Questions often will ask about missing information. Notice what is missing as well as what is given.

3. Which of the following types of reaction is the opposite of a synthesis reaction?
   A. displacement
   B. reversible
   C. combustion
   D. decomposition

4. Which substance is the precipitate in the following reaction?
   $$Ba(NO_3)_2(aq) + K_2SO_4(aq) \longrightarrow BaSO_4(s) + 2KNO_3(aq)$$
   A. $Ba(NO_3)_2$
   B. K_2SO_4
   C. $BaSO_4$
   D. KNO_3

5. Which of the following reactions is endothermic?
   A. iron rusting
   B. burning wood
   C. exploding dynamite
   D. mixing Epsom salt in water

Use the figure below to answer questions 6 and 7.

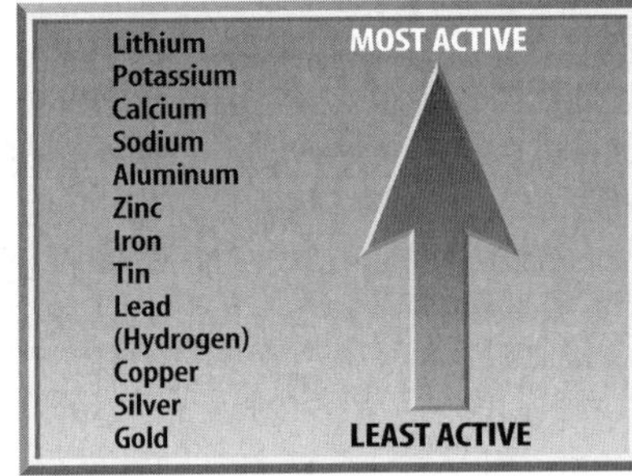

6. Which of the metals in the activity series shown above would you expect to be mostly found in nature as a deposit of a relatively pure element?
   A. copper
   B. lithium
   C. silver
   D. iron

7. Which of the following metals would most likely replace lead in a solution?
   A. potassium
   B. copper
   C. silver
   D. gold

Part 3 Open Ended

13. An inhibitor slows down the rate of a reaction. Preservatives slow down the rate of food spoilage.
14. reactants, products
15. A chemical reaction is exergonic if it releases energy. A reaction is exothermic if it gives off energy in the form of heat. The reaction shown is exergonic because it releases heat and produces visible light. It is exothermic because it produces warmth and burning.
16. The unbalanced chemical equation is $Mg(s) + O_2(g) \longrightarrow MgO(s)$. To balance the equation, adjust the coefficient with MgO to balance oxygen and with Mg to balance magnesium. The equation is balanced as $2Mg(s) + O_2(g) \longrightarrow 2MgO(s)$.

Part 2 Short Response/Grid In

Record your answers on the answer sheet provided by your teacher or on a sheet of paper.

8. What is a synthesis reaction?
9. What is the source of the heat, light, sound, and electricity that can be produced during a chemical reaction?

Use the photograph below to answer questions 10 and 11.

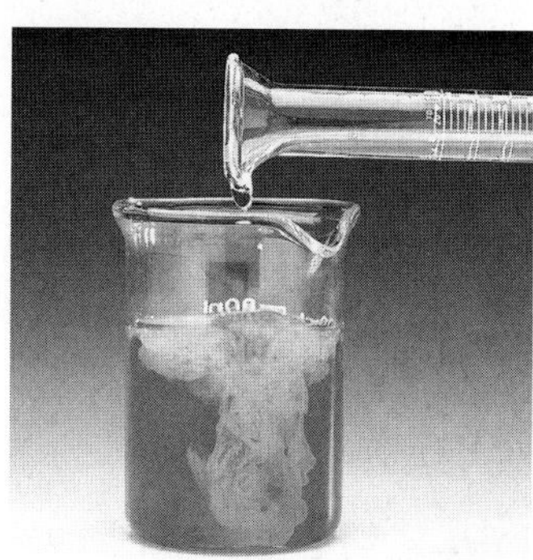

10. The photograph above shows the reaction of aqueous nickel(II) chloride, $NiCl_2$, and aqueous sodium hydoxide, NaOH, to form solid nickel(II) hydroxide, $Ni(OH)_2$, and aqueous sodium chloride, NaCl. Write a balanced chemical equation for this reaction.
11. State the conservation of mass as it applies to the chemical reaction in the photograph above.
12. What do the symbols *s*, *aq*, *g*, and *l* mean when they are placed in parentheses next to the formulas for substances in chemical equations?
13. Food preservatives are a type of inhibitor. Explain why this is useful in foods.
14. What are the substances that react and the substances that are produced in a chemical reaction called?

Part 3 Open Ended

Record your answers on a sheet of paper.

Use the photograph below to answer questions 15 and 16.

15. The photograph above shows a chemical reaction between, Mg, and oxygen gas, O_2. This reaction is exergonic and exothermic. Explain what these terms mean and how you can tell that a chemical reaction is exergonic or exothermic.
16. The reaction of magnesium and oxygen gas forms magnesium oxide, MgO. Write chemical equation for this reaction and explain the process you use to balance the equation.
17. Name and describe three notations that may be used above the arrow in a chemical equation.
18. Explain what is wrong with the following balanced equation:

    $4Al(s) + 6O(g) \longrightarrow 2Al_2O_3(s)$

    What is the correct form of the equation?
19. What is a double-displacement reaction? Describe the double-displacement reaction shown in the following chemical equation in which lead nitrate, $Pb(NO_3)_2$, and potassium iodide, KI, react to form lead iodide, PbI_2, and potassium nitrate, KNO_3.

    $Pb(NO_3)_2 + 2KI \longrightarrow PbI_2 + 2KNO_3$

17. The notation "heat" means the reactants are heated, "light" means the reactants are exposed to light, and "elec" means an electric current is applied to the reactants.
18. The equation has oxygen as a single atom; however, oxygen gas is a diatomic molecule, O_2. The correct form of the equation is $4Al(s) + 3O_2(g) \longrightarrow 2Al_2O_3(s)$.
19. In a double-displacement reaction, the positive ion of one reactant compound replaces the positive ion of the other reactant compound to form two new compounds. In this reaction, a lead ion replaces the potassium ion in potassium iodide. The potassium ion replaces the lead ion in lead nitrate. The two new substances formed are lead iodide and potassium nitrate.

Rubrics

The following rubrics are sample scoring devices for short response and open-ended questions.

Short Response

Points	Description
2	The student demonstrates a thorough understanding of the science of the task. The response may contain minor flaws that do not detract from the demonstration of a thorough understanding.
1	The student has provided a response that is only partially correct.
0	The student has provided a completely incorrect solution or no response at all.

Open Ended

Points	Description
4	The student demonstrates a thorough understanding of the science of the task. The response may contain minor flaws that do not detract from the demonstration of a thorough understanding.
3	The student demonstrates an understanding of the science of the task. The response is essentially correct and demonstrates an essential but less than thorough understanding of the science.
2	The student demonstrates only a partial understanding of the science of the task. Although the student may have used the correct approach to a solution or may have provided a correct solution, the work lacks an essential understanding of the underlying science concepts.
1	The student demonstrates a very limited understanding of the science of the task. The response is incomplete and exhibits many flaws.
0	The student provides a completely incorrect solution or no response at all.

Unit Contents

WebQuest *Chemistry of Fireworks* is designed to engage students in researching the chemical components of fireworks, how chemicals are used to produce different colors, the history of fireworks, and how firework displays are created. Students will answer a set of questions following their Web research to demonstrate the knowledge they have gained.

unit 6 Interactions of Matter

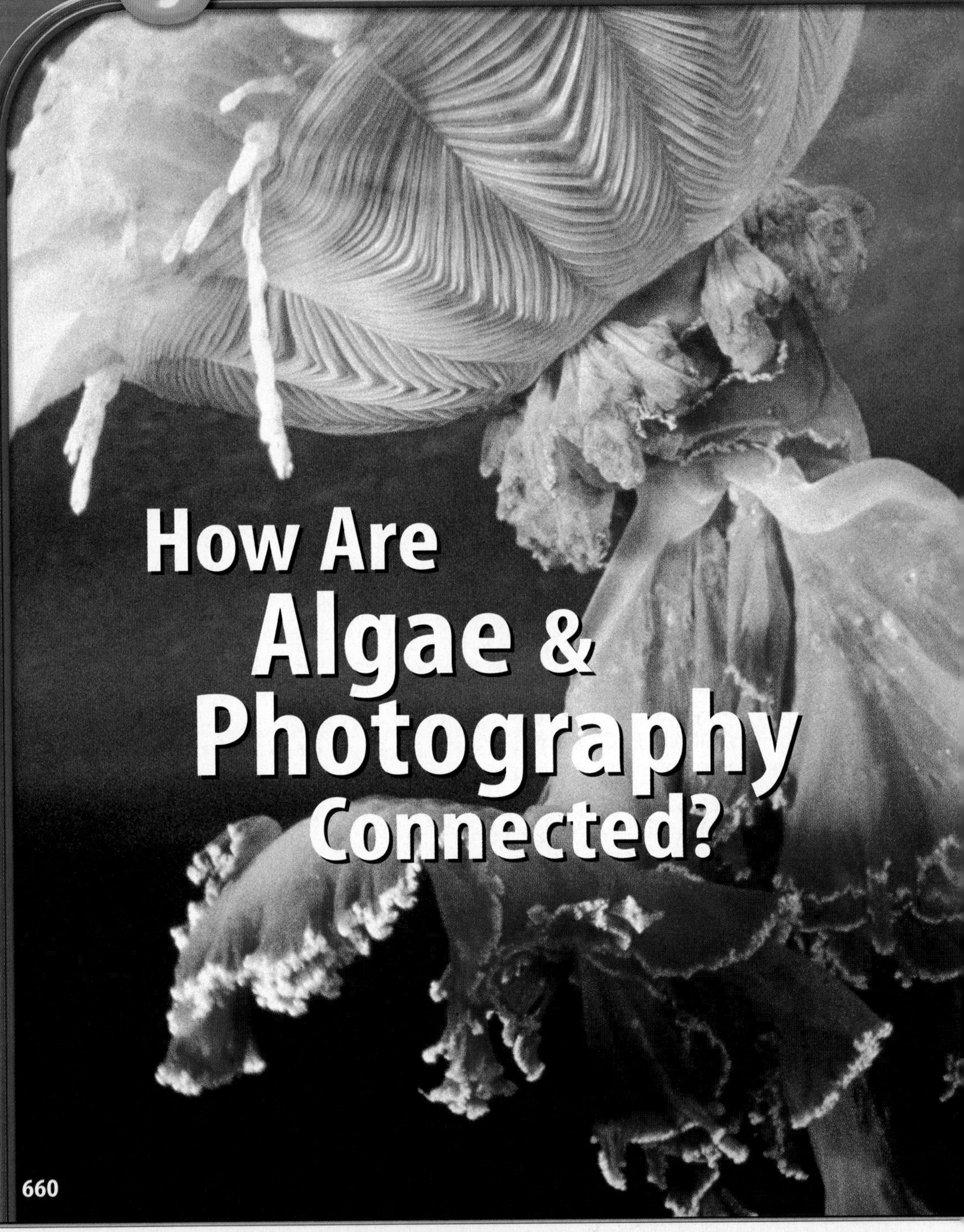

How Are Algae & Photography Connected?

660

PROJECT CRISS℠

Study Skills

Organize Information Main idea-detail notes help students organize content from reading assignments. After studying solutions and chemical reactions, students use the two-column strategy. In the left column, students list a variety of acids and bases. In the right-hand column, students write pertinent details about each, such as the properties, pH, and uses.

Main Idea	Detail
Acid	Properties: • ________ • ________ pH: ________ Uses: ________
Base	

In the mid-1800s, scientists experimented with light-sensitive chemicals. They found that when paper was treated with such chemicals and then exposed to light, the resulting reaction changed the paper's color. If an object blocked some of the light, a silhouette of the object was created. One set of chemicals produced prints—called cyanotypes—of white images on a blue background. A botanist named Anna Atkins saw the potential of this process. Until that time, the only way to create pictures of plants had been to draw them. Atkins used cyanotypes to create impressions of the plants. In 1843, she published a book of cyanotype images of algae, including the two seen at lower right. It was the first book ever to be illustrated by photography. Since Atkins' time, photography has gone through many changes. But it is still a powerful tool for making images of the natural world—which includes this giant jellyfish, whose image is being captured by an underwater photographer.

unit projects

Visit gpscience.com/unit_project to find project ideas and resources.
Projects include:

- **Career** Explore the field of pharmaceutical research. Develop a list of questions, interview a professional, and compile class data.
- **Technology** Discover what elements are used to make salts, how they are made, where they can be found, and where they are used. Create a formula for personal bath salts or salt scrubs.
- **Model** Design a creative review game—board game, card game, or quiz game—to offer practice with chemical elements and their properties.

WebQuest *Chemistry of Fireworks* explores the chemical compounds of fireworks, what chemicals are used, and how firework displays are created.

NATIONAL GEOGRAPHIC How Are Algae & Photography Connected?

- Students are probably familiar with a specific application of the cyanotype process—blueprints. If any of their families have blueprints of their homes, have students share them with the class.
- Ask students to hypothesize how cyanotypes can be used to photocopy something. The item to be photocopied can be placed over treated paper, and then exposed to light. Tell students that this type of copying was first done in the mid-1800s.
- Tell students that they will study many such interactions of matter and energy. All chemical reactions involve energy transfer.

unit projects

Career Have students explore the field of pharmaceutical research. As a class, brainstorm a list of 15–20 questions to investigate about this revolutionary and innovative career. Through the use of personal interview, have students pose their questions, and then share their answers with the group as a class flowchart or concept map.

Technology Assign a specific salt to a pair of students. Using a variety of resources, have students research what elements are used to make their salt, how it is made, where it can be found, and where it is used. Some students may be interested in researching bath salts and their popularity in today's society. Salt research suggestions might include: sodium chloride ($NaCl$), potassium chloride (KCl), ammonium chloride (NH_4Cl), magnesium sulfate ($MgSO_4$), sodium sulfate (Na_2SO_4), potassium acetate (CH_3CO_2K), sodium nitrate ($NaNO_3$), barium sulfate ($BaSO_4$), copper (II) acetate ($Cu(CH_3CO_2)$), or ammonium sulfate ($(NH_4)_2SO_4$).

Model In small groups, have students design a review game to offer practice with chemical reactions, formulas, elements, molecules, reactants, chemical symbols, chemical names, and common names. Students may want to include spinners, dice, game pieces, money, cards of chance, or a lotto format.

Additional Resources For more information, resources, and assessment rubrics, visit gpscience.com/unit_project

Solutions

BIG Idea A solution is a homogeneous mixture of a solvent and a solute.

	Content Standards	Learning Objectives	Resources to Assess Mastery
Section 1	**5–8:** UCP.1–3, 5; A.1, 2; B.1 **9–12:** UCP.1–3, 5; A.1, 2; B.1–3	**How Solutions Form** 1. **Determine** how things dissolve. 2. **Examine** the factors that affect the rates at which solids and gases dissolve in liquids. ***Main Idea*** A solution forms when particles of solute become evenly mixed among particles of solute.	Formative Assessment Reading Check, pp. 665, 667 Section Review, p. 670 Summative Assessment *ExamView® Assessment Suite*
Section 2	**5–8:** UCP.1–3, 5; A.1, 2; B.1, 3 **9–12:** UCP.1–3, 5; A.1, 2; B.2, 6	**Solubility and Concentration** 3. **Define** the concept of solubility. 4. **Identify** how to express the concentration of solutions. 5. **List** and define three types of solutions. 6. **Describe** the effects of pressure and temperature on the solubility of gases. ***Main Idea*** Solubility is the maximum amount of solute that can dissolve and concentration is the amount of solute actually dissolved in a given amount of solute.	Formative Assessment Reading Check, pp. 671, 673 Section Review, p. 675 Summative Assessment *ExamView® Assessment Suite*
Section 3	**5–8:** UCP.1–3, 5; A.1, 2; B.1, 3 **9–12:** UCP.1–3, 5; A.1, 2; B.2	**Particles in Solution** 7. **Examine** how some solutes break apart in water solutions to form positively and negatively charged particles. 8. **Determine** how some solutions conduct electricity. 9. **Describe** how antifreeze works. ***Main Idea*** Dissolved particles can both lower the freezing point and raise the boiling point of a solution.	Formative Assessment Reading Check, p. 677 Section Review, p. 679 Summative Assessment *ExamView® Assessment Suite*
Section 4	**5–8:** UCP.1–3, 5; A.1, 2; B.1; F.1; G.1 **9–12:** UCP.1–3, 5; A.1, 2; B.2; F.1; G.1 See pp. 16T–17T for a Key to Standards.	**Dissolving Without Water** 10. **Identify** several kinds of solutes that do not dissolve well in water. 11. **Explain** how solvents work in terms of polarity. 12. **Determine** how to choose the right solvent for the job. ***Main Idea*** Nonpolar solvents can dissolve many nonpolar solutes.	Formative Assessment Reading Check, pp. 682, 683, 685 Section Review, p. 685 Summative Chapter Assessment MindJogger, Ch. 22 *ExamView® Assessment Suite* Leveled Chapter Test Test A L1 Test B L2 Test C L3 Test Practice, pp. 692–693

Suggested Pacing				
Period	**Instruction**	**Labs**	**Review & Assessment**	**Total**
Single	3.5 days	2.5 days	2 days	8 days
Block	1.75 blocks	1.25 blocks	1 block	4 blocks

<table>
<tr><th rowspan="2">Core Instruction</th><th rowspan="2">Leveled Resources</th><th rowspan="2">Leveled Labs</th><th colspan="3">Pacing</th></tr>
<tr><th colspan="2">Period</th><th>Block</th></tr>
<tr><td rowspan="2">Student Text, pp. 662–670
Section Focus Transparency, Ch. 22, Section 1
Interactive Chalkboard, Ch. 22, Section 1
Differentiated Instruction, pp. 666, 667, 669
Visualizing Metal Alloys, p. 666
Applying Math, p. 669</td><td rowspan="2">Chapter Fast File Resources
Directed Reading for Content Mastery, p. 20 [L1]
Note-taking Worksheet, pp. 35–37
Reinforcement, p. 27 [L2]
Enrichment, p. 31 [L3]
Reading Essentials, p. 378 [L1] ELL
Science Notebook, p. 253 ELL</td><td>Launch Lab, p. 633: bottled water, sports drinks, 100-mL beakers (3), hot plate 15 min [L2]</td><td>1</td><td>Section 1, pp. 663–666 (includes Launch Lab)</td><td rowspan="2">1</td></tr>
<tr><td>MiniLAB, p. 668: sugar cubes (4), distilled water, glasses (2), stirring rods (2) 15 min [L2]</td><td>2</td><td>Section 1, pp. 667–670 (includes MiniLAB and Section Review)</td></tr>
<tr><td>Student Text, pp. 671–675
Section Focus Transparency, Ch. 22, Section 2
Interactive Chalkboard, Ch. 22, Section 2
Identifying Misconceptions, p. 672
Differentiated Instruction, pp. 672, 674</td><td>Chapter Fast File Resources
Directed Reading for Content Mastery, p. 21 [L1]
Note-taking Worksheet, pp. 35–37
Reinforcement, p. 28 [L2]
Enrichment, p. 32 [L3]
Reading Essentials, p. 383 [L1] ELL
Science Notebook, p. 257 ELL</td><td></td><td>3</td><td>Section 2, pp. 671–675 (includes Section Review)</td><td rowspan="2">2</td></tr>
<tr><td rowspan="2">Student Text, pp. 676–680
Section Focus Transparency, Ch. 22, Section 3
Teaching Transparency, Ch. 22, Section 3
Interactive Chalkboard, Ch. 22, Section 3
Differentiated Instruction, p. 678</td><td rowspan="2">Chapter Fast File Resources
Directed Reading for Content Mastery, p. 20 [L1]
Note-taking Worksheet, pp. 35–37
Reinforcement, p. 29 [L2]
Enrichment, p. 33 [L3]
Reading Essentials, p. 388 [L1] ELL
Science Notebook, p. 260 ELL</td><td rowspan="2">*Lab, p. 680: distilled water, Celsius thermometer, table salt, ring stand, hot plate, 250-mL beaker 35 min [L1] [L2] [L3]</td><td>4</td><td>Section 3, pp. 676–679 (includes Section Review)</td></tr>
<tr><td>5</td><td>LAB—Boiling Points of Solutions, p. 680</td><td rowspan="2">3</td></tr>
<tr><td rowspan="3">Student Text, pp. 681–687
Section Focus Transparency, Ch. 22, Section 4
Interactive Chalkboard, Ch. 22, Section 4
Differentiated Instruction, pp. 683, 684
Chapter Study Guide, p. 689</td><td rowspan="3">Chapter Fast File Resources
Directed Reading for Content Mastery, pp. 20, 22 [L1]
Note-taking Worksheet, pp. 35–37
Reinforcement, p. 30 [L2]
Enrichment, p. 33 [L3]
Reading Essentials, p. 393 [L1] ELL
Science Notebook, p. 263 ELL</td><td rowspan="3">MiniLAB, p. 683: water, pennies (2), paper towel, dropper (2), rubbing alcohol 10 min [L2]

*Lab, pp. 686–687: distilled water, large test tube, Celsius thermometer, sugar, stirrer, test-tube holder, 25-mL graduated cylinder, 250-mL beaker, water, hot plate, ring stand 40 min [L1] [L2] [L3]

*Lab version A [L1]
version B [L2] [L3]</td><td>6</td><td>Section 4, pp. 681–685 (includes MiniLAB and Section Review)</td></tr>
<tr><td>7</td><td>LAB—Saturated Solutions, pp. 686–687</td><td rowspan="2">4</td></tr>
<tr><td>8</td><td>Study Guide, Chapter Review, and Test Practice, pp. 689–693</td></tr>
</table>

Transparencies

Section Focus

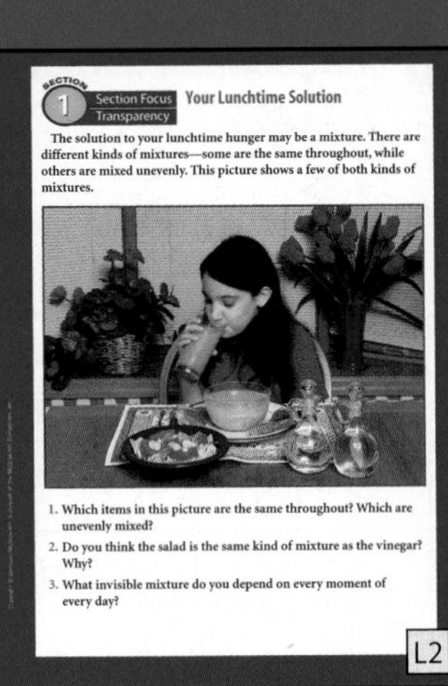
Section 1 Section Focus Transparency **Your Lunchtime Solution**

The solution to your lunchtime hunger may be a mixture. There are different kinds of mixtures—some are the same throughout, while others are mixed unevenly. This picture shows a few of both kinds of mixtures.

1. Which items in this picture are the same throughout? Which are unevenly mixed?
2. Do you think the salad is the same kind of mixture as the vinegar? Why?
3. What invisible mixture do you depend on every moment of every day?

L2

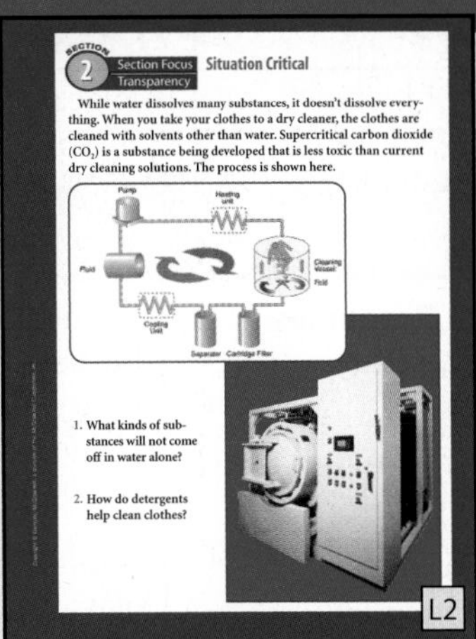
Section 2 Section Focus Transparency **Situation Critical**

While water dissolves many substances, it doesn't dissolve everything. When you take your clothes to a dry cleaner, the clothes are cleaned with solvents other than water. Supercritical carbon dioxide (CO_2) is a substance being developed that is less toxic than current dry cleaning solutions. The process is shown here.

1. What kinds of substances will not come off in water alone?
2. How do detergents help clean clothes?

L2

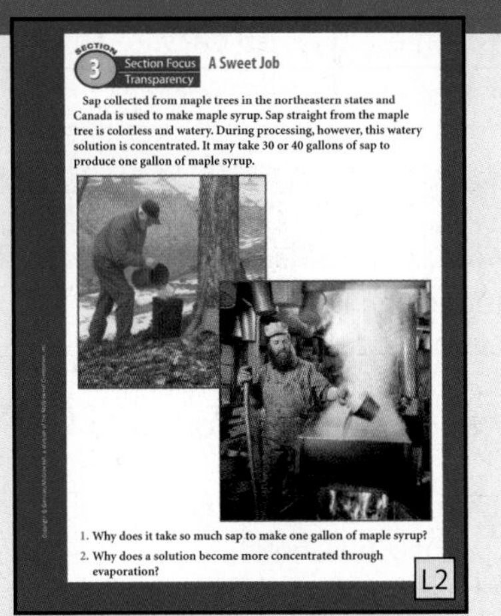
Section 3 Section Focus Transparency **A Sweet Job**

Sap collected from maple trees in the northeastern states and Canada is used to make maple syrup. Sap straight from the maple tree is colorless and watery. During processing, however, this watery solution is concentrated. It may take 30 or 40 gallons of sap to produce one gallon of maple syrup.

1. Why does it take so much sap to make one gallon of maple syrup?
2. Why does a solution become more concentrated through evaporation?

L2

This is a representation of key blackline masters available in the Teacher Classroom Resources. See Resource Manager boxes within the chapter for additional information.

Assessment

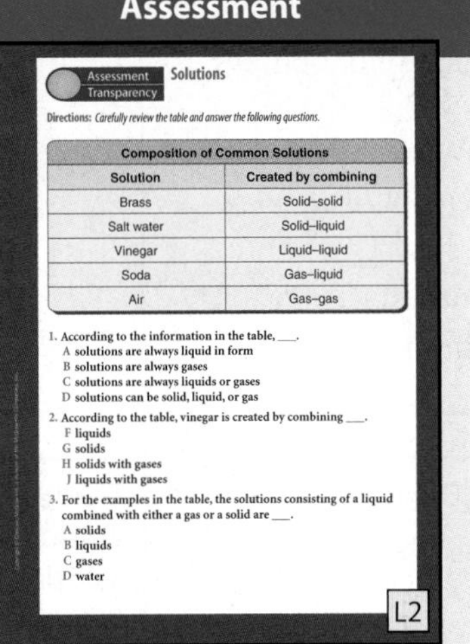
Assessment Transparency **Solutions**

Directions: Carefully review the table and answer the following questions.

Composition of Common Solutions	
Solution	Created by combining
Brass	Solid–solid
Salt water	Solid–liquid
Vinegar	Liquid–liquid
Soda	Gas–liquid
Air	Gas–gas

1. According to the information in the table, ___.
   A solutions are always liquid in form
   B solutions are always gases
   C solutions are always liquids or gases
   D solutions can be solid, liquid, or gas
2. According to the table, vinegar is created by combining ___.
   F liquids
   G solids
   H solids with gases
   J liquids with gases
3. For the examples in the table, the solutions consisting of a liquid combined with either a gas or a solid are ___.
   A solids
   B liquids
   C gases
   D water

L2

Teaching

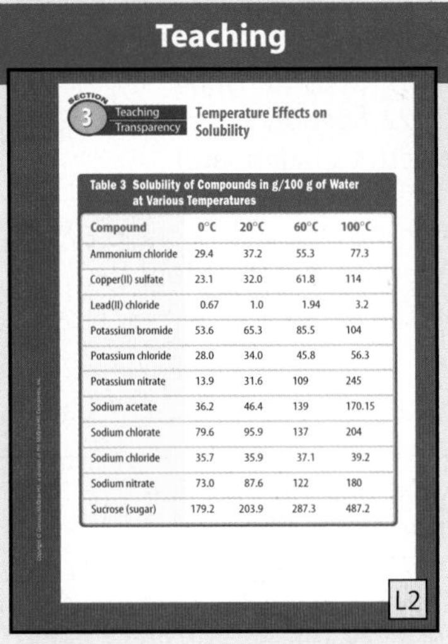
Section 3 Teaching Transparency **Temperature Effects on Solubility**

Table 3 Solubility of Compounds in g/100 g of Water at Various Temperatures

Compound	0°C	20°C	60°C	100°C
Ammonium chloride	29.4	37.2	55.3	77.3
Copper(II) sulfate	23.1	32.0	61.8	114
Lead(II) chloride	0.67	1.0	1.94	3.2
Potassium bromide	53.6	65.3	85.5	104
Potassium chloride	28.0	34.0	45.8	56.3
Potassium nitrate	13.9	31.6	109	245
Sodium acetate	36.2	46.4	139	170.15
Sodium chlorate	79.6	95.9	137	204
Sodium chloride	35.7	35.9	37.1	39.2
Sodium nitrate	73.0	87.6	122	180
Sucrose (sugar)	179.2	203.9	287.3	487.2

L2

Key to Teaching Strategies

The following designations will help you decide which activities are appropriate for your students.

- **L1** Level 1 activities should be appropriate for students with learning difficulties.
- **L2** Level 2 activities should be within the ability range of all students.
- **L3** Level 3 activities are designed for above-average students.
- **ELL** ELL activities should be within the ability range of English Language Learners.
- **COOP LEARN** Cooperative Learning activities are designed for small group work.
- **LS** Multiple Learning Styles logos, as described on page 12T, are used throughout to indicate strategies that address different learning styles.
- **P** These strategies represent student products that can be placed into a best-work portfolio.
- **PBL** Problem-Based Learning activities apply real-world situations to learning.

Hands-on Activities

Student Text Lab Worksheet

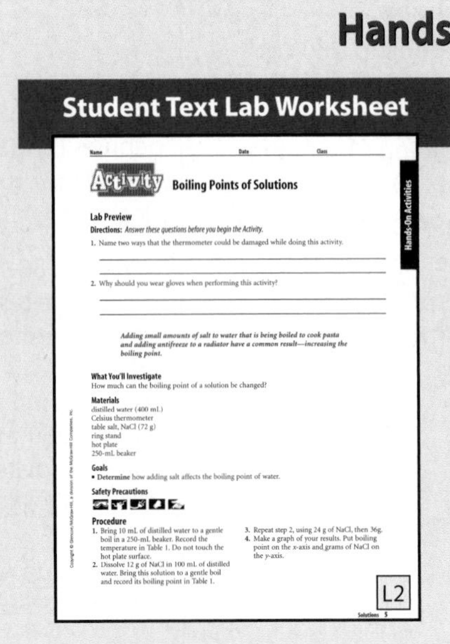
Activity **Boiling Points of Solutions**

Lab Preview

Directions: Answer these questions before you begin the Activity.

1. Name two ways that the thermometer could be damaged while doing this activity.
2. Why should you wear gloves when performing this activity?

Adding small amounts of salt to water that is being boiled to cook pasta and adding antifreeze to a radiator have a common result—increasing the boiling point.

What You'll Investigate
How much can the boiling point of a solution be changed?

Materials
distilled water (400 mL)
Celsius thermometer
table salt, NaCl (72 g)
ring stand
hot plate
250-mL beaker

Goals
• Determine how adding salt affects the boiling point of water.

Safety Precautions

Procedure
1. Bring 10 mL of distilled water to a gentle boil in a 250-mL beaker. Record the temperature in Table 1. Do not touch the hot plate surface.
2. Dissolve 12 g of NaCl in 100 mL of distilled water. Bring this solution to a gentle boil and record its boiling point in Table 1.
3. Repeat step 2, using 24 g of NaCl, then 36g.
4. Make a graph of your results. Put boiling point on the x-axis and grams of NaCl on the y-axis.

L2

Laboratory Activities

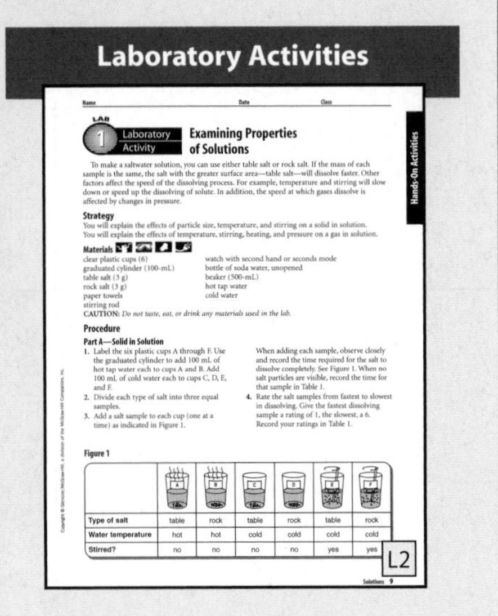
Lab 1 Laboratory Activity **Examining Properties of Solutions**

To make a saltwater solution, you can use either table salt or rock salt. If the mass of each sample is the same, the salt with the greater surface area—table salt—will dissolve faster. Other factors affect the speed of the dissolving process. For example, temperature and stirring will slow down or speed up the dissolving of solute. In addition, the speed at which gases dissolve is affected by changes in pressure.

Strategy
You will explain the effects of particle size, temperature, and stirring on a solid in solution.
You will explain the effects of temperature, stirring, heating, and pressure on a gas in solution.

Materials
clear plastic cups (6)
graduated cylinder (100-mL)
table salt (3 g)
rock salt (3 g)
paper towels
stirring rod
watch with second hand or seconds mode
bottle of soda water, unopened
beaker (500-mL)
hot tap water
cold water

CAUTION: *Do not taste, eat, or drink any materials used in the lab.*

Procedure

Part A—Solid in Solution
1. Label the six plastic cups A through F. Use the graduated cylinder to add 100 mL of hot tap water each to cups A and B. Add 100 mL of cold water each to cups C, D, E, and F.
2. Divide each type of salt into three equal samples.
3. Add a salt sample to each cup (one at a time) as indicated in Figure 1.

When adding each sample, observe closely and record the time required for the salt to dissolve completely. See Figure 1. When no salt particles are visible, record the time for that sample in Table 1.

4. Rate the salt samples from fastest to slowest in dissolving. Give the fastest dissolving sample a rating of 1, the slowest, a 6. Record your ratings in Table 1.

Figure 1

	A	B	C	D	E	F
Type of salt	table	rock	table	rock	table	rock
Water temperature	hot	hot	cold	cold	cold	cold
Stirred?	no	no	no	no	yes	yes

L2

Meeting Different Ability Levels

Content Outline

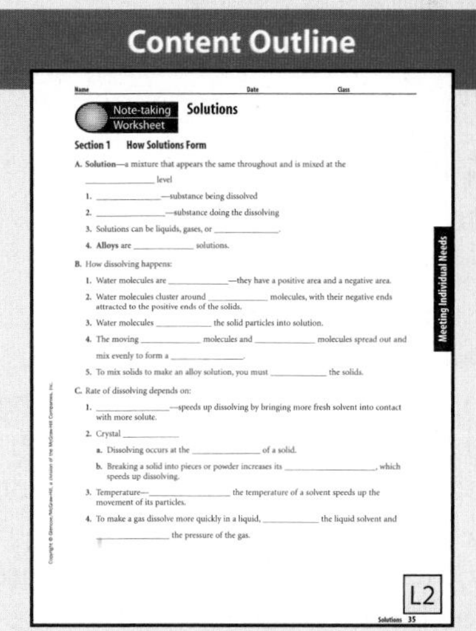

Note-taking Worksheet — Solutions

Section 1 How Solutions Form

L2

Reinforcement

Section 1 Reinforcement — How Solutions Form

Directions: Complete the table below by writing the missing information in the appropriate box. Then answer the question below.

Solution type	Solvent	Solute	Example
1. gas		gas	
2.		solid	salt water
3. solid			dental amalgam
4.	liquid		club soda
5.	liquid	liquid	
6.	solid		brass

7. Study the information in your table carefully. What is true about the state of the solvent and the type of solution produced?

Directions: Circle the term in parentheses that makes each statement true.

8. When a solid is being dissolved in a liquid, stirring (speeds up, slows down) the dissolving process.
9. A gas dissolves faster in a liquid if the temperature of the liquid is (increased, decreased).
10. A gas's solubility is faster in a liquid when under (high, low) pressure.
11. By stirring a gas in a liquid, its solubility (speeds up, slows down) the dissolving process.
12. A solid dissolves faster in a liquid if the temperature of the liquid is (increased, decreased).
13. The (larger, smaller) the surface area of a solid, the faster it will dissolve.

Directions: Study your responses to the exercise above. Use your responses to answer the following question.

14. How do the methods of speeding the rate of solution for dissolving a solid in a liquid compare to the methods of speeding the rate of solution when dissolving a gas in a liquid?

L2

Enrichment

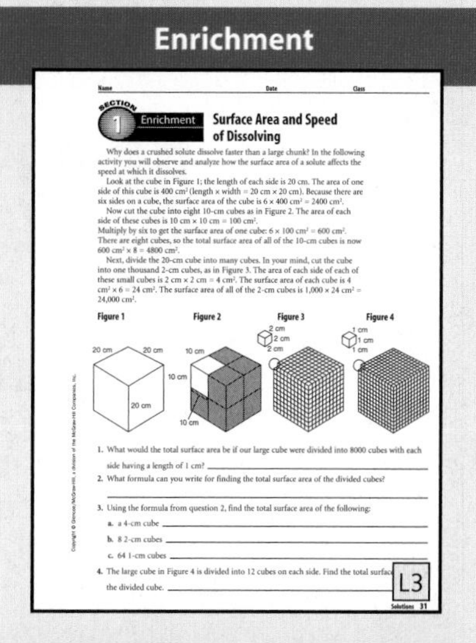

Section 1 Enrichment — Surface Area and Speed of Dissolving

L3

Student Text Lab Worksheet

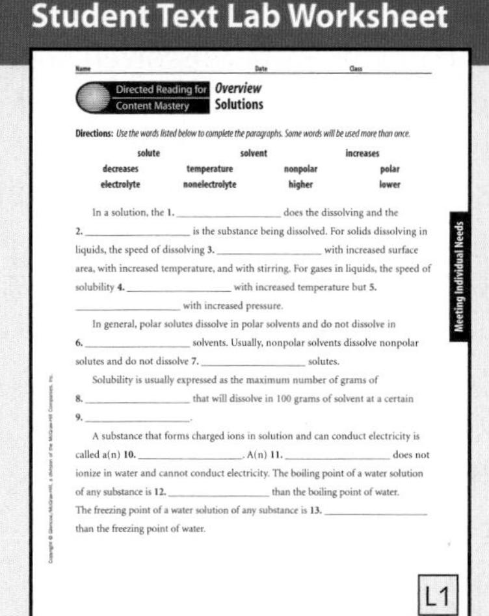

Directed Reading for Content Mastery — Overview Solutions

L1

Study Guide

Study Guide

L1

Reading Essentials

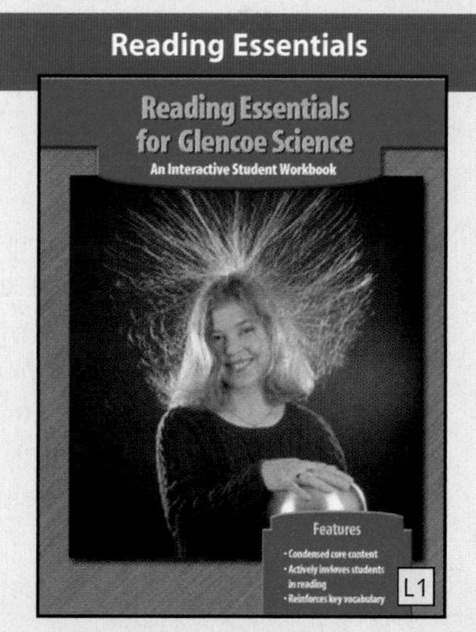

Reading Essentials for Glencoe Science

An Interactive Student Workbook

L1

Assessment

Test Practice Workbook

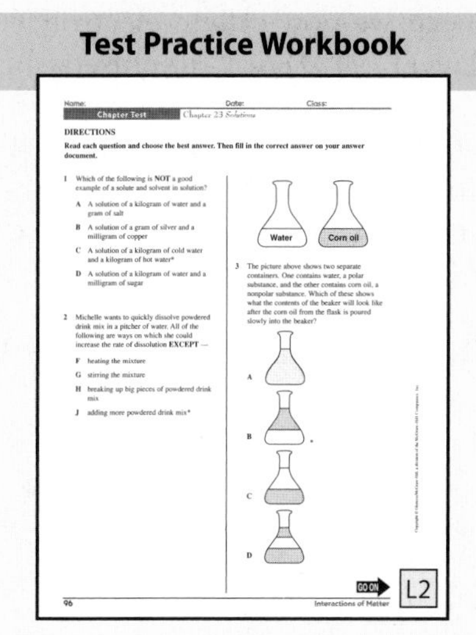

Chapter Test

L2

Chapter Review

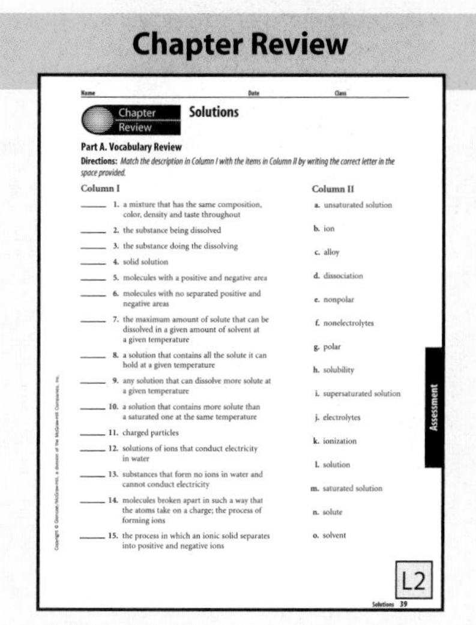

Chapter Review — Solutions

L2

Chapter Tests

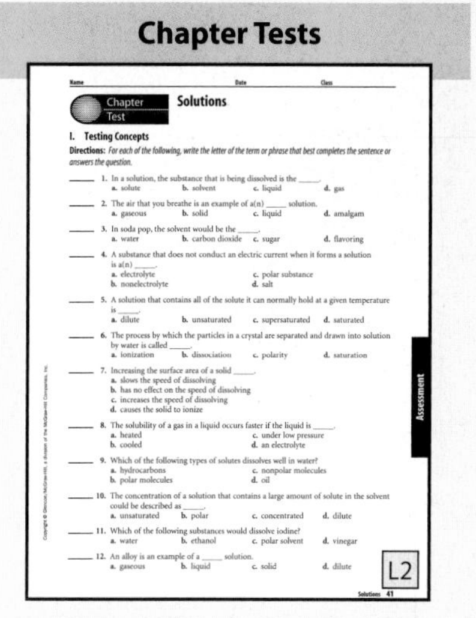

Chapter Test — Solutions

L2

Science Content Background

section 1 How Solutions Form

How Substances Dissolve?

Attractive forces between the atoms, ions, or molecules of a substance hold liquid and solid substances together. When a substance is surrounded by a solvent, particles of the substance may be attracted to the solvent molecules by various forces. If these attractive forces are strong enough to overcome the internal attractive forces of the solute, the substance will be soluble to some extent. A substance with an extremely low solubility is usually said to be insoluble.

The process of dissolving, called dissolution, involves energy. Energy is absorbed when the structure of a molecular solid or liquid is broken down or the ions of an ionic crystal are separated. Energy is released when the particles of solute form new bonds with the solvent. In the cold packs used by athletic trainers, more energy is absorbed in the first part of the dissolution process than is released in the second. For that reason, the overall process is endothermic, and the liquid becomes colder.

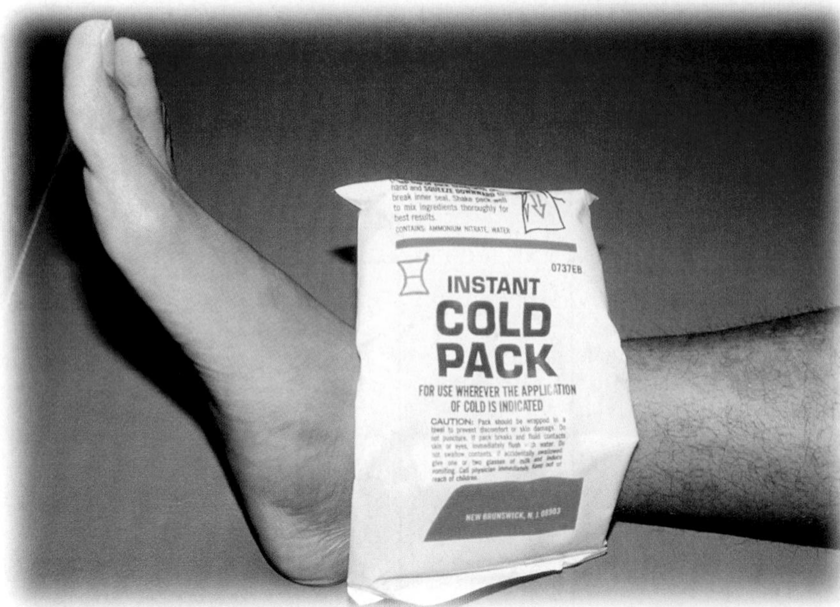

David R. Frazier/ Photo Researchers,Inc.

section 2 Solubility and Concentration

Types of Solutions

A solution is saturated when equilibrium between the undissolved solute and dissolved solute is established at a particular temperature. It is important to state the temperature of a saturated solution. Because a solution that is saturated at one temperature may not be saturated at another temperature. In the state known as solution equilibrium, the solute is dissolving into the solution and coming out of solution at exactly the same rate.

If a solution contains more dissolved solute than it usually can hold at a given temperature, the solution is said to be supersaturated. Supersaturated solutions are unstable and disturbances such as jarring, stirring, scratching the walls of the container, or dropping in a "seed" crystal cause the solution to return to the saturated state.

section 3 Particles in Solution

Particles With a Charge

It was British scientists William Nicholson and Anthony Carlisle who in 1800 first used electricity to decompose aqueous salt solutions into hydrogen and oxygen. The salt aided current flow, acting as what we now call an electrolyte. Michael Faraday (1791–1867) first used the term *electrolyte*, as well as the terms *ion*, *cation*, *anion*, *cathode*, *anode*, and *electrode*. In 1884, Svante Arrhenius (1859–1927) introduced the idea that salt ions dissociate as soon as they are dissolved in water, without the aid of electrical current.

Dissolving Without Water

Useful Nonpolar Molecules

One nonpolar solvent with which many people are familiar is turpentine, which is used to dissolve oil-based paint. Turpentine is made up of a mixture of cyclic monoterpene hydrocarbons with the molecular formula $C_{10}H_{16}$. About 85 percent of the turpentine made in the United States is sulfate turpentine, produced in the process that converts the wood from longleaf and slash pines into pulp.

The molecules contained in soap and detergent have both a polar and a nonpolar end. The polar end makes them soluble in water while the nonpolar end dissolves grease and dirt. In hard water—water that contains dissolved calcium and magnesium salts—ordinary soap reacts with the calcium and magnesium ions to form an insoluble greasy scum. Detergents, however, do not form precipitates with hard water and have excellent cleaning ability. Hard water is also undesirable because it causes "scale" to form on the walls of water heaters, teakettles, coffeepots, and irons, which greatly reduces their efficiency. Hard water can be "softened" by distillation, precipitating the calcium and magnesium, ion exchange, and demineralization.

Teacher to Teacher

Pam K. Hintz,
Elgin/New Leipzig Public School
Elgin, North Dakota

"To show how solutions can be useful in analytical applications, I prepare a simple chromatography demonstration. I place a dot of permanent marker near the bottom of a strip of coffee filter paper and a dot of water-based marker ink on another strip. Then I dip the strips in separate beakers with a small amount of water (water line below the ink dots) and let them sit for about 45 minutes. We take a minute for the students to predict what will happen and we come back to the beakers at the end of class. Students should see that the water-based ink dissolved in the water and, as the water was absorbed up the paper, separated out to show the colors that combined to make the ink. Chromatography techniques like this one are used to isolate and analyze the individual components of unknown substances."

Pam K. Hintz

chapter content resources

Internet Resources

For additional content background, visit gpscience.com to:

- access your book online
- find references to related articles in popular science magazines
- access Web links with related content background
- access current events with science journal topics

Print Resources

Clean Solvents: alternative media for chemical reactions and processing, by M. A. Abraham, American Chemical Society (symposium series 819), 2000

Properties of Liquids and Solutions, by J. N. Murrell, Wiley & Sons, 1994

Elements, compounds, and mixtures, by B. J. Knapp, Grolier Educational, 1998

Properties of Solvents, by X. Marcus, Wiley & Sons, 1998

The Experimental Determination of Solubilities, by G. T. Hefter and R. P. T. Tomkins, Wiley–VCH, 2003

chapter 22

About the Photo

Underwater Solutes This diver may not know it, but the underwater environment is full of solutes in solution. Water dissolves many substances, and the salty seawater itself is a solution. The oxygen tank that makes this dive possible also contains a solution–a gas solution of nitrogen or possibly helium mixed with oxygen.

Science Journal Student responses will vary at the beginning, but all students should come to recognize that all liquids are not necessarily solutions and all solutions are not necessarily liquids.

BIG Idea

Intermolecular Forces A solution is a homogeneous mixture. Intermolecular forces cause the ions, atoms, or molecules in the solute to be evenly distributed throughout the molecules of the solvent. For example, when a salt dissolves in water, the water molecules exert attractive electrical forces on the ions in a salt crystal. A number of water molecules at the surface of a crystal can exert a combined force on an ion that is large enough to pull the ion away from the crystal lattice. Water molecules then surround the ion, forming a cage that isolates the ion and prevents it from interacting with other ions.

Introduce the Chapter Ask students to imagine dissolving a teaspoon of sugar in a glass of water. Ask them what happens to the sugar when it dissolves. Would the weight and the volume of the liquid in the glass change? What would happen to the sugar if all the water evaporated after the sugar was dissolved?

chapter 22

Solutions

BIG Idea A solution is a homogeneous mixture of a solvent and a solute.

22.1 How Solutions Form

MAIN Idea A solution forms when particles of solute become evenly mixed among particles of solute.

22.2 Solubility and Concentration

MAIN Idea Solubility is the maximum amount of solute that can dissolve and concentration is the amount of solute actually dissolved in a given amount of solute.

22.3 Particles in Solution

MAIN Idea Dissolved particles can both lower the freezing point and raise the boiling point of a solution.

22.4 Dissolving Without Water

MAIN Idea Nonpolar solvents can dissolve many nonpolar solutes.

Mixed-Up Chemistry

Seawater, lemonade, and suntan lotion are liquids. They have something else in common, too—they are all solutions. In this chapter, you will learn about solutions.

Science Journal

Are all liquids necessarily solutions, and are all solutions liquids? Check your answer later and revise it if you've learned differently.

Interactive Chalkboard

This CD-ROM is an editable Microsoft® PowerPoint® presentation that includes:

- an editable presentation for every chapter
- additional chapter questions
- animated graphics
- image bank
- links to gpscience.com

Start-Up Activities

Solution Identification by Solvent Subtraction

What do you like to drink when you're thirsty? Do you prefer water from the faucet, bottled water, or a sports drink that contains substances added to replace those lost during sweating? What do these thirst quenchers contain? Try the following lab to find out.

1. Obtain three solution samples from your teacher and place equal amounts of each in separate, marked, 100-mL beakers.
2. Carefully, boil each solution on a hot plate. As soon as the liquid is gone, remove each beaker to a heat-proof surface using a thermal mitt. Let cool.
3. Examine the inside of your cooled beakers. What do you see? Guess the identity of each solution.
4. **Think Critically** Describe in your Science Journal what remained in each of the three containers and explain how solutions may look alike but contain different substances.

FOLDABLES™ Study Organizer

Solvent-Solute Comparison Make the following Foldable to compare and contrast the characteristics of solvents and solutes.

STEP 1 **Fold** one sheet of paper lengthwise.

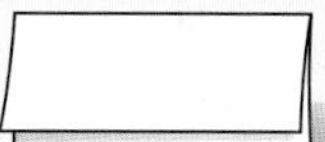

STEP 2 **Fold** into thirds.

STEP 3 **Unfold and draw** overlapping ovals. **Cut** the top sheet along the folds.

STEP 4 **Label** the ovals as shown.

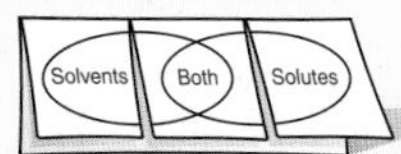

Construct a Venn Diagram As you read the chapter, list characteristics that are unique to solvents under the left tab, those unique to solutes under the right tab, and characteristics common to both under the middle tab.

Preview this chapter's content and activities at gpscience.com

663

Additional Chapter Media

- Virtual Lab: *How is the solubility of a compound determined?*
- Video Lab: *Identify the Solution by Solvent Subtraction*

Purpose Students will investigate the solid solute content of liquid samples. L2 ELL

LS **Visual-Spatial**

Preparation Purchase samples of bottled water and common sports drinks.

Materials bottled water, sports drinks, three small beakers per group, hot plate, oven mitt

Teaching Strategy Display the labels of the bottled water and sports drinks. Ask students to note the amounts of dissolved solutes.

Think Critically

Results will vary depending on the minerals dissolved in local tap water and the bottled water and sports drinks used. The sports drinks will likely produce the most precipitate, which will have a dark color. Because solutes are dissolved, it is impossible to tell by looking at a solution how much solute is present.

Assessment

Process Show two types of sweetened drinks. Ask students how they might decide which had the most dissolved solute without heating the samples. Determine the density of both. The one with more dissolved solute is denser. Use **Performance Assessment in the Science Classroom,** p. 95.

Dinah Zike Study Fold

Student preparation materials for this Foldable are available in the **Chapter *Fast File* Resources.**

1 Motivate

Bellringer

Section Focus Transparencies also are available on the Interactive Chalkboard CD-ROM. L2 

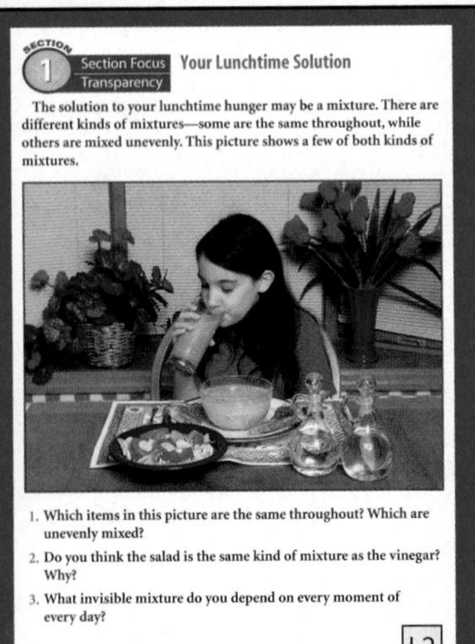
Section 1 Section Focus Transparency — Your Lunchtime Solution

The solution to your lunchtime hunger may be a mixture. There are different kinds of mixtures—some are the same throughout, while others are mixed unevenly. This picture shows a few of both kinds of mixtures.

1. Which items in this picture are the same throughout? Which are unevenly mixed?
2. Do you think the salad is the same kind of mixture as the vinegar? Why?
3. What invisible mixture do you depend on every moment of every day?

L2

Tie to Prior Knowledge

Mixtures Have students recall what they know about heterogeneous and homogeneous mixtures. In a homogeneous mixture, the particles are distributed evenly throughout. In a heterogeneous mixture, the mixed materials are not distributed evenly. A homogeneous mixture is one in which the particles are distributed evenly at the molecular or ionic level. L2

section 1

How Solutions Form

Reading Guide

***What* You'll Learn**

- **Determine** how things dissolve.
- **Examine** the factors that affect the rates at which solids and gases dissolve in liquids.

***Why* It's Important**

Many chemical reactions take place in solution—the food you eat is digested, or chemically changed, by the solution that is in your stomach.

Review Vocabulary

alloy: a mixture of elements that has metallic properties

New Vocabulary

- solution
- solute
- solvent
- polar

What is a solution?

Hummingbirds are fascinating creatures. They can hover for long periods while they sip nectar from flowers through their long beaks. To attract hummingbirds, many people use feeder bottles containing a red liquid, as shown in **Figure 1.** The liquid is a solution of sugar and red food coloring in water.

Suppose you are making some hummingbird food. When you add sugar to water and stir, the sugar crystals disappear. When you add a few drops of red food coloring and stir, the color spreads evenly throughout the sugar water. Why does this happen?

Hummingbird food is one of many solutions. A **solution** is a mixture that has the same composition, color, density, and even taste throughout. The reason you no longer see the sugar crystals and the reason the red dye spreads out evenly is that they have formed a completely homogeneous mixture. The sugar crystals broke up into sugar molecules, the red dye into its molecules, and both mixed evenly among the water molecules.

Figure 1 Liquid solutions, like this hummingbird food, which has sugar and food coloring, may contain gases, other liquids, or solids.

Section 1 Resource Manager 

Chapter *FAST FILE* Resources
- Transparency Activity, p. 46
- Note-taking Worksheets, pp. 35–37
- Directed Reading for Content Mastery, pp. 19, 20
- Enrichment, p. 31
- Lab Activity, pp. 9–12
- MiniLAB, p. 3
- Reinforcement, p. 13

Reading and Writing Skill Activities, p. 17

Mathematics Skill Activities, p. 13

Solutes and Solvents

To describe a solution, you may say that one substance is dissolved in another. The substance being dissolved is the **solute,** and the substance doing the dissolving is the **solvent.** When a solid dissolves in a liquid, the solid is the solute and the liquid is the solvent. Thus, in salt water, salt is the solute and water is the solvent. In carbonated soft drinks, carbon dioxide gas is one of the solutes and water is the solvent. When a liquid dissolves in another liquid, the substance present in the larger amount is usually called the solvent.

Reading Check *How do you know which substance is the solute in a solution?*

Nonliquid Solutions Solutions can also be gaseous or even solid. Examples of all three solution phases are shown in **Figure 1** and **Figure 2.** Did you know that the air you breathe is a solution? In fact, all mixtures of gases are solutions. Air is a solution of 78 percent nitrogen, 21 percent oxygen, and small amounts of other gases such as argon, carbon dioxide and hydrogen. The sterling silver and brass used in musical instruments is an example of a solid solution. The sterling silver contains 92.5 percent silver and 7.5 percent copper. The brass is a solution of copper and zinc metals. Solid solutions are known as alloys. They are made by melting the metal solute and solvent together. Most coins, as shown in **Figure 3,** are alloys.

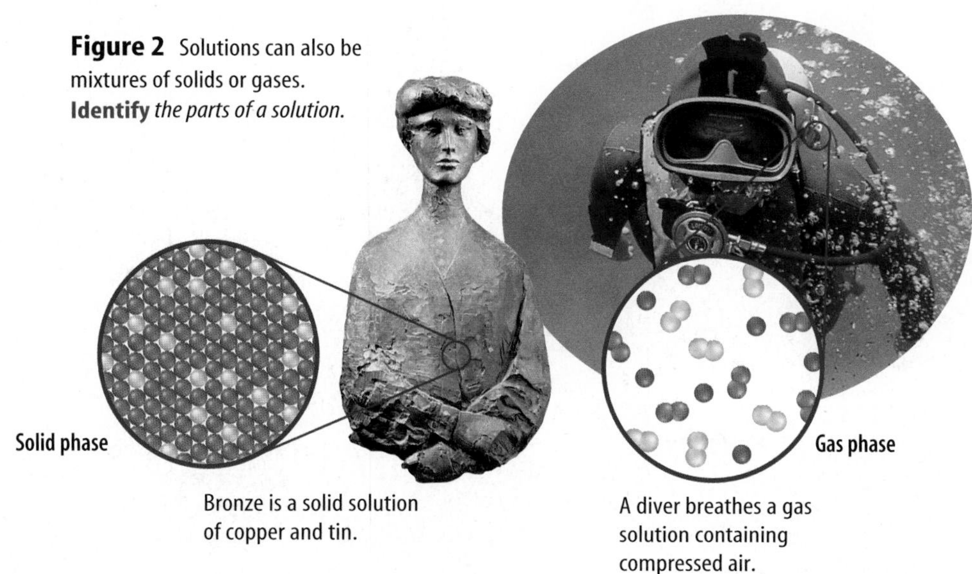
Solid phase
Gas phase
Bronze is a solid solution of copper and tin.
A diver breathes a gas solution containing compressed air.

Figure 2 Solutions can also be mixtures of solids or gases.
Identify *the parts of a solution.*

2 Teach

Quick Demo

Dissolve a Crystal

Materials petri dish, water, potassium permanganate

Estimated Time 5 minutes

Procedure Partially fill a petri dish with water and place it on the overhead projector. Place a crystal of potassium permanganate in the water. The purple color will stream out from the crystal as it dissolves. L1 ELL
LS **Visual-Spatial**

Reading Check

Answer It is the substance being dissolved and is usually the substance that is present in the lesser amount.

Activity

Salt Residue Have students stir table salt into 50 mL of water until no more salt dissolves. Then have them add 5 mL of powdered chalk and stir again. Have them pour the liquid through filter paper. They should observe the chalk on the filter paper. Have them evaporate the filtered liquid and observe the residue remaining (salt). Explain that if filter paper can separate a substance out of a liquid, the substance was not dissolved. The chalk did not dissolve; the salt did. L2 ELL
LS **Visual-Spatial**

Teacher FYI

Alloys Steel is an alloy of mostly iron with various other metals and semimetals added. Chromium, carbon, and nickel are solutes added to molten iron, which is cooled to make a solid alloy.

Science Journal

Everyday Solvents and Solutes Have students recall that solvents and solutes are all around them. Ask them to list in their Science Journals solvents and solutes they encounter in their daily lives. Their bodies contain solutes dissolved in water. Paint thinner, spot removers, and nail polish remover are all solvents that do not contain water. L2 P LS **Linguistic**

Visualizing Metal Alloys

Have students examine the pictures and read the captions. Then ask the following questions.

Why is it necessary for vending machines to be able to recognize a coin by its size, weight, and electrical conductivity? All three properties are difficult to duplicate in counterfeit coins or slugs. It also compensates for the machine's lack of visual recognition.

Look at the photograph of the two types of dollars. Do they appear to be made from the same alloy? No, the Susan B. Anthony dollar appears to be made of a material, such as nickel or silver, that is silver in color. The Sacagawea dollar is copper in color, similar to the element copper.

Activity

Coin Composition Have students find the composition of the Susan B. Anthony dollar and construct circle graphs for the Susan B. Anthony dollar similar to the one shown in the text for the Sacagawea dollar. L2

LS **Logical-Mathematical**

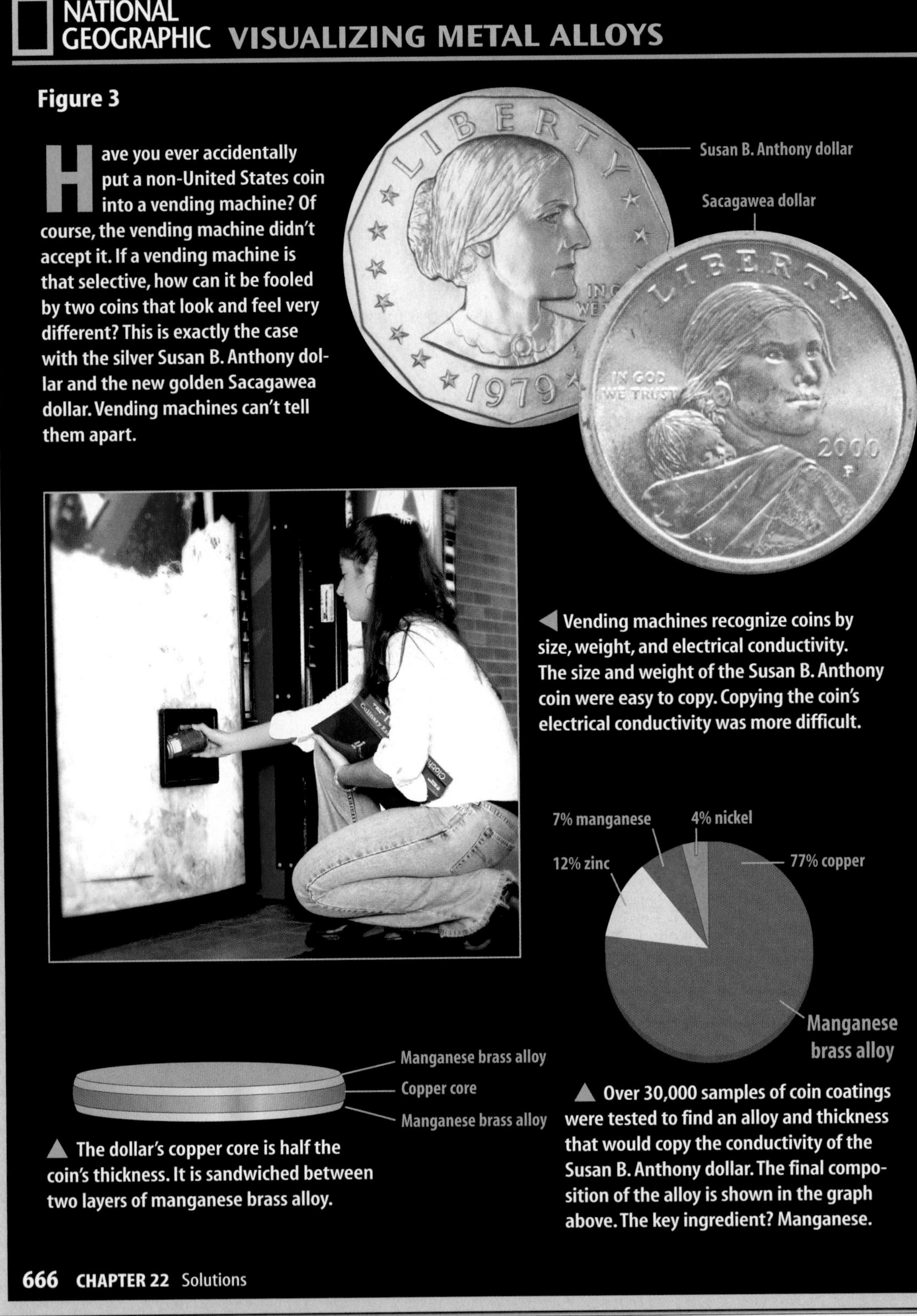

NATIONAL GEOGRAPHIC VISUALIZING METAL ALLOYS
Figure 3
Have you ever accidentally put a non-United States coin into a vending machine? Of course, the vending machine didn't accept it. If a vending machine is that selective, how can it be fooled by two coins that look and feel very different? This is exactly the case with the silver Susan B. Anthony dollar and the new golden Sacagawea dollar. Vending machines can't tell them apart.
Susan B. Anthony dollar
Sacagawea dollar
LIBERTY
1979
IN GOD WE TRUST
2000
Vending machines recognize coins by size, weight, and electrical conductivity. The size and weight of the Susan B. Anthony coin were easy to copy. Copying the coin's electrical conductivity was more difficult.
7% manganese
4% nickel
12% zinc
77% copper
Manganese brass alloy
Over 30,000 samples of coin coatings were tested to find an alloy and thickness that would copy the conductivity of the Susan B. Anthony dollar. The final composition of the alloy is shown in the graph above. The key ingredient? Manganese.
Manganese brass alloy
Copper core
Manganese brass alloy
The dollar's copper core is half the coin's thickness. It is sandwiched between two layers of manganese brass alloy.
666 CHAPTER 22 Solutions

Differentiated Instruction

Challenge Have students find out how vending machines check the size, weight, and electrical conductivity of coins. Have students report their findings to their class. L3 LS **Linguistic**

How Substances Dissolve

Fruit drinks and sports drinks are examples of solutions made by dissolving solids in liquids. Like hummingbird food, both contain sugar as well as other substances that add color and flavor. How do solids such as sugar dissolve in water?

The dissolving of a solid in a liquid occurs at the surface of the solid. To understand how water solutions form, keep in mind two things you have learned about water. Like the particles of any substance, water molecules are constantly moving. Also, water molecules are **polar,** which means they have a positive area and a negative area. Molecules of sugar are also polar.

How It Happens **Figure 4** shows molecules of sugar dissolving in water. First, water molecules cluster around sugar molecules with their negative ends attracted to the positive ends of the sugar. Then, the water molecules pull the sugar molecules into solution. Finally, the water molecules and the sugar molecules mix evenly, forming a solution.

Reading Check *How do water molecules help sugar molecules dissolve?*

The process described in **Figure 4** repeats as layer after layer of sugar molecules moves away from the crystal, until all the molecules are evenly spread out. The same three steps occur for any solid solute dissolving in a liquid solvent.

Dissolving Liquids and Gases A similar but more complex process takes place when a gas dissolves in a liquid. Particles of liquids and gases move much more freely than do particles of solids. When gases dissolve in gases or when liquids dissolve in liquids, this movement spreads solutes evenly throughout the solvent, resulting in a homogenous solution.

Dissolving Solids in Solids How can you mix solids to make alloys? Although solid particles do move a little, this movement is not enough to spread them evenly throughout the mixture. The solid metals are first melted and then mixed together. In this liquid state, the metal atoms can spread out evenly and will remain mixed when cooled.

Figure 4 Dissolving sugar in water can be thought of as a three-step process.

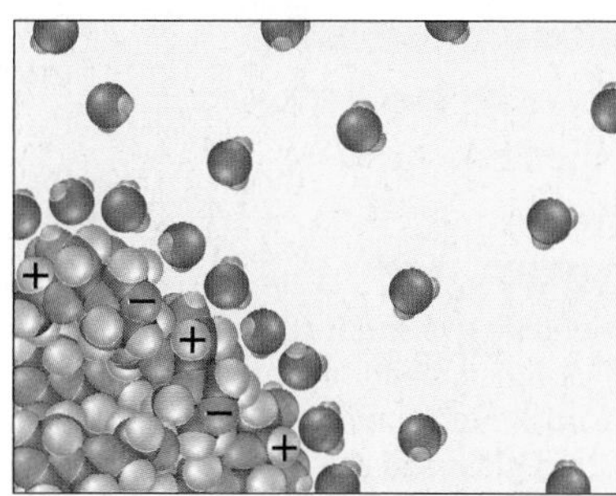

Step 1 Moving water molecules cluster around the sugar molecules as their negative ends are attracted to the positive ends of the sugar molecules.

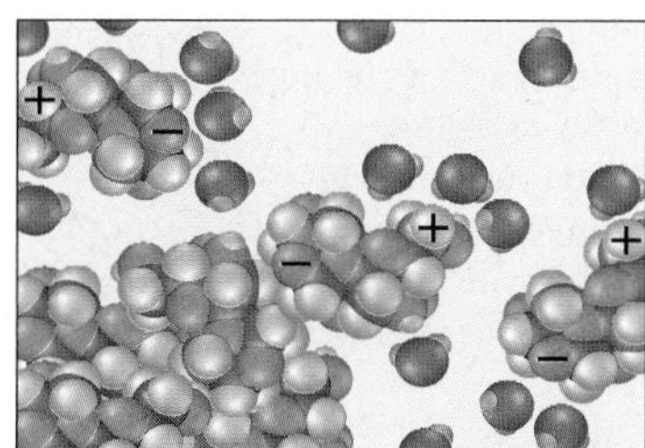

Step 2 Water molecules pull the sugar molecules into solution.

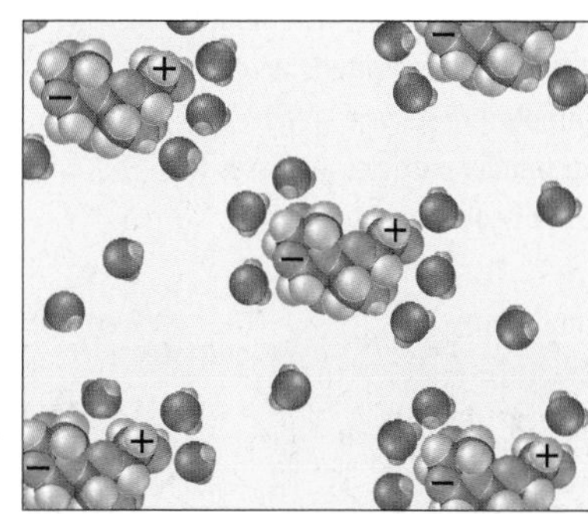

Step 3 Water molecules and sugar molecules spread out to form a homogeneous mixture.

Visual Learning

Figure 4 Place a box of foam spheres in the center of a group of students who have linked arms. Tell students that they are solvent particles and the spheres are solute particles. In order for a sphere to dissove, it must be held by a student. Discuss the three dissolving steps presented on the page. Then have students act out the steps with the spheres as you call out Step 1, Step 2, and Step 3. The activity can also be used to discuss the advantage of making the solute more available by stirring it among the solvent particles. L2 ELL IS **Kinesthetic**

Reading Check

Answer The negative ends of the water molecules pull on the positive ends of sugar molecules.

Quick Demo

Water Polarity

Materials balloon, wool cloth

Estimated Time 5 minutes

Procedure To show the polarity of water, blow up a balloon and rub its surface with a wool cloth. Turn on the water faucet so it delivers a thin steady stream. Bring the statically charged balloon near the stream, but do not touch the balloon to it. Have students observe that the stream bends dramatically. L2 ELL IS **Visual-Spatial**

Cultural Diversity

Sandbox Trees The sap from the tall sandbox trees, found in the jungles of Central and South America, is acidic. Fishers throw this sap into lakes and streams, which have been dammed, to stun the fish so they can gather them for food. Then they remove the dams. The sap becomes sufficiently dilute, and the fish recover completely.

Differentiated Instruction

Learning Disabled As you do the various demonstrations, help students follow what you are doing by moving slowly and deliberately through each step and explaining what you are doing as you do it. Make sure all students can see what you do and can see the results. Make sure you describe the results to the class. L1 ELL **Auditory-Musical**

Purpose Students will observe differences in the rates of dissolution of particles with different surface areas. L2 ELL LS **Visual-Spatial**

Materials four sugar cubes, distilled water, two glasses, two stirring rods per group

Teaching Strategy Have students do the activity twice, once stirring the sugar and once not stirring. Stirring increases rate of dissolving.

Analysis

1. The granules dissolved faster than the cubes even though they were treated identically.
2. The greater the surface area of the solute, the faster it dissolves.

Assessment

Oral Have students use their MiniLAB results and **Figure 5** to explain how the surface area of the two cubes increases when they are ground. Use **Performance Assessment in the Science Classroom,** p. 89.

Discussion

Surface Area Discuss with students how rapidly surface area increases as an object is divided into smaller pieces. Have students calculate the surface area of a 2-cm cube. $6 \times 4\ cm^2 = 24\ cm^2$ Ask students to predict how much larger the surface area would be if the cube were divided into 1-cm cubes. How many 1-cm cubes would there be? 8 What is their surface area? $8 \times 6 \times 1\ cm^2 = 48\ cm^2$ L2

Observing the Effect of Surface Area

Procedure

1. Grind up two **sugar cubes.**
2. Place the ground sugar particles into a **medium-sized glass** and place two **unground sugar cubes** into a similar glass.
3. Add an equal amount of **distilled water** at room temperature to each glass.

Analysis

1. Compare the times required to dissolve each.
2. What do you conclude about the dissolving rate and surface area?

Try at Home

Rate of Dissolving

If two substances will form a solution, they will do so at a particular rate. Sometimes the rate at which a solute dissolves into a solvent is fast and other times slow. There are several things you can do to speed up the rate of dissolving—stirring, reducing crystal size, and increasing temperature are three of the most effective techniques.

Stirring How can you speed up the dissolving process? Think about how you make a drink from a powdered mix. After you add the mix to water, you stir it. Stirring a solution speeds up dissolving because it brings more fresh solvent into contact with more solute. The fresh solvent attracts the particles of solute, causing the solid solute to dissolve faster.

Crystal Size Another way to speed the dissolving of a solid in a liquid is to grind large crystals into smaller ones. Suppose you want to use a 5-g crystal of rock candy to sweeten your water. If you put the whole crystal into a glass of water, it might take several minutes to dissolve, even with stirring. However, if you first grind the crystal of rock candy into a powder, it will dissolve in the same amount of water in a few seconds.

Why does breaking up a solid cause it to dissolve faster? Breaking the solid into smaller pieces greatly increases its surface area, as you can see in **Figure 5.** Because dissolving takes place at the surface of the solid, increasing the surface area allows more solvent to come into contact with more solid solute. Therefore, the speed of the dissolving process increases.

Figure 5 Crystal size affects solubility. Large crystals dissolve in water slowly because the amount of surface area is limited. Increasing the amount of surface area by creating smaller particles increases the rate of dissolving.

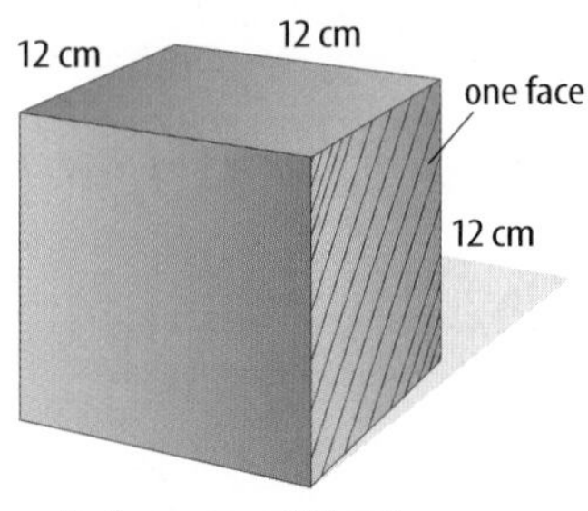

A face of a cube is the outer surface that has four edges.

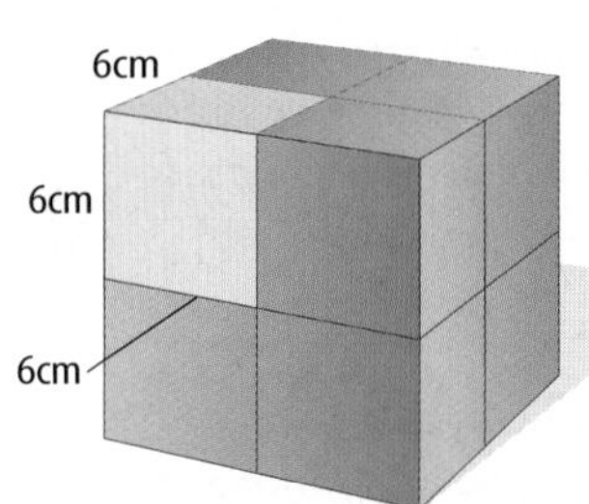

Pull apart the cube into smaller cubes of equal size. You now have eight cubes and forty-eight faces.

If you divide the cube into smaller cubes that are 1 cm on a side, you will have 1,728 cubes and 10,368 faces.

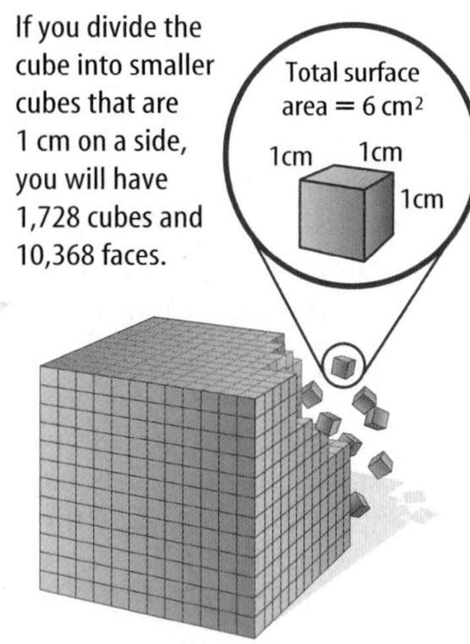

Active Reading

Quickwrites Let students spontaneously discover what they already know about solutions, solvents, and solutes. Have students list their ideas and thoughts about these topics freely in a paragraph. Then, during or after a learning experience, share those ideas and thoughts with the class. L2

668 CHAPTER 22 Solutions

SURFACE AREA EQUATION

Calculating Surface Area The length, height, and width of a cube are each 1 cm. If the cube is cut in half to form two rectangles, what is the total surface area of the new pieces?

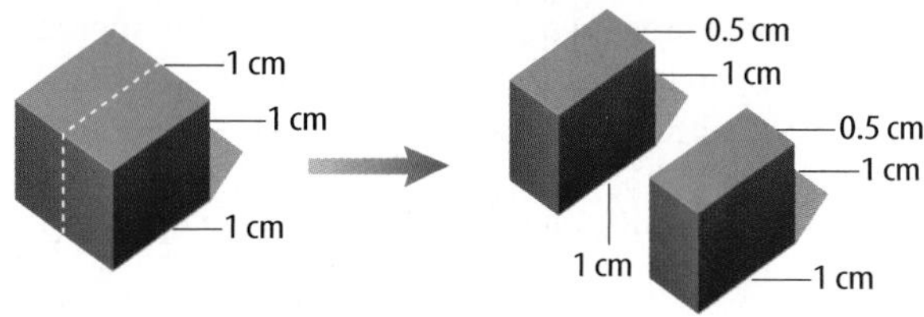

1 This is what you know: Each new piece has the dimensions: $l = 1$ cm $h = 1$ cm $w = 0.5$ cm

2 This is what you need to find: Total surface area of the two new pieces

3 Use this formula: The rectangular solids each have six faces:
SA front and back = $2(\mathbf{h} \times \mathbf{w})$
SA left and right = $2(\mathbf{h} \times \mathbf{l})$
SA top and bottom = $2(\mathbf{w} \times \mathbf{l})$
Total *SA* of one piece:
Total *SA* = $2(\mathbf{h} \times \mathbf{w}) + 2(\mathbf{h} \times \mathbf{l}) + 2(\mathbf{w} \times \mathbf{l})$

4 Substitute: $2(\mathbf{1\ cm} \times \mathbf{0.5\ cm}) + 2(\mathbf{1\ cm} \times \mathbf{1\ cm}) + 2(\mathbf{0.5\ cm} \times \mathbf{1\ cm})$
$= 4\ cm^2$

Because there are two identical pieces, their total surface area: $2\ (4\ cm^2) = 8\ cm^2$

5 Determine the units: units of *SA* = (cm × cm) + (cm × cm) + (cm × cm)
units of *SA* = $cm^2 + cm^2 + cm^2$
units of *SA* = cm^2

Answer: The total surface area of the two rectangles is $8\ cm^2$

Science Online
For more practice problems, go to page 834, and visit gpscience.com/extra_problems.

Practice Problems

1. A cube of salt with a length, height, and width of 5 cm is attached along a face to another cube of salt with the same dimensions. What is the combined surface area of the new rectangular solid?
2. **Challenge** How much surface area was lost by combining cubes?

SURFACE AREA EQUATION

National Math Standards

Correlation to Mathematics Objectives

4, 6, 9

Answers to Practice Problems

1. Solve the equations
- For the attached cubes:
  $h = 5$ cm, $l = 5$ cm, $w = 10$ cm
  $2(5\ cm \times 10\ cm) + 2(5\ cm \times 5\ cm) + 2(10\ cm \times 5\ cm)$
  $= 250\ cm^2$
- For the original cubes:
  $h = l = w = 5$ cm
  $2(5\ cm \times 5\ cm) + 2(5\ cm \times 5\ cm) + 2(5\ cm \times 5\ cm)$
  $= 150\ cm^2$

2. Because there were two cubes, $150\ cm^2 + 150\ cm^2 = 300\ cm^2$, so $50\ cm^2$ of surface area was lost.

Fun Fact

Moisturizers have long been used to protect and rehydrate the skin. These products contain compounds called humectants and emollients that increase the water content of the skin in different ways. Humectants add water to the skin by attracting water vapor from the air. Emollients cover the skin with a layer of material that is immiscible with water. This prevents water from within the skin from evaporating.

Differentiated Instruction

Challenge Air is a solution of gases, primarily nitrogen. Ask students to discover the other gases and the relative amounts of each in air. Students can then present their research to the class in a format of their choosing. Although charts and graphs make good visual representation, challenge students to invent another creative way to illustrate their findings. L2

3 Assess

DAILY INTERVENTION

Check for Understanding

Kinesthetic Have two or three students stand in a group and have another student pull at the hand of a student in the group. Relate this activity to the job of a solvent pulling a solute into solution. Have students identify which person is the solvent and which is the solute. L1

Reteach

Surface Area Bring in two boxes of different sizes to represent different surface areas. Use a new crayon and color all six sides of the larger box. Then use another new crayon and color all six sides of the smaller box. Explain that the difference in surface area affected the amount of crayon that was needed to color it. L2 LS **Visual Spatial**

Assessment

Content Have students work in groups to write a story or a poem about what happens to one NaCl crystal as it is put into water and dissolves. Use **Performance Assessment in the Science Classroom,** p. 157. L2

Temperature In addition to stirring and decreasing particle size, a third way to increase the rate at which most solids dissolve is to increase the temperature of the solvent. Think about making hot chocolate from a mix. You can make the sugar in the chocolate mix dissolve faster by putting it in hot water instead of cold water. Increasing the temperature of a solvent speeds up the movement of its particles. This increase causes more solvent particles to bump into the solute. As a result, solute particles break loose and dissolve faster.

Controlling the Process Think about how the three factors you just learned affect the rate of dissolving. Can these factors combine to further increase the rate or perhaps control the rate of dissolving? Each technique, stirring, crushing, and heating, is known to speed up the rate of dissolving by itself. However, when two or more techniques are combined, the rate of dissolving is even faster. Consider a sugar cube placed in cold water. You know that the sugar cube will eventually dissolve. You can predict that heating the water will increase the rate by some amount. You can also predict that heat and stirring will increase the rate further. Finally, you can predict that crushing the cube combined with heating and stirring will result in the fastest rate of dissolving. Knowing how much each technique affects the rate will allow you to control the rate of dissolving more precisely.

section 1 review

Summary

What is a solution?

- A solution is a uniform mixture.
- Solutions have the same composition, color, density, and taste throughout.

Solutes and Solvents

- In a solution, the solute is the substance that is being dissolved; the solvent is the substance that is doing the dissolving.

How Substances Dissolve

- The process of dissolving happens at the surface and is aided by polarity and molecular movement.

Rate of Dissolving

- Stirring, surface area, and temperature affect the rate of dissolving.

Self Check

1. **List** possible ways that phases of matter could combine to form a solution.
2. **Describe** how temperature affects the rate of dissolving.
3. **Describe** how the metal atoms in an alloy are mixed.
4. **Think Critically** Amalgrams, which are sometimes used in tooth fillings, are alloys of mercury with other metals. Is an amalgam a solution? Explain.

Applying Math

5. **Find Surface Area** Calculate the surface area of a rectangular solid with dimensions $l = 2$ cm, $w = 1$ cm, and $h = 0.5$ cm.
6. **Calculate Percent Increase** If the length of the rectangle in question 5 is increased by 10%, by how much will the surface area increase?

gpscience.com/self_check_quiz

section  review

1. Possible answer: liquid/liquid, solid/liquid, gas/liquid, gas/gas, solid/solid.
2. Increasing temperature causes particles to move faster which causes solutes to dissolve faster.
3. Metals are melted, mixed evenly, then cooled to a solid.
4. Yes, one metal acts as the solute while the other metal acts as a solvent.
5. $2(2\text{ cm} \times 1\text{ cm}) + 2(2\text{ cm} \times 0.5\text{ cm}) + 2(1\text{ cm} \times 0.5\text{ cm}) = 7\text{ cm}^2$
6. new $l = 2.2$ cm; therefore, new surface area = 7.6 cm. $\left[\frac{(7.6\text{ cm} - 7\text{ cm})}{7\text{ cm}}\right] \times 100 = 8.5\%$ increase

670 CHAPTER 22 Solutions

section

Solubility and Concentration

Reading Guide

What **You'll Learn**

- **Define** the concept of solubility.
- **Identify** how to express the concentration of solutions.
- **List** and define three types of solutions.
- **Describe** the effects of pressure and temperature on the solubility of gases.

Why **It's Important**

Solutions such as medicine and lemonade work and taste a particular way because of the specific solution concentrations

Review Vocabulary

concentration: describes how much solute is present in a solution compared to the amount of solvent

New Vocabulary

- solubility
- saturated solution
- unsaturated solution
- supersaturated solution

How much can dissolve?

You can stir several teaspoons of sugar into lemonade, and the sugar will dissolve. However, if you continue adding sugar, eventually the point is reached when no more sugar dissolves and the excess granules sink to the bottom of the glass. This indicates how soluble sugar is in water. **Solubility** (sol yuh BIH luh tee) is the maximum amount of a solute that can be dissolved in a given amount of solvent at a given temperature.

Reading Check *What is solubility?*

Comparing Solubilities The amount of a substance that can dissolve in a solvent depends on the nature of these substances. **Figure 6** shows two beakers with the same volume of water and two different solutes. In one beaker, 1 g of solute A dissolves completely, but additional solute does not dissolve and falls to the bottom of the beaker. On the other hand, 1 g of solute B dissolves completely, and two more grams also dissolve before solute begins to fall to the bottom. If the temperature of the water is the same in both beakers, you can conclude that substance B is more soluble than substance A. **Table 1** shows how the solubility of several substances varies at 20°C. For solutes that are gases, the pressure also must be given.

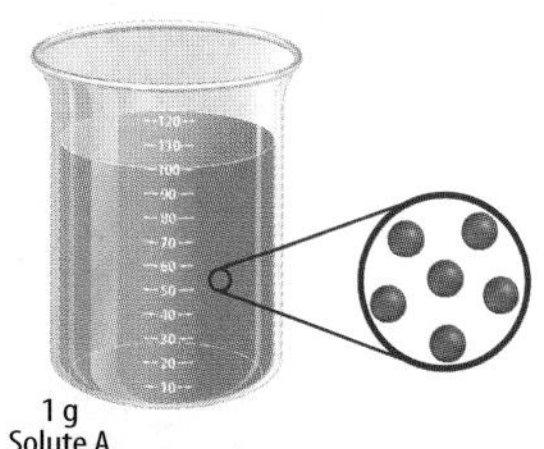

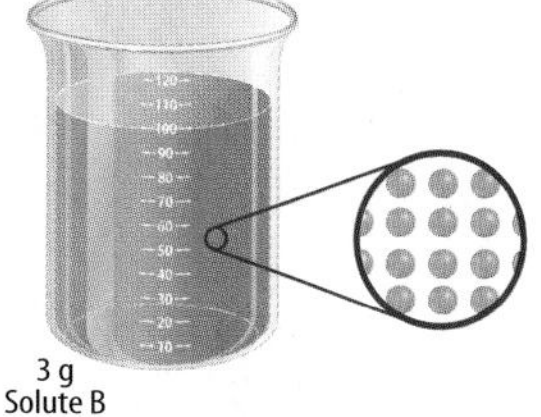

Figure 6 Substance B is more soluble in water than substance A at the same temperature.

1 Motivate

Bellringer

Section Focus Transparencies also are available on the Interactive Chalkboard CD-ROM.  

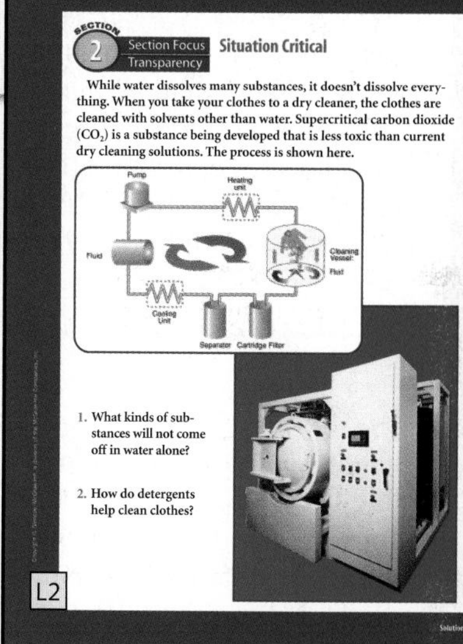

Tie to Prior Knowledge

Nutritious Milk Students are familiar with milk as a nutritious food. Bring in a milk carton and go over the percent concentrations of various nutrients dissolved in the milk. Point out that solute percentages can provide important information. L2

Virtual Lab

Solute How is the solubility of a compound determined?

Section 2 Resource Manager

Chapter *Fast File* Resources

Transparency Activity, p. 47
Directed Reading for Content Mastery, p. 21
MiniLAB, p. 4
Enrichment, p. 32
Reinforcement, p. 28

2 Teach

Reading Check

Answer the maximum amount of solute that can be dissolved in a given amount of solvent at a given temperature

Misconceptions

Concentrated Acids Some people think that all concentrated acids are 100% acid. Explain to students that concentrated hydrochloric acid is 37% HCl, concentrated nitric acid is 70% HNO_3, and sulfuric acid is 96% H_2SO_4.

Activity

Ranking Concentration Bring a colored drink to class and dilute it into several glasses of equal volume but different concentration. Have students place the solutions in sequence from low to high concentration. (The basis for the sequencing is the intensity of the color.) Once the students are satisfied with the sequence, tell them the concentrations of the solutions in %v/v. L1 ELL LS **Visual-Spatial**

Visual Learning

Table 2 Prepare 50 mL of a saturated solution of any substance from **Table 2.** Place a small amount of this solution in a petri dish. Place a small amount of the same solution in a second petri dish and add water to make it unsaturated. Place both petri dishes on the overhead projector. Have a student drop a crystal of the salt into each dish and slowly stir both solutions. The crystal will dissolve in the unsaturated solution, but it will remain visible in the saturated solution. L2 ELL LS **Visual-Spatial**

Table 1 Solubility of Substances in Water at 20°C

Substance	Solubility in g/100 g of Water
Solid Substances	
Salt (sodium chloride)	35.9
Baking soda (sodium bicarbonate)	9.6
Washing soda (sodium carbonate)	21.4
Lye (sodium hydroxide)	109.0
Sugar (sucrose)	203.9
Gaseous Substances*	
Hydrogen	0.00017
Oxygen	0.005
Carbon dioxide	0.16

*at normal atmospheric pressure

Concentration

Suppose you add one teaspoon of lemon juice to a glass of water to make lemonade. Your friend adds four teaspoons of lemon juice to another glass of water the same size. You could say that your glass of lemonade is dilute and your friend's lemonade is concentrated, because your friend's drink now has more lemon flavor than yours. A concentrated solution is one in which a large amount of solute is dissolved in the solvent. A dilute solution is one that has a small amount of solute in the solvent.

Precise Concentrations How much real fruit juice is there in one of those boxed fruit drinks? You can read the label to find out. *Concentrated* and *dilute* are not precise terms. However, concentrations of solutions can be described precisely. One way is to state the percentage by volume of the solute. The percentage by volume of the juice in the drink shown in **Figure 7** is 10 percent. Adding 10 mL of juice to 90 mL of water makes 100 mL of this drink. Commonly, fruit-flavored drinks can contain from ten percent to 100 percent fruit juice. Generally, if two or more liquids are being mixed, the concentration is given in percentage by volume. To be certain of the concentration of your beverage, chose a product that is 100% juice.

Figure 7 The concentrations of fruit juices often are given in percent by volume like these. Concentrations commonly range from 10 percent to 100 percent juice.
Identify *the product that has the highest concentration.*

Science Journal

General and Precise Terms In general terms, solutions can be described as *concentrated* or *dilute*. Precise concentrations are expressed in other terms. Have students record in their Science Journals some other examples in which general and precise terms can be used. A baseball player may be described as a "good hitter" or by batting average,—" a .320 hitter." L2 P LS **Linguistic**

Differentiated Instruction

Challenge Have students contact a representative from a local wastewater facility and find out what is commonly found to be dissolved in the water. Have them prepare a chart or graph that shows the solutes and their approximate quantities in the water. Ask students to define all terms and units (such as parts per million) they use. L3

Types of Solutions

How much solute can dissolve in a given amount of solvent? That depends on a number of factors, including the solubility of the solute. Here you will examine the types of solutions based on the amount of a solute dissolved.

Saturated Solutions If you add 35 g of copper(II) sulfate, $CuSO_4$, to 100 g of water at 20°C, only 32 g will dissolve. You have a saturated solution because no more copper(II) sulfate can dissolve. A **saturated solution** is a solution that contains all the solute it can hold at a given temperature. However, if you heat the mixture to a higher temperature, more copper(II) sulfate can dissolve. Generally, as the temperature of a liquid solvent increases, the amount of solid solute that can dissolve in it also increases. **Table 2** shows the amounts of a few solutes that can dissolve in 100 g of water at different temperatures, forming saturated solutions. Some of these data also are shown on the accompanying graph.

Solubility Curves Each line on the graph from **Table 2** is called a solubility curve for a particular substance. You can use a solubility curve to figure out how much solute will dissolve at any temperature given on the graph. For example, about 78 g of KBr (potassium bromide) will form a saturated solution in 100 g of water at 47°C. How much NaCl (sodium chloride) will form a saturated solution with 100 g of water at the same temperature?

Unsaturated Solutions An **unsaturated solution** is any solution that can dissolve more solute at a given temperature. Each time a saturated solution is heated to a higher temperature, it becomes unsaturated. The term *unsaturated* isn't precise. If you look at **Table 2,** you'll see that at 20°C, 35.9 g of NaCl (sodium chloride) forms a saturated solution in 100 g of water. However, an unsaturated solution of NaCl could be any amount less than 35.9 g in 100 g of water at 20°C.

Reading Check *What happens to a saturated solution if it is heated?*

Table 2 Solubility of Compounds in g/100 g of Water

Compound	0°C	20°C	100°C
Copper(II) sulfate	23.1	32.0	114
Potassium bromide	53.6	65.3	104
Potassium chloride	28.0	34.0	56.3
Potassium nitrate	13.9	31.6	245
Sodium chlorate	79.6	95.9	204
Sodium chloride	35.7	35.9	39.2
Sucrose (sugar)	179.2	203.9	487.2

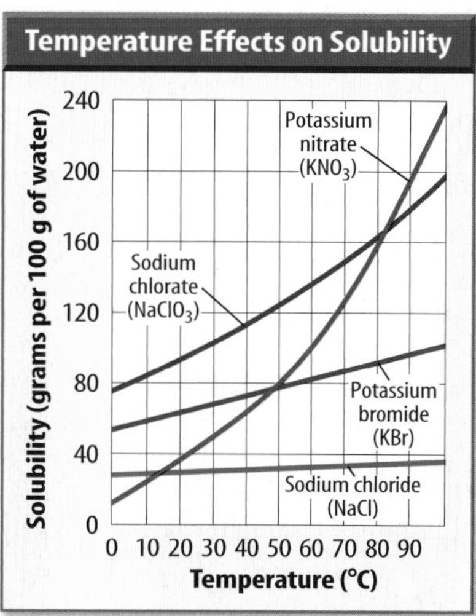

Text Question Answer

approximately 37 g of NaCl

Inquiry Lab

Saturation Point

Purpose Students witness the saturation point of a solution of their choice and have the opportunity to compare results with others for a wider experience.

Possible Materials water, rubbing alcohol, juices or drinks for solvents; granular sugar, powdered sugar, flour, salt for solutes

Estimated Time 30 minutes

Give each student a beaker and have them add an amount of the solvent of their choice. Then instruct them to begin adding the solute of their choice, slowly and with stirring. Have students keep close track of how much solute they add until the solution becomes saturated. Encourage students to repeat the activity to find out how other solutes work with the solvent they chose or how other solvents work with the solute they chose. Prepare a class chart of the results.

Teaching Strategies

- Discuss this activity before doing it and let the students brainstorm to list possible solutes and solvents that could be available for the activity.
- Do not limit their possible materials to only those substances you know will dissolve.
- Encourage students to investigate the variables that apply to this activity, such as volume of solvent, degree of agitation, and temperature. L2

For additional inquiry activities, see *Science Inquiry Labs.*

Answer It may become unsaturated.

Caption Answer

Figure 7 the product labeled "100% pure orange juice"

Teacher FYI

Solubility Temperature Most solid solutes dissolve better as the solution is warmed. However, the solubility of some solids decreases as temperature increases. Calcium acetate, $Ca(C_2H_3O_2)_2$, has a solubility of 37.4 g/100 mL of water at 0° C, but at 100° C, only 29.7 g dissolve per 100 mL of water.

Curriculum Connection

Math Ask students to refer to **Table 2** and answer the following question. If you were to graph the solubility of a solute on the y axis and the temperature of the solution on the x axis, which solute would have the line with the steepest slope, potassium chloride or sodium chloride? potassium chloride L2

Make a Model

Beaker Solutions On the board draw three identical oversized beakers. Draw the same number of small circles in each beaker. These represent particles of a solvent. Ask students to copy your drawings and add, using a different color of pen or pencil, circles in the beakers to represent unsaturated, saturated, and supersaturated solutions. L1 LS **Analytical-Mathematical**

Quick Demo

Gas in Solution

Materials full, unopened bottle of soda (any size)

Estimated Time 10 minutes

Procedure Open a soda bottle. Point out that when a soda is sealed, pressure keeps the gas in solution. Once opened, pressure is reduced and then bubbles become visible again.

Use an Analogy

Saturated Class Describe the types of solutions using the analogy of adding students to a classroom. In a room with 25 desks, a class with fewer than 25 students is analogous to an unsaturated solution. More students can be added to fill the desks. The 25th student takes the last desk and makes the classroom saturated. Adding more students beyond 25 causes some students to be displaced from desks and fall out into the aisles, representing precipitation. L1

Discussion

Reaction Energy Review the concepts of endothermic and exothermic reactions and talk about several practical applications for each type.

Caption Answer

Figure 8 because a change in temperature causes solute to fall out

Topic: Crystallization

Visit gpscience.com for Web links to information about crystals and crystallization.

Activity Find instructions for a safe "do-it-yourself" home crystallization experiment. Grow the crystals as directed and share the results with the class.

Supersaturated Solutions If you make a saturated solution of potassium nitrate at 100°C and then let it cool to 20°C, part of the solute comes out of solution. This is because, at the lower temperature, the solvent cannot hold as much solute. Most other saturated solutions behave in a similar way when cooled. However, if you cool a saturated solution of sodium acetate from 100°C to 20°C without disturbing it, no solute comes out. At this point, the solution is supersaturated. A **supersaturated solution** is one that contains more solute than a saturated solution at the same temperature. Supersaturated solutions are unstable. For example, if a seed crystal of sodium acetate is dropped into the supersaturated solution, excess sodium acetate crystallizes out, as shown in **Figure 8.**

Solution Energy As the supersaturated solution of sodium acetate crystallizes, the solution becomes hot. Energy is given off as new bonds form between the ions and the water molecules. Some portable heat packs use crystallization from supersaturated solutions to produce heat. After crystallization, the heat pack can be reused by heating it to again dissolve all the solute.

Another result of solution energy is to reduce the temperature of the solution. Some substances, such as ammonium nitrate, must draw energy from the surroundings to dissolve. This is what happens when a cold pack is activated to treat minor injuries or to reduce swelling. When the inner bags of ammonium nitrate and water are broken, the ammonium nitrate draws energy from the water, which causes the temperature of the water to drop and the pack cools.

Figure 8 A supersaturated solution is unstable.
Explain *why this is so.*

A seed crystal of sodium acetate is added to a supersaturated solution of sodium acetate.

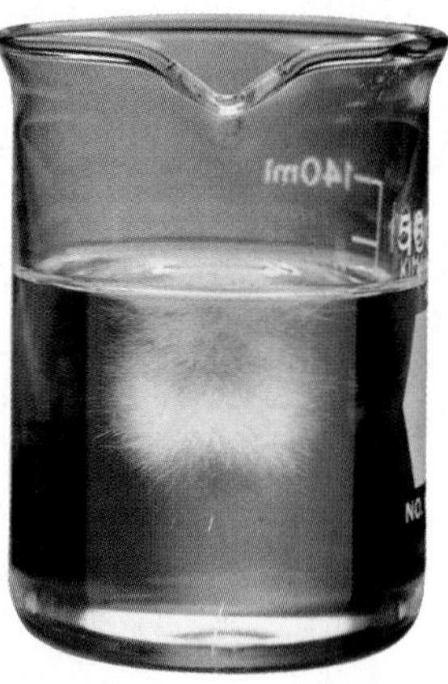

Excess solute immediately crystallizes from solution.

The crystallization reaction continues to draw solute from the solution.

Science Journal

The Solution Is in the Solution Have students imagine they have a crystal and a solution of zinc chloride. Have them explain how to use the crystal to tell whether the solution is unsaturated, saturated, or supersaturated. Drop the crystal into the solution. If it dissolves, the solution is unsaturated; if not, the solution is saturated; if the solution crystallizes, it is supersaturated. L2 LS **Linguistic**

Differentiated Instruction

Learning Disabled Break the words *supersaturated* and *unsaturated* into their respective prefixes and root. Use common terms to define the word *saturated* and each prefix, then redefine both scientific terms in clear language.

674 CHAPTER 22 Solutions

Solubility of Gases

When you shake an opened bottle of soda, it bubbles up and may squirt out. Shaking or pouring a solution of a gas in a liquid causes gas to come out of solution. Agitating the solution exposes more gas molecules to the surface, where they escape from the liquid.

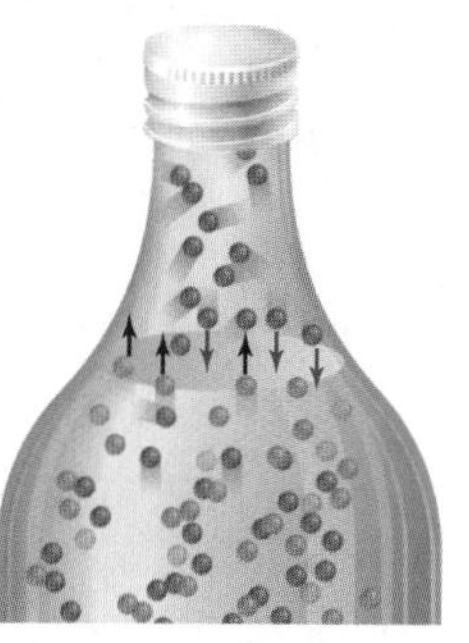

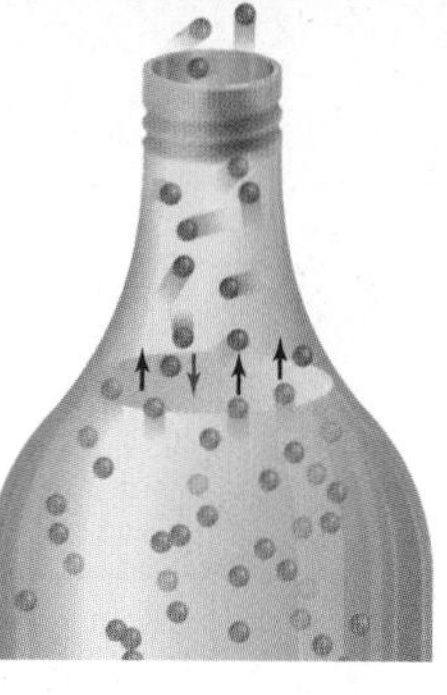

Figure 9 Solutions of gases behave differently from those of solids or liquids. This soda is bottled under pressure to keep carbon dioxide in solution. When the bottle is opened, pressure is released and carbon dioxide bubbles out of solution.

Pressure Effects What might you do if you want to dissolve more gas in a liquid? One thing you can do is increase the pressure of that gas over the liquid. Soft drinks are bottled under increased pressure. This increases the amount of carbon dioxide that dissolves in the liquid. When the pressure is released, the carbon dioxide bubbles out.

Temperature Effects Another way to increase the amount of gas that dissolves in a liquid is to cool the liquid. This is just the opposite of what you do to increase the speed at which most solids dissolve in a liquid. Imagine what happens to the carbon dioxide when a bottle of soft drink is opened. Even more carbon dioxide will bubble out of a soft drink as it gets warmer.

section 2 review

Summary

How much can dissolve?

- Solubility tells how much solute can dissolve in a solvent at a particular temperature.

Concentration

- A concentrated solution has a large amount of dissolved solute. A dilute solution has a small amount of dissolved solute.

Types of Solutions

- Saturated, unsaturated, and supersaturated solutions are defined by how much solute is dissolved.
- Solubility curves help predict how much solute can dissolve at a particular temperature.
- Some supersaturated solutions absorb or give off energy.

Gases in Solution

- Pressure and temperature affect gases in solution. High pressure and low temperature allow more gas to dissolve.

Self Check

1. **Explain** Do all solutes dissolve to the same extent in the same solvent? How do you know?
2. **Interpret** from **Table 2** the mass of sugar that would have to be dissolved in 100 g of water to form a saturated solution at 20°C.
3. **Determine** which is more soluble in water: 17 g of solute X dissolved in 100 mL of water at 23°C or 26 g of solute Z dissolved in 100 mL of water at 23°C.
4. **Identify** the type of solution you have if, at 35°C, solute continues to dissolve as you add more.
5. **Think Critically** Explain how keeping a carbonated beverage capped helps keep it from going "flat."

Applying Math

6. **Calculate Cost** By volume, orange drink is ten percent each of orange juice and corn syrup. A 1.5-L can of the drink costs \$0.95. A 1.5-L can of orange juice is \$1.49, and 1.5 L of corn syrup is \$1.69. Per serving, does it cost less to make your own orange drink or buy it ?

gpscience.com/self_check_quiz

3 Assess

DAILY INTERVENTION

Check for Understanding

Honey Crystals Describe, or bring to class if available, an old jar of honey. Ask students to describe why there are crystals of sugar forming in the previously smooth solution. As the water evaporates from the solution, the dissolved sugar becomes more concentrated. As the concentration exceeds the saturation limit, sugar will begin to precipitate, crystallizing out of the solution. L2 LS **Linguistic**

Reteach

Aromas Open a small bottle of ammonia in the back of the room without telling students. Ask if anyone can detect any type of chemical aroma. As the ammonia fumes mix in the air, point out to students that the air is diluting the ammonia. L2

Assessment

Performance Have students use the data in **Table 2** to plot solubility versus temperature for sucrose. Have them use a different color and sketch a line on the same graph that they think would show qualitatively how the solubility of oxygen gas in water changes with temperature. The first line slopes up, and the second line slopes down. Use **Performance Assessment in the Science Classroom,** p. 111. L2

section 2 review

1. No; you can determine this experimentally.
2. 203.9 g
3. solute Z
4. unsaturated
5. When capped, carbon dioxide stays in solution, which keeps the soda "fizzy."
6. Making it is cheaper. If you were making 1,500 mL of orange drink you would need 150 mL of orange juice @ \$1.49/1,500 mL = 14.9 cents per 150 mL; 150 mL of syrup @ \$1.69/1,500 mL = 16.9 cents per 150 mL; so, to make 1,500 mL of drink you need only 14.9 + 16.9 cents = 31.8 cents of ingredients per 1,500 mL of drink

section 3

Particles in Solution

1 Motivate

Bellringer

Section Focus Transparencies also are available on the Interactive Chalkboard CD-ROM. L2 ELL

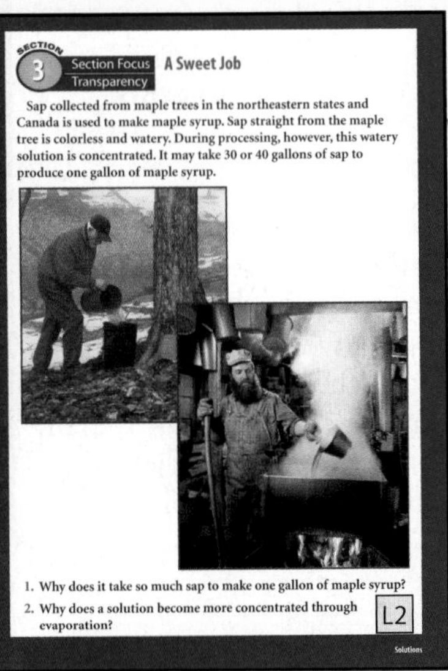

Section Focus Transparency — A Sweet Job

Sap collected from maple trees in the northeastern states and Canada is used to make maple syrup. Sap straight from the maple tree is colorless and watery. During processing, however, this watery solution is concentrated. It may take 30 or 40 gallons of sap to produce one gallon of maple syrup.

1. Why does it take so much sap to make one gallon of maple syrup?
2. Why does a solution become more concentrated through evaporation? L2

Solutions

Tie to Prior Knowledge

Material States Ask students to describe situations in which the boiling point or the freezing point of a material was changed. If they have trouble, explain that adding antifreeze to automobile radiators raises the boiling point. Explain that they will learn how this process works. L2

Reading Guide

What You'll Learn

- **Examine** how some solutes break apart in water solutions to form positively and negatively charged particles.
- **Determine** how some solutions conduct electricity.
- **Describe** how antifreeze works.

Why It's Important

Many of the products we use every day rely on the effects of solutes in solution.The name and the formula convey information about the compound.

Review Vocabulary

conductivity: property of metals and alloys that allows them to be good conductors of heat and electricity

New Vocabulary

- ion
- electrolyte
- nonelectrolyte
- ionization
- dissociation

Particles with a Charge

Did you know that there are charged particles in your body that conduct electricity? In fact, you could not live without them. Some help nerve cells transmit messages. Each time you blink your eyes or wave your hand nerves control how muscles will respond. These charged particles, called **ions,** are in the fluids that are in and around all the cells in your body. The compounds that produce solutions of ions that conduct electricity in water are known as **electrolytes.** Some substances, like sodium chloride, are strong electrolytes and conduct a strong current. Strong electrolytes exist completely in the form of ions in solution. Other substances, like acetic acid in vinegar, remain mainly in the form of molecules when they dissolve in water. They produce few ions and conduct current only weakly. They are called weak electrolytes. Substances that form no ions in water and cannot conduct electricity are called **nonelectrolytes.** Among these are organic molecules like ethyl alcohol and sucrose.

Ionization Ionic solutions form in two ways. Electrolytes, such as hydrogen chloride, are molecules made up of neutral atoms. To form ions, the molecules must be broken apart in such a way that the atoms take on a charge. This process of forming ions is called **ionization.** The process is shown in **Figure 10,** using hydrogen chloride as a model.

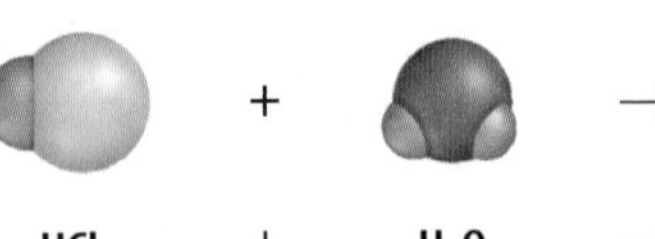

$HCl + H_2O \rightarrow H_3O^+ + Cl^-$

Figure 10 Both hydrogen chloride and water are polar molecules. Water surrounds the hydrogen chloride molecules and pulls them apart, forming positive hydrogen ions and negative chloride ions. Hydrogen ions are often shown as H_3O^+ to emphasize the role water plays in ionization.

Section 3 Resource Manager

Chapter *Fast File* Resources
- Transparency Activity, pp. 48, 51–52
- Directed Reading for Content Mastery, p. 20
- Lab Activity, pp. 13–16
- Enrichment, p. 33
- Reinforcement, p. 29

Physical Science Critical Thinking/Problem Solving, p. 1

Cultural Diversity, p. 37

Dissociation The second way that ionic solutions form is by the separation of ionic compounds. The ions already exist in the ionic compound and are attracted into the solution by the surrounding polar water molecules. **Dissociation** is the process in which an ionic solid, such as sodium chloride, separates into its positive and negative ions. A model of a sodium chloride crystal is shown in **Figure 11.** In the crystal, each positive sodium ion is attracted to six negative chloride ions. Each of the negative chloride ions is attracted to six sodium ions, a pattern that exists throughout the crystal.

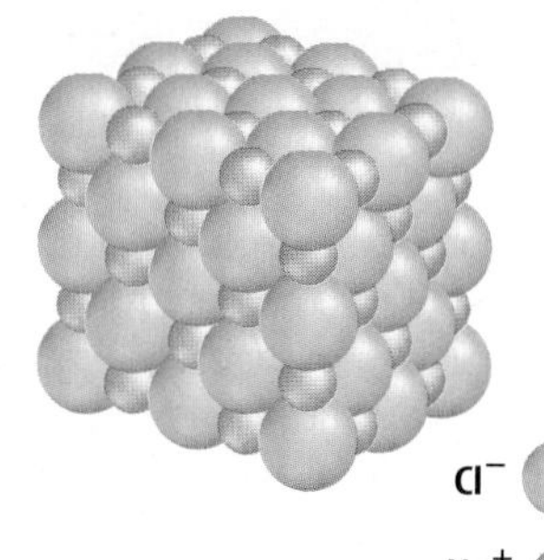

Figure 11 This is a model of a sodium chloride crystal. Each chloride ion is surrounded by six sodium ions and vice versa.

When placed in water, the crystal begins to break apart under the influence of water molecules. Remember that water is polar, which means that the positive areas of the water molecules are attracted to the negative chloride ions. Likewise the negative oxygen part of the water molecules is attracted to the sodium ions.

In **Figure 12,** water molecules are approaching the sodium and chloride ions in the crystal. The water molecules surround the sodium and chloride ions, having pulled them away from the crystal and into solution. The sodium and chloride ions have dissociated from one another. The solution now consists of sodium and chloride ions mixed with water. The ions move freely through the solution and are capable of conducting an electric current.

Reading Check *What are the differences and similarities between dissociation and ionization?*

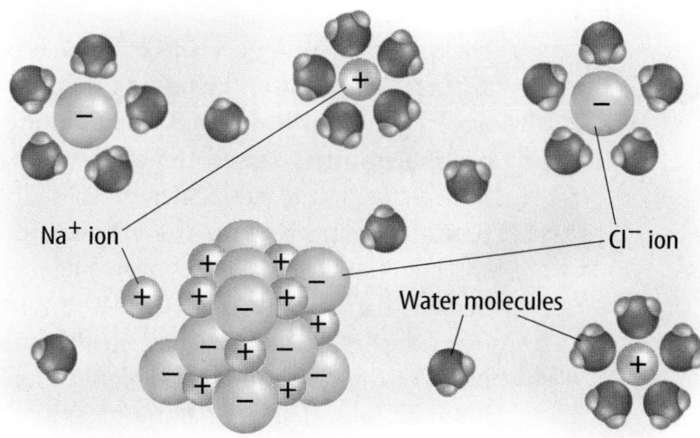

Figure 12 Sodium chloride dissociates as water molecules attract and pull the sodium and chloride ions from the crystal. Water molecules then surround and separate the Na^+ and Cl^- ions.
Predict *Will sodium chloride in solution conduct electricity?*

2 Teach

Visual Learning

Figure 12 Have students follow the dissolution process as you read the caption aloud. Emphasize that ionization is a process in which particles obtain a charge, while dissociation is a process in which already charged particles are separated from one another. L2

Teacher FYI

Dissolved Solute or Osmosis The diffusion of solute is directly affected by the amount of dissolved solute in a solution. A dissolved solute will travel through a membrane from an area of higher concentration to an area of lower concentration until an equilibrium is reached.

Reading Check

Answer dissociation: ions are separated from ionic crystals; ionization: process that forms ions

Caption Answer

Figure 12 yes

LAB DEMONSTRATION

Purpose to show that dissolved ionic compounds conduct an electrical current

Materials conductivity tester, distilled water, NaCl, Epsom salt, rubbing alcohol, sugar

Preparation List the solutes on the board. Dissolve each in distilled water.

Procedure Test the conductivity of each solution. Make sure students can see the results of each test.

Expected Outcome NaCl and Epsom salt solutions will conduct electricity; alcohol and sugar solutions will not.

Assessment

What occurs in the conducting solutions? Ions are moving out of crystals and into water where they can move in the solution and conduct electricity.

Why don't the other solutions conduct electricity? The solutes in the other solutions don't form ions. L2

Quick Demo

Freezing Points

Materials soda bottles with caps (2), water , rubbing alcohol

Estimated Time 45 min, or one class period

Procedure Fill one bottle with water (100 mL) and replace the cap. Fill the second with 100 mL of a solution of alcohol (70%) and water (30%). Label the containers and place them in a freezer. At the end of the class period, retrieve the bottles and check the extent of freezing. water should be more frozen

Use Science Words

Word Usage Have students find out why the word *electrolyte* is used when discussing sports drinks and the contents of batteries. Sports drinks contain electrolytes (sodium and potassium ions) that transport signals in the body. Batteries contain electrolytes (ammonium ions, sulfate ions, hydrogen ions) that conduct electricity in the battery. They both conduct electricity, but they contain different elements. L2 LS **Linguistic**

Discussion

Road Salt Review with the class the benefits of using salt on icy roads. Also discuss the detrimental effects of salt on icy roads. deteriorates roads, corrodes cars and bridges, kills roadside plant life

Activity

Practical Application Almost any substance that will dissolve in water can be used to raise the boiling point of water. Have students work in groups and brainstorm some substances that would *not* be good radiator coolants. Answers will vary but may include volatile substances that would vaporize or substances that might corrode the radiator.

Effects of Solute Particles

All solute particles—polar and nonpolar, electrolyte and nonelectrolyte—affect the physical properties of the solvent, such as its freezing point and its boiling point. These effects can be useful. For example, adding antifreeze to water in a car radiator lowers the freezing point of the radiator fluid. Sugar and salt also would do the same thing, however, both would damage the cooling system. The effect that a solute has on the freezing point or boiling point of a solvent depends on the number of solute particles in solution, not on the chemical nature of the particles.

Lowering Freezing Point Adding a solute such as antifreeze to a solvent lowers the freezing point of the solvent. How much the freezing point goes down depends upon how many solute particles you add. How does this work?

As a substance freezes, its particles arrange themselves in an orderly pattern. The added solute particles interfere with the formation of this pattern, making it harder for the solvent to freeze as shown in **Figure 13.** To overcome this interference, a lower temperature is needed to freeze the solvent.

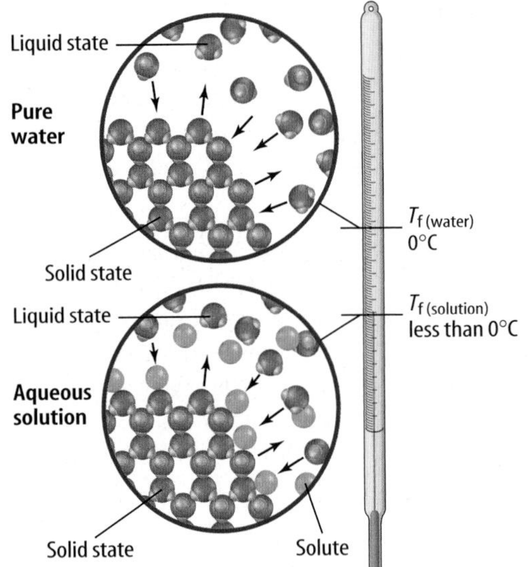

Figure 13 Solute molecules interfere with the freezing process by blocking molecules of solvent as they try to join the growing crystal lattice. For example, antifreeze molecules added to water block the formation of ice crystals.

INTEGRATE Life Science **Animal Antifreeze** Certain animals that live in extremely cold climates have their own kind of antifreeze. Caribou, for example, contain substances in the lower section of their legs that prevent freezing in subzero temperatures. The caribou can stand for long periods of time in snow and ice with no harm to their legs. Fish that live in polar waters also have a natural chemical antifreeze called glycoprotein in their bodies. Glycoprotein prevents ice crystals from forming in the moist tissues. Many insects also have a similar antifreeze chemical to protect them from freezing temperatures.

Raising Boiling Point Surprisingly, antifreeze also raises the boiling point of the water. How can it do this? The amount the boiling point is raised depends upon the number of solute molecules present. Solute particles interfere with the evaporation of solvent particles. Thus, more energy is needed for the solvent particles to escape from the liquid surface, and so the boiling point of the solution will be higher than the boiling point of solvent alone.

Differentiated Instruction

Visually Impaired When the Quick Demo on freezing points is concluded, have visually impaired students feel and shake the containers to experience the difference in the extent of freezing.

Challenge Have students refresh their knowledge of osmosis and research the medical treatment called dialysis. Ask students to write a paragraph explaining how particles in solution relate to osmosis and dialysis. L3

Car Radiators The beaker in **Figure 14** represents a car radiator when it contains water molecules only—no antifreeze. Some of those molecules on the surface will vaporize, and the number of molecules that do vaporize depends upon the temperature of the solvent. As temperature increases, water molecules move faster, and more molecules vaporize. Finally, when the pressure of the water vapor equals atmospheric pressure, the water boils. Have you ever seen a vehicle at the side of the road with vapors rising from the radiator?

The result of adding antifreeze is shown in **Figure 14.** Particles of solute are distributed evenly throughout the solution, including the surface area. Now fewer water molecules can reach the surface and evaporate, making the vapor pressure of the solution lower than that of the solvent. This means that it will take a higher temperature to make the car's radiator boil over.

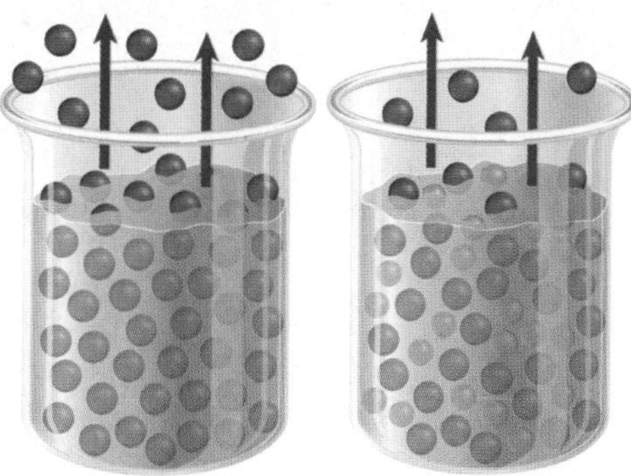

Solvent particles vaporize freely from the surface.

Solute particles block part of the surface, making it more difficult for solvent to vaporize.

Figure 14 Solute particles raise the boiling point of a solution.
Describe *how antifreeze works in a car.*

section 3 review

Summary

Particles with a Charge

- Ions, charged particles, are formed from neutral compounds in such a way that the atoms take on a charge.
- Electrolytes can conduct electricity.
- Dissociation is the process of breaking an ionic compound into its positive and negative ions.
- Ions are found in the fluids that are in and around the cells in your body.

Effects of Solute Particles

- Solutes affect the physical properties of a solution by the number of solute particles, not by the chemical nature of the solute.
- Solute particles change the freezing and boiling points of solutions.
- Fish that live in polar waters have a natural chemical antifreeze called glycoprotein.
- When a substance freezes, its particles arrange themselves in an orderly pattern.

Self Check

1. **Determine** what has taken place, ionization or dissociation, if calcium phosphate ($Ca_3(PO_4)_2$) breaks into Ca^{2+} and PO_4^{3-}.
2. **Identify** what kinds of solute particles are present in water solutions of electrolytes and nonelectrolytes.
3. **Describe** how an ionic substance dissociates in water.
4. **Describe** how the concentration of a solution influences its boiling point.
5. **Think Critically** In cold weather, people often put salt on ice that forms on sidewalks and driveways. The salt helps melt the ice, forming a saltwater solution. Explain why this solution may not refreeze.

Applying Math

6. **Graph Data** Use the following data points (0,12), (10,8),(20,4), and (30,0), to graph the effect of a solute on the freezing point of a solvent. Label the *x*-axis *Grams solute* and the *y*-axis *Freezing point.*
7. **Calculate Slope** Find the slope of the line you graphed in question 6.

Science Online gpscience.com/self_check_quiz

3 Assess

DAILY INTERVENTION

Check for Understanding

Model Concepts Make or bring in a molecular model of a neutral compound and an ionic compound. Have students simulate ionization and dissociation by breaking the compounds apart as they would break apart in solution. L2

Reteach

Particle Interference To emphasize that the number of solute particles is the major factor in changing freezing and boiling points, have students predict the number of solute particles expected per starting particle of:

- $NaCl \rightarrow Na^+ + Cl^-$ two
- $CaCl_2 \rightarrow Ca^{2+} + 2Cl^-$ three
- $Mg(OH)2 \rightarrow Mg^{2+} + 2\ OH^-$ three
- $C_6H_{12}O_6 \rightarrow C6H_{12}O_6$ one, nonelectrolyte

L1 LS **Analytical-Mathematical**

Content Have students draw and label diagrams showing the process of dissociation of an ionic salt. Use **Performance Assessment in the Science Classroom,** p. 127. L2

section 3 review

1. dissociation
2. electrolytes: ions; nonelectrolytes: molecules
3. The particles in the crystal are separated and drawn into solution by water molecules.
4. As the concentration rises, the boiling point increases until saturation is reached.
5. The ions from the salt have disrupted the crystal lattice formed by water when it freezes. The temperature will have to be lower for the molecules of water to freeze.
6. Check students' graphs.
7. slope = 0.4

Real-World Question

Purpose Students will determine the effect of added solute on the boiling point of a solution. L3 ELL **Analytical-Mathematical**

Process Skills observe, predict, classify, recognize cause and effect, interpret data

Time Required 35 minutes

Procedure

Safety Precautions Students should not let the thermometer touch the sides or bottom of the beaker. Have them use care around boiling solutions.

Teaching Strategies

- Have one student measure out the next amount of solute while the other heats the solution.
- Start the graph at 90° C.

Toubleshooting Make sure the thermometer bulb is submerged but not touching the bottom or sides of the beaker during temperature readings.

Conclude and Apply

1. The boiling point of the water solution is higher due to impurities.
2. The boiling point would still have been higher than that of pure water, but not as high as before.
3. The boiling point would continue to rise until the solution was saturated, then the boiling point would level off.

Boiling Points of Solutions

Adding small amounts of salt to water that is being boiled and adding antifreeze to a radiator have a common result—increasing the boiling point.

Real-World Question

How much can the boiling point of a solution be changed?

Goals

- **Determine** how adding salt affects the boiling point of water.

Possible Materials

distilled water (400 mL)
Celsius thermometer
table salt, NaCl (72 g)
ring stand
hot plate
250-mL beaker

Safety Precautions

Procedure

1. Copy the data table as shown in the next column. Bring 100 mL of distilled water to a gentle boil in a 250-mL beaker. Record the temperature. Do not touch the hot plate surface.

2. Dissolve 12 g of NaCl in 100 mL of distilled water. Bring this solution to a gentle boil and record its boiling point.
3. Repeat step 2, using 24 g of NaCl, then 36 g.
4. Make a graph of your results. Put boiling point on the *x*-axis and grams of NaCl on the *y*-axis.

Effects of Solute on Boiling Point

Grams of NaCl Solute	Boiling Point (°C)
0	~100°C
12	~102°C
24	~104°C
36	~106°C

Conclude and Apply

1. **Explain** the difference between the boiling points of pure water and a water solution.
2. **Predict** what would have been the effect of doubling the amount of water instead of the amount of NaCl in step 3.
3. **Predict** what would happen if you continued to add more salt. Would your graph continue in the same pattern or eventually level off? Explain your prediction.

Communicating Your Data

Compare your results with those of other groups and discuss any differences in the results obtained. **For more help, refer to the** Science Skill Handbook.

680 CHAPTER 22 Solutions

Assessment

Process Have students use their graphs to predict the boiling point of a solution that contains 18 g NaCl. about 103°C Use **Performance Assessment in the Science Classroom,** p. 101. L3

Communicating Your Data

Some differences arise because lab grade thermometers may vary and measurements of water and salt may vary. Also, as solutions boil, they become more concentrated, so variations in the length of time they boil can cause differences.

section 4

Dissolving Without Water

Reading Guide

What You'll Learn
- **Identify** several kinds of solutes that do not dissolve well in water.
- **Explain** how solvents work in terms of polarity.
- **Determine** how to choose the right solvent for the job.

Why It's Important
Many solutes do not dissolve in water, yet there are useful applications for solutions that make use of these solutes.

Review Vocabulary
hydrocarbon: Saturated or unsaturated compound that contains only carbon and hydrogen atoms.

New Vocabulary
- nonpolar

When Water Won't Work

Water often is referred to as the universal solvent because it can dissolve so many things. However, there are some things, such as oil, that it can't dissolve. Why?

As you learned in the first section, water has positive and negative areas that allow it to attract polar solutes. However, **nonpolar** materials have no separated positive and negative areas. Because of this, they are not attracted to polar materials, which means they are not attracted to water molecules. Nonpolar materials do not dissolve in water except to a small extent, if at all.

Nonpolar Solutes An example of a nonpolar substance that does not dissolve in water can be seen on many dinner tables. The vinegar-and-oil salad dressing shown in **Figure 15** has two distinct layers—the bottom layer is vinegar, which is a solution of acetic acid in water, and the top layer is salad oil.

Most salad oils contain large molecules made of carbon and hydrogen atoms, which are called hydrocarbons. In hydrocarbons, carbon and hydrogen atoms share electrons in a nearly equal manner. This equal distribution of electrons means that the molecule has no separate positive and negative areas. Therefore, the nonpolar oil molecule is not attracted to the polar water molecules in the vinegar solution. That's why you must shake this kind of dressing to mix it just before you pour it on your salad.

Figure 15 Oil and vinegar do not form a solution.
Infer *How do the particles in this substance disperse so it is tasteful to eat?*

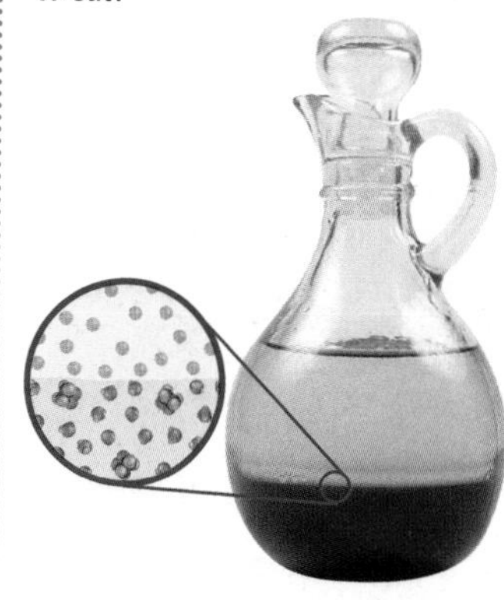

1 Motivate

Bellringer

Section Focus Transparencies also are available on the Interactive Chalkboard CD-ROM. L2 

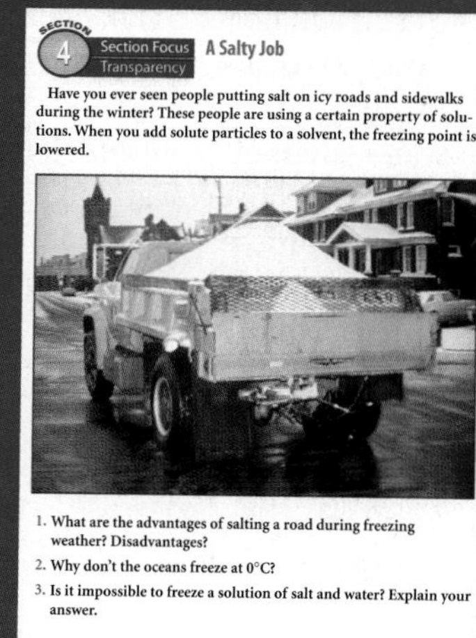

Tie to Prior Knowledge

Paint Solvents Ask students if they have ever had to clean paintbrushes with a solvent other than water. Explain that some paints are not water soluble. L2

Text Question

Answer because polar water does not dissolve nonpolar substances.

Caption Answer

Figure 15 Shaking the dressing temporarily distributes the molecules relatively evenly so the taste and texture are acceptable.

Section 4 Resource Manager

Chapter *FAST FILE* Resources
- Transparency Activity, p. 49
- Directed Reading for Content Mastery, pp. 20, 22
- Enrichment, p. 34
- Reinforcement, p. 30
- Lab Worksheet, pp. 5–6, 7–8

Performance Assessment in the Science Classroom, p. 41

SECTION 4 Dissolving Without Water 681

2 Teach

Activity

"Pet Drop" Tell students how to make a "pet drop!" Obtain a small vial with a very tight-sealing screw cap. Pour water tinted with food coloring into the vial until it is half full. Add rubbing alcohol until the vial is nearly full. Then add a large drop of cooking oil. The drop should float near the center of the vial. As you move the vial, the oil will float and change locations. (Do not shake the mixture.) The density of the water-alcohol solution allows the oil to hover near the center of the solution. The nonpolar oil will not dissolve in the polar water-alcohol solution. L2

ELL **Kinesthetic**

Answer The molecule has both a polar end and a nonpolar end.

Quick Demo

Nail Polish Remover

Materials nail polish remover (acetone), nail polish, water, cotton balls

Estimated Time 15 minutes

Procedure Apply nail polish to two of your fingernails. Do not apply on students. Allow the polish to dry, then soak one cotton ball with remover and one with water and attempt to remove the polish with each solvent. Discuss why water did not remove the polish.

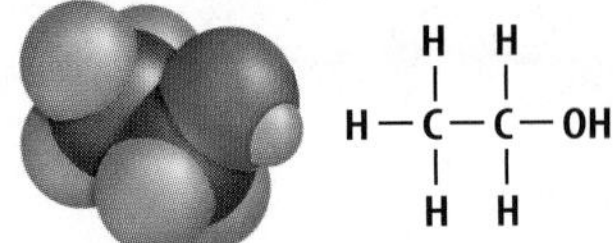

Figure 16 Ethanol, C_2H_5OH, has a polar –OH group at one end but the $-C_2H_5$ section is nonpolar. **Determine** *the molecular weight for ethanol.*

Versatile Alcohol Some substances form solutions with polar as well as nonpolar solutes because their molecules have a polar and a nonpolar end. Ethanol, shown in **Figure 16,** is such a molecule. The polar end dissolves polar substances, and the nonpolar end dissolves nonpolar substances. For example, ethanol dissolves iodine, which is nonpolar, as well as water, which is polar.

Reading Check *How can alcohol dissolve both polar and nonpolar substances?*

Useful Nonpolar Molecules

Some materials around your house may be useful as nonpolar solvents. For example, mineral oil may be used as a solvent to remove candle wax from glass or metal candleholders. Both the mineral oil and the candle wax are nonpolar materials. Mineral oil can also aid in removing bubble gum from some surfaces for the same reason. Oil-based paints contain pigments that are dissolved in oils. In order to thin or remove such paints, a nonpolar solvent must be used. The gasoline you use in your car and lawnmower is a solution of hydrocarbons, which are nonpolar substances.

Dry cleaners use nonpolar solvents when removing oily stains. The word *dry* refers to the fact that no water is used in the process. Molecules of a nonpolar solute can slip easily among molecules of a nonpolar solvent. That is why dry cleaning can remove stains of grease and oil that you cannot clean easily yourself. A general statement that describes which substance dissolves which is the phrase "like dissolves like."

Many nonpolar solvents are connected with specific jobs. People who paint pictures using oil-based paints probably use the solvent turpentine. It comes from the sap of a pine tree. **Figure 17** shows how well turpentine dissolves non-polar paint.

Figure 17 With no polarity to interfere, paint molecules slide smoothly among molecules of turpentine.

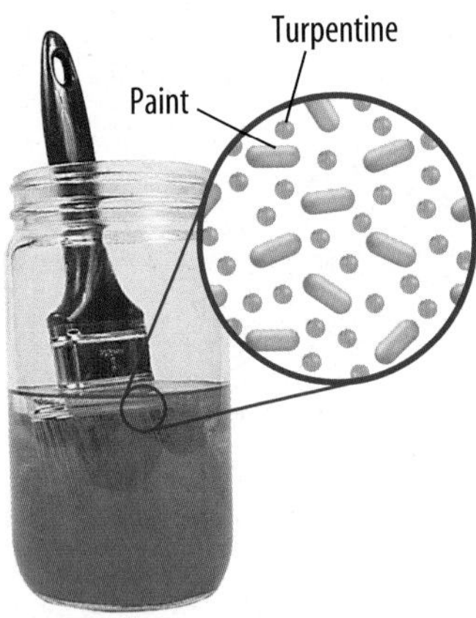

Drawbacks of Nonpolar Solvents Although nonpolar solvents have many uses, they have some drawbacks, too. First, many nonpolar solvents are flammable. Also, some are toxic, which means they are dangerous if they come into contact with the skin or if their vapors are inhaled. For these reasons, you must always be careful when handling these materials and never use them in a closed area. Good ventilation is critical, because nonpolar solvents tend to evaporate more readily than water, and even small amounts of a nonpolar liquid can produce high concentrations of harmful vapor in the air.

Teacher FYI

Acetone The solvent acetone has three carbons joined in a chain. The middle carbon is double-bonded to an oxygen atom. Both end carbons have three hydrogen atoms attached. The electrons in the oxygen-carbon bond are pulled toward the more electronegative oxygen atom, making the bond polar. Therefore, acetone dissolves easily in water.

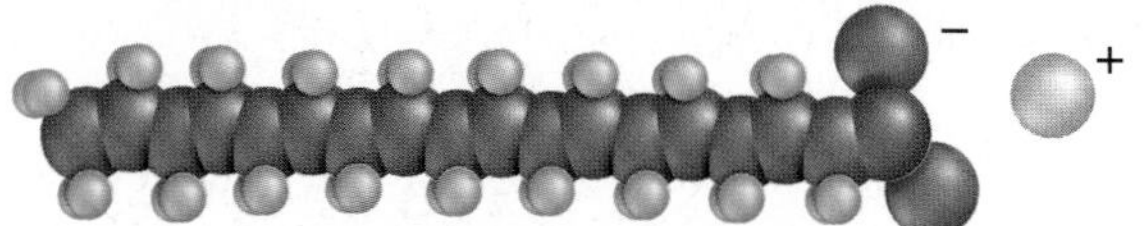

Figure 18 The long hydrocarbon tail of sodium stearate is nonpolar. The head is ionic.

How Soap Works The oils on human skin and hair keep them from drying out, but the oils can also attract and hold dirt. The oily dirt is a nonpolar mixture, so washing with water alone won't clean away the dirt. This is where soap comes in. Soaps, you might say, have a split personality. They are substances that have polar and nonpolar properties. Soaps are salts of fatty acids, which are long hydrocarbon molecules with a carboxylic acid group –COOH at one end. When a soap is made, the hydrogen atom of the acid group is removed, leaving a negative charge behind, and a positive ion of sodium or potassium is attached. This is shown in **Figure 18.**

Thus, soap has an ionic end that will dissolve in water and a long hydrocarbon portion that will dissolve in oily dirt. In this way, the dirt is removed from your skin, hair, or a fabric, suspended in the wash water, and washed away, as shown in **Figure 19.**

Reading Check *Why doesn't water alone clean oily dirt?*

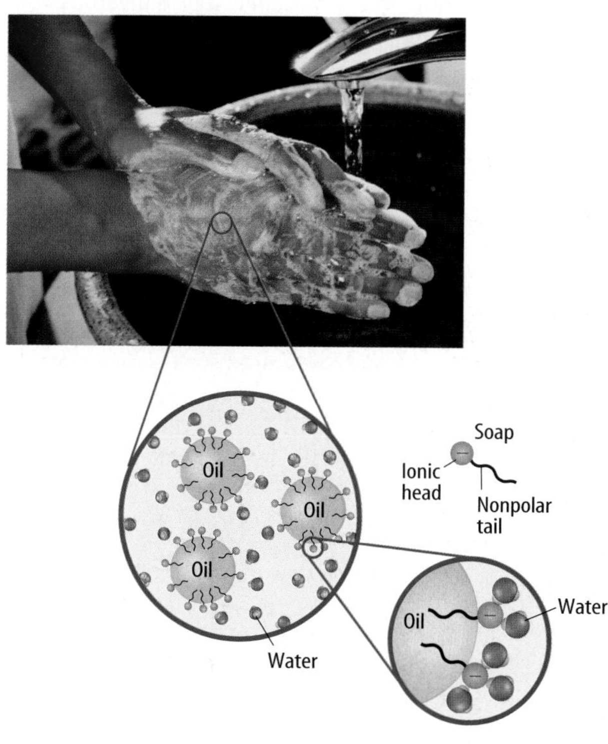

Figure 19 Soap cleans because its nonpolar hydrocarbon part dissolves in oily dirt and its ionic part interacts strongly with water. The oil and water mix and the dirt is washed away.

Mini LAB

Observing Clinging Molecules

Procedure

1. Lay **two clean pennies** side by side and heads up on a **paper towel.**
2. Slowly place drops of **water** from a **dropper** onto the head of one penny. Count each drop and continue until the accumulated water spills off the edge of the penny.
3. With adult supervision, repeat step 2 using **rubbing alcohol,** which is approximately 30 percent isopropyl alcohol, and the other penny.

Analysis

1. Which penny held the most drops before liquid spilled over the edge of the penny?
2. Isopropyl alcohol has the formula C_3H_7OH. How polar do you think it is?
3. How do the results of the experiment support the concept of polarity and molecules sticking to each other?

Reading Check

Answer Oily dirt won't dissolve in water because oil is nonpolar.

Mini LAB

Purpose Students compare the clinging ability of polar molecules with that of nonpolar molecules

L2 ELL IS **Kinesthetic**

Materials two clean pennies, paper towel, two droppers, water, rubbing alcohol

Teaching Strategy Tell students to hold the dropper close to but not touching the penny or liquid surface. Remind them that the distance used with water should be the same as that used with the alcohol.

Analysis

1. the penny containing water drops
2. slightly polar, but not as polar as water
3. The polar water molecules stick to each other better than the less polar alcohol molecules.

Assessment

Process Have students describe the variables that may cause different students to have different answers. Possible answers: size of opening in droppers, distance between dropper and surface, cleanliness of the pennies Use **Performance Assessment in the Science Classroom,** p. 89.

Differentiated Instruction

Physically Disabled Suggest that any student who cannot manipulate the dropper work with a partner who can. L1

Vitamins in Excess vitamin B-6: nerve damage causing changes in touch sensation; vitamin D: nausea, vomiting, headache, dizziness; niacin: headache, nausea, flushing, rashes, tingling, liver damage, glucose intolerance, cramping, eye damage, heart injury

Career invite a dietician to the classroom to talk about vitamins and solubility and the impact on health and diet.

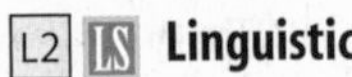

Linguistic

Discussion

Vitamins Talk with the class about the importance of eating a well-balanced diet to ensure adequate amounts of essential vitamins. Bring in some recipes that might make healthy eating appealing to young people.

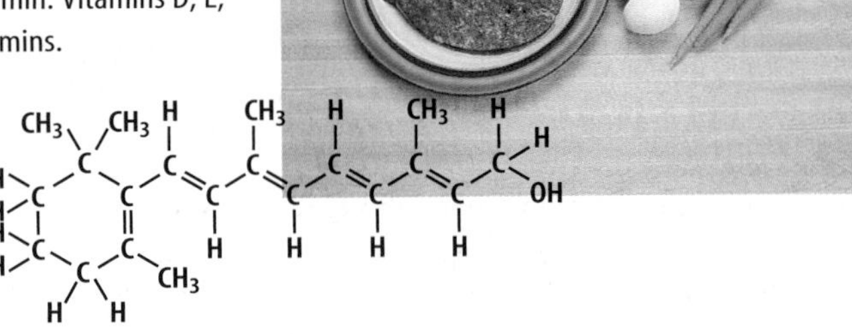

Figure 20 The structural formula of vitamin A shows a long hydrocarbon chain that makes it nonpolar. Foods such as liver, lettuce, cheese, eggs, carrots, sweet potatoes, and milk are good sources of this fat-soluble vitamin. Vitamins D, E, and K are also fat-soluble vitamins.

Science Online

Topic: Vitamins
Visit gpscience.com for Web links to information about vitamins.

Activity Copy the ingredients list from a container of multivitamins and use the links at gpscience.com to research those listed. Make a chart that categorizes each as either a water-soluble vitamin or a fat-soluble vitamin.

Polarity and Vitamins

Having the right kinds and amounts of vitamins is important for your health. Some of the vitamins you need, such as vitamin A, shown in **Figure 20,** are nonpolar and can dissolve in fat, which is another nonpolar substance. Because fat and fat-soluble vitamins do not wash away with the water that is present in the cells throughout your body, the vitamins can accumulate in your tissues. Some fat-soluble vitamins are toxic in high concentrations, so taking large doses or taking doses that are not recommended by your physician can be dangerous.

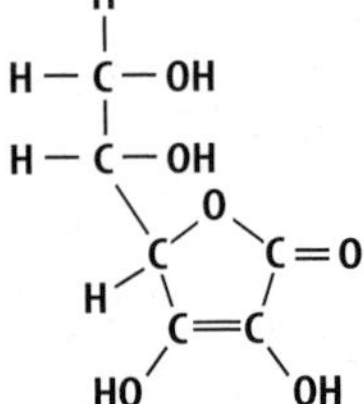

Figure 21 Although vitamin C has carbon-to-carbon bonds, it also has polar groups and is water soluble. Foods such as those shown here are good sources of vitamin C, which helps heal wounds and helps the body absorb iron.

Table 3 Sources of Vitamin C

Food	Amount	mg
Orange juice, fresh	1 cup	124
Green peppers, raw	1/2 cup	96
Broccoli, raw	1/2 cup	70
Cantaloupe	1/4 melon	70
Strawberries	1/2 cup	42

Differentiated Instruction

Challenge Using the structure of vitamin C as shown in **Figure 21**, have students create a 3–D model of the substance. Encourage creativity in their choice of materials, but ensure that the structure is accurate. L3

Visual Learning

Figure 21 How does cooking in water affect foods that contain vitamin C? Vitamin C is water soluble, so cooking in water removes some of the vitamin from the food. Explain that vitamin C deficiency (scurvy) was the first deficiency disease identified in humans. In 1753, Scottish naval surgeon James Lind showed that scurvy could be cured and prevented by eating citrus fruits. L2

Other vitamins, such as vitamins B and C, are polar compounds. When you look at the structure of vitamin C, shown in **Figure 21,** you will see that it has several carbon-to-carbon bonds. This might make you think that it is nonpolar. But, if you look again, you will see that it also has several oxygen-to-hydrogen bonds that resemble those found in water. This makes vitamin C polar.

Polar vitamins dissolve readily in the water that is in your body. These vitamins do not accumulate in tissue because any excess vitamin is washed away with the water in the body. For this reason, you must replace water-soluble vitamins by eating enough of the foods that contain them or by taking vitamin supplements. **Table 3** lists some good sources of vitamin C. In general, the best way to stay healthy is to eat a variety of healthy foods. Such a diet will supply the vitamins you need with no risk of overdoses.

Why do you need to replace some of the vitamins used in your body?

Vitamins in Excess
Drinking too much carrot juice, which is rich in beta carotene, a substance related to vitamin A, can cause the palms of your hands and soles of your feet to turn orange. Though this condition is not serious and the color fades in time, taking too much of some vitamins can be dangerous. Research what might result from taking too much vitamin B-6, vitamin D, and niacin.

section  review

Summary

When Water Won't Work

- Water cannot dissolve all substances.
- Nonpolar molecules are not attracted to polar molecules.

Useful Nonpolar Molecules

- Nonpolar solvents have many household and industrial uses.
- Nonpolar solvents may have drawbacks including flammability and toxicity.
- Some molecules have both polar and nonpolar properties. Solvents made from these kinds of substances can dissolve things that water alone cannot.

Polarity and Vitamins

- Nonpolar vitamins may dissolve in fat and accumulate to sometimes dangerous levels in your body.
- Polar vitamins dissolve readily in water and can be flushed from the body before absorption.

Self Check

1. **Explain** how a solute can dissolve in polar and nonpolar solvents.
2. **Explain** the phrase "like dissolves like" and give an example of two polar "like" substances.
3. **Describe** how soap cleans greasy dirt from your hands.
4. **Infer** Some small engines require a mixture of oil and gasoline. Gasoline evaporates easily. What conclusion can be drawn about the polarity of the engine oil?
5. **Think Critically** What might happen to your skin if you washed with soap too often?

Applying Math

6. **Calculate Mass** If 60 mg of vitamin C in a multivitamin provides only 75 percent of the recommended daily dosage for children, how much is recommended?
7. **Interpret Data** To get the recommended 80 mg of vitamin C, refer to **Table 3** to determine approximately how much fresh orange juice you must drink.

gpscience.com/self_check_quiz

Fun Fact

All of the B vitamins are water soluble, as is vitamin C. Vitamins E, D, and A are fat soluble.

Reading Check

Answer Vitamins that are water soluble are eliminated with body wastes and therefore need to be constantly replaced.

3 Assess

DAILY INTERVENTION

Check for Understanding

Vitamin Solubility Bring in a juice bottle for which the label indicates that 100% daily requirement of vitamin C is included. Have students explain why it is OK to have more than one serving of that juice without worrying about overdosing on vitamin C. L2

Reteach

Explain Concepts Ask students to explain how nonpolar solvents dissolve nonpolar solutes. The nonpolar molecules have no attraction for one another, so the nonpolar solute can slip easily among the molecules of a nonpolar solvent. L1 LS **Linguistic**

Assessment

Performance Have students examine the molecular structure of antifreeze (ethylene glycol) and write advertisements and slogans describing why it dissolves so well in water. It has two –OH groups, one on each of the two carbon atoms. These make it very polar. Use **Performance Assessment in the Science Classroom,** p. 129. L2

section  review

1. Its molecules have a polar part and a nonpolar part.
2. Polar substances dissolve in polar solvents and nonpolar substances dissolve in nonpolar solvents. Water and alcohol are two like substances because they are polar.
3. Soap has one polar end and one nonpolar end. Grease dissolves in the nonpolar end and is carried away when the polar end of the soap is dissolved in water.
4. Since gasoline easily evaporates, it is probably nonpolar. Engine oil dissolves in gasoline, so engine oil must also be nonpolar.
5. You would lose natural oils.
6. $.75X = 60$ mg
   $X = 60/.75$
   $X = 80$ mg
7. approx. $\frac{1}{2}$ cup; more precisely, 5 oz.

Real-World Question

Purpose Students compare the solubility of a solute at various temperatures. L2 ELL

LS **Logical-Mathematical**

Process Skills measure, use numbers, communicate, make and use graphs, make and use tables, infer

Time Required 40 minutes

Procedure

Alternate Materials In addition to sugar, other solutes such as $CuSO_4$ (**WARNING:** *toxic*) or KBr could be used.

Safety Precautions Students should use test tube holders when handling hot test tubes. They should not stir solutions with a thermometer.

Teaching Strategy Keep the hot plate setting low so the temperature changes will be slow.

Tie to Prior Knowledge Remind students about dissolving sugar in hot tea versus cold tea.

Troubleshooting Experiment with making the copper stirrers before the lab. Coil the copper wire around a pencil and check to be sure the coil fits into the test tubes being used.

Saturated Solutions

Goals
- **Observe** the effects of temperature on the amount of solute that dissolves.

Materials
distilled water at room temperature
large test tubes
Celsius thermometer
table sugar
copper wire stirrer, bent into a spiral as shown on the next page
test-tube holder
graduated cylinder (25-mL)
beaker (250-mL) with 150 mL of water
electric hot plate
test-tube rack
ring stand

Safety Precautions

WARNING: *Do NOT touch the test tubes or hot plate surface when hot plate is turned on or cooling down. When heating a solution in a test tube, keep it pointed away from yourself and others. Do NOT remove goggles until clean up including washing hands is completed.*

Real-World Question

Two major factors to consider when you are dissolving a solute in water are temperature and the ratio of solute to solvent. What happens to a solution as the temperature changes? To be able to draw conclusions about the effect of temperature, you must keep other variables constant. For example, you must be sure to stir each solution in a similar manner. How does solubility change as temperature is increased?

Procedure

1. Place 20 mL of distilled water in a test tube.
2. Add 30 g of sugar.
3. Stir. Does this dissolve?
4. If it dissolves completely, add another 5 g of sugar to the test tube. Does it dissolve?
5. Continue adding 5-g amounts of sugar until no more sugar dissolves.
6. Now place the beaker of water on the hot plate and hang the thermometer from the ring stand so that the bulb is immersed about halfway into the beaker, making sure it does not touch the sides or bottom. Record the starting temperature.

686

Alternative Inquiry Lab

Change Variables Make this Lab an Inquiry Lab by asking students what they think will happen if two or more different kinds of solutes are dissolved in a solvent? In other words, how will this experiment result if multiple solutes are dissolved in the water? Let the students investigate solutes of their choosing with safety guidance from the teacher. Some students may want to go further and investigate solute solubility in different solvents. Have students record their alternative activities and results in their Science Journals. L2

7. Using a test-tube holder, place the test tube into the water.
8. Gradually increase the temperature of the hot plate, while stirring the solution in the tube, until all the sugar dissolves.
9. Note the temperature at which this happens.
10. Add another 5 g of sugar and continue. Note the temperature at which this additional sugar dissolves.
11. Continue in this manner until you have at least four data points. Note the total amount of sugar that has dissolved. Record your data on the data table.

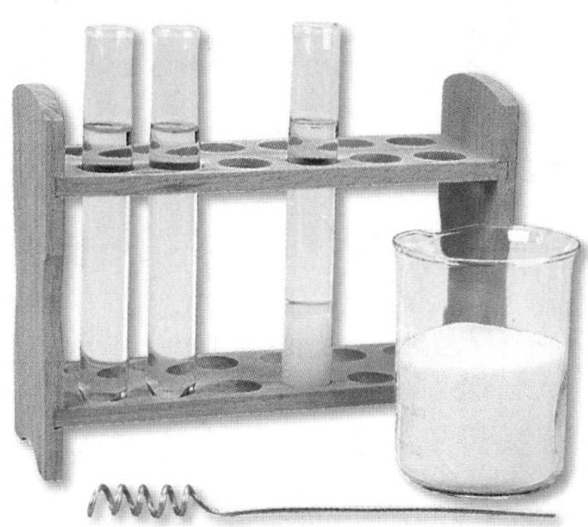

Analyze Your Data

1. **Graph** your results using a line graph. Place grams of solute per 100 g of water (multiply the number of grams by five because you used only 20 mL of water) on the *y*-axis and place temperature on the *x*-axis.
2. **Interpret Data** Using your graph, estimate the solubility of sugar at 100°C and at 0°C, the boiling and freezing point of water, respectively.

Dissolving Sugar in Water

Temperature	Total Grams of Sugar Dissolved
20°C–25°C	about 40g
30°C–35°C	about 45g
50°C	about 50g
55°C–60°C	about 55g

Conclude and Apply

1. How did the saturation change as the temperature was increased?
2. **Compare** your results with those given in **Table 2.**

Communicating Your Data

Compare your results with those of other groups and discuss any differences noted. Why might these differences have occurred? **For more help, refer to the** Science Skill Handbook.

Analyze Your Data

Expected Outcome At higher temperatures, more sugar will dissolve.

Answers to Questions

1. Check student graphs against their results for accuracy.
2. approximately 490 g per 100mL at 100°C and 179 g per 100 mL at 0°C

Error Analysis It may be difficult to tell whether the solute is dissolved when the solution is near saturation. Be sure students pause at each temperature long enough to give the solute time to dissolve. Otherwise, the amount of solute may be less than expected for saturation.

Conclude and Apply

1. The amount of solute needed to cause saturation was greater with increasing temperature steps.
2. Answers will vary.

Assessment

Oral Have students explain how the relationship between saturation and temperature shown in this activity can be used in making candy. Large amounts of sugar may be dissolved at a very high temperature, then cooled quickly to form sugar crystals used in candy making. Students should also observe how stirring influences crystal size. Use **Performance Assessment in the Science Classroom,** p. 93. L2

Communicating Your Data

Keeping the temperature constant while observing possible saturation is difficult. It is easy to go beyond the saturation level without knowing it. If the temperature increases at different rates, results will be different.

SCIENCE Stats

Content Background

The stomach is protected from stomach acid by a mucous layer. Ulcers can result if this layer does not completely cover the stomach lining.

Many mixtures are heterogeneous but contain solutions. For example, blood is heterogeneous because it contains blood cells that are not dissolved in it. However, the dissolved solids and gases in blood plasma form a solution.

Discussion

Glue and Solvents Water is the solvent in many glues, such as the washable school glue used by younger students. When would you need to use glue that contains a solvent that is not water? When items that are being glued will be exposed to moisture, water should not be the solvent.

Find Out About It

Before finding the volume of the solutions in the human body, have students brainstorm the types of solutions present. Such solutions include blood plasma, lymph, saliva, urine, and stomach acid.

Visual Learning

The acidity of a solution is measured by pH. The pH scale ranges from 0 to 14, and the lower the pH, the more acidic the solution. Have students read about the solution that is present in the stomach. On the board, draw a pH scale and have students indicate the pH of vinegar and tomatoes if the pH of stomach acid is 2. The pH of vinegar is 3; the pH of tomatoes is 4. L2

SCIENCE Stats

Weird Solutions

Did you know...

... The "brightest" solutions can glow like a streetlight. Glowing rods called light sticks are an example. Each rod contains two liquids in separate glass or plastic containers. When you flex the rod, the containers break, and the solutions mix and react to produce luminescence, or glowing light. A similar process called bioluminescence allows some living organisms, like fireflies, to glow.

... One of the hardest solutions is steel, a solid solution of iron, carbon, and other elements. When you add some chromium and nickel to the mix, you get stainless steel, which is a tough, rust-resistant solution. In 1998, the United States produced nearly 100 million metric tons of raw steel—enough to make more than 1,800 Empire State Buildings.

... The saltiest and largest body of solution in the western hemisphere is the Great Salt Lake in Utah. If all the salt in the lake dried out and hardened, the result would be a rock with a mass of about 4 1/2 trillion kg—as heavy as 300 million large trucks.

Applying Math

1. Great Salt Lake's salinity is 5 percent when the water is highest and 30 percent when the water is lowest. What is the lake's salinity when the water level is halfway between its highest and lowest levels?
2. Glow sticks shine for about 10 h. If you kept a glow stick glowing continuously in your window for seven days, how many sticks would you need?

Applying Math

Teaching Strategies

- For question 1, review with students how to interpolate values between two known values.
- For question 3, suggest students first set up an equation that relates the amount of chromium to the amount of nickel in stainless steel, then incorporate that in an equation that includes the total percentage of material needed to complete the stainless steel. L2

Answers

1. $30\% - 5\% = 25\%; \frac{1}{2} \times 25\% = 12.5\%; 5\% + 12.5\% = 17.5\%$
2. $\frac{(7 \times 24)}{10} = 16.8 = 17$ glow sticks

Reviewing Main Ideas

Section 1 How Solutions Form

1. A solution is a mixture that has the same composition, color, density, and taste throughout.
2. The substance being dissolved is called a solute, and the substance that does the dissolving is called a solvent.
3. The rate of dissolving can be increased by stirring, increasing surface area, or increasing temperature.
4. Under similar conditions, small particles of solute dissolve faster than large particles.

Section 2 Solubility and Concentration

1. Some compounds are more soluble than others, and this can be measured.
2. *Concentrated* and *dilute* are not precise terms used to describe concentration of solutions.
3. Concentrations can be expressed as percent by volume.
4. An unsaturated solution can dissolve more solute, and a saturated solution, like this tea, cannot. A supersaturated solution is made by raising the temperature of a saturated solution and adding more solute. If it is cooled carefully, the supersaturated solution will retain the dissolved solute.

Section 3 Particles in Solution

1. Substances that dissolve in water to produce solutions that conduct electricity are called electrolytes.
2. When water pulls apart the molecules of a polar substance, forming ions, the process is called ionization.
3. When ionic solids dissolve in water, the process is called dissociation, because the ions are already present in the solid.

Section 4 Dissolving Without Water

1. Water cannot dissolve all solutes.
2. Nonpolar solvents are needed to dissolve nonpolar solutes.
3. Some vitamins are nonpolar and dissolve in the fat contained in some body cells.
4. Nonpolar solvents can be dangerous as well as helpful. Many products, including the substances shown here, are packaged with cautions of flammability and toxicity.

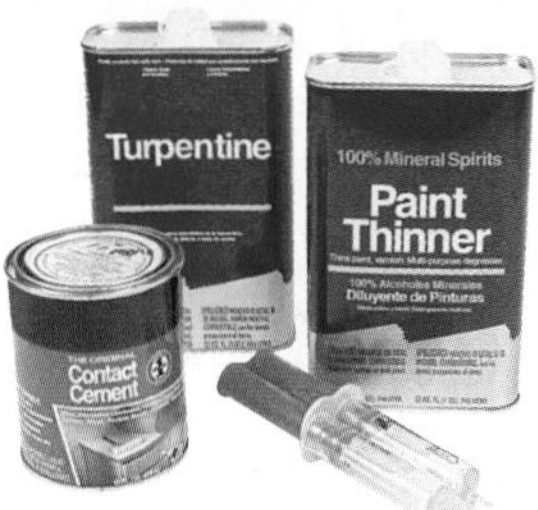

FOLDABLES™ Use the Foldable that you made at the beginning of this section to help you review the characteristics of solvents and solutes.

Science Online gpscience.com/interactive_tutor

chapter 22 Study Guide

Reviewing Main Ideas

Summary statements can be used by students to review the major concepts of the chapter.

Visit gpscience.com
/self_check_quiz
/interactive_tutor
/vocabulary_puzzlemaker
/chapter_review
/standardized_test

Assessment Transparency

For additional assessment questions, use the *Assessment Transparency* located in the transparency book.

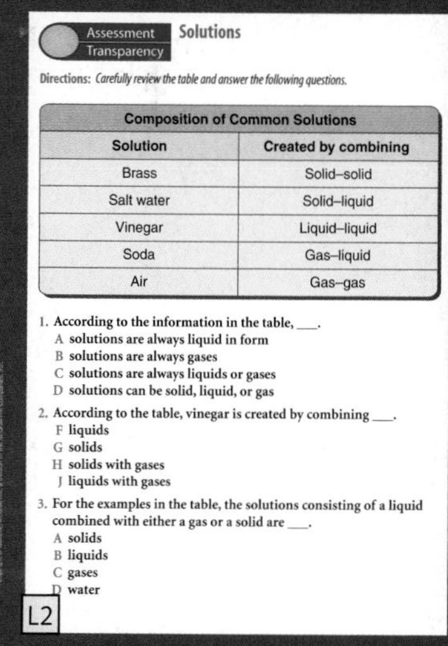

Assessment

Assessment Transparency — Solutions

Directions: *Carefully review the table and answer the following questions.*

Composition of Common Solutions	
Solution	**Created by combining**
Brass	Solid–solid
Salt water	Solid–liquid
Vinegar	Liquid–liquid
Soda	Gas–liquid
Air	Gas–gas

1. According to the information in the table, ___.
   A solutions are always liquid in form
   B solutions are always gases
   C solutions are always liquids or gases
   D solutions can be solid, liquid, or gas
2. According to the table, vinegar is created by combining ___.
   F liquids
   G solids
   H solids with gases
   J liquids with gases
3. For the examples in the table, the solutions consisting of a liquid combined with either a gas or a solid are ___.
   A solids
   B liquids
   C gases
   D water

L2

Solutions

FOLDABLES™ Have students use their Foldables to review the content of the chapter. Using the same idea, draw another Venn diagram and write a task or situation that requires a water-based solvent, one that requires a non-water-based solvent, and one that could utilize either type of solvent. L2

chapter 22 Review

Using Vocabulary

1. solute, solvent
2. dissociation
3. solubility
4. supersaturated solution
5. unsaturated solution
6. nonelectrolyte

Checking Concepts

7. D
8. A
9. B
10. A
11. B
12. B
13. B
14. A
15. B
16. C

Interpreting Graphics

17. See student page.
18. See student page.

chapter 22 Review

Using Vocabulary

dissociation p. 677
electrolyte p. 676
ion p. 676
ionization p. 676
nonelectrolyte p. 676
nonpolar p. 681
polar p. 667
saturated solution p. 673
solubility p. 671
solution p. 664
solute p. 665
solvent p. 665
supersaturated solution p. 674
unsaturated solution p. 673

Fill in the blanks with correct vocabulary or words.

1. In lemonade, sugar is the ________ and water is the ________.
2. During ________, particles in an ionic solid are separated and drawn into solution.
3. If more of substance B dissolves in water than substance A, then substance B has a higher ________ than substance A.
4. Adding a seed crystal may cause solute to crystallize from a(n) ________.
5. More solute can be added to a(n) ________.
6. Nonpolar solutes in a solution are called ________.

Checking Concepts

Choose the word or phrase that best answers the question.

7. Which of the following is NOT a solution?
   A) glass of flat soda
   B) air in a scuba tank
   C) bronze alloy
   D) mud in water tank
8. What term is NOT appropriate to use when describing solutions?
   A) heterogeneous **C)** liquid
   B) gaseous **D)** solid
9. When iodine is dissolved in alcohol, what term is used to describe the alcohol?
   A) alloy **C)** solution
   B) solvent **D)** solute
10. What word is used to describe a mixture that is 85 percent copper and 15 percent tin?
    A) alloy **C)** saturated
    B) solvent **D)** solute
11. Solvents such as paint thinner and gasoline evaporate more readily than water because they are what type of compounds?
    A) ionic
    B) nonpolar
    C) dilute
    D) polar

12. What can a polar solvent dissolve?
    A) any solute **C)** a nonpolar solute
    B) a polar solute **D)** no solute
13. If a water solution conducts electricity, what must the solute be?
    A) gas **C)** liquid
    B) electrolyte **D)** nonelectrolyte
14. In forming a water solution, what process does an ionic compound undergo?
    A) dissociation **C)** ionization
    B) electrolysis **D)** no change
15. What can you increase to make a gas more soluble in a liquid?
    A) particle size **C)** stirring
    B) pressure **D)** temperature
16. If a solute crystallizes out of a solution when a seed crystal is added, what kind of solution is it?
    A) unsaturated **C)** supersaturated
    B) saturated **D)** dilute

Science Online gpscience.com/vocabulary_puzzlemaker

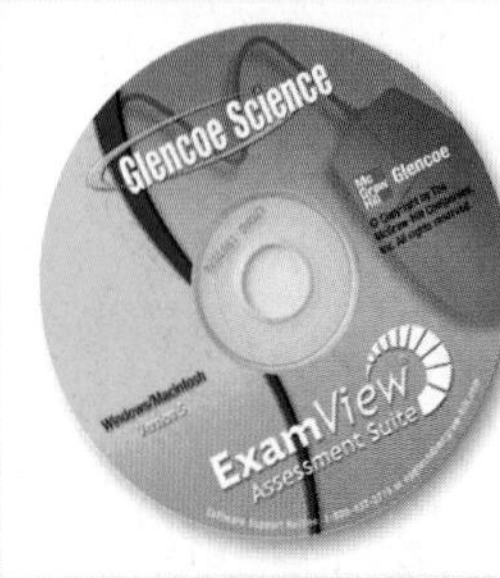

Interpreting Graphics

17. Copy and complete the following concept map on solutions.

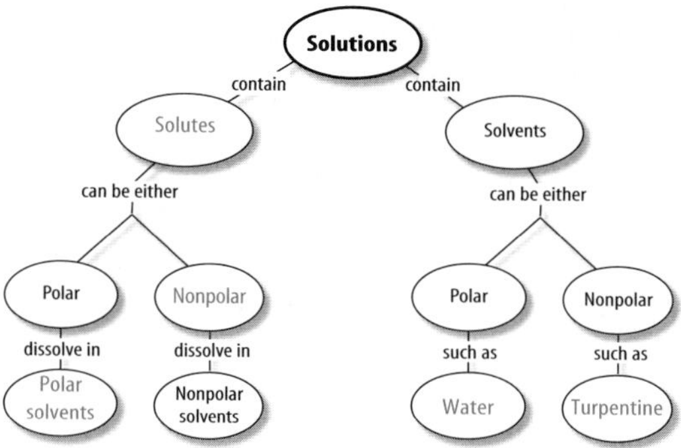

Use the table below to answer question 18.

Limits of Solubility

Compound	Type of Solution	Solubility in 100 g Water at 20°C
$CuSO_4$	saturated	32.0 g
KCl	supersaturated	34.0 g
KNO_3	saturated	31.6 g
$NaClO_3$	unsaturated	95.9 g

18. **Identify** Using the data in **Table 2,** fill in the following table. Use the terms *saturated*, *unsaturated*, and *supersaturated* to describe the type of solution.

Thinking Critically

19. **Explain** why potatoes might cook more quickly in salted water than in unsalted water.

20. **Explain** what happens when an ionic compound such as copper(II) sulfate, $CuSO_4$, dissolves in water.

21. **Explain** why the term *dilute* is not precise.

22. **Explain** why the statement, "Water is the solvent in a solution," is not always true.

Applying Math

23. **Measure in SI** 153 g of potassium nitrate have been dissolved in enough water to make 1 L of this solution. You use a graduated cylinder to measure 80 mL of solution. What mass of potassium nitrate is in the 80-mL sample?

Use the graph below to answer question 24.

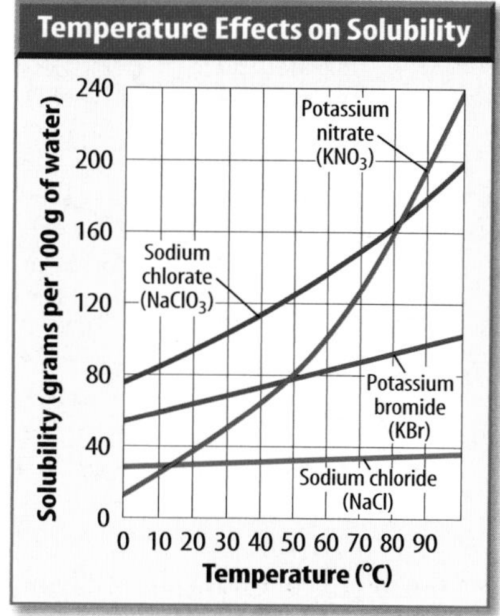

24. **Interpret Data** Determine the temperature at which a solution of 80 g potassium nitrate (KNO_3) in 100 mL of water is saturated.

25. **Use Numbers** How would you make a 25 percent solution by volume of apple juice?

26. **Make and Use Graphs** Using **Table 2,** make a graph of solubility versus temperature for $CuSO_4$ (copper(II) sulfate) and KCl. How would you make a saturated solution of each substance at 80°C?

Science Online gpscience.com/chapter_review

Assessment Resources

Reproducible Masters

Chapter *Fast File* Resources
- Chapter Review, pp. 39–40
- Chapter Tests, pp. 41–44
- Assessment Transparency Activity, p. 53

Glencoe Science Web site
- Chapter Review Test
- Standardized Test Practice

Glencoe Technology
- Assessment Transparency
- *ExamView® Assessment Suite*
- MindJogger Videoquiz
- Interactive Chalkboard

Thinking Critically

19. The salted water boils at a slightly higher temperature than unsalted water because of the presence of dissolved ions. At the higher temperature, the potatoes cook more quickly.
20. It dissociates into Cu^{2+} and SO_4^{2-} ions that are attracted to the polar water molecules.
21. Dilute indicates not much solute is present, but it does not specify exactly how much solute and solvent are present.
22. Water can be the solute in a solution. For example, water may be dissolved in alcohol.

Applying Math

National Math Standards

1, 2, 5, 9

Answers to Practice Problems

23. $\frac{153\text{ g}}{1000\text{ mL}} \times 80.0\text{ mL} = 12.2\text{ g } KNO_3$
24. 50°C
25. Place 25 mL of concentrated apple juice in 75 mL of water.
26. $CuSO_4$: use approximately 87g per 100 g of water.

FAST FILE

Answer Sheet A practice answer sheet can be found at gpscience.com/answer_sheet.

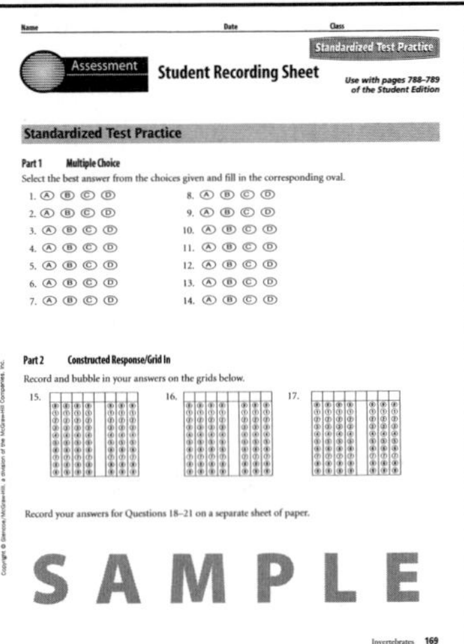
Name Date Class

Standardized Test Practice

Assessment Student Recording Sheet

Use with pages 788–789 of the Student Edition

Standardized Test Practice

Part 1 Multiple Choice

Select the best answer from the choices given and fill in the corresponding oval.

Part 2 Constructed Response/Grid In

Record and bubble in your answers on the grids below.

Record your answers for Questions 18–21 on a separate sheet of paper.

SAMPLE

Invertebrates 169

Part 1 Multiple Choice

1. B
2. D
3. B
4. D
5. C
6. B

Part 2 Short Response

7. The temperature in the room could have dropped. This would make the solution cooler and excess sugar would settle out at a lower temperature. Or some of the water could have evaporated from the solution and the excess sugar would settle out.
8. You could cool the liquid or you could increase the pressure of the carbon dioxide over the liquid.
9. Shaking or pouring the drink exposes more gas molecules to the surface, where they escape from the liquid.
10. Solubility in 100 g water = 34 g; therefore, solubility in 200 g water = 68 g. Solubility in warm water = 100 g; therefore, 100 g − 68 g = 32 g will come out of solution.

chapter 22 Standardized Test Practice

Part 1 Multiple Choice

Record your answers on the answer sheet provided by your teacher or on a sheet of paper.

Use the graph below to answer questions 1–3.

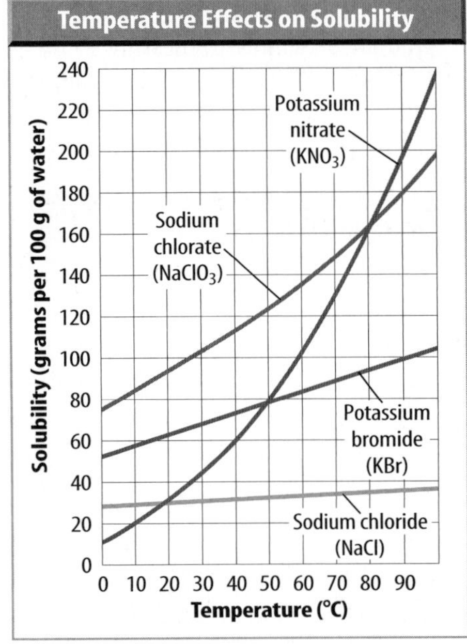

1. How much potassium nitrate will you have to add to 100 g of water at 40°C to make a saturated solution?
   A. 60 g **C.** 100 g
   B. 60 g **D.** 240 g

2. If 25 g of sodium chlorate are dissolved in 100 g of water at 70°C, how would you describe the solution?
   A. concentrated **C.** saturated
   B. supersaturated **D.** dilute

Test-Taking Tip

Answer Bubbles Double check that you are filling in the correct answer bubble for the question number you are working on.

3. Which of the following will make a saturated solution if added to 100 g of water?
   A. 20 g of NaCl if the water is 50°C
   B. 100 g of KBr if the water is 90°C
   C. 80 g of $NaClO_3$ if the water is 30°C
   D. 60 g of KNO_3 if the water is 100°C

4. Which of the following statements about solubility is true as the temperature increases?
   A. The solubility of both gases and solids increases.
   B. The solubility of both gases and solids decreases.
   C. The solubility of gases increases, while the solubility of solids decreases.
   D. The solubility of gases decreases, while the solubility of solids increases.

Use the illustration below to answer questions 5 and 6.

5. Which of the following will NOT make the crystal of rock candy dissolve faster in water?
   A. stirring **C.** cooling
   B. heating **D.** shaking

6. Which of the following statements is true about how grinding the crystal would affect its dissolving rate?
   A. Grinding would increase the surface area and slow down dissolving.
   B. Grinding would increase the surface area and speed up dissolving.
   C. Grinding would decrease the surface are and slow down dissolving.
   D. Grinding would decrease the surface area and speed up dissolving.

Part 2 Short Response/Grid In

11. The bubbles contain air that was dissolved in the water. When the water is heated, less air can be dissolved in the water, so the air comes out of solution and forms bubbles.
12. Turpentine is a nonpolar solvent and water is a polar solvent. Oil-based paints are nonpolar, so a nonpolar solvent like turpentine will dissolve nonpolar paint.
13. The salt lowers the temperature of the ice-water mixture, thus allowing the ice cream to form below 0°C.

Part 2 Short Response/Grid In

Record your answers on the answer sheet provided by your teacher or on a sheet of paper.

7. A girl mixes a saturated solution of sugar in water in science lab on a Friday. On Monday, the open container has particles of sugar on the bottom. Explain possible reasons to explain why this happened.

Use the illustration below to answer questions 8 and 9.

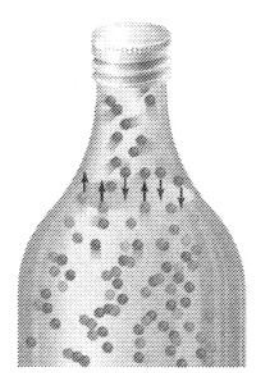
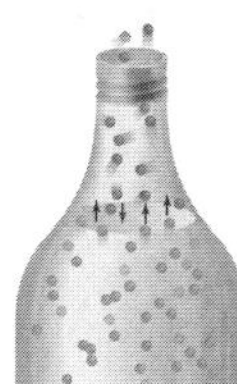

8. The drawing above shows carbon dioxide gas dissolved in water. What are two ways you could make more gas dissolve in the water?

9. Why does shaking or pouring a carbonated drink cause gas to come out of solution?

10. The solubility of potassium chloride in water is 34 g per 100 g of water at 20°C. A warm solution containing 100 g of potassium chloride in 200 g of water is cooled to 20°C. How many grams of potassium chloride will come out of solution?

11. When water is heated slowly, small bubbles form in the liquid. These bubbles do not contain water vapor. What is in the bubbles and why do they form?

12. Why will turpentine remove oil-based paint from a paint brush while water will not?

13. Why is salt mixed with the ice in a hand-crank ice cream maker?

Part 3 Open Ended

Record your answers on a sheet of paper.

14. Why can carp, catfish, and other fish with low oxygen needs live in warmer waters than can trout, which need large amounts of oxygen?

Use the illustration below to answer questions 15 and 16.

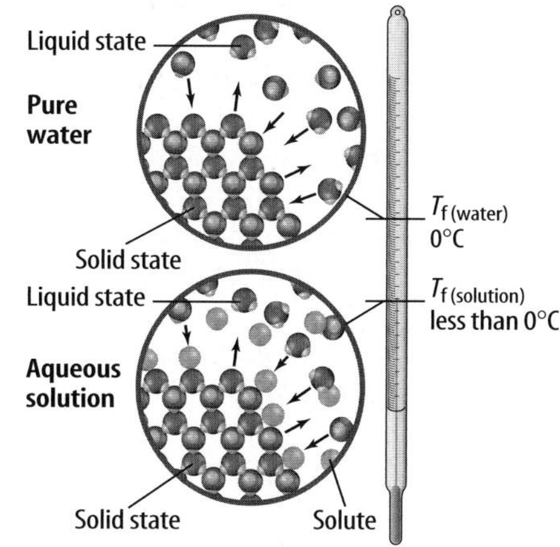

15. The drawing shows what happens to the freezing point of water when antifreeze is dissolved in the water to form a solution. Explain how this happens.

16. How can antifreeze also raise the boiling point of water?

17. When you take clothing to the dry cleaner, it is important to identify any stains that are on the clothing. Why does the dry cleaner need this information?

18. You are given a clear water solution containing potassium nitrate. How could you determine whether the solution is unsaturated, saturated, or supersaturated?

19. A solution conducts electricity. What do you know about the solution?

Part 3 Open Ended

14. Cold water holds more dissolved oxygen that warm water does. Cold water is therefore more likely to supply trout with enough oxygen. Carp, catfish, and other fish with low oxygen needs can survive in water waters where the amount of dissolved oxygen is much lower.

15. The antifreeze molecules block the water molecules as they try to join the growing crystal lattice to form ice. So antifreeze molecules block the formation of ice crystals, and this lowers the temperature needed to freeze the water.

16. Without antifreeze, water particles vaporize freely from the surface. But the antifreeze molecules keep fewer water molecules from reaching the surface to evaporate. The means that it will take a higher temperature to make the water boil.

17. The dry cleaner needs to know what the stains are to select an appropriate solvent to remove the stains. If the stains are from polar molecules, a polar solvent must be used to remove the stains. If the stains are from nonpolar molecules, a nonpolar solvent must be used to remove the stains.

18. You could add a single crystal of potassium nitrate to the solution. If the crystal dissolved, the solution is unsaturated. If the crystal sank to the bottom, the solution is saturated. If, when the crystal was added, more potassium nitrate crystallizes out, the solution was supersaturated.

19. If the solution conducts electricity, it contains ions. The solution is not pure water, nor it is likely to be a nonpolar solvent.

Rubrics

For more help evaluating open-ended assessment questions, see the rubric on p. 10T.

Acids, Bases, and Salts

BIG Idea Some substances can be classified as acids, bases, or salts.

	Content Standards	Learning Objectives	Resources to Assess Mastery
Section 1	**5–8:** UCP.1–3, 5; A.1, 2; B.1 **9–12:** UCP.1–3, 5; A.1, 2; B.2, 3	**Acids and Bases** **1. Compare and contrast** acids and bases and identify the characteristics they have. **2. Examine** some formulas and uses of common acids and bases. **3. Determine** how the process of ionization and dissociation apply to acids and bases. ***Main Idea*** Acids produce hydronium ions (H_3O^+) in water, and bases produce hydroxide ions (OH^-) in water.	**Formative Assessment** Reading Check, pp. 697, 701 Section Review, p. 701 **Summative Assessment** *ExamView® Assessment Suite*
Section 2	**5–8:** UCP.1–3, 5; A.1, 2; B.1 **9–12:** UCP.1–3, 5; A.1, 2; B.2, 3	**Strength of Acids and Bases** **4. Determine** what is responsible for the strength of an acid or a base. **5. Compare and contrast** strength and concentration. **6. Examine** the relationship between pH and acid or base strength. **7. Examine** electrical conductivity. ***Main Idea*** Acid strength describes the ease with which an acid dissociates into ions. Acid concentration describes the amount of acid dissolved in water.	**Formative Assessment** Reading Check, p. 705 Section Review, p. 705 **Summative Assessment** *ExamView® Assessment Suite*
Section 3	**5–8:** UCP.1–3, 5; A.1, 2; B.1; F.1, 2 **9–12:** UCP.1–3, 5; A.1, 2; B.2, 3; F.1, 4, 5 See pp. 16T–17T for a Key to Standards.	**Salts** **8. Identify** a neutralization reaction. **9. Determine** what a salt is and how salts form. **10. Compare and contrast** soaps and detergents. **11. Examine** how esters are made and what they are used for. ***Main Idea*** An acid and a base react to form a salt and water.	**Formative Assessment** Reading Check, pp. 713, 714 Section Review, p. 715 **Summative Chapter Assessment** MindJogger, Ch. 23 *ExamView® Assessment Suite* Leveled Chapter Test Test A L1 Test B L2 Test C L3 Test Practice, pp. 722–723

Suggested Pacing				
Period	**Instruction**	**Labs**	**Review & Assessment**	**Total**
Single	3.5 days	3 days	1.5 days	8 days
Block	1.75 blocks	1.5 blocks	.75 block	4 blocks

Core Instruction	Leveled Resources	Leveled Labs	Pacing: Period		Block
Student Text, pp. 694–701 Section Focus Transparency, Ch. 23, Section 1 Teaching Transparency, Ch. 23, Section 1 Interactive Chalkboard, Ch. 23, Section 1 Differentiated Instruction, pp. 699, 700	**Chapter *Fast File* Resources** Directed Reading for Content Mastery, p. 20 L1 Note-taking Worksheet, pp. 33–35 Reinforcement, p. 27 L2 Enrichment, p. 30 L3 **Reading Essentials**, p. 398 L1 ELL **Science Notebook**, p. 267 ELL ***Active*Folders**: *Acids and Bases* L1 ELL	**Launch Lab**, p. 695: chalk, mortar and pestle, bottles of fresh soda (several), water, 100-mL beakers, graduated cylinders (50- or 100-mL), funnels, filter paper *25 min* (over 2 days) L2 **MiniLAB**, p. 698: water, 250-mL beaker, HCL (1M), universal indicator, antacid tablets, graduated cylinder, dropper *25 min* L2	**1**	Section 1, pp. 695–697 (includes Launch Lab)	**1**
			2	Section 1, pp. 698–701 (includes MiniLAB and Section Review)	
Student Text, pp. 702–706 Section Focus Transparency, Ch. 23, Section 2 Interactive Chalkboard, Ch. 23, Section 2 Identifying Misconceptions, pp. 703, 704 Differentiated Instruction, pp. 703, 704	**Chapter *Fast File* Resources** Directed Reading for Content Mastery, p. 20 L1 Note-taking Worksheet, pp. 33–35 Reinforcement, p. 28 L2 Enrichment, p. 31 L3 **Reading Essentials**, p. 403 L1 ELL **Science Notebook**, p. 271 ELL ***Active*Folders**: *Acids and Bases* L1 ELL	***Lab**, p. 706: cabbage indicator, coffee filter, wax paper, grease pencil or masking tape, pencil *30 min* L1 L2 L3	**3**	Section 2, pp. 702–705 (includes Section Review)	**2**
			4	Lab: Acid Concentrations, p. 706	
Student Text, pp. 707–717 Section Focus Transparency, Ch. 23, Section 3 Interactive Chalkboard, Ch. 23, Section 3 Visualizing Salt, p. 709 Applying Science, p. 711 Differentiated Instruction, pp. 708, 709, 712 Chapter Study Guide, p. 719	**Chapter *Fast File* Resources** Directed Reading for Content Mastery, pp. 21, 22 L1 Note-taking Worksheet, pp. 33–35 Reinforcement, p. 29 L2 Enrichment, p. 32 L3 **Reading Essentials**, p. 407 L1 ELL **Science Notebook**, p. 274 ELL ***Active*Folders**: *Acids and Bases* L1 ELL	**MiniLAB**, p. 711: water, small glasses (2), purple grape juice, baking soda, white vinegar *15 min* L2 ***Lab**, pp. 716–717: colorless soft drinks (3), test tubes (3), 25-mL graduated cylinder, dropper (2), phenolphthalein (1%), diluted NaOH solution (0.1M) *45 min* L1 L2 L3 (Video Lab) *Lab version A L1 version B L2 L3	**5**	Section 3, pp. 707–711 (includes MiniLAB)	**3**
			6	Section 3, pp. 712–715 (includes Section Review)	
			7	Lab: Be a Soda Scientist, pp. 716–717	**4**
			8	Study Guide, Chapter Review, and Test Practice, pp. 719–723	

Video Lab

 chapter 23 Acids, Bases, and Salts

Transparencies

Section Focus

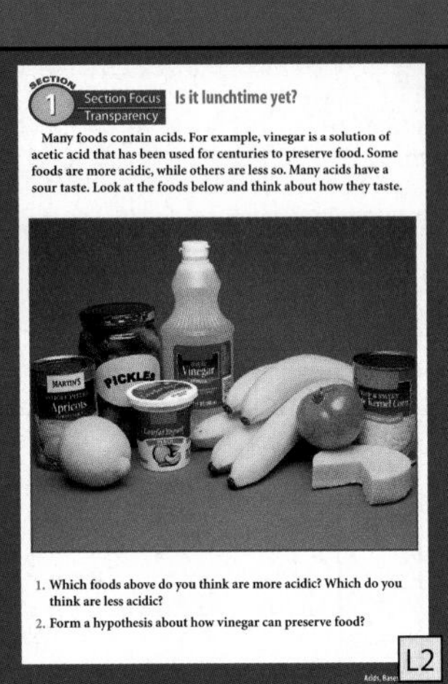
Section 1 Section Focus Transparency **Is it lunchtime yet?**

Many foods contain acids. For example, vinegar is a solution of acetic acid that has been used for centuries to preserve food. Some foods are more acidic, while others are less so. Many acids have a sour taste. Look at the foods below and think about how they taste.

1. Which foods above do you think are more acidic? Which do you think are less acidic?
2. Form a hypothesis about how vinegar can preserve food?

L2

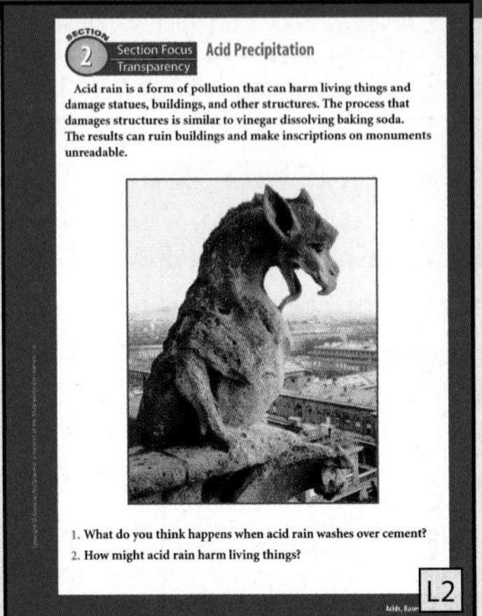
Section 2 Section Focus Transparency **Acid Precipitation**

Acid rain is a form of pollution that can harm living things and damage statues, buildings, and other structures. The process that damages structures is similar to vinegar dissolving baking soda. The results can ruin buildings and make inscriptions on monuments unreadable.

1. What do you think happens when acid rain washes over cement?
2. How might acid rain harm living things?

L2

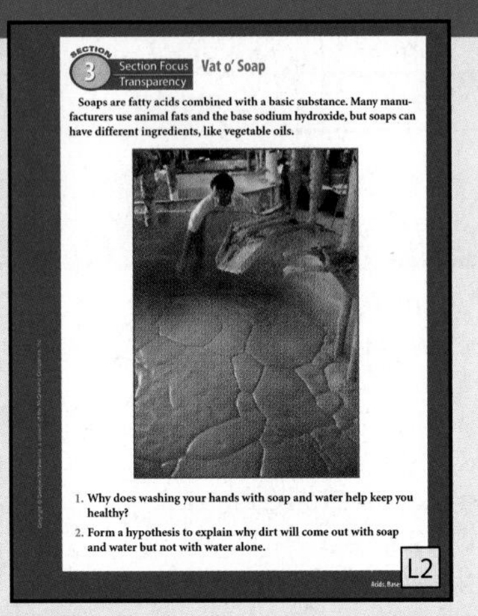
Section 3 Section Focus Transparency **Vat o' Soap**

Soaps are fatty acids combined with a basic substance. Many manufacturers use animal fats and the base sodium hydroxide, but soaps can have different ingredients, like vegetable oils.

1. Why does washing your hands with soap and water help keep you healthy?
2. Form a hypothesis to explain why dirt will come out with soap and water but not with water alone.

L2

This is a representation of key blackline masters available in the Teacher Classroom Resources. See Resource Manager boxes within the chapter for additional information.

Assessment

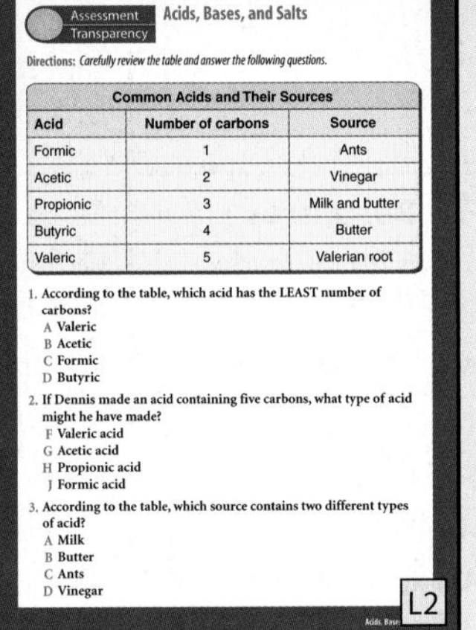
Assessment Transparency **Acids, Bases, and Salts**

Directions: Carefully review the table and answer the following questions.

Common Acids and Their Sources		
Acid	Number of carbons	Source
Formic	1	Ants
Acetic	2	Vinegar
Propionic	3	Milk and butter
Butyric	4	Butter
Valeric	5	Valerian root

1. According to the table, which acid has the LEAST number of carbons?
   A Valeric
   B Acetic
   C Formic
   D Butyric
2. If Dennis made an acid containing five carbons, what type of acid might he have made?
   F Valeric acid
   G Acetic acid
   H Propionic acid
   J Formic acid
3. According to the table, which source contains two different types of acid?
   A Milk
   B Butter
   C Ants
   D Vinegar

L2

Teaching

Section 1 Teaching Transparency **Common Acids**

Table 1 Common Acids and Their Uses

Name, Formula	Use
Acetic Acid, CH_3COOH	Food preservation and preparation
Acetylsalicylic Acid, $HOOC-C_6H_4-OOCCH_3$	Pain relief, fever relief, to reduce inflammation
Ascorbic Acid, $H_2C_6H_6O_6$	Antioxidant, vitamin
Carbonic Acid, H_2CO_3	Carbonated drinks
Hydrochloric Acid, HCl	Digestion as gastric juice in stomach, to clean steel in a process called pickling
Nitric Acid, HNO_3	To make fertilizers
Phosphoric Acid, H_3PO_3	To make detergents, fertilizers, and soft drinks
Sulfuric Acid, H_2SO_4	Car batteries, to manufacture fertilizers and other chemicals

L2

Key to Teaching Strategies

The following designations will help you decide which activities are appropriate for your students.

- **L1** Level 1 activities should be appropriate for students with learning difficulties.
- **L2** Level 2 activities should be within the ability range of all students.
- **L3** Level 3 activities are designed for above-average students.
- **ELL** ELL activities should be within the ability range of English Language Learners.
- **COOP LEARN** Cooperative Learning activities are designed for small group work.
- **LS** Multiple Learning Styles logos, as described on page 12T, are used throughout to indicate strategies that address different learning styles.
- **P** These strategies represent student products that can be placed into a best-work portfolio.
- **PBL** Problem-Based Learning activities apply real-world situations to learning.

Hands-on Activities

Student Text Lab Worksheet

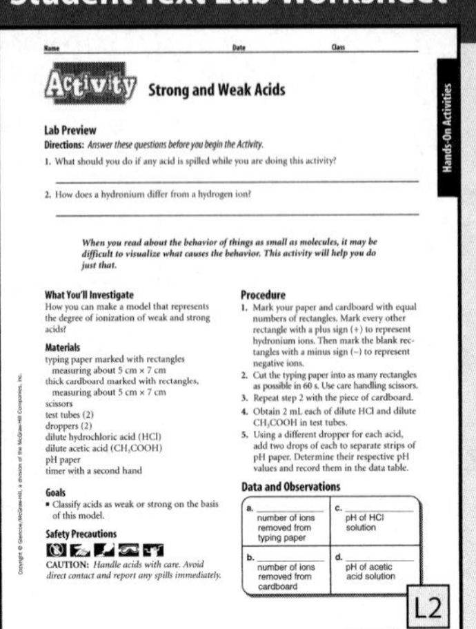
Name Date Class

Activity **Strong and Weak Acids**

Lab Preview

Directions: *Answer these questions before you begin the Activity.*

1. What should you do if any acid is spilled while you are doing this activity?
2. How does a hydronium differ from a hydrogen ion?

When you read about the behavior of things as small as molecules, it may be difficult to visualize what causes the behavior. This activity will help you do just that.

What You'll Investigate

How you can make a model that represents the degree of ionization of weak and strong acids?

Materials

typing paper marked with rectangles measuring about 5 cm × 7 cm
thick cardboard marked with rectangles, measuring about 5 cm × 7 cm
scissors
test tubes (2)
droppers (2)
dilute hydrochloric acid (HCl)
dilute acetic acid (CH_3COOH)
pH paper
timer with a second hand

Goals

- Classify acids as weak or strong on the basis of this model.

Safety Precautions

CAUTION: *Handle acids with care. Avoid direct contact and report any spills immediately.*

Procedure

1. Mark your paper and cardboard with equal numbers of rectangles. Mark every other rectangle with a plus sign (+) to represent hydronium ions. Then mark the blank rectangles with a minus sign (–) to represent negative ions.
2. Cut the typing paper into as many rectangles as possible in 60 s. Use care handling scissors.
3. Repeat step 2 with the piece of cardboard.
4. Obtain 2 mL each of dilute HCl and dilute CH_3COOH in test tubes.
5. Using a different dropper for each acid, add two drops of each to separate strips of pH paper. Determine their respective pH values and record them in the data table.

Data and Observations

a. ______ number of ions removed from typing paper	c. ______ pH of HCl solution
b. ______ number of ions removed from cardboard	d. ______ pH of acetic acid solution

L2

Acids, Bases, and Salts 5

Laboratory Activities

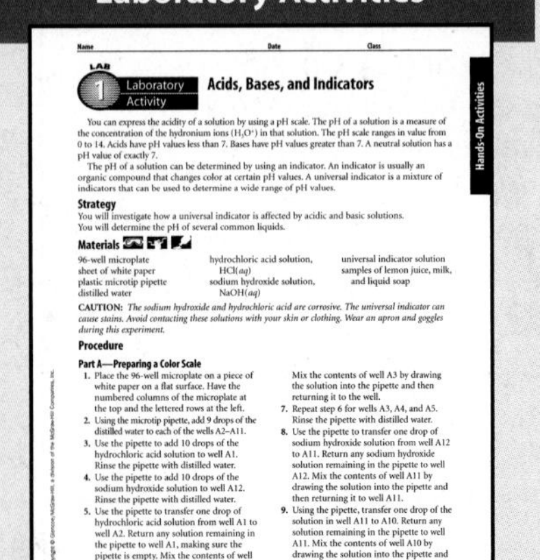
Name Date Class

Lab 1 Laboratory Activity **Acids, Bases, and Indicators**

You can express the acidity of a solution by using a pH scale. The pH of a solution is a measure of the concentration of the hydronium ions (H_3O^+) in that solution. The pH scale ranges in value from 0 to 14. Acids have pH values less than 7. Bases have pH values greater than 7. A neutral solution has a pH value of exactly 7.

The pH of a solution can be determined by using an indicator. An indicator is usually an organic compound that changes color at certain pH values. A universal indicator is a mixture of indicators that can be used to determine a wide range of pH values.

Strategy

You will investigate how a universal indicator is affected by acidic and basic solutions. You will determine the pH of several common liquids.

Materials

96-well microplate
sheet of white paper
plastic microtip pipette
distilled water
hydrochloric acid solution, HCl(*aq*)
sodium hydroxide solution, NaOH(*aq*)
universal indicator solution
samples of lemon juice, milk, and liquid soap

CAUTION: *The sodium hydroxide and hydrochloric acid are corrosive. The universal indicator can cause stains. Avoid contacting these solutions with your skin or clothing. Wear an apron and goggles during this experiment.*

Procedure

Part A—Preparing a Color Scale

1. Place the 96-well microplate on a piece of white paper on a flat surface. Have the numbered columns of the microplate at the top and the lettered rows at the left.
2. Using the microtip pipette, add 9 drops of the distilled water to each of the wells A2–A11.
3. Use the pipette to add 10 drops of the hydrochloric acid solution to well A1. Rinse the pipette with distilled water.
4. Use the pipette to add 10 drops of the sodium hydroxide solution to well A12. Rinse the pipette with distilled water.
5. Use the pipette to transfer one drop of hydrochloric acid solution from well A1 to well A2. Return any solution remaining in the pipette to well A1, making sure the pipette is empty. Mix the contents of well A2 by drawing the solution into the pipette and then returning it to well A2.
6. Using the pipette, transfer one drop of the solution in well A2 to well A3. Return any solution remaining in the pipette to well A2. Mix the contents of well A3 by drawing the solution into the pipette and then returning it to the well.
7. Repeat step 6 for wells A3, A4, and A5. Rinse the pipette with distilled water.
8. Use the pipette to transfer one drop of sodium hydroxide solution from well A12 to A11. Return any sodium hydroxide solution remaining in the pipette to well A12. Mix the contents of well A11 by drawing the solution into the pipette and then returning it to well A11.
9. Using the pipette, transfer one drop of the solution in well A11 to A10. Return any solution remaining in the pipette to well A11. Mix the contents of well A10 by drawing the solution into the pipette and then returning it to the well.
10. Repeat step 9 for wells A10 and A9. Do not transfer solution from well A8 to well A7. Well A7 will contain only distilled water. Rinse the pipette with distilled water.

L2

Acids, Bases, and Salts 9

Resource Manager

Meeting Different Ability Levels

Content Outline

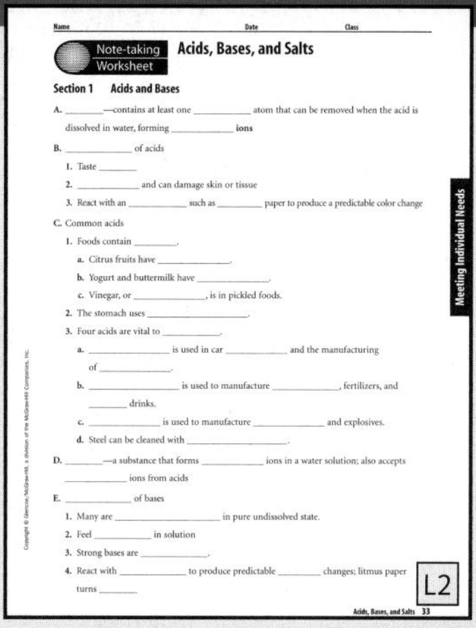

Reinforcement

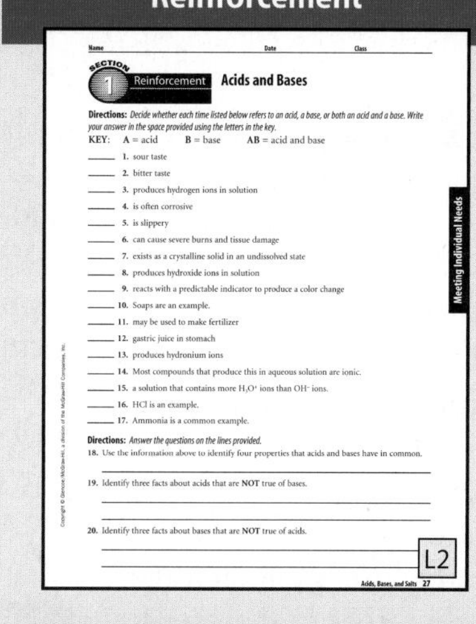

Enrichment

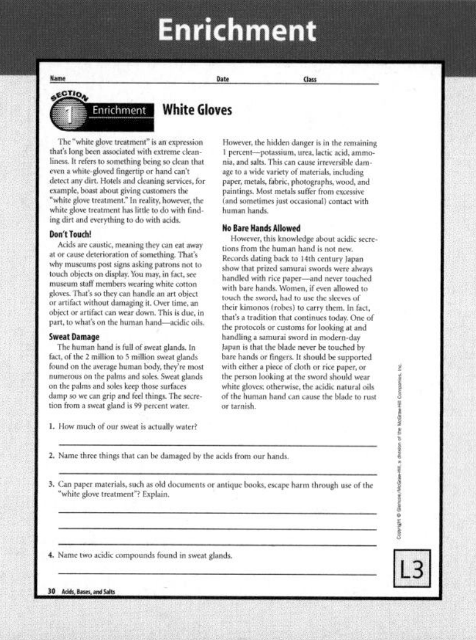

Directed Reading (English/Spanish)

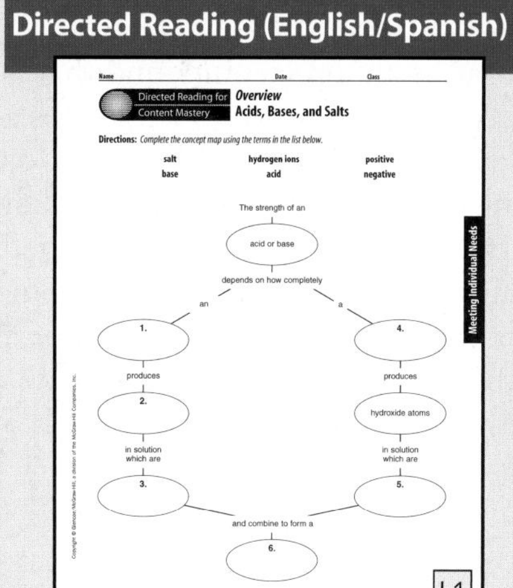

Study Guide

Study Guide
Features
• Contains a study guide page for each section of the chapter
• Reviews key concepts
• Includes answer pages
L1

Reading Essentials

Reading Essentials for Glencoe Science
An Interactive Student Workbook
Features
• Condensed core content
• Actively involves students in reading
• Reinforces key vocabulary
L1

Assessment

Test Practice Workbook

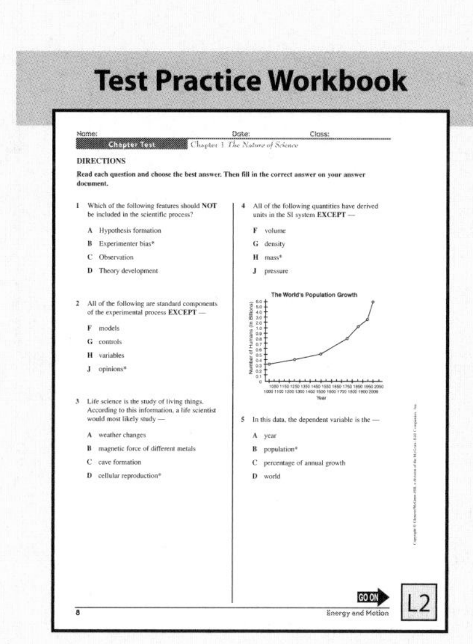

Chapter Review

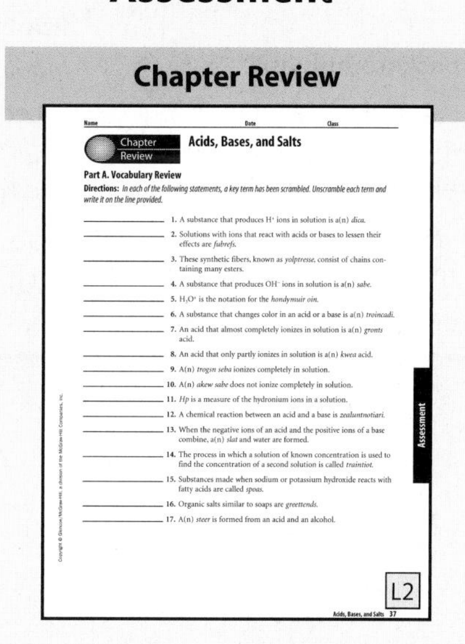

Chapter Tests

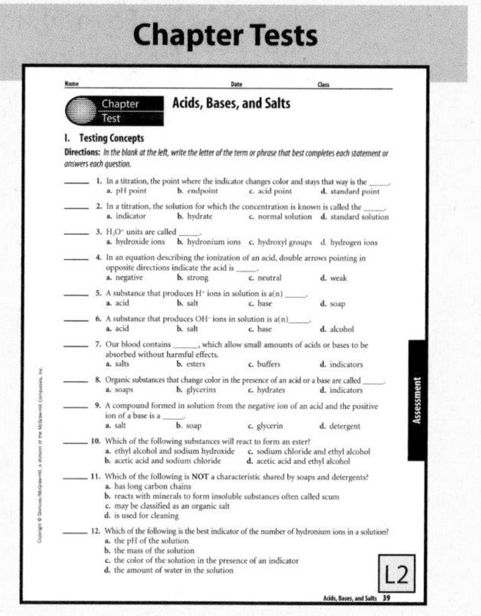

Science Content Background

section 1 Acids and Bases

Solutions of Acids and Bases

A good operational definition of acids and bases is that acids increase the concentration of hydronium ions (H_3O^+) when dissolved in water and bases increase the concentration of hydroxide ions when dissolved in water. Other characteristics come from work by Robert Boyle in the 1600s. Acids have a sour taste, are corrosive, turn litmus from blue to red, and lose their acidity when they react with alkaline (basic) materials. Bases feel slippery, change litmus from red to blue, and become less *alkaline* when they react with acids. The word alkaline became synonymous with basic because alkalines are the "basis" for making salts.

section 2 Strength of Acids and Bases

pH of a Solution

The term pH is derived from the German *potenz* (power) and H for hydrogen. It refers to the power of 10 used to express the molar H_3O^+ concentration. The approximate pH of a solution can be determined by using an acid-base indicator. Bromothymol blue, for instance, changes color in the pH range 6.0–7.6 from yellow in its acid form to blue in its base form. Phenolphthalein changes in the pH range of 8.2–9.8 from colorless in its acid form to pink in its base form. A mixture of indicators called universal indicator can be used that measures the range of pH from 0–14.

section 3 Salts

Salt Formation

A salt is an ionic compound that is formed when an acid neutralizes a base. Salt solutions can be neutral, acidic, or basic, depending on the acid-base properties of the constituents. As a general rule, salts formed by the reaction of a strong acid with a strong base are neutral, salts formed by reaction of a strong acid with a weak base are acidic, and salts formed by the reaction of a weak acid with a strong base are basic.

chapter content resources

Internet Resources

For additional content background, visit gpscience.com to:

- access your book online
- find references to related articles in popular science magazines
- access Web links with related content background
- access current events with science journal topics

Print Resources

Inquiry-Based Experiments in Chemistry, Valerie Lechtanski, Oxford University Press, 2000

Acids, Bases, and Salts, Brian J. Knapp, Grolier Educational, Danbury, CT, 1998

Acids, Bases, and Salts (CHEMLAB), Keith Walshaw, Atlantic Europe Publishing Co., 1998

IDENTIFYING Misconceptions

Find Out What Students Think

Students may think that . . .

pH is only a measure of the degree of acidity.
From lemon juice to vinegar, examples of acids seem common in our lives. Thus it is no wonder that students think of pH in terms of acidity and may not consider the basic or alkaline components of pH.

Activity L2

Ask students to record their responses as you read each statement:

- Explain what is meant by pH.
- List three substances that are acids in water.
- List three substances that are bases in water.

Promote Understanding

Activity

Before class:

- Place 5 mL of each of the following materials into beakers: 4 drops of HCl in 5 mL of water, milk of magnesia, ammonia-based cleaner, baking soda in water, vinegar, lemon juice, and orange juice.
- Create stations with these solutions in a well-ventilated area. Have a glass rod in each beaker and a small plate at each station. Place caution signs at the HCl and ammonia-based cleaner stations. Students should wear goggles, an apron, and gloves. Have water available in case chemicals contact the body.

In class:

- Distribute goggles, aprons, and universal pH strips to each student.
- Draw a scale from 0 to 14 on the board. Directly over the number 7, write H_2O (*HOH*). Explain that a material with a pH of 7 is neutral.
- Write H^+ above the numbers 0–6 and OH^- above the numbers 8–14. Explain that solutions with a pH <7 have more H^+ ions than OH^- ions in water and are acidic. Solutions with a pH of >7 have more OH^- ions than H^+ ions in water and are basic.
- Hydrochloric acid is a very acidic material. Write *concentrated hydrochloric acid* between 0 and 1 on the scale. A very basic material is drain cleaner, with a pH of 14. Write *drain cleaner* above 14.
- Explain that students will work in groups to find materials for each number on the pH scale. Students will test materials and use their textbooks, library, and the Internet to complete the activity. Materials have already been found for pH 1, 7, 13, and 14.
- Instruct students to put the pH strip on the plate and add one drop of liquid using the stirring rod. Have them leave the pH test strips on the plates for you to dispose of later.

Assess

After completing the chapter, see *Identifying Misconceptions* in the Study Guide at the end of the chapter.

chapter 23

About the Photo

Salt Sources Salt is an essential element for most creatures on Earth, and Earth provides salt for its creatures. Natural salt sources are found all over the world, and animals flock to them. These parrots know where to get salt, as do most animals from elephants to butterflies.

Science Journal Salt is an electrolyte, an electrically charged substance, that is used by the body for such tasks as transporting nutrients in and out of cells and carrying electrical messages along the nervous system that control all of the muscles of the body, including the heart.

BIG Idea

The Self-Ionization of Water In pure water, some water molecules dissociate into hydronium (H_3O^+) and hydroxide (OH^-) ions. The equilibrium concentrations of H_3O^+ and OH^- ions both equal 10^{-7} molar, and pure water has a pH of 7. This means that about one in every 555 million water molecules has dissociated. The product of the two concentrations is always 10^{-14}, so that when an acid is added to pure water, the hydronium ion concentration increases, and the hydroxide ion concentration decreases. For example, for an acidic solution of pH 5, the concentration of H_3O^+ is 10^{-5} molar and the concentration of OH^- is 10^{-9} molar.

Introduce the Chapter Ask students how they would define an acid. Then have students give examples of acids or mixtures that contain acids. Ask them how well their definition describes their examples.

chapter 23

Acids, Bases, and Salts

BIG Idea Some substances can be classified as acids, bases, or salts.

23.1 Acids and Bases

MAIN Idea Acids produce hydronium ions (H_3O^+) in water, and bases produce hydroxide ions (OH^-) in water.

23.2 Strength of Acids and Bases

MAIN Idea Acid strength describes the ease with which an acid dissociates into ions. Acid concentration describes the amount of acid dissolved in water.

23.3 Salts

MAIN Idea An acid and a base react to form a salt and water.

The Well-Seasoned You

Salt is essential for most animals, including humans. Birds, such as these macaws, arrive each day to eat the clay at Macaw Clay Lick in Peru. In this chapter, you'll learn about salts and about the acids and bases that react to form them.

Science Journal

Research to find out why your body needs salt, then write a brief summary and identify several ways that you can safely get the salt you need.

694

Interactive Chalkboard

This CD-ROM is an editable Microsoft® PowerPoint® presentation that includes:

- an editable presentation for every chapter
- additional chapter questions
- animated graphics
- image bank
- links to gpscience.com

Start-Up Activities

The Effects of Acid Rain

Many limestone caves and rock formations are shaped by water containing carbon dioxide. Higher levels of carbon dioxide in acid rain can damage marble structures. Observe this reaction using soda water to represent acid rain and chalk, which like limestone and marble, is calcium carbonate.

1. Measure approximately 5 g of classroom chalk.
2. Crush it slightly and place it in a 100-mL beaker.
3. Add 50 mL of plain, bottled, carbonated water to the beaker.
4. After several minutes, stir the mixture.
5. When the mixture stops reacting, filter it using a paper filter in a glass funnel.
6. Dry the residue overnight and determine its mass.
7. **Think Critically** Record your observations in your Science Journal. How did the mass change? Write your conclusions about the effect of acid rain on marble buildings and monuments.

Acids, Bases, and Salts The very essence of life, DNA, is an acid. You also may be familiar with ascorbic acid, or vitamin C. Make the following Foldable to compare and contrast the characteristics of acids, bases, and salts.

STEP 1 **Fold** one sheet of paper lengthwise.

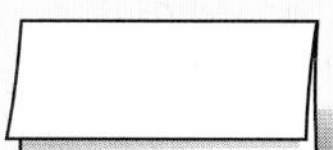

STEP 2 **Fold** into thirds.

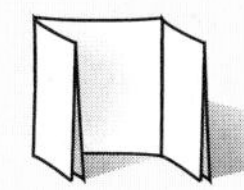

STEP 3 **Unfold** and **draw** overlapping ovals. Cut the top sheet along the folds.

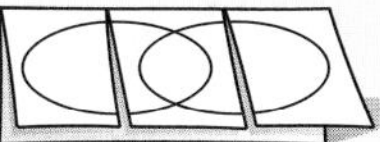

STEP 4 **Label** the ovals *Acids, Salts,* and *Bases.*

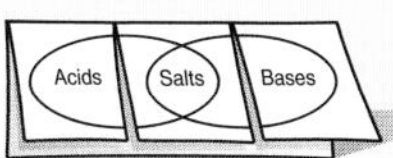

Construct a Venn Diagram As you read the chapter, list the characteristics of acids, bases, and salts under the appropriate tabs.

Preview this chapter's content and activities at gpscience.com

695

Purpose Use the Launch Lab to show evidence of a chemical reaction between the carbonic acid in soda and the base calcium carbonate. L2 IS **Kinesthetic**

Preparation Chalk pieces may be massed ahead of time and placed in beakers, each labeled with the mass of the chalk. Keep soda water sealed until immediately before use.

Materials classroom chalk, mortar and pestle to crush the chalk, several bottles of fresh soda water, 100-mL beakers, 50-mL or 100-mL graduated cylinder, funnels, filter paper

Teaching Strategies

- Provide the filter paper folded into funnels.
- The residue may be dried in the air overnight or with an electric heater.

Think Critically

The mass of the residue is less than the mass of the chalk. Acid rain can dissolve limestone.

Assessment

Oral Ask students to explain how increasing the level of acidity in rainwater would affect ancient marble sculptures. More acid in rainwater would cause marble sculptures to decompose more quickly.

Dinah Zike Study Fold

Student preparation materials for this Foldable are available in the **Chapter *Fast File* Resources.**

Additional Chapter Media

- BrainPOP *Acids and Bases*
- Video Lab: *Be a Soda Scientist*
- Virtual Lab: *How is the acidic concentration of a solution determined?*

section 1

Acids and Bases

1 Motivate

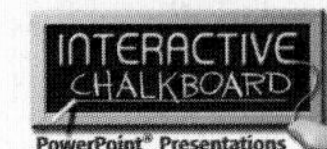

Bellringer

Section Focus Transparencies also are available on the Interactive Chalkboard CD-ROM. L2 

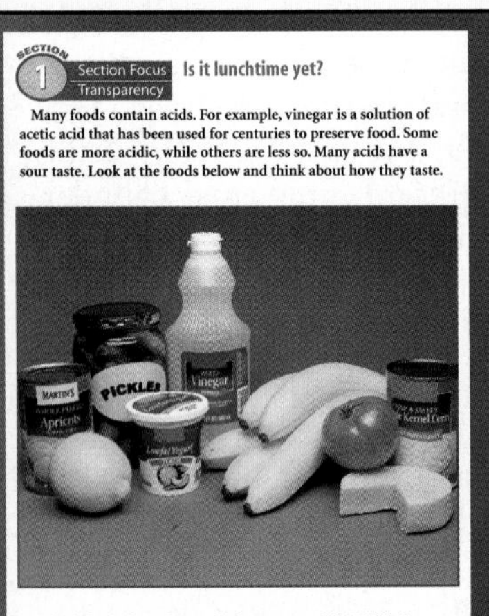
Section Focus Transparency 1 — Is it lunchtime yet?

Many foods contain acids. For example, vinegar is a solution of acetic acid that has been used for centuries to preserve food. Some foods are more acidic, while others are less so. Many acids have a sour taste. Look at the foods below and think about how they taste.

1. Which foods above do you think are more acidic? Which do you think are less acidic?
2. Form a hypothesis about how vinegar can preserve food?

L2

Tie to Prior Knowledge

Upset Stomach Ask students whether they have heard of someone using an antacid for an upset stomach. What does this indicate about the contents of our stomachs? Our stomachs must contain an acid. Medical antacid preparations typically contain weak bases. L1

Reading Guide

What You'll Learn

- **Compare and contrast** acids and bases and identify the characteristics they have.
- **Examine** some formulas and uses of common acids and bases.
- **Determine** how the process of ionization and dissociation apply to acids and bases.

Why It's Important

Acids and bases are found almost everywhere—from fruit juice and gastric juice to soaps.

Review Vocabulary

electrolyte: compound that breaks apart in water, forming charged particles (ions) that can conduct electricity

New Vocabulary

- acid
- hydronium ion
- indicator
- base

Acids

What comes to mind when you hear the word *acid?* Do you think of a substance that can burn your skin or even burn a hole through a piece of metal? Do you think about sour foods like those shown in **Figure 1?** Although some acids can burn and are dangerous to handle, most acids in foods are safe to eat. What acids have in common, however, is that they contain at least one hydrogen atom that can be removed when the acid is dissolved in water.

Figure 1 The acids in these common foods give each their distinctive sour taste.

Properties of Acids When an acid dissolves in water, some of the hydrogen is released as hydrogen ions, H^+. An **acid** is a substance that produces hydrogen ions in a water solution. It is the ability to produce these ions that gives acids their characteristic properties. When an acid dissolves in water, H^+ ions interact with water molecules to form H_3O^+ ions, which are called **hydronium ions** (hi DROH nee um • I ahnz).

Acids have several common properties. For one thing, all acids taste sour. The familiar, sour taste of many foods is due to acids. However, taste never should be used to test for the presence of acids. Some acids can damage tissue by producing painful burns. Acids are corrosive. Some acids react strongly with certain metals, seeming to eat away the metals as metallic compounds and hydrogen gas form. Acids also react with indicators to produce predictable changes in color. An **indicator** is an organic compound that changes color in acid and base. For example, the indicator litmus paper turns red in acid.

Section 1 Resource Manager

Chapter FAST FILE Resources
- Transparency Activity, pp. 44, 47–48
- Directed Reading for Content Mastery, pp. 19, 20
- Note-taking Worksheets, pp. 33–35
- MiniLAB, p. 3
- Reinforcement, p. 27
- Enrichment, p. 30
- Lab Activity, pp. 13–16

Home and Community Involvement, p. 36

Science Inquiry Labs, pp. 45–46

Common Acids Many foods contain acids. In addition to citric acid in citrus fruits, lactic acid is found in yogurt and buttermilk, and any pickled food contains vinegar, also known as acetic acid. Your stomach uses hydrochloric acid to help digest your food. At least four acids (sulfuric, phosphoric, nitric, and hydrochloric) play vital roles in industrial applications.

Reading Check *Which four acids are important for industry?*

Table 1 lists the names and formulas of a few acids, their uses, and some properties. Three acids are used to make fertilizers—most of the nitric acid and sulfuric acid and approximately 90 percent of phosphoric acid produced are used for this purpose. Many acids can burn, but sulfuric acid can burn by removing water from your skin as easily as it takes water from sugar, as shown in **Figure 2.**

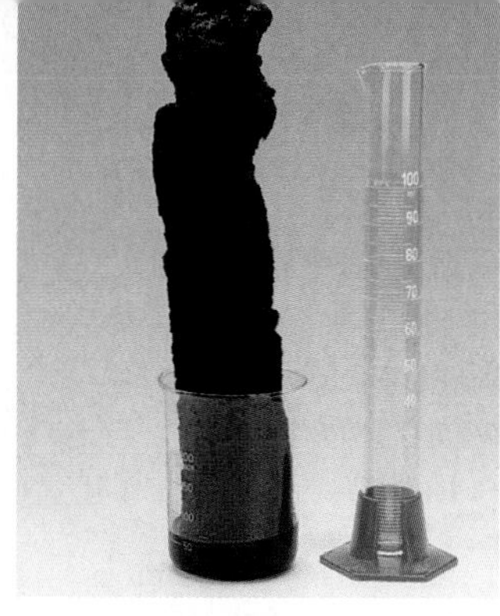

Figure 2 When sulfuric acid is added to sugar the mixture foams, removing hydrogen and oxygen atoms as water and leaving air-filled carbon.

Table 1 Common Acids and Their Uses

Name, Formula	Use	Other Information
Acetic acid, CH_3COOH	Food preservation and preparation	When in solution with water, it is known as vinegar.
Acetylsalicylic acid, $HOOC{-}C_6H_4{-}OOCCH_3$	Pain relief, fever relief, to reduce inflammation	Known as aspirin
Ascorbic acid, $H_2C_6H_6O_6$	Antioxidant, vitamin	Called vitamin C
Carbonic acid, H_2CO_3	Carbonated drinks	Involved in cave, stalactite, and stalagmite formation and acid rain
Hydrochloric acid, HCl	Digestion as gastric juice in stomach, to clean steel in a process called pickling	Commonly called muriatic acid
Nitric acid, HNO_3	To make fertilizers	Colorless, yet yellows when exposed to light
Phosphoric acid, H_3PO_4	To make detergents, fertilizers and soft drinks	Slightly sour but pleasant taste, detergents containing phosphates cause water pollution
Sulfuric acid, H_2SO_4	Car batteries, to manufacture fertilizers and other chemicals	Dehydrating agent, causes burns by removing water from cells

2 Teach

Activity

Acid Formulas Have students note the formulas of the inorganic acids listed in **Table 1.** Ask what they observe about the way formulas of these acids are typically written. Chemists commonly indicate that a compound is an acid by writing the formula with "H" as the first element. L2 IN **Logical-Mathematical**

Use Science Words

Word Meaning Have students use the word *indicator* in a sentence, and then explain how the meaning of *indicator* in their sentence parallels its meaning in the context of acid and base identification. L2 IN **Linguistic**

Visual Learning

Table 1 If an acid contains a structure that includes COOH, it is an organic acid. Other acids, including H_2CO_3, are inorganic. Have students work in small groups to classify the acids from **Table 1** as organic or inorganic. All are inorganic except acetic acid and acetylsalicylic acid. L2 IN **Linguistic**

Reading Check

Answer sulfuric, phosphoric, nitric, and hydrochloric acids

Visual Learning

Figure 2 This reaction produces irritating fumes and should not be attempted in the classroom.

Curriculum Connection

Art Etching is using the reaction between an acid and a metal to make a piece of art. Have students find out more about this process and make posters illustrating it. A metal plate, usually copper or zinc, is coated with acid-resistant resin. The artist draws lines through the resin, then puts the plate in an acid bath. The acid reacts with the metal exposed by the drawing and not through the resin. L2 P IN **Visual-Spatial**

Purpose to observe how an indicator changes color as a base is neutralized L2 ELL

LS **Kinesthetic**

Materials water, 250-mL beaker, 1 *M* HCl, universal indicator, antacid tablets, graduated cylinder, dropper

Teaching Strategy A blue or violet color may occur when the HCl is added, depending on the brand of antacid used.

Analysis

1. The color changed from red to orange to yellow to green.
2. The base neutralized the HCl, changing the color of the indicator.

Caption Answer

Figure 3 slipperiness

Quick Demo

Test a Base

Materials drain cleaner, distilled water, litmus

Estimated Time 15 minutes

Procedure Add a small amount (less than 5 mL) of drain cleaner to distilled water. Test the solution with litmus to demonstrate the base properties of the cleaner. **WARNING:** *Keep the solution out of reach of students. Dispose of it properly.* L2 ELL

LS **Visual-Spatial**

Assessment

Portfolio Have students write complete lab reports of this activity in their Science Journals. Encourage them to include both diagrams and written descriptions. Make sure they include the materials used, the procedure, and all of their observations. Use **Performance Assessment in the Science Classroom,** p. 119. P L2

Observing Acid Relief

WARNING: *Do not eat antacid tablets.*

Procedure

1. Add 150 mL of **water** to a **250-mL beaker.**
2. Add three drops **1*M* HCl** and 12 drops of **universal indicator.**
3. Observe the color of the solution.
4. Add an **antacid tablet** and observe for 15 minutes.

Analysis

1. Describe any changes that took place in the solution.
2. Explain why these changes occurred.

Bases

You might not be as familiar with bases as you are with acids. Although you can eat some foods that contain acids, you don't consume many bases. Some foods, such as egg whites, are slightly basic. Other examples of basic materials are baking powder and amines found in some foods. Medicines, such as milk of magnesia and antacids, are basic, too. Still, you come in contact with many bases every day. For example, each time you wash your hands using soap, you are using a base. One characteristic of bases is that they feel slippery, like soapy water. Bases are important in many types of cleaning materials, as shown in **Figure 3.** Bases are important in industry, also. For example, sodium hydroxide is used in the paper industry to separate fibers of cellulose from wood pulp. The freed cellulose fibers are made into paper.

Bases can be defined in two ways. Any substance that forms hydroxide ions, OH^-, in a water solution is a **base.** In addition, a base is any substance that accepts H^+ from acids. The definitions are related, because the OH^- ions produced by some bases do accept H^+ ions.

Properties of Bases One way to think about bases is as the complements, or opposites, of acids. Although acids and bases share some common features, the bases have their own characteristic properties. In the pure, undissolved state, many bases are crystalline solids. In solution, bases feel slippery and have a bitter taste. Like strong acids, strong bases are corrosive, and contact with skin can result in severe burns. Therefore, taste and touch never should be used to test for the presence of a base. Finally, like acids, bases react with indicators to produce changes in color. The indicator litmus turns blue in bases.

Figure 3 Bases are commonly found in many cleaning products used around the home.
Identify *the property of bases evident in soaps.*

Teacher FYI

Base Attractions All bases attract H^+ to a pair of unshared electrons in their structures. OH^- ions have a negative charge, which helps attract positive H^+ ions. Bases containing nitrogen have an unshared pair of electrons around the nitrogen. Typically, nitrogen-containing bases are not as strong as OH^--containing bases.

Figure 4 Two applications of bases are shown here.

Aluminum hydroxide is a base used in water-treatment plants. Its sticky surface collects impurities, making them easier to filter from the water.

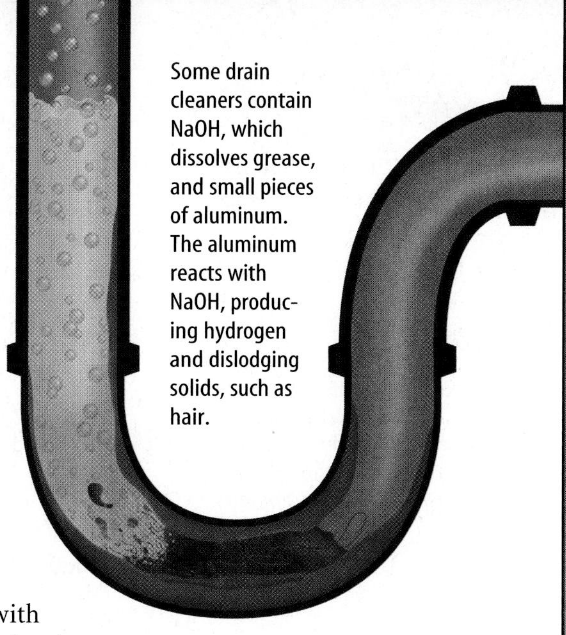

Some drain cleaners contain NaOH, which dissolves grease, and small pieces of aluminum. The aluminum reacts with NaOH, producing hydrogen and dislodging solids, such as hair.

Common Bases You probably are familiar with many common bases because they are found in cleaning products used in the home. These and some other bases are shown in **Table 2,** which also includes their uses and some information about them. **Figure 4** shows two uses of bases that you might not be familiar with.

Table 2 Common Bases and Their Uses

Name, Formula	Use	Other Information
Aluminum hydroxide, $Al(OH)_3$	Color-fast fabrics, antacid, water purification as shown in **Figure 4**	Sticky gel that collects suspended clay and dirt particles on its surface
Calcium hydroxide, $Ca(OH)_2$	Leather-making, mortar and plaster, lessen acidity of soil	Called caustic lime
Magnesium hydroxide, $Mg(OH)_2$	Laxative, antacid	Called milk of magnesia when in water
Sodium hydroxide, NaOH	To make soap, oven cleaner drain cleaner, textiles, and paper	Called lye and caustic soda; generates heat (exothermic) when combined with water, reacts with metals to form hydrogen
Ammonia, NH_3	Cleaners, fertilizer, to make rayon and nylon	Irritating odor that is damaging to nasal passages and lungs

IDENTIFYING Misconceptions

OH Bases Most of the bases examined in this section have OH bonded to a metal. Students may have seen the OH symbols connected to other compounds called alcohols. This does not make alcohols fit the definition of a base. The —OH in an alcohol is called a hydroxyl group and is not the same thing as the hydroxide ion, OH^-.

Fun Fact

The formula for caffeine, the stimulant found in coffee, tea, and many soft drinks, is $C_8H_{10}N_4O_2$. Caffeine is a weak acid with a pH of 6.9. Caffeinated beverages may stimulate the secretion of stomach acid, which may worsen ulcer symptoms.

Use an Analogy

Football Pass In a football game, a quarterback holding the ball cannot complete a pass unless a receiver catches the ball. An H^+ ion from an acid is like the football. The quarterback (the acid) must have a receiver (the base) to receive the football (the H^+ ion) to complete the pass (the reaction between the acid and the base). This could be demonstrated in class with a foam football labeled H^+. L1 ELL **Kinesthetic**

Differentiated Instruction

Challenge Amino acids make up the building blocks of proteins. Write out the structure of the amino acid glycine, NH_2CH_2 COOH. Ask students to identify the areas of the molecule that cause it to have acidic properties. The H at the end of COOH can be donated to produce H^+ ions. Also ask students to look for another area that allows it to have base properties. The N atom has unshared electrons that can attract and accept H^+ ions, as bases do. L3 **Logical-Mathematical**

Acidic Stings HCOOH, or formic acid, has the simplest structure of the organic acids. One of the first preparations of this acid included the crushing and heating of ants and the recovery of the vapor that contained the acid.

Discussion

Natural Acids and Bases Talk about other examples of acids and bases in nature. Students may not know of specific examples, but the discussion could focus on logical possibilities such as defense mechanisms.

Make a Model

Ionization To illustrate the dissociation that takes place when an acid is dissolved in water, have students hold a capped ink pen in the right hand. On your signal, have them use the left hand to remove the cap and cover it in that hand. In this model, water (the left hand) detaches H^+ (the pen cap) from an acid (the pen) and surrounds and holds it. This same process takes place with billions of acid molecules as they dissociate in water. L1 ELL LS **Kinesthetic**

Visual Learning

Figure 5 With students, review the two parts of the illustration. Draw a diagram on the chalkboard showing how hydrogen chloride gas molecules form hydronium ions in water. Draw a similar diagram for formic acid. L2 LS **Visual-Spatial**

Reading Check

Answer NH_3 removes H^+ from water to leave behind OH^- ions and form NH_4^+.

Acidic Stings *Some ants add sting to their bite by injecting a solution of formic acid. In fact, formic acid was named for ants, which make up the genus Formica.* Still, ants are considered tasty treats by many animals. For example, one woodpecker called a *flicker has saliva that is basic enough to take the sting out of ants.*

Solutions of Acids and Bases

Many of the products that rely on the chemistry of acids and bases are solutions, such as the cleaning products and food products mentioned previously. Because of its polarity, water is the main solvent in these products.

Dissociation of Acids You have learned that substances such as HCl, HNO_3, and H_2SO_4 are acids because of their ability to produce hydrogen ions (H^+) in water. *When an acid dissolves in water, the negative areas of nearby water molecules attract the positive hydrogen in the acid.* The acid dissociates—or separates—into ions and the hydrogen atom combines with a water molecule to form hydronium ions (H_3O^+). Therefore, an acid can more accurately be described as a compound that produces hydronium ions when dissolved in water. This process is shown in **Figure 5.**

Dissociation of Bases Compounds that can form hydroxide ions (OH^-) in water are classified as bases. If you look at **Table 2,** you will find that most of the substances listed contain –OH in their formulas. *When bases that contain –OH dissolve in water, the negative areas of nearby water molecules attract the positive ion in the base.* The positive areas of nearby water molecules attract the –OH of the base. *The base dissociates into a positive ion and a negative ion—a hydroxide ion (OH^-).* This process also is shown in **Figure 5.** Unlike acid dissociation, *water molecules do not combine with the ions formed from the base.*

$$NaOH(s) \xrightarrow{H_2O} Na^+(aq) + OH^-(aq)$$

Figure 5 Acids and bases are classified by the ions they produce when they dissolve in water. Acids produce hydronium ions in water. Bases produce hydroxide ions in water.

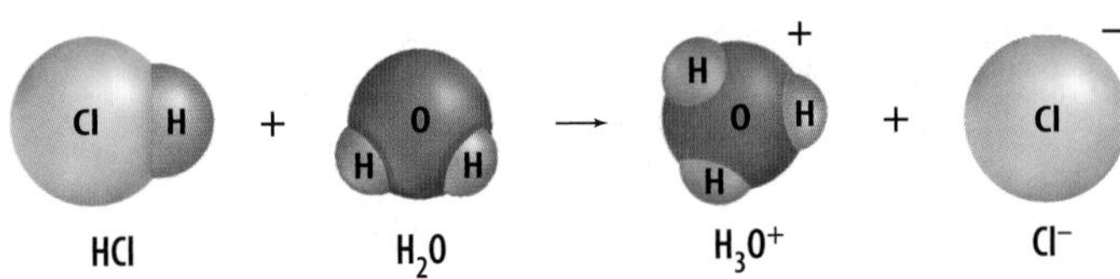

When hydrogen chloride dissolves in water, a hydronium ion and a chloride ion are produced.

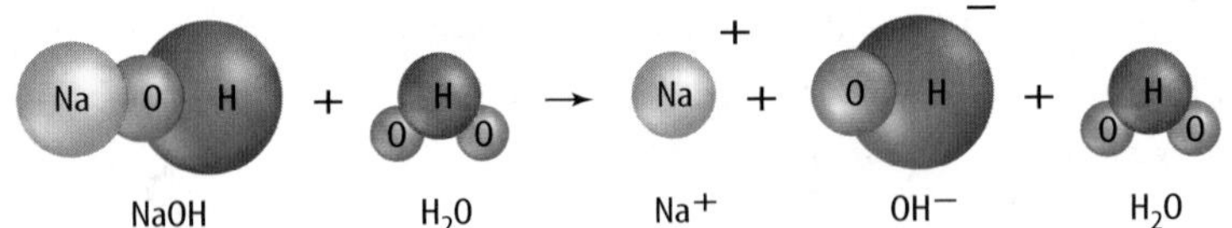

When sodium hydroxide dissolves in water, a sodium ion and a hydroxide ion are produced.

Science Journal

Oil of Vitriol Sulfate compounds used to be called vitriols because the compounds look glassy. The old name for sulfuric acid was *oil of vitriol.* The words *vitriol* and *vitriolic* have taken on broader meanings. Ask students to write the meaning of *vitriol* in their Science Journals and explain how it is connected to sulfuric acid. *Vitriol* means "something caustic," or "virulence of feeling or speech." L2

Differentiated Instruction

Visually Impaired Figure 5 is referred to several times in the teaching suggestions; therefore, this figure should be made accessible to visually impaired students. Bring models of the molecules in the figure and have sighted students work with visually impaired students to clarify the structures.

Figure 6 Ammonia reacts with water to produce some hydroxide ions, therefore, it is a base.

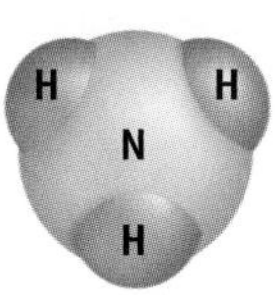

+

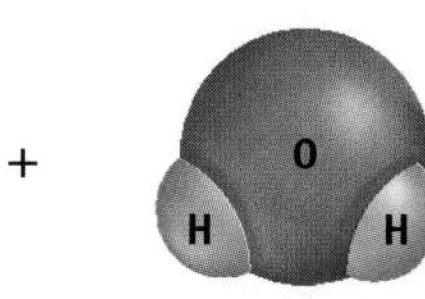

→

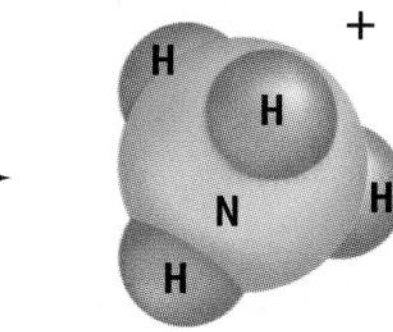

+

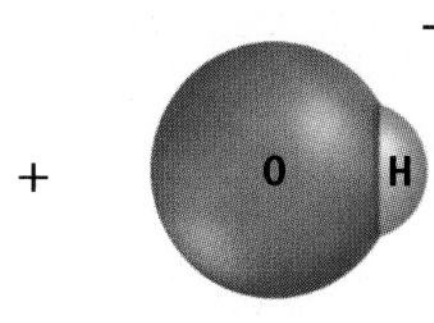

Ammonia Ammonia is a base that does not contain −OH. In a water solution, dissociation takes place when the ammonia molecule attracts a hydrogen ion from a water molecule, forming an ammonium ion (NH_4^+). This leaves a hydroxide ion (OH^-), as shown in **Figure 6.**

Reading Check *How does ammonia react in a water solution?*

Ammonia is a common household cleaner. However, products containing ammonia never should be used with other cleaners that contain chlorine (sodium hypochlorite), such as some bathroom bowl cleaners and bleach. A reaction between sodium hypochlorite and ammonia produces the toxic gases hydrazine and chloramine. Breathing these gases can severely damage lung tissues and cause death.

Solutions of both acids and bases produce some ions that are capable of carrying electric current to some extent. Thus, they are said to be electrolytes.

Science Online

Topic: Cleaner Chemistry

Visit gpscience.com for Web links to information about the dangers of mixing ammonia cleaners with chlorine or hydrochloric acid cleaners.

Activity Visit the cleaning products and laundry sections of the grocery store. Read the labels on several products. Make a list of products that include warnings on the labels and those that do not. Share your findings with the class.

section 1 review

Summary

Acids

- Acids, when dissolved in water, release H^+, which forms hydronium ions (H_3O^+).
- Acids are sour tasting, corrosive, and reactive with indicators.

Bases

- Bases, when dissolved in water, form OH^-.
- Bases exist as crystals in the solid state, are slippery, have a bitter taste, are corrosive, and are reactive with indicators.

Solutions of Acids and Bases

- The polar nature of water allows acids and bases to dissolve in water.
- Dissociation is the separation of substances, such as acids and bases, into ions in water.

Self Check

1. **Identify** three important acids and three important bases and describe their uses.
2. **Describe** an indicator.
3. **Predict** what metallic compound forms when sulfuric acid reacts with magnesium metal.
4. **Infer** If an acid donates H^+ and a base produces OH^-, what compound is likely to be produced when acids react with bases?
5. **Think Critically** Vinegar contains acetic acid, CH_3COOH. Is acetic acid organic or inorganic? How do you know?

Applying Math

6. **Calculate** the molecular weight of acetylsalicylic acid, $C_9H_8O_4$.

Science Online gpscience.com/self_check_quiz

3 Assess

DAILY INTERVENTION

Check for Understanding

Linguistic Conduct a discussion about the properties of acids and bases by going around the room and having each student make a true statement about what they've learned in this section. L2

Reteach

Litmus Test Provide several unlabeled dilute solutions of acids and bases. Give students litmus paper to test the solutions to determine which are acids and which are bases. Litmus is red in an acid and blue in a base. L2 LS **Visual-Spatial**

Assessment

Performance Ask students to write the balanced chemical equation for the reaction of an aqueous solution of ammonia with vapors of hydrogen chloride. $NH_4OH + HCl \rightarrow NH_4Cl + H_2O$. Use **Performance Assessment in the Science Classroom,** p. 101. L2

section 1 review

1. Accept all reasonable responses.
2. an organic compound that changes color in acid or base
3. magnesium sulfate
4. HOH, which is water
5. Acetic acid is organic. It has a COOH group.
6. 180.16

section 2

Strength of Acids and Bases

Reading Guide

What You'll Learn
- **Determine** what is responsible for the strength of an acid or a base.
- **Compare and contrast** strength and concentration.
- **Examine** the relationship between pH and acid or base strength.
- **Examine** electrical conductivity.

Why It's Important
Understanding the strength of acids and bases helps you use them safely.

Review Vocabulary
acid strength: the ability of an acid to dissociate completely

New Vocabulary
- strong acid
- weak acid
- strong base
- weak base
- pH
- buffer

Strong and Weak Acids and Bases

Some acids must be handled with great care. For example, sulfuric acid found in car batteries can burn your finger, yet you drink acids such as citric acid in orange juice and carbonic acid in soft drinks. Obviously, some acids are stronger than others. One measure of acid strength is the ability to dissociate in solution.

The strength of an acid or base depends on how many acid or base particles dissociate into ions in water. When a **strong acid** dissolves in water, nearly all the acid molecules dissociate into ions. HCl, HNO_3, and H_2SO_4 are examples of strong acids. When a **weak acid** dissolves in water, only a small fraction of the molecules dissolve in water. Acetic acid and carbonic acid are examples of weak acids.

Ions in solution can conduct an electric current. The more ions a solution contains, the more current it can conduct. The ability of a solution to conduct a current can be demonstrated using a lightbulb connected to a battery with leads placed in the solution, as shown in **Figure 7.** The strong acid solution conducts more current and the lightbulb burns brightly. The weak acid solution does not conduct as much current as a strong acid solution and the bulb burns less brightly.

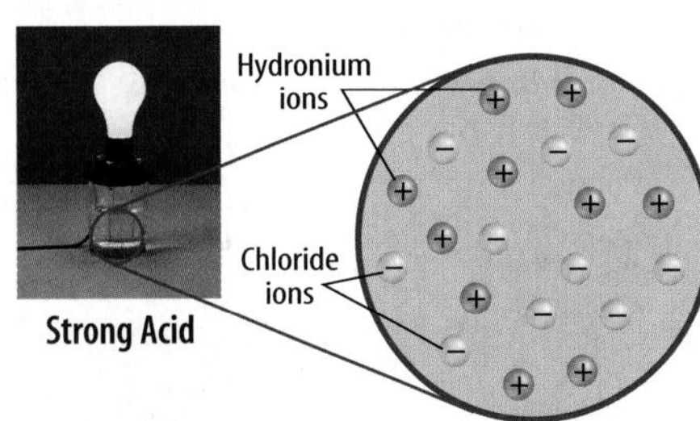

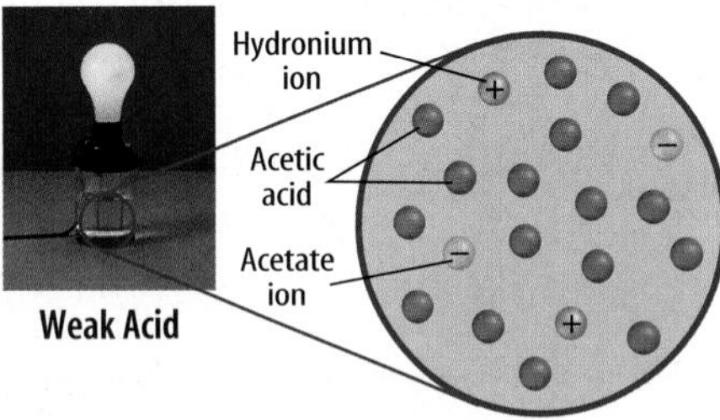

Figure 7 Nearly all molecules of HCl, a strong acid, dissociate into ions in water. The bulb burns brightly. Only a few molecules of acetic acid, a weak acid, dissociate. The bulb is dimmer.

1 Motivate

Bellringer

Section Focus Transparencies also are available on the Interactive Chalkboard CD-ROM.

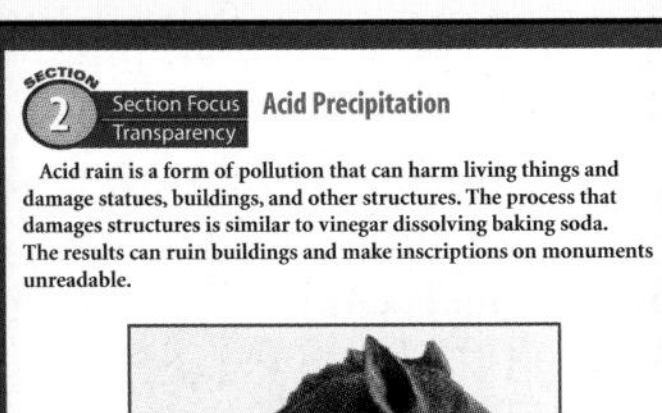

Section 2 Section Focus Transparency — Acid Precipitation

Acid rain is a form of pollution that can harm living things and damage statues, buildings, and other structures. The process that damages structures is similar to vinegar dissolving baking soda. The results can ruin buildings and make inscriptions on monuments unreadable.

1. What do you think happens when acid rain washes over cement?
2. How might acid rain harm living things?

L2

Tie to Prior Knowledge

Acid Strength Ask students to name acids they have encountered that weren't harmful and acids that were. Possible answers: Fruit juices with weak acids are not harmful; battery acid is harmful. Tell students that in this section, they will learn why some acids are stronger than others. L2

Section 2 Resource Manager

Chapter *Fast File* Resources
- Transparency Activity, p. 45
- Directed Reading for Content Mastery, p. 20
- Enrichment, p. 31
- Lab Activity, pp. 9–11
- Reinforcement, p. 28
- Lab Worksheet, pp. 5–6

Physical Science Critical Thinking/Problem Solving, p. 16

Strong and Weak Acids Equations describing dissociation can be written in two ways. In strong acids, such as HCl, nearly all the acid dissociates. This is shown by writing the equation using a single arrow pointing toward the ions that are formed.

$$HCl(g) + H_2O(l) \rightarrow H_3O^+(aq) + Cl^-(aq)$$

Almost 100 percent of the particles in solution are H_3O^+ and Cl^- ions, and only a negligible number of HCl molecules are present.

Equations describing the dissociation of weak acids, such as acetic acid, are written using double arrows pointing in opposite directions. This means that only some of the CH_3COOH dissociates and the reaction does not go to completion.

$$CH_3COOH(l) + H_2O(l) \rightleftharpoons H_3O^+(aq) + CH_3COO^-(aq)$$

In an acetic acid solution, most of the particles are CH_3COOH molecules, and only a few CH_3COO^- and H^+ ions are in solution.

Strong and Weak Bases Remember that many bases are ionic compounds that dissociate to produce ions when they dissolve. A **strong base** dissociates completely in solution. The following equation shows the dissociation of sodium hydroxide, a strong base.

$$NaOH(s) \rightarrow Na^+(aq) + OH^-(aq)$$

The dissociation of ammonia, which is a weak base, is shown using double arrows to indicate that not all the ammonia ionizes. A **weak base** is one that does not dissociate completely.

$$NH_3(aq) + H_2O(l) \rightleftharpoons NH_4^+(aq) + OH^-(aq)$$

Because ammonia produces only a few ions and most of the ammonia remains in the form of NH_3, ammonia is a weak base.

Strength and Concentration Sometimes, when talking about acids and bases, the terms *strength* and *concentration* can be confused. The terms *strong* and *weak* are used to classify acids and bases. The terms refer to the ease with which an acid or base dissociates in solution. *Strong* acids and bases dissociate completely; *weak* acids and bases dissociate only partially. In contrast, the terms *dilute* and *concentrated* are used to indicate the concentration of a solution, which is the amount of acid or base dissolved in the solution. It is possible to have dilute solutions of strong acids and bases and concentrated solutions of weak acids and bases, as shown in **Figure 8.**

Figure 8 You can have a dilute solution of a strong acid and a concentrated solution of a weak acid.

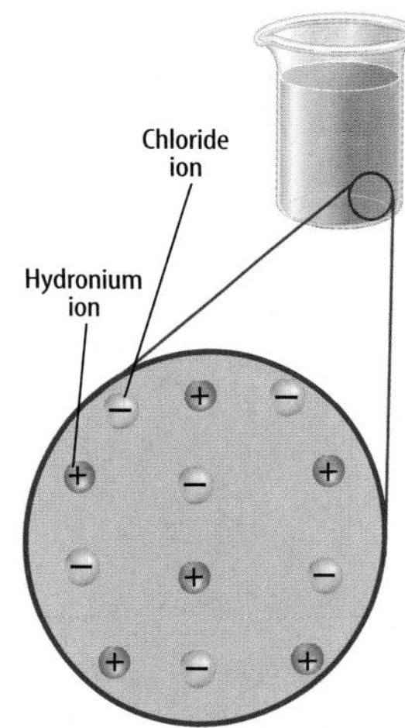

This is a dilute solution of HCl.

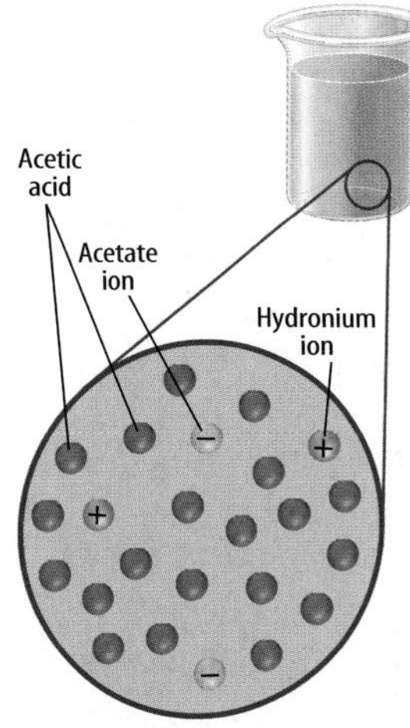

This is a concentrated solution of acetic acid.

2 Teach

Fun Fact

Hydrochloric acid is essential for digestion and is secreted by the lining of the stomach in quantities of 1.2 to 1.5 L per day.

IDENTIFYING Misconceptions

Strong Disconnect In connection with acid, the word *strong* means that the acid forms ions easily. Some students may confuse the concept, thinking it is a contradiction to use the word *strong* with something that comes apart easily.

Use Science Words

Word Usage Have students complete the following sentence: A ___________ will ionize only to a small extent because its molecules have a strong hold on their H atoms. weak acid L1 ELL IS

Virtual Labs

Titrations *How is the acidic concentration of a solution determined?*

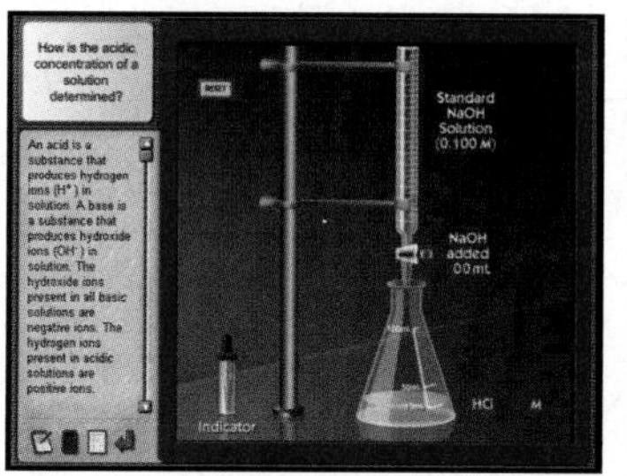

Teacher FYI

Logarithmic Value The value of pH is based on a logarithmic scale. Each unit increment is a tenfold change in hydrogen ion concentration. So, if one solution has a pH of 3 and another has a pH of 2, the second is 10 times more acidic than the first.

Differentiated Instruction

English-Language Learners The difference between ionization and dissociation is subtle. Review these terms by stressing that ionization happens when nonionic substances break apart, interact with water, and produce ions. Dissociation is the separation of ionic substances, such as a salt. Use a model to visually represent these concepts. ELL

Activity

Measure pH Provide samples, other than those shown in **Figure 9,** with which students can measure pH using universal pH paper. Examples may include spoiled milk, lemon juice, soap solutions, and dissolved antacids. L2 ELL IS **Visual-Spatial**

Quick Demo

Examine pH Changes

Materials indicator paper (litmus or universal), vinegar, milk of magnesia, pH meter

Estimated Time 20 minutes

Procedure Use litmus paper or universal indicator paper to show that vinegar has an acidic pH value. Then add a small amount of milk of magnesia to the vinegar. Check the pH again to see whether it has changed. As the milk of magnesia is added, OH^- is brought into the solution. OH^- ions react with the H_3O^+ ions, so the pH should rise. Continue adding milk of magnesia until this effect is noticed on the pH indicator. If one is available, do this demonstration with a pH meter. L2 ELL IS **Visual-Spatial**

IDENTIFYING Misconceptions

Degree of Acidity Students may think that pH is only a measure of degree of acidity. See page F at the beginning of this chapter for teaching strategies that address this misconception.

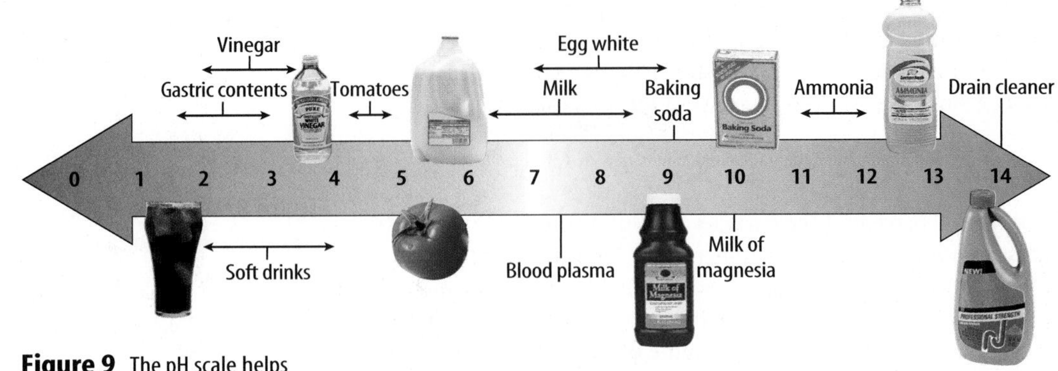

Figure 9 The pH scale helps classify solutions as acidic or basic.

pH of a Solution

If you have a swimming pool or keep tropical fish, you know that the pH of the water must be controlled. Also, many products such as shampoos claim to control pH so it suits your type of hair. The **pH** of a solution is a measure of the concentration of H^+ ions in it. The greater the H^+ concentration is, the lower the pH is and the more acidic the solution is. The pH measures how acidic or basic a solution is. To indicate pH, a scale ranging from 0 to 14 has been devised, as shown in **Figure 9.**

As the scale shows, solutions with a pH lower than 7 are described as acidic, and the lower the value is, the more acidic the solution is. Solutions with a pH greater than 7 are basic, and the higher the pH is, the more basic the solution is. A solution with a pH of exactly 7 indicates that the concentrations of H^+ ions and OH^- ions are equal. These solutions are considered neutral. Pure water at 25°C has a pH of 7.

One way to determine pH is by using a universal indicator paper. This paper undergoes a color change in the presence of H_3O^+ ions and OH^- ions in solution. The final color of the pH paper is matched with colors in a chart to find the pH, as shown in **Figure 10.** Is this an accurate way to determine pH?

An instrument called a pH meter is another tool to determine the pH of a solution. This meter is operated by immersing the electrodes in the solution to be tested and reading the dial. Small, battery-operated pH meters with digital readouts are precise and convenient for use outside the laboratory when testing the pH of soils and streams, as shown in **Figure 10.**

Figure 10 The pH of a sample can be measured in several ways. Indicator paper gives an approximate value quickly, however, a pH meter is quick and more precise.

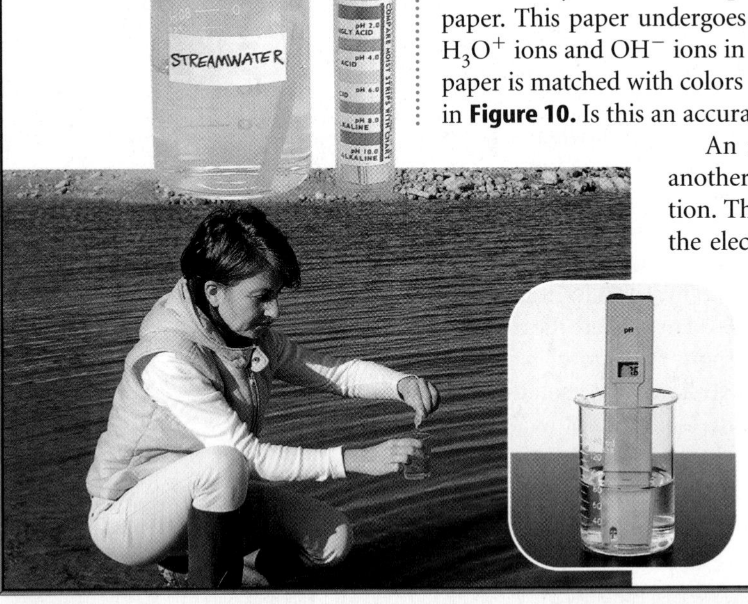

Science Journal

Sour Milk Have students describe the changes in pH that occur in milk as it spoils. They may need to examine the process in a nutrition reference or biology source. Lactose, commonly called milk sugar, is changed through bacterial action into lactic acid. This change lowers the pH of the solution. L2 IS **Logical-Mathematical**

Differentiated Instruction

Challenge Have students write chemical equations that show HCO_3^- acting to neutralize the addition of OH^- ions and the addition of H^+ ions. This would show how one of the blood buffers works. $HCO_3^- + OH^- \rightarrow H_2O + CO_3^{2-}$; $HCO_3^- + H^+ \rightarrow H_2CO_3$ L3 IS **Logical-Mathematical**

Blood pH Your blood circulates throughout your body carrying oxygen, removing carbon dioxide, and absorbing nutrients from food that you have eaten. In order to carry out its many functions properly, the pH of blood must remain between 7.0 and 7.8. The main reason for this is that enzymes, the protein molecules that act as catalysts for many reactions in the body, cannot work outside this pH range. Yet you can eat foods that are acidic without changing the pH of your blood. How can this be? The answer is that your blood contains compounds called buffers that enable small amounts of acids or bases to be absorbed without harmful effects.

Buffers are solutions containing ions that react with additional acids or bases to minimize their effects on pH. One buffer system in blood involves bicarbonate ions, HCO_3^-. Because of these buffer systems, small amounts of even concentrated acid will not change pH much, as shown in **Figure 11.** Buffers help keep your blood close to a nearly constant pH of 7.4.

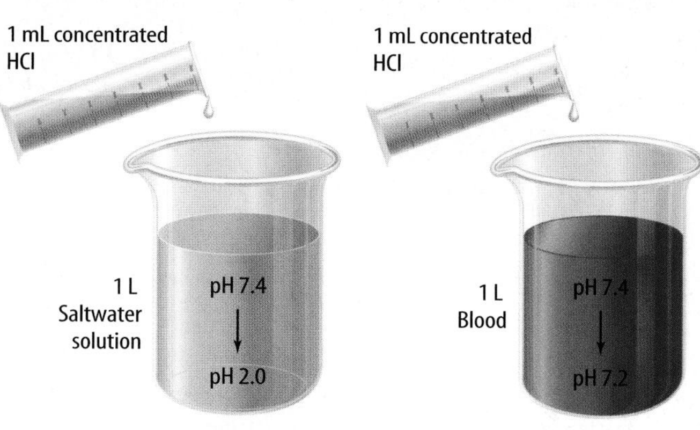

Figure 11 This experiment shows how well blood plasma acts as a buffer. Adding 1 mL of concentrated HCl to 1 L of salt water changes the pH from 7.4 to 2.0. Adding the same amount of concentrated HCl to 1 L of blood plasma changes the pH from 7.4 to 7.2.

What are buffers and how are they important for health?

section 2 review

Summary

Strong and Weak Acids and Bases

- When strong acids dissolve in water, nearly all the acid molecules dissociate into ions. When weak acids dissolve in water, few molecules dissociate.
- When strong bases dissolve in water, nearly all base particles dissociate. When weak bases dissove, only a few particles dissociate.
- Ions in solution can conduct electricity.
- Strength refers to the ability of an acid or base to dissociate in water; concentration refers to how much acid or base is in solution.

pH of a Solution

- pH describes a substance as acidic or basic.
- Buffers are substances that minimize the effects of an acid or base on pH.

Self Check

1. **Describe** what determines the strength of an acid. A base?
2. **Explain** how to make a dilute solution of a strong acid.
3. **Explain** how electricity can be conducted by solutions.
4. **Describe** pH values of 9.1, 1.2, and 5.7 as basic, acidic, or very acidic.
5. **Think Critically** The proper pH range for a swimming pool is between 7.2 and 7.8. Most pools use two substances, Na_2CO_3 and HCl, to maintain this range. How would you adjust the pH if you found it was 8.2? 6.9?

Applying Math

6. **Use Equations** To determine the difference in pH strength, calculate 10^n, where n = difference between pHs. How much more acidic is a solution of pH 2.4 than a solution of pH 4.4?

Reading Check

Answer Buffers are solutions containing ions that react with acids or bases to minimize their effects. This is important because our blood needs to maintain a pH of about 7.4.

3 Assess

DAILY INTERVENTION

Check for Understanding

Visual-Spatial Bring in a can of frozen orange juice and a gallon container. Explain to the students that the orange juice in the can is a concentrated form (more OJ per unit of water), then add water and explain that the orange juice is now diluted (less OJ per same unit of water). To reinforce the concept, on the blackboard, draw diagrams similar to **Figure 8** illustrating dilute and concentrated forms of the orange juice.

Reteach

Acid Strength Place a small piece of magnesium ribbon in a petri dish and add a few drops of 1*M* HCl. **WARNING:** *Wear goggles, an apron, and gloves when working with HCl.* Note that the reaction produces hydrogen gas. Repeat the activity with another small piece of magnesium metal, but use a few drops of 1*M* acetic acid. Ask which is a strong acid and which is a weak acid. The HCl is a strong acid because it reacts with magnesium to produce more hydrogen than acetic acid does. L2 LS **Visual-Spatial**

section 2 review

1. The strength of an acid is determined by its ability to produce H^+ ions in solution. The strength of a base is determined by its ability to produce OH^- ions in solution.
2. You can dilute hydrochloric acid, a strong acid, by adding a small amount of acid to a much larger amount of water.
3. An ionic compound breaks into its ions, which conduct electricity.
4. 9.1–basic; 1.2–very acidic; 5.7–acidic
5. pH of 8.2–add HCl; pH of 6.9–add Na_2CO_3
6. $4.4 - 2.4 = 2.0$
   $10^2 = 100$

Assessment

Oral Sometimes soil pH must be changed to encourage plant growth. Ask students whether adding $Ca(OH)_2$, sometimes referred to as slaked lime, would raise or lower the pH of soil. The OH^- ions released by $Ca(OH)_2$ would raise the pH. Use **PASC,** p. 89. L2

Real-World Question

Purpose Students will test several substances and rank the relative acid concentration by the color of the indicator. L2

Process Skills Lab techniques, observe, sequence, draw conclusions

Time Required 30 minutes

Procedure

Alternative Materials Other common acidic substances such as vinegar, catsup, soda pop

Safety Precautions Have students wash hands after the experiment.

Teaching Strategies

- Prepare the indicator ahead of class according to the following recipe. Fill a glass quart jar with uncooked purple cabbage leaves that have been torn into small pieces. Heat distilled water to boiling, then fill the jar with the cabbage. Allow to cool to room temperature. Pour the cooled cabbage solution through a tea strainer into a second container and discard the cabbage leaves.
- Acids turn this indicator red, bases turn it green.

Conclude and Apply

1. yes, shades of red
2. Each substance has a different acid concentration.
3. Actual rank (most concentrated to least) is fruit preservative, cream of tartar, alum. Students may rank least to most concentrated if they interpret the colors in reverse sequence.
4. Sodium hydroxide is a base, so the indicator would turn green. Students may indicate simply a different color.

Acid Concentrations

Real-World Question

The science of acids and bases is not practiced only in a high-tech laboratory by degreed scientists. You can investigate the acidic concentrations of things in your own home using a simple home-made indicator solution. How can you tell if a substance is a strong or weak acid?

Goals

- **Determine** the relative concentrations of common acid substances.

Materials

home-made cabbage indicator (indicates both acids and bases)
coffee filter
wax paper
grease pencil or masking tape
teaspoons (3)
alum
cream of tartar
fruit preservative

Safety Precautions

Procedure

1. Use the grease pencil or masking tape and a pencil to label three areas on the wax paper *alum, cream of tartar,* and *fruit preservative.* These areas should be about 8 cm apart.
2. Place approximately 1/2 teaspoon of each of the three powders on the wax paper where labeled. Use a separate teaspoon for each substance.
3. Cut three strips from the coffee filter, about 1 cm wide by 8 cm long.
4. Dip the end of one of the strips into the cabbage indicator solution, then lay the wet end on top of the alum.
5. Wet a second strip and lay it in on top of the cream of tartar.
6. Wet the third strip and lay on top of the fruit preservative.
7. Wait 5 minutes, then check the indicator strips and record your observations.

Conclude and Apply

1. Determine if all three substances were acids. Did the indicator strips turn a similar color?
2. Explain why each substance produced a different color.
3. Propose a possible rank of the concentrations.
4. Predict what you would have observed if you used sodium hydroxide instead of alum.

Communicating Your Data

Compare your results with other groups in the class. Discuss any differences in the results you obtained.

Assessment

Process This investigation indicated the relative concentration of several acids. Using these results, can you draw conclusions about the strength of the acids? No reliable conclusion can be made. Concentration and strength are independent of each other. L2

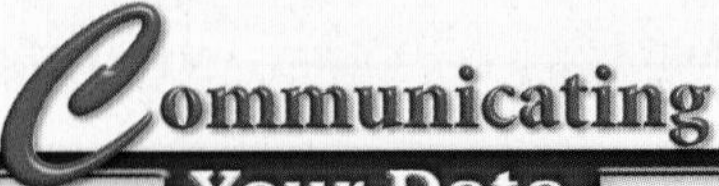

Communicating Your Data

Conduct a discussion of the results and possible differences in outcomes. L2

section 3

Salts

Reading Guide

What You'll Learn
- **Identify** a neutralization reaction.
- **Determine** what a salt is and how salts form.
- **Compare and contrast** soaps and detergents.
- **Examine** how esters are made and what they are used for.

Why It's Important
You need salt to live and soaps and detergents to keep yourself and your clothing clean.

Review Vocabulary
ester: organic compounds made from acids and alcohols

New Vocabulary
- neutralization
- salt
- titration
- soap

Neutralization

Advertisements for antacids claim that these products neutralize the excess stomach acid that causes indigestion. Normally, gastric juice contains a dilute solution of hydrochloric acid. Too much acid can produce discomfort. Antacids contain bases or other compounds containing sodium, potassium, calcium, magnesium, or aluminum that react with acids to lower acid concentration. **Figure 12** shows what happens when you take an antacid tablet containing sodium bicarbonate—$NaHCO_3$. The equation is:

$$HCl(aq) + NaHCO_3(s) \rightarrow NaCl(aq) + CO_2(g) + H_2O(l)$$

In this case, the acid (HCl) is neutralized by the base ($NaHCO_3$).

Neutralization is a chemical reaction between an acid and a base that takes place in a water solution. For example, when HCl is neutralized by NaOH, hydronium ions from the acid combine with hydroxide ions from the base to produce neutral water.

$$H_3O^+(aq) + OH^- \rightarrow 2H_2O(l)$$

Salt Formation The equation above accounts for only half of the ions in the solution. The remaining ions react to form a salt. A **salt** is a compound formed when the negative ions from an acid combine with the positive ions from a base. In the reaction between HCl and NaOH the salt formed in water solution is sodium chloride.

$$Na^+(aq) + Cl^-(aq) \rightarrow NaCl(aq)$$

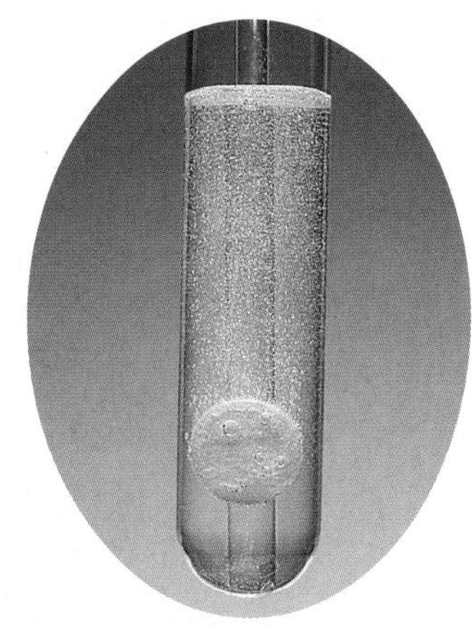

Figure 12 An antacid tablet reacts in your stomach much as it does in this dilute HCl. Usually, people chew antacid tablets before swallowing them. **Explain** *how this would affect the rate of the reaction.*

1 Motivate

Bellringer

Section Focus Transparencies also are available on the Interactive Chalkboard CD-ROM. L2 

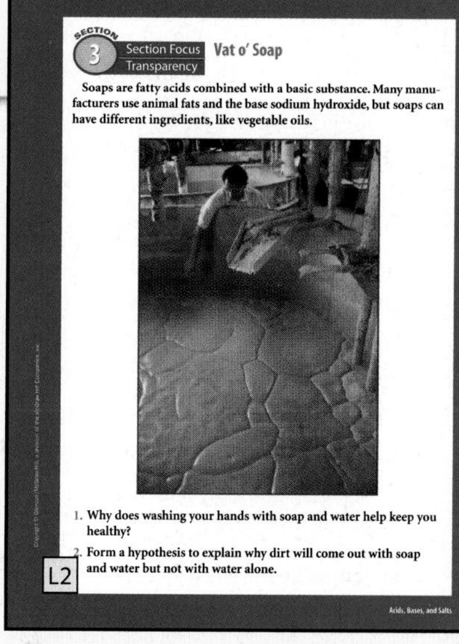

Tie to Prior Knowledge

Antacids Bring several antacid medications to class and show students the labels. Ask them which acid is being neutralized when a person uses an antacid. HCl L2

Caption Answer

Figure 12 It would speed it up by providing more surface area, allowing more of the antacid to come in contact quickly with stomach acid.

Section 3 Resource Manager

Chapter *FAST FILE* Resources
- Transparency Activity, pp. 46, 47–48
- Directed Reading for Content Mastery, pp. 21, 22
- Enrichment, p. 32
- MiniLAB, p. 4
- Reinforcement, p. 29

Physical Science Critical Thinking/Problem Solving, p. 15
Mathematics Skill Activities, p. 1
Cultural Diversity, p. 37
Performance Assessment in the Science Classroom, p. 40

2 Teach

Quick Demo

Produce a Salt

Materials zinc metal piece, HCl (5 mL, 1*M*), 2 test tubes, wood splint

Estimated Time 15 minutes

Procedure Place a pea-size piece of zinc metal in a medium-sized test tube. Add about 5 mL of 0.1*M* HCl to the zinc metal. **WARNING:** *Handle HCl with care. Wear goggles, an apron, and gloves.* Using a test-tube holder, invert another test tube over the first to collect the gas (H_2) that is generated. Then bring a glowing splint near the mouth of the second tube. The hydrogen will give a small "bark" as the hydrogen and oxygen react. **WARNING:** *Wear goggles, ensure that students wear goggles, and demonstrate a safe distance from students.* Ask students to balance the equation and name the salt that is produced. $Zn + 2HCl \rightarrow H_2 + ZnCl_2$; zinc chloride L3

LS **Logical-Mathematical**

Discussion

Base/Acid Prediction Ask students to use the information in **Table 3** to predict the acid and base that most likely produced each salt.

$NaCl$: $NaOH$; HCl
$NaHCO_3$: $NaOH$; H_2CO_3
$CaCO_3$: $Ca(OH)_2$; H_2CO_3
KNO_3: KOH; HNO_3
K_2CO_3: KOH; H_2CO_3
Na_3PO_4: $NaOH$; H_3PO_4
NH_4Cl: NH_3; HCl

Figure 13 Like many animals, elephants get salt from natural deposits. Salt helps to maintain body processes.

Acid-Base Reactions The following general equation represents acid-base reactions in water.

Acid-Base Reactions

acid + base → salt + water

Another neutralization reaction occurs between HCl, an acid, and $Ca(OH)_2$, a base producing water and the salt $CaCl_2$.

$$2HCl(aq) + Ca(OH)_2(aq) \rightarrow CaCl_2(aq) + 2H_2O(l)$$

Salts

Salt is essential for many animals large and small. Some animals find it at natural deposits, as shown in **Figure 13.** Even insects, such as butterflies, need salt and often are found clustered on moist ground. You need salt too, especially because you lose salt in perspiration. How humans obtain one salt—sodium chloride—is shown in **Figure 14.**

There are many other salts, however, a few of which are shown in **Table 3.** Most salts are composed of a positive metal ion and an ion with a negative charge, such as Cl^- or CO_3^{2-}. Ammonium salts contain the ammonium ion, NH_4^+, rather than a metal.

Table 3 Some Common Salts and Their Uses

Name, Formula	Common Name	Uses
Sodium chloride, $NaCl$	Salt	Food, manufacture of chemicals
Sodium hydrogen carbonate, $NaHCO_3$	Sodium bicarbonate Baking soda	Food, antacids
Calcium carbonate, $CaCO_3$	Calcite, chalk	Manufacture of paint and rubber tires
Potassium nitrate, KNO_3	Saltpeter	Fertilizers
Potassium carbonate, K_2CO_3	Potash	Manufacture of soap and glass
Sodium phosphate, Na_3PO_4	TSP	Detergents
Ammonium chloride, NH_4Cl	Sal ammoniac	Dry-cell batteries

Science Journal

Epsom Salt Another salt students may know is Epsom salt. Have them find out the chemical formula for Epsom salt, what it is used for, and how it was named. Have them record their findings in their Science Journals. Epsom salt is $MgSO_4 \cdot 7H_2O$. It is used for soaking bruises and sprains. It was named after the mineral-rich waters of Epsom, England, which contained magnesium sulfate. L2 LS **Linguistic**

Differentiated Instruction

Learning Disabled React a small amount of dilute HCl with the same amount of dilute NaOH. Gently boil away the liquid. Collect the white residue and show the resulting salt (NaCl) of the neutralization reaction. **WARNING:** *Do not taste the salt as it may contain impurities.* L1 LS **Visual-Spatial**

NATIONAL GEOGRAPHIC VISUALIZING SALT

Figure 14

The salt you use every day comes from both the land and the sea. Some salt can be mined from the ground in much the same way as coal, or salt can be obtained by the process of evaporation in crystallizing ponds.

▲ MINING SALT Underground salt deposits are found where there was once a sea. Salt mines can be located deep underground or near Earth's surface in salt domes. Salt domes, such as the one above on Avery Island, Louisiana, form when pressure from Earth pushes buried salt deposits close to the surface, where they are easily mined.

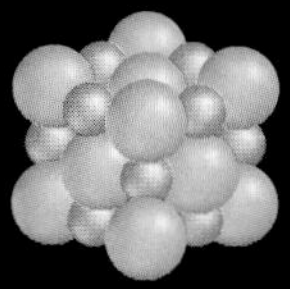

◀ EVAPORATION PROCESS Workers fill evaporation ponds, like these near San Francisco Bay, California, with salt water, or brine. They move the brine from pond to pond as it becomes saltier through evaporation. (Red-tinted ponds have a higher salt content.) The saltiest water is then pumped from evaporation ponds into crystallizing ponds, where the remaining water is drained off. In the five years it takes to produce a crop of salt, brine may move through as many as 23 different ponds.

Unit cell of sodium chloride (NaCl)

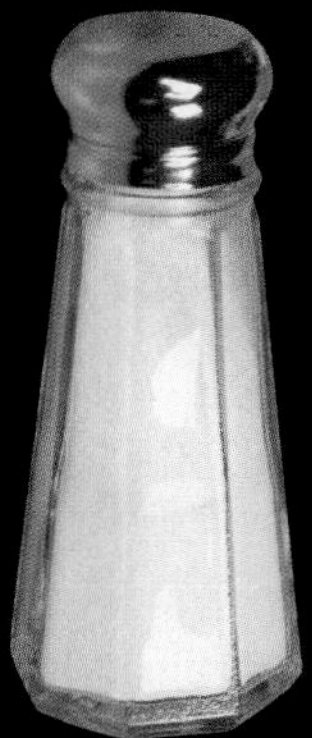

◀ TABLE SALT Raw sodium chloride is washed in chemicals and water to remove impurities before it appears on your dining-room table as salt. Iodine is added to table salt to ensure against iodine deficiency in the diet.

▼ SALT MOUNDS When the crystallizing ponds are drained, the result is huge piles of salt, like these on the Caribbean island of Bonaire.

Visualizing Salt

Have students examine the pictures and read the captions. Then ask the following questions.

In which geographic locations would the evaporation process be an obvious choice for obtaining salt? areas that are located near oceans or other salt water sources

What are some of the advantages and disadvantages of each process? Answers will vary but may include: removing salt from a mine is a much faster process than evaporation. The evaporation process requires a lot of land for evaporation ponds.

Would the land near San Francisco Bay that is used for the evaporation process be useful for farming should the salt evaporation process cease? No, because the concentration of salt in the soil is too high. L2

Activity

Salt Mining Challenge students to find the areas throughout the world where salt mining occurs. Use a world map and mark these locations. Ask them to find out what these locations have common. L2 LS **Visual-Spatial**

Differentiated Instruction

Challenge Ask students to research how salt was used to pay soldiers in ancient times and report to the class the information they find. L3 LS **Linguistic**

Caption Answer

Figure 15 when the solution turns pink and stays pink

Inquiry Lab

Acid Neutralization

Purpose Students will design an experiment to determine the effectiveness of antacid products by determining neutralization capability. L2

Materials pencil and paper

Estimated Time 45 minutes

Teaching Strategies

- Explain to students that there are several ways to determine the neutralization point of an acid. Let them decide which analytical method to use (titration, pH indicator paper, litmus paper, etc.).
- Students may choose the approach to use (test a single tablet, test the recommended dosage on the package, test liquid products).
- Encourage students to develop experiments to compare products. They can compare two national brands, a national brand vs a store brand, a tablet and liquid form of the same product, expired vs fresh, etc.
- Have some experimental materials on hand. If time permits, let students perform the experiments they designed. Alternatively, schedule another class period to perform the experiments.

For additional inquiry activities, see *Science Inquiry Labs*.

Topic: Acid/Base Indicators

Visit gpscience.com for Web links to information about acids, bases, and indicators.

Activity Obtain several strips of pH indicator paper and test various liquids around your house to determine if they are acidic, basic, or neutral. You might try the liquids in your refrigerator, rain from a puddle, or swimming pool water.

Titration

Sometimes you need to know the concentration of an acidic or basic solution; for example, to determine the purity of a commercial product. This can be done using a process called **titration** (ti TRAY shun), in which a solution of known concentration is used to determine the concentration of another solution. **Figure 15** shows a titration experiment.

Titration involves a solution of known concentration, called the standard solution. This is added slowly and carefully to a solution of unknown concentration to which an acid/base indicator has been added. If the solution of unknown concentration is a base, a standard acid solution is used. If the unknown is an acid, a standard base solution is used.

The Endpoint Has a Color The titration shown in **Figure 15** shows how you could find the concentration of an acid solution. First, you would add a few drops of an indicator, such as phenolphthalein (fee nul THAY leen), to a carefully measured amount of the solution of unknown concentration. Phenolphthalein is colorless in an acid but turns bright pink in the presence of a base.

Then, you would slowly and carefully add a base solution of known concentration to this acid-and-indicator mixture. Toward the end of the titration you must add a base drop by drop until one last drop of the base turns the solution pink and the color persists. The point at which the color persists is known as the end point, the point at which the acid is completely neutralized by the base. When you know what volume of base was used, you use that value and the known concentration of the base to calculate the concentration of the acid solution.

Figure 15 In this titration, a base of known concentration is being added to an acid of unknown concentration. The swirl of pink color shows that the end point is near.
Explain *How do you know when the endpoint has been reached?*

Teacher FYI

Molarity The most common method for expressing the concentration of solutions in chemistry is molarity (*M*). Molarity is the ratio between the number of moles of solute dissolved in the solution and the volume of the solution. A mole of any substance is 6.02×10^{23} units, typically molecules or ions. In an acid-base titration, the number of moles of acid required to neutralize the unknown basic solution is determined by the ratio of coefficients of acid and base in the chemical equation. If the volume, in liters, of a solution is multiplied by the molarity, the number of moles can be determined.

Figure 16 Natural indicators include red cabbage, radishes, and roses.

Many natural substances are acid–base indicators. In fact, the indicator litmus comes from a lichen—a combination of a fungus and an algae or a cyanobacterium. Flowers that are indicators include hydrangeas, which produce blue blossoms when the pH of the soil is acidic and pink blossoms when the soil is basic. This is just the opposite of litmus.

Other natural indicators possess a range of color. For example, the color of red cabbage varies from deep red at pH 1 to lavender at pH 7 and yellowish green at pH 10. Grape juice is also an indicator, as you can find out by doing the Try at Home MiniLAB.

Testing a Grape Juice Indicator

Procedure

1. Add one-half cup of **water** to each of **two small glasses.**
2. Add 1 tablespoon of **purple grape juice** to each glass.
3. To one glass, add 1 teaspoon of **baking soda.** Stir.
4. To the other glass add 1 teaspoon of **white vinegar.**
5. Note the color after each addition in steps 2, 3, and 4.

Analysis

1. Did the color change when you added baking soda? Why?
2. Did the color change when you added vinegar? Did your grape juice contain any citric or ascorbic acid? How would this affect your experiment?

Try at Home

Applying Science

How can you handle an upsetting situation?

Most of us have, at some time, experienced an upset stomach. Often, the cause is the excess acid within our stomachs. For digestive purposes, our stomachs contain dilute hydrochloric acid with a pH between 1.6 and 3.0. A doctor might recommend an antacid treatment for an upset stomach. What type of compound is "anti acid"?

Identifying the Problem

You have learned that neutralization reactions change acids and bases into salts. Antacids typically contain small amounts of $Ca(OH)_2$, $Al(OH)_3$, or $NaHCO_3$, which are bases. Whereas having an excess of acid lowers the pH of your stomach contents, these compounds raise the pH of your stomach contents. How does this change of pH make you feel better?

Solving the Problem

1. What compounds are produced from a reaction of HCl and $Mg(OH)_2$?
2. Why is it important to have some acid in your stomach?
3. How could you compare how well antacid products neutralize acid? Describe the procedure you would use.

Active Reading

Reflective Journal In this strategy, students record responses to an activity. Have students divide sheets of paper into columns. Have them record their thoughts under headings such as *What I did, What I learned, What questions I have, What surprises I experienced,* and *Overall response.* Have students write a Reflective Journal entry for the MiniLAB on this page. L2

Purpose Students use an acid-base indicator to demonstrate a change in the pH of a solution. L2 LS **Kinesthetic**

Materials water glasses (2), grape juice, baking soda, white vinegar, measuring spoon

Safety Precaution Remind students not to taste chemicals used in the lab.

Analysis

1. Yes; from the original red-purple to a blue tone to a greenish tone. The solution became more basic.
2. The color became reddish. The grape juice contains citric and ascorbic acids. Acids lower the pH, so the addition of a base has less effect on the color because the acid already present neutralizes the added hydrogen carbonate.

Assessment

Performance Provide another unknown solution and have students use the grape juice to determine whether it is an acid or a base. A soap solution should register as basic. Use **PASC,** p. 97.

Applying Science

Answers

1. water and magnesium chloride, $MgCl_2$
2. Acid in your stomach is needed for the digestion of protein.
3. You would need an indicator to change color when the HCl was neutralized. To make the test fair, you would have to have a constant amount of acid and carefully measure the mass of the antacid tablets that were needed to neutralize that amount of acid. Also, you would have to ensure that the time needed for complete neutralization was adequate.

Quick Demo

Detergent Effects

Materials petri dish, whole milk, food dye (four colors), detergent, toothpicks

Estimated time 15 minutes

Procedure To show the effect of detergent on other nonpolar substances, pour 4% (whole) milk into a petri dish. Place one drop of each of four different colored food dyes in different areas around the edges of the dish. Next, dip a toothpick into some detergent. Touch the surface of the milk with the toothpick. The detergent changes the attractions between the water molecules and interacts with the nonpolar fat molecules. The resulting motion in the milk can be seen as the food dyes begin to mix. L2 LS **Visual-Spatial**

Caption Answer

Figure 17 $C_{17}H_{35}CO_2Na$

Figure 17 Soaps that contain sodium like this one made from stearic acid are solids, those that contain potassium are liquids. **Write** *the chemical formula for this soap.*

COO Na

Ionic head

Nonpolar hydrocarbon tail

Soaps and Detergents

The next time you are in a supermarket, go to the aisle with soaps and detergents. You'll see all kinds of products—solid soaps, liquid soaps, and detergents for washing clothes and dishes. What are all these products? Do they differ from one another? Yes, they do differ slightly in how they are made and in the ingredients included for color and aroma. Still, all these products are classified into two types—soaps and detergents.

Soaps The reason soaps clean so well is explained by polar and nonpolar molecules. **Soaps** are organic salts. They have a nonpolar organic chain of carbon atoms on one end and either a sodium or potassium salt of a carboxylic acid (kar bahk SIHL ihk), $-COOH$, group at the other end. Look at **Figure 17.** The nonpolar, hydrocarbon end interacts with oils and dirt so that they can be removed readily, and the ionic end, COONa or COOK, helps them dissolve in water.

To make an effective soap, the acid must contain 12 to 18 carbon atoms. If it contains fewer than 12 atoms, it will not be able to mix well with and clean oily dirt. If it has too many carbon atoms, its sodium or potassium salt will not be soluble in water. **Figure 18** shows how soap interacts with dirt particles to clean your hands.

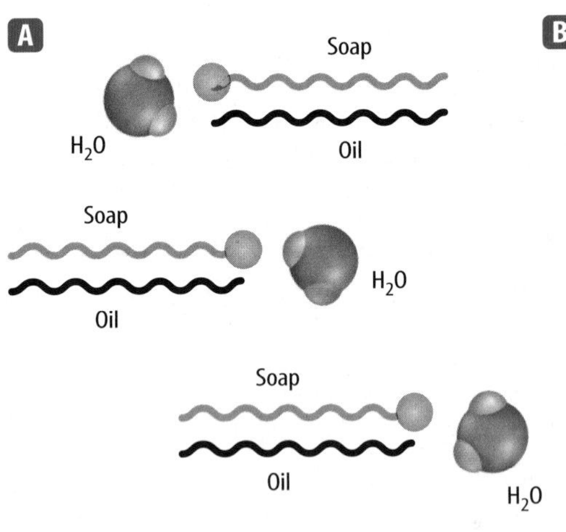

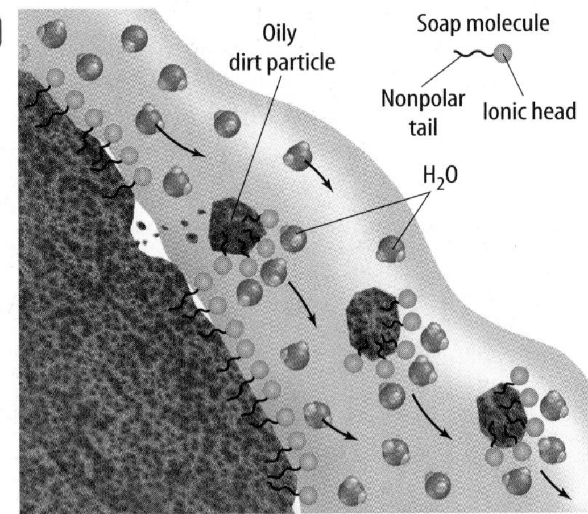

Figure 18 This is how soaps clean. **A** The long hydrocarbon tail of a soap molecule mixes well with oily dirt while the ionic head attracts water molecules. **B** Dirt now linked with the soap rinses away as water flows over it.

Cultural Diversity

Soap Science African American scientist George Washington Carver made many discoveries in the late 1800s and early 1900s. Have students research to find information about his contribution to the making of soap. He found a way to extract peanut oil and convert the oil to soap, using lye, NaOH. L3 LS **Linguistic**

Differentiated Instruction

Challenge Have students explain what causes polarity and nonpolarity in molecules. In some chemical bonds, some of the electrons of the bonded atoms spend more time around one atom than around the other. This causes uneven charge distribution which results in a polar bond. When electrons are shared almost equally between bonded atoms, the result is nonpolarity. L3 LS **Logical-Mathematical**

712 CHAPTER 23 Acids, Bases, and Salts

Commercial Soaps A simple soap like the one shown in **Figure 17** can be made by reacting a long-chain fatty acid with sodium or potassium hydroxide. The fatty acids used to make commercial soaps come from natural sources, such as canola, palm, and coconut oils. One problem with all soaps, however, is that the sodium and potassium ions can be replaced by ions of calcium, magnesium, and iron found in some water known as hard water. When this happens, the salts formed are insoluble. They precipitate out of solution in the form of soap scum. Detergents were developed to avoid this problem.

Reading Check *How are simple soaps made?*

Detergents Detergents are synthetic products that are made from petroleum molecules, instead of from natural fatty acids like their soap counterparts. Similar to soaps, detergents have long hydrocarbon chains, but instead of a carboxylic acid group (–COOH) at the end, they may contain instead a sulfonic acid group. These acids form more soluble salts with the ions in hard water and thereby lessen the problem of soap scum. Detergents can also be used in cold water. Most detergents contain additional ingredients called builders and surfactants to enhance sudsing and further improve cleaning in hard water.

Despite solving the problem of cleaning in hard water, detergents are not the complete solution to our needs. Some detergents contained phosphates, the use of which has been restricted or banned in many states, and these are no longer produced because they cause water pollution. Certain sulfonic acid detergents also present problems in the form of excess foaming in water treatment plants and streams, as shown in **Figure 19.** These detergents do not break down easily by bacteria and remain in the environment for long periods of time.

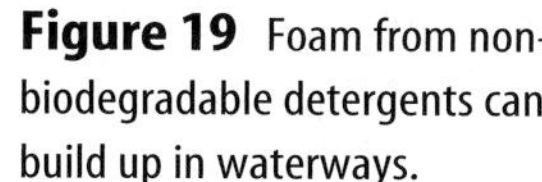

Figure 19 Foam from nonbiodegradable detergents can build up in waterways.

Ecology Before the environmental impact of phosphates was understood, phosphates were added to detergents. Eventually water/detergent mixtures would be washed into streams where the phosphates acted like strong fertilizers, causing algae and water plants to grow uncontrollably. Research this problem and, in your Science Journal, write a pamphlet or speech that an environmental activist might have used to convince law makers of the need for change.

Ecology In the 1960s, it could not be denied that the nation's streams, lakes, and rivers were becoming clogged with excessive amounts of vegetation, which in effect was choking the life out of those bodies of water. One of the primary contributors was phosphates in detergents, and many states and jurisdictions have banned the use of these agents in detergents; however, the ban is not global across all states and products. Local situations and varying levels of opposition and support have resulted in "patchwork" legislation to control the problem.

Career Invite an environmental scientist to class to discuss current priorities and the role of environmental scientists today.

Reading Check

Answer by reacting long-chain fatty acids with NaOH or KOH

Activity

Suds and Residue Have students place 10 mL of hard water and 10 mL of soft water in separate test tubes. Have them add 1 mL of cooking oil to each, add 5 drops of soap to each, then stopper the tubes and shake them vigorously to see which produces more suds. Then have them drain the water and allow the moist tubes to dry. Compare the residues left behind. Soft water produces more suds and leaves less residue. L1 ELL LS **Kinesthetic**

LAB DEMONSTRATION

Purpose to show the soap-making process

Materials solid vegetable shortening, ethanol, NaOH, NaCl, water, cheesecloth

Procedure Place 25 g of solid vegetable shortening, 10 mL of ethanol, and 5 mL of 6*M* NaOH in a 250-mL beaker. Heat the mixture on a hot plate and stir for 15 minutes. **WARNING:** *Ethanol is flammable. Wear goggles, an apron, and gloves.* Cool the mixture in an ice water bath. Add 25 mL of water and 25 mL of saturated NaCl solution. Usable soap will begin to appear as curds. Filter the soap through cheesecloth and press it into a dish. Allow the soap to dry for a few days.

Assessment

Which ingredients reacted to form the soap? vegetable shortening and sodium hydroxide Why were the NaCl and water added? NaCl was added to make the soap precipitate, and water was added to wash out the excess hydroxide. L2

Caption Answer

Figure 20 butyl alcohol (C_4H_9OH)

Reading Check

Answer soaps, flavors and perfumes, and fibers used to make clothing

Fun Fact

Aromas are detected when molecules or particles interact with receptors inside our noses. Research has shown that the shape of an aroma molecule plays a major role in its detection. The receptors are often in cavities into which the aroma molecule must fit to cause a sensation.

Discussion

Hydrolysis The reverse reaction to the formation of an ester is hydrolysis, which splits the ester into its acid and base components. The compound pentyl butyrate is associated with apricots. After studying the equation in **Figure 20,** ask students to determine what acid and base would result from the hydrolysis of this ester. The pentyl part comes from pentanol, $C_5H_{11}OH$; the acid part comes from butyric acid, C_3H_7COOH. L2

LS **Logical-Mathematical**

Visual Learning

Figure 20 Look at the equation as it is given and have students count the number of C, H, and O atoms on each side of the arrow. This will reinforce the concept of balanced chemical equations and the law of conservation of matter that was learned previously.

```
    H  H  H                H  H              H  H  H           H  H
    |  |  |                |  |              |  |  |           |  |
H — C— C— C— C — OH + HO — C— C— H  →  H — C— C— C— C— O — C— C— H + H2O
    |  |  |  ||            |  |              |  |  |  ||       |  |
    H  H  H  O             H  H              H  H  H  O        H  H

      Butyric acid         Ethyl alcohol          Ethyl butyrate         Water
```

Figure 20 This structural equation shows the formation of the ester ethyl butyrate, an ester that tastes and smells like pineapple. **Predict** *which alcohol you would use to prepare butyl butyrate.*

Versatile Esters

In a way esters can be thought of as the organic counterparts of salts. Like salts, esters are made from acids, and water is formed in the reaction used to prepare them. The difference is that salts are made from bases and esters come from alcohols that are not bases but have a hydroxyl group.

Esters have many different applications. Esters of the alcohol glycerine are used commercially to make soaps. Other esters are used widely in flavors and perfumes, and still others can be transformed into fibers to make clothing.

Reading Check *What are three types of products that are made from esters?*

Esters for Flavor Many fruit-flavored soft drinks and desserts taste like the real fruit. If you look at the label though, you might be surprised to find that no fruit was used—only artificial flavor. Most likely this artificial flavor contains some esters.

The reaction to prepare esters involves removing a molecule of water from an acid and an alcohol. Often concentrated sulfuric acid is added to aid this reaction. **Figure 20** shows the reaction of butyric (byew TIHR ihk) acid and ethyl alcohol to produce water and the ester, ethyl butyrate, which is a component in pineapple flavor.

Although natural and artificial flavors often contain a blend of many esters, the odor of some individual esters immediately makes you think of particular fruits, as shown in **Figure 21.** For example, octyl acetate smells much like oranges, and both pentyl and butyl acetates smell like bananas.

Making realistic synthetic flavors is an art, in which chemists vary the composition to achieve the desired taste. Strawberry flavor, for example, may contain several esters.

Figure 21 These esters have strong fruity aromas.

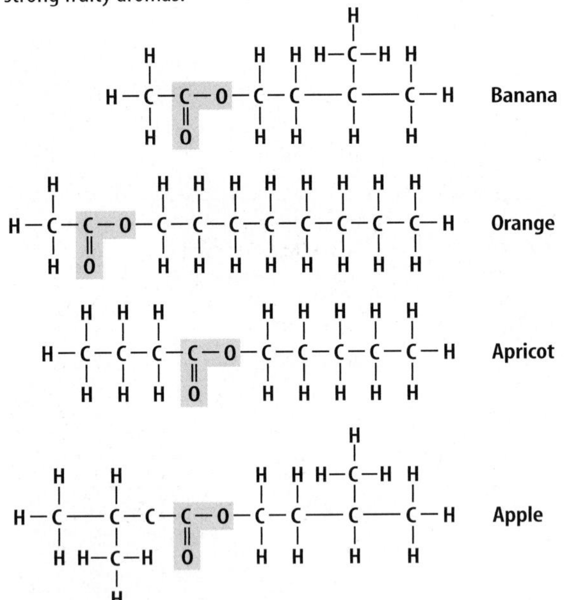

714 CHAPTER 23 Acids, Bases, and Salts

Figure 22 Polyesters and nylons are polymers most often used for clothing fibers.

$$HO-\overset{O}{\overset{\|}{C}}-C_6H_4-\overset{O}{\overset{\|}{C}}-OH + HO-\underset{H}{\overset{H}{C}}-\underset{H}{\overset{H}{C}}-OH \rightarrow \left[\overset{O}{\overset{\|}{C}}-C_6H_4-\overset{O}{\overset{\|}{C}}-O-\underset{H}{\overset{H}{C}}-\underset{H}{\overset{H}{C}}-O\right] + 2H_2O$$

Organic acid — Alcohol — Polymer (1 unit) — Water

Polyesters Synthetic fibers known as polyesters are polymers; that is, they are chains containing many or *poly* esters. They are made from an organic acid that has two $-COOH$ groups and an alcohol that has two $-OH$ groups, as shown in **Figure 22.** The two compounds form long nonpolar chains that are closely packed together. This adds strength to the polymer fiber. Many varieties of polyesters can be made, depending on what alcohols and acids are used. They can be woven or knitted into fabrics that are durable, water repellent, colorfast, and do not wrinkle easily. Because of their low moisture content however, they tend to build up a static electric charge that causes them to cling. Polyesters often are combined with natural fibers, as shown in **Figure 22.**

Blends of polyester and cotton fibers make comfortable activewear.

section 3 review

Summary

Salts

- Salts are solid compounds formed from the negative ions of an acid and the positive ions from a base.
- Salt is a dietary essential.

Neutralization and Titration

- Acids and bases in solution can combine to bring pH closer to neutral. Products such as stomach antacids use this principle.
- Titration is a method used to determine the concentration of an acidic or basic solution.

Soaps, Detergents, and Esters

- Soaps and detergents are polar, which allows one end to attract dirt and grease molecules and the other end to attract water to wash the dirt away.
- Esters are organic compounds that are made from acids and alcohols.

Self Check

1. **Describe** a neutralization reaction. What are the products of such reactions?
2. **Identify** the purpose of an indicator in a titration experiment.
3. **Explain** how the composition of detergents differs from that of soaps.
4. **Identify** the molecule that is produced in the reaction between an alcohol and an acid to form an ester.
5. **Think Critically** Give the names and formulas of the salts formed in these neutralizations: sulfuric acid and calcium hydroxide, nitric acid and potassium hydroxide, and carbonic acid and aluminum hydroxide.

Applying Math

6. **Calculate Ratios** In the following reaction: $2HCl(aq) + Ca(OH)_2(aq) \rightarrow CaCl_2(aq) + 2H_2O(l)$ acid reacts with base in what ratio? How many molecules of HCl are needed to produce four molecules of H_2O?

Science Online gpscience.com/self_check_quiz

section 3 review

1. A reaction between an acid and a base; water and a salt are produced.
2. The indicator changes color when the substance of unknown concentration has completely reacted with the substance of known concentration, allowing to determine the concentration of the unknown.
3. Detergents may contain a sulfonic acid group at the end of their hydrocarbon chains.
4. water
5. **(a)** calcium sulfate, $CaSO_4$ **(b)** potassium nitrate, KNO_3 **(c)** aluminum carbonate, $Al_2(CO_3)_3$
6. One molecule of base reacts with two molecules of acid. Four molecules of HCl produce four molecules of H_2O.

3 Assess

DAILY INTERVENTION

Check for Understanding

Visual-Spatial Review with students that a salt is the compound formed when the negative ions of an acid react with the positive ions of a base. Write the chemical equations for several reactions of acids and bases to form salts, and use colored chalk to draw lines connecting the ions on the left side to the salt substance on the right.

Reteach

OH My! The formula OH has been seen on three types of compounds. Write the following compounds on the chalkboard, and have students determine which is an acid, which is a base, and which is an alcohol. $Ca(OH)_2$ base; C_2H_5COOH acid; CH_3CH_2 CH_2OH alcohol L2 **Logical-Mathematical**

Assessment

Performance Bring several well-known antacid products to class and write components from the labels on the chalkboard. Do the same for some soap and detergent samples. Ask students to identify which compounds most likely are from an antacid, which are from a soap, and which are from a detergent. Use **Performance Assessment in the Science Classroom,** p. 89. L2

Real-World Question

Purpose Students will design and carry out an experiment to find the level of acidity in soft drinks. L2 COOP LEARN

LS Interpersonal

Process Skills observe, compare, measure, communicate, make and use tables, recognize cause and effect, form a hypothesis, design an experiment, separate and control variables, interpret data

Time Required 45 minutes

Possible Materials To prepare a 0.1*M* NaOH solution, dissolve 2.0 g of NaOH pellets in enough water to make 500 mL of solution. **CAUTION:** *Sodium hydroxide is highly caustic. Do not touch the pellets or the solution. Wear goggles, an apron, and gloves.* Be sure the carbonated beverages are freshly opened so that the escape of CO_2 does not affect the acidity.

Safety Precautions Students should avoid direct contact with NaOH. Wash any affected area immediately. Make sure students do not drink any of the beverages.

Form a Hypothesis

Possible Hypotheses

- A neutralization reaction can be used as a method of comparing acid levels in solutions.
- The NaOH solution will neutralize the acidity of soft drinks. The number of drops of NaOH solution needed for neutralization is proportional to the acidity level of the soft drinks.

Design Your Own

Be a Soda Scientist

Goals

- **Observe** evidence of a neutralization reaction using an indicator.
- **Compare** the acidity levels in soft drinks.
- **Design** an experiment that uses the independent variable of acid content of soft drinks and the dependent variable of amount of base added to determine the relative acidity of the drinks.

Possible Materials

different colorless soft drinks (3)
test tubes (3)
25-mL graduated cylinder
droppers (2)
1% phenolphthalein
dilute NaOH solution (0.1*M*)

Safety Precautions

WARNING: *Sodium hydroxide is caustic. Wear eye protection and avoid any skin contact with the solution. Flush thoroughly under a stream of water if any of the NaOH touches your skin. Keep your hands away from your face.*

Real-World Question

The next time you drink a can of soda, take a look at the ingredients label. Carbonated soft drinks contain carbonic acid and sometimes phosphoric acid. You have learned that bases can neutralize acids. Using a proper indicator and a base solution, how could you compare the acidity levels in soft drinks?

Form a Hypothesis

Based on your knowledge of acids and bases, develop a hypothesis about how neutralization reactions can be used to rank the acidity of soft drinks.

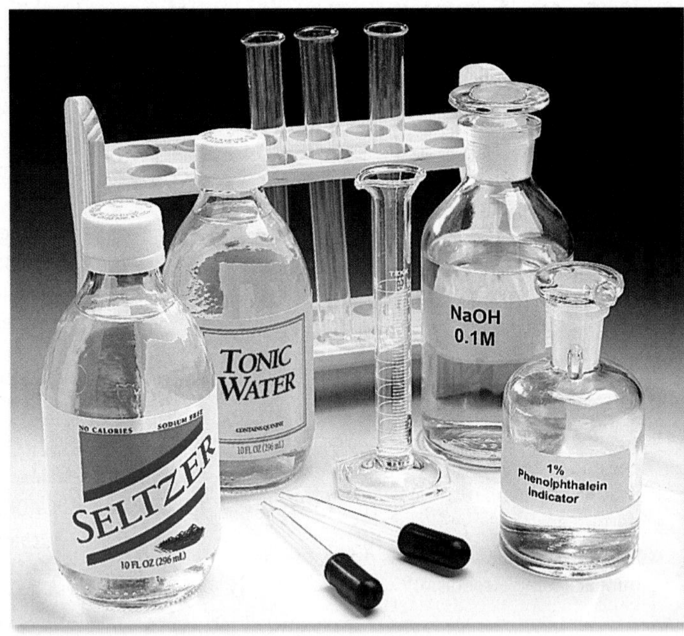

Alternative Inquiry Lab

Extend the Activity Encourage students to think of other types of beverages and foods that they eat. Some students may want to evaluate the acid levels of a complete meal. Others may opt to compare similar items obtained from different sources. Some students may wish to evaluate the same soda with different indicators. L2

Using Scientific Methods

Test Your Hypothesis

Make a Plan

1. As a group, agree upon and write the hypothesis statement.
2. In a logical manner, list the specific steps that you will use to test your hypothesis.
3. **List** all of the materials that you will need to test your hypothesis.
4. **Design** a data table in your Science Journal that will allow you to record the amount of NaOH that was required to neutralize each soda sample.
5. **Decide** the amount of soda to be tested in each trial as a control. Decide also how many times to repeat each trial.
6. **Predict** whether you can test only colorless solutions with this procedure and explain why.

Follow Your Plan

1. Make sure your teacher approves your plan before you start.
2. **Observe** the color change that the indicator phenolphthalein undergoes in a solution that changes from an acidic pH to a basic pH.
3. While doing the experiment, write your observations and complete the data table in your Science Journal.

Analyze Your Data

1. **Classify** the sodas you tested based on their acidities. Rank them in the order of most acidic to least acidic.
2. **Predict** if your acidity values can be compared with those of other groups if they used different amounts of soda.

Conclude and Apply

1. **Evaluate** the results. Do they support your hypothesis? Explain why or why not.
2. **Predict** At warmer temperatures less gas dissolves in a liquid. How would this affect the results of an experiment comparing two sodas stored at different temperatures?

Communicating Your Data

Compare your soda rankings with those of other class groups. **Discuss** possible reasons for any differences observed.

Teaching Strategies Be sure to test the selected beverages ahead of time to ensure that there is a measurable difference in the number of NaOH drops required.

Expected Outcome The acidity of a carbonated soda is directly related to the number of drops of NaOH solution needed to neutralize the acid. When the NaOH has no more acid to neutralize, the phenolphthalein stays pink.

Analyze Your Data

1. Answers between groups should be similar although not necessarily identical.
2. only if drops used per milliliter of soda are reported

Error Analysis Different droppers may produce slightly different volumes in the drops, causing slightly different results. The judgment that the acid has been neutralized and that it is time to stop the addition of NaOH may not be consistent from group to group.

Conclude and Apply

1. Answers will vary.
2. Warmer sodas tend to lose CO_2 gas, which lowers the acidity of the soda. Thus, the same soda at a warmer temperature may require fewer drops of NaOH solution for neutralization.

Test Your Hypothesis

Possible Procedures

- Mix the solutions well after each addition of NaOH.
- The pink color can be seen best if the test tubes are held against a piece of white paper.
- For most carbonated beverages, about 30–50 drops of the NaOH solution will neutralize 5 mL.

Communicating Your Data

Make a chart on the board showing the results of the different groups. Combine the data to get a class average for each soft drink.

Assessment

Performance Have one student from each group demonstrate the procedure the group used to compare the soft drinks. Use **Performance Assessment in the Science Classroom,** p. 143.

Content Background

Acid rain is caused by water falling through polluted air. A number of factors determine the severity of the effects of acid rain. Among them are the amount and type of chemicals contained in the clouds and the contours and composition of the soil on which it falls. For example, soils formed over limestone or chalk can tolerate much higher levels of acid than those based on granite or sandstone. The alkalinity of limestone and chalk neutralizes acids before they can have a corrosive effect. Quartzite granite does not react with the acids, leaving them in the soil to be washed into streams and lakes. There is some disagreement over the extent of the harm caused by acid rain, but not over the fact that it is harmful.

Activity

Place a clean glass container in a safe place outside prior to an expected rainstorm. Collect a rain sample and check the pH using pH paper. Have students find the position of the pH of rainwater on the chart in **Figure 9.** L2 LS **Kinesthetic**

Investigate the Issue

Research the patterns of acid rain across the country and the presumed sources. Note them on a national map and use it to discuss how the local area is affected. Find out whether you are in an area of acid rainfall, a source area or both. L2

TIME SCIENCE AND Society

SCIENCE ISSUES THAT AFFECT YOU!

Acid Rain

Protecting Earth from the damaging effects of chemically loaded precipitation

Acid rain is rain, snow, or sleet that is more acidic than unpolluted precipitation. It's caused by the burning of fossil fuels, such as coal, oil, and natural gas. In the United States, most gasoline and electricity come from fossil fuels. People burn fossil fuels each time they drive a car, heat a building, or turn on a light.

Normally, raindrops pick up particles and natural chemicals in the air. When rain falls, it mixes with the carbon dioxide in the atmosphere, giving clean rain a slightly acidic pH of 5.6. Then, natural chemicals found in the air and soil balance out the acidity, giving most lakes and streams a pH between 6.0 and 8.0. But when pollutants are introduced, these natural bases are not strong enough to neutralize these solutions. Wind can carry this acidic moisture for hundreds of miles before it falls to Earth as acid rain.

Eating Away at History

Like all acids, acid rain can corrode, or eat away at, substances. Many historical monuments, such as the Mayan temples in Mexico and the Parthenon in Greece, have been slowly but steadily damaged by acid rain. This kind of damage can be fixed, though it costs billions of dollars to ensure that ancient monuments and buildings are not destroyed.

Some Solutions

In some countries, high acid levels in lakes and streams have been lowered by adding lime to the water. Lime, a natural base, balances out the damaging chemicals. In the United States, all new cars must have catalytic converters, which help reduce the amount of exhaust pollution that vehicles give off.

You also can make a difference. Turning off the lights when you are not using them means a power plant does not have to produce as much electricity. By carpooling, using public transportation, and walking, there is less pollution from cars. The results of all these individual actions can make a huge difference in preserving our environment.

Ride a bike! It saves fuel, is nonpolluting, and helps preserve the environment.

List Go to a local park or forest. List any effects of acid rain that you see. Make a list of the things you do that use energy or cause pollution. Think about what your family can do to reduce pollution and save energy. Share your list with an adult.

For more information, visit gpscience.com/time

List If your local park shows symptoms of acid rain, try to determine the source of the acid rain. In many cases, the sources of acid rain are also major contributors to the local economy. Find out if the economic activity of your community produces acid rain-causing pollutants and what steps local industries and government have taken to address the problem. L3

Resources for Teachers and Students

Acid Rain, Sally Morgan, Franklin Watts: New York, 1999

Acid Rain, Louise Petheram, Bridgestone Books, Mankato, MN, 2003

Reviewing Main Ideas

Section 1 Acids and Bases

1. An acid is a substance that produces hydrogen ions, H^+, in solution. A base produces hydroxide ions, OH^-, in solution.
2. Some foods can be classified as acidic or basic. Properties of acids and bases are due, in part, to the presence of the H^+ and OH^- ions.

3. Common acids include hydrochloric acid, sulfuric acid, nitric acid, and phosphoric acid. Common bases include sodium hydroxide, calcium hydroxide, and ammonia.
4. Acidic solutions form when certain polar compounds ionize as they dissolve in water. Except for ammonia, basic solutions form when certain ionic compounds dissociate upon dissolving in water.

Section 2 Strength of Acids and Bases

1. The strength of an acid or base is determined by how completely it forms ions when it is in solution.
2. Strength and concentration are not the same thing. Concentration involves the relative amounts of solvent and solute in a solution, whereas strength is related to the extent to which a substance dissociates.
3. pH measures the concentration of hydronium ions in water solution using a scale ranging from 0 to 14.
4. For acidic solutions of equal concentration, the stronger the acid is, the lower its pH is. For basic solutions of equal concentration, the stronger the base is, the higher its pH is.

Section 3 Salts

1. In a neutralization reaction, the H_3O^+ ions from an acid react with the OH^- ions from a base to produce water molecules. The products of a neutralization reaction are a salt and water.
2. Salts form when negative ions from an acid combine with positive ions from a base.
3. Soaps and detergents are organic salts. Unlike soaps, detergents do not react with compounds in hard water to form soap scum as shown here.

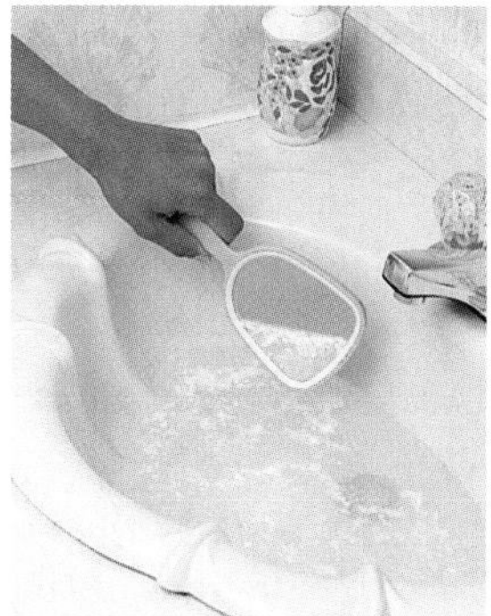

4. Esters are organic compounds formed by the reaction of an organic acid and an alcohol.

FOLDABLES Use the Foldable that you made at the beginning of this chapter to help you review acids, bases, and salts.

Identifying Misconceptions

Assess

After students have done the activity on page F at the beginning of the chapter, have them perform this activity.

Materials paper and pencil

Procedure Have students make cartoon posters of a basketball game between the Acids and the Bases. Each team should have five players, which will be the names of acids or bases. Each player's number will be its pH value.

Expected Outcome Students should realize that the pH scale includes both acids and bases. L2

chapter 23 Study Guide

Reviewing Main Ideas

Summary statements can be used by students to review the major concepts of the chapter.

Visit gpscience.com
/self_check_quiz
/interactive_tutor
/vocabulary_puzzlemaker
/chapter_review
/standardized_test

Assessment Transparency

For additional assessment questions, use the *Assessment Transparency* located in the transparency book.

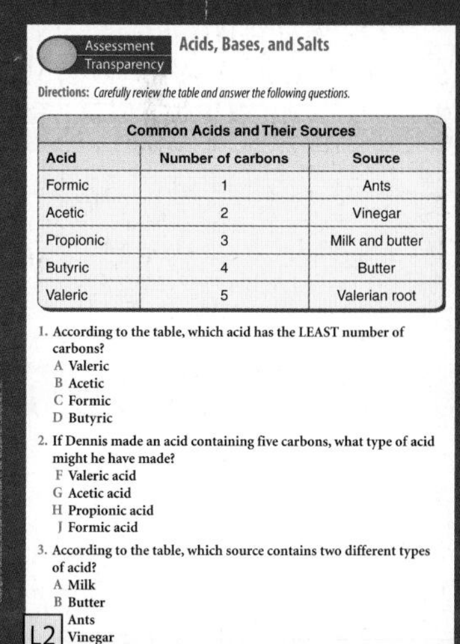

Assessment

Assessment Transparency **Acids, Bases, and Salts**

Directions: *Carefully review the table and answer the following questions.*

Common Acids and Their Sources		
Acid	Number of carbons	Source
Formic	1	Ants
Acetic	2	Vinegar
Propionic	3	Milk and butter
Butyric	4	Butter
Valeric	5	Valerian root

1. According to the table, which acid has the LEAST number of carbons?
   A Valeric
   B Acetic
   C Formic
   D Butyric
2. If Dennis made an acid containing five carbons, what type of acid might he have made?
   F Valeric acid
   G Acetic acid
   H Propionic acid
   J Formic acid
3. According to the table, which source contains two different types of acid?
   A Milk
   B Butter
   Ants
   Vinegar

L2

Acids, Bases, and Salts

FOLDABLES Have students use their Foldables to review the content of the chapter. Have students look at the information they have under the *Salts* tab.

chapter 23 Review

Using Vocabulary

1. An acid produces hydrogen ions in solutions. A base forms hydroxide ions in solutions and accepts hydrogen ions from acids.
2. A salt forms when an acid and base combine.
3. Soaps are organic salts.
4. Soaps are organic salts. Salts are formed when an acid and base combine.
5. Neutralization reactions produce salts.
6. A strong acid has a pH <7.
7. When acids dissolve in water, hydronium ions are formed.
8. Titrations and indicators are used to determine the concentration of acid or base solutions.
9. pH is a measure of the concentration of hydronium ions in a solution. A buffer is a solution that contains ions that react with additional acids and bases to minimize their effects.
10. A strong base ionizes completely in solution. A weak base does not.

Checking Concepts

11. A	14. C	17. B
12. C	15. A	18. C
13. D	16. C	

Interpreting Graphics

19. ammonia
20. sample B

chapter 23 Review

Using Vocabulary

acid p. 696
base p. 698
buffer p. 705
hydronium ion p. 696
indicator p. 696
neutralization p. 707
pH p. 704
salt p. 707
soap p. 712
strong acid p. 702
strong base p. 703
titration p. 710
weak acid p. 702
weak base p. 703

Explain the differences between each set of vocabulary words given below. Then explain how the words are related.

1. acid—base
2. acid—salt
3. salt—soap
4. base—soap
5. neutralization—salt
6. strong acid—pH
7. hydronium ion—acid
8. indicator—titration
9. pH—buffer
10. weak base—strong base

Checking Concepts

Choose the word or phrase that best answers the question.

11. What best describes solutions of equal concentrations of HCl and CH_3COOH?
    A) do not have the same pH
    B) will react the same with metals
    C) will make the same salts
    D) have the same amount of ionization
12. What is hydrochloric acid also known as?
    A) battery acid **C)** stomach acid
    B) citric acid **D)** vinegar
13. Which of the following acids ionizes only partially in water?
    A) HCl **C)** HNO_3
    B) H_2SO_4 **D)** CH_3COOH
14. Which of the following is another name for sodium hydroxide (NaOH)?
    A) ammonia **C)** lye
    B) caustic lime **D)** milk of magnesia
15. Carrots have a pH of 5.0, so how would you describe them?
    A) acidic **C)** neutral
    B) basic **D)** an indicator
16. What is the pH of pure water at 25°C?
    A) 0 **C)** 7
    B) 5.2 **D)** 14
17. A change of what property permits certain materials to act as indicators?
    A) acidity **C)** concentration
    B) color **D)** taste
18. Which of the following might you use to titrate an oxalic acid solution?
    A) HBr **C)** NaOH
    B) $Ca(NO_3)_2$ **D)** NH_4Cl

Interpreting Graphics

Use the table below to answer question 19.

19. Which of the substances listed in the table would be most effective for neutralizing battery acid?

pH Readings

Substance	pH
Battery acid	1.5
Lemon juice	2.5
Apple	3
Milk	6.7
Seawater	8.5
Ammonia	12

gpscience.com/vocabulary_puzzlemaker

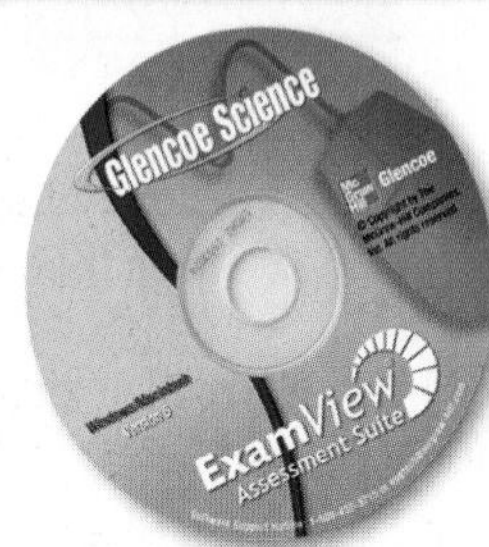

Use the *ExamView® Assessment Suite* CD-ROM to:

- create multiple versions of tests
- create modified tests with one mouse click for inclusion students
- edit existing questions and add your own questions
- build tests aligned with state standards using built-in State Curriculum Tags
- change English tests to Spanish with one mouse click and vice versa

Use the illustration below to answer question 20.

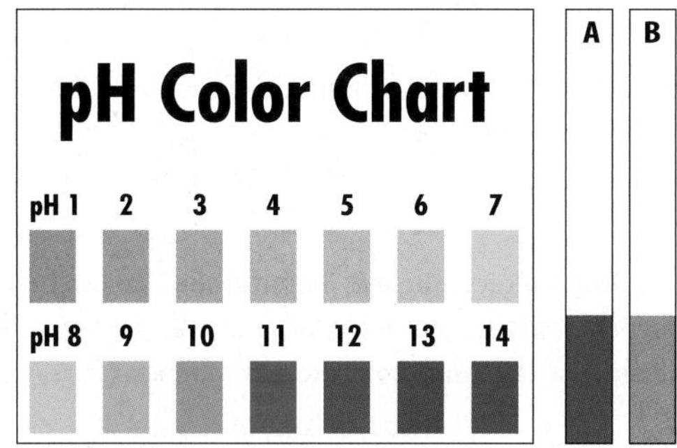

20. Compare the pH test strips for Sample A and Sample B and determine which sample is the acid.

Thinking Critically

21. **Describe** what happens to hydrogen chloride, HCl, when dissolved in water to form hydrochloric acid.
22. **Explain** how the hydroxide ion in NaOH differs from the −OH group in an alcohol.
23. **Explain** why ammonia is considered a base, even though it contains no hydroxide ions. Is it a strong or weak base?
24. **Explain** why a concentrated acid is not necessarily a strong acid.
25. **Explain** why the substances CH_4 and SiO_2 do not conduct electricity.
26. **Compare and Contrast** How would the pH of a dilute solution of HCl compare with the pH of a concentrated solution of the same acid?
27. **Recognize Cause and Effect** Ramón often saw his mother cleaning white deposits from inside her teakettle using vinegar. When she added vinegar, bubbles formed. When she finished, all the white deposits were gone. What do you think these white deposits might be? Do you think dish detergent would have worked as well?
28. **Draw Conclusions** You have equal amounts of three colorless liquids: A, B, and C. You add several drops of phenolphthalein to each liquid. A and B remain colorless, but C turns pink. Next, you add some C to A and the pink color disappears. Then, you add the rest of C to B and the mixture remains pink. What can you infer about each of these liquids? Which original liquid could have had a pH of 7?

Applying Math

29. **Calculate pH** If an acid is added to a solution of pH 10 and the solution changes 4 pH units, what is the new pH?
30. **Use Proportions** To make an indicator solution, a student mixes 3 mL of a concentrated solution to 100 mL water. How much concentrate is needed to make 3 liters of the indicator?

Use the graph below to answer question 31.

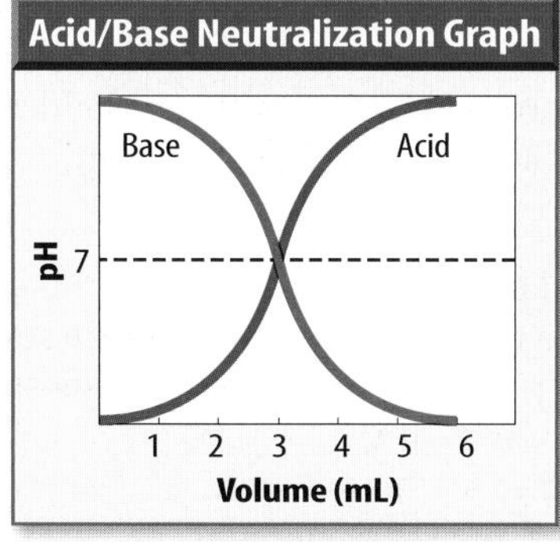

31. **Interpret Graphs** The graph illustrates an acid-base neutralization reaction. Which line (red or blue) represents a base being neutralized by an acid?
32. **Interpret Graphs** Using the graph above, how much acid must be added to the base to neutralize it?

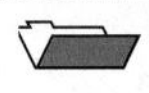

Thinking Critically

21. Water interacts forming H_3O^+ and Cl^- ions in the ionization process.
22. OH^- is part of an ionic compound that dissociates in water. The OH found in alcohol molecules is covalently bonded to a carbon atom and does not ionize or dissociate in water.
23. Ammonia can accept H^+ ions from water, forming NH_4^+ ions and thus producing OH^- in water. It is a weak base.
24. A concentrated acid has a large amount of acid dissolved in a solution. A strong acid easily donates H^+ ions. A concentrated acid could be a large amount of weak acid in a solution.
25. They do not dissociate into ions in solution. Such substances are nonelectrolytes and do not conduct.
26. A concentrated solution of HCl has a low pH. A dilute solution has a higher pH that is still below 7.
27. It is likely that the deposits contained carbonate and the gas was carbon dioxide. Detergent would have had little effect on the white deposits.
28. Liquid A is acidic. Liquid B is likely near neutral. Liquid C is basic. Liquid A contains more acid than a small amount of liquid C can neutralize. Liquid B contains less acid than liquid A and could have a pH near 7.

Applying Math

National Math Standards

1, 2, 5, 9

29. new pH = 6
30. 90 mL
31. red
32. 3 mL

Assessment Resources

Reproducible Masters

Chapter *Fast File* Resources
- Chapter Review, pp. 37–38
- Chapter Tests, pp. 39–42
- Assessment Transparency Activity, p. 49

Glencoe Science Web site
- Chapter Review Test
- Standardized Test Practice

Glencoe Technology
- Assessment Transparency
- *ExamView® Assessment Suite*
- MindJogger Videoquiz
- Interactive Chalkboard

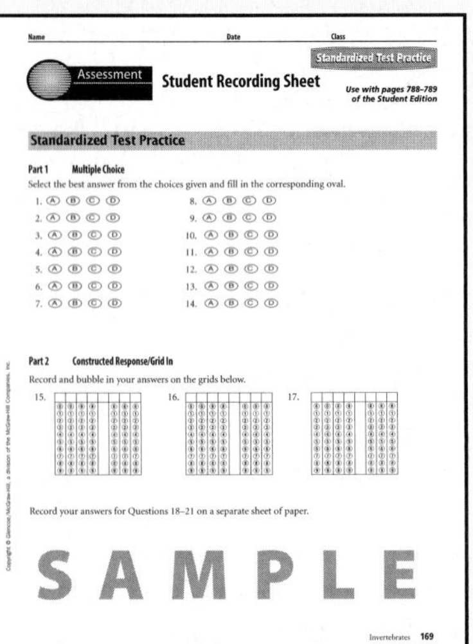

Answer Sheet A practice answer sheet can be found at gpscience.com/answer_sheet.

Part 1 Multiple Choice

1. B
2. B
3. D
4. B
5. A
6. A
7. C
8. C
9. B

Part 2 Short Response

10. H_2S
11. two
12. $H_2S + 2H_2O \rightarrow 2H_3O^+ + S_2^-$
13. Only a small percent will ionize.
14. The bulb will begin to glow as Na^+ and Cl^- dissociate.
15. 0.10 (100×0.0010)
16. Strength has to do with the degree to which a substance dissociates into ions and concentration has to do with the number of atoms of an acid or base that are in solution.
17. 31%
18. Sodium Chloride; potassium nitrate; calcium sulfate

Part 1 Multiple Choice

Record your answers on the answer sheet provided by your teacher or on a sheet of paper.

Use the table below to answer questions 1 and 2.

Acid Solution Data		
Solution	**pH**	**Dissociation**
W	7	none
X	2	complete
Y	6	partial
Z	4	??

1. Which word best describes the dissociation of acid solution Z?
   A. complete **C.** none
   B. partial **D.** exactly 50%

2. Which solution contains a strong acid?
   A. solution W **C.** solution Y
   B. solution X **D.** solution Z

3. Hard water often contains various amounts of metallic substances. Which of the following ions does NOT contribute to hard water?
   A. calcium **C.** magnesium
   B. iron **D.** sodium

4. An unknown substance in solution is slippery to the touch, dissolves easily in water, and turns litmus paper blue. The substance is most likely a(n)
   A. acid. **C.** salt.
   B. base. **D.** ester.

Test-Taking Tip

Answer All Questions Never skip a question. If you are unsure of an answer, mark your best guess on another sheet of paper and mark the question in your test booklet to remind you to come back to it at the end of the test.

5. Which chemical formula below describes a hydronium ion?
   A. H_3O^+ **C.** COOH
   B. OH^- **D.** H_2O

The titration curve (below) indicates the changes that happened to the solution as drops of a strong base are added. Use the graph below to answer questions 6–9.

Acids, Bases, and Salts

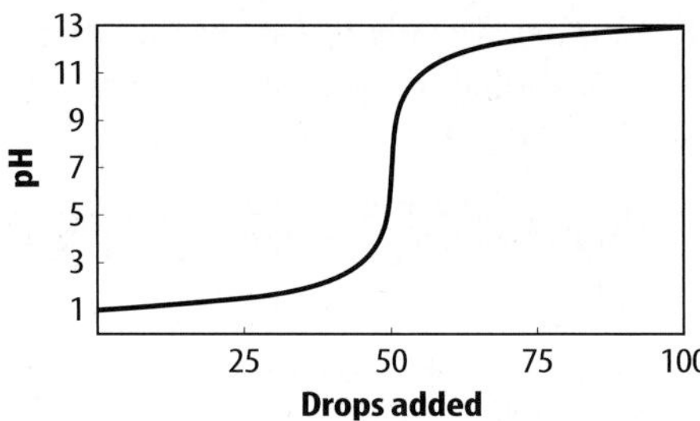

6. Before any drops were added, what was the pH of the solution?
   A. 1 **C.** 9
   B. 3 **D.** 13

7. At what drop count are the acid and base exactly neutralized?
   A. 0 **C.** 50
   B. 25 **D.** 75

8. At the instant of neutralization, what is in the beaker besides water?
   A. acid only **C.** salt only
   B. base only **D.** equal amounts of each

9. If the chemical equation for this reaction is $2HCl + Ca(OH)_2 \rightarrow CaCl_2 + 2H_2O$, how many water molecules are formed as x molecules of $CaCl_2$ form?
   A. 2
   B. twice as many, $2x$
   C. half as many, $x/2$
   D. an equal number, x

Part 2 Short Response/Grid In

Record your answers on the answer sheet provided by your teacher or on a sheet of paper.

Use the model below of hydrogen sulfide to answer questions 10–13.

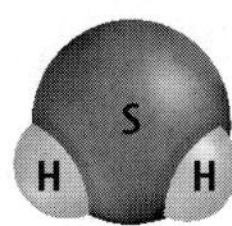

10. What is the chemical formula for this substance?

11. How many hydronium ions can it form in water?

12. Write the chemical equation for this dissociation reaction.

13. Hydrogen sulfide is a weak acid. Describe how much this substance will dissociate in water.

14. A conductivity apparatus is inserted into a beaker of water, but the light bulb does not glow. Describe what will happen if NaCl crystals are added with stirring.

15. When the pH of a solution drops from 3.0 to 1.0, the hydronium ion concentration increases by a factor of one hundred fold from 0.0010. What is the concentration at pH = 1.0?

16. Compare and contrast the terms *strength* and *concentration* as they apply to acids and bases in solution.

17. An environmental scientist tested rain puddles with pH test strips and a pH meter. The test strips indicated pH = 2.0 and the meter indicated pH = 2.9. By percent, calculate by how much these results differ.

18. Name the salt that is produced by each of the following acid-base pairs. HCl + NaOH; HNO_3 + KOH; H_2SO_4 + $Ca(OH)_2$

Part 3 Open Ended

Record your answers on a sheet of paper.

One of the solutions has a pH of 10, the other pH of 12. In one beaker the bulb glows more brightly than does the other. Use the figures below to answer questions 19 and 20.

19. Are the two solutions acids or bases? Explain how you know.

20. Explain why the bulbs glow with different intensities. Use the words *strong* and *weak* in your answer.

21. Describe how dishwashing liquid cleans dirty plates.

22. Na_2SO_4 is a soluble salt. Write the chemical equation describing its dissociation in water.

23. Identify the acid and base that are neutralized to form the salt Na_2SO_4 in a titration reaction.

24. Assume you have a HCl solution of unknown concentration. If 25.0 mL of this solution requires 50.0 mL of a known concentration of a NaOH solution to neutralize, how much more concentrated is the HCl solution than the NaOH solution?

25. Explain why a weak acid in solution has a higher pH than a strong acid of the same concentration.

Part 3 Open Ended

19. bases; they both have pH values above 7.

20. The base with the higher pH is a stronger base and therefore dissociates more completely than does the one with the lower pH. The stronger base releases more OH^- ions and conducts more electricity.

21. The nonpolar end of the soap molecule attracts dirt while the polar end is attracted by water molecules. Swirling the water and rinsing removes the dirt-laden soap molecules from the plate.

22. $Na_2SO_4^- \rightarrow 2Na^+(aq) + (SO_4)^{-2}(aq)$

23. sulfuric acid (H_2SO_4) and sodium hydroxide (NaOH)

24. twice as concentrated

25. The pH of a weak acid is higher because a weak acid produces fewer H_3O^- ions than a strong acid at the same concentration.

Rubrics

The following rubrics are sample scoring devices for short response and open-ended questions.

Short Response

Points	Description
2	The student demonstrates a thorough understanding of the science of the task. The response may contain minor flaws that do not detract from the demonstration of a thorough understanding.
1	The student has provided a response that is only partially correct.
0	The student has provided a completely incorrect solution or no response at all.

Open Ended

Points	Description
4	The student demonstrates a thorough understanding of the science of the task. The response may contain minor flaws that do not detract from the demonstration of a thorough understanding.
3	The student demonstrates an understanding of the science of the task. The response is essentially correct and demonstrates an essential but less than thorough understanding of the science.
2	The student demonstrates only a partial understanding of the science of the task. Although the student may have used the correct approach to a solution or may have provided a correct solution, the work lacks an essential understanding of the underlying science concepts.
1	The student demonstrates a very limited understanding of the science of the task. The response is incomplete and exhibits many flaws.
0	The student provides a completely incorrect solution or no response at all.

Organic Compounds

BIG Idea **Most compounds containing the element carbon are organic compounds.**

	Content Standards	Learning Objectives	Resources to Assess Mastery
Section 1	**5–8:** UCP.1–3, 5; A.1, 2; B.1; C.1 **9–12:** UCP.1–3, 5; A.1, 2; B.2; C.5	**Simple Organic Compounds** 1. **Identify** the difference between organic and inorganic compounds. 2. **Examine** the structure of some organic compounds. 3. **Differentiate** between saturated and unsaturated hydrocarbons. 4. **Identify** isomers of organic compounds. ***Main Idea*** Hydrocarbons are compounds made only of carbon and hydrogen atoms.	Formative Assessment Reading Check, pp. 727, 728, 730 Section Review, p. 730 Summative Assessment *ExamView® Assessment Suite*
Section 2	**5–8:** UCP.1–3, 5; A.1, 2; B.1; C.1 **9–12:** UCP.1–3, 5; A.1, 2; B.2; C.5	**Other Organic Compounds** 5. **Define** aromatic compounds. 6. **Identify** the nature of alcohols and acids. 7. **Identify** organic compounds you use in daily life. ***Main Idea*** Substituted hydrocarbons contain other elements besides carbon and hydrogen.	Formative Assessment Reading Check, pp. 731, 732, 733 Section Review, p. 734 Summative Assessment *ExamView® Assessment Suite*
Section 3	**5–8:** UCP.1–3, 5; A.1, 2; B.1; C.1 **9–12:** UCP.1–3, 5; A.1, 2; B.2; C.5	**Petroleum—A Source of Carbon Compounds** 8. **Explain** how carbon compounds are obtained from petroleum. 9. **Determine** how carbon compounds can form long chains. 10. **Define** the terms *polymerization* and *depolymerization.* ***Main Idea*** Petroleum is the source of carbon compounds used to make plastics, fossil fuels, and many other products.	Formative Assessment Reading Check, pp. 739, 740 Section Review, p. 741 Summative Assessment *ExamView® Assessment Suite*
Section 4	**5–8:** UCP.1–3, 5; A.1, 2; B.1; C.1; G.3 **9–12:** UCP.1–3, 5; A.1, 2; B.2; C.5; G.3 See pp. 16T–17T for a Key to Standards.	**Biological Compounds** 11. **Compare and contrast** proteins, nucleic acids, carbohydrates, and lipids. 12. **Identify** the structure of polymers found in basic food groups. 13. **Identify** the structure of large biological polymers. ***Main Idea*** Proteins, nucleic acids, carbohydrates, and lipids are polymers made by plants and animals.	Formative Assessment Reading Check, p. 743 Section Review, p. 747 Summative Chapter Assessment MindJogger, Ch. 24 *ExamView® Assessment Suite* Leveled Chapter Test Test A L1 Test B L2 Test C L3 Test Practice, pp. 754–755

Suggested Pacing				
Period	Instruction	Labs	Review & Assessment	Total
Single	3.5 days	2.5 days	2 days	8 days
Block	1.75 blocks	1.25 blocks	1 block	4 blocks

Core Instruction	Leveled Resources	Leveled Labs	Pacing Period		Pacing Block
Student Text, pp. 724–730 Section Focus Transparency, Ch. 24, Section 1 Teaching Transparency, Ch. 24, Section 1 Interactive Chalkboard, Ch. 24, Section 1 Differentiated Instruction, pp. 727, 728	**Chapter *Fast File* Resources** Directed Reading for Content Mastery, p. 20 L1 Note-taking Worksheet, pp. 35–38 Reinforcement, p. 27 L2 Enrichment, p. 31 L3 **Reading Essentials,** p. 412 L1 ELL **Science Notebook,** p. 279 ELL	**Launch Lab**, p. 725: white bread, white paper, laboratory burner, test tubes *15 min* L2 **MiniLAB**, p. 729: gumdrops (one color), raisins, toothpicks *15 min* L2	1	Section 1, pp. 725–727 includes Launch Lab)	1
			2	Section 1, pp. 728–731 (includes MiniLAB and Section Review)	
Student Text, pp. 731–735 Section Focus Transparency, Ch. 24, Section 2 Interactive Chalkboard, Ch. 24, Section 2 Identifying Misconceptions, p. 732	**Chapter *Fast File* Resources** Directed Reading for Content Mastery, p. 20 L1 Note-taking Worksheet, pp. 35–38 Reinforcement, p. 28 L2 Enrichment, p. 32 L3 **Reading Essentials,** p. 418 L1 ELL **Science Notebook,** p. 283 ELL	***Lab**, p. 735: large test tube, stopper, potassium permanganate solution (0.01*M*), sodium hydroxide solution (6*M*), ethanol, 10-mL graduated cylinder *25 min* L1 L2 L3	3	Section 2, pp. 731–734 (includes Section Review)	2
			4	Lab: Alcohol and Organic Acids, p. 735	
Student Text, pp. 736–741 Section Focus Transparency, Ch. 24, Section 3 Interactive Chalkboard, Ch. 24, Section 3 Visualizing Petroleum Products, p. 738 Differentiated Instruction, pp. 738, 739, 740	**Chapter *Fast File* Resources** Directed Reading for Content Mastery, p. 21 L1 Note-taking Worksheet, pp. 35–38 Reinforcement, p. 29 L2 Enrichment, p. 33 L3 **Reading Essentials,** p. 422 L1 ELL **Science Notebook,** p. 286 ELL	**MiniLAB**, p. 739: markers, scissors, tape, or stapler, colored paper, paper clips (20) *20 min* L2	5	Section 3, pp. 736–741 (includes MiniLAB and Section Review)	3
Student Text, pp. 742–749 Section Focus Transparency, Ch. 24, Section 4 Interactive Chalkboard, Ch. 24, Section 4 Applying Science, p. 744 Differentiated Instruction, pp. 745, 746 Chapter Study Guide, p. 751	**Chapter *Fast File* Resources** Directed Reading for Content Mastery, pp. 21, 22 L1 Note-taking Worksheet, pp. 35–38 Reinforcement, p. 30 L2 Enrichment, p. 34 L3 **Reading Essentials,** p. 427 L1 ELL **Science Notebook,** p. 289 ELL	***Lab**, pp. 748–749: test tubes, test-tube holder, 250-mL beaker, 10-mL graduated cylinder, water, hot plate, ring stand, thermometer, salicylic acid, amyl alcohol, concentrated sulfuric acid *25 min* L1 L2 L3 *Lab version A L1 version B L2 L3	6	Section 4, pp. 742–747	
			7	Lab: Preparing an Ester, pp. 748–749	4
			8	Study Guide, Chapter Review, and Test Practice, pp. 751–755	

Video Lab

Transparencies

Section Focus

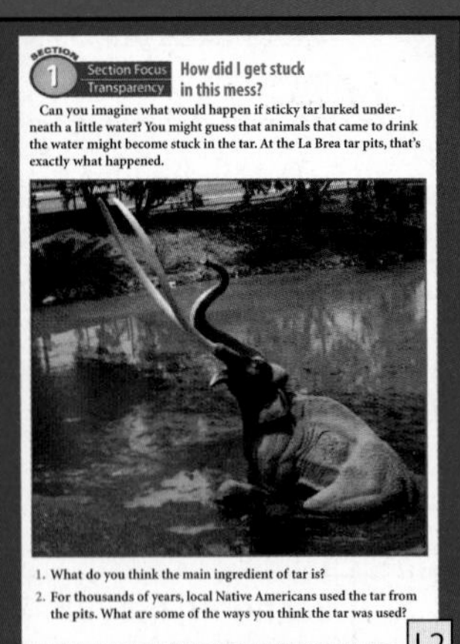
Section Focus Transparency 1 — How did I get stuck in this mess?

Can you imagine what would happen if sticky tar lurked underneath a little water? You might guess that animals that came to drink the water might become stuck in the tar. At the La Brea tar pits, that's exactly what happened.

1. What do you think the main ingredient of tar is?
2. For thousands of years, local Native Americans used the tar from the pits. What are some of the ways you think the tar was used?

L2

Section Focus Transparency 2 — Slick Idea

In 1823, Charles Macintosh discovered how to waterproof fabric with dissolved rubber. Later developments improved his method of waterproofing, but the term *mackintosh* still refers to a waterproof overcoat.

1. Where does rubber come from?
2. What other uses for rubber can you think of?

L2

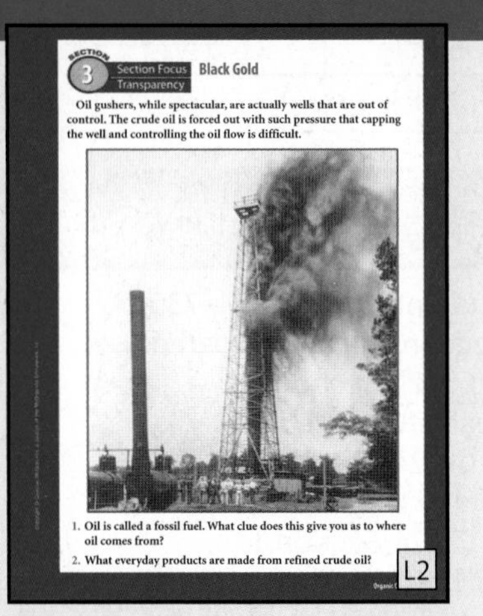
Section Focus Transparency 3 — Black Gold

Oil gushers, while spectacular, are actually wells that are out of control. The crude oil is forced out with such pressure that capping the well and controlling the oil flow is difficult.

1. Oil is called a fossil fuel. What clue does this give you as to where oil comes from?
2. What everyday products are made from refined crude oil?

L2

This is a representation of key blackline masters available in the Teacher Classroom Resources. See Resource Manager boxes within the chapter for additional information.

Assessment

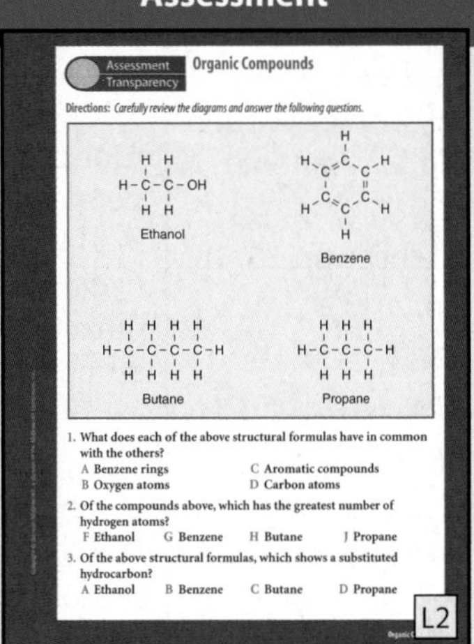
Assessment Transparency — Organic Compounds

Directions: Carefully review the diagrams and answer the following questions.

1. What does each of the above structural formulas have in common with the others?
   A Benzene rings C Aromatic compounds
   B Oxygen atoms D Carbon atoms
2. Of the compounds above, which has the greatest number of hydrogen atoms?
   F Ethanol G Benzene H Butane J Propane
3. Of the above structural formulas, which shows a substituted hydrocarbon?
   A Ethanol B Benzene C Butane D Propane

L2

Teaching

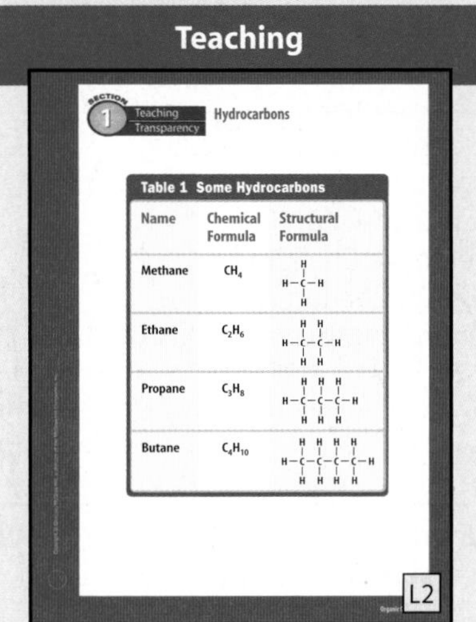
Teaching Transparency 1 — Hydrocarbons

Table 1 Some Hydrocarbons

Name	Chemical Formula	Structural Formula
Methane	CH_4	
Ethane	C_2H_6	
Propane	C_3H_8	
Butane	C_4H_{10}	

L2

Key to Teaching Strategies

The following designations will help you decide which activities are appropriate for your students.

- L1 Level 1 activities should be appropriate for students with learning difficulties.
- L2 Level 2 activities should be within the ability range of all students.
- L3 Level 3 activities are designed for above-average students.
- ELL ELL activities should be within the ability range of English Language Learners.
- COOP LEARN Cooperative Learning activities are designed for small group work.
- LS Multiple Learning Styles logos, as described on page 12T, are used throughout to indicate strategies that address different learning styles.
- P These strategies represent student products that can be placed into a best-work portfolio.
- PBL Problem-Based Learning activities apply real-world situations to learning.

Hands-on Activities

Student Text Lab Worksheet

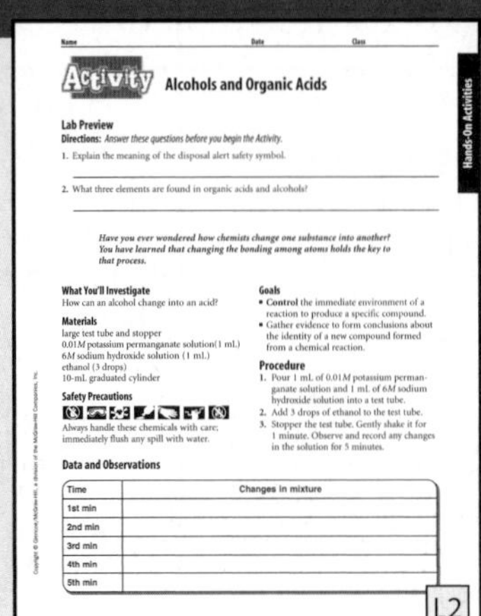
Activity — Alcohols and Organic Acids

Lab Preview

Directions: Answer these questions before you begin the Activity.

1. Explain the meaning of the disposal alert safety symbol.
2. What three elements are found in organic acids and alcohols?

Data and Observations

Time	Changes in mixture
1st min	
2nd min	
3rd min	
4th min	
5th min	

L2

Laboratory Activities

Laboratory Activity 1 — The Breakdown of Starch

L2

Meeting Different Ability Levels

Content Outline

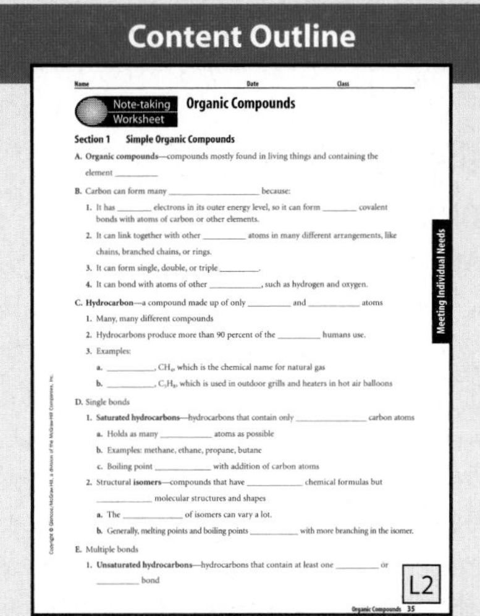

Note-taking Worksheet — Organic Compounds

Section 1 Simple Organic Compounds

L2

Reinforcement

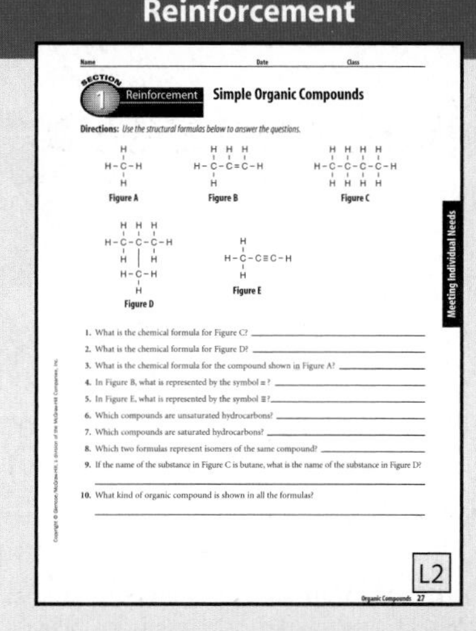

Section 1 Reinforcement — Simple Organic Compounds

L2

Enrichment

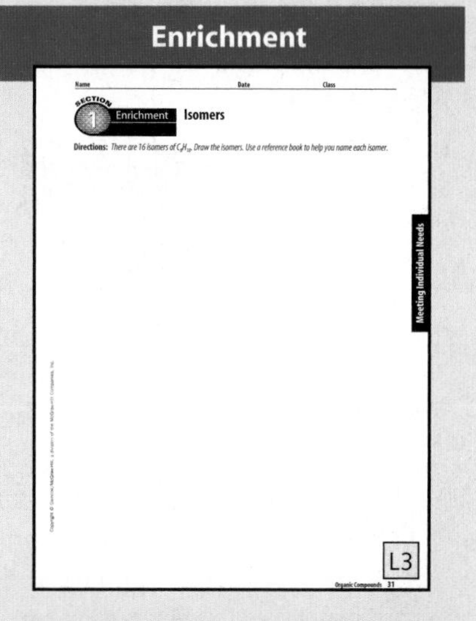

Section 1 Enrichment — Isomers

L3

Directed Reading (English/Spanish)

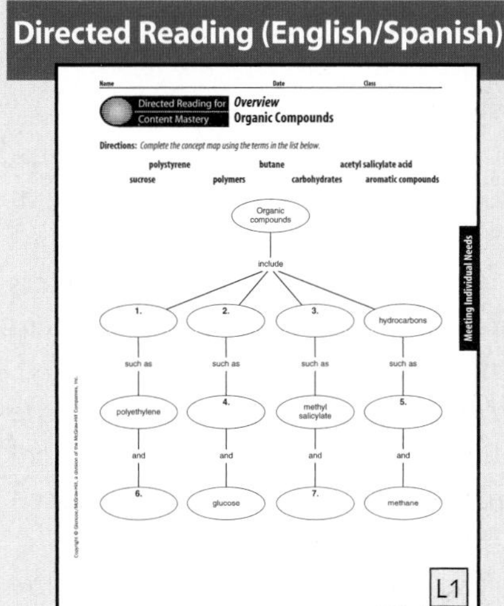

Directed Reading for Content Mastery — Overview: Organic Compounds

L1

Study Guide

Study Guide
Features
• Contains a study guide page for each section of the chapter
• Reviews key concepts
• Includes answer pages
L2

Reading Essentials

Reading Essentials for Glencoe Science
An Interactive Student Workbook
Features
• Condensed core content
• Actively involves students in reading
• Reinforces key vocabulary
L1

Assessment

Test Practice Workbook

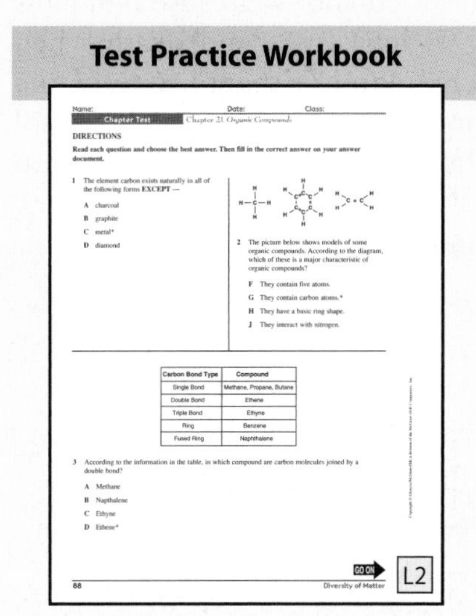

Chapter Test — Chapter 24 Organic Compounds

L2

Chapter Review

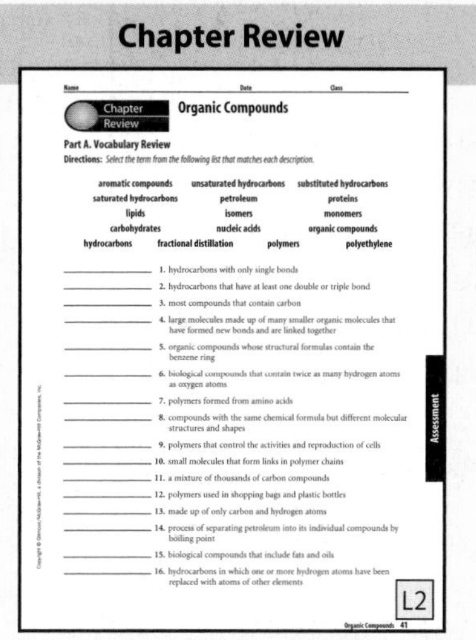

Chapter Review — Organic Compounds

L2

Chapter Tests

Chapter Test — Organic Compounds

L2

Science Content Background

section 1 Simple Organic Compounds

Single Bonds

Alkanes, hydrocarbons that contain all single bonds, are generally very unreactive. However, they will react with oxygen under certain conditions. The chemical reaction of alkanes with oxygen occurs during combustion in an engine or a furnace when the alkane is burned as a fuel. Carbon dioxide and water are formed as products, and a large amount of heat is released. At room temperature, alkanes with one to four carbons per molecule are gases (methane, propane), five to about sixteen carbons are liquid (gasoline, kerosene), and those with more than sixteen carbons per molecule are solids (wax, petroleum jelly).

Multiple Bonds

Ethene, or ethylene, the simplest of the alkenes, is an important commercial organic chemical. Annual United States production of ethylene is more than 20 billion kg. More than half of this amount goes into the manufacture of the plastic, polyethylene. Another 15 percent is converted to ethylene glycol, the major component of antifreeze.

Teacher to Teacher
Steve Federman
Loveland Middle School
Loveland, Ohio

"Casein is the part of the milk that makes plastic. I have students pour $\frac{1}{2}$ cup milk and 1 tablespoon vinegar into a saucepan and heat slowly, stirring constantly until lumps form. Then, they remove the pan from the heat and continue stirring until the curds (solid protein) float in the whey (liquid). The polymers are linked together making it moldable and plastic."

Steve Federman

section 2 Other Organic Compounds

Aromatic Hydrocarbons

In the early days of organic chemistry, the word *aromatic* was used to describe certain fragrant substances from natural sources such as fruits and trees. Chemists soon realized, however, that these substances behaved differently from most other organic compounds. Benzene is the simplest aromatic compound, but other compounds such as aspirin, hydrocortisone, and Valium also contain aromatic rings.

Substituted Hydrocarbons

Organic compounds can undergo substitution reactions in which some or all of the hydrogen atoms are replaced with other atoms or groups of atoms. For example, when benzene reacts with nitric acid in the presence of sulfuric acid as a catalyst, trinitrotoluene (TNT) is produced. Nitration of aromatic rings is a key step in the synthesis of many important pharmaceutical agents and of many brightly colored dyes used in clothing.

Methanol, the simplest alcohol with one carbon, is also known as wood alcohol because it was once produced by heating wood in the absence of air. Today, more than eight billion gallons of methanol are manufactured each year. Toxic to humans, methanol will cause blindness when ingested in low doses and death when taken in larger amounts. Ethanol, one of the oldest known organic compounds, is an alcohol with two carbons. Sometimes called grain alcohol, ethanol is present in all wines, beers, and distilled liquors.

section 3 Petroleum—A Source of Carbon Compounds

Uses for Petroleum

The gasoline that is distilled directly from petroleum is a poor fuel because it causes engines to "knock." The knock comes from uncontrolled combustion in the engine and can waste fuel and damage the engine. The octane number of gasoline indicates how good or bad the gasoline is as a fuel. Heptane, a straight-chain hydrocarbon and a very bad fuel, is assigned a value of 0. A branched-chain hydrocarbon commonly known as isooctane has a rating of 100. To obtain gasoline, the kerosene fraction which contains hydrocarbons ranging in the number of 12 to 14 carbons, is "cracked" into smaller molecules. The major gasoline products of cracking are branched-chain molecules containing from 7 to 10 carbons. These have high octane ratings. Tetraethlyl lead was used for many years to boost a gasoline's octane rating, but now compounds such as ethanol are used.

section 4 Biological Compounds

Proteins

Enzymes are large proteins that act as catalysts for biological reactions. Enzymes are made to catalyze only very specific reactions. The enzyme amylase found in human digestive systems, for example, is able to catalyze the breakdown of starch to yield glucose but has no effect on cellulose, even though the two compounds are similar. This is why humans can digest potatoes but not grass.

Lipids

Steroids are lipids that are made up of tetracyclic (four-ring) hydrocarbons. Three of the rings have six carbons and one has five carbons. Steroids have many diverse roles in both plants and animals. Cholesterol and a variety of hormones have this structure.

chapter content resources

Internet Resources

For additional content background, visit **gpscience.com** to:

- access your book online
- find references to related articles in popular science magazines
- access Web links with related content background
- access current events with science journal topics

Print Resources

The Way Science Works, Robin Kerrod and Sharon Ann Holgate, Darling Kindersley, 2002

Chemistry Demystified, Linda Williams, McGraw-Hill, 2003

Girls Think of Everything, Catherine Thimmesh, Haughton Mifflen Co., 2000

Napoleon's Buttons, Penny Le Couteur and Jay Burreson, J.P. Tarcher, 2003

Hans Pfletschinger/Peter Arnold, Inc.

chapter 24

About the Photo

The photo shows willow trees in the Boston Public Garden in Boston, Massachusetts. The Public Garden was established in 1837 and is the oldest botanical garden in the United States. The active ingredient in willow bark is salicin, which is converted to salicyclic acid in the body.

Science Journal Answers will vary, depending on the students' backgrounds. Some may mention herbal remedies, such as St. John's wort, Ginseng, or *Ginkgo biloba*. Tamoxifen for treating cancer has been in the news.

BIG Idea

Carbon Bonds Carbon atoms can form strong single, double, and triple bonds. Carbon bonds point in different directions, depending on the number of bonds a carbon atom forms. If a carbon atom forms four single bonds, the bonds point toward the vertices of a triangular pyramid, or tetrahedron. If three bonds are formed, one bond is a double bond. Then the double bond and the two single bonds point toward the vertices of an equilateral triangle. If two bonds are formed, one bond is a triple bond, and the two bonds are linear.

Introduce the Chapter Ask students to define the word *organic*. Have them discuss how they think the element carbon and their definition of *organic* might be connected.

chapter 24

Organic Compounds

BIG Idea Most compounds containing the element carbon are organic compounds.

24.1 Simple Organic Compounds

MAIN Idea Hydrocarbons are compounds made only of carbon and hydrogen atoms.

24.2 Other Organic Compounds

MAIN Idea Substituted hydrocarbons contain other elements besides carbon and hydrogen.

24.3 Petroleum—A Source of Carbon Compounds

MAIN Idea Petroleum is the source of carbon compounds used to make plastics, fossil fuels, and many other products.

24.4 Biological Compounds

MAIN Idea Proteins, nucleic acids, carbohydrates, and lipids are polymers made by plants and animals.

What's in the willows?

The bark of willow trees has been used to treat pain and fever. Willow bark contains a compound related to aspirin. Today, aspirin and thousands of other useful substances are synthesized from compounds found in petroleum.

Science Journal

List other medicines from natural sources, such as plants.

724

Interactive Chalkboard

This CD-ROM is an editable Microsoft® PowerPoint® presentation that includes:

- an editable presentation for every chapter
- additional chapter questions
- animated graphics
- image bank
- links to gpscience.com

Start-Up Activities

Carbon, the Organic Element

The element carbon exists in three very different forms: dull, black charcoal; slippery, gray graphite; and bright, sparkling diamond. However, this is nothing compared with the millions of different compounds that carbon can form. In this lab, you will seek out the carbon hidden in two common substances.

WARNING: *Always use extreme caution around an open flame. Point test tubes away from yourself and others.*

1. Place a small piece of bread in a test tube.
2. Using a test-tube holder, hold the tube over the flame of a laboratory burner until you observe changes in the bread.
3. Using a clean test tube and a small amount of paper instead of bread, repeat step 2.
4. **Think Critically** Based on what you observed and what remained in the test tubes, infer what these residues might be.

Organic Compounds Make the following Foldable to help you understand the vocabulary terms in this chapter.

STEP 1 **Fold** a vertical sheet of notebook paper from side to side.

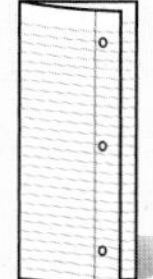

STEP 2 **Cut** along every third line of only the top layer to form tabs.

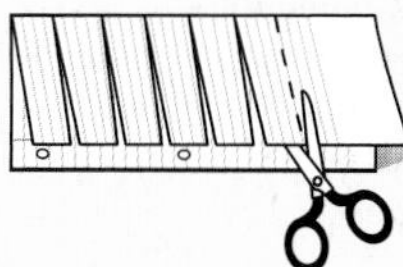

Build Vocabulary As you read the chapter, list the vocabulary words about organic compounds on the tabs. As you learn the definitions, write them under the tab for each vocabulary word.

Preview this chapter's content and activities at gpscience.com

725

Purpose Use the Launch Lab to introduce students to some of the common materials around them that contain carbon. This lab also points out that although two substances can appear very different, their basic makeup may be very similar. L2 ELL

LS **Visual-Spatial**

Preparation Cut fresh bread into thin strips, 2 cm long, that will fit into a test tube.

Materials white bread, white paper, laboratory burner, test tubes

Teaching Strategy Bring some carbon ground from charcoal to class and have students examine it before they do this lab.

Think Critically

The black ash left in the test tubes is carbon. Many students may write that what remained was burned bread. Remind them of what they saw leaving the test tube, which was water vapor.

Assessment

Oral After students have done the lab, hold up a burnt piece of bread and ask them if they can identify whether it is bread or paper. Use **Performance Assessment in the Science Classroom,** p. 89

Dinah Zike Study Fold

Student preparation materials for this Foldable are available in the Chapter *Fast File* Resources.

Additional Chapter Media

- Virtual Lab: *What are the energy outputs of different types of fuels?*
- Virtual Lab: *Alcohols and Organic Acids*

1 Motivate

Bellringer

Section Focus Transparencies also are available on the Interactive Chalkboard CD-ROM. L2

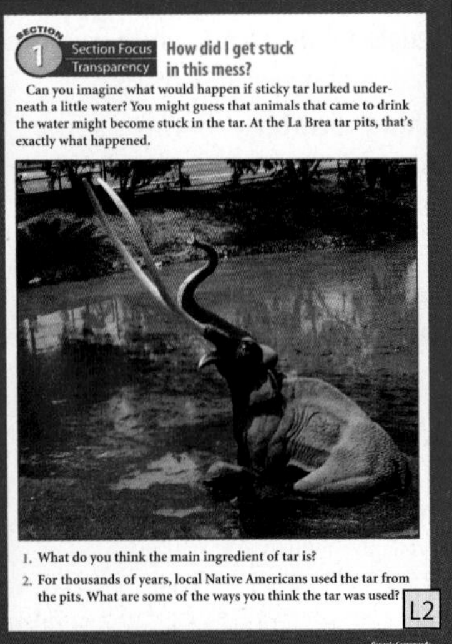
SECTION 1 Section Focus Transparency **How did I get stuck in this mess?**

Can you imagine what would happen if sticky tar lurked underneath a little water? You might guess that animals that came to drink the water might become stuck in the tar. At the La Brea tar pits, that's exactly what happened.

1. What do you think the main ingredient of tar is?
2. For thousands of years, local Native Americans used the tar from the pits. What are some of the ways you think the tar was used? L2

Organic Compounds

Tie to Prior Knowledge

Forms of Carbon Ask students to identify forms of carbon that they know. Remind them that diamonds and the graphite in pencils are both forms of carbon. Explain that the element carbon is able to bond with itself and other elements in many different ways. L2

section 1

Simple Organic Compounds

Reading Guide

What You'll Learn

- **Identify** the difference between organic and inorganic carbon compounds.
- **Examine** the structures of some organic compounds.
- **Differentiate** between saturated and unsaturated hydrocarbons.
- **Identify** isomers of organic compounds.

Why It's Important

Carbon compounds surround you—they're in your food, your body, and most materials you use every day.

Review Vocabulary

compound: substance formed from two or more elements

New Vocabulary

- organic compound
- hydrocarbon
- saturated hydrocarbon
- isomer
- unsaturated hydrocarbon

Organic Compounds

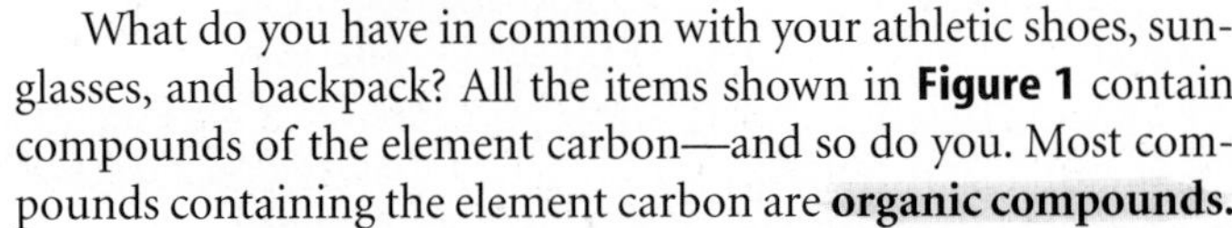

What do you have in common with your athletic shoes, sunglasses, and backpack? All the items shown in **Figure 1** contain compounds of the element carbon—and so do you. Most compounds containing the element carbon are **organic compounds.**

At one time, scientists thought that only living organisms could make organic compounds, which is how they got their name. By 1830, scientists could make organic compounds in laboratories, but they continued to call them organic.

Of the millions of carbon compounds known today, more than 90 percent of them are considered organic. The others, including carbon dioxide and the carbonates, are considered inorganic.

Figure 1 Most items used every day contain carbon.

Bonding You may wonder why carbon can form so many organic compounds. The main reason is that a carbon atom has four electrons in its outer energy level. This means that each carbon atom can form four covalent bonds with atoms of carbon or with other elements. As you have learned, a covalent bond is formed when two atoms share a pair of electrons. This large number of bonds allows carbon to form many types of compounds ranging from small compounds used as fuel, to complex compounds found in medicines and dyes, and the polymers used in plastics and textile fibers.

Section 1 Resource Manager

Chapter *Fast File* Resources

- Transparency Activity, pp. 48, 53–54
- Directed Reading for Content Mastery, pp. 19, 20
- Note-taking Worksheets, pp. 35–38
- MiniLAB, p. 3
- Reinforcement, p. 27
- Enrichment, p. 31

726 CHAPTER 24 Organic Compounds

Arrangement Another reason carbon can form so many compounds is that carbon can link together with other carbon atoms in many different arrangements—chains, branched chains, and even rings. It also can form double and triple bonds as well as single bonds. In addition, carbon can bond with atoms of many other elements, such as hydrogen and oxygen. **Figure 2** shows some possible arrangements for carbon compounds.

Hydrocarbons

Carbon forms an enormous number of compounds with hydrogen alone. A compound made up of only carbon and hydrogen atoms is called a **hydrocarbon.** Does the furnace, stove, or water heater in your home burn natural gas? A main component of the natural gas used for these purposes is the hydrocarbon methane. The chemical formula of methane is CH_4.

Methane can be represented in two other ways, as shown in **Figure 3.** The structural formula uses lines to show that four hydrogen atoms are bonded to one carbon atom in a methane molecule. Each line between atoms represents a single covalent bond. The second way, the space-filling model, shows a more realistic picture of the relative size and arrangement of the atoms in the molecule. Most often, however, chemists use chemical and structural formulas to write about reactions.

Reading Check *Name three ways that chemists represent organic compounds.*

Another hydrocarbon used as fuel is propane. Some stoves, most outdoor grills, and the heaters in hot-air balloons burn this hydrocarbon, which is found in bottled gas. Propane's structural formula and space-filling model also are shown in **Figure 3.**

Methane and other hydrocarbons produce more than 90 percent of the energy humans use. Carbon compounds also are important in medicines, foods, and clothing. To understand how carbon can play so many roles, you must understand how it forms bonds.

Figure 2 Carbon atoms bond to form straight, branched, and cyclic chains.

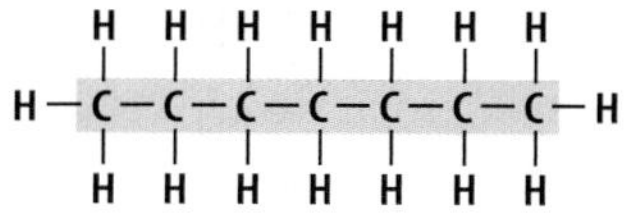

Heptane is found in gasoline.

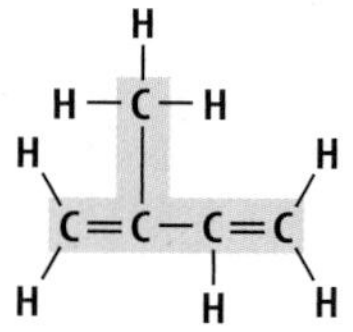

Isoprene exists in natural rubber.

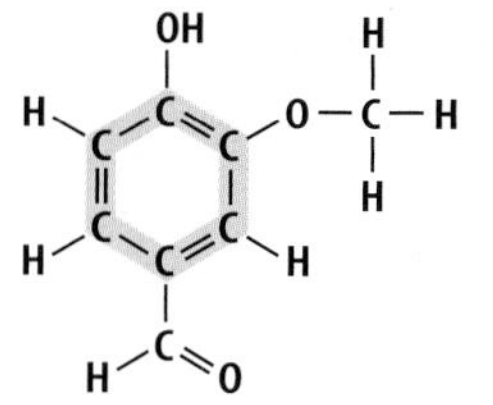

Vanillin is found in vanilla flavoring.

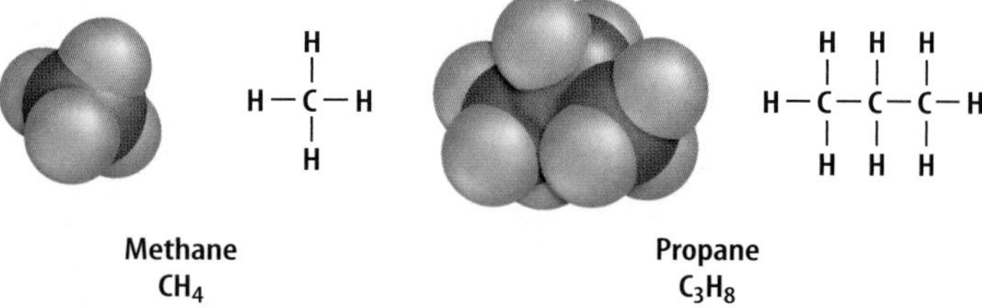

Figure 3 Natural gas is mostly methane, CH_4, but bottled gas is mostly propane, C_3H_8.
Compare and contrast *the two gases.*

2 Teach

Teacher FYI

Unreactive Alkanes Alkanes are extremely unreactive compounds. Their most notable reaction is combustion, in which the products are CO_2 and H_2O. The amount of heat released by burning is also known as the heat of combustion. The heats of combustion for some short-chain alkanes are: methane: 890.8 kJ/mol; ethane, 1560.7 kJ/mol; propane: 2,219.2 kJ/mol; butane: 2,877.6 kJ/mol; pentane: 3,509.0 kJ/mol; hexane: 4,163.2 kJ/mol; and heptane: 4,817.0 kJ/mol.

Activity

Hydrocarbon Models Have students make models of the three compounds shown in **Figure 2** using varying colors of gumdrops for atoms and toothpicks for bonds. Ask them to make sure that each carbon atom has exactly four bonds. L2

Reading Check

Answer chemical formula, structural formula, and space-filling model

Caption Answer

Figure 3 Both gases are hydrocarbons. Methane is the smallest with one carbon atom and four hydrogen atoms. Propane has three carbon atoms and eight hydrogen atoms.

Differentiated Instruction

Challenge Ask students to research the work of Friedrich Wöhler, the first organic chemist, and report on it to the class. They should learn the name and structure of urea, the compound he made in the laboratory in 1828. Before this, people thought that urea could be made only by living systems. L2

Visual Learning

Figure 2 Point out to students that in this figure, each line between atoms represents a single bond and each double line represents a double bond. Ask students to count the number of double bonds in heptane 0, isoprene 2, and vanillin 4. Point out that in vanillin, carbon is attached to oxygen atoms as well as to hydrogen atoms. L1 ELL IN **Visual-Spatial**

SECTION 1 Simple Organic Compounds 727

Table 1 Some Hydrocarbons

Name	Chemical Formula	Structural Formula
Methane	CH_4	H | H—C—H | H
Ethane	C_2H_6	H H | | H—C—C—H | | H H
Propane	C_3H_8	H H H | | | H—C—C—C—H | | | H H H
Butane	C_4H_{10}	H H H H | | | | H—C—C—C—C—H | | | | H H H H

Single Bonds

In some hydrocarbons, the carbon atoms are joined by single covalent bonds. Hydrocarbons containing only single-bonded carbon atoms are called **saturated hydrocarbons.** Saturated means that a compound holds as many hydrogen atoms as possible—it is saturated with hydrogen atoms.

Reading Check *What are saturated hydrocarbons?*

Table 1 lists four saturated hydrocarbons. Notice how each carbon atom appears to be a link in a chain connected by single covalent bonds. **Figure 4** shows a graph of the boiling points of some hydrocarbons. Notice the relationship between boiling points and the addition of carbon atoms.

Structural Isomers Perhaps you have seen or know about butane, which is a gas that sometimes is burned in camping stoves and lighters. The chemical formula of butane is C_4H_{10}. Another hydrocarbon called isobutane has exactly the same chemical formula. How can this be? The answer lies in the arrangement of the four carbon atoms. Look at **Figure 5.** In a molecule of butane, the carbon atoms form a continuous chain. The carbon chain of isobutane is branched. The arrangement of carbon atoms in each compound changes the shape of the molecule, and very often affects its physical properties, as you will soon see. Isobutane and butane are isomers.

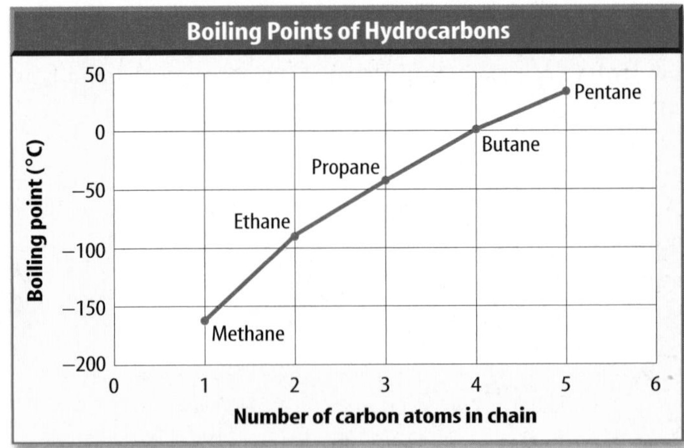

Figure 4 Boiling points of hydrocarbons increase as the number of carbon atoms in the chain increases.
Predict *the approximate boiling point of hexane.*

Use Science Words

Word Origin Explain to students that in the word *isomer* the prefix *iso-* means "equal." Ask students what is equal about different isomers. their chemical formulas Have students name other words they know that have the prefix *iso-*, and tell what the words mean. Possible answers: *isobar*—line of equal pressure; *isotherm*—line of equal temperature; *isotope*—atoms with the same atomic number but different numbers of neutrons. L2 IS **Linguistic**

Quick Demo

Hydrocarbon Fuels

Materials small butane lighter

Estimated Time five minutes

Procedure Light the lighter and draw the structure of butane on the board. Point out that it has only one more carbon than propane, which is used as fuel in outdoor grills.

Fun Fact

Methane is also known as marsh gas because it forms from decaying vegetation. When pockets of this gas ignited, primitive peoples believed the bluish flames were evil spirits.

Caption Answer

Figure 4 Actual boiling point is 69°C. Accept 60° to 80°.

Discussion

Heat from Hydrocarbons You have read that many alkane hydrocarbons are used as fuel. How do you think changing a single bond into a double bond affects the amount of heat released when the substance burns? Possible answer: Burning means combining with oxygen. When alkanes burn their hydrogens combine with oxygen. If fewer hydrogens are present as in a double-bonded compound, there are fewer hydrogens to combine. Therefore the amount of heat released during combustion decreases. L2

Differentiated Instruction

English-Language Learners Ask students to make models of organic compounds. Have them paint polystyrene foam balls different colors to represent specific elements (carbon–black, hydrogen–yellow, etc.). Have them combine the atoms to form models of some of the compounds shown in this chapter. L2 ELL IS P **Kinesthetic**

Visual Learning

Figure 4 Have students look at the graph and determine the boiling point of propane. −40°C Ask them to use the data in the graph to estimate the boiling point of octane. Accept 100 to 125°C. L2 ELL
IS **Visual-Spatial**

728 CHAPTER 24 Organic Compounds

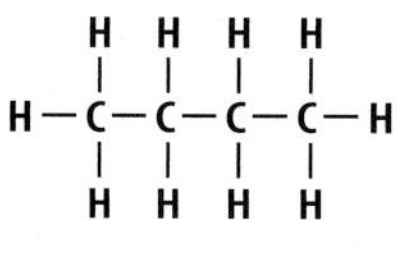

Butane
C_4H_{10}

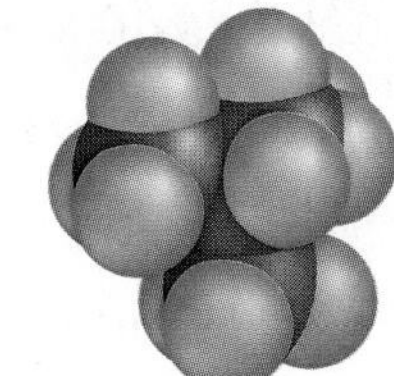

Isobutane
C_4H_{10}

Figure 5 Butane has two isomers, one with a straight chain and the other isomer with a branched chain.

Isomers are compounds that have identical chemical formulas but different molecular structures and shapes. Thousands of isomers exist among the hydrocarbons. Generally, melting points and boiling points are lowered as the amount of branching in an isomer increases. You can see this pattern in **Table 2,** which lists properties of butane and isobutane.

Sometimes properties of isomers can vary amazingly. For example, the isomer of octane having all eight carbons in a straight chain melts at −56.8°C, but the most branched octane melts at 100.7°C. In this case, the high melting point results from the symmetry of the molecule and its globular shape. Look for this isomer when you do the Try at Home MiniLAB.

Other Isomers There are many other kinds of isomers in organic and inorganic chemistry. Some isomers differ only slightly in how their atoms are arranged in space. Such isomers form what often are called right- and left-handed molecules, like mirror images. Two such isomers may have nearly identical physical and chemical properties.

Table 2 Properties of Butane Isomers

Property	Butane	Isobutane
Description	Colorless gas	Colorless gas
Density	0.60 kg/L	0.603 kg/L
Melting point	−135°C	−145°C
Boiling point	−0.5°C	−10.2°C

Modeling Structures of Octane

Procedure

1. To model octane, C_8H_{18}, a hydrocarbon found in gasoline, use soft **gumdrops** to represent carbon atoms.
2. Use **raisins** to represent hydrogen atoms.
3. Use **toothpicks** for chemical bonds.
   WARNING: *NEVER eat any food in the laboratory.*

Analysis

1. How do you distinguish one structure from another?
2. What was the total number of different molecules found in your class?

Try at Home

Mini LAB

Purpose Students use models to determine the structures of isomers of octane. L2 ELL

LS **Kinesthetic**

Materials gumdrops of one color, raisins, toothpicks

Teaching Strategies This activity can be done at home or in class. If it is done in class have each student build the straight-chain isomer of octane. This ensures that everyone will have all carbons and hydrogens in correct relative positions.

Safety Precaution Remind students that toothpicks are sharp and to use care when piercing gumdrops.

Troubleshooting Monitor the structure comparisons so students do not consider identical structures to be different because they are oriented differently.

Analysis

1. by the positions and arrangements of the carbon atoms
2. There can be a maximum of 18 different structures.

Assessment

Oral Have students explain why different structures have different properties. Some shapes form stronger intermolecular bonds than others. Use **Performance Assessment in the Science Classroom,** p. 89.

Reading Check

Answer hydrocarbons in which all of the bonds are single covalent bonds

Science Journal

Isomers Have students draw and label in their Science Journals all the isomers of the short-chain hydrocarbons, ethane, propane, butane, pentane, hexane, and heptane. After students have drawn the isomers, have them check carefully and cross out any isomers that are equivalent to ones they have already drawn. Ask students to record the number of different isomers possible for each compound. ethane: 1; propane: 1; butane: 2; pentane: 3; hexane: 5; heptane: 9 L3 ELL LS **Logical-Mathematical**

Answer ethylene

3 Assess

DAILY INTERVENTION

Check for Understanding

Interpersonal Have students work in pairs. Tell each to individually make 5 flash cards having the name of a hydrocarbon on one side and its structure on the other. Then let them take turns quizzing the other. Tell them to include single, double, and triple bonds in their compounds. L2

Reteach

Alkane Fuels Write the names and structures of the first eight alkanes on the board in a tabular form leaving two columns open, one headed *Physical State* and the other *Use*. Fill in these columns with student participation. L2

Assessment

Performance Provide the boiling points and structural formulas of the three isomers of pentane, *n*-pentane: 36.0°C; isopentane: 27.8°C, and neopentane: 9.4°C. Have students graph the boiling points and use the graph to infer a relationship between branching and boiling points. The greater the branching, the lower the boiling point. Use **Performance Assessment in the Science Classroom,** p. 89. L3

Figure 6 Hydrocarbons can contain double or triple bonds between carbon atoms. Ethyne, also called acetylene, is used in torches for welding. Ethene or ethylene gas ripens fruit.

Multiple Bonds

Peaches are among the many fruits that can form small quantities of ethylene gas, which aids in ripening. Ethylene is another name for the hydrocarbon ethene, C_2H_4. This contains one double bond in which two carbon atoms share two pairs of electrons. The hydrocarbon ethyne contains a triple bond in which three pairs of electrons are shared. Hydrocarbons, such as ethene and ethyne, that contain at least one double or triple bond are called **unsaturated hydrocarbons.** They are shown in **Figure 6.**

Reading Check *What is another name for ethene?*

An easy way to remember what type of bond a hydrocarbon has is to look at the last three letters. Compounds ending with *–ane* have a single bond; the ending *–ene* indicates a double bond, and *–yne* indicates a triple bond.

section 1 review

Summary

Organic Compounds

- Most compounds containing the element carbon are organic compounds.
- Carbon can form many compounds because it has four electrons in its outer energy level.
- Carbon can bond with atoms of other elements, such as hydrogen, oxygen, and nitrogen.

Hydrocarbons

- A compound containing only carbon and hydrogen atoms is a hydrocarbon.
- Saturated hydrocarbons contain only single bonds.

Isomers and Multiple Bonds

- Compounds that have identical chemical formulas but different molecular structures are called isomers.
- Unsaturated hydrocarbons contain double and triple bonds.

Self Check

1. **Explain** how organic compounds got this name.
2. **Compare and contrast** ethane, ethene, and ethyne.
3. **Explain** the term *saturated* in relation to hydrocarbons. With what are such compounds saturated?
4. **Describe** how boiling and melting points generally vary as branching in a hydrocarbon chain increases.
5. **Think Critically** Cyclopropane is a cyclic, saturated hydrocarbon containing three carbon atoms. Draw its structural formula. Are cyclopropane and propane isomers? Explain.

Applying Math

6. **Ratios** The formula for the saturated hydrocarbon octane is C_8H_{18}. Adding one double bond makes the hydrocarbon octene, having the formula C_8H_{16}. Write the formulas of the hydrocarbons formed by adding one, two, and three more double bonds to octene. Find the ratio of hydrogen decrease to the number of double bonds?

section 1 review

1. Organic refers to living. Originally it was thought that these carbon-based compounds came only from living organisms.
2. They are hydrocarbons with two carbon atoms each. Ethane has a single bond between the two carbon atoms, ethene has a double bond, and ethyne has a triple bond.
3. Saturated with respect to hydrocarbons means that they contain only single bonds, or all the hydrogen atoms possible. In a sense, they are "saturated" with hydrogen.
4. Generally more branching results in a lowering of boiling and melting points.
5. No; cyclopropane, C_3H_6, is not an isomer of propane, C_3H_8, because it has a different chemical formula.
6. For one double bond, C_8H_{16}; For two double bonds, C_8H_{14}; For three double bonds, C_8H_{12}; Ratio is two hydrogens decrease to each double bond.

section 2

Other Organic Compounds

Reading Guide

What You'll Learn

- **Define** aromatic compounds.
- **Identify** the nature of alcohols and acids.
- **Identify** organic compounds you use in daily life.

Why It's Important

Aromatic compounds are building blocks of thousands of useful compounds, such as flavorings and medicines.

Review Vocabulary

structural formula: a molecular model that uses symbols and bonds to show relative positions of atoms

New Vocabulary

- aromatic compound
- substituted hydrocarbon
- alcohol

Aromatic Compounds

Chewing flavored gum or dissolving a candy mint in your mouth releases pleasant flavors and aromas. Many chemical compounds produce pleasant odors but others have less pleasant flavors and smells. For example, aspirin, which has an unpleasant, sour taste, and methyl salicylate, the compound that produces the fresh fragrance of wintergreen, shown in **Figure 7.** Both of these compounds are considered aromatic compounds. In addition to the fragrances mentioned here, aromatic compounds contribute to the smell of cloves, cinnamon, anise, and vanilla.

You might assume that aromatic compounds are so named because they are smelly—and most of them are. However, smell is not what makes a compound aromatic in the chemical sense. To a chemist, an **aromatic compound** is one that contains a benzene structure having a ring with six carbons.

What structure is found in all aromatic compounds?

Figure 7 You can see the six-carbon benzene ring in these aromatic compounds.

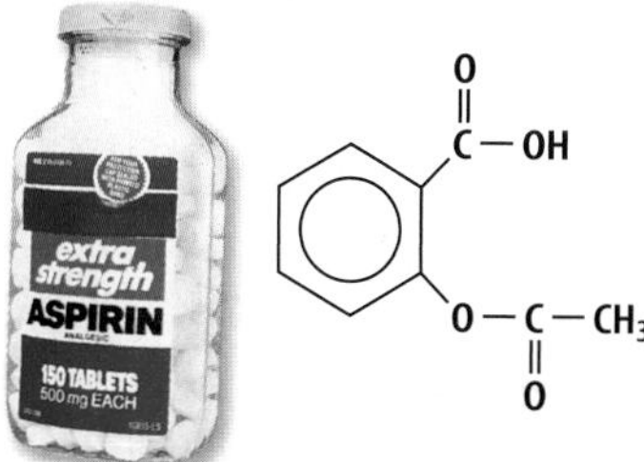

Aspirin is acetyl salicylic acid.

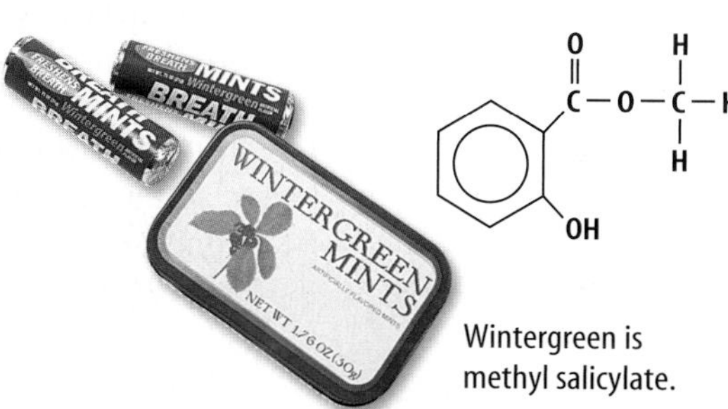

Wintergreen is methyl salicylate.

Section 2 Resource Manager

Chapter *Fast File* Resources

Transparency Activity, p. 49

Directed Reading for Content Mastery, p. 20

Enrichment, p. 32

Reinforcement, p. 28

Lab Worksheet, pp. 5–6

Reinforcement, p. 28

Home and Community Involvement, p. 42

1 Motivate

Bellringer

Section Focus Transparencies also are available on the Interactive Chalkboard CD-ROM. L2

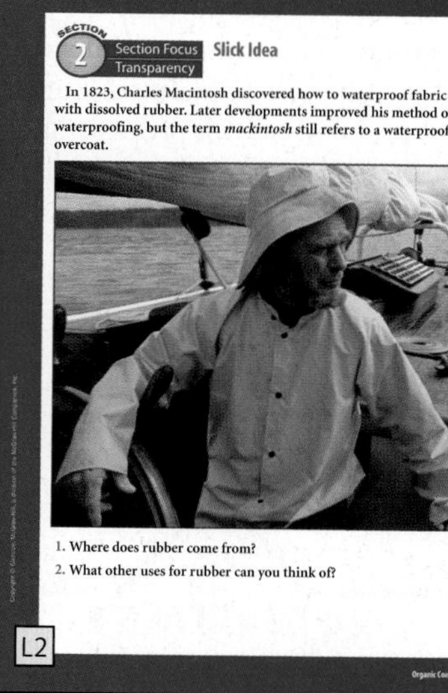

Tie to Prior Knowledge

Organic Compounds Remind students that organic compounds contain carbon. Review principles of bonding with students before beginning this section. L2

Answer benzene ring structure

Fun Fact

Saccharin, the first artificial sweetener, is 200 to 700 times as sweet as sugar. Saccharin is made from a substituted benzene molecule.

2 Teach

Reading Check

Answer the equal sharing of electrons by the 6 carbon atoms of the benzene ring

Quick Demo

Substituted Benzene

Materials Model or drawing of a benzene ring

Estimated Time five minutes

Procedure Remove or erase one H and replace it with an –OH group. This forms the disinfectant phenol. Explain to students that chemists with proper training cause this substitution on billions of molecules during reactions. L1 LS **Visual-Spatial**

Caption Answer

Figure 8 Benzene symbol

IDENTIFYING Misconceptions

Artificial Sweeteners Some artificial sweeteners are not made from any kind of sugar. One kind is made from two amino acids, aspartic acid and phenylalanine, connected by a peptide bond.

Figure 8 Benzene, C_6H_6, can be represented in three ways.
Infer *Which method of representing benzene do you think chemists use most often?*

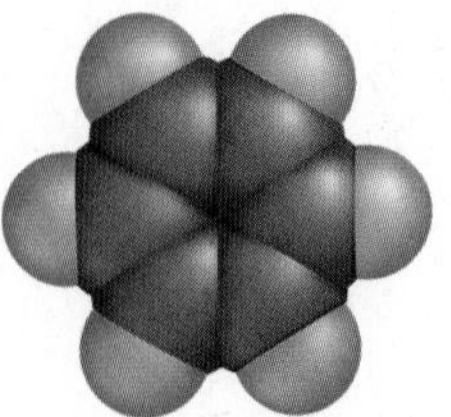

Space-filling model

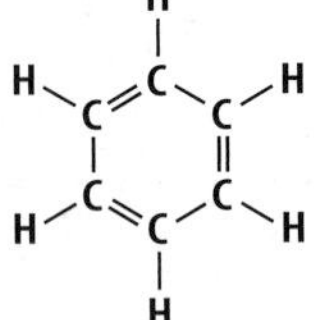

Structural formula

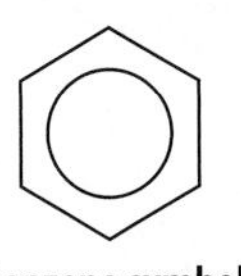

Benzene symbol

Benzene Look at a model of benzene, C_6H_6, and its structural formula in **Figure 8.** As you can see, the benzene molecule has six carbon atoms bonded into a ring. The electrons shown as alternating double and single bonds that form the ring are shared by all six carbon atoms in the ring. This equal sharing of electrons is represented by the special benzene symbol—a circle in a hexagon. The sharing of these electrons causes the benzene molecule to be very stable because all six carbon atoms are bound in a rigid, flat structure. Many compounds contain this stable ring structure. The stable ring acts as a framework upon which new molecules can be built.

Reading Check *What is responsible for the stability of the benzene ring?*

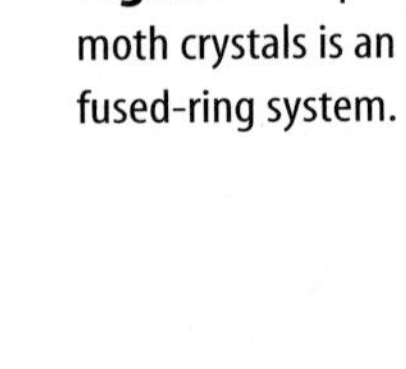

Naphthalene
$C_{10}H_8$

Figure 9 Naphthalene used in moth crystals is an example of a fused-ring system.

Fused Rings Moth crystals have a distinct odor. One type of moth crystal is made of naphthalene (NAF thuh leen). This is a different type of aromatic compound that is made up of two ring structures fused together, as shown in **Figure 9.** Many known compounds contain three or more rings fused together. Tetracycline (teh truh SI kleen) antibiotics are based on a fused ring system containing four fused rings.

Substituted Hydrocarbons

Usually a cheeseburger is a hamburger covered with melted American cheese and served on a bun. However, you can make a cheeseburger with Swiss cheese and serve it on toast. Such substitutions would affect the taste of this cheeseburger.

In a similar way, chemists change hydrocarbons into other compounds having different physical and chemical properties. They may include a double or triple bond or add different atoms or groups of atoms to compounds. These changed compounds are called **substituted hydrocarbons.**

LAB DEMONSTRATION

Safety Precautions

Purpose to show the odorous compounds that result when an organic acid reacts with an organic alcohol

Materials concentrated sulfuric acid, acetic acid, ethanol, isopentanol, 1-octanol, test tubes, warm water bath

Safety Acid is corrosive; alcohols are flammable. Check aromas by using a wafting motion to direct fumes toward your nose.

Procedure Put 6 mL each of the acid and alcohol combinations listed below in a test tube. Add 5 drops of sulfuric acid, mix, and heat in a warm water bath.

Expected Outcome acetic acid + ethanol = apple; acetic acid + isopentanol = banana; acetic acid + 1-octanol = orange

Assessment

You know chemical changes took place because new substances were formed.

A substituted hydrocarbon has one or more of its hydrogen atoms replaced by atoms or groups of other elements. Depending on what properties are needed, chemists decide what to add. Examples of substituted hydrocarbons are shown in **Figure 10.**

Alcohols and Acids Rubbing alcohol gets its name from the fact that it was used for rubbing on aching muscles. Rubbing alcohol is a substituted hydrocarbon. Alcohols are an important group of organic compounds. They serve often as solvents and disinfectants, and more importantly can be used as pieces to assemble larger molecules. An **alcohol** is formed when –OH groups replace one or more hydrogen atoms in a hydrocarbon. **Figure 10** shows ethanol, an alcohol produced by the fermentation of sugar in grains and fruit.

Reading Check *Why are alcohols considered substituted hydrocarbons?*

Organic acids form when a carboxyl group, –COOH, is substituted for one of the hydrogen atoms attached to a carbon atom. Look at **Figure 10.** The structures of ethane, ethanol, and acetic acid are similar. Do you see that acetic acid, found in vinegar, is a substituted hydrocarbon? You know some other organic acids, too—citric acid found in citrus fruits, such as oranges and lemons, and lactic acid found in sour milk.

Carbon Compounds in Space About five percent of meteorites contain water and carbon compounds. Carbon compounds, such as formic acid and a form of acetylene, have been detected in outer space using radio telescopes. The areas where they are found are thought to be regions of space where new stars are forming.

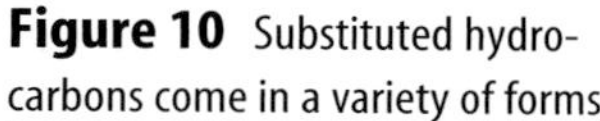

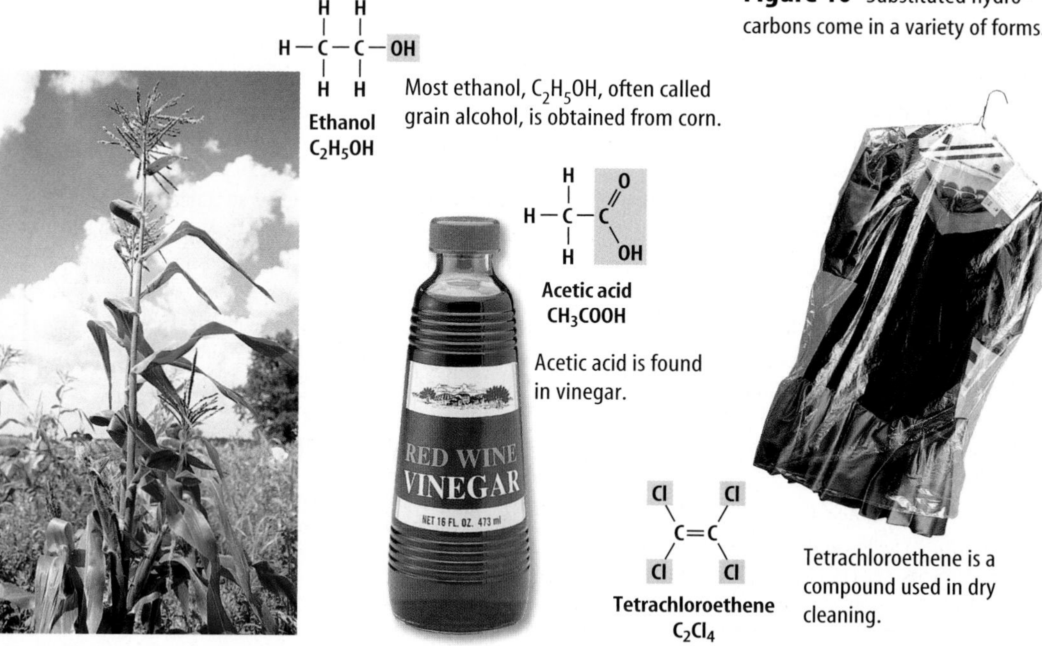

Ethanol
C_2H_5OH
Most ethanol, C_2H_5OH, often called grain alcohol, is obtained from corn.
Acetic acid
CH_3COOH
Acetic acid is found in vinegar.
RED WINE
VINEGAR
Tetrachloroethene
C_2Cl_4
Tetrachloroethene is a compound used in dry cleaning.

Figure 10 Substituted hydrocarbons come in a variety of forms.

Carbon Compounds in Space Carbonaceous chondrites are stony meteorites that contain material associated with life, such as amino acids and hydrocarbons. They are similar in texture to volcanic tuffs, a type of terrestrial rock. This indicates that they have been fragmented and recemented.

Reading Check

Answer because they are formed when hydrogen atoms are replaced by atoms or groups of atoms, in this case an OH group

Visual Learning

Figure 10 Have students copy the formulas from the examples on this page, then have them highlight the basic hydrocarbon chain in each formula. This will help students identify the parts that have been substituted onto the chain. L1 ELL LS **Visual-Spatial**

Activity

Fermentation Write the formula $C_6H_{12}O_6$ on the board and tell students that this is the formula for the simple sugar glucose. Tell them to write a series of letters on a piece of paper; six C's, 12 H's, and six O's. Then tell them that in fermentation glucose breaks down into two molecules of ethanol and another substance. Ask them to identify this substance. They can do this by circling or crossing out letters, corresponding to two molecules of ethanol. Tell them to look at **Figure 10** if they are not sure of the formula for ethanol. L2

They should have two C's and 4 O's remaining. If they do not recognize what this is tell them that these make up two molecules of carbon dioxide or CO_2.

Active Reading

Write-Draw-Discuss This strategy encourages students to actively participate in reading and lectures, assimilating content creatively. Have students write about an idea, clarify it, then make an illustration or drawing. Ask students to share responses with the class and display several examples. Have students Write-Draw-Discuss as they read about aromatic compounds and substituted hydrocarbons. L2

3 Assess

DAILY INTERVENTION

Check for Understanding

Kinesthetic Have students reuse the gumdrop models to form other substituted hydrocarbons. For example, formic acid, HCOOH, the compound that provides the sting in some insect stings, could be assembled along with others pictured in the text. L1 ELL LS **Kinesthetic**

Reteach

Isomers Present the isomers of propyl alcohol to students using magnets marked with C's, H's, and O or other moveable letters (possibly felt or hook-and-loop tape). Show them the two isomers of normal propanol by moving the OH group from the end carbon atom of propanol to the middle carbon of 2-propanol. Then add another carbon and two hydrogens and ask them how many isomers are possible for butanol. Allow them to place the atoms and record each on paper. Depending how they write the structures, they may think there are three isomers, but only two are possible. Have them find which of their structures are identical. L2

Assessment

Oral Ask students to report the number of bonds made to each carbon atom in every structure they have studied in this section. four L2

Discussion

Helpful Odors Can you think of other ways in which pleasant or unpleasant odors are helpful? Possible Answers: Ripe fruit produces good odors, aroma therapy, the smell of smoke can alert people to a fire, the odor of spoiled food makes it unappetizing.

Figure 11 Strangely, small concentrations of foul-smelling compounds are often found in pleasant-smelling substances. For example, the mercaptan in skunk spray is among the 834 components of coffee aroma.

Substituting Other Elements Other atoms besides hydrogen and oxygen can be added to hydrocarbons. One is chlorine. When four chlorine atoms replace four hydrogen atoms in ethylene, the result is tetrachloroethene (teh truh klor uh eth EEN), a solvent used in dry cleaning. It is shown in **Figure 10.** Adding four fluorine atoms to ethylene makes a compound that can be transformed into a black, shiny material used for nonstick surfaces in cookware. Among other possible substituted hydrocarbons are molecules containing nitrogen, bromine, and sulfur.

When sulfur replaces oxygen in the –OH group of an alcohol, the resulting compound is called a thiol, or more commonly a mercaptan. Most mercaptans have unpleasant odors. This can be useful to animals like the skunk shown in **Figure 11.**

Mercaptan odors are not only unpleasant, they are also powerful. You can smell skunk spray even in concentrations as low as 0.5 parts per million. Though you might not think so, such a powerful stink can be an asset, and not just for skunks. In fact, smelly mercaptans can save lives. Recall that natural gas has no odor of its own so it is impossible to smell a gas leak. For this reason, gas companies add small amounts of a mercaptan to the gas to make people aware of leaks before they become dangerous.

section 2 review

Summary

Aromatic Compounds

- A compound that contains a benzene ring is called an aromatic compound.
- A benzene molecule contains six carbon atoms bonded into a ring having alternating double and single bonds.
- Aromatic compounds can contain two or more fused rings.

Substituted Hydrocarbons

- A hydrocarbon having one or more hydrogen atoms replaced by other atoms or groups of atoms is called a substituted hydrocarbon.
- In alcohols, the —OH group is substituted for a hydrogen atom.
- Organic acids contain the group —COOH.
- Substituted hydrocarbons may contain atoms of elements, such as chlorine, bromine, fluorine, nitrogen, and sulfur.

Self Check

1. **Describe** three ways of representing a benzene molecule.
2. **Explain** why each of the following is considered a substituted hydrocarbon: tetrachloroethene, ethanol, and acetic acid.
3. **Explain** why the benzene ring is so stable.
4. **Explain** why chemists might want to prepare substituted hydrocarbons. Give two examples of possible substitutions.
5. **Think Critically** Chloroethane, C_2H_5Cl, can be used as a spray-on anesthetic for localized injuries. How does chloroethane fit the definition of a substituted hydrocarbon? Diagram its structure.

Applying Math

6. **Use Percentages** As you have read, the odor of mercaptans can be detected in concentrations as low as 0.5 parts per million. Express this concentration as a percent.

gpscience.com/self_check_quiz

section 2 review

1. Benzene may be represented by a structural formula, a space-saving model, or by the benzene symbol.
2. tetrachloroethene: chlorine atoms have replaced four hydrogen atoms; ethanol: —OH group has replaced a hydrogen atom; acetic acid: —COOH group has replaced a hydrogen atom
3. The benzene ring is so stable because of the equal sharing of electrons by the six carbon atoms.
4. to make compounds with properties they want; substituted compounds carbon tetrachloride, CCl_4, and phenol, C_6H_5OH
5. Ethane is C_2H_6. In chloroethane a hydrogen atom has been replaced with a chlorine atom. Check diagrams.
6. The concentration is 0.0005%.

Alcohol and Organic Acids

Have you ever wondered how chemists change one substance into another? You have learned that changing the bonding among atoms holds the key to that process.

Real-World Question

How can an alcohol change into an acid?

Goals

- **Control** the immediate environment of a reaction to produce a specific compound.
- Gather evidence to form conclusions about the identity of a new compound formed from a chemical reaction.

Materials

large test tube and stopper
0.01*M* potassium permanganate solution (1 mL)
6*M* sodium hydroxide solution (1 mL)
ethanol (3 drops)
10-mL graduated cylinder

Safety Precautions

WARNING: *Always handle chemicals with care; immediately flush any spill with water.*

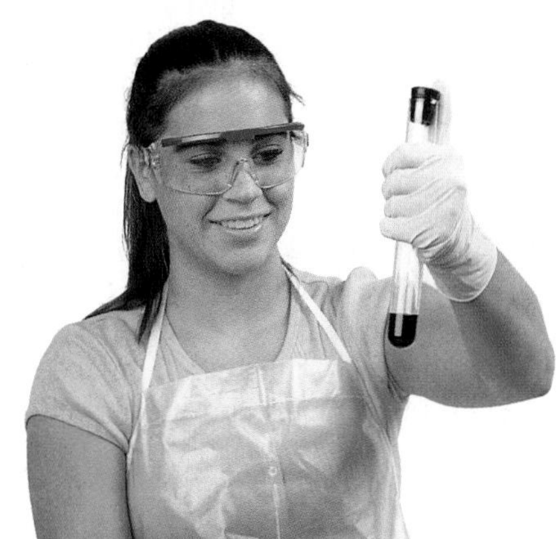

Procedure

1. Pour 1 mL of 0.01*M* potassium permanganate solution and 1 mL of 6*M* sodium hydroxide solution into a test tube.
2. Add 3 drops of ethanol to the test tube.
3. Stopper the test tube. Gently shake it for 1 min. Observe and record any changes in the solution for 5 min.

Conclude and Apply

1. **Identify** the structural formula for ethanol.
2. **Identify** the part of a molecule that makes a compound an alcohol.
3. **Identify** the part of a molecule that identifies a compound as an organic acid.
4. **Explain** how you know that a chemical change took place in the test tube.
5. **Predict** the formula of the acid produced when ethanol undergoes a chemical reaction in the presence of potassium permanganate.
6. **Identify** the chemical name of the acid produced from ethanol that is found in vinegar.

Communicating Your Data

Design a table and record what changes take place in the color of the solution. Compare your observations with those of other students in your class. **For more help, refer to the** Science Skill Handbook.

Assessment

Process Write the formulas C_3H_8O and $C_3H_6O_2$ on the board and ask students to explain how to determine which formula is for an acid and which is for an alcohol. Organic acids must have at least two oxygen atoms per molecule. L2

Communicating Your Data

Students may want to use an electronic spreadsheet to generate the Data Table.

Real-World Question

Purpose Students recognize the evidence of the chemical reaction of an organic compound. L2 LS **Visual-Spatial**

Process Skills observe, predict, classify, recognize cause and effect, interpret data

Time Required 25 minutes

Procedure

Safety Precautions Caution students against spilling, skin contact with, or inhaling fumes of any chemicals used. If a spill does occur, immediately rinse the area with water.

Teaching Strategies

- Show students how to shake a tube by holding it at the lip with the fingers of one hand while swinging it gently against the palm of the other hand.
- Prepare 6.0*M* NaOH by dissolving 24 grams of solid NaOH in 100 mL distilled water. **CAUTION:** NaOH is caustic, and dissolving it generates heat. Use a heat-resistant glass container.
- Prepare 0.01*M* $KMnO_4$ by dissolving 0.16 g $KMnO_4$ in 100 mL distilled water.

Conclude and Apply

1. 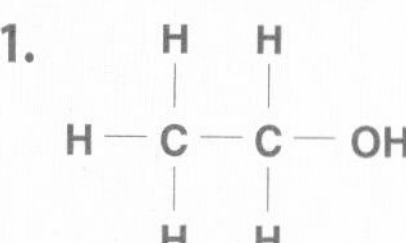

2. the –OH group attached to a carbon not attached to any other O
3. the carboxyl group, –COOH
4. The color of the solution changed from purple to green to brown.
5. CH_3COOH
6. acetic acid

Petroleum—A Source of Carbon Compounds

1 Motivate

Bellringer

Section Focus Transparencies also are available on the Interactive Chalkboard CD-ROM. L2 

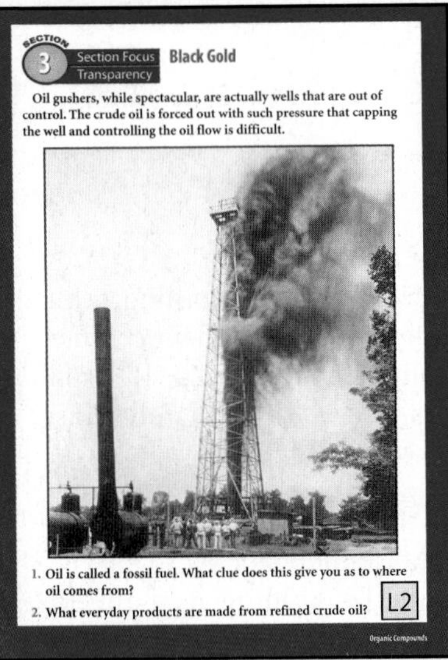

Tie to Prior Knowledge

String Confetti Ask students if they have ever seen string confetti. Get a can and spray a string from the can. Tell students that the string is made of a polymer—many molecules attached together to form a long string. L2

Reading Guide

What You'll Learn

- **Explain** how carbon compounds are obtained from petroleum.
- **Determine** how carbon compounds can form long chains.
- **Define** the terms *polymerization* and *depolymerization.*

Why It's Important

Petroleum gives us fuels, plastics, clothing, and many other products.

Review Vocabulary

condense: to change from gaseous to liquid state

New Vocabulary

- polymer
- monomer
- polyethylene
- depolymerization

What is petroleum?

Do you carry a comb in your pocket or purse? What is it made from? If you answer plastic, you are probably right, but do you know where that plastic came from? Chances are it came from petroleum—a dark, flammable liquid, often called crude oil, that is found deep within Earth. Like coal and natural gas, this dark, foul-smelling substance is formed from the remains of fossilized material. For this reason these substances often are called fossil fuels.

How can a thick, dark liquid like petroleum be transformed into a hard, brightly colored, useful object like a comb? The answer lies in the nature of petroleum. Petroleum is a mixture of thousands of carbon compounds. To make items such as combs, the first step is to extract the crude oil from its underground source, as shown in **Figure 12.** Then, chemists and engineers separate the crude oil into fractions containing compounds with similar boiling points. The separation process is known as fractional distillation. It takes place in petroleum refineries. If you have ever driven past a refinery, you may have seen big, metal towers called fractionating towers. They often rise as high as 35 m and can be 18 m wide and have pipes and metal scaffolding attached to the outside.

Figure 12 Drilling for petroleum beneath the ocean floor requires huge platforms.

Section 3 Resource Manager

Chapter FAST FILE Resources

Transparency Activity, p. 50

Directed Reading for Content Mastery, p. 21

MiniLAB, p. 4

Enrichment, p. 33

Reinforcement, p. 29

Cultural Diversity, pp. 45, 49

Physical Science Critical Thinking/Problem Solving, p. 13

The Tower Inside the tower is a series of metal plates arranged like the floors of a building. These plates have small holes so that vapors can pass through. On the outside you can see a maze of pipes at various levels. The tower separates crude oil into fractions containing compounds having a range of boiling points. Within a fraction, boiling points may range more than 100°C.

How It Happens The crude petroleum at the base of the tower is heated to more than 350°C. At this temperature most hydrocarbons in the mixture become vapor and start to rise. The higher boiling fractions reach only the lower plates before they condense, forming shallow pools that drain off through pipes on the sides of the tower and are collected.

Fractions with lower boiling points may climb higher to the middle plates before condensing. Finally, those with the lowest boiling points condense on the topmost plates or never condense at all and are collected as gases at the top of the tower. **Figure 13** shows some typical fractions and how they are used.

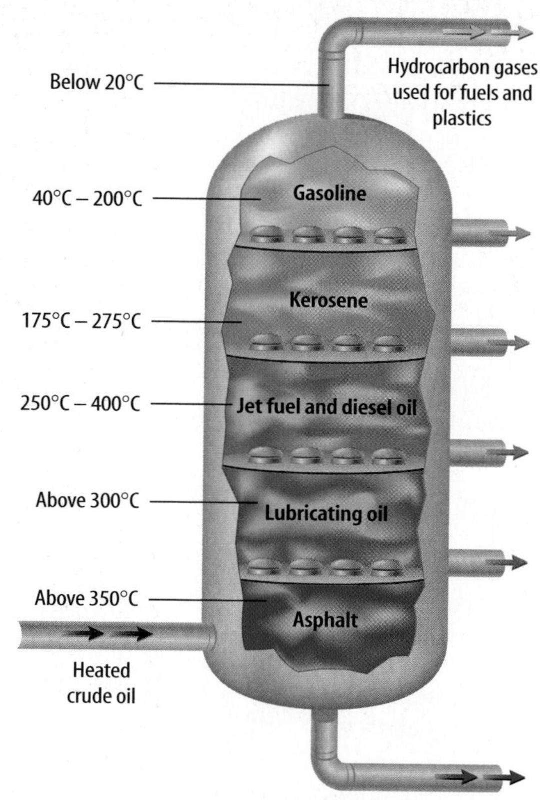

Figure 13 Typical fractions are separated in a fractionating tower by their boiling points.
Infer *How might these fractions be separated further?*

Why don't the condensed liquids fall back through the holes? The reason is that pressure from the rising vapors prevents this. In fact, the separation of the fractions is improved by the interaction of rising vapors with condensed liquid. The processes involved vary. For example, some towers add steam at the bottom to aid vaporization. The design and process used depend on the type of crude oil and on the fractions desired.

Uses for Petroleum Compounds

Some fractions are used directly for fuel—the lightest fractions from the top of the tower include butane and propane. The fractions that condense on the upper plates and contain from five to ten carbons are used for gasoline and solvents. Below these are fractions with 12 to 18 carbons that are used for kerosene and jet fuel. The bottom fractions go into lubricating oil, and the residue is used for paving asphalt. **Figure 14** shows the variety of useful products that can be obtained from petroleum, in addition to its use as a fuel.

2 Teach

Quick Demo

Separating Components

Materials rectangular piece of filter paper, three food colors, beaker, water

Estimated Time 15 minutes

Procedure Before class mix three liquid food colors together in a beaker. You need enough liquid to fill the beaker to a depth of 1 cm. Then with the class watching, place the filter paper in the beaker. As the liquid rises up the paper, the three components will separate showing bands of each color. This illustrates another way that components can be separated based on their physical properties, in this case solubility.

Discussion

Distilled Water Bring in a label from a bottle of distilled water. Ask students to describe the distillation of water and compare it to the distillation of petroleum. Distilled water has been separated by distillation from any materials dissolved in it. The water was boiled off and collected, separating it from the nonboiling or higher-boiling materials. The distillation of petroleum also separates components in the crude oil mixture through the differences in boiling points. L2 IN **Logical-Mathematical**

Teacher FYI

Cracking Another process used in petroleum refining is to break the larger hydrocarbon molecules into smaller ones that can be used in gasoline. This process is called cracking. In this way the gasoline yield from a petroleum sample can be increased.

Visual Learning

Figure 13 Ask students to explain which hydrocarbons would be found and removed from the top of a fractionating tower. butane, propane, and ethylene, which have the lowest boiling points L2

Caption Answer

Figure 13 by repeating the fractional distillation

NATIONAL GEOGRAPHIC

Visualizing Petroleum Products

Have students examine the pictures and read the captions. Then ask the following questions.

All of the products in the figures are made from petroleum, so which elements would you expect them to include? carbon and hydrogen

How might the production of these products be different if people didn't have a reliable supply of crude oil? Without crude oil, these products might be made from another source, such as coal, or corn-based organic compounds.

Activity

Polymers Among Us We are so accustomed to using polymer materials that we rarely notice how widespread they are. Examine your desk, pockets, purse, and backpack and count the items that contain polymer materials. Then count those items that are completely natural. Compare your findings with those of other students. L2

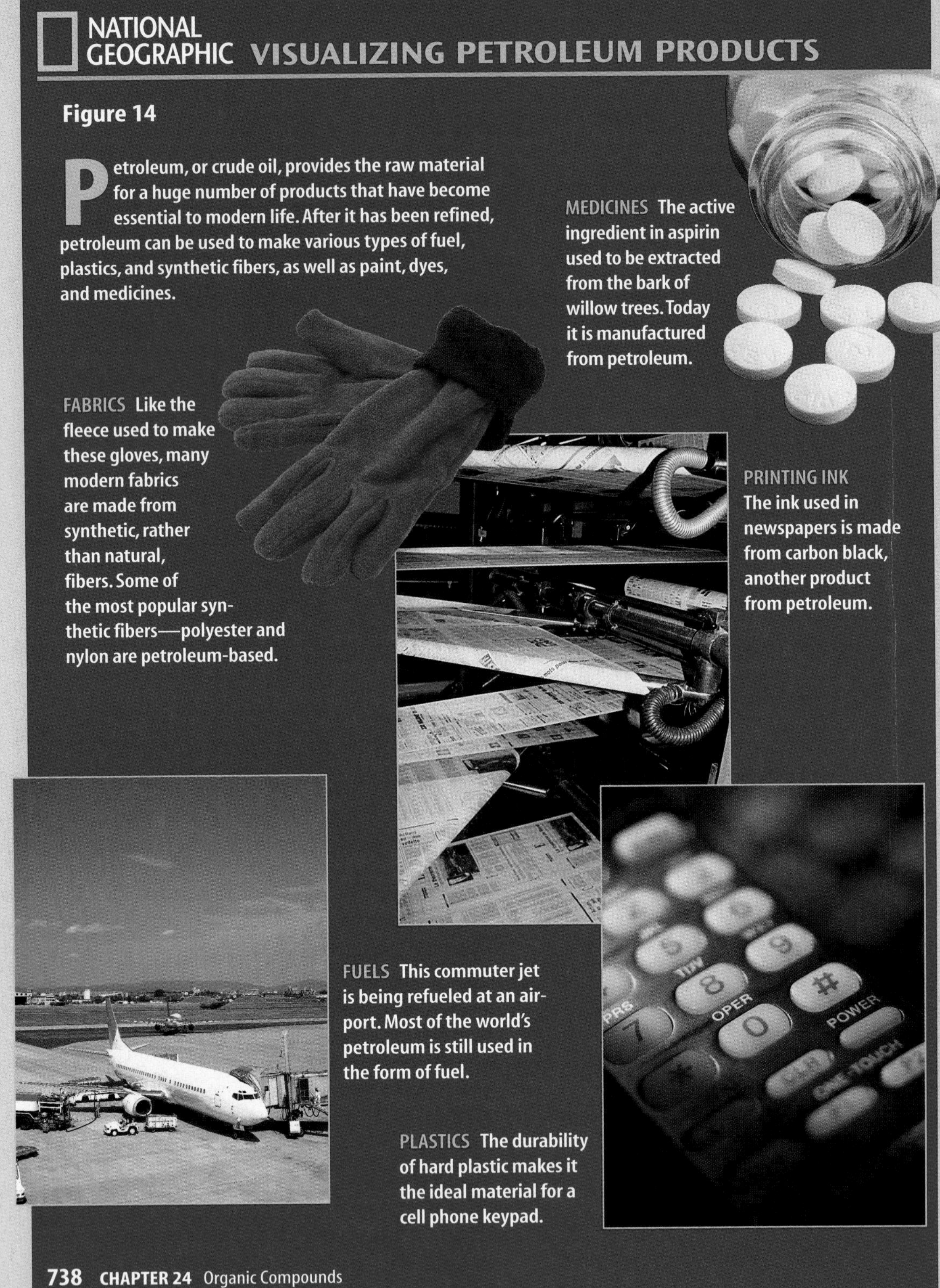

NATIONAL GEOGRAPHIC VISUALIZING PETROLEUM PRODUCTS
Figure 14
Petroleum, or crude oil, provides the raw material for a huge number of products that have become essential to modern life. After it has been refined, petroleum can be used to make various types of fuel, plastics, and synthetic fibers, as well as paint, dyes, and medicines.
MEDICINES The active ingredient in aspirin used to be extracted from the bark of willow trees. Today it is manufactured from petroleum.
FABRICS Like the fleece used to make these gloves, many modern fabrics are made from synthetic, rather than natural, fibers. Some of the most popular synthetic fibers—polyester and nylon are petroleum-based.
PRINTING INK The ink used in newspapers is made from carbon black, another product from petroleum.
FUELS This commuter jet is being refueled at an airport. Most of the world's petroleum is still used in the form of fuel.
PLASTICS The durability of hard plastic makes it the ideal material for a cell phone keypad.
PRS
OPER
POWER
738 CHAPTER 24 Organic Compounds

Differentiated Instruction

Challenge Challenge students to research the process by which crude oil is refined. Ask them to make posters explaining the process using diagrams or flow charts where possible. L3

LS **Visual-Spatial** P

Polymers

Did you ever loop together strips of paper to make paper chains for decorations, or have you ever strung paper clips together? A paper chain can represent the structure of a polymer as shown in **Figure 15.** Some of the smaller molecules from petroleum can act like links in a chain. When these links are hooked together, they make new, extremely large molecules known as **polymers.** The small molecule, which forms a link in the polymer chain, is called a **monomer.** *Mono* means one.

Reading Check *How are polymers similar to paper chains or linked paper clips?*

Common Polymers One common polymer or plastic is made from the monomer ethene or ethylene. Under standard room-temperature conditions, this small hydrocarbon is a gas. However, when ethylene combines with itself repeatedly, it forms a polymer called **polyethylene.** Polyethylene (pah lee EH thuh leen) is used widely in shopping bags and plastic bottles. Another common polymer is polypropylene (pah lee PRO puh leen) used to make glues and carpets. Often two or more different monomers, known as copolymers, combine to make one polymer molecule.

Polymers can be made light and flexible or so strong that they can be used to make plastic pipes, boats, and even some auto bodies. In many cases, they have replaced natural building materials, such as wood and metal. Because so many things used today are made of synthetic polymers, some people call this "The Age of Plastics."

Visualizing Polymers

Procedure

1. Use **paper clips** to represent monomers in a synthetic polymer. Hook about 20 together to make a chain.
2. Cut 20 **strips of colored paper** and mark each with a different letter of the alphabet from A to T.
3. Assemble these strips in random order to make a paper chain.

Analysis

1. Imagine both chains extended to contain 10,000 or more units. Compare them in terms of ease of construction and degree of complexity.
2. Compare the paper chains made by your class. How many different combinations of letters are there?

Figure 15 Imagine this paper chain extended by 10,000 units. Then imagine each link as a monomer. Now you have an idea of what a typical polymer used to make plastic looks like.

Reading Check

Answer They are made of many small parts linked together.

Purpose Students model the bonding between monomers found in synthetic and natural polymers. L1 ELL

LS **Kinesthetic**

Materials markers, scissors, tape or stapler, colored paper, paper clips

Teaching Strategy Explain that the pieces of colored paper could represent amino acids in a protein.

Analysis

1. They would both be easy to construct, but the paper chain would be more complex.
2. There are probably as many arrangements as there are class members. There are 20! (20 factorial) possibilities.

Assessment

Process Give students pieces of construction paper of four different colors. Ask students to link the pieces of paper in different orders to make as many different 4-link paper chains as they can, using each color only once in each chain. Ask them how many different chains they can make. 4! or 24

Curriculum Connection

Geography Have students locate on a world map areas that have high concentrations of crude oil. Countries having high concentrations of crude oil include Saudi Arabia, the United States (Alaska), Russia, Iraq, Iran, Venezuela, Kuwait, United Arab Emirates, Egypt, Mexico, China, Canada, and Libya. High concentrations are also claimed by England and Norway in the North Sea. L2

Differentiated Instruction

Visually Impaired For the MiniLAB, pair visually impaired students with students who see well. Make sure the visually impaired students have the opportunity to run the paper clip polymer and the paper chain polymer through their hands. Have the sighted student name the colors of the paper chain in order. L2

SECTION 3 Petroleum—A Source of Carbon Compounds 739

Use An Analogy

Human Polymers Have each student assume the role of a monomer. Have students loop their arms together to form polymers. Have several 5- or 6-member polymer chains in the room. Have students move around to show how monomers can twist and turn and one chain can get intertwined with another chain. Now place one student between two chains and have the student hold on to one chain with one hand and on to the other chain with the other hand. This mimics cross-linking in polymers. This limits the flexibility of both chains, much the same way cross-linking limits the flexibility of chains in true polymers. L1 ELL LS **Kinesthetic**

Reading Check

Answer suitcases, backpacks, bulletproof vests, light-weight exercise garments

Fun Fact

Every year the U. S. produces enough plastic film to shrink-wrap the State of Texas

Virtual Labs

Energy Output *What are the energy outputs of different types of fuel?*

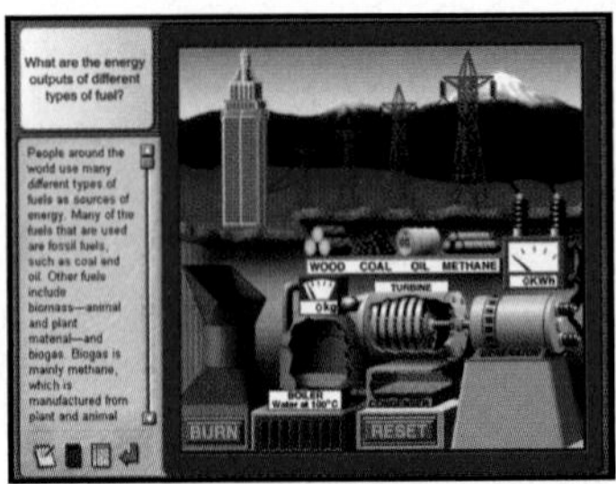

Figure 16 Processing can modify a polymer's properties. Polystyrene used in CD cases is clear, hard, and brittle. Polystyrene used in cups is opaque, lightweight, and foamy.

Science Online

Topic: Polymers
Visit gpscience.com for Web Links to information about polymers and plastics.

Activity Find out which polymers can be recycled and how to identify them.

Designing Polymers The properties of polymers depend mostly on which monomers are used to make them. Also, like hydrocarbons, polymers can have branches in their chains. The amount of branching and the shape of the polymer greatly affect its properties.

Polymer materials can be shaped in many ways. Some are molded to make containers or other rigid materials. Sometimes the same polymer can take two completely different forms. For example, polystyrene (pah lee STI reen) that is made from styrene, shown in **Figure 16,** forms brittle, transparent cases for CDs and lightweight, opaque foam cups and packing materials. To make this transformation, a gas such as carbon dioxide is blown into melted polystyrene as it is molded. Bubbles remain within the polymer when it cools, making polystyrene foam an efficient insulator.

Other polymers can be spun into threads, which are used to make clothing or items such as suitcases and backpacks. Fibers can be made strong and durable for products that receive wear and tear. Others can resist strong impacts. For example, bulletproof vests are made of a tightly woven, synthetic polymer. Polymer fibers also can be made stretchy and resilient for fabric products like exercise garments. Some polymers remain rigid when heated, but others become soft and pliable when heated and harden again when cooled.

Reading Check *Name some applications of polymer fibers.*

Differentiated Instruction

Challenge Tell students that there are two basic types of polymers, addition polymers and condensation polymers. Have students research these designations and name some polymers of each type. In addition polymers such as polyethylene, the monomer is identical to the repeating unit of the polymer. In condensation polymers, such as polyesters, the monomer has lost atoms to form the polymer. L3 LS **Intrapersonal**

Science Journal

Fullerene Buckminsterfullerene is a form of carbon first discovered in the late 1900s. Have students find out what it is and who Buckminster Fuller was, and write their findings in their Science Journals. The molecule contains 60 carbon atoms arranged in the shape of a ball, not unlike a soccer ball or a geodesic dome, which is a structure Buckminster Fuller developed. L3 LS **Linguistic**

Other Petroleum Products are obtained by further purifying petroleum fractions using different techniques to isolate individual compounds. After these are separated, they can be converted into substituted hydrocarbons, as you learned in the last section. Chemists use these to make products ranging from medicines such as aspirin to insecticides, printers' ink, and flavorings. Also, aromatic dyes from petroleum have replaced natural dyes, such as indigo and alizarin, almost completely. The first synthetic dye was a bright purple called mauve that was discovered accidentally in coal tar compounds.

Figure 17 This gazebo, like many other structures, is built from 100 percent recycled plastics.

Depolymerization Polymers have been used so widely that disposal has caused problems, because many polymers do not decompose. One way to combat this is by recycling, which recovers clean plastics for reuse in new products, as shown in **Figure 17.** Many communities recycle plastics.

Another approach involves a process called **depolymerization,** that uses heat or chemicals to break the long polymer chain into its monomer fragments. These monomers can then be reused. However, each polymer requires a different process, and much research is needed to make this type of recycling economical.

section 3 review

Summary

What is petroleum?

- Petroleum, often called crude oil, is a dark, flammable liquid that is formed from fossilized materials.
- Carbon compounds in petroleum can be separated using fractional distillation.
- Petroleum fractions are used directly for fuel and to make useful substances, such as plastics.

Polymers

- Polymers are long chains of repeating chemical units called monomers.
- Polymers can be designed with specific properties, such as strength and flexibility.
- Common polymers are polyethylene and polypropylene.
- Depolymerization is the process of breaking a polymer into its components.

Self Check

1. **Identify** what physical property is used to separate petroleum fractions.
2. **Explain** why some fuels are referred to as fossil fuels.
3. **Explain** why polymers made from the same monomer can have physical properties that vary greatly.
4. **List** some of the fuels obtained from petroleum by fractional distillation.
5. **Describe** why depolymerization can be an expensive process.
6. **Think Critically** Based on the names of the polymers in this section, what do you think polymers made from the monomers terpene and urethane are called?

Applying Math

7. **Calculate** If the average molecular weight of an amino acid is 112, find the approximate molecular weight of a protein containing 122 amino acids.

3 Assess

DAILY INTERVENTION

Check for Understanding

Kinesthetic Allow students to handle strings of beads and let them see how the strings represent polymers. Each bead is a monomer. Strings having all the same color and shape beads are similar to polymers like polyethylene in which all monomers are the same. Strings having two differently colored or shaped beads resemble copolymers. The strings are flexible.

Reteach

Recycling Use the same strings of beads to discuss recycling. If a long string is separated into two shorter strings without removing the beads, this resembles most common form of recycling that reforms used plastics into new shapes. But removing the beads and restringing in different orders resembles depolymerization.

Assessment

Oral Ask students to name materials or fibers that contain *poly-* as a prefix. polyvinyl chloride (PVC), polypropylene, polyester, polystyrene, polyvinyl alcohol (used to absorb water in some disposable diapers), polyethylene terephthalate (PETE) soft drink bottles, and polybutadiene (used in automobile tires). L2

section 3 review

1. Boiling point is used in fractional distillation.
2. They are formed from fossilized remains.
3. Polymers may vary because the chains may be cross-linked, twisted, or treated differently in the manufacturing process.
4. Fuels are propane, butane, gasoline, kerosene, diesel fuel, jet fuel, and fuel oil.
5. Depolymerization can be expensive because each polymer requires a different process.
6. polyterpene, polyurethane
7. The approximate molecular weight would be 13,664.

Biological Compounds

1 Motivate

Bellringer

Section Focus Transparencies also are available on the Interactive Chalkboard CD-ROM.  

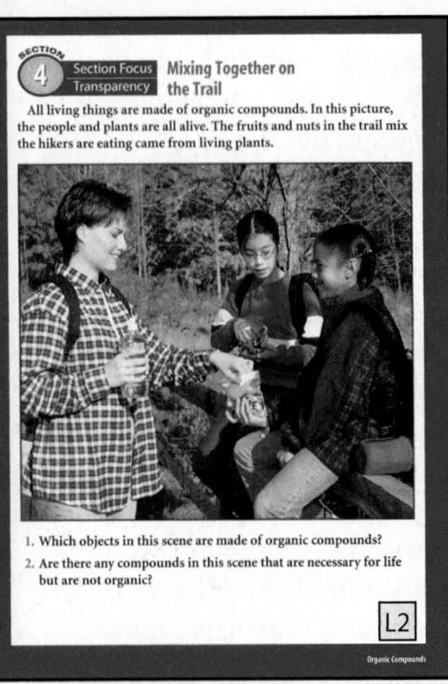

Tie to Prior Knowledge

Proteins in the Body Discuss with students what they already know about proteins and how they are used by the body. Remind them that proteins form cartilage, muscle, tendons, and hair. Explain that proteins are polymers made up of hundreds of amino acids strung together. L2

Reading Guide

What You'll Learn

- **Compare and contrast** proteins, nucleic acids, carbohydrates, and lipids.
- **Identify** the structure of polymers found in basic food groups.
- **Identify** the structure of large biological polymers.

Why It's Important

All life processes depend on large biological compounds.

Review Vocabulary

molecule: neutral particle formed when atoms share electrons

New Vocabulary

- protein
- nucleic acid
- deoxyribonucleic acid (DNA)
- carbohydrate
- lipid

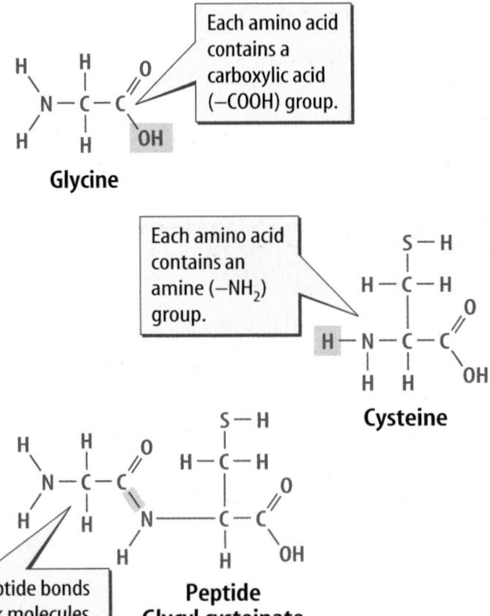

Figure 18 In a protein polymer, peptide bonds link together molecules of amino acids.

Biological Polymers

Like the polymers that are used to make the plastics and fibers, biological polymers are huge molecules. Also, they are made of many smaller monomers that are linked together. The monomers of biological polymers are usually larger and more complex in structure. Still, you can picture a biological monomer as one link in a very long chain.

Many of the important biological compounds in your body are polymers. Among them are the proteins, which often contain hundreds of units.

Proteins

Proteins are large organic polymers formed from organic monomers called amino acids. Even though only 20 amino acids are commonly found in nature, they can be arranged in so many ways that millions of different proteins exist. Proteins come in numerous forms and make up many of the tissues in your body, such as muscles and tendons, as well as your hair and fingernails. In fact, proteins account for 15 percent of your total body weight.

Section 4 Resource Manager

Chapter *FAST FILE* Resources

Transparency Activity, p. 51
Directed Reading for Content Mastery, pp. 21, 22
Enrichment, p. 34
Lab Activity, pp. 9–11, 13–15
Reinforcement, p. 30
Lab Worksheet, pp. 7–8
Mathematics Skill Activity, p. 23

Figure 19 Four peptide chains coil around each other in the protein polymer hemoglobin. Each chain has an atom of iron, which carries oxygen.

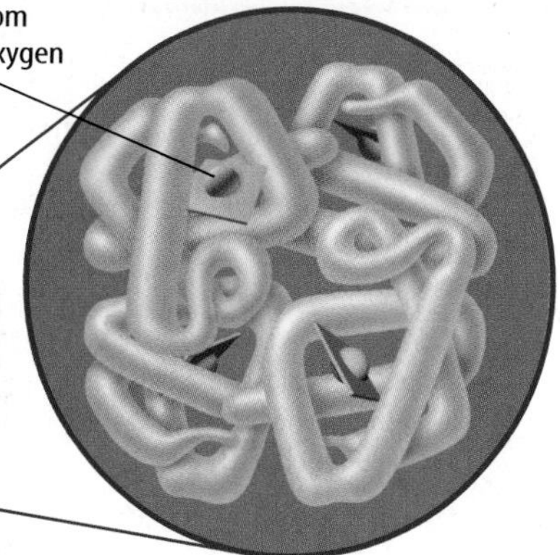

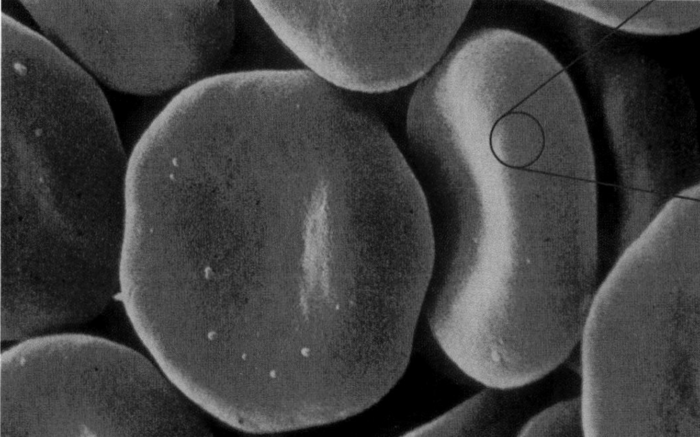

Protein Monomers Amino acids are the monomers that combine to form proteins. Two amino acids are shown in **Figure 18.** The $-NH_2$ group is the amine group and the $-COOH$ group is the carboxylic acid group. Both groups appear in every amino acid.

Amine groups of one amino acid can combine with the carboxylic acid group of another amino acid, linking them together to form a compound called a peptide as also shown in **Figure 18.** The bond joining them is known as a peptide bond. When a peptide contains a large number of amino acids—about 50 or more—the molecule is called a protein.

Reading Check *Approximately how many amino acid units does a protein contain?*

Protein Structure Long protein molecules tend to twist and coil in a manner unique to each protein. For example, hemoglobin, which carries oxygen in your blood, has four chains that coil around each other as shown in **Figure 19.** Each chain contains an iron atom that carries the oxygen. If you look closely, you can see all four iron atoms in hemoglobin.

When you eat foods that contain proteins, such as meat, dairy products, and some vegetables, your body breaks down the proteins into their amino acid monomers. Then your body uses these amino acids to make new proteins that form muscles, blood, and other body tissues.

Organic Chemist Organic chemists find challenges in many industries. Areas such as pharmaceuticals, polymers, adhesives, fuels, food additives, cosmetics, and environmental science all involve organic chemistry. To prepare for this career, students should study as much science as possible in high school, and not neglect math. Math is important in both applied and theoretical organic chemistry.

2 Teach

Quick Demo

Peptide Bonds

Materials plastic pop-it beads or plastic building toy having differently shaped connections on each end

Procedure Point out that the beads or toys have differently shaped connections on each end. Hook them together to make a chain and tell students that the connectors resemble the amino groups and carboxylic acids of an amino acid that connect to hook peptide chains together.

Reading Check

Answer more than 50

Organic Chemist In the early days of organic chemistry its boundaries were well defined. Chemists worked in laboratories and synthesized compounds. Modern organic chemistry has many branches, such as physical chemistry, biochemistry, electrochemistry, and organometallic chemistry. Along with test tubes and flasks, organic chemists use tools such as computers, UV, IR, and mass spectroscopes, electrophoresis and X-ray diffractometers.

Research Ask students to choose one of the tools mentioned here, and find out how it helps chemists in their work.

Teacher FYI

The two organic bases cytosine, C, and guanine, G, attract each other when they are aligned on opposite strands of a DNA molecule. Thymine, T, and adenine, A, do the same. The attractive forces between these base pairs hold the two strands of DNA together.

Applying Science

Answers

1. Protein: cheddar cheese, hamburger, soybeans, wheat; carbohydrates: wheat, potato chips; they would give you too much fat.
2. Possible answers: soybeans are rich in protein, soybean products are low in fat; people with lactose intolerance may eat them for protein.

Teacher FYI

Lactic Acid Students may have heard of lactic acid $C_3H_6O_3$. This organic acid builds up in muscle tissue during exercise. Also, as milk spoils, the lactose it contains is converted to lactic acid. Lactic acid has three carbon atoms. The middle carbon has an $-OH$ group attached, and one end carbon has a double bonded oxygen and an $-OH$ group.

Topic: DNA Fingerprinting
Visit gpscience.com for Web links to information about DNA fingerprinting.

Activity Research how DNA fingerprints are being used besides solving crimes and prepare a short report on one of them.

Nucleic Acids

The **nucleic acids** are another important group of organic polymers that are essential for life. They control the activities and reproduction of cells. One kind of nucleic acid, called **deoxyribonucleic** (dee AHK sih ri boh noo klay ihk) **acid** or DNA, is found in cells where it codes and stores genetic information. This is known as the genetic code.

Nucleic Acid Monomers The monomers that make up DNA are called nucleotides. A nucleotide is a complex molecule that contains one of four organic bases, a sugar, and a phosphate unit. DNA nucleotides are in chains that are unique to an organism. Two nucleotide chains twist around each other forming what resembles a twisted ladder called a double helix. The rungs of the ladder are paired organic bases. There only are two different pairs that can form, as shown in **Figure 20.** Your genetic code gives instructions for making other nucleotides and proteins needed by your body.

Applying Science

Selecting a Balanced Diet

What do you like to eat? You probably choose your foods by how good they taste. A better way might be to look at their nutritional value. Your body needs nutrients like proteins, carbohydrates, and fats to give it energy and help it build cells. Almost every food has some of these nutrients in it. The trick is to pick your foods so you don't get too much of one thing and not enough of another.

Identifying the Problem

The table on the right lists some basic nutrients for a variety of foods. The amount of the protein, carbohydrate, and fat is recorded as the number of grams in 100 g of the food. By examining these data, can you select the foods that best provide each nutrient?

Solving the Problem

1. Using the table, list the foods that supply the most protein and carbohydrates. What might be the problem with eating too many potato chips?
2. In countries where meat and dairy products are hard to get, people eat a lot of food made from soybeans. Can you think of reasons why people might wish to substitute meat and dairy products with soybean based products?

Nutritional Values for Some Common Foods

Food (100 g)	Protein (g)	Carbohydrate (g)	Fat (g)
Cheddar cheese	25	1	33
Hamburger	17	23	17
Soybeans	13	11	7
Wheat	15	68	2
Potato chips	7	53	35

Cultural Diversity

Hold the Cheese! Lactase is an enzyme that allows us to break down lactose, the sugar in milk. Normally, infants produce lactase, but lactase production stops in humans as we age. This causes a condition know as lactose intolerance. If a person lacks lactase, digesting milk products is difficult. Only about 18% of adult Americans of northern European ancestry are lactose intolerant, but about 80% of African American adults and 60% of Mexican-American adults do not produce lactase. In some Asian populations, such as Thai, as many as 98% do not produce lactase. Scientists suggest that populations that have used dairy farming as an important food resource for thousands of years have adapted by retaining the ability to produce lactase into adulthood.

DNA Fingerprinting Human DNA contains more than 5 billion base pairs. The DNA of each person differs in some way from that of everyone else, except for identical twins, who share the same DNA sequence. The unique nature of DNA offers crime investigators a way to identify criminals from hair or fluids left at a crime scene. DNA from bloodstains or cells in saliva found on a cigarette can be extracted in the laboratory. Then, chemists can break up the DNA into its nucleotide components and use radioactive and X-ray methods to obtain a picture of the nucleotide pattern. Comparing this pattern to one made from the DNA of a suspect can link that suspect to the crime scene.

Carbohydrates

If you hear the word *carbohydrate,* you may think of bread, cookies, or pasta. Have you heard of carbohydrate loading by athletes? Runners, for example, often prepare for a long-distance race by eating, or loading up on, carbohydrates in foods such as vegetables and pasta. **Carbohydrates** are compounds containing carbon, hydrogen, and oxygen, that have twice as many hydrogen atoms as oxygen atoms. Carbohydrates include the sugars and starches.

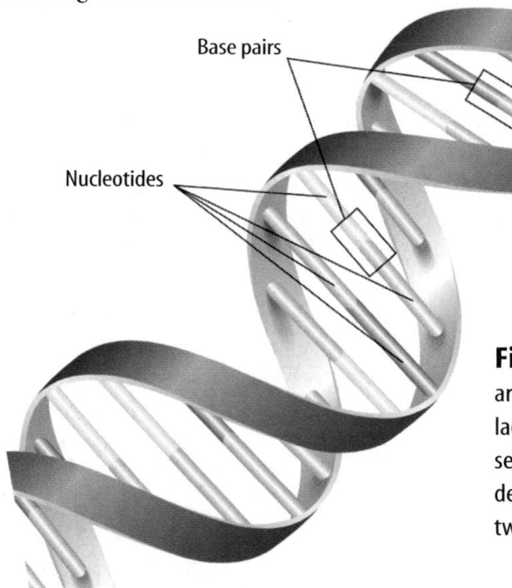

Figure 20 DNA models show how nucleotides are arranged in DNA. Each nucleotide looks like half of a ladder rung with an attached side piece. As you can see, each pair of nucleotides forms a rung on the ladder, while the side pieces give the ladder a little twist that gives DNA the name *double helix.*

Make a Model

DNA Helix Have students make 3-D models of the DNA twisted helix. Details could vary, but could include the phosphate and sugar groups that make up the structure along with the four bases of guanine, cytosine, thymine, and adenine. L2

LS **Visual-Spatial**

Teacher FYI

Living Energy The process of breaking down carbohydrates into CO_2 and H_2O provides most of the energy used by living things. Most plants store the carbohydrates they need in the form of starch. Starch contains more than 5,000 glucose monomers. Animals store carbohydrates in the form of glycogen. Glycogen contains fewer glucose units than starch and has more branches, which allows them to be broken faster to release the energy animals need to move.

Activity

Safety Precaution Before doing this activity, check to see if any students have dietary restrictions.

Starch to Glucose During digestion, enzymes break down starch into monomers of glucose, a simple sugar. Give each student a small piece of unsweetened cracker. Have students chew the cracker many times without swallowing until they notice a taste change. The taste change shows that the enzyme ptyalin in the mouth's saliva is beginning the process of breaking the starch polymer into monomers of glucose. L1 ELL LS **Kinesthetic**

Differentiated Instruction

Challenge Have students research the genetic disease sickle cell anemia and write a report in their Science Journals on their findings. The genetic basis for the disease is in a change in only two of the more than 500 amino acids in hemoglobin. If both parents carry the gene for this disease, it is likely to be passed on to children. L2

LS **Linguistic**

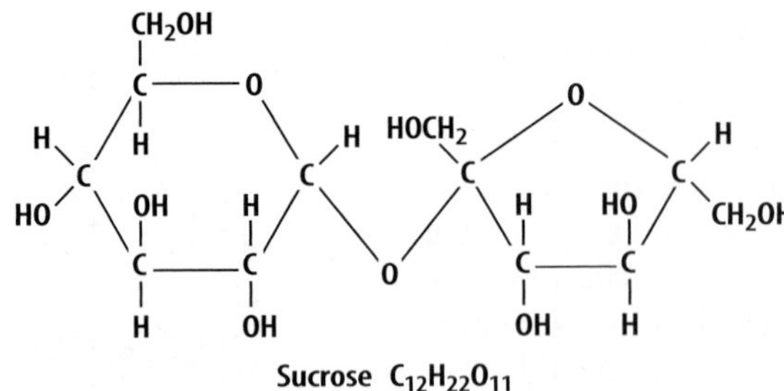

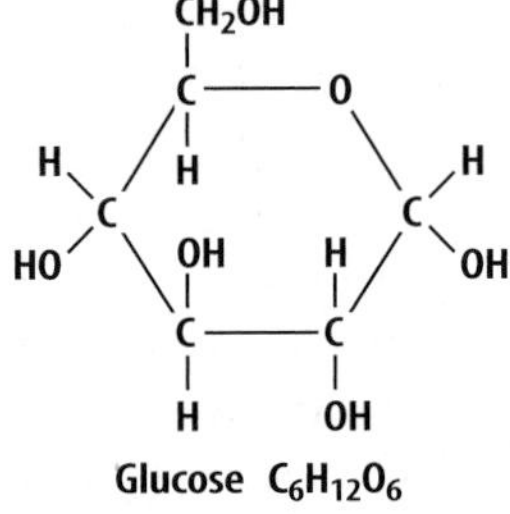

Figure 21 Sucrose and glucose are sugars found in foods. Fruits contain glucose and another simple sugar called fructose.
Explain *why sugars are carbohydrates.*

Sugars Sugars are a major group of carbohydrates, as shown in **Figure 21.** The sugar glucose is found in your blood and also in many sweet foods such as grapes and honey. Common table sugar, known as sucrose, is broken down by digestion into two simpler sugars—fructose, often called fruit sugar, and glucose. Unlike starches, sugars provide quick energy soon after eating.

Starches Starch, shown in **Figure 22,** is a carbohydrate that is also a polymer. It is made of units or monomers of the sugar glucose. During digestion, the starch is broken down into smaller molecules of glucose and other similar sugars, which release energy in your body cells.

Athletes, especially long-distance runners, use starches to provide high-energy, long-lasting fuel for the body. The energy from starches can be stored in liver and muscle cells in the form of a compound called glycogen. During a long race, this stored energy is released, giving the athlete a fresh burst of power.

Lipids

Fats, oils, and related compounds make up a group of organic compounds known as **lipids.** Lipids include animal fats such as butter, and vegetable oils such as corn oil. Lipids contain the same elements as carbohydrates but in different proportions. For example, lipids have fewer oxygen atoms and contain carboxylic acid groups.

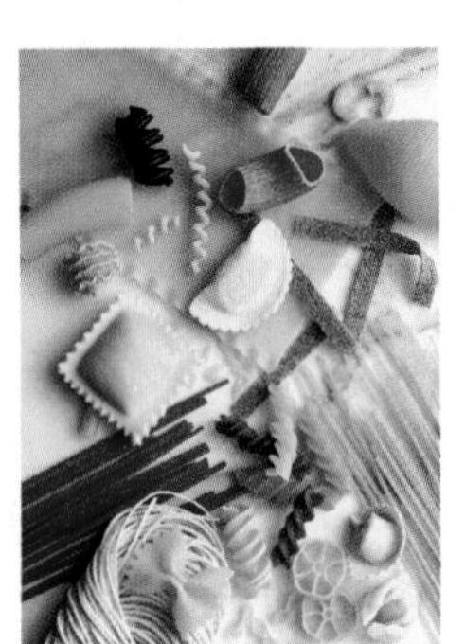

Figure 22 Starch is the major component of pasta.

Caption Answer

Figure 21 because they contain twice as many hydrogen atoms as oxygen atoms

Inquiry Lab

Crosslinking Polymers

Purpose To observe how crosslinking changes the properties of a polymer, students mix 15 mL of white school glue with 5 mL of water. They can make two separate polymers; one by adding 5 mL of borax solution and another by adding 15 mL liquid starch. Then they can examine and compare the properties of the two polymers.

Possible Materials white school glue, borax or borax laundry additive, liquid starch, water, plastic or foam cups, plastic wrap (to protect desks), wooden stirrers, metric rulers, and plastic bags to preserve polymers

Estimated Time 45 minutes

Teaching Strategies

- Before class, prepare borax solution by dissolving about 2.5 g of borax or borax laundry additive in 200 mL of water.
- The glue contains the polymer polyvinyl acetate. Normally, chains of this polymer slide over each other helping the polymer to flow easily. Borax and laundry starch (which contains borax and corn starch) can form cross-links between the polymer chains. This changes their properties.
- Let students choose which properties to investigate and how to do it objectively. Possibilities are stretchiness, ability to flow, and bounce.
- If time permits let them vary proportions of ingredients to see how this affects properties. L2

For additional inquiry activities, see *Science Inquiry Labs.*

Differentiated Instruction

Challenge Have students compare labels on various margarine and butter products. Have them report the percent of unsaturated and saturated fats in each one. Then have them research why saturated fats have been associated with circulation problems. L2 LS **Linguistic**

Visual Learning

Figure 21 Point out the structure of glucose. Explain to students that fructose also has the formula $C_6H_{12}O_6$, but differs in the position of the oxygen atom in the ring. L2

Fats and Oils These substances are similar in structure to hydrocarbons. They can be classified as saturated or unsaturated, according to the types of bonds in their carbon chains. Saturated fats contain only single bonds between carbon atoms. Unsaturated fats having one double bond are called monounsaturated, and those having two or more double bonds are called polyunsaturated. Animal lipids or fats tend to be saturated and are solids at room temperature. Plant lipids called oils are unsaturated and are usually liquids, as shown in **Figure 23.** Sometimes hydrogen is added to vegetable oils to form more saturated solid compounds known as hydrogenated vegetable shortenings.

Have you heard that eating too much fat can be unhealthy? Evidence shows that too much saturated fat and cholesterol in the diet may contribute to some heart disease and that unsaturated fats may help to prevent heart disease. It appears that saturated fats are more likely to be converted to substances that can block the arteries leading to the heart. A balanced diet includes some fats, just as it includes proteins and carbohydrates.

Cholesterol is another lipid that is often in the news. It is found in meats, eggs, butter, cheese, and fish. Also, some cholesterol is produced by the body to build cell membranes. It is also found in bile, a digestive fluid. Too much cholesterol may cause serious damage to heart and blood vessels, similar to the damage caused by saturated fats.

Figure 23 At room temperature, fats are normally solids, and oils are usually liquids.

section 4 review

Summary

Proteins

- Proteins are large organic polymers made from units called amino acids. Proteins form the muscles, blood, and other body tissues.

Nucleic Acids

- DNA is a nucleic acid built of complex molecules called nucleotides.
- DNA is found in the cell nucleus. It codes and stores genetic information.

Other Large Organic Compounds

- Carbohydrates contain carbon, hydrogen, and oxygen.
- Sugars are carbohydrates that provide energy to your body and starches are large polymers built of sugar units.
- Lipids include fats and oils.

Self Check

1. **List** the monomers that make up the following biological polymers: proteins, nucleic acids, and starches.
2. **Explain** where your body gets the amino acids it needs to build proteins.
3. **Identify** the name given to the information transmitted by DNA.
4. **Explain** the difference between saturated and unsaturated fats and oils.
5. **Think Critically** Whole milk contains about 4 percent butterfat. Explain why you might choose to drink milk containing 2 percent fat.

Applying Math

6. **Use Percentages** You have read that your body is about 15 percent protein. Calculate the weight of protein in your body in kilograms.

section 4 review

1. The monomers for proteins are amino acids, for nucleic acids, nucleotides, and for starch, sugars.
2. Some amino acids can be synthesized in our bodies, but others must come from plant and animal protein in our diet.
3. The information transmitted by DNA is known as the genetic code.
4. Saturated fats have only single bonds between carbon atoms. Unsaturated fats have one or more double or triple bonds between carbon atoms.
5. Answers may vary, but should mention that reduced fat milk may be healthier. However, skim milk with 0% fat may not be desirable because we all need some fat in our diet.
6. The answer depends on the individual student. Student must first determine his or her weight in kilograms and then multiply by 0.15 to get kilograms of protein.

3 Assess

DAILY INTERVENTION

Check for Understanding

Interpersonal Linguistic Hand out a three-column chart with the headings *Monomer, Polymer, Occurrence* or *Use*. Tell half the class to list as many monomers as they can in the first column. Tell the other half to list as many polymers as they can in the second column. Now have them work in pairs to combine their lists and complete the third column. L2

Reteach

Name Origin To show where carbohydrates got their name, write the formula for glucose as $C_6H_{12}O_6$ and as $C_6(H_2O)_6$. The second way emphasizes the carbon, and shows that the hydrogen to oxygen ratio is the same as that in water. L2 ELL LS **Linguistic**

Assessment

Content Have each student make a small poster identifying the monomers in each of the biologically important polymers described in this section. It should include the structures of the monomers and examples of the polymers that show how the monomers connect. Use **Performance Assessment Science Classroom,** p. 145. L2 P

Discussion

DNA Screening Is DNA screening of humans a good thing? Possible answers: DNA screening may detect risks of certain diseases allowing people to get treatment or change their lifestyle to avoid illness. However, DNA testing could be used by employers to avoid hiring those considered risks or by insurers to deny coverage to those bearing risky genes. L2

Real-World Question

Purpose Students investigate the reaction between an acid and an alcohol to produce an ester. They will determine the presence of the ester by detecting its aroma.
L2 COOP LEARN LS **Kinesthetic**

Process Skills observe, experiment

Time Required 25 minutes

Safety Precautions **WARNING:** Sulfuric acid is corrosive. Avoid all skin contact. Detect aromas carefully. Gently waft a current of air from the tube toward your nose by waving your hand over the tube. Demonstrate the correct technique shown in the illustration.

Procedure

Teaching Strategies Have students work in pairs. Have one student in the pair get the acid, while the other obtains the alcohol.

Tie to Prior Knowledge Before the experiment, tell students that the aroma of this ester is one that they have detected before. During the experiment ask them to report where they have smelled this aroma before.

PREPARING AN ESTER

Goals
- Prepare an ester from an alcohol and an acid.
- Detect the results of the reaction by the odor of the product.

Materials
medium-size test tube
test-tube holder
250-mL beaker
10-mL graduated cylinder
water
hot plate
ring stand
thermometer
salicylic acid (1.0 g)
amyl alcohol (2 mL)
concentrated sulfuric acid (1 mL to be added by teacher)

Safety Precautions

WARNING: *Sulfuric acid is caustic. Avoid all contact. Mix all the contents together using a glass stirring rod. Do not use the thermometer as a stirring rod.*

Real-World Question

Are esters aromatic compounds? Organic compounds known as acids and alcohols react to form another type of organic compound called an ester. Esters frequently produce a recognizable and often pleasant fragrance, even though they are not aromatic in the chemical sense—they might not contain a benzene ring. Esters are responsible for many fruit flavors, such as apple, pineapple, pear, and banana. How do an acid and an alcohol combine to produce a compound with different characteristics? Can the presence of the new compound formed be detected by its odor?

Procedure

WARNING: *Any compound you can smell has entered your body, and unknown compounds can be toxic or corrosive. To detect an aroma safely, hold the container about 10 cm in front of your face and wave your hand over the opening to direct air currents to your nose.*

See the illustration below for the proper way to detect odors in the laboratory.

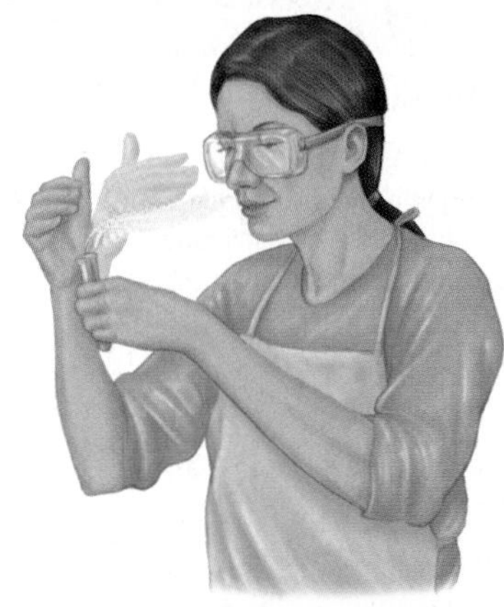

1. Add about 150 mL of water to the beaker and heat it on the hot plate to 70°C.
2. Place approximately 1 g of salicylic acid in a test tube. Does this material have an odor?

Differentiated Instruction

Behaviorally Disordered Tell these students about this lab and give them copies of the procedure so they can see what they will be expected to do. Tell them to read through the procedure and ask any questions they have about it. When they do the lab, pair them with students who work well in the lab and make sure that the nonbehaviorly disordered student handles the acid.

Alternative Inquiry Lab

Extend the Experience Ask students to brainstorm questions that arose or any negative results encountered. Have them suggest modified procedures to answer their questions or solve problems. Allow them to test their modifications as time permits.

3. Add 2 mL of amyl alcohol to the test tube. Before adding it, check to see if this compound has an odor. If so, try to remember what it smells like.
4. Ask your teacher to add carefully 1 mL of concentrated sulfuric acid.
5. Place the test tube in the hot water and leave it untouched for about 12 to 15 minutes.
6. Remove the tube from the hot water using a test-tube holder and allow it to cool. Check to see if you can detect a new aroma.

Analyze Your Data

1. What did you smell in step 6?
2. Look closely at the surface of the liquid in the test tube. Do you see any small droplets of an oily substance? What do you think it is?

Conclude and Apply

1. **Predict** What esters would form if amyl alcohol was replaced by the following alcohols; methyl, ethyl, propyl, and isobutyl.
2. **Predict** Look at the equation for the reaction below. One product is given. What do you think is the second product formed in this reaction?

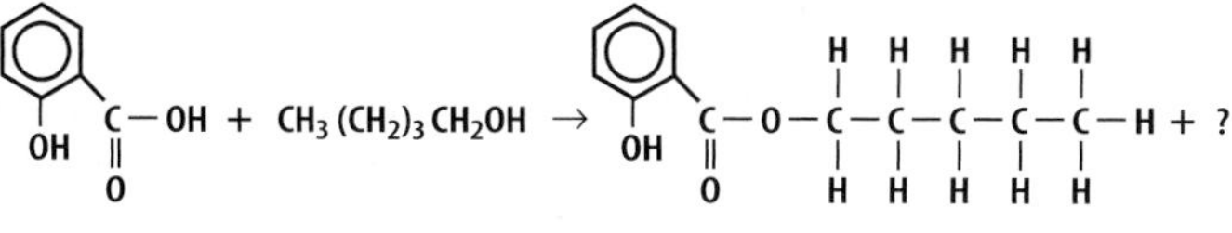

Communicating Your Data

Write a description of your experiment in your Science Journal. Suggest how you might modify the experiment to produce a different ester. **For more help, refer to the** Science Skill Handbook.

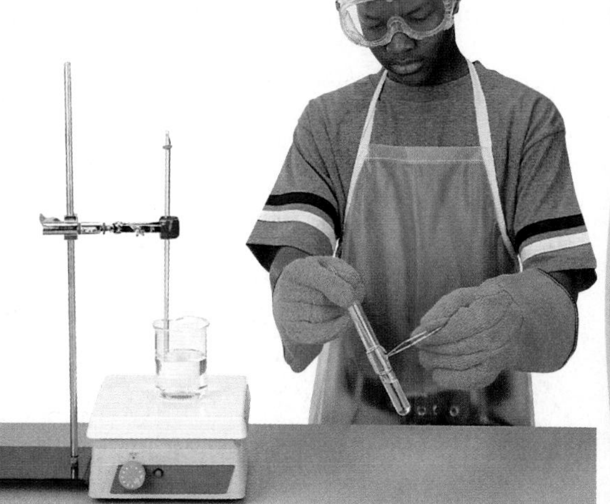

Expected Outcome The aroma of pineapple should appear soon after the mixture is heated.

Analyze Your Data

1. pineapple (amyl salicylate)
2. Yes; it is the ester. The ester is not very polar, so it does not dissolve in the polar water solvent.

Conclude and Apply

1. methyl salicylate, ethyl salicylate, propyl salicylate, isobutyl salicylate
2. water, H_2O

Error Analysis If the pineapple aroma is not detected, too much heating may have decomposed the ester or driven it out of the tube.

Communicating Your Data

Have selected students share their ideas for modifying the experiment with the class. L1 LS **Interpersonal**

Content Background

Fabric-protecting chemicals come in many forms, each engineered for a particular type of surface. What is really special about these molecules, is that they are sticky on one side and slippery on the other. This allows one side to stick to the surface of a fabric while the other side repels molecules that potentially might stain the fabric.

Discussion

To Coat or Not to Coat What kinds of items would you want to have coated with a water and stain-resistant coating? What items would you not like to have coated? Possible answers: Coatings desirable for tents, rain gear, baby bibs, and dog beds, but not for towels, wash cloths, and sponges. L2

Analyze the Event

An Open Mind Patsy Sherman never did find the new rubber for jet airplane fuel she had sought originally. What she did find became a new industry. What characteristics do you think a scientist must have to take advantage of an accidental discovery? Possible answers: a good imagination and the ability to recognize potential opportunity, even if it is not what they are looking for L2

Oops! Accidents in SCIENCE

SOMETIMES GREAT DISCOVERIES HAPPEN BY ACCIDENT!

A SPILL FOR A SPILL

In 1953, American chemist Patsy Sherman invented a way to protect fabrics from accidental spills. Strangely enough, this discovery came about because of an accidental spill in her lab.

The technicians were trying to develop a new kind of latex rubber for jet aircraft fuel lines when some of the latex mixture accidentally splashed on an assistant's canvas tennis shoe. The result was remarkable.

The latex mixture didn't stain the shoe or change it in any way. But it simply would not come off. Neither soap nor alcohol nor any other cleaning material could remove the stubborn mixture from the shoe. In fact, water beaded and ran off the shoe, much as water runs off a duck's back.

Although her assistant was frustrated by the mixture's staying power, Sherman was inspired. She realized that it could be used to protect fabrics from oil, water, and dirt. She spent three years working with another chemist to perfect the product, which came on the market in 1956. The substituted hydrocarbon compound that Sherman developed makes fabrics more durable as well as stain resistant. It bonds to the fibers in the fabric and protects them like an invisible shield.

The fabric protector invented by Sherman was used widely to protect many household products, and some clothing, for over 40 years. It was long believed to be chemically inert, however, later studies showed that it does break down slowly, yielding a chemical called PFOS. This substance can persist for long periods in the environment and can bind to human and animal proteins. For this reason, Sherman's original product was removed from the market and replaced by a similar compound that has been shown to present no danger to the environment.

Now retired, Patsy Sherman often speaks to students. She stresses that a creative mind is a scientist's best tool. "Anyone can become an inventor," she insists, "as long as they keep an open and inquiring mind and never overlook the possible significance of an accident or apparent failure."

"How many great discoveries would never have occurred were it not for accidents?" asks Sherman.

Experiment Pour a small amount of water on a piece of cloth that has been treated with fabric protector. Do the same to a piece of untreated cloth. What happened to the water in both cases? What happened to the pieces of cloth?

Science Online
For more information, visit gpscience.com/oops

Experiment Students should see the water on the treated cloth bead up and not soak into the cloth. The water should soak into the untreated cloth.

Resources for Teachers and Students

Serendipity: Accidental Discoveries in Science, by Royston M. Roberts, John Wiley & Sons, Inc., 1989

Accidents May Happen, Charlotte Foltz Jones, Delacorte Press, 1998

They All Laughed..., Ira Flatow, Perennial, 1993

Reviewing Main Ideas

Section 1 Simple Organic Compounds

1. Carbon is an element with a structure that enables it to form a large number of compounds, known as organic compounds.
2. Saturated hydrocarbons contain only single bonds between carbon atoms. Unsaturated hydrocarbons contain double or triple bonds.

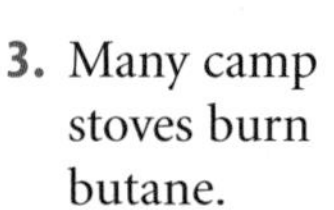

3. Many camp stoves burn butane.
4. Isomers of organic compounds have identical formulas but different molecular shapes.

Section 2 Other Organic Compounds

1. Aromatic compounds, many of which have odors, contain the benzene ring structure.
2. Cookware often has a nonstick coating. This coating is a hydrocarbon polymer in which fluorine replaces some hydrogen atoms.

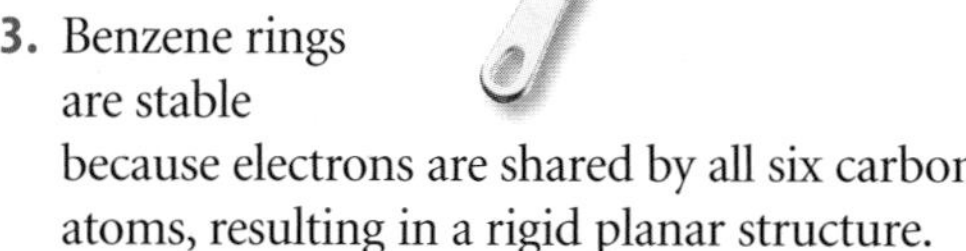

3. Benzene rings are stable because electrons are shared by all six carbon atoms, resulting in a rigid planar structure.
4. Aromatic compounds include those having two or more rings fused together.

Section 3 Petroleum—A Source of Carbon Compounds

1. Petroleum is a mixture of thousands of carbon compounds.
2. A fractionating tower separates petroleum into groups of compounds or fractions based on their boiling points.
3. Small hydrocarbons obtained from petroleum can be combined to make long chains called polymers, which are used for plastics.

4. Polymers can be spun into fibers designed to have specific properties.

Section 4 Biological Compounds

1. Proteins, nucleic acids, carbohydrates, and lipids are major groups of biological organic compounds.
2. Many important biological compounds are polymers, huge organic molecules made of smaller units, or monomers.

3. The pain-producing components of wasp venom are peptides.

FOLDABLES Use the Foldable that you made at the beginning of this chapter to help you review organic compounds.

Science Online gpscience.com/interactive_tutor

chapter Study Guide 24

Reviewing Main Ideas

Summary statements can be used by students to review the major concepts of the chapter.

Science Online

Visit gpscience.com
/self_check_quiz
/interactive_tutor
/vocabulary_puzzlemaker
/chapter_review
/standardized_test

Assessment Transparency

For additional assessment questions, use the *Assessment Transparency* located in the transparency book.

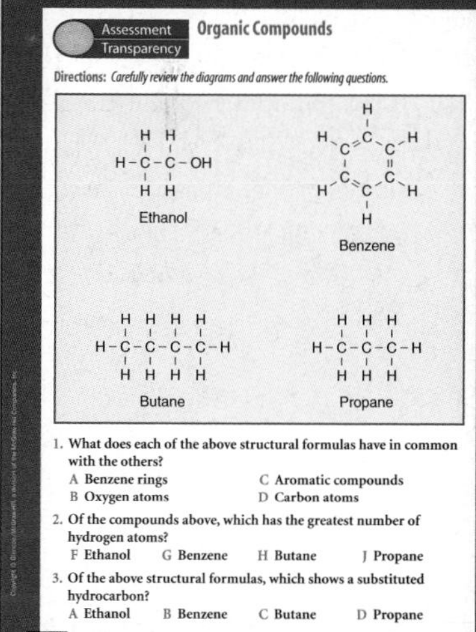

Assessment

Assessment Transparency **Organic Compounds**

Directions: *Carefully review the diagrams and answer the following questions.*

1. What does each of the above structural formulas have in common with the others?
   A Benzene rings C Aromatic compounds
   B Oxygen atoms D Carbon atoms
2. Of the compounds above, which has the greatest number of hydrogen atoms?
   F Ethanol G Benzene H Butane J Propane
3. Of the above structural formulas, which shows a substituted hydrocarbon?
   A Ethanol B Benzene C Butane D Propane

L2

Organic Compounds

FOLDABLES Have students use their Foldables to review the content of the chapter. On the back of the paper, have students write a paragraph about the nature of the forces between magnets. What does the forces between magnets depend on?

CHAPTER STUDY GUIDE 751

chapter 24 Review

Using Vocabulary

1. Organic compounds
2. proteins
3. DNA
4. aromatic compound
5. carbohydrates
6. lipids
7. Isomers

Checking Concepts

8. B
9. A
10. D
11. B
12. C
13. D
14. D
15. C

Interpreting Graphics

16. See student page.
17. Answers should be close to -1°C, 126°C, and 216°C, respectively.
18. The boiling point would be lower, so the graph would dip at that spot.
19. Graphs will differ depending on several factors. Probably synthetics will be more than 50 percent of most students' wardrobes.

chapter 24 Review

Using Vocabulary

alcohol p. 733
aromatic compound p. 731
carbohydrate p. 745
deoxyribonucleic acid (DNA) p. 744
depolymerization p. 741
hydrocarbon p. 727
isomer p. 729
lipid p. 746
monomer p. 739
nucleic acid p. 744
organic compound p. 726
polyethylene p. 739
polymer p. 739
protein p. 742
saturated hydrocarbon p. 728
substituted hydrocarbon p. 732
unsaturated hydrocarbon p. 730

Fill in the blanks with the correct vocabulary word(s).

1. ________ are defined as compounds that contain the element carbon.
2. Amino acids combine to form large organic polymers known as ________.
3. ________ is the nucleic acid that contains your genetic information.
4. A(n) ________ is defined as a compound containing the benzene-ring structure.
5. Organic compounds such as sugars and starches are called ________.
6. Organic compounds such as fats and oils are called ________.
7. ________ are compounds with identical chemical formulas but different structures.

Checking Concepts

Choose the word or phrase that best answers the question.

8. How would you describe a benzene ring?
   A) rare
   B) stable
   C) unstable
   D) saturated
9. What are the small units that make up polymers called?
   A) monomers **C)** plastics
   B) isomers **D)** carbohydrates
10. What type of compound is hemoglobin found in red blood cells?
    A) carbohydrate **C)** nucleic acid
    B) lipid **D)** protein
11. What type of compounds form the DNA molecule?
    A) amino acids **C)** polymers
    B) nucleotides **D)** carbohydrates
12. Glucose and fructose both have the formula $C_6H_{12}O_6$. What are such compounds called?
    A) amino acids **C)** isomers
    B) alcohols **D)** polymers
13. If a carbohydrate has 16 oxygen atoms, how many hydrogen atoms does it have?
    A) 4 **C)** 16
    B) 8 **D)** 32
14. What type of compound is cholesterol?
    A) sugar **C)** protein
    B) starch **D)** lipid
15. Which petroleum fractions are collected at the top of a fractionating tower?
    A) highest boiling **C)** lowest boiling
    B) liquid **D)** polymer

Interpreting Graphics

16. Copy and complete the following concept map about types of hydrocarbons.

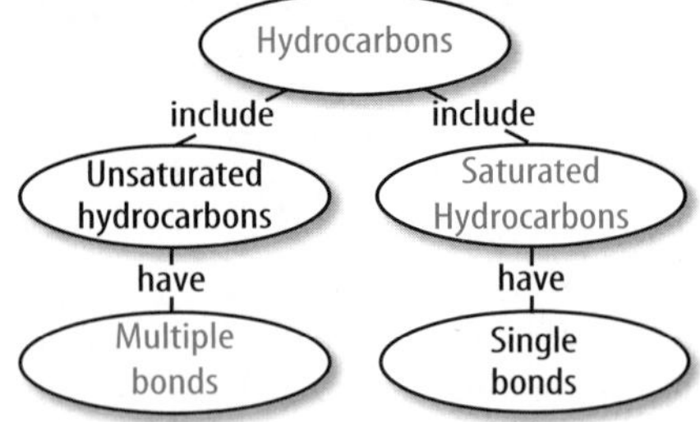

gpscience.com/vocabulary_puzzlemaker

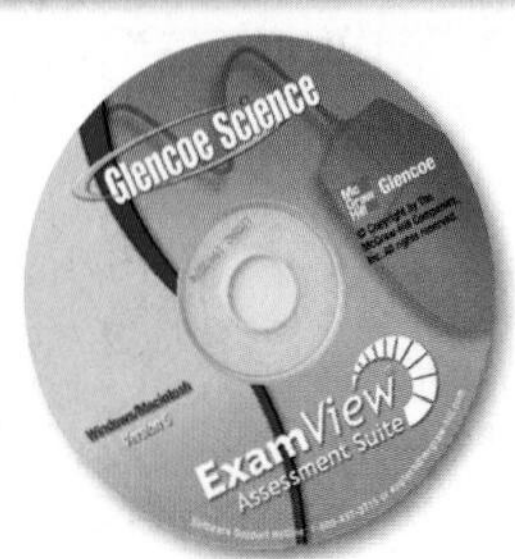

Use the *ExamView® Assessment Suite* CD-ROM to:
- create multiple versions of tests
- create modified tests with one mouse click for inclusion students
- edit existing questions and add your own questions
- build tests aligned with state standards using built-in State Curriculum Tags
- change English tests to Spanish with one mouse click and vice versa

Use the table below to answer questions 17 and 18.

Hydrocarbons		
Name	Formula	Boiling Point (°C)
Methane	CH_4	−162
Ethane	C_2H_6	−89
Propane	C_3H_8	−42

17. Using the table above, plot the number of carbon atoms on one axis and the boiling point on the other axis on a graph. Use the graph to predict the boiling points of butane, octane, and dodecane ($C_{12}H_{26}$).

18. How might your graph be different, if one of the hydrocarbons you plotted had a branched chain instead of a straight chain?

19. Look at the fiber content of ten items of your clothing. Note the percentages of synthetic or natural fibers. Determine the contents of these items by making a circle graph comparing the average percentages of natural and synthetic fibers. *Hint: cotton, linen, wool, and silk are natural fibers.*

Thinking Critically

20. **Infer** A healthy diet contains a variety of nutrients, including fats. However, as you have read, saturated fats have some drawbacks. Based on this knowledge, how would you modify your diet to make it healthier? What general rule would you apply in making your choices?

21. **Classify** the following compounds as saturated, unsaturated, or substituted hydrocarbons: *hexene, isopropyl alcohol, 2-chlorobutane, pentadiene,* and *butyric acid.*

22. **Explain** why the toughness and durability of many plastic polymers can be both an asset and a liability.

23. **Describe** how the structures of propyl alcohol and isopropyl alcohol might differ, although both have the formula C_3H_8O.

24. **Explain** single, double, and triple bonds in hydrocarbons by drawing a chain of carbon that shows each type of bond.

Applying Math

25. **Solve One-Step Equations** Although physicians disagree about what is a healthy level of blood cholesterol, many feel that levels above 200 mg/dL are harmful. A patient's blood cholesterol level measured 228 mg/dL. After two months on a low-fat diet, it dropped to 210 mg/mL. By what percent did the patient's cholesterol level decrease?

26. **Use Percentages** The label on a bottle of vinegar containing 473 mL says that the contents contain 6 percent acid by volume. How many milliliters of acid does this bottle contain?

Use the graph below to answer question 27.

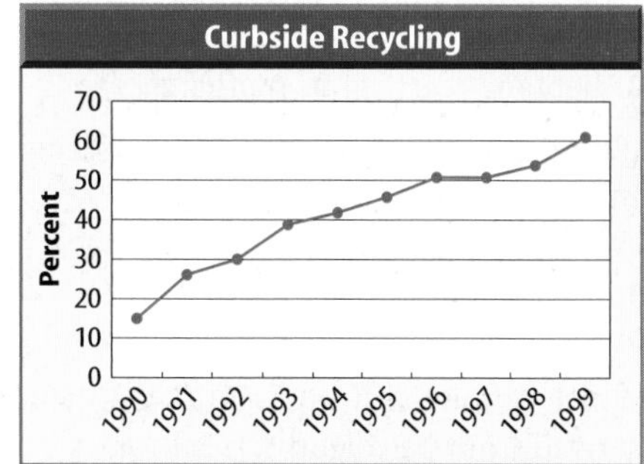

27. **Use Statistics** The graph above shows the percent of the U. S. population served by curbside recycling from 1990 to 1999. Calculate what percent of the population received service from 1992 to 1999.

Science Online gpscience.com/chapter_review

chapter Review 24

Thinking Critically

20. The general rule would be to limit consumption of saturated fats, choosing foods containing unsaturated or polyunsaturated fats instead. Students should understand, however that small amounts of saturated fat are not harmful and may even be needed.

21. Hexene and pentadiene are unsaturated hydrocarbons. All the others are substituted hydrocarbons.

22. They can be a liability because they do not decompose in a landfill and might persist in the environment.

23. The OH group may be on the middle carbon atom or one of the end carbon atoms. They are isomers.

24. Single bond atoms share a pair of electrons, double bond atoms share two electron pairs, and triple bonded atoms share three electron pairs. Student diagrams should show four bonds for each carbon atom in a chain that looks like:

H H H H
H–C–C–C=C–C–C≡C–H
H H H H

Single bond Double bond Triple bond

Applying Math

National Math Standards

1, 2, 5, 9

25. The cholesterol was lowered 7.89 percent or about 8%.

26. The bottle contains 28.4 mL acid. This is determined by multiplying 473 by 0.06.

27. By reading the graph the student will see that 30 % had recycling in 1992 and about 62% had recycling in 1999, therefore the answer is 32%.

Assessment Resources

Reproducible Masters

Chapter *Fast File* Resources
Chapter Review, pp. 41–42
Chapter Tests, pp. 43–47
Assessment Transparency Activity, p. 55

Glencoe Science Web site
Chapter Review Test
Standardized Test Practice

Glencoe Technology
Assessment Transparency
ExamView® Assessment Suite
MindJogger Videoquiz
Interactive Chalkboard

FAST FILE

Answer Sheet A practice answer sheet can be found at gpscience.com/answer_sheet.

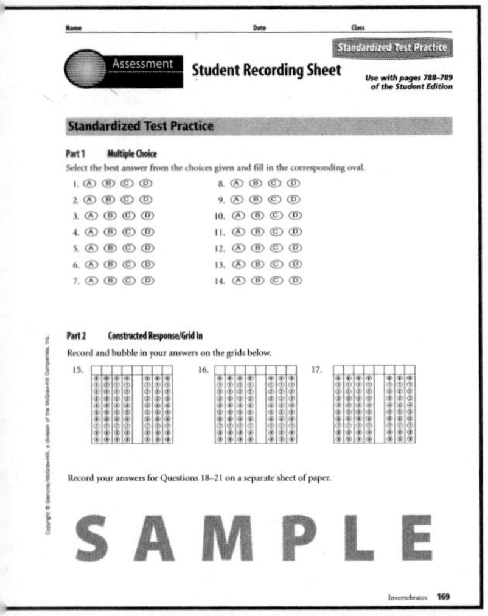

Assessment — Student Recording Sheet — Standardized Test Practice

SAMPLE

Part 1 Multiple Choice

1. C
2. D
3. A
4. B
5. B
6. D
7. C
8. A
9. B

Part 2 Short Response

10. Carbon forms covalent bonds, in which atoms share electrons. Carbon can form single, double, or triple bonds with carbon atoms and bond with many other elements.
11. Isomers are compounds with identical chemical formulas but different molecular structures. The formula for these compounds is C_4H_{10}.
12. Generally, melting points and boiling points are lowered as the amount of branching increases.

Part 1 Multiple Choice

Record your answers on the answer sheet provided by your teacher or on a sheet of paper.

1. What atoms make up a hydrocarbon molecule?
   A. oxygen, carbon, and hydrogen
   B. nitrogen and carbon
   C. carbon and hydrogen
   D. oxygen and hydrogen

Use the illustrations below to answer questions 2 and 3.

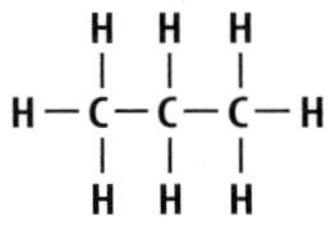

```
    H   H   H
    |   |   |
H — C — C — C — H
    |   |   |
    H   H   H
```

2. What is the chemical formula of the compound shown above?
   A. C_3H_3 **C.** C_6H_6
   B. CH_8 **D.** C_3H_8
3. What is the name of this compound?
   A. propane **C.** isoprene
   B. heptane **D.** methane
4. Which of these contains carbon, hydrogen, and oxygen, and has twice as many hydrogen atoms as oxygen atoms?
   A. hydrocarbon **C.** alcohol
   B. carbohydrate **D.** isomer
5. Which of the following is NOT a polymer derived from petroleum?
   A. polypropylene **C.** polyethylene
   B. acetylene **D.** polystyrene
6. Which of the following is a type of recycling that breaks up the polymers into their original monomers?
   A. fractionation **C.** isomerization
   B. saturation **D.** depolymerization

Use the illustrations below to answer questions 7 and 8.

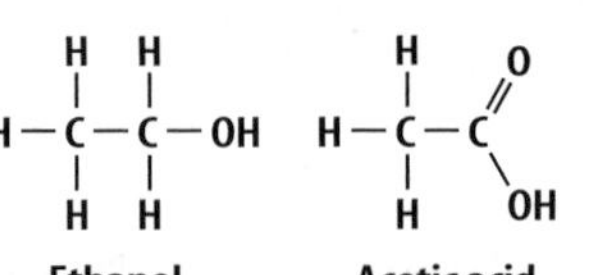

Ethanol C_2H_5OH Acetic acid CH_3COOH

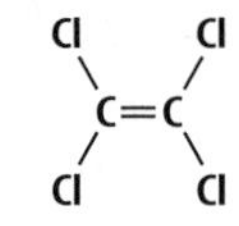

Tetrachloroethene C_2Cl_4

7. Each of these compounds can be considered to be a substituted hydrocarbon. What does this mean?
   A. Their basic structural unit is a benzene ring.
   B. They are inorganic compounds.
   C. One or more of the hydrogen atoms is replaced by atoms or groups of other elements.
   D. They are polymers.
8. Which of these compounds is an alcohol that is often obtained from corn?
   A. ethanol
   B. acetic acid
   C. tetrachloroethene
   D. ethene
9. Which of these best shows the shape of the nucleic acid DNA?

A.

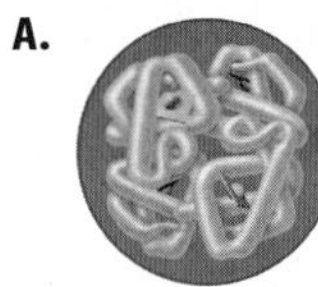

C.

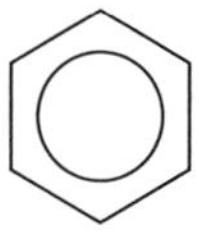

B.

D.

Part 2 Short Response/Grid In

13. Alcohols are organic compounds and are considered substituted hydrocarbons. In alcohols —OH groups replace one or more hydrogen atoms of a hydrocarbon. They are used as solvents and disinfectants and are the building blocks of many molecules.
14. The process of fractional distillation is based on the fact that each compound in petroleum has its own boiling point.
15. Fractions include gasoline, kerosene, jet fuel, diesel oil, lubricating oil, and asphalt.

Part 3 Open Ended

16. Polymers are light, and can be made flexible or very strong. Objects made from polymers include eyeglass frames, chairs, and eating utensils.
17. Polystyrene is brittle and transparent when hardened into the material used to make CD cases.

Part 2 Short Response/Grid In

Record your answers on the answer sheet provided by your teacher or on a sheet of paper.

10. Describe the type of bonds carbon can form.

Use the illustrations below to answer question 11.

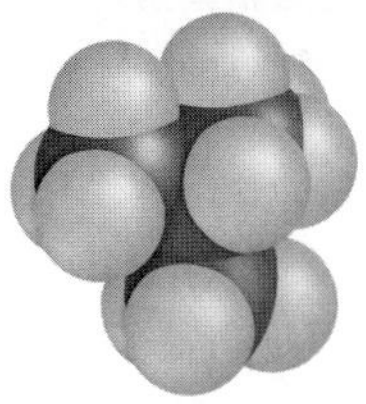

11. These molecules are isomers. Given the information that these are hydrocarbons, write their chemical formulas.

12. Describe the general relationship between melting point, boiling point, and the amount of branching in an isomer.

13. Describe some properties and uses of alcohols.

14. What is the process used to separate petroleum compounds called? On what physical property is this process based?

15. Identify some fractions into which crude petroleum is separated.

Test-Taking Tip

Formulas Think about structural formulas before answering the question.

Question 11 Remember how many bonds each carbon atom can form.

Part 3 Open Ended

Record your answers on a sheet of paper.

16. Describe useful properties of polymers. List several objects made of polymer material that would likely have been made of wood or metal in the past.

17. Identify the polymer material used to make CD cases and foam drinking cups. How can it be used to create two types of containers that have such different properties?

Use the illustration below to answer questions 18 and 19.

18. How is this paper chain a good representation of a protein? Describe the importance of proteins in the human body.

19. Draw a section of this polymer with three or four links using the formulas of the two amino acids given in the chapter and label each link.

20. When you read or hear about cholesterol in the news, it is usually associated with negative effects on the heart and blood vessels. Why does the body make a substance that can potentially damage the circulatory system?

21. Plastic polymers can be prepared cheaply to replace more expensive natural substances. However, disposal presents problems because they do not decompose readily in landfills. Describe two ways of solving this problem.

To make foam cups, a gas is blown into melted polystyrene as it is molded.

18. Proteins are polymers, which are very large molecules made up of units of amino acids. Proteins make up tissues found throughout the body, including muscles, tendons, hair, fingernails, and blood.

19. Amino acids should include glycine and cysteine in any order.

20. While too much cholesterol can cause damage, a small amount is needed to build cell membranes and to be part of a body fluid which aids in digestion.

21. They can be recyled into new products or depolymerized into their components and reused.

Rubrics

The following rubrics are sample scoring devices for short response and open-ended questions.

Short Response

Points	Description
2	The student demonstrates a thorough understanding of the science of the task. The response may contain minor flaws that do not detract from the demonstration of a thorough understanding.
1	The student has provided a response that is only partially correct.
0	The student has provided a completely incorrect solution or no response at all.

Open Ended

Points	Description
4	The student demonstrates a thorough understanding of the science of the task. The response may contain minor flaws that do not detract from the demonstration of a thorough understanding.
3	The student demonstrates an understanding of the science of the task. The response is essentially correct and demonstrates an essential but less than thorough understanding of the science.
2	The student demonstrates only a partial understanding of the science of the task. Although the student may have used the correct approach to a solution or may have provided a correct solution, the work lacks an essential understanding of the underlying science concepts.
1	The student demonstrates a very limited understanding of the science of the task. The response is incomplete and exhibits many flaws.
0	The student provides a completely incorrect solution or no response at all.

New Materials Through Chemistry

BIG Idea Materials are compounds and mixtures that are made by nature or by humans.

	Content Standards	Learning Objectives	Resources to Assess Mastery
Section 1	**5–8:** UCP.1–3, 5; A.1, 2; B.1; G.3 **9–12:** UCP.1–3, 5; A.1, 2; B.2; G.3	**Materials with a Past** 1. **Identify** how different alloys are used. 2. **Explain** how the properties of alloys determine their use. ***Main Idea*** An alloy is a mixture of elements that has metallic properties such as luster, ductility, malleability, and conductivity.	**Formative Assessment** Reading Check, pp. 759, 761, 762 Section Review, p. 763 **Summative Assessment** *ExamView® Assessment Suite*
Section 2	**5–8:** UCP.1–3, 5; A.1, 2; B.1 **9–12:** UCP.1–3, 5; A.1, 2; B.1, 2	**Versatile Materials** 3. **Examine** the versatile properties of ceramics. 4. **Identify** how ceramic materials are used. 5. **Explain** what a semiconductor is. ***Main Idea*** Ceramics and semiconductors have conductivities that can range from highly insulating to superconductive.	**Formative Assessment** Reading Check, p. 764 Section Review, p. 770 **Summative Assessment** *ExamView® Assessment Suite*
Section 3	**5–8:** UCP.1–3, 5; A.1, 2; B.1 **9–12:** UCP.1–3, 5; A.1, 2; B.2; G.3 See pp. 16T–17T for a Key to Standards.	**Polymers and Composites** 6. **Identify** what a polymer is and the variety of polymers around us. 7. **Explain** what a composite material is and why composites are used. ***Main Idea*** A huge variety of human-made products, from plastics to aircraft components, are made from polymers and composites.	**Formative Assessment** Reading Check, pp. 774, 776 Section Review, p. 776 **Summative Chapter Assessment** MindJogger, Ch. 25 *ExamView® Assessment Suite* Leveled Chapter Test Test A L1 Test B L2 Test C L3 Test Practice, pp. 784–785

Suggested Pacing				
Period	**Instruction**	**Labs**	**Review & Assessment**	**Total**
Single	3 days	4 days	2 days	9 days
Block	1.5 blocks	2 blocks	1 block	4.5 blocks

Core Instruction	Leveled Resources	Leveled Labs	Pacing: Period		Block
Student Text, pp. 756–763 Section Focus Transparency, Ch. 25, Section 1 Interactive Chalkboard, Ch. 25, Section 1 Identifying Misconceptions, p. 761 Differentiated Instruction, pp. 759, 761, 762	**Chapter *Fast File* Resources** Directed Reading for Content Mastery L1 Note-taking Worksheet, pp. 33–35 Reinforcement L2 Enrichment L3 **Reading Essentials,** p. 432 L1 ELL **Science Notebook,** p. 293 ELL	**Launch Lab**, p. 757: lab burner, tongs, thin steel wire, beaker, cold water, heat-proof surface *15 min* L2	1	Section 1, pp. 757–759 (includes Launch Lab)	1
		MiniLAB, p. 759 conductivity tester, paper, pencil, ink pen, paper clip, aluminum foil *10 min* L2	2	Section 2, pp. 759–763 (includes MiniLAB and Section Review)	
Student Text, pp. 764–770 Section Focus Transparency, Ch. 25, Section 2 Interactive Chalkboard, Ch. 25, Section 2 Applying Science, p. 766 Differentiated Instruction, p. 767 Visualizing the History of Computers, p. 769	**Chapter *Fast File* Resources** Directed Reading for Content Mastery L1 Note-taking Worksheet, pp. 33–35 Reinforcement L2 Enrichment L3 **Reading Essentials,** p. 436 L1 ELL **Science Notebook,** p. 297 ELL	**MiniLAB**, p. 765: sand, aquarium gravel or small pebbles, white glue, water, paper cup, large spoon *20 min* L2	3	Section 2, pp. 764–766 (includes MiniLAB)	2
			4	Section 2, pp. 766–770 (includes Section Review)	
Student Text, pp. 771–779 Section Focus Transparency, Ch. 25, Section 3 Teaching Transparency, Ch. 25, Section 3 Interactive Chalkboard, Ch. 25, Section 3 Differentiated Instruction, pp. 773, 775 Chapter Study Guide, p. 781	**Chapter *Fast File* Resources** Directed Reading for Content Mastery L1 Note-taking Worksheet, pp. 33–35 Reinforcement, p. 29 L2 Enrichment, p. 32 L3 **Reading Essentials,** p. 441 L1 ELL **Science Notebook,** p. 300 ELL	***Lab**, p. 777: white glue, borax laundry soap, warm water, beakers or cups (250- and 100-mL), graduated cylinder, craft stick *35 min* L1 L2 L3 ELL (Video Lab)	5	Section 3, pp. 771–776 (includes Section Review)	3
			6	Lab: What can you do with this stuff?, p. 777	
		***Lab**, pp. 778–779: meterstick, spring scale, composite rods (wood, steel, fiberglass), supports, graph paper *80 min* L1 L2 L3 *Lab version A L1 version B L2 L3	7	Lab: Can polymer composites be stronger than steel?, pp. 778–779	4
			8	Lab: Can polymer composites be stronger than steel?, pp. 778–779	
			9	Study Guide, Chapter Review, and Test Practice, pp. 781–785	4.5

Video Lab

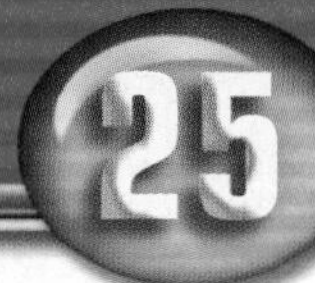

New Materials Through Chemistry

Transparencies

Section Focus

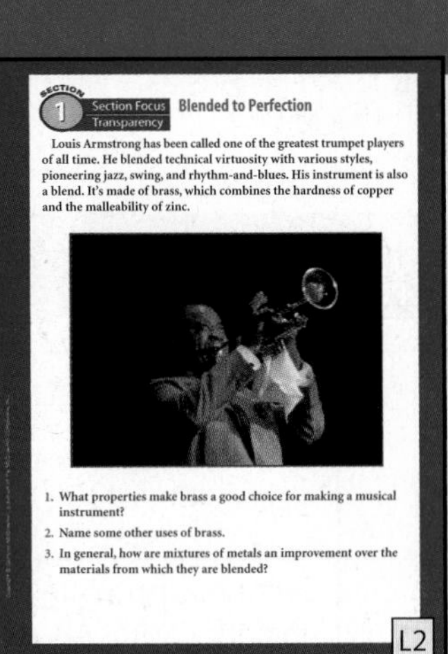
Section 1 Section Focus Transparency **Blended to Perfection**

Louis Armstrong has been called one of the greatest trumpet players of all time. He blended technical virtuosity with various styles, pioneering jazz, swing, and rhythm-and-blues. His instrument is also a blend. It's made of brass, which combines the hardness of copper and the malleability of zinc.

1. What properties make brass a good choice for making a musical instrument?
2. Name some other uses of brass.
3. In general, how are mixtures of metals an improvement over the materials from which they are blended?

L2

Section 2 Section Focus Transparency **Into the Fire**

Ceramics have many applications in advanced technologies like superconductors and space travel, but the process is ancient. Pottery is a type of ceramics that dates to prehistoric times. The earliest firing method involved placing the pots in small pits and building fires over them, but modern potters use special ovens called kilns.

1. What is pottery like before it is fired?
2. What properties of finished pottery make it useful?

L2

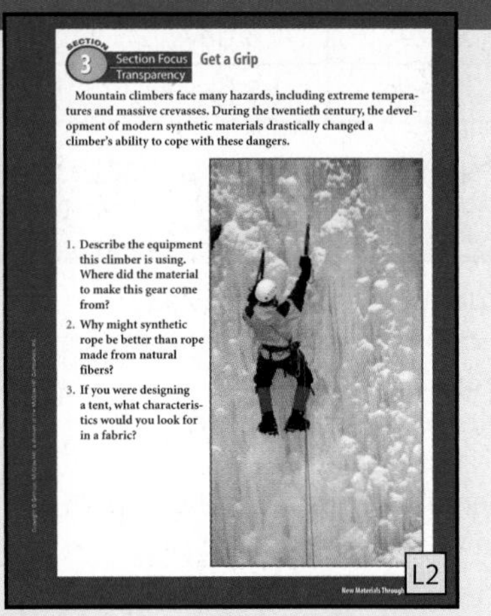
Section 3 Section Focus Transparency **Get a Grip**

Mountain climbers face many hazards, including extreme temperatures and massive crevasses. During the twentieth century, the development of modern synthetic materials drastically changed a climber's ability to cope with these dangers.

1. Describe the equipment this climber is using. Where did the material to make this gear come from?
2. Why might synthetic rope be better than rope made from natural fibers?
3. If you were designing a tent, what characteristics would you look for in a fabric?

L2

This is a representation of key blackline masters available in the Teacher Classroom Resources. See Resource Manager boxes within the chapter for additional information.

Assessment

Assessment Transparency **New Materials Through Chemistry**

Directions: *Carefully review the table and answer the following questions.*

Polymer name	Uses	Production method
Polyethylene	Tubing, prosthetic devices, packaging materials	Synthetic
Silk	Textiles	Silkworm
Dacron	Textiles, arterial grafts	Synthetic
Nylon 66	Tire cord, textiles, netting, carpet, athletic turf, sutures	Synthetic

1. Which of the above is most likely a natural polymer?
   A Polyethylene C Dacron
   B Silk D Nylon 66
2. According to the above data, which polymer is not found in textiles?
   F Polyethylene H Dacron
   G Silk J Nylon 66
3. According to the above information, it is possible to infer that polymers can ___.
   A have just one use
   B have multiple uses
   C have no use whatsoever
   D be made only synthetically

L2

Teaching

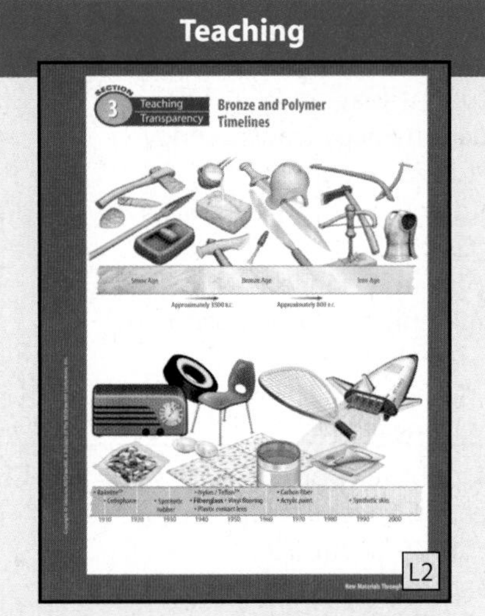
Section 3 Teaching Transparency **Bronze and Polymer Timelines**

L2

Key to Teaching Strategies

The following designations will help you decide which activities are appropriate for your students.

- **L1** Level 1 activities should be appropriate for students with learning difficulties.
- **L2** Level 2 activities should be within the ability range of all students.
- **L3** Level 3 activities are designed for above-average students.
- **ELL** ELL activities should be within the ability range of English Language Learners.
- **COOP LEARN** Cooperative Learning activities are designed for small group work.
- **LS** Multiple Learning Styles logos, as described on page 12T, are used throughout to indicate strategies that address different learning styles.
- **P** These strategies represent student products that can be placed into a best-work portfolio.
- **PBL** Problem-Based Learning activities apply real-world situations to learning.

Hands-on Activities

Student Text Lab Worksheet

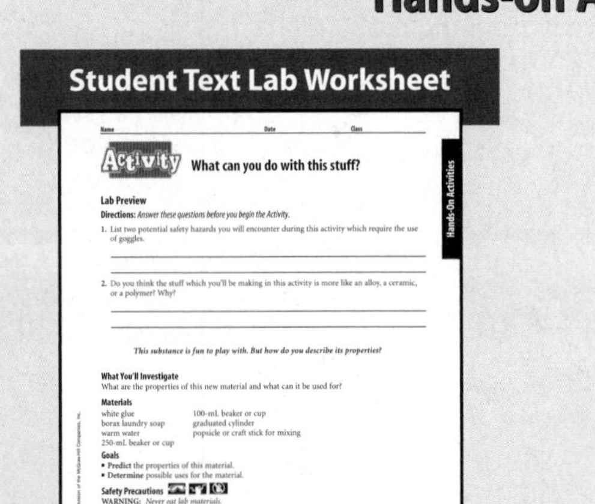
Name Date Class

Activity **What can you do with this stuff?**

Lab Preview

Directions: *Answer these questions before you begin the Activity.*

1. List two potential safety hazards you will encounter during this activity which require the use of goggles.
2. Do you think the stuff which you'll be making in this activity is more like an alloy, a ceramic, or a polymer? Why?

This substance is fun to play with. But how do you describe its properties?

What You'll Investigate

What are the properties of this new material and what can it be used for?

Materials

white glue
borax laundry soap
warm water
250-mL beaker or cup
100-mL beaker or cup
graduated cylinder
popsicle or craft stick for mixing

Goals

- **Predict** the properties of this material.
- **Determine** possible uses for the material.

Safety Precautions

WARNING: *Never eat lab materials.*

Procedure

1. Study the data table on the next page that you will use to record your observations of the following: stretched slowly, stretched quickly, rolled into a ball and left alone, pressed onto newspaper ink, dropped on a hard surface.
2. Put about 100 mL of warm water in the larger beaker or cup and add borax laundry soap until soap no longer dissolves.
3. Put 5 mL of water and 10 mL of white glue into the smaller beaker and mix completely.
4. Add 5 mL of the borax solution to the glue solution and continue mixing for a couple of minutes.
5. When the substance firms up, remove it from the container and continue to mix it by pressing with your fingers until it is like soft clay.
6. **Examine** the properties of this material and record them in your data table.

Hands-On Activities

L2

New Materials Through Chemistry 5

Laboratory Activities

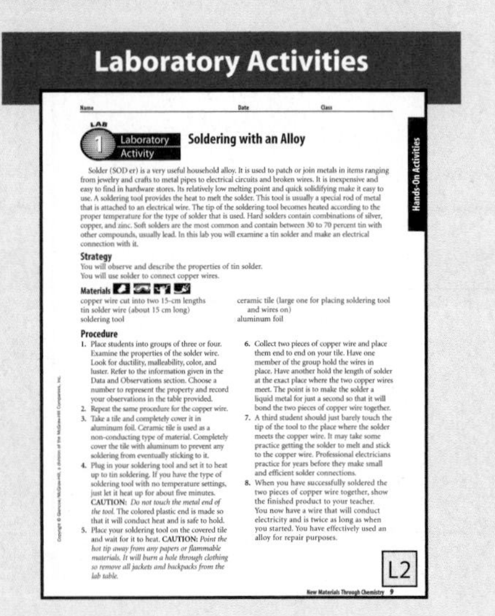
Name Date Class

Lab 1 Laboratory Activity **Soldering with an Alloy**

Solder (SOD er) is a very useful household alloy. It is used to patch or join metals in items ranging from jewelry and crafts to metal pipes to electrical circuits and broken wires. It is inexpensive and easy to find in hardware stores. Its relatively low melting point and quick solidifying make it easy to use. A soldering tool provides the heat to melt the solder. This tool is usually a special rod of metal that is attached to an electrical wire. The tip of the soldering tool becomes heated according to the proper temperature for the type of solder that is used. Hard solders contain combinations of silver, copper, and zinc. Soft solders are the most common and contain between 30 to 70 percent tin with other compounds, usually lead. In this lab you will examine a tin solder and make an electrical connection with it.

Strategy

You will observe and describe the properties of tin solder.
You will use solder to connect copper wires.

Materials

copper wire cut into two 15-cm lengths
tin solder wire (about 15 cm long)
soldering tool
ceramic tile (large one for placing soldering tool and wires on)
aluminum foil

Procedure

1. Place students into groups of three or four. Examine the properties of the solder wire. Look for ductility, malleability, color, and luster. Refer to the information given in the Data and Observations section. Choose a number to represent the property and record your observations in the table provided.
2. Repeat the same procedure for the copper wire.
3. Take a tile and completely cover it in aluminum foil. Ceramic tile is used as a non-conducting type of material. Completely cover the tile with aluminum to prevent any soldering from eventually sticking to it.
4. Plug in your soldering tool and set it to heat up to tin soldering. If you have the type of soldering tool with no temperature settings, just let it heat up for about five minutes. **CAUTION:** *Do not touch the metal end of the tool.* The colored plastic end is made so that it will conduct heat and is safe to hold.
5. Place your soldering tool on the covered tile and wait for it to heat. **CAUTION:** *Point the hot tip away from any papers or flammable materials. It will burn a hole through clothing so remove all jackets and backpacks from the lab table.*
6. Collect two pieces of copper wire and place them end to end on your tile. Have one member of the group hold the wires in place. Have another hold the length of solder at the exact place where the two copper wires meet. The point is to make the solder a liquid metal for just a second so that it will bond the two pieces of copper wire together.
7. A third student should just barely touch the tip of the tool to the place where the solder meets the copper wire. It may take some practice getting the solder to melt and stick to the copper wire. Professional electricians practice for years before they make small and efficient solder connections.
8. When you have successfully soldered the two pieces of copper wire together, show the finished product to your teacher. You now have a wire that will conduct electricity and is twice as long as when you started. You have effectively used an alloy for repair purposes.

Hands-On Activities

L2

New Materials Through Chemistry 9

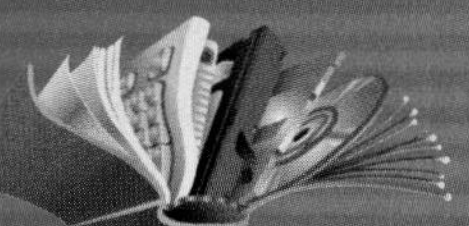

Meeting Different Ability Levels

Content Outline

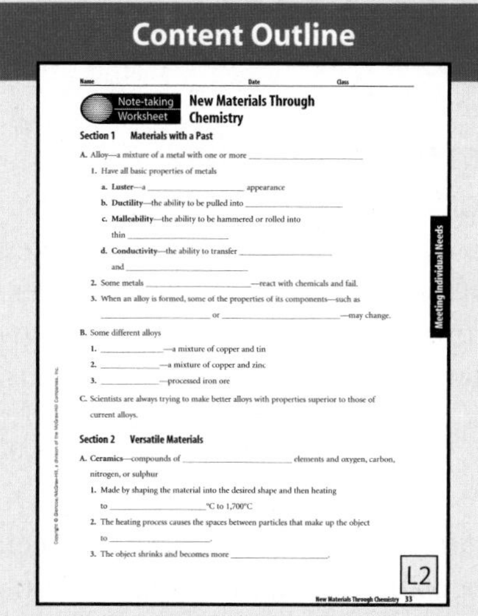

Note-taking Worksheet **New Materials Through Chemistry**

Section 1 Materials with a Past

A. Alloy—a mixture of a metal with one or more ______

1. Have all basic properties of metals
   a. Luster—a ______ appearance
   b. Ductility—the ability to be pulled into ______
   c. Malleability—the ability to be hammered or rolled into thin ______
   d. Conductivity—the ability to transfer ______ and ______
2. Some metals ______—react with chemicals and fail.
3. When an alloy is formed, some of the properties of its components—such as ______ or ______—may change.

B. Some different alloys

1. ______—a mixture of copper and tin
2. ______—a mixture of copper and zinc
3. ______—processed iron ore

C. Scientists are always trying to make better alloys with properties superior to those of current alloys.

Section 2 Versatile Materials

A. Ceramics—compounds of ______ elements and oxygen, carbon, nitrogen, or sulphur

1. Made by shaping the material into the desired shape and then heating to ______°C to 1,700°C
2. The heating process causes the spaces between particles that make up the object to ______.
3. The object shrinks and becomes more ______.

Meeting Individual Needs

L2

New Materials Through Chemistry 33

Reinforcement

Section 1 Reinforcement **Materials with a Past**

Directions: *On the lines provided, write the letters of the substances in Column II that make up each alloy listed in Column I.*

Column I	Column II
______ 1. bronze	a. copper
	b. mercury
______ 2. brass	c. zinc
	d. tin
______ 3. dental fillings	e. gold
	f. silver
______ 4. 14-karat gold	g. iron
______ 5. steel	h. carbon

Directions: *Name one practical use for each alloy listed below.*

6. brass
7. steel
8. bronze
9. gold alloys

Directions: *Answer the following questions on the lines provided.*

10. Identify four properties of metals.
11. Explain why brass is not used for boat propellers.
12. Give two examples of how properties of alloys can be altered to serve different needs.

Meeting Individual Needs

L2

New Materials Through Chemistry 27

Enrichment

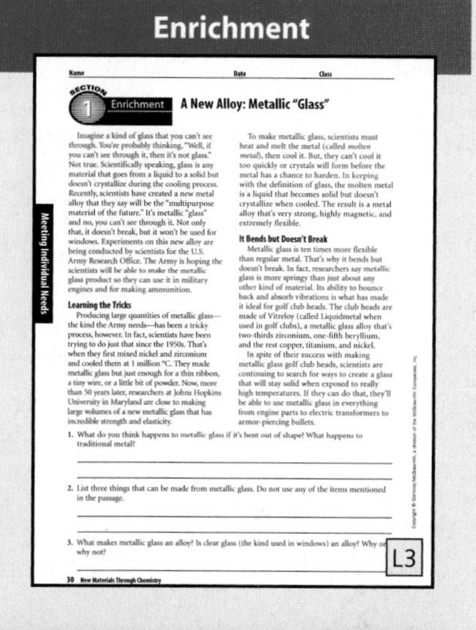

Section 1 Enrichment **A New Alloy: Metallic "Glass"**

It Bends but Doesn't Break

Learning the Tricks

1. What do you think happens to metallic glass if it's bent out of shape? What happens to traditional metal?
2. List three things that can be made from metallic glass. Do not use any of the items mentioned in the passage.
3. What makes metallic glass an alloy? Is clear glass (the kind used in windows) an alloy? Why or why not?

Meeting Individual Needs

L3

30 New Materials Through Chemistry

Directed Reading (English/Spanish)

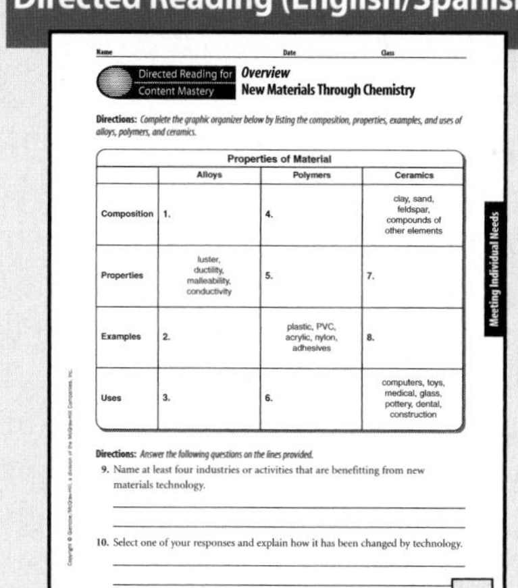

Directed Reading for Content Mastery *Overview* **New Materials Through Chemistry**

Directions: *Complete the graphic organizer below by listing the composition, properties, examples, and uses of alloys, polymers, and ceramics.*

Properties of Material	Alloys	Polymers	Ceramics
Composition	1.	4.	clay, sand, feldspar, compounds of other elements
Properties	luster, ductility, malleability, conductivity	5.	7.
Examples	2.	plastic, PVC, acrylic, nylon, adhesives	8.
Uses	3.	6.	computers, toys, medical, glass, pottery, dental, construction

Directions: *Answer the following questions on the lines provided.*

9. Name at least four industries or activities that are benefitting from new materials technology.
10. Select one of your responses and explain how it has been changed by technology.

Meeting Individual Needs

L1

New Materials Through Chemistry 19

Study Guide

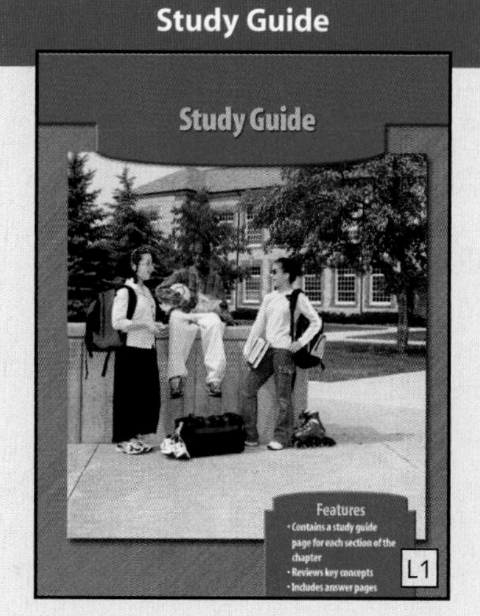

Study Guide

Features
- Contains a study guide page for each section of the chapter
- Reviews key concepts
- Includes answer pages

L1

Reading Essentials

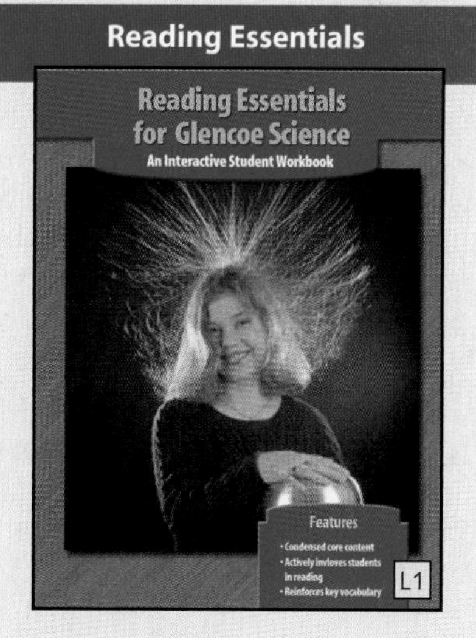

Reading Essentials for Glencoe Science

An Interactive Student Workbook

Features
- Condensed core content
- Actively involves students in reading
- Reinforces key vocabulary

L1

Assessment

Test Practice Workbook

Chapter Test — Chapter 22 New Materials Through Chemistry

DIRECTIONS

Read each question and choose the best answer. Then fill in the correct answer on your answer document.

1. An alloy is a mixture of one or more types of what material?
   - A Plastic
   - B Ceramic
   - C Metal*
   - D Polymer

Properties of Alloys

Alloy	Properties
Manganese Steel	Hard
Duriron	Acid Resistant
Invar	Does Not Expand or Contract
Stainless Steel	Corrosion Resistant

2. Which of the alloys in the table below would make a good storage container for vinegar?
   - F Manganese steel
   - G Duriron*
   - H Invar
   - J Stainless steel

3. Most ceramics have all of these properties EXCEPT —
   - A ability to withstand high temperatures
   - B strength
   - C brittleness
   - D malleability*

GO ON

L2

92 Diversity of Matter

Chapter Review

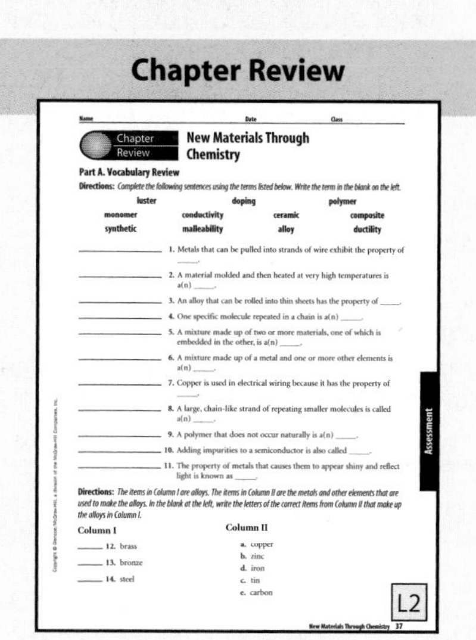

Chapter Review **New Materials Through Chemistry**

Part A. Vocabulary Review

Directions: *Complete the following sentences using the terms listed below. Write the terms in the blank on the left.*

luster, doping, polymer, monomer, conductivity, ceramic, composite, synthetic, malleability, alloy, ductility

1. Metals that can be pulled into strands of wire exhibit the property of ______.
2. A material molded and then heated at very high temperatures is a(n) ______.
3. An alloy that can be rolled into thin sheets has the property of ______.
4. One specific molecule repeated in a chain is a(n) ______.
5. A mixture made up of two or more materials, one of which is embedded in the other, is a(n) ______.
6. A mixture made up of a metal and one or more other elements is a(n) ______.
7. Copper is used in electrical wiring because it has the property of ______.
8. A large, chain-like strand of repeating smaller molecules is called a(n) ______.
9. A polymer that does not occur naturally is a(n) ______.
10. Adding impurities to a semiconductor is also called ______.
11. The property of metals that causes them to appear shiny and reflect light is known as ______.

Directions: *The items in Column I are alloys. The items in Column II are the metals and other elements that are used to make the alloys. In the blank at the left, write the letters of the correct items from Column II that make up the alloys in Column I.*

Column I	Column II
______ 12. brass	a. copper
______ 13. bronze	b. zinc
______ 14. steel	d. iron
	c. tin
	e. carbon

Assessment

L2

New Materials Through Chemistry 37

Chapter Tests

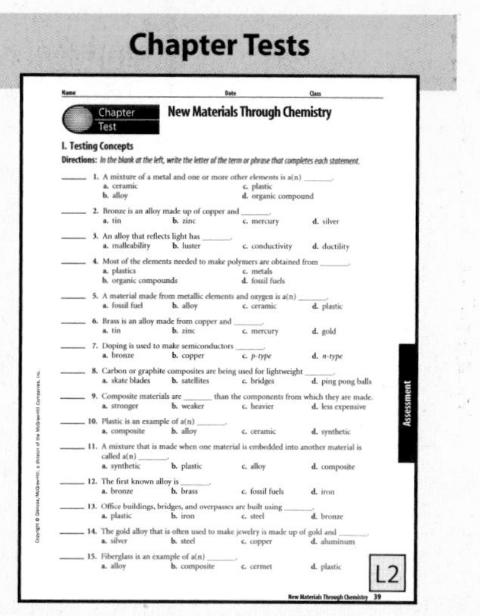

Chapter Test **New Materials Through Chemistry**

I. Testing Concepts

Directions: *In the blank at the left, write the letter of the term or phrase that completes each statement.*

1. A mixture of a metal and one or more other elements is a(n) ______. a. ceramic b. alloy c. plastic d. organic compound
2. Bronze is an alloy made up of copper and ______. a. tin b. zinc c. mercury d. silver
3. An alloy that reflects light has ______. a. malleability b. luster c. conductivity d. ductility
4. Most of the elements needed to make polymers are obtained from ______. a. plastics b. organic compounds c. metals d. fossil fuels
5. A material made from metallic elements and oxygen is a(n) ______. a. fossil fuel b. alloy c. ceramic d. plastic
6. Brass is an alloy made from copper and ______. a. tin b. zinc c. mercury d. gold
7. Doping is used to make semiconductors ______. a. bronze b. copper c. p-type d. n-type
8. Carbon or graphite composites are being used for lightweight ______. a. skate blades b. satellites c. bridges d. ping pong balls
9. Composite materials are ______ than the components from which they are made. a. stronger b. weaker c. heavier d. less expensive
10. Plastic is an example of a(n) ______. a. composite b. alloy c. ceramic d. synthetic
11. A mixture that is made when one material is embedded into another material is called a(n) ______. a. synthetic b. plastic c. alloy d. composite
12. The first known alloy is ______. a. bronze b. brass c. fossil fuels d. iron
13. Office buildings, bridges, and overpasses are built using ______. a. plastic b. iron c. steel d. bronze
14. The gold alloy that is often used to make jewelry is made up of gold and ______. a. silver b. steel c. copper d. aluminum
15. Fiberglass is an example of a(n) ______. a. alloy b. composite c. cermet d. plastic

Assessment

L2

New Materials Through Chemistry 39

chapter 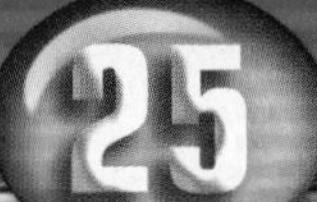 New Materials Through Chemistry

Science Content Background

section 1 Materials with a Past

Alloys

Iron is separated from iron ore in a huge chimney-like oven called a blast furnace. The raw materials that go into the furnace are iron ore (iron oxide), carbon, and limestone (calcium carbonate). The iron from the blast furnace, called pig iron, has a fairly low melting point, so it is easily cast into molds, hence the name cast iron.

Cast iron is brittle, and still has many impurities, so most cast iron is converted to steel. In another furnace, pressurized oxygen reacts with impurities still left in the iron. Properties of steel can be made to vary over a wide range by adjusting the amount of carbon in it. Low carbon steel is ductile and malleable, whereas high carbon steel is hard and strong.

Steel is commonly alloyed with other metals to give it special properties. For example, tungsten imparts high temperature strength, manganese imparts hardness, and additions of chromium and nickel produce stainless steel.

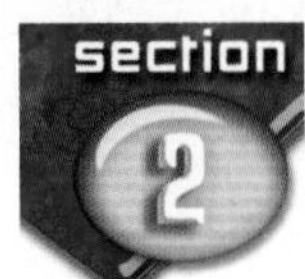

section 2 Versatile Materials

Ceramics

One type of new ceramics is called advanced ceramics. Advanced ceramics are ceramics that have high-tech engineering, electronic, and biomedical applications. These ceramics include oxide ceramics such as alumina (Al_2O_3) and nonoxide ceramics such as silicon carbide (SiC). These ceramics have melting points 500 to 1500 °C higher than steel, are almost twice as hard, and much less elastic.

section 3 Polymers and Composites

Composites

Ceramic composites are hybrid materials that have been strengthened and toughened by mixing ceramic powder with fibers of a second ceramic material, such as carbon, boron, or silicon carbide. An example is the composite consisting of fine grains of alumina reinforced with single crystals, or whiskers, of silicon carbide. Silicon carbide-reinforced alumina possesses high strength and high shock resistance, even at high temperatures, and is used to make high-speed cutting tools for machining very hard steel.

chapter content resources

Internet Resources

For additional content background, visit gpscience.com to:

- access your book online
- find references to related articles in popular science magazines
- access Web links with related content background
- access current events with science journal topics

Print Resources

The Physics of Superconductors, by K. H. Bennemann (Ed.), Springer Verlag, 2003

Modern materials and manufacturing processes, John E. Neely, Prentice Hall, 1998

Superstuff!: Materials That Have Changed Our Lives, by Alfred B. Bortz, Franklin Watts, 1990

Physical Ceramics: Principles for Ceramic Science and Engineering, John Wiley & Sons, 1996

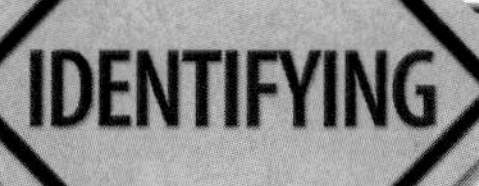

IDENTIFYING Misconceptions

Find Out What Students Think

Students may think that . . .

Scientific research is done at universities strictly for the purpose of gaining knowledge. In fact, there are two general categories that most scientific research fits into: pure science and applied science. The goal of pure science is to extend what is known, and the goal of applied science is to produce new technology. And universities are not the only place where scientific research is conducted. Academic research and industrial research and development can both contribute to the banks of pure science and applied science. Commonly, pure scientists contribute their work to society by publishing their findings in journals and books. Applied scientists contribute their work to society by developing new products and materials.

Demonstration

Have students do a Two-Minute Essay. Give each student a sheet of paper and ask them to describe the differences between a pure scientist and an engineer. L2 LS **Linguistic, Interpersonal**

Promote Understanding

Activity

Prior to class:

- Explore the Web site of your nearest research university, and find descriptions of the research being done by the science faculty and the engineering faculty. For example, if you live near Texas A&M University, you can go to the Chemistry Department's Internet link.
- Print the descriptions of three faculty engaged in pure science research and three engaged in applied science research.

In class:

- Describe to students the differences between the goals and methods of pure science and those of applied science.
- Distribute the descriptions you printed from the Internet.
- Ask students to classify the work of each faculty member as either pure or applied research. L2 LS **Logical-Mathematical**
- Discuss students' classifications and any reasons for different opinions. L2 LS **Logical-Mathematical**

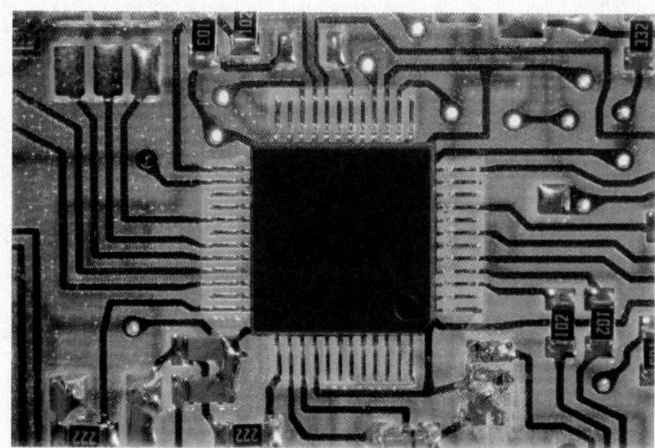

Jeffrey Sylvester/FPG International

Assess

After completing the chapter, see *Identifying Misconceptions* in the Study Guide at the end of the chapter.

About the Photo

Snowboard Materials Snowboards are made of several layers. The core is usually made of wood with layers of fiberglass above and below. The bottom layer is a dense, abrasion-resistant polyethylene plastic called P-tex that slides easily over snow.

Science Journal Materials might have to be developed through a research program that involves modification of existing materials.

BIG Idea

Polyethylene Chains The most commonly used plastic is polyethylene, which is made from ethylene gas, C^2H^4. A chemical reaction causes long chains of the monomer CH^2 to form. A single chain might contain thousands of monomers. If a chain were as wide as a strand of spaghetti, it could be a kilometer in length. The chains are intertwined, but are not chemically bonded to each other. Low-density polyethylene is made of polymers that have side branches and contain about 500 monomers. High-density polyethylene contains unbranched, linear chains that can contain 10,000 monomers. These linear chains can be parallel to each other, forming a more rigid structure than is formed by the randomly tangled chains in low-density polyethylene.

Introduce the Chapter Have students make a list of objects that are plastic or have plastic parts. Ask them to identify some of the properties of the various plastic materials. Ask them to discuss how the properties of various plastics makes them useful.

chapter 25

New Materials Through Chemistr

BIG Idea

Materials are compounds and mixtures that are made by nature or by humans.

25.1 Materials with a Past

MAIN Idea An alloy is a mixture of elements that has metallic properties such as luster, ductility, malleability, and conductivity.

25.2 Versatile Materials

MAIN Idea Ceramics and semiconductors have conductivities that can range from highly insulating to superconductive.

25.3 Polymers and Composites

MAIN Idea A huge variety of human-made products, from plastics to aircraft components, are made from polymers and composites.

Chemistry on the Slopes

If you enjoy boarding down a snowy slope, you'll appreciate that most of your equipment is made from materials that have been engineered specifically to meet the challenges of a demanding sport.

Science Journal
How do manufacturers find materials to meet theirneeds?

Interactive Chalkboard

This CD-ROM is an editable Microsoft® PowerPoint® presentation that includes:

- an editable presentation for every chapter
- additional chapter questions
- animated graphics
- image bank
- links to gpscience.com

Start-Up Activities

Chemistry and Properties of Materials

When an engineer designs a vehicle, bridge, or building, the materials used for construction must be selected to match the function. Can the manufacturing process affect a material's performance?

WARNING: *Use proper protection when handling hot objects or working near an open flame. Tie back hair; roll up sleeves.*

1. Using tongs, hold a 5-cm piece of steel wire in a lab burner flame until the wire glows red-hot for 30 seconds.
2. Quickly drop the hot wire into a beaker of cold water.
3. Repeat step 1 with another 5-cm piece of steel wire, but place this hot wire on a heat-proof surface to cool instead of in water.
4. After both pieces of wire are cool, compare the flexibility of the wires.
5. **Think Critically** Write what you observe about the flexibility of the two wires. Suggest reasons.

Materials Classification Make the following Foldable to help you organize materials into groups based on their common features.

STEP 1 **Draw** a mark at the midpoint of a sheet of paper along the side edge. Then **fold** the top and bottom edges in to touch the midpoint.

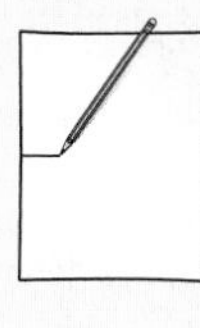

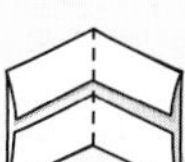

STEP 2 **Fold** in half from side to side.

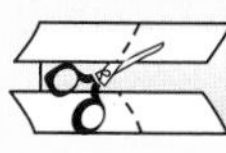

STEP 3 **Turn** the paper horizontally. **Open and cut** along the inside fold lines to form four tabs.

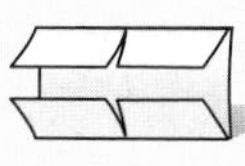

STEP 4 **Label** the tabs *Alloys*, *Ceramics*, *Polymers*, and *Composites*.

Classify As you read Chapter 25, list three or more examples of common materials for each group.

Preview this chapter's content and activities at gpscience.com

757

Additional Chapter Media

- What's Science Got to Do With It?: *Cell Phones*
- Virtual Lab: *How do ratios of elements affect the physical properties of an alloy?*
- Video Lab: *What can you do with this stuff?*

Purpose to investigate how metals may respond to fast and slow temperature change L2 ELL

LS **Kinesthetic**

Preparation Prepare several beakers of ice water.

Materials lab burner, tongs, pieces of thin steel wire, beaker of cold water

Teaching Strategies

- Point out that both wire pieces are heated to the same temperature, so the only variable is the rate at which they cool.
- Remind students that heating metals to high temperature and then allowing them to cool occurs in engines and heating elements.

Think Critically

Before heating, both wires were somewhat flexible. After being heated to red-hot, then cooled, the wire that cooled slowly was still somewhat flexible. However, the wire that was cooled quickly became brittle and snapped easily when bent.

Assessment

Oral What happened to the atoms in the metal as it was heated? The atoms began to move faster and their relationship to each other changed and weakened. Why might cooling quickly not restore the flexibility to the metal wire? The heated atoms were not given time to return to their original stable positions. Use **Performance Assessment in the Science Classroom**, p. 89.

L3 LS **Kinesthetic, Visual-Spatial, Logical-Mathematical**

Dinah Zike Study Fold

Student preparation materials for this Foldable are available in the Chapter *Fast File* Resources.

section 1

Materials with a Past

Reading Guide

What You'll Learn

- **Identify** how different alloys are used.
- **Explain** how the properties of alloys determine their use.

Why It's Important

Alloys make modern cities, space travel, and many other things possible.

Review Vocabulary

physical properties: characteristics that can be observed or measured without changing the composition of the material

New Vocabulary

- alloy
- luster
- ductility
- malleability
- conductivity

Alloys

For ages, people have searched for better materials to use to make their lives more comfortable and their tasks easier. Ancient cultures used stone tools until methods for processing metals became known. Today, advances in metal processing are still occurring as scientists continue to improve the art of blending metals, or making alloys, to make better metal products. An **alloy** is a mixture of elements that has metallic properties. For example, pewter is a mixture of the elements tin, copper, and antimony. If you were to see a pewter mug or a pewter figurine, you probably would not hesitate to say that the objects are metallic. Alloys can produce materials with improved properties such as greater hardness, strength, lightness, or durability.

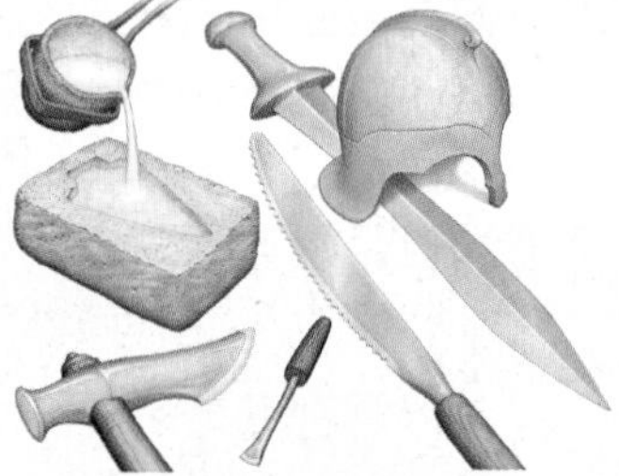

Figure 1 Artifacts from the Bronze Age prove that alloys of metal were used as early as 3500 B.C.

Alloys Through Time In about 3500 B.C., historians believe that ancient Sumerians in the Tigris-Euphrates Valley (now Iraq) accidentally discovered bronze. They believe that Sumerians used rocks rich in copper and tin ore to make fire rings to keep their campfires from spreading. The hot campfire melted the copper and tin ores within the rocks, creating bronze. This first known mixture of metals became so popular and widely used that a 2,000-year span of history is known as the Bronze Age. The ancients did not have a chemical language for their discovery, but the bronze tools and objects, such as those shown in **Figure 1,** helped change the history of civilization.

1 Motivate

Bellringer

Section Focus Transparencies also are available on the Interactive Chalkboard CD-ROM. L2

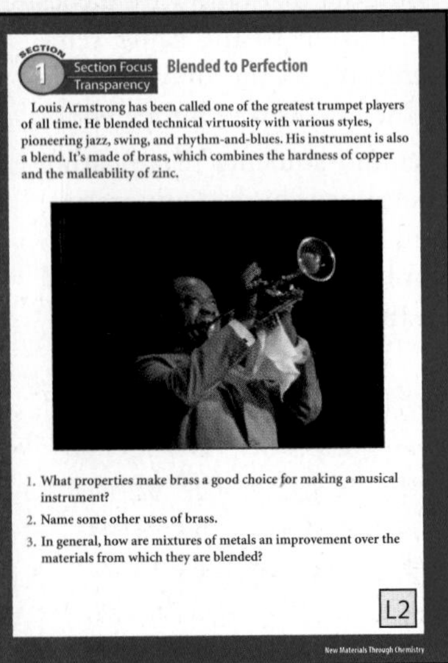
Section 1 Section Focus Transparency — Blended to Perfection

Louis Armstrong has been called one of the greatest trumpet players of all time. He blended technical virtuosity with various styles, pioneering jazz, swing, and rhythm-and-blues. His instrument is also a blend. It's made of brass, which combines the hardness of copper and the malleability of zinc.

1. What properties make brass a good choice for making a musical instrument?
2. Name some other uses of brass.
3. In general, how are mixtures of metals an improvement over the materials from which they are blended?

L2

New Materials Through Chemistry

Tie to Prior Knowledge

Made of Metal Ask students to name things that are made of metal and the elements that make up these metals. Possible answers: steel supports in buildings and bridges (mostly iron), wire (copper, among others), pots, pans, and bicycle frames (aluminum, among others) Explain that brass and bronze are metal alloys—metal solutions whose properties depend on the ratio of the elements each contains. L2

Caption Answer

Figure 2 Malleability allows metals to be rolled or hammered into thin sheets. Ductility allows metals to be pulled into wires.

Section 1 Resource Manager

Chapter *Fast File* Resources

- Transparency Activity, p. 44
- Directed Reading for Content Mastery, pp. 19, 20
- MiniLAB, p. 3
- Note-taking Worksheets, pp. 33–35
- Enrichment, p. 30
- Transparency Activity, pp. 47–48
- Reinforcement, p. 27
- Lab Activity, pp. 9–11

Physical Science Critical Thinking/Problem Solving, p. 23

Figure 2 This roll of coated copper wire has the metallic properties of ductility and conductivity. The French horn has the properties of malleability and luster.
Explain *the difference between malleability and ductility.*

Materials Change Typical objects from the Bronze Age and the following Iron Age include spearheads, tools, and even body armor. Bronze and iron are still used today, but it is doubtful that ancient people would recognize them. The methods of processing these alloys have undergone many changes. Other alloys also have been developed through the ages, giving people a large selection of materials to choose from today.

Properties of Metals and Alloys

Alloys retain the metallic properties of metals, some of which are shown in **Figure 2,** but what are the properties of metals? Metals have **luster,** which means they reflect light or have a shiny appearance. The shiny appearance of aluminum foil and a new copper coin demonstrates the property of luster. **Ductility** (duk TIH luh tee) means the metal can be pulled into wires. The copper electrical wire in your home demonstrates the ductility of metals and alloys. **Malleability** (mal yuh BIH luh tee) is the property that allows metals and alloys to be hammered or rolled into thin sheets. Aluminum foil that is used in food preparation and food storage demonstrates the malleability of aluminum. The French horn above demonstrates the luster and malleability of brass. **Conductivity** (kahn duk TIH vuh tee) means that heat or electrical charges can move easily through the material. Metals and alloys have high conductivity because some of their electrons are not tightly held by their atoms. Metals and alloys usually are good conductors of heat and electricity because of these loosely bound electrons. Copper is used to carry electricity because it is conductive and ductile.

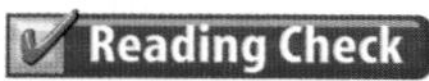
Reading Check *What are five other examples of items that you know of that have metallic properties?*

Mini LAB

Observing Properties of Alloys

Procedure

1. Observe a small sheet of **aluminum foil.**
2. Using a **conductivity tester,** test the following items for their ability to conduct electric current: aluminum foil, **paper, pencil, ink pen,** and **paper clip.**

Analysis

1. What metallic properties of the foil do you observe?
2. Explain why each item was or was not able to conduct electric current.

2 Teach

Mini LAB

Purpose observe properties of aluminum and compare the conductivity of several common materials. L2 IS **Kinesthetic**

Materials conductivity tester, paper, pencil, ink pen, and paper clip, aluminum foil

Teaching Strategy Inexpensive, continuity testers that are available in hardware stores can be substituted for the conductivity tester.

Safety Precautions Some conductivity testers have sharp points.

Analysis

1. ductility, malleability, and conductivity
2. Conductors (aluminum foil, paper clip) have loosely held electrons; nonconductors (paper, pencil, pen) have tightly held electrons.

Assessment

Process Have students make a list of ten items in their homes—five conductors and five nonconductors. Ask them to hypothesize the materials used to make each item. Use **Performance Assessment in the Science Classroom,** p. 93. L3 P IS **Logical-Mathematical, Linguistic, Intrapersonal**

Reading Check

Answer Possible answers include coins, silver or gold jewelry, toasters, keys, and paper clips.

Curriculum Connection

Language Arts Have students write science fiction stories involving a new alloy with unusual properties. Have students tell how the alloy is made and what its properties are. An example is the legend surrounding frontiersman Jim Bowie's knife. It was said to be made from the metal of a meteorite he found. The blade was said to be indestructible and never to need sharpening. L2 P IS **Linguistic**

Differentiated Instruction

English-Language Learners Have students create a three column chart and write the words *Ductility*, *Malleability*, and *Conductivity* at the top of each column. Then have students work with a partner to define each word and use it in a sentence.

Panning for Gold Gold is not soluble in water and is very dense (19.3 g/cm^3), so it sinks in water. Prospectors panned for gold by scooping up dirt and soil samples thought to contain gold and washing water over them. Less dense materials floated away, leaving the bright yellow and very dense particles of gold in the bottom of the pan.

Activity

Periodic Table Have students locate copper, zinc, and tin on the periodic table and find the melting point of each. Cu 1,085°C, Zn 420°C, Sn 232°C L2 IS **Linguistic**

Visual Learning

Figure 2 Explain to students that one karat is one-twenty-fourth part of pure gold. Therefore pure gold is 24-karat. Have students express the amount of gold in each ring in twenty-fourths. 22 karat ring is $\frac{22}{24} = \frac{11}{12}$; 14 karat ring is $\frac{14}{24} = \frac{7}{12}$; 12 karat ring is $\frac{12}{24} = \frac{1}{2}$ L2 IS **Logical-Mathematical**

Make a Model

Ice Cube Metals Have students bring to class plastic molds for making ice cubes. Then, have them mix water with a colored solution, such as fruit juice, and pour it into the molds. Next, freeze the molds and later remove the solid material to display. Tell students that mixing the liquids represents the mixing of copper and zinc to make brass. Pouring the solution into molds represents the process by which various doorknobs, plumbing fixtures, bronze jewelry, and wrought iron fences are made. L2 ELL IS **Kinesthetic, Visual-Spatial**

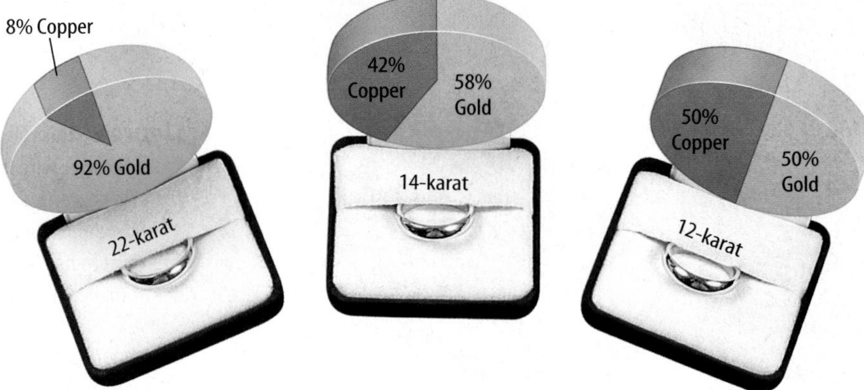

Figure 3 These gold rings appear to look alike, but they vary in the amount of copper that has been added to the gold. The composition of the alloy that was used to make the ring will determine its properties.

Panning for Gold During the California gold rush, prospectors obtained gold by panning. Panning is a process in which dirt and gravel are washed away with water, leaving gold in the bottom of the pan. In your Science Journal describe the properties of gold that were important in making this technique useful.

Choosing an Alloy What properties of an alloy are most important? The answer depends upon how the alloy will be used and which characteristics are the most desirable. Look at the characteristics of familiar objects made from alloys such as the gold jewelry shown in Figure 3. The rings appear to be made of pure gold, but they are made from alloys.

Gold is a bright, expensive metal that is soft and bends easily. Copper, on the other hand, is an inexpensive metal that is harder than gold. When gold and copper are melted, mixed, and allowed to cool, an alloy forms. The properties will vary depending upon the amount of each metal that is added. A ring made with a higher percentage of gold will bend easily due to gold's softness. This ring will be more valuable because it contains a higher percentage of gold. A ring with a higher percentage of copper will not bend as easily because copper is harder than gold. This ring will be less valuable because it contains more copper, a less-expensive metal.

Which properties are needed? The alloy chosen for jewelry and the alloy chosen for a drill bit probably will not be the same. However, the characteristics of the final product must be considered in both situations before the product is constructed.

How hard does the alloy have to be to prevent the object from breaking when it is used? Will the object be exposed to chemicals that will react with the alloy and cause the alloy to fail? These questions relate to the properties of the alloy and its intended use. This represents only two of the many possible questions that must be answered while a product is being designed.

Cultural Diversity

Industrial Parks K. Aslihan Yener was born in Turkey. She became interested in archaeology and applied chemical technology to archaeology in the "analysis of lead isotopes found in the mines and metals located throughout the Near East." Yener knew that the ratio of lead isotopes to other metals in Bronze Age objects would be like fingerprints. This insight enabled Yener to match the objects to the mine from which the metal originated. By doing this, Yener not only found large industrial parks in the Taurus Mountains of Turkey but she also located a subterranean city built into the mountainside. Have students explain how determining which mine a metal came from enabled Yener to find those Bronze Age industrial parks.

Uses of Alloys

Alloys are used in a variety of products, as shown in **Table 1.** If you see an object that looks metallic, it is most likely an alloy. Alloys that are exceptionally strong are used to manufacture industrial machinery, construction beams, and railroad cars and rails. Automobile and aircraft bodies that require strong materials are constructed of alloys that are corrosion resistant and lightweight but able to carry heavy loads. Other types of alloys are used in products such as food cans, carving knives, and roller skates. **Figure 4** shows some additional examples of alloys.

Table 1 Common Alloys

Name	Composition	Use
Bronze	copper, tin	jewelry, marine hardware
Brass	copper, zinc	hardware, musical instruments
Sterling silver	silver, copper	tableware
Pewter	tin, copper, antimony	tableware
Solder	lead, tin	plumbing
Wrought iron	iron, carbon	porch railings, fences, sculpture

If you have a tooth filling, your dentist might have used a silver and mercury alloy to fill it, preventing further tooth decay. Other alloys that are resistant to tissue rejection can be used inside the human body. Special pins and screws made from alloys are used by surgeons to connect broken bones, as shown in **Figure 4.** Alloys also are used as metal plates to repair damage to the skull. These plates protect the brain from injury and are safe to use inside the body.

Reading Check *What are several uses for alloys?*

Figure 4 The fork and saw blade, on the right, are both steel alloys, but they differ in chemical composition. Surgical steel, shown below, can be used to join bones.
Identify *the properties of steel that are most important.*

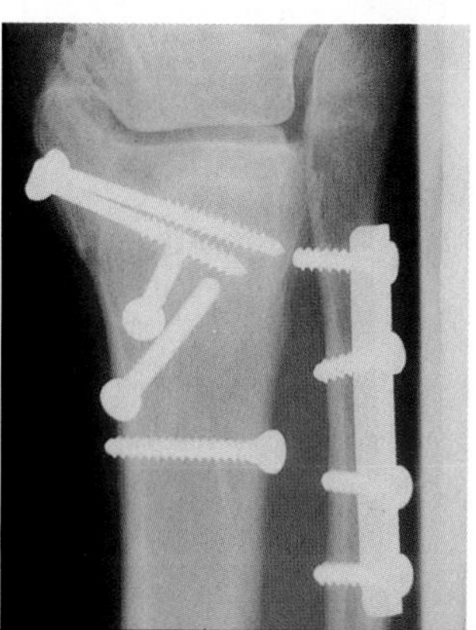

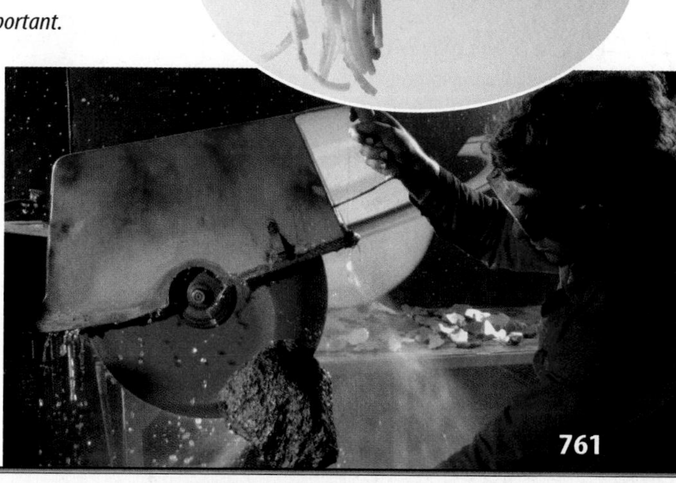

761

Wood's Metal Not every alloy is made to produce a stronger substance. An alloy called Wood's metal is actually a soft metal that melts around 70°C. It is made from bismuth, lead, tin, and cadmium. Its low melting point makes Wood's metal a good material to use in overhead sprinkler systems. A fire would heat the metal alloy to its melting point, when it would no longer hold back the water in a sprinkler system.

Quick Demo

Get A Reaction

Materials copper and zinc metal samples; HCl (5 *M*); large test tubes (2)

Estimated Time 10 minutes

Procedure Place each metal sample in a test tube that contains a small amount of hydrochloric acid. Zinc will react quickly to form hydrogen gas, but copper will not. **WARNING:** *Exercise care with the acid, using only small amounts well below the top of the test tube. Use pea-sized pieces of the metals and do not pressurize the hydrogen gas.*

Reading Check

Answer Possible answers include brass door handles, sterling silver spoons, wrought iron fences, steel automobile bodies, and alloy metal wheel rims.

Differentiated Instruction

Learning Disabled Give students a photocopy of the periodic table. Use vertical, horizontal, and diagonal hash marks of different colors to shade in elements used to make alloys. For example, the metals used to make bronze could be colored in with vertical red lines. Point out how some elements are used over and over. L2 ELL LS **Visual-Spatial, Hearing Impaired**

Caption Answer

Figure 4 resistance to tissue rejection, strength, and the ability to resist corrosion

Figure 5 Alloys can be designed and manufactured to meet specific physical properties.

Teacher FYI

Recycled Steel Steel is recycled easily. The magnetic properties of iron in steel products make it easy to separate from other wastes. Steel also can withstand the high temperatures used to clean old steel objects. Approximately 65 percent of steel made annually is made from recycled steel.

Use an Analogy

Music Analogy Remind students that steel is mostly iron, but with the addition of even small amounts of other elements the properties of the resulting alloy can be changed. Liken this to a band in which three members—a guitarist, drummer, and bassist —make good music, but the addition of a keyboardist adds a different tone to the songs.

Answer It is strong.

Fun Fact

Steel cans contain approximately 25 percent recycled material and are themselves completely recyclable. Nearly 600 steel cans are recycled each second.

Virtual Labs

Elements and Alloys *How do ratios of elements affect the physical properties of an alloy?*

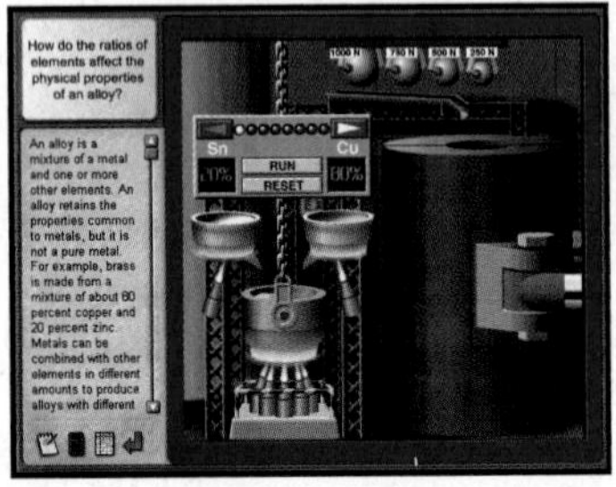

Steel—An Important Alloy There are various classes of steel. They are classified by the amount of carbon and other elements present, as well as by the manufacturing process that is used to refine the iron ore. The classes of steel have different properties and therefore different uses. Steel is a strong alloy and is used often if a great deal of strength is required. Office buildings have steel beams to support the weight of the structure. Bridges, overpasses, and streets also are reinforced with steel. Ship hulls, bedsprings, and automobile gears and axles are made from steel. Another class of steel, called stainless steel, is used in surgical instruments, cooking utensils, and large vessels where food products are prepared.

Reading Check *Why is steel an important alloy?*

Topic: Materials for Space Vehicles
Visit gpscience.com for Web links to recent news on research for new materials that can be used for space travel.

Activity Write a newspaper article or present a newscast story about your findings.

New Alloys

Steel is not the only common type of alloy. Aluminum is familiar because it is used to make soda cans and cooking foil. Did you know that engineers also are using new aluminum and titanium alloys to build large commercial aircraft? The aircraft shown in **Figure 5** shows how extensively alloys are used in new aircraft construction. The new alloys are strong, lightweight and last longer than alloys used in the past. Also, a lighter plane is less expensive to fly.

Space-Age Alloys Titanium alloy panels, developed for the space shuttle heat shield, might be used on future reusable launch vehicles that are designed to carry payloads to the International Space Station. Titanium and metallic alloys with similar heat-resistive and strength properties may prove to be key materials for other space applications as well.

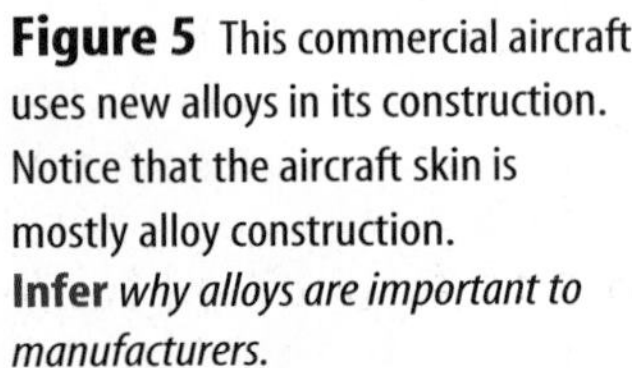

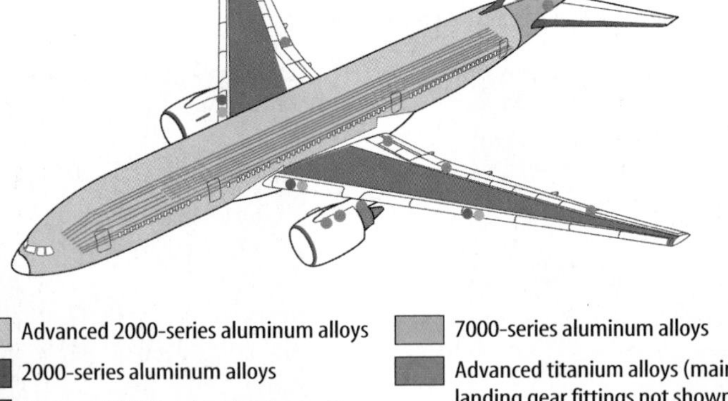

Figure 5 This commercial aircraft uses new alloys in its construction. Notice that the aircraft skin is mostly alloy construction.
Infer *why alloys are important to manufacturers.*

- Advanced 2000-series aluminum alloys
- 2000-series aluminum alloys
- Advanced 7000-series aluminum alloys
- 7000-series aluminum alloys
- Advanced titanium alloys (main landing gear fittings not shown)

Curriculum Connection

Math Students can calculate the small amount of carbon used in a sample of steel. High-carbon steel, used to make tools and springs, may contain only 0.7 percent carbon. Calculate the grams of carbon needed to make 1.0 kg of high-carbon steel. $0.007 \times 1{,}000 \text{ grams} = 7 \text{ grams}$
L2 LS **Logical-Mathematical**

Differentiated Instruction

Challenge Have students identify some of the most common brasses, the metals they contain, and what they are used for. Common brasses include cartridge brass (70% copper, 30% zinc), used for plumbing fixtures; naval brass (contains less than 2% tin), used in naval construction; Dutch metal (80-85% copper, 15-20% zinc), used as substitute for gold leaf. L3 LS **Linguistic**

New Titanium Alloy Heat Shield

The original heat shield on the space shuttle uses ceramic tiles that are prone to cracking as a result of the high temperature and stress they experience during reentry into Earth's atmosphere. Each broken ceramic tile must be removed carefully and a new one glued into place before the shuttle can be used on another mission. This maintenance is expensive, and damaged tiles are physically difficult to replace.

The new titanium alloy tiles, shown in **Figure 6,** are much larger and easier to attach to the heat shield than the ceramic tiles are. A lower maintenance cost for the heat shield is expected by using the new alloy. Scientists and engineers also predict that the new alloy will protect the space shuttle as well as the old ceramic tiles did.

Figure 6 New alloys are being tested for use on the space shuttle. An experimental titanium alloy heat-resistant tile similar to this example may cover space shuttles in future flights.

section 1 review

Summary

Alloys

- Alloy metals defined several historical time periods, including the Bronze Age and the Iron Age.
- An alloy has characteristics that are different from, and often improved upon, the individual elements of the alloy.

Properties of Metals and Alloys

- Alloy materials are defined by their physical properties.

Uses of Alloys

- Alloy materials are used in industry, food service, medicine, and aeronautics.

New Alloys

- New alloys that are strong and lightweight can be used for high-tech applications including aircraft and spacecraft.

Self Check

1. **Identify** two medical uses of alloys.
2. **List** the properties of metals and alloys.
3. **Describe** how steels are classified.
4. **Explain** the effects of adding small amounts of another substance to a material.
5. **Think Critically** If you were designing a skyscraper in an earthquake zone, what properties would the structural materials need?

Applying Math

6. **Calculate** Use the information from **Figure 3** to calculate the actual amount of gold in a 65-g, 14-karat gold necklace.
7. **Find Mass** If a 7.6-g sample of copper can be hammered into a 2-cm × 2-cm sheet, calculate the number of grams necessary to hammer a 17-cm × 17-cm sheet under the same manufacturing conditions.

Science Online gpscience.com/self_check_quiz

3 Assess

DAILY INTERVENTION

Check for Understanding

Linguistic Ask students to write a recipe card for making steel or another alloy of their choice. Have them include a list of ingredients and step-by-step instructions for preparation. L3 LS **Linguistic**

Reteach

Pewter Example Bring a pewter object to class. Explain to students that pewter is an alloy. Ask whether that means pewter is a type of solution. yes Ask students to locate the positions of tin, antimony, and copper on the periodic table. These are the ingredients in pewter. L2 LS **Visual-Spatial**

Assessment

Oral The strongest known permanent magnet is an alloy. Ask students what they know about the magnet when they know it is an alloy. It is made from more than one type of metallic element. The alloy metals are neodymium, iron, and boron. Have students locate the metals on the periodic table by their atomic numbers. Nd is 60; Fe is 26, B is 5. L1 LS **Visual-Spatial**

section 1 review

1. Possible answers include tooth fillings and protective metal plates in the skull.
2. They are malleable and ductile and conduct electricity and heat. They also have luster.
3. by the amount of carbon and other elements present
4. Adding different components to a material changes its chemical identity and can also change its physical properties and performance.
5. strength to support the weight of the structure and the flexibility to withstand the forces generated by seismic shaking
6. $65 \text{ g} \times 0.58 = 38 \text{ g}$ of gold
7. $\frac{7.6 \text{ g}}{4 \text{ cm}^2} = \frac{x \text{ g}}{289 \text{ cm}^2}$

   $4x = 2196.4$

   $x = 549.1 \text{ g}$

1 Motivate

Bellringer

Section Focus Transparencies also are available on the Interactive Chalkboard CD-ROM.

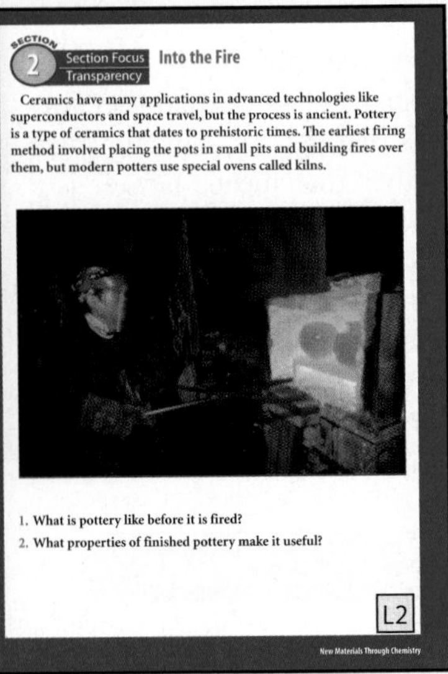

Section 2 Section Focus Transparency — Into the Fire

Ceramics have many applications in advanced technologies like superconductors and space travel, but the process is ancient. Pottery is a type of ceramics that dates to prehistoric times. The earliest firing method involved placing the pots in small pits and building fires over them, but modern potters use special ovens called kilns.

1. What is pottery like before it is fired?
2. What properties of finished pottery make it useful?

L2

New Materials Through Chemistry

Tie to Prior Knowledge

Ceramics Most students have seen painted ceramic figurines. Bring some examples to class. Students are also familiar with glass. Explain that glass is a type of ceramic that doesn't have a consistent crystal structure.

section 2

Versatile Materials

Reading Guide

What You'll Learn

- **Examine** the versatile properties of ceramics.
- **Identify** how ceramic materials are used.
- **Explain** what a semiconductor is.

Why It's Important

Ceramics and semiconductors are classes of materials that make computers, electronic games, and many medical devices practical.

Review Vocabulary

compound: a chemical combination of two or more different elements into a substance that has properties different than the component elements

New Vocabulary

- ceramics
- semiconductor
- doping
- integrated circuit

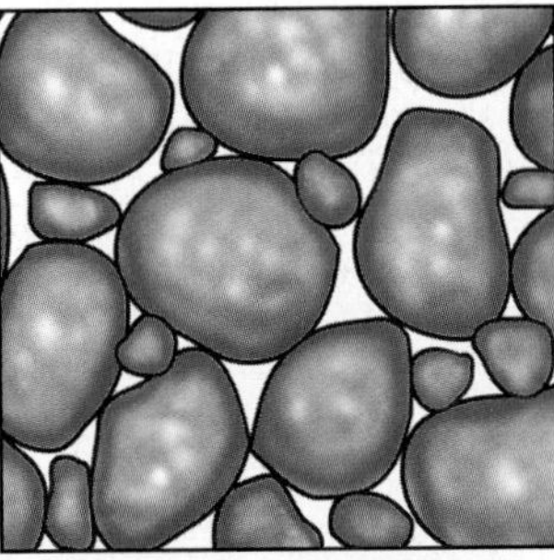

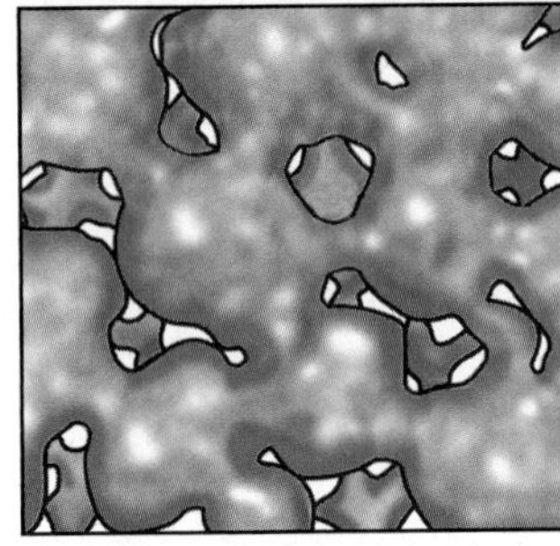

Figure 7 Ceramics are molded and then heated to high temperatures to force the particles to merge. The object shrinks and the structure becomes more dense.

Ceramics

Do you think of floor tiles, pottery, or souvenir nicknacks when you see the word *ceramic?* By definition, **ceramics** are materials that are made from dried clay or claylike mixtures. Ceramics have been around for centuries—in fact, pieces of clay pottery from 10,000 B.C. have been found. The first walled town, Jericho, was built about 8,000 B.C. The wall surrounding Jericho, as well as the homes inside the walls were constructed of bricks made from mud and straw that were baked in the Sun. Around 1,500 B.C., the first glass vessels were made and kilns were used to fire and glaze pottery. By 50 B.C. the Romans developed concrete and used it as a building material. Some of the structures built by the Romans still stand today. About the same time that Romans were developing concrete, the Syrians were developing glass-blowing techniques to make glass vessels. Pottery, bricks, glass, and concrete are examples of ceramics.

How are ceramics made? Traditional ceramics are made from easily obtainable raw materials—clay, silica (sand), and feldspar (crystalline rocks). These raw materials were used by ancient civilizations to make ceramic materials and still are used today. However, some of the more recent ceramics are made from compounds of metallic elements and carbon, nitrogen, or sulfur.

What raw materials are used to make traditional ceramic objects?

Section 2 Resource Manager

Chapter *FAST FILE* Resources

- Transparency Activity, p. 45
- Directed Reading for Content Mastery, p. 21
- MiniLAB, p. 4
- Reinforcement, p. 28
- Enrichment, p. 31

Reading and Writing Skill Activities, p. 9

Cultural Diversity, p. 49

Figure 8 Ceramic materials are used for a wide range of products. Glass, pottery, bricks, and tile are all made from ceramics.
Explain *how ceramics and alloys are similar.*

Firing Ceramics After the raw materials are processed, ceramics usually are made by molding the ceramic into the desired shape, then heating it to temperatures between 1,000°C and 1,700°C. The heating process, called firing, causes the spaces between the particles to shrink, as shown in **Figure 7.** The entire object shrinks as the spaces become smaller. This extremely dense internal structure gives ceramics their strength. This is demonstrated by the use of ceramics on the space shuttle heat shield. They are able to withstand the high temperatures and stress of reentry into Earth's atmosphere. However, these same ceramics also are fragile and will break if they are dropped or if the temperature changes too quickly.

Traditional Ceramics Ceramics are known also for their chemical resistance to oxygen, water, acids, bases, salts, and strong solvents. These qualities make ceramics useful for applications where they may encounter these substances. For instance, ceramics are used for tableware because your foods contain acids, water, and salts. Ceramic tableware is not damaged by contact with foods containing these substances.

Traditional ceramics also are used as insulators because they do not conduct heat or electricity. You may have seen electric wires attached to poles or posts with ceramic insulators. These insulators keep the current flowing through the wire instead of into the ground.

The properties of ceramics can be customized, which makes them useful for a wide variety of applications as shown in **Figure 8.** Changing the composition of the raw materials or the manufacturing process changes the properties of the ceramic. Manufacturing ceramics is similar to manufacturing alloys because scientists determine which properties are required and then attempt to create the ceramic material.

Modeling a Composite Material

Procedure

WARNING: *Wear goggles and an apron while doing this lab. Wash your hands before leaving the lab.*

1. Mix four tablespoons of **sand,** four tablespoons of **aquarium gravel or small pebbles,** and six tablespoons of **white glue** in a paper cup.
2. Add enough water to thoroughly mix the ingredients.
3. Stir the mixture until it is smooth.
4. Allow the mixture to sit for several days and observe.
5. Dispose of the cup as instructed by your teacher.

Analysis

1. Describe what happened to your mixture after several days. Is it a ceramic?
2. How is your mixture similar to concrete?
3. What are some of the properties of your product?

2 Teach

Reading Check

Answer clay, silica, and feldspar

Purpose Students make concrete. L2 **Kinesthetic**

Materials sand, aquarium gravel, white glue, water, paper cup, and large spoon

Analysis

1. The mixture hardened into a stone-like material and is a ceramic.
2. Both mix sand, gravel, and a sticking agent with water to form a rock-hard material.
3. Answers will vary, but should describe the appearance and apparent strength of the material.

Assessment

Oral Ask students how life might be different had concrete and other stone building materials never been developed. Answers will vary but could include that stone building materials were necessary to construct the large, permanent cities where culture developed. Use **Performance Assessment in the Science Classroom,** p. 89. L2

Caption Answer

Figure 8 Ceramics and alloys both contain metallic elements.

Curriculum Connection

Art If possible, invite the school art teacher to demonstrate for the class the properties of clay before and after kiln firing to show how the clay becomes brittle. L2 **Visual-Spatial**

Fun Fact

The color of an unglazed ceramic is very likely to be white if it was made from the pure clay called kaolinite, $Al_2Si_2O_5(OH)_4$. Red brick ceramic gets its color from additional iron oxide present in the clay.

Teacher FYI

Firing Ceramics Firing ceramics must be done very carefully. The rate of heating and of cooling can influence the small structural relationships among the fine particles. Microwave heating can be better controlled than flame heating and is used for making some specialty ceramics. If ceramics are not heated gradually, the sudden application of heat causes the internal water to vaporize with enough pressure to shatter the ceramic object.

Applying Science

Answers

1. Ceramic A; it does not wear out easily, and would not likely react with fuel chemicals. In addition, it could withstand the high temperatures often found in engines. The overall mass of the engine needs to be kept low, so the density of the ceramic could be a factor.
2. Ignoring cost, ceramic D or C would possibly provide the qualities of electrical conductivity needed in some computer parts. Neither appears to have corrosion problems.
3. cost and availability of the material and its ability to withstand impacts that occur in collisions. It may be suitable if it is able to absorb the energy of an impact without permanent distortion or splintering.

Caption Answer

Figure 9 Examples are knee, shoulders, teeth, and fingers.

Figure 9 This ceramic hip socket is used to replace damaged sockets in the human body.
Identify *other parts of the body that can be helped by ceramics.*

Modern Ceramics Ceramics can be customized to have nontraditional properties, too. Ceramics traditionally are used as insulators, but there are exceptions. For instance, chromium dioxide conducts electricity as well as most metals, and some copper-based ceramics have superconductive properties. One application of nontraditional ceramics uses a transparent, electrically conductive ceramic in aircraft windshields to keep them free of ice and snow.

Ceramics have medical uses. **Figure 9** shows a ceramic replacement hip socket for use in the human body. Ceramics can be used in the body because they are strong and resistant to body fluids, which can damage other materials. In the medical field, surgeons use ceramics for the repair and replacement of joints such as hips, knees, shoulders, elbows, fingers, and wrists. Dentists use ceramics for tooth replacements, repair, and braces.

Applying Science

Can you choose the right material?

Scientists continue to learn about atoms and how they bond. With this new knowledge, chemists today are able to create substances with a wide range of properties. This is especially evident in the production of specialized ceramics.

Ceramic Properties

Material	Wear Resistant	Conducts Electricity	React with Chemicals	Melting Point
ceramic A	highly resistant	no	no	3,000°C
ceramic B	wears easily	no	yes	100°C
ceramic C	moderately resistant	yes	no	1,500°C
ceramic D	resistant	yes	no	500°C

Identifying the Problem

As an engineer working on the design of a new car, you need to select the right ceramic materials to build parts of the car's engine and its onboard computer. The table above shows the materials you have to choose from. Using the properties given in the table, decide which materials should be used for the engine parts and the onboard computer. Be prepared to explain your answer.

Solving the Problem

1. Which of the above materials would you use when you build the engine? Explain the factors that you considered to make your decision.
2. Which of the above materials would you select when building the onboard computer? Explain your selection.
3. If you had to choose a material for building the car's bumper, what factors would you consider? Do you think that a ceramic material would be the best choice? Explain your answer.

LAB DEMONSTRATION

Purpose to show that traditional ceramics are strong and brittle

Materials small ceramic tiles (from a home-improvement store), hammer, heavy cloth, container for the wrapped tile

Preparation Obtain tile that can demostrate breakage without undue force.

Procedure Demonstrate strength: stand on a tile. Demonstrate brittleness: wrap a tile in heavy cloth, place it in a container, and strike the wrapped tile with a hammer. Unwrap the tile and observe.

Expected Outcome The tile can support heavy objects without cracking, but the blow shatters the tile.

Assessment

If traditional ceramics are so brittle why are they used in some places instead of metal? Ceramics can withstand extremely high temperatures at which most metals would melt. Also, they may be cheaper or less massive than metal. L2

Semiconductors

Another class of versatile materials is semiconductors. Semiconductors are the materials that make computers and other electronic devices possible.

The Periodic Table What are semiconductors? To answer this, think about the periodic table. The elements on the left side and in the center of the table are metals. Metals are good conductors of electricity. Nonmetals, located on the right side of the table, are poor conductors of electricity and are electrical insulators. The small number of elements found along the staircase-shaped border shown in **Figure 10** between the metals and nonmetals are metalloids. Some metalloids, such as silicon (Si) and germanium (Ge), are semiconductors. **Semiconductors** are poorer conductors of electricity than metals but better conductors than nonmetals, and their electrical conductivity can be controlled. This property makes semiconductor devices useful.

Controlling Conductivity Adding other elements to some metalloids can change their electrical conductivities. For example, the conductivity of silicon can be increased by replacing silicon atoms with atoms of other elements, such as arsenic (As) or gallium (Ga), as shown in **Figure 11.** If the added atoms, called impurities, have fewer electrons than silicon atoms, the silicon crystals will contain holes, or areas with fewer electrons. Electrons now can move from hole to hole across the crystal, increasing conductivity.

Adding even a single atom of one of these elements to a million silicon atoms significantly changes the conductivity. By controlling the type and number of atoms added, the conductivity of silicon can vary over a wide range.

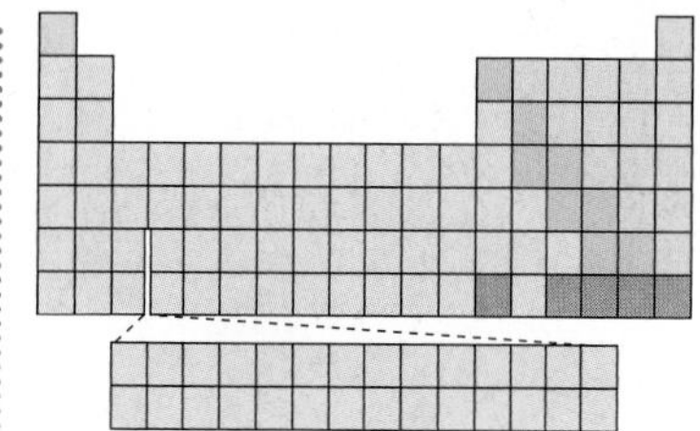

Figure 10 This outline of the periodic table clearly shows the metalloids, which appear in green.

Figure 11 Pure silicon is a poor conductor of electricity. Adding another element with fewer outer electrons, as an impurity, creates an area of fewer electrons called a hole.

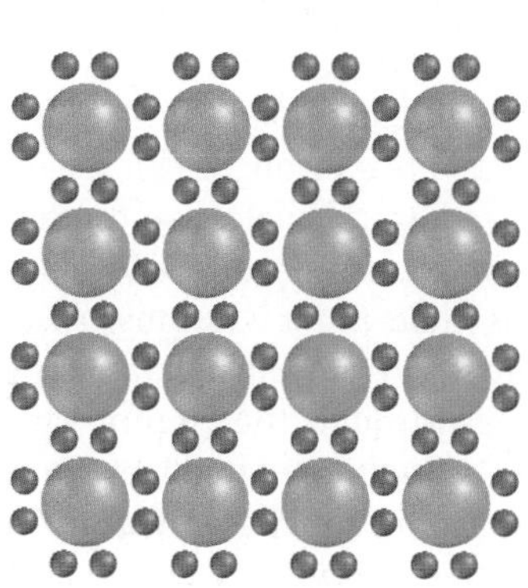

Pure silicon crystal

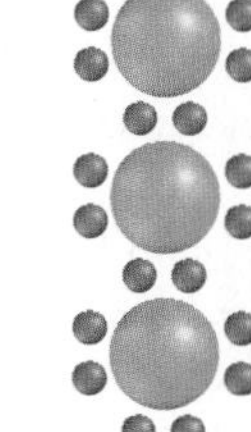

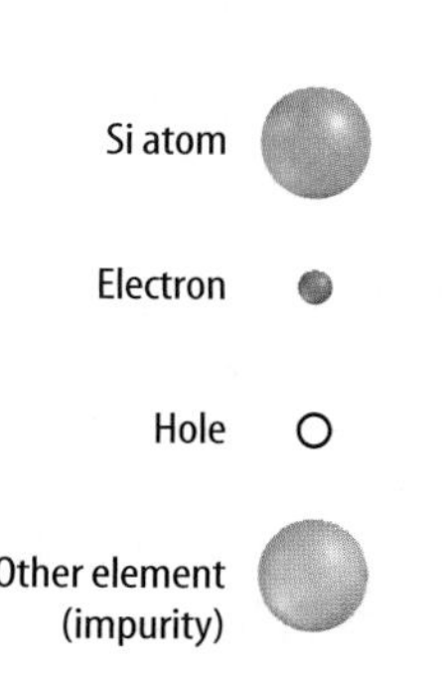

Silicon crystal with impurities

Visual Learning

Figure 11 Ask a volunteer to point out the holes in the doped semiconductor, and to describe the movement of electrons and holes in it. L2 LS **Visual-Spatial**

Discussion

Silicon Semiconductor Why would silicon be a popular and inexpensive material for making semiconductors? It is found in most rocks and is one of the most plentiful elements on Earth. In addition, its conductive properties can be changed by adding impurities to the crystalline structure. L2 LS **Logical-Mathematical**

Quick Demo

Seeing Semiconductors

Materials various electronic components

Estimated Time 15 minutes

Procedure Bring in several electronic components and show students the integrated circuitry of each. Explain that the circuit chips are made of semiconducting materials and that the circuits can be tailored to each application by the material it is made of and by doping with other elements.

Differentiated Instruction

Challenge The first semiconductor materials used were the elements germanium, silicon, and a form of tin known as gray tin. Now some compounds are also used as semiconductors. Have students find out what some of these compounds are. Gallium arsenide, indium antimonide, and aluminum phosphide are three compounds used as semiconductors. L3 LS **Linguistic**

Visually Impaired As they examine computer chips, ask sighted students to describe to visually impaired students what is on the chips and how small they are. Suggest that they describe size by using analogies to items whose size can be determined by touch. L2 LS **Kinesthetic**

Use Science Words

Word Meaning Tell students that the word *integrate* means "to blend into a functioning or unified whole." Ask students to explain how this applies to integrated circuits. In an integrated circuit, all the components are blended into a functioning whole on a single chip of semiconductor material. L2 IS **Linguistic, Logical-Mathematical**

Activity

Circuitry Have some microchips with integrated circuits on them available for students to observe and examine through a microscope. They should realize how tiny the components can be and still be effective. L2 IS **Visual-Spatial, Logical-Mathematical**

Fun Fact

A transistor is a semiconductor that amplifies or strengthens an electric signal or acts as a tiny electric on-off switch. Transistors, which have been used in electronic circuits as amplifiers, rectifiers, detectors, or switches, paved the way for the development of the integrated circuit used in today's myriad electronic devices.

Caption Answer

Figure 12 n-type semiconductor has an increase in the overall number of electrons; p-type semiconductor has a decrease in electrons

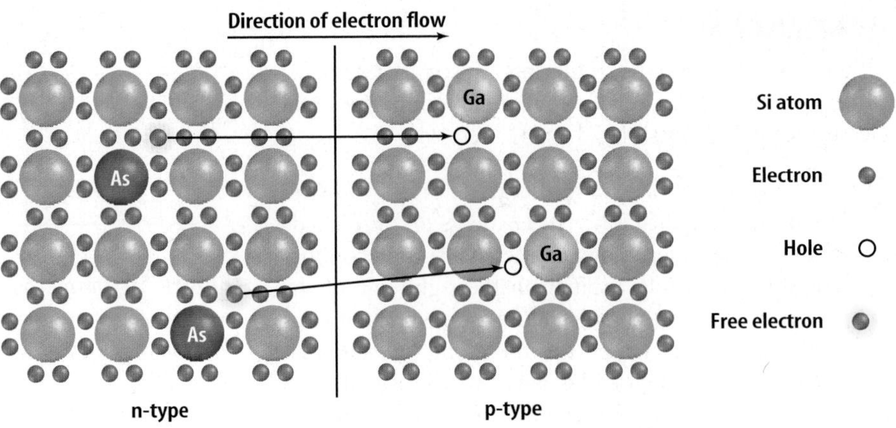

Figure 12 The electrons flow from the arsenic-doped silicon to the germanium-doped silicon, filling the available holes. The electron flow is controlled by the sequence of n-type or p-type semiconductors.
Summarize *the difference between n-type and p-type semiconductors.*

Doping The process of adding impurities or other elements to a semiconductor to modify the conductivity is called **doping.** Depending on the element added, the overall number of electrons in the semiconductor is increased or decreased. If the impurity causes the overall number of electrons to increase, the semiconductor is called an *n-type* semiconductor. If doping reduces the overall number of electrons, the semiconductor is called a *p-type* semiconductor.

Integrated Circuits By placing n-type and p-type semiconductors together, semiconductor devices such as transistors and diodes can be made. These devices are used to control the flow of electrons in electrical circuits, as shown in **Figure 12.** During the 1960s, methods were developed for making these components extremely small. At the same time, the integrated circuit was developed.

An **integrated circuit** contains many semiconducting devices. Integrated circuits as small as 1 cm on a side can contain millions of semiconducting devices. Because of their small size, integrated circuits are sometimes called microchips. **Figure 13** shows how small an integrated circuit chip can be.

Being able to pack so many circuit components onto a tiny integrated circuit was a technological breakthrough. This makes it possible for today's televisions, radios, calculators, and other devices to be smaller in size, cheaper to manufacture, and capable of more advanced functions than older versions. Also, because the circuit components are so close together, it takes less time for electric current to travel through the circuit. This enables electronic signals to be processed more rapidly by computers, cell phones, and other electronic appliances. **Figure 14** illustrates how integrated circuits have given us faster, smaller, and more capable computers since the 1940s.

Figure 13 A single integrated circuit fits easily on a fingertip. This small size allows computers and other electronic devices to be compact.

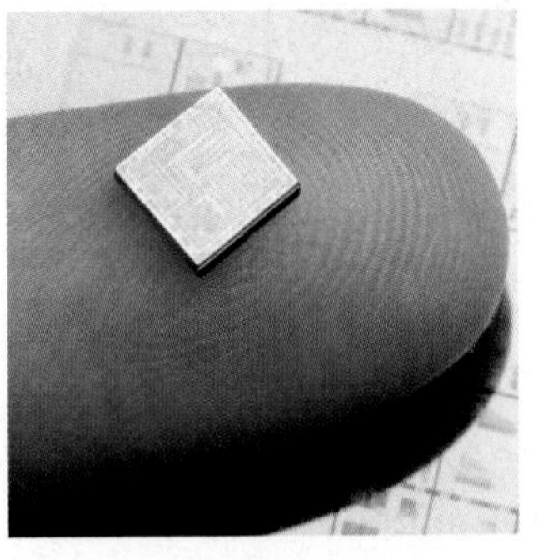

Science Journal

Integrated Circuits Have students make note of all the devices they use in a week that contain integrated circuits. Ask students to write their lists in their Science Journals. Devices include computers, printers, televisions, calculators, VCRs, automobiles, digital watches, radios, CD players, microwave ovens, and cellular phones. L2 IS **Visual-Spatial** P **Linguistic**

VISUALIZING THE HISTORY OF COMPUTERS

Figure 14

The earliest, room-size computers relied on vacuum tubes to store data. Today's computers use microchips, tiny flakes of silicon engraved with millions of circuit components. A selection of computers is shown here, beginning with the Electronic Numerical Integrator and Computer (ENIAC), developed by the Army in 1946.

Ⓐ A technician programs the ENIAC, the first electronic computer. Some of the 18,000 vacuum tubes that ran the ENIAC are shown at right.

Ⓑ A young woman operates a 1960s-era computer. The inset photo shows an integrated circuit from such a computer.

Ⓒ Teenagers surf the Internet on a modern personal computer. The microchips that store computer programs are now smaller than a fingernail.

Visualizing the History of Computers

Have students examine the pictures and read the captions. Then ask the following questions.

How have the changes in the size of computers affected their use? Possible answer: Old computers were too large to be used in schools, homes, and many offices.

How might your lives be different if personal computers had not been developed? Possible answer: You wouldn't be able to do research on the Internet; e-mail friends and family; do homework on the computer; play computer games. L2 LS **Visual-Spatial, Logical-Mathematical**

Activity

Computer Uses Divide the class into four groups. Assign each group one of the following topics: business and industry; government and law enforcement; engineering and science; medicine and health. Have students in each group research how computers are being used in the area they were assigned. Each group should present an oral report to the class. L2 COOP LEARN LS **Linguistic**

Active Reading

Learning Journal The Learning Journal encourages students to interact with the reading, allowing personal responses. Students should draw a vertical line down each page of their Learning Journal. The left column entries can be research notes, lecture notes, or vocabulary terms. The right column entries can be the student's response to, interpretation of, question about, or analysis of the left column entries. Have students write a Learning Journal related to the versatile materials described in this section. L3 LS **Linguistic, Logical-Mathematical, Intrapersonal**

3 Assess

DAILY INTERVENTION

Check for Understanding

Visual-Spatial Review **Figure 7** with students and describe again how ceramics are made from the raw materials and what the desired physical properties are.

Reteach

Spark Plugs Bring a spark plug from a car engine to class. Ask students to identify the metal component of the plug. The tip is metallic. Show them the white ceramic part and ask students for its properties. nonconductor, withstands high heat surrounding the plug L2 ELL IS **Visual-Spatial**

Assessment

Oral Describe how semiconductors control the flow of electrons in integrated circuits. Electrons only flow from n-type to p-type semiconductors. Use **Performance Assessment in the Science Classroom,** p. 89. L2

Caption Answer

Figure 15 Accept all answers.

Figure 15 Desktop computers use semiconductors to perform their tasks.
Infer *what you think computers will look like in twenty years.*

Semiconductors and Computers

Semiconductors make today's computers possible. A desktop computer is an example of a device that uses semiconductors. A computer has three main jobs. First, it must be able to receive and store the information that is needed to solve a problem. Next, it must be able to follow instructions to perform tasks in a logical way. Finally, a computer must communicate information to the outside world. All three jobs can be done with a combination of hardware and software components.

Computer hardware refers to the major permanent components of a computer, such as the keyboard, monitor, mouse, and central processing unit (CPU). These components are shown in **Figure 15.** Software refers to the instructions that tell the computer what to do. When a computer system is functioning properly, the hardware and software work together to perform tasks.

section 2 review

Summary

Ceramics

- Ceramics are dense composites that are strong and heat resistant.
- Resistance to oxygen, water, acids, bases, and solvents makes ceramics useful for a wide range of applications.
- The properties of ceramics can be customized by changing raw materials and manufacturing processes.
- Ceramics are used as insulators because they do not conduct heat or electicity.

Semiconductors

- Semiconductors conduct electricity moderately well.
- The degree of semiconductor conductivity can be controlled, making these materials versatile.
- Doping is the process of adding impurities to a semiconductor to change its conductivity.
- Integrated circuits are microchips that contain many semiconducting devices.

Self Check

1. **Describe** how ceramic materials are made.
2. **List** five uses of ceramic materials.
3. **Describe** electrical conductivity of ceramics.
4. **Explain** what semiconductors are and where they are used.
5. **Think Critically** Computers and software have changed the way businesses operate. If you operated a distribution center for a manufacturer, how would you use computers to assist you?

Applying Math

6. **Calculate** Ceramic A forms when heated to 1,400°C and has a density of 5.3 g/cm^3. Ceramic B forms at a temperature 675°C cooler and is four times as dense. What temperature is required to form Ceramic B and what is its density?
7. **Solve a Problem** A developmental ceramic is designed to be 35% silica and 65% sulfur. If a researcher needs 75 g of this material for a test, how many grams of each component will she need?

Science Online gpscience.com/self_check_quiz

section 2 review

1. They are molded into form and heated to force the particles to merge.
2. Answers may include engine parts, insulators, floor tile, containers, and replacement joints, and teeth.
3. Some ceramics do not conduct, those that contain chromium dioxide conduct well, and some containing copper are superconductors.
4. metalloids such as silicon and germanium that are poorer conductors of electricity than metals but better conductors than nonmetals; they are used in computer chips, integrated circuits, and computers
5. to track inventories, check customer credit, transfer funds electronically
6. 1400°C − 675°C = 725°C
   $\frac{5.3\text{ g}}{\text{cm}^3} \times 4 = \frac{21.2\text{ g}}{\text{cm}^3}$
7. 75 g × .35 = 26.25 g silica
   75 g × .65 = 48.75 g sulfur

section 3

Polymers and Composites

Reading Guide

What You'll Learn

- **Identify** what a polymer is and the variety of polymers around us.
- **Explain** what a composite material is and why composites are used.

Why It's Important

Synthetic polymers and composite materials can replace natural materials such as engine oil, wood, and paper to conserve natural resources.

Review Vocabulary

polymerization: a chemical reaction in which two or more molecules combine to form a larger molecule with repeating structural units (polymer)

New Vocabulary

- polymer
- monomer
- synthetic
- composite

Polymers

Polymers are a class of natural or manufactured substances that are composed of molecules arranged in large chains with small, simple, repeating units called monomers. A **monomer** is one specific molecule that is repeated in the polymer chain. Each link in the chain is a monomer. Polypropylene, for example, might have 50,000 to 200,000 monomers in its chain. Several examples of manufactured polymers are shown in **Table 2.**

Not all polymers are manufactured. Some occur naturally. Proteins, cellulose, and nucleic acids are polymers found in living things. In this section, the focus will be on manufactured or synthetic polymers. **Synthetic** means that the polymer does not occur naturally, but it was manufactured in a laboratory or chemical plant. Many synthetic polymers are designed to out perform their natural counterparts.

Table 2 Common Polymers

Polymer	Monomer	Uses
Polyethylene	$\left[CH_2 - CH_2 \right]$	bottles, garment bags
Polyvinyl chloride (PVC)	$\left[CH_2 - CHCl \right]$	pipe, bottles, compact discs, computer housing
Polypropylene	$\left[CH_2 - CH(CH_3) \right]$	rope, luggage, carpet, film
Polystyrene	$\left[CH(C_6H_5) - CH_2 \right]$	toys, packaging, egg cartons, flotation devices

Section 3 Resource Manager

Chapter FAST FILE Resources

Transparency Activity, p. 46, 47–48

Directed Reading for Content Mastery, pp. 21, 22

Enrichment, p. 32

Lab Activity, pp. 13–16

Reinforcement, p. 29

Lab Worksheet, pp. 5–6, 7–8

Reading and Writing Skill Activities, p. 17

Physical Science Critical Thinking/Problem Solving, p. 5, 15

Mathematics Skill Activities, p. 19

1 Motivate

Bellringer

Section Focus Transparencies also are available on the Interactive Chalkboard CD-ROM. L2 

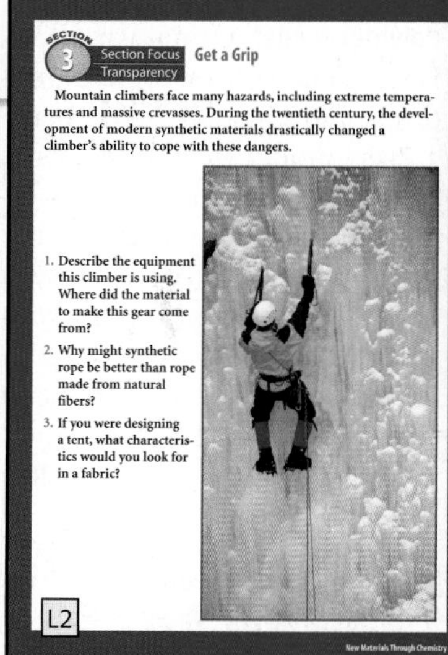

Tie to Prior Knowledge

Everyday Polymers Bring labels from clothing and other items made of materials whose names start with *poly-* (for example, polyester and polypropylene). Explain to students that the materials used to make these items are polymers. In this section they will learn more about what polymers are and how they are used.

2 Teach

Activity

Plastic Products Have students bring in plastic products. Arrange them from soft to rigid as a display representing the various properties of polymers. Have students identify the names of the polymers and their monomers. Possible polymers include those listed in **Table 2.** L2 IN **Visual-Spatial**

Make a Model

Polymer Model Using a molecular modeling kit or colored gum drops and chenille sticks, make a class model of polyethylene. Have each student make a polyethylene monomer, then join the monomers together to make a polyethylene chain. Discuss with students the formation of polymers and show how the chain could have many twists and turns. L2 ELL IN **Kinesthetic, Visual Spatial**

Synthetic Polymers Students may want to contact a local landfill agency and obtain comments about the synthetic polymers being placed there. Why are the polymers so stable? When they polymerize, the monomers form new bonds that are very stable. L3 IN **Logical-Mathematical**

Career Have students locate chemical companies that manufacture polymers. The Internet is a good resource for information about such companies. Have students look at descriptions of the manufacturing facilities and locate listings of career opportunities. Ask them if they would be interested in working for any of the companies they locate. L2 IN **Linguistic**

Synthetic Polymers Many disposable items such as plates, diapers, trash bags, and utensils are made from synthetic polymers. These products are used once, then thrown away. Most synthetic polymers do not decompose in landfills. In your Science Journal, infer the problems that this might cause and suggest solutions to these problems.

History of Synthetic Polymers Humankind has used natural polymers for centuries. The ancient Egyptians soaked their burial wrappings in natural resins to help preserve their dead. Animal horns and turtle shells, which contain natural resins, were used to make combs and buttons for many years. In the 1800s, scientists began developing processes to improve natural polymers and to create new ones in the laboratory.

In 1839, Charles Goodyear, an American inventor, found that heating sulfur and natural rubber together improved the qualities of natural rubber. By treating the rubber with sulfur, the natural rubber was no longer brittle when it became cold or soft when it became hot. In the late 1860s, John Hyatt developed celluloid as a replacement for ivory in billiard balls. Celluloid was used in other products such as umbrella handles and toys. These early polymers had many drawbacks, but they were the beginning of the development of a huge class of materials now referred to as polymers. Today, so many types of synthetic polymers exist that they tend to be divided into groups such as plastics, synthetic fibers, adhesives, surface coatings, and synthetic rubbers. **Figure 16** shows a time line of when some of these materials were created.

Hydrocarbons Today, synthetic polymers usually are made from fossil fuels such as oil, coal, or natural gas. Fossil fuels are composed primarily of carbon and hydrogen and are referred to as hydrocarbons. Because synthetic polymers are made from hydrocarbons, carbon and hydrogen are the primary components of most synthetic polymers.

Figure 16 Polymers were developed in the late 1800s, but they did not become widely used until after World War II in 1945.

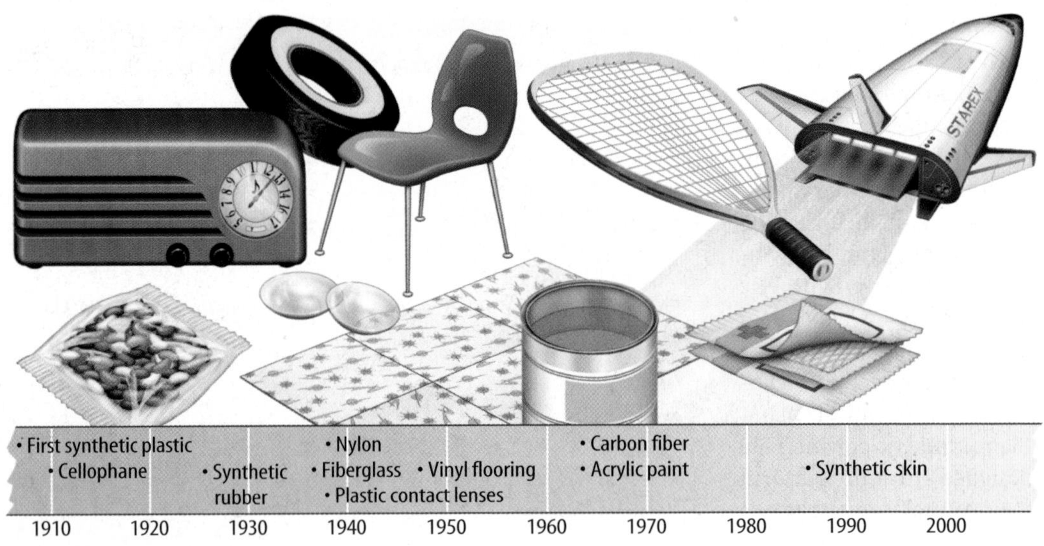

Cultural Diversity

South American Rubber Rubber was first used in Central and South America. Rubber was harvested from local trees and used for balls, containers, and shoes and for waterproofing fabrics. Later, rubber was harvested from pará rubber trees found in Brazil's Amazon basin. Have students find out about the history of rubber in Brazil. In the late nineteenth century, the need for electrical insulation and the invention of pneumatic tires dramatically increased the world's demand for rubber. Most of the world's rubber came from Brazil's Amazon basin, which went through a rubber boom from 1880–1910. After 1910, competition from Asian rubber decreased the importance of Brazil's rubber, and the development of relatively inexpensive synthetic rubber during World War II made natural rubber unnecessary. L3 IN **Linguistic, Intrapersonal**

772 CHAPTER 25 New Materials Through Chemistry

Changing Properties Polymers are a class of materials with a wide range of uses. The reason that polymers can be used for so many applications is directly related to the ease with which their properties can be modified. Polymers are long chains of monomers. If the composition or arrangement of monomers is changed, then the properties of the material will change.

Figure 17 shows that the monomer ethylene can be modified to produce a polymer with different properties and uses. Ethylene has only two carbon atoms and six bonding sites. The number of carbon atoms in the polymer can be high, and each bonding site represents a possibility of a change in properties. Polyethylene can be high density or low density depending upon how the molecules are attached to the monomer. One of the substances on the monomer can be replaced by another substance or a group of substances and the properties will change, too. The possibilities for creating new materials are almost limitless.

The Plastics Group Plastics are widely used for many products because they have desirable properties. Plastics are usually lightweight, strong, impact resistant, waterproof, moldable, chemical resistant, and inexpensive. Examples of plastics are easy to find. They are used to make toys, computer housing, telephones, containers, plates, and so on. The properties of plastics vary widely within this group. Some plastics are clear, some melt at high temperature, and some are flexible. Transparency, melting temperature, and flexibility are properties of plastics that relate to the composition of the polymer.

Science Online

Topic: Changing Properties
Visit gpscience.com for Web links to information about how changing the monomer changes the properties of the polymer.

Activity Write a paragraph describing a scientific experiment in which you test the theory that changing the monomer changes the polymer.

Figure 17 The arrangement of the branches along the chain can affect the properties of the polymer. **Compare and contrast** *the different types of plastics.*

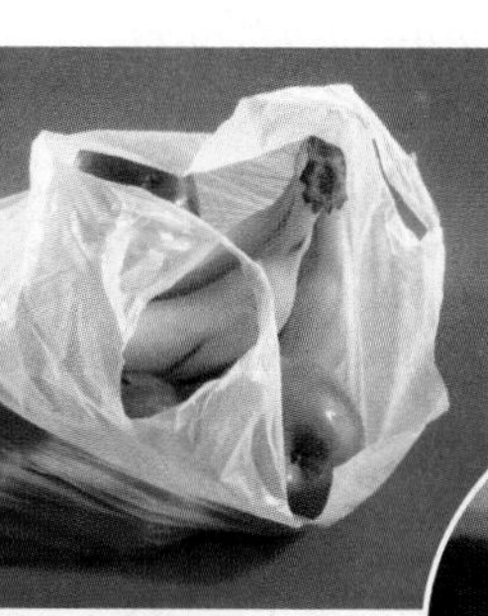

Low-density polyethylene, LDPE, is flexible, tough, and chemical resistant. The chain has a great deal of side-branching, which causes low density.

High-density polyethylene, HDPE, is firmer, stronger, and less translucent than LDPE. This chain has little side-branching, which allows the chain to pack closer together, thus giving it a higher density and different properties.

Polyvinyl chloride (PVC) is used in building materials. The substitution of chlorine for a hydrogen in the polyethylene chain makes the polymer harder and more heat resistant.

Activity

Polypropylene Forms Have students find out how polypropylene forms and make posters with drawings and explanations to display their findings. Polypropylene is made from propene, a three-carbon monomer with one double bond. To start the polymer chain, one propene molecule joins another at the double bond, reducing the bond to a single bond. Each succeeding propene monomer adds to the chain at the double bond, which changes to a single bond. L3 IS Visual-Spatial P Logical-Mathematical

Visual Learning

Figure 17 Draw on the board a polyethylene chain with many side branches to illustrate low-density polyethylene. Draw three polyethylene chains with few side branches and show how these chains can pack together to form high-density polyethylene. L2 ELL IS Visual-Spatial

Quick Demo

Puffed Polymer

Materials small dish, fingernail polish remover or acetone, foam cup

Estimated Time 5 minutes

Procedure Place some fingernail polish remover in a small dish. Keep it away from flames. Set a foam cup in the fingernail polish remover. The acetone in the fingernail polish remover breaks down some of the foam, which reforms into a small puddle. Tell students that foam is polystyrene that has been puffed into a lightweight form. The foam cup contains very little polystyrene. L2 ELL IS Visual-Spatial

Differentiated Instruction

Visually Impaired Bring in samples of LDPE, HDPE, and PVC and let students feel each type of polymer. Review some of the uses of each so students can relate the material by its feel to its function.

Fun Fact

Many polymers exist in nature. For example, silk from silkworms is a polymer, a turtle's shell is constructed of polymers, natural rubber and latex are polymers that come from trees, and our hair and fingernails are made from keratin—a polymer.

Caption Answer

Figure 17 The three different types of plastic are all polymers with different types of branching, substitution, and physical properties. LDPE has a lot of side-branching. HDPE has very little side-branching. PVC is a polymer where the chlorine is substituted for a hydrogen. This makes it harder and heat resistant.

Discussion

Clothing Fibers How can synthetic fibers provide greater versatility in clothing? Synthetic fibers can be developed to meet specific needs, such as warmth, weight, and durability. In addition, they can be combined with natural fibers. L1 LS **Logical-Mathematical**

Reading Check

Answer Adhesives are used in the manufacture of automobile parts, home building, window and door sealant, braces, pressure-sensitive tape.

Inquiry Lab

Cool Composites

Purpose Students apply the concept of composites to devise a new material to meet a specific need.

Possible Materials pencil and paper

Estimated Time 20 minutes

Teaching Strategies

- Pose this question "Wouldn't it be cool if there was something that could ______?" Have students "invent" a composite of two or more materials with which they are familiar that could potentially fill the need.
- Do not focus on the actual combination of components (can they chemically or mechanically combine); rather, focus on the concept that a composite is a mixture of two or more things.
- Select several "inventions" that are suitable for classroom demonstration and try them, as time allows. L2
- Have students prepare a scientific document to be submitted to a patent attorney. They should include the purpose of each invention and the details on how it is made and how it works.

LS **Logical-Mathematical, Linguistic**

For additional inquiry activities, see *Science Inquiry Labs*.

Figure 18 Some synthetic polymers make hazardous conditions safer. Firefighters' jackets are made with an aramid fiber that is fireproof. Motorcycle clothing are manufactured from another aramid, which provides protection for the rider during a crash.

Synthetic Fibers Nylon, polyester, acrylic, and polypropylene are examples of polymers that can be manufactured as fibers. Most synthetic fibers are composed of carbon chains because they are produced from petroleum or natural gas. Synthetic fibers can be mass-produced to almost any set of desired properties. Nylon is often used in wind and water-resistant clothing such as lightweight jackets. Polyester and polyester blended with natural fibers such as cotton often are used in clothing. Polyester fiber also is used to fill pillows and quilts. Polyurethane is the foam used in mattresses and pillows.

Synthetic fibers called aramids are a family of nylons with special properties. **Figure 18** shows some uses for these materials. Aramids are used to make fireproof clothing. Firefighters, military pilots, and race car drivers are examples of professionals that make use of this special fabric. Another aramid fiber is used to make bulletproof vests, race car survival cells, puncture-resistant gloves, and motorcycle clothing. Although they are lightweight, these aramids are five times stronger than steel.

Adhesives Synthetic polymers are used to make adhesives that can be modified to provide the best properties for a particular application. Contact cements are used in the manufacture of automobile parts, furniture, leather goods, and decorative laminates. They adhere instantly and the bond gets stronger after it dries. Structural adhesives are used in construction projects. One structural adhesive, silicone, is used to seal windows and doors to prevent heat loss in homes and other buildings. Ultraviolet-cured adhesives are used by orthodontists to adhere brace brackets to teeth. These adhesives bond after exposure to ultraviolet light. Other types of adhesives are hot-melts and transparent, pressure-sensitive tape.

Reading Check *What are five uses of adhesives?*

Teacher FYI

Adhesives For an adhesive to stick to an object, the surface of the adhesive must contact the surface of the object. The surfaces bond to each other by mechanical adhesion or by chemical reaction. During bonding, the adhesive must change from a liquid to a tough, nonflowing solid. The exact nature of these bonds is a matter of continuing scientific research. There are two main types of adhesives, thermoplastic and thermosetting. Thermoplastic adhesives set on cooling or evaporation of a solvent, whereas thermosetting adhesives set on heating or when mixed with a catalyst.

Surface Coatings and Elastic Polymers Many surface coatings use synthetic polymers. Polyurethane is a popular polymer that is used to protect and enhance wood surfaces. Many paints use synthetic polymers in their composition, too.

Synthetic rubber is a synthetic elastic polymer. It is used to manufacture tires, gaskets, belts, and hoses. The soles of some shoes also are made from this rubber.

INTEGRATE Life Science

Taking a Cue from Nature Spinning long fibers into threads and fabrics is not an original idea. Spiders spun fibers for their webs long before humans copied the idea and began spinning fibers themselves. Nylon fiber is another idea borrowed from nature. The silkworm produces a highly desirable fiber that is woven into fabric for items such as blouses and stockings. Can you imagine how long it would take a silkworm to produce enough silk for one blouse? Nylon was produced in the laboratory as a possible substitute for silk. Why do you think natural silk fabric is more expensive than nylon fabric?

Composites

The properties of a synthetic polymer can be altered by using more than one material. A **composite** is a mixture of two or more materials—one embedded or layered in the other. Composite materials of plastic are used to construct boat and car bodies, as shown in **Figure 19.** These bodies are made of a glass-fiber composite that is a mixture of small threads or fibers of glass embedded in a plastic. The structure of the fiberglass reinforces the plastic, making a strong, lightweight composite. If a substance is lightweight but brittle, such as some plastics, embedding flexible fibers into it can alter the brittleness property. After the substance has the flexible fibers embedded, the product is less brittle and can withstand greater forces before it breaks. Glass fibers are used often to reinforce plastics because glass is inexpensive, but other materials can be used as well.

Figure 19 Composite materials are used to make some cars and boats. The glass fiber embedded in the plastic reinforces the plastic structure. This composite material is strong, lightweight, and corrosion resistant.
Define *the term* glass-fiber composite.

Topic: Polymers
Visit gpscience.com for Web links to recent news on newly created polymers and new uses for existing polymers.

Activity Research the use of polymer adhesives for use on spacecraft and other high-performance applications. Present your finding to the class.

Text Question Answer

Its supply is limited.

Use Science Words

Word Origins The word *composite* can be broken down into the parts *com-* and *-posit.* Have students find the origins and meanings of these word parts. *Com-* comes from Latin and means "with." *-Posit* comes from the Latin word *ponere*, meaning "to put or place." Thus the word *composite* means to put or place together. L3
LS **Linguistic**

Fun Fact

Dragline silk, the web-making polymer produced by some spiders, is estimated to be up to five times as strong, by weight, as steel.

Discussion

Reinforcing Fibers Make two batches of dessert gelatin—one according to the instructions and one with pieces of uncooked spaghetti set in the gel. Bring these samples to class and have students compare the rigidity and density of both products. Discuss how embedding one material in another results in a change in the properties. L2
ELL LS **Visual-Spatial**

Caption Answer

Figure 19 Glass-fiber composite is a mixture of small threads or fibers of glass embedded in a plastic.

Differentiated Instruction

Challenge Have students research and write reports on the material used to replace natural ivory in piano keys. Reports should include why the ivory needed to be replaced and what problems had to be overcome. Several hard plastics, such as cellulose-based polymers, replaced ivory when it became illegal to use elephant ivory. Creating something with the feel and texture of ivory was difficult. L3 P LS
Linguistic, Logical Mathematical, Interpersonal

Reading Check

Answer Composite materials can be strong and lightweight. Reduced weight reduces the amount of fuel required. Composites provide corrosion resistance and are simple to repair.

3 Assess

DAILY INTERVENTION

Check for Understanding

Kinesthetic Bring a molecular model of a polymer to class and, with student volunteers, break it apart into its subunits. Review how polymers are built from monomers.

Reteach

Composites Bring to class an article of sports equipment that is manufactured from a known composite (graphite tennis racquet, fishing rod, golf club, etc.). Tell students the object is a composite and demonstrate one of its properties (flexibility, strength, corrosion resistance, etc.). Ask students what they can determine about the object knowing it is a composite. The material it is made of is a combination of different materials. L2 LS **Visual-Spatial**

Assessment

Oral Ask students to give examples and explain the benefits of composites. They combine the qualities, such as flexibility and strength, of the different materials used to make them. Use **Performance Assessment in the Science Classroom**, p. 89. L2

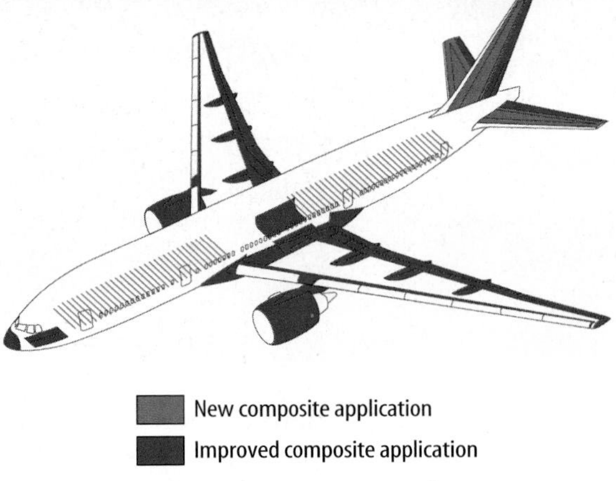

Figure 20 Commercial aircraft use composite materials in some locations. Composites provide corrosion resistance and are easy to repair.

Composites in Flight Composite materials are used in the construction of satellites. Lighter-weight satellites are less expensive to launch into orbit, yet the structure still is able to withstand the stress of the launch. Carbon fibers are used to strengthen the plastic body, creating a material that is four times more firm and 40 percent stronger than aluminum. Satellites made of graphite composites are about 13 percent lighter than satellites made of aluminum. The composite material is stronger and lighter in weight than aluminum, therefore it is less expensive to launch and can endure the stress of the launch better.

Commercial aircraft use composite materials in their construction, as shown in **Figure 20.** Aircraft made of composites also benefit from the strong yet lightweight properties of composite materials. The weight of this aircraft was reduced by more than 2,600 kg by using advanced alloys and composite materials. The lower weight results in cost savings by reducing the amount of fuel required to operate the aircraft.

Reading Check *Why are composites used in aircraft?*

section 3 review

Summary

Polymers

- The composition and chemistry of the polymers allows almost limitless modifications.
- Synthetic polymers are those that have been developed in the lab or manufacturing facility; they do not occur naturally.
- Some of the common classes of synthetic polymers include plastics, fibers, adhesives, and surface coatings.

Composites

- Composites are a class of materials made by embedding one or more components into another.
- Composite materials often are selected for products because their properties offer savings and performance benefits.

Self Check

1. **Explain** what a polymer is and give three examples of items that are made from polymers.
2. **Identify** the raw materials that are used to make most synthetic polymers.
3. **Explain** what a composite material is and give three examples of items that are made from composites.
4. **Classify** synthetic polymers into groups based upon their uses.
5. **Think Critically** How are synthetic polymers creating waste-disposal problems? Discuss possible solutions to this problem.

Applying Math

6. **Find Mass** A telecommunications company launches 10,000-kg satellites. A new satellite made from composites promises to reduce that mass by 25%. What is the mass of the new satellite?

Science Online gpscience.com/self_check_quiz

section 3 review

1. a large molecule made from joining smaller molecules, monomers, into chains; packaging, carpet, toys
2. fossil fuels, such as oil, coal, natural gas
3. a material made from two or more materials that have been mixed so that one material is embedded in the other; boat and car bodies, parts for commercial aircraft
4. Synthetic polymer groups include plastics, synthetic fibers, adhesives, surface coatings, and synthetic rubbers.
5. Some synthetic materials resist the breakdown action of bacteria in landfills. This can cause the volume of the landfill waste to increase rapidly. One possible solution is to recycle plastic materials.
6. $10{,}000 \text{ kg} - 25\% = 7{,}500 \text{ kg}$
   $(10{,}000 \times 0.25 = 2{,}500$
   $10{,}000 - 2{,}500 = 7{,}500)$

776 CHAPTER 25 New Materials Through Chemistry

WHAT CAN YOU DO WITH THIS STUFF?

This substance is fun to play with. But how do you describe its properties?

Real-World Question

What are the properties of this new material and what can it be used for?

Goals

- **Predict** the properties of this material.
- **Determine** possible uses for the material.

Materials

white glue
borax laundry soap
warm water
250-mL beaker or cup
100-mL beaker or cup
graduated cylinder
craft stick for mixing

Safety Precautions

WARNING: *Never eat lab materials.*

Procedure

1. Prepare a data table to record your observations of the following: stretched slowly, stretched quickly, rolled into a ball and left alone, pressed onto newspaper ink, dropped on a hard surface.
2. Put about 100 mL of warm water in the larger beaker and add borax laundry soap until soap no longer dissolves.
3. Put 5 mL of water and 10 mL of white glue into the smaller beaker and mix completely.
4. Add 5 mL of the borax solution to the glue solution and continue mixing for a couple of minutes.

5. When the substance firms up, remove it from the container and continue to mix it by pressing with your fingers until it is like soft clay.
6. **Examine** the properties of this material and record them in your data table.

Conclude and Apply

1. **Identify** the properties of this material.
2. **Evaluate** Get together with other students and brainstorm. What could this material be used for, and which of its properties would make it useful for that purpose?
3. **Apply** You're in charge of marketing this product. Prepare an advertisement with text and graphics on a sheet of notebook paper. Which magazine would you place this ad in and why?

Communicating Your Data

Compare your conclusions with those of other students in your class. **For more help, refer to the** Science Skill Handbook.

Real-World Question

Purpose to produce a new material and learn to investigate its properties

Process Skills observe, predict, classify, recognize cause and effect, interpret data

Time Required 35 minutes

Procedure

Alternative Materials Try various brands of white glue to see which one works best.

Safety Precautions The materials should never be tasted.

Teaching Strategies

- Color the material made by adding food coloring to the glue mixture.
- The new material will mold within a few minutes.
- The new material can leave water spots on wooden surfaces.

Troubleshooting Make sure students squeeze any pockets of solution from the polymer. The liquid pockets interfere with the final product.

Conclude and Apply

1. The material was a puttylike substance. It had form but could be easily molded. It bounced like a ball.
2. The product could be a new toy, or it could be an insulator that would harden after being poured like a liquid into small cracks.
3. Possible answer: Solquid! Is it a liquid or a solid or a new phase of matter? Advertise it in magazines that appeal to young people.

Communicating Your Data

Put a large version of the student data table on the board. Have students put their observations on the large summary board. L2 IS **Visual-Spatial**

Assessment

Process Have students vary the ratio of glue to borax solution. What properties appear when there is too much glue for the borax? The material is more liquid-like. Use **Performance Assessment in the Science Classroom**, p. 97. L2 IS **Kinesthetic, Visual-Spatial**

Real-World Question

Purpose Students will measure the flexibility of various rods. L2 LS **Kinesthetic**

Process Skills collect data, measure, make and use tables, record data, interpret data

Time Required 80 minutes

Materials Wood and steel rods are available as 1/4" 3 36" rods from a hardware store. Fiberglass rods that are used as supports for driveway reflectors also are available in hardware stores.

Alternative Materials Instead of fiberglass, other types of composite materials can be used, or you can choose to compare something other than wood and steel to fiberglass.

Safety Precautions It is extremely important that during this lab everyone in the classroom be wearing safety goggles. It is possible that rods will break and fly across the room.

Can polymer composites be stronger than STEEL?

Goals

- **Model** appropriate equipment to test wood, steel, and fiberglass composite rods.
- **Measure** the force required to flex the test rods.
- **Calculate** the relative flexibility of each rod.
- **Estimate** the performance of each material.

Possible Materials

meterstick
spring scale (0–12-kg range and 0–2-kg range)
wood, steel, and fiberglass composite rods (6.35 mm in diameter by 50 cm long)
supports to hold the test rods
graph paper

Safety Precautions

WARNING: *Wear safety goggles at all times during this lab.*

Real-World Question

Why are composite materials used instead of wood or metal in high-performance applications? Scientists and engineers test many materials before selecting the best one for a specific use. Composites are used in aircraft parts, sports equipment, and space vehicles because of their strength and low weight. What other factors might be important? How do you measure performance and choose the best material for an application?

Procedure

1. Hook the spring scale to the center of the fiberglass rod. Have a team member pull down on the spring scale until the top of the test rod moves down 1 cm from the zero point. Record the scale reading on the data table.

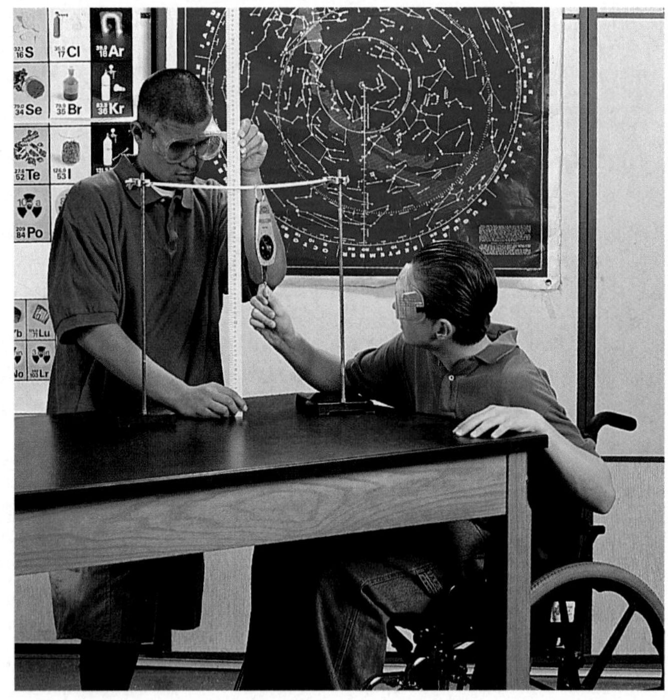

Differentiated Instruction

Learning Disabled These students can work with other students to make the calculations and generate the graphs. All students should construct graphs and make the calculations. L2 LS COOP LEARN **Visual-Spatial, Logical-Mathematical, Interpersonal**

Alternative Inquiry Lab

Extend the Activity Challenge students to design an experiment to compare different properties of other materials, perhaps related to hobbies or interests. Students might investigate properties such as adhesion or color. Encourage students to follow their investigative trail in any safe direction. Lead students in discussions about their investigations. L3 LS **Linguistic, Logical-Mathematical**

2. Pull down on the spring scale until the rod flexes 2 cm, then 3 cm. Record both of the spring scale readings on the data chart.
3. Repeat steps 1 and 2 on the steel and wood rods. Record the data in your table. Refer to the example table shown here.

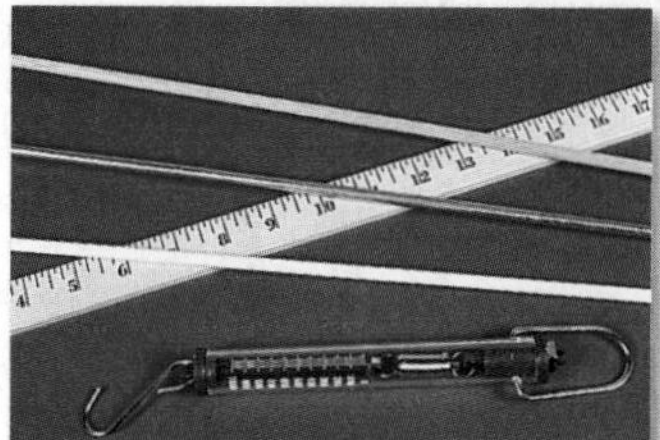

Analyze Your Data

1. **Graph** For each of the rods, graph the force measured on the *y*-axis and the distances on the *x*-axis.
2. **Calculate** the slope of each line in kilograms per centimeter. The slope is a relative measure of the flexibility of the samples.
3. **Determine** the specific performance number, which is used to compare different materials, by dividing the slope of each line by the density of the corresponding material. The densities are: composite = 1.2 g/cm^3, steel = 7.9 g/cm^3, and wood = 0.5 g/cm^3.

Data Table

Material	Distance Flexed (cm)	Force Required (kg)
composite	1	1.0
composite	2	2.0
composite	3	3.5
steel	1	4.5
steel	2	9.0
steel	3	12.0
wood	1	0.34
wood	2	0.80
wood	3	1.0

Conclude and Apply

1. **Identify** which rod had the highest specific performance number. What is meant by the statement that a polymer composite is twice as strong as steel?
2. **Analyze** which variables could affect the flexibility measurement.
3. **Model** Using the data that you have gathered, create a model exhibit showing possible construction uses for each of these materials. Indicate the reason the specific material was chosen.

Communicating Your Data

Give an oral presentation on choosing the best material for a specific application to another class of students using your model.

Communicating Your Data

Students may want to make posters as visual aids for their presentations. L1 ELL IS **Visual-Spatial**

Assessment

Oral Discuss the advantages of fiberglass over steel in some applications? Possible answers: Flexibility. Fiberglass does not rust. It is inexpensive to produce. It can be molded into the desired shape. Use **Performance Assessment in the Science Classroom,** p. 89. L2 IS **Logical-Mathematical**

Procedure

Teaching Strategies

- Have students work in pairs to collect data. One student should hold the meterstick in place while the other student flexes the rod and reads the spring scale.
- To make the performance numbers easier to compare, have the students multiply the answer they calculated by 1,000. Explain that as long as each calculation is multiplied by the same number the comparison is still valid.

Analyze Your Data

Expected Outcome Most results will show that steel had the least flex and the composite had the most.

Answers to Questions

1. Check students' graphs
2. Slopes: steel 3.75; composite 1.25; wood 0.33
3. Performance numbers: steel 0.48 (×1000 = 480); composite 1.08 (×1000 = 1080); wood 0.66 (×1000 = 660)

Error Analysis Students who do not get the correct outcome should check the slope and performance number calculations. Review the procedure to calculate slope.

Conclude and Apply

1. composite; The polymer composite material is the strongest of the three materials on a per mass basis.
2. Possible answers: the specific type of material, diameter of rod, distance between rod supports
3. Check students' work.

Content Background

When Stephanie Kwolek made her discovery, DuPont was looking for a polymer-based product to replace steel in belted automobile tires. Polymers are molecules that form chains when bonded together. Aramid polymers are immensely strong because they are exceptionally long and when bent form a crystalline structure, making them very hard.

The features that make Kevlar® strong also make it difficult to form into useful shapes. Impervious to solvents, it is difficult to dissolve and, with a melting point of 500°C, molding it with heat is not practical. As a result, it took almost ten years for the first Kevlar® products to reach the public.

Discussion

Polymers Are there any examples of naturally occurring polymers? Possible Answer: Yes. Tree sap, honey, and latex are examples. Modern polymer chemistry began in 1839 when Charles Goodyear developed vulcanization, a way to harden natural rubber in molded shapes without losing its flexibility. L2

Activity

Chains Form students into parallel, single-file lines of five to eight students each. Placing their right hand on the shoulder of the person in front of them they should try walking around the classroom. Now add the additional link of placing their left hand on the right shoulder of the person next to them. Have them try moving in this formation. The first exercise is similar to single polymer chains, the second to cross-linked polymers. Lessened mobility equates to higher material strength.

L2 ELL IS COOP LEARN **Hearing Impaired, Kinesthetic, Learning Disabled, Interpersonal, Visually Impaired**

Wonder Fiber

In 1964, Stephanie Kwolek was a chemist working at a research laboratory. Her assignment? Create a new type of tough, lightweight fiber. Kwolek's routine at the lab was about the same each day. She combined different substances in test tubes. She stirred them. She heated them. Then she would have any new substance spun into fibers and tested.

A Shocking Discovery

At one point, Kwolek was working with two polymers. She wanted to use heat to combine them, but they would not melt. So she decided to use a solvent to dissolve them. But when she poured the solvent onto one of the polymers, she got something unlike anything she had ever seen. Not only did it look different, it behaved differently when she stirred it. It separated into two distinct layers.

Kwolek thought this strange liquid might be something special. She asked one of her coworkers to spin it into fibers using a machine called a spinneret. The other chemist refused at first, saying the liquid wouldn't form fibers. And besides, it would probably gum up the equipment. But Kwolek had a hunch about this liquid. So she persisted until the other chemist agreed to try to spin the liquid into fibers.

Stephanie Kwolek

A New Type of Fiber

What they found was shocking. The fibers that formed in the spinneret were very lightweight, but also extremely stiff and strong. Kwolek had accidentally discovered a new type of synthetic fiber—a fiber made from a new substance called a liquid-crystal solution.

This new fiber was five times stronger than steel, and over the decades since its discovery, it has been put to many uses, such as in bulletproof vests, boat hulls, fiber-optic cables, cut-resistant gloves, airplane parts, skis, tennis rackets, and parts of spacecraft. The discovery was a huge accomplishment for Kwolek and has benefited many people in the form of bulletproof vests used by police officers and the tough clothing used by firefighters.

This police dog can thank Stephanie Kwolek for its bulletproof vest!

Research Visit your school's media center or the link to the right to find out more about the superfiber Kwolek discovered. Compare what you uncover with what others in the class find.

For more information, visit gpscience.com/time

Research While researching Kevlar® students will come across information about other polymers and their development. Some were discovered accidentally. Two of these were Bakelite and Teflon. Have students discuss the similarities and differences between these materials and compare the uses of each.

Resources for Teachers and Students

Girls Think of Everything: Stories of Ingenious Inventions by Women, by Catherine Thimmesh, Houghton Mifflin, 2000

Mistakes That Worked, by Charlotte Foltz Jones, Doubleday, 1991

Reviewing Main Ideas

Section 1 Materials with a Past

1. People have been making and using alloys for thousands of years. Some common alloys include bronze, brass, and various alloys of iron.
2. An alloy is a mixture of a metal with one or more other elements. Metals and alloys, like these shown here, have the properties of luster, ductility, malleability, and conductivity.

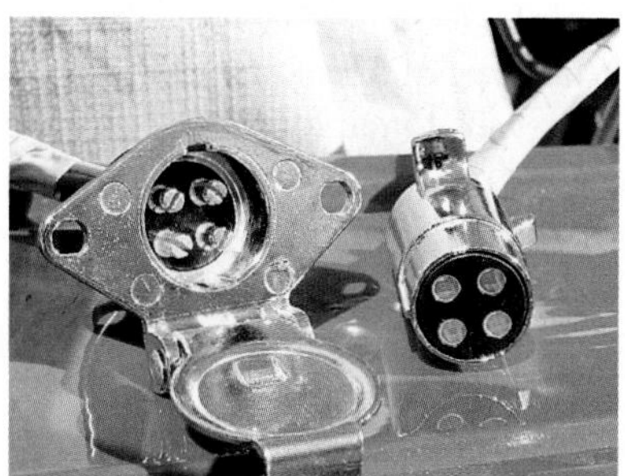

Section 2 Versatile Materials

1. Ceramics are used in a wide range of products, such as aircraft windshields. This is due to the ability of scientists to customize the properties of ceramics.

2. Semiconductors are made from silicon doped with other elements.
3. Ceramic materials are made by molding the object, and then heating the object to high temperatures. This process increases the density of the material.
4. Integrated circuits contain n-type and p-type semiconducting devices.

Section 3 Polymers and Composites

1. Polymers are a class of natural or human-made substances that are composed of molecules that are in large chains with simple repeating units called monomers.
2. Synthetic polymers can be produced in many forms, ranging from thin films to thick slabs or blocks. Synthetic fibers are produced in thin strands that can be woven into fabrics.
3. A composite is a mixture of two materials, one embedded in the other. Reinforced concrete and fiberglass are examples of composites. The skateboard in the figure to the right is constructed of a fiberglass composite. The composite material is strong and flexible.

FOLDABLES Use the Foldable that you made at the beginning of this chapter to help you review classifications of materials.

chapter 25 Study Guide

Reviewing Main Ideas

Summary statements can be used by students to review the major concepts of the chapter.

Science Online

Visit gpscience.com
/self_check_quiz
/interactive_tutor
/vocabulary_puzzlemaker
/chapter_review
/standardized_test

Assessment Transparency

For additional assessment questions, use the *Assessment Transparency* located in the transparency book.

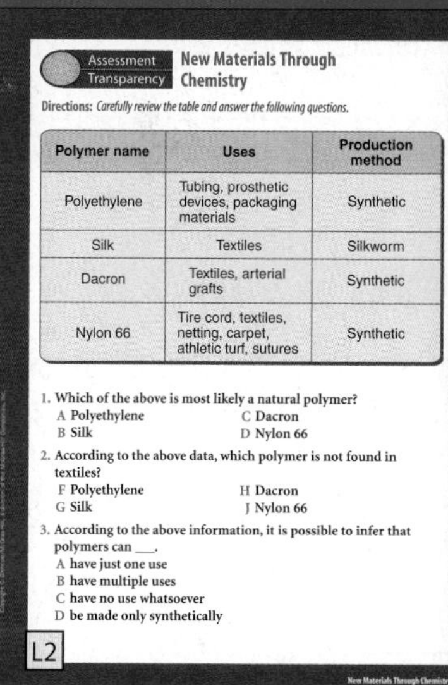

Assessment

Assessment Transparency **New Materials Through Chemistry**

Directions: *Carefully review the table and answer the following questions.*

Polymer name	Uses	Production method
Polyethylene	Tubing, prosthetic devices, packaging materials	Synthetic
Silk	Textiles	Silkworm
Dacron	Textiles, arterial grafts	Synthetic
Nylon 66	Tire cord, textiles, netting, carpet, athletic turf, sutures	Synthetic

1. Which of the above is most likely a natural polymer?
   A Polyethylene C Dacron
   B Silk D Nylon 66
2. According to the above data, which polymer is not found in textiles?
   F Polyethylene H Dacron
   G Silk J Nylon 66
3. According to the above information, it is possible to infer that polymers can ___.
   A have just one use
   B have multiple uses
   C have no use whatsoever
   D be made only synthetically

L2

New Materials Through Chemistry

Identifying Misconceptions

Assess

Perform this activity.

Materials paper and pencil

Procedure Divide a sheet of paper into two columns, one labeled *Pure Science*, the other *Applied Science*. Place the following in the appropriate columns: (a) finding the best electrical material to use in a computer, (b) researching the causes of cancer, (d) finding a non-flammable alternative to hydrogen for balloon travel.

Expected Outcome Examples (a) and (d) are applied while (b) and is pure science. L2 IS **Linguistic, Logical-Mathematical, Intrapersonal**

FOLDABLES Have students use their Foldables to review the content of the chapter. On the back of the paper, have students write some actual or possible applications of the materials they have listed. Can they add other materials and list some applications?

CHAPTER STUDY GUIDE 781

Using Vocabulary

1. Malleability
2. Ceramics
3. synthetic
4. composite
5. luster
6. Polymer

Checking Concepts

7. D
8. A
9. D
10. A
11. D
12. B
13. C
14. D
15. D
16. D

Interpreting Graphics

17. See student edition.
18. Check students' work.

Thinking Critically

19. Gold that is 10-karat would be less likely to bend out of shape.
20. Answers will vary. One example could be that composite tennis rackets allow players to stroke the ball faster due to the lighter mass of the newer rackets. This gives an advantage to a strong server. Lighter rackets may add so much serve power that other aspects of the game are overshadowed. This may require rule changes such as a higher net that would de-emphasize the importance of a powerful serve.
21. The synthetic material may not decompose, thus adding more volume to overcrowded landfills.

chapter 25 Review

Using Vocabulary

alloy p. 758	luster p. 759
ceramics p. 764	malleability p. 759
composite p. 775	monomer p. 771
conductivity p. 759	polymer p. 771
doping p. 768	semiconductor p. 767
ductility p. 759	synthetic p. 771
integrated circuit p. 768	

Fill in the blank with the correct word or words.

1. ________ is the property of metals and alloys that describes their ability to be hammered or rolled into thin sheets.
2. ________ are used to make heat shield tiles for the space shuttle, but may be replaced by an alloy that is less fragile.
3. Fiberglass is a(n) ________ material that is used to make boats and skateboards.
4. Fiberglass is a(n) ________.
5. Chrome and other shiny, reflective surfaces illustrate the property of ________.
6. ________ are used to make plastics for products such as food containers, toys and electronic cases.

Checking Concepts

Choose the word or phrase that best answers the question.

7. Which metal replaces bronze as a widely used metal?
   A) copper **C)** zinc
   B) tin **D)** iron
8. Why are metals and alloys good conductors of heat and electricity?
   A) They have loosely bound electrons within the atom.
   B) They have luster and malleability.
   C) They are composed of mixtures.
   D) They have a shiny appearance.
9. An alloy of steel will contain iron and what element?
   A) mercury **C)** zinc
   B) tin **D)** carbon
10. What raw materials are many synthetic polymers made from?
    A) hydrocarbons **C)** fiberglass
    B) iron ore **D)** ceramics

Use the photo below to answer question 11.

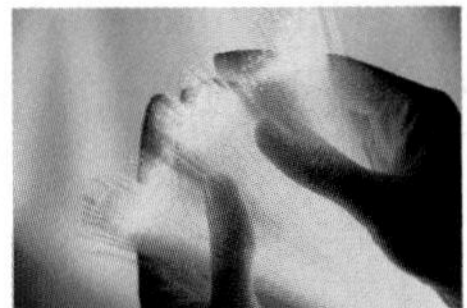

11. What type of fibers, shown above, are often used to reinforce polymers in automobile bodies?
    A) ceramic **C)** hydrocarbon
    B) metal alloy **D)** glass
12. Which element below is found in both brass and bronze?
    A) mercury **C)** tin
    B) copper **D)** zinc
13. Which of the following is a natural fiber?
    A) nylon **C)** silk
    B) polyester **D)** acrylic
14. Which group of materials below is not classified as synthetic?
    A) ceramics **C)** composites
    B) alloys **D)** metal ores
15. Customizing properties is NOT likely in which of the following?
    A) alloys **C)** ceramics
    B) synthetic polymers **D)** pure metals
16. Which of the following elements is used to dope silicon crystals?
    A) carbon **C)** copper
    B) zinc **D)** gallium

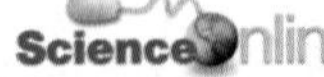

gpscience.com/vocabulary_puzzlemaker

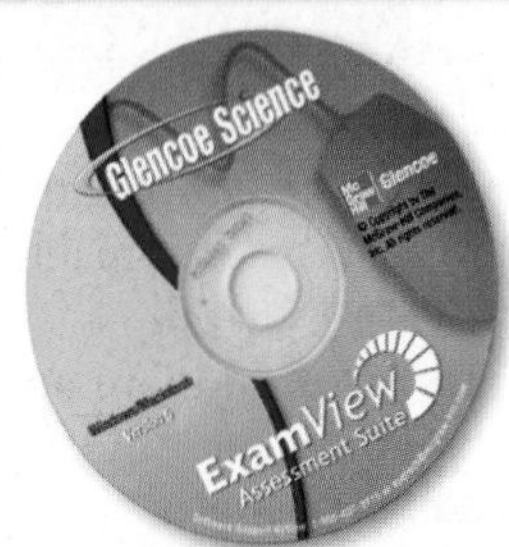

Use the *ExamView®* *Assessment Suite* CD-ROM to:

- create multiple versions of tests
- create modified tests with one mouse click for inclusion students
- edit existing questions and add your own questions
- build tests aligned with state standards using built-in State Curriculum Tags
- change English tests to Spanish with one mouse click and vice versa

Interpreting Graphics

17. Copy and complete the following concept map using the terms *composites, hydrocarbons, polymers, adhesives, plastics, synthetic fibers,* and *surface coatings.*

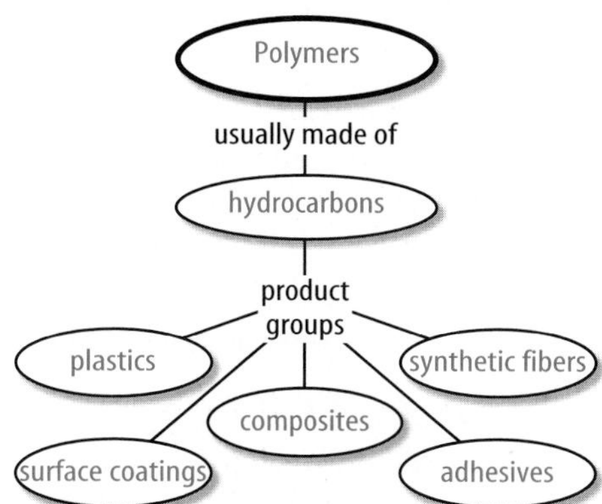

18. Look at the polymer below. Draw the monomer upon which the polymer is based.

$$\left[\begin{array}{cccccc} H & H & H & H & H & H \\ | & | & | & | & | & | \\ -C- & C- & C- & C- & C- & C- \\ | & | & | & | & | & | \\ H & CN & H & CN & H & CN \end{array}\right]$$

Thinking Critically

19. Infer A lower-karat gold has less gold in it than a higher-karat gold. Why might you prefer a ring that is 10-karat gold over a ring that is 20-karat gold?

20. Explain the advantages and disadvantages of using composites in the world of sports.

21. Explain A synthetic fiber might be preferred over a natural fiber for use outdoors because it will not rot. How could this negatively affect the environment?

22. Compare and contrast alloys and ceramics.

23. Recognize Cause and Effect A student performing the two-page lab did not see any difference in the flexing of the rods. What are some possible causes of this result?

24. Measure in SI A bronze trophy has a mass of 952 g. If the bronze is 85 percent copper, how many grams of tin are contained in the trophy?

Applying Math

Use the graph below to answer questions 25 and 26.

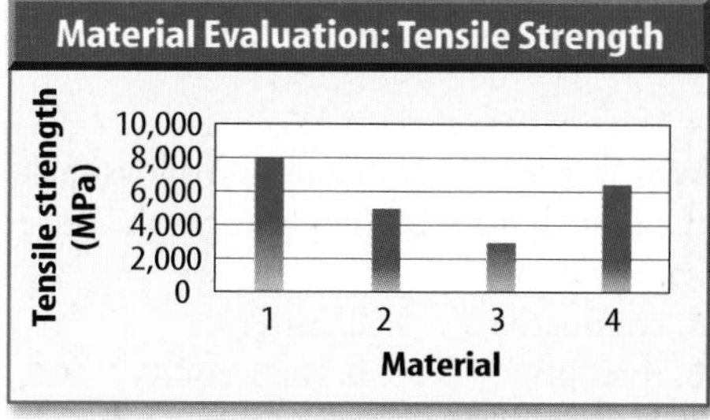

25. Interpret Graphs Tensile strength is a measure of the amount of "pulling" stress an object can withstand before it breaks or becomes damaged. The graph above shows a comparison of tensile strength for four materials that an engineer is considering for a new product. Which material should be considered if the product must be tear-resistant?

26. Compare Materials Refer to the chart above and calculate, in percent, how much more stress material 4 can withstand than material 3.

27. Find Mass An experimental alloy is made up of 28 percent gold and equal parts of two other elements, X and Y. How many grams of the other elements are in a 75-g sample of the alloy?

Assessment Resources

Reproducible Masters

Chapter *Fast File* Resources
- Chapter Review, pp. 37–38
- Chapter Tests, pp. 39–42
- Assessment Transparency Activity, p. 49

Glencoe Science Web site
- Chapter Review Test
- Standardized Test Practice

Glencoe Technology
- Assessment Transparency
- *ExamView® Assessment Suite*
- MindJogger Videoquiz
- Interactive Chalkboard

chapter 25 Review

22. Alloys and ceramics are made from more than one substance in varying ratios. Alloys are made from a metal and one or more other elements. Ceramics are made from metallic elements and oxygen, nitrogen, and sulfur. Alloys are typically less brittle than ceramics.

23. The measuring equipment might have been calibrated differently for each rod or the amount of force used to bend the rod might have been inconsistent.

24. $952 \text{ g} \times (1 - 0.85) = 142.8 \text{ g}$, or approximately 143 g

Applying Math

National Math Standards

Correlation to Mathematics Objectives

1, 5, 6, 9

Answers to Practice Problems

25. material 1

26. $\frac{(6{,}500 - 3{,}000)}{6{,}500} \times 100\% = 54\%$

27. $100\% - 28\% = 72\%$

$\frac{72\%}{2} = 36\%$ of each of the other two.

In grams there would be 27 g of elements *X* and *Y* and 21 g of gold.

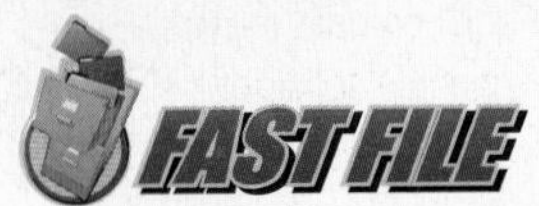

Answer Sheet A practice answer sheet can be found at gpscience.com/answer_sheet.

Assessment Student Recording Sheet

Standardized Test Practice

SAMPLE

Part 1 Multiple Choice

1. C
2. D
3. D
4. A
5. B
6. D
7. B
8. D

Part 2 Short Response

9. The left is an n-type semiconductor, and the right is a p-type semiconductor.The p-type semiconductor has less electrons, meaning it has holes. The n-type has more electrons.
10. Excess electrons can move from the n-type semiconductor to the p-type semiconductor.
11. Ceramics are strong and resistant to high temperatures. However, they are also fragile and break if they are exposed to rapid changes in temperature.

chapter 25 Standardized Test Practice

Part 1 Multiple Choice

Record your answers on the answer sheet provided by your teacher or on a sheet of paper.

Use the photo below to answer questions 1–3.

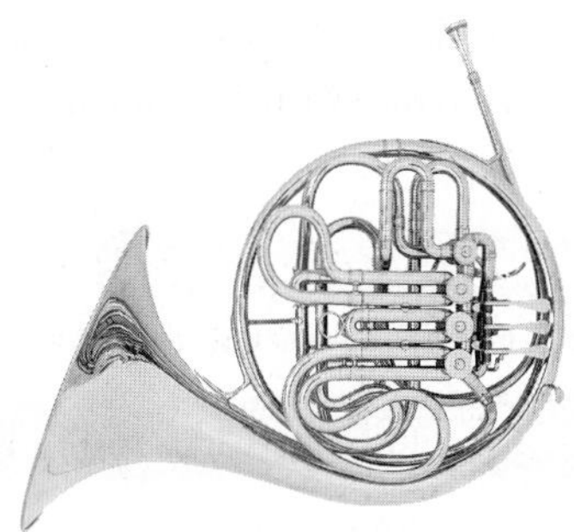

1. Which property of metals and alloys makes the French horn in the photograph above appear shiny?

A. conductivity **C.** luster
B. ductility **D.** malleability

2. The French horn is made of brass. What element was combined with copper to make the brass?

A. antimony **C.** tin
B. silver **D.** zinc

3. What property allowed the metal from which the instrument is made to be shaped into a French horn?

A. conductivity **C.** luster
B. ductility **D.** malleability

4. Approximately when was the alloy bronze first discovered?

A. 3500 B.C. **C.** 1400 A.D.
B. 350 B.C. **D.** 1800 A.D.

Test-Taking Tip

Relax Stay calm during the test. If you feel yourself getting nervous, close your eyes and take five slow, deep breaths.

5. A 14-karat gold ring is 58% gold and 42% copper by mass. If the ring has a mass of 5.3 g, what is the mass of the gold used to make the ring?

A. 2.2 g **C.** 5.3 g
B. 3.1 g **D.** 5.8 g

6. Which of the following terms refers to substances and materials that are created in a laboratory or chemical plant?

A. component **C.** integrated
B. composite **D.** synthetic

Use the photo below to answer questions 7 and 8.

7. The photograph above shows a roll of copper electrical wire with a polymer coating. Which of the following properties are needed for the wire?

A. ductility and malleability
B. ductility and conductivity
C. malleability and luster
D. malleability and conductivity

8. What property should the polymer coating on the wire have?

A. low melting point
B. high conductivity
C. high malleability
D. high resistivity

Part 2 Short Response/Grid In

12. spiders and silkworms
13. Semiconductors are some of the metalloids located along the staircase-shaped border between metals and nonmetals.
14. Traditional ceramics are chemically resistant to acids, water, and salts.
15. Alloys have many of the same properties of metals, but they have improved properties as well, such as greater hardness, strength, lightness, and durability.
16. After the raw materials are processed, the ceramics usually are molded into a desired shape. The ceramics are then heated to temperatures between 1,000°C and 1,700°C. This heating process, called firing, causes the spaces between the particles to shrink. The entire object then shrinks. This dense internal structure causes ceramics to be very strong. Ceramics also can withstand very high temperatures.

784 STANDARDIZED TEST PRACTICE

Part 2 Short Response/Grid In

Record your answers on the answer sheet provided by your teacher or on a sheet of paper.

Use the illustration below to answer questions 9 and 10.

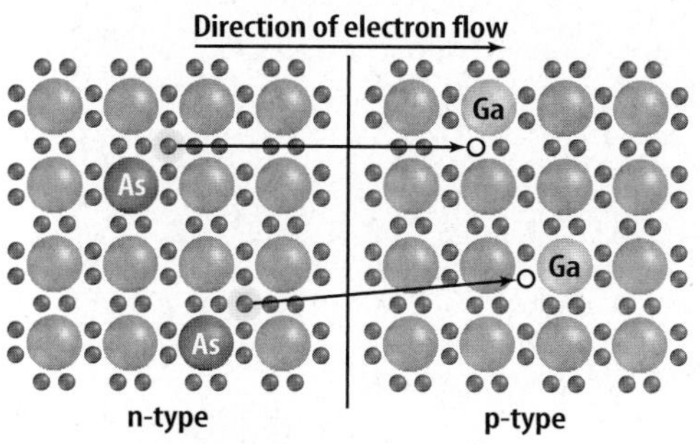

9. Which of the two semiconductors shown in the illustration above is an n-type and which is a p-type? How can you tell?
10. Explain how adding an impurity increases the conductivity of the semiconductor shown in the illustration.
11. What properties of ceramics makes them suitable for use as heat shields on the space shuttles? What properties of ceramics are drawbacks to their use as shields?
12. The production of fibers from nylon is an idea that was borrowed from nature. Name two animals that produce fibers.
13. Where on the periodic table are semiconductors located?
14. Name three properties of traditional ceramics that make them useful as food serving bowls.
15. Why do manufacturers frequently use alloys when making different products, rather than just using metals?

Part 3 Open Ended

Record your answers on a sheet of paper.

16. Describe the process of firing traditional ceramics. Explain how this process affects the properties of the ceramics.
17. Explain what polymers are. There are so many types of polymers that they are divided into different groups. What are some of these groups?
18. Explain what is meant by a *hole* in a semiconductor. Describe what happens to holes as current flows through the semiconductor.
19. Describe some properties of modern ceramics that traditional ceramics do not have. What are some uses of modern ceramics?

Use the illustration below to answer questions 20 and 21.

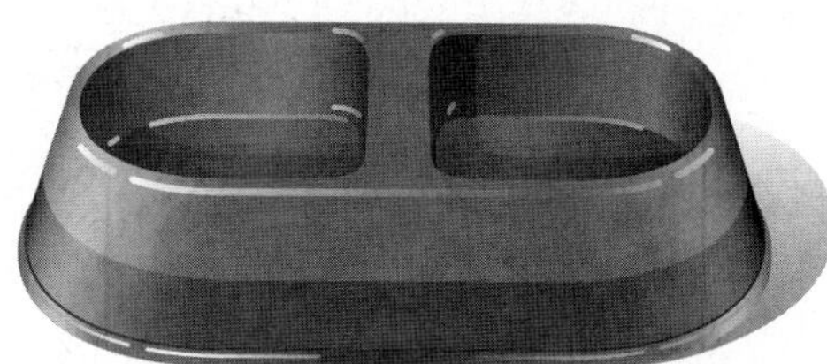

20. The pet food and water bowl shown in the figure above is made of high-density polyethylene, HDPE. Describe the structure of HDPE and explain how its properties make it a good material for use as a pet bowl.
21. Explain why the pet bowl could not be made from low-density polyethylene, LDPE. What are some products that could be made from LDPE?
22. Name and describe the glass-fiber composite that is often used to make boat and car bodies. What are some properties of this composite?

Science Online gpscience.com/standardized_test

19. Modern ceramics can be customized to be more electrically conductive and stronger than traditional ceramics. Some copper-based ceramics are superconductive. Modern ceramics can be used as electrically conductive aircraft windshields to keep them free of ice and snow. Strong, chemically resistant modern ceramics can be used as bone replacements in the human body.
20. HDPE is made from an ethylene monomer, $—CH_2—CH_2—$. It has very little side-branching, allowing it to pack closely and giving it high density. The high density of HDPE makes it a hard and durable polymer.
21. Like HDPE, LDPE is made from an ethylene monomer. However, LDPE has a great deal of side-branching. This makes it have low density. The LDPE is tough and chemically resistant, but it is also flexible—unsuitable for a pet bowl.
22. The glass-fiber composite is called fiberglass. It is a mixture of small fibers of glass embedded in a plastic. The structure of the fiberglass reinforces the plastic, making a strong, lightweight composite. The embedded fibers also reduce the brittleness of the plastic. Additionally, fiberglass is corrosion resistant.

Rubrics

For more help evaluating open-ended assessment questions, see the rubric on p. 10T. Wrap the extra questions around the bottom to the side.

Part 3 Open Ended

17. Polymers are a class of natural or manufactured substances that are composed of molecules arranged in large chains of monomers. A monomer is a small, simple, repeating unit. It is a molecule that is repeated in the polymer chain. Some types of polymers are plastics, synthetic fibers, adhesives, surface coatings, and natural and synthetic rubbers.
18. A p-type semiconductor is formed by doping a metalloid with tiny amounts of certain elements that reduce the overall number of electrons in the semiconductor. A hole is a location in the semiconductor that is missing the electron that normally would be there. When a current flows through the semiconductor, an electron is attracted to the hole location. The electron's former position then becomes the location of a hole. This movement maintains the flow of current through the semiconductor.

Student Resources

CONTENTS

Scientific Methods

Scientists use an orderly approach called the scientific method to solve problems. This includes organizing and recording data so others can understand them. Scientists use many variations in this method when they solve problems.

Identify a Question

The first step in a scientific investigation or experiment is to identify a question to be answered or a problem to be solved. For example, you might ask which gasoline is the most efficient.

Gather and Organize Information

After you have identified your question, begin gathering and organizing information. There are many ways to gather information, such as researching in a library, interviewing those knowledgeable about the subject, testing and working in the laboratory and field. Fieldwork is investigations and observations done outside of a laboratory.

Researching Information Before moving in a new direction, it is important to gather the information that already is known about the subject. Start by asking yourself questions to determine exactly what you need to know. Then you will look for the information in various reference sources, like the student is doing in **Figure 1.** Some sources may include textbooks, encyclopedias, government documents, professional journals, science magazines, and the Internet. Always list the sources of your information.

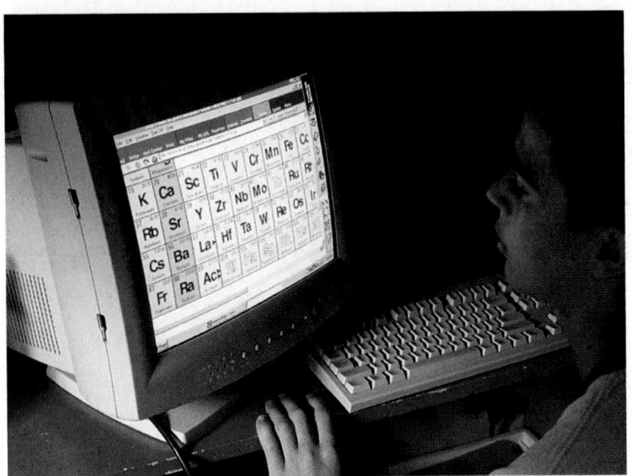

Figure 1 The Internet can be a valuable research tool.

Evaluate Sources of Information Not all sources of information are reliable. You should evaluate all of your sources of information, and use only those you know to be dependable. For example, if you are researching ways to make homes more energy efficient, a site written by the U.S. Department of Energy would be more reliable than a site written by a company that is trying to sell a new type of weatherproofing material. Also, remember that research always is changing. Consult the most current resources available to you. For example, a 1985 resource about saving energy would not reflect the most recent findings.

Sometimes scientists use data that they did not collect themselves, or conclusions drawn by other researchers. This data must be evaluated carefully. Ask questions about how the data were obtained, if the investigation was carried out properly, and if it has been duplicated exactly with the same results. Would you reach the same conclusion from the data? Only when you have confidence in the data can you believe it is true and feel comfortable using it.

Interpret Scientific Illustrations As you research a topic in science, you will see drawings, diagrams, and photographs to help you understand what you read. Some illustrations are included to help you understand an idea that you can't see easily by yourself, like the tiny particles in an atom in **Figure 2.** A drawing helps many people to remember details more easily and provides examples that clarify difficult concepts or give additional information about the topic you are studying. Most illustrations have labels or a caption to identify or to provide more information.

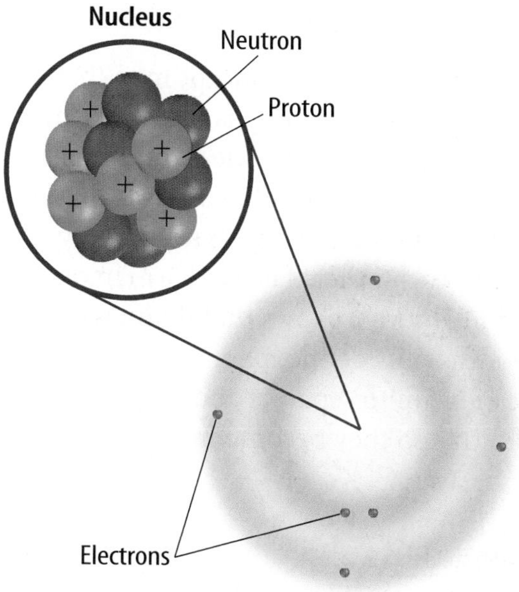

Figure 2 This drawing shows an atom of carbon with its six protons, six neutrons, and six electrons.

Concept Maps One way to organize data is to draw a diagram that shows relationships among ideas (or concepts). A concept map can help make the meanings of ideas and terms more clear, and help you understand and remember what you are studying. Concept maps are useful for breaking large concepts down into smaller parts, making learning easier.

Network Tree A type of concept map that not only shows a relationship, but how the concepts are related is a network tree, shown in **Figure 3.** In a network tree, the words are written in the ovals, while the description of the type of relationship is written across the connecting lines.

When constructing a network tree, write down the topic and all major topics on separate pieces of paper or notecards. Then arrange them in order from general to specific. Branch the related concepts from the major concept and describe the relationship on the connecting line. Continue to more specific concepts until finished.

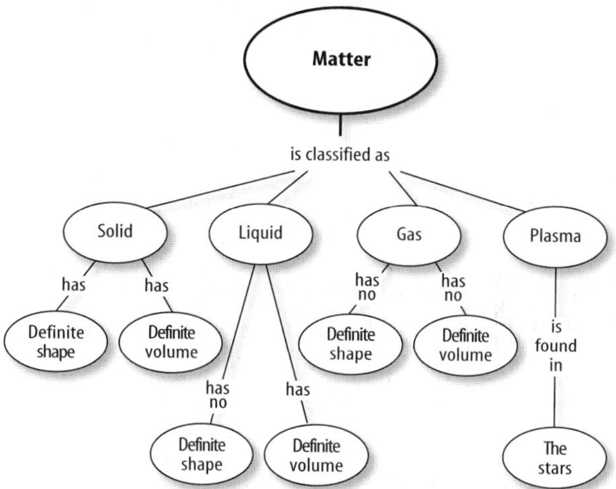

Figure 3 A network tree shows how concepts or objects are related.

Events Chain Another type of concept map is an events chain. Sometimes called a flow chart, it models the order or sequence of items. An events chain can be used to describe a sequence of events, the steps in a procedure, or the stages of a process.

When making an events chain, first find the one event that starts the chain. This event is called the initiating event. Then, find the next event and continue until the outcome is reached, as shown in **Figure 4.**

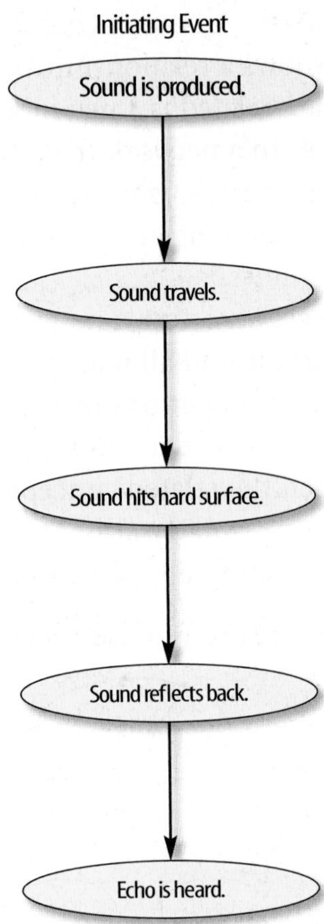

Figure 4 Events-chain concept maps show the order of steps in a process or event. This concept map shows how a sound makes an echo.

Cycle Map A specific type of events chain is a cycle map. It is used when the series of events do not produce a final outcome, but instead relate back to the beginning event, such as in **Figure 5.** Therefore, the cycle repeats itself.

To make a cycle map, first decide what event is the beginning event. This is also called the initiating event. Then list the next events in the order that they occur, with the last event relating back to the initiating event. Words can be written between the events that describe what happens from one event to the next. The number of events in a cycle map can vary, but usually contain three or more events.

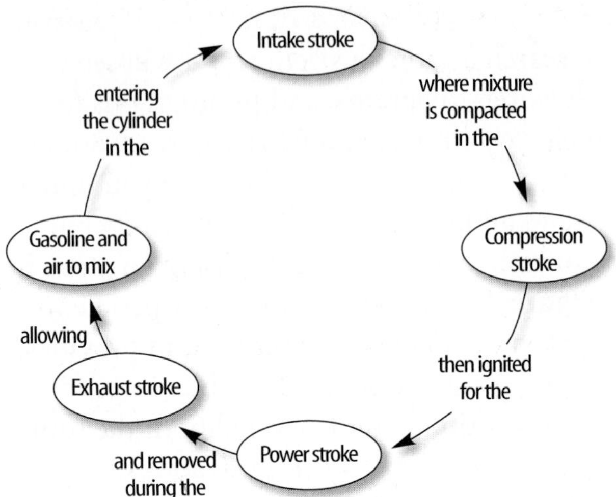

Figure 5 A cycle map shows events that occur in a cycle.

Spider Map A type of concept map that you can use for brainstorming is the spider map. When you have a central idea, you might find that you have a jumble of ideas that relate to it but are not necessarily clearly related to each other. The spider map on sound in **Figure 6** shows that if you write these ideas outside the main concept, then you can begin to separate and group unrelated terms so they become more useful.

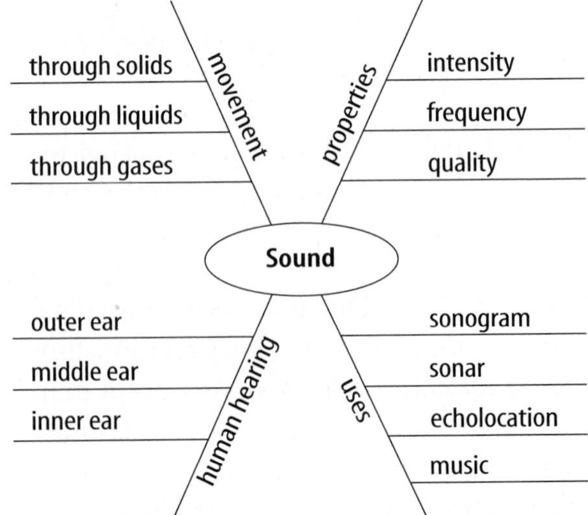

Figure 6 A spider map allows you to list ideas that relate to a central topic but not necessarily to one another.

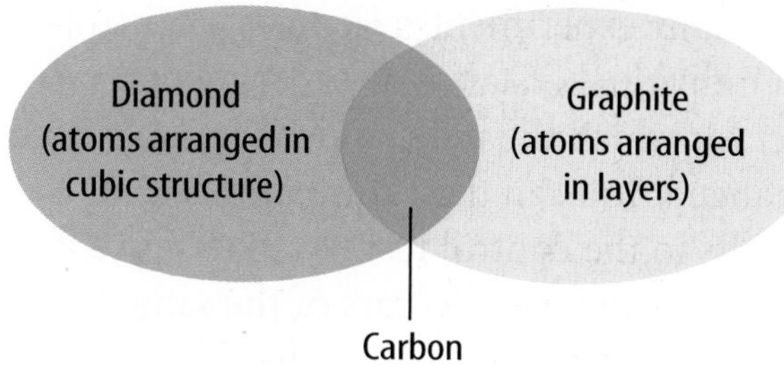

Figure 7 This Venn diagram compares and contrasts two substances made from carbon.

Venn Diagram To illustrate how two subjects compare and contrast you can use a Venn diagram. You can see the characteristics that the subjects have in common and those that they do not, shown in **Figure 7.**

To create a Venn diagram, draw two overlapping ovals that that are big enough to write in. List the characteristics unique to one subject in one oval, and the characteristics of the other subject in the other oval. The characteristics in common are listed in the overlapping section.

Make and Use Tables One way to organize information so it is easier to understand is to use a table. Tables can contain numbers, words, or both.

To make a table, list the items to be compared in the first column and the characteristics to be compared in the first row. The title should clearly indicate the content of the table, and the column or row heads should be clear. Notice that in **Table 1** the units are included.

Table 1 Recyclables Collected During Week

Day of Week	Paper (kg)	Aluminum (kg)	Glass (kg)
Monday	5.0	4.0	12.0
Wednesday	4.0	1.0	10.0
Friday	2.5	2.0	10.0

Make a Model One way to help you better understand the parts of a structure, the way a process works, or to show things too large or small for viewing is to make a model. For example, an atomic model made of a plastic-ball nucleus and pipe-cleaner electron shells can help you visualize how the parts of an atom relate to each other. Other types of models can by devised on a computer or represented by equations.

Form a Hypothesis

A possible explanation based on previous knowledge and observations is called a hypothesis. After researching gasoline types and recalling previous experiences in your family's car you form a hypothesis—our car runs more efficiently because we use premium gasoline. To be valid, a hypothesis has to be something you can test by using an investigation.

Predict When you apply a hypothesis to a specific situation, you predict something about that situation. A prediction makes a statement in advance, based on prior observation, experience, or scientific reasoning. People use predictions to make everyday decisions. Scientists test predictions by performing investigations. Based on previous observations and experiences, you might form a prediction that cars are more efficient with premium gasoline. The prediction can be tested in an investigation.

Design an Experiment A scientist needs to make many decisions before beginning an investigation. Some of these include: how to carry out the investigation, what steps to follow, how to record the data, and how the investigation will answer the question. It also is important to address any safety concerns.

Test the Hypothesis

Now that you have formed your hypothesis, you need to test it. Using an investigation, you will make observations and collect data, or information. This data might either support or not support your hypothesis. Scientists collect and organize data as numbers and descriptions.

Follow a Procedure In order to know what materials to use, as well as how and in what order to use them, you must follow a procedure. **Figure 8** shows a procedure you might follow to test your hypothesis.

Procedure

1. Use regular gasoline for two weeks.
2. Record the number of kilometers between fill-ups and the amount of gasoline used.
3. Switch to premium gasoline for two weeks.
4. Record the number of kilometers between fill-ups and the amount of gasoline used.

Figure 8 A procedure tells you what to do step by step.

Identify and Manipulate Variables and Controls In any experiment, it is important to keep everything the same except for the item you are testing. The one factor you change is called the independent variable. The change that results is the dependent variable. Make sure you have only one independent variable, to assure yourself of the cause of the changes you observe in the dependent variable. For example, in your gasoline experiment the type of fuel is the independent variable. The dependent variable is the efficiency.

Many experiments also have a control—an individual instance or experimental subject for which the independent variable is not changed. You can then compare the test results to the control results. To design a control you can have two cars of the same type. The control car uses regular gasoline for four weeks. After you are done with the test, you can compare the experimental results to the control results.

Collect Data

Whether you are carrying out an investigation or a short observational experiment, you will collect data, as shown in **Figure 9.** Scientists collect data as numbers and descriptions and organize it in specific ways.

Observe Scientists observe items and events, then record what they see. When they use only words to describe an observation, it is called qualitative data. Scientists' observations also can describe how much there is of something. These observations use numbers, as well as words, in the description and are called quantitative data. For example, if a sample of the element gold is described as being "shiny and very dense" the data are qualitative. Quantitative data on this sample of gold might include "a mass of 30 g and a density of 19.3 g/cm^3."

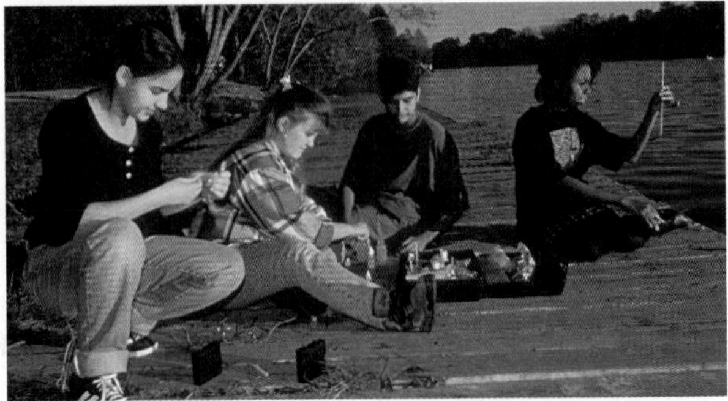

Figure 9 Collecting data is one way to gather information directly.

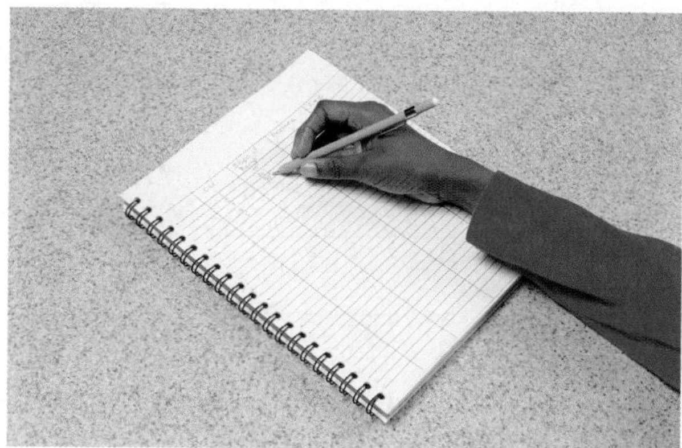

Figure 10 Record data neatly and clearly so it is easy to understand.

When you make observations you should examine the entire object or situation first, and then look carefully for details. It is important to record observations accurately and completely. Always record your notes immediately as you make them, so you do not miss details or make a mistake when recording results from memory. Never put unidentified observations on scraps of paper. Instead they should be recorded in a notebook, like the one in **Figure 10.** Write your data neatly so you can easily read it later. At each point in the experiment, record your observations and label them. That way, you will not have to determine what the figures mean when you look at your notes later. Set up any tables that you will need to use ahead of time, so you can record any observations right away. Remember to avoid bias when collecting data by not including personal thoughts when you record observations. Record only what you observe.

Estimate Scientific work also involves estimating. To estimate is to make a judgment about the size or the number of something without measuring or counting. This is important when the number or size of an object or population is too large or too difficult to accurately count or measure.

Sample Scientists may use a sample or a portion of the total number as a type of estimation. To sample is to take a small, representative portion of the objects or organisms of a population for research. By making careful observations or manipulating variables within that portion of the group, information is discovered and conclusions are drawn that might apply to the whole population. A poorly chosen sample can be unrepresentative of the whole. If you were trying to determine the rainfall in an area, it would not be best to take a rainfall sample from under a tree.

Measure You use measurements everyday. Scientists also take measurements when collecting data. When taking measurements, it is important to know how to use measuring tools properly. Accuracy also is important.

Length To measure length, the distance between two points, scientists use meters. Smaller measurements might be measured in centimeters or millimeters.

Length is measured using a metric ruler or meter stick. When using a metric ruler, line up the 0-cm mark with the end of the object being measured and read the number of the unit where the object ends. Look at the metric ruler shown in **Figure 11.** The centimeter lines are the long, numbered lines, and the shorter lines are millimeter lines. In this instance, the length would be 4.50 cm.

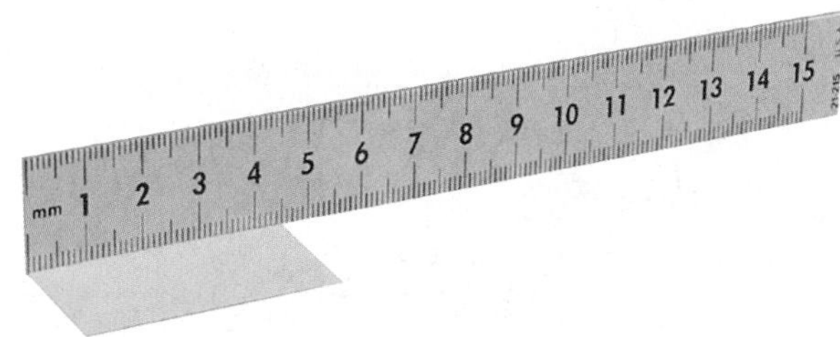

Figure 11 This metric ruler has centimeter and millimeter divisions.

Mass The SI unit for mass is the kilogram (kg). Scientists can measure mass using units formed by adding metric prefixes to the unit gram (g), such as milligram (mg). To measure mass, you might use a triple-beam balance similar to the one shown in **Figure 12.** The balance has a pan on one side and a set of beams on the other side. Each beam has a rider that slides on the beam.

When using a triple-beam balance, place an object on the pan. Slide the largest rider along its beam until the pointer drops below zero. Then move it back one notch. Repeat the process for each rider proceeding from the larger to smaller until the pointer swings an equal distance above and below the zero point. Sum the masses on each beam to find the mass of the object. Move all riders back to zero when finished.

Instead of putting materials directly on the balance, scientists often take a tare of a container. A tare is the mass of a container into which objects or substances are placed for measuring their masses. To mass objects or substances, find the mass of a clean container. Remove the container from the pan, and place the object or substances in the container. Find the mass of the container with the materials in it. Subtract the mass of the empty container from the mass of the filled container to find the mass of the materials you are using.

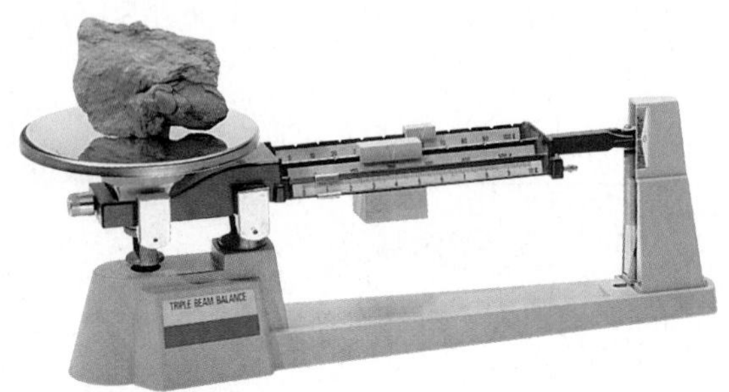

Figure 12 A triple-beam balance is used to determine the mass of an object.

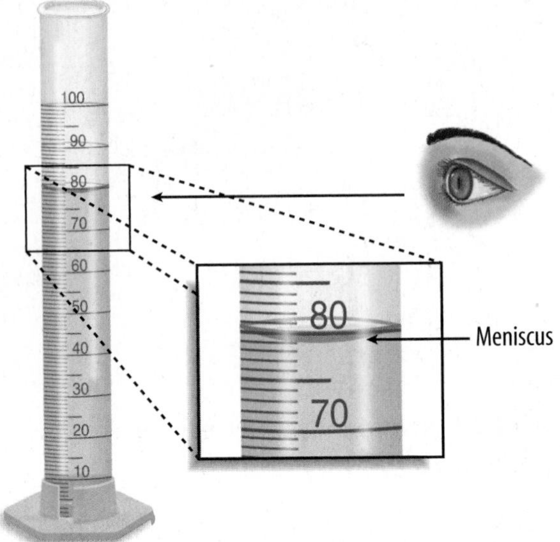

Figure 13 Graduated cylinders measure liquid volume.

Liquid Volume To measure liquids, the unit used is the liter. When a smaller unit is needed, scientists might use a milliliter. Because a milliliter takes up the volume of a cube measuring 1 cm on each side it also can be called a cubic centimeter ($cm^3 = cm \times cm \times cm$).

You can use beakers and graduated cylinders to measure liquid volume. A graduated cylinder, shown in **Figure 13,** is marked from bottom to top in milliliters. In lab, you might use a 10-mL graduated cylinder or a 100-mL graduated cylinder. When measuring liquids, notice that the liquid has a curved surface. Look at the surface at eye level, and measure the bottom of the curve. This is called the meniscus. The graduated cylinder in **Figure 13** contains 79.0 mL, or 79.0 cm^3, of a liquid.

Temperature Scientists often measure temperature using the Celsius scale. Pure water has a freezing point of 0°C and boiling point of 100°C. The unit of measurement is degrees Celsius. Two other scales often used are the Fahrenheit and Kelvin scales.

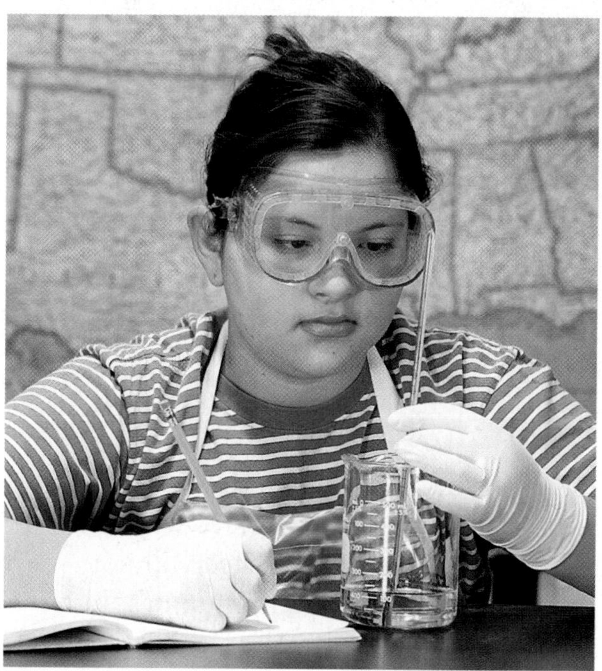

Figure 14 A thermometer measures the temperature of an object.

Scientists use a thermometer to measure temperature. Most thermometers in a laboratory are glass tubes with a bulb at the bottom end containing a liquid such as colored alcohol. The liquid rises or falls with a change in temperature. To read a glass thermometer like the thermometer in **Figure 14,** rotate it slowly until a red line appears. Read the temperature where the red line ends.

Form Operational Definitions An operational definition defines an object by how it functions, works, or behaves. For example, when you are playing hide and seek and a tree is home base, you have created an operational definition for a tree.

Objects can have more than one operational definition. For example, a ruler can be defined as a tool that measures the length of an object (how it is used). It can also be a tool with a series of marks used as a standard when measuring (how it works).

Analyze the Data

To determine the meaning of your observations and investigation results, you will need to look for patterns in the data. Then you must think critically to determine what the data mean. Scientists use several approaches when they analyze the data they have collected and recorded. Each approach is useful for identifying specific patterns.

Interpret Data The word *interpret* means "to explain the meaning of something." When analyzing data from an experiement, try to find out what the data show. Identify the control group and the test group to see whether or not changes in the independent variable have had an effect. Look for differences in the dependent variable between the control and test groups.

Classify Sorting objects or events into groups based on common features is called classifying. When classifying, first observe the objects or events to be classified. Then select one feature that is shared by some members in the group, but not by all. Place those members that share that feature in a subgroup. You can classify members into smaller and smaller subgroups based on characteristics. Remember that when you classify, you are grouping objects or events for a purpose. Keep your purpose in mind as you select the features to form groups and subgroups.

Compare and Contrast Observations can be analyzed by noting the similarities and differences between two more objects or events that you observe. When you look at objects or events to see how they are similar, you are comparing them. Contrasting is looking for differences in objects or events.

Recognize Cause and Effect A cause is a reason for an action or condition. The effect is that action or condition. When two events happen together, it is not necessarily true that one event caused the other. Scientists must design a controlled investigation to recognize the exact cause and effect.

Draw Conclusions

When scientists have analyzed the data they collected, they proceed to draw conclusions about the data. These conclusions are sometimes stated in words similar to the hypothesis that you formed earlier. They may confirm a hypothesis, or lead you to a new hypothesis.

Infer Scientists often make inferences based on their observations. An inference is an attempt to explain observations or to indicate a cause. An inference is not a fact, but a logical conclusion that needs further investigation. For example, you may infer that a fire has caused smoke. Until you investigate, however, you do not know for sure.

Apply When you draw a conclusion, you must apply those conclusions to determine whether the data supports the hypothesis. If your data do not support your hypothesis, it does not mean that the hypothesis is wrong. It means only that the result of the investigation did not support the hypothesis. Maybe the experiment needs to be redesigned, or some of the initial observations on which the hypothesis was based were incomplete or biased. Perhaps more observation or research is needed to refine your hypothesis. A successful investigation does not always come out the way you originally predicted.

Avoid Bias Sometimes a scientific investigation involves making judgments. When you make a judgment, you form an opinion. It is important to be honest and not to allow any expectations of results to bias your judgments. This is important throughout the entire investigation, from researching to collecting data to drawing conclusions.

Communicate

The communication of ideas is an important part of the work of scientists. A discovery that is not reported will not advance the scientific community's understanding or knowledge. Communication among scientists also is important as a way of improving their investigations.

Scientists communicate in many ways, from writing articles in journals and magazines that explain their investigations and experiments, to announcing important discoveries on television and radio. Scientists also share ideas with colleagues on the Internet or present them as lectures, like the student is doing in **Figure 15.**

Figure 15 A student communicates to his peers about his investigation.

SAFETY SYMBOLS	HAZARD	EXAMPLES	PRECAUTION	REMEDY
DISPOSAL	Special disposal procedures need to be followed.	certain chemicals, living organisms	Do not dispose of these materials in the sink or trash can.	Dispose of wastes as directed by your teacher.
BIOLOGICAL	Organisms or other biological materials that might be harmful to humans	bacteria, fungi, blood, unpreserved tissues, plant materials	Avoid skin contact with these materials. Wear mask or gloves.	Notify your teacher if you suspect contact with material. Wash hands thoroughly.
EXTREME TEMPERATURE	Objects that can burn skin by being too cold or too hot	boiling liquids, hot plates, dry ice, liquid nitrogen	Use proper protection when handling.	Go to your teacher for first aid.
SHARP OBJECT	Use of tools or glassware that can easily puncture or slice skin	razor blades, pins, scalpels, pointed tools, dissecting probes, broken glass	Practice common-sense behavior and follow guidelines for use of the tool.	Go to your teacher for first aid.
FUME	Possible danger to respiratory tract from fumes	ammonia, acetone, nail polish remover, heated sulfur, moth balls	Make sure there is good ventilation. Never smell fumes directly. Wear a mask.	Leave foul area and notify your teacher immediately.
ELECTRICAL	Possible danger from electrical shock or burn	improper grounding, liquid spills, short circuits, exposed wires	Double-check setup with teacher. Check condition of wires and apparatus.	Do not attempt to fix electrical problems. Notify your teacher immediately.
IRRITANT	Substances that can irritate the skin or mucous membranes of the respiratory tract	pollen, moth balls, steel wool, fiberglass, potassium permanganate	Wear dust mask and gloves. Practice extra care when handling these materials.	Go to your teacher for first aid.
CHEMICAL	Chemicals can react with and destroy tissue and other materials	bleaches such as hydrogen peroxide; acids such as sulfuric acid, hydrochloric acid; bases such as ammonia, sodium hydroxide	Wear goggles, gloves, and an apron.	Immediately flush the affected area with water and notify your teacher.
TOXIC	Substance may be poisonous if touched, inhaled, or swallowed.	mercury, many metal compounds, iodine, poinsettia plant parts	Follow your teacher's instructions.	Always wash hands thoroughly after use. Go to your teacher for first aid.
FLAMMABLE	Flammable chemicals may be ignited by open flame, spark, or exposed heat.	alcohol, kerosene, potassium permanganate	Avoid open flames and heat when using flammable chemicals.	Notify your teacher immediately. Use fire safety equipment if applicable.
OPEN FLAME	Open flame in use, may cause fire.	hair, clothing, paper, synthetic materials	Tie back hair and loose clothing. Follow teacher's instruction on lighting and extinguishing flames.	Notify your teacher immediately. Use fire safety equipment if applicable.

Eye Safety
Proper eye protection should be worn at all times by anyone performing or observing science activities.

Clothing Protection
This symbol appears when substances could stain or burn clothing.

Animal Safety
This symbol appears when safety of animals and students must be ensured.

Handwashing
After the lab, wash hands with soap and water before removing goggles.

Safety in the Science Laboratory

The science laboratory is a safe place to work if you follow standard safety procedures. Being responsible for your own safety helps to make the entire laboratory a safer place for everyone. When performing any lab, read and apply the caution statements and safety symbol listed at the beginning of the lab.

General Safety Rules

1. Obtain your teacher's permission to begin all investigations and use laboratory equipment.
2. Study the procedure. Ask your teacher any questions. Be sure you understand safety symbols shown on the page.
3. Notify your teacher about allergies or other health conditions which can affect your participation in a lab.
4. Learn and follow use and safety procedures for your equipment. If unsure, ask your teacher.
5. Never eat, drink, chew gum, apply cosmetics, or do any personal grooming in the lab. Never use lab glassware as food or drink containers. Keep your hands away from your face and mouth.
6. Know the location and proper use of the safety shower, eye wash, fire blanket, and fire alarm.

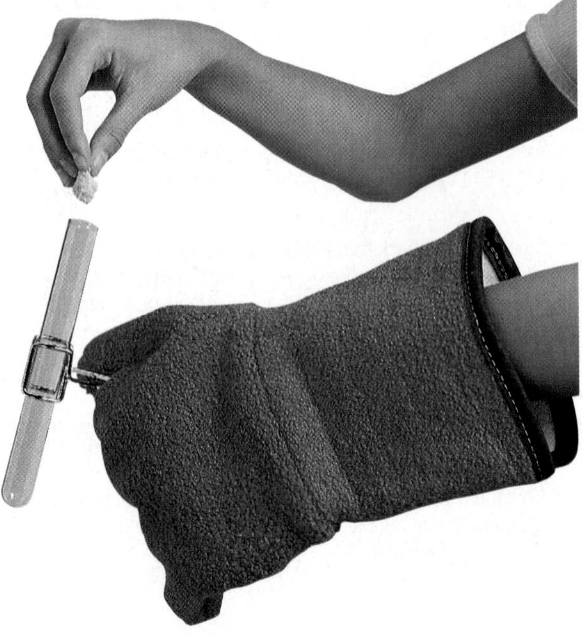

Prevent Accidents

1. Use the safety equipment provided to you. Goggles and a safety apron should be worn during investigations.
2. Do NOT use hair spray, mousse, or other flammable hair products. Tie back long hair and tie down loose clothing.
3. Do NOT wear sandals or other open-toed shoes in the lab.
4. Remove jewelry on hands and wrists. Loose jewelry, such as chains and long necklaces, should be removed to prevent them from getting caught in equipment.
5. Do not taste any substances or draw any material into a tube with your mouth.
6. Proper behavior is expected in the lab. Practical jokes and fooling around can lead to accidents and injury.
7. Keep your work area uncluttered.

Laboratory Work

1. Collect and carry all equipment and materials to your work area before beginning a lab.
2. Remain in your own work area unless given permission by your teacher to leave it.

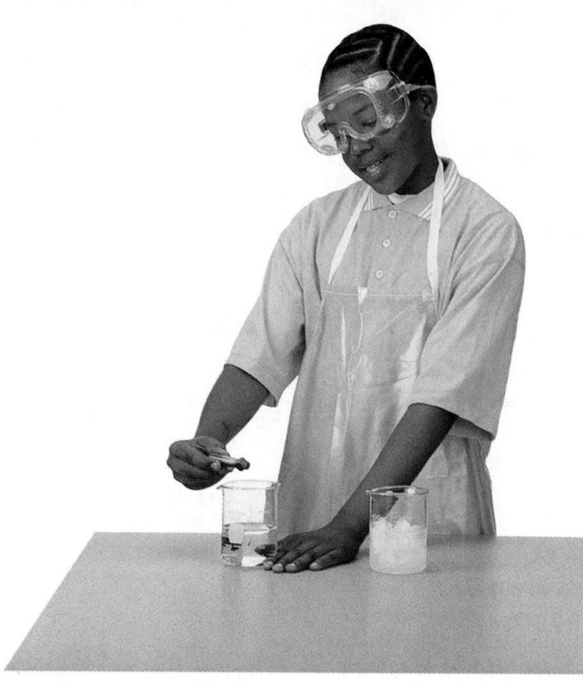

3. Always slant test tubes away from yourself and others when heating them, adding substances to them, or rinsing them.
4. If instructed to smell a substance in a container, hold the container a short distance away and fan vapors towards your nose.
5. Do NOT substitute other chemicals/substances for those in the materials list unless instructed to do so by your teacher.
6. Do NOT take any materials or chemicals outside of the laboratory.
7. Stay out of storage areas unless instructed to be there and supervised by your teacher.

Laboratory Cleanup

1. Turn off all burners, water, and gas, and disconnect all electrical devices.
2. Clean all pieces of equipment and return all materials to their proper places.
3. Dispose of chemicals and other materials as directed by your teacher. Place broken glass and solid substances in the proper containers. Never discard materials in the sink.
4. Clean your work area.
5. Wash your hands with soap and water thoroughly BEFORE removing your goggles.

Emergencies

1. Report any fire, electrical shock, glassware breakage, spill, or injury, no matter how small, to your teacher immediately. Follow his or her instructions.
2. If your clothing should catch fire, STOP, DROP, and ROLL. If possible, smother it with the fire blanket or get under a safety shower. NEVER RUN.
3. If a fire should occur, turn off all gas and leave the room according to established procedures.
4. In most instances, your teacher will clean up spills. Do NOT attempt to clean up spills unless you are given permission and instructions to do so.
5. If chemicals come into contact with your eyes or skin, notify your teacher immediately. Use the eyewash or flush your skin or eyes with large quantities of water.
6. The fire extinguisher and first-aid kit should only be used by your teacher unless it is an extreme emergency and you have been given permission.
7. If someone is injured or becomes ill, only a professional medical provider or someone certified in first aid should perform first-aid procedures.

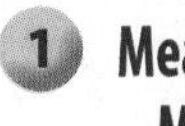

Measure for Measure

Time Required 30 minutes

Teaching Strategy
Students also could weigh an object on a kitchen scale and a bathroom scale and compare results.

Conclude and Apply
1. Possible answers: measuring around the curved surfaces and needing to estimate some measures; students might have thought to use a string around the pot to measure the curved surface.
2. Answers will vary.
3. Answers depend on the precision of the carpenter's tape and ruler that they use.
4. Students may say the sewing tape because it curved around the pot, or they may say the most precise instrument. Any answer with a reasonable explanation should be accepted.

Extra Try at Home Labs

EXTRA Try at Home Labs

From Your Kitchen, Junk Drawer, or Yard

1 Measure for Measure

Real-World Question
What is the difference in the precision of different measuring instruments?

Possible Materials
- kitchen pot
- ruler
- sewing measuring tape
- carpenter's measuring tape

Procedure
1. Before you begin the lab, review this procedure and make an appropriate data table to record your results. For more information, refer to the *Precision and Significant Digits* section in the **Math Skills Handbook.**
2. With the ruler, measure the diameter, the height, and the circumference of the pot.
3. Measure the same three things with both the sewing tape and the carpenter's tape.
4. The precision is one-half of the smallest division on the measuring device. Subtract this amount from each measurement and calculate the volume in each case.
5. Add half the smallest division to each measurement and calculate the volume in each case.

Conclude and Apply
1. What difficulties did you encounter while measuring? How did you overcome them?
2. Use the measurement of the diameter to calculate what the circumference should be. How does that compare with the measurement you had for circumference?
3. Which measuring tool gave the most precise calculation of volume? Why?
4. Which measuring tool do you think was the best for the job? Explain why.

2 Finding Forces

Real-World Question
What forces act on a moving ball?

Possible Materials
- tennis ball
- softball
- plastic baseball
- football
- rubber ball

Procedure
1. Go outside and stand in an empty field or lawn where there are no other people, buildings, or cars for 20–30 meters.
2. Throw a plastic baseball as far as you can in a straight line.
3. Observe the baseball as it moves through the air, falls to the ground, and eventually stops.

Conclude and Apply
1. Identify all the forces that acted on the ball from the time you threw it to the time it came to a stop.
2. Infer why baseball batters want the grass of a baseball field cut short.
3. Infer and describe the ball's motion if no outside forces ever acted on it.

Adult supervision required for all labs.

These labs are available at gpscience.com.

Finding Forces

Time Required ten minutes

Materials Students more easily can see the force of air resistance working against the motion of a plastic baseball with holes in it (whiffle ball) than a heavier ball such as a tennis ball.

Safety Precaution Tell students not to throw anything toward people, buildings, cars, or property that can be damaged.

Teaching Strategy Show a football bloopers video segment to your class. Have students identify all the forces that act on a football during a play.

Conclude and Apply
1. Forces include: the initial force of the throw, air resistance, gravity, ground (grass) friction, and possibly an object on the ground.
2. Short grass creates less friction than long grass and allows the ball to move faster for a longer period of time.
3. The ball would orbit Earth at the same height that it was thrown.

Extra Try at Home Labs

3 Look Out Below

Real-World Question
How does an object's mass affect the amount of force it has?

Possible Materials
- aluminum pie pan
- clay
- foam ball
- tennis ball
- baseball
- basketball
- 1-in steel ball-bearing
- metric ruler
- meterstick

Procedure
1. Fill an aluminum pie pan with modeling clay to a depth of 10 cm.
2. Place the pan on a level cement or asphalt surface outside.
3. Measure and record the mass of each ball you will test.
4. Hold the foam ball 2 m above the clay and drop it into the center of the clay.
5. Measure the depth of the crater made by the foam ball in the clay and record it in your Science Journal.
6. Smooth out the clay.
7. Repeat steps 4, 5, and 6 for each ball.

Conclude and Apply
1. Infer what the depth of each crater measures.
2. Compare the crater depth of each ball.
3. Infer the relationship between the mass of each ball and its force.

Extra Try at Home Labs

4 Energy Conversion

Real-World Question
How does energy from solid wax change ice to water?

Possible Materials
- short candle
- matches or lighter
- glass measuring cup
- dry, very cold ice (below 0°C)
- thermometer
- pot
- cooling racks for baked goods

Procedure
1. Set the candle upright in the pot and place the cooling rack on top, resting the rack on the pot. Light the candle. *CAUTION:* Flame will be hot.
2. Transfer the ice straight out of the freezer into the glass measuring cup and set it on the cooling rack directly above the candle. If the ice has started to melt, pat it dry.
3. Note the time and temperature of the water. Record its temperature every minute.

Conclude and Apply
1. List all the energy changes that occur as the candle burns and the ice melts.
2. Graph your temperature data v. time. Mark the changes you listed. How would your graph be different if a Bunsen burner were used instead of a candle? What if a heat lamp were used?
3. The temperature stays at 0°C for a long time before heating up again. Where is the energy from the candle going during this time?

Adult supervision required for all labs.

3 Look Out Below

Time Required 40 minutes

Materials
- The clay layers should measure about 25 cm wide, 25 cm long, and 10 cm deep.
- Students can use mud instead of clay or rocks instead of balls.

Safety Precaution
Students should not throw the balls.

Teaching Strategies
- Explain to students that all falling objects have an acceleration of 9.8 m/s^2 in the absence of air resistance.
- Drop a bowling ball on the clay as a demo to end the lab.

Conclude and Apply
1. the force of each falling ball
2. Students should record the depths of the craters they made.
3. The mass of the ball is directly proportional to its force of impact with the clay.

4 Energy Conversion

Time Required one class period

Safety Precaution Make sure that students tie back long hair and loose clothing.

Conclude and Apply
1. Potential energy from the chemical bonds in the wax are converted to heat and light as the candle burns. Some of the heat and all of the light energy are lost to the surroundings, while the rest warms the beaker and the ice. When the ice reaches its melting point, the energy from the candle breaks the bonds between water molecules and the ice melts (a potential energy change). When all of the ice has melted, the energy from the candle increases the kinetic energy of the water, heating it up.
2. The graph would be the same shape in all cases, though maybe with a shorter time if more heat is added.
3. It breaks bonds between water molecules in the ice.

5 Levers that Cut

Time Required 25 minutes

Materials Students also can measure the mechanical advantage of hedge clippers, pruning clippers, and other scissor-like tools.

Safety Precautions
- Students should wear safety goggles.
- Caution students to handle the scissors with care.

Teaching Strategy
Explain to students that scissors, seesaws, and pliers are all the same type of lever with the fulcrum between the effort arm and resistance arm.

Conclude and Apply
1. The center bolt is the fulcrum; the distance from the bolt to the paper is the resistance arm, and the distance from the bolt to the center of the handles is the effort arm.
2. Answers will vary, but the mechanical advantage of a pair of scissors normally ranges between 4 and 12.

Extra Try at Home Labs

Extra Try at Home Labs

5 Levers that Cut

Real-World Question
What are the ideal mechanical advantages of the scissors in your home?

Possible Materials
- several pairs of scissors
- metric ruler
- sheet of paper
- calculator

Procedure
1. Open the blades of a pair of scissors wide, insert a sheet of paper, and close the scissors until they just start to cut the paper.
2. Measure the distance from the bolt in the center of the scissors to the spot where the blades are starting to cut the paper.
3. Measure the distance from the bolt in the center of the scissors to the center of the handles.
4. Record your measurements in your Science Journal.
5. Repeat steps 1–3 with several other pairs of scissors.

Conclude and Apply
1. Draw a labeled diagram of a pair of scissors and identify the fulcrum, resistance arm, and effort arm.
2. Calculate the ideal mechanical advantage of each pair of scissors you measured.

6 Ice Melts, Water Cools

Real-World Question
What can a thermometer tell you about water?

Materials
- polystyrene cups (2)
- thermometer
- scale
- ice
- lid with a hole for the thermometer

Procedure
1. Place one cup inside the other and measure their mass.
2. Half fill the inner cup with water and determine the water's mass and temperature.
3. Pat the ice dry if necessary. Measure its mass.
4. Put the ice in the water and place the lid on the cup. When the ice has almost melted, insert the thermometer through the hole in the lid and measure the water's temperature. Record the lowest temperature of the water.
5. The heat gained by the ice is lost by the water. Use the equation $m_{ice} \times 335\ J/g = m_{water} \times (t_f - t_i) \times c_{water}$ to calculate the specific heat capacity of water.
6. Try the experiment again with heated water.

Conclude and Apply
1. Should you get the same result for c if you start with ice and water at different temperatures than your original trial? Explain. Try to experiment with this if you have time.
2. Why is the lid important?
3. List sources of experimental error. What would you do differently next time?

Adult supervision required for all labs.

These labs are available at gpscience.com.

6 Ice Melts, Water Cools

Time Required one class period

Teaching Strategies
- The formula given is a simplified adaptation of $nH_{ice} = m \times (t_f - t_i) \times c_{water}$.
- The error should be less with heated water, because less time is required to melt the ice. Therefore, there is less time to lose heat to the surroundings.

Conclude and Apply
1. You should get the same result because specific heat capacity is a constant for each substance and is not temperature dependent.
2. The lid reduces loss of heat to the surroundings.
3. Answers will vary. Possible answers include: loss of heat to the surroundings, wet ice, reader error

802 STUDENT RESOURCES

Extra Try at Home Labs

7 Glowing Bulbs

Real-World Question
How can you make a lightbulb glow without plugging it into an outlet?

Possible Materials
- fluorescent bulb
- soft wool fabric
- silk fabric
- flannel fabric
- flashlight

Procedure
1. Turn the flashlight on and carry your materials into a completely dark room, such as a closet or bedroom with thick curtains.
2. Hold a fluorescent bulb and soft wool in one hand. Turn off the flashlight. Place the wool in your other hand and rub the wool vigorously against the bulb. Observe any change in the bulb. Put down the wool and turn on the flashlight.
3. Repeat step 2 using the silk fabric, and then the flannel fabric.

Conclude and Apply
1. Describe how the fluorescent bulb changed when you rubbed it with each cloth.
2. Identify the type of fabric that caused the greatest change.

8 Magnetic Attraction

Real-World Question
What things in your home are magnetic?

Possible Materials
- refrigerator door magnet
- bar magnet
- horseshoe magnet

Procedure
1. Obtain a magnet from your refrigerator door, hobby shop, or science store.
2. Test a wide variety of items in your home to find out what materials are magnetic. To test an object, simply hold the magnet against it and observe whether or not the magnet attaches to it.
3. Test materials in your home including tools, kitchen food cans, aluminum foil, bolts, screws, appliances, lamps, bicycles, car parts, and anything else you can think of.
4. Record all the magnetic objects you find in your Science Journal.
5. Research what the magnetic objects found in your home are made of.

Conclude and Apply
1. List the things you tested and found to be magnetic.
2. Infer what types of materials are magnetic.

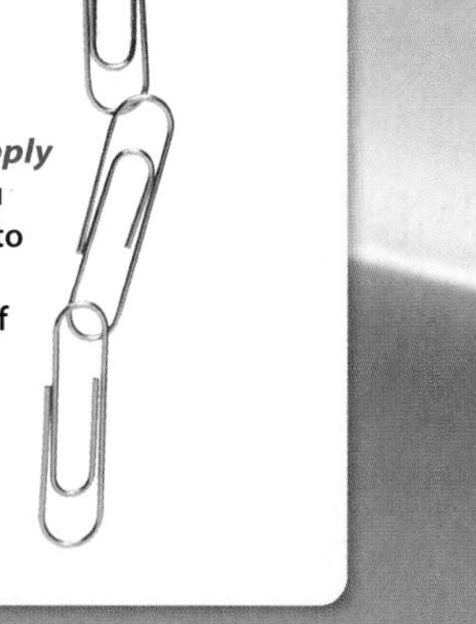

Adult supervision required for all labs.

Extra Try at Home Labs

7 Glowing Bulbs

Time Required 15 minutes

Materials
- The fluorescent bulbs should be new.
- Students should check their fabrics to be certain they are 100% wool and 100% silk. The wool should be soft, not coarse.

Safety Precaution
Caution students not to rub hard enough to break the glass. A chemical coating on the interior of the bulbs can be harmful.

Teaching Strategy
Explain to the class that the tube is filled with mercury vapor. Rubbing the fabrics against the tubes causes electrons to shoot into them and collide with the mercury atoms. The mercury atoms emit UV light, which causes a phosphor coating on the inside of the bulb to glow.

Conclude and Apply
1. Each type of cloth should cause the tube to glow.
2. Answers will vary depending on the types of cloth used, but silk usually produces the brightest glow and flannel the faintest.

8 Magnetic Attraction

Time Required 30 minutes

Materials Collect a wide variety of metal objects for students to test.

Safety Precaution Caution students to be careful when handling jagged metal edges. Cuts from metal may require a tetanus shot. Any injuries should be reported immediately.

Teaching Strategy Explain to students that different alloys use a variety of metals and nonmetals. Some alloys are made with magnetic metals but are not magnetic. For example, some stainless steel alloys are made of magnetic iron, but they are not magnetic.

Conclude and Apply
1. Answers will vary.
2. Iron, steel, nickel, and cobalt are magnetic metals.

9 Energy Graphs

Time Required 45 minutes

Materials Students should use colored pencils to distinguish between the energy consumption data of the different countries on their graphs.

Safety Precaution Students should not search the Internet without adult supervision.

Teaching Strategies
- Have students research the most current energy consumption data and other countries not listed.
- Display students' graphs on a class bulletin board.

Conclude and Apply
1. 25.4%
2. 24.4%
3. 4.6%

Extra Try at Home Labs

9 Energy Graphs

Real-World Question
How much energy does the United States use compared to the rest of the world?

Possible Materials
- calculator
- colored pencils
- white paper
- metric ruler
- compass and pencil

Procedure
1. Study the energy consumption chart.
2. Use the data to make a bar graph of the oil consumption of the countries in the chart.
3. Construct a circle graph showing the total energy consumption of the countries in the chart.

Conclude and Apply
1. Calculate the percentage of the world's oil that the USA uses.
2. Calculate the percentage of the world's total energy the USA uses.
3. The population of the United States is 290,300,000, and the world population is 6,300,000,000. Calculate what percentage of the world's population is made up of the U.S. population.

2002 Energy Consumption (Equivalent of Millions of Metric Tons of Oil)

	Oil	Natural Gas	Coal	Hydroelectric	Nuclear	Total Energy Use
USA	894.3	600.7	553.8	58.2	185.8	2,293.0
China	245.7	27.0	663.4	55.8	5.9	997.8
Russia	122.9	349.6	98.5	37.2	32.0	640.2
Japan	242.6	69.7	105.3	20.5	71.3	509.4
Germany	127.2	74.3	84.6	5.9	37.5	329.4
Rest of the world	1,889.9	1,160.7	892.3	414.5	278.3	4,635.2

10 Measuring Refraction

Real-World Question
Do some liquids refract light more than others?

Possible Materials
- glasses (3)
- straws or pencils (3)
- water
- white vinegar
- vegetable oil
- metric ruler or protractor

Procedure
1. Pour 300 mL of water into a glass, 300 mL of vinegar into a second glass, and 300 mL of vegetable oil into a third glass.
2. Place a straw into each glass so that each straw is resting at the same angle.
3. Set the glasses side by side, view them from eye level, and observe the angle of refraction caused by each liquid.
4. Use a metric ruler or protractor to measure the refraction caused by the water, vinegar, and oil.

Conclude and Apply
1. List the amount of refraction created by each liquid.
2. Define *refraction*.

Adult supervision required for all labs.

Extra Try at Home Labs

These labs are available at gpscience.com.

10 Measuring Refraction

Time Required 15 minutes

Materials Encourage students to test other liquids such as clear soda, juices, and other types of oil.

Safety Precaution Warn students never to eat or drink anything in science class.

Teaching Strategy Students can measure the angle of refraction created by a liquid by measuring the gap between the straw above the liquid and its reflection under the liquid.

Conclude and Apply
1. The refraction caused by the water will be about 2 mm; the vinegar, 3 mm; and the oil, 5 mm.
2. Refraction is the bending of a wave caused by a change in its speed as it moves from one medium to another.

Extra Try at Home Labs

11 It Sounds Different

Real-World Question
How do sounds change when heard through different mediums?

Possible Materials
- wood block
- water
- balloon
- ticking watch

Procedure
1. Hold a wood block next to your ear and have a partner hold a ticking watch next to the block. Note the sound of the watch through the wood.
2. Blow up a balloon and hold the balloon next to your ear. Have a friend hold the ticking watch against the other side of the balloon and note the sound of the watch through the air in the balloon.
3. Fill the balloon with water and securely tie its neck. Hold the water balloon next to your ear and have a partner hold the ticking watch against the other side of the balloon. Note the sound of the watch through the water in the balloon.

Conclude and Apply
1. Compare the sound of the watch when it traveled through the three different mediums.
2. Infer why the watch sounded different in the different mediums.

12 Electromagnetic Waves

Real-World Question
How do polarized sunglasses stop electromagnetic waves and prevent glare?

Possible Materials
- 2 sets of polarized sunglasses (or one set, broken in half)

Procedure
1. On a sunny day, observe the bright glare from a shiny object without sunglasses.
2. Now close one eye and use the other to look through the polarized lens. Hold the lens in front of your eye, then turn it a quarter turn. Record your observations of how the electromagnetic rays of the sunlight changed in each case.
3. Hold one lens in front of another. Look through both lenses at the shiny object and slowly rotate one lens. Record your observations of what happened to the light.

Conclude and Apply
1. Describe what happened to the sunlight glare when you looked through the double lenses of the glasses and rotated them.
2. Why do you think the brightness is different when holding the glasses horizontally and vertically?
3. Infer how polarized sunglasses block electromagnetic energy from the Sun.

Extra Try at Home Labs

11 It Sounds Different

Time Required 25 minutes

Materials
- Large wooden toy building blocks work well for this activity.
- Students can place a funnel in the neck of the balloon to make it easier to fill with water.

Safety Precautions
- Caution students not to pop the balloons.
- Students should never place objects that make loud noises near their ears.

Teaching Strategy
Be considerate of students who have hearing disabilities and provide them with an alternative activity or a specific job to do during this lab.

Conclude and Apply
1. The ticking of the watch will sound louder when heard through the wood and water than it does when heard through the air.
2. Sounds travel faster and more efficiently through liquids and solids than they do through gases, and they will sound louder and fuller in these mediums.

12 Electromagnetic Waves

Time Required 30 minutes

Materials
- Clip-on polarized sunglasses are available cheaply at pharmacies and dollar stores.
- Students also can use polarizing filters for camera lenses or sheets of polarizing plastic (available from science supply outlets).

Teaching Strategy A sunny late morning or early afternoon works best for this activity.

Conclude and Apply
1. The light dims as the lenses are turned. Perpendicular lenses will completely block sunlight.
2. The light comes in at a perpendicular angle. Light bounces off the object at a horizontal angle and the sunglasses are designed to block that. If you hold the glasses vertically they don't block much of the horizontal light waves from the glare.
3. Glare is made when sunlight reflects off a shiny object at a horizontal angle. The materials in polarized lenses are made in planes perpendicular to the reflected glare.

13 Light Show

Time Required 15 minutes

Materials
- Students also can experiment with different colors of plastic wrap.
- Laser pointers can be used with caution instead of flashlights.

Safety Precaution
Flashlights or laser pointers should never be directed toward a person's eyes.

Teaching Strategy
Students first can shine their lights on the wall without holding any paper up to serve as a comparison for the amount of light that passes though the different materials.

Conclude and Apply
1. The light will shine through the plastic wrap, but the foil will block the light. As the wax paper is folded, less light will pass through it.
2. Answers will vary but may include lamp shades and curtains.

Extra Try at Home Labs

13 Light Show

Real-World Question
What does light look like when it passes through different materials?

Possible Materials
- aluminum foil
- clear plastic wrap
- wax paper
- flashlight

Procedure
1. Have a partner hold a 30-cm × 30-cm square of plastic wrap about 30 cm from a white wall.
2. Darken the room and shine a flashlight through the plastic wrap. Observe the amount of light that passes through the wrap and shines on the wall. Be sure to keep the flashlight location constant.
3. Hold a 30-cm × 30-cm square of aluminum foil in front of the wall, darken the room, and shine the light on the foil. Observe what happens to the light.
4. Hold a 30-cm × 30-cm square of wax paper in front of the wall, darken the room, and shine the light on the paper. Observe the amount of light that strikes the wall.
5. Repeat step 4 after folding the wax paper once, then twice, and then several times.

Conclude and Apply
1. Describe your observations of the light when you shined it on the different materials.
2. Identify translucent materials in your home that are used to partially block light.

14 Mirror, Mirror on the Car

Real-World Question
Why are car side-view mirrors convex mirrors?

Possible Materials
- plane mirror
- tennis balls, cans, or other objects (15)
- meterstick

Procedure
1. Measure a distance of 10 m directly behind your family car. Be certain you are not walking into traffic. (If you do not have access to a car, set up chairs and mirrors to simulate where they are positioned in a car.)
2. Line up 15 objects behind the car. The objects should be perpendicular to the car and about 0.5 m apart. Place the first object in line with the back bumper and line up the other objects so that they extend beyond the rear side view of the driver.
3. Sit in the driver's seat, with a parent or guardian present, and look in the side view mirror. Count the number of objects you can see.
4. Sit in the same position and have a partner place a plane mirror over the side-view mirror. Count the number of objects you can see.

Conclude and Apply
1. Compare the number of objects you saw in the convex, side-view mirror with the number of objects you saw in the plane mirror.
2. Infer why convex mirrors are used for side view mirrors on cars.

Adult supervision required for all labs.

These labs are available at gpscience.com.

14 Mirror, Mirror on the Car

Time Required 20 minutes

Materials The plane mirror should be approximately the same size as the side-view mirror.

Safety Precautions
- Students should complete this lab away from traffic or busy parking lots.
- Caution students to handle the mirrors with care and never to touch broken glass.

Teaching Strategy Instruct students to adjust the side-view mirror as they would if they were driving the car. The plane mirror should be held up at the same angle and location as the side-view mirror.

Conclude and Apply
1. Answers will vary, but students should see more balls in the convex side-view mirror.
2. Convex mirrors spread out light allowing the driver to view a larger area of the road behind the car.

15 Lemon Clean

Real-World Question

What chemical changes happen to coins?

Possible Materials

- lemon
- paring knife
- tarnished penny
- tarnished nickel
- tarnished dime
- tarnished quarter
- metric ruler

Procedure

1. Cut a slit in a lemon 1 cm wide and 1 cm deep. Insert a tarnished penny halfway into the slit.
2. On the same side of the lemon, repeat step 1 for the nickel and the dime.
3. Cut a 1.5 cm wide and 1.5 cm deep slit on the same side of the lemon and insert the quarter halfway into the slit.
4. Leave the coins in the lemon for two days before removing them. Observe the chemical change that happened to the sides of the coins that were in the lemon.

Conclude and Apply

1. Describe the change that happened to the coins.
2. Infer why this change happened.

16 Overflowing Ice

Real-World Question

What happens to water when it freezes?

Possible Materials

- plastic drink bottle
- plate
- water
- freezer

Procedure

1. Fill a clean, plastic drink bottle with water. The water should come to the top brim of the bottle.
2. Place a plate in a freezer. Be certain the plate is level and not tilted to one side.
3. Carefully place the bottle on the plate without spilling any of the water. If water spills, refill the bottle.
4. Leave the bottle in the freezer overnight and observe the ice that forms the next day.

Conclude and Apply

1. Describe what the ice looks like.
2. Infer why the ice formed this way.
3. Infer how the results of your experiment would be different if you had used rubbing alcohol instead of water. *Hint: Look up the freezing point of rubbing alcohol.*

Adult supervision required for all labs.

15 Lemon Clean

Time Required 15 minutes set-up; five-minute observation period two days later

Materials

- Use fresh lemons.
- Dull kitchen knives will work for this lab with less chance for accidents.

Safety Precaution

Caution students to handle the knives carefully.

Teaching Strategy

Place the lemons in a cool place away from direct sunlight.

Conclude and Apply

1. The parts of the coins that were in the lemon will be clean and shiny.
2. The acid in the lemon chemically reacted with the tarnish on the coins removing it from their surfaces.

16 Overflowing Ice

Time Required 10 minutes to set up; five-minute observation period the next day

Materials

- Dark-colored plates work best.
- Choose bottles with narrow necks.

Safety Precautions

- Do not use glass bottles.
- Caution students not to eat or drink anything during science class.

Teaching Strategies

- Instruct students not to put the lids on the bottles.
- Have students fill the bottles near the freezer to reduce spilling accidents.

Conclude and Apply

1. The water in the bottle is frozen solid. Rivulets of ice are down the sides of the bottle, and a small pool of ice is on the plate.
2. As the water in the bottle started to freeze, the expanding ice forced water out of the bottle.
3. The alcohol would not freeze.

17 How big is an atom?

Time Required one to two class sessions

Teaching Strategies

- The orbit would be about 100 m.
- If time is tight, you might want to do this together, as a class. If you have a double period, you might want to walk around a field with a clip board to see what each group comes up with.
- If you want to demonstrate the solution to question 1, use cross-multiplication.

Conclude and Apply

1. Earth would be 7×10^{13} m away. This is ten times Pluto's current orbit.
2. about 100,000 times

Extra Try at Home Labs

Extra Try at Home Labs

17 How big is an atom?

Real-World Question

If an atom's nucleus were as big as the head of a pin, how far away would the nearest electron be?

Possible Materials

- pins
- measuring tapes
- outdoor playing field
- masking or duct tape

Procedure

1. The diameter of an atom's nucleus is about 1×10^{-15} m. The orbit of an electron is about 1×10^{-10} m. Calculate how big the orbit would be if the nucleus were the size of the head of a pin (about 0.0001 m).
2. Put your pin through a piece of tape so you can find it later. Measure out the distance to the first electron, and mark the spot with a second pin and tape.

Conclude and Apply

1. Earth orbits the Sun at about 150 million km. This is 214 times the Sun's radius. How many km away would Earth orbit the Sun, if it were on the same scale as an atom's first electron?
2. How many times the nucleus' radius is the orbit of an electron?

18 Get a Half-life

Real-World Question

How would you determine the half-life of a radioactive substance?

Possible Materials

- pennies (200)
- shoe box

Procedure

1. To model the half-life of 200 atoms of a radioactive substance, place 200 pennies in a shoe box, with the "heads" side up.
2. Close the shoe box and shake it for 3 s.
3. Open the shoe box, shift the pennies around until they are all flat, and remove all pennies that are now "tails" side up. Record the number of pennies that you removed from the box and the number of pennies that are left in the box.
4. Repeat steps 2 and 3 until all pennies are removed from the box or you have done this process ten times. Record each shake-and-remove step as increments of 3 s—3 s, 6 s, 9 s, etc. This is the time interval.
5. Graph the data as number of pennies left versus time.

Conclude and Apply

1. According to the graph, how much decay (shaking) time was required for half of your atoms (pennies) to decay (go "tails" up)?
2. If you increased the number of atoms (pennies), would your results change?
3. How would you define the term *half-life*? How would you measure half-life?

Adult supervision required for all labs.

These labs are available at gpscience.com.

 18 Get a Half-life

Time Required 45 minutes

Materials Use rubber bands to keep shoe boxes closed tight when shaking.

Teaching Strategy To improve the results of the model, have a class do this in groups of two. Combine results and then graph them. Have each group graph their results and compare their graphs to the class graph. Explain why the combined class results are more consistent than individual results.

Conclude and Apply

1. It took about 3 s for half to decay.
2. No
3. Half-life describes the rate of decay of a radioactive substance. Use a large amount of the substance to measure half-life.

Extra Try at Home Labs

19 Mining for Metals

Real-World Question

How do miners get metal from ore?

Possible Materials

- potato chips
- rolling pin or heavy book
- plastic bags (2)
- water
- hotplate, kettle, or stove
- tea leaf strainer, flour sifter, or other mesh device

Procedure

1. Pretend that the potato chips represent ore taken from the ground, and the fat represents a metal compound.
2. Research the mining process and develop a procedure to process the "ore" to refine the "metal."

Conclude and Apply

1. Were you satisfied with your procedure and results? What could you do better next time?
2. How does your procedure compare to the real mining process?

20 Disappearing Peanuts

Real-World Question

How can you observe chemical bonds breaking?

Possible Materials

- polystyrene packing peanuts or polystyrene cups
- acetone fingernail polish remover
- glass jar or shallow dish
- measuring cup

Procedure

1. Work in a well-ventilated area.
2. Pour 30 mL of acetone into a glass jar or shallow dish.
3. Drop a polystyrene packing peanut into the acetone and observe how the polystyrene and acetone react.
4. Drop several peanuts into the acetone and observe what happens to them.
5. Drop a handful of peanuts into the acetone so that they stack up above the liquid observe the reaction that occurs.

Conclude and Apply

1. Describe what happened to the polystyrene peanuts.
2. Infer why this happened to the peanuts.

Adult supervision required for all labs.

Extra Try at Home Labs

19 Mining for Metals

Time Required one class session

Safety Precaution

Students should have their procedures approved before completing the lab.

Teaching Strategies

- Possible procedure: Place chips in doubled plastic bags to prevent leaks. Crush the chips with a rolling pin or heavy book. Remove large pieces by running the crushed "ore" through a sifter. Add the chips to water and boil. The fat rises to the top. Larger pieces of chip rise to the top as well if the mixture is not sifted.
- To make this procedure quantitative: Have students weigh the chips preprocessing. Collect the fat by touching filter paper to the top of the liquid mixture, and leave it overnight to evaporate the water. Compare the mass of the fat to the original mass of the chips.

Conclude and Apply

1. Accept appropriate answers and improvements.
2. In the real mining process, detergent is used to make the metal rise to the top of the boiling mixture. Finely crushing the ore is necessary to get the best metal yield.

20 Disappearing Peanuts

Time Required 15 minutes

Materials Students also can place a polystyrene cup in a shallow dish of acetone to watch it melt.

Safety Precautions

- Students must wear safety goggles.
- Students should not touch the acetone.
- Have students wash their hands after the lab or if acetone splashes on them.

Teaching Strategies

- Dispose of the acetone by diluting it with water to ten times its volume and slowly pouring it down the drain.
- The residue of the polystyrene can be reclaimed, washed, and dried.
- Some packing peanuts are made of cornstarch and can be dissolved in water.

Conclude and Apply

1. They disappeared immediately.
2. A chemical reaction happened that broke the chemical bonds holding the polystyrene molecules together.

21 Balanced Reactions

Time Required one class period

Materials This lab could be done with chemical modeling sets.

Teaching Strategy The kinesthetic nature of this lab will help some students who have a hard time remembering with abstract imagery.

Conclude and Apply

1. There are the same number of atoms of reactants and products.
2. Add a molecule or atom on one side or the other to balance the equation.
3. New compounds were formed when bonds were broken and formed.

Extra Try at Home Labs

21 Balanced Reactions

Real-World Question

What would a balanced chemical reaction look like, in terms of atoms and molecules?

Possible Materials

- round fruit (grapes, oranges, apples), marshmallows, foam balls, or any other suitable objects to represent atoms
- sharp toothpicks or straightened paper clips to represent bonds

Procedure

1. Look through the chapter to find two examples of chemical reactions. Balance the equations, if necessary.
2. Make a key for your modeling set. For example, grape = carbon, marshmallow = oxygen, apple = magnesium.
3. Model each balanced chemical reaction that you have written down by bonding the "atoms" together with toothpicks or straightened paper clips to make the reactants. Sketch what you have modeled.
4. Using only the atoms from the reactants, break bonds and make new bonds to form the products. Sketch what you have modeled.

Conclude and Apply

1. How do you know that the law of conservation of mass is followed in the reactions you modeled?
2. What would you do to fix a reaction that did not follow the conservation of mass?
3. What is the evidence that a reaction has occurred?

Extra Try at Home Labs

22 Sticky Solution

Real-World Question

How can heat change a solution?

Possible Materials

- cornstarch
- pot
- kitchen stove or hotplate
- glass
- measuring cup
- tablespoon
- wooden spoon
- oven mitt

Procedure

1. Pour 300 mL of water into a clean glass.
2. Add a tablespoon of cornstarch to the water and stir the water until a solution is formed. Observe what the solution looks like.
3. Pour your solution into a pot and boil the solution over a hotplate or stove-top burner.
4. Once the solution is boiling, stir it with a wooden spoon.
5. Boil the solution for 2 min and observe how the solution changes.

Conclude and Apply

1. Describe the water and cornstarch solution before it boiled.
2. Describe how heat changed the water and cornstarch solution.

Adult supervision required for all labs.

These labs are available at gpscience.com.

22 Sticky Solution

Time Required ten minutes

Materials Students can use the highest setting on their hotplates.

Safety Precautions

- Students should wear safety goggles, cloth aprons, and heat-resistant gloves.
- Caution students not to touch the pot or stove.
- The solution will remain hot for a long time after it is removed from the heat source.

Teaching Strategy Starch is made of large granules that burst in hot water to form a thick paste. The granules do not burst in cold water.

Conclude and Apply

1. Before boiling, the solution is cloudy and is milky white.
2. After boiling, a thick, clear gelatinlike solution formed.

Extra Try at Home Labs

23 Kitchen Indicator

Real-World Question

How many pHs can you measure around your home?

Possible Materials

- purple cabbage
- water
- pot
- hotplate or stove
- knife
- several clear glasses
- spoons
- baking soda, juice, soda, vinegar, and milk

Procedure

1. Chop up the purple cabbage and put it in the pot. Boil it until the water turns purple.
2. Discard the cabbage, but keep the water.
3. Add a spoonful of the cabbage water to a spoonful of each household substance you plan to test. What color is the mixture? (The color change indicates if the substance is acidic or basic. If the color is red or pink, the substance is an acid. If the color is blue, green, or yellow, it is a base.)
4. Record your colors on a chart.
5. Ask an adult to select other substances for you to test. By adding more of the acidic and basic substances, you can get several interesting colors from this indicator.

Conclude and Apply

How can you prove that vinegar is between drinking soda and baking soda on the pH scale by using the cabbage indicator?

24 Organic Bonding

Real-World Question

How can you and your family represent organic bonding?

Possible Materials

- family members or friends
- large construction paper rings
- pins or tape

Procedure

1. You are a carbon atom. Each of your arms and legs is a place for a bond. Link the paper rings to your arms or legs to represent the correct number of hydrogen atoms.
2. Get together with friends to form ethane, propane, butane, and isobutane.
3. With five friends, make a benzene ring. To make a double bond, touch a neighbor's foot with yours while holding his or her hand. Make a single bond with your other neighbor by holding hands.
4. After forming each molecule, try to move from one side of the room to the other. Which molecules twist and bend easily, and which don't? Make a table of your observations.

Conclude and Apply

1. Use your observations to explain why the boiling point of hydrocarbons increases with the number of carbon atoms.
2. Use your observations to explain why benzene is so stable.
3. How many people would you need to form a protein molecule? Are there enough students in your school?

Isobutane

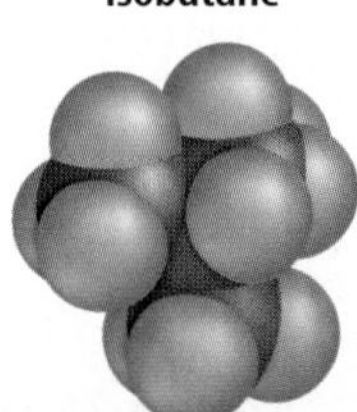

Adult supervision required for all labs.

Extra Try at Home Labs

23 Kitchen Indicator

Time Required one and a half class periods

Safety Precaution

Warn students to use caution and to wear goggles when using any chemical.

Conclude and Apply

1. Find the color of the indicator in each substance. Put some baking soda with the indicator in a glass. Add drinking soda until you get the color of vinegar.

24 Organic Bonding

Time Required one class

Safety Precaution Clear a space in the classroom, or use a gym or other open space. Gymnastics mats would be useful for the benzene part, as students may fall down while learning to construct this ring.

Teaching Strategy Extend this lab to encompass other molecules. This is a good model to show the restricted movement of double and triple bonds, and the rotational, vibrational, and translational ability of different molecules.

Conclude and Apply

1. With more atoms, the molecules are bulkier and not as free to move. More energy is required to vaporize larger molecules.
2. The molecule is very tightly bonded.
3. Protein molecules contain thousands of atoms. No.

25 Quick Dry

Time Required 20 minutes

Materials

- Use nylon from an old jacket or athletic shorts, not nylon stockings.
- Students also can place the squares under a heat lamp.
- Purchase old clothing at a thrift store for sample squares.

Safety Precaution

Inquire about student allergies to wool before the lab.

Teaching Strategies

- This lab works well outside on a hot, sunny day.
- Students should not wring their cloth squares dry before placing them on the towels.
- If you complete this lab inside, use the classroom windowsills.

Conclude and Apply

1. The wool will stay wet, and the cotton will be very damp. The nylon and polyester should be dry.
2. Athletic clothing quickly becomes wet with sweat. Synthetic fibers are quick-drying and lightweight, making them more comfortable.

Extra Try at Home Labs

Extra Try at Home Labs

25 Quick Dry

Real-World Question

Do synthetic fibers dry more quickly than natural fibers?

Possible Materials

- **measuring cup**
- **drinking glasses (4)**
- **water**
- **3-cm × 3-cm squares of:**
  cotton cloth
  wool cloth
  polyester cloth
  nylon cloth

Procedure

1. **Pour 400 mL of water into each of the four glasses.**
2. **Submerge a square of fabric in each beaker and soak the squares for 3 min.**
3. **Remove the fabric squares, lay them flat on several layers of paper towels, and place them in direct sunlight.**
4. **Check the dampness of each cloth square every 3 min for 15 min.**

Conclude and Apply

1. **Describe the results of your activity.**
2. **Infer why athletes wear polyester or nylon clothing.**

Adult supervision required for all labs.

These labs are available at gpscience.com.

Computer Skills

People who study science rely on computers, like the one in **Figure 16,** to record and store data and to analyze results from investigations. Whether you work in a laboratory or just need to write a lab report with tables, good computer skills are a necessity.

Using the computer comes with responsibility. Issues of ownership, security, and privacy can arise. Remember, if you did not author the information you are using, you must provide a source for your information. Also, anything on a computer can be accessed by others. Do not put anything on the computer that you would not want everyone to know. To add more security to your work, use a password.

Use a Word Processing Program

A computer program that allows you to type your information, change it as many times as you need to, and then print it out is called a word processing program. Word processing programs also can be used to make tables.

Figure 16 A computer will make reports neater and more professional looking.

Learn the Skill To start your word processing program, a blank document, sometimes called "Document 1," appears on the screen. To begin, start typing. To create a new document, click the *New* button on the standard tool bar. These tips will help you format the document.

- The program will automatically move to the next line; press *Enter* if you wish to start a new paragraph.
- Symbols, called non-printing characters, can be hidden by clicking the *Show/Hide* button on your toolbar.
- To insert text, move the cursor to the point where you want the insertion to go, click on the mouse once, and type the text.
- To move several lines of text, select the text and click the *Cut* button on your toolbar. Then position your cursor in the location that you want to move the cut text and click *Paste.* If you move to the wrong place, click *Undo.*
- The spell check feature does not catch words that are misspelled to look like other words, like "cold" instead of "gold." Always reread your document to catch all spelling mistakes.
- To learn about other word processing methods, read the user's manual or click on the *Help* button.
- You can integrate databases, graphics, and spreadsheets into documents by copying from another program and pasting it into your document, or by using desktop publishing (DTP). DTP software allows you to put text and graphics together to finish your document with a professional look. This software varies in how it is used and its capabilities.

Use a Database

A collection of facts stored in a computer and sorted into different fields is called a database. A database can be reorganized in any way that suits your needs.

Learn the Skill A computer program that allows you to create your own database is a database management system (DBMS). It allows you to add, delete, or change information. Take time to get to know the features of your database software.

- Determine what facts you would like to include and research to collect your information.
- Determine how you want to organize the information.
- Follow the instructions for your particular DBMS to set up fields. Then enter each item of data in the appropriate field.
- Follow the instructions to sort the information in order of importance.
- Evaluate the information in your database, and add, delete, or change as necessary.

Use the Internet

The Internet is a global network of computers where information is stored and shared. To use the Internet, like the students in **Figure 17,** you need a modem to connect your computer to a phone line and an Internet Service Provider account.

Learn the Skill To access internet sites and information, use a "Web browser," which lets you view and explore pages on the World Wide Web. Each page is its own site, and each site has its own address, called a URL. Once you have found a Web browser, follow these steps for a search (this also is how you search a database).

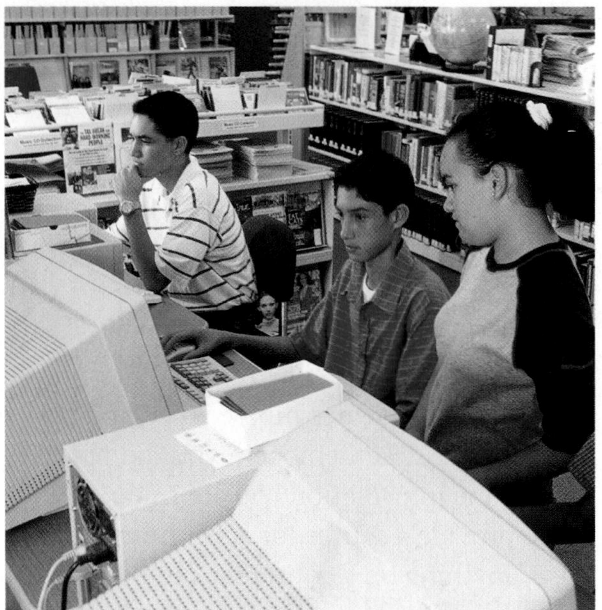

Figure 17 The Internet allows you to search a global network for a variety of information.

- Be as specific as possible. If you know you want to research "gold," don't type in "elements." Keep narrowing your search until you find what you want.
- Web sites that end in *.com* are commercial Web sites; *.org, .edu,* and *.gov* are non-profit, educational, or government Web sites.
- Electronic encyclopedias, almanacs, indexes, and catalogs will help locate and select relevant information.
- Develop a "home page" with relative ease. When developing a Web site, NEVER post pictures or disclose personal information such as location, names, or phone numbers. Your school or community usually can host your Web site. A basic understanding of HTML (hypertext mark-up language), the language of Web sites, is necessary. Software that creates HTML code is called authoring software, and can be downloaded free from many Web sites. This software allows text and pictures to be arranged as the software is writing the HTML code.

Use a Spreadsheet

A spreadsheet, shown in **Figure 18,** can perform mathematical functions with any data arranged in columns and rows. By entering a simple equation into a cell, the program can perform operations in specific cells, rows, or columns.

Learn the Skill Each column (vertical) is assigned a letter, and each row (horizontal) is assigned a number. Each point where a row and column intersect is called a cell, and is labeled according to where it is located—Column A, Row 1 (A1).

- Decide how to organize the data, and enter it in the correct row or column.
- Spreadsheets can use standard formulas or formulas can be customized to calculate cells.
- To make a change, click on a cell to make it activate, and enter the edited data or formula.
- Spreadsheets also can display your results in graphs. Choose the style of graph that best represents the data.

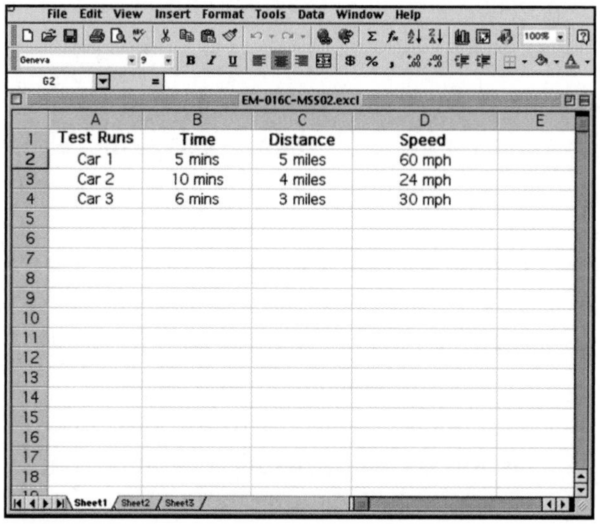

	A	B	C	D	E
1	Test Runs	Time	Distance	Speed	
2	Car 1	5 mins	5 miles	60 mph	
3	Car 2	10 mins	4 miles	24 mph	
4	Car 3	6 mins	3 miles	30 mph	

Figure 18 A spreadsheet allows you to perform mathematical operations on your data.

Use Graphics Software

Adding pictures, called graphics, to your documents is one way to make your documents more meaningful and exciting. This software adds, edits, and even constructs graphics. There is a variety of graphics software programs. The tools used for drawing can be a mouse, keyboard, or other specialized devices. Some graphics programs are simple. Others are complicated, called computer-aided design (CAD) software.

Learn the Skill It is important to have an understanding of the graphics software being used before starting. The better the software is understood, the better the results. The graphics can be placed in a word-processing document.

- Clip art can be found on a variety of internet sites, and on CDs. These images can be copied and pasted into your document.
- When beginning, try editing existing drawings, then work up to creating drawings.
- The images are made of tiny rectangles of color called pixels. Each pixel can be altered.
- Digital photography is another way to add images. The photographs in the memory of a digital camera can be downloaded into a computer, then edited and added to the document.
- Graphics software also can allow animation. The software allows drawings to have the appearance of movement by connecting basic drawings automatically. This is called in-betweening, or tweening.
- Remember to save often.

Presentation Skills

Develop Multimedia Presentations

Most presentations are more dynamic if they include diagrams, photographs, videos, or sound recordings, like the one shown in **Figure 19.** A multimedia presentation involves using stereos, overhead projectors, televisions, computers, and more.

Learn the Skill Decide the main points of your presentation, and what types of media would best illustrate those points.

- Make sure you know how to use the equipment you are working with.
- Practice the presentation using the equipment several times.
- Enlist the help of a classmate to push play or turn lights out for you. Be sure to practice your presentation with him or her.
- If possible, set up all of the equipment ahead of time, and make sure everything is working properly.

Figure 19 These students are engaging the audience using a variety of tools.

Computer Presentations

There are many different interactive computer programs that you can use to enhance your presentation. Most computers have a compact disc (CD) drive that can play both CDs and digital video discs (DVDs). Also, there is hardware to connect a regular CD, DVD, or VCR. These tools will enhance your presentation.

Another method of using the computer to aid in your presentation is to develop a slide show using a computer program. This can allow movement of visuals at the presenter's pace, and can allow for visuals to build on one another.

Learn the Skill In order to create multimedia presentations on a computer, you need to have certain tools. These may include traditional graphic tools and drawing programs, animation programs, and authoring systems that tie everything together. Your computer will tell you which tools it supports. The most important step is to learn about the tools that you will be using.

- Often, color and strong images will convey a point better than words alone. Use the best methods available to convey your point.
- As with other presentations, practice many times.
- Practice your presentation with the tools you and any assistants will be using.
- Maintain eye contact with the audience. The purpose of using the computer is not to prompt the presenter, but to help the audience understand the points of the presentation.

Math Review

Use Fractions

A fraction compares a part to a whole. In the fraction $\frac{2}{3}$, the 2 represents the part and is the numerator. The 3 represents the whole and is the denominator.

Reduce Fractions To reduce a fraction, you must find the largest factor that is common to both the numerator and the denominator, the greatest common factor (GCF). Divide both numbers by the GCF. The fraction has then been reduced, or it is in its simplest form.

Example Twelve of the 20 chemicals in the science lab are in powder form. What fraction of the chemicals used in the lab are in powder form?

Step 1 Write the fraction.

$$\frac{\text{part}}{\text{whole}} = \frac{12}{20}$$

Step 2 To find the GCF of the numerator and denominator, list all of the factors of each number.

Factors of 12: 1, 2, 3, 4, 6, 12 (the numbers that divide evenly into 12)

Factors of 20: 1, 2, 4, 5, 10, 20 (the numbers that divide evenly into 20)

Step 3 List the common factors.

1, 2, 4.

Step 4 Choose the greatest factor in the list.

The GCF of 12 and 20 is 4.

Step 5 Divide the numerator and denominator by the GCF.

$$\frac{12 \div 4}{20 \div 4} = \frac{3}{5}$$

In the lab, $\frac{3}{5}$ of the chemicals are in powder form.

Practice Problem At an amusement park, 66 of 90 rides have a height restriction. What fraction of the rides, in its simplest form, has a height restriction?

Add and Subtract Fractions To add or subtract fractions with the same denominator, add or subtract the numerators and write the sum or difference over the denominator. After finding the sum or difference, find the simplest form for your fraction.

Example 1 In the forest outside your house, $\frac{1}{8}$ of the animals are rabbits, $\frac{3}{8}$ are squirrels, and the remainder are birds and insects. How many are mammals?

Step 1 Add the numerators.

$$\frac{1}{8} + \frac{3}{8} = \frac{(1+3)}{8} = \frac{4}{8}$$

Step 2 Find the GCF.

$$\frac{4}{8} \quad \text{(GCF, 4)}$$

Step 3 Divide the numerator and denominator by the GCF.

$$\frac{4}{4} = 1, \quad \frac{8}{4} = 2$$

$\frac{1}{2}$ of the animals are mammals.

Example 2 If $\frac{7}{16}$ of the Earth is covered by freshwater, and $\frac{1}{16}$ of that is in glaciers, how much freshwater is not frozen?

Step 1 Subtract the numerators.

$$\frac{7}{16} - \frac{1}{16} = \frac{(7-1)}{16} = \frac{6}{16}$$

Step 2 Find the GCF.

$$\frac{6}{16} \quad \text{(GCF, 2)}$$

Step 3 Divide the numerator and denominator by the GCF.

$$\frac{6}{2} = 3, \quad \frac{16}{2} = 8$$

$\frac{3}{8}$ of the freshwater is not frozen.

Practice Problem A bicycle rider is going 15 km/h for $\frac{4}{9}$ of his ride, 10 km/h for $\frac{2}{9}$ of his ride, and 8 km/h for the remainder of the ride. How much of his ride is he going over 8 km/h?

Reduce Fractions

$$\frac{66 \div 6}{90 \div 6} = \frac{11}{15}$$

Add and Subtract Fractions

$$\frac{4}{9} + \frac{2}{9} = \frac{6}{9}$$

$$\frac{6 \div 3}{9 \div 3} = \frac{2}{3}$$

Math Skill Handbook

MATH SKILL HANDBOOK 817

Unlike Denominators

Problem 1

$1 \times 5 = 5, 8 \times 5 = 40$

$1 \times 4 = 4, 10 \times 4 = 40$

$\frac{5}{40} + \frac{4}{40} = \frac{9}{40}$

Problem 2

If $\frac{7}{10}$ are involuntary, the remainder are voluntary.

$\frac{10}{10} - \frac{7}{10} = \frac{3}{10}$

Unlike Denominators To add or subtract fractions with unlike denominators, first find the least common denominator (LCD). This is the smallest number that is a common multiple of both denominators. Rename each fraction with the LCD, and then add or subtract. Find the simplest form if necessary.

Example 1 A chemist makes a paste that is $\frac{1}{2}$ table salt (NaCl), $\frac{1}{3}$ sugar ($C_6H_{12}O_6$), and the rest water (H_2O). How much of the paste is a solid?

Step 1 Find the LCD of the fractions.

$\frac{1}{2} + \frac{1}{3}$ (LCD, 6)

Step 2 Rename each numerator and each denominator with the LCD.

$1 \times 3 = 3, \; 2 \times 3 = 6$

$1 \times 2 = 2, \; 3 \times 2 = 6$

Step 3 Add the numerators.

$\frac{3}{6} + \frac{2}{6} = \frac{(3 + 2)}{6} = \frac{5}{6}$

$\frac{5}{6}$ of the paste is a solid.

Example 2 The average precipitation in Grand Junction, CO, is $\frac{7}{10}$ inch in November, and $\frac{3}{5}$ inch in December. What is the total average precipitation?

Step 1 Find the LCD of the fractions.

$\frac{7}{10} + \frac{3}{5}$ (LCD, 10)

Step 2 Rename each numerator and each denominator with the LCD.

$7 \times 1 = 7, \; 10 \times 1 = 10$

$3 \times 2 = 6, \; 5 \times 2 = 10$

Step 3 Add the numerators.

$\frac{7}{10} + \frac{6}{10} = \frac{(7 + 6)}{10} = \frac{13}{10}$

$\frac{13}{10}$ inches total precipitation, or $1\frac{3}{10}$ inches.

Practice Problem On an electric bill, about $\frac{1}{8}$ of the energy is from solar energy and about $\frac{1}{10}$ is from wind power. How much of the total bill is from solar energy and wind power combined?

Example 3 In your body, $\frac{7}{10}$ of your muscle contractions are involuntary (cardiac and smooth muscle tissue). Smooth muscle makes $\frac{3}{15}$ of your muscle contractions. How many of your muscle contractions are made by cardiac muscle?

Step 1 Find the LCD of the fractions.

$\frac{7}{10} - \frac{3}{15}$ (LCD, 30)

Step 2 Rename each numerator and each denominator with the LCD.

$7 \times 3 = 21, \; 10 \times 3 = 30$

$3 \times 2 = 6, \; 15 \times 2 = 30$

Step 3 Subtract the numerators.

$\frac{21}{30} - \frac{6}{30} = \frac{(21 - 6)}{30} = \frac{15}{30}$

Step 4 Find the GCF.

$\frac{15}{30}$ (GCF, 15)

$\frac{1}{2}$

$\frac{1}{2}$ of all muscle contractions are cardiac muscle.

Example 4 Tony wants to make cookies that call for $\frac{3}{4}$ of a cup of flour, but he only has $\frac{1}{3}$ of a cup. How much more flour does he need?

Step 1 Find the LCD of the fractions.

$\frac{3}{4} - \frac{1}{3}$ (LCD, 12)

Step 2 Rename each numerator and each denominator with the LCD.

$3 \times 3 = 9, \; 4 \times 3 = 12$

$1 \times 4 = 4, \; 3 \times 4 = 12$

Step 3 Subtract the numerators.

$\frac{9}{12} - \frac{4}{12} = \frac{(9 - 4)}{12} = \frac{5}{12}$

$\frac{5}{12}$ of a cup of flour.

Practice Problem Using the information provided to you in Example 3 above, determine how many muscle contractions are voluntary (skeletal muscle).

Multiply Fractions To multiply with fractions, multiply the numerators and multiply the denominators. Find the simplest form if necessary.

Example Multiply $\frac{3}{5}$ by $\frac{1}{3}$.

Step 1 Multiply the numerators and denominators.

$$\frac{3}{5} \times \frac{1}{3} = \frac{(3 \times 1)}{(5 \times 3)} = \frac{3}{15}$$

Step 2 Find the GCF.

$\frac{3}{15}$ (GCF, 3)

Step 3 Divide the numerator and denominator by the GCF.

$\frac{3}{3} = 1, \ \frac{15}{3} = 5$

$\frac{1}{5}$

$\frac{3}{5}$ multiplied by $\frac{1}{3}$ is $\frac{1}{5}$.

Practice Problem Multiply $\frac{3}{14}$ by $\frac{5}{16}$.

Find a Reciprocal Two numbers whose product is 1 are called multiplicative inverses, or reciprocals.

Example Find the reciprocal of $\frac{3}{8}$.

Step 1 Inverse the fraction by putting the denominator on top and the numerator on the bottom.

$\frac{8}{3}$

The reciprocal of $\frac{3}{8}$ is $\frac{8}{3}$.

Practice Problem Find the reciprocal of $\frac{4}{9}$.

Divide Fractions To divide one fraction by another fraction, multiply the dividend by the reciprocal of the divisor. Find the simplest form if necessary.

Example 1 Divide $\frac{1}{9}$ by $\frac{1}{3}$.

Step 1 Find the reciprocal of the divisor.

The reciprocal of $\frac{1}{3}$ is $\frac{3}{1}$.

Step 2 Multiply the dividend by the reciprocal of the divisor.

$$\frac{\frac{1}{9}}{\frac{1}{3}} = \frac{1}{9} \times \frac{3}{1} = \frac{(1 \times 3)}{(9 \times 1)} = \frac{3}{9}$$

Step 3 Find the GCF.

$\frac{3}{9}$ (GCF, 3)

Step 4 Divide the numerator and denominator by the GCF.

$\frac{3}{3} = 1, \ \frac{9}{3} = 3$

$\frac{1}{3}$

$\frac{1}{9}$ divided by $\frac{1}{3}$ is $\frac{1}{3}$.

Example 2 Divide $\frac{3}{5}$ by $\frac{1}{4}$.

Step 1 Find the reciprocal of the divisor.

The reciprocal of $\frac{1}{4}$ is $\frac{4}{1}$.

Step 2 Multiply the dividend by the reciprocal of the divisor.

$$\frac{\frac{3}{5}}{\frac{1}{4}} = \frac{3}{5} \times \frac{4}{1} = \frac{(3 \times 4)}{(5 \times 1)} = \frac{12}{5}$$

$\frac{3}{5}$ divided by $\frac{1}{4}$ is $\frac{12}{5}$ or $2\frac{2}{5}$.

Practice Problem Divide $\frac{3}{11}$ by $\frac{7}{10}$.

Multiply Fractions

$$\frac{3}{14} \times \frac{5}{16} = \frac{(3 \times 5)}{(14 \times 16)} = \frac{15}{224}$$

Find a Reciprocal

$\frac{9}{4}$

Divide Fractions

The reciprocal of $\frac{7}{10}$ is $\frac{10}{7}$.

$$\frac{3}{11} \times \frac{10}{7} = \frac{(3 \times 10)}{(11 \times 7)} = \frac{30}{77}$$

Math Skill Handbook

MATH SKILL HANDBOOK 819

Use Ratios

$\frac{100 \text{ cm}}{144 \text{ cm}} = \frac{100 \div 4}{144 \div 4} = \frac{25}{36}$

25:36

Add or Subtract Decimals

$$\begin{array}{r} {}^{1} \\ 1.245 \\ +\ 3.842 \\ \hline 5.087 \end{array}$$

Use Ratios

When you compare two numbers by division, you are using a ratio. Ratios can be written 3 to 5, 3:5, or $\frac{3}{5}$. Ratios, like fractions, also can be written in simplest form.

Ratios can represent probabilities, also called odds. This is a ratio that compares the number of ways a certain outcome occurs to the number of outcomes. For example, if you flip a coin 100 times, what are the odds that it will come up heads? There are two possible outcomes, heads or tails, so the odds of coming up heads are 50:100. Another way to say this is that 50 out of 100 times the coin will come up heads. In its simplest form, the ratio is 1:2.

Example 1 A chemical solution contains 40 g of salt and 64 g of baking soda. What is the ratio of salt to baking soda as a fraction in simplest form?

Step 1 Write the ratio as a fraction.

$\frac{\text{salt}}{\text{baking soda}} = \frac{40}{64}$

Step 2 Express the fraction in simplest form.

The GCF of 40 and 64 is 8.

$\frac{40}{64} = \frac{40 \div 8}{64 \div 8} = \frac{5}{8}$

The ratio of salt to baking soda in the sample is 5:8.

Example 2 Sean rolls a 6-sided die 6 times. What are the odds that the side with a 3 will show?

Step 1 Write the ratio as a fraction.

$\frac{\text{number of sides with a 3}}{\text{number of sides}} = \frac{1}{6}$

Step 2 Multiply by the number of attempts.

$\frac{1}{6} \times 6 \text{ attempts} = \frac{6}{6} \text{ attempts} = 1 \text{ attempt}$

1 attempt out of 6 will show a 3.

Practice Problem Two metal rods measure 100 cm and 144 cm in length. What is the ratio of their lengths in simplest form?

Use Decimals

A fraction with a denominator that is a power of ten can be written as a decimal. For example, 0.27 means $\frac{27}{100}$. The decimal point separates the ones place from the tenths place.

Any fraction can be written as a decimal using division. For example, the fraction $\frac{5}{8}$ can be written as a decimal by dividing 5 by 8. Written as a decimal, it is 0.625.

Add or Subtract Decimals When adding and subtracting decimals, line up the decimal points before carrying out the operation.

Example 1 Find the sum of 47.68 and 7.80.

Step 1 Line up the decimal places when you write the numbers.

$$\begin{array}{r} 47.68 \\ +\ 7.80 \end{array}$$

Step 2 Add the decimals.

$$\begin{array}{r} 47.68 \\ +\ 7.80 \\ \hline 55.48 \end{array}$$

The sum of 47.68 and 7.80 is 55.48.

Example 2 Find the difference of 42.17 and 15.85.

Step 1 Line up the decimal places when you write the number.

$$\begin{array}{r} 42.17 \\ -15.85 \end{array}$$

Step 2 Subtract the decimals.

$$\begin{array}{r} 42.17 \\ -15.85 \\ \hline 26.32 \end{array}$$

The difference of 42.17 and 15.85 is 26.32.

Practice Problem Find the sum of 1.245 and 3.842.

Multiply Decimals To multiply decimals, multiply the numbers like any other number, ignoring the decimal point. Count the decimal places in each factor. The product will have the same number of decimal places as the sum of the decimal places in the factors.

Example Multiply 2.4 by 5.9.

Step 1 Multiply the factors like two whole numbers.
$24 \times 59 = 1416$

Step 2 Find the sum of the number of decimal places in the factors. Each factor has one decimal place, for a sum of two decimal places.

Step 3 The product will have two decimal places.
14.16

The product of 2.4 and 5.9 is 14.16.

Practice Problem Multiply 4.6 by 2.2.

Divide Decimals When dividing decimals, change the divisor to a whole number. To do this, multiply both the divisor and the dividend by the same power of ten. Then place the decimal point in the quotient directly above the decimal point in the dividend. Then divide as you do with whole numbers.

Example Divide 8.84 by 3.4.

Step 1 Multiply both factors by 10.
$3.4 \times 10 = 34,\ 8.84 \times 10 = 88.4$

Step 2 Divide 88.4 by 34.

```
     2.6
34)88.4
  -68
   204
  -204
     0
```

8.84 divided by 3.4 is 2.6.

Practice Problem Divide 75.6 by 3.6.

Use Proportions

An equation that shows that two ratios are equivalent is a proportion. The ratios $\frac{2}{4}$ and $\frac{5}{10}$ are equivalent, so they can be written as $\frac{2}{4} = \frac{5}{10}$. This equation is a proportion.

When two ratios form a proportion, the cross products are equal. To find the cross products in the proportion $\frac{2}{4} = \frac{5}{10}$, multiply the 2 and the 10, and the 4 and the 5. Therefore $2 \times 10 = 4 \times 5$, or $20 = 20$.

Because you know that both proportions are equal, you can use cross products to find a missing term in a proportion. This is known as solving the proportion.

Example The heights of a tree and a pole are proportional to the lengths of their shadows. The tree casts a shadow of 24 m when a 6-m pole casts a shadow of 4 m. What is the height of the tree?

Step 1 Write a proportion.
$$\frac{\text{height of tree}}{\text{height of pole}} = \frac{\text{length of tree's shadow}}{\text{length of pole's shadow}}$$

Step 2 Substitute the known values into the proportion. Let h represent the unknown value, the height of the tree.
$$\frac{h}{6} = \frac{24}{4}$$

Step 3 Find the cross products.
$h \times 4 = 6 \times 24$

Step 4 Simplify the equation.
$4h = 144$

Step 5 Divide each side by 4.
$$\frac{4h}{4} = \frac{144}{4}$$
$h = 36$

The height of the tree is 36 m.

Practice Problem The ratios of the weights of two objects on the Moon and on Earth are in proportion. A rock weighing 3 N on the Moon weighs 18 N on Earth. How much would a rock that weighs 5 N on the Moon weigh on Earth?

Multiply Decimals

Multiply 4.6 and 2.2 by 10.

$46 \times 22 = 1012$

Each factor had one decimal place.

10.12

Divide Decimals

Multiply both factors by 10.

Divide 756 by 36.

```
    21
36)756
   72
    36
    36
     0
```

Use Proportions

$$\frac{3}{18} = \frac{5}{w}$$

$w \times 3 = 5 \times 18$

$$\frac{3w}{3} = \frac{90}{3}$$

$w = 30$

Math Skill Handbook

MATH SKILL HANDBOOK 821

Use Percentages

$$\frac{73}{365} = \frac{x}{100}$$

$$\frac{7300}{365} = \frac{365x}{365}$$

$$20\% = x$$

Solve One-Step Equations

$$h = gd$$

$$\frac{17.4}{12.3} = \frac{12.3d}{12.3}$$

$$1.41 = d$$

Use Percentages

The word *percent* means "out of one hundred." It is a ratio that compares a number to 100. Suppose you read that 77 percent of the Earth's surface is covered by water. That is the same as reading that the fraction of the Earth's surface covered by water is $\frac{77}{100}$. To express a fraction as a percent, first find the equivalent decimal for the fraction. Then, multiply the decimal by 100 and add the percent symbol.

Example Express $\frac{13}{20}$ as a percent.

Step 1 Find the equivalent decimal for the fraction.

```
     0.65
20)13.00
   12 0
    1 00
    1 00
       0
```

Step 2 Rewrite the fraction $\frac{13}{20}$ as 0.65.

Step 3 Multiply 0.65 by 100 and add the % sign.

$0.65 \times 100 = 65 = 65\%$

So, $\frac{13}{20} = 65\%$.

This also can be solved as a proportion.

Example Express $\frac{13}{20}$ as a percent.

Step 1 Write a proportion.

$\frac{13}{20} = \frac{x}{100}$

Step 2 Find the cross products.

$1300 = 20x$

Step 3 Divide each side by 20.

$\frac{1300}{20} = \frac{20x}{20}$

$65\% = x$

Practice Problem In one year, 73 of 365 days were rainy in one city. What percent of the days in that city were rainy?

Solve One-Step Equations

A statement that two things are equal is an equation. For example, $A = B$ is an equation that states that A is equal to B.

An equation is solved when a variable is replaced with a value that makes both sides of the equation equal. To make both sides equal the inverse operation is used. Addition and subtraction are inverses, and multiplication and division are inverses.

Example 1 Solve the equation $x - 10 = 35$.

Step 1 Find the solution by adding 10 to each side of the equation.

$x - 10 = 35$

$x - 10 + 10 = 35 + 10$

$x = 45$

Step 2 Check the solution.

$x - 10 = 35$

$45 - 10 = 35$

$35 = 35$

Both sides of the equation are equal, so $x = 45$.

Example 2 In the formula $a = bc$, find the value of c if $a = 20$ and $b = 2$.

Step 1 Rearrange the formula so the unknown value is by itself on one side of the equation by dividing both sides by *b*.

$a = bc$

$\frac{a}{b} = \frac{bc}{b}$

$\frac{a}{b} = c$

Step 2 Replace the variables *a* and *b* with the values that are given.

$\frac{a}{b} = c$

$\frac{20}{2} = c$

$10 = c$

Step 3 Check the solution.

$a = bc$

$20 = 2 \times 10$

$20 = 20$

Both sides of the equation are equal, so $c = 10$ is the solution when $a = 20$ and $b = 2$.

Practice Problem In the formula $h = gd$, find the value of d if $g = 12.3$ and $h = 17.4$.

Use Statistics

The branch of mathematics that deals with collecting, analyzing, and presenting data is statistics. In statistics, there are three common ways to summarize data with a single number—the mean, the median, and the mode.

The **mean** of a set of data is the arithmetic average. It is found by adding the numbers in the data set and dividing by the number of items in the set.

The **median** is the middle number in a set of data when the data are arranged in numerical order. If there were an even number of data points, the median would be the mean of the two middle numbers.

The **mode** of a set of data is the number or item that appears most often.

Another number that often is used to describe a set of data is the range. The **range** is the difference between the largest number and the smallest number in a set of data.

A **frequency table** shows how many times each piece of data occurs, usually in a survey. **Table 2** below shows the results of a student survey on favorite color.

Table 2 Student Color Choice

Color	Tally	Frequency
red	||||	4
blue	~~||||~~	5
black	||	2
green	|||	3
purple	~~||||~~ ||	7
yellow	~~||||~~ |	6

Based on the frequency table data, which color is the favorite?

Example The speeds (in m/s) for a race car during five different time trials are 39, 37, 44, 36, and 44.

To find the mean:

Step 1 Find the sum of the numbers.
$39 + 37 + 44 + 36 + 44 = 200$

Step 2 Divide the sum by the number of items, which is 5.
$200 \div 5 = 40$

The mean is 40 m/s.

To find the median:

Step 1 Arrange the measures from least to greatest.
36, 37, 39, 44, 44

Step 2 Determine the middle measure.
36, 37, <u>39</u>, 44, 44

The median is 39 m/s.

To find the mode:

Step 1 Group the numbers that are the same together.
44, 44, 36, 37, 39

Step 2 Determine the number that occurs most in the set.
<u>44, 44</u>, 36, 37, 39

The mode is 44 m/s.

To find the range:

Step 1 Arrange the measures from largest to smallest.
44, 44, 39, 37, 36

Step 2 Determine the largest and smallest measures in the set.
<u>44</u>, 44, 39, 37, <u>36</u>

Step 3 Find the difference between the largest and smallest measures.
$44 - 36 = 8$

The range is 8 m/s.

Practice Problem Find the mean, median, mode, and range for the data set 8, 4, 12, 8, 11, 14, 16.

Use Statistics

mean
$8 + 4 + 12 + 8 + 11 + 14 + 16 = 73$
$73 \div 7 = 10.4$

median
4, 8, 8, <u>11</u>, 12, 14, 16

mode
4, <u>8</u>, <u>8</u>, 11, 12, 14, 16

range
<u>4</u>, 8, 8, 11, 12, 14, <u>16</u>
$16 - 4 = 12$

Perimeter

Problem 1

$P = 2(18 \text{ m} + 7 \text{ m})$

$P = 2(25 \text{ m})$

$P = 50 \text{ m}$

Problem 2

$P = 1.6 \text{ cm} + 2.4 \text{ cm} + 2.4 \text{ cm}$

$P = 6.4 \text{ cm}$

Area of a Rectangle

$A = (4 \text{ m} \times 4 \text{ m})$

$A = 16 \text{ m}^2$

Area of a Triangle

$A = \frac{1}{2}(27 \text{ cm} \times 17 \text{ cm})$

$A = \frac{1}{2}(459 \text{ cm}^2)$

$A = 229.5 \text{ cm}^2$

Math Skill Handbook

Use Geometry

The branch of mathematics that deals with the measurement, properties, and relationships of points, lines, angles, surfaces, and solids is called geometry.

Perimeter The **perimeter** (P) is the distance around a geometric figure. To find the perimeter of a rectangle, add the length and width and multiply that sum by two, or $2(l + w)$. To find perimeters of irregular figures, add the length of the sides.

Example 1 Find the perimeter of a rectangle that is 3 m long and 5 m wide.

Step 1 You know that the perimeter is 2 times the sum of the width and length.

$P = 2(3 \text{ m} + 5 \text{ m})$

Step 2 Find the sum of the width and length.

$P = 2(8 \text{ m})$

Step 3 Multiply by 2.

$P = 16 \text{ m}$

The perimeter is 16 m.

Example 2 Find the perimeter of a shape with sides measuring 2 cm, 5 cm, 6 cm, 3 cm.

Step 1 You know that the perimeter is the sum of all the sides.

$P = 2 + 5 + 6 + 3$

Step 2 Find the sum of the sides.

$P = 2 + 5 + 6 + 3$

$P = 16$

The perimeter is 16 cm.

Practice Problem Find the perimeter of a rectangle with a length of 18 m and a width of 7 m.

Practice Problem Find the perimeter of a triangle measuring 1.6 cm by 2.4 cm by 2.4 cm.

Area of a Rectangle The **area** (A) is the number of square units needed to cover a surface. To find the area of a rectangle, multiply the length times the width, or $l \times w$. When finding area, the units also are multiplied. Area is given in square units.

Example Find the area of a rectangle with a length of 1 cm and a width of 10 cm.

Step 1 You know that the area is the length multiplied by the width.

$A = (1 \text{ cm} \times 10 \text{ cm})$

Step 2 Multiply the length by the width. Also multiply the units.

$A = 10 \text{ cm}^2$

The area is 10 cm^2.

Practice Problem Find the area of a square whose sides measure 4 m.

Area of a Triangle To find the area of a triangle, use the formula:

$$A = \frac{1}{2}(\text{base} \times \text{height})$$

The base of a triangle can be any of its sides. The height is the perpendicular distance from a base to the opposite endpoint, or vertex.

Example Find the area of a triangle with a base of 18 m and a height of 7 m.

Step 1 You know that the area is $\frac{1}{2}$ the base times the height.

$A = \frac{1}{2}(18 \text{ m} \times 7 \text{ m})$

Step 2 Multiply $\frac{1}{2}$ by the product of 18×7. Multiply the units.

$A = \frac{1}{2}(126 \text{ m}^2)$

$A = 63 \text{ m}^2$

The area is 63 m^2.

Practice Problem Find the area of a triangle with a base of 27 cm and a height of 17 cm.

Circumference of a Circle The **diameter** (d) of a circle is the distance across the circle through its center, and the **radius** (r) is the distance from the center to any point on the circle. The radius is half of the diameter. The distance around the circle is called the **circumference** (C). The formula for finding the circumference is:

$$C = 2\pi r \text{ or } C = \pi d$$

The circumference divided by the diameter is always equal to 3.1415926... This nonterminating and nonrepeating number is represented by the Greek letter π (pi). An approximation often used for π is 3.14.

Example 1 Find the circumference of a circle with a radius of 3 m.

Step 1 You know the formula for the circumference is 2 times the radius times π.
$C = 2\pi(3)$

Step 2 Multiply 2 times the radius.
$C = 6\pi$

Step 3 Multiply by π.
$C = 19$ m

The circumference is 19 m.

Example 2 Find the circumference of a circle with a diameter of 24.0 cm.

Step 1 You know the formula for the circumference is the diameter times π.
$C = \pi(24.0)$

Step 2 Multiply the diameter by π.
$C = 75.4$ cm

The circumference is 75.4 cm.

Practice Problem Find the circumference of a circle with a radius of 19 cm.

Area of a Circle The formula for the area of a circle is:
$A = \pi r^2$

Example 1 Find the area of a circle with a radius of 4.0 cm.

Step 1 $A = \pi(4.0)^2$

Step 2 Find the square of the radius.
$A = 16\pi$

Step 3 Multiply the square of the radius by π.
$A = 50 \text{ cm}^2$

The area of the circle is 50 cm^2.

Example 2 Find the area of a circle with a radius of 225 m.

Step 1 $A = \pi(225)^2$

Step 2 Find the square of the radius.
$A = 50625\pi$

Step 3 Multiply the square of the radius by π.
$A = 158962.5$

The area of the circle is $158{,}962 \text{ m}^2$.

Example 3 Find the area of a circle whose diameter is 20.0 mm.

Step 1 You know the formula for the area of a circle is the square of the radius times π, and that the radius is half of the diameter.
$A = \pi\left(\frac{20.0}{2}\right)^2$

Step 2 Find the radius.
$A = \pi(10.0)^2$

Step 3 Find the square of the radius.
$A = 100\pi$

Step 4 Multiply the square of the radius by π.
$A = 314 \text{ mm}^2$

The area is 314 mm^2.

Practice Problem Find the area of a circle with a radius of 16 m.

Circumference of a Circle

$C = 2\pi r$

$C = 2\pi(19)$

$C = 38\pi$

$C = 119.3$

Area of a Circle

$A = \pi r^2$

$A = \pi(16 \text{ m})^2$

$A = \pi\, 256 \text{ m}^2$

$A = 803.8 \text{ m}^2$

Math Skill Handbook

MATH SKILL HANDBOOK 825

Volume

Problem 1

$V = 8\text{ m} \times 4\text{ m} \times 4\text{ m}$

$V = 128\text{ m}^3$

Problem 2

$V = \pi r^2 \times \text{height}$

$V = \left[\pi\left(\frac{1}{2} \times 7\right)^2\right] \times 16$

$V = [\pi(3.5)^2] \times 16$

$V = [\pi(12.25)] \times 16$

$V = 38.46 \times 16$

$V = 615.36$

Volume The measure of space occupied by a solid is the **volume** (V). To find the volume of a rectangular solid multiply the length times width times height, or $V = l \times w \times h$. It is measured in cubic units, such as cubic centimeters (cm^3).

Example Find the volume of a rectangular solid with a length of 2.0 m, a width of 4.0 m, and a height of 3.0 m.

Step 1 You know the formula for volume is the length times the width times the height.

$V = 2.0\text{ m} \times 4.0\text{ m} \times 3.0\text{ m}$

Step 2 Multiply the length times the width times the height.

$V = 24\text{ m}^3$

The volume is 24 m^3.

Practice Problem Find the volume of a rectangular solid that is 8 m long, 4 m wide, and 4 m high.

To find the volume of other solids, multiply the area of the base times the height.

Example 1 Find the volume of a solid that has a triangular base with a length of 8.0 m and a height of 7.0 m. The height of the entire solid is 15.0 m.

Step 1 You know that the base is a triangle, and the area of a triangle is $\frac{1}{2}$ the base times the height, and the volume is the area of the base times the height.

$V = \left[\frac{1}{2}(b \times h)\right] \times 15$

Step 2 Find the area of the base.

$V = \left[\frac{1}{2}(8 \times 7)\right] \times 15$

$V = \left(\frac{1}{2} \times 56\right) \times 15$

Step 3 Multiply the area of the base by the height of the solid.

$V = 28 \times 15$

$V = 420\text{ m}^3$

The volume is 420 m^3.

Example 2 Find the volume of a cylinder that has a base with a radius of 12.0 cm, and a height of 21.0 cm.

Step 1 You know that the base is a circle, and the area of a circle is the square of the radius times π, and the volume is the area of the base times the height.

$V = (\pi r^2) \times 21$

$V = (\pi 12^2) \times 21$

Step 2 Find the area of the base.

$V = 144\pi \times 21$

$V = 452 \times 21$

Step 3 Multiply the area of the base by the height of the solid.

$V = 9490\text{ cm}^3$

The volume is 9490 cm^3.

Example 3 Find the volume of a cylinder that has a diameter of 15 mm and a height of 4.8 mm.

Step 1 You know that the base is a circle with an area equal to the square of the radius times π. The radius is one-half the diameter. The volume is the area of the base times the height.

$V = (\pi r^2) \times 4.8$

$V = \left[\pi\left(\frac{1}{2} \times 15\right)^2\right] \times 4.8$

$V = (\pi 7.5^2) \times 4.8$

Step 2 Find the area of the base.

$V = 56.25\pi \times 4.8$

$V = 176.63 \times 4.8$

Step 3 Multiply the area of the base by the height of the solid.

$V = 847.8$

The volume is 847.8 mm^3.

Practice Problem Find the volume of a cylinder with a diameter of 7 cm in the base and a height of 16 cm.

Science Applications

Measure in SI

The metric system of measurement was developed in 1795. A modern form of the metric system, called the International System (SI), was adopted in 1960 and provides the standard measurements that all scientists around the world can understand.

The SI system is convenient because unit sizes vary by powers of 10. Prefixes are used to name units. Look at **Table 3** for some common SI prefixes and their meanings.

Table 3 Common SI Prefixes

Prefix	Symbol	Meaning	
kilo-	k	1,000	thousand
hecto-	h	100	hundred
deka-	da	10	ten
deci-	d	0.1	tenth
centi-	c	0.01	hundredth
milli-	m	0.001	thousandth

Example How many grams equal one kilogram?

Step 1 Find the prefix *kilo* in **Table 3.**

Step 2 Using **Table 3,** determine the meaning of *kilo.* According to the table, it means 1,000. When the prefix *kilo* is added to a unit, it means that there are 1,000 of the units in a "*kilo*unit."

Step 3 Apply the prefix to the units in the question. The units in the question are grams. There are 1,000 grams in a kilogram.

Practice Problem Is a milligram larger or smaller than a gram? How many of the smaller units equal one larger unit? What fraction of the larger unit does one smaller unit represent?

Dimensional Analysis

Convert SI Units In science, quantities such as length, mass, and time sometimes are measured using different units. A process called dimensional analysis can be used to change one unit of measure to another. This process involves multiplying your starting quantity and units by one or more conversion factors. A conversion factor is a ratio equal to one and can be made from any two equal quantities with different units. If 1,000 mL equal 1 L then two ratios can be made.

$$\frac{1{,}000 \text{ mL}}{1 \text{ L}} = \frac{1 \text{ L}}{1{,}000 \text{ mL}} = 1$$

One can covert between units in the SI system by using the equivalents in **Table 3** to make conversion factors.

Example 1 How many cm are in 4 m?

Step 1 Write conversion factors for the units given. From **Table 3,** you know that 100 cm = 1 m. The conversion factors are

$$\frac{100 \text{ cm}}{1 \text{ m}} \text{ and } \frac{1 \text{ m}}{100 \text{ cm}}$$

Step 2 Decide which conversion factor to use. Select the factor that has the units you are converting from (m) in the denominator and the units you are converting to (cm) in the numerator.

$$\frac{100 \text{ cm}}{1 \text{ m}}$$

Step 3 Multiply the starting quantity and units by the conversion factor. Cancel the starting units with the units in the denominator. There are 400 cm in 4 m.

$$4 \cancel{\text{m}} \times \frac{100 \text{ cm}}{1 \cancel{\text{m}}} = 400 \text{ cm}$$

Practice Problem How many milligrams are in one kilogram? (Hint: You will need to use two conversion factors from **Table 3.**)

Math Skill Handbook

Measure in SI

smaller; 1000; one thousandth

Dimensional Analysis

$$x \text{ mg} = 1 \cancel{\text{kg}} \times \frac{1000 \cancel{\text{g}}}{1 \cancel{\text{kg}}} \times \frac{1000 \text{ mg}}{1 \cancel{\text{g}}} =$$

1,000,000 mg

1,000,000 mg = 1 kg

Math Skill Handbook

MATH SKILL HANDBOOK 827

Convert Between Unit Systems

$$\frac{(1\ \text{in})^3}{(2.54\ \text{cm})^3} = \frac{1\ \text{in} \times 1\ \text{in} \times 1\ \text{in}}{2.54\ \text{cm} \times 2.54\ \text{cm} \times 2.54\ \text{cm}} = \frac{1\ \text{in}^3}{16.39\ \text{cm}^3}$$

Table 4 Unit System Equivalents

Type of Measurement	Equivalent
Length	1 in = 2.54 cm 1 yd = 0.91 m 1 mi = 1.61 km
Mass and Weight*	1 oz = 28.35 g 1 lb = 0.45 kg 1 ton (short) = 0.91 tonnes (metric tons) 1 lb = 4.45 N
Volume	1 in^3 = 16.39 cm^3 1 qt = 0.95 L 1 gal = 3.78 L
Area	1 in^2 = 6.45 cm^2 1 yd^2 = 0.83 m^2 1 mi^2 = 2.59 km^2 1 acre = 0.40 hectares
Temperature	$°C = \frac{(°F - 32)}{1.8}$ K = °C + 273

*Weight is measured in standard Earth gravity.

Convert Between Unit Systems **Table 4** gives a list of equivalents that can be used to convert between English and SI units.

Example If a meterstick has a length of 100 cm, how long is the meterstick in inches?

Step 1 Write the conversion factors for the units given. From **Table 4,** 1 in = 2.54 cm.

$$\frac{1\ \text{in}}{2.54\ \text{cm}} \quad \textit{and} \quad \frac{2.54\ \text{cm}}{1\ \text{in}}$$

Step 2 Determine which conversion factor to use. You are converting from cm to in. Use the conversion factor with cm on the bottom.

$$\frac{1\ \text{in}}{2.54\ \text{cm}}$$

Step 3 Multiply the starting quantity and units by the conversion factor. Cancel the starting units with the units in the denominator. Round your answer based on the number of significant figures in the conversion factor.

$$100\ \cancel{\text{cm}} \times \frac{1\ \text{in}}{2.54\ \cancel{\text{cm}}} = 39.37\ \text{in}$$

The meterstick is 39.4 in long.

Practice Problem A book has a mass of 5 lbs. What is the mass of the book in kg?

Practice Problem Use the equivalent for in and cm (1 in = 2.54 cm) to show how 1 in^3 = 16.39 cm^3.

Math Skill Handbook

Math Skill Handbook

Precision and Significant Digits

When you make a measurement, the value you record depends on the precision of the measuring instrument. This precision is represented by the number of significant digits recorded in the measurement. When counting the number of significant digits, all digits are counted except zeros at the end of a number with no decimal point such as 2,050, and zeros at the beginning of a decimal such as 0.03020. When adding or subtracting numbers with different precision, round the answer to the smallest number of decimal places of any number in the sum or difference. When multiplying or dividing, the answer is rounded to the smallest number of significant digits of any number being multiplied or divided.

Example The lengths 5.28 and 5.2 are measured in meters. Find the sum of these lengths and record your answer using the correct number of significant digits.

Step 1 Find the sum.

5.28 m	2 digits after the decimal
+ 5.2 m	1 digit after the decimal
10.48 m	

Step 2 Round to one digit after the decimal because the least number of digits after the decimal of the numbers being added is 1.

The sum is 10.5 m.

Practice Problem How many significant digits are in the measurement 7,071,301 m? How many significant digits are in the measurement 0.003010 g?

Practice Problem Multiply 5.28 and 5.2 using the rule for multiplying and dividing. Record the answer using the correct number of significant digits.

Scientific Notation

Many times numbers used in science are very small or very large. Because these numbers are difficult to work with scientists use scientific notation. To write numbers in scientific notation, move the decimal point until only one non-zero digit remains on the left. Then count the number of places you moved the decimal point and use that number as a power of ten. For example, the average distance from the Sun to Mars is 227,800,000,000 m. In scientific notation, this distance is 2.278×10^{11} m. Because you moved the decimal point to the left, the number is a positive power of ten.

The mass of an electron is about 0.000 000 000 000 000 000 000 000 000 000 911 kg. Expressed in scientific notation, this mass is 9.11×10^{-31} kg. Because the decimal point was moved to the right, the number is a negative power of ten.

Example Earth is 149,600,000 km from the Sun. Express this in scientific notation.

Step 1 Move the decimal point until one non-zero digit remains on the left.
1.496 000 00

Step 2 Count the number of decimal places you have moved. In this case, eight.

Step 3 Show that number as a power of ten, 10^8.

The Earth is 1.496×10^8 km from the Sun.

Practice Problem How many significant digits are in 149,600,000 km? How many significant digits are in 1.496×10^8 km?

Practice Problem Parts used in a high performance car must be measured to 7×10^{-6} m. Express this number as a decimal.

Practice Problem A CD is spinning at 539 revolutions per minute. Express this number in scientific notation.

Precision and Significant Digits

Problem 1
7; 4

Problem 2
$5.28 \times 5.2 = 27.456$

5.28 has 3 significant digits.

5.2 has 2 significant digits.

When multiplying and dividing, the answer is rounded to the smallest number of significant digits of the numbers being multiplied or divided—in this case, 2.

27.456 is rounded to 27.

Scientific Notation

Problem 1
4; 4

Problem 2
0.000007

Problem 3
5.39×10^2

Math Skill Handbook

MATH SKILL HANDBOOK 829

Line Graph

x	y
3	52
6	72
9	83
12	86

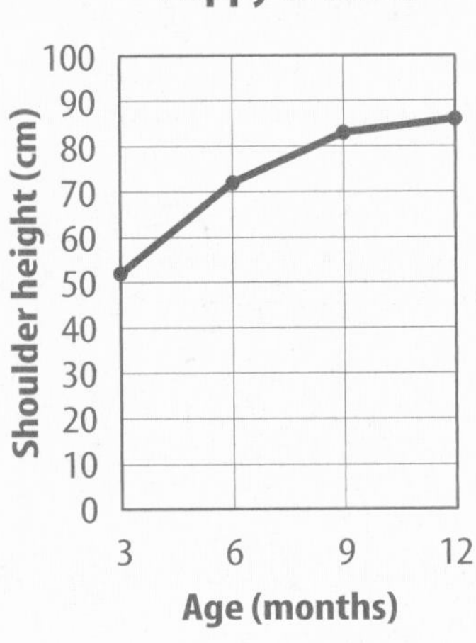

Make and Use Graphs

Data in tables can be displayed in a graph—a visual representation of data. Common graph types include line graphs, bar graphs, and circle graphs.

Line Graph A line graph shows a relationship between two variables that change continuously. The independent variable is changed and is plotted on the x-axis. The dependent variable is observed, and is plotted on the y-axis.

Example Draw a line graph of the data below from a cyclist in a long-distance race.

Table 5 Bicycle Race Data

Time (h)	Distance (km)
0	0
1	8
2	16
3	24
4	32
5	40

Step 1 Determine the x-axis and y-axis variables. Time varies independently of distance and is plotted on the x-axis. Distance is dependent on time and is plotted on the y-axis.

Step 2 Determine the scale of each axis. The x-axis data ranges from 0 to 5. The y-axis data ranges from 0 to 40.

Step 3 Using graph paper, draw and label the axes. Include units in the labels.

Step 4 Draw a point at the intersection of the time value on the x-axis and corresponding distance value on the y-axis. Connect the points and label the graph with a title, as shown in **Figure 20.**

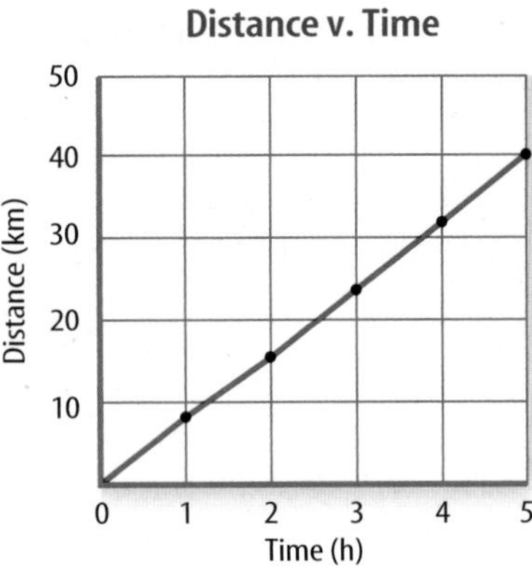

Figure 20 This line graph shows the relationship between distance and time during a bicycle ride.

Practice Problem A puppy's shoulder height is measured during the first year of her life. The following measurements were collected: (3 mo, 52 cm), (6 mo, 72 cm), (9 mo, 83 cm), (12 mo, 86 cm). Graph this data.

Find a Slope The slope of a straight line is the ratio of the vertical change, rise, to the horizontal change, run.

$$\text{Slope} = \frac{\text{vertical change (rise)}}{\text{horizontal change (run)}} = \frac{\text{change in } y}{\text{change in } x}$$

Example Find the slope of the graph in **Figure 20.**

Step 1 You know that the slope is the change in y divided by the change in x.

$$\text{Slope} = \frac{\text{change in } y}{\text{change in } x}$$

Step 2 Determine the data points you will be using. For a straight line, choose the two sets of points that are the farthest apart.

$$\text{Slope} = \frac{(40-0)\text{ km}}{(5-0)\text{ hr}}$$

Step 3 Find the change in y and x.

$$\text{Slope} = \frac{40\text{ km}}{5\text{h}}$$

Step 4 Divide the change in y by the change in x.

$$\text{Slope} = \frac{8\text{ km}}{\text{h}}$$

The slope of the graph is 8 km/h.

Bar Graph To compare data that does not change continuously you might choose a bar graph. A bar graph uses bars to show the relationships between variables. The *x*-axis variable is divided into parts. The parts can be numbers such as years, or a category such as a type of animal. The *y*-axis is a number and increases continuously along the axis.

Example A recycling center collects 4.0 kg of aluminum on Monday, 1.0 kg on Wednesday, and 2.0 kg on Friday. Create a bar graph of this data.

Step 1 Select the *x*-axis and *y*-axis variables. The measured numbers (the masses of aluminum) should be placed on the *y*-axis. The variable divided into parts (collection days) is placed on the *x*-axis.

Step 2 Create a graph grid like you would for a line graph. Include labels and units.

Step 3 For each measured number, draw a vertical bar above the *x*-axis value up to the *y*-axis value. For the first data point, draw a vertical bar above Monday up to 4.0 kg.

Aluminum Collected During Week

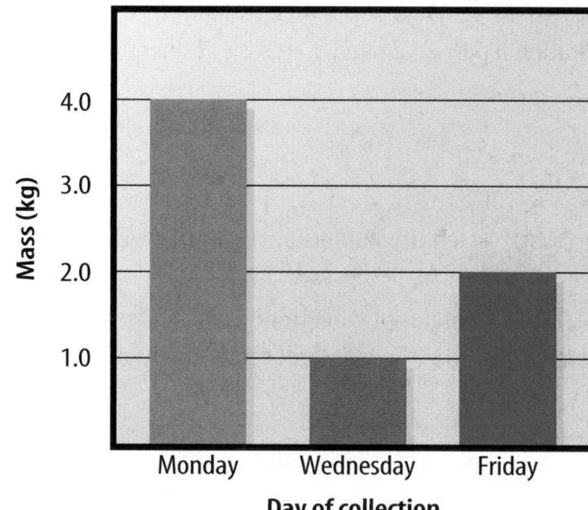

Practice Problem Draw a bar graph of the gases in air: 78% nitrogen, 21% oxygen, 1% other gases.

Circle Graph To display data as parts of a whole, you might use a circle graph. A circle graph is a circle divided into sections that represent the relative size of each piece of data. The entire circle represents 100%, half represents 50%, and so on.

Example Air is made up of 78% nitrogen, 21% oxygen, and 1% other gases. Display the composition of air in a circle graph.

Step 1 Multiply each percent by 360° and divide by 100 to find the angle of each section in the circle.

$$78\% \times \frac{360°}{100} = 280.8°$$

$$21\% \times \frac{360°}{100} = 75.6°$$

$$1\% \times \frac{360°}{100} = 3.6°$$

Step 2 Use a compass to draw a circle and to mark the center of the circle. Draw a straight line from the center to the edge of the circle.

Step 3 Use a protractor and the angles you calculated to divide the circle into parts. Place the center of the protractor over the center of the circle and line the base of the protractor over the straight line.

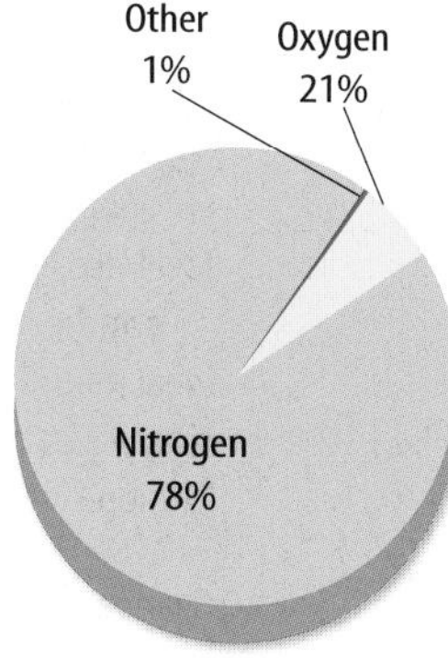

Practice Problem Draw a circle graph to represent the amount of aluminum collected during the week shown in the bar graph to the left.

Math Skill Handbook

Bar Graph

Composition of Air

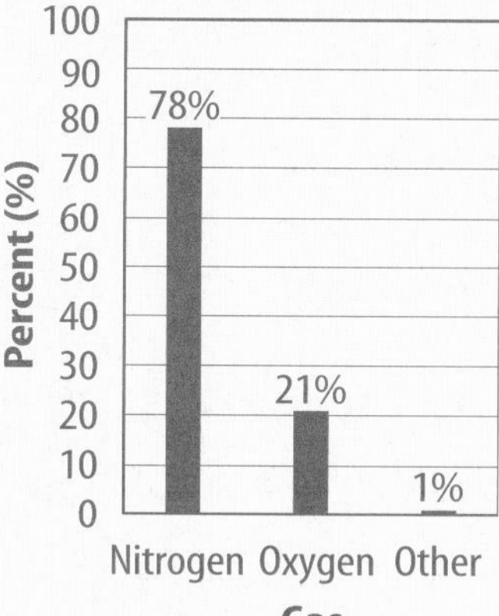

Circle Graph

The total amount of aluminum collected is:

$4.0\text{ kg} + 1.0\text{ kg} + 2.0\text{ kg} = 7.0\text{ kg}$

$\frac{4.0\text{ kg}}{7.0\text{ kg}} = \frac{x}{360°};\ x = 206°$

$\frac{1.0\text{ kg}}{7.0\text{ kg}} = \frac{x}{360°};\ x = 51°$

$\frac{2.0\text{ kg}}{7.0\text{ kg}} = \frac{x}{360°};\ x = 103°$

Math Skill Handbook

MATH SKILL HANDBOOK 831

Formulas

Chapter 1
The Nature of Science

Density = mass/volume
Kelvin = °Celsius + 273
% Error = [(Accepted value − Experimental value)/Accepted value] × 100

Chapter 2
Motion

Speed = distance/time
Acceleration = change in velocity/time
Change in velocity = final velocity − initial velocity

Chapter 3
Forces

Acceleration = net force/mass
Force = mass × acceleration
Gravitational force = mass × (acceleration due to gravity)
Weight = mass × 9.8 m/s^2
Momentum (p) = mass × velocity
Force = $(mv_f - mv_i)$/time
change in displacement = initial velocity (change in time) + $\frac{1}{2}$ acceleration(change in time)^2
average velocity = change in displacement/change in time = (final velocity + initial velocity)/2
average acceleration = change in velocity/change in time

Chapter 4
Energy

Kinetic energy = $\frac{1}{2}$ mass × (velocity)^2
Gravitational potential energy (GPE) = mass × 9.8 m/s^2 × height
Mechanical energy = gravitational potential energy + kinetic energy

Chapter 5
Work and Machines

Work = force × distance
Power = work/time
Efficiency = $(work_{out}/work_{in})$ × 100%
Ideal mechanical advantage (IMA) = length of effort arm/length of resistance arm = L_e/L_r
Ideal mechanical advantage (IMA) = radius of wheel/radius of axle = r_w/r_a
IMA = effort distance/resistance distance = length of slope/height of slope = l/h

Chapter 6
Thermal Energy

Change in thermal energy = mass × change in temperature × specific heat
or
$Q = m \times (T_{final} - T_{initial}) \times C_p$
Q = mass × heat of fusion = mH_f
Q = mass × heat of vaporization = mH_v

Math Skill Handbook

Math Skill Handbook

Chapter 7
Electricity

Electric current = voltage difference/resistance or $I = V/R$
Electric power = current × voltage difference or $P = I \times V$
Electric energy = power × time or $E = P \times t$

Series Circuits

$I_t = I_1 = I_2 = I_3 = \ldots$
$V_t = V_1 + V_2 + V_3 + \ldots$
$R_t = R_1 + R_2 + R_3 + \ldots$

Parallel Circuits

$I_t = I_1 + I_2 + I_3 + \ldots$
$V_t = V_1 = V_2 = V_3 = \ldots$
$1/R_t = 1/R_1 + 1/R_2 + 1/R_3 + \ldots$

Chapter 10
Waves

Wave velocity = wavelength × frequency or $v_w = \lambda \times f$

Chapter 13
Light

Index of refraction =
speed of light in a vacuum/speed of light in a substance or $n = c/v$

Chapter 16
Solids, Liquids, and Gases

Pressure = force/area or $P = F/A$
Boyle's law $P_1 \times V_1 = P_2 \times V_2$
Charles's law $V_1/T_1 = V_2/T_2$

Chapter 22
Solutions

Surface area of a rectangular solid = $2(h \times w) + 2(h \times l) + 2(w \times l)$

Math Skill Handbook

MATH SKILL HANDBOOK 833

Answers

Chapter 1

1. 400 cm
2. 5 dL
3. 2.54 L
4. 40,000 g
5. 42.7 kg
6. 0.002 m^3
7. 5,760 s
8. −270°C
9. 25 s
10. 3%

Chapter 2

11. 3.7 km
12. 2.5 m
13. 15 cm/s
14. 84.6 km/h
15. 100 km/h
16. 3 m/s
17. 0.5 m/s^2
18. −0.3 m/s^2
19. 300 N
20. 3,000 N toward team B
21. 4 h
22. 7.92 h
23. 2.5 m/s^2
24. −5 m/s^2

Chapter 3

25. 467.5 N
26. 20 m/s^2

Extra Math Problems

EXTRA Math Problems

For help and hints with these problems, visit gpscience.com/extra_problems.

Chapter 1 The Nature of Science

1. How many centimeters are in four meters?
2. How many deciliters are in 500 mL?
3. How many liters are in 2540 cm^3?
4. A young child has a mass of 40 kg. What is the mass of the child in grams?
5. Iron has a density of 7.9 g/cm^3. What is the mass in kg of an iron statue that has a volume of 5.4 L?
6. A 2-L bottle of soda has a volume of 2000 cm^3. What is the volume of the bottle in cubic meters?
7. A big summer movie has a running time of 96 minutes. What is the movie's running time in seconds?
8. The temperature in space is approximately 3 K. What is this temperature in degrees Celsius?
9. The *x*-axis of a certain graph is distance traveled in meters and the *y*-axis is time in seconds. Two points are plotted on this graph with coordinates (2, 43) and (5, 68). What is the elapsed time between the two points?
10. A circle graph has labeled segments of: 57%, 21%, 13%, and 6%. What percentage does the unlabeled segment have?

Chapter 2 Motion

11. John rides his bike 2.3 km to school. After school, he rides an additional 1.4 km to the mall in the opposite direction. What is his total distance traveled?
12. A squirrel runs 4.8 m across a lawn, stops, then runs 2.3 m back in the opposite direction. What is the squirrel's displacement from its starting point?
13. An ant travels 75 cm in 5 s. What was the ant's speed?
14. It took you 6.5 h to drive 550 km. What was your speed?
15. A bus leaves at 9 A.M. with a group of tourists. They travel 350 km before they stop for lunch. Then they travel an additional 250 km until the end of their trip at 3 P.M. What was the average speed of the bus?
16. Halfway through a cross-country meet, a runner's speed is 4 m/s. In the last stretch, she increases her speed to 7 m/s. What is her change in speed?
17. It takes a car one minute to go from rest to 30 m/s. What is the acceleration of this car?
18. You are running at a speed of 10 km/h and hit a patch of mud. Two seconds later your speed is 8 km/h. What is your acceleration in units of m/s^2?
19. A weight lifter is trying to lift a 1500-N weight but can apply a force of only 1200 N on the weight. One of his friends helps him lift it all the way. What force was applied to the weight by the weight lifter's friend?
20. During a tug-of-war, Team A is applying a force of 5000 N while Team B is applying a force of 8000 N. What is the net force applied to the rope?
21. You are in a car traveling an average speed of 60 km/h. The total trip is 240 km. How long does the trip take?
22. You are riding in a train that is traveling at a speed of 120 km/h. How long will it take to travel 950 km?
23. A car goes from rest to a speed of 90 km/h in 10 s. What is the car's acceleration in m/s^2?
24. A cart rolling at a speed of 10 m/s comes to a stop in 2 s. What is the cart's acceleration?

Chapter 3 Forces

25. A 85-kg mass has an acceleration of 5.5 m/s^2. What is the net force applied?
26. A 3200-N force is applied to a 160-kg mass. What is the acceleration of the mass?

834 STUDENT RESOURCES

27. If you are pushing on a box with a force of 20 N and there is a force of 7 N on the box due to sliding friction, what is the net force on the box?
28. A 2-kg object is dropped from a height of 1000 m. What is the force of air resistance on the object when it reaches terminal velocity?
29. How much force is needed to lift a 25-kg mass?
30. A person is on an elevator that moves downward with an acceleration of 1.8 m/s^2. If the person weighs 686 N, what is the net force on the person?
31. The acceleration due to gravity on the moon is about 1.6 m/s^2. If you weigh 539 N on Earth, how much would you weigh on the moon?
32. If a 5000-kg mass is moving at a speed of 43 m/s, what is its momentum?
33. How fast must a 50-kg mass travel to have a momentum of 1500 kg m/s?
34. What is the net force on a 4000-kg car that doubles its speed from 15 m/s to 30 m/s over 10 seconds?
35. A book with a mass of 1 kg is sliding on a table. If the frictional force on the book is 5 N, calculate the book's acceleration. Is it speeding up or slowing down?
36. What is the weight of a person with a mass of 80 kg?
37. A car with a mass of 1,200 kg has a speed of 30 m/s. What is the car's momentum?

Chapter 4 Energy

38. What is the kinetic energy of a 5-kg object moving at 7 m/s?
39. An object has kinetic energy of 600 J and a speed of 10 m/s. What is its mass?
40. If you throw a 0.4-kg ball at a speed of 20 m/s, what is the ball's kinetic energy?
41. A rollercoaster car moving around a high turn has 100,000 J of GPE and 23,000 J of KE. What is its mechanical energy?
42. If you have a mass of 80 kg and you are standing on a platform 3 m above the ground, what is your gravitational potential energy?
43. A 2-kg book is moved from a shelf that is 2 m off the ground to a shelf that is 1.5 m off the ground. What is its change in GPE?
44. A car is traveling at 30 m/s with a kinetic energy of 900 kJ. What is its mass?
45. At top of a hill, a rollercoaster has 67,500 J of kinetic energy and 290,000 J of potential energy. Gradually the roller coaster comes to a stop due to friction. If the roller coaster has 30,000 J of potential when it stops, how much heat energy is generated by friction from the top of the hill until it stops?
46. A system has a total mechanical energy of 350 J and kinetic energy of 220 J. What is its potential energy?
47. An object held in the air has a GPE of 470 J. The object then is dropped. Halfway down, what is the object's kinetic energy?
48. A car with a mass of 900 kg is traveling at a speed of 25 m/s. What is the kinetic energy of the car in joules?
49. What is the gravitational potential energy of a diver with a mass of 60 kg who is 10 m above the water?
50. If your weight is 500 N, and you are standing on a floor that is 20 m above the ground, what is your gravitational potential energy?

Chapter 5 Work and Machines

51. When moving a couch, you exert a force of 400 N and push it 4 m. How much work have you done?
52. How much work is needed to lift a 50-kg weight to a shelf 3 m above the floor?
53. By applying a force of 50 N, a pulley system can lift a box with a mass of 20 kg. What is the mechanical advantage of the pulley system?
54. How much energy do you save per hour if you replace a 60-watt lightbulb with a 55-watt lightbulb?
55. Suppose you supply energy to a machine at a rate of 700 W and that the machine converts 560 J into heat every second. At what rate does the machine do work?

Answers

Chapter 3 cont.

27. 140 N
28. 19.6 N
29. 245 N
30. 126 N
31. 114 N
32. 215,000 kg·m/s
33. 30 m/s
34. 6,000 N
35. 5 m/s^2
36. 784 N
37. 36,000 kg·m/s

Chapter 4

38. 122.5 J
39. 12 kg
40. 80 J
41. 123,000 J
42. 2,350 J
43. 9.8 J
44. 2,000 kg
45. 327,000 J
46. 130 J
47. 235 J
48. 281,000 J
49. 5,880 J
50. 10,000 J

Chapter 5

51. 1,600 J
52. 120 J
53. 3.92
54. 18,000 J
55. 140 W

EXTRA MATH PROBLEMS 835

Answers

Chapter 5 cont.

56. 1,120 N
57. 25%
58. 1.33
59. 8.75
60. 3.0 m
61. 32 W
62. 81.7%
63. 196 N

Chapter 6

64. 20,920 J
65. 2 kg
66. 13,280 J
67. 418,400 J
68. 6 kg
69. 343 K
70. 710 J/(kg K)
71. 198 K
72. 1,300 J
73. 2,967 J/(kg K)
74. 20,900 J
75. 397 J/(kg K)

Chapter 7

76. 5.6 V
77. 3 A
78. 2 Ω
79. 360 W
80. 5.8 A
81. 220 V
82. 330 kWh

Extra Math Problems

56. You exert a force of 200 N on a machine over a distance of 0.3 m. If the machine moves an object a distance of 0.5 m, how much force does the machine exert on the object? Assume friction can be ignored.
57. What is the efficiency of a machine if you do work on the machine at a rate of 1200 W and the machine does work at a rate of 300 W?
58. What is the IMA of a seesaw with a 1.6-m effort arm and a 1.2-m resistance arm?
59. What is the IMA of a wheel with a radius of 0.35 m and an axle radius of 0.04 m?
60. An inclined plane has an IMA of 1.5 and a height of 2.0 m. How long is this inclined plane?
61. What power is used by a machine to perform 800 J of work in 25 s?
62. A person pushes a box up a ramp that is 3 m long, and 1 m high. If the box has a mass of 20 kg, and the person pushes with a force of 80 N, what is the efficiency of the ramp?
63. A first class lever has a mechanical advantage of 5. How large would a force need to be to lift a rock with a mass of 100 kg?

Chapter 6 Thermal Energy

64. Water has a specific heat of 4184 J/(kg K). How much energy is needed to increase the temperature of a kilogram of water 5°C?
65. The temperature of a block of iron, which has a specific heat of 450 J/(kg K), increases by 3 K when 2700 J of energy are added to it. What is the mass of this block of iron?
66. How much energy is needed to heat 1 kg of sand, which has a specific heat of 664 J/(kg K), from 30°C to 50°C?
67. 1 kg of water (specific heat = 4184 J/(kg K)) is heated from freezing (0°C) to boiling (100°C). What is the change in thermal energy?
68. A concrete statue (specific heat = 600 J/(kg K)) sits in sunlight and warms up to 40°C. Overnight, it cools to 15°C and loses 90,000 J of thermal energy. What is its mass?
69. A glass of water has temperature of 70°C. What is its temperature in K?
70. A substance with a mass of 10 kg loses 106.5 kJ of heat when its temperature drops 15°C. What is this substance's specific heat?
71. Air is cooled from room temperature (25°C) to 100 K. What is the temperature change in K?
72. To remove 800 J of heat from a refrigerator, the compressor in the refrigerator does 500 J of work. How much heat is released into the surrounding room?
73. A calorimeter contains 1 kg of water [specific heat = 4184 J/(kg K)]. An object with a mass of 4.23 kg is added to the water. If the water temperature increases by 3 K and the temperature of the object decreases by 1 K, what is the specific heat of the object?
74. How much heat is needed to raise the temperature of 100 g of water by 50 K, if the specific heat of water is 4,184 J/kg K?
75. A sample of an unknown metal has a mass of 0.5 kg. Adding 1,985 J of heat to the metal raises its temperature by 10 K. What is the specific heat of the metal?

Chapter 7 Electricity

76. A circuit has a resistance of 4 Ω. What voltage difference will cause a current of 1.4 A to flow in the circuit?
77. How many amperes of current will flow in a circuit if the voltage difference is 9 V and the resistance in the circuit is 3 Ω?
78. If a voltage difference of 3 V causes a 1.5 A current to flow in a circuit, what is the resistance in the circuit?
79. The current in an appliance is 3 A and the voltage difference is 120 V. How much power is being supplied to the appliance?
80. What is the current into a microwave oven that requires 700 W of power if the voltage difference is 120 V?
81. What is the voltage difference in a circuit that uses 2420 W of power if 11 A of current flows into the circuit?
82. How much energy is used when a 110 kW appliance is used for 3 hours?

83. A television has a power rating of 210 W. If the television uses 1.68 kWh of energy, for how long has the television been on?

84. How much does it cost to light six 100-W lightbulbs for six hours if the price of electrical energy is $0.09/kWh?

85. An electric clothes dryer uses 4 kW of electric power. How long did it take to dry a load of clothes if electric power costs $0.09/kWh, and the cost of using the dryer was $0.27?

86. What is the resistance of a lightbulb that draws 0.5 amp of current when plugged into a 120-V outlet?

87. How much current flows through a 100-W lightbulb that is plugged into a 120-V outlet?

88. Eight amps of current flow through a hair dryer connected to a 120-V outlet. How much electrical power does the hair dryer use?

89. Compare the electrical energy that is used by a 100-W lightbulb that burns for 10 h, and a 1,200-W hair dryer that is used for 15 min.

Chapter 8 Magnetism and Its Uses

90. How many turns are in the secondary coil of a step-down transformer that reduces a voltage from 900 V to 300 V and has 15 turns in the primary coil?

91. A step-down transformer reduces voltage from 2400 V to 120 V. What is the ratio of the number of turns in the primary coil to the number of turns in the secondary coil of the transformer?

92. The current produced by an AC generator switches direction twice for each revolution of the coil. How many times does a 110-Hz alternating current switch direction each second?

93. What is the output voltage from a step-down transformer with 200 turns in the primary coil and 100 turns in the secondary coil if the input voltage was 750 V?

94. What is the output voltage from a step-up transformer with 25 turns in the primary coil and 75 turns in the secondary coil if the input voltage was 120 V?

95. How many turns are in the primary coil of a step-down transformer that reduces a voltage from 400 V to 100 V and has 80 turns in the secondary coil?

96. How many turns are in the secondary coil of a step-up transformer that increases voltage from 30 V to 150 V and has seven turns in the primary coil?

97. The coil of a 60-Hz generator makes 60 revolutions each second. How many revolutions does the coil make in five minutes?

98. If a generator coil makes 6000 revolutions in two minutes, how many revolutions does it make each second?

Chapter 9 Energy Sources

99. A gallon of gasoline contains about 2800 g of gasoline. If burning one gram of gasoline releases about 48 kJ of energy, how much energy is released when a gallon of gasoline is burned? (1 kJ = 1000 J)

100. An automobile engine converts the energy released by burning gasoline into mechanical energy with an efficiency of about 25%. If burning 1 kg of gasoline releases about 48,000 kJ of energy, how much mechanical energy is produced by the engine when 1 kg of gasoline is burned?

101. You heat a cup of water in a 750-W microwave oven for 40 s, and warm the water by 20°C. If it takes about 20 kJ of energy to raise the temperature of a cup of water by 20°C, what is the efficiency of the microwave oven?

102. On average, solar energy strikes Earth's surface with an intensity of about 200 W/m^2. If solar cells are 10% efficient, how large an area would have to be covered by solar cells to generate enough electrical power to light a 100-W lightbulb?

103. What is the overall efficiency of a hydroelectric plant if the process of falling water turning a turbine is 80% efficient, the turbine spinning an electric generator is 95% efficient, and the transmission through power lines is 90% efficient?

Answers

Chapter 7 cont.

83. 8 h
84. $0.32
85. 0.75 h
86. 240 Ω
87. 0.833 A
88. 906 W
89. 1 kWh : 0.30 kWh

Chapter 8

90. 5
91. 20:1
92. 220
93. 375 V
94. 360 V
95. 320
96. 35
97. 18,000
98. 50

Chapter 9

99. 134,400 kJ
100. 12,000 kJ
101. 67%
102. 5 m^2
103. 68%

EXTRA MATH PROBLEMS 837

Answers

Chapter 9 cont.

104. 3
105. 4,000 kg
106. 32
107. 10.8%
108. 5.7

Chapter 10

109. 0.04 m
110. 1,632 Hz
111. 3 cm
112. 3 m
113. 18 m/s
114. 35°
115. 1 m/s
116. 5,600,000 Hz
117. 43°
118. 3 Hz

Chapter 11

119. 0.79 m
120. 11.8 m
121. 150 m/s
122. 14.7
123. 3.9%
124. 331.6 m/s
125. 880 Hz
126. 5.1 s

Extra Math Problems

104. When a certain $^{235}_{92}U$ nucleus is struck by a neutron, it forms the two nuclei $^{91}_{36}Kr$ and $^{142}_{56}Ba$. How many neutrons are emitted when this occurs?

105. A nuclear reactor contains 100,000 kg of enriched uranium. About 4% of the enriched uranium is the isotope uranium-235. What is the mass of uranium-235 in the reactor core?

106. Suppose the number of uranium-235 nuclei that are split doubles at each stage of a chain reaction. If the chain reaction starts with one nucleus split in the first stage, how many nuclei will have been split after six stages?

107. From 1970 to 1995 the carbon dioxide concentration in Earth's atmosphere increased from about 325 parts per million to about 360 parts per million. What was the percentage change in the concentration of carbon dioxide?

108. About 85% of the energy used in the U.S. comes from fossil fuels. How many times greater is the amount of energy used from fossil fuel than the amount used from all other energy sources?

Chapter 10 Waves

109. What is the wavelength of a wave with a frequency of 0.4 kHz traveling at 16 m/s?

110. Two waves are traveling in the same medium with a speed of 340 m/s. What is the difference in frequency of the waves if the one has a wavelength of 5 m and the other has a wavelength of 0.2 m?

111. Transverse wave A has an amplitude of 7 cm. This wave constructively interferes with wave B. While the two waves overlap, the amplitude of the resulting wave is 10 cm. What is the amplitude of wave B?

112. What is the wavelength of a wave with a frequency of 5 Hz traveling at 15 m/s?

113. What is the velocity of a wave that has a wavelength of 6 m and a frequency of 3 Hz?

114. A ray of light hits a mirror at an angle of 35° to the normal. What is the angle of the reflected ray to the normal?

115. A wave has a wavelength of 250 cm and a frequency of 4 Hz. What is its speed?

116. A wave has a frequency of 5.6 MHz. What is the frequency of this wave in Hz?

117. A light ray strikes a mirror and is reflected. The angle between the incident and reflected rays is 86°. What is the angle of the incident ray to the normal?

118. What is the frequency of a wave with a wavelength of 7 m traveling at 21 m/s?

Chapter 11 Sound

119. What is the wavelength of a 440-Hz sound wave traveling with a speed of 347 m/s?

120. A sound wave with a frequency of 440 Hz travels in steel with a speed of 5200 m/s. What is the wavelength of the sound wave?

121. A wave traveling in water has a wavelength of a 750 m and a frequency of 2 Hz. How fast is this wave moving?

122. At 0°C sound travels through air with a speed of about 331 m/s and through aluminum with a speed of 4877 m/s. How many times longer is the wavelength of a sound wave in aluminum compared to the wavelength of a sound wave in air if both waves have the same frequency?

123. The speed of sound in air at 0°C is 331 m/s, and at 20°C is 344 m/s. What is the percentage change in the speed of sound at 20°C compared to 0°C?

124. In a lab experiment, measurements of the speed of sound in air were 329.7 m/s, 333.6 m/s, 330.8 m/s, 331.7 m/s, and 332.2 m/s. What is the average value of these measurements?

125. What is the frequency of the first overtone of a 440-Hz wave?

126. The wreck of the *Titanic* is at a depth of about 3800 m. A sonar unit on a ship above the *Titanic* emits a sound wave that travels at a speed of 1500 m/s. How long does it take a sound wave reflected from the *Titanic* to return to the ocean surface?

127. A sonar unit on a ship emits a sound wave. The echo from the ocean floor is detected two seconds later. If the speed of sound in water is 1500 m/s, how deep is the ocean beneath the ship?

128. One flute plays a note with a frequency of 443 Hz, and another flute plays a note with a frequency of 440 Hz. What is the frequency of the beats that the flute players hear?

129. A sound wave has a wavelength of 50 m and a frequency of 22 cycles per second. What is the speed of the sound wave?

130. A tsunami travels across the ocean at a speed of 500 km/h. If the distance between the wave crests is 200 km, what is the frequency of the wave?

Chapter 12 Electromagnetic Waves

131. Express the number 20,000 in scientific notation.

132. An electromagnetic wave has a wavelength of 0.054 m. What is the wavelength in scientific notation?

133. Earth is about 4,500,000,000 years old. Express this number in scientific notation.

134. The speed of electromagnetic waves in air is 300,000 km/s. What is the frequency of electromagnetic waves that have a wavelength of 5×10^{-3} km?

135. The speed of radio waves in water Is about 2.26×10^5 km/s. What is the frequency of radio waves that have a wavelength of 3.0 km?

136. Radio waves with a frequency of 125,000 Hz have a wavelength of 1.84 km when traveling in ice. What is the speed of the radio waves in ice?

137. Some infrared waves have a frequency of 10,000,000,000,000 Hz. Express this frequency in scientific notation.

138. An infrared wave has a frequency of 1×10^{13} Hz and a wavelength of 3×10^{-5} m. Express this wavelength as a decimal number.

139. An AM radio station broadcasts at a frequency of 620 kHz. Express this frequency in Hz using scientific notation.

140. An FM radio station broadcasts at a frequency of 101 MHz. Express this frequency in Hz using scientific notation.

Chapter 13 Light

141. A ray of light hits a plane mirror at 35° from the normal. What angle does the reflected ray make with the normal?

142. A light ray strikes a plane mirror. The angle between the light ray and the surface of the mirror is 25°. What angle does the reflected ray make with the normal?

143. About 8% of men and 0.5% of women have some form of color blindness. The number of men who experience color blindness is how many times larger than the number of women who experience color blindness?

144. The index of refraction of a material is the speed of light in a vacuum divided by the speed of light in the material. If the index of refraction of the mineral rock salt is 1.52, and the speed of light in a vacuum is 300,000 km/s, what is the speed of light in rock salt?

145. A laser is used to measure the distance from Earth to the Moon. The laser beam is reflected from a mirror on the Moon's surface. If the time needed for the laser to reach the Moon and be reflected back is 2.56 s, and the laser beam travels at 300,000 km/s, what is the distance to the Moon?

146. A light ray is reflected from a plane mirror. If the angle between the incident ray and the reflected ray is 104°, what is the angle of incidence?

147. In the human eye, there are about 7,000,000 cone cells distributed over an area of 5 cm^2. If cone cells are evenly distributed over this region, how many cone cells are distributed over an area of 2 cm^2? Express your answer in scientific notation.

148. What will happen to a ray of light leaving water and entering air if it hits the boundary at an angle of 49° to the normal? (The critical angle for water and air is 49°.)

Answers

Chapter 11 cont.

127. 1,500 m
128. 3 Hz
129. 1,100 m/s
130. 2.5 wavelengths/h

Chapter 12

131. 2×10^4
132. 5.4×10^{-2}
133. 4.5×10^9
134. 6×10^7 Hz
135. 7.5×10^{-4} Hz
136. 2.30×10^5 km/s
137. 1×10^{13} Hz
138. 0.00003 m
139. 6.2×10^5 Hz
140. 1.01×10^8 Hz

Chapter 13

141. 35°
142. 65°
143. 16
144. 197,000 km/s
145. 384,000 km
146. 52°
147. 2.8×10^6
148. It will travel along the boundary between air and water.

EXTRA MATH PROBLEMS 839

Answers

Chapter 13 cont.

149. 30°
150. 1:0.0016

Chapter 14

151. 55°
152. 80×
153. < 5 cm
154. > one focal length from the mirror
155. 2.3 cm
156. 1,000,000:1
157. 200×
158. 1.2 cm
159. 0.96 or 25:24
160. 0.058%

Chapter 15

161. 675 g
162. 320 g
163. 1,176 g

Extra Math Problems

Extra Math Problems

149. A ray of light hits a plane mirror at 60° from the normal. What is the angle between the reflected ray and the surface of the mirror?

150. When a light beam is reflected from a glass surface, only 4% of the energy carried by the beam is reflected. If a light beam is reflected from one glass surface and then another, what is the ratio of the energy carried by the beam after the second reflection, compared to the energy carried by the beam before the first reflection?

Chapter 14 Mirrors and Lenses

151. A light ray strikes a plane mirror. The angle between the incident light ray and the normal to the mirror is 55°. What is the angle between the reflected ray and the normal?

152. The magnification of a mirror or lens equals the image size divided by the object size. If a plant cell with a diameter of 0.0035 mm is magnified so that the diameter of the image is 0.028 cm, what is the magnification?

153. A convex lens in a magnifying glass has a focal length of 5 cm. How far should the lens be from an object if the image formed is virtual, enlarged, and upright?

154. A concave mirror forms a real image that is 3/4 the size of the object. How far is the object from the mirror?

155. Magnification equals the image size divided by the object size. Magnification also equals the distance of the image from the lens divided by the distance of the object from the lens. A penny has a diameter of 2.0 cm. A convex lens forms an image with a diameter of 5.2 cm and is 6.0 cm from the lens. What is the distance between the penny and the lens?

156. Light enters the human eye through the pupil. In the dark, the pupil is dilated and has a diameter of about 1 cm. The Keck telescope has a mirror with a diameter of 10 m. If both the pupil and the Keck mirror are circles, what is the ratio of the area of the Keck telescope mirror to the area of a dilated human pupil?

157. A small insect is viewed in a compound microscope. The objective lens of the microscope forms a real image 20 times larger than the insect. The eyepiece lens then magnifies this real image by 10 times. What is the magnification of the microscope?

158. A light source is placed a distance of 1.2 m from a concave mirror on the optical axis. The reflected light rays are parallel and form a light beam. What is the focal length of the mirror?

159. In some types of reflecting telescopes the eyepiece is located behind the concave mirror. A small curved mirror in front of the concave mirror reflects light through a hole in the concave mirror to the eyepiece. Suppose a circular concave mirror with a diameter of 50 cm has a hole with a diameter of 10 cm. What is the ratio of the reflecting area of the mirror with the 10-cm hole to the reflecting area of the same mirror without the hole?

160. Astronomers have proposed building the OWL telescope (**o**ver**w**helmingly **l**arge telescope) with a mirror 100 m in diameter. The diameter of the *Hubble Space Telescope* mirror is 2.4 m. What percentage of the surface area of the OWL mirror would be covered by the surface area of the *Hubble* mirror?

Chapter 15 Classification of Matter

161. Two solutions, one with a mass of 450 g and the other with a mass of 350 g, are mixed. A chemical reaction occurs and 125 g of solid crystals are produced that settle on the bottom of the container. What is the mass of the remaining solution?

162. Carbon reacts with oxygen to form carbon dioxide according to the following equation: $C + O_2 \rightarrow CO_2$. When 120 g of carbon reacts with oxygen, 440 g of carbon dioxide are formed. How much oxygen reacted with the carbon?

163. Salt water is distilled by boiling it and condensing the vapor. After distillation, 1,164 g of water have been collected and 12 g of salt are left behind in the original container. What was the original mass of the salt water?

164. Calcium carbonate, $CaCO_3$, decomposes according to the reaction: $CaCO_3 \rightarrow CaO + CO_2$. When 250 g of $CaCO_3$ decompose completely, the mass of CaO is 56% of the mass of the products of this reaction. What is the mass of CO_2 produced?

165. Water breaks down into hydrogen gas and oxygen gas according to the reaction: $2H_2O \rightarrow 2H_2 + O_2$. In this reaction the mass of oxygen produced is eight times greater than the mass of hydrogen produced. If 36 g of water form hydrogen and oxygen gas, what is the mass of hydrogen gas produced?

166. The size of particles in a solution is about 1 nm (1 nm = 0.000000001 m). Write 0.000000001 m in scientific notation.

167. A chemical reaction produces two new substances, one with a mass of 34 g and the other with a mass of 39 g. What was the total mass of the reactants?

168. The human body is about 65% oxygen. If a person has a mass of 75.0 kg, what is the mass of oxygen in their body?

169. A 112-g serving of ice cream contains 19 g of fat. What percentage of the serving is fat?

170. The mass of the products produced by a chemical reaction is measured. The reaction is repeated five times, with the same mass of reactants used each time. The measured product masses are 50.17 g, 50.12 g, 50.17 g, 50.10 g, and 50. 14 g. What is the average of these measurements?

Chapter 16 Solids, Liquids, and Gases

171. A book is sitting on a desk. The area of contact between the book and the desk is 0.06 m^2. If the book's weight is 30 N, what is the pressure the book exerts on the desk?

172. A skater has a weight of 500 N. The skate blades are in contact with the ice over an area of 0.001 m^2. What is the pressure exerted on the ice by the skater?

173. The weight of the water displaced by a person floating in the water is 686 N. What is the person's mass?

174. The pressure on a balloon that has a volume of 7 L is 100 kPa. If the temperature stays the same and the pressure on the balloon is increased to 250 kPa, what is the new volume of the balloon?

175. Two cylinders contain pistons that are connected by fluid in a hydraulic system. A force of 1,300 N is exerted on one piston with an area of 0.05 m^2. What is the force exerted on the other piston which has an area of 0.08 m^2?

176. A gas-filled weather balloon floating in the atmosphere has an initial volume of 850 L. The weather balloon rises to a region the pressure is 56 kPa, and its volume expands to 1700 L. If the temperature remains the same, what was the initial pressure on the weather balloon?

177. The air in a tire pump has a volume of 1.50 L at a temperature of 5°C. If the temperature is increased to 30°C and the pressure remains constant, what is the new volume?

178. A block of wood with a mass of 1.2 kg is floating in a container of water. If the density of water is 1.0 g/cm^3, what is the volume of water displaced by the floating wood?

179. In a hydraulic system, a force of 7,500 N is exerted on a piston with an area of 0.05 m^2. If the force exerted on a second piston in the hydraulic system is 1,500 N, what is the area of this second piston?

180. A gold bar weighs 17.0 N. If the density of gold is 19.3 g/cm^3, what is the volume of the gold bar?

181. A book is sitting on a desk. If the surface area of the book's cover is 0.05 m^2, and atmospheric pressure is 100.0 kPa, what is the downward force of the atmosphere on the book?

182. A piston applies a pressure of 5,000 N/m^2. If the piston has a surface area of 0.1 m^2, how much force can the piston apply?

Chapter 17 Properties of Atoms and the Periodic Table

183. Boron has a mass number of 11 and an atomic number of 5. How many neutrons are in a boron atom?

Answers

Chapter 15 cont.

164. 110 g
165. 4 g
166. 1×10^{-9}
167. 73 g
168. 48.8 g
169. 17%
170. 50.14 g

Chapter 16

171. 500 Pa
172. 500,000 N/m^2
173. 70 kg
174. 2.8 L
175. 2,080 N
176. 112 kPa
177. 1.63 L
178. 1,200 cm^3
179. 0.01 m^2
180. 90.0 cm^3
181. 5,000 N
182. 500 N

Chapter 17

183. 6

EXTRA MATH PROBLEMS 841

Answers

Chapter 17 cont.

184. 24
185. 42%
186. 16
187. 1.66 or 73:44
188. 24.3 amu
189. 4.88×10^{10}
190. 1.25 g
191. 1.5 minutes
192. 5

Chapter 18

193. 36
194. 30
195. 0.65 or 95:146
196. 1
197. 1
198. $^{222}_{86}Rn$
199. 2.1 s
200. 16.08 days
201. 17,190 years
202. 37.2 minutes

Chapter 19

203. 770 L
204. 150
205. 5.5×10^{-5}
206. 8.0 g
207. 44.4 g
208. 1,220°F
209. 5,660 g

Extra Math Problems

Extra Math Problems

184. A magnesium atom has 12 protons and 12 neutrons. What is its mass number?

185. Iodine-127 has a mass number of 127 and 74 neutrons. What percentage of the particles in an iodine-127 nucleus are protons?

186. How many neutrons are in an atom of phosphorus-31?

187. What is the ratio of neutrons to protons in the isotope radium-234?

188. About 80% of all magnesium atoms are magnesium-24, about 10% are magnesium-25, and about 10% are magnesium-26. What is the average atomic mass of magnesium?

189. The half-life of the radioactive isotope rubidium-87 is 48,800,000,000 years. Express this half-life in scientific notation.

190. The radioactive isotope nickel-63 has a half-life of 100 years. How much of a 10.0-g sample of nickel-63 is left after 300 years?

191. A sample of the radioactive isotope cobalt-62 is prepared. The sample has a mass of 1.00 g. After three minutes, the mass of cobalt-62 remaining is 0.25 g. What is the half-life of cobalt-62?

192. A neutral phosphorus atom has 15 electrons. How many electrons are in the third energy level?

Chapter 18 Radioactivity and Nuclear Reactions

193. How many protons are in the nucleus $^{81}_{36}Kr$?

194. How many neutrons are in the nucleus $^{56}_{26}Fe$?

195. What is the ratio of neutrons to protons in the nucleus $^{241}_{95}Am$?

196. How many alpha particles are emitted when the nucleus $^{222}_{86}Rn$ decays to $^{218}_{84}Po$?

197. How many beta particles are emitted when the nucleus $^{40}_{19}K$ decays to the nucleus $^{40}_{20}Ca$?

198. An alpha particle is the same as the helium nucleus $^{4}_{2}He$. What nucleus is produced when the nucleus $^{226}_{88}Ra$ decays by emitting an alpha particle?

199. How long will it take a sample of $^{194}_{84}Po$ to decay to 1/8 of its original amount if $^{194}_{84}Po$ has a half-life of 0.7 s?

200. The half-life of $^{131}_{53}I$ is 8.04 days. How much time would be needed to reduce 1 g of $^{131}_{53}I$ to 0.25 g?

201. A sample of radioactive carbon-14 sample has decayed to 12.5% of its original amount. If the half-life of carbon-14 is 5730 years, how old is this sample?

202. A sample of $^{38}_{17}Cl$ is observed to decay to 25% of the original amount in 74.4 minutes. What is the half-life of $^{38}_{17}Cl$?

Chapter 19 Elements and Their Properties

203. In seawater the concentration of fluoride ions, F^-, is 1.3×10^{-3} g/L. How many liters of seawater would contain 1.0 g of F^-?

204. There are three isotopes of hydrogen. The isotope deuterium, with one proton and one neutron in the nucleus, makes up 0.015% of all hydrogen atoms. Of every million hydrogen atoms, how many are deuterium?

205. A vitamin and mineral supplement pill contains 1.0×10^{-5} g of selenium. According to the label on the bottle, this amount is 18% of the recommended daily value. What is the recommended daily value of selenium in g?

206. The density of silver is 10.5 g/cm^3 and the density of copper is 8.9 g/cm^3. What is the difference in mass between a piece of silver with a volume of 5 cm^3 and a piece of copper with a volume of 5 cm^3?

207. A person has a mass of 68.3 kg. If 65% of the mass of a human body is oxygen, what is the mass of oxygen in this person's body?

208. The melting point of aluminum is 660.0°C. What is the melting point of aluminum on the Fahrenheit temperature scale?

209. A certain gold ore produces about 5 g of gold for every 1,000 kg of ore that is mined. If one ounce = 28.3 g, how many kg of ore must be mined to produce an ounce of gold?

210. A metal bolt with a mass of 26.6 g is placed in a 50-mL graduated cylinder containing water. The water level in the cylinder rises from 27.0 mL to 30.5 mL. What is the density of the bolt in g/cm^3?

211. On a circle graph showing the percentage of elements in the human body, the wedge representing nitrogen takes up 10.8°. What is the percentage of nitrogen in the human body?

212. The synthetic element hassium-261 has a half-life of 9.3 s. The synthetic element fermium-255 has a half-life of 20.1 h. How many times longer is the half-life of fermium-255 than the half-life of hassium-261?

Chapter 20 Chemical Bonds

213. What is the formula of the compound formed when ammonium ions, NH_4^+, and phosphate ions, PO_4^{3-}, combine?

214. Show that the sum of positive and negative charges in a unit of calcium chloride ($CaCl_2$) equals zero.

215. What is the formula for iron(III) oxide?

216. How many hydrogen atoms are in three molecules of ammonium phosphate, $(NH_4)_3PO_4$?

217. The overall charge on the polyatomic phosphate ion, PO_4^{3-}, is 3−. What is the oxidation number of phosphorus in the phosphate ion?

218. The overall charge on the polyatomic dichromate ion, $Cr_2O_7^{2-}$, is 2−. What is the oxidation number of chromium in this polyatomic ion?

219. What is the formula for lead(IV) oxide?

220. What is the formula for potassium chlorate?

221. What is the formula for carbon tetrachloride?

222. What percentage of the mass of a sulfuric acid molecule, H_2SO_4, is sulfur?

Chapter 21 Chemical Reactions

223. Lithium reacts with oxygen to form lithium oxide according to the equation: $4Li + O_2 \rightarrow 2Li_2O$. If 27.8 g of Li react completely with 32.0 g of O_2, how many grams of Li_2O are formed?

224. What coefficients balance the following equation: $\_Zn(OH)_2 + \_H_3PO_4 \rightarrow \_Zn_3(PO_4)_2 + \_H_2O$?

225. Aluminum hydroxide, $Al(OH)_3$, decomposes to form aluminum oxide, Al_2O_3, and water according to the reaction: $2Al(OH)_3 \rightarrow Al_2O_3 + 3H_2O$. If 156.0 g of $Al(OH)_3$ decompose to from 102.0 g of Al_2O_3, how many grams of H_2O are formed?

226. In the following balanced chemical reaction one of the products is represented by the symbol *X*: $BaCO_3 + C + H_2O \rightarrow Ba(OH)_2 + H_2O + 2X$. What is the formula for the compound represented by *X*?

227. When propane, C_3H_8, is burned, carbon dioxide and water vapor are produced according to the following reaction: $C_3H_8 + 5O_2 \rightarrow 3CO_2 + 4H_2O$. How much propane is burned if 160.0 g of O_2 are used and 132.0 g of CO_2 and 72.0 g of H_2O are produced?

228. Increasing the temperature usually causes the rate of a chemical reaction to increase. If the rate of a chemical reaction doubles when the temperature increases by 10°C, by what factor does the rate of reaction increase if the temperature increases by 30°C?

229. When acetylene gas, C_2H_2, is burned, carbon dioxide and water are produced. Find the coefficients that balance the chemical equation for the combustion of acetylene: $\_C_2H_2 + \_O_2 \rightarrow \_CO_2 + \_H_2O$.

230. What coefficients balances the following equation: $\_CS_2 + \_O_2 \rightarrow \_CO_2 + \_SO_2$?

231. When methane, CH_4, is burned, 50.1 kJ of energy per gram are released. When propane, C_3H_8, is burned, 45.8 kJ of energy are released. If a mixture of 1 g of methane and 1 g of propane is burned, how much energy is released per gram of mixture?

232. A chemical reaction produces 0.050 g of a product in 0.18 s. In the presence of a catalyst, the reaction produces 0.050 g of the same product in 0.007 s. How much faster is the rate of reaction in the presence of the enzyme?

Answers

Chapter 19 cont.

210. 7.6 g/cm^3
211. 3%
212. 7,780×

Chapter 20

213. $(NH_4)_2SO_4$
214. −2 + 2 = 0
215. Fe_2O_3
216. 36
217. +5
218. +6
219. PbO_2
220. $KClO_3$
221. CCl_4
222. 32.6%

Chapter 21

223. 59.8 g
224. 3, 2, 1, 6
225. 54.0 g
226. CO
227. 44.0 g
228. 8
229. 2, 5, 4, 2
230. 1, 3, 1, 2
231. 48.0 kJ/g
232. 25.7 times

EXTRA MATH PROBLEMS 843

Answers

Chapter 22

233. 1.5
234. 4%
235. 24 cm^2
236. 32 cm^2
237. 24 cm^2
238. 32 cm^2
239. 155 g
240. 26.4%
241. 17.4 mL
242. 50 mL

Chapter 23

243. 4
244. 4.7
245. 26.0 mL
246. 9
247. 100 times
248. $H_2SO_4 + 2KOH \rightarrow K_2SO_4 + 2H_2O$
249. $3HBr + Al(OH)_3 \rightarrow AlBr_3 + 3H_2O$
250. 180 amu
251. $HNO_3 + H_2O \rightarrow NO_3^- + H_3O^+$
252. $Na_2O + H_2O \rightarrow 2NaOH$

Chapter 24

253. 126°C
254. 370 million gallons
255. 4,210 million
256. C_6H_{14}

Extra Math Problems

Chapter 22 Solutions

233. A cup of orange juice contains 126 mg of vitamin C and 1/2 cup of strawberries contain 42 mg of vitamin C. How many cups of strawberries contain as much vitamin C as one cup of orange juice?

234. A Sacagawea dollar coin is made of manganese brass alloy that is 1/25 nickel. Express this number as a percentage.

235. What is the total surface area of a 2-cm cube?

236. A cube has 2-cm sides. If it is split in half, what is the total surface area of the two pieces?

237. What is the increase in surface area when a cube with 2-cm sides is divided into eight equal parts?

238. How much surface area is lost if two 4-cm cubes are attached at one face?

239. At 20°C, the solubility in water of potassium bromide, KBr, is 65.3 g/100 mL. What is the maximum amount of potassium bromide that will dissolve in 237 mL of water?

240. At 20°C, the solubility of sodium chloride, NaCl, in water is 35.9 g/100 mL. If the maximum amount of sodium chloride is dissolved in 500 mL of water at 20°C, the mass of the dissolved sodium chloride is what percentage of the mass of the solution?

241. At 60°C, the solubility of sucrose (sugar) in water is 287.3 g/100 mL. At this temperature, what is the minimum amount of water needed to dissolve 50.0 g of sucrose?

242. A fruit drink contains 90% water and 10% fruit juice. How much fruit juice does 500 mL of fruit drink contain?

Chapter 23 Acids, Bases, and Salts

243. The difference between the pH of an acidic solution and the pH of pure water is 3. What is the pH of the solution?

244. The pH of rain that fell over a region had measured values of 4.6, 5.1, 4.8, 4.5, 4.5, 4.9, 4.7, and 4.8. What was the mean value of the measured pH?

245. If 5.5% of 473.0 mL of vinegar is acetic acid, how many milliliters of acetic acid are there?

246. The difference between the pH of a basic solution and the pH of pure water is 2. What is the pH of the solution?

247. On the pH scale, a decrease of one unit means that the concentration of H^+ ions increases 10 times. If the pH of a solution changes from 6.5 to 4.5, how has the concentration of H^+ ions changed?

248. Write the balanced chemical equation for the neutralization of H_2SO_4, sulfuric acid, by KOH, potassium hydroxide.

249. Write the balanced chemical equation for the neutralization of HBr, hydrobromic acid, by $Al(OH)_3$, aluminum hydroxide.

250. A molecule of acetylsalicylic acid, or aspirin, has the chemical formula $COOHC_6H_4COOCH_3$. What is the mass of a molecule of acetylsalicylic acid in amu?

251. Write the equation for the reaction when HNO_3, nitric acid, ionizes in water.

252. When Na_2O, sodium oxide, reacts with water, the base NaOH, sodium hydroxide, is formed. Write the balanced equation for this reaction.

Chapter 24 Organic Compounds

253. The hydrocarbon octane, C_8H_{18}, has a boiling point of 259°F. What is its boiling point on the Celsius temperature scale?

254. A barrel of oil is 42.0 gallons. About 45% of a barrel of oil is turned into gasoline during the fractional distillation process. In 2001, about 19.6 million barrels of crude oil were refined each day. How many gallons of gasoline were produced each day?

255. In 2001, about 56% of the crude oil used by the United States was imported. If the United States used 20.6 million barrels of crude oil a day, how many million barrels of crude oil were imported in 2001?

256. Four molecules of a hydrocarbon contain carbon atoms and 56 hydrogen atoms. What is the formula for a molecule of this hydrocarbon?

257. For saturated hydrocarbons, the number of hydrogen atoms in a molecule can be calculated by the formula $N_H = 2N_C + 2$, where N_H is the number of hydrogen atoms and N_C is the number of carbon atoms in the molecule. If a molecule of the saturated hydrocarbon decane has 22 hydrogen atoms, how many carbon atoms does a decane molecule contain?

258. Fats supply 9 Calories per gram, carbohydrates and proteins each supply 4 Calories per gram. If 100 g of potato chips contain 7 g of protein, 53 g of carbohydrates, and 35 g of fats, how many Calories are in 100 g of potato chips?

259. The basal metabolism rate (BMR) is the amount of energy required to maintain basic body functions. The BMR is approximately 1.0 Calories/hr per kilogram of body mass. For a person with a mass of 65 kg, how many Calories are needed each day to maintain basic body functions?

260. A food Calorie is an energy unit equal to 4,184 joules. If a person uses 2,070 Calories in one day, what is the power being used? Express your answer in watts.

261. In each 100 g of cheddar cheese there are 33 g of fat. Calculate how many grams of fat are in 250 g of cheddar cheese.

262. A car gets 25 miles per gallon of gas. If the car is driven 12,000 miles in one year and gasoline costs $1.55 per gallon, what was the cost of the gasoline used in one year?

Chapter 25 New Materials Through Chemistry

263. A stainless steel spoon contains 30.0 g of iron, 6.8 g of chromium, and 3.2 g of nickel. What percentage of the stainless steel is chromium?

264. A 14-karat gold earring has a mass of 10 g. What is the mass of gold in the earring?

265. In 1997, about 6,400,000,000 kg of polyvinyl chloride were used in the United States. About 6% of the PVC used was for packaging. Express in scientific notation how many kilograms of PVC were used for packaging in 1997.

266. The molecules in a sample of polypropylene have an average length of 60,000 monomers. The monomer of polypropylene has the formula CH_2CHCH_3. Express in scientific notation the mass, in amu, of a polypropylene molecule made of 60,000 monomers.

267. A certain process for manufacturing integrated circuits packs 47,600,000 transistors into an area of 340 mm^2. If this process is used to produce an integrated circuit with an area of 1 cm^2, express in scientific notation the number of transistors in this integrated circuit.

268. The melting points of five different samples of a new aluminum alloy have measured values of 631.5°C, 632.3°C, 636.1°C, 637.4°C, and 630.2°C. What is the mean of these measurements?

269. Rounded to the nearest degree, eight measured values of the melting point of a stainless steel alloy are 1,421°C, 1,420°C, 1,421°C, 1,423°C, 1,423°C, 1,421°C, 1,424°C, and 1,419°C. What is the mode of these measurements?

270. The measured values of the copper content of seven bronze buttons found at an archaeological site are 83%, 90%, 91%, 72%, 79%, 87%, and 89%. What is the median of these measurements?

271. The number of transistors and other components per mm^2 on an integrated circuit has doubled, on average, every two years. If integrated circuits contained 100,000 transistors in 1982, estimate how many transistors an integrated circuit of the same size contained in 1998.

272. A car contains 200 kg of plastic parts instead of steel parts. The density of steel is twice the density of plastic. If the volume of the plastic parts equals the volume of the same parts made of steel, how much less is the mass (kg) of the car by using plastic parts instead of steel?

Extra Math Problems

Answers

Chapter 24 cont.

257. 10
258. 555 Calories
259. 1,560 Calories/day
260. 100 W
261. 82.5 g
262. $744.00

Chapter 25

263. 17.0%
264. 5.8 g
265. 3.84×10^8 kg
266. 2.52×10^6 amu
267. 1.40×10^7
268. 633.5°C
269. 1,421°C
270. 87%
271. 25,600,000
272. 200 kg

EXTRA MATH PROBLEMS 845

Physical Science Reference Tables

Standard Units

Symbol	Name	Quantity
m	meter	length
kg	kilogram	mass
Pa	pascal	pressure
K	kelvin	temperature
mol	mole	amount of a substance
J	joule	energy, work, quantity of heat
s	second	time
C	coulomb	electric charge
V	volt	electric potential
A	ampere	electric current
Ω	ohm	resistance

Physical Constants and Conversion Factors

Acceleration due to gravity	g	9.8 m/s/s or m/s^2
Avogadro's Number	N_A	6.02×10^{23} particles per mole
Electron charge	e	1.6×10^{-19} C
Electron rest mass	m_e	9.11×10^{-31} kg
Gravitation constant	G	6.67×10^{-11} N $\times$ m^2/kg^2
Mass-energy relationship		1 u (amu) = 9.3×10^2 MeV
Speed of light in a vacuum	c	3.00×108 m/s
Speed of sound at STP	331 m/s	
Standard Pressure	1 atmosphere 101.3 kPa 760 Torr or mmHg 14.7 lb/in.^{2}	

Wavelengths of Light in a Vacuum

Violet	$4.0 - 4.2 \times 10^{-7}$ m
Blue	$4.2 - 4.9 \times 10^{-7}$ m
Green	$4.9 - 5.7 \times 10^{-7}$ m
Yellow	$5.7 - 5.9 \times 10^{-7}$ m
Orange	$5.9 - 6.5 \times 10^{-7}$ m
Red	$6.5 - 7.0 \times 10^{-7}$ m

The Index of Refraction for Common Substances

($\lambda = 5.9 \times 10^{-7}$ m)

Air	1.00
Alcohol	1.36
Canada Balsam	1.53
Corn Oil	1.47
Diamond	2.42
Glass, Crown	1.52
Glass, Flint	1.61
Glycerol	1.47
Lucite	1.50
Quartz, Fused	1.46
Water	1.33

Heat Constants

	Specific Heat (average) (kJ/kg × °C) (J/g × °C)	Melting Point (°C)	Boiling Point (°C)	Heat of Fusion (kJ/kg) (J/g)	Heat of Vaporization (kJ/kg) (J/g)
Alcohol (ethyl)	2.43 (liq.)	−117	79	109	855
Aluminum	0.90 (sol.)	660	2467	396	10500
Ammonia	4.71 (liq.)	−78	−33	332	1370
Copper	0.39 (sol.)	1083	2567	205	4790
Iron	0.45 (sol.)	1535	2750	267	6290
Lead	0.13 (sol.)	328	1740	25	866
Mercury	0.14 (liq.)	−39	357	11	295
Platinum	0.13 (sol.)	1772	3827	101	229
Silver	0.24 (sol.)	962	2212	105	2370
Tungsten	0.13 (sol.)	3410	5660	192	4350
Water (solid)	2.05 (sol.)	0	–	334	–
Water (liquid)	4.18 (liq.)	–	100	–	–
Water (vapor)	2.01 (gas)	–	–	–	2260
Zinc	0.39 (sol.)	420	907	113	1770

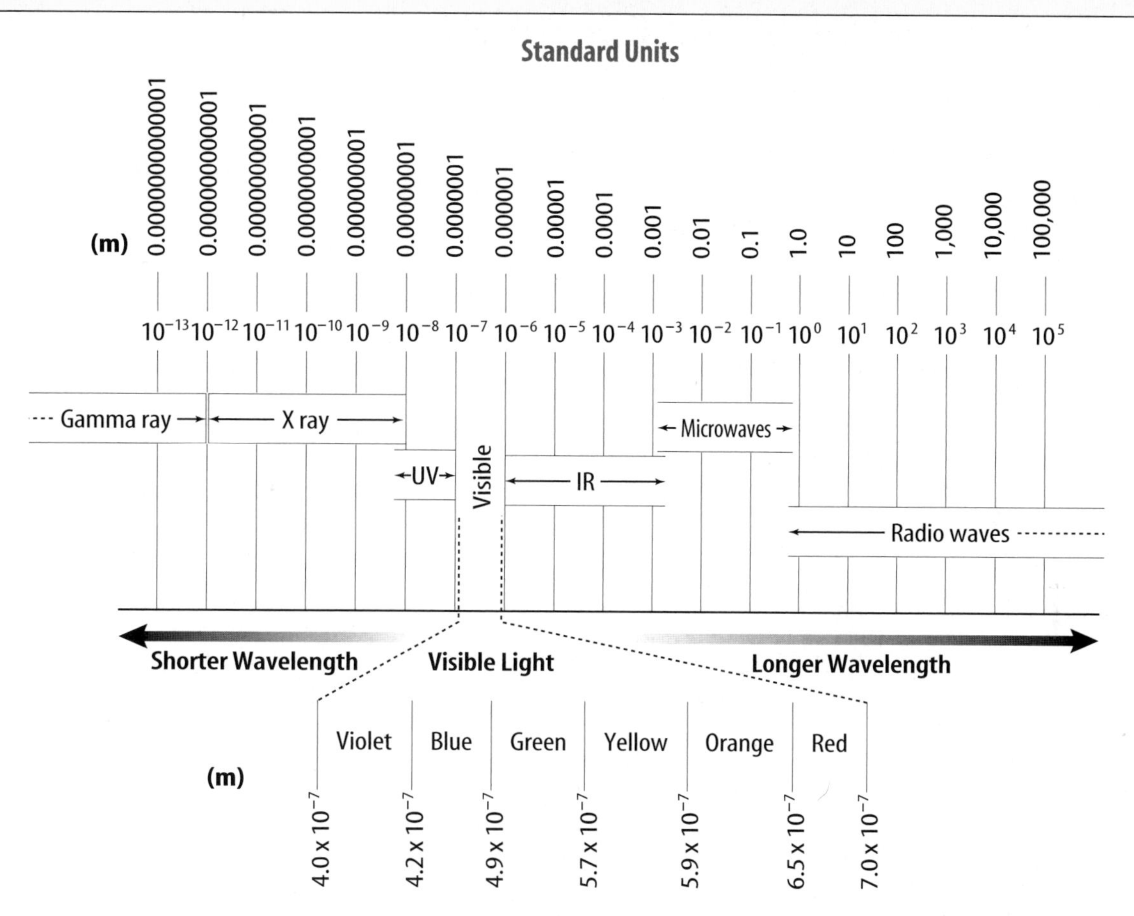
Standard Units
(m)
0.0000000000001
0.000000000001
0.00000000001
0.0000000001
0.000000001
0.00000001
0.0000001
0.000001
0.00001
0.0001
0.001
0.01
0.1
1.0
10
100
1,000
10,000
100,000
10^-13 10^-12 10^-11 10^-10 10^-9 10^-8 10^-7 10^-6 10^-5 10^-4 10^-3 10^-2 10^-1 10^0 10^1 10^2 10^3 10^4 10^5
Gamma ray
X ray
UV
Visible
IR
Microwaves
Radio waves
Shorter Wavelength
Visible Light
Longer Wavelength
Violet
Blue
Green
Yellow
Orange
Red
(m)
4.0 x 10^-7
4.2 x 10^-7
4.9 x 10^-7
5.7 x 10^-7
5.9 x 10^-7
6.5 x 10^-7
7.0 x 10^-7

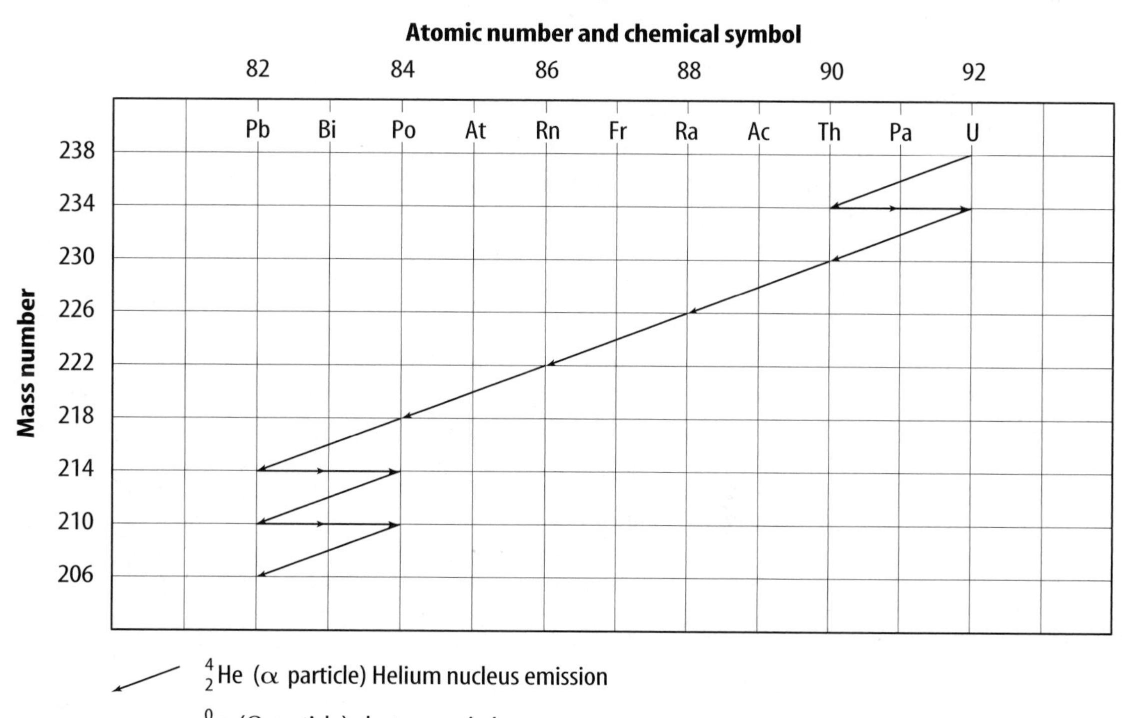
Uranium Disintegration Series
Atomic number and chemical symbol
82
84
86
88
90
92
Pb
Bi
Po
At
Rn
Fr
Ra
Ac
Th
Pa
U
Mass number
238
234
230
226
222
218
214
210
206
$^4_2$He (α particle) Helium nucleus emission
$^0_{-1}$e (β particle) electron emission

PERIODIC TABLE OF THE ELEMENTS

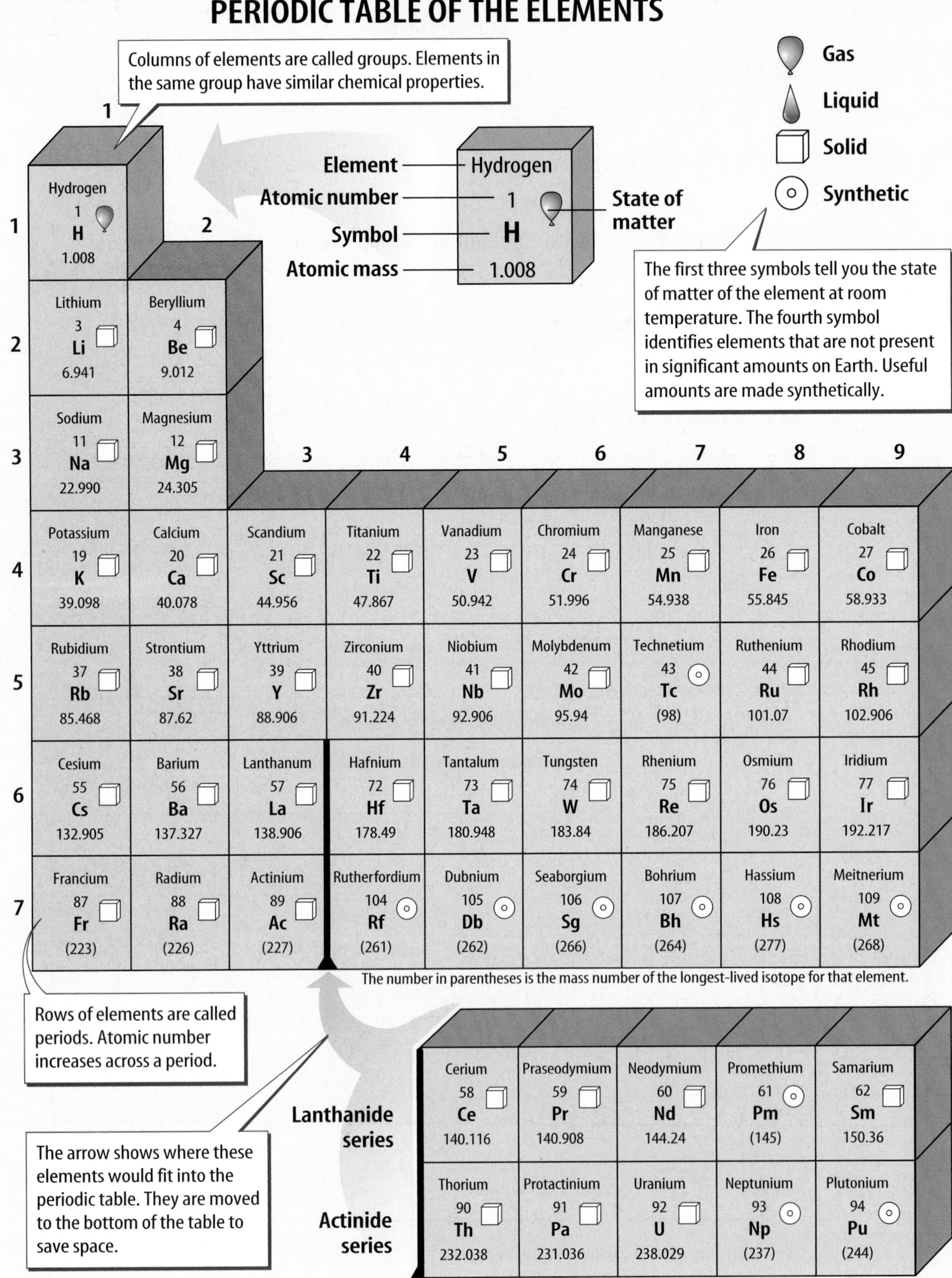
Columns of elements are called groups. Elements in the same group have similar chemical properties.
Gas
Liquid
Solid
Synthetic
Element
Atomic number
Symbol
Atomic mass
Hydrogen 1 H 1.008
State of matter
The first three symbols tell you the state of matter of the element at room temperature. The fourth symbol identifies elements that are not present in significant amounts on Earth. Useful amounts are made synthetically.
1 2 3 4 5 6 7 8 9
1 2 3 4 5 6 7
Hydrogen 1 H 1.008
Lithium 3 Li 6.941
Beryllium 4 Be 9.012
Sodium 11 Na 22.990
Magnesium 12 Mg 24.305
Potassium 19 K 39.098
Calcium 20 Ca 40.078
Scandium 21 Sc 44.956
Titanium 22 Ti 47.867
Vanadium 23 V 50.942
Chromium 24 Cr 51.996
Manganese 25 Mn 54.938
Iron 26 Fe 55.845
Cobalt 27 Co 58.933
Rubidium 37 Rb 85.468
Strontium 38 Sr 87.62
Yttrium 39 Y 88.906
Zirconium 40 Zr 91.224
Niobium 41 Nb 92.906
Molybdenum 42 Mo 95.94
Technetium 43 Tc (98)
Ruthenium 44 Ru 101.07
Rhodium 45 Rh 102.906
Cesium 55 Cs 132.905
Barium 56 Ba 137.327
Lanthanum 57 La 138.906
Hafnium 72 Hf 178.49
Tantalum 73 Ta 180.948
Tungsten 74 W 183.84
Rhenium 75 Re 186.207
Osmium 76 Os 190.23
Iridium 77 Ir 192.217
Francium 87 Fr (223)
Radium 88 Ra (226)
Actinium 89 Ac (227)
Rutherfordium 104 Rf (261)
Dubnium 105 Db (262)
Seaborgium 106 Sg (266)
Bohrium 107 Bh (264)
Hassium 108 Hs (277)
Meitnerium 109 Mt (268)
The number in parentheses is the mass number of the longest-lived isotope for that element.
Rows of elements are called periods. Atomic number increases across a period.
The arrow shows where these elements would fit into the periodic table. They are moved to the bottom of the table to save space.
Lanthanide series
Cerium 58 Ce 140.116
Praseodymium 59 Pr 140.908
Neodymium 60 Nd 144.24
Promethium 61 Pm (145)
Samarium 62 Sm 150.36
Actinide series
Thorium 90 Th 232.038
Protactinium 91 Pa 231.036
Uranium 92 U 238.029
Neptunium 93 Np (237)
Plutonium 94 Pu (244)

Metal

Metalloid

Nonmetal

The color of an element's block tells you if the element is a metal, nonmetal, or metalloid.

Science Online
Visit gpscience.com for updates to the periodic table.

10	11	12	13	14	15	16	17	18
								Helium 2 He 4.003
			Boron 5 B 10.811	Carbon 6 C 12.011	Nitrogen 7 N 14.007	Oxygen 8 O 15.999	Fluorine 9 F 18.998	Neon 10 Ne 20.180
			Aluminum 13 Al 26.982	Silicon 14 Si 28.086	Phosphorus 15 P 30.974	Sulfur 16 S 32.065	Chlorine 17 Cl 35.453	Argon 18 Ar 39.948
Nickel 28 Ni 58.693	Copper 29 Cu 63.546	Zinc 30 Zn 65.409	Gallium 31 Ga 69.723	Germanium 32 Ge 72.64	Arsenic 33 As 74.922	Selenium 34 Se 78.96	Bromine 35 Br 79.904	Krypton 36 Kr 83.798
Palladium 46 Pd 106.42	Silver 47 Ag 107.868	Cadmium 48 Cd 112.411	Indium 49 In 114.818	Tin 50 Sn 118.710	Antimony 51 Sb 121.760	Tellurium 52 Te 127.60	Iodine 53 I 126.904	Xenon 54 Xe 131.293
Platinum 78 Pt 195.078	Gold 79 Au 196.967	Mercury 80 Hg 200.59	Thallium 81 Tl 204.383	Lead 82 Pb 207.2	Bismuth 83 Bi 208.980	Polonium 84 Po (209)	Astatine 85 At (210)	Radon 86 Rn (222)
Darmstadtium 110 Ds (281)	Roentgenium 111 Rg (272)	Ununbium * 112 Uub (285)		Ununquadium * 114 Uuq (289)				

* The names and symbols for elements 112 and 114 are temporary. Final names will be selected when the elements' discoveries are verified.

Europium 63 Eu 151.964	Gadolinium 64 Gd 157.25	Terbium 65 Tb 158.925	Dysprosium 66 Dy 162.500	Holmium 67 Ho 164.930	Erbium 68 Er 167.259	Thulium 69 Tm 168.934	Ytterbium 70 Yb 173.04	Lutetium 71 Lu 174.967
Americium 95 Am (243)	Curium 96 Cm (247)	Berkelium 97 Bk (247)	Californium 98 Cf (251)	Einsteinium 99 Es (252)	Fermium 100 Fm (257)	Mendelevium 101 Md (258)	Nobelium 102 No (259)	Lawrencium 103 Lr (262)

Glossary/Glosario

Cómo usar el glosario en español:
1. Busca el término en inglés que desees encontrar.
2. El término en español, junto con la definición, se encuentran en la columna de la derecha.

Pronunciation Key

Use the following key to help you sound out words in the glossary.

a	back (BAK)	**ew**	food (FEWD)
ay	day (DAY)	**yoo**	pure (PYOOR)
ah	father (FAH thur)	**yew**	few (FYEW)
ow	flower (FLOW ur)	**uh**	comma (CAH muh)
ar	car (CAR)	**u (+ con)**	rub (RUB)
e	less (LES)	**sh**	shelf (SHELF)
ee	leaf (LEEF)	**ch**	nature (NAY chur)
ih	trip (TRIHP)	**g**	gift (GIHFT)
i (i + con + e)	idea (i DEE uh)	**j**	gem (JEM)
oh	go (GOH)	**ing**	sing (SING)
aw	soft (SAWFT)	**zh**	vision (VIH zhun)
or	orbit (OR buht)	**k**	cake (KAYK)
oy	coin (COYN)	**s**	seed, cent (SEED, SENT)
oo	foot (FOOT)	**z**	zone, raise (ZOHN, RAYZ)

English — A — Español

acceleration: rate of change of velocity; can be calculated by dividing the change in the velocity by the time it takes the change to occur. (p. 47)

acid: any substance that produces hydrogen ions, H^+, in a water solution. (p. 696)

acoustics: the study of sound. (p. 339)

air resistance: force that opposes the motion of objects that move through the air. (p. 73)

alcohol: compound, such as ethanol, that is formed when $-OH$ groups replace one or more hydrogen atoms in a hydrocarbon. (p. 733)

allotropes: different forms of the same element having different molecular structures. (p. 585)

alloy: a mixture of elements that has metallic properties. (p. 758)

alpha particle: particle consisting of two protons and two neutrons that is emitted from a decaying atomic nucleus. (p. 541)

alternating current (AC): electric current that reverses its direction of flow in a regular pattern. (p. 242)

amplitude: a measure of the energy carried by a wave. (p. 300)

aromatic compound: an organic compound that contains the benzene ring structure and may have a pleasant or unpleasant odor and flavor. (p. 731)

atom: the smallest particle of an element that still retains the properties of the element. (p. 507)

aceleración: tasa de cambio de la velocidad; se calcula dividiendo el cambio en la velocidad por el tiempo que toma para que ocurra el cambio. (p. 47)

ácido: sustancia que produce iones de hidrógeno, H^+, en una solución de agua. (p. 696)

acústica: el estudio del sonido. (p. 339)

resistencia del aire: fuerza que se opone al movimiento de los objetos que se mueven por el aire. (p. 73)

alcohol: compuesto, como el etanol, que se forma cuando grupos $-OH$ reemplazan a uno o más átomos de hidrógeno en un hidrocarburo. (p. 733)

alótropos: formas diferentes del mismo elemento que tienen diferentes estructuras moleculares. (p. 585)

aleación: una mezcla de elementos que tiene propiedades metálicas. (p. 758)

partícula alfa: partícula compuesta por dos protones y dos neutrones y que es emitida por un núcleo atómico en descomposición. (p. 541)

corriente alterna (CA): corriente eléctrica que invierte su dirección de flujo en un patrón regular. (p. 242)

amplitud: medida de la energía transportada por una onda. (p. 300)

compuesto aromático: compuesto orgánico que contiene la estructura del anillo bencénico y que puede tener un olor y un sabor agradables o desagradables. (p. 731)

átomo: la partícula más pequeña de un elemento que mantiene las propiedades del elemento. (p. 507)

atomic number: number of protons in an atom's nucleus. (p. 513)

average atomic mass: weighted-average mass of the mixture of an element's isotopes. (p. 515)

average speed: total distance an object travels divided by the total time it takes to travel that distance. (p. 42)

número atómico: número de protones en el núcleo de un átomo. (p. 513)

masa atómica promedio: masa de peso promedio resultado de la mezcla de los isótopos de un elemento. (p. 515)

velocidad promedio: distancia que recorre un objeto dividida por el tiempo que dura en recorrer dicha distancia. (p. 42)

B

balanced chemical equation: chemical equation with the same number of atoms of each element on both sides of the equation. (p. 638)

balanced forces: forces on a object that combine to give a zero net force and do not change the motion of the object. (p. 53)

base: any substance that forms hydroxide ions, OH^-, in a water solution. (p. 698)

beta particle: electron that is emitted from a decaying atomic nucleus. (p. 543)

bias: occurs when a scientist's expectations change how the results of an experiment are viewed. (p. 10)

binary compound: compound that is composed of two elements. (p. 615)

biomass: renewable organic matter from plants and animals, such as wood and animal manure, that can be burned to provide heat. (p. 276)

boiling point: the temperature at which the pressure of the vapor in the liquid is equal to the external pressure acting on the surface of the liquid. (p. 479)

bubble chamber: radiation detector, consisting of a container of superheated liquid under high pressure, that is used to detect the paths of charged particles. (p. 547)

buffer: solution containing ions that react with added acids or bases and minimize their effects on pH. (p. 705)

buoyancy: ability of a fluid—a liquid or a gas—to exert an upward force on an object immersed in the fluid. (p. 485)

ecuación química Fnceada: ecuación química con el mismo número de átomos de cada elemento en los dos lados de la ecuación. (p. 638)

fuerzas equilibradas: fuerzas en un objeto que se combinan para dar una fuerza neta de cero y no cambiar el movimiento del objeto. (p. 53)

base: sustancia que forma iones de hidróxido, OH^-, en una solución de agua. (p. 698)

partícula beta: electrón emitido por un núcleo atómico en descomposición. (p. 543)

predisposición: ocurre cuando las expectativas de un científico cambian la forma en que son vistos los resultados de un experimento. (p. 10)

compuesto binario: compuesto conformado por dos elementos. (p. 615)

biomasa: materia orgánica renovable proveniente de plantas y animales, tales como madera y estiércol animal, que puede ser incinerada para producir calor. (p. 276)

punto de ebullición: temperatura a la cual la presión del vapor de un líquido es igual a la presión externa que actúa sobre la superficie del líquido. (p. 479)

cámara de burbujas: detector de radiación que consiste de un contenedor de un líquido sobrecalentado a alta presión, usado para detectar la trayectoria de las partículas cargadas. (p. 547)

buffer: solución que contiene iones que reaccionan con los ácidos o bases agregados y que minimiza los efectos de éstos en el pH. (p. 705)

fuerza flotante: capacidad de un fluido, líquido o gas, para ejercer una fuerza ascendente sobre un objeto inmerso en un fluido. (p. 485)

C

carbohydrates: group of biological compounds, such as sugars and starches, with twice as many hydrogen atoms as oxygen atoms. (p. 745)

carbohidratos: grupo de compuestos biológicos tales como azúcares y almidones que contienen el doble de átomos de hidrógeno que de oxígeno. (p. 745)

Glossary/Glosario

carrier wave: specific frequency that a radio station is assigned and uses to broadcast signals. (p. 367)

catalyst: substance that speeds up a chemical reaction without being permanently changed itself. (p. 650)

cathode-ray tube: sealed vacuum tube that produces one or more beams of electrons that produce an image when they strike the coating on the inside of a TV screen. (p. 370)

centripetal acceleration: acceleration of an object toward the center of a curved or circular path. (p. 81)

centripetal force: a net force that is directed toward the center of a curved or circular path. (p. 81)

ceramics: versatile materials made from dried clay or clay-like mixtures with customizable properties; produced by a process in which an object is molded and then heated to high temperatures, increasing its density. (p. 764)

chain reaction: ongoing series of fission reactions. (p. 552)

charging by contact: process of transferring charge between objects by touching or rubbing. (p. 195)

charging by induction: process of rearranging electrons on a neutral object by bringing a charged object close to it. (p. 196)

chemical bond: force that holds atoms together in a compound. (p. 606)

chemical change: change of one substance into a new substance. (p. 462)

chemical equation: shorthand method to describe chemical reactions using chemical formulas and other symbols. (p. 635)

chemical formula: chemical shorthand that uses symbols to tell what elements are in a compound and their ratios. (p. 603)

chemical potential energy: energy stored in chemical bonds. (p. 103)

chemical property: any characteristic of a substance, such as flammability, that indicates whether it can undergo a certain chemical change. (p. 461)

chemical reaction: process in which one or more substances are changed into new substances. (p. 632)

circuit: closed conducting loop through which an electric current can flow. (p. 201)

cloud chamber: radiation detector that uses water or ethanol vapor to detect the paths of charged particles. (p. 546)

cochlea: spiral-shaped, fluid-filled structure in the inner ear that converts sounds waves to nerve impulses. (p. 326)

onda transportadora: frecuencia específica que se le asigna a una estación de radio y que la usa para emitir señales. (p. 367)

catalizador: sustancia que acelera una reacción química sin cambiar el mismo permanentemente. (p. 650)

tubo de rayos catódicos: tubo vacío sellado que produce uno o más haces de electrones para producir una imagen al chocar con el revestimiento del interior de una pantalla de televisor. (p. 370)

aceleración centrípeta: aceleración de un objeto dirigida hacia el centro de un trayecto curvo o circular. (p. 81)

fuerza centrípeta: fuerza neta dirigida hacia el centro de un trayecto curvo o circular. (p. 81)

cerámicas: materiales versátiles hechos con arcilla seca o mezclas parecidas a la arcilla con propiedades adaptables, producidos mediante un proceso en el cual un objeto es moldeado y luego sujeto a altas temperaturas, aumentando su densidad. (p. 764)

reacción en cadena: serie continua de reacciones de fisión. (p. 552)

carga por contacto: proceso de transferir carga entre objetos por contacto o frotaciòn. (p. 195)

carga por inducción: proceso de redistribución de los electrones en un objeto neutro acercándoles un objeto con carga. (p. 196)

enlace químico: fuerza que mantiene a los átomos juntos dentro de un compuesto. (p. 606)

cambio químico: transformación de una sustancia en una nueva sustancia. (p. 462)

ecuación química: método simplificado para describir reacciones químicas usando fórmulas químicas y otros símbolos. (p. 635)

fórmula química: nomenclatura química que usa símbolos para expresar qué elementos están en un compuesto y en qué proporción. (p. 603)

energía química potencial: energía almacenada en los enlaces químicos. (p. 103)

propiedad química: cualquier característica de una sustancia, como por ejemplo la combustibilidad, que indique si puede someterse a determinado cambio químico. (p. 461)

reacción química: proceso en el cual una o más sustancias son cambiadas por nuevas sustancias. (p. 632)

circuito: circuito conductor cerrado a través del cual puede fluir una corriente eléctrica. (p. 201)

cámara de vapor: detector de radiaciones que usa vapor de agua o de etanol para detectar la trayectoria de las partículas cargadas. (p. 546)

cóclea: estructura en el oído interno, con forma de espiral y llena de un fluido, la cual convierte las ondas sonoras en impulsos nerviosos. (p. 326)

coefficient: number in a chemical equation that represents the number of units of each substance taking part in a chemical reaction. (p. 636)

coherent light: light of a single wavelength that travels in a single direction with its crests and troughs aligned. (p. 398)

colloid (KAHL oyd): heterogeneous mixture whose particles never settle. (p. 454)

combustion reaction: a type of chemical reaction that occurs when a substance reacts with oxygen to produce energy in the form of heat and light. (p. 641)

composite: mixture of two materials, one of which is embedded in the other. (p. 775)

compound: substance formed from two or more elements in which the exact combination and proportion of elements is always the same. (p. 452)

compound machine: machine that is a combination of two or more simple machines. (p. 146)

compressional wave: a wave for which the matter in the medium moves back and forth along the direction that the wave travels. (p. 292)

concave lens: a lens that is thicker at the edges than in the middle; causes light rays to diverge and forms reduced, upright, virtual images; and is usually used in combination with other lenses. (p. 426)

concave mirror: a reflective surface that curves inward and can magnify objects or create beams of light. (p. 418)

conduction: transfer of thermal energy by collisions between particles in matter at a higher temperature and particles in matter at a lower temperature. (p. 164)

conductivity (kahn duk TIHV ut ee): property of metals and alloys that allows heat or electrical charges to pass through the material easily. (p. 759)

conductor: material, such as copper wire, in which electrons can move easily. (p. 194)

constant: in an experiment, a variable that does not change when other variables change. (p. 9)

control: standard used for comparison of test results in an experiment. (p. 9)

convection: transfer of thermal energy in a fluid by the movement of warmer and cooler fluid from one place to another. (p. 165)

convex lens: a lens that is thicker in the middle than at the edges and can form real or virtual images. (p. 424)

coeficiente: número en una ecuación química que representa el número de unidades de cada una de las sustancias que participan en una reacción química. (p. 636)

luz coherente: luz de una sola longitud de onda que viaja en una sola dirección con sus crestas y sus depresiones alineadas. (p. 398)

coloide: mezcla heterogénea cuyas partículas nunca se sedimentan. (p. 454)

reacción de combustión: un tipo de reacción química que ocurre cuando una sustancia reacciona con oxígeno para producir energía en forma de calor y luz. (p. 641)

compuesto: mezcla de dos materiales, uno de los cuales está embebido en el otro. (p. 775)

compuesto: sustancia formada por dos o más elementos en la que la combinación y proporción exacta de los elementos es siempre la misma. (p. 452)

máquina compuesta: máquina compuesta por dos o más máquinas simples. (p. 146)

onda de compresión: onda para la cual la materia en el medio se mueve hacia adelante y hacia atrás en la dirección en que viaja la onda. (p. 292)

lente cóncavo: lente que es más delgado en los bordes que en el centro; hace que los rayos de luz se desvíen y forma imágenes reducidas, verticales y virtuales, y generalmente se utiliza en combinación con otros lentes. (p. 426)

espejo cóncavo: superficie reflexiva que se curva hacia el interior y que puede amplificar los objetos o crear rayos de luz. (p. 418)

conducción: transferencia de energía térmica por colisiones entre partículas de materia a una temperatura alta y partículas de materia a una temperatura más baja. (p. 164)

conductividad: propiedad de los metales y aleaciones que permite fácilmente el paso de calor o cargas eléctricas a través del material. (p. 759)

conductor: material, como el alambre de cobre, a través del cual los electrones se pueden mover con facilidad. (p. 194)

constante: en un experimento, una variable que no cambia cuando cambian otras variables. (p. 9)

control: estándar usado para la comparación de resultados de pruebas en un experimento. (p. 9)

convección: transferencia de energía térmica en un fluido por el movimiento de fluidos con mayores y menores temperaturas de un lugar a otro. (p. 165)

lente convexo: lente que es más delgado en el centro que en los bordes y que puede formar imágenes reales o virtuales. (p. 424)

convex mirror: a reflective surface that curves outward and forms a reduced, upright, virtual image. (p. 421)

cornea: transparent covering on the eyeball through which light enters the eye. (p. 427)

covalent bond: attraction formed between atoms when they share electrons. (p. 611)

crest: the highest points on a transverse wave. (p. 296)

critical mass: amount of fissionable material required so that each fission reaction produces approximately one more fission reaction. (p. 552)

espejo convexo: una superficie reflexiva que se curva hacia el exterior y forma una imagen reducida, vertical y virtual. (p. 421)

córnea: cubierta transparente del globo ocular a través de la cual entra la luz al ojo. (p. 427)

enlace covalente: atracción formada entre átomos que comparten electrones. (p. 611)

cresta: los puntos más altos en una onda transversal. (p. 296)

masa crítica: cantidad de material fisionable requerido de manera que cada reacción de fisión produzca aproximadamente una reacción de fisión adicional. (p. 552)

D

decibel: unit for sound intensity; abbreviated dB. (p. 329)

decomposition reaction: chemical reaction in which one substance breaks down into two or more substances. (p. 642)

density: mass per unit volume of a material. (p. 19)

deoxyribonucleic (dee AHK sih ri boh noo klay ihk) acid: a type of essential biological compound found in the nuclei of cells that codes and stores genetic information and controls the production of RNA. (p. 744)

dependent variable: factor that changes as a result of changes in the other variables. (p. 9)

depolymerization: process using heat or chemicals to break a polymer chain into its monomers. (p. 741)

diatomic molecule: a molecule that consists of two atoms of the same element. (p. 579)

diffraction: the bending of waves around an obstacle; can also occur when waves pass through a narrow opening. (p. 306)

diffusion: spreading of particles throughout a given volume until they are uniformly distributed. (p. 479)

direct current (DC): electric current that flows in only one direction. (p. 242)

displacement: distance and direction of an object's change in position from the starting point. (p. 39)

dissociation: process in which an ionic compound separates into its positive and negative ions. (p. 677)

distance: how far an object moves. (p. 39)

distillation: process than can separate two substances in a mixture by evaporating a liquid and recondensing its vapor. (p. 461)

decibel: unidad que mide la intensidad del sonido; se abrevia dB. (p. 329)

reacción de descomposición: reacción química en la cual una sustancia se descompone en dos o más sustancias. (p. 642)

densidad: masa por unidad de volumen de un material. (p. 19)

ácido desoxirribonucleico: compuesto biológico esencial encontrado en el núcleo de células que codifican y almacenan información genética y que controla la producción de ARN. (p. 744)

variable dependiente: factor que varía como resultado de los cambios en las otras variables. (p. 9)

despolimerización: proceso en el que se utilizan calor o químicos para descomponer una cadena de polímeros en sus monómeros. (p. 741)

molécula diatómica: molécula formada por dos átomos del mismo elemento. (p. 579)

difracción: curvatura de las ondas alrededor de un obstáculo, la cual también puede ocurrir cuando éstas pasan a través de una abertura angosta. (p. 306)

difusión: propagación de partículas en la totalidad de un volumen determinado hasta que se distribuyen de manera uniforme. (p. 479)

corriente directa (CD): corriente eléctrica que fluye en una sola dirección. (p. 242)

desplazamiento: distancia y dirección del cambio de posición de un objeto desde el punto inicial. (p. 39)

disociación: proceso en el cual un compuesto iónico se separa en sus iones positivos y negativos. (p. 677)

distancia: qué tan lejos se mueve un objeto. (p. 39)

destilación: proceso que puede separar dos sustancias de una mezcla por medio de la evaporación de un líquido y la recondensación de su vapor. (p. 461)

doping: process of adding impurities to a semiconductor to increase its conductivity. (p. 768)

Doppler effect: change in pitch or frequency that occurs when a source of a sound is moving relative to a listener. (p. 331)

double-displacement reaction: chemical reaction that produces a precipitate, water, or a gas when two ionic compounds in solution are combined. (p. 643)

ductile: ability of metals to be drawn into wires. (p. 570)

ductility (duk TIHL uh tee): ability of metals or alloys to be pulled into wires. (p. 759)

dopaje: proceso que consiste en añadir impurezas a un semiconductor para aumentar su conductividad. (p. 768)

efecto Doppler: cambio en la altura o frecuencia que ocurre cuando una fuente de sonido se mueve en relación con un oyente. (p. 331)

reacción de doble desplazamiento: reacción química que produce un precipitado, agua o gas cuando se combinan dos compuestos iónicos en una solución. (p. 643)

ductibilidad: capacidad de los metales para convertirse en alambres. (p. 570)

ductilidad: capacidad de los metales o aleaciones para ser convertidos en alambres. (p. 759)

E

eardrum: tough membrane in the outer ear that is about 0.1 mm thick and transmits sound vibrations into the middle ear. (p. 325)

echolocation: process in which objects are located by emitting sounds and interpreting sound waves that are reflected. (p. 339)

efficiency: ratio of the output work done by the machine to the input work done on the machine, expressed as a percentage. (p. 136)

elastic potential energy: energy stored when an object is compressed or stretched. (p. 103)

electrical power: rate at which electrical energy is converted to another form of energy; expressed in watts (W). (p. 210)

electric current: the net movement of electric charges in a single direction, measured in amperes (A). (p. 201)

electric motor: device that converts electrical energy to mechanical energy by using the magnetic forces between an electromagnet and a permanent magnet to make a shaft rotate. (p. 235)

electrolyte: compound that breaks apart in water, forming charged particles (ions) that can conduct electricity. (p. 676)

electromagnet: temporary magnet made by wrapping a wire coil, carrying a current, around an iron core. (p. 232)

electromagnetic induction: process in which electric current is produced in a wire loop by a changing magnetic field. (p. 238)

electromagnetic waves: waves created by vibrating electric charges, can travel through a vacuum or through matter, and have a wide variety of frequencies and wavelengths. (p. 354)

tímpano: membrana fuerte del oído externo que tiene más o menos 0.1 mm de grosor y transmite las vibraciones del sonido al oído medio. (p. 325)

ecolocalización: proceso en el cual los objetos son localizados emitiendo sonidos e interpretando ondas de sonido que se reflejan. (p. 339)

eficiencia: relación del trabajo efectuado por una máquina y el trabajo hecho en ésta, expresada en porcentaje. (p. 136)

energía elástica potencial: energía almacenada cuando un objeto es comprimido o estirado. (p. 103)

potencia eléctrica: proporción a la cual la energía eléctrica se convierte en otra forma de energía; se expresa en vatios (V). (p. 210)

corriente eléctrica: movimiento neto de cargas eléctricas en una sola dirección, medido en amperios (A). (p. 201)

motor eléctrico: dispositivo que convierte la energía eléctrica en energía mecánica usando las fuerzas magnéticas entre un electroimán y un imán permanente para que el eje gire. (p. 235)

electrolito: compuesto que se descompone en agua formando partículas cargadas (iones) que pueden conducir electricidad. (p. 676)

electroimán: imán temporal que se hace envolviendo una bobina de cable que conduce una corriente, alrededor de un núcleo de hierro. (p. 232)

inducción electromagnética: proceso en el cual una corriente eléctrica es producida en un circuito cerrado de cable mediante un campo magnético cambiante. (p. 238)

ondas electromagnéticas: ondas creadas por la vibración de cargas eléctricas, que pueden viajar a través del vacío o de la materia y que tienen una amplia variedad de frecuencias y de longitudes de onda. (p. 354)

electron cloud: area around the nucleus of an atom where the atom's electrons are most likely to be found. (p. 511)

electron dot diagram: uses the symbol for an element and dots representing the number of electrons in the element's outer energy level. (p. 522)

electrons: particles surrounding the center of an atom that have a charge of 1−. (p. 507)

element: substance with atoms that are all alike. (p. 450)

endergonic reaction: chemical reaction that requires energy input (heat, light, or electricity) in order to proceed. (p. 649)

endothermic reaction: chemical reaction that requires heat energy in order to proceed. (p. 649)

exergonic reaction: chemical reaction that releases some form of energy, such as light or heat. (p. 648)

exothermic reaction: chemical reaction in which energy is primarily given off in the form of heat. (p. 648)

experiment: organized procedure for testing a hypothesis; tests the effect of one thing on another under controlled conditions. (p. 8)

nube de electrones: área alrededor del núcleo de un átomo en donde hay más probabilidad de encontrar los electrones de los átomos. (p. 511)

diagrama de punto de electrones: usa el símbolo de un elemento y puntos que representan el número de electrones en el nivel de energía externo del elemento. (p. 522)

electrones: partículas que rodean el centro de un átomo que tienen la carga de 1−. (p. 507)

elemento: sustancia en la cual todos los átomos son iguales. (p. 450)

reacción endergónica: reacción química que requiere entrada de energía (calor, luz o electricidad) para poder proceder. (p. 649)

reacción endotérmica: reacción química que requiere energía de calor para proceder. (p. 649)

reacción exergónica: reacción química que libera una forma de energía, tal como, luz o calor. (p. 648)

reacción exotérmica: reacción química en la cual la energía es inicialmente emitida en forma de calor. (p. 648)

experimento: procedimiento organizado para probar una hipótesis; prueba el efecto de una cosa sobre otra bajo condiciones controladas. (p. 8)

F

first law of thermodynamics: states that the increase in thermal energy of a system equals the work done on the system plus the heat added to the system. (p. 175)

fluorescent light: light that results when ultraviolet radiation produced inside a fluorescent bulb causes the phosphor coating inside the bulb to glow. (p. 395)

focal length: distance from the center of a lens or mirror to the focal point. (p. 418)

focal point: the point on the optical axis of a concave mirror or convex lens where light rays, that are initially parallel to the optical axis, pass through after they strike the mirror or lens. (p. 418)

force: a push or pull exerted on an object. (p. 52)

fossil fuels: oil, natural gas, and coal; formed from the decayed remains of ancient plants and animals. (p. 257)

frequency: the number of wavelengths that pass a fixed point each second; is expressed in hertz (Hz). (p. 297)

friction: force that opposes the sliding motion between two touching surfaces. (p. 70)

primera ley de la termodinámica: establece que el aumento en la energía térmica de un sistema es igual al trabajo realizado sobre el sistema más el calor agregado a éste. (p. 175)

luz fluorescente: luz que resulta cuando una radiación ultravioleta producida dentro de una bombilla fluorescente hace que brille el revestimiento de fósforo dentro de la bombilla. (p. 395)

longitud focal: distancia desde el centro de un lente o espejo al punto focal. (p. 418)

punto focal: el punto en el eje óptico de un espejo cóncavo o lente convexo en el cual los rayos de luz, que inicialmente son paralelos al eje óptico, cruzan luego de chocar con el espejo o lente. (p. 418)

fuerza: impulso o tracción sobre un objeto. (p. 52)

combustibles fósiles: petróleo, gas natural y carbón formados por los restos descompuestos de plantas y animales ancestrales. (p. 257)

frecuencia: el número de longitudes de onda que pasan por un punto fijo en un segundo; se expresa en hertz (Hz). (p. 297)

fricción: fuerza que se opone al movimiento deslizante entre dos superficies en contacto. (p. 70)

G

galvanometer: a device that uses an electromagnet to measure electric current. (p. 234)

gamma ray: electromagnetic wave with no mass and no charge that travels at the speed of light and is usually emitted with alpha or beta particles from a decaying atomic nucleus; has a wavelength less than about ten trillionths. (pp. 365, 543)

Geiger counter: radiation detector that produces a click or a flash of light when a charged particle is detected. (p. 548)

generator: device that uses electromagnetic induction to convert mechanical energy to electrical energy. (p. 238)

geothermal energy: thermal energy in hot magma; can be converted by a power plant into electrical energy. (p. 275)

Global Positioning System (GPS): a system of satellites and ground monitoring stations that enable a receiver to determine its location at or above Earth's surface. (p. 373)

graph: visual display of information or data that can provide a quick way to communicate a lot of information and allow scientists to observe patterns. (p. 22)

gravitational potential energy: energy stored by objects due to their position above Earth's surface; depends on the distance above Earth's surface and the object's mass. (p. 104)

gravity: attractive force between two objects that depends on the masses of the objects and the distance between them. (p. 75)

group: vertical column in the periodic table. (p. 520)

galvanómetro: dispositivo que usa un electroimán para medir la corriente eléctrica. (p. 234)

rayo gama: onda electromagnética sin masa ni carga que viaja a la velocidad de la luz y que usualmente es emitida con partículas alfa o beta a partir de un núcleo atómico en descomposición; tiene una electromagnética con longitudes de onda menores a diez trillonésimas de metro. (pp. 365, 543)

contador Geiger: detector de radiación que produce un sonido seco o un destello de luz al detectar una partícula cargada. (p. 548)

generador: dispositivo que usa inducción electromagnética para convertir energía mecánica en energía eléctrica. (p. 238)

energía geotérmica: energía térmica en el magma caliente, la cual se puede convertir mediante una planta industrial en energía eléctrica. (p. 275)

Sistema de Posicionamiento Global (GPS): sistema de satélites y estaciones de monitoreo en tierra que permiten que un receptor determine su ubicación en o sobre la superficie terrestre. (p. 373)

gráfica: presentación visual de información que puede suministrar una forma rápida de comunicar gran cantidad de información y que permite que los científicos puedan observar los patrones. (p. 22)

energía gravitacional potencial: energía almacenada por objetos debido a su posición sobre la superficie terrestre, la cual depende de la distancia sobre la superficie terrestre y de la masa del objeto. (p. 104)

gravedad: fuerza de atracción entre dos objetos que depende de las masas de los objetos y de la distancia entre ellos. (p. 75)

grupo: columna vertical en la tabla periódica. (p. 520)

H

half-life: amount of time it takes for half the nuclei in a sample of a radioactive isotope to decay. (p. 544)

heat: thermal energy that flows from a warmer material to a cooler material. (p. 160)

heat engine: device that converts thermal energy into work. (p. 176)

heat of fusion: amount of energy required to change a substance from the solid phase to the liquid phase. (p. 478)

vida media: tiempo requerido para que se descomponga la mitad de los núcleos de una muestra de isótopo radiactivo. (p. 544)

calor: energía térmica que fluye de un material caliente a uno frío. (p. 160)

motor de calor: dispositivo que convierte la energía térmica en trabajo. (p. 176)

calor de fusión: cantidad de energía necesaria para cambiar una sustancia del estado sólido al líquido. (p. 478)

heat of vaporization: the amount of energy required for the liquid at its boiling point to become a gas. (p. 479)

heterogeneous (het uh ruh JEE nee us) mixture: mixture, such as mixed nuts or a dry soup mix, in which different materials are unevenly distributed and are easily identified. (p. 453)

holography: technique that produces a complete three-dimensional photographic image of an object. (p. 401)

homogeneous (hoh moh JEE nee us) mixture: solid, liquid, or gas that contains two or more substances blended evenly throughout. (p. 454)

hydrate: compound that has water chemically attached to its ions and written into its chemical formula. (p. 620)

hydrocarbon: saturated or unsaturated compound containing only carbon and hydrogen atoms. (p. 727)

hydroelectricity: electricity produced from the energy of falling water. (p. 273)

hydronium ions (hi DROH nee um • I ahnz): H_3O^+ ions, which form when an acid dissolves in water and H^+ ions interact with water. (p. 696)

hypothesis: educated guess using what you know and what you observe. (p. 8)

incandescent light: light produced by heating a piece of metal, usually tungsten, until it glows. (p. 394)

inclined plane: simple machine that consists of a sloping surface, such as a ramp, that reduces the amount of force needed to lift something by increasing the distance over which the force is applied. (p. 144)

incoherent light: light that contains more than one wavelength, and travels in many directions with its crests and troughs unaligned. (p. 398)

independent variable: factor that, as it changes, affects the measure of another variable. (p. 9)

index of refraction: property of a material indicating how much light slows down when traveling in the material. (p. 386)

indicator: organic compound that changes color in acids and bases. (p. 696)

inertia: resistance of an object to a change in its motion. (p. 54)

infrared waves: electromagnetic waves that have a wavelength between about 1 mm and 750 billionths of a meter. (p. 362)

calor de vaporización: cantidad de energía necesaria para que un líquido en su punto de ebullición se convierta en gas. (p. 479)

mezcla heterogénea: mezcla, tal como una mezcla de nueces o una mezcla seca para hacer sopa, en la cual diferentes materiales están distribuidos en forma desigual y se pueden identificar fácilmente. (p. 453)

holografía: técnica que produce una imagen fotográfica tridimensional completa de un objeto. (p. 401)

mezcla homogénea: sólido, liquido, o gas que contiene dos o más sustancias mezcladas de manera uniforme en toda la mezcla. (p. 454)

hidrato: compuesto que contiene agua químicamente conectada a sus iones y representada en su fórmula química. (p. 620)

hidrocarburos: compuestos saturados o no saturados que contienen únicamente átomos de carbono e hidrógeno. (p. 727)

hidroelectricidad: electricidad producida a partir de la energía generada por una caída de agua. (p. 273)

iones de hidronio: iones H_3O^+ que se forman cuando un ácido se disuelve en agua y los iones H^+ interactúan con el agua. (p. 696)

hipótesis: suposición fundamentada que se basa en lo que se sabe y lo que se observa. (p. 8)

luz incandescente: luz que se produce al calentar una pieza de metal, generalmente tungsteno, hasta que brille. (p. 394)

plano inclinado: máquina simple que consiste de una superficie inclinada, tal como una rampa, que reduce la fuerza necesaria para levantar un objeto aumentando la distancia sobre la cual se aplica dicha fuerza. (p. 144)

luz incoherente: luz que contiene más de una longitud de onda y que viaja en varias direcciones con sus crestas y depresiones no alineadas. (p. 398)

variable independiente: factor que, a medida que cambia, afecta la medida de otra variable. (p. 9)

índice de refracción: propiedad de un material para indicar la cantidad de luz que se frena al pasar a través del material. (p. 386)

indicador: compuesto orgánico que cambia de color en presencia de ácidos y bases. (p. 696)

inercia: resistencia de un objeto a cambiar su movimiento. (p. 54)

ondas infrarrojas: ondas electromagnéticas que tienen una longitud de onda entre aproximadamente 1 mm y 750 billonésimas de metro. (p. 362)

inhibitor: substance that slows down a chemical reaction or prevents it from occurring by combining with a reactant. (p. 650)

instantaneous speed: speed of an object at a given point in time; is constant for an object moving with constant speed, and changes with time for an object that is slowing down or speeding up. (p. 42)

insulator: material in which electrons are not able to move easily. (p. 195)

insulator: material in which heat flows slowly. (p. 169)

integrated circuit: tiny chip of semiconductor material that can contain millions of transistors, diodes, and other components. (p. 768)

intensity: amount of energy that flows through a certain area in a specific amount of time. (p. 328)

interference: occurs when two or more waves overlap and combine to form a new wave. (p. 308)

internal combustion engine: heat engine that burns fuel inside the engine in chambers or cylinders. (p. 176)

ion: charged particle that has either more or fewer electrons than protons. (pp. 608, 676)

ionic bond: attraction formed between oppositely charged ions in an ionic compound. (p. 610)

ionization: process in which electrolytes dissolve in water and separate into charged particles. (p. 676)

isomers: compounds with identical chemical formulas but different molecular structures and shapes. (p. 729)

isotopes: atoms of the same element that have different numbers of neutrons. (p. 514)

inhibidor: sustancia que reduce una reacción química o previene que ocurra por una combinación con un reactivo. (p. 650)

velocidad instantánea: velocidad de un objeto en un punto dado en el tiempo; es constante para un objeto que se mueve a una velocidad constante y cambia con el tiempo en un objeto que está reduciendo o aumentando su velocidad. (p. 42)

aislador: material a través del cual los electrones no se pueden mover con facilidad. (p. 195)

aislador: material en el cual el calor fluye lentamente. (p. 169)

circuito integrado: pedazo minúsculo de material semiconductor que puede contener millones de transistores, diodos y otros componentes. (p. 768)

intensidad: cantidad de energía que fluye a través de cierta área en un tiempo específico. (p. 328)

interferencia: ocurre cuando dos o más ondas se sobreponen y combinan para formar una nueva onda. (p. 308)

motor de combustión interna: motor de calor que quema combustible en su interior en cámaras o cilindros. (p. 176)

ion: partícula cargada que tiene ya sea más o menos electrones que protones. (pp. 608, 676)

enlace iónico: atracción formada entre iones con cargas opuestas en un compuesto iónico. (p. 610)

ionización: proceso en el cual los electrolitos se disuelven en agua y se separan en partículas cargadas. (p. 676)

isómeros: compuestos con fórmulas químicas idénticas pero diferentes estructuras y formas moleculares. (p. 729)

isótopos: átomos del mismo elemento que tienen diferente número de neutrones. (p. 514)

J

joule: SI unit of energy. (p. 102)

julio: unidad SI de energía. (p. 102)

K

kinetic energy: energy a moving object has because of its motion; depends on the mass and speed of the object. (p. 102)

kinetic theory: explanation of the behavior of molecules in matter; states that all matter is made of constantly moving particles that collide without losing energy. (p. 476)

energía cinética: energía que tiene un cuerpo debido a su movimiento, la cual depende de la masa y velocidad del objeto. (p. 102)

teoría cinética: explicación del comportamiento de las moléculas en la materia, la cual establece que todas las sustancias están compuestas de partículas en constante movimiento que colindan sin perder energía. (p. 476)

L

law of conservation of charge: states that charge can be transferred from one object to another but cannot be created or destroyed. (p. 193)

law of conservation of energy: states that energy can never be created or destroyed. (p. 111)

law of conservation of mass: states that the mass of all substances present before a chemical change equals the mass of all the substances remaining after the change. (p. 465)

lever: simple machine consisting of a bar free to pivot about a fixed point called the fulcrum. (p. 138)

lipids: group of biological compounds that contains the same elements as carbohydrates but in different arrangements and combinations, and includes saturated and unsaturated fats and oils. (p. 746)

loudness: human perception of sound intensity. (p. 329)

luster: property of metals and alloys that describes having a shiny appearance or reflecting light. (p. 759)

ley de la conservación de carga: establece que la carga puede ser transferida entre un objeto y otro pero no puede ser creada o destruida. (p. 193)

ley de la conservación de energía: establece que la energía nunca puede ser creada ni destruida. (p. 111)

ley de conservación de la masa: establece que la masa de todas las sustancias presente antes de un cambio químico es igual a la masa de todas las sustancias resultantes después del cambio. (p. 465)

palanca: máquina simple que consiste de una barra que puede girar sobre un punto fijo llamado pivote. (p. 138)

lípidos: grupo de compuestos biológicos que contienen los mismos elementos que los carbohidratos pero en diferentes disposiciones y combinaciones, y que incluye grasas y aceites saturados o no saturados. (p. 746)

volumen de sonido: percepción humana de la intensidad del sonido. (p. 329)

lustre: propiedad de los metales y aleaciones que describe que tienen una apariencia brillante o que reflejan la luz. (p. 759)

M

machine: device that makes doing work easier by increasing the force applied to an object, changing the direction of an applied force, or increasing the distance over which a force can be applied. (p. 132)

magnetic domain: group of atoms in a magnetic material with the magnetic poles of the atoms pointing in the same direction. (p. 229)

magnetic field: surrounds a magnet and exerts a force on other magnets and objects made of magnetic materials. (p. 225)

magnetic pole: region on a magnet where the magnetic force exerted by a magnet is strongest; like poles repel and opposite poles attract. (p. 225)

magnetism: the properties and interactions of magnets. (p. 224)

malleability (mal yuh BIHL yt ee): ability of metals and alloys to be rolled or hammered into thin sheets. (pp. 570, 759)

mass: amount of matter in an object. (p. 19)

mass number: sum of the number of protons and neutrons in an atom's nucleus. (p. 513)

máquina: artefacto que facilita la ejecución del trabajo aumentando la fuerza que se aplica a un objeto, cambiando la dirección de una fuerza aplicada o aumentando la distancia sobre la cual se puede aplicar una fuerza. (p. 132)

dominio magnético: grupo de átomos en un material magnético en el cual los polos magnéticos de los átomos apuntan en la misma dirección. (p. 229)

campo magnético: rodea a un imán y ejerce una fuerza sobre otros imanes y objetos hechos de materiales magnéticos. (p. 225)

polo magnético: zona en un imán en donde la fuerza magnética ejercida por un imán es la más fuerte; los polos iguales se repelen y los polos opuestos se atraen. (p. 225)

magnetismo: propiedades e interacciones de los imanes. (p. 224)

maleabilidad: capacidad de los metales y aleaciones de ser rolados o martillados para formar láminas delgadas. (pp. 570, 759)

masa: cantidad de materia en un objeto. (p. 19)

número de masa: suma del número de protones y neutrones en el núcleo de un átomo. (p. 513)

mechanical advantage (MA): ratio of the output force exerted by a machine to the input force applied to the machine. (p. 136)

mechanical energy: sum of the potential energy and kinetic energy in a system. (p. 108)

medium: matter in which a wave travels. (p. 291)

melting point: temperature at which a solid begins to liquefy. (p. 478)

metal: element that typically is a hard, shiny solid, is malleable, and is a good conductor of heat and electricity. (p. 570)

metallic bonding: occurs because electrons move freely among a metal's positively charged ions and explains properties such as ductility and the ability to conduct electricity. (p. 571)

metalloid: element that shares some properties with metals and some with nonmetals. (p. 584)

microscope: uses convex lenses to magnify small, close objects. (p. 435)

microwaves: radio waves with wavelengths of between about 1 m and 1 mm. (p. 361)

mirage: image of a distant object produced by the refraction of light through air layers of different densities. (p. 388)

model: can be used to represent an idea, object, or event that is too big, too small, too complex, or too dangerous to observe or test directly. (p. 11)

molecule: a neutral particle that forms as a result of electron sharing. (p. 611)

momentum: property of a moving object that equals its mass times its velocity. (p. 86)

monomer: small molecule that forms a link in a polymer chain and can be made to combine with itself repeatedly. (pp. 739, 771)

music: sounds that are deliberately used in a regular pattern. (p. 333)

ventaja mecánica (MA): relación de la fuerza ejercida por una máquina y la fuerza aplicada a dicha máquina. (p. 136)

energía mecánica: suma de la energía potencial y energía cinética en un sistema. (p. 108)

medio: materia a través de la cual viaja una onda. (p. 291)

punto de fusión: temperatura a la cual un sólido comienza a licuarse. (p. 478)

metal: elemento típicamente duro, sólido brillante, maleable y buen conductor del calor y la electricidad. (p. 570)

enlace metálico: ocurre debido a que los electrones se mueven libremente entre los iones de un metal cargados positivamente y explica propiedades tales como la ductibilidad y la capacidad para conducir electricidad. (p. 571)

metaloide: elemento que tiene algunas propiedades de los metales y algunas de los no metales. (p. 584)

microscopio: instrumento que usa lentes convexos para amplificar objetos pequeños cercanos. (p. 435)

microondas: ondas de radio con longitudes de onda entre aproximadamente 1 mm y 1 m. (p. 361)

espejismo: imagen de un objeto distante producida por la refracción de la luz a través de capas de aire de diferentes densidades. (p. 388)

modelo: puede ser usado para representar una idea, objeto o evento que es demasiado grande, demasiado pequeño, demasiado complejo o demasiado peligroso para ser observado o probado directamente. (p. 11)

molécula: partícula neutra que se forma al compartir electrones. (p. 611)

inercia: propiedad de un objeto en movimiento que es igual a su masa por su velocidad. (p. 86)

monómero: pequeña molécula que forma una conexión en una cadena de polímeros y que se puede combinar consigo misma repetidamente. (pp. 739, 771)

música: sonidos que se usan deliberadamente en un patrón regular. (p. 333)

N

net force: sum of the forces that are acting on an object. (p. 53)

neutralization: chemical reaction that occurs when the H_3O^+ ions from an acid react with the OH^- ions from a base to produce water molecules. (p. 707)

neutron: neutral particle, composed of quarks, inside the nucleus of an atom. (p. 507)

fuerza neta: suma de fuerzas que actúan sobre un objeto. (p. 53)

neutralización: reacción química que ocurre cuando los iones H_3O^+ de un ácido reaccionan con los iones OH^- de una base para producir moléculas de agua. (p. 707)

neutrón: partícula neutra, compuesta por quarks, dentro del núcleo de un átomo. (p. 507)

Glossary/Glosario

Newton's second law of motion: states that the acceleration of an object is in the same direction as the net force on the object, and that the acceleration equals the net force divided by the mass. (p. 69)

Newton's third law of motion: states that when one object exerts a force on a second object, the second object exerts a force on the first object that is equal in strength and in the opposite direction. (p. 83)

nonelectrolyte: substance that does not ionize in water and cannot conduct electricity. (p. 676)

nonmetal: element that usually is a gas or brittle solid at room temperature, is not malleable or ductile, is a poor conductor of heat and electricity, and typically is not shiny. (p. 578)

nonpolar: not having separated positive and negative areas; nonpolar materials do not attract water molecules and do not dissolve easily in water. (p. 681)

nonpolar molecule: molecule that shares electrons equally and does not have oppositely charged ends. (p. 614)

nonrenewable resources: natural resource, such as fossil fuels, that cannot be replaced by natural processes as quickly as it is used. (p. 263)

nuclear fission: process of splitting an atomic nucleus into two or more nuclei with smaller masses. (p. 551)

nuclear fusion: reaction in which two or more atomic nuclei form a nucleus with a larger mass. (p. 553)

nuclear reactor: uses energy from a controlled nuclear chain reaction to generate electricity. (p. 264)

nuclear waste: radioactive by-product that results when radioactive materials are used. (p. 268)

nucleic acids: essential organic polymers that control the activities and reproduction of cells. (p. 744)

nucleotides: complex, organic molecules that make up RNA and DNA; contain an organic base, a phosphoric acid unit, and a sugar. (p. 744)

nucleus: positively charged center of an atom that contains protons and neutrons and is surrounded by a cloud of electrons. (p. 507)

segunda ley de movimiento de Newton: establece que la aceleración de un objeto es en la misma dirección que la fuerza neta del objeto y que la aceleración es igual a la fuerza neta dividida por su masa. (p. 69)

tercera ley de movimiento de Newton: establece que cuando un objeto ejerce una fuerza sobre un segundo objeto, el segundo objeto ejerce una fuerza igual de fuerte sobre el primer objeto y en dirección opuesta. (p. 83)

no electrolito: sustancia que no se ioniza en el agua y no puede conducir electricidad. (p. 676)

no metal: elemento que por lo general es un gas o un sólido frágil a temperatura ambiente, no es maleable o dúctil, es mal conductor del calor y la electricidad, y por lo general no es brillante. (p. 578)

no polar: sustancia que no tiene áreas positivas y negativas separadas; los materiales no polares no atraen las moléculas de agua y no se disuelven fácilmente en ésta. (p. 681)

molécula no polar: molécula que comparte equitativamente los electrones y que no tiene extremos con cargas opuestas. (p. 614)

recursos no renovables: recursos naturales, tales como combustibles fósiles, que no pueden ser reemplazados por procesos naturales tan pronto como son usados. (p. 263)

fisión nuclear: proceso de división de un núcleo atómico en dos o más núcleos con masas más pequeñas. (p. 551)

fusión nuclear: reacción en la cual dos o más núcleos atómicos forman un núcleo con mayor masa. (p. 553)

reactor nuclear: usa energía de una reacción nuclear controlada en cadena para generar electricidad. (p. 264)

desperdicio nuclear: subproducto radioactivo que resulta del uso de materiales radiactivos. (p. 268)

ácidos nucleicos: polímeros orgánicos esenciales que controlan las actividades y la reproducción de las células. (p. 744)

nucleótidos: moléculas orgánicas complejas que componen el ARN y el ADN y que contienen una base orgánica, una unidad de ácido fosfórico y un azúcar. (p. 744)

núcleo: centro de un átomo con carga positiva que contiene protones y neutrones y está rodeado por una nube de electrones. (p. 507)

O

Ohm's law: states that the current in a circuit equals the voltage difference divided by the resistance. (p. 205)

ley de Ohm: establece que la corriente en un circuito es igual a la diferencia de voltaje dividida por la resistencia. (p. 205)

opaque: material that absorbs or reflects all light and does not transmit any light. (p. 384)

optical axis: imaginary straight line that is perpendicular to the center of a concave mirror or convex lens. (p. 418)

organic compounds: large number of compounds containing the element carbon. (p. 726)

overtone: vibration whose frequency is a multiple of the fundamental frequency. (p. 334)

oxidation: the loss of electrons from the atoms of a substance. (p. 645)

oxidation number: positive or negative number that indicates how many electrons an atom has gained, lost, or shared to become stable. (p. 615)

opaco: material que absorbe o refleja toda la luz pero no la transmite. (p. 384)

eje óptico: línea recta imaginaria perpendicular al centro de un espejo cóncavo o lente convexo. (p. 418)

compuestos orgánicos: un gran número de compuestos que contienen el elemento carbono. (p. 726)

armónico: vibración cuya frecuencia es un múltiplo de la frecuencia fundamental. (p. 334)

oxidación: la pérdida de electrones de los átomos de una sustancia. (p. 645)

número de oxidación: número positivo o negativo que indica cuántos electrones ha ganado, perdido o compartido un átomo para poder ser estable. (p. 615)

P

parallel circuit: circuit in which electric current has more than one path to follow. (p. 208)

pascal: SI unit of pressure. (p. 490)

period: horizontal row in the periodic table. (p. 523); the amount of time it takes one wavelength to pass a fixed point; is expressed in seconds. (p. 297)

periodic table: organized list of all known elements that are arranged by increasing atomic number and by changes in chemical and physical properties. (p. 516)

petroleum: liquid fossil fuel formed from decayed remains of ancient organisms; can be refined into fuels and used to make plastics. (p. 259)

pH: a measure of the concentration of hydronium ions in a solution using a scale ranging from 0 to 14, with 0 being the most acidic and 14 being the most basic. (p. 704)

photon: particle that electromagnetic waves sometimes behave like; has energy that increases as the frequency of the electromagnetic wave increases. (p. 358)

photovoltaic cell: device that converts solar energy into electricity; also called a solar cell. (p. 271)

physical change: any change in size, shape, or state of matter in which the identity of the substance remains the same. (p. 460)

physical property: any characteristic of a material, such as size or shape, that you can observe or attempt to observe without changing the identity of the material. (p. 458)

circuito paralelo: circuito en el cual la corriente eléctrica tiene más de una trayectoria para seguir. (p. 208)

pascal: unidad SI de presión. (p. 490)

período: fila horizontal en la tabla periódica. (p. 523); la cantidad de tiempo que requiere una longitud de onda para pasar un punto fijo; se expresa en segundos. (p. 297)

tabla periódica: lista organizada de todos los elementos conocidos y que han sido ordenados de manera ascendente por número atómico y por cambios en sus propiedades químicas y físicas. (p. 516)

petróleo: combustible fósil líquido que se forma a partir de residuos en descomposición de organismos ancestrales y que puede ser refinado para producir combustibles y usado para hacer plásticos. (p. 259)

pH: medida de la concentración de iones de hidronio en una solución, usando una escala de 0 a 14, en la cual 0 es la más ácida y 14 la más básica. (p. 704)

fotón: partícula como la cual algunas veces se comportan las ondas electromagnéticas; tiene energía que aumenta a medida que la frecuencia de la onda electromagnética aumenta. (p. 358)

células fotovoltaicas: dispositivo que convierte la energía solar en electricidad; también llamada celda solar. (p. 271)

cambio físico: cualquier cambio en tamaño, forma o estado de una sustancia en la cual la identidad de la sustancia sigue siendo la misma. (p. 460)

propiedad física: cualquier característica de un material, tal como tamaño o forma, que se puede haber observar o tratado de observar sin cambiar la identidad del material. (p. 458)

Glossary/Glosario

pigment: colored material that is used to change the color of other substances. (p. 392)

pitch: how high or low a sound seems; related to the frequency of the sound waves. (p. 330)

plane mirror: flat, smooth mirror that reflects light to form upright, virtual images. (p. 473)

plasma: matter consisting of positively and negatively charged particles. (p. 480)

polar: having separated positive and negative areas; polar materials attract water molecules and dissolve easily in water. (p. 667)

polarized light: light whose waves vibrate in only one direction. (p. 400)

polar molecule: molecule with a slightly positive end and a slightly negative end as a result of electrons being shared unequally. (p. 614)

polyatomic ion: positively or negatively charged, covalently bonded group of atoms. (p. 619)

polyethylene: polymer formed from a chain containing many ethylene units; often used in plastic bags and plastic bottles. (p. 739)

polymer: class of natural or synthetic substances made up of many smaller, simpler molecules, called monomers, arranged in large chains. (pp. 739, 771)

potential energy: stored energy an object has due to its position. (p. 103)

power: amount of work done, or the amount of energy transferred, divided by the time required to do the work or transfer the energy; measured in watts (W). (p. 129)

precipitate: insoluble compound that comes out of solution during a double-displacement reaction. (p. 643)

pressure: amount of force exerted per unit area; SI unit is the pascal (Pa). (p. 486)

product: in a chemical reaction, the new substance that is formed. (p. 632)

proteins: large, complex, biological polymers formed from amino acid units; make up many body tissues such as muscles, tendons, hair, and fingernails. (p. 742)

proton: particle, composed of quarks, inside the nucleus of an atom that has a charge of 1+. (p. 507)

pulley: simple machine that consists of a grooved wheel with a rope, chain, or cable running along the groove; can be either fixed or movable. (p. 141)

pigmento: material de color que se usa para cambiar el color de otras sustancias. (p. 392)

altura: qué tan alto o bajo parece un sonido; tiene relación con la frecuencia de las ondas sonoras. (p. 330)

espejo plano: espejo plano y liso que refleja la luz para formar imágenes verticales y virtuales. (p. 473)

plasma: materia consistente de partículas con cargas positivas y negativas. (p. 480)

polar: sustancia que tiene áreas positivas y negativas separadas; los materiales polares atraen las moléculas de agua y se disuelven fácilmente en ésta. (p. 667)

luz polarizada: luz cuyas ondas vibran en una sola dirección. (p. 400)

molécula polar: molécula con un extremo ligeramente positivo y otro ligeramente negativo como resultado de un compartir desigual de los electrones. (p. 614)

ion poliatómico: grupo de átomos enlazados covalentemente, con carga positiva o negativa. (p. 619)

polietileno: polímero formado por una cadena que contiene varias unidades de etileno; es comúnmente usado en la fabricación de bolsas y envases plásticos. (p. 739)

polímero: clase de sustancias naturales o sintéticas compuestas por muchas moléculas más simples y pequeñas, llamadas monómeros, ordenadas en largas cadenas. (pp. 739, 771)

energía potencial: energía almacenada que un objeto tiene debido a su posición. (p. 103)

potencia: cantidad de trabajo realizado o cantidad de energía transferida, dividida por el tiempo requerido para realizar el trabajo o transferir la energía; medida en vatios (V). (p. 129)

precipitado: compuesto insoluble que resulta de una solución durante una reacción de doble desplazamiento. (p. 643)

presión: cantidad de fuerza ejercida por unidad de área; la unidad SI es el pascal (Pa). (p. 486)

producto: es la nueva sustancia que se forma en una reacción química. (p. 632)

proteínas: polímeros biológicos extensos y complejos formados por unidades de aminoácidos; conforman muchos tejidos del cuerpo como los músculos, los tendones, el pelo y las uñas. (p. 742)

protón: partícula, compuesta por quarks, dentro del núcleo de un átomo que tiene una carga de 1+. (p. 507)

polea: máquina simple que consiste de una rueda acanalada con una cuerda, cadena o cable que se desliza por el canal y que puede ser fija o móvil. (p. 141)

Q

quarks: particles of matter that make up protons and neutrons. (p. 507)

quarks: partículas de materia que constituyen los protones y neutrones. (p. 507)

R

radiant energy: energy carried by an electromagnetic wave. (p. 357)

radiation: transfer of thermal energy by electromagnetic waves. (p. 167)

radioactive element: element, such as radium, whose nucleus breaks down and emits particles and energy. (p. 572)

radioactivity: process that occurs when a nucleus decays and emits alpha, beta, or gamma radiation. (p. 538)

radio waves: electromagnetic waves with wavelengths longer than about 1 mm, used for communications. (p. 361)

rarefaction: the least dense regions of a compressional wave. (p. 296)

reactant: in a chemical reaction, the substance that reacts. (p. 632)

real image: an image formed by light rays that converge to pass through the place where the image is located. (p. 419)

reduction: the gain of electrons by the atoms of a substance. (p. 645)

reflecting telescope: uses a concave mirror, plane mirror, and convex lens to collect and focus light from distant objects. (p. 433)

refracting telescope: uses two convex lenses to gather and focus light from distant objects. (p. 433)

refraction: the bending of a wave as it changes speed in moving from one medium to another. (p. 304)

renewable resource: energy source that is replaced almost as quickly as it is used. (p. 271)

resistance: tendency for a material to oppose electron flow and change electrical energy into thermal energy and light; measured in ohms (Ω). (p. 203)

resonance: the process by which an object is made to vibrate by absorbing energy at its natural frequencies. (p. 311)

resonator: hollow, air-filled chamber that amplifies sound when the air inside it vibrates. (p. 335)

energía radiante: energía transportada por una onda electromagnética. (p. 357)

radiación: transferencia de energía térmica mediante ondas electromagnéticas. (p. 167)

elemento radiactivo: elemento, como el radio, cuyo núcleo se divide y emite partículas y energía. (p. 572)

radiactividad: proceso que ocurre cuando un núcleo se descompone y emite radiación alfa, beta o gama. (p. 538)

ondas de radio: ondas electromagnéticas con longitudes de onda más largas de aproximadamente 1 mm y que se usan en las comunicaciones. (p. 361)

rarefacción: las regiones menos densas de una onda de compresión. (p. 296)

reactante: es la sustancia que reacciona en una reacción química. (p. 632)

imagen real: imagen formada por rayos de luz que convergen para pasar a través del sitio donde está localizada la imagen. (p. 419)

reducción: la obtención de electrones por los átomos de una sustancia. (p. 645)

telescopio reflexivo: usa un espejo cóncavo, un espejo plano y lentes convexos para recolectar y enfocar la luz proveniente de objetos distantes. (p. 433)

telescopio refractivo: usa dos lentes convexos para reunir y enfocar la luz proveniente de objetos distantes. (p. 433)

refracción: curvatura de una onda al cambiar su velocidad al pasar de un medio a otro. (p. 304)

recursos renovables: fuente de energía que es reemplazada casi tan pronto como es usada. (p. 271)

resistencia: tendencia de un material de oponerse al fluido de los electrones y convertir la energía eléctrica en energía térmica y luz; se mide en ohmios (Ω). (p. 203)

resonancia: el proceso por el cual un objeto vibra al absorber energía en sus frecuencias naturales. (p. 311)

resonador: cámara hueca, llena de aire, que amplifica el sonido cuando vibra el aire en su interior. (p. 335)

retina: inner lining of the eye that has cells which convert light images into electrical signals for interpretion by the brain. (p. 427)

retina: capa interna del ojo que posee células que convierten imágenes iluminadas en señales eléctricas para que el cerebro las interprete. (p. 427)

S

salt: compound formed when negative ions from an acid combine with positive ions from a base. (pp. 580, 707)

sal: compuesto iónico que se forma cuando un halógeno adquiere un electrón de un metal. (pp. 580, 707)

saturated hydrocarbon: compound, such as propane or methane, that contains only single bonds between carbon atoms. (p. 728)

hidrocarburo saturado: compuesto, como el propano y el metano, que contiene únicamente enlaces simples entre los átomos de carbono. (p. 728)

saturated solution: any solution that contains all the solute it can hold at a given temperature. (p. 673)

solución saturada: cualquier solución que contiene todo el soluto que puede retener a una temperatura determinada. (p. 673)

scientific law: statement about what happens in nature that seems to be true all the time; does not explain why or how something happens. (p. 12)

ley científica: enunciado acerca de lo que ocurre en la naturaleza, lo cual parece ser cierto en todo momento, sin explicar cómo o por qué algo ocurre. (p. 12)

scientific method: organized set of investigation procedures that can include stating a problem, forming a hypothesis, researching and gathering information, testing a hypothesis, analyzing data, and drawing conclusions. (p. 7)

método científico: conjunto organizado de procedimientos de investigación que puede incluir el planteamiento de un problema, formulación de una hipótesis, investigación y recopilación de información, comprobación de la hipótesis, análisis de datos y elaboración de conclusiones. (p. 7)

screw: simple machine that consists of an inclined plane wrapped in a spiral around a cylindrical post. (p. 145)

tornillo: máquina simple que consiste de un plano inclinado envuelto en espiral alrededor de un poste cilíndrico. (p. 145)

second law of thermodynamics: states that is impossible for heat to flow from a cool object to a warmer object unless work is done. (p. 175)

segunda ley de la termodinámica: establece que es imposible que el calor fluya de un objeto frío a uno caliente, a menos que se realice un trabajo. (p. 175)

semiconductor: materials having conductivity properties between that of metals (good conductors) and nonmetals (insulators) and having controllable conductivity parameters. (pp. 585, 767)

semiconductor: materiales que tienen propiedades de conductividad entre aquellas de los metales (buenos conductores) y los no metales (aisladores) y que tienen parámetros de conductividad controlables. (pp. 585, 767)

series circuit: circuit in which electric current has only one path to follow. (p. 207)

circuito en serie: circuito en el cual la corriente eléctrica tiene una sola trayectoria para seguir. (p. 207)

SI: International System of Units—the improved, universally accepted version of the metric system that is based on multiples of ten and includes the meter (m), liter (L), and kilogram (kg). (p. 15)

SI: Sistema Internacional de Unidades: la versión mejorada y aprobada universalmente del sistema métrico que se basa en múltiplos de diez e incluye el metro (m), el litro (L) y el kilogramo (Kg). (p. 15)

simple machine: machine that does work with only one movement—lever, pulley, wheel and axle, inclined plane, screw, and wedge. (p. 138)

máquina simple: máquina que realiza el trabajo con un solo movimiento: palanca, polea, rueda y eje, plano inclinado, tornillo y cuña. (p. 138)

single-displacement reaction: chemical reaction in which one element replaces another element in a compound. (p. 643)

reacción de un solo desplazamiento: reacción química en la cual un elemento reemplaza a otro elemento en un compuesto. (p. 643)

sliding friction: frictional force that opposes the motion of two surfaces sliding past each other. (p. 72)

fricción deslizante: fuerza de fricción que se opone al movimiento de dos superficies que se deslizan entre sí. (p. 72)

soaps: organic salts with nonpolar, hydrocarbon ends that interact with oils and dirt and polar ends that helps them dissolve in water. (p. 712)

solar collector: device used in an active solar heating system that absorbs radiant energy from the Sun. (p. 174)

solenoid: a wire wrapped into a cylindrical coil. (p. 232)

solubility: maximum amount of a solute that can be dissolved in a given amount of solvent at a given temperature. (p. 671)

solute: in a solution, the substance being dissolved. (p. 665)

solution: homogeneous mixture that remains constantly and uniformly mixed and has particles that are so small they cannot be seen with a microscope. (pp. 454, 664)

solvent: in a solution, the substance in which the solute is dissolved. (p. 665)

sonar: system that uses the reflection of sound waves to detect objects underwater. (p. 341)

sound quality: difference between sounds having the same pitch and loudness. (p. 334)

specific heat: amount of thermal energy needed to raise the temperature of 1 kg of a material 1°C. (p. 161)

speed: distance an object travels per unit of time. (p. 39)

standard: exact, agreed-upon quantity used for comparison. (p. 14)

standing wave: a wave pattern that forms when waves of equal wavelength and amplitude, but traveling in opposite directions, continuously interfere with each other; has points called nodes that do not move. (p. 310)

static electricity: the accumulation of excess electric charge on an object. (p. 192)

static friction: frictional force that prevents two surfaces from sliding past each other. (p. 71)

strong acid: any acid that dissociates almost completely in solution. (p. 702)

strong base: any base that dissociates completely in solution. (p. 703)

strong force: attractive force that acts between protons and neutrons in an atomic nucleus. (p. 537)

sublimation: the process of a solid changing directly to a vapor without forming a liquid. (p. 581)

jabones: sales orgánicas con extremos de hidrocarburos no polares que interactúan con aceites y suciedad, y con extremos polares que ayudan a disolverlos en agua. (p. 712)

recolector solar: dispositivo utilizado en un sistema activo de calefacción solar, el cual absorbe la energía radiante del sol. (p. 174)

solenoide: cable envuelto en forma de bobina cilíndrica. (p. 232)

solubilidad: máxima cantidad de soluto que puede ser disuelto en una cantidad dada de solvente a una temperatura determinada. (p. 671)

soluto: en una solución, la sustancia que está disuelta. (p. 665)

solución: mezcla homogénea que permanece constante y uniformemente mezclada y que tiene partículas tan pequeñas que no pueden ser vistas en un microscopio. (pp. 454, 664)

solvente: en una solución, la sustancia en la cual se disuelve el soluto. (p. 665)

sonar: sistema que usa la reflexión de las ondas sonoras para detectar objetos bajo el agua. (p. 341)

calidad del sonido: diferencia entre sonidos que tienen la misma altura e intensidad sonora. (p. 334)

calor específico: cantidad de energía térmica necesaria para aumentar un grado centígrado la temperatura de un kilogramo de material. (p. 161)

velocidad: distancia que recorre un objeto por unidad de tiempo. (p. 39)

estándar: cantidad exacta y acordada, usada para hacer comparaciones. (p. 14)

onda estacionaria: patrón de una onda que se forma cuando ondas con la misma longitud de onda y amplitud, pero que viajan en direcciones opuestas, interfieren continuamente entre sí; tiene puntos llamados nodos que no se mueven. (p. 310)

electricidad estática: la acumulación del exceso de carga eléctrica en un objeto. (p. 192)

fricción estática: fuerza que evita que dos superficies en contacto se deslicen una sobre otra. (p. 71)

ácido fuerte: cualquier ácido que se disocie casi por completo en una solución. (p. 702)

base fuerte: cualquier base que se disocie completamente en una solución. (p. 703)

fuerza de atracción: fuerza de atracción que actúa entre protones y neutrones en un núcleo atómico. (p. 537)

sublimación: proceso mediante el cual un sólido se convierte directamente en vapor sin pasar por estado líquido. (p. 581)

substance: element or compound that cannot be broken down into simpler components and maintain the properties of the original substance. (p. 450)

substituted hydrocarbon: hydrocarbon with one or more of its hydrogen atoms replaced by atoms or groups of other elements. (p. 732)

supersaturated solution: any solution that contains more solute than a saturated solution at the same temperature. (p. 674)

suspension: heterogeneous mixture containing a liquid in which visible particles settle. (p. 456)

synthesis reaction: chemical reaction in which two or more substances combine to form a different substance. (p. 642)

synthetic: describes polymers, such as plastics, adhesives, and surface coatings, that are made from hydrocarbons. (p. 771)

sustancia: elemento o compuesto que no se puede descomponer en componentes más simples y que mantiene las propiedades de la sustancia original. (p. 450)

hidrocarburo sustituido: un hidrocarburo en el cual uno o más de sus átomos de hidrógeno son reemplazados por átomos o grupos de otros elementos. (p. 732)

solución sobresaturada: cualquier solución que contenga más solutos que una solución saturada a la misma temperatura. (p. 674)

suspensión: mezcla heterogénea que contiene un líquido en el cual las partículas visibles se sedimentan. (p. 456)

reacción síntesis: reacción química en la cual se combinan dos o más sustancias para formar una sustancia diferente. (p. 642)

sintético: describe a los polímeros, tales como plásticos, adhesivos y recubrimientos de superficies, hechos de hidrocarburos. (p. 771)

T

technology: application of science to help people. (p. 13)

temperature: measure of the average kinetic energy of all the particles in an object. (p. 159)

theory: explanation of things or events that is based on knowledge gained from many observations and investigations. (p. 12)

thermal energy: sum of the kinetic and potential energy of the particles in an object; is transferred by conduction, convection, and radiation. (p. 159)

thermal expansion: increase in the size of a substance when the temperature is increased. (p. 481)

thermodynamics: study of the relationship between thermal energy, heat, and work. (p. 174)

titration (ti TRAY shun): process in which a solution of known concentration is used to determine the concentration of another solution. (p. 710)

total internal reflection: occurs when light strikes a boundary between two materials and is completely reflected. (p. 402)

tracer: radioactive isotope, such as iodine-131, that can be detected by the radiation it emits after it is absorbed by a living organism. (p. 554)

transceiver: device that transmits one radio signal and receives another radio signal at the same time, allowing a cordless phone user to talk and listen at the same time. (p. 371)

tecnología: aplicación de la ciencia en beneficio de la población. (p. 13)

temperatura: medida de la energía cinética promedio de todas las partículas en un objeto. (p. 159)

teoría: explicación de las cosas o eventos que se basa en el conocimiento obtenido a partir de numerosas observaciones e investigaciones. (p. 12)

energía térmica: suma de la energía cinética y potencial de las partículas en un objeto, la cual se transfiere por conducción, convección y radiación. (p. 159)

expansión térmica: aumento del tamaño de una sustancia al aumentar la temperatura. (p. 481)

termodinámica: estudio de la relación entre la energía térmica, el calor y el trabajo. (p. 174)

titulación: proceso mediante el cual una solución con una concentración conocida es usada parea determinar la concentración de otra solución. (p. 710)

reflexión interna total: ocurre cuando la luz choca con el límite entre dos materiales y se refleja completamente. (p. 402)

indicador radiactivo: isótopo radioactivo, tal como el yodo-131, que puede ser detectado por la radiación que emite después de ser absorbido por un organismo vivo. (p. 554)

radio transmisor-receptor: dispositivo que transmite y recibe una señal de radio al mismo tiempo, permitiendo que un usuario de un teléfono inalámbrico pueda hablar y escuchar al mismo tiempo. (p. 371)

transformer: device that uses electromagnetic induction to increase or decrease the voltage of an alternating current. (p. 243)

transition elements: elements in Groups 3 through 12 of the periodic table; occur in nature as uncombined elements and include the iron triad and coinage metals. (p. 574)

translucent: material that transmits some light but not enough to see objects clearly through it. (p. 384)

transmutation: process of changing one element to another through radioactive decay. (p. 542)

transparent: material that transmits almost all the light striking it so that objects can be clearly seen through it. (p. 384)

transuranium elements: elements having more than 92 protons, all of which are synthetic and unstable. (p. 589)

transverse wave: wave for which the matter in the medium moves back and forth at right angles to the direction the wave travels; has crests and troughs. (p. 292)

trough: the lowest points on a transverse wave. (p. 296)

turbine: large wheel that rotates when pushed by steam, wind, or water and provides mechanical energy to a generator. (p. 240)

Tyndall effect: scattering of a light beam as it passes through a colloid. (p. 455)

transformador: dispositivo que usa inducción electromagnética para aumentar o disminuir el voltaje de una corriente alterna. (p. 243)

elementos de transición: los elementos de los grupos 3 al 12 de la tabla periódica que se encuentran en la naturaleza como elementos sin combinar e incluyen la tríada de hierro y los metales con los que se fabrican las monedas. (p. 574)

translúcido: material que transmite alguna luz pero no la suficiente para ver claramente los objetos a través del mismo. (p. 384)

transmutación: proceso de cambio de un elemento a otro mediante la descomposición radioactiva. (p. 542)

transparente: material que transmite casi toda la luz, chocándola de tal manera que los objetos pueden ser claramente vistos a través del mismo. (p. 384)

elementos transuránicos: elementos que tienen más de 92 protones, todos los cuales son sintéticos e inestables. (p. 589)

onda transversal: onda para la cual la materia en el medio se mueve hacia adelante y hacia atrás en ángulos rectos respecto a la dirección en que viaja la onda; ésta tiene cresta y depresiones. (p. 292)

depresión: los puntos más bajos en una onda transversal. (p. 296)

turbina: rueda grande que gira al ser impulsada por vapor, viento o agua y que suministra energía mecánica a un generador. (p. 240)

efecto Tyndall: difusión de un rayo de luz al pasar a través de un coloide. (p. 455)

ultrasonic: sound waves with frequencies above 20,000 Hz. (p. 330)

ultraviolet waves: electromagnetic waves with wavelengths between about 400 billionths and 10 billionths of a meter. (p. 363)

unsaturated hydrocarbon: compound, such as ethene or ethyne, that contains at least one double or triple bond between carbon atoms. (p. 730)

unsaturated solution: any solution that can dissolve more solute at a given temperature. (p. 673)

ultrasónico: ondas de sonido con frecuencia superiores a 20,000 Hz. (p. 330)

ondas ultravioleta: ondas electromagnéticas con longitudes de onda entre aproximadamente 10 y 400 billonésimas de metro. (p. 363)

hidrocarburo no saturado: compuesto, como el etileno, que contiene al menos un enlace doble o triple entre los átomos de carbono. (p. 730)

solución no saturada: cualquier solución que puede disolver más solutos a una temperatura determinada. (p. 673)

V

variable: factor that can cause a change in the results of an experiment. (p. 9)

variable: factor que puede causar un cambio en los resultados de un experimento. (p. 9)

velocity: the speed and direction of a moving object. (p. 44)

velocidad direccional: la rapidez y dirección de un objeto en movimiento. (p. 44)

virtual image: an image formed by diverging light rays that is perceived by the brain, even though no actual light rays pass through the place where the image seems to be located. (p. 418)

imagen virtual: la imagen que se forma al divergir los rayos de luz, la cual es percibida por el cerebro, aún cuando ningún rayo de luz real pase por el sitio donde la imagen parezca estar localizada. (p. 418)

viscosity: a fluid's resistance to flow. (p. 489)

viscosidad: resistencia de un fluido al flujo. (p. 489)

visible light: electromagnetic waves with wavelengths of 750 to 400 billionths of a meter that can be detected by human eyes. (p. 363)

luz visible: ondas electromagnéticas con longitudes de onda entre 400 y 750 billonésimas de metro y que pueden ser detectadas por el ojo humano. (p. 363)

voltage difference: related to the force that causes electric charges to flow; measured in volts (V). (p. 200)

diferencia de voltaje: se refiere a la fuerza que causa que las cargas eléctricas fluyan; se mide en voltios (V). (p. 200)

volume: amount of space occupied by an object. (p. 18)

volumen: espacio ocupado por un objeto. (p. 18)

W

wave: a repeating disturbance or movement that transfers energy through matter or space. (p. 290)

onda: alteración o movimiento repetitivo que transfiere energía a través de la materia o el espacio. (p. 290)

wavelength: distance between one point on a wave and the nearest point just like it. (p. 297)

longitud de onda: distancia entre un punto en una onda y el punto semejante más cercano. (p. 297)

weak acid: any acid that only partly dissociates in solution. (p. 702)

ácido débil: cualquier ácido que solamente se disocie parcialmente en una solución. (p. 702)

weak base: any base that does not dissociate completely in solution. (p. 703)

base débil: cualquier base que no se disocie completamente en una solución. (p. 703)

wedge: simple machine that is an inclined plane with one or two sloping sides. (p. 145)

cuña: máquina simple que consiste de un plano inclinado con uno o dos lados en declive. (p. 145)

weight: gravitational force exerted on an object. (p. 77)

peso: fuerza gravitacional ejercida sobre un objeto. (p. 77)

wheel and axle: simple machine that consists of a shaft or axle attached to the center of a larger wheel, so that the shaft and the wheel rotate together. (p. 143)

rueda y eje: máquina simple que consiste de una barra o eje sujeto al centro de una rueda de mayor tamaño de manera que el eje y la rueda giran juntos. (p. 143)

work: transfer of energy that occurs when a force makes an object move; measured in joules. (p. 126)

trabajo: transferencia de energía que se produce cuando una fuerza hace mover un objeto y que se mide en julios. (p. 126)

X

X rays: electromagnetic waves with wavelengths between about 10 billionths of a meter and 10 trillionths of a meter, that are often used for medical imaging. (p. 365)

rayos X: ondas electromagnéticas con longitudes de onda entre 10 billonésimas de metro y 10 trillonésimas de metro, las cuales se utilizan con frecuencia para producir imágenes de uso médico. (p. 365)

Italic numbers = illustration/photo **Bold numbers = vocabulary term**
lab = a page on which the entry is used in a lab
act = a page on which the entry is used in an activity

A

Index

Index

Index

L

Index

Index

Index

Index

W

Magnification Key: Magnifications listed are the magnifications at which images were originally photographed.
LM–Light Microscope
SEM–Scanning Electron Microscope
TEM–Transmission Electron Microscope

Acknowledgments: Glencoe would like to acknowledge the artists and agencies who participated in illustrating this program: Absolute Science Illustration; Andrew Evansen; Argosy; Articulate Graphics; Craig Attebery represented by Frank & Jeff Lavaty; CHK America; John Edwards and Associates; Gagliano Graphics; Pedro Julio Gonzalez represented by Melissa Turk & The Artist Network; Robert Hynes represented by Mendola Ltd.; Morgan Cain & Associates; JTH Illustration; Laurie O'Keefe; Matthew Pippin represented by Beranbaum Artist's Representative; Precision Graphics; Publisher's Art; Rolin Graphics, Inc.; Wendy Smith represented by Melissa Turk & The Artist Network; Kevin Torline represented by Berendsen and Associates, Inc.; WILDlife ART; Phil Wilson represented by Cliff Knecht Artist Representative; Zoo Botanica.

Photo Credits

Cover Roger Ressmeyer/CORBIS; **i ii** Roger Ressmeyer/CORBIS; **viii** SuperStock; **ix** Peter Ardito/Index Stock; **x** Russell D. Curtis/Photo Researchers; **xi** CMCD/PhotoDisc; **xiii** (t)Richard Megna/Fundamental Photographs; **xiii** (b)Alfred Pasieka/Science Photo Library/Photo Researchers; **xiv** George B. Diebold/The Stock Market; **xv** Ginger Chih/Peter Arnold, Inc.; **xvi** NASA; **xvii** AISI/Visuals Unlimited; **xxi** Dominic Oldershaw; **1** James H. Karales/Peter Arnold, Inc.; **2-3** John Terence Turner/FPG/Getty Images; **3** (l)Artville, (r)Lisa Pines/Getty Images; **4-5** Roger Ressmeyer/CORBIS; **6** Ron Sachs/CORBIS; **7** Will McIntyre/Photo Researchers; **9** James L. Amos/CORBIS; **10** David Young-Wolff/PhotoEdit; **11** (l)Roger Ressmeyer/CORBIS, (r)imagebroker/Alamy Images; **12** J. Marshall/The Image Works; **13** (t)Jonathan Nourok/PhotoEdit, (b)Tony Freeman/PhotoEdit; **14** First Image; **15** AFP/Getty Images; **16** Matt Meadows; **17** (t)Amanita Pictures, (bl)Stockbyte, (br)CORBIS; **24** First Image; **28** Bob Daemmrich; **29** Icon Images; **30** Rosalie Winard; **31** (l)TSADO/NCDC/NOAA/Tom Stack & Associates, (r)Getty Images; **32** Amanita Pictures; **36-37** Lester Lefkowitz/CORBIS; **38** Icon Images; **42** Paul Silverman/Fundamental Photographs; **44** (t)SuperStock, (b)Robert Holmes/CORBIS; **49** (t)RDF/Visuals Unlimited, (c)Ron Kimball, (b)Richard Megna/Fundamental Photographs; **50** (l)The Image Finders, (r)Richard Hutchings; **51** Dan Feicht/Cedar Point Amusement Park; **52** Jupiterimages/Creatas/Alamy Images; **53** Tim Courlas/Horizons Companies; **54** Neal Haynes/Rex USA, Ltd.; **55** (t)David Leah/Getty Images, (b)courtesy Insurance Institute for Highway Safety; **56** Donald Johnston/Stone; **57** First Image; **58** Icon Images; **59** Icon Images; **60** Sylvain Grandadam/Stone; **61** (tl)Tony Freeman/PhotoEdit, (bl)Tony Freeman/PhotoEdit, (br)Peter Newton/Stone; **66-67** Tim Wright/CORBIS; **68** David Young-Wolff/PhotoEdit; **70** (t)Russell Sadur/Getty Images, (c)M.W. Davidson/Photo Researchers, (b)Getty Images; **71** Bob Daemmrich, **72** (t)Bob Daemmrich, (b)Alen Penton/Alamy Images; **73** (t)Jim Sugar/Getty Images, (b)Michael Newman/PhotoEdit; **74** Keith Kent/Peter Arnold, Inc.; **76** StockTrek/CORBIS; **77** Peticolas-Megna/Fundamental Photographs; **78** NASA; **80** (tl)KS Studios, (tr)David Young-Wolff/PhotoEdit, (b)Richard Megna/Fundamental Photographs; **81** PhotoLink/Getty Images; **83** Steven Sutton/PCN Photography; **84** Jupiter Images; **85** (l)NASA, (tr cr br)(NASA-JSC); **87** (l)Jeff Smith/Fotosmith, (r)Richard Megna/Fundamental Photographs; **88** Amanita Pictures; **90** Matt Meadows; **91** Tim Courlas/Horizons Companies; **92** (t)Tony Craddock/Photo Researchers, Inc., (b)Bettmann/CORBIS; **93** (l)Keith Kent/Peter Arnold, Inc., (r)Richard Megna/Fundamental Photographs; **98-99** Jim Cummins/CORBIS; **100** Jens Johnson 2008; **101** (l)Tony Walker/PhotoEdit, (c)Mark Burnett, (r)D. Boone/CORBIS; **105** KS Studios; **109** Walter H. Hodge/Peter Arnold, Inc.; **110** RFD/Visuals Unlimited; **114** David H. Wells/CORBIS; **117** Matt Meadows; **118** (tl)Brompton Studios, (bl)TIME, (r)Hank Morgan/Photo Researchers; **119** (tl)SuperStock, (bl)Jana R. Jirak/Visuals Unlimited, (cr)Steve Fitchett/Getty Images; **124-125** Jakob Helbig/Getty Images; **125** Timothy Fuller; **126** Tim Courlas/Horizons Companies; **127** (t)Tim Courlas/Horizons Companies, (b)Michael Newman/PhotoEdit; **129** Michelle Bridwell/PhotoEdit; **131** Jules Frazier/Getty Images; **132** Michael Newman/PhotoEdit; **133** (t)Mark Burnett, (b)Tony Freeman/PhotoEdit; **134** Joseph P. Sinnot/Fundamental Photographs; **135** Richard Megna/Fundamental Photographs; **139** (tl)Tom Pantages, (tr)Mark Burnett, (br)Tony Freeman/PhotoEdit; **140** (l)Lori Adamski Peek/Getty Images, (tr)Amos Morgan/Getty Images, (br)CORBIS/Jupiter Images; **141** A.J. Copley/Visuals Unlimited; **143** Mark Burnett; **144** Tom Pantages; **145** (tl)file photo, (tr)Mark Burnett, (b)Amanita Pictures; **146** SuperStock; **147** Mark Burnett; **149** Hickson-Bender; **150** (t)courtesy D. Carr & H. Craighead, Cornell University, (b)Joe Lertola; **151** (t) Alistair Berg/Getty Images, (bl)file photo, (br)C. Squared Studios/PhotoDisc; **155** Michael Newman/PhotoEdit; **156-157** Charles E. Rotkin/CORBIS; **160** Aaron Haupt; **165** Peter Ardito/Index Stock; **166** (t)Earth Imaging/Stone, (bl)Martin Harvey/Alamy Images, (br)Charles & Josette Lenars/CORBIS; **168** (l)Doug Cheeseman/Peter Arnold, Inc., (c)Tim Davis/The Stock Market, (r)Ed Reschke/Peter Arnold, Inc.; **169** David Madison; **171** Richard Day/Animals Animals; **174** Stu Rosner/Stock Boston; **180** Tim Courlas/Horizons Companies; **182** (tl bl) NASA, (r)Roy Johnson/Tom Stack & Associates; **183** (l)Dean Conger/CORBIS, (r)Michael Newman/PhotoEdit; **186** Doug Martin; **188-189** Photodisc/Alamy Images; **189** CORBIS; **190-191** John Lawrence/Getty Images; **191** Michael Newman/PhotoEdit; **193** Geoff Butler; **195** KS Studios; **196** Tim Courlas/Horizons Companies; **197** T. Wiewandt/DRK Photo; **198** Dale Sloat/Phototake; **203** Ray Ellis/Photo Researchers; **204** Thomas Veneklasen; **206 207 208** Geoff Butler; **210** (tl)Geoff Butler, (tr)Tony Freeman/PhotoEdit, (c b)Aaron Haupt; **214 215** Geoff Butler; **216** Bernard Gotfryd/Hulton Archive/Getty Images; **217** (t)file photo, (bl)Image Ideas/PictureQuest, (br)Harold Stucker/Black Star; **222-223** Kennan Ward/CORBIS; **224** Don Smetzer/Getty Images; **225 226** Richard Megna/Fundamental Photographs; **229** (l)Stephen Frisch/Stock Boston, (r)Mark Burnett; **230** Mark Burnett; **233** Icon Images; **235** (t)Allen Zak, (b)Tim Courlas/Horizons Companies; **238** Tim Courlas/Horizons Companies; **240** (t)Paiwei Wei/Getty Images, (b)Russell D. Curtis/Photo Researchers;

Credits

241 (tl)Stockbyte/PunchStock, (tr)ImageSource/AGE footstock, (cl)Tim Ridley/DK Images, (cr)Comstock Images/Alamy, (bl)Ingram Publishing/AGE Fotostock, (br)Tim Ridley/DK Images; **242** Mark Burnett; **245** Tim Courlas/Horizons Companies; **246 247** KS Studios; **248** (t)Brian Blauser/Stock Shop, (b)Laurence Dutton/Stone; **249** (l)Richard Megna/Fundamental Photographs, (r)Jeff Greenberg/Peter Arnold, Inc.; **254-255** Sandy Felsenthal/CORBIS; **256** (t)James Sugar/Black Star, (b)Bill Heinsohn/Stone; **258** Robert E. Pratt; **259** Amanita Pictures; **260** (t)Digital Vision/PictureQuest, (b)Doug Martin; **264** Robert Essel/CORBIS; **265** Photo Researchers; **268** Laski Diffusion/Liaison/Getty Images; **269** Tim Wright/CORBIS; **271** Amanita Pictures; **273** S.K. Patrick/ Tom Stack & Associates; **274** (t)John Elk III/Stock Boston, (b)Lester Lefkowitz/The Stock Market; **276** Martin Bond/Science Photo Library/Photo Researchers; **278** Timothy Fuller; **279** Martin B. Withers/Frank Lane Picture Agency/CORBIS; **280** Dan Lamont/CORBIS; **281** (tl)Amanita Pictures, (bl)US Department of Energy/Photo Researchers, (r)Kathy Ferguson/PhotoEdit; **285** Robert Essel/CORBIS; **286** (inset)Wallace Weeks/Alamy; **286-287** Jim Wehtje/Getty Images; **288-289** CORBIS; **290** James H. Karales/Peter Arnold, Inc.; **294** VStock/Alamy Images; **302 303** Tim Courlas/Horizons Companies; **304** (t)Richard Megna/Fundamental Photographs, (b)SIU/Visuals Unlimited; **306** (t)photo by John S. Shelton, (b)Richard Megna/Fundamental Photographs; **307** Richard Megna/Fundamental Photographs; **310** Kodansha; **312** Doug Martin; **313** Tim Courlas/Horizons Companies; **314** (t)Ralph White/CORBIS, (b)Ralph White/CORBIS; **315** (tl)Ryan McVay/Stone/Getty Images, (tr)Bruce Heinemann/PhotoDisc, (b)SIU/Visuals Unlimited; **320-321** AFP; **324** Tim Courlas/Horizons Companies; **326** Prof. Pl Motta/Dept. of Anatomy/University la Sapienza, Rome/Photo Researchers; **328** Michael Newman/PhotoEdit; **329** (tl)Ian O'Leary/Stone, (tr)David Young-Wolff/PhotoEdit, (bl)Mark A. Schneider/Visuals Unlimited, (bc)Rafael Macia/Photo Researchers, (br)SuperStock; **332** NOAA/OAR/ERL/National Severe Storms Laboratory (NSSL); **333** (t)UKraft/Alamy Images, (b)First Image; **335** (t)Charles Gupton/Stone, (b)Will Hart/PhotoEdit; **336** (t)Nick Rowe/PhotoDisc, (b)Derick A. Thomas, Dat's Jazz/CORBIS; **338** Doug Martin; **339** Araldo de Luca/CORBIS; **340** Dr. Merlin D. Tuttle/Photo Researchers, Inc.; **342** Doug Martin; **344** John Wang/PhotoDisc; **345** David Young-Wolff/PhotoEdit; **346** (tl)Australian Picture Library/CORBIS, (tr)Zig Leszczynski/Earth Scenes, (b)David Sacks; **347** (tl)John Waters/Getty Images, (tr)CMCD/PhotoDisc, (b)Robert Brenner/PhotoEdit; **352-353** Bob Burch/Index Stock Imagery; **357** Mat Jacob/The Image Works; **362** (t)CORBIS, (bl)NASA/GSFC/JPL, MISR and AirMISR Teams, (br)NASA/GSFC/MITI/ERSDAC/JAROS, and USA/Japan ASTER Science Team; **363** AP/Wide World Photos; **365** Getty Images; **367** StudiOhio; **368** (tr bl)First Image, (br)PhotoDisc; **369** (tl)Design Pics Inc./Alamy, (tr)David R. Frazier Photolibrary Inc./Alamy, (bl)CORBIS, (bc)Dorling Kindersley, (br)David Young-Wolff/PhotoEdit Inc.; **370** Nino Mascardi/The Image Bank; **371** Photolink/PhotoDisc; **372** Adastra/Getty Images; **374** Len Delessio/Index Stock; **375** Jim Wark/Index Stock; **376** (t)Getty Images, (b)Bettman/CORBIS; **377** (tl)Martin Dohrn/Science Photo Library/Photo Researchers, (bl)Joe McDonald/Tom Stack & Associates, (r)CORBIS; **380** PhotoDisc; **382-383** Brandon Cole; **384** First Image; **386** (tl)Bruce Iverson, (tr)Myrleen Cate/Index Stock/PictureQuest, (b)Scott Peterson/Jupiter Images; **387** David Parker/Science Photo Library/Photo Researchers; **388** Charles O'Rear/CORBIS; **390** First Image; **391** (t)Ralph C. Eagle, Jr./Photo Researchers, (b)Diane Hirsch/Fundamental Photographs; **392** Matt Meadows; **395** Ginger Chih/Peter Arnold, Inc.; **396** First Image; **397** Will & Deni McIntyre/Photo Researchers; **399** Andrew Syred/Science Photo Library/Photo Researchers; **401** Larry Mulvehill/Photo Researchers; **403** Paul Silverman/Fundamental Photographs; **404** David Young-Wolff/PhotoEdit; **405** Doug Martin; **406 407** Dominic Oldershaw; **408** (t)Archivo Iconografico, S.A./CORBIS, (b)Ashmolean Museum, Oxford, UK/Bridgeman Art Library, London/New York; **409** (l)Dick Poe/Visuals Unlimited, (r)Timothy Fuller; **414-415** David R. Frazier Photolibrary, Inc./Alamy Images; **416** CORBIS; **417** David Young-Wolff/PhotoEdit; **420** George B. Diebold/CORBIS; **421** Paul A. Souders/CORBIS; **423** Matt Meadows; **424** David Parker/Science Photo Library/Photo Researchers; **430** (l)National Eye Institute, National Institutes of Health, (r) United States coin images from the United States Mint; **434** NASA Marshall Space Flight Center (NASA-MSFC); **436 437** Breck P. Kent/Earth Scenes; **438 439** Dominic Oldershaw; **440** (t)Hemsey/Liaison Agency, (b)Louis Psihoyos/Matrix; **441** (t)Jeff Greenberg/Visuals Unlimited, (bl)Mark Burnett, (br)John Durham/Science Photo Library/Photo Researchers; **446-447** The Granger Collection, New York; **447** Jules Frazier/Getty Images; **448-449** Michael Newman/PhotoEdit; **449** Matt Meadows; **450** (t)Siede Pries/PhotoDisc, (c)Ryan McVay/PhotoDisc, (b)PhotoDisc; **451** (tl)James L. Amos/CORBIS, (tr)Ingram Publishing/Alamy, (cl)Yann Arthus-Bertrand/CORBIS, (cr)Reed Saxon/AP Images, (bl)David Young-Wolff/Alamy, (br)Dorling Kindersley; **452** (t)Richard Megna/Fundamental Photographs, (b)Icon Images; **453** (l)Icon Images, (tr)Icon Images, (br)Andrew Syred/Science Photo Library/Photo Researchers; **454** (t)Icon Images, (bl)PhotoDisc, (br)C. Squared Studios/PhotoDisc; **455** (tl)bildagentur-online.com/th-foto/Alamy Images, (tr)Kaj R. Svensson/Science Photo Library/Photo Researchers, (b)Kip & Pat Peticolas/Fundamental Photographs; **456** Cameron Davidson/Getty Images; **457** Icon Images; **458** Matt Meadows; **459** (t)Amanita Pictures, (b)Doug Martin; **460** Richard Megna/Fundamental Photographs; **461** Jed & Kaoru Share/Stone; **462** Richard Megna/Fundamental Photographs; **464** (l)M. Romesser, (r)SuperStock; **465** Chris Rogers/CORBIS; **466** Icon Images; **467** (t)Icon Images, (b)Matt Meadows; **468** (t)Dominic Oldershaw, (c)Doug Martin, (b)Punchstock; **469** (tl)Icon Images, (tr)Stockdisc/PunchStock, (bl)Tony Freeman/PhotoEdit, (br)Icon Images; **473** (tl bl br)Doug Martin, (tr)Chris Rogers/Corbis; **474-475** The Stock Market; **475** Matt Meadows; **476** Icon Images; **479** Doug Martin; **480** JISAS/Lockheed/Science Photo Library/Photo Researchers; **481** (t)CORBIS, (b)Mark E. Gibson/Visuals Unlimited; **483** Amanita Pictures; **484** Matt Meadows; **488** (t)Bob Daemmrich, (b)Tim Courlas/Horizons Companies; **490** file photo; **492** Mark Burnett/Photo Researchers; **495** Matt Meadows; **496** John Evans; **498** (t)Geoff Tomkinson/Science Photo Library/Photo Researchers, (b)Michael Dwyer/Stock Boston; **499** (t)Breck P. Kent/Animals Animals, (bl)Icon Images, (br)Aaron Haupt; **503** (l)Mark Burnett/Photo Researchers, (r)Mark E.

Gibson/Visuals Unlimited; **504-505** Walter Bibikow/Index Stock Imagery, NY; **508** (tl)Science Photo Library/Photo Researchers, (tr)Hank Morgan/Science Source/Photo Researchers, (b)Photo Researchers; **509** Sheila Terry/Science Photo Library/Photo Researchers; **512** Matt Meadows;

516 SSPL/The Image Works; **524** CORBIS; **525** The Image Bank; **526** Tom Pantages; **527** PhotoEdit; **528** (t)Roger Ressmeyer/CORBIS, (b)Maria Stenzel/National Geographic Image Collection; **534-535** Paul Souders/Getty Images; **535** Aaron Haupt; **536** (t)First Image, (b)David Frazier/The Image Works; **540** American Institute of Physics/Emilio Segrè Visual Archives; **542** Amanita Pictures; **546** (l)Courtesy Supersaturated Environments, (r)Science Photo Library/Photo Researchers; **547** (t)CERN, P. Loiez/Science Photo Library/Photo Researchers, (b)Richard Megna/Fundamental Photographs; **549** Hank Morgan/Photo Researchers; **554** Oliver Meckes/Nicole Ottawa/Photo Researchers; **555** Hank Morgan/Photo Researchers, Inc.; **556** J.L. Carson/Custom Medical Stock Photo; **557** Tim Courlas/Horizons Companies; **558** (l)Fermilab/Visuals Unlimited, (r)Matt Meadows; **559** Matt Meadows; **560** (t)C. Powell, P. Fowler & D. Perkins/Science Photo Library/Photo Researchers, Inc., (cr)CORBIS, (b)CORBIS; **561** (l)Martha Cooper/Peter Arnold, Inc., (r)Oliver Meckes/Nicole Ottawa/Photo Researchers; **566-567** Lawrence Lawry/Getty Images; **567** Dorling Kindersley; **568-569** Georg Gerster/Photo Researchers; **570** (t)Henry Groskinsky/Time & Life Pictures/Getty Images, (b)Nubar Alexanian/CORBIS; **572** (l)Stephen Frisch/Stock Boston, (r)Jerry Mason/Science Photo Library/Photo Researchers; **573** Firefly Productions/The Stock Market; **574** Mark Burnett/Photo Researchers; **575** (tl)Matt Meadows, (tr)Icon Images, (b)Jeff J. Daly/Fundamental Photographs; **577** Melvyn P. Lawes/Papilio/CORBIS; **579** (l to r)Russ Lappa/Science Source/Photo Researchers, Gregory G. Dimijian/Photo Researchers, Stephen Frisch/Stock Boston, Andrew J. Martinez/Photo Researchers, Doug Martin, Charles Gupton/Stock Boston; **580** (t)Spencer Grant/Photo Edit, (b)Brand X Pictures/Punchstock; **581** (t)Norris Blake/Visuals Unlimited, (b)Steven Senne/AP/Wide World Photos; **582** Gene J. Puskar/AP/Wide World Photos; **584** George Hall/CORBIS; **585** (l)Icon Images, (r)Charles D. Winters/Photo Researchers; **586** (l)Aaron Haupt, (c)Comstock/JupiterImages, (r)Alfred Pasieka/Science Photo Library/Photo Researchers; **588** (l)RMIP/Richard Haynes, (r)PhotoDisc; **590** (l to r, t to b)Gianni Dagli Orti/CORBIS, Jonathan Blair/CORBIS, The McGraw-Hill Companies, Inc./Stephen Frisch, CORBIS, FogStock/Alamy Images, PhotoDisc, Paul A. Souders/CORBIS, Bettmann/CORBIS, Steve Cole/Getty Images, Artville, AP Photo/GSI, Achim Zschau; **592** (t)Charles D. Winters/Photo Researchers, (b)Richard Hutchings; **593** Richard Hutchings; **594** Lynn Johnson/Aurora; **595** (cw from top)Charles D. Winters/Photo Researchers, Stephen Frisch/Stock Boston, Charles E. Zirkle, Doug Martin, Karl Hartmann/Sachs/PhotoTake NYC, Russ Lappa/Science Source/Photo Researchers; **599** George Hall/CORBIS; **600-601** Tom Sanders/CORBIS; **601** Amanita Pictures; **602** (t)John Evans, (b)CORBIS; **603** (l)Andrew Lambert Photography/Photo Researchers, Inc., (c)Richard Megna/Fundamental Photographs, (r)Syndicated Features Limited/The Image Works; **607** First Image; **608** John Paul Kay/Peter Arnold, Inc.; **612** John Evans; **613** (c)Image Source Black/Getty Images; **615** Bettmann/CORBIS; **620** Amanita Pictures; **622** (l)Amanita Pictures, (r)Richard Hutchings; **623** Richard Hutchings; **624** Daniel Belknap; **625** Syndicated Features Limited/The Image Works;

630-631 Transglobe/Index Stock; **633** Mansell Collection/TimePix/Getty Images; **635** Richard Megna/Fundamental Photographs; **637** CORBIS; **638** Richard Megna/Fundamental Photographs; **639** Doug Martin/Photo Researchers; **640** Richard Megna/Fundamental Photographs; **641** Emory Kristof/National Geographic Image Collection; **642** (t)Charles D. Winters/Photo Researchers, (b)Lester V. Bergman/CORBIS; **643** Richard Megna/Fundamental Photographs; **645** Royalty-Free/CORBIS; **646** Tim Matsui/Liaison Agency; **647** (l cl)Bettmann/CORBIS, (cr)Roger Ressmeyer/NASA/CORBIS, (r)NASA/CORBIS; **648** Matt Meadows; **649** (t)Jeff J. Daly/Fundamental Photographs, (c)Matt Meadows, (b)Matt Meadows; **651** Timothy Fuller; **652** UNEP-Topham/The Image Works; **653** Michael Newman/PhotoEdit; **654** (t)SSPL/The Image Works, (b)Brad Maushart/Graphistock; **655** (l)Charles D. Winters/Photo Researchers, (r)Joseph P. Sinnot/Fundamental Photographs; **658** Charles D. Winters/Photo Researchers; **659** (l)Richard Megna/Fundamental Photographs, (r)Firefly Productions/The Stock Market; **660-661** Norbert Wu/Getty Images; **661** Spencer Collection, New York Public Library, Astor, Lenox & Tilden Foundation; **662-663** Stephen Frink/Index Stock Imagery; **664** Annie Griffiths Belt/CORBIS; **665** (l)Christie's Images, (r)Flip Schulke/Black Star; **666** (tl)Bettmann/CORBIS, (tr)Marilyn Angel Wynn/Nativestock Pictures/CORBIS, (b)VStock/Alamy; **672** Mark Thayer; **674** Richard Megna/Fundamental Photographs; **680** Tim Courlas/Horizons Companies; **681** **682** Icon Images; **683** Steve Mason/PhotoDisc; **684** KS Studios; **686** (l)Matt Meadows, (r)Tim Courlas/Horizons Companies; **687** Matt Meadows; **688** (t)Tony Freeman/PhotoEdit, (c)AISI/Visuals Unlimited, (b)Standard-Examiner, Kort Duce/AP/Wide World Photos; **689 690 692** Icon Images; **694-695** Frans Lanting/Minden Pictures; **696** KS Studios; **697** Matt Meadows; **698** Geoff Butler; **699** Rick Poley/Index Stock; **702** Matt Meadows; **704** (l to r, t to b) Elaine Shay, Brent Turner/BLT Productions, Matt Meadows, Elaine Shay, CORBIS, Icon Images, StudiOhio, Dominic Oldershaw, Digital Vision/Alamy, Matt Meadows; **706** Tim Courlas/Horizons Companies; **707** Charles D. Winters/Photo Researchers; **708** The Purcell Team/CORBIS; **709** (tl)Kevin Schafer/CORBIS, (tr)VOLKMAR K. WENTZEL/National Geographic Image Collection, (c)CORBIS, (b)Kevin Schafer/CORBIS; **710** Richard Megna/Fundamental Photographs; **711** (t)Matt Meadows, (b)Amanita Pictures; **713** Chinch Gryniewicz/Ecoscene/CORBIS; **714** Amanita Pictures; **715** PhotoDisc; **716** (t)vario images GmbH & Co.KG/Alamy Images, (b)Richard Megna/Fundamental Photographs; **717** Richard Megna/Fundamental Photographs; **718** TIME; **719** (l)KS Studios, (r)Matt Meadows; **723** Matt Meadows; **724-725** Walter Bibikow/Index Stock Imagery; **726** KS Studios; **730** (t)U.S. Department of Energy, (b)PhotoDisc; **731** (t)Aaron Haupt, (b)First Image; **732** Ken Frick; **733** (l)Aaron Haupt, (c)Timothy Fuller, (r)Timothy Fuller; **734** Lynn M. Stone/Index Stock; **735** Tim Courlas/Horizons Companies; **738** (tl)Hemera Technologies/Picturequest, (tr)CORBIS, (c)Bernard Roussel/The Image Bank/Getty Images, (bl)Digital Archive Japan/Alamy Images, (br)Getty Images; **740** (l)Geoff Butler, (r)Charles D. Winters/Photo Researchers; **741** Milmar;

743 David M. Phillips/Visuals Unlimited; **746** (t)Bob Mullenix, (b)Corbis Premium RF/Alamy Images; **747** Ken Frick; **749** Matt Meadows; **750** courtesy 3M; **751** (tl)Francis & Donna Caldwell/Visuals Unlimited, (tr)Richard Hutchings/Photo Researchers, (bl)Getty Images, (br)Bob Coates/Index Stock; **756-757** David Stoecklein/CORBIS; **757** Matt Meadows; **759** (l)Icon Images, (r)Martin Fox/Index Stock; **760** Icon Images; **761** (l)SIU/Visuals Unlimited, (tr)Laura Sifferlin, (br)Jonathan Blair/CORBIS; **762** courtesy Boeing; **763** NASA; **765** Aaron Haupt; **766** (tl)BSIP/Phototake; **768** Technology And Industry Concepts/Alamy Images; **769** (tl)L. Mulvehill/Photo Researchers, (tr)Bettmann/CORBIS, (cl)courtesy Texas Instruments, (cr)Bettmann/CORBIS,(bl)David Young-Wolff/PhotoEdit, (br)Charles O'Rear/CORBIS; **770** Amanita Pictures; **773** (l)Leonard Lessin/Peter Arnold, Inc., (c)Myrleen Ferguson/PhotoEdit, (r)Robert Rathe/Stock Boston; **774** (t)Doug Wilson/CORBIS, (c)Gady Cojocaru/Alamy, (b)Jon Eisberg/FPG/Getty Images; **775** (l)Astrid & Hanns-Frieder Michler/Photo Researchers, (r)Car Culture/Corbis; **776** courtesy Boeing; **777** Aaron Haupt; **778** Timothy Fuller; **779** Icon Images; **780** (t)Bernard Roussel/The Image Bank/Getty Images, (c)courtesy 3M, (b)Steve Labadessa/Timepix; **781** (t)Tony Freeman/PhotoEdit, (bl)Paul Loven/Getty Images, (br)Stockdisc/Getty Images; **782** George B. Diebold/The Stock Market; **784** (l)Martin Fox/Index Stock, (r)Icon Images; **786** Getty Images; **788** Tom Pantages; **792** Michell D. Bridwell/PhotoEdit; **793** (t)Mark Burnett, (b)Dominic Oldershaw; **794** StudiOhio; **795** Timothy Fuller; **796** Aaron Haupt; **798** KS Studios; **799** Matt Meadows; **800** Rod Joslin; **802** C. Squared Studios/PhotoDisc; **803** Amanita Pictures; **806** (t)Geoff Butler, (b)Amanita Pictures; **807** KS Studios/Mullenix; **808** KS Studios; **813** Amanita Pictures; **814** Bob Daemmrich; **816** Davis Barber/PhotoEdit

PERIODIC TABLE OF THE ELEMENTS

Columns of elements are called groups. Elements in the same group have similar chemical properties.

Element — Hydrogen
Atomic number — 1
Symbol — H
Atomic mass — 1.008
State of matter

Gas
Liquid
Solid
Synthetic

The first three symbols tell you the state of matter of the element at room temperature. The fourth symbol identifies elements that are not present in significant amounts on Earth. Useful amounts are made synthetically.

Period	1	2	3	4	5	6	7	8	9
1	Hydrogen 1 H 1.008 (Gas)								
2	Lithium 3 Li 6.941 (Solid)	Beryllium 4 Be 9.012 (Solid)							
3	Sodium 11 Na 22.990 (Solid)	Magnesium 12 Mg 24.305 (Solid)							
4	Potassium 19 K 39.098 (Solid)	Calcium 20 Ca 40.078 (Solid)	Scandium 21 Sc 44.956 (Solid)	Titanium 22 Ti 47.867 (Solid)	Vanadium 23 V 50.942 (Solid)	Chromium 24 Cr 51.996 (Solid)	Manganese 25 Mn 54.938 (Solid)	Iron 26 Fe 55.845 (Solid)	Cobalt 27 Co 58.933 (Solid)
5	Rubidium 37 Rb 85.468 (Solid)	Strontium 38 Sr 87.62 (Solid)	Yttrium 39 Y 88.906 (Solid)	Zirconium 40 Zr 91.224 (Solid)	Niobium 41 Nb 92.906 (Solid)	Molybdenum 42 Mo 95.94 (Solid)	Technetium 43 Tc (98) (Synthetic)	Ruthenium 44 Ru 101.07 (Solid)	Rhodium 45 Rh 102.906 (Solid)
6	Cesium 55 Cs 132.905 (Solid)	Barium 56 Ba 137.327 (Solid)	Lanthanum 57 La 138.906 (Solid)	Hafnium 72 Hf 178.49 (Solid)	Tantalum 73 Ta 180.948 (Solid)	Tungsten 74 W 183.84 (Solid)	Rhenium 75 Re 186.207 (Solid)	Osmium 76 Os 190.23 (Solid)	Iridium 77 Ir 192.217 (Solid)
7	Francium 87 Fr (223) (Solid)	Radium 88 Ra (226) (Solid)	Actinium 89 Ac (227) (Solid)	Rutherfordium 104 Rf (261) (Synthetic)	Dubnium 105 Db (262) (Synthetic)	Seaborgium 106 Sg (266) (Synthetic)	Bohrium 107 Bh (264) (Synthetic)	Hassium 108 Hs (277) (Synthetic)	Meitnerium 109 Mt (268) (Synthetic)

The number in parentheses is the mass number of the longest-lived isotope for that element.

Rows of elements are called periods. Atomic number increases across a period.

The arrow shows where these elements would fit into the periodic table. They are moved to the bottom of the table to save space.

Lanthanide series	Cerium 58 Ce 140.116 (Solid)	Praseodymium 59 Pr 140.908 (Solid)	Neodymium 60 Nd 144.24 (Solid)	Promethium 61 Pm (145) (Synthetic)	Samarium 62 Sm 150.36 (Solid)
Actinide series	Thorium 90 Th 232.038 (Solid)	Protactinium 91 Pa 231.036 (Solid)	Uranium 92 U 238.029 (Solid)	Neptunium 93 Np (237) (Synthetic)	Plutonium 94 Pu (244) (Synthetic)